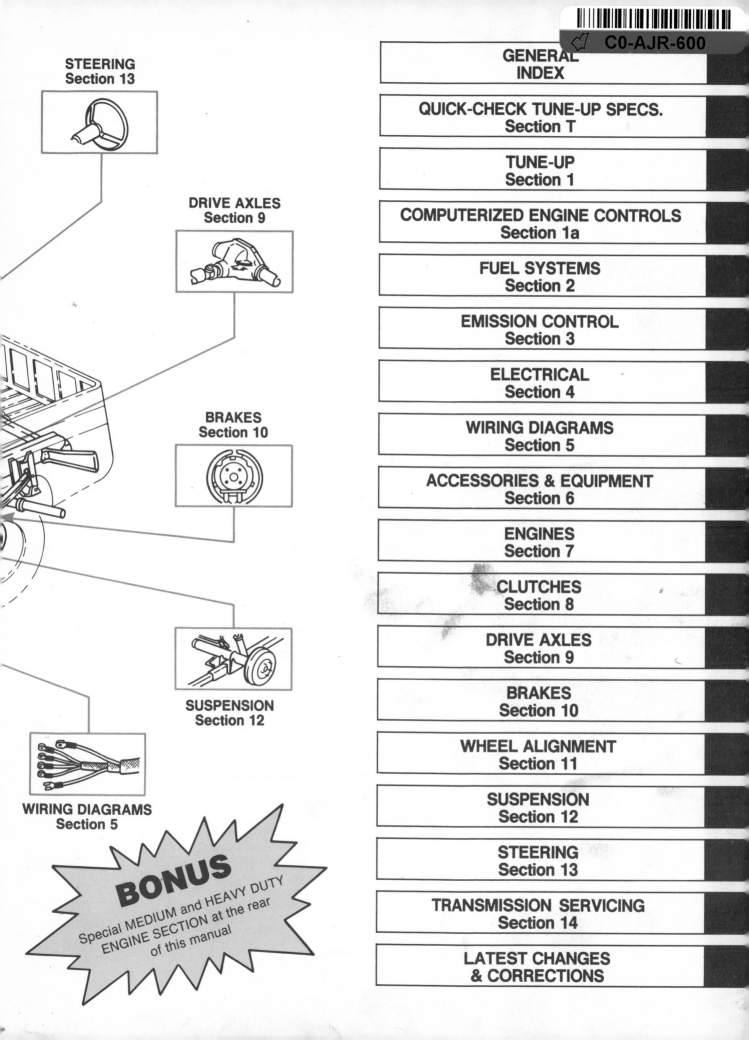

STEERING
Section 13

DRIVE AXLES
Section 9

BRAKES
Section 10

SUSPENSION
Section 12

WIRING DIAGRAMS
Section 5

BONUS
Special MEDIUM and HEAVY DUTY
ENGINE SECTION at the rear
of this manual

C0-AJR-600

PREFACE

This is the 1983 edition of Mitchell Manuals'
Light Truck Service & Repair Manual.
This book, like the many Mitchell publications which have preceded it,
represents our commitment to professionalism
in the automotive service market.

The automotive industry advances every year.
As a participant and contributor, Mitchell Manuals pledges to advance and improve its products
in order to maintain the quality and utility of all our publications.

We cordially acknowledge the goodwill
and mutual goals that exist in the automotive business.
It is in this spirit that we thank the manufacturers, distributors,
dealers, independents and the entire automotive industry.
Your cooperation and assistance make this publication possible.

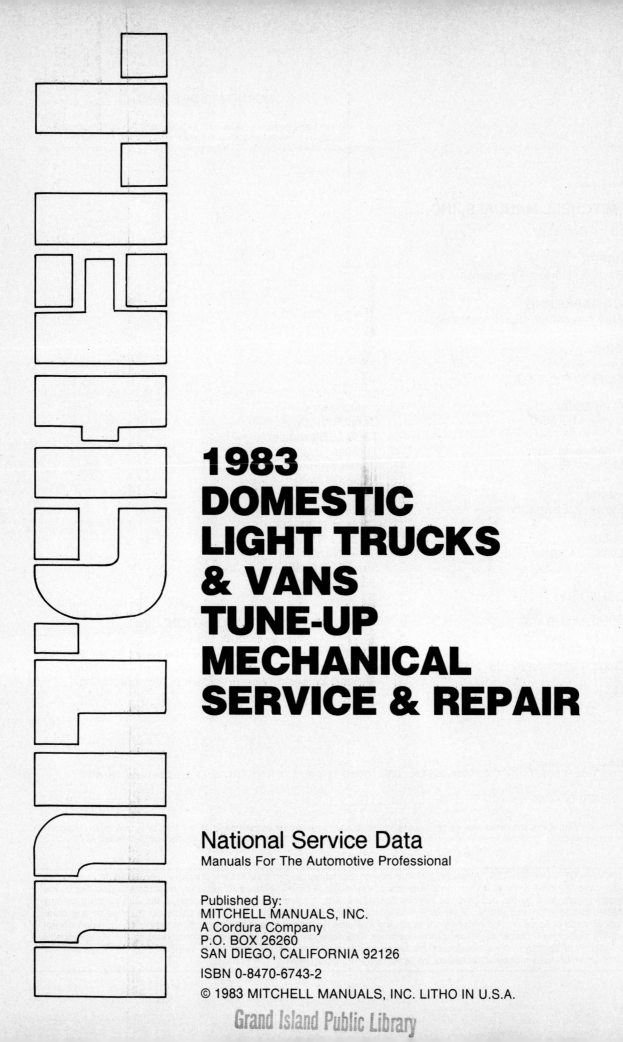

1983 DOMESTIC LIGHT TRUCKS & VANS TUNE-UP MECHANICAL SERVICE & REPAIR

National Service Data
Manuals For The Automotive Professional

Published By:
MITCHELL MANUALS, INC.
A Cordura Company
P.O. BOX 26260
SAN DIEGO, CALIFORNIA 92126

ISBN 0-8470-6743-2

ACKNOWLEDGEMENT

Mitchell Manuals thanks the automotive and equipment manufacturers, distributors, dealers and the entire automotive industry for their fine cooperation and assistance which makes the publication of this manual possible.

MITCHELL MANUALS, INC.

A Cordura Company

PUBLISHER
Barry A. Norton, President

DIRECT MARKETING
Alan Hirschfeld, Vice President

EDITORIAL
Editorial Director
Kenneth A. Young

Managing Editor
Daniel M. Kelley

Ass't. Managing Editor
Michael Roeder

Art Director
Eloise S. Stiverson

Detroit Editor
Lynn D. Meeker

Technical Editors
Daryl F. Visser
Terry L. Blomquist
Thomas L. Landis
Daniel D. Fleming
Philip G. Wallan
Cliff Herrin
Jeffrey C. Wedeking
Thomas J. Kelley
Barbara A. Siesel
Eddie Santangelo
Patrick T. Rice

PUBLISHED BY

MITCHELL MANUALS, INC.
9889 Willow Creek Road
P.O. Box 26260
San Diego, California 92126

a subsidiary of
CORDURA PUBLICATIONS, INC.
C.L. Kobrin, President
John Opelt, Senior Vice President of Finance & Administration
Malcolm Ferrier, Senior Vice President of Technology
Robert W. Ladd, Vice President of Manufacturing

For Subscription Information:
CALL TOLL FREE 800 - 854-7030. In California CALL COLLECT 619 - 578-8770. Or WRITE: P.O. Box 26260, San Diego, CA 92126

ISBN 0-8470-6743-2

Introduction

You now have the most complete and up to date Service and Repair Manual currently available to the professional mechanic. Our staff of experts has spent many hundreds of hours gathering and processing service and repair information from sources throughout the automotive industry. More than 200 separate articles provide specific step-by-step Testing, Adjusting and Repair procedures for 1983 Domestic Light Trucks and Vans.

To use this manual in the most efficient and profitable way possible, please take the time to read the following instructions, "How To Find the Information." This will enable you to quickly locate the car model and the mechanical procedure you need, without wasting time thumbing through unnecessary pages.

HOW TO FIND THE INFORMATION
3 Quick Steps

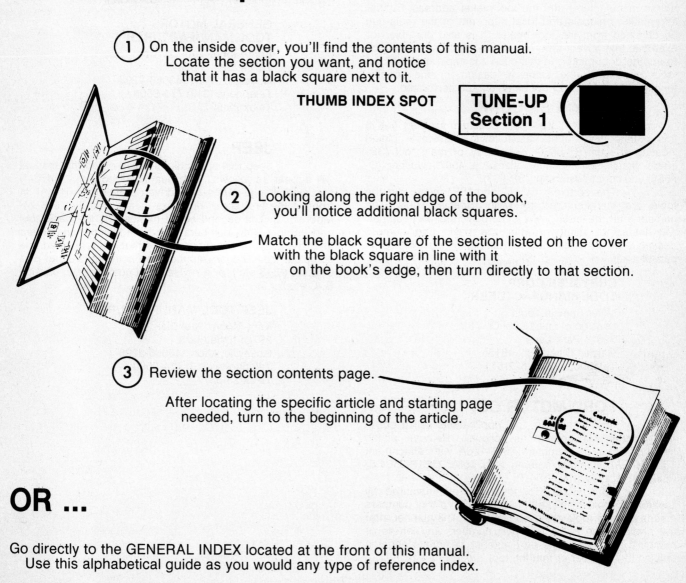

(1) On the inside cover, you'll find the contents of this manual. Locate the section you want, and notice that it has a black square next to it.

THUMB INDEX SPOT

TUNE-UP
Section 1

(2) Looking along the right edge of the book, you'll notice additional black squares.

Match the black square of the section listed on the cover with the black square in line with it on the book's edge, then turn directly to that section.

(3) Review the section contents page.

After locating the specific article and starting page needed, turn to the beginning of the article.

OR ...

Go directly to the GENERAL INDEX located at the front of this manual.
Use this alphabetical guide as you would any type of reference index.

Tool Applications

ALL MANUFACTURERS

DESCRIPTION

Tool applications used in this manual are noted in the text of all articles where applicable. These tools are usually specific tools that must be used to perform a specific function in Removal, Installation, Overhaul or Testing of a component.

For example; "Using Spline Adapter (J-28513) and Holding Wrench (J-28514), tighten pinion nut until end play is taken up." Although other tools could possibly be substituted, the tool references in text are those that are recommended by the vehicle manufacturer. These tools should be used whenever possible. In cases where a non-specific tool is called for, no tool number will be given.

For example; "Place bearing insert in rod and install guides on rod bolts. Compress piston rings using ring compressor." Since just about any ring compressor that works and does not damage the components can be used, no specific tool number will be called out.

The following descriptions show an example of the reference in text, the maker of the tools recommended by the manufacturer and the tool maker address. Further information on tools and local suppliers of the tools can be obtained from the tool maker. It is also possible, for example, that a Kent-Moore tool may be cross-referenced to another tool maker. In this case it is imperative that the tools be exactly the same in design, or the specific function of the tool may not be able to be performed.

CHRYSLER CORP.

Chrysler Corp. tool applications called out in this manual will appear as follows: "Assemble pinion locating spacer (SP-6030) over body of main tool (SP-5385). Install shaft locating sleeve (L-4507), washer (C-4656) and compression nut (SP-533)."

The prefixes "C," "L" and "SP" mean that the tools are manufactured by Miller Special Tools. The number after the letter prefix is the basic tool part number. Any letters or numbers after the basic part number designate either a revised tool number or that the tool is part of a set.

CHRYSLER CORP. TOOL MANUFACTURER

Miller Special Tools
Division of Utica Tool Co., Inc.
32615 Park Lane
Garden City, Mich. 48135
Telephone (313) 522-6717

FORD MOTOR CO.

Ford Motor Co. tool applications called out in this manual will appear as follows: "Remove pinion bearing with slide hammer (T50T-100A with attachment T58L-101-A). Remove bearing with puller (T81P-3504-S, T58L-101-A and T81P-3504-T)."

Ford Motor Co. tools are manufactured by Owatonna Tools. The prefix used with Ford tool numbers means that the tools are essential tools. The number after the prefix is the basic tool part number. Any letters or numbers after the basic part number designate either a revised tool number or that the tool is part of a set.

FORD MOTOR CO. TOOL MANUFACTURER

Owatonna Tool Co. Inc.
Owatonna, Minn. 55060
Telephone (507) 455-2626
Telex 29-0876

GENERAL MOTORS

General Motors tool applications called out in this manual will appear as follows; "Install pivot pin remover (J-21854-1) and remove pins. Using pin punch (J-22635), drive out lever pin."

The "J" in front of the first set of numbers means that it is a Kent-Moore tool. The second set of numbers is the basic tool part number. Part numbers with no additional characters after the basic part number means that the tool listed is a complete tool. The last number means that it is either part of a set (-2,-3 etc.), or a revised tool number (-02,-03, or -B,-C etc,).

GENERAL MOTORS TOOL MANUFACTURER

Kent-Moore Tool Division
29784 Little Mack
Roseville, Mich., 48066-2298
Telephone (313) 774-9500
Telex 23-5377

JEEP

Jeep tool applications called out in this manual will appear as follows: "Use bearing remover (J-21473-1) and extension (J-21054-1) to drive out bearing." The "J" in front of the first set of numbers means that it is a Kent-Moore tool. The second set of numbers is the basic tool part number. Part numbers with no additional characters after the basic part number means that the tool listed is a complete tool. The last number means that it is either part of a set (-2,-3 etc.), or a revised tool number (-02,-03, or -B,-C etc,).

JEEP TOOL MANUFACTURER

Kent-Moore Tool Division
29784 Little Mack
Roseville, Mich., 48066-2298
Telephone (313) 774-9500
Telex 23-5377

1983 Light Truck Model Identification

In this manual, Light Truck models will be referred to by the manufacturer's model and/or series designation. When a specific model does not have a designated model or series designation, it will be referred to by model name.

NOTE: When General Motors is referred to within this manual (rather than Chevrolet or GMC), the Chevrolet numerical vehicle series designations will be abbreviated for common reference to both Chevrolet and GMC models. The GMC counterpart models will be identified as follows: 10 = 1500 (except S15); 20 = 2500; 30 = 3500.

CHEVROLET

MODEL IDENTIFICATION

Model	Description
C10	[1] 1/2 Ton Conventional Cab 2WD
C20	[1] 3/4 Ton Conventional Cab 2WD
C30	1 Ton Conventional Cab 2WD
K10	[1] 1/2 Ton Conventional Cab 4WD & Blazer
K20	[1] 3/4 Ton Conventional Cab 4WD
K30	1 Ton Conventional Cab 4WD
G10	1/2 Ton Van
G20	3/4 Ton Van
G30	[2] 1 Ton Van
P20	3/4 Ton Parcel Delivery Van
P30 (42)	1 Ton Parcel Delivery Van
S10	1/2 Ton Conventional Cab 2WD & Blazer
T10	1/2 Ton Conventional Cab 4WD & Blazer

[1] — Includes Suburban models.
[2] — Includes Front Section and Hi-Cube models.

DODGE

MODEL IDENTIFICATION

Model	Description
AD150	Ramcharger 2WD
AW150	Ramcharger 4WD
B150	1/2 Ton Van
B250	3/4 Ton Van
B350	1 Ton Van
CB350	1 Ton Van (Kary Van)
CB450	1 1/2 Ton Van (Kary Van)
MB250	3/4 Ton Van (Front Section)
MB350	1 Ton Van (Front Section)
MB450	1 1/2 Ton Van (Front Section)
D150	Heavy Duty 1/2 Ton Conventional Cab 2WD
D250	3/4 Ton Conventional Cab 2WD
D350	1 Ton Conventional Cab 2WD
W150	Heavy Duty 1/2 Ton Conventional Cab 4WD
W250	1/2 Ton Conventional Cab 4WD
W350	1 Ton Conventional Cab 4WD

FORD

MODEL IDENTIFICATION

Model	Description
Bronco	Family 4WD Wagon
Bronco II	Family 4WD Wagon

FORD (Cont.)

MODEL IDENTIFICATION

Model	Description
E100	1/2 Ton Van
E150	Heavy Duty 1/2 Ton Van
E250	3/4 Ton Van
E350	[1] 1 Ton Van
F100	1/2 Ton Conventional Cab 2WD
F150	Heavy Duty 1/2 Ton Conventional Cab 2WD & 4WD
F250	3/4 Ton Conventional Cab 2WD & 4WD
F350	1 Ton Conventional Cab 2WD & 4WD
Ranger	1/2 Ton Conventional Cab 2WD & 4WD

[1] — Includes Front Section and Parcel Delivery models.

GMC

MODEL IDENTIFICATION

Model	Description
C1500	[1] 1/2 Ton Conventional Cab 2WD
C2500	[1] 3/4 Ton Conventional Cab 2WD
C3500	1 Ton Conventional Cab 2WD
K1500	[1] 1/2 Ton Conventional Cab 4WD & Jimmy
K2500	[1] 3/4 Ton Conventional Cab 4WD
K3500	1 Ton Conventional Cab 4WD
G1500	1/2 Ton Van
G2500	3/4 Ton Van
G3500	[2] 1 Ton Van
P2500	3/4 Ton Parcel Delivery Van
P3500 (42)	1 Ton Parcel Delivery Van
S15	1/2 Ton Conventional Cab 2WD & Jimmy
T15	1/2 Ton Conventional Cab 4WD & Jimmy

[1] — Includes Suburban models.
[2] — Includes Front Sections and Hi-Cube models.

JEEP

MODEL IDENTIFICATION

Model	Description
Cherokee	Cherokee 4WD
CJ5	84" Wheelbase Utility Vehicle 4WD
CJ7	94" Wheelbase Utility Vehicle 4WD
J10	1/2 Ton Conventional Cab 4WD
J20	3/4 Ton Conventional Cab 4WD
Scrambler	104" Wheelbase Utility Vehicle 4WD
Wagoneer	Wagoneer 4WD

PLYMOUTH

MODEL IDENTIFICATION

Model	Description
PB150	1/2 Ton Van
PB250	3/4 Ton Van
PB350	1 Ton Van

1983 Engine Size Conversion Charts

CHRYSLER CORP. ENGINES

Liters	Cubic Inches
6-Cylinder	
3.7	225
V8	
5.2	318
5.9	360

FORD MOTOR CO. ENGINES

Liters	Cubic Inches
4-Cylinder	
2.0	122
2.2 Diesel	134
2.3	140
V6	
2.8	170
3.8	232
6-Cylinder	
4.9	300
V8	
5.0	302
5.8	351
6.9 Diesel	420
7.5	460

GENERAL MOTORS ENGINES

Liters	Cubic Inches
4-Cylinder	
1.9	119
2.0	122
V6	
2.8	173
6-Cylinder	
4.1	250
4.8	292
V8	
5.0	305
5.7	350
6.2 Diesel	378
7.4	454

JEEP ENGINES

Liters	Cubic Inches
4-Cylinder	
2.5	151
6-Cylinder	
4.2	258
V8	
6.0	360

GENERAL INDEX

The first step in using these pages
is to locate the listed components that you require
information on. Go down the list under the specific component heading
to the model or engine size of the vehicle you are working on. On the
right-hand side of the column will appear the corresponding
page number of the article, specification,
or wiring diagram you require.

1983 General Index

1983 General Index

SECTION T
1983
QUICK-CHECK
TUNE-UP
SPECIFICATIONS

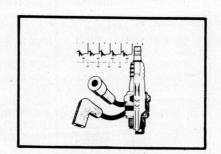

1983 Light Truck Tune-Up

TUNE-UP SPECIFICATIONS

ENGINE	IGNITION TIMING *		SPARK PLUGS		FUEL SYSTEM	No.
	Man. Trans.	Auto. Trans.	Type	Gap In. (mm)	Make & Type	
CHRYSLER CORP.						
3.7L (225") 6-Cyl.						
Fed. 1-Bbl.	12@600	16@650	CH RBL-16Y	.035 (.9)	Holley 1945	1
Fed. 2-Bbl.	12@700	.....	CH RBL-16Y	.035 (.9)	Carter BBD	2
Calif.	12@750	16@750	CH RBL-16Y	.035 (.9)	Holley 6145	3
5.2L (318") V8 2-Bbl.	16@700 [1]	16@700 [1]	CH RN-12Y	.035 (.9)	Carter BBD [3]	4
5.2L (318") V8 4-Bbl.						
Fed.	12@750 [2]	16@750 [2]	CH RN-12Y	.035 (.9)	Carter Thermo-Quad	5
Calif.	16@750 [2]	.....	CH RN-12Y	.035 (.9)	Carter Thermo-Quad	6
5.9L (360") V8						
Fed.	4@700	4@700	CH RN-12Y	.035 (.9)	Carter Thermo-Quad	7
Calif.	10@750	10@750	CH RN-12Y	.035 (.9)	Carter Thermo-Quad	8
FORD MOTOR CO.						
2.0L (122") 4-Cyl.	6@800	6@800	MCFTAWSF-42	.035 (.9)	Carter YFA	9
2.3L (140") 4-Cyl.						
Fed.	6@800 [1]	6@800	MCFTAWSF-42	.035 (.9)	Carter YFA	10
Calif.	6@800	8@800	MCFTAWSF-42	.035 (.9)	Carter YFA	11
4.9L (300") 6-Cyl.						
Light Duty	6@800 [4]	10@800	MCFT BSF-42	.044 (1.2)	Carter YFA [5]	12
Heavy Duty	12@800 [6]	12@800	MCFT BSF-42	.044 (1.2)	Carter YFA	13
2.8L (170") V6	10@Idle	10@Idle	MCFTAWSF-42	.044 (1.2)	Motorcraft 2150A	14
3.8L (232") V6	2@800	10@800	MCFTAGSP-52	.044 (1.2)	Motorcraft 2150-A	15
5.0L (305") V8						
Fed.	8@800 [7]	8@800 [7]	MCFT ASF-42	.044 (1.2)	Motorcraft 2150	16
Calif.	[8]	[8]	MCFT ASF-42	.044 (1.2)	Motorcraft 7200VV	17
5.8L (351") V8						
Light Duty	10@800 [8]	14@800 [8]	MCFT ASF-42	.044 (1.2)	Motorcraft 2150 [9]	18
Heavy Duty	8@800	8@800	MCFT ASF-42	.044 (1.2)	Motorcraft 2150	19
7.5L (460") V8						
Fed.	8@800	8@800	MCFT ASF-42	.044 (1.2)	Holley 4180-C	20
Calif.	6@800	6@800	MCFT ASF-42	.044 (1.2)	Holley 4180-C	21
GENERAL MOTORS						
1.9L (119") 4-Cyl.	6@900 [1]	6@900	AC R42XLS	.043 (1.1)	Hitachi DCH340	22
2.0L (122") 4-Cyl.	2@800	2@800	AC R42CTS	.043 (1.1)	Rochester 2SE	23
4.1L (250") 6-Cyl.						
Fed.	10@Idle	10@Idle	AC R45TS [4]	.035 (.9)	Rochester 2SE	24
Calif.	6@700	6@650 [5]	R45TS [4]	.045 (1.2)	Rochester 2SE [6]	25
4.8L (292") 6-Cyl.	8@700	8@700	AC R545TS [4]	.035 (.9)	Rochester 1ME	26
2.8L (173") V6						
Fed.	8@650 [8]	12@650 [9]	AC R43CTS	.045 (1.2)	Rochester 2SE	27
Calif.	10@750	10@650	AC R43CTS	.045 (1.2)	Rochester E2SE	28
5.0L (305") V8						
Fed.	4@600 [11]	4@500 [12]	AC R45TS [4]	.045 (1.2)	Rochester E4ME [13]	29
Calif.	.....	8@550	AC R45TS [4]	.045 (1.2)	Rochester E4ME [13]	30
5.7L (350") V8						
Fed.						
Light Duty	8@700	8@500 [14]	AC R45TS	.045 (1.2)	Rochester M4ME	31
Heavy Duty	6@700	6@700	AC R44T	.045 (1.2)	Rochester M4MC	32
Calif.						
Light Duty	.....	8@550	AC R45TS	.045 (1.2)	Rochester E4ME	33
Heavy Duty	4@700	4@700	AC R44T	.045 (1.2)	Rochester M4MC	34
7.4 (454") V8	4@700 [12]	4@700	AC R44T	.045 (1.2)	Rochester M4MC	35
JEEP						
2.5L (151") 4-Cyl.	12@900	12@900	AC R44TSX	.060 (1.5)	Rochester 2SE [1]	36
4.2L (258") 6-Cyl.						
Fed.	7@600 [2]	7@500 [3]	CH RFN14LY	.035 (.9)	Carter BBD	37
Calif.	7@650	7@550	CH RFN14LY	.035 (.9)	Carter BBD	38
6.0L (360") V8	10@600 [6]	10@600 [6]	CH RN12Y	.035 (.9)	Motorcraft 2150	39

Spark Plugs — **AC** = AC Delco; **CH** = Champion; **MCFT** = Motorcraft
* — All specifications are BTDC; transmission in "D" unless otherwise noted.

TUNE-UP SPECIFICATIONS (Cont.)

No.	HOT IDLE •		FAST IDLE †			REMARKS
	Man. Trans.	Auto. Trans.	M/T RPM	Cam Step	A/T RPM	
1	600/800	650/800	1600	2nd High	1600	[1] — 12@750 on Fed. models.
2	700	.....	1600	2nd High	.....	[2] — 8@750 on Hvy. Duty models.
3	750/850	750/850	1600	2nd High	1600	[3] — Holley 2280 on some Fed. models.
4	800/850 [4] [6]	800/850 [5] [6]	1400 [7]	2nd High	1400 [7]	[4] — 740/850 on Calif. models.
5	750	750	1600 [8]	2nd High	1600 [8]	[5] — 700/850 on Calif. models.
6	750	750	1600 [8]	2nd High	1600 [8]	[6] — 750 with Holley 2280.
7	700	700	1500	2nd High	1500	[7] — 1500 with Holley 2280.
8	750	750	1700	2nd High	1700	[8] — 1800 on Hvy. Duty models.
9	800/700	800/700	2000	High	2000	[1] — 10@800 on Hi. Alt. models.
10	850/700 [2]	800/700 [3]	2000	High	2000	[2] — 800/700 without power steering.
11	850/700 [2]	800/700 [3]	2000	High	2000	[3] — 750/700 without power steering.
12	600/700	550	1400	2nd	1400	[4] — 10@800 on Hi. Alt. models. Calibration No. 2-51P-R0 and 2-51P-R0 10@600.
13	500/600	500/550	1600	2nd	1600	[5] — YFA Feedback on Calif. & Hi. Alt. models.
14	.....	.....	3000	High	3000	[6] — Calibration No. 9-78J-R0 10@800.
15	700/850	650/750	2200	High	1300	[7] — 12@800 on Hi. Alt. models.
16	700/800	600/625	2100	High	2000	[8] — Calif. models not adjustable.
17	.....	575/650	.....	High	2000	[9] — Motorcraft 7200VV on Calif. models.
18	550/625	550/625	1700 [10]	2nd [11]	1650 [12]	[10] — 2000 on Hi. Alt. Calibration No. 2-64X-R00 and all Calif. models.
19	525/650	525/650	1500	1st	1500	[11] — High step on Hi. Alt. models with automatic transmission.
20	650	650	1500	High	1600	[12] — 2000 on Hi. Alt. No. 2-64X-R00, Fed. No. 1-64H-R11 and all Calif. models. 1700 on Hi. Alt. No. 2-63Y-R11 and -R12.
21	650	650	2000	High	1600	
22	900/900 [2]	900/1900	3200	1st	3200	[1] — 6@800 on Fed. & Hi. Alt. models.
23	800/1075	800/1075	2600	High	2600	[2] — 800 on Fed. models.
24	[7]	[7]	2000	High	2200	[3] — 900 on Man. Trans. models.
25	[7]	[7]	2000	High	2200	[4] — AC R44T on HD models.
26	450/700	450/700	2400	High	2400	[5] — 6@700 on models with air conditioning.
27	650/850 [10]	650/850 [10]	1800	High	2100	[6] — Rochester E2SE on models with HEI-EST.
28	750/950	650/850	2100	High	2100	[7] — Varies with decal number. See Tune-Up article.
29	600/700	500/600	1300 [15] [16]	High	1600	[8] — 10@700 on Hi. Alt. models.
30	.....	550/600	.....	High	1800 [16]	[9] — 12@700 on Hi. Alt. models.
31	600/750	500/600	1300 [15]	High	1600	[10] — 700/850 on Hi. Alt. models.
32	700	700	1900	High	1900	[11] — 4@700 on Hi. Alt. models.
33	.....	550/600	.....	High	1800	[12] — 4@600 on Hi. Alt. models.
34	700	700	1900	High	1900	[13] — Rochester M4MC on Hvy. Duty models.
35	700	700	1900	High	1900	[14] — 8@600 on Hi. Alt. models. [15] — 1600 on Hi. Alt. models. [16] — 1900 on Hvy. Duty models.
36	500/900	500/900	2500	High	2500	[1] — Rochester E2SE on Calif. models.
37	600 [4]	500 [6]	1700	2nd	1850	[2] — 14@700 on Hi. Alt. models.
38	650	550	1700	2nd	1850	[3] — 14@650 on Hi. Alt. models. [4] — 700 on Hi. Alt. models.
39	500/600	500/600	1500	2nd	1600	[5] — 650 on Hi. Alt. models. [6] — 16@600 on Hi. Alt. models.

• — When idle solenoid is used, lower RPM is with solenoid disconnected; higher RPM is with solenoid connected.

† — All specifications are with transmission in neutral unless otherwise noted.

SECTION 1

TUNE-UP

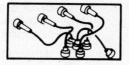

CONTENTS

NOTE: **ALSO SEE GENERAL INDEX.**

IMPORTANT: Because of the many model names used by vehicle manufacturers, accurate identification of models is important. See Model Identification at the front of this publication.

Tune-Up

TUNE-UP TROUBLE SHOOTING

CONDITION	POSSIBLE CAUSE	CORRECTION
SPARK PLUG DIAGNOSIS		
Normal Spark Plug Condition	Light Tan or Gray deposits on insulator Electrode not burned or fouled Gap tolerance not changed	
Cold Fouling or Carbon Deposits	Over-rich air/fuel mixture Faulty choke Clogged air filter Incorrect idle speed or dirty carburetor Faulty ignition wiring Prolonged operation at idle Sticking valves or worn valve guide seals	Adjust air/fuel mixture, see TUNE-UP Replace choke assembly, see FUEL Clean and/or replace air filter Reset idle speed and/or clean carburetor Replace ignition wiring Shut engine off during long idle Check valve train
Wet Fouling or Oil Deposits	Worn rings and pistons Excessive cylinder wear Worn or loose bearings	Install new rings and pistons Rebore or replace block Tighten or replace bearings
Gap Bridged	Deposits in combustion chamber becoming fused to electrode	Clean combustion chamber of deposits
Blistered Electrode	Engine overheating Wrong type of fuel Loose spark plugs Over-advanced ignition timing	Check cooling system Replace with correct fuel Re-tighten spark plugs Reset ignition timing, see TUNE-UP
Pre-Ignition or Melted Electrodes	Incorrect type of fuel Incorrect ignition timing Burned valves Engine overheating Wrong type of spark plug, too hot	Replace with correct fuel Reset ignition timing, see TUNE-UP Replace valves Check cooling system Replace with correct spark plug, see TUNE-UP
Chipped Insulators	Severe detonation Improper gapping procedure	Check for over-advanced timing or combustion chamber deposits Re-gap spark plugs
Rust Colored Deposits	Additives in unleaded fuel Water in combustion chamber	Try different fuel brand These deposits do not affect plug performance
ELECTRONIC IGNITION DIAGNOSIS		

Before diagnosing an electronic ignition system, ensure that all wiring is properly connected between distributor, wiring connector and spark plugs. Ignition problems will show up either as: Engine Will Not Start or Engine Runs Rough.

CONDITION	POSSIBLE CAUSE	CORRECTION
Engine Won't Start	Open circuits in the following locations: Between distributor and bulkhead connector Between bulkhead connector and ignition switch Between ignition switch and starter solenoid	 Repair circuit Repair circuit Repair circuit
Engine Runs Rough	Fuel lines leaking or clogged Ignition timing incorrect Centrifugal advance malfunction Defective spark plugs, or wiring	Tighten fitting, remove restriction Reset ignition timing, see TUNE-UP Check distributor advance, see ELECTRICAL Replace plugs or plug wiring
Component Failure	Spark arc-over on rotor, coil or cap Defective pick-up coil Defective ignition coil Defective vacuum unit Defective control module	Replace rotor, cap or coil Replace pick-up coil, see ELECTRICAL Replace ignition coil Replace vacuum unit, see ELECTRICAL Replace control module

TUNE-UP TROUBLE SHOOTING (Cont.)

CONDITION	POSSIBLE CAUSE	CORRECTION
ELECTRONIC IGNITION DIAGNOSIS BY OSCILLOSCOPE PATTERN		
Firing Voltage Lines are the Same, But Abnormally High	Retarded ignition timing	Reset ingition timing, see TUNE-UP
	Fuel mixture too lean	Re-adjust carburetor, see TUNE-UP
	High resistance in coil wire	Replace coil wire
	Corrosion in coil tower terminal	Clean and/or replace coil
	Corrosion in distributor coil terminal	Clean or replace distributor cap
Firing Voltage Lines are the Same, But Abnormally Low	Fuel mixture too rich	Re-adjust carburetor, see TUNE-UP
	Breaks in coil wire causing arcing	Replace coil wire
	Cracked coil tower causing arcing	Replace coil
	Low coil output	Replace coil
	Low engine compression	Determine cause and repair
One or More, But Not All Firing Voltage Lines Are Higher Than the Others	Carburetor idle mixture not balanced	Re-adjust idle mixture, see TUNE-UP
	EGR valve stuck open	Inspect and/or replace EGR valve
	High resistance in spark plug wire	Replace spark plug wires
	Cracked or broken spark plug insulator	Replace spark plugs
	Intake vacuum leak	Repair leak
	Defective spark plugs	Replace spark plugs
	Corroded spark plug terminals	Replace spark plugs
One or More, But Not All Firing Voltage Lines Are Lower	Curb idle mixture not balanced.	Re-adjust idle mixture, see TUNE-UP
	Breaks in plug wires causing arcing.	Replace spark plug wires
	Cracked coil tower causing arcing.	Replace coil
	Low compression.	Determine cause and repair
	Defective or fouled spark plugs	Replace spark plugs
Cylinders Not Firing	Cracked distributor cap terminals.	Replace distributor cap
	Shorted spark plug wire.	Determine cause of short and replace wire
	Mechanical problem in engine.	Determine problem and correct
	Defective spark plugs.	Replace spark plugs
	Spark plugs fouled.	Replace spark plugs
GENERAL DIAGNOSIS		
Hard Starting	Binding carburetor linkage	Eliminate binding
	Binding choke linkage	Eliminate binding
	Binding choke piston	Eliminate binding
	Restricted choke vacuum	Check vacuum lines for blockage
	Worn or dirty needle valve and seat	Clean carburetor, see FUEL
	Float sticking	Re-adjust or replace float, see FUEL
	Incorrect choke adjustment.	Reset choke adjustment, see TUNE-UP
	Defective coil.	Replace coil
	Improper spark plug gap.	Re-gap spark plugs
	Incorrect ignition timing.	Reset ignition timing, see TUNE-UP
Detonation	Over-advanced ignition timing	Reset ignition timing, see TUNE-UP
	Defective spark plugs	Replace spark plugs
	Fuel lines clogged	Clean out fuel lines
	EGR system malfunction	Check EGR system
	PCV system malfunction	Check PCV system
	Vacuum leaks	Check and repair vacuum system
	Loose fan belts	Tighten or replace fan belts, see TUNE-UP
	Restricted air flow	Remove restriction
	Vacuum advance malfunction	Check distributor operation, see ELECTRICAL
Dieseling	Binding carburetor linkage	Free carburetor linkage
	Binding throttle linkage	Free throttle linkage
	Binding choke linkage or fast idle cam	Free binding linkage
	Defective idle solenoid	Replace solenoid, see FUEL
	Improper base idle speed	Reset idle speed, see TUNE-UP
	Incorrect ignition timing	Reset ignition timing, see TUNE-UP
	Incorrect idle mixture setting	Reset idle mixture setting, see TUNE-UP

Tune-Up

TUNE-UP TROUBLE SHOOTING (Cont.)

CONDITION	POSSIBLE CAUSE	CORRECTION
GENERAL DIAGNOSIS (Cont.)		
Faulty Acceleration	Incorrect ignition timing	Reset ignition timing, see TUNE-UP
	Engine cold and choke too lean	Adjust choke and allow engine to warm-up
	Defective spark plugs	Replace spark plugs
	Defective coil	Replace coil
Faulty Low Speed Operation	Clogged idle transfer slots	Clean idle transfer slots, see FUEL
	Restricted idle air bleeds and passages.	Disassemble carburetor and clean, see FUEL
	Clogged air cleaner filter	Replace air cleaner
	Defective spark plugs	Replace spark plugs
	Defective ignition wires	Replace ignition wires, see TUNE-UP
	Defective distributor cap	Replace distributor cap
Faulty High Speed Operation	Incorrect ignition timing	Reset ignition timing, see TUNE-UP
	Defective distributor centrifugal advance.	Replace mechanism, see ELECTRICAL
	Defective distributor vacuum advance	Replace adcanve unit, see ELECTRICAL
	Incorrect spark plugs or plug gap	Check gap and/or replace spark plugs
	Faulty choke operation	Check choke and repair as required
	Clogged vacuum passages	Remove restrictions
	Improper size or clogged main jet	Check jet size and clean, see FUEL
	Restricted air cleaner	Check filter and replace as required
	Defective distributor cap, rotor or coil	Replace cap, rotor or coil
	Worn distributor shaft	Replace distributor
Misfire At All Speeds	Defective spark plugs	Replace spark plugs
	Defective spark plug wires	Replace spark plug wires
	Defective distributor cap, rotor or coil	Replace cap, rotor, or coil
	Cracked or broken vacuum hoses	Replace vacuum hoses
	Vacuum leaks	Seal leaks
	Fuel lines clogged	Remove restriction
Hesitation	Cracked or broken vacuum hoses	Replace vacuum hoses
	Vacuum leaks	Repair leaks
	Binding carburetor linkage	Eliminate binding
	Binding throttle linkage	Eliminate binding
	Binding choke linkage or fast idle cam	Eliminate binding
	Improper float setting	Re-adjust float setting, see FUEL
	Cracked or broken ignition wires	Replace ignition wires
Rough Idle, Missing or Stalling	Incorrect curb idle or fast idle speed.	Reset idle speeds, see TUNE-UP
	Incorrect basic timing	Reset ignition timing, see TUNE-UP
	Improper idle mixture adjustment	Reset idle mixture adjustment, see TUNE-UP
	Improper feedback system operation	Check feedback system, see FUEL
	Incorrect spark plug gap	Reset spark plug gap, see TUNE-UP
	Moisture in ignition components	Dry components
	Loose or broken ignition wires	Replace ignition wires
	Damaged distributor cap or rotor	Replace cap or rotor
	Faulty ignition coil	Replace coil
	Fuel filter clogged or worn	Replace fuel filter
	Damaged idle mixture screw	Replace idle mixture screw, see FUEL
	Improper fast idle cam adjustment	Reset fast idle cam adjustment, see TUNE-UP
	Improper EGR valve operation	Replace EGR valve
	Faulty PCV valve air flow	Replace PCV valve
	Choke binding, or improper setting	Reset choke and eliminate binding
	Vacuum leak	Eliminate leak
	Improper float bowl fuel level	Reset float adjustment, see FUEL
	Clogged air bleed or idle passages	Clean carburetor passages, see FUEL
	Clogged or worn air cleaner filter	Replace air filter
	Faulty choke vacuum diaphragm	Replace diaphragm, see FUEL
	Exhaust manifold heat valve inoperative	Replace heat valve
	Improper distributor spark advance	Check distributor operation, see ELECTRICAL

TUNE-UP TROUBLE SHOOTING (Cont.)

CONDITION	POSSIBLE CAUSE	CORRECTION
	GENERAL DIAGNOSIS (Cont.)	
Rough Idle, Missing or Stalling (Cont.)	Leaking valves or valve components	Check valve train
	Improper carburetor mounting	Remove and remount carburetor
	Excessive play in distributor shaft	Replace distributor, see ELECTRICAL
	Loose or corroded wiring connections	Repair or replace as required
Engine Surges	Improper PCV valve air flow	Replace PCV valve
	Vacuum leaks	Eliminate leaks
	Clogged main jets	Remove restriction
	Clogged air bleeds	Remove restriction
	EGR valve malfunction	Replace EGR valve
	Restricted air cleaner filter	Replace air filter
	Cracked or broken vacuum hoses	Repair or replace hoses
	Cracked or broken ignition wires	Replace ignition wires
	Vacuum advance malfunction	Check unit and replace if required
	Defective or fouled spark plugs	Replace spark plugs
Ping or Spark Knock	Incorrect ignition timing	Reset ignition timing, see TUNE-UP
	Distributor centrifugal or vacuum advance malfunction	Check operation amd replace as required
	Carburetor setting too lean	Re-adjust mixture setting, see TUNE-UP
	Vacuum leak	Eliminate leak
	EGR valve malfunction	Replace EGR valve
Poor Gasoline Mileage	Cracked or broken vacuum hoses	Replace vacuum hoses
	Vacuum leaks	Eliminate leaks
	Defective ignition wires	Replace wires
	Incorrect choke setting	Re-adjust setting, see FUEL
	Defective vacuum advance	Replace vacuum advance, see ELECTRICAL
	Defective spark plugs	Replace spark plugs
	Binding carburetor power piston	Eliminate binding
	Dirt in carburetor jets	Clean jets and/or replace, see FUEL
	Incorrect float adjustment	Re-adjust float setting, see FUEL
	Defective power valves	Replace power valve, see FUEL
Engine Stalls	Incorrect idle speed	Re-adjust idle speed, see TUNE-UP
	Improper float level	Re-adjust float level, see FUEL
	Leaking needle valve and seat	Replace needle valve and seat, see FUEL
	Vacuum Leaks	Eliminate leaks

1983 Chrysler Corp. 6 Tune-Up

TUNE-UP

ENGINE IDENTIFICATION

The engine can be identified by a number stamped on right side of block below No. 6 spark plug. The first digit indicates model year. The next 3 digits indicate cubic inch displacement.

The engine can also be identified by the eighth digit of the Vehicle Identification Number (VIN). The VIN number is located on a label on upper left corner of instrument panel, near windshield.

VIN ENGINE CODES

Application	VIN Code
3.7L (225") 1-Bbl.	H
3.7L (225") 2-Bbl.	M

TUNE-UP NOTES

NOTE: **When performing tune-up procedures described in this article, the following notes and precautions must be followed.**

In order to comply with emission standards, specifications shown on engine compartment emission control tune-up decal must be used in all instances. In the event of a conflict between specifications given in this manual and decal specifications, use the decal specifications.

When performing tune-up on vehicles equipped with catalytic converters, do not allow or create a condition of engine misfire in more than one cylinder for an extended period of time. Damage to converter may occur due to loading converter with unburned air/fuel mixture.

ENGINE COMPRESSION

Before making a compression test or cranking engine using a remote starting switch, disconnect coil wire from distributor and secure to a good ground. With engine warm, spark plugs removed and throttle wide open, compression pressure should be as specified.

COMPRESSION SPECIFICATIONS

Compression Ratio	8.4:1
Compression Pressure	Min. 100 psi (7.0 kg/cm²)
Maximum Pressure Variation	25 psi (1.8 kg/cm²)

VALVE CLEARANCE

All engines are equipped with hydraulic valve lifters. Lifters should be adjusted to zero lash.

VALVE ARRANGEMENT

E-I-E-I-E-I-I-E-I-E-I-E (Front to rear)

SPARK PLUGS

SPARK PLUG SPECIFICATIONS

Application	Gap In. (mm)	Torque Ft. Lbs. (N.m)
All Models	.035 (0.9)	.... 10 (14)

SPARK PLUG TYPE

Application	Champion No.
All Models	RBL-16Y

HIGH TENSION WIRE RESISTANCE

1) Carefully remove spark plug wire from spark plug. DO NOT remove wire from distributor cap. Connect an ohmmeter between spark plug end terminal and corresponding electrode inside cap.

2) If resistance is not within specifications, remove wire and repeat test. To check coil wire resistance, remove distributor cap from distributor without removing wire from cap or coil. Connect an ohmmeter between center contact in cap and other end of wire.

3) If resistance is not within specifications, remove wire at coil tower and repeat test. If resistance of any wire is not within specifications, replace wire.

RESISTANCE (Ohms)

Application	Specification
All Wires	
Minimum	3000 per foot
Maximum	7200 per foot

DISTRIBUTOR

All models are equipped with Chrysler Electronic Spark Advance (ESA) system with dual pick-up distributor. No adjustments are required.

Fig. 1: Timing Marks and Firing Order

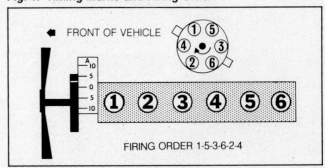

Magnetic probe located at 10° ATDC.

TUNE-UP (Cont.)

IGNITION TIMING

NOTE: **All models are equipped with socket for magnetic timing equipment, located at 10° ATDC. Do not use this location for timing with a conventional timing light.**

1) Connect power timing light to number 1 cylinder and tachometer to engine. Start engine, set parking brake and place transmission in Neutral. Bring engine to normal operating temperature. With engine at operating temperature, momentarily open throttle and make sure idle speed screw returns against its stop.

2) On vehicles with carburetor switch, connect a jumper wire between switch and ground. Disconnect and plug vacuum line at Spark Control Computer (SCC). On vehicles not equipped with SCC, disconnect and plug vacuum line at distributor.

3) Adjust idle speed screw if necessary to obtain curb idle. Aim power timing light at timing plate on chain case cover or read magnetic timing unit.

4) If timing is not within 2° of specification, loosen distributor hold-down arm screw and rotate distributor housing to obtain correct timing. Tighten distributor hold-down screw when timing is correct. Recheck idle set RPM and timing.

CAUTION: **DO NOT use distributor vacuum advance unit as a handle when turning distributor housing.**

TIMING SPECIFICATIONS (Degrees BTDC@RPM)

Application	Man. Trans.	Auto. Trans.
1-Bbl.		
Federal	12@600	16@650
Calif.	12@750	16@750
2-Bbl.	12@700	.....

HOT (SLOW) IDLE RPM

MODELS WITH 1-BARREL CARBURETOR

1) Before checking idle speed, check and adjust ignition timing. Disconnect and plug EGR valve hose and 3/16" control hose at canister. Pull PCV valve from valve cover and allow to draw fresh air. Ground carburetor switch with jumper wire, if equipped.

2) Set parking brake, place transmission in Neutral and warm engine to normal operating temperature. Turn A/C "ON" with blower set to "LOW" position and disconnect compressor clutch wire. If not equipped with A/C, connect a jumper wire between positive battery terminal and solenoid lead wire.

NOTE: **Be sure jumper wire is connected to solenoid wire. Wrong connections may damage wiring harness.**

3) Open throttle slightly to allow solenoid plunger to extend. Remove external screw and spring from solenoid. Insert a 1/8" Allen wrench into solenoid and adjust solenoid idle speed. Turn A/C "OFF" and reconnect compressor, or remove jumper wire.

4) On California models with model 6145 carburetor, disconnect and ground oxygen sensor lead. Remove and plug vacuum hose at vacuum transducer on

computer. Connect auxiliary vacuum supply to vacuum transducer and apply 16" Hg.

NOTE: **DO NOT pull wire at oxygen sensor. Oxygen sensor connector is about 4" away from sensor.**

5) On all models, allow engine to run at least 2 minutes, then check idle speed. Replace idle speed screw on solenoid and adjust curb idle. Stop engine, remove test equipment and reconnect all hoses.

MODELS WITH 2-BARREL CARBURETOR

1) Before checking or adjusting idle speed, check and adjust ignition timing. Disconnect and plug vacuum hose at EGR valve. Ground carburetor switch with jumper wire, if equipped.

2) Disconnect and plug carburetor vacuum hose at heated air temperature sensor and OSAC valve. Remove air cleaner and plug 3/16" control hose at canister.

3) Remove PCV valve at cylinder head cover and allow valve to draw underhood air. Connect tachometer. Start engine. Allow engine to run for 1 minute and check RPM. If RPM is not correct, turn idle speed screw to obtain proper idle set RPM.

IDLE SPEED (RPM)

Application	Curb Idle	Solenoid Energized
All Models		
1-Bbl.		
Federal		
Man. Trans.	600	800
Auto. Trans.	650	800
Calif.	750	850
2-Bbl.	700	.....

IDLE MIXTURE

NOTE: **Idle mixture adjustment is not part of a regular tune-up. DO NOT adjust mixture unless carburetor has been disassembled or vehicle fails emissions testing.**

MIXTURE SCREW PLUG REMOVAL
Models With 1-Barrel Carburetor

1) Remove air cleaner assembly, vacuum hoses and linkage as required to gain access to mixture plug. Using a center punch, mark an index point 1/4" from end of mixture screw housing at 2 o'clock position. See Fig. 2.

2) Using a 3/16" drill, drill through outer section of housing at index point. Plug should pop out. If not, use a small tool to pry plug out. Do not tamper with mixture screw setting. Retain plug for reinstallation. Replace all disconnected components and air cleaner.

Models With 2-Barrel Carburetor

1) Remove air cleaner assembly, vacuum hoses and linkage as required to gain access to mixture plugs. Using a center punch, mark an index point 5/16" from front of mixture screw housing on outside surface of both housings.

TUNE-UP (Cont.)

Fig. 2: Mixture Screw Plug Location

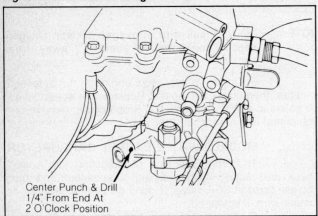

Center Punch & Drill
1/4" From End At
2 O'Clock Position

Use for Holley model 1945 & 6145 carburetors.

2) Using a 3/16" drill, drill at a right angle (90°) to housing through outer surface of housing. Use a small tool to pry plug out. Do not tamper with mixture screw setting. Retain plug for reinstallation. Replace all disconnected components and air cleaner.

PROPANE ENRICHMENT PROCEDURE

1) Remove concealment plug. Set parking brake and place transmission in Neutral. Turn all lights and accessories off. Connect tachometer to engine. Start engine and allow to warm up on 2nd highest step of fast idle cam until normal operating temperature is reached. Return to idle.

2) Disconnect and plug vacuum hose at EGR valve. Ground carburetor switch with jumper wire, if equipped. On 2-barrel carburetor, disconnect and plug vacuum hose at heated air temperature sensor. Remove air cleaner (prop up on models with computer). On all other models, disconnect vacuum supply hose from choke diaphragm at the "T".

3) Install propane supply hose to "T" (to heated air door sensor on 2-barrel carburetor). With the propane bottle upright, remove PCV valve from the cylinder head cover and allow valve to draw underhood air. Disconnect and plug 3/16" control hose from canister.

4) On California models, disconnect and ground oxygen sensor lead. Remove and plug vacuum hose at vacuum transducer on computer. Using auxiliary vacuum supply, apply 16" Hg to vacuum transducer.

5) On all models, allow engine to run for 2 minutes. Open main propane valve. Slowly open the metering valve until maximum RPM is reached. With propane flowing, adjust idle speed screw to reach specified RPM.

6) Adjust metering valve again to reach maximum RPM. If there has been a change in maximum RPM, readjust idle speed screw to specified RPM. Turn off propane and allow engine speed to stabilize. Adjust idle mixture screws 1/16 turn at a time, waiting 30 seconds between adjustments, until smoothest idle at specified RPM is reached.

7) If RPM is more than 25 RPM different from specified RPM, repeat steps **5)** and **6)**. Turn off the propane valves. Remove propane supply hose, reconnect all vacuum hoses and remove test equipment. Install new concealment plugs and perform Slow and Fast Idle Speed Adjustments.

PROPANE MIXTURE ADJUSTMENT (RPM)

Application	Propane RPM (Man. Trans.)	Propane RPM (Auto. Trans.)
All Models		
1-Bbl.		
Federal	675	725
Calif.	850	850
2-Bbl.	750	

COLD (FAST) IDLE RPM

1) Warm engine to operating temperature and place transmission in Neutral. Disconnect and plug hoses at EGR valve and canister. Ground carburetor switch with jumper wire, if equipped. Remove PCV valve from valve cover and allow to draw fresh air. Install tachometer to engine.

2) On 2-barrel carburetor without computer, disconnect and plug vacuum hose at heated air temperature sensor and remove air cleaner. On 2-barrel carburetor with computer, disconnect and plug vacuum hose at vacuum transducer and prop up air cleaner.

3) On all models, disconnect and ground oxygen sensor lead, if equipped. Allow engine to run for 2 minutes. Place fast idle adjustment screw on 2nd highest step of fast idle cam. With choke fully open, adjust fast idle speed by turning screw.

4) Return to idle speed and recheck fast idle speed with fast idle speed screw on 2nd highest step of fast idle cam. Readjust if required. Remove test equipment and reconnect all components.

FAST IDLE SPEED (RPM)

Application	Man. Trans.	Auto. Trans.
All Models	1600	1600

BOWL VENT VALVE ADJUSTMENT

NOTE: Idle speed must be properly set before performing this adjustment.

2-BARREL CARBURETOR ONLY

1) Warm engine to normal operating temperature. Operate engine at curb idle. Remove air cleaner, step-up piston cover plate and gasket.

2) Using pin gauge, measure clearance between top of bowl vent valve and seat. Clearance should be .080" (.20 mm). To adjust, bend bowl vent lever tab until specification is obtained. Support bowl vent lever while bending vent tab.

3) Stop engine. Install step-up piston, gasket and air cleaner.

AUTOMATIC CHOKE SETTING

Vehicles over 6000 lbs. GVW are equipped with a non-adjustable thermostatically controlled automatic choke using engine heat only in positioning valve. All other vehicles have an electric assist choke requiring no adjustment.

TUNE-UP (Cont.)

FUEL PUMP

Measure fuel pump output and pressure with engine running at 500 RPM.

FUEL PUMP SPECIFICATIONS

Application	Pressure psi (kg/cm²)	Volume Quarts (Liters)
All Models	3.0-4.5 (.21-.32)	1 in 1 min. (.95 in 1 min.)

MANIFOLD HEAT CONTROL VALVE

Apply solvent to both ends of valve shaft where it rotates in bushing every 18,000 miles. Work valve back and forth several times.

CAUTION: Apply solvent only when manifold is cold.

EMISSION CONTROL SYSTEMS

NOTE: See appropriate article in Emission Control Section.

GENERAL SERVICING

IGNITION

DISTRIBUTOR

All models are equipped with Chrysler Electronic Spark Advance (ESA) system with dual pick-up. No adjustments are necessary.

DISTRIBUTOR PICKUP COIL RESISTANCE (Ohms)

All Models	150-900

IGNITION COIL

COIL RESISTANCE (Ohms)@75°F (24°C)

Application	Primary	Secondary
Essex	1.34-1.55	9000-12,200
Prestolite	1.60-1.79	9400-11,700

FUEL SYSTEMS

CARBURETORS

Application	Model
Fed. 2-Bbl. Man. Trans.	Carter BBD
Fed. 1-Bbl. All Trans.	Holley 1945
Calif. 1-Bbl. All Trans.	Holley 6145

ELECTRICAL

BATTERY

BATTERY SPECIFICATIONS

Application	Cold Cranking Amps [1]	Reserve Capacity Minutes
Standard	370	86
Optional	500	120

[1] — At 0°F (-18°C).

STARTER

All models use Chrysler Corp. reduction gear type starters.

STARTER SPECIFICATIONS

Application	Volts	Amps	Test RPM
All Models	11	90	3700

ALTERNATORS

All models use Chrysler Corp. alternator.

ALTERNATOR SPECIFICATIONS

Tag Color	Rated Amp. Output
Violet	41
Yellow	
"D", "W", "AW" & "PW" Models	117
All Other Models	60

Field Current Draw@12 Volts

All Models	[1] 4.5-6.5 amps

[1] — While rotating alternator by hand.

ALTERNATOR REGULATORS

All models use Chrysler Corp. Electronic Voltage Regulator. Unit is non-adjustable.

REGULATOR OPERATING VOLTAGE@80°F (27°C)

All Models	13.9-14.6 volts.

ADJUSTMENTS

BELT ADJUSTMENT

With 10 pounds (4.5 kg) pressure applied midway between pulleys, belt deflection for new belts should be .25-.50" (6.0-12 mm). Belt deflection for used belts should be .25-.31" (6.0-8.0 mm). Used belts are any operated more than 15 minutes.

1983 Chrysler Corp. 6 Tune-Up

GENERAL SERVICING (Cont.)

SERVICE INTERVALS

REPLACEMENT INTERVALS

Component	Interval (Miles)
Oil Filter	15,000
Fuel Filter	18,000
PCV Valve	24,000
Air Filter	30,000
Spark Plugs	
With Cat. Converter	30,000
Without Cat. Converter	15,000

CAPACITIES

FLUID CAPACITIES

Application	Quantity
Crankcase	[1] 5.0 qts. (4.7L)
Cooling System	
Standard	[2] 12.0 qts. (11.4L)
Optional	[2] 14.0 qts. (13.2L)
Auto. Trans. (Dexron II)	
A-727	[3] 7.7 pts. (3.6L)
All Others	17.1 pts. (8.1L)
Man. Trans.	
A-833 4-Speed Overdrive	
(Dexron II)	7.5 pts. (3.5L)
N. P. 435 4-Speed	
(SAE 80W-90)	7.0 pts. (3.3L)
Transfer Case	
N. P. 205 (SAE 80W-90)	4.5 pts. (2.1L)
N. P. 208 (Dexron II)	6.0 pts. (2.8L)
Rear Axle (SAE 80W-90)	
8 1/4" Ring Gear	4.5 pts. (2.1L)
9 1/4" Ring Gear	4.5 pts. (2.1L)
9 3/4" Ring Gear	6.0 pts. (2.8L)
10 1/2" Ring Gear	6.5 pts. (3.1L)
Front Axle (SAE 80W-90)	
Model 44	3.5 pts. (1.7L)
Model 60	6.5 pts. (3.1L)
Fuel Tank	
Van Models	
Standard	22.0 gals. (83.3L)
Optional	36.0 gals. (136.3L)
Pickup Models	
Standard (Sport Utility)	35.0 gals. (132.4L)
Standard (Light Duty)	20.0 gals. (75.7L)
Optional	30.0 gals. (113.6L)

[1] — Add 1 quart (.95L) with filter change.
[2] — Add 1 quart (.95L) with rear heater.
[3] — Without torque converter drain.

TUNE-UP

ENGINE IDENTIFICATION

Engine identification number is stamped on a pad located at rear of the right engine mount. First digit indicates model year. The next 3 digits indicate engine size in cubic inches.

Engine can also be identified by the eighth digit in the Vehicle Identification Number (VIN). VIN is located on a plate attached to upper left corner of instrument panel, near windshield.

VIN ENGINE CODES

Application	VIN Code
5.2L (318") 2-Bbl.	T
5.2L (318") 4-Bbl.	U
5.9L (360") 4-Bbl. (Federal)	W
5.9L (360") 4-Bbl. (Calif.)	I
5.9L (360") 4-Bbl. (Heavy Duty)	V

TUNE-UP NOTES

NOTE: **When performing tune-up procedures described in this article, the following notes and precautions must be followed.**

When performing tune-up on vehicles equipped with a catalytic converter, do not allow or create a condition of engine misfire in one or more cylinders for an extended period of time. Damage to converter may occur due to loading with unburned air/fuel mixture.

Due to production changes, always refer to Engine Tune-Up Decal in engine compartment before attempting tune-up. In the event of a conflict between specifications given in this manual and decal specifications, use the decal specifications.

On vehicles equipped with catalytic converters do not add fuel system cleaning agents to fuel tank or carburetor as their use may be detrimental to the catalytic converter.

For tune-up purposes, "Light Duty" refers to vehicles 8500 lbs. GVW or less and "Heavy Duty" refers to vehicles over 8500 lbs. GVW.

ENGINE COMPRESSION

Before making a compression test or cranking engine using a remote starting switch, disconnect coil wire from distributor and secure to a good ground. With engine warm, all spark plugs removed and throttle wide open, compression should be as specified.

COMPRESSION SPECIFICATIONS

Compression Ratio	
5.2L	8.6:1
5.9L	8.5:1
Compression Pressure	Min. 100 psi (7.0 kg/cm²)
Maximum Pressure Variation	40 psi (2.8 kg/cm²)

VALVE CLEARANCE

All engines are equipped with hydraulic lifters. Lifters should be adjusted to zero lash.

VALVE ARRANGEMENT

E-I-I-E-E-I-I-E (Front to rear, both banks)

SPARK PLUGS

SPARK PLUG SPECIFICATIONS

Application	Gap In. (mm)	Torque Ft. Lbs. (N.m)
All Models	.035 (0.9)	.... 30 (41)

SPARK PLUG TYPE

Application	Champion No.
All Models	RN-12Y

HIGH TENSION WIRE RESISTANCE

1) Carefully remove spark plug wire from spark plug. DO NOT remove wire from distributor cap. Connect an ohmmeter between spark plug end terminal and corresponding electrode inside cap. If resistance is not within specifications, remove wire and repeat test.

2) To check coil wire resistance, remove disributor cap from distributor without removing wire from cap or coil. Connect an ohmmeter between center contact in cap and other end of wire. If resistance is not within specifications, remove wire at coil tower and repeat test. If resistance of any wire is not to specification, replace wire.

RESISTANCE (Ohms)

Application	Specification
All Wires	
Minimum	3000 per foot
Maximum	7200 per foot

DISTRIBUTOR

All models are equipped with Chrysler Electronic Ignition system and no adjustments are required. Automatic transmission models use a dual pick-up distributor, while manual transmission models have a single pick-up.

Fig. 1: Timing Marks and Firing Order

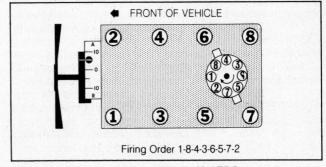

Firing Order 1-8-4-3-6-5-7-2

Magnetic probe socket located at 10° ATDC.

1983 Chrysler Corp. V8 Tune-Up

TUNE-UP (Cont.)

NOTE: All models are equipped with a receptacle for magnetic timing light equipment, located 10° ATDC. Do not use this location for timing with a conventional timing light.

IGNITION TIMING

1) Connect power timing light to number 1 cylinder and connect tachometer to engine. Start engine, set parking brake and place transmission in Neutral. Bring engine to normal operating temperature. With engine at operating temperature, momentarily open throttle and make sure idle speed screw returns against its stop.

2) On vehicles with a carburetor switch, connect a jumper wire between switch and ground. On vehicles not equipped with Spark Control Computer (SCC), disconnect and plug vacuum line at distributor. Adjust idle speed screw if necessary to obtain curb idle.

3) If timing is not within 2° of specification, loosen distributor hold-down arm screw and rotate distributor housing to obtain correct timing. Tighten distributor hold-down screw when timing is correct. Recheck idle set RPM and timing.

CAUTION: DO NOT use distributor vacuum advance unit as a handle when turning distributor housing.

TIMING SPECIFICATIONS (Degrees BTDC@RPM)

Application	Man. Trans.	Auto Trans.
5.2L 2-Bbl.		
Federal	12@750	12@750
Calif.	16@700	16@700
High Alt.	16@700	16@700
5.2L 4-Bbl.		
Light Duty		
Federal	12@750	16@750
Calif.	16@750	.....
Heavy Duty	8@750	8@750
5.9L 4-Bbl.		
Federal	4@700	4@700
Calif.	10@750	10@750

HOT (SLOW) IDLE RPM

1) Before checking or adjusting idle speed, check and adjust ignition timing. Disconnect and plug vacuum hose at EGR valve. Ground carburetor switch with jumper wire, if equipped. On all models not equipped with Spark Control Computer (SCC), disconnect and plug carburetor vacuum hose at heated air temperature sensor.

2) Remove air cleaner (prop up on models with SCC). Remove and plug 3/16" control hose at canister. Remove PCV valve at cylinder head cover and allow valve to draw underhood air. Connect tachometer to engine. Start and warm engine to normal operating temperature.

3) On models equipped with solenoid idle stop (model BBD carburetor), turn A/C "ON" with blower set on "LOW" position. Disconnect A/C compressor clutch wire. On models without A/C, connect a jumper wire between battery positive terminal and solenoid idle stop lead wire.

NOTE: Be sure jumper wire is connected to solenoid wire. Wrong connections may damage wiring harness.

4) Open throttle slightly and allow solenoid plunger to extend. Adjust solenoid idle speed by turning screw on solenoid. Turn A/C "OFF" and reconnect compressor, or remove jumper wire.

5) On models with oxygen sensor, disconnect and ground oxygen sensor lead. Remove and plug vacuum hose at vacuum transducer on computer. Connect auxiliary vacuum supply to vacuum transducer and apply 16" Hg to vacuum transducer.

NOTE: DO NOT pull wire at oxygen sensor. Oxygen sensor connector is about 4" away from sensor.

6) On all models, allow engine to run at least 2 minutes, then check idle speed. Turn idle speed screw and adjust curb idle. Stop engine, remove test equipment and reconnect all hoses. Proceed to fast idle adjustment.

IDLE SPEED (RPM)

Application	Curb Idle	Solenoid Energized
5.2L 2-Bbl. (Carter BBD)		
Calif.		
Man. Trans.	740	850
Auto. Trans.	700	850
All Others	800	850
5.2L 2-Bbl. (Holley 2280)		
All Models	750	
5.2L 4-Bbl.	750	
5.9L 4-Bbl.		
Federal	700	
Calif.	750	

IDLE MIXTURE

NOTE: Idle mixture adjustment is not part of a normal tune-up. DO NOT adjust mixture unless carburetor has been disassembled or vehicle fails emissions testing.

MIXTURE SCREW PLUG REMOVAL

1) Remove air cleaner assembly, vacuum hoses and linkage as required to gain access to mixture plugs. Using a center punch, mark an index point 5/16" (1/4" on Holley 2280 and Carter Thermo-Quad) from end of mixture screw housing on outside surface.

Fig. 2: Mixture Screw Plug Location

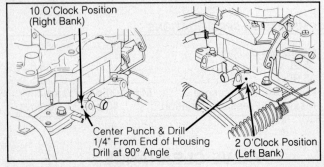

Use for 4-barrel carburetors.

TUNE-UP (Cont.)

2) On Holley 2280, punch right bank in center of housing and left bank slightly above center of housing. On Carter Thermo-Quad, mark right bank at 10 o'clock position and left bank at 2 o'clock position. *See Fig. 2.*.

3) Using a 3/16" drill, drill at a 90° angle (45° angle on Holley 2280) to housing through outer surface of housing. Use a small tool to pry plug out. Do not tamper with mixture screw setting. Retain plug for reinstallation. Replace all disconnected components and air cleaner.

PROPANE ENRICHMENT PROCEDURE

1) Remove concealment plug. Set parking brake and place transmission in Neutral. Turn all lights and accessories off. Connect tachometer. Start engine and allow to warm up on the second highest step of fast idle cam. Return to idle.

2) On 2-barrel models (Carter BBD), disconnect and plug vacuum hose at EGR valve. Ground carburetor switch with jumper wire, if equipped. On models without computer, disconnect and plug vacuum hose at heated air temperature sensor. Remove air cleaner (prop up on models with computer).

3) Connect propane supply hose to heated air temperature sensor vacuum connection. Remove PCV valve from cylinder head cover and allow valve to draw underhood air. Disconnect and plug 3/16" control hose at canister.

4) Disconnect and ground oxygen sensor lead, if equipped. If equipped with oxygen sensor, remove and plug vacuum line at vacuum transducer. Using an auxiliary vacuum supply, apply 16" Hg to vacuum transducer.

5) On all other models, disconnect and plug vacuum hoses at EGR valve, distributor, heated air temperature sensor and OSAC valve, if equipped. Remove air cleaner.

6) Disconnect vacuum supply hose from choke diaphragm "T" (bowl vent vacuum hose at carburetor nipple on 4-barrel models). Remove PCV valve from the cylinder head cover and allow valve to draw underhood air. Disconnect and plug 3/16" control hose at canister.

7) On all models, allow engine to idle for 2 minutes. Open propane main valve. Slowly open the metering valve until maximum RPM is reached. With propane flowing, adjust idle speed screw to reach specified RPM. Adjust metering valve again to reach maximum RPM.

PROPANE MIXTURE ADJUSTMENT (RPM)

Application	Propane RPM (Man. Trans.)	Propane RPM (Auto. Trans.)
5.2L 2-Bbl.		
Carter BBD		
Calif.	825	760
All Others	800	800
Holley 2280		
W/Aspirator	850	850
W/O Aspirator		880
5.2L 4-Bbl.		
Light Duty	840	840
Heavy Duty	810	810
5.9L 4-Bbl.	800	800

8) If there has been a change in maximum RPM, readjust idle speed screw to specified RPM. Turn

off propane and allow engine speed to stabilize. Adjust the idle mixture screws 1/16 turn at a time, waiting 30 seconds between adjustments, until smoothest idle at specified RPM is reached.

9) If RPM is more than 25 RPM different from specified RPM, repeat steps **7)** and **8)**. Turn off propane valves. Remove propane supply hose and test equipment. Reconnect all components and install concealment plugs. Perform Idle Set RPM and Fast Idle Speed Adjustment.

COLD (FAST) IDLE RPM

1) Warm engine to operating temperature and place transmission in Neutral. Disconnect and plug hoses at EGR valve and canister. Ground carburetor switch with jumper wire, if equipped. Remove PCV valve from valve cover and allow to draw fresh air. Install tachometer to engine.

2) On 2-barrel carburetor without computer, disconnect and plug vacuum hose at heated air temperature sensor and remove air cleaner. On 2-barrel carburetor with computer, disconnect and plug vacuum hose at vacuum transducer and prop up air cleaner.

3) On all models, disconnect and ground oxygen sensor lead, if equipped. Allow engine to run for 2 minutes. Place fast idle adjustment screw on 2nd highest step of fast idle cam. With choke fully open, adjust fast idle speed by turning screw.

4) Return to idle speed and recheck fast idle speed with fast idle speed screw on 2nd highest step of fast idle cam. Readjust if required. Remove test equipment and reconnect all components.

NOTE: Idle speeds in the normal operating condition may vary from set speeds.

FAST IDLE SPEED (RPM)

Application	RPM
5.2L 2-Bbl.	
Carter BBD	1400
Holley 2280	1500
5.2L 4-Bbl.	
Light Duty	1600
Heavy Duty	1800
5.9L 4-Bbl.	
Federal	1500
Calif.	1700

DASHPOT ADJUSTMENT

5.2L & 5.9L 4-BBL.

1) With idle speed and idle mixture properly set, connect tachometer to engine. Start engine and position throttle lever actuating tab so that tab is touching dashpot stem. Throttle lever actuating tab should not be depressing dashpot stem.

2) Wait 30 seconds for engine speed to stabilize. Engine speed should be 2300 RPM. To adjust, loosen dashpot lock nut and turn screw until specification is obtained. After adjustment, tighten lock nut and make sure throttle lever returns to idle position.

TUNE-UP (Cont.)

BOWL VENT VALVE ADJUSTMENT

NOTE: Idle speed must be properly set before performing this adjustment.

5.2L 2-BBL.

1) Warm engine to normal operating temperature. Operate engine at curb idle. Remove air cleaner, step-up piston cover plate and gasket.

2) Using pin gauge, measure clearance between top of bowl vent valve and seat. Clearance should be .080" (.20 mm). If adjustment is required, bend bowl vent lever tab until specification is obtained. Support bowl vent lever while bending vent tab.

3) Stop engine. Install step-up piston, gasket and air cleaner.

SOLENOID BOWL VENT VALVE

5.2L & 5.9L 4-BBL.

1) Remove air cleaner assembly. Disconnect hose to solenoid bowl vent diaphragm. Connect outside vacuum source and apply at least 15" Hg to diaphragm.

2) Look down through air horn vent tube and observe valve movement. *See Fig. 3.* Turn ignition switch "ON". Remove outside vacuum source from diaphragm. Valve should remain in down position until ignition switch is turned "OFF".

Fig. 3: Cutaway View of Solenoid Vent Valve for Checking Vent Valve Operation

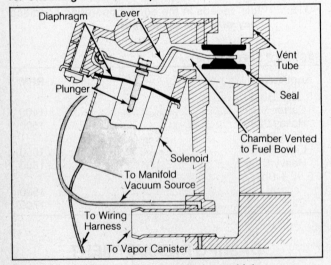

Perform test with carburetor installed on vehicle.

3) If valve does not move with vacuum applied, diaphragm is leaking and must be replaced. If valve does not remain in down position when ignition switch is turned "ON" and vacuum source is removed, solenoid or its related wiring is faulty.

VACUUM THROTTLE POSITIONER ADJUSTMENT

5.2L & 5.9L 4-BBL. VANS

1) Start engine and allow to idle in Neutral. Accelerate engine to above 2000 RPM. Make sure the

vacuum positioner operates and can withstand being pushed on by hand when in the operating position.

Fig. 4: Vacuum Throttle Positioner

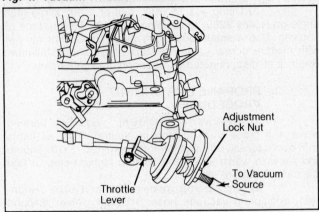

Make adjustment in 1/4 turn increments.

2) Accelerate to 2000 RPM and loosen positioner adjustment lock nut. Rotate complete vacuum positioner assembly until positioner just contacts throttle lever. *See Fig. 4.* Release throttle and slowly adjust positioner to decrease engine speed until a sudden drop of at least 1000 RPM occurs.

3) Turn positioner 1/4 turn further and tighten lock nut. Accelerate engine to 2300 RPM and release throttle. Engine should return to normal idle.

AUTOMATIC CHOKE SETTING

All models use an electric assist choke which requires no adjustment.

FUEL PUMP

Measure fuel pump pressure and volume with engine running at 500 RPM.

FUEL PUMP SPECIFICATIONS

Application	Pressure psi (kg/cm²)	Volume Quarts (Liters)
All Models	4.75-6.25 (.33-.44)	1 in 1 min. (.95 in 1 min.)

MANIFOLD HEAT CONTROL VALVE

Apply solvent to both ends of valve shaft where it rotates in bushing every 18,000 miles. Work valve back and forth several times.

CAUTION: Apply solvent only when manifold is cold.

EMISSION CONTROL SYSTEMS

NOTE: See appropriate article in Emission Control Section.

GENERAL SERVICING

IGNITION

DISTRIBUTOR

All models are equipped with Chrysler Corp. Electronic Ignition System. Units are entirely self-contained and require no outside adjustments.

DISTRIBUTOR PICKUP COIL RESISTANCE (Ohms)

All Models 150-900

TOTAL SPARK ADVANCE@2200 RPM

Application (Distributor No.)	With Vac. Advance	Without Vac. Advance
4111950 & 4111501	20°	9°
4145602	18°	7°
4091661 [1]	19°	7°

[1] — At 2000 RPM.

IGNITION COIL

COIL RESISTANCE (Ohms)@75°F (24°C)

Application	Primary	Secondary
Essex	1.3-1.6	9000-12,200
Prestolite	1.6-1.8	9400-11,700

FUEL SYSTEMS

CARBURETORS

Application	Model
5.2L 2-Bbl.	
Federal Only	Holley 2280
Federal, High Alt., & Calif.	Carter BBD
5.2L 4-Bbl.	Carter Thermo-Quad
5.9L 4-Bbl.	Carter Thermo-Quad

ELECTRICAL

BATTERY

BATTERY SPECIFICATIONS

Application	Cold Cranking Amps. [1]	Reserve Capacity Minutes
Standard	370	86
Optional	500	120

[1] — At 0°F (-18°C).

STARTER

All models use a Chrysler Corp. reduction gear type starter.

STARTER SPECIFICATIONS

Application	Volts	Amps.	Test RPM
All Models	11	90	3700

ALTERNATORS

All models use Chrysler Corp. alternators.

ALTERNATOR SPECIFICATIONS

Tag Color	Rated Amp. Output
Violet	41
Yellow	
"D", "W", "AW" & "PW" Models	117
All Other Models	60

Field Current Draw@12 Volts

| All Models .... | [1] 4.5-6.5 amps |

[1] — While rotating alternator by hand.

ALTERNATOR REGULATOR

All models use Chrysler Corp. Electronic Voltage Regulator. Unit is non-adjustable.

REGULATOR OPERATING VOLTAGE@80°F (27°C)

All Models 13.9-14.6

CAPACITIES

FLUID CAPACITIES

Application	Quantity
Crankcase	[1] 5.0 qts. (4.7L)
Cooling System	
5.2L	[2] 16.0 qts. (15.1L)
5.9L	14.5 qts. (13.7L)
Auto. Trans. (Dexron II)	
A-727	[3] 7.7 pts. (3.6L)
All Others	17.1 pts. (8.1L)
Man. Trans.	
4-Speed Overdrive	
A-833 (Dexron II)	7.5 pts. (3.5L)
N.P. 435 4-Speed	
(SAE 80W-90)	7.0 pts. (3.3L)
Transfer Case	
N.P. 205 (SAE 80W-90)	4.5 pts. (2.1L)
N.P. 208 (Dexron II)	6.0 pts. (2.8L)
Rear Axle (SAE 80W-90)	
8 1/4" Ring Gear	4.5 pts. (2.1L)
9 1/4" Ring Gear	4.5 pts. (2.1L)
9 3/4" Ring Gear	6.0 pts. (2.8L)
10 1/2" Ring Gear	6.5 pts. (3.1L)
Front Axle (SAE 80W-90)	
Model 44	3.5 pts. (1.7L)
Model 60	6.5 pts. (3.1L)
Fuel Tank	
Van Models	
Standard	22.0 gals. (83.3L)
Optional	36.0 gals. (136.3L)
Pickup Models	
Standard (Sport Utility)	35.0 gals. (132.4L)
Standard (Light Duty)	20.0 gals. (75.7L)
Optional	30.0 gals. (113.6L)

[1] — Add 1 qt. (.95L) with filter change.
[2] — Add 1 qt. (.95L) with A/C or increased cooling.
[3] — Without torque converter drain.

1983 Chrysler Corp. V8 Tune-Up

GENERAL SERVICING (Cont.)

ADJUSTMENTS

BELT ADJUSTMENT

With 10 pounds (4.5 kg) pressure applied midway between pulleys, belt deflection for new belts should be .25-.50" (6.0-12 mm). Belt deflection for used belts should be .25-.31" (6.0-8.0 mm). Used belts are any operated more than 15 minutes.

SERVICE INTERVALS

REPLACEMENT INTERVALS

Component	Light Duty Interval (Miles)	Heavy Duty Interval (Miles)
Oil Filter	15,000	12,000
Fuel Filter	30,000	18,000
Air Filter	30,000	[1] 24,000
PCV Valve	30,000	24,000
Spark Plugs		
W/Cat. Conv.	30,000	18,000
W/O Cat. Conv.	15,000	18,000

[1] — Clean at 12,000 mile intervals.

TUNE-UP

ENGINE IDENTIFICATION

Engine is identified by letter code in eighth position of Vehicle Identification Number (VIN). The VIN is stamped on a metal tab, attached to upper left side of instrument panel and is visible through windshield. The VIN can also be found on Safety Standard Certification Label attached to left door lock edge.

ENGINE IDENTIFICATION CODES

Engine	Code
2.0L (122") 1-Bbl.	C
2.3L (140") 1-Bbl.	A

TUNE-UP NOTES

NOTE: **When performing tune-up procedures described in this article, the following notes and precautions must be followed.**

When performing tune-up on vehicles equipped with a catalytic converter, do not allow or create a condition of engine misfire in one or more cylinders for an extended period of time. Damage to converter may occur due to loading with unburned air/fuel mixture.

Due to production changes, always refer to Engine Tune-Up Decal in engine compartment before attempting tune-up. In the event of a conflict between specifications given in this manual and decal specifications, use the decal specifications.

ENGINE COMPRESSION

Test compression pressure with engine at normal operating temperature, all spark plugs removed, and throttle wide open. Crank engine through at least 5 compression strokes before recording pressure. Maximum compression variation between highest and lowest cylinder must not exceed 25%.

VALVE CLEARANCE

All engines have hydraulic lifters. Lifters should be adjusted to zero lash.

VALVE ARRANGEMENT

E-I-E-I-E-I-E-I

SPARK PLUGS

SPARK PLUG SPECIFICATIONS

Application	Gap In. (mm)	Torque Ft. Lbs. (N.m)
All Models	.032-.036 (0.8-0.9) ...	.... 5-10 (7-13)

SPARK PLUG TYPE

Application	Motorcraft No.
All Models	AWSF-42

HIGH TENSION WIRE RESISTANCE

1) Loosen wires from spark plugs by twisting spark plug boot carefully to loosen seal on spark plug. Remove wires by pulling on plug boot. Remove distributor cap from distributor, leaving wires connected to cap.

NOTE: **DO NOT disconnect wires from distributor cap unless replacement is necessary.**

2) Using an ohmmeter, check resistance of each wire by connecting one ohmmeter lead to spark plug terminal and other lead to distributor cap insert. If more than 5000 ohms resistance per inch, remove wire and test again. If still over 5000 ohms per inch, replace wire.

NOTE: **Whenever a high tension wire is disconnected, the interior of the spark plug terminal boot must be coated with silicone grease before reconnection.**

DISTRIBUTOR

All models are equipped with the Dura-Spark II ignition system. The Dura-Spark II ignition system uses a standard Dura-Spark II ignition module or a Universal Ignition Module (UIM), depending on engine calibration.

Fig. 1: 2.0L and 2.3L Timing Mark and Firing Order

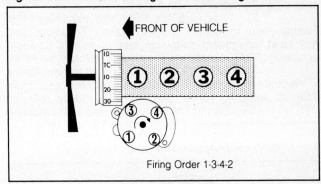

Firing Order 1-3-4-2

IGNITION TIMING

NOTE: **Timing instrument should be connected to number one spark plug wire using an adapter or snap-on connector. Do not puncture spark plug wire or boot to make connection.**

1) Place transmission in Neutral (man. trans.) or "P" (auto. trans.). Turn A/C and heater off. Disconnect and plug vacuum lines at distributor. Connect inductive-type timing light and tachometer to engine.
2) On 2.3L High Altitude models, disconnect 2-wire connector on ignition module and install jumper wire between pins. On 2.3L models with EEC-IV, disconnect wire 324 (between distributor and engine harness) at in-line connector.
3) On all models, start engine and warm to normal operating temperature. With engine running at timing RPM, adjust initial ignition timing. Remove test equipment and reconnect all components. Remove jumper

1983 Ford 4 Tune-Up

GENERAL SERVICING (Cont.)

wire on 2.3L High Altitude models. Reconnect wire on 2.3L models with EEC-IV.

TIMING SPECIFICATIONS (Degrees BTDC@RPM)

Application	Specification
2.0L	6@800
2.3L	
Federal	6@800
Calif.	
Man. Trans.	6@800
Auto. Trans.	8@800
High Altitude	
Man. Trans.	10@800
Auto. Trans.	[1] 8@800

[1] — With feedback carburetor;
without feedback carburetor set to 10@800.

IDLE SPEED (RPM)

Application	Curb Idle & TSP-On RPM	TSP-Off [1]
2.0L	800	700
2.3L		
High Alt.		
Man. Trans.	850	700
Auto. Trans.	800	700
All Others		
Man. Trans.		
W/Power Steer.	850	700
W/O Power Steer.	800	700
Auto. Trans.		
W/Power Steer.	800	700
W/O Power Steer.	750	700

[1] — Transmission in Neutral for TSP-Off.

HOT (SLOW) IDLE RPM

CAUTION: Do not idle engine for over 3 minutes at a time. If idle adjustment is not completed within 3 minutes, run engine at 2200-2800 RPM for 30 seconds before continuing. Repeat as required.

1) Place transmission in Neutral (man. trans.) or "P" (auto. trans.). Start engine and warm to normal operating temperature. Turn A/C off.

2) Check curb idle RPM with transmission in Neutral (man. trans.) or "D" (auto. trans.). To adjust, turn hex head adjustment screw on rear of throttle solenoid positioner (TSP). Accelerate engine and recheck idle RPM.

3) Check TSP-Off RPM with all transmissions in Neutral. If adjustment is required, remove seal from TSP-Off adjusting screw. *See Fig. 2.* Manually collapse TSP by pushing on throttle shaft lever until TSP adjusting screw contacts carburetor body. Adjust TSP-Off RPM.

Fig. 2: Carburetor Adjustment Screw Locations

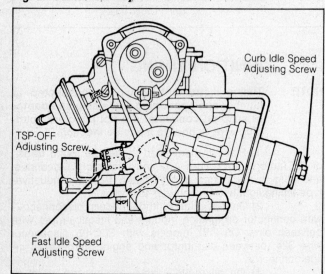

Locations are identical for feedback and non-feedback models.

IDLE MIXTURE

CAUTION: Do not idle engine for over 3 minutes at a time. If idle adjustment is not completed within 3 minutes, run engine at 2200-2800 RPM for 30 seconds before continuing. Repeat as required.

MIXTURE SCREW PLUG REMOVAL

NOTE: Mixture adjustment is not a normal tune-up procedure. DO NOT remove idle mixture plugs unless vehicle fails emissions testing or throttle body has been disassembled.

1) Remove carburetor from engine. Drain fuel from carburetor. Using a hacksaw, carefully cut a lengthwise slot through metal cup around mixture screw.

NOTE: DO NOT contact throttle body with hacksaw blade.

2) Insert a screwdriver into hacksaw slot and twist screwdriver to spread cup. Spread cup just enough to remove mixture screw plug. Reinstall carburetor on engine.

PROPANE ENRICHMENT PROCEDURE

1) Apply parking brake and block drive wheels. Connect tachometer to engine. Make sure hot idle compensator is closed (if equipped). Disconnect fuel evaporative purge hose at air cleaner and plug fitting on air cleaner.

2) Disconnect fresh air duct from air cleaner. Insert propane supply hose 3/4 way into air cleaner duct. Leave all vacuum hoses connected to air cleaner. Air cleaner may be positioned aside for adjustments, but must be in place during speed checks.

3) Revise dump valve vacuum hose configuration as follows, if equipped with thermactor air system (air injection pump).

• Dump valve with 2 vacuum fittings — Disconnect and plug hoses.

1983 Ford 4 Tune-Up

TUNE-UP (Cont.)

- Dump valve with 1 vacuum fitting or combination air by-pass/air control valve — Remove and plug hose at dump valve. Connect slave hose from dump valve fitting to intake manifold vacuum source.
- Combination dump valve and air diverter valve — Disconnect and plug both hoses at dump valve portion.

4) On models with feedback carburetor, disconnect electrical lead wire from electric ported vacuum switch (PVS). Check and adjust curb idle and ignition timing. Remove PCV valve from valve cover and allow to draw fresh air. Briefly run engine at 2500 RPM.

NOTE: Propane bottle must be in a vertical position.

5) With engine idling and transmission in Neutral (man. trans.) or "D" (auto. trans.), slowly open propane valve and watch for RPM gain. When RPM begins to drop off, note maximum speed gain. If gain is within "RPM Gain" specification, do not adjust.

6) If measured speed gain is higher than specification, turn mixture screw counterclockwise (rich) slightly, then repeat steps **4)** and **5)** until gain matches "Reset RPM".

NOTE: After turning idle mixture screw, wait 15 seconds for idle to stabilize before turning screw again.

7) If measured speed gain is lower than specification, turn mixture screw clockwise (lean) slightly, then repeat steps **4)** and **5)** until gain matches "Reset RPM".

8) Reconnect PCV valve and other disconnected components. Readjust idle speed if necessary, then remove test equipment.

PROPANE MIXTURE ADJUSTMENT (RPM)

Application	RPM Gain	Reset RPM
All Models	20-30	30

COLD (FAST) IDLE RPM

1) Place transmission in Neutral (man. trans.) or "P" (auto. trans.). Start engine and warm to normal operating temperature. Stop engine and turn ignition and A/C off. Disconnect and plug vacuum hose at EGR valve.

2) Place fast idle speed adjusting screw on kickdown step of fast idle cam. Adjust idle speed to specification by turning fast idle speed adjusting screw. See Fig. 2. Reconnect vacuum hose at EGR and remove test equipment.

FAST IDLE SPEED (RPM)

Application	RPM
All Models	2000

BOWL VENT VALVE ADJUSTMENT

NOTE: Idle speed must be properly set before performing this adjustment.

1) Turn ignition switch on. Open throttle so that TSP plunger extends. Secure choke plate in wide open position. Open throttle so that throttle vent lever does not contact bowl vent rod.

2) Close throttle to idle set position and measure travel of fuel bowl vent rod from idle to full throttle. See Fig. 3, Dimension "A".

3) Bowl vent rod travel should be .10-.15" (2.5-3.8 mm). If adjustment is required, bend throttle vent lever at point shown in Fig. 3.

Fig. 3: Bowl Vent Valve Adjustment

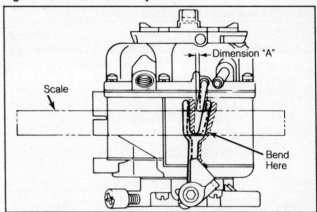

Bend throttle vent lever to obtain specification.

AUTOMATIC CHOKE

NOTE: Although automatic choke is of tamper-proof design, these steps are used if automatic choke is damaged or when carburetor is rebuilt.

1) Choke housing is non-adjustable. Setting is fixed by an index plate located between carburetor and choke cover. Color of index plate indicates calibration setting.

2) To replace index plate, loosen choke thermostat cover. Remove 2 rivets and retaining screw. Separate cover from carburetor and exchange index plates. Replace cover. Install and tighten new rivets and screw.

FUEL PUMP

Make all tests with engine at normal operating temperature, engine at idle speed and transmission in Neutral.

FUEL PUMP SPECIFICATIONS

Application	Pressure psi (kg/cm²)	Volume Pints (Liters)
All Models	5.0-7.0 (34.5-41.5)	1 in 25 sec. (.47 in 25 sec.)

EMISSION CONTROL SYSTEMS

NOTE: See appropriate article in Emission Control Section.

1983 Ford 4 Tune-Up
GENERAL SERVICING

IGNITION
DISTRIBUTOR
All models are equipped with Dura-Spark II ignition systems. No adjustments are required.

DISTRIBUTOR PICKUP COIL RESISTANCE (Ohms)

Application	Specification
All Models	400-1300

TOTAL SPARK ADVANCE@2500 RPM

Application	With Vac. Advance	Without Vac. Advance
Distributor No.		
E27E-12127-AA	38-49	17-21
E27E-12127-BA	37-48	16-21
E37E-12127-FA	33-45	15-20
E37E-12127-GA	34-46	15-20

IGNITION COIL

IGNITION COIL RESISTANCE (Ohms)

Application	Primary	Secondary
All Models	0.8-1.6	7700-10,500

FUEL SYSTEMS
CARBURETORS

Application	Model
2.0L & 2.3L 1-Bbl.	Carter YFA

ELECTRICAL
BATTERY

BATTERY SPECIFICATIONS

Application	Capacity (Amps.)	Discharge Rate (Amps.)
All Models		
Standard	45	190
Optional	63	260

STARTER
All models use Motorcraft positive engagement type starter.

STARTER SPECIFICATIONS

Application	Volts	Amps	Test RPM
All Models			
4" Armature	12	70	[1]
4 1/2" Armature	12	80	[1]

[1] — Information not available from manufacturer.

ALTERNATORS
All models use Motorcraft external regulator alternator.

ALTERNATOR SPECIFICATIONS

Stamp Color	Rated Amp. Output
Orange	40
Green	60
Black	65

Field Current Draw@12 Volts

All Models	4

ALTERNATOR REGULATOR
All models use Motorcraft Solid State Electronic Regulator, calibrated and preset by manufacturer. No adjustment is required or possible.

ADJUSTMENTS
BELT ADJUSTMENT
Using a strand tension gauge, measure belt tension midway between pulleys. If tension is not as specified in Belt Adjustment table, adjust tension or replace belt. Used belts are any operated for more than 10 minutes.

BELT ADJUSTMENT
Tension in Lbs. (Kg) Using Strand Tension Gauge

Application	New Belt	Used Belt
All Models		
Standard V-Belts		
1/4"	50-80	40-60
	(23-36)	(18-27)
15/32"	120-160	90-120
	(54-73)	(41-54)
Ribbed V-Belts	140-180	130-160
	(64-82)	(59-73)

SERVICE INTERVALS
REPLACEMENT INTERVALS

Component	Interval (Miles)
Oil Filter	7500
Air Filter	30,000
PCV Filter	30,000
Spark Plugs	30,000
Fuel Filter	50,000

GENERAL SERVICING (Cont.)

CAPACITIES

FLUID CAPACITIES

Application	Quantity
Cooling System	
Without A/C	6.5 qts. (6.2L)
With A/C	7.2 qts. (6.8L)
Crankcase	
2.0L Engine	[1] 4.0 qts. (3.8L)
2.3L Engine	[1] 5.0 qts. (4.7L)
Auto. Trans.	
C-3 (Dexron II)	8.0 qts. (7.6L)
C-5 (Motorcraft Type H)	
2WD Ranger	17.5 qts. (7.1L)
4WD Ranger	17.9 qts. (7.5L)
Man. Trans.	
4-Speed	3.0 pts. (1.4L)
5-Speed	3.6 pts. (1.7L)
Transfer Case (Dexron II)	3.0 pts. (1.4L)
Rear Axle (Hypoid Gear Lube)	
6 3/4" Ring Gear	3.0 pts. (1.4L)
7 1/2" Ring Gear	4.0 pts. (1.9L)
Front Axle (Hypoid Gear Lube)	
Model 28	1.0 pts. (0.5 L)
Fuel Tank	
Standard	
Short Wheelbase	15.2 gals. (57.5L)
Long Wheelbase	17.0 gals. (64.3L)
Optional Auxiliary	13.0 gals. (49.2L)

[1] — Add 1 qt. (.95L) with filter change.

1983 Ford 6 Tune-Up

TUNE-UP

ENGINE IDENTIFICATION

The engine can be identified by the eighth digit of the Vehicle Identification Number. The number is located on the Safety Compliance label on the left front door pillar. It also is located on a metal plate, riveted to the driver's side of the dash and visible through windshield.

VIN ENGINE CODE

Application	Code
4.9L (300") 1-Bbl.	Y

TUNE-UP NOTES

NOTE: **When performing tune-up procedures described in this article, the following notes and precautions must be followed:**

For tune-up purposes, "Light Duty" refers to vehicles up to 8500 lbs. GVW. "Heavy Duty" refers to vehicles exceeding 8500 lbs. GVW.

Due to late changes and corrections, always refer to Engine Tune-Up Decal in engine compartment before performing tune-up procedures. In the event manual specifications and decal specifications are different, always use the specifications on the Engine Tune-Up Decal.

If the Dura-Spark 2-piece distributor cap must be removed, first remove top portion, then rotor, then bottom portion. If any spark plug wire is disconnected with this system, connection must be first greased with silicone grease before it is reattached.

When connecting a tachometer to Dura-Spark ignition coil, install the alligator clip on tachometer into the "DEC" (TACH TESTING) cavity.

On vehicles equipped with catalytic converter, do not allow or create a condition of engine misfire in more than one cylinder for more than 30 seconds. Damage to converter may result due to loading converter with unburned air/fuel mixture.

ENGINE COMPRESSION

Test compression with all spark plugs removed and engine at normal operating temperature. Crank engine through at least 5 compression strokes before recording reading. Maximum compression variation should not exceed 25% between highest and lowest cylinder.

COMPRESSION SPECIFICATIONS

Application	Compression Ratio
All Models	8.9:1

VALVE CLEARANCE

VALVE CLEARANCE SPECIFICATIONS

Application	Clearance
All Models	[1] .100-.200" (2.5-5.1 mm)

[1] — Clearance allowable with tappet collapsed. Desired clearance is .125-.175" (3.2-4.5 mm).

VALVE ARRANGEMENT

E-I-E-I-E-I-E-I-E-I (Front to rear)

SPARK PLUGS

SPARK PLUG TYPE

Application	Motorcraft No.
All Models	BSF-42

SPARK PLUG SPECIFICATIONS

Application	Gap In. (mm)	Torque Ft. Lbs. (N.m)
All Models	.044 (1.15)	15-22 (20-30)

HIGH TENSION WIRE RESISTANCE

1) Loosen wires from spark plugs by twisting spark plug boot carefully to loosen seal on spark plug. Remove wires by pulling on plug boot. Remove distributor cap from distributor, leaving wires connected to cap.

2) Using an ohmmeter, check resistance of each wire. Connect one ohmmeter lead to spark plug terminal and other lead to distributor cap insert.

3) Replace any wire with over 5000 ohms resistance per inch. New wires should have a resistance of 7000 ohms per foot.

NOTE: **Whenever a high tension wire is disconnected, the interior of spark plug terminal boot must be coated with dielectric silicone grease before reconnection.**

DISTRIBUTOR

All models are equipped with Dura-Spark II ignition system. No adjustments are required.

Fig. 1: Timing Mark & Firing Order

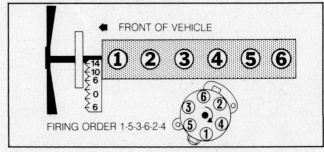

FRONT OF VEHICLE

① ② ③ ④ ⑤ ⑥

FIRING ORDER 1-5-3-6-2-4

Receptacle for magnetic pick-up timing light is located at 135° ATDC.

IGNITION TIMING

CAUTION: **Engines are equipped with a receptacle for use with magnetic pick-up timing lights, located at 135° ATDC. Do not use this location for timing with a conventional timing light.**

TUNE-UP (Cont.)

1) Place transmission in Neutral (man. trans.) or "P" (auto. trans.). Remove vacuum hose from distributor vacuum advance connection, and plug hose.

2) Place mark on proper degree line of damper (or of pointer and damper notch). Connect timing light using inductive pick-up or adapter.

3) Do not puncture spark plug leads. Connect an accurate tachometer. Disconnect barometric pressure switch from ignition module, if equipped.

4) Connect a jumper wire across pins at ignition module connector. Start engine and warm to operating temperature. With engine idling in Neutral, check timing.

5) If within 2° of specification, do not reset. If not to specifications, loosen distributor hold-down bolt and rotate distributor to set timing. Recheck after tightening bolt.

IGNITION TIMING (Degrees BTDC@RPM)

Application	Auto. Trans.	Man. Trans.
All Models		
Light Duty		
High Altitude	10@800	10@800
All Others	10@800	[1] 6@800
Heavy Duty	12@800	[2] 12@800

[1] — Set Calibration No. 2-51P-R0 to 10@600 RPM and No. 2-51P-R10 to 12@600 RPM.

[2] — Set Calibration No. 9-78J-R0 to 10@800 RPM.

HOT (SLOW) IDLE RPM

LIGHT DUTY

1) Place transmission in Neutral (man. trans.) or "P" (auto. trans.) with engine at normal operating temperature. Turn A/C heat selector off. Allow engine speed to stabilize, and measure curb idle speed.

Fig. 2: Adjustment Points for YFA 1-Bbl. Carburetor on Light Duty Engines

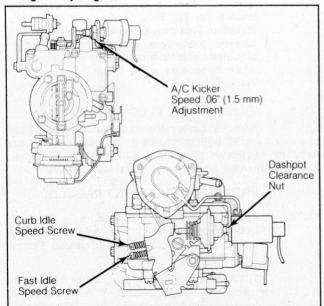

A/C Kicker Speed .06" (1.5 mm) Adjustment

Dashpot Clearance Nut

Curb Idle Speed Screw

Fast Idle Speed Screw

Use 3/8" end wrench on dashpot clearance nut.

2) Ensure Throttle Solenoid Positioner (TSP) is activated. Adjust RPM by turning nut directly behind dashpot housing. *See Fig. 2.* Check anti-diesel RPM (TSP-Off).

3) Manually collapse the TSP-dashpot by rotating carburetor shaft lever until TSP-Off adjusting screw contacts carburetor body.

4) Place transmission in Neutral. Increase engine RPM momentarily, and then recheck idle RPM. If final curb idle speed adjustment is required, bowl vent setting must be checked.

5) Stop engine, and turn ignition key "ON". Secure choke plate in wide open position. Open the throttle so that throttle vent lever does not touch fuel bowl vent rod. Close throttle, and measure travel of fuel bowl vent rod at point "A" from open position. *See Fig. 3.*

Fig. 3: Bowl Vent Setting

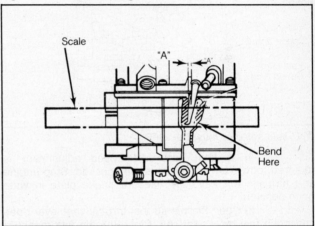

Scale

"A"

Bend Here

Bend throttle vent lever to adjust setting.

6) Travel should be within .10-.15" (2.5-3.8 mm). If out of specification, bend vent lever to obtain required travel. Move A/C heat selector to maximum cooling (blower switch in high position). Disconnect A/C clutch wire. Check and adjust for A/C-On RPM.

LIGHT DUTY IDLE SPEED (RPM)

Application	Curb Idle (A/C Off)	Solenoid Energized (A/C On)
All Models		
Man. Trans.	600	700
Auto. Trans.	550	....

HEAVY DUTY

1) Place transmission in Neutral (man. trans.) or "P", (auto. trans.) with engine at normal operating temperature. Turn A/C heat selector off.

2) Activate (TSP). Set curb idle to specification by turning solenoid in or out. *See Fig. 4.*

3) With transmission selector lever in Neutral (man. trans.) or "P" (auto. trans.), increase engine speed momentarily, letting it return to normal curb idle. Check RPM, and readjust if necessary.

1983 Ford 6 Tune-Up

TUNE-UP (Cont.)

Fig. 4: Adjustment Points for YFA 1-Bbl. Carburetor on Heavy Duty Engines

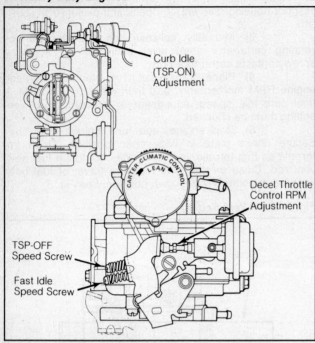

A/C heat selector must be "OFF."

4) If final curb idle speed adjustment is required, bowl vent setting must be checked. Stop engine and turn ignition key "ON". Secure choke plate in wide open position.

5) Open throttle so that throttle vent lever does not touch fuel bowl vent rod. Close throttle and measure travel of fuel bowl vent rod at point "A" from open position.

6) Travel should be within .10-.15" (2.5-3.8 mm). If out of specification, bend vent lever to obtain required travel. To set TSP-Off RPM, run engine to normal operating temperature.

7) Place A/C heat selector in "OFF" position. Disconnect TSP wire. Place transmission in Neutral. Using TSP-Off adjusting screw, set TSP-Off RPM to specifications. Reconnect TSP wire to terminal.

HEAVY DUTY IDLE SPEED (RPM)

Application	Curb Idle TSP-On	TSP-Off
All Models		
Man. Trans.	600	500
Auto. Trans.	550	500

COLD (FAST) IDLE RPM

LIGHT DUTY

1) Place transmission in Neutral. Bring engine to normal operating temperature. Disconnect vacuum hoses at EGR, purge valve or purge solenoid valve, and plug hoses.

2) Disconnect and plug vacuum hose from cold start vacuum switch (Orange vacuum switch on valve cover). Using a slave vacuum hose, connect manifold vacuum to cold start vacuum switch.

3) Place fast idle screw on second step (kickdown) of fast idle cam. Adjust fast idle speed to specifications. *See Fig. 2.* Remove plugs from vacuum hoses, and restore all hoses to their original locations.

LIGHT DUTY FAST IDLE SPEED (RPM)

Application	RPM	Cam Step
All Models		
Man. Trans.	1400	2nd (Kickdown)
Auto. Trans.	1400	2nd (Kickdown)

HEAVY DUTY

NOTE: **Procedure includes setting Decel Throttle Control.**

1) Place transmission in Neutral. Bring engine to normal operating temperature. Disconnect and plug vacuum hose at EGR valve and decel throttle control diaphragm.

2) Place fast idle adjusting screw on second step (kickdown) of fast idle cam. Adjust fast idle speed to specifications. Momentarily depress throttle to rotate fast idle cam.

3) Using a slave vacuum hose, connect manifold vacuum to decel throttle control diaphragm. Adjust diaphragm shaft length until specified RPM is obtained. Remove plugs, and restore vacuum hoses to their original locations.

HEAVY DUTY FAST IDLE SPEED (RPM)

Application	Fast Idle Speed	Decel Throttle Control Speed
All Models	1600	1400-1500

IDLE MIXTURE

NOTE: **If adjustments to air/fuel mixture are made that require removing idle limiter caps, it is imperative that Blue service limiter caps be installed. This procedure is not part of normal tune-up procedure. Idle mixture should be adjusted only during carburetor repair or when necessary as a result of government inspection laws.**

IDLE MIXTURE PLUG REMOVAL

Remove carburetor from vehicle. Drain fuel bowl. Drill a 3/32" hole in mixture screw plug. Use a screw extractor to remove plug. Reinstall carburetor and make adjustments. After adjustments, install new mixture plug.

PROPANE ENRICHMENT PROCEDURE

NOTE: **Propane enrichment procedure is for Light Duty Vehicles only. For adjustments for Heavy Duty Vehicles, see Emission Control Tune-Up Decal.**

1) Leave all vacuum signal hoses attached to air cleaner assembly when relocating air cleaner for

TUNE-UP (Cont.)

carburetor adjustments. Air cleaner MUST be installed for engine speed checks.

2) Apply parking brake and block wheels. Disconnect automatic brake release, and plug vacuum connection, if equipped. Connect tachometer.

3) Disconnect and plug fuel evaporative purge valve signal hose at engine. Disconnect purge hose at air cleaner and plug nipple.

4) Disconnect flexible fresh air tube from air cleaner duct or adapter. Insert hose from propane enrichment tool (Rotunda T75L-9600-A) about 3/4 of the way into duct or fresh air tube. Disconnect PCV valve from grommet, and allow valve to draw underhood air during adjustment.

5) For vehicles equipped with thermactor, disconnect and plug hoses of dump valves equipped with 2 fittings. If valves have one fitting, remove and plug hose at valve. Connect slave hose to dump valve and intake manifold vacuum source.

6) Verify ignition timing is set to specification and adjust if necessary. With engine at normal operating temperature, check curb idle speed or A/C-Off RPM. Adjust as necessary. Run engine at 2500 RPM for 15 seconds before each mixture check.

7) With engine idling in Neutral, gradually open propane tool valve and watch for engine speed gain on tachometer. When speed reaches maximum and begins to drop off, note amount of speed gain.

NOTE: **Propane cartridge must be in vertical position. If engine speed will not drop off, check bottle gas supply. If necessary, repeat test with new bottle.**

8) Compare measured speed gain with specifications. If mixture adjustment is necessary, adjust so gain is within "Reset RPM" specifications. If propane enrichment speed gain is within "RPM Gain" specifications, proceed to step **11)**.

9) If measured speed gain is greater than specification, turn mixture screws counterclockwise in equal amounts, and recheck until measured speed rise is within "'Reset RPM" specifications. Proceed to step **11)**.

10) If measured speed gain is less than specification, turn mixture screws clockwise in equal amounts, and recheck until measured speed rise is within "Reset RPM" specifications. Proceed to step **11)**.

11) Check curb idle, and remove all test equipment. Reconnect hoses in original positions, and connect PCV valve.

PROPANE MIXTURE ADJUSTMENT (RPM)

Calibration Number [1]	RPM Gain	Reset RPM
Light Duty 2-52K-R0 & 2-52L-R0	20-110	60
All Others	10-50	20

[1] — Calibration No. is located on an identification label on front of valve cover. On some engines, label may be on same component as Emission Certification Decal.

ADJUSTMENT

AUTOMATIC CHOKE

NOTE: **Some models may have tamper-proof choke assemblies.**

Drill heads from 2 rivets, and remove. Loosen retaining screw, and turn choke cover in direction indicated on cover to specified setting. Install new rivets and tighten screw.

AUTOMATIC CHOKE SPECIFICATIONS

Application	Choke Setting
Light Duty	Non-Adjustable
Heavy Duty	Index

FUEL PUMP

Check fuel pump at idle RPM with engine at normal operating temperature.

FUEL PUMP SPECIFICATIONS

Application	Pressure psi (kg/cm²)	Volume Pints (Liters)
All Models	5.0-7.0 (.35-.50)	1 in 20 sec. (.47 in 20 sec.)

EMISSION CONTROL

NOTE: **See appropriate article in EMISSION CONTROL Section.**

GENERAL SERVICING

IGNITION

DISTRIBUTOR

All units are equipped with Motorcraft Dura-Spark II Ignition system. Units are self-contained and require no outside adjustments.

DISTRIBUTOR PICK-UP COIL RESISTANCE (Ohms)

All Models	400-1000

1983 Ford 6 Tune-Up

GENERAL SERVICING (Cont.)

TOTAL SPARK ADVANCE@2500 RPM

Distributor No.	W/Vac. Advance	W/O Vac. Advance
Light Duty		
E2TE-12127-FA	42-53°	13-18°
E3TE-12127-TA	[1] 38-50°	15-20°
E3TE-12127-VA	[2] 39-53°	13-18°
E3UE-12127-GA	[3] 38-50°	13-18°
E3UE-12127-JA	41-53°	13-18°
E2TE-12127-RA	42-53°	17-22°
E3TE-12127-NA	39-52°	14-19°
E3UE-12127-HA	41-54°	14-19°
E3TE-12127-UA	[4] 40-52°	15-20°
E3TE-12127-KA	44-55°	15-20°
E3TE-12127-RA	[5] 40-52°	14-19°
E1TE-12127-GA	40-51°	18-23°
Heavy Duty		
D5TE-12127-FA	29-40°	16-21°
D9TE-12127-AEA	24-34°	18-23°
D9TE-12127-ADA	24-34	18-23°

[1] — Calibration number 3—51Z—R00 W/Vac. 42-54° and W/O Vac. 19-24°.

[2] — Calibration number 3—51X—R00 W/Vac. 43-57° and W/O Vac. 17-22°.

[3] — Calibration number 3—51V—R00 W/Vac. 42-54° and W/O Vac. 17-22°.

[4] — Calibration number 3—52Z—R00 W/Vac. 44-56° and W/O Vac. 19-24°.

[5] — Calibration number 3—52V—R00 W/Vac. 44-56° and W/O Vac. 18-23°.

IGNITION COIL

COIL RESISTANCE (Ohms)

Application	Primary	Secondary
All Models	0.8-1.6	7700-10,500

FUEL SYSTEMS

CARBURETORS

Application	Model
Light Duty	
Federal	Carter YFA 1-Bbl.
Calif. & High Alt.	Carter YFA 1-Bbl. Feedback
Heavy Duty	Carter YFA 1-Bbl.

ELECTRICAL

BATTERY

BATTERY SPECIFICATIONS

Application	Capacity (Amp. Hours)	Discharge Rate (Amps.)
Standard		
Federal	36	155
California	45	190
Optional	54, 63, 81	225, 260, 175

STARTER

All models use Motorcraft positive engagement type starters with either a 4" or 4 1/2" armature.

STARTER SPECIFICATIONS

Application	Volts	Amps.	Test RPM
4" Armature	12	70	6700 Min.
4 1/2" Armature	12	80	7380-9356

ALTERNATORS

All models use Motorcraft alternators.

ALTERNATOR SPECIFICATIONS

I.D. Tag Color	Rated Amp. Output
Rear Terminal	
Orange	40
Green	60
Side Terminal	
Black	70
Red	100

Field Current Draw@12 Volts

All Models	4.0 Amps.

ALTERNATOR REGULATORS

Two Motorcraft electronic voltage regulators are used. Although both look alike, they are not interchangeable.

REGULATOR IDENTIFICATION

Application	Color Coding
Used with Ammeter	Blue label
Used with Indicator Lamp	Black label

ADJUSTMENTS

BELT ADJUSTMENT

Using a strand tension gauge, measure belt tension midway between pulleys. If tension is not as specified in Belt Adjustment table, adjust tension or replace belt. Used belts are any operated for more than 10 minutes.

BELT ADJUSTMENT
Tension in Lbs. (Kg) Using Strand Tension Gauge

Application	New Belt	Used Belt
All Models		
1/4" Belt	50-80 (23-36)	18-27 (40-60)
Air Conditioning	135-145 (61-66)	90-100 (41-45)
Alternator	120-160 (54-72)	90-120 (41-54)
All Others	120-130 (54-59)	70-80 (32-36)

GENERAL SERVICING (Cont.)

SERVICE INTERVALS

REPLACEMENT INTERVALS

Application	Miles
Oil Filter	
E100/150, F100/150	10,000
Bronco	7500
All Others	15,000
Air Filter	30,000
PCV Filter	30,000
Spark Plugs	30,000

CAPACITIES

FLUID CAPACITIES (EXCEPT FUEL & COOLING)

Application	Quantity
Crankcase	[1] 6.0 qts. (5.6L)
Rear Axle (Hypoid Gear Lube)	
Ford Standard & Traction-Lok	6.5 pts. (3.0L)
Dana 60	5.0 pts. (2.4L)
Dana 61-1	6.0 pts. (2.8L)
Dana 61-2	6.0 pts. (2.8L)
Dana 70	
Standard	6.5 pts. (3.0L)
Heavy Duty	7.4 pts. (3.5L)
Front Axle (Hypoid Gear Lube)	
Dana 44-IFS	
F150 & Bronco	3.9 pts. (1.8L)
F250	3.8 pts. (1.8L)
Dana IFS	4.1 pts. (1.9L)
Transfer Case (Dexron II Series D)	
Warner 1345	6.5 pts. (3.0L)
New Process 208	7.0 pts. (3.3L)
Auto. Trans. (Dexron II)	
C-5 3-Speed	22 pts. (10.4L)
C-6 3-Speed	
2WD	24 pts. (11.2L)
4WD	27 pts. (12.7L)
AOT 4-Speed	24 pts. (11.7L)
Man. Trans. (SAE 80W-90)	
Ford 3.03 3-Speed	3.5 pts. (1.6L)
T-18 4-Speed	7.0 pts. (3.3L)
New Process 435 4-Speed W/Ext.	7.0 pts. (3.3L)
New Process 435 4-Speed W/O Ext.	6.5 pts. (3.0L)
4-Speed Overdrive	4.5 pts. (2.1L)

[1] — Includes 1 qt. (.95L) for filter change.

COOLING CAPACITIES

Application	Quarts (Liters)
"E" Models	
With Heater	15.0 (14.2)
With Heater & A/C	20.0 (18.9)
Bronco & "F" Models	
With Heater	13.0 (12.2)
With Heater & A/C	14.0 (13.2)

FUEL TANK CAPACITIES

Application	Gallons (Liters)
F100/150, F250 (Short W.B.)	
Standard	16.5 (62.4)
Auxiliary	19.0 (72.0)
F100/350 (Long W.B.)	
Standard	19.0 (72.0)
Auxiliary	19.0 (72.0)
E100/150, Club Wagon (Short W.B.)	
Standard	18.0 (68.1)
Auxiliary	18.0 (68.1)
All Other "E" Models (Long W.B.)	
Standard	22.1 (83.7)
Auxiliary	18.0 (68.1)
Bronco	
Standard	25.0 (94.6)
Optional	32.0 (121.1)

1983 Ford V6 Tune-Up

TUNE-UP

ENGINE IDENTIFICATION

The engine can be identified by the eighth digit of the Vehicle Identification Number (VIN), which is stamped on a metal plate located at upper left corner of dash.

VIN ENGINE CODES

Application	VIN Code
Bronco II & Ranger	
2.8L V6	S
All Others	
3.8L V6	3

TUNE-UP NOTES

NOTE: **When performing tune-up procedures described in this article, the following notes and precautions must be followed:**

Due to production changes, always refer to Engine Tune-Up Decal in engine compartment before attempting tune-up. In the event of a conflict between specifications given in this manual and decal specifications, use the decal specifications.

When performing tune-up on vehicles equipped with a catalytic converter, do not allow or create a condition of engine misfire in 1 or more cylinders for an extended period of time. Damage to converter from overheating may occur due to loading with unburned fuel.

ENGINE COMPRESSION

Test compression with spark plugs removed, engine at normal operating temperature and throttle wide open. Crank engine through at least 5 compression strokes before recording reading. Minimum compression reading must be at least 75% of maximum reading.

VALVE CLEARANCE

VALVE CLEARANCE ADJUSTMENT

Application	Intake In. (mm)	Exhaust In. (mm)
2.8L	[1] .014 (.35)	[1] .016 (.40)
3.8L	Zero Lash	Zero Lash

[1] — Engine cold.

VALVE ARRANGEMENT

2.8L

Right Bank — I-E-I-I-E-E (Front-to-Rear)
Left Bank — E-E-I-I-E-I (Front-to-Rear)

3.8L

I-E-I-E-I-E (Front-to-Rear, both sides)

SPARK PLUGS

SPARK PLUG TYPE

Application	Motorcraft No.
2.8L	AWSF-42
3.8L	AGSP-52

SPARK PLUG SPECIFICATIONS

Application	Gap In. (mm)	Torque Ft. Lbs. (N.m)
All Models	.044 (1.2)	20 (28)

HIGH TENSION WIRE RESISTANCE

1) Remove wires from spark plugs by twisting spark plug boot carefully to loosen seal on plug. Remove wires by pulling on plug boot. Remove distributor cap from distributor, leaving wires connected to cap.

2) Using an ohmmeter, check resistance of each wire. Connect one ohmmeter lead to spark plug terminal and other lead to distributor cap insert.

3) Replace any wire with over 5000 ohms resistance per inch. New wires should have a resistance of 7000 ohms per foot.

DISTRIBUTOR

All 2.8L engines are equipped with the TFI-IV ignition system. Models with the 3.8L use either the Dura-Spark II or Dura-Spark III ignition system. No adjustments are required on any of these systems.

Fig. 1: Timing Mark & Firing Order — 2.8L V6

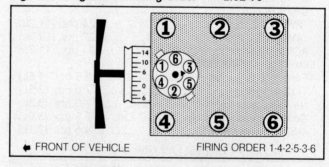

FRONT OF VEHICLE   FIRING ORDER 1-4-2-5-3-6

Fig. 2: Timing Mark and Firing Order — 3.8L V6

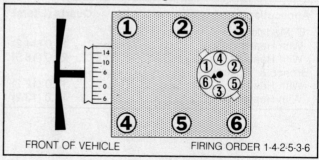

FRONT OF VEHICLE   FIRING ORDER 1-4-2-5-3-6

TUNE-UP (Cont.)

IGNITION TIMING

2.8L

1) Bring engine to normal operating temperature and shut off engine. Disconnect single wire (Black) connector from near distributor. Attach timing light.

2) Start engine and check initial ignition timing. Adjust as needed.

3.8L

1) Place transmission in neutral or "Park". Remove vacuum hose from distributor vacuum advance connection and plug hose. Connect timing light and tachometer.

2) Start engine and warm to operating temperature. With engine idling in neutral, check timing. If within 2° of specification, do not reset. If outside of this range, loosen distributor hold-down bolt and rotate distributor to set timing. Recheck after tightening bolt.

IGNITION TIMING (Degrees BTDC@RPM)

Application	Auto. Trans.	Man. Trans.
2.8L [1]	10@Idle	10@Idle
3.8L	10@800	2@800

[1] — Idle speed not adjustable.

HOT (SLOW) IDLE RPM

NOTE: The following procedures apply to 3.8L engines, only. The 2.8L engine is equipped with automatic idle speed control and cannot be adjusted.

NOTE: On vehicles equipped with air conditioning, set *A/C-On Idle* before making basic curb idle adjustment.

A/C-ON IDLE

1) Bring engine to normal operating temperature. Disconnect A/C clutch wire. Turn A/C to maximum cooling and high blower position.

Fig. 3: Idle Speed Adjustments

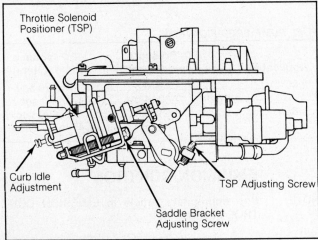

Throttle Solenoid Positioner (TSP)

Curb Idle Adjustment

TSP Adjusting Screw

Saddle Bracket Adjusting Screw

All models equipped with air conditioning.

2) With manual transmission in neutral, automatic in "D", check idle speed. If incorrect, adjust by turning saddle bracket adjusting screw. *See Fig. 3.* Reconnect A/C clutch wire.

CURB IDLE

1) Bring engine to normal operating temperature. With A/C off (if equipped) and transmission in neutral ("D" on automatics), check basic idle speed.

2) If incorrect, adjust by turning screw at rear of Throttle Solenoid Positioner (TSP) diaphragm assembly (with air) or saddle bracket adjustment screw (without air).

3) Disconnect TSP wire and check TSP Off idle speed. If incorrect, adjust by turning TSP adjusting screw. Reconnect TSP wire.

Fig. 4: Idle Speed Adjustments

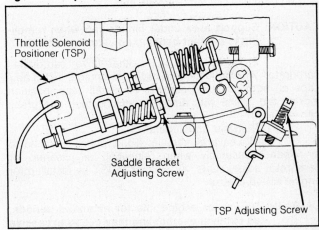

Throttle Solenoid Positioner (TSP)

Saddle Bracket Adjusting Screw

TSP Adjusting Screw

All models without air conditioning.

IDLE SPEED SPECIFICATIONS (RPM)

Application	Auto. Trans.	Man. Trans.
Basic Idle	650	700
A/C-On Idle	750	850
TSP Off	550	550

COLD (FAST) IDLE RPM

NOTE: Before performing Cold (Fast) Idle RPM adjustment, perform Hot (Slow) Idle RPM preliminary adjustments.

1) With transmission in neutral or park and engine at normal operating temperature, disconnect and plug EGR vacuum line. Place fast idle screw on highest step of fast idle cam.

2) Adjust idle speed to specification as given in *Fast Idle RPM* table. Remove plug from vacuum line and reconnect to EGR valve.

FAST IDLE RPM

Application	Man. Trans.	Auto. Trans.
2.8L	3000	3000
3.8L	1300	2200

IDLE MIXTURE

NOTE: Idle mixture adjustment is not part of a normal tune-up. DO NOT adjust mixture unless carburetor has been disassembled or vehicle fails emissions testing.

PROPANE ENRICHMENT PROCEDURE
Limiter Cap Removal
Before any idle mixture adjustment can be made, idle mixture limiter caps must be removed. If adjustment is required, use the following procedure to remove caps.

1) Remove carburetor from vehicle and drain fuel. Turn carburetor over and locate locking tab on limiter cap. Use a blunt punch and light hammer to tap tab in until locking detent is cleared. Remove cap.

CAUTION: Support area under limiter cap when removing to prevent bending adjustment needle.

2) Repeat step **1)** for other limiter cap. Install carburetor. After adjustments have been made, install new caps on both adjusting screws. To install caps, position locking tab in line with detent in locking plug and press cap into plug.

Propane Enrichment
1) Leave all vacuum signal hoses attached to air cleaner assembly when relocating air cleaner for carburetor adjustments. Air cleaner MUST be installed for engine speed checks.

CAUTION: Do not let engine idle for extended periods, as catalyst overheating may cause excessive underbody temperatures.

2) Apply parking brake and block wheels. Disconnect vacuum parking brake release (if equipped), and plug vacuum connection. Connect tachometer.

3) Disconnect and plug fuel evaporative purge valve signal hose at engine. Disconnect purge hose at air cleaner and plug nipple.

4) Disconnect flexible fresh air tube from air cleaner duct or adapter. Insert hose from propane enrichment tool (Rotunda T75L-9600-A) about 3/4 of the way into duct or fresh air tube. Disconnect PCV valve from grommet, and allow valve to draw underhood air during adjustment.

5) For vehicles equipped with thermactor, disconnect and plug hoses of dump valves equipped with 2 fittings. If valve has 1 fitting, remove and plug hose at valve. Connect slave hose to dump valve from intake manifold vacuum source.

6) Verify ignition timing is set to specification and adjust if necessary. With engine at normal operating temperature, check curb idle speed and adjust as needed. Run engine at 2500 RPM for 15 seconds before each mixture check.

7) With engine idling in neutral, gradually open propane tool valve and watch for engine speed gain on tachometer. When speed reaches maximum and begins to drop off, note amount of speed gain.

NOTE: Propane cartridge must be in vertical position. If engine speed will not drop off, check

bottle gas supply. If necessary, repeat test with new bottle.

8) Compare measured speed gain with specifications. If mixture adjustment is required, limiter caps must first be removed. Refer to *Limiter Cap Removal* procedure. With caps removed and carburetor installed, adjust mixture until RPM gain is within "Reset RPM" specifications. If adjustment is not required, go to step **11)**.

9) If measured speed gain is greater than specification, turn mixture screws counterclockwise in equal amounts, and recheck until measured speed rise is within "Reset RPM" specifications. Then go to step **11)**.

10) If measured speed gain is less than specification, turn mixture screws clockwise in equal amounts, and recheck until measured speed rise is within "Reset RPM" specifications.

11) Check and adjust curb idle as needed. Remove all test equipment. Reconnect hoses in original positions and connect PCV valve.

IDLE MIXTURE SPECIFICATIONS (PROPANE ENRICHMENT)

Application	RPM Gain (Check)	Reset RPM (Adjust)
2.8L	[1]	[1]
3.8L	10-30	20

[1] — Information not available.

AUTOMATIC CHOKE

Loosen choke thermostat cover screws and turn cover in direction indicated on cover to specified setting. Tighten screws.

AUTOMATIC CHOKE SPECIFICATIONS

Application	Choke Setting
All Models	"V" Notch

FUEL PUMP

Check fuel pump with engine idling at normal operating temperature. Pinch off fuel return line during test.

FUEL PUMP SPECIFICATIONS

Application	Pressure psi (kg/cm²)	Volume Pints (Liters)
2.8L	4.5-6.5 (.32-.46)	1 in 30 sec. (.47 in 30 sec.)
3.8L	6.0-8.0 (.42-.56)	1 in 20 sec. (.47 in 20 sec.)

EMISSION CONTROL

NOTE: See appropriate article in EMISSION CONTROL Section.

1983 Ford V6 Tune-Up

GENERAL SERVICING

IGNITION

DISTRIBUTOR

All models with the 2.8L engine are equipped with the TFI-IV ignition system. All ignition advance is computer controlled on the TFI-IV system. Therefore, no vacuum or mechanical advance mechanisms are used. No pickup coil is used on this system so no resistance measurements can be made.

All with the 3.8L engine use either the Dura-Spark II or Dura-Spark III system. All units are self-contained and require no adjustments.

DISTRIBUTOR PICKUP COIL RESISTANCE

Application	Resistance (Ohms)
2.8L TFI-IV	[1]
3.8L Dura-Spark II & III	400-1000

[1] — The 2.8L TFI-IV system does not include a pickup coil.

TOTAL SPARK ADVANCE@2500 RPM (°BTDC)

Application	W/Vac. Advance	W/O Vac. Advance
2.8L	[1]	[1]
3.8L		
Man. Trans.	42-56	13-17
Auto. Trans.	38-49	14-19

[1] — Timing controlled by computer.

IGNITION COIL

COIL RESISTANCE (Ohms)

Application	Primary	Secondary
TFI-IV	0.3-1.0	8000-11,500
Dura-Spark II & III	0.8-1.6	7700-10,500

FUEL SYSTEMS

CARBURETORS

Application	Model
All Models	Motorcraft 2150A

ELECTRICAL

BATTERY

BATTERY SPECIFICATIONS

Application	Capacity (Amp Hours)	Discharge Rate (Amps)
Standard	54	225
Premium HD	81	175
Optional	45	190
	63	260

STARTER

Motorcraft positive engagement type with either a 4" or 4.5" armature.

STARTER SPECIFICATIONS

Application	Volts	Amps.	Test RPM
4" Armature	12	70	6700 Min.
4.5" Armature	12	80	7380-9356

ALTERNATORS

All models use Motorcraft alternators.

ALTERNATOR SPECIFICATIONS

I.D. Tag Color	Rated Amp Output
Rear Terminal	
Orange	40
Green	60
Side Terminal	
Black	70
Red	100
Field Current Draw@12 Volts	
All Models	4.0 Amps

ALTERNATOR REGULATORS

Two Motorcraft electronic voltage regulators are used. Though similar in appearance, they are different internally and must never be interchanged.

REGULATOR IDENTIFICATION

Application	Color Coding
All with Ammeter	Gray
All with Indicator Light	Black

ADJUSTMENTS

BELT ADJUSTMENT

	Tension Using Strand Tension Gauge	
Application	Lbs. (Kg)
New Belts	
2.8L	
Air Conditioning	120-160 (55-73)
Alternator	120-160 (55-73)
All Others	120-160 (55-73)
3.8L Single Belt	150-190 (68-86)
Used Belts [1]	
2.8L	
Air Conditioning	110-130 (50-59)
Alternator	110-130 (50-59)
All Others	110-130 (50-59)
3.8L Single Belt	140-160 (64-73)

[1] — Any belt operated 10 minutes or more.

1983 Ford V6 Tune-Up
GENERAL SERVICING (Cont.)

SERVICE INTERVALS

REPLACEMENT INTERVALS

Application	Miles
Oil Filter	
2.8L	7500
3.8L	10,000
Air Filter	30,000
PCV Filter	30,000
Fuel Filter	5000
Spark Plugs	30,000

CAPACITIES

FLUID CAPACITIES

Application	Quantity
Cooling System	
2.8L	
With A/C	7.8 qts. (7.4L)
Without A/C	7.2 qts. (6.8L)
3.8L	
With A/C	11.0 qts. (10.4L)
Without A/C	10.0 qts. (9.5L)
Crankcase [1]	
2.8L	5.0 qts. (4.7L)
3.8L	6.0 qts. (5.6L)
Auto. Trans.	
C-3 3-Speed	16.0 pts. (7.6L)
C-5 3-Speed	
All Except Bronco II & Ranger	22.0 pts. (10.4L)
2WD Ranger	15.0 pts. (7.1L)
Bronco II & 4WD Ranger	15.8 pts. (7.5L)
C-6 Transmission	
2WD Models	23.6 pts. (11.2L)
4WD Models	27.0 pts. (12.8L)
Man. Trans.	
Ford 3.03 3-Speed	3.5 pts. (1.6L)
New Process 435 4-Speed	
W/Ext. Housing	7.0 pts. (3.3L)
W/O Ext. Housing	6.5 pts. (3.0L)
S.R.O.D. 4-Speed	4.5 pts. (2.1L)
Bronco II & Ranger	
4-Speed	3.0 pts. (1.5L)
5-Speed	3.0 pts. (1.4L)
Transfer Case	
Bronco II & Ranger w/Warner 13-50	3.0 pts. (1.4L)
Fuel Tank	
Bronco II	
Standard	17.0 gals. (64.3L)
Optional	21.0 gals (79.4L)
Ranger	
Standard Short Bed	15.2 gals. (57.5L)
Standard Long Bed	17.0 gals. (64.3L)
Optional Auxiliary	13.0 gals. (49.2L)
All Other Models	
Standard	16.5 gals. (62.0L)
Optional [2]	19.0 gals. (72.0L)

[1] — Includes 1 qt. (.9L) for filter change.
[2] — Standard on some models.

TUNE-UP

ENGINE IDENTIFICATION

Engine can be identified by the eighth digit of Vehicle Identification Number. Number is stamped on a metal plate, which is riveted to upper left corner of instrument panel and visible through left side of windshield.

VIN ENGINE CODE

Application	Code
5.0L (302") 2-Bbl.	F
5.8L (351") 2-Bbl.	G
7.5L (460") 4-Bbl.	L

TUNE-UP NOTES

NOTE: **When performing tune-up procedures described in this article, the following notes and precautions must be followed:**

In some applications within this article it will be necessary to refer to the engine calibration number. Most numbers for V8 engines are located on an identification label on front of right valve cover.

For Tune-Up purposes, "Light Duty" refers to vehicles up to 8500 lbs. GVW. "Heavy Duty" refers to vehicles exceeding 8500 lbs. GVW.

When connecting a tachometer to SSI coil, install the alligator clip on tachometer into the "DEC" (TACH TEST) cavity.

For other items affecting Tune-Up, see FUEL SYSTEMS Section or EMISSION CONTROL Section.

Due to production changes, always refer to Engine Tune-Up Decal in engine compartment before attempting tune-up. In the event of a conflict between specifications given in this manual and decal specifications, use the decal specifications.

When performing tune-up on vehicles equipped with a catalytic converter, do not allow or create a condition of engine misfire in one or more cylinders for an extended period of time. Damage to converter from overheating may occur due to loading with unburned fuel.

ENGINE COMPRESSION

Test compression with all spark plugs removed and engine at normal operating temperature. Crank engine through at least five compression strokes before recording reading. Maximum compression variation should not exceed 25% between highest and lowest cylinder.

VALVE CLEARANCE

All engines are equipped with hydraulic lifters. Adjust all valves to zero lash.

VALVE ARRANGEMENT

All Models
E-I-E-I-E-I-E-I (Left bank, front to rear)
I-E-I-E-I-E-I-E (Right bank, front to rear)

SPARK PLUGS

SPARK PLUG SPECIFICATIONS

Application	Gap In. (mm)	Torque Ft. Lbs. (N.m)
5.0L & 5.8L	.044 (1.1)	10-15 (14-20)
7.5L	.044 (1.1)	5-7 (7-14)

SPARK PLUG TYPE

Application	Motorcraft No.
All Engines	ASF-42

HIGH TENSION WIRE RESISTANCE

1) Loosen wires from spark plugs by twisting spark plug boot carefully to loosen seal on spark plug. Remove wires by pulling on plug boot. Remove distributor cap from distributor, leaving wires connected to cap.

NOTE: **DO NOT disconnect wires from distributor cap unless replacement is necessary.**

2) Using an ohmmeter, check resistance of each wire by connecting one ohmmeter lead to spark plug terminal and other lead to distributor cap insert. Replace any wire with over 5,000 ohms resistance per inch.

NOTE: **Whenever a high tension wire is disconnected, the interior of spark plug terminal boot must be coated with dielectric silicone grease before connection.**

DISTRIBUTOR

Calif. 5.0L and 5.8L models are equipped with Dura-Spark III ignition system. All other models are equipped with Dura-Spark II ignition system. No adjustments are required.

Fig. 1: 5.0L & 7.5L Timing Mark and Firing Order

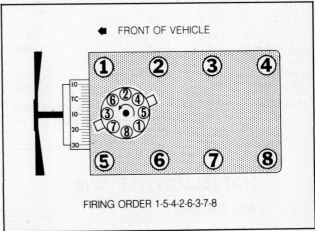

FIRING ORDER 1-5-4-2-6-3-7-8

Magnetic probe located at 135° ATDC.

1983 Ford V8 Tune-Up

TUNE-UP (Cont.)

IGNITION TIMING

NOTE: Magnetic probe timing device may be used if instrument is available and engine is so equipped. Timing probe offset is 135° ATDC on all V8 engines.

1) Determine specified timing and mark degree line on damper (some vehicles mark both pointer and damper notch). Disconnect vacuum line(s) at distributor and plug.

Fig. 2: 5.8L Timing Mark & Firing Order

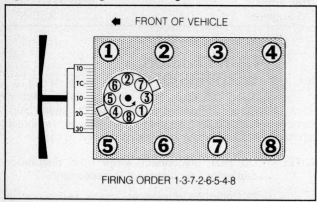

FIRING ORDER 1-3-7-2-6-5-4-8

Magnetic probe located at 135° ATDC.

2) Connect tachometer. Connect timing light to No. 1 spark plug wire. If vehicle is equipped with barometric sensor, disconnect sensor from module. Connect Black and Yellow wires in module connector. Set timing to specifications if more than 2° variation is found.

3) To adjust, loosen distributor hold-down bolt and rotate distributor to align marks in step **1)**. Tighten hold-down bolt and recheck timing.

TIMING SPECIFICATIONS (Degrees BTDC@RPM)

Application	Man. Trans.	Auto. Trans.
5.0L		
Calif.	1	1
High Altitude	12@800	12@800
All Other Models	8@800	8@800
5.8L		
Calif.	1	1
Light Duty	10@800	14@800
Heavy Duty	8@800	8@800
7.5L		
Calif.	6@800	6@800
All Other Models	8@800	8@800

1 — Calif. 5.0L & 5.8L engines are equipped with Electronic Engine Control (EEC III) system and no adjustment is required.

HOT (SLOW) IDLE RPM

ALL MODELS

NOTE: After engine adjustments are complete reconnect all vacuum lines or hoses to their original positions. Reinstall air cleaner assembly. Run engine at 2500 RPM for 15 seconds and recheck curb idle speed. Final curb idle speed check must be made with air cleaner installed. Adjust as necessary and recheck dashpot clearance.

5.0L ENGINES
FEDERAL VEHICLES

Curb Idle & A/C "OFF" RPM

1) With transmission in neutral or in "PARK", start engine and let it run until it reaches normal operating temperature. Place air conditioning and heater in "OFF" position.

2) Disconnect and plug vacuum hose at thermactor air by-pass valve. Check curb idle RPM. If adjustment is necessary, adjust to specification by turning saddle bracket adjusting screw on 5.0L models with automatic overdrive transmisson.

3) Adjust with curb idle speed screw on all other models. Place transmission in neutral or "PARK" and increase engine speed momentarily. Recheck curb idle RPM. Readjust if necessary. Unplug and reconnect vacuum hose at thermactor air by-pass valve.

Kicker RPM (A/C "ON")

1) With engine at normal operating temperature, place A/C in maximum cooling position and blower in high position. Disconnect A/C compressor clutch wire. Place transmission in neutral or "PARK".

2) Check and or adjust A/C "ON" (A/C-On) RPM. Adjust by turning nut behind dashpot housing on 5.0L models with automatic overdrive transmission. Adjust by turning saddle bracket adjusting screw on all other models. Reconnect A/C compressor clutch wire.

CURB IDLE & A/C "ON" RPM

Application	A/C-On	Curb Idle (A/C-Off)
5.0L		
Man. Trans.	800	700
Auto. Trans.	625	600

5.0L ENGINES
CALIFORNIA VEHICLES

Curb Idle and VOTM RPM

1) Place transmission in neutral or "PARK". With engine at normal operating temperature, disconnect EVAP purge solenoid connector. Disconnect and plug vacuum line to VOTM kicker. Check curb idle. If adjustment is necessary, use curb idle screw. *See Emission Control Decal for specification.*

2) Increase engine speed momentarily. Recheck curb idle. Adjust if required. Connect a slave vacuum hose to manifold vacuum and VOTM. Check VOTM-On RPM. Remove slave vacuum hose and check VOTM-Off RPM. If necessary, adjust with adjusting nut on VOTM.

VOTM RPM

Application	VOTM-On	VOTM-Off
5.0L	650	575

TUNE-UP (Cont.)

5.8L ENGINES
FEDERAL LIGHT DUTY VEHICLES

Curb Idle

1) With transmission in neutral or "PARK", start engine and let run until it reaches normal operating temperature. Disconnect and plug the vacuum hose to the VOTM kicker. Turn off engine then restart.

2) Check/adjust curb idle RPM, if adjustment required, use hex rod on back of solenoid. Adjustment must be mamde within 120 seconds of hot restart.

3) Remove plug from vacuum hose to VOTM and reconnect to VOTM. Apply a slight pressure to the nylon nut located on the accelerator pump. Turn the nylon nut on the accelerator pump rod clockwise until a clearance of .005-.015" is obtained between the top of the carburetor and the pump lever.

4) Turn the nut on the accelerator pump rod one turn counterclockwise to set the lever lash preload. Increase engine speed momentarily. Recheck curb idle. Readjust if necessary.

5.8L ENGINES
CALIF. LIGHT DUTY VEHICLES

Curb Idle and VOTM RPM

1) Place transmission in neutral or "PARK". With engine at normal operating temperature, disconnect EVAP purge solenoid connector. Disconnect and plug vacuum line to VOTM kicker.

2) Place transmission in specified position. Check curb idle. If adjustment is necessary, use curb idle screw.

3) Place transmission in "PARK" or neutral, increase engine speed momentarily. Place engine in specified position, recheck curb idle. Adjust if required. Disconnect EEC harness from processor assembly and install Rotunda EEC tester.

4) Check/adjust throttle position sensor. Remove plug from vacuum hose on VOTM kicker and reconnect.

5) Apply a slight pressure on top of the nylon nut located on the accelerator linkage. Turn the nylon nut on the linkage clockwise until a .005-.015" clearance is obtained between the top of the carburetor and the pump lever.

6) Turn the accelerator pump rod nut one turn counterclockwise to set the lever lash preload.

7) Trigger EEC-III System Self-Test. If test is not a passing service code take corrective action indicated. Remove tester and reconnect assembly to EEC harness.

CURB IDLE (RPM)

Application	A/C-On	A/C-Off
All Models	625	550

5.8L ENGINES
ALL HEAVY DUTY VEHICLES

Curb Idle and Decel Throttle Control Speed

1) With transmission in neutral or "PARK", start engine and let run until it reaches normal operating temperature.

2) Place A/C and heater switch in "OFF" position. Disconnect and plug vacuum hose from throttle kicker or from throttle kicker portion of TSP (Throttle Solenoid Positioner).

3) Install a slave vacuum hose from throttle kicker portion of TSP to intake manifold vacuum. Speed up engine momentarily. Check and adjust the decel throttle kicker RPM to specification by turning throttle kicker screw located in mounting bracket.

4) Disconnect slave vacuum hose from throttle kicker and intake manifold vacuum source. On automatic transmsisson models, increase engine speed momentarily and check and adjust curb idle speed (TSP-On) by adjusting bolt on back of TSP.

5) Disconnect Blue electrical wiring clip connecting TSP to engine wiring harness. Using curb idle set screw, check and adjust TSP-Off RPM on automatic transmission models, and check and adjust curb idle RPM to specifications on manual transmission models.

6) Remove plug and reconnect vacuum hose to throttle kicker or throttle kicker portion of TSP. Reconnect Blue electrical clip to TSP wire (if necessary).

CURB IDLE (RPM)

Application	Curb Idle TSP-On	TSP-Off
5.8L	650	525

DECEL THROTTLE KICKER RPM

5.8L	1750-1950

7.5L ENGINES

Curb Idle and Decel Throttle Control Speed

1) With transmission in neutral or "PARK", and A/C in "OFF" position, start engine and let it run until it reaches normal operating temperature.

2) Remove air cleaner. Disconnect and plug decel throttle control kicker diaphragm vacuum hose. Connect a slave vacuum hose from intake manifold vacuum to decel throttle control kicker.

3) Run engine at 2500 RPM for 15 seconds, and then release throttle. If decel throttle control RPM is not within 50 RPM of specified RPM, adjust decel throttle control kicker until specified RPM is reached.

4) Disconnect slave vacuum hose and allow engine to return to idle. Check and adjust idle if necessary using idle speed adjusting screw. Unplug and reconnect vacuum hose to decel throttle control kicker diaphragm and reinstall air cleaner.

CURB IDLE (RPM)

All Models	650

DECEL THROTTLE KICKER RPM

All Models	1800

COLD (FAST) IDLE RPM

NOTE: Before adjusting Cold (Fast) Idle RPM, perform Hot (Slow) Idle RPM preliminary adjustments.

1983 Ford V8 Tune-Up

TUNE-UP (Cont.)

5.0L ENGINES

1) With transmission in neutral or "PARK", start engine and let run until it reaches normal operating temperature.

2) Disconnect and plug hoses at both EGR valve and thermactor air by-pass valve. Disconnect vacuum hose and electrical connector on EVAP purge solenoid.

3) On all models, place fast idle adjusting screw on top step of fast idle cam. Check and adjust (if necessary) fast idle by turning fast idle adjusting screw.

4) Reconnect vacuum hoses and electrical connector removed in step **2)**.

5.8L ENGINES
LIGHT DUTY VEHICLES

1) With transmission in neutral or "PARK", start engine and let run until it reaches normal operating temperature.

2) On California models, disconnect purge hose on canister and ensure that purge vacuum is present. Reconnect hose.

3) On all models, disconnect and plug vacuum hose at EGR valve and purge valve. On Federal high altitude models with auto. trans., place fast idle adjusting screw on highest step of fast idle cam. On all other models, place adjusting screw on second highest step.

4) Check and adjust (if necessary) fast idle by turning fast idle adjusting screw. Unplug and reconnect vacuum hoses removed in step **3)**.

5.8L ENGINES
HEAVY DUTY VEHICLES

1) With transmission in neutral or "PARK", start engine and let it run until it reaches normal operating temperature.

2) On all models, disconnect and plug vacuum hose at EGR valve. Disconnect and plug vacuum hose at throttle kicker or at throttle kicker portion of TSP.

3) Place fast idle adjusting screw on first step of fast idle cam and adjust fast idle to specified RPM by turning fast idle adjusting screw.

4) Unplug and reconnect all vacuum hoses removed in step **2)**.

FAST IDLE SPEED (RPM)

Application	Man. Trans.	Auto. Trans.
5.0L		
Federal	2100	2000
Calif.	......	2000
5.8L		
Light Duty		
Federal	1700	[1] 1650
Calif.	2000	2000
High Alt.	[2] 1650	[2] 1650
Heavy Duty	1500	1500
7.5		
Federal	1500	1600
Calif.	2000	1600

[1] — Set 1-64H-R11 to 2000 RPM.

[2] — Set 2-63Y-R11 and 2-63Y-R12 to 1700 RPM. Set 2-64X-R00 to 2000 RPM.

7.5L ENGINES

1) With transmission in neutral or "PARK" and A/C in "OFF" position, start engine and let run until it reaches normal operating temperature. Remove the air cleaner.

2) Disconnect and plug distributor advance vacuum hose and EGR valve vacuum hose.

3) Depress throttle lever and turn fast idle cam, by hand, until fast idle adjusting screw sets on first step of fast idle cam. Adjust fast idle to specified RPM by turning fast idle adjusting screw.

4) Unplug and reconnect all vacuum hoses removed in step **2)**. Reinstall air cleaner.

IDLE MIXTURE

NOTE: Idle mixture adjustment is not part of a normal tune-up. DO NOT adjust mixture unless carburetor has been disassembled or vehicle fails emissions testing.

NOTE: No idle mixture adjustment is possible on vehicles with 7200VV 2-Bbl. carburetors. If engine performance is unsatisfactory, see Ford Electronic Engine Control in EMISSION CONTROL Section.

PROPANE ENRICHMENT PROCEDURE

NOTE: This procedure is for light duty vehicles only. For adjustments for heavy duty vehicles, see Emission Control Tune-Up Decal.

1) Leave all vacuum signal hoses attached to air cleaner assembly when relocating air cleaner for carburetor adjustments. Air cleaner MUST be installed for engine speed checks.

CAUTION: Do not let engine idle for extended periods, as catalyst overheating may cause excessive underbody temperatures.

2) Apply parking brake and block wheels. Disconnect automatic brake release, and plug vacuum connection. Connect tachometer.

3) Disconnect and plug fuel evaporative purge valve signal hose at engine. Disconnect purge hose at air cleaner and plug nipple.

4) Disconnect flexible fresh air tube from air cleaner duct or adapter. Insert hose from propane enrichment tool (Rotunda T75L-9600-A) about 3/4 of the way into duct or fresh air tube. Disconnect PCV valve from grommet, and allow valve to draw underhood air during adjustment.

5) For vehicles equipped with thermactor, except 5.0L truck, disconnect and plug hoses of dump valves equipped with 2 fittings. If valves have one fitting, remove and plug hose at valve. Connect slave hose to dump valve and intake manifold vacuum source.

6) Verify ignition timing is set to specification and adjust if necessary. With engine at normal operating temperature, check curb idle speed or A/C-Off RPM. Adjust as necessary. Run engine at 2500 RPM for 15 seconds before each mixture check.

TUNE-UP (Cont.)

7) With engine idling in neutral, gradually open propane tool valve and watch for engine speed gain on tachometer. When speed reaches maximum and begins to drop off, note amount of speed gain.

NOTE: Propane cartridge must be in vertical position. If engine speed will not drop off, check bottle gas supply. If necessary, repeat test with new bottle.

8) Compare measured speed gain with specifications. If mixture adjustment is necessary, adjust so gain is within "Reset RPM" specifications. If propane enrichment speed gain is within "RPM Gain" specifications, proceed to step **11).**

9) If measured speed gain is greater than specification, turn mixture screws counterclockwise in equal amounts, and recheck until measured speed rise is within '"Reset RPM" specifications. Then proceed to step **11).**

10) If measured speed gain is less than specification, turn mixture screws clockwise in equal amounts, and recheck until measured speed rise is within "Reset RPM" specifications. Then proceed to step **11).**

11) Check curb idle, and remove all test equipment. Reconnect hoses in original positions, and connect PCV valve.

IDLE MIXTURE SPECIFICATIONS (PROPANE ENRICHMENT)

Application	RPM Gain (Check)	Reset RPM (Adjust)
5.0L	Federal	
Man. Trans.	40-80	60
Auto. Trans.	20-100	60
Calif.		
Auto. Trans.	90-120	150
5.8L		
Auto. Trans.	30-80	60

[1] — For calibration 3-54T-R00 RPM gain 60-170, RPM reset 100.

DASHPOT ADJUSTMENT

With idle speed and mixture properly adjusted, remove air cleaner and loosen dashpot lock nut. With choke open, hold throttle plate closed (idle position), and check clearance between throttle lever pad and dashpot plunger tip. Plunger MUST be completely collapsed to check clearance. Turn dashpot in or out to obtain .090-.140" (2.3-3.6 mm) clearance. Tighten lock nut.

SOLENOID BOWL VENT VALVE TEST
California 5.0 & 5.8L Models
1) Remove air cleaner, then turn ignition on and off. A "click" should be heard if solenoid is operating properly.

2) If not, disconnect electrical lead, and connect a voltmeter between lead and ground. Turn ignition on and check for battery voltage. If not present, repair wiring as required.

3) If 12 volts are present at lead connector, check valve for binding and/or plugged condition. Repair as required. If valve is not binding and/or plugged, replace solenoid valve assembly. Reinstall air cleaner.

AUTOMATIC CHOKE ADJUSTMENT

Loosen choke thermostat cover screws and turn choke cover in direction indicated on cover to specified setting.

AUTOMATIC CHOKE SPECIFICATIONS

Application	Setting
5.0L	"V" Notch
5.8L	Index [1]
7.5L	3 Rich

[1] — Calibration Nos. 1-64H-R02 and 2-64X-R00 adjust to "V" notch.

FUEL PUMP

Check mechanical fuel pump at curb idle RPM with engine at normal operating temperature and transmission in neutral.

FUEL PUMP SPECIFICATIONS

Application	Pressure psi (kg/cm²)	Volume Pints (Liters)
All Models	6.0-8.0 (.45-.56)	1 in 20 sec. (.47 in 20 sec.)

EMISSION CONTROL

NOTE: See appropriate article in EMISSION CONTROL Section.

GENERAL SERVICING

IGNITION

DISTRIBUTORS
Calif. 5.0L and 5.8L models are equipped with Motorcraft Dura-Spark III ignition system. All other models are equipped with Motorcraft Dura-Spark II ignition system. Units are self-contained and require no outside adjustments.

IGNITION COIL

COIL RESISTANCE (Ohms)

Application	Primary	Secondary
All Models	0.8-1.6	7700-10,500

1983 Ford V8 Tune-Up
GENERAL SERVICING (Cont.)

TOTAL SPARK ADVANCE@2500 RPM

Engine & Calibration No.	W/O Vacuum Advance	W/Vacuum Advance
5.0L		
Auto. Trans.		
3-54E-R00	14-19	28-37
3-54F-R00	13-17	30-40
3-54J-R00	16-21	33-34
3-54L-R00	13-18	39-48
3-54T-R00	17-21	40-52
3-54Y-R00	18-22	36-45
3-54Z-R00	18-22	36-45
3-54P-R00	[1]	[1]
3-54R-R00	[1]	[1]
3-54T-R00	[1]	[1]
Man. Trans.		
3-53F-R00	15-20	32-43
3-53G-R00	15-20	32-43
3-53K-R00	16-22	34-44
3-53L-R00	16-22	34-44
3-53W-R00	19-24	36-47
3-53Y-R00	19-24	36-47
3-53Z-R00	19-22	36-47
5.8L		
Auto. Trans.		
1-64H-R02	10-15	35-46
1-64T-R12	[1]	[1]
1-64T-R13	[1]	[1]
2-64X-R00	14-19	39-50
2-64Y-R11	[1]	[1]
2-64Y-R12	[1]	[1]
Man. Trans		
1-63T-R12	[1]	[1]
1-63T-R13	[1]	[1]
1-63Y-R11	[1]	[1]
1-63Y-R12	[1]	[1]
7.5L		
9-97J-R13	18-24	36-46
9-49S-R00	16-21	37-48
9-98S-R00	18-23	28-37

[1] — Engines equipped with Dura-Spark III have computerized spark advance.

DISTRIBUTOR PICK-UP COIL RESISTANCE (Ohms)

All Models .... 400-1000 ohms

ELECTRICAL
BATTERY

BATTERY SPECIFICATIONS

Application	Capacity (Amp. Hours)	Discharge Rate (Amps.)
Standard		
Federal	36	155
California	45	190
Optional	54, 63, 81	225, 260, 175

STARTER
All models use Motorcraft positive engagement type starters with either a 4" or 4 1/2" armature.

STARTER SPECIFICATIONS

Application	Volts	Amps.	Test RPM
4" Armature	12	70	6700 Min.
4½" Armature	12	80	7380-9356

ALTERNATORS
All models use Motorcraft alternators.

ALTERNATOR SPECIFICATIONS

I.D. Tag Color	Rated Amp. Output
Rear Terminal	
Orange	40
Green	60
Green	65
Side Terminal	
Black	70
Red	100

Field Current Draw@12 Volts

Rear Terminal	4.25 Amps
Side Terminals	4.0 Amps.

ALTERNATOR REGULATORS
Two Motorcraft electronic voltage regulators are used. Although both look alike, they are not interchangeable.

REGULATOR IDENTIFICATION

Application	Color Coding
Used with Ammeter	Grey Label
Used with Indicator Lamp	Black Label

FUEL SYSTEMS

CARBURETORS

Application	Model
Federal 5.0L & 5.8L	Motorcraft 2150 2-Bbl.
Calif. 5.0L & 5.8L	Motorcraft 7200VV 2-Bbl.
7.5L	Holley 4180-C 4-Bbl.

ADJUSTMENTS

BELT ADJUSTMENT
Tension Using Strand Tension Gauge

Application	Lbs. (Kg)
New Belt	
1/4" Belt	50-80 (23-36)
All Others	110-140 (49-63)
Used Belt [1]	
1/4" Belt	40-60 (18-27)
All Others	90-110 (41-49)

[1] — Any belt that has been operated 10 minutes or more.

GENERAL SERVICING (Cont.)

CAPACITIES

FLUID CAPACITIES (Except Cooling)

Application	Quantity
Crankcase (Including Filter)	
All Engines	6.0 qts. (5.6L)
Man. Trans. (SAE 80W-90)	
3.03 3-Speed	3.5 pts. (1.6L)
New Process 435 4-Speed	
W/Extension	7.0 pts. (3.3L)
W/O Extension	6.5 pts. (3.0L)
T-18 4-Speed	7.0 pts. (3.3L)
4-Speed Overdrive	4.5 pts. (2.1L)
Auto. Trans. (Dexron II Series D)	
C-5 3-Speed	22.0 pts. (10.4L)
AOD 4-Speed	24.0 pts. (11.4L)
C-6 3-Speed	
2-WD	23.8 pts. (11.2L)
4-WD	26.8 pts. (12.7L)
Rear Axle (Hypoid Gear Lube)	
Ford Standard & Traction-Lok	5.5 pts. (3.0L)
Dana 60	6.0 pts. (2.4L)
Dana 61-1	6.0 pts. (2.8L)
Dana 61-2	6.0 pts. (2.8L)
Dana 70	
Standard	6.5 pts. (3.0L)
Heavy Duty	7.4 pts. (3.5L)
Front Axle (Hypoid Gear Lube)	
Dana 44-IFS	
F150 & Bronco	3.8 pts. (1.8L)
F250	3.8 pts. (1.8L)
Dana IFS	3.8 pts. (1.8L)
Transfer Case (Dexron II Series D)	
Warner 1345	6.5 pts. (3.0L)
New Process 208	7.0 pts. (3.3L)
Fuel Tank	
F100/150 & F150/250 Super Cab	
Short Wheel Base	
Standard	16.5 gal. (62.5L)
Auxiliary	19.0 gal. (71.9L)
All Other "F" Models	
Standard	19.0 gal. (71.9L)
Auxiliary	19.0 gal. (71.9L)
Bronco	
Standard	25.0 gal. (94.6L)
Auxiliary	32.0 gal. (121.1L)
E100 Van & Club Wagon,	
E150 Van (W/124" W.B.)	
Standard	18.0 gal. (68.1L)
Auxiliary	18.0 gal. (68.1L)
E-100/150 with M4-OD trans.	
Standard	19.6 gal. (74L)
Auxiliary	18.0 gal. (68.1L)
All Other "E" Models	
Standard	22.1 gal. (83.6L)
Auxiliary	18.0 gal. (68.1L)

COOLING SYSTEM CAPACITIES

Application	Quantity
5.0L	
F150/350 & Bronco	
Standard or Extra Cooling	13.0 qts. (12.3L)
Super Cooling	14.0 qts. (13.2L)
E100/250 Federal	
Standard Cooling	15.0 qts. (14.2L)
Extra Cooling	17.5 qts. (16.6L)
Super Cooling	18.5 qts. (17.5L)
5.8L	
E100/250 Calif. Only	
Standard or Extra Cooling	20.0 qts. (19.2L)
Super Cooling	21.0 qts. (19.9L)
5.8L	
F150/350 & Bronco	
Standard or Extra Cooling	15.0 qts. (14.2L)
Super Cooling	16.0 qts. (15.1L)
7.5L	
F250 HD, F350	
Man. Trans. Extra Cooling	16.5 qts. (15.5L)
All Other Options	17.5 qts. (16.5L)
E250, E350	
All Models	28.0 qts. (26.5L)

SERVICE INTERVALS

REPLACEMENT INTERVALS

Component	Interval (Miles)
Oil Filter	7500
Air Filter	30,000
Fuel Filter	15,000
PCV Valve	30,000
Spark Plugs	30,000

1983 Ford Diesel Tune-Up

TUNE-UP

ENGINE IDENTIFICATION

Engine is identified by letter code in eighth position of Vehicle Identification Number (VIN). The VIN is stamped on a metal tab, attached to upper left side of instrument panel and is visible through windshield. The VIN can also be found on Safety Standard Certification Label attached to left door lock edge.

VIN ENGINE CODES

Application	VIN Code
2.2L (134") 4-Cyl. Diesel	P
6.9L (420") V8 Diesel	1

TUNE-UP NOTES

NOTE: **When performing tune-up procedures described in this article, the following notes and precautions must be followed:**

Due to late changes and corrections, always refer to engine compartment Emission Control Tune-Up Decal before attempting tune-up procedures. In the event manual specifications and decal specifications are different, always use decal specifications.

Ensure that all diesel injection lines and fittings are thoroughly cleaned before removing. Cap all lines, nozzles and fittings when removed. Dirt in system may damage injection pump.

Some models are equipped with water separator units. Check periodically for presence of water and drain off if needed or when "Water-in-Fuel" indicator light glows (if equipped).

ENGINE COMPRESSION

Prior to checking compression, be sure batteries are fully charged. During compression check, crank engine with ignition off through at least 6 compression strokes and note number of strokes required to obtain highest reading. Repeat check on each cylinder, cranking engine same number of compression strokes. DO NOT add oil to cylinder. Adding oil may cause hydrostatic lock and extensive engine damage. Maximum variation between cylinders on 6.9L should not exceed 25%.

1) Start and warm engine to normal operating temperature. Turn ignition off. Remove air cleaner and/or intake opening cover. Disconnect injection pump solenoid leads (fuel cutoff solenoid leads on 2.2L). On 2.2L engine, disconnect glow plug harness (Blue/Red stripe wire) from engine wiring harness.

2) On all models, remove all glow plugs and insert compression gauge in No. 1 cylinder glow plug hole. Crank engine (ignition off on 6.9L engine) and note compression reading. Repeat compression test.

COMPRESSION SPECIFICATIONS

Compression Ratio	
2.2L	22:1
6.9L	20.7:1
Compression Pressure	
2.2L	Min. 384 psi (27 kg/cm²)
Maximum Pressure Variation	
2.2L	42.7 psi (3 kg/cm²)

VALVE CLEARANCE

The 6.9L engine is equipped with hydraulic valve lifters which are adjusted to zero lash. On 2.2L engines, warm engine to normal operating temperature. Turn engine off and check valve clearance.

VALVE CLEARANCE ADJUSTMENT

Application	Clearance
2.2L	
Intake & Exhaust	.012" (.030 mm)

VALVE ARRANGEMENT

2.2L
I-E-I-E-I-E-I-E

6.9L
I-E-I-E-I-E-I-E (Right Bank, Front to rear)
E-I-E-I-E-I-E-I (Left Bank, Front to rear)

GLOW PLUGS

Glow plugs on 2.2L engine are variable voltage type heaters. Glow plugs on 6.9L engine are 6 volt heaters. Each cylinder has a glow plug screwed into the cylinder head. The tip of the glow plug projects into the combustion chamber to preheat cylinder and aid in cold engine starting.

On 2.2L engine, full system voltage is supplied to glow plugs when ignition is turned "ON". Depending on coolant temperature, glow plug voltage is cycled between 12 and 4 volts or maintained at reduced voltage of 4-5 volts for a short period of time after engine start.

On 6.9L engine, glow plugs are activated when ignition switch is turned "ON". Glow plugs are controlled by a control switch based upon coolant temperature. Control switch allows glow plug operation only when coolant temperature is below 165°F (91°C).

GLOW PLUG TYPE

Application	Motorcraft Part No.
2.2L	E3TZ-12A342-B
6.9L	E3TZ-12A342-A

Fig.1: 2.2L Diesel Firing Order

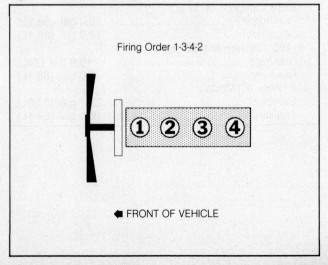

Firing Order 1-3-4-2

① ② ③ ④

◄ FRONT OF VEHICLE

TUNE-UP (Cont.)

Fig.2: 6.9L Diesel Firing Order

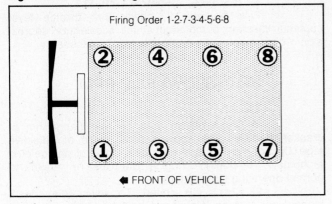

Firing Order 1-2-7-3-4-5-6-8

◀ FRONT OF VEHICLE

INJECTION TIMING

2.2L

1) Disconnect ground cables from both batteries. Remove air inlet hose between air cleaner and intake manifold. Disconnect fuel injection pipes from fuel injection pump. Remove hydraulic head plug bolt from injection pump. Align 2° ATDC timing mark on crankshaft pulley with indicator pin by turning crankshaft. *See Fig. 3.*

Fig. 3: 2.2L Initial Timing Mark Setup

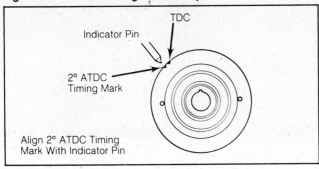

Make sure marks align at 2° ATDC.

2) Mount static timing gauge adapter with metric dial indicator (14-0303 & D82L-4201-A) in hydraulic head plug hole. Mount adapter and indicator assembly so indicator pointer is in contact with injection pump plunger and gauge reads about .08" (2 mm). *See Fig. 4.*

Fig. 4: 2.2L Timing Gauge Adapter Installation

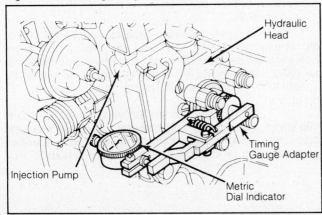

Indicator pointer should contact injection pump plunger.

3) Slowly rotate crankshaft counterclockwise (reverse direction of engine rotation) until dial indicator pointer stops moving. Crankshaft 2° ATDC timing mark should be about 30-50° away from initial setup position. *See Fig. 5.*

Fig. 5: Position of 2° ATDC Timing Mark After Rotation

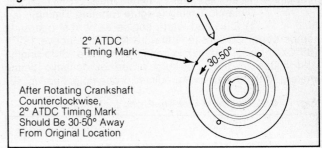

Mark should be about 30-50° away from initial setup position.

4) Set dial indicator pointer to zero. Turn crankshaft left and right slightly to make sure that indicator pointer does not move from zero setting.

5) Turn crankshaft clockwise (in direction of engine rotation) until 2° ATDC timing mark aligns with indicator pin. When mark is aligned with pin, dial indicator reading should be .04" ±.0008" (1 mm ±.02 mm).

6) If timing is not to specification, loosen injection pump attaching bolt and nuts. Turn injection pump housing counterclockwise (reverse direction of engine rotation) past correct position. Rotate pump housing clockwise until timing is correct. Repeat steps **3)** through **5)** to check timing.

6.9L

NOTE: Models with C-6 transmissions and late production models with manual transmissions are equipped with a pump-mounted fast idle bracket and solenoid. Bracket and solenoid must be removed on these models to provide access for pump wrench and rotating tool during timing procedure.

Static Timing (Engine Stopped Timing)

1) Loosen (keep snug) 3 nuts attaching fuel injection pump to pump mounting adapter with injector

Fig. 6: 6.9L Static Timing Mark Alignment

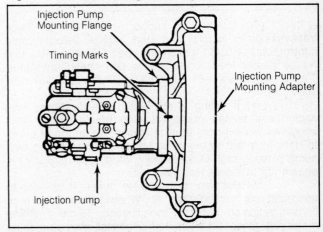

Keep mounting nuts snug during static timing check.

TUNE-UP (Cont.)

pump wrench (T83T-9000-B). Install injection pump rotating tool (T83T-9000-C) on front of pump. Rotate pump to align injection pump mounting flange timing mark with pump mounting adapter timing mark. *See Fig. 6.*

2) Remove tools and tighten mounting nuts to specifications. Visually recheck timing to ensure that marks are still aligned after tightening nuts.

Dynamic Timing (Engine Running Timing)

1) Start and warm engine to normal operating temperature. Coolant temperature MUST be above 192°F (89°C) to perform dynamic timing procedure. Stop engine and install magnetic pick-up probe of dynamic timing meter (78-0100) into timing pointer probe hole. *See Fig. 7.*

Fig. 7: 6.9L Magnetic Pick-Up Probe Installation

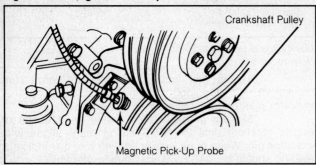

2) Remove No. 1 cylinder glow plug. Install luminosity probe in place of glow plug and tighten to 12 ft. lbs. (16 N.m). *See Fig. 8.* Connect photocell over luminosity probe and connect to dynamic timing meter. Connect dynamic timing meter to battery and set to 20° offset.

Fig. 8: 6.9L Luminosity Probe Installation

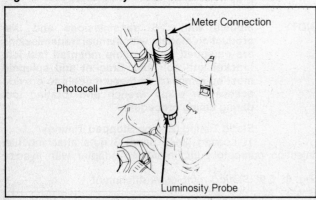

3) Raise and support rear wheels. Place transmission in Neutral and start engine. Using throttle control tool (14-0302), set engine speed at 1400 RPM with no accessory load. Observe injection timing on meter. Timing should be 4-6° ATDC. Add 1° for altitudes over 3000 feet.

4) If timing is not within specifications, stop engine and loosen pump retaining nuts (keeping nuts snug). As viewed from front of engine, rotate top of pump to right to retard timing or to left to advance timing with pump rotating tool. Moving timing mark .030" (.75 mm) is equal to 2° of timing. Retighten nuts.

5) Recheck timing using meter. If still not to specifications, repeat step **4)**. When timing is correct, tighten retaining nuts to specification. Remove timing meter and other test equipment. Reinstall glow plug using anti-seize compound on threads.

LINKAGE ADJUSTMENT

With engine off, check that throttle lever contacts injection pump stop at full accelerator depression. Adjust stop screw on throttle lever if necessary.

HOT (SLOW) IDLE RPM

2.2L

1) Clean off an area on rear flange rim of crankshaft pulley and apply a small piece of reflective tape. Do not overlap tape onto belt. Connect photoeletric tachometer (99-0001) to engine. Start and run engine to normal operating temperature.

2) Check idle speed. To adjust idle speed, loosen lock nut on idle speed adjusting bolt. Turn bolt clockwise to increase idle speed or counterclockwise to decrease idle speed. *See Fig. 9.* After adjustment, race engine several times to make sure accelerator cable is returning properly.

Fig. 9: 2.2L Idle Adjusting Locations

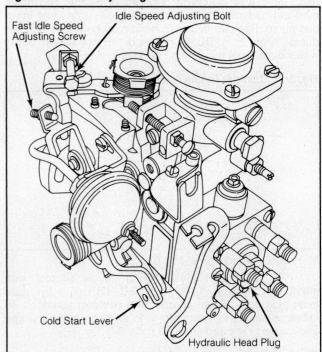

6.9L

1) Apply reflective tape to rear flange rim of the crankshaft pulley. Start and run engine to normal operating temperature. Connect a photoelectric tachometer (99-0001) to engine and check idle speed. Measure idle speed with transmission in Neutral (man. trans.) or "D" (auto. trans.).

2) Turn idle speed adjusting screw to adjust idle speed. *See Fig. 10.* Shift transmission out of gear and momentarily accelerate engine. Shift back into specified gear and recheck idle speed. Readjust if necessary.

TUNE-UP (Cont.)

Fig. 10: 6.9L Idle Adjusting Locations

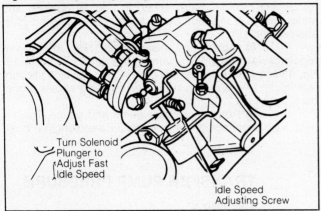

Turn Solenoid Plunger to Adjust Fast Idle Speed

Idle Speed Adjusting Screw

IDLE SPEED (RPM)

Application	RPM
2.2L	780-830
6.9L	650-700

COLD (FAST) IDLE SPEED

2.2L

1) Apply reflective tape to rear flange rim of crankshaft pulley. Attach photoelectric tachometer to engine. Pull cold start knob (located on instrument panel) out to fullest extent of travel.

2) Check fast idle speed. Turn fast idle speed adjusting screw to adjust engine speed to specification. *See Fig. 9.*

6.9L

1) Apply reflective tape to rear flange rim of crankshaft pulley. Attach photoelectric tachometer to engine. Disconnect wiring harness from fast idle solenoid. Apply battery voltage to solenoid to activate it. Momentarily accelerate engine to set solenoid plunger.

2) Check fast idle speed. Adjust fast idle speed by turning solenoid plunger in or out. *See Fig. 10.* Momentarily accelerate engine and recheck fast idle speed. Readjust if necessary.

3) Stop engine. Remove battery voltage from solenoid and reconnect wiring harness to solenoid. Remove tachometer.

FAST IDLE SPEED (RPM)

Application	RPM
2.2L	1150-1250
6.9L	850-900

VACUUM PUMP & RESERVOIR

Diesel engines do not produce manifold vacuum; therefore, all models are equipped with a belt-driven vacuum pump. The pump produces vacuum for operation of power brake and speed control systems. A brake/low-vacuum warning light on the instrument panel glows if system vacuum is not adequate to operate brake booster or other vacuum systems. The warning light remains on after engine start-up until vacuum builds up in system.

1) The vacuum pump is required to operate accessories. The reservoir is a holding tank for vacuum. Test pump and reservoir periodically.

2) Locate reservoir on right fender apron. Disconnect Grey stripe (2.2L) vacuum hose at speed control servo and connect hose to vacuum gauge. Start engine and observe vacuum gauge.

3) Vacuum should be 20-23" Hg. If not to specification, check for leaking vacuum hose or defective vacuum pump.

4) After vacuum has stabilized above 20" Hg, turn engine off. Vacuum should hold steady. After 24 hours, vacuum should be a minimum 15" Hg. If vacuum fails to hold, replace vacuum reservoir.

VACUUM REGULATOR VALVE

6.9L AUTO. TRANS. ONLY

1) The vacuum regulator valve provides vacuum signals to control transmission shift points. Vacuum setting of valve should be checked periodically, using the following procedure. Engine MUST NOT be running during this procedure.

2) Disconnect 2-port vacuum connector from vacuum regulator valve, located on left side of pump. *See Fig. 11.* Remove throttle cable from pump throttle lever, located on right side of pump.

Fig. 11: Location of Vacuum Regulator Valve on 6.9L Fuel Injection Pump

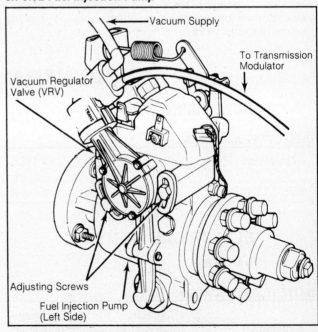

Vacuum Supply

To Transmission Modulator

Vacuum Regulator Valve (VRV)

Adjusting Screws

Fuel Injection Pump (Left Side)

3) Remove throttle return spring and reposition. Place end of spring over throttle lever ball stud and other end over throttle cable support bracket. Insert gauging block (T83T-7B200-AH) between pump boss and wide open throttle stop screw. *See Fig. 12.*

4) Attach a vacuum pump to upper port (labeled "VAC") of vacuum regulator valve. Attach vacuum gauge to lower port (labeled "TRANS") of regulator valve.

1983 Ford Diesel Tune-Up

TUNE-UP (Cont.)

Fig. 12: Repositioning Throttle Return Spring on 6.9L

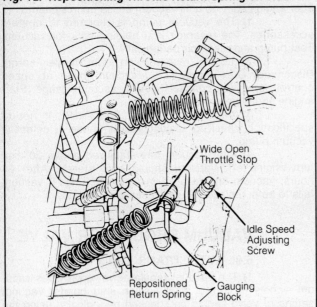

Wide Open Throttle Stop

Idle Speed Adjusting Screw

Repositioned Return Spring

Gauging Block

Insert gauging block between pump boss and wide open throttle stop screw.

5) Apply and maintain 20" Hg to vacuum regulator valve. Vacuum gauge attached to regulator valve should indicate 6.4-7.4" Hg. If vacuum reading is not to specification, adjust regulator valve.

6) To adjust valve, loosen 2 vacuum regulator valve-to-injection pump mounting screws and rotate valve until vacuum gauge reads 6.4-7.4" Hg. Tighten screws. If valve cannot be adjusted to obtain vacuum reading, replace regulator valve.

7) Release vacuum and remove gauging block. Reconnect throttle return spring in original position and make sure fuel injection pump lever returns and stays at idle position.

8) Apply and maintain 20" Hg to vacuum regulator valve again. Vacuum gauge MUST indicate 13" Hg. If vacuum reading is less than 13" Hg, replace vacuum regulator valve and adjust new valve using above procedure.

9) Remove vacuum pump and gauge. Reconnect all disconnected components in their original positions.

TRANSFER PUMP PRESSURE

6.9L ONLY

1) Remove screw from transfer pump pressure port cover and install transfer pump pressure connector (T83T-9000-A). Connector should go through cover and into pressure port. Install adapter (5650) onto connector and connect pressure tester (19-0002).

2) Connect photoelectric tachometer to engine. Place transmission in Neutral and run engine at 3000 RPM with no accessory load. Pressure should be 95-110 psi (6.8-7.7 kg/cm²). If not to specification, replace fuel injection pump.

EMISSION CONTROL

NOTE: See appropriate article in EMISSION CONTROL Section.

GENERAL SERVICING

FUEL INJECTION

DIESEL FUEL INJECTION

Application	Type
2.2L	Kiki VE
6.9L	Stanadyne DB-2

ELECTRICAL SYSTEM

BATTERY

BATTERY SPECIFICATIONS

Application	Capacity (Amp Hours)	Discharge Rate (Amps)
2.2L	63	260
6.9L	83	350

STARTER

The 2.2L engine uses a Mitsubishi positive engagement starter with solenoid actuated drive. The 6.9L engine uses a Motorcraft positive engagement starter.

STARTER SPECIFICATIONS

Application	Volts	Amps	Test RPM
2.2L	12	500	[1]
6.9L			
4" Armature	12	70	[1]
4 1/2" Armature	12	80	[1]

[1] — Information not available from manufacturer.

ALTERNATORS

All models use Motorcraft external regulator alternator.

ALTERNATOR REGULATOR

All models use Motorcraft Solid State Electronic Regulator, calibrated and preset by manufacturer. No adjustment is required or possible.

GENERAL SERVICING (Cont.)

ALTERNATOR SPECIFICATIONS

Stamp Color	Rated Amp Output
2.2L (Rear Terminal)	
Orange	40
Green	60
6.9L (Side Terminal)	
Green	65
Black	70
Red	100

Field Current Draw@12 Volts	
2.2L	4
6.9L	4.25

ADJUSTMENTS

BELT ADJUSTMENT

Using a strand tension gauge, measure belt tension midway between pulleys. If tension is not as specified in Belt Adjustment table, adjust tension or replace belt. Used belts are any operated for more than 10 minutes.

BELT ADJUSTMENT
Tension in Lbs. (Kg) Using Strand Tension Gauge

Application	New Belt	Used Belt
2.2L		
Vacuum Pump	90-130 (41-59)	80-100 (36-45)
Alternator	120-160 (54-73)	110-130 (50-59)
Power Steering	150-190 (68-86)	140-160 (64-73)
6.9L		
Thermactor	90-130 (41-59)	80-100 (36-45)
All Others	120-160 (54-73)	110-130 (50-59)

SERVICE INTERVALS

REPLACEMENT INTERVALS

Component	Interval (Miles)
Oil Filter	5000
Oil By-Pass Filter (2.2L)	10,000
Air Filter	30,000
Fuel Filter	
2.2L	15,000
6.9L (Secondary)	30,000

CAPACITIES

COOLING SYSTEM CAPACITIES

Application	Quantity
2.2L	
With A/C	10.7 qts. (10.1L)
Without A/C	10.0 qts. (9.5L)
6.9L	29.0 qts. (27L)

ENGINE OIL & FUEL CAPACITIES

Application	Quantity
Crankcase (Including Filter)	
2.2L	7.0 qts. (6.6L)
6.9L	10.0 qts. (9.3L)
Fuel Tank	
2.2L	
Standard	
Short Wheelbase	15.2 gals. (57.5L)
Long Wheelbase	17.0 gals. (64.3L)
Optional Auxiliary	13.0 gals. (49.2L)
6.9L	
Standard (Front)	19.0 gals. (72.0L)
Optional (Rear)	19.0 gals. (72.0L)

TRANSMISSION & DIFFERENTIAL CAPACITIES

Application	Quantity
Auto. Trans.	
Ranger	
C-3 (Dexron II)	8.0 qts. (7.6L)
C-5 (Motorcraft Type H)	
2WD Models	17.5 qts. (7.1L)
4WD Models	17.9 qts. (7.5L)
F-250/350	
C-5 (Motorcraft Type H)	11.0 qts. (10.4L)
C-6 (Dexron II)	
2WD Models	11.9 qts. (11.2L)
4WD Models	13.4 qts. (12.7L)
AOT (Dexron II)	12.0 qts. (11.7L)
Man. Trans.	
Ranger	
4-Speed	3.0 pts. (1.4L)
5-Speed	3.6 pts. (1.7L)
F-250/350	
3-Speed	1.8 qts. (1.6L)
4-Speed	
T-18	3.5 qts. (3.3L)
Overdrive	2.3 qts. (2.1L)
New Process 435	
With Extension	3.5 qts. (3.3L)
Without Extension	3.3 qts. (3.0L)
Transfer Case (Dexron II)	
Ranger	3.0 pts. (1.4L)
F-250/350	
New Process 208	7.0 pts. (3.3L)
Borg-Warner 13-45	6.5 pts. (3.0L)
Rear Axle (Hypoid Gear Lube)	
Ranger	
6 3/4" Ring Gear	3.3 pts. (1.6L)
7 1/2" Ring Gear	5.0 pts. (2.4L)
F-250/350	
Ford Axles	
8 3/4" Ring Gear	5.5 pts. (2.6L)
All Others	4.5 pts. (2.1L)
Dana (Spicer) Axles	
Model 60 & 61	6.0 pts. (2.8L)
Front Axle (Hypoid Gear Lube)	
Ranger	
Model 28	1.0 pts. (0.5 L)
F-250/350	
Model 44	3.8 pts. (1.7L)
Model 50	4.1 pts. (1.9L)

1983 General Motors 4 Tune-Up

TUNE-UP

ENGINE IDENTIFICATION

Engines can be identified by the 8th digit of the Vehicle Identification Number (VIN). The VIN number is stamped on a plate attached to the left top side of dash.

VIN ENGINE CODES

Application	VIN Code
1.9L (119") 2-Bbl.	A
2.0L (122") 2-Bbl.	Y

TUNE-UP NOTES

NOTE: **When performing tune-up procedures described in this article, the following notes and precautions must be followed:**

Due to changes and corrections, always refer to Engine Tune-Up Decal in engine compartment before attempting Tune-Up. In the event of a conflict between specifications given in this manual and decal specifications, always use decal specifications.

When performing tune-up on vehicles equipped with a catalytic converter, do not allow or create a condition of engine misfire in one or more cylinders for an extended period of time. Damage to converter from overheating may occur due to loading with unburned fuel.

ENGINE COMPRESSION

When making compression checks, disconnect the ignition switch connector Pink wire from High Energy Ignition (HEI) system. With air cleaner removed and throttle and choke wide open, crank engine through at least 4 compression strokes.

COMPRESSION SPECIFICATIONS

Compression Ratio	
1.9L	8.4:1
2.0L	9.3:1
Compression Pressure	
1.9L	170 psi (12 kg/cm²)
2.0L	100 psi (7 kg/cm²)
Minimum Pressure	
1.9L	100 psi (7 kg/cm²)
Maximum Variation	
1.9L	10 psi (0.7 kg/cm²)
2.0L	30 psi (2.1 kg/cm²)

VALVE CLEARANCE

Check rocker arm bracket nuts for looseness and retighten as necessary before adjusting valves. Adjust valves with engine cold.

VALVE ADJUSTMENT

Application	Clearance
1.9L	
Intake	.006" (.15 mm)
Exhaust	.010" (.25 mm)
2.0L	
All	1 1/2 turns past zero lash.

VALVE ARRANGEMENT

1.9L
Intake — Left side.
Exhaust — Right Side.
2.0L
E-I-I-E-E-I-I-E (Front to rear)

SPARK PLUGS

SPARK PLUG TYPE

Application	AC Number
1.9L	R42XLS
2.0L	R42CTS

SPARK PLUG SPECIFICATIONS

Application	Gap In. (mm)	Torque Ft. Lbs. (N.m)
All Models	.043 (1.1)	7-19 (9-26)

HIGH TENSION WIRE RESISTANCE

Carefully remove ends of wire from spark plug and distributor. Using an ohmmeter, check resistance while gently twisting wire. If resistance is not within specifications, or fluctuates from infinity to any value, replace cable.

RESISTANCE (Ohms)

Application	Ohms
All Models	31,500-73,500 per foot

DISTRIBUTOR

All 1.9L engines are equipped with a Nippon-denso electronic ignition distributor. All 2.0L engines are equipped with a Delco-Remy HEI ignition system. No adjustments are necessary.

Fig. 1: 1.9L 4-Cyl. Firing Order

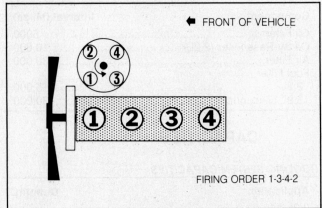

← FRONT OF VEHICLE

FIRING ORDER 1-3-4-2

TUNE-UP (Cont.)

Fig. 2: 2.0L 4-Cyl. Firing Order and Timing Marks

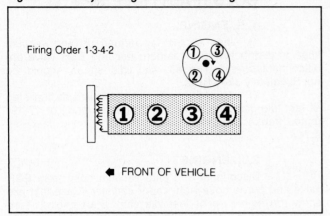

Firing Order 1-3-4-2

◀ FRONT OF VEHICLE

IGNITION TIMING

1) Install timing light with an adapter between No. 1 spark plug and No. 1 spark plug wire, or use an inductive type pickup. Do not puncture wire.

2) Run engine until it reaches normal operating temperature. Disconnect and plug distributor advance, EGR, and canister purge vacuum lines. Place transmission in Neutral (man. trans.) or "D" (auto. trans.). Check ignition timing and adjust if necessary. Reconnect all hoses.

TIMING SPECIFICATIONS (Degrees BTDC@RPM)

Application	Man. Trans.	Auto. Trans.
1.9L	[1] 6@900	6@900
2.0L	2@800	2@800

[1] — Federal and High Altitude models 6°@800 RPM.

HOT (SLOW) IDLE RPM

1.9L ENGINE

1) Warm engine to normal operating temperature and place transmission in Neutral. California models must be in closed loop operation before checking or adjusting. Disconnect and plug distributor vacuum hose, canister purge line and EGR vacuum line.

2) Pinch off idle compensator vacuum line by bending rubber hose. Adjust throttle adjusting screw to obtain specified idle RPM. If vehicle is equipped with air conditioning, turn A/C on maximum cold and high blower.

3) On California vehicles with automatic transmissions, disconnect and ground single wire from back of A/C compressor. On all models, open throttle momentarily to assure solenoid is fully extended and allow to close. Adjust screw on throttle lever to obtain solenoid RPM. Reconnect wires and hoses.

2.0L ENGINE

1) Disconnect and plug vacuum hose at EGR valve and canister purge hose at canister. Make adjustment with engine at normal operating temperature, choke fully open, air cleaner installed and air conditioning off. Disconnect solenoid wire and set base idle speed with idle speed screw.

2) Reconnect solenoid wire. If vehicle is equipped with air conditioner, disconnect electrical lead from compressor and turn A/C switch "ON". Open throttle slightly to allow solenoid to extend, then adjust curb idle by turning screw on back of solenoid. Reconnect wires and hoses.

IDLE SPEED (RPM)

Application	Idle RPM	Solenoid RPM
1.9L	[1] 900	[2] 1900
2.0L	800	1075

[1] — Federal manual transmission models 800 RPM.
[2] — Manual transmission models 900 RPM.

IDLE MIXTURE

NOTE: Idle mixture adjustment is not a part of normal tune-up. DO NOT adjust mixture unless carburetor has been disassembled or vehicle fails emissions testing.

MIXTURE SCREW PLUG REMOVAL

1.9L Engine

Remove carburetor from vehicle. Remove idle mixture screw plug using a screwdriver inserted into slit on base of carburetor.

2.0L Engine

1) Remove carburetor from engine. Invert throttle body and make two parallel cuts on each side of the locator point with a hacksaw. Cuts should not extend more than 1/8" (3.2 mm) beyond the locator point.

2) Place a flat punch near the end of the saw marks. Hold the punch at a 45° angle. Drive it into the throttle body until the casting breaks away, exposing the steel plug.

3) Hold a center punch in a vertical position and drive it into the plug. Now hold punch at a 45° angle, and drive plug out of casting.

MIXTURE ADJUSTMENT

1.9L Federal Models

1) Remove carburetor. Remove idle mixture screw plug. Reinstall carburetor. Block drive wheels and place transmission in Neutral.

2) Disconnect and plug distributor vacuum line, idle compensator and EGR vacuum lines. With engine at normal operating temperature, turn idle mixture screw all the way in and back out 1 1/2 turns. Adjust throttle screw to 850 RPM (man. trans.) or 950 RPM (auto. trans.).

3) Adjust setting of idle mixture screw to achieve maximum speed. Reset throttle screw to reach RPM listed in step 2). Turn idle mixture screw clockwise until engine speed drops 50 RPM.

4) If vehicle has air conditioner, turn A/C on to maximum cold and high blower. Open throttle about 1/3 and allow to close. Adjust speed up controller to set idle at 900 RPM.

1.9L California Models

1) Remove carburetor. Remove idle mixture screw plug. Reinstall carburetor. Make idle speed and mixture adjustment with engine at normal operating temperature.

2) Disconnect and plug distributor vacuum line. Block idle compensator line by bending hose. Connect

TUNE-UP (Cont.)

dwell meter (set to 6-cylinder scale) to dwell meter lead on carburetor. Turn idle mixture screw all the way in and back out 1 1/2 turns. Adjust throttle screw to obtain an idle of 850-950 RPM.

3) Adjust idle mixture screw to obtain an average dwell of 36°. Reset throttle adjusting screw to 850-950 RPM.

4) If vehicle is equipped with air conditioning, turn on A/C to maximum cold and set blower on high. Open throttle 1/3 and allow to close. Adjust speed up controller screw to set idle at 900 RPM.

2.0L Models

1) Engine must be at normal operating temperature and air conditioning off. Set parking brake and block drive wheels. On vehicles equipped with vacuum parking brake release, disconnect and plug hose at brake.

2) Disconnect and plug vacuum as directed on the Vehicle Emission Control Information label. Connect tachometer to engine. Adjust timing and reconnect vacuum advance hose. Set idle speed.

3) Disconnect crankcase ventilation tube from air cleaner. Using tool J-26911 (or equivalent), insert hose with rubber stopper (from propane valve) into air cleaner snorkel. Be sure propane cartridge is vertical.

4) With engine idling in "D" (auto. trans.) or Neutral (man. trans.), open propane supply control valve slowly. Engine speed will increase. Add propane until engine speed begins to drop from over-richness. Note maximum enriched idle RPM.

5) The maximum enriched idle RPM is the idle RPM plus propane enrichment RPM. Engine speed should rise above normal idle by amount specified. If so, mixture is correct. Proceed to step **9)**.

6) If speed is incorrect, remove idle mixture screw plugs. Carburetor must be removed and punch driven through bottom of throttle body to remove plug. Seat screws, then back out 3 turns.

7) Place transmission in "D" (auto. trans.) or Neutral (man. trans.), then back out screw slowly until maximum idle speed is reached. Then set maximum enriched idle speed.

8) Turn each mixture screw in (clockwise) 1/8 turn at a time until idle speed is correct. Recheck maximum enriched speed with propane. If incorrect, repeat step **7)**. Check and adjust fast idle speed.

9) Turn off engine. Remove propane tool, connect crankcase ventilation tube and reconnect all vacuum hoses.

PROPANE MIXTURE ADJUSTMENT (RPM)

Application	Man. Trans.	Auto. Trans.
2.0L Engine		
Federal	20	20
High Alt.	20	20

COLD (FAST) IDLE RPM

1.9L ENGINE

1) When engine is warmed up and vacuum lines of distributor, idle compensator and EGR valve are disconnected and plugged, fast idle speed should be approximately 3200 RPM.

2) Adjusted throttle valve opening at first step of fast idle cam should be 15-17° (man. trans.) or 17-19° (auto. trans.). Adjust if necessary by turning fast idle screw.

2.0L ENGINE

Disconnect and plug vacuum hose from EGR valve and purge hose from vapor canister. Place fast idle screw on high step of fast idle cam. Start engine. Turn screw to adjust fast idle RPM to 2600 RPM. Open throttle to release fast idle cam. Stop engine and reconnect hoses.

COLD (FAST) IDLE RPM

Application	RPM
1.9L	3200 [1]
2.0L	2600

[1] — Approximate speed. Throttle angle must be 15-17° for man. trans. or 17-19° for auto. trans.

AUTOMATIC CHOKE

Automatic choke is non-adjustable.

FUEL PUMP

NOTE: **Information not available from manufacturer.**

EMISSION CONTROL

NOTE: **For information on emission controls, see appropriate article in EMISSION CONTROL Section.**

GENERAL SERVICING

IGNITION

DISTRIBUTOR

All 1.9L engines are equipped with a Nippondenso solid state distributor. All 2.0L engines are equipped with a Delco-Remy HEI solid state distributor. No adjustments are necessary.

DISTRIBUTOR PICKUP COIL RESISTANCE (Ohms)

All Models	500-1500

GENERAL SERVICING (Cont.)

IGNITION COIL

COIL RESISTANCE (Ohms)

Application	Primary	Secondary
1.9L	0.9-1.4	7300-11,100
2.0L	0-1	6,000-30,000

FUEL SYSTEMS

CARBURETORS

Application	Model
1.9L	Hitachi DCH340
2.0L	Rochester 2SE

ELECTRICAL

BATTERY

BATTERY SPECIFICATIONS

Application	Cold Cranking Amps. [1]	Reserve Capacity Minutes
1.9L	315	75
2.0L	405	75
Heavy Duty	515	115

[1] — At 0°F (-18°C).

STARTER

All 1.9L engines are equipped with Hitachi starters. All 2.0L engines are equipped with Delco-Remy 5MT starters.

STARTER SPECIFICATIONS

Application	Volts	Amps.	Test RPM
1.9L	12	70	6000
2.0L	9	50-75	6000-11,900

ALTERNATORS

All models are equipped with Delco alternators with integral voltage regulator.

ALTERNATOR SPECIFICATIONS

Application	Rated Amp. Output
All Models	37, 66, 78

Field Current Draw @ 12 volts [1]	
All Models	4.0-5.0 amps.

[1] — At 80°F (27°C).

ALTERNATOR REGULATORS

All models are equipped with Delco-Remy non-adjustable voltage regulators, integral with alternator.

ADJUSTMENTS

BELT ADJUSTMENT

Using a strand tension gauge, measure belt tension midway between pulleys. If tension is not as specified in Belt Adjustment table, adjust tension or replace belt. Used belts are any that have been rotate at least 1 complete revolution by engine pulley.

BELT ADJUSTMENT
Tension in Lbs. (Kg) Using Strand Tension Gauge

Application	New Belt	Used Belt
All Models		
Air Conditioning	145	65-100
	(66)	(29-45)
Power Steering	130	50-80
	(59)	(23-36)

SERVICE INTERVALS

REPLACEMENT INTERVALS

Component	Interval (Miles)
Fuel Filter	15,000
Spark Plugs	30,000
PCV Valve & Filter	30,000
Air Filter	30,000

CAPACITIES

FLUID CAPACITIES

Application	Quantity
Cooling System	9.5 qts. (9.0L)
Crankcase	4.0 qts. (3.8L)
Automatic Transmission	
Overhaul	
3-Speed	19.0 pts. (8.9L)
4-Speed	23.0 pts. (10.9L)
Refill	
3-Speed	7.0 pts. (3.3L)
4-Speed	10.0 pts. (4.7L)
Manual Transmission	[1]
Rear Axle	3.0 pts. (1.4L)
Fuel Tank	
Standard	13.0 gals. (49.2L)
Optional	20.0 gals. (75.7L)

[1] — Add fluid to bottom of filler plug hole.

TUNE-UP

ENGINE IDENTIFICATION

Engines can be identified by the eighth digit of the Vehicle Identification Number (VIN). The VIN number is stamped on a plate located at the base of the steering column on "P" (Van conversion) models, and on the upper left corner of the dash on all other models.

VIN ENGINE CODES

Application	VIN Code
4.1L (250") 2-Bbl.	D
4.8L (292") 1-Bbl.	T

TUNE-UP NOTES

NOTE: **When performing tune-up procedures described in this article, the following notes and precautions must be observed:**

Due to changes and corrections, always refer to Engine Tune-Up Decal in engine compartment before attempting tune-up. In the event of a conflict between specifications given in this manual and decal specifications, decal specifications prevail.

When performing tune-up on vehicles equipped with a catalytic converter, do not allow or create a condition of engine misfire in one or more cylinders for an extended period of time. Damage to converter from overheating may occur due to loading with unburned fuel.

For tune-up purposes, "Light Duty" refers to vehicles up to 8500 lbs. GVW. "Heavy Duty" refers to vehicles exceeding 8500 lbs. GVW.

ENGINE COMPRESSION

When making compression checks, disconnect ignition switch Pink wire from High Energy Ignition system. With air cleaner removed and throttle and choke wide open, crank engine through at least four compression strokes.

COMPRESSION SPECIFICATIONS

Compression Ratio	
4.1L	8.3:1
4.8L	8.0:1
Compression Pressure	130 psi (9.1 kg/cm²)
Maximum Pressure Variation	30 psi (2.1 kg/cm²)

VALVE CLEARANCE

All engines have hydraulic lifters which should be adjusted to 1 turn down from zero lash.

VALVE ARRANGEMENT

E-I-I-E-E-I-I-E-E-I-I-E (Front to rear)

SPARK PLUGS

SPARK PLUG SPECIFICATIONS

Application	Gap In. (mm)	Torque Ft. Lbs. (N.m)
All Models	.035 (.90)	17-27 (23-37)

SPARK PLUG TYPE

Application	AC No.
All Models	
Light Duty	R45TS
Heavy Duty	R44T

HIGH TENSION WIRE RESISTANCE

Carefully remove ends of wire from spark plug and distributor. Using an ohmmeter, check resistance while gently twisting wire. If resistance is incorrect, or fluctuates from infinity to any value, replace cable.

RESISTANCE (Ohms)

Wire Length	Maximum
Under 24"	30,000
Over 24"	50,000

DISTRIBUTOR

Most models are equipped with High Energy Ignition (HEI) systems and no adjustments are required. In California, the 4.1L engine will be equipped with the Electronic Spark Timing (HEI-EST) system.

Fig. 1: Timing Mark and Firing Order

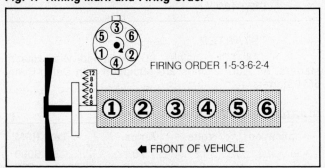

Magnetic probe located at 10° ATDC.

IGNITION TIMING

NOTE: **Engines are equipped with a receptacle for magnetic probe timing equipment, located 10° ATDC. Do not use this location for timing with a conventional light.**

1) Install timing light with an adapter between No. 1 spark plug and No. 1 spark plug wire, or use an inductive type pickup. Do not puncture wire.

2) Ignition timing is set with the engine at normal operating temperature, choke full open, air cleaner installed and air conditioner off. On HEI equipped vehicles, disconnect and plug vacuum hose at distributor. Set ignition timing at specified engine speed.

3) On HEI-EST equipped engines, disconnect 4 wire connector at distributor and set ignition timing at specified engine speed. Reconnect 4 wire connector and clear ECM trouble code.

TUNE-UP (Cont.)

IGNITION TIMING (Degrees BTDC @ RPM)

Application	Man. Trans.	Auto Trans.
4.1L		
Fed.	[1] 10	[1] 10
Cal.	6@700	[2] 6@650
4.8L		
Fed.	8@700	8@700
Cal.	8@700	8@700

[1] — Set timing at curb idle.
[2] — 700 RPM with air conditioning.

HOT (SLOW) IDLE RPM

4.1L MODELS

1) Make adjustments with engine at normal operating temperature, choke full open, air cleaner installed and air conditioning off. Disconnect solenoid wire and set base idle speed with idle speed screw.

2) Reconnect solenoid wire and all hoses. If vehicle is equipped with air conditioner, disconnect electrical lead from compressor and turn A/C switch ON. Open throttle slightly to allow solenoid to extend, then adjust curb idle by turning screw in back of solenoid.

4.8L MODELS

1) Make adjustments with engine at normal operating temperature, choke full open, air cleaner installed, air conditioning off and transmission in neutral. Disconnect solenoid wire and set base idle speed with hex head screw in rear of solenoid.

2) Reconnect solenoid wire. Set curb idle speed by turning solenoid assembly in or out. Ensure solenoid is energized and fully extended.

SLOW IDLE SPEED (RPM)

Application (Decal No.)	Solenoid Idle	Curb Idle
4.1L		
DHK, DHN, & DHR	850	700
DKF, DKD DWS & DWT	650	475
DJH, DJJ DJU & DJW	700	550
DJK & DJM	750	550
DJZ, DKA, DKB, DKC & DKZ	650	525
DJR, DJN, DJS, DJT, DKH, DKJ DKR & DKS	750	600
DHK, DHN, DHR DHT, DHU, DHW	850	700
DKM, DKN, DKT & DKU	650	550
DHX, DHY, DHZ, DJA, DJB, DJC, DJD & DJF	[1] 650	500
4.8L		
Man. Trans.	700	450
Auto. Trans.	700	450

[1] — 700 RPM with air conditioning.

IDLE MIXTURE

NOTE: Mixture adjustment is not a normal tune-up procedure. DO NOT remove idle mixture plugs unless vehicle fails emissions testing or throttle body has been disassembled.

MIXTURE SCREW PLUG REMOVAL

4.1L Models

1) Remove carburetor from engine. Invert throttle body and make two parallel cuts on each side of the locator point with a hacksaw. Cuts should not extend more than 1/8" (3.2 mm) beyond the locator point. *See Fig. 2.*

Fig. 2: Removing Idle Mixture Plug

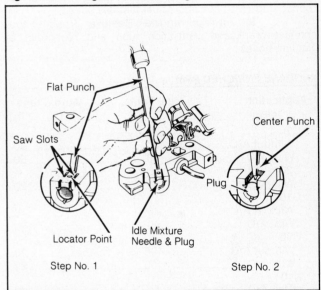

Distance between saw cuts depends on the size of the punch to be used.

2) Place a flat punch near the end of the saw marks. Hold the punch at a 45° angle. Drive it into the throttle body until the casting breaks away, exposing the steel plug.

3) Hold a center punch in a vertical position and drive it into the plug. Now hold punch at a 45° angle, and drive plug out of casting.

PROPANE ENRICHMENT PROCEDURE

4.1L Models (HEI Ignition)

1) Engine must be at normal operating temperature and air conditioning off. Set parking brake and block drive wheels. On vehicles equipped with vacuum parking brake release, disconnect and plug hose at brake.

2) Disconnect and plug vacuum as directed on the Vehicle Emission Control Information label. Connect tachometer to engine. Adjust timing and reconnect vacuum advance hose. Set idle speed.

3) Disconnect crankcase ventilation tube from air cleaner. Using tool J-26911 (or equivalent), insert hose with rubber stopper (from propane valve) into air cleaner snorkel. Be sure propane cartridge is vertical.

4) With engine idling in "D" (Automatic) or "Neutral" (Manual), open propane supply control valve slowly. Engine speed will increase. Add propane until

1983 General Motors 6 Tune-Up

TUNE-UP (Cont.)

engine speed begins to drop from over-richness. Note maximum enriched idle RPM.

5) The maximum enriched idle RPM is the idle RPM plus propane enrichment RPM. Engine speed should rise above normal idle by amount specified. If so, mixture is correct. Proceed to step **9)**.

6) If speed is incorrect, remove idle mixture screw plugs. Carburetor must be removed and punch driven through bottom of throttle body to remove plug. Seat screws, then back out 3 turns.

7) Place transmission in "D" (Automatic) or "Neutral" (Manual), then back out screw slowly until maximum idle speed is reached. Then set maximum enriched idle speed.

8) Turn each mixture screw in (clockwise) 1/8 turn at a time until idle speed is correct. Recheck maximum enriched speed with propane. If incorrect, repeat step **7)**. Check and adjust fast idle speed.

9) Turn off engine. Remove propane tool, connect crankcase ventilation tube and reconnect all vacuum hoses.

PROPANE ENRICHED RPM

Application	Man. Trans.	Auto. Trans.
4.1L (2SE)		
C10		
Without A/C	60	50
With A/C	60	50
C20		
Without A/C	60	20
G10		
Without A/C	40	10
With A/C	40	
G30		
Without A/C	100	20
With A/C	100	20
K10		
With A/C	60	20

IDLE MIXTURE ADJUSTMENT
California Models (HEI-EST Ignition)

1) Remove carburetor from engine and remove idle mixture screw plug. Turn mixture screw in until lightly seated and back out 4 turns. If plug in air horn covering idle air bleed has been removed, replace air horn.

2) Remove vent stack screen assembly to gain access to lean mixture screw. Turn lean mixture screw until lightly bottomed and back out 2 1/2 turns. Some resistance should be felt. If no resistance, remove screw and check for spring.

3) Install carburetor on engine. Do not install air cleaner. Disconnect bowl vent line at carburetor. Disconnect the EGR valve hose and canister purge hose at carburetor and cap carburetor ports.

4) Disconnect carburetor-to-temperture sensor hose on air cleaner and plug open hose. Connect a dwell meter lead to the mixture control solenoid dwell test lead (green connector).

5) Set dwell meter to 6-cylinder position. Connect a tachometer to distributor lead (brown connector). Transmission should be in "PARK" or "NEUTRAL". Start engine and bring to operating temperature.

6) Run engine at 3000 RPM and adjust the lean mixture screw slowly to allow time for dwell to stabilize. It is normal for dwell to vary over a narrow range of approximately 5°.

7) Turn screw to obtain a average dwell of 35°. If unable to adjust, inspect main metering circuit for leaks or resistrictions. Return engine to idle.

8) Adjust idle mixture screw to obtain average dwell of 25° with cooling fan in off cycle. Adjustment is very sensitive. Make final check with adjusting tool removed.

9) If unable to adjust, inspect idle system for leaks or resistrictions. Disconnect mixture control solenoid when cooling fan is in off cycle and check for an RPM change of at least 50 RPM. If RPM does not change, check idle air bleed circuit.

10) Run engine at 3000 RPM for a few moments and note dwell reading. Dwell should show an average of 35°. If not, reset lean mixture screw. Then reset idle mixture screw to obtain 25° dwell.

11) When dwell readings have been set, reconnect all hoses and install vent screen and air cleaner. Set idle speed.

LEAN DROP PROCEDURE
4.8L Models Only

1) Set parking brake and block drive wheels. Remove air cleaner for access to carburetor, but keep vacuum hoses connected. Disconnect and plug other hoses if directed on Emission Control Tune-Up decal.

2) Warm engine to normal operating temperature. Make sure choke is open and air conditioning "OFF". Connect a tachometer to engine. Disconnect and plug distributor vacuum advance hose.

3) Check ignition timing and adjust if necessary. Reconnect vacuum advance hose. Carefully remove limiter cap from idle mixture screw. Lightly seat mixture screw, then back out just enough so engine will run.

4) Place transmission in neutral. Back out mixture screw slowly until maximum idle speed is obtained. Reset curb idle speed to 775 RPM. Turn mixture screw in until idle speed is 700 RPM.

5) Reset curb idle speed to 775 RPM. Reconnect all hoses and install air cleaner, then recheck idle speed.

COLD (FAST) IDLE RPM

4.1L Engine

Place fast idle screw on high step of fast idle cam. Turn screw to adjust fast idle RPM.

4.8L Engine

Place cam follower on high step of fast idle cam. Support lever with pliers and bend tang in or out to adjust fast idle RPM.

NOTE: **On models with manual choke, rotate fast idle cam clockwise to farthest "UP" position.**

FAST IDLE SPEED (RPM)

Application	Man. Trans.	Auto. Trans.
4.1L	2000	2200
4.8L	2400	2400

TUNE-UP (Cont.)

THROTTLE POSITION SENSOR (TPS)

ADJUSTMENT

1) DO NOT remove the TPS adjustment screw plug unless the TPS is not adjusted correctly or it is necessary to replace the air horn assembly, float bowl, TPS sensor, or TPS adjustment screw.

2) Using a .078" (1.98 mm) drill, carefully drill a hole in the steel cup plug covering the TPS adjustment screw. Plug is located next to the TPS plunger bore. Remove steel plug using a small slide hammer.

3) Disconnect the TPS connector and jumper all three terminals. Connect a digital voltmeter from TPS connector center terminal (B) to bottom terminal (C).

4) With ignition on, engine stopped, turn the TPS screw with flat bladed screwdriver to obtain .26 volts at curb idle position. Air conditioner must be off and Idle Speed Control fully retracted.

5) After adjustment, a new cup plug or silicone sealant rubber RTV must be inserted in the air horn.

AUTOMATIC CHOKE

All choke caps are retained with rivets and are non-adjustable.

FUEL PUMP

To test pressure, pinch off fuel return line (if equipped) and connect pressure gauge to fuel line at carburetor. Hold pressure gauge at level of pump outlet.

FUEL PUMP

Application	Pressure psi (kg/cm²)	Volume Pints (Liters)
All Models	4.5-6.0 (.3-.4)	1 pt in 30 sec. (.47 in 30 sec.)

EMISSION CONTROL

NOTE: See appropriate article in EMISSION CONTROL Section.

GENERAL SERVICING

IGNITION

DISTRIBUTOR

All vehicles are equipped with Delco-Remy High Energy Ignition. In California, the 4.1L engine is equipped with the HEI-EST system.

DISTRIBUTOR PICKUP COIL RESISTANCE (Ohms)

All Models	500-1500

IGNITION COIL

COIL RESISTANCE (Ohms)@75°F (24°C)

Application	Primary	Secondary
All Models	0.4-1.0	6000-30,000

COIL OUTPUT

At all engine speeds	25-35KV Minimum

FUEL SYSTEMS

CARBURETORS

Application	Model
4.1L	[1] Rochester 2SE 2-Bbl.
4.8L	Rochester 1ME 1-Bbl.

[1] — California models with HEI-EST uses Rochester E2SE 2-Bbl.

ELECTRICAL

BATTERY SPECIFICATIONS

Application	Cold Cranking Amps. [1]	Reserve Capacity Minutes
4.1L	315	75
4.8L	405	75

[1] — At 0°F (-18°C).

STARTER

All starters are Delco-Remy overrunning clutch models.

STARTER SPECIFICATIONS

Application	Volts	Amps.	Test RPM
4.1L	10	60-85	6800-10,300
4.8L	10	60-85	6800-10,300

ALTERNATOR

All models are equipped with Delco-Remy Integral Regulator Alternators.

1983 General Motors 6 Tune-Up

GENERAL SERVICING (Cont.)

ALTERNATOR SPECIFICATIONS

Application	Rated Amp. Output
Standard	
4.1L	37
4.8L	
"P" Models	42
Optional (All)	66, 80
Field Current Draw @ 12 volts [1]	
All Models	4.0-4.5 amps.

[1] — At 80°F(27®C).

ALTERNATOR REGULATOR

All models are equipped with Delco-Remy non-adjustable regulator, integral with alternator.

REGULATOR SPECIFICATIONS

Operating Voltage @85°F(29°C)	13.5-16

ADJUSTMENTS

BELT ADJUSTMENT (USING STRAND TENSION GAUGE)

Application	Lbs. (Kg)
New Belt	
Air Conditioning	135-145 (61-66)
All Others	120-130 (54-59)
Used Belt [1]	
Air Conditioning	90-100 (41-45)
All Others	70-80 (32-36)

[1] — Any belt that has been operated 10 minutes or more.

SERVICE INTERVALS

REPLACEMENT INTERVALS

Components	Intervals (Miles)
Oil Filter	7500
Fuel Filter	12,000
Spark Plugs	30,000
PCV Valve and Filter	30,000
Air Filter	30,000

CAPACITIES

COOLING SYSTEM

Application	Quantity
4.1L	
Van Models	17.0 qts. (16.1L)
All Other Models	15.5 qts. (14.7L)
4.8L	
"P" Models	13.5 qts. (12.8L)
All Other Models	15.5 qts. (14.7L)

CAPACITIES (EXCEPT COOLING)

Application	Quantity
Crankcase [1]	
4.1L	5.0 qts. (3.8L)
4.8L	6.0 qts. (4.7L)
Automatic Transmission (Dexron)	
THM 350	
Overhaul	10.0 qts. (9.5L)
Refill	6.0 pts. (2.8L)
THM 400	
Overhaul	10.0 qts. (9.5L)
Refill	7.0 pts. (3.8L)
Manual Transmission (SAE 80W-90)	
3-Speed	3.0 pts. (1.4L)
4-Speed	4.0 pts. (1.9L)
Transfer Case (SAE 10W-30)	5.0 pts. (2.4L)
Front Axle (SAE 80W-90)	5.0 pts. (2.4L)
Rear Axle (SAE 80W-90)	[2]
Power Take-Off (SAE 80W-90)	5.0 pts. (2.4L)
Fuel Tank	
Pickup Models	
Short Wheelbase (Each Tank)	16.0 gals. (61.0L)
Long Wheelbase (Each Tank)	20.0 gals. (76.0L)
Van Models	
Standard	22.0 gals. (84.0L)
Optional	33.0 gals. (125.0L)
"P" Models	
Standard	31.0 gals. (118.0L)
Optional	40.0 gals. (152.0L)

[1] — Including 1 quart for filter change.
[2] — Fill to bottom of filler hole.

TUNE-UP

ENGINE IDENTIFICATION

Engines can be identified by the eighth digit of the Vehicle Identification Number (VIN). The VIN number is stamped on a plate attached to the left top side of dash.

VIN ENGINE CODE

Application	VIN Code
2.8L (173") 2-Bbl.	B

TUNE-UP NOTES

NOTE: **When performing tune-up procedures described in this article, the following notes and precautions must be observed:**

Due to changes and corrections, always refer to Engine Tune-Up Decal in engine compartment before attempting tune-up. In the event of a conflict between specifications given in this manual and decal specifications, decal specifications prevail.

When performing tune-up on vehicles equipped with a catalytic converter, do not allow or create a condition of engine misfire in one or more cylinders for an extended period of time. Damage to converter from overheating may occur due to loading with unburned fuel.

ENGINE COMPRESSION

When making compression checks, disconnect the ignition switch connector Pink wire from high energy ignition system. With air cleaner removed and throttle and choke wide open, crank engine through at least 4 compression strokes.

COMPRESSION SPECIFICATIONS

Compression Ratio	8.5:1
Compression Pressure	100 psi (7.0 kg/cm²) min.
Maximum Pressure Variation	30%

VALVE CLEARANCE

All engines have hydraulic lifters. Lifters should be adjusted to 1 1/2 turns down from zero lash.

VALVE ARRANGEMENT

E-I-I-E-I-E (Left bank, front to rear)
E-I-E-I-I-E (Right bank, front to rear)

SPARK PLUGS

SPARK PLUG SPECIFICATIONS

Application	Gap In. (mm)	Torque Ft. Lbs. (N.m)
All Models	.045 (1.2)	.... 7-15 (9-20)

SPARK PLUG TYPE

Application	AC Number
All Models	R43CTS

HIGH TENSION WIRE RESISTANCE

Carefully remove ends of wire from spark plug and distributor. Spark plug boot should be turned 1/2 turn before removing. Using an ohmmeter, check resistance while gently twisting wire. If resistance is not to specifications, or fluctuates from infinity to any value, replace cable.

RESISTANCE (Ohms)

Wire Length	Maximum
Under 24"	30,000
Over 24"	50,000

DISTRIBUTOR

All models are equipped with a Delco High Energy Ignition system and no adjustments are required.

Fig. 1: Firing Order and Timing Mark

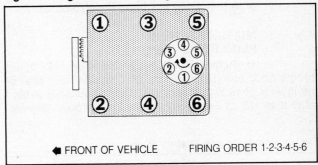

FRONT OF VEHICLE   FIRING ORDER 1-2-3-4-5-6

Magnetic probe located at 9.5°ATDC.

IGNITION TIMING

1) Install timing light with an adapter between No. 1 spark plug and No. 1 spark plug wire, or use an inductive type pickup. Do not puncture wire.

2) Check or adjust ignition timing with engine at normal operating temperature, distributor advance line disconnected and plugged, and automatic transmission in "D" (if equipped).

TIMING SPECIFICATIONS (Degrees BTDC@RPM)

Application	Man. Trans.	Auto. Trans.
Federal Models	[1] 8@650	[2] 12@650
Calif. Models	10@750	10@650

[1] — High altitude specification: 10@700.
[2] — High altitude specification: 12@700.

HOT (SLOW) IDLE RPM

ALL MODELS

1) Make adjustments with engine at normal operating temperature, choke full open, air cleaner installed and air conditioning off. Disconnect solenoid wire and set base idle speed with idle speed screw.

2) Reconnect solenoid wire and all hoses. If vehicle is equipped with air conditioner, disconnect

1983 General Motors V6 Tune-Up

TUNE-UP (Cont.)

electrical lead from compressor and turn A/C switch ON. Open throttle slightly to allow solenoid to extend, then adjust curb idle by turning screw in back of solenoid.

SLOW IDLE SPEED (RPM)

Application	Solenoid Idle	Curb Idle
Federal Models		
Man. Trans.	850	[1] 650
Auto. Trans.	850	[1] 650
Calif. Models		
Man. Trans.	950	750
Auto. Trans.	850	650

[1] — 700 RPM for high altitude models.

IDLE MIXTURE

NOTE: **Mixture adjustment is not a normal tune-up procedure. DO NOT remove idle mixture plugs unless vehicle fails emissions testing or throttle body has been disassembled.**

MIXTURE SCREW PLUG REMOVAL

1) Remove carburetor from engine. Invert throttle body and make two parallel cuts on each side of the locator point with a hacksaw. Cuts should not extend more than 1/8" (3.2 mm) beyond the locator point. *See Fig. 2.*

Fig. 2: Removing Idle Mixture Plug

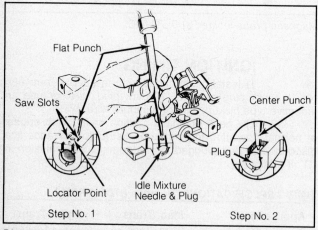

Distance between saw cuts depends on the size of the punch to be used.

2) Place a flat punch near the end of the saw marks. Hold the punch at a 45° angle. Drive it into the throttle body until the casting breaks away, exposing the steel plug.

3) Hold a center punch in a vertical position and drive it into the plug. Now hold punch at a 45° angle, and drive plug out of casting.

PROPANE ENRICHMENT PROCEDURE
Federal Models (HEI Ignition)

1) Engine must be at normal operating temperature and air conditioning off. Set parking brake and block drive wheels. On vehicles equipped with vacuum parking brake release, disconnect and plug hose at brake.

2) Disconnect and plug vacuum as directed on the Vehicle Emission Control Information label. Connect tachometer to engine. Adjust timing and reconnect vacuum advance hose. Set idle speed.

3) Disconnect crankcase ventilation tube from air cleaner. Using tool J-26911 (or equivalent), insert hose with rubber stopper (from propane valve) into air cleaner snorkel. Be sure propane cartridge is vertical.

4) With engine idling in "D" (Automatic) or "Neutral" (Manual), open propane supply control valve slowly. Engine speed will increase. Add propane until engine speed begins to drop from over-richness. Note maximum enriched idle RPM.

5) The maximum enriched idle RPM is the idle RPM plus propane enrichment RPM. Engine speed should rise above normal idle by amount specified. If so, mixture is correct. Proceed to step 9).

6) If speed is incorrect, remove idle mixture screw plugs. Carburetor must be removed and punch driven through bottom of throttle body to remove plug. Seat screws, then back out 3 turns.

7) Place transmission in "D" (Automatic) or "Neutral" (Manual), then back out screw slowly until maximum idle speed is reached. Then set maximum enriched idle speed.

8) Turn each mixture screw in (clockwise) 1/8 turn at a time until idle speed is correct. Recheck maximum enriched speed with propane. If incorrect, repeat step 7). Check and adjust fast idle speed.

9) Turn off engine. Remove propane tool, connect crankcase ventilation tube and reconnect all vacuum hoses.

PROPANE ENRICHED RPM

Application	RPM
Federal Models	40

IDLE MIXTURE ADJUSTMENT
California Models (HEI-EST Ignition)

1) Remove carburetor from engine and remove idle mixture screw plug. Turn mixture screw in until lightly seated and back out 4 turns. If plug in air horn covering idle air bleed has been removed, replace air horn.

2) Remove vent stack screen assembly to gain access to lean mixture screw. Turn lean mixture screw until lightly bottomed and back out 2 1/2 turns. Some resistance should be felt. If no resistance, remove screw and check for spring.

3) Install carburetor on engine. Do not install air cleaner. Disconnect bowl vent line at carburetor. Disconnect the EGR valve hose and canister purge hose at carburetor and cap carburetor ports.

4) Disconnect carburetor-to-temperture sensor hose on air cleaner and plug open hose. Connect a dwell meter lead to the mixture control solenoid dwell test lead (green connector).

5) Set dwell meter to 6-cylinder position. Connect a tachometer to distributor lead (brown connector). Transmission should be in "PARK" or "NEUTRAL". Start engine and bring to operating temperature.

6) Run engine at 3000 RPM and adjust the lean mixture screw slowly to allow time for dwell to stabilize. It is normal for dwell to vary over a narrow range of approximately 5°.

TUNE-UP (Cont.)

7) Turn screw to obtain a average dwell of 35°. If unable to adjust, inspect main metering circuit for leaks or resistrictions. Return engine to idle.

8) Adjust idle mixture screw to obtain average dwell of 25° with cooling fan in off cycle. Adjustment is very sensitive. Make final check with adjusting tool removed.

9) If unable to adjust, inspect idle system for leaks or resistrictions. Disconnect mixture control solenoid when cooling fan is in off cycle and check for an RPM change of at least 50 RPM. If RPM does not change, check idle air bleed circuit.

10) Run engine at 3000 RPM for a few moments and note dwell reading. Dwell should show an average of 35°. If not, reset lean mixture screw. Then reset idle mixture screw to obtain 25° dwell.

11) When dwell readings have been set, reconnect all hoses and install vent screen and air cleaner. Set idle speed.

COLD (FAST) IDLE RPM

Warm up vehicle. Remove and plug vacuum lines listed on emission label. Place fast idle screw on highest step of fast idle cam. Adjust fast idle screw to obtain fast idle RPM.

FAST IDLE RPM

Application	Man. Trans.	Auto. Trans.
Federal	1800	2100
Calif.	2100	2100

THROTTLE POSITION SENSOR (TPS)

ADJUSTMENT

1) DO NOT remove the TPS adjustment screw plug unless the TPS is not adjusted correctly or it is necessary to replace the air horn assembly, float bowl, TPS sensor, or TPS adjustment screw.

2) Using a .078" (1.98 mm) drill, carefully drill a hole in the steel cup plug covering the TPS adjustment screw. Plug is located next to the TPS plunger bore. Remove steel plug using a small slide hammer.

3) Disconnect the TPS connector and jumper all three terminals. Connect a digital voltmeter from TPS connector center terminal (B) to bottom terminal (C).

4) With ignition on, engine stopped, turn the TPS screw with flat bladed screwdriver to obtain .26 volts at curb idle position. Air conditioner must be off and Idle Speed Control fully retracted.

5) After adjustment, a new cup plug or silicone sealant rubber RTV must be inserted in the air horn.

AUTOMATIC CHOKE

Automatic choke is non-adjustable.

FUEL PUMP

FUEL PUMP SPECIFICATIONS

Application	Pressure psi (kg/cm²)	Volume Pints (Liters)
All Models	5.5-6.5 (2.6-4.6)	1 in 30 sec. (.47 in 30 sec.)

EMISSION CONTROL

NOTE: See appropriate article in EMISSION CONTROL Section.

GENERAL SERVICING

IGNITION

DISTRIBUTOR

California models use Delco Electronic Spark Timing system with detonation sensor and 5-pin module. All other models use a standard HEI system with 4-pin module.

DISTRIBUTOR PICKUP COIL RESISTANCE (Ohms)

All Models	500-1500

IGNITION COIL

COIL RESISTANCE (Ohms)@75°F (24°C)

Application	Primary	Secondary
All Models	0.4-1.0	6000-30,000

FUEL SYSTEMS

CARBURETORS

Application	Model
Federal Models	Rochester 2SE
California Models	Rochester E2SE

ELECTRICAL

BATTERY

Application	Cold Cranking Amps. [1]	Reserve Capacity Minutes
All Models	465	115

[1] — At 0°F (-18°C).

1983 General Motors V6 Tune-Up

GENERAL SERVICING (Cont.)

STARTER

All models are equipped with Delco overrunning clutch starters.

STARTER SPECIFICATIONS

Application	Volts	Amps.	Test RPM
All Models	10.6	50-80	7500-11,400

ALTERNATOR

All models are equipped with Delco alternators with integral voltage regulator.

ALTERNATOR SPECIFICATIONS

Application	Rated Ampere Output
Standard	37
Optional	63
Field Current Draw @ 12 volts	
All Models	[1] 4.5-5.5 amps.

[1] — At 80°F (27°C).

ALTERNATOR REGULATOR

All models are equipped with Delco nonadjustable voltage regulators, integral with alternator.

ADJUSTMENTS

BELT ADJUSTMENT

Tension Using Strand Tension Gauge

Application	Lbs. (Kg)
New Belt	
Air Conditioning	146 (66)
Power Steering	135 (61)
Alternator	146 (66)
Air Pump	135 (61)
Used Belt [1]	
All Belts	67 (30)

[1] — Any belt that has been rotated at least one complete revolution of the engine pulley.

SERVICE INTERVALS

REPLACEMENT INTERVALS

Component	Interval (Miles)
Fuel Filter	15,000
Spark Plugs	30,000
PCV Valve & Filter	30,000
Air Filter	30,000

CAPACITIES

FLUID CAPACITIES

Application	Quantity
Cooling System	12.0 qts. (11.4L)
Crankcase	[1] 4.0 qt. (3.8L)
Automatic Transmission	
Overhaul	19.0 pts. (8.9L)
Refil	7.0 pts. (3.3L)
Man. Trans.	[2]
Fuel Tank	
Standard	13.0 gal. (49.2L)
Optional	20.0 gal. (75.7L)

[1] — With or without filter.
[2] — Fill to bottom of fill hole.

TUNE-UP

ENGINE IDENTIFICATION

Engines can be identified by eighth digit of Vehicle Identification Number (VIN). Number is located on plate at top left corner of dashboard and at base of steering column on van models.

Engine code numbers are located at front of block, at right cylinder head on 5.0 and 5.7L engines and in front of intake manifold on 7.4L engines.

VIN ENGINE CODES

Application	VIN Code
5.0L (305") 4-Bbl.	
Federal	H
Calif.	F
5.7L (350") 4-Bbl.	
Light Duty	L
Heavy Duty	M
7.4L (454") 4-Bbl.	
Heavy Duty	W

TUNE-UP NOTES

NOTE: **When performing tune-up procedures described in this article, the following notes and precautions must be observed:**

Due to changes and corrections, always refer to Engine Tune-Up Decal in engine compartment before attempting tune-up. In the event of a conflict between specifications given in this manual and decal specifications, decal specifications prevail.

For tune-up purposes, "Light Duty" refers to vehicles up to 8500 lbs. "Heavy Duty" refers to vehicles exceeding 8500 lbs.

When performing tune-up on vehicles equipped with a catalytic converter, do not allow or create a condition of engine misfire in one or more cylinders for an extended period of time. Damage to converter from overheating may occur due to loading with unburned fuel.

ENGINE COMPRESSION

When making compression checks, disconnect the ignition switch connector pink wire from high energy ignition system. With air cleaner removed and throttle and choke wide open, crank engine through at least four compression strokes.

COMPRESSION SPECIFICATIONS

Compression Ratio	
5.0L	
Federal	9.2:1
Calif.	8.6:1
5.7L	
Light Duty	8.2:1
Heavy Duty	8.3:1
7.4L	8.0:1
Compression Pressure	150 psi (10.5 kg/cm²)
Maximum Pressure Variation	20 psi (1.4 kg/cm²)

VALVE CLEARANCE

All vehicles are equipped with hydraulic lifters. Lifters should be adjusted to 1 turn down from zero lash.

VALVE ARRANGEMENT

5.0L & 5.7L
  E-I-I-E-E-I-I-E (Both banks, front-to-rear)
7.4L
  E-I-E-I-E-I-E-I (Left bank, front-to-rear)
  I-E-I-E-I-E-I-E (Right bank, front-to-rear)

SPARK PLUGS

SPARK PLUG SPECIFICATIONS

Application	Gap In. (mm)	Torque Ft. Lbs. (N.m)
All Models	.045 (1.14)	17-27 (23-37)

SPARK PLUG TYPE

Application	AC No.
Light Duty Emissions	R45TS
Heavy Duty Emissions	R44T

HIGH TENSION WIRE RESISTANCE

Carefully remove ends of wire from spark plug and distributor. Using an ohmmeter, check resistance while gently twisting wire. If resistance is not to specifications, or fluctuates from infinity to any value, replace cable.

RESISTANCE (Ohms)

Wire Length	Resistance
0-24"	30,000 Max.
Over 24"	50,000 Max.

DISTRIBUTOR

The California models of the 5.0L and 5.7L engines will be equipped with the Electronic Spark Timing

Fig. 1: Timing Mark and Firing Order

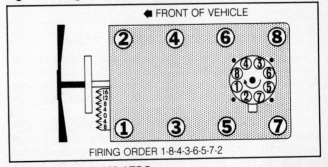

FIRING ORDER 1-8-4-3-6-5-7-2

Timing Socket at 10° ATDC.

TUNE-UP (Cont.)

(HEI-EST) ignition system. 5.0L (4-Bbl.) Federal engines are high compression (9.2:1) models and use an Electronic Spark Control (ESC) ignition system with detonation sensor. All other models are equipped with High Energy Ignition systems and no adjustments are required.

IGNITION TIMING

NOTE: **Engines are equipped with a receptacle for magnetic probe timing lights, located 10° ATDC. Do not use this location for timing with a conventional light.**

1) Connect an adapter between No. 1 spark plug wire or use an inductive type pickup. Do not puncture wires. Connect timing light according to manufacturer's instructions.

2) Check or adjust ignition timing with engine at normal operating temperature, distributor vacuum line disconnected and plugged. Light Duty models with automatic transmission should be in "D", all others in neutral.

3) On HEI-EST and HEI-ESC distributors, disconnect the plug connector at the distributor when checking ignition timing.

TIMING SPECIFICATIONS (Degrees BTDC@RPM)

Application	Man. Trans.	Auto. Trans
5.0L		
Federal	[1] 4@600	[2] 4@500
Calif.		8@550
5.7L		
Light Duty		
Federal	8@700	[3] 8@500
Calif.		8@550
Heavy Duty		
Federal	6@700	6@700
Calif.	4@700	4@700
7.4L	4@700	4@700

[1] — High altitude specification: 4@700.
[2] — High altitude specification: 4@600.
[3] — High altitude specification: 8@600.

HOT (SLOW) IDLE RPM

NOTE: **See engine compartment Emission Control Tune-Up Decal to prepare engine for idle speed adjustment.**

M4MC & M4ME CARBURETORS

1) Set ignition timing to specifications. Disconnect lead from idle solenoid (if equipped). Adjust curb idle speed to specifications using idle speed screw. Transmission should be in "D" for Light Duty with automatic transmission, and in neutral on all others.

2) Disconnect lead from air conditioning compressor. Reconnect lead at idle solenoid, then turn air conditioning "ON". Open throttle slightly to allow solenoid to fully extend. Adjust solenoid idle speed by turning solenoid screw.

3) On heavy duty engines equipped with throttle return control, connect a hand vacuum pump to control diaphragm. With engine idling, apply sufficient vacuum to extend the plunger fully.

4) Open throttle slightly to allow plunger to fully extend. Screw plunger in or out as necessary to obtain specified RPM. See Throttle Return Control table.

THROTTLE RETURN CONTROL (RPM)

Application	Federal	Calif.
Heavy Duty		
5.7L	[1] 1600	1500
7.4L	1500	1500

[1] — Except California "C" & "K" models with automatic transmission: 1400 RPM.

E4ME CARBURETOR (CALIF.)
Idle Speed Control (ISC)

1) Prior to adjustment, check for an identification letter on the ISC plunger. If no letter appears, remove plunger from unit.

2) Measure length of plunger from back side of plunger head to end of plunger screw. This is dimension "A". See Fig. 2.

Fig. 2: Adjusting Idle Speed Control Unit

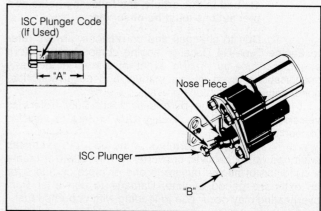

After plunger adjustment, dimension "B" must not exceed specification.

3) Install plunger so that the distance measured from the back side of the plunger to ISC nosepiece is LESS than dimension "B". See ISC Plunger Identificaion table. Follow Vehicle Emission Information Lable to prepare vehicle for adjustments.

CAUTION: **DO NOT disconnect or connect ISC connector with ignition "ON" as damage to the ECM may occur.**

4) Connect tachometer to engine. Connect dwell meter to mixture control solenoid dwell lead. Set dwell meter to 6-cylinder scale regardless of engine being tested. Turn A/C off. Start engine and run until dwell meter starts to vary.

5) Turn ignition off and unplug connector from ISC motor. Retract ISC plunger by applying 12V to terminal "C" of ISC motor connection and ground lead to terminal "D" of the ISC motor connection. See Fig. 3.

Fig. 3: ISC Motor Connections

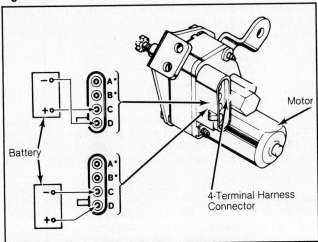

NEVER connect voltage across terminals "A" & "B".

6) Start engine and wait until dwell meter needle begins to vary. On automatic transmissions, block wheels and place transmission in "D". With ISC plunger fully retracted, adjust carburetor IDLE STOP screw to curb idle specification.

7) Place automatic transmission in "P". Fully extend plunger by applying 12V to terminal "D" and ground lead to terminal "C". Leave power applied only long enough to extend plunger.

8) On manual transmissions, use tool (J-29607 or BT-8022) to adjust idle speed. See IDLE SPEED table. On automatic transmissions, preset plunger to 1500 RPM. Set parking brake and block drive wheels. Set idle speed to specifications.

9) Recheck idle speed with voltage applied to motor. After adjustment of ISC plunger, measure distance from back side of plunger to ISC nosepiece (dimension "B" in Fig. 2).

10) Dimension must not exceed specification. Plunger type is identified by plunger length or letter identification. See ISC PLUNGER IDENTIFICATION table.

IDLE SPEED CONTROL PLUNGER IDENTIFICATION

Letter	Dimension "A" In. (mm)	Dimension "B" In. (mm)
None	9/16 (14.1)	7/32 (5.6)
None	41/64 (16.3)	5/16 (8.0)
X	47/64 (18.5)	25/64 (10.0)
A	49/64 (19.3)	27/64 (10.8)
Y	51/64 (20.5)	15/32 (12.0)
S	27/32 (21.2)	1/2 (12.7)
Z	7/8 (22.5)	35/64 (14.0)
G	29/32 (23.2)	37/64 (14.7)
E	1 (25.6)	43/64 (17.1)
L	1 3/32 (27.5)	3/4 (19.0)
J	1 3/16 (30.0)	27/32 (21.5)
N	1 17/64 (32.0)	59/64 (23.5)
T	1 11/32 (34.0)	1 (25.5)

11) Fully retract ISC plunger and turn ignition off. Disconnect battery leads, tachometer and dwell meter. Reconnect 4-terminal harness connector.

12) The procedure described above will cause code to be stored as an "Intermittent" problem. It will be necessary to clear the diagnostic trouble codes. *See appropriate article in EXHAUST EMISSION SYSTEMS Section.*

Idle Load Compensator (ILC)

1) With transmission in "P", brakes set and wheels blocked, prepare vehicle for adjustments. Remove air cleaner and plug hose to thermal vacuum valve (TVV). Disconnect and plug hoses to EGR, canister purge port and idle load compensator (ILC).

2) Back out idle stop screw 3 turns. Turn A/C "OFF". With engine running and transmission selector in "D", check that ILC plunger is fully extended. Adjust plunger to obtain 725 RPM. Hold jam nut on plunger to avoid damaging ILC.

3) Remove plug from vacuum hose, reconnect hose to ILC. Idle speed should be 500 RPM in "D". If speed is correct, no further adjustment is necessary. If speed is NOT correct, procede to next step.

4) Stop engine and remove the ILC. Plug vacuum hose to ILC. With the ILC hose removed, remove the rubber cap from the center outlet tube. Remove the metal plug (if used) from this same tube.

5) Install ILC and all related parts on carburetor. Remove plug from vacuum hose and reconnect hose to ILC. Using a spare rubber cap with a hole punched to accept a .090" (3/32") Allen wrench, install cap on center outlet tube.

6) Start engine and turn adjusting screw to obtain 500 RPM in "D". Remove wrench and cap and install new rubber cap. With engine running and transmission in "D", measure distance from the jam nut to the tip of plunger.

7) This distance must not exceed 1" (25 mm). *See Fig. 4.*

Fig. 4: Adjusting Idle Load Compensator On E4ME

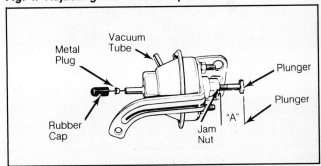

Measure with engine running and transmission in "DRIVE".

8) Disconnect and plug vacuum hose to ILC. Apply vacuum source to ILC inlet tube to fully retract plunger. Adjust idle stop screw on carburetor float bowl to obtain 500 RPM in "D".

9) Stop engine. Reconnect all hoses and remove test equipment.

A/C Idle Speed Control Solenoid (ISS)

1) Prepare vehicle for adjustments according to directions on Emission Lable on vehicle. Disconnect solenoid and turn air conditioning off. Set curb idle speed with idle speed screw.

2) Connect solenoid. Disconnect A/C lead at compressor and turn A/C on. Place automatic transmission in "D" and manual transmission in neutral.

3) Open throttle to extend solenoid plunger. Turn solenoid screw to adjust RPM. Reconnect A/C lead.

IDLE SPEED (RPM)

Application	Curb Idle	Solenoid Energized
Light Duty		
5.0L		
Federal		
Man. Trans.	600	700
Auto. Trans.	500	600
Calif.		
Auto. Trans.	550	600
5.7L		
Federal		
Man. Trans.	600	750
Auto. Trans.	500	600
Calif.		
Auto. Trans	550	600
Heavy Duty		
5.7L	700	.....
7.4L	700	.....

Throttle Position Sensor (TPS)

1) DO NOT readjust the TPS unless the TPS is not adjusted correctly or it is necessary to replace the air horn assembly, float bowl, TPS sensor or TPS adjustment screw.

2) Using a 5/64" (2 mm) drill, drill a 1/16" to 1/8" deep hole in aluminum plug covering TPS adjustment screw. Use care not to damage screw head. See Fig. 5.

Fig. 5: TPS Adjustment Screw Location for E4ME

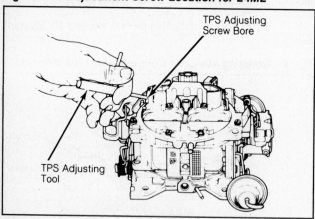

Plug must be drilled out to adjust screw.

3) Start a No. 8 1/2" long self-tapping screw in drilled hole turning screw in only far enough to ensure good thread engagement. Using a screw driver between screw head and air horn, pry out plug.

4) Using tool (J-28696), remove TPS adjustment screw. Connect digital voltmeter from TPS connector center terminal (B) to bottom terminal (C).

5) With ignition on, engine stopped, install TPS adjustment screw to obtain specified TPS voltage with A/C off. See TPS VOLTAGE ADJUSTMENT table.

TPS VOLTAGE ADJUSTMENT

Engine	Voltage
"F" & "L"	.4V
"H"	.51V

6) Install new plug in air horn. If new plug not available, use Delco Threadlock Adhesive X-10 on screw threads then adjust voltage.

IDLE MIXTURE

MIXTURE SCREW PLUG REMOVAL

1) Remove carburetor from engine and drain fuel. Invert carburetor and make 2 parallel cuts in the throttle body on either side of the locator points beneath the idle mixture needle plug (manifold side) with a hacksaw.

2) The cuts should reach down to the steel plug but should not extend more than 1/8" beyond the locator points. The distance between the saw marks depends on the size of the punch to be used.

3) Place a flat punch at a point near the ends of the saw marks in the throttle body. Holding the punch at a 45° angle, drive it into the throttle body until casting breaks away, exposing the steel plug.

4) Holding a center punch vertical, drive it into the steel plug. Holding the punch at a 45° angle, drive out the steel plug.

PROPANE ENRICHMENT PROCEDURE
Federal Light Duty Models Only

1) With engine at normal operating temperature, choke fully open and A/C "OFF" (if equipped), set parking brake and block drive wheels. Disconnect and plug hoses as directed on Emission Control/Tune-Up decal.

2) Connect tachometer to engine. Disconnect vacuum advance and set timing to specification. Reconnect vacuum advance. Disconnect crankcase ventilation tube from air cleaner.

3) Insert hose with rubber stopper (tool J-26911) from propane valve into PCV tube opening in air cleaner. Propane bottle must be in vertical position.

4) Slowly open control valve until maximum engine speed is reached with transmission in "D" (automatic) or neutral (manual).

NOTE: **Too much propane will cause engine speed to drop.**

5) Observe propane flow meter to ensure propane cartridge is full. With propane flowing, adjust idle speed screw or solenoid so speed rises above normal idle by specified amount.

6) Readjust propane flow to be certain of maximum engine speed and adjust idle speed if necessary. Turn off propane. Run engine at 2000 RPM in neutral for 30 seconds, return to idle, and place in "D".

7) Check idle speed. If correct, no adjustment of mixture is necessary. If not correct, proceed with adjustment procedure. If idle speed is too low, carefully remove caps from mixture screws and back out screws (richen) 1/8 turn at a time until correct speed is reached.

8) If RPM is too high, turn screws in (leaner) 1/8 turn at a time until correct speed is reached. Turn propane on again to check maximum engine idle speed.

9) If RPM does not meet specifications, readjust idle speed screw or solenoid screw to obtain specified enriched RPM with propane flowing.

TUNE-UP (Cont.)

10) Turn off propane, place transmission in neutral and run engine at 3000 RPM for 30 seconds. Recheck idle speed and repeat procedure if necessary.

PROPANE ENRICHED RPM (Fed. Light Duty)

Application	Man. Trans.	Auto. Trans.
5.0L 4-Bbl.		
High Alt.	100	20
All Others	[1] 150	50
5.7L 2-Bbl.		
5.7L 4-Bbl.		
Federal	100	40
Calif.	50	
High Alt.	100	20

[1] — Set carburetor number 1708223 to 100 RPM.

BEST IDLE PROCEDURE
Heavy Duty Models Only

1) Set parking brake and block drive wheels. Remove air cleaner after engine reaches normal operating temperature. Place transmission in neutral and connect tachometer.

2) As a starting point, turn idle mixture screws in lightly to seat and then back out 2 turns. Do not turn screws tightly against seat or damage may result.

3) With engine running, choke open, and transmission in neutral, adjust idle speed to specification. Adjust mixture screws to obtain maximum RPM.

4) Readjust idle speed screw to specification and readjust mixture screws to obtain highest RPM. Turn ignition off, remove gauges and install air cleaner.

E4ME MIXTURE ADJUSTMENT
Mixture Control Solenoid Plunger Travel

1) Idle mixture control solenoid plunger travel should be checked before any mixture adjustments or disassembly. Use float gauge J-9789-130 or BT-7720 to check float level externally.

2) Insert gauge in the vertical "D" shaped vent hole in the air horn casting, next to the Idle Air Bleed cover. It may be necessary to file material off the gauge to allow it to enter the vent hole.

3) Engine must be off and air cleaner and gasket removed. Check that gauge moves freely in vent hole. With gauge released, record the reading of the gauge mark that lines up with the top of air horn casting.

4) Lightly press down on gauge and record reading of gauge mark that lines up with top of air horn casting. Total plunger travel must be between 1/16" (1.6 mm) and 3/16" (4.8 mm).

5) If plunger travel is within specifications, proceed to Idle Air Bleed Valve Adjustment. If plunger travel is incorrect, carburetor must be disassembled and adjusted. See appropriate article in FUEL SYSTEMS Section.

Idle Air Bleed Valve Adjustment

1) Mixture must not be adjusted unless carburetor has been disassembled for cleaning or parts replacement or "Systems Performance Check" indicates the carburetor is the cause of any malfunction.

2) If adjustment is necessary, check ignition timing according to directions on Emission Control Label under hood. Connect a tachometer to engine. Connect dwell meter to Green wire of mixture control solenoid on carburetor.

3) Set dwell meter to 6-cylinder scale. Bring engine to operating temperature and check idle speed. Adjust idle and curb idle speed if necessary. On models with ILC or ISC curb idle is controlled by ECM.

4) With engine idling in "DRIVE" ("NEUTRAL" for manual transmissions), observe dwell reading. If varying within the 10-50° range, adjustment is correct and no further checks are necessary. If not, perform the following procedure.

5) Turn engine off. Cover internal bowl vents, air inlets to the bleed valve and carburetor air inlets with masking tape to prevent metal chips from entering carburetor.

6) Use a No. 35 (.110") drill to drill out the rivet heads on either side of the idle air bleed valve cover. Lift off idle air bleed valve cover and remove any rivet pieces from carburetor.

7) Look for a letter identification code on top of the idle air bleed valve. Not all valves will have an identification code.

NOTE: On idle air bleed valves WITHOUT a letter code: the following procedure (setting valve to gauge dimension) is not necessary unless the idle air bleed valve was serviced prior to on-vehicle adjustment.

Fig. 6: Idle Air Bleed Valve Identification

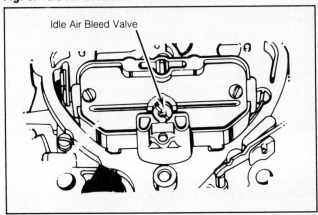

Idle Air Bleed Valve

Check for letter identification code on top of valve.

8) To set idle air bleed valve to a gauge dimension, install air bleed valve gauging tool (J-33815-2 or BT-8253-B) in throttle side "D" shaped hole in the air horn casting. See Fig. 7.

9) The upper end of the tool should be positioned over the open cavity next to the air bleed valve. Hold the gauging tool down lightly against the solenoid stop.

10) Adjust the idle air bleed valve so that the gauging tool will pivot over and just contact the top of the valve. The valve is now ready for adjustment.

NOTE: If the idle air bleed valve HAS a letter code, the air bleed valve does NOT have an adjustment. Proceed to Adjusting Idle Mixture Needles.

TUNE-UP (Cont.)

Fig. 7: Positioning Idle Air Bleed Valve

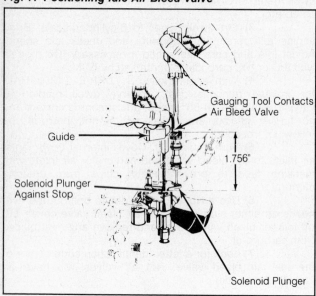

Hold gauging tool down lightly.

11) Start engine and bring to operating temperature. While idling in "DRIVE" ("NEUTRAL" for manual transmissions), use a screwdriver to adjust valve until a dwell reading of 25-35° is obtained.

12) If dwell reading is NOT within the 25-35° range, remove the mixture needle plugs and adjust the mixture needles.

Adjusting Idle Mixture Needles

1) Turn each needle clockwise until lightly seated. Back out needles 3 turns. Bring engine to operating temperature.

2) For valves WITH letter code, adjust both needles equally, in or out, until dwell meter reads as close to 30° as possible. After adjustment is complete, seal mixture needle openings with RTV sealant.

3) For valves WITHOUT letter code, readjust air bleed valve. If unable to set dwell to 25-35° range, turn mixture needles equally in or out to bring dwell reading within range. Readjust air bleed valve and seal mixture needle openings with RTV sealant.

COLD (FAST) IDLE RPM

1) Place transmission in neutral. Move cam follower onto highest step of fast idle cam. Disconnect and plug vacuum hose to EGR valve, canister purge hose and purge signal hose at canister.

2) Start engine without touching throttle. Turn fast idle speed screw to adjust speed to specification.

FAST IDLE SPEED (RPM)

Application	Man. Trans.	Auto. Trans.
Light Duty		
Federal	[1] 1300	1600
Calif.		1800
Heavy Duty	1900	1900

[1] — High Altitude models set to 1600 RPM.

AUTOMATIC CHOKE

The choke cover on all engines is riveted in place and no adjustments are possible or necessary.

FUEL PUMP

FUEL PUMP SPECIFICATIONS

Application	Pressure psi (kg/cm²)	Volume Pints (Liters)
7.4L [1]	7.5-9.0	1 in 30 sec.
	(.52-.63)	(.47 in 30 sec.)
All Others	5.5-7.0	1 in 30 sec.
	(.38-.50)	(.47 in 30 sec.)

[1] — Without vapor return line.

EMISSION CONTROL

NOTE: See appropriate article in EMISSION CONTROL Section.

GENERAL SERVICING

IGNITION

DISTRIBUTOR

The 5.0L and 5.7L California engines are equipped with the Electronic Spark Timing system. 5.0L 4-Bbl. Federal engines use Electronic Spark Control (ESC) system with detonation sensor and 5-pin module. All other models use a standard HEI system with 4-pin module.

NOTE: High energy ignition system module must be replaced as a unit. A liberal coat of silicone grease MUST be applied to both the module and the surface on which it will be mounted.

DISTRIBUTOR PICKUP COIL RESISTANCE (Ohms)

All Models	500-1500

IGNITION COIL

COIL RESISTANCE (Ohms)@At75°F (24°C)

Application	Primary	Secondary
All Models	0.4-1.0	6000-30,000

GENERAL SERVICING (Cont.)

COIL OUTPUT

At all engine speeds .... 30 KV Min.

FUEL SYSTEMS

CARBURETORS

Application	Model
Light Duty	
5.0L & 5.7L	
Federal	Rochester M4ME
California	Rochester E4ME
Heavy Duty	
All	Rochester M4MC

ELECTRICAL

BATTERY

Application	Cold Cranking Amps. [1]	Reserve Capacity Minutes
5.0L & 5.7L		
Standard	405	75
Optional	515	115
7.4L	475	130

[1] — At 0°F (-18°C).

STARTER

All models are equipped with Delco overrunning clutch starters.

STARTER SPECIFICATIONS

Application	Volts	Amps.	Test RPM
5.0L	10	45-70	7000-11,900
5.7L & 7.4L	10	65-95	7500-10,500

ALTERNATOR

All models are equipped with Delco alternators with integral voltage regulators.

ALTERNATOR SPECIFICATIONS

Application	Rated Amp. Output
Standard	
"P" Models	42
All Others	37
Optional	
All Models	66, 80

Field Current Draw @ 12 Volts [1]

All Models .... 4.0-4.5 amps.

[1] — At 80°F (27°C).

ALTERNATOR REGULATOR

Regulators are Delco nonadjustable, integral with alternator.

REGULATOR SPECIFICATIONS

Application	Operating Voltage
All Models	13.5-16.0

SERVICE INTERVALS

REPLACEMENT INTERVALS

Components	Intervals (Miles)
Oil Filter	7500
Fuel Filter	12,000
Spark Plugs	30,000
PCV Valve and Filter	30,000
Air Filter	30,000

CAPACITIES

FLUID CAPACITIES

Application	Quantity
Cooling System	
5.0 & 5.7L	
With A/C	18.0 qts. (17.0L)
Without A/C	17.5 qts. (16.5L)
7.4L	
With A/C	24.5 qts. (23.3L)
Without A/C	23.0 qts. (22.0L)
Crankcase	
5.0 & 5.7L	[1] 4.0 qts. (3.8L)
7.4L	[1] 6.0 qts. (5.7L)
Automatic Transmission (Dexron)	
THM 350	6.0 pts. (2.8L)
THM 400	7.0 pts. (3.8L)
THM 700-R4	10.0 pts. (4.7L)
Manual Transmission (SAE 80W-90)	
3-Speed	3.0 pts. (1.4L)
4-Speed	4.0 pts. (1.9L)
Transfer Case (SAE 10W-30)	5.0 pts. (2.4L)
Front Axle (SAE 80W-90)	5.0 pts. (2.4L)
Rear Axle (SAE 80W-90)	[2]
Power Take-Off (SAE 80W-90)	5.0 pts. (2.4L)
Fuel Tank	
Pickup Models	
Short Wheelbase (Each Tank)	16.0 gals. (60.6L)
Long Wheelbase (Each Tank)	20.0 gals. (75.7L)
Van Models	
Standard	22.0 gals. (83.3L)
Optional	33.0 gals. (124.9L)
Suburban Models	
Standard	25.0 gals. (94.6L)
Optional	31.0 or 40.0 gals. (117.3L or 151.4)
Blazer Models	
Standard	25.0 gals. (94.6L)
Optional	31.0 gals. (117.3L)
"P" Models	
Standard	31.0 gals. (117.3L)
Optional	40.0 gals. (151.4L)

[1] — Add one quart with filter change.

[2] — Fill to bottom of filler hole.

1983 General Motors V8 Tune-Up
GENERAL SERVICING (Cont.)

ADJUSTMENTS

BELT ADJUSTMENT

Tension Using Strand Tension Gauge

Application	Lbs. (Kg)
New Belt	
Air Conditioning	135-145 (61-66)
All Others	120-130 (54-59)
Used Belt [1]	
Air Conditioning	90-100 (41-45)
All Others	70-80 (32-36)

[1] — Any belt that has been rotated at least one complete revolution of the engine pulley.

TUNE-UP

ENGINE IDENTIFICATION

Engine can be identified by the 8th digit of Vehicle Identification Number (VIN) which is stamped on a tag at the top left corner of dashboard. The engine is also identified by code letters located on a label at rear of left valve cover and stamped into block on left front corner.

VIN ENGINE CODES

Application	Code
6.2L (379") V8 Diesel (Light Duty)	C
6.2L (379") (Heavy Duty)	J

TUNE UP NOTES

NOTE: **When performing tune-up procedures described in this article, the following notes and precautions must be followed:**

Due to late changes and corrections, always refer to Engine Tune-Up Decal in engine compartment before attempting tune-up. If the decal specifications are different than the specifications presented here, use decal specifications.

Adjustment of injectors or internal adjustment of injection pump must be done in a properly equipped injector shop with clean environment.

Prior to checking compression, be sure battery is fully charged to avoid battery run down. When turning engine over during test, 6 "puffs" per cylinder should be used to obtain reading.

ENGINE COMPRESSION

1) Remove air cleaner and install screen cover over air crossover. Disconnect electrical wire from fuel injection pump solenoid terminal.

2) Disconnect glow plug wiring and remove all glow plugs. Use compression gauge (J-26999) to test individual cylinders.

CAUTION: Do not add oil to cylinders during compression check as extensive engine damage will result.

COMPRESSION SPECIFICATIONS

Compression Ratio	21.5:1
Compression Pressure (Min.)	275 psi (19 kg/cm)
Max. Pressure Variation	1

1 — Lowest cylinder must read within 70% of highest.

VALVE CLEARANCE

Lifters are hydraulic and are not adjustable. They should have zero lash. Some engines were produced with both standard and .010" (.25 mm) oversize lifters installed.

NOTE: **Oversize lifters can be identified by an "O" etched on side of lifter boss. Diesel engine lifters are NOT interchangeable with gasoline engine lifters.**

VALVE ARRANGEMENT

I-E-I-E-I-E-I-E (Left bank, Front to rear)
E-I-E-I-E-I-E-I (Right bank, Front to rear)

GLOW PLUGS

Glow plugs are small 6-volt heaters operated by an electronic relay. They cycle on and off, powered by 12 volts to give rapid heating. Glow plug light on dash should cycle on and off as plugs cycle on and off.

If test lamp is connected to glow plugs and ground, it should flash on and off. Relay can be heard clicking on and off after ignition has been on for approximately 6 seconds.

GLOW PLUG SPECIFICATIONS

GM Part No.	5613680
Torque	12 Ft. Lbs. (16 N.m)

Fig. 1: Diesel Firing Order

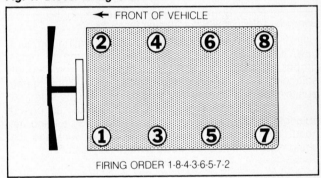

FIRING ORDER 1-8-4-3-6-5-7-2

INJECTOR TIMING

1) Check alignment of injection pump marks. If marks are not within tolerance shown in *Fig. 2*, timing is necessary. Loosen 3 retaining nuts and turn pump with 3/4" (19 mm) wrench (J-29872) on boss at front of pump.

2) Tighten nuts and adjust throttle linkage. Disconnect cruise control and transmission linkage. Disconnect pump rod, loosen lock nut, and shorten rod several turns.

3) Rotate throttle lever to full-throttle position and lengthen rod until it fits with lever just contacting full-throttle stop. Reconnect linkage from cruise control or transmission.

Fig. 2: Timing Marks on Adapter & Injection Pump

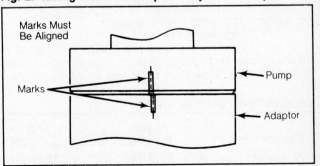

Marks must be aligned within this tolerance.

TUNE-UP (Cont.)

IDLE SPEED (RPM)

NOTE: Use magnetic tachometer (J-26925) to check idle speed. Insert probe in timing indicator hole.

Fig. 3: Adjustment Locations on Diesel Injection Pump

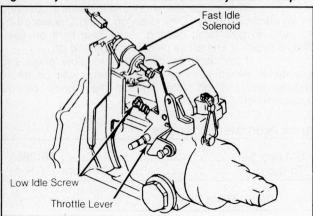

Energize solenoid when adjusting fast idle.

1) Warm engine to normal operating temperature. Adjust low speed idle screw on pump to obtain proper RPM. *See Fig. 3.* Remove connector from fast idle solenoid. Run an insulated jumper wire from battery positive terminal to solenoid terminal to energize solenoid.

2) Start engine and open throttle to ensure solenoid is fully extended. Adjust solenoid by turning hex head. Turn engine off and remove jumper wire and test equipment. Reinstall fast idle solenoid connector.

IDLE SPEED (RPM)

Application	Curb Idle	Fast Idle
All Models	650	800

VACUUM PUMP

GEAR-DRIVEN MECHANICAL PUMP

The vacuum pump is designed to aid the engine in maintaining a proper vacuum level for the power brake system. The gear-driven vacuum pump is a diaphragm pump which requires no periodic maintenance.

Pump is driven by a cam inside the drive assembly to which it mounts. Drive housing assembly has a drive gear on lower end which meshes with cam gear in engine. Drive gear causes cam in drive housing to rotate. Drive gear also powers engine oil pump.

Diagnosis & Testing

Install hose and vacuum gauge to pump. With engine running read gauge. Shut off engine, vacuum level should not drop below 19 in. Hg in less than 1.5 seconds.

VACUUM PUMP SPECIFICATIONS

Application	Engine Running	Engine Off
All Models	20 in. Hg	¹ 19 in. Hg

¹ — Minimum reading after 1.5 seconds.

VACUUM REGULATOR VALVE

Vacuum is regulated at idle and during heavy loads by the vacuum regulator valve. Valve is mounted to the diesel fuel pump and can be identified by the 2 vacuum ports extending from valve chamber.

Diagnosis & Testing

1) Loosely assemble throttle position switch to fuel injection pump with throttle lever in closed position. Attach a continuity meter across terminals (light duty vehicles IGN Pink and EGR Yellow).

2) Insert the proper "switch-closed" gauge block, between gauge boss on injection pump and wide open stop screw on throttle shaft. Rotate and hold throttle lever against gauge block.

3) Rotate throttle switch clockwise (facing throttle switch) until continuity pivot occurs (high meter reading) across terminals. Hold switch body at this position and tighten mounting bolts to 4-5 ft. lbs. (5-7 N.M).

NOTE: Switch point must be set only while rotating switch body in clockwise direction.

4) Release throttle lever and allow it to return to idle position. Remove "switch-closed" gauge block and insert "switch-open" gauge block. Rotate throttle lever against "switch-open" gauge block. There should be no continuity across terminals.

5) If no continuity exists, switch is set properly. However, if there is continuity, then switch must be reset by returning to step **1)** and repeating the entire procedure.

Fig. 4: Adjusting Throttle Position Switch

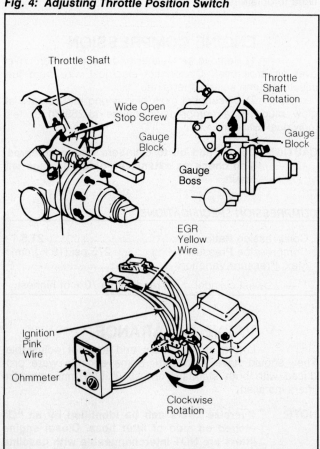

Rotate clockwise until continuity occurs.

TUNE-UP (Cont.)

INJECTION NOZZLES

If engine starts, but idles roughly, check injection nozzles as described:

1) Start engine. Loosen injection line fitting at each nozzle, one at a time. Be sure to direct fuel away from sources which could cause fire.

2) If, when an injection line fitting is loosened, idle speed or quality does NOT change, replace that nozzle and repeat test.

3) Disconnect fuel return system from nozzles on one bank of engine at a time. Start engine and observe fuel seepage from each nozzle. Replace any nozzle that leaks excessively. Torque nozzle clamp bolt to 25 ft. lbs. (34 N.m).

ADJUSTMENTS

THROTTLE POSITION SWITCH (TPS)

1) Remove air cleaner assembly. With throttle lever in closed position, loosen TPS-to-fuel injection pump retaining screws. Attach an ohmmeter across ignition (Pink) and EGR terminals or wires. *See Fig. 4.*

2) Using the proper size "switch-closed" gauge block, insert block between gauge boss on injection pump housing and throttle shaft wide open stop screw. Rotate and hold throttle lever against gauge block.

3) Rotate TPS clockwise (facing TPS) until continuity just occurs on ohmmeter. Hold switch body in this position and tighten retaining screws. TPS must be set only while rotating switch body in clockwise rotation.

4) Remove "switch-closed" gauge block and insert proper "switch-open" gauge block. Rotate throttle lever so it rests against "switch-open" gauge block.

5) Ohmmeter reading should indicate no continuity. If no continuity is measured, switch is properly adjusted. If continuity is registered, repeat entire adjustment procedure.

GENERAL SERVICING

FUEL INJECTION

All models are equipped with General Motors Diesel Fuel Injection.

ELECTRICAL

BATTERIES

Diesel vehicles use two 12 volt negative ground sealed top units. One battery is located on each side of engine compartment and they are wired in parallel.

BATTERY SPECIFICATIONS

Application	Cold Crank Amps @0°F (-18°C)	Reserve Capacity Minutes
All Models	550	115

STARTER

STARTER SPECIFICATIONS

Application	Volts	Amps.	Test RPM
6.2L	9	65-95	7500-10,500

ALTERNATORS

Alternator supplies current to both batteries. There are no switches or relays in charging circuit.

ALTERNATOR SPECIFICATIONS

Application	Amp. Output
Standard	61

ALTERNATOR REGULATOR

Delco non-adjustable, integral with alternator.

REGULATOR SPECIFICATIONS

Operating Voltage	[1] 13.8-14.8 V

[1] — At 85°F (29°C).

ADJUSTMENTS

BELT ADJUSTMENT

Application	Tension in Lbs. (kg) Using Strand Tension Gauge	
	New Belt	Used Belt
Air Conditioning	145 (66)	90 (41)
All Others	125 (57)	75 (34)

SERVICE INTERVALS

REPLACEMENT INTERVALS

Component	Interval (Miles)
Oil Filter	3000
Air Cleaner Element	30,000
Fuel Filter	15,000
Automatic Transmission Filter	100,000
Breather Cap and Filter	[1] 30,000
Ventilation Regulator Valve	30,000

[1] — Check every 6000 miles.

GENERAL SERVICING (Cont.)

CAPACITIES

FLUID CAPACITIES

Application	Quantity
Crankcase	[1] 7.0 qts. (6.6L)
Auto. Trans. (Dexron)	[2] 6.0 pts. (2.8L)
Rear Axle (SAE 80W-90)	[3]
Cooling System	
Without A/C	23.0 qts. (21.7L)
With A/C	24.5 qts. (23.2L)
Fuel Tank	
Short W.B. (Main or Aux.)	16 gals. (61L)
Long W.B. (Main or Aux.)	20 gals. (76L)

[1] — Includes filter. Oil MUST be designated BOTH SE & CC. If CD appears anywhere on can, do not use.

[2] — Total fill is 10.0 qts. (9.5L).

[3] — Fill to bottom of filler hole.

TUNE-UP

ENGINE IDENTIFICATION

Engine can be identified by the fourth digit of the Vehicle Identification Number (VIN), which is stamped on a plate attached to top left corner of instrument panel.

VIN ENGINE CODE

Application	Code
2.5L (151") 2-Bbl.	B

ENGINE IDENTIFICATION

Engine code is stamped into a pad on the front left top corner of engine block. On engines built for sale in Georgia and Tennessee, a second code number is stamped into the left rear flange.

TUNE-UP NOTES

NOTE: **When performing tune-up procedures described in this article, the following notes and precautions must be followed.**

Due to production changes, always refer to Engine Tune-Up Decal in engine compartment before attempting tune-up. In the event of a conflict between specifications given in this manual and decal specifications, use the decal specifications.

When performing tune-up on vehicles equipped with catalytic converters, do not allow or create a condition of engine misfire in one or more cylinders for an extended period of time. Damage to converter may occur due to loading converter with unburned air/fuel mixture.

ENGINE COMPRESSION

Check compression pressure with engine at normal operating temperature, all spark plugs removed, and throttle and choke valves wide open.

COMPRESSION SPECIFICATIONS

Compression Ratio	8.2:1
Compression Pressure	140 psi (9.8 kg/cm²)
Maximum Variation Between Cylinders	30 psi (2.1 kg/cm²)

VALVE CLEARANCE

All engines have hydraulic lifters. Lifters should be adjusted to zero lash.

VALVE ARRANGEMENT

I-E-I-E-E-I-E-I (front-to-rear)

SPARK PLUGS

SPARK PLUG SPECIFICATIONS

Application	Gap In. (mm)	Torque Ft. Lbs. (N.m)
All Models	.060 (1.5)	7-15 (9-20)

SPARK PLUG TYPE

Application	AC No.
All Models	R44TSX

HIGH TENSION WIRE RESISTANCE

Do not puncture spark plug wires with any type of probe. Remove spark plug wire and check resistance using an ohmmeter.

RESISTANCE (Ohms)

Wire Length	Minimum	Maximum
0-15"	3000	10,000
15-25"	4000	15,000
25-35"	6000	20,000
Over 35"	8000	25,000

DISTRIBUTOR

All models are equipped with a Delco High Energy Ignition system distributor. No adjustments are necessary.

IGNITION TIMING

NOTE: **Engines are equipped with a receptacle for a magnetic probe timing light, located 9.5° ATDC. Do not use this location for timing with a conventional light.**

Check or adjust ignition timing with engine at normal operating temperature, distributor vacuum hose disconnected and plugged, and engine at curb idle speed.

TIMING SPECIFICATIONS (Degrees BTDC@RPM)

Application	Specification
All Models	12@900

Fig. 1: Timing Mark and Firing Order

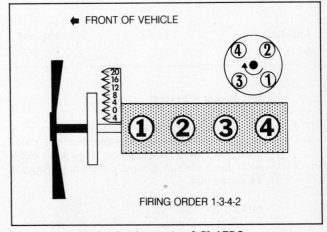

Magnetic timing socket located at 9.5° ATDC.

HOT (SLOW) IDLE RPM

CAUTION: Do not idle engine for over 3 minutes at a time. If idle adjustment is not completed within 3 minutes, run engine at 2000 RPM for 1 minute before continuing. Repeat as necessary.

1) Warm engine to normal operating temperature and connect tachometer. Disconnect and plug deceleration valve hose and canister purge hose. Remove air cleaner.

2) On California models with model E2SE carburetor, insert positive dwell meter probe into terminal 14 and negative probe into terminal 7 of diagnostic connector. *See Fig. 2.*

Fig. 2: Diagnostic Connector Terminal Positions

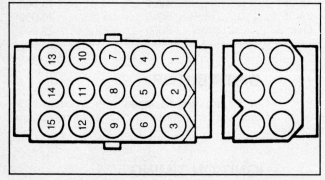

Insert dwell meter probes to No. 14 and No. 7.

3) Dwell meter should be oscillating (15° sweep maximum) and pointer should be in the 10-50° range. If equipped with air conditioning, adjust idle speed screw to obtain correct RPM. Turn A/C control switch "ON".

4) Open throttle momentarily to extend solenoid arm. Adjust solenoid idle speed screw to obtain solenoid RPM. Turn nut on solenoid plunger to obtain solenoid RPM.

5) If not equipped with air conditioning, adjust solenoid idle speed screw with solenoid energized to obtain specified RPM. Disconnect solenoid wire connector and adjust idle speed screw to obtain curb idle speed.

IDLE SPEED (RPM)

Application	Curb Idle	Solenoid Energized
All Models	500	900

IDLE MIXTURE

NOTE: Do not idle engine for over 3 minutes at a time. If idle mixture adjustment is not completed within 3 minutes, run engine at 2000 RPM for 1 minute before continuing. Repeat as necessary.

MIXTURE SCREW PLUG REMOVAL

NOTE: Mixture adjustment is not a normal tune-up procedure. DO NOT remove idle mixture plugs unless vehicle fails emissions testing or throttle body has been disassembled.

1) Remove carburetor and drain fuel. Place upside down on holding fixture. Place a punch in locator point in throttle body (beneath mixture plug).

2) Drive punch through locator until plug breaks, then drive out loose pieces by holding punch at a 45° angle. Reinstall carburetor and make adjustments using a thin wall 3/16" deep socket.

LEAN DROP PROCEDURE
Federal Vehicles

1) Connect an accurate tachometer, start engine, and warm to normal operating temperature. Place transmission in Neutral. Starting from full rich position, turn mixture screw leaner (clockwise) until a noticeable RPM loss is indicated.

2) Turn mixture screw richer (counterclockwise) until highest RPM reading is obtained. Do not turn screw any further than point at which highest RPM is first obtained.

3) As final adjustment, turn mixture screw clockwise to obtain specified drop in engine RPM. If final RPM differs more than 30 RPM from specified curb idle speed, reset curb idle to specification and repeat mixture adjustment.

LEAN DROP (RPM)

Application	RPM Drop
All Federal Models	100

DWELL METER PROCEDURE
California Vehicles

1) Remove mixture screw plug. While carburetor is removed from vehicle, turn mixture screw in until lightly seated, then back out 2 1/2 turns.

2) If plug in air horn which covers idle air bleed screw is already removed, turn screw in until seated and back out 1 1/4 turns. If plug is in place, DO NOT remove.

3) Install carburetor on engine. Disconnect bowl vent line at carburetor. Disconnect EGR and canister purge line at carburetor and plug carburetor ports. Connect dwell meter (set on 6-cylinder scale) to mixture solenoid test lead near carburetor. Connect tachometer to connector on distributor.

4) Place transmission in Neutral and start engine. Operate at fast idle for at least 3 minutes to allow oxygen sensor to warm up, and system to shift to closed loop operation. Return engine to idle and adjust speed to 700 RPM.

5) Adjust idle mixture screw carefully to obtain 25° dwell reading. Back screw out to raise dwell; turn screw in to lower dwell reading. Allow engine to operate between adjustments to stabilize readings.

6) Disconnect mixture control solenoid wire and check that idle speed drops at least 50 RPM. If not, check idle air bleed circuit. If not correct, repeat adjustment procedure. Replace all hoses and set idle speed to specification. Remove test equipment.

COLD (FAST) IDLE RPM

Set idle with engine at normal operating temperature and EGR disconnected. Position fast idle

TUNE-UP (Cont.)

screw on high step of fast idle cam and turn to obtain fast idle RPM.

FAST IDLE SPEED (RPM)

Application	RPM
All Models	2500

AUTOMATIC CHOKE

Choke coil cover is riveted in place and no adjustment is necessary or possible.

FUEL PUMP

Perform fuel pump test with air cleaner removed and fuel inlet line or filter disconnected at carburetor.

Disconnect fuel return line at fuel filter and plug nipple or filter. Make all tests at idle speed.

FUEL PUMP SPECIFICATIONS

Application	Pressure psi (kg/cm²)	Volume Pints (Liters)
All Models	6.5-8.0 (.46-.56)	1 in 30 sec. (.47 in 30 sec.)

EMISSION CONTROL

NOTE: **See appropriate article in EMISSION CONTROL Section.**

GENERAL SERVICING

IGNITION

DISTRIBUTOR

All models are equipped with Delco High Energy Ignition (HEI) system distributor which requires no servicing.

TOTAL SPARK ADVANCE@2000 RPM

Application	With Vac. Advance	Without Vac. Advance
Federal	23°	5°
Calif.	25°	5°

DISTRIBUTOR PICKUP COIL RESISTANCE (Ohms)

Application	
All Models	500-1500

IGNITION COIL

Primary resistance should be zero or nearly zero, secondary resistance should be less than infinity.

COIL OUTPUT

Application	
All Models	25-35 KV Minimum

FUEL SYSTEMS

CARBURETORS

Application	Model
Federal	Rochester 2SE
California	Rochester E2SE

ELECTRICAL

BATTERY

BATTERY SPECIFICATIONS

Application	Cold Cranking Amps [1]	Reserve Capacity Minutes
Standard	380	75
Optional	450	90

[1] — At 0°F (-18°C).

STARTER

Delco-Remy solenoid actuated with overrunning clutch.

STARTER SPECIFICATIONS

Application	Volts	Amps	Test RPM
All Models	9	45-70	7000-11,900

ALTERNATOR

All models are equipped with Delco solid state alternators with internal voltage regulators.

ALTERNATOR SPECIFICATIONS

Application	Rated Amp. Output
Standard	42
Optional	63

Field Current Draw

Application	
All Models	[1] 4.0-5.0

[1] — At 80°F (27°C).

1983 Jeep 4 Tune-Up
GENERAL SERVICING (Cont.)

ALTERNATOR REGULATORS
Delco-Remy non-adjustable, integral with alternator.

REGULATOR SPECIFICATIONS

Operating Voltage [1]	13.9-14.9

[1] — At 50-100°F (10-38°C).

ADJUSTMENT

BELT ADJUSTMENT

Tension Using Strand Tension Gauge

Application	Lbs. (Kg)
New Belts	125-155 (57-70)
Used Belts	90-115 (41-52)

SERVICE INTERVALS

REPLACEMENT INTERVALS

Component	Interval (Miles)
Oil Filter	7500
Fuel Filter	15,000
Air Filter	30,000
PCV Filter & Valve	30,000
Oxygen Sensor (Calif.)	30,000
Charcoal Canister Filter	30,000
Spark Plugs	30,000

CAPACITIES

FLUID CAPACITIES

Application	Quantity
Crankcase (Includes Filter)	3.0 qts. (2.8L)
Cooling System	7.8 qts. (7.4L)
Man. Trans. (SAE 85W-90)	
T4 4-Speed	3.0 pts. (1.7L)
T5 5-Speed	4.0 pts. (1.9L)
Transfer Case (SAE 85W-90)	4.0 pts. (1.9L)
Front Axle (SAE 85W-90)	2.5 pts. (1.2L)
Rear Axle (SAE 85W-90)	4.8 pts. (2.3L)
Fuel Tank	
Standard	14.8 gals. (56.0L)
Optional	20.0 gals. (75.5L)

TUNE-UP

ENGINE IDENTIFICATION

Engine can be identified by the fourth digit of engine Build Date Code number, located on a tag attached to right side of block between No. 2 and 3 cylinders. The same code letter is also the fourth digit in the Vehicle Identification Number (VIN), located at top left corner of dashboard.

VIN ENGINE CODE

Application	Code
4.2L (258") 2-Bbl.	C

TUNE-UP NOTES

NOTE: **When performing tune-up procedures described in this article, the following notes and precautions must be followed:**

When performing tune-up on vehicles equipped with a catalytic converter, do not allow or create a condition of engine misfire in one or more cylinders for an extended period of time. Damage to converter from overheating may occur due to loading with unburned air/fuel mixture.

Due to production changes, always refer to Engine Tune-Up Decal in engine compartment before attempting tune-up. In the event of a conflict between specifications given in this manual and decal specifications, use the decal specifications.

ENGINE COMPRESSION

Check compression pressure with engine at normal operating temperature, all spark plugs removed, throttle and choke valves wide open and engine at cranking speed.

COMPRESSION SPECIFICATIONS

Compression Ratio	9.2:1
Compression Pressure . 120-150 psi (8.4-10.5 kg/cm²)	
Maximum Variation	
Between Cylinders	30 psi (2.1 kg/cm²)

VALVE CLEARANCE

All engines have hydraulic lifters. Lifters should be adjusted to zero lash.

VALVE ARRANGEMENT

E-I-I-E-I-E-E-I-E-I-I-E (Front to rear)

SPARK PLUG SPECIFICATIONS

Application	Gap In. (mm)	Torque Ft. Lbs. (N.m)
All Models	.035 (0.9)	.... 7-15 (9-20)

SPARK PLUG TYPE

Application	Champion No.
All Models	RFN14LY

HIGH TENSION WIRE RESISTANCE

Do not puncture spark plug wires with any type of probe. Remove spark plug wire and check resistance using an ohmmeter.

RESISTANCE (Ohms)

Wire Length	Minimum	Maximum
0-15"	3000	 10,000
15-25"	4000	 15,000
25-35"	6000	 20,000
Over 35"	8000	 25,000

DISTRIBUTOR

All models are equipped with Motorcraft Solid State Ignition (SSI) systems. No adjustments are required.

Fig. 1: Timing Mark and Firing Order

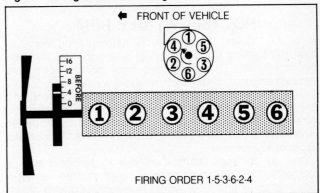

Magnetic probe located at 10° ATDC.

IGNITION TIMING

NOTE: **Engines are equipped with a receptacle for a magnetic probe timing light, located 10° ATDC. Do not use this location to check timing with a conventional light.**

PRIMARY PROCEDURE

1) Set parking brake and place transmission in Neutral. Start engine and run at idle to obtain normal operating temperature. Turn ignition off and connect timing light using inductive pick-up or adapter. Do not puncture spark plug wire.

2) Connect tachometer. Disconnect and plug vacuum hose at distributor. Disconnect vacuum switch assembly wire connector. Start engine and increase engine speed to 1600 RPM. Adjust timing. Set timing by loosening distributor clamp bolt and turning distributor. Recheck timing after clamp bolt is tightened.

PRIMARY TIMING SPECIFICATIONS (Degrees BTDC@RPM)

Application	Man. Trans.	Auto. Trans.
Federal	6@1600	.... 6@1600
Calif.	6@1600	.... 6@1600
High Alt.	13@1600	.... 13@1600

1983 Jeep 6 Tune-Up

TUNE-UP (Cont.)

ALTERNATE PROCEDURE

1) Set parking brake and place transmission in Neutral. Start engine and run at idle to obtain normal operating temperature. Turn ignition off and connect timing light using inductive pick-up or adapter. Do not puncture spark plug wire.

2) Disconnect and plug 4" Hg vacuum switch hose (Red and Black wires connected to switch). Disconnect knock sensor wire connector. Using a jumper wire, ground knock sensor wire connector to engine block. Start engine.

3) With engine at idle speed, check timing. If required, adjust timing to specification.

ALTERNATE TIMING SPECIFICATIONS (Degrees BTDC@RPM)

Application	Man. Trans.	Auto. Trans.
Federal	7@600	7@500
Calif.	7@650	7@550
High Alt.	14@700	14@650

HOT (SLOW) IDLE RPM

1) Warm engine to normal operating temperature. Set parking brake and place automatic transmission selector in "D". Disconnect and plug vacuum hose from vacuum actuator. Disconnect solenoid wire connector.

2) Adjust curb idle screw to obtain correct curb idle. Apply direct manifold vacuum to vacuum actuator. When throttle positioner is fully extended, adjust screw on throttle lever to set vacuum actuator RPM. Disconnect vacuum source.

3) Apply battery voltage to solenoid with a jumper wire. Turn A/C on and open throttle to allow solenoid to extend fully. Adjust hex-head screw to obtain solenoid RPM. Reconnect solenoid connector and vacuum hose.

IDLE SPEED (RPM)

Application	Man. Trans.	Auto. Trans.
Federal	600	500
Calif.	650	550
High Alt.	700	650

VACUUM ACTUATOR & SOLENOID IDLE (RPM)

Application	Vacuum Actuator	Solenoid Energized
High Alt.		
Man. Trans.	1000	950
Auto. Trans.	850	750
All Others		
Man. Trans.	950	750
Auto. Trans.	850	650

IDLE MIXTURE

NOTE: Be sure idle speed and timing are set before performing idle mixture adjustment. If mixture setting takes more than 3 minutes, run engine at 2000 RPM in Neutral for 1 minute, then resume adjustment.

Fig. 2: Adjustment Points for Carter BBD Carburetor

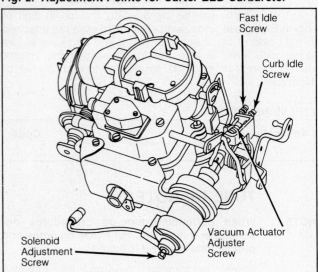

Holding solenoid maintains throttle position.

TACHOMETER (LEAN DROP) PROCEDURE

NOTE: Idle mixture adjustment is not part of a normal tune-up. DO NOT adjust mixture unless carburetor has been disassembled or vehicle fails emissions testing.

1) Remove carburetor and locate roll pins blocking idle mixture screws. Drill through throttle body on closed end of roll pin hole, then drive pins out with punch. Reinstall carburetor.

2) Warm vehicle to operating temperature and adjust idle speed. Place automatic transmission selector in "D". Turn mixture screws in (lean) until RPM drops, then turn screw out until highest RPM is reached.

3) Turn mixture screws in until specified "Lean Drop" is obtained. Adjust both screws equally. When mixture is correctly adjusted, replace roll pin to block adjustment screws.

NOTE: If final RPM differs more than 30 RPM from specified curb idle speed, reset curb idle and repeat mixture adjustment.

LEAN DROP (RPM)

Application	Man. Trans.	Auto. Trans.
All Models	50	50

COLD (FAST) IDLE RPM

Disconnect EGR solenoid line and plug carburetor ports. With engine running at normal operating temperature, place fast idle screw on second step of fast idle cam and against shoulder of high step. Turn screw to adjust fast idle speed.

FAST IDLE SPEED (RPM)

Application	Man. Trans.	Auto. Trans.
All Models	1700	1850

1983 Jeep 6 Tune-Up

TUNE-UP (Cont.)

AUTOMATIC CHOKE SETTING

Choke coil cover is riveted in place and no adjustment is necessary or possible.

FUEL PUMP

Perform fuel pump test with air cleaner removed and fuel inlet line or filter disconnected at carburetor. Disconnect fuel return line at fuel filter and plug nipple or filter. Make all tests at idle speed.

FUEL PUMP SPECIFICATIONS

	Pressure	Volume
Application	psi (kg/cm²)	Pts. (Liters)
All Models	4.0-5.0	1 in 30 sec.
	(.28-.35)	(.47 in 30 sec.)

EMISSION CONTROL

NOTE: See appropriate article in EMISSION CONTROL Section.

GENERAL SERVICING

IGNITION

DISTRIBUTOR

All vehicles use a Motorcraft breakerless solid state distributor.

TOTAL SPARK ADVANCE@2000 RPM

	With	Without
Application	Vac. Advance	Vac. Advance
All Models	33°	10°

DISTRIBUTOR PICKUP COIL RESISTANCE (Ohms)@75°F (24°C)

All Models	400-800

IGNITION COIL

IGNITION COIL RESISTANCE (Ohms)@75°F (24°C)

Application	Primary	Secondary
All Models	1.13-1.23	7700-9300

COIL OUTPUT

All Models	24KV Minimum

ELECTRICAL

BATTERY

BATTERY SPECIFICATIONS

	Cold Cranking	Reserve Capacity
Application	Amps ¹	Minutes
Standard	380	75
Optional	450	90
Police	440	135

¹ — At 0°F (-18°C).

STARTER

All models use Motorcraft positive engagement starters.

STARTER SPECIFICATIONS

Application	Volts	Amps.	Test RPM
All Models	12	67	7380-9356

ALTERNATOR

All models use Delco solid state alternators with internal voltage regulator.

ALTERNATOR SPECIFICATIONS

	Rated
Application	Amp. Output
Standard	42
Optional	56
Police	78

Field Current Draw

All Models	4.0-5.0 amps.

¹ — At 80°F (27°C)

ALTERNATOR REGULATORS

All models use Delco solid state regulators, integral with alternator. Regulator is non-adjustable.

FUEL SYSTEMS

CARBURETORS

Application	Model
All Models	Carter BBD 2-Bbl.

1983 Jeep 6 Tune-Up
GENERAL SERVICING (Cont.)

ADJUSTMENTS

BELT ADJUSTMENT

Tension Using Strand Tension Gauge

Application	Lbs. (Kg)
New Belts	
Air Pump & Pwr. Strg. [1]	65-75 (29-34)
Serpentine	180-200 (82-91)
All Other Belts	125-155 (57-70)
Used Belts	
Air Pump & Power Steering [1]	60-70 (27-32)
Serpentine	140-160 (64-73)
All Other Belts	90-115 (40-52)

[1] — 3/8" belt only.

SERVICE INTERVALS

REPLACEMENT INTERVALS

Component	Interval (Miles)
Oil Filter	7500
Fuel Filter	15,000
Air Filter	30,000
PCV Valve	30,000
Spark Plugs	30,000

CAPACITIES

FLUID CAPACITIES

Application	Capacity
Cooling System (Includes Heater)	10.5 qts. (9.9L)
Crankcase (Includes Filter)	6.0 qts. (5.7L)
Man. Trans. (SAE 85W-90)	
T4 4-Speed	3.5 pts. (1.7L)
T176 4-Speed	3.5 pts. (1.7L)
T18 4-Speed	6.5 pts. (3.1L)
T5 5-Speed	4.0 pts. (1.9L)
Auto. Trans. (Dexron II)	
Refill	8.5 pts. (4.0L)
Overhaul	17.0 pts (8.0L)
Transfer Case	
CJ & Scrambler (SAE 85W-90)	4.0 pts. (1.9L)
All Others (DEXRON II)	6.0 pts. (2.8L)
Drive Axles	Fill to bottom of filler plug hole
Fuel Tank	
CJ & Scrambler	
Standard	14.8 gals. (56.0L)
Optional	20.0 gals. (75.5L)
Cherokee & Wagoneer	20.3 gals. (76.8L)
Truck	18.2 gals. (68.8L)

1983 Jeep V8 Tune-Up

TUNE-UP

ENGINE IDENTIFICATION

Engine can be identified by the fourth digit of engine Build Date Code, located on a tag attached to the right cylinder head cover. The same code letter is also the fourth digit of Vehicle Identification Number (VIN), located on a plate attached to top left corner of instrument panel.

VIN ENGINE CODES

Application	Code Letter
6.0L (360") 2-Bbl.	N

TUNE-UP NOTES

NOTE: **When performing tune-up procedures described in this article, the following notes and precautions must be followed.**

Due to production changes, always refer to Engine Tune-Up Decal in engine compartment before attempting tune-up. In the event of a conflict between specifications given in this manual and decal specifications, use the decal specifications.

When performing tune-up on vehicles equipped with a catalytic converter, do not allow or create a condition of engine misfire in one or more cylinders for an extended period of time. Damage to converter may occur due to loading with unburned air/fuel mixture.

ENGINE COMPRESSION

Measure compression pressure with engine at normal operating temperature, spark plugs removed, throttle and choke valves wide open and engine at cranking speed.

COMPRESSION SPECIFICATIONS

Compression Ratio	8.3:1
Compression Pressure ... 120-140 psi (8.4-9.8 kg/cm²)	
Maximum Pressure Variation .... 30 psi (2.1 kg/cm²)	

VALVE CLEARANCE

All models are equipped with hydraulic lifters which should be adjusted to zero lash.

VALVE ARRANGEMENT

E-I-I-E-E-I-I-E (Front to rear, both banks)

SPARK PLUGS

SPARK PLUG SPECIFICATIONS

Application	Gap In. (mm)	Torque Ft. Lbs. (N.m)
All Models	.035 (0.9)	22-33 (30-45)

SPARK PLUG TYPE

Application	Champion No.
All Models	RN12Y

HIGH TENSION WIRE RESISTANCE

Do not puncture spark plug wires with any type of probe. Remove spark plug wire and check resistance using an ohmmeter.

RESISTANCE (Ohms)

Wire Length	Minimum	Maximum
0-15"	3000	10,000
15-25"	4000	15,000
25-35"	6000	20,000
Over 35"	8000	25,000

DISTRIBUTOR

All models are equipped with Solid State Ignition (SSI) systems and no adjustments are required.

Fig. 1: Timing Mark and Firing Order

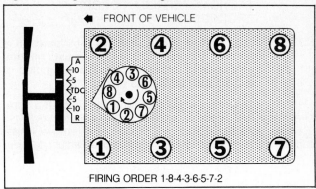

FIRING ORDER 1-8-4-3-6-5-7-2

Timing socket located at 9.5° ATDC.

IGNITION TIMING

NOTE: **Engines are equipped with a receptacle for a magnetic probe timing light, located 9.5° ATDC. Do not use this location for timing with a conventional light.**

Warm engine and allow to idle. Disconnect and plug distributor vacuum line, then check ignition timing. Adjust by turning distributor.

TIMING SPECIFICATIONS (Degrees BTDC@RPM)

Application	Specification
All Models	
High Alt.	16@600
All Others	10@600

1983 Jeep V8 Tune-Up

TUNE-UP (Cont.)

HOT (SLOW) IDLE RPM

1) Set parking brake and block drive wheels. Connect tachometer to engine. Warm engine to operating temperature and place in Neutral (manual) or "D" (automatic). Turn hex head screw on solenoid carriage to adjust solenoid RPM. Disconnect solenoid wire and adjust idle speed screw to obtain curb idle.

2) If equipped with dashpot, depress stem fully and measure clearance between stem and throttle lever. Turn dashpot to adjust to .093" (2.4 mm). Tighten lock nut and remove test equipment.

IDLE SPEED (RPM)

Application	Curb Idle	Solenoid Energized
All Models	500	550-650

IDLE MIXTURE

NOTE: Be sure idle speed and timing are set before performing idle mixture adjustment. If mixture setting takes more than 3 minutes, run engine at 2000 RPM in neutral for 1 minute, then resume adjustment.

TACHOMETER (LEAN DROP) PROCEDURE

NOTE: Idle mixture adjustment is not part of a regular tune-up. DO NOT adjust mixture unless carburetor has been disassembled or vehicle fails emissions testing.

1) Warm engine to normal operating temperature. Turn idle mixture screws to full counterclockwise position, note position of screw slot, and remove limiter caps. If screw moved during cap removal, adjust to prior position.

2) Start engine and run in Neutral (manual) or "D" (automatic). Turn mixture screw clockwise (leaner) until engine speed begins to drop. Then turn screw counterclockwise (richer) until highest RPM reading is obtained. This is lean best idle. Finally, turn screw clockwise until specified "Lean Drop" is obtained.

NOTE: If final RPM differs more than 30 RPM from specified curb idle speed, reset curb idle and repeat mixture adjustment.

3) Carefully install new limiter caps with tabs positioned against full rich stop. Press caps fully into place.

LEAN DROP (RPM)

Application	Man. Trans.	Auto. Trans.
All Models	50	20

COLD (FAST) IDLE RPM

Disconnect EGR vacuum line and plug carburetor port. With engine idling at normal operating temperature, place fast idle screw on second step of fast idle cam and against shoulder of high step. Adjust screw to set fast idle RPM.

FAST IDLE SPEED (RPM)

Application	Man. Trans.	Auto. Trans.
All Models	1500	1600

AUTOMATIC CHOKE SETTING

To adjust automatic choke, loosen cover retaining screws and rotate cover in direction indicated by arrow on face of cover. Adjust to specified setting.

AUTOMATIC CHOKE SETTING

High Alt.	1NR
All Others	2NR

FUEL PUMP

Perform fuel pump test with air cleaner removed and fuel inlet line or filter disconnected at carburetor. Disconnect fuel return line at fuel filter and plug nipple or filter. Make all tests at idle speed.

FUEL PUMP SPECIFICATIONS

Application	Pressure psi (kg/cm²)	Volume Pints (Liters)
All Models	5.0-6.5 (.35-.46)	1 in 30 sec. (.47 in 30 sec.)

EMISSION CONTROL

NOTE: See appropriate article in EMISSION CONTROL Section.

GENERAL SERVICING

IGNITION

DISTRIBUTOR

All models are equipped with Motorcraft breakerless solid state distributors. No adjustments are required.

TOTAL SPARK ADVANCE@2000 RPM

Application	With Vac. Advance	Without Vac. Advance
All Models	32°	8°

GENERAL SERVICING (Cont.)

DISTRIBUTOR PICKUP COIL RESISTANCE (Ohms)@75°F (24°C)

All Models 400-800

IGNITION COIL

IGNITION COIL RESISTANCE (Ohms)@75°F (24°C)

Application	Primary	Secondary
All Models	1.13-1.23	 7700-9300

COIL OUTPUT@1000 RPM

All Models .... 24 KV min.

FUEL SYSTEMS

CARBURETORS

Application	Model
All Models	Motorcraft 2150 2-Bbl.

ELECTRICAL

BATTERY

BATTERY SPECIFICATIONS

Application	Cold Cranking Amps. [1]	Reserve Capacity Minutes
Standard	380	 75
Optional	450	 90
Police	440	 135

[1] — At 0°F (-18°C.)

STARTER

All models are equipped with Motorcraft positive engagement starters.

STARTER SPECIFICATIONS

Application	Volts	Amps.	Test RPM
All Models	12	 67	 7380-9356

ALTERNATORS

All models are equipped with Delco solid state alternators with integral voltage regulator.

ALTERNATOR REGULATORS

All models use Delco solid state regulators, integral with alternator. Regulator is non-adjustable.

ALTERNATOR SPECIFICATIONS

Application	Rated Amp. Output
Standard	42
Optional	56
Police	78

Field Current Draw

All Models .... 4.0-5.0 amps.

[1] — At 80°F (27°C)

ADJUSTMENTS

BELT ADJUSTMENT

Tension Using Strand Tension Gauge	
Application	Lbs. (Kg)
New Belts	125-155 (57-70)
Used Belts	90-115 (40-52)

SERVICE INTERVALS

REPLACEMENT INTERVALS

Component	Interval (Miles)
Oil Filter	7500
Fuel Filter	15,000
Air Filter	30,000
Charcoal Canister Filter	30,000
PCV Valve	30,000
Spark Plugs	30,000

FLUID CAPACITIES

Application	Capacity
Cooling System (Includes Heater)	14.0 qts. (13.2L)
Crankcase (Includes Filter)	5.0 qts. (4.7L)
Man. Trans. (SAE 85W-90)	
T18 4-Speed	6.5 pts. (3.1L)
T176 4-Speed	3.5 pts. (1.7L)
Auto. Trans. (Dexron II)	
Refill	8.5 pts. (4.0L)
Overhaul	17.0 pts. (8.0L)
Transfer Case (Dexron II)	6.0 pts. (2.8L)
Drive Axles	Fill to bottom of filler plug hole
Fuel Tank	
Cherokee & Wagoneer	20.3 gals. (76.8L)
Truck	18.2 gals. (68.8L)

SECTION 1a

COMPUTERIZED ENGINE CONTROLS

CONTENTS

NOTE: ALSO SEE GENERAL INDEX.

IMPORTANT: Because of the many model names used by vehicle manufacturers, accurate identification of models is important. See Model Identification at the front of this publication.

1983 Computerized Engine Controls

CHRYSLER CORP. ELECTRONIC FUEL CONTROL

DESCRIPTION

The Electronic Fuel Control (EFC) system is an electronically controlled system that closely manages air/fuel ratio and ignition timing. The Spark Control Computer (SCC) is the heart of the system. This computer provides the capability of igniting a lean air/fuel mixture according to different modes of engine operation; plus, during closed loop operation, the computer maintains the air/fuel mixture close to the ideal ratio of 14.7:1.

OPERATION

The EFC system consists of the following subsystems: fuel control, electronic throttle control, spark control, data sensors. Spark Control Computer (SCC), electronic exhaust gas recirculation (EGR), electronic air switching and catalytic converter.

FUEL CONTROL

All models are equipped with feedback carburetors which contain an electronically operated duty cycle solenoid. This solenoid meters the main fuel system of the carburetor and operates in parallel with the conventional fixed main metering jets. The computer controls the operation of the solenoid with electrical signals, in response to input from data sensors. See Fig. 1.

Fig. 1: Sectional View of Thermo-Quad Feedback Carburetor With Duty Cycle Solenoid

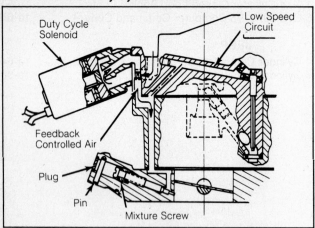

Fig. 2: Sectional View of Holley 6145 Feedback Carburetor With Duty Cycle Solenoid

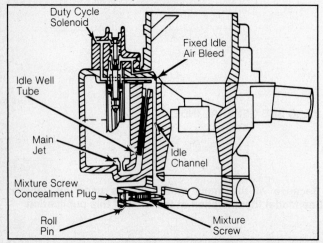

When the solenoid is de-energized by the computer, the solenoid valve spring pushes upward through main system fuel valve. When de-energized, the solenoid main metering orifice is fully uncovered, providing the richest mixture for any given air flow.

When the solenoid is energized by the computer, the solenoid main metering orifice is fully sealed. This solenoid position offers the leanest mixture within the carburetor for any given air flow.

Main system fuel may be regulated between richest and leanest mixture conditions by controlling the amount of time that the solenoid is energized and de-energized. The computer controls the duration of time that solenoid is energized in comparison to total time of solenoid operation.

This duration of time is determined by engine operating conditions and/or oxygen sensor signals. In this manner, the ideal air/fuel ratio can be constantly maintained.

ELECTRONIC THROTTLE CONTROL

The Electronic Throttle Control system and 2 electric timers are incorporated within the SCC. A solenoid, mounted on the carburetor, is energized whenever the air conditioning, rear window defogger or electric timers are activated. The 2 timers operate when the throttle is closed, providing a 2 second time delay, or after engine is started.

SPARK CONTROL

Spark Control allows the computer to determine the exact instant that ignition is required; then signals ignition coil to produce electrical impulses which fire the spark plugs. The computer eliminates the need for either vacuum advance units or centrifugal advance weights. Spark control operates in 1 of the following modes:

Start Mode

During cranking, an electrical signal from the distributor is fed into the computer, which causes the computer to fire the spark plugs at a fixed amount of advance.

Run Mode

Once the engine starts and is operating normally, the timing will be controlled by the computer, based upon information received by the data sensors.

Spark timing and dwell cannot be adjusted in the run mode. If the computer fails, the system will go into the start mode. This enables the vehicle to be driven in for repair; but performance and fuel economy will be poor. If the start mode fails, the engine will not start or run.

The amount of spark advance is determined by engine speed and engine vacuum. However, where it happens depends upon the following conditions:

Advance From Vacuum

Advance based upon engine vacuum is allowed by the computer when the carburetor switch is open. The amount of advance is programmed into the computer and is proportionate to the amount of vacuum and engine RPM.

Advance From Speed

Advance based upon engine speed (RPM) is allowed by the computer when the carburetor switch is open and vacuum level is steady. This advance from speed is programmed into the computer, controlled by engine RPM, and will build at a slow rate. If carburetor switch closes, advance from speed will be cancelled.

CHRYSLER CORP. ELECTRONIC FUEL CONTROL (Cont.)

DATA SENSORS

Each sensor furnishes electrical impulses to the SCC. The SCC computes ignition timing and air/fuel mixture ratio necessary to maintain proper engine operation. The function of each sensor is closely related to each of the other sensors. Operation of each sensor is as follows:

Magnetic Pick-Up Assembly

The magnetic pick-up assembly consists of 2 pick-up coils: start pick-up coil and run pick-up coil. Both are located in the distributor and operate as follows:

- **Start Pick-Up Coil** — Supplies a signal to SCC which will cause the spark plugs to fire at a fixed amount of advance during cranking only. This coil is permanently attached to distributor and the amount of advance is determined by distributor position. *See Fig. 3.*
- **Run Pick-Up Coil** — Once engine begins to run, the start pick-up coil signal is by-passed and the run pick-up coil supplies advance information to SCC. The SCC then modifies advance to reflect engine operating conditions reported by other sensors. *See Fig. 3.*

Fig. 3: View of Distributor with Cap & Rotor Removed

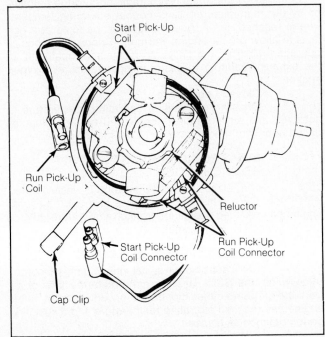

Note location of magnetic pick-up coil assembly.

NOTE: See Figs. 4, 5 and 6 for location of data sensors.

Coolant Temperature Sensor/Switch

The coolant sensor/switch informs the SCC when the engine has reached normal operating temperature, preventing any changes until such temperature is reached so that proper adjustment can be made to the air/fuel ratio. The coolant sensor/switch also controls amount of ignition timing advance or retard when the engine is cold.

Fig. 4: Location of Data Sensors on 3.7L Engine

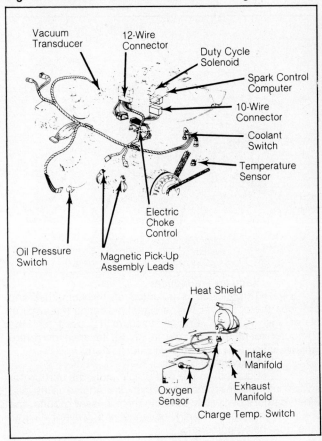

Fig. 5: Location of Data Sensors on 5.2L Engine (Rear View)

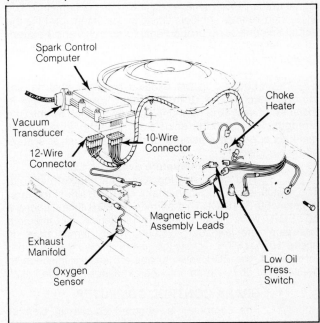

CHRYSLER CORP. ELECTRONIC FUEL CONTROL (Cont.)

Fig. 6: Location of Data Sensors on 5.2L Engine (Front View)

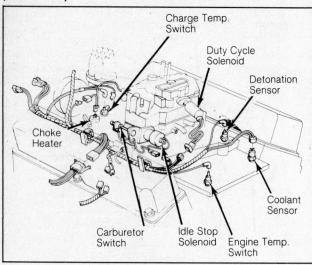

Fig. 7: Internal View of Spark Control Computer

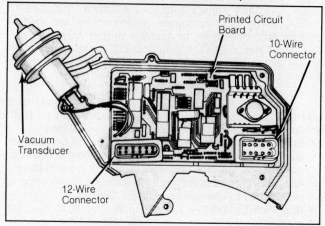

Vacuum Transducer

This sensor is mounted on the computer and provides the computer with a signal indicating the amount of engine vacuum. Engine vacuum is used by the computer to determine how much to advance or retard ignition timing and to change air/fuel mixture.

Carburetor Switch

Located on the end of idle stop, the carburetor switch informs the computer when the engine is at idle. When carburetor switch contacts throttle lever ground, the computer will cancel spark advance and prevent air/fuel ratio from being adjusted.

Detonation Sensor

Used only on the 5.2L engine, this sensor is mounted in the intake manifold and sends a low voltage signal to the SCC whenever engine knock is detected. The SCC then retards ignition timing a maximum of 11°, the actual amount being proportional to strength and frequency of detonation. When the condition no longer exists, ignition timing is advanced to original value.

Oxygen Sensor

Located in the exhaust manifold, this sensor informs the computer of the amount of oxygen present in exhaust gases. The amount is proportional to mixture strength. The computer adjusts air/fuel ratio so that it will maintain operating efficiency of the 3-way catalyst system and the engine.

Charge Temperature Switch

This sensor is located in the intake manifold. The switch is closed when intake charge (air/fuel mixture) is below 60°F (16°C). This permits no EGR timer function, no EGR valve operation and switches air injection upstream into exhaust system. When temperature is above 60°F (16°C), the switch opens, allowing EGR timer to time out, the EGR valve to operate and air injection to be switched downstream into the exhaust system.

SPARK CONTROL COMPUTER

The computer is mounted on the air cleaner housing and consists of a printed circuit board which simultaneously receives signals from all data sensors and analyzes these signals to determine spark advance and air/fuel mixture. Incorporated within the computer are the electronics for the throttle control, EGR and air switching

systems. After determining spark advance, the computer will operate the engine in one of the following modes:

Open Loop Mode

During cold engine operation, the air/fuel ratio is controlled by information programmed into the computer by the manufacturer. Until normal operating temperature is reached, the air/fuel mixture will be fixed at a rich level to allow proper engine warm-up. During this mode of operation, air from the air pump is injected "upstream" in the exhaust manifold to assist in heating-up the oxygen sensor.

Closed Loop Mode

Once normal engine operating temperature is achieved, the air/fuel ratio is controlled by the computer based upon information received from the oxygen sensor.

ELECTRONIC EXHAUST GAS RECIRCULATION

The electronic EGR system is incorporated within the SCC. This system prevents EGR flow until engine has reached normal operating temperature (after a predetermined length of time).

ELECTRONIC AIR SWITCHING

The electronic air switching system is incorporated within the SCC. This system directs the flow of air from the air pump either "upstream" or "downstream" after engine has reached operating temperature and a specified period of time has elapsed.

CATALYTIC CONVERTER

Proper emission control is accomplished with the special catalytic converter system used with the EFC system. All models are equipped with a front converter located below exhaust manifold (2 converters on 5.2L engines; 1 on each side of engine). A second (main) converter is placed behind the front converter(s) in exhaust system.

NOTE: **Similarities exist between external characteristics of each converter system. However, extreme care must be exercised during replacement of converters due to internal design differences.**

CHRYSLER CORP. ELECTRONIC FUEL CONTROL (Cont.)

TESTING

A malfunction in the EFC system may result in engine surge, hesitation, rough idle and/or poor fuel economy. Before performing any tests, check all vacuum and electrical wiring for proper routing and connections and check for exhaust and intake manifold leaks. If these are in order, proceed with testing.

NOTE: **The Spark Control Computer controls ignition timing as well as air/fuel mixture. Before testing EFC system, perform Spark Control Tests first.**

ELECTRONIC SPARK CONTROL SYSTEM TESTS

Ignition System Starting Test
1) Measure and record battery voltage. Check battery specific gravity, which must be 1.220 (temperature corrected) to deliver proper voltage to ignition system.
2) Turn ignition on and remove coil wire from distributor cap. Hold end of wire 1/4" from a good engine ground. Intermittently jump coil negative terminal to ground, while watching for spark at coil wire. If there is a spark, it must be constant and bright blue.
3) If there is a good spark, continue cranking engine while slowly moving secondary wire away from ground. Look for arcing at coil tower. If arcing occurs, replace coil. If spark is weak or not constant, or if there is no spark, proceed to "Failure to Start Test".
4) If spark is good and there is no arcing at coil tower, secondary voltage is satisfactory. Make sure it is reaching spark plugs by checking distributor rotor, cap, spark plug wires and spark plugs.
5) If all of these components check okay, ignition system is not at fault. Check fuel system or mechanical engine damage.

CAUTION: **Perform "Ignition System Starting Test" first. Failure to do so may result in lost diagnostic time or incorrect test results.**

Failure to Start Test
1) Turn ignition switch off and disconnect 10-wire connector from SCC. Repeat Ignition System Starting Test, step **2)**. If spark results, replace computer.
2) If no spark is obtained, check voltage at coil positive terminal. With ignition switch on, connect positive voltmeter lead to coil positive terminal and negative lead to a good ground. Reading should be within 1 volt of battery voltage. If not, check wiring between battery and coil positive terminal.
3) If voltage at positive coil terminal was correct, connect positive voltmeter lead to coil negative terminal and negative lead to a good ground. Again, voltage should be within 1 volt of battery voltage. If not, replace ignition coil.

NOTE: **Primary and secondary resistance may be checked before replacing ignition coil. However, if battery voltage exists on positive side, but not on negative side of coil, ignition coil normally requires replacement.**

4) If voltage was correct at negative coil terminal, but no spark resulted in Ignition System Starting Test, step **2)**, replace ignition coil.

5) If spark results, but engine will not start, turn ignition switch to "RUN" position. Connect positive voltmeter lead to terminal 1 of 10-wire connector and negative lead to a good ground. *See Fig. 8.* Reading should be within 1 volt of battery voltage. If not, check wire for open and repair it. Repeat this step after repairing wire. Reconnect 10-wire connector to computer.

Fig. 8: Voltmeter Hookup for Checking Terminal 1 Voltage

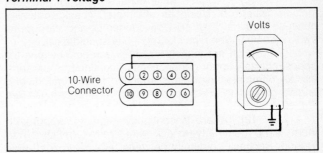

Reading should be within 1 volt of battery voltage.

Fig. 9: Checking Voltage at Carburetor Switch

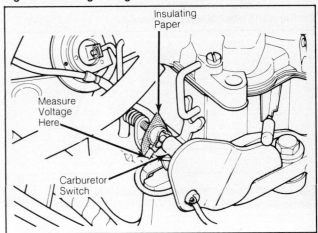

Voltage should read about 5 volts.

6) If battery voltage was recorded in step **5)**, place a thin insulator (thin piece of cardboard) between curb idle adjusting screw and carburetor switch or make sure screw does not touch switch. *See Fig. 9.* Connect negative lead of voltmeter to a good ground.
7) Turn ignition switch to "RUN" position and touch positive voltmeter lead to carburetor switch terminal. Reading should be about 5 volts. If so, proceed to step **13)**.

Fig. 10: Voltmeter Hookup for Checking Terminal 2 Voltage

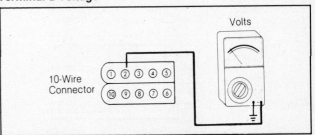

Voltage should be within 1 volt of battery voltage.

CHRYSLER CORP. ELECTRONIC FUEL CONTROL (Cont.)

8) If voltage was not at least 5 volts, turn ignition switch off. Disconnect 10-wire connector from computer. Turn ignition switch back to "RUN" position. Connect positive voltmeter lead to terminal 2 of 10-wire connector and negative lead to ground. *See Fig. 10.*

9) Voltage reading should again be within 1 volt of battery voltage. If not, check wiring between terminal 2 and ignition switch for opens, shorts or poor connections.

10) If voltage at terminal 2 was correct, turn ignition switch off. Using an ohmmeter, check continuity between terminal 7 of 10-wire connector and carburetor switch terminal. *See Fig. 11.* Continuity should exist.

11) If not, check wire between connections for opens, shorts or poor connections. If continuity is present, use an ohmmeter with leads attached to terminal 10 and engine ground to check continuity of ground circuit. *See Fig. 12.*

12) If there is continuity, replace computer. If there is no continuity, check wire from terminal 10 to ground. Recheck continuity between terminal 7 of 10-wire connector and carburetor switch. Try to start engine. If engine fails to start, go on to next step.

Fig. 11: Ohmmeter Hookup for Checking Carburetor Switch Wiring Harness

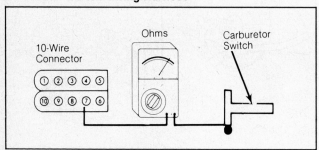

Fig. 12: Ohmmeter Hookup for Checking Computer Ground Circuit

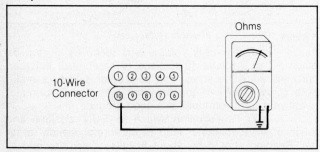

Fig. 13: Ohmmeter Hookup for Checking Pick-Up Coil Resistance

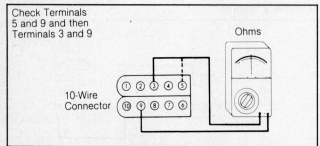

Resistance should be between 150 and 900 ohms.

13) Turn ignition switch off. Attach ohmmeter leads to terminals 5 and 9 of 10-wire harness connector to check run pick-up coil resistance and to terminals 3 and 9 to check start pick-up coil resistance. *See Fig. 13.* Resistance should be 150-900 ohms. If so, proceed to step **15)**.

14) If not, disconnect distributor connectors and attach ohmmeter leads to run pick-up coil leads and then to start pick-up coil leads coming from distributor. If resistance is now okay, wiring harness is defective. If resistance is still not 150-900 ohms, replace pick-up coils, as necessary.

15) Next, connect one lead of an ohmmeter to engine ground and touch other lead to each terminal of leads coming from 2 distributor pick-up coils. There should be no continuity. If continuity is indicated, replace pick-up coil.

16) Remove distributor cap and rotor and check reluctor-to-pick-up coil(s) air gap. Air gap for single pick-up coil distributor should be .006" (.15 mm). On dual pick-up distributors, air gap should be .006" (.15 mm) for start pick-up coil and .012" (.30 mm) for run pick-up coil.

17) If not to specification, adjust gap using a non-magnetic feeler gauge. *See Fig. 14.* To adjust, loosen pick-up coil hold-down screws, move up coil against feeler gauge, resting against reluctor tooth. Tighten hold-down screw, remove feeler gauge and recheck gap.

Fig. 14: Checking Distributor Pick-Up Air Gap

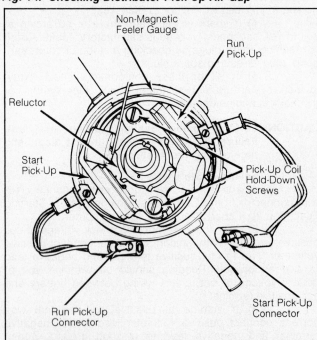

A non-magnetic feeler gauge must be used when checking and/or adjusting air gap.

18) Install distributor cap and reinstall all wiring. If engine fails to start, replace spark control computer. If it still fails to start, install original computer and retest.

Spark Control Computer Spark Test

1) Warm engine to normal operating temperature. Disconnect carburetor switch or unground it by placing a thin piece of cardboard between curb idle adjusting screw and switch. Be sure coolant temperature sensor/switch is connected and working properly.

CHRYSLER CORP. ELECTRONIC FUEL CONTROL (Cont.)

2) Remove and plug vacuum hose at vacuum transducer. Connect an auxiliary vacuum supply to vacuum transducer and apply 16 in. Hg. Increase engine speed to 1500 RPM and wait 1 minute before checking specifications. Advance specifications are in addition to basic advance. See Spark Advance Test Specifications table.

3) If computer fails to obtain settings, replace computer.

NOTE: **The 3.7L engine is equipped with an accumulator (timer). The carburetor switch MUST be ungrounded for 30 seconds before checking specified spark advance schedule.**

SPARK ADVANCE TEST SPECIFICATIONS

Application	Computer No.	Spark Advance [1]
Pickup		
3.7L		
Man. Trans.		
Fed.		
1-Bbl.		
W/Overdrive	4289097	21-29°
W/O Overdrive	4289099	17-25°
2-Bbl.		
W/Mizer Option	4289024	28-36°
W/O Mizer Option	4289089	24-32°
Calif.	4289067	12-20°
Auto. Trans.		
Fed.	4289091	18-26°
Calif.	4289069	0-8° [2]
5.7L		
Man. Trans.	4289075	9-17°
Auto. Trans.	4289077	4-12°
Van		
3.7L		
Man. Trans.		
Fed.	4289103	21-29°
Calif.	4289081	12-20°
Auto. Trans.		
Fed.	4289145	18-26°
Calif.	4289083	0-8° [2]
5.2L		
Man. Trans.	4289086	9-17°
Auto. Trans.	4289094	4-12°

[1] — With engine speed at 1500 RPM and 16 in. Hg vacuum applied.

[2] — With engine speed at 2000 RPM and 16 in. Hg vacuum applied.

ELECTRONIC FUEL CONTROL SYSTEM TESTS

NOTE: **The "Spark Control Computer Spark Test" should be tested prior to beginning any test on EFC system. The following test MUST then be performed in the sequence given.**

Air Switching System Diagnosis (Vacuum Supply)

1) Remove vacuum hose for air switching/diverter valve and connect a vacuum gauge to hose. Set parking brake. Start engine and observe gauge reading.

2) On a cold engine, engine vacuum should be present until engine coolant temperature reaches 60°F (16°C). When temperature is reached and time delay has elapsed as shown in Air Switching Delay Specifications table, vacuum should drop to zero. If no vacuum is present on gauge, check vacuum supply air switching solenoid, coolant switch, charge temperature switch and computer wiring and connections. If all check okay, computer may be defective, preventing air switching function. Proceed to step **4)**.

3) On a warm engine, vacuum should be present for the specified time shown in the Air Switching Delay Specifications table after engine starts, then drop to zero. If there is no vacuum, check vacuum supply, air switching solenoid, coolant switch, charge temperature switch and computer wiring and connections. If all check okay, computer may be defective, preventing air switching function. Proceed to step **4)**.

4) If no vacuum was recorded in step **2)** and **3)** and all components are operating properly, connect a voltmeter to Light Green wire on air switching solenoid. With engine at normal operating temperature, start engine. Voltage should be less than 1 volt.

5) After specified time shown in Air Switching Delay Specifications table, voltmeter should read the same as charging system voltage. If voltmeter does not register charging system voltage or charging system voltage is shown prior to specified time, replace computer.

AIR SWITCHING DELAY SPECIFICATIONS

Application	Computer No.	Delay (Seconds)
Pickup		
3.7L		
Man. Trans.		
Fed.		
1-Bbl.		
W/Overdrive	4289097	0
W/O Overdrive	4289099	0
2-Bbl.		
W/Mizer Option	4289024	0
W/O Mizer Option	4289089	0
Calif.	4289067	60
Auto. Trans.		
Fed.	4289091	0
Calif.	4289069	60
5.7L		
Man. Trans.	4289075	0
Auto. Trans.	4289077	0
Van		
3.7L		
Man. Trans.		
Fed.	4289103	0
Calif.	4289081	60
Auto. Trans.		
Fed.	4289145	0
Calif.	4289083	60
5.2L		
Man. Trans.	4289086	0
Auto. Trans.	4289094	0

Air Switching Diagnosis (Air Switching Valve)

1) Remove air supply hose from air switching valve. Remove vacuum hose from valve and install an auxiliary vacuum supply.

CHRYSLER CORP. ELECTRONIC FUEL CONTROL (Cont.)

2) Set parking brake. Start engine. Air should blow out of side port. Apply vacuum to valve. Air should blow out bottom port.

Coolant Sensor Test

Turn ignition switch off and disconnect wire connector from sensor. Connect ohmmeter leads to sensor terminals. With engine cold and ambient temperature below 90°F (32°C), resistance should read 500-1000 ohms. With a hot engine, resistance should be greater than 1300 ohms. If specifications are not obtained, replace sensor.

NOTE: **The coolant sensor resistance will continually change with changes in engine temperature. It is not a switch.**

Charge Temperature & Coolant Switch

1) Turn ignition off and disconnect wire from temperature switch. Connect 1 lead of ohmmeter to good engine ground or to switch's ground terminal. Connect other lead to center terminal of coolant switch. Check for continuity.

2) On a cold engine, continuity should be present (resistance less than 100 ohms). If not, replace switch. The charge temperature switch must be cooler than 60°F (16°C) to obtain this reading. On an engine at normal operating temperature, the terminal should show no continuity. If it does, replace coolant switch.

Carburetor Duty Cycle Solenoid Test

1) Remove and plug vacuum hose at vacuum transducer. Connect a tachometer. Connect an auxiliary vacuum supply to vacuum transducer and apply 16 in. Hg. Set parking brake and start engine. Allow engine to reach normal operating temperature. DO NOT ground carburetor switch. Run engine at 1500 RPM.

NOTE: **After any hot start, maintain 1500 RPM for at least 2 minutes before proceeding with test.**

2) Disconnect duty cycle solenoid connector at solenoid. Average engine speed should increase a minimum of 50 RPM. Reconnect solenoid connector. Engine speed should slowly return to 1500 RPM.

3) Disconnect 12-pin connector at computer. Connect a ground to harness connector pin 11. Engine speed should decrease 50 RPM (minimum). If speed does not change as outlined, service carburetor (check for air leaks).

Electronic Fuel Control Computer Test

1) Connect a tachometer and set parking brake. Start engine, warm to normal operating temperature and maintain engine speed of 1500 RPM. DO NOT ground carburetor switch. Connect a voltmeter to duty cycle solenoid output wire going to carburetor (Green wire).

NOTE: **Do not separate the solenoid connector from the wiring harness.**

2) Disconnect electrical connector at oxygen sensor and connect a jumper to a good ground. Engine speed should increase at least 50 RPM and voltmeter should indicate more than 9 volts.

3) Hold jumper wire with 1 hand and with the other hand, touch the battery positive terminal with jumper wire. Engine speed should decrease at least 50 RPM and voltmeter should indicate less than 3 volts. If computer fails both tests, replace it. Reconnect oxygen sensor harness.

CAUTION: **Before performing next test, ensure fuel control computer is operating properly.**

Oxygen Sensor Test

1) Set parking brake and connect tachometer. Run engine at 1500 RPM and connect voltmeter to carburetor-to-computer output wire (Green). DO NOT ground carburetor switch. Hold choke blade closed. During the next 10 seconds, the voltage should decrease to 3 volts or less and maintain that level. If engine does not respond, proceeed to step 2).

2) Disconnect PCV system. During the next 10 seconds, the voltage should increase to 9 volts or greater and maintain that level until vacuum hose is reconnected. If sensor fails both tests, replace it. Reconnect all hoses and wires.

NOTE: **This test should not be performed for more than 90 seconds.**

POOR PERFORMANCE TESTS

NOTE: **Be sure basic timing and hot curb idle speed are set to specifications before performing these tests.**

Carburetor Switch Test

1) Turn ignition off and disconnect 10-wire connector from computer. With throttle completely closed, check continuity with ohmmeter leads connected to cavity 7 and ground.

NOTE: **Grounding carburetor switch eliminates all spark advance on systems.**

2) If no continuity is read, check wire from cavity 7 to carburetor switch terminal. Also check carburetor switch for proper operation.

3) Open throttle and again check for continuity from cavity 7 to ground. There should be none.

NOTE: **After performing carburetor switch test, perform tests on the spark control system and fuel control system.**

ELECTRONIC THROTTLE CONTROL SYSTEM TEST

1) Connect a tachometer to engine. Start and run engine until normal operating temperature is obtained. On vehicles without air conditioning, depress and release accelerator. An RPM higher than curb idle speed should be seen for specified time shown in EGR and Throttle Control Specifications table.

2) On vehicles equipped with air conditioning or rear window defogger, turning on the air conditioner or defogger and depressing accelerator for a moment should give an RPM higher than curb idle speed. Turning off the air conditioner or rear window defogger will result in normal idle speed.

NOTE: **The air conditioning clutch will cycle on and off as it is running. DO NOT mistake this for electronic throttle control operation.**

CHRYSLER CORP. ELECTRONIC FUEL CONTROL (Cont.)

3) On all vehicles, if speed increases do not occur as outlined above, turn engine off and disconnect 3-wire connector at carburetor (idle stop solenoid and duty cycle solenoid). Using an ohmmeter, check resistance of the solenoid by measuring from the 3-wire connector containing the Black wire to ground. Resistance should be 15-35 ohms. If not, replace idle stop solenoid.

4) On vehicles without air conditioning or rear window defogger, start vehicle and before specified time has elapsed, measure voltage at Black wire of 3-wire connector. Voltmeter reading should equal charging system voltage. If voltmeter reading does not equal charging system voltage, replace the Gray starter timer on 3.7L Federal models. On all other models, replace the computer.

5) On air conditioned vehicles, start engine and turn on air conditioner. Measure voltage at Black wire of 3-wire connector. Voltmeter reading should equal charging system voltage AFTER specified time has elapsed. If not, check wiring back to instrument panel for an open circuit.

ELECTRONIC EGR SYSTEM TEST

NOTE: **Ensure engine temperature sensors are working properly before performing test.**

1) With the engine temperature cold and ignition switch off, connect a voltmeter between Gray wire on EGR solenoid and ground. Start engine. Voltage should read less than 1 volt. This reading should be maintained until normal operating temperature is reached and specified time has elapsed as shown in EGR and Throttle Control Specifications table.

2) After normal operating temperature is reached and specified time has elapsed, voltmeter should register charging system voltage. If readings are not obtained as outlined, replace EGR solenoid and repeat test. If the voltmeter indicates charging system voltage before specified time elapses, replace computer.

EGR & THROTTLE CONTROL SPECIFICATIONS

Application	Computer No.	Delay (Seconds)
Pickup		
3.7L		
Man. Trans.		
Fed.		
1-Bbl.		
W/Overdrive	4289097	60
W/O Overdrive	4289099	60
2-Bbl.		
W/Mizer Option	4289024	0
W/O Mizer Option	4289089	0
Calif.	4289067	65
Auto. Trans.		
Fed.	4289091	60
Calif.	4289069	65
5.7L		
Man. Trans.	4289075	20
Auto. Trans.	4289077	20
Van		
3.7L		
Man. Trans.		
Fed.	4289103	60
Calif.	4289081	65
Auto. Trans.		
Fed.	4289145	60
Calif.	4289083	60
5.2L		
Man. Trans.	4289086	20
Auto. Trans.	4289094	20

Fig. 15: Wiring Diagram for 3.7L and 5.2L EFC System

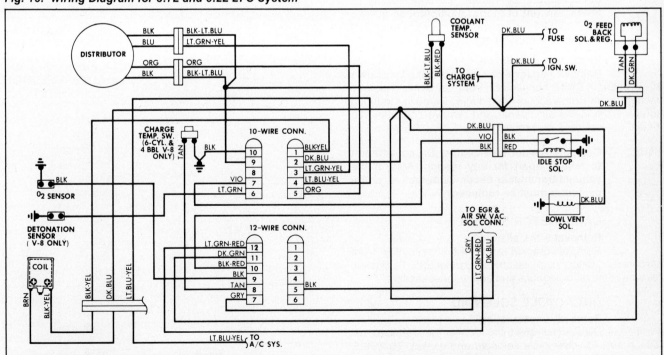

Also see chassis wiring in WIRING DIAGRAM Section.

CHRYSLER CORP. ELECTRONIC FUEL CONTROL (Cont.)

NOTE: If an engine is restarted while still at normal operating temperature, the voltmeter reading should register 1 volt for the specified time, then register charging system voltage.

ELECTRONIC AIR SWITCHING TESTS

NOTE: Follow test procedure for Air Switching System Diagnosis (Vacuum Supply and Air Switching Valve) described in ELECTRONIC FUEL CONTROL SYSTEM TESTS.

DETONATION SENSOR TEST

NOTE: This test applies to 5.2L engines only.

1) Connect a variable timing light to engine. Start engine and run it on second highest step of fast idle cam (about 1200 RPM). Connect an auxiliary vacuum supply of 16 in. Hg vacuum.

2) Using a small wrench, tap lightly on manifold, near the sensor. With timing light, look for a decrease in spark advance. Amount of timing decrease should be proportional to strength and frequency of tapping. Maximum decrease in timing should be 11°. Turn engine off and remove timing light.

REMOVAL & INSTALLATION

SPARK CONTROL COMPUTER

NOTE: Do not remove grease from either harness connectors or connector cavities in computer. The grease is used in order to prevent moisture from corroding the terminals. If there is not at least 1/2" of grease on bottom of computer connector cavities, apply a liberal amount of Mopar multipurpose grease No. 2932524 (or equivalent) over entire end of plug before reinstalling.

Removal & Installation
Remove negative battery terminal. Disconnect 10-wire and 12-wire connectors from computer. Remove vacuum hose from vacuum transducer. Remove mounting screws from inside air cleaner and remove computer. To install, reverse removal procedure.

NOTE: Computer is not serviceable. Do not attempt to take it apart for any reason. Also, if the vacuum transducer becomes defective, entire computer must be replaced.

CARBURETOR SWITCH
Removal & Installation
Remove bracket and switch assembly from carburetor. Disconnect electrical connector. To install, reverse removal procedure and adjust if necessary.

DUTY CYCLE SOLENOID
Removal & Installation
Disconnect electrical connector. Remove retaining screws, duty cycle solenoid and gasket. To install, reverse removal procedure.

OXYGEN SENSOR
Removal & Installation
Disconnect battery cable and electrical lead at sensor. Remove sensor. To install, coat threads of new sensor with nickel-based anti-seize compound. Do not use graphite or other compounds. Hand-start sensor, then tighten to 35 ft. lb. (48 N.m). Connect electrical connector and battery cable.

FORD MCU ENGINE CONTROL SYSTEM

Federal 2.0L, Low Alt. 2.3L, Federal F100 4.9L, Calif. Light Duty 4.9L

DESCRIPTION

The MCU control system is named for and commanded by a Microprocessor Control Unit. This micro-computer is located in the engine compartment and is capable of controlling engine air/fuel ratios, air injection, and on some models, canister purge, spark retard and idle speed. The system consists of the MCU module, air/fuel control and air injection solenoids, engine sensors, feedback carburetor, and related circuitry.

OPERATION

MICROPROCESSOR CONTROL UNIT (MCU)

The MCU is a solid-state micro-computer located on the left fender panel. It is the "brain" of the system and receives inputs and sends signals through a 24-pin connector. The MCU is capable of operating in 3 modes: Initialization, Open loop and Closed loop.

Initialization mode occurs when the engine is started. In this mode the MCU richens the fuel mixture for easy starting. Open loop operation is controlled by MCU programming. Air/fuel ratio is fixed at a pre-determined level and allows good driveability at idle, moderate-to-heavy acceleration, and deceleration.

Closed loop operation occurs when the engine is warm and vehicle is operated at light load conditions. In closed loop, the MCU controls the air/fuel mixture in response to signals from an oxygen sensor in the exhaust manifold.

ENGINE SENSORS
Coolant Temperature

The coolant temperature switch is used to signal temperature changes to the MCU. The MCU uses this signal to improve cold engine operation. The coolant switch is mounted on the Ported Vacuum Switch (PVS).

Fig. 1: MCU System Layout

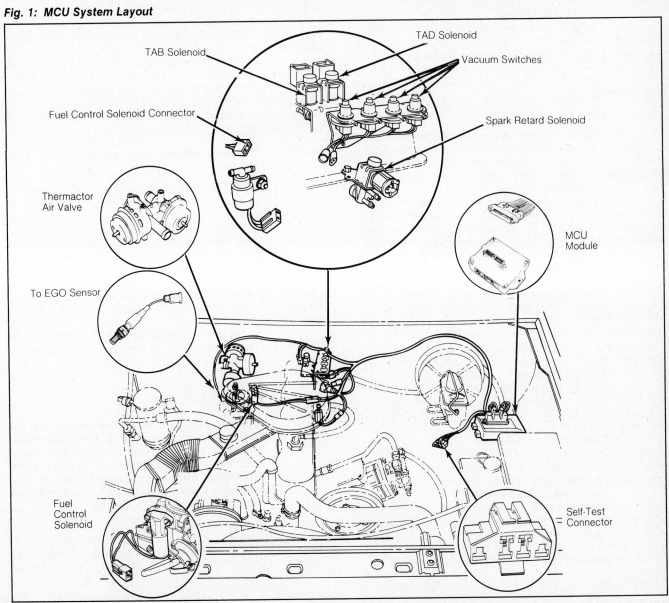

FORD MCU ENGINE CONTROL SYSTEM (Cont.)

Engine Load Sensor

Engine load is determined by vacuum level, and throttle position. An idle tracking switch signals the MCU when the throttle is closed. A vacuum switch signals wide open conditions.

Oxygen Sensor

All models use an oxygen sensor mounted in the exhaust manifold. This sensor sends a low voltage signal to the MCU to indicate rich or lean mixture. When mixture is lean, the signal is less than 0.2 volts. When rich, the sensor voltage is slightly above 0.6 volts.

Knock Sensor

The knock sensor is used to help reduce detonation. It allows a voltage signal to pass through when it senses detonation. The MCU uses this signal to bleed off distributor vacuum. The MCU does not otherwise control ignition timing.

Engine Speed

The MCU receives a direct signal from the "Tach Test" terminal on the coil. It uses this signal to calculate engine speed and alters the air/fuel correction based on this speed.

Self-Test Connector

The MCU can self-diagnose most common operating problems. In order to initiate and read the diagnostic program, connections are made to the Self-Test connector. It provides voltage pulses which can be read by a specialized tester (Rotunda 07-0004) or a dial-type voltmeter.

ENGINE CONTROLS

Engine controls are the devices the MCU operates to accomplish its task of improving driveability and reducing emissions. These devices vary with engine type, but are all controlled electrically.

Thermactor Controls

These controls direct the flow of air from an air pump to either the exhaust manifold, the catalytic converter, or the atmosphere. On all models, a pair of solenoid valves control vacuum flow which operates a Thermactor Air Valve assembly. These valves are called the Thermactor Air By-Pass (TAB) and Thermactor Air Diverter (TAD) valves.

In normal operation, the air is injected into the catalytic converter to improve reduction of emissions. When the engine is idling or decelerating for long periods of time, air is diverted to atmosphere. When the engine is first warming, air is injected into the exhaust manifold to help heat exhaust gases before they reach the converter.

Air/Fuel Controls

The MCU provides a pulsed voltage signal which operates a fuel control solenoid/vacuum regulator. The vacuum is applied to a mixture control diaphragm in the carburetor.

Canister Purge Solenoid

A canister purge solenoid is controlled by the MCU. When engine conditions are correct, the solenoid is opened and the fuel vapor canister is purged.

Spark Retard Solenoid

The spark retard solenoid works in conjunction with the knock sensor. When the knock sensor signals the MCU that detonation is taking place, the MCU opens the spark retard solenoid. Opening the solenoid bleeds off distributor advance vacuum, which retards timing.

DIAGNOSIS & TESTING

The MCU system is capable of diagnosing some problems which may occur. To determine which components should be checked, perform the "Functional Test" which follows. If problems do exist, a service code will be displayed (as pulses on a voltmeter).

Locate the appropriate test chart and follow the repair procedure as instructed. Do not use the test charts unless referred to them by the "Functional Test", or you may replace some components unnecessarily. Testing procedures require the following equipment:

- Dial Voltmeter (0-20v scale)
- Digital Voltmeter (DVOM — Min. impedance 10 megohms)
- Vacuum Gauge (0-30 in. Hg)
- Vacuum pump
- Tachometer
- Jumper Wire

PREPARATION FOR TESTING

1) Check vacuum hoses for leaks, cracks, or improper routing. Repair or replace as necessary.

2) Check electrical connections. Repair any frayed or broken wires. Ensure that all connections are clean and tight.

3) Check coolant level. Turn all accessories off. Place transmission in neutral and set parking brake. Warm engine to normal operating temperature. If air cleaner must be moved, leave all vacuum hoses attached. If engine will start, start engine and check for voltage at electric choke terminal.

NOTE: **If vehicle will not start, go to No Start Test (No. 1).**

4) Turn ignition off. Locate Self-Test connector and insert a jumper wire between ground and Trigger sockets. Connect the positive lead of a needle-type voltmeter to vehicle battery positive terminal, and the negative lead to Self-Test output socket. Set voltmeter on 15-20 volt scale. Battery voltage may be shown.

5) Disable canister purge system by disconnecting the hose that runs from the canister to the purge valve (if equipped). Reconnect hose after testing. Make sure that the carburetor throttle linkage is off the high cam and that the choke is open.

6) On engines equipped with an EGR vacuum load control valve, plug the vent holes on the valve with a piece of tape. Remove tape after testing.

4-CYLINDER FUNCTIONAL TEST

NOTE: **Service codes are shown by voltage pulses. The first digit is indicated by a series of pulses, then the needle drops to zero for 2 seconds, then the second digit of the code is displayed. After each service code is displayed, a 5 second pause will occur and then the next code will be displayed.**

Key On, Engine Off Test

Turn key on, but do not start engine. Watch voltmeter for code pulses which should appear within 5-30 seconds. Ignore any initial surge of voltage when ignition

FORD MCU ENGINE CONTROL SYSTEM (Cont.)

is turned on. If code 11 is displayed proceed to "Engine Running Test". If any code(s) other than code 11 are displayed, perform test for code(s) indicated and repair problem(s) before proceeding to "Engine Running Test".

NOTE: If voltmeter does not pulse, but shows steady high or low readings, see "Functional Test Not Operating".

Fig. 2: Connections for Functional Test

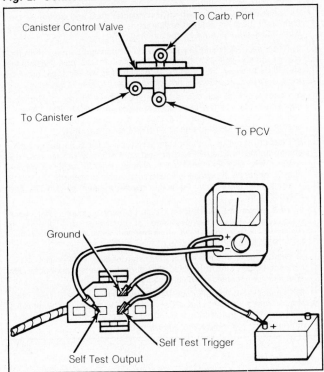

Engine Running Test

1) Start engine and raise speed to 3000 RPM within 20 seconds after start. Hold RPM until initial pulses appear (2-3). Continue holding speed until code pulses begin (10-40 seconds).

2) Return engine to idle when codes begin. If code 11 is displayed proceed to "Canister Purge Quick Check". If any code(s) other than code 11 are displayed,

perform test for code(s) indicated and repair problem(s) before proceeding to next test.

NOTE: If no initial pulses or more than 3 initial pulses occur, perform test for code 33.

NOTE: If voltmeter does not pulse, but shows steady high or low readings, see "Functional Test Not Operating".

Canister Purge Quick Check

Tee in a vacuum gauge between canister purge solenoid and canister. Turn engine off and restart. Increase speed to 2500 RPM to initiate "Functional Test". Observe vacuum gauge during initialization pulses. If vacuum pulses 0-1 in. Hg 3 times, system is ok. If vacuum is steadily high or low, perform "Canister Purge Test".

SUB-ROUTINE TESTS

INSTRUCTIONS FOR USING THE SUB-ROUTINE TESTS

Sub-routines are the following checks which are performed to correct a service code. Be sure to perform check as instructed. After replacing components or repairing circuits, repeat "Functional Test" and check engine operation.

Observe the following instructions when performing sub-routines:

- Do not measure voltage or resistance at MCU module, or connect test lamps to it (unless specific instructions say to do so).
- Disconnect both ends of a circuit when looking for continuity or shorts. Be sure ignition is turned off.
- Disconnect solenoids and switches from harness before measuring resistance or continuity.
- When more than one service code is indicated, start service with the first code received.
- Use wiring diagrams to locate pin locations and connectors.

NOTE: Complete system wiring diagram is located before Sub-Routine Tests. Each individual test has a partial schematic to aid in servicing.

Fig. 3: 4-Cylinder MCU System Wiring Diagram

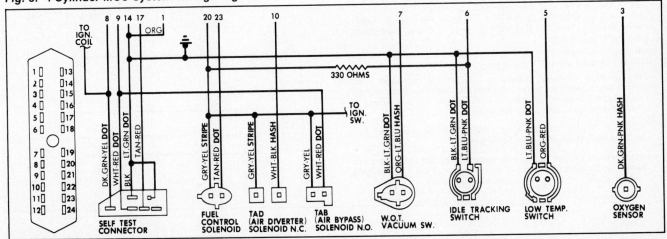

Also see chassis wiring in WIRING DIAGRAMS Section.

TEST 1 — 4-CYL.

NO START TEST

This test detects faults in the MCU only.

1) Check Tach lead for a ground short. Leave harness connected to MCU; disconnect coil and ignition module connectors. Measure resistance between ground and Self-Test connector, then tach connector. If resistance is less than 1000 ohms, go to step 2). If higher than 1000 ohms, MCU is not shorted.

2) Disconnect harness from MCU and measure resistance again. If resistance is less than 1000, repair circuit. If greater than 1000, replace MCU module.

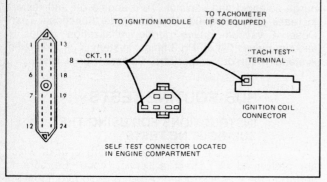

TEST 2 — 4-CYL.

DIAGNOSTIC CODE 33
RUNNING TEST NOT INITIATED

It is necessary to increase speed to more than 2500 RPM within 20 seconds after start in order to initiate "Functional Test". Turn key off and repeat procedure.

TEST 3 — 4-CYL.

DIAGNOSTIC CODE 41
FUEL ALWAYS LEAN

After starting engine, allow engine to idle for at least 2 minutes before testing. Disconnect "Functional Test" trigger wire.

1) Disconnect MCU connector, fuel control solenoid and oxygen sensor. Turn all accessories off. Measure resistance between ground and MCU connector pins 3 and 23. If resistance is less than 1000 ohms in either case, repair short. If resistance is greater than 1000 ohms, go to next step.

2) Check continuity between MCU connector pin 3 and oxygen sensor connector (harness side). If resistance is greater than 5 ohms, repair wire. If less than 5 ohms, go to next step.

3) Reconnect MCU and oxygen sensor. Disconnect harness from fuel control solenoid (FCS). Check resistance of FCS coil. Resistance should be between 28-66 ohms. If resistance is within range, proceed to next step. If resistance is not within range, replace FCS.

4) Reconnect FCS and connect voltmeter to back of solenoid harness connector. Start engine and maintain a speed of 2500 RPM. Observe voltmeter after 55 seconds. If voltage is less tham 10 volts, proceed to next step. If voltage is greater than 10 volts, replace MCU.

5) Disconnect and plug thermactor air supply hose at air pump. Raise engine speed to 2500 RPM and hold choke 3/4 closed to force the system rich. With voltmeter still connected to FCS, observe voltage after 55 seconds. If voltage is less than 10 volts, proceed to next step. If voltage is more than 10 volts, check for lean carburetor, and thermactor air.

6) Turn engine off. Disconnect oxygen sensor connector and check resistance between harness side of connector and ground. If resistance is less than 1000 ohms, replace MCU module. If greater than 1000 ohms, go to next step.

7) With oxygen sensor disconnected, start engine. With engine idling, connect jumper wire to harness side of oxygen sensor connector. Be sure this connection cannot contact ground.

8) Connect other end of jumper to battery positive terminal, then raise engine speed to 2500-2800 RPM. Measure voltage at FCS after 55 seconds. If voltage is less than 10 volts, replace MCU. If voltage is more than 10 volts, replace oxygen sensor.

TEST 4 — 4-CYL.

DIAGNOSTIC CODE 42
FUEL ALWAYS RICH

After starting engine, allow engine to idle at least 2 minutes before testing. Disconnect "Functional Test" trigger jumper. Do not block throttle open as idle tracking switch will be activated and invalidate test.

1) Check choke valve for sticking or binding and repair as necessary.

2) Disconnect MCU connector and connector at fuel control solenoid (FCS). Measure resistance between MCU pin 20 and FCS connector, then between MCU pin 23 and FCS connector. Resistance in both wires should be less than 5 ohms. If so, go to next step. If resistance is higher, repair wiring.

3) Check resistance of FCS. If within 28-66 ohms, go to next step. If resistance is not within 28-66 ohm range, replace FCS.

4) Connect a voltmeter to back of FCS harness connector. Start engine and raise engine speed to 2500 RPM. Measure voltage after 55 seconds. If voltage is less than 10 volts, replace MCU. If voltage is more than 10 volts, proceed to next step.

NOTE: For the following step, a DVOM must be used which has an input impedance of at least 10 megohms.

5) Disconnect oxygen sensor from harness. Connect DVOM between sensor and ground, with switch in lowest voltage position. Start engine and run at 2000 RPM for 1 minute to warm up sensor.

6) Turn engine off and immediately check DVOM reading. If greater than 0.4 volts, go to next step. If less than 0.4 volts, check carburetor (too rich).

7) Purge exhaust system by immediately disconnecting coil "horseshoe" connector and cranking engine for 10 seconds with throttle wide open. Observe DVOM. If greater than 0.4 volts, replace oxygen sensor. If less than 0.4 volts, check carburetor (too rich).

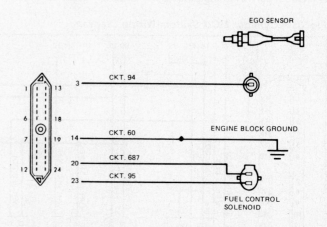

FORD MCU ENGINE CONTROL SYSTEM (Cont.)

TEST 5 — 4-CYL.

DIAGNOSTIC CODE 44
THERMACTOR SYSTEM

1) Remove vacuum hose from TAB valve and connect gauge to hose. Start engine and increase speed to above 2500 RPM to activate "Functional Test". Observe vacuum gauge.

2) If vacuum pulses are above and below or constantly above 5 in. Hg, proceed to next step. If pulses are always below 5 in. Hg, proceed to step 12).

3) Reconnect hose to TAB. Disconnect hose at TAD valve and connect vacuum gauge. Start engine and raise speed above 2500 RPM to start "Functional Test".

4) Observe vacuum readings. If above and below or constantly above 5 in. Hg, go to next step. If pulses are always below 5 in. Hg, go to step 16).

5) Reconnect hose to TAD valve. Remove upstream air hose at TAD valve. Start engine and raise speed above 2500 RPM to activate "Functional Test" and maintain speed.

6) Check for air at TAD nipple 20 seconds after initialization (air will last for about 6 seconds). If air is present, proceed with test. If air is not present at TAD outlet, check air pump and hoses.

7) Turn engine off and reconnect air hose. Disconnect harness from oxygen sensor and jumper harness to ground. Start engine, increase speed to initiate Self-Test (2 or 3 pulses on dial voltmeter connected to diagnostic connector).

8) Maintain speed until diagnostic codes are received (ignore any pulses longer than 1 second). If code 41 is read on voltmeter, check choke system, then go to next step. If code 44 is received, replace MCU module.

CAUTION: For the next step, a DVOM must be used which has an input impedance of at least 10 megohms.

9) Place DVOM selector in lowest voltage position and connect it between oxygen sensor and ground. Start engine and run at 2000 RPM for 1 minute to warm up sensor.

10) Turn engine off and immediately check DVOM. If voltage is less than 0.4 volts, check carburetor (too rich). If voltage is greater than 0.4 volts, go to next step.

11) Immediately purge exhaust system. Disconnect coil "horseshoe" connector and crank engine for 10 seconds with throttle wide open. If voltage is greater than 0.4 volts, replace oxygen sensor. If voltage is less than 0.4 volts, check carburetor (too rich).

12) Check vacuum hose between TAD and TAB solenoid, then between source and TAB solenoid. Repair as necessary. If hoses are okay, go to next step.

13) Check thermal vacuum switch (TVS) and retard delay valve (RDV) for proper installation and operation. Check vacuum schematic for usage and location. Service valves if necessary, otherwise go to next step.

14) Check at TAB solenoid output to be sure vacuum is present when the solenoid is energized (12 volts). If vacuum is not present, replace TAB solenoid. If vacuum is present, go to next step.

15) Disconnect MCU connector, then connectors at TAD and TAB solenoids. Check continuity between MCU connector pin 20 and TAD solenoid, then between pin 9 and TAB solenoid. If less than 5 ohms resistance, replace MCU. If greater than 5 ohms resistance is measured, repair wiring.

16) Check vacuum hoses between TAD valve and TAD solenoid, then between TAD solenoid and vacuum source. Repair if necessary. If vacuum source and hoses are okay, go to next step.

17) Check retard delay valve (RDV) for proper installation and operation. Check thermal vacuum switch (TVS) for proper installation and operation (if used). Replace if necessary. If okay, go to next step.

18) Measure resistance of TAD solenoid. If not between 50-110 ohms, replace solenoid. If resistance is okay, go to next step.

19) Check at TAD solenoid to be sure vacuum is present when solenoid is energized (12 volts). If vacuum is not present, replace solenoid. If vacuum is present, go to next step.

20) Disconnect wiring at TAD solenoid and MCU. Measure between MCU pin 20 and TAD solenoid, then between pin 10 and solenoid. If resistance is greater than 5 ohms, repair wiring. If less than 5 ohms, replace MCU module.

TEST 6 — 4-CYL.

DIAGNOSTIC CODE 45
THERMACTOR AIR DIVERTER

1) Remove vacuum hose from TAD valve and connect vacuum gauge to hose. Start engine and raise speed to 2500 RPM to begin "Functional Test". Observe gauge during initial pulses.

2) If pulses are above and below 5 in. Hg, MCU is okay, check thermactor pump. If pulses are always above or always below 5 in. Hg, go to next step.

3) Check vacuum hoses between vacuum source, TAD solenoid, and TAD valve. If vacuum source or hoses are faulty, repair. If okay, go to next step.

4) Measure resistance of TAD solenoid. If within 50-110 ohms, go to next step. If not, replace TAD solenoid.

5) Check at TAD solenoid output for vacuum when solenoid is energized (12 volts). If no vacuum, replace solenoid. If vacuum is present, go to next step.

6) Disconnect MCU connector and TAD connector. Measure resistance between MCU pin 10 and TAD connector, then between pin 20 and TAD connector.

7) If resistance is less than 5 ohms, replace MCU module. If resistance is greater than 5 ohms, repair circuit.

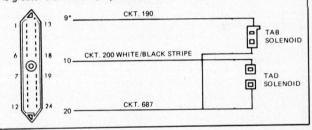

TEST 7 — 4-CYL.

DIAGNOSTIC CODE 46
THERMACTOR AIR BY-PASS

1) Remove vacuum hose at TAB valve and connect gauge to hose. Start engine and raise speed above 2500 RPM to start "Functional Test". Observe gauge during initial pulses.

2) If pulses are above and below 5 in. Hg, MCU is okay, check thermactor pump. If pulses are always above or always below 5 in. Hg, go to next step.

3) Check vacuum hoses between vacuum source, TAD solenoid, and TAB valve for leaks or blockage. Repair if necessary. If hoses are okay, go to next step.

4) Measure resistance of TAB solenoid. If within 50-110 ohms, go to next step. If not, replace TAB solenoid.

5) Check at TAB solenoid output to be sure vacuum is present when solenoid is deactivated. If no vacuum is present, replace solenoid. If vacuum is present, go to next step.

6) Check continuity of wires from MCU connector pins 9 and 20 to TAB solenoid connector. If resistance is more than 5 ohms, repair wire(s). If resistance is less than 5 ohms, proceed with test.

7) Disconnect MCU and TAB solenoid connectors. Measure resistance between ground and MCU pin 9. If resistance is less than 1000 ohms, repair short to ground. If resistance is greater than 1000 ohms, replace MCU module.

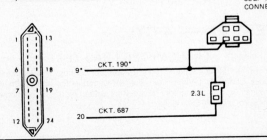

TEST 8 — 4-CYL.

DIAGNOSTIC CODE 51
LOW TEMPERATURE SWITCH

1) Ensure that coolant temperature was above 95°F (35°C) during "Functional Test" when code was observed.

2) Check contacts of midtemperature switch (should be closed above 95°F/35°C). If resistance measures less than 5 ohms, go to step **3)**. If above 5 ohms, replace low temperature switch.

3) Measure resistance in wiring between MCU (pins 5 & 14) and midtemperature switch. If resistance is less than 5 ohms, proceed with test. If greater than 5 ohms, repair wiring.

4) Disconnect harness from midtemperature switch and measure resistance between wire leading to MCU pin 14 and ground. If resistance is less than 1000 ohms, repair wire leading to MCU pin 14. If resistance is greater than 1000 ohms, replace MCU.

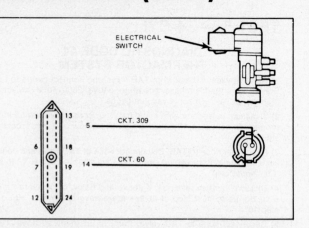

TEST 9 — 4-CYL.

DIAGNOSTIC CODES 52,
53, 55, 62, 63 & 65
WOT VACUUM SWITCH

1) Verify correct amount of vacuum is present at switches (use vacuum gauge). At least 10 in. Hg should be present. If vacuum level is too low, check vacuum lines and thermal switches. If vacuum is okay, go to next step.

2) Check switch contacts. Continuity should be present without vacuum. If resistance is greater than 5 ohms, replace vacuum switch(es). If less than 5 ohms, go to next step.

3) Check switch contacts with at least 10 in. Hg vacuum applied to switches. If resistance is less than 5 ohms, replace switch(es). If greater than 5 ohms, go to next step.

4) Check continuity from pin 14 in MCU connector to bottom pin in 2-wire connector at vacuum switches (circuit 60). If resistance is less than 5 ohms, go to next step. If greater than 5 ohms, repair wiring.

5) Check continuity of switch circuits from MCU connector to switches. Use MCU pins 6, 7 and 18, and appropriate switch connector pin. If resistance is greater than 5 ohms, repair circuit. If less than 5 ohms, go to next step.

6) Check same circuit for short to ground. Measure between ground and MCU pins 6, 7 and 18. If resistance is less than 1000 ohms, repair short in circuit. If greater than 1000 ohms, MCU module must be replaced.

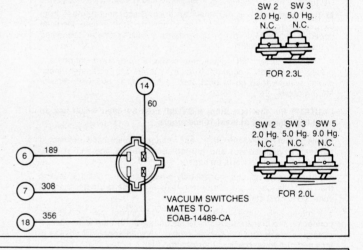

*VACUUM SWITCHES
MATES TO:
EOAB-14489-CA

TEST 10 — 4-CYL.

NO DIAGNOSTIC CODE
FUNCTIONAL TEST NOT OPERATING

1) Ensure that test connections, jumper wires, and VOM were all correctly hooked up.

2) Disconnect MCU connector. With ignition on, battery voltage should be present at pin 20. If not, check fuse. With ignition off, pin 14 should have continuity to ground. If not, repair. If wiring is okay, go to next step.

3) Check for continuity between Self-Test connector and MCU. See wiring diagram at end of this test for wire connections. Check to ensure circuit from MCU to TAD solenoid is not shorted to ground.

4) Measure TAB solenoid resistance. If within 50-110 ohms, replace MCU module. If not within 50-110 ohms, replace solenoid. Repeat "Functional Test".

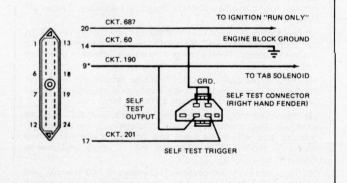

TEST 11 — 4-CYL.

TACHOMETER LEAD TEST

Disconnect MCU connector and "horseshoe" connector at ignition coil. Check continuity between pin 8 in MCU connector and "Tach Test" terminal in coil connector. If circuit is open, repair. If continuity is found, replace MCU module.

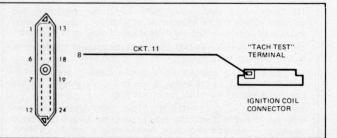

FORD MCU ENGINE CONTROL SYSTEM (Cont.)

TEST 12 — 4-CYL.

CANISTER PURGE SOLENOID

1) Check vacuum hoses for leaks or blockage and check vacuum source. Repair leaks or blockage, if present. Proceed with test.

2) Check to ensure canister purge solenoid passes vacuum when energized with 12 volts, and blocks vacuum when de-energized. Check housing and hose for leaks. If solenoid is okay, proceed to next step. If not, replace solenoid and retest.

3) Disconnect MCU and canister purge connector. Check continuity between MCU connector pin 24 and canister purge connector. Also check between pin 20 and canister purge connector. If resistance of each circuit is less than 5 ohms, go to next step. If not, repair circuits.

4) Connect ohmmeter between ground and MCU connector pin 24. If resistance is greater than 1000 ohms, replace MCU. If less, repair short circuit to ground.

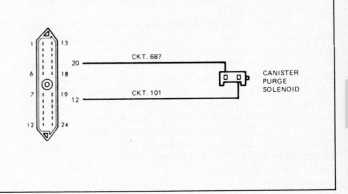

6-CYLINDER FUNCTIONAL TEST

NOTE: Service codes are shown by voltage pulses. The first digit is indicated by a series of pulses, then the needle drops to zero for 2 seconds, then the second digit of the code is displayed. After each service code is displayed, a 5 second pause will occur and then the next code will be displayed.

Key On, Engine Off Test

1) Turn key on, but do not start engine. Watch voltmeter for code pulses which should appear within 5-30 seconds. Ignore any initial surge of voltage when ignition is turned on.

2) If code 11 is displayed proceed to "Engine Running Test". If any code(s) other than code 11 are displayed, perform test for code(s) indicated and repair problem(s) before proceeding to "Engine Running Test".

NOTE: If voltmeter does not pulse, but shows steady high or low readings, see "Functional Test Not Operating".

Fig. 4: Connections for Functional Test

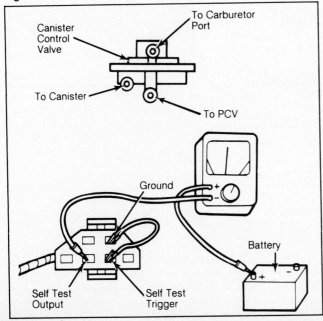

Engine Running Test

1) Start engine and raise speed to 3000 RPM within 20 seconds after start. Hold RPM until initial pulses appear (2-3).

2) On vehicles equipped with knock sensor, when initial pulses occur, immediately simulate spark knock by tapping a steel rod on intake manifold near base of knock sensor for about 16 seconds. Continue holding speed until code pulses begin (10-40 seconds).

3) Return engine to idle when codes begin. If code 11 is displayed proceed to "Spark Retard Solenoid Quick Check". If any code(s) other than code 11 are displayed, perform test for code(s) indicated and repair problem(s) before proceeding to next test.

NOTE: If no initial pulses or more than 3 initial pulses occur, repeat "Engine Running Test".

NOTE: If voltmeter does not pulse, but shows steady high or low readings, see "Functional Test Not Operating".

Spark Retard Solenoid Quick Check

1) Remove air filter from spark control solenoid and connect a vacuum gauge to solenoid port. Restart engine and increase speed to 2500 RPM to initiate "Functional Test".

2) Observe vacuum gauge during initialization pulses. If vacuum is always high or always low, perform "Spark Retard Solenoid Test". If vacuum pulses 3 times, system is ok on models not equipped with universal ignition module.

3) If vacuum pulses 3 times on models equipped with a universal ignition module that exhibit a WOT detonation/poor performance problem, proceed to next step.

4) Disconnect knock sensor and verify initial timing. Correct timing as necessary. Engine should be at normal operating temperature. Disconnect 2-wire connector at ignition module (Yel & Blk/Wht wires) and jumper module connector terminals together. Read and note ignition timing.

5) Remove jumper and re-read ignition timing. If timing does not retard 16-20°, replace ignition module. If timing retards 16-20°, reconnect module and proceed with test.

6) With engine running at normal operating temperature, set fast idle cam on lowest step that will maintain 1200 RPM. Read and note ignition timing.

1983 Computerized Engine Controls

FORD MCU ENGINE CONTROL SYSTEM (Cont.)

Disconnect and plug vacuum hose from zone vacuum switch. Re-read timing. If timing does not retard more than 5°, proceed to step **7)**.

7) If timing retards more than 5°, on models without knock sensor, testing is complete; on models with knock sensor, proceed to step **8)**.

8) While still at 1200 RPM, disconnect 2-wire ignition module connector. If timing does not retard, check Yellow wire for opens. If wire is ok, replace MCU and retest. If timing retards, check Yellow wire for shorts to ground. If wire is ok, replace MCU and retest.

9) Reconnect knock sensor. Re-run "Engine Running Test", but do not tap on manifold. If service code 25 appears, MCU is ok. If any other code appears, replace knock sensor and retest.

SUB-ROUTINE TESTS

INSTRUCTIONS FOR USING THE SUB-ROUTINE TESTS

Sub-routines are the following checks which are performed to correct a service code. Be sure to perform check as instructed. After replacing components or repairing circuits, repeat "Functional Test" and check engine operation.

Observe the following instructions when performing sub-routines:

- Do not measure voltage or resistance at MCU module, or connect test lamps to it (unless specific instructions say to do so).
- Disconnect both ends of a circuit when looking for continuity or shorts. Be sure ignition is turned off.
- Disconnect solenoids and switches from harness before measuring resistance or continuity.
- When more than one service code is indicated, start service with the first code received.
- Use wiring diagrams to locate pin locations and connectors.

NOTE: **Complete system wiring diagram is located before Sub-Routine Tests. Each individual test has a partial schematic to aid in servicing.**

Fig. 5: 6-Cylinder MCU System Wiring Diagram

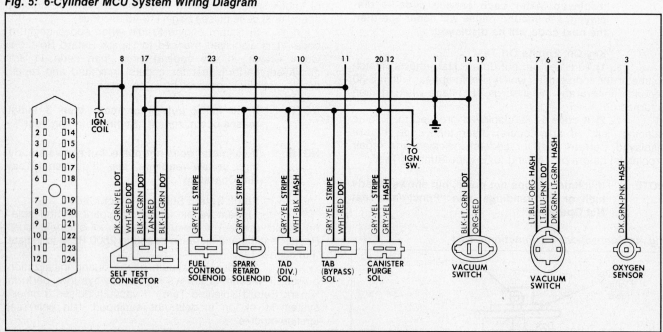

Also see chassis wiring in WIRING DIAGRAMS Section.

FORD MCU ENGINE CONTROL SYSTEM (Cont.)

TEST 1 — 6-CYL.

NO START TEST

This test detects faults in the MCU only.

1) Check Tach lead for a ground short. Leave harness connected to MCU; disconnect coil and ignition module connectors. Measure resistance between ground and Self-Test connector, then tach connector. If resistance is less than 1000 ohms, go to step **2)**. If higher than 1000 ohms, MCU is not shorted.

2) Disconnect harness from MCU and measure resistance again. If resistance is less than 1000, repair circuit. If greater than 1000, replace MCU module.

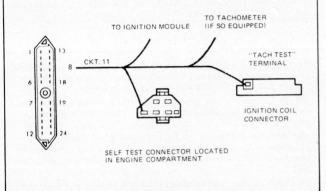

SELF TEST CONNECTOR LOCATED IN ENGINE COMPARTMENT

TEST 2 — 6-CYL.

DIAGNOSTIC CODE 25
KNOCK DETECTION TEST

1) Verify that knock simulation during "Functional Test" took place within 2" of knock sensor. Disconnect grounded jumper wire from Self-Test connector. If knock simulation was more than 2" from sensor, repeat "Engine Running Test". Otherwise, proceed with test.

2) Turn ignition off and disconnect knock sensor harness. Verify that knock sensor is tightened to 12-18 ft. lbs. (16-24 N.m).

3) Disconnect wiring harness from MCU and knock sensor. Connect an ohmmeter between ground and MCU harness connector pin 13. If resistance is less than 1000 ohms, correct short to ground. If resistance is 1000 ohms or more, proceed with test.

4) Check continuity of wire from knock sensor to MCU harness connector pin 13. If resistance is more than 5 ohms, repair wire. If resistance is 5 ohms or less, proceed with test.

5) Check continuity of wire from knock sensor to MCU harness connector pin 14. If resistance is more than 5 ohms, repair wire. If resistance is 5 ohms or less, reconnect MCU and proceed with test.

6) Reconnect the grounded jumper wire to the Self-Test connector. Connect a test lamp to positive terminal of battery. Disconnect knock sensor.

7) Repeat "Engine Running Test" noting the following: When the initialization pulses occur, tap wire that leads to pin 14 of MCU with test lamp for 5 seconds. If diagnostic code 25 is displayed, replace MCU. If any other diagnostic code is displayed, replace knock sensor.

TEST 3 — 6-CYL.

DIAGNOSTIC CODE 33
RUNNING TEST NOT INITIATED

It is necessary to increase speed to more than 2500 RPM within 20 seconds after start in order to initiate "Functional Test". Turn key off and repeat procedure.

TEST 4 — 6-CYL.

DIAGNOSTIC CODE 41
FUEL ALWAYS LEAN

After starting engine, allow at least 2 minutes of idling before testing. Disconnect "Functional Test" trigger wire.

1) Disconnect MCU connector, fuel control solenoid and oxygen sensor. Turn all accessories off. Measure resistance between ground and MCU connector pins 3 and 23. If resistance is less than 1000 ohms in either case, repair short. If resistance is greater than 1000 ohms, go to next step.

2) Check continuity between MCU connector pin 3 and oxygen sensor connector (harness side). If resistance is greater than 5 ohms, repair wire. If less than 5 ohms, go to next step.

3) Reconnect MCU and oxygen sensor. Disconnect harness from fuel control solenoid (FCS). Check resistance of FCS coil. Resistance should be between 28-66 ohms. If resistance is within range, proceed to next step. If resistance is not within range, replace FCS.

4) Reconnect FCS and connect voltmeter to back of solenoid harness connector. Start engine and maintain a speed of 2500 RPM. Observe voltmeter after 55 seconds. If voltage is less tham 10 volts, proceed to next step. If voltage is greater than 10 volts, replace MCU.

5) Disconnect and plug thermactor air supply hose at air pump. Raise engine speed to 2500 RPM and hold choke 3/4 closed to force the system rich. With voltmeter still connected to FCS, observe voltage after 55 seconds.

6) If voltage is less than 10 volts, proceed to next step. If voltage is more than 10 volts, check for lean carburetor, and thermactor air.

7) Turn engine off. Disconnect oxygen sensor connector and check resistance between harness side of connector and ground. If resistance is less than 1000 ohms, replace MCU module. If greater than 1000 ohms, go to next step.

8) With oxygen sensor disconnected, start engine. With engine idling, connect a jumper wire to harness side of oxygen sensor connector. Be sure this connection cannot contact ground.

9) Connect other end of jumper to battery positive terminal, then raise engine speed to 2500-2800 RPM. Measure voltage at FCS after 55 seconds. If voltage is less than 10 volts, replace MCU. If voltage is more than 10 volts, replace oxygen sensor.

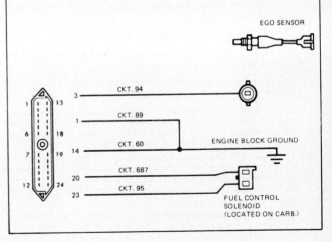

TEST 5 — 6-CYL.

DIAGNOSTIC CODE 42
FUEL ALWAYS RICH

After starting engine, allow at least 2 minutes at idle before testing. Disconnect "Functional Test" trigger jumper. Do not block throttle open as idle tracking switch will be activated and invalidate test.

1) Check choke valve for sticking or binding and repair as necessary.

2) Disconnect MCU connector and connector at fuel control solenoid (FCS). Measure resistance between MCU pin 20 and FCS connector, then between MCU pin 23 and FCS connector. Resistance in both wires should be less than 5 ohms. If so, go to next step. If resistance is higher, repair wiring.

3) Check resistance of FCS. If within 28-66 ohms, go to next step. If resistance is not within 28-66 ohm range, replace FCS.

4) Connect a voltmeter to back of FCS harness connector. Start engine and raise engine speed to 2500 RPM. Measure voltage after 55 seconds. If voltage is less than 10 volts, replace MCU. If voltage is more than 10 volts, proceed to next step.

NOTE: For the following step, a DVOM must be used which has an input impedance of at least 10 megohms.

5) Disconnect oxygen sensor from harness. Connect DVOM between sensor and ground, with switch in lowest voltage position. Start engine and run at 2000 RPM for 1 minute to warm up sensor.

6) Turn engine off and immediately check DVOM reading. If greater than 0.4 volts, go to next step. If less than 0.4 volts, check carburetor (too rich).

7) Purge exhaust system by immediately disconnecting coil "horseshoe" connector and cranking engine for 10 seconds with throttle wide open. Observe DVOM. If greater than 0.4 volts, replace oxygen sensor. If less than 0.4 volts, check carburetor (too rich).

TEST 6 — 6-CYL.

DIAGNOSTIC CODE 44
THERMACTOR SYSTEM

1) Remove vacuum hose from TAB valve and connect gauge to hose. Start engine and increase speed to above 2500 RPM to activate "Functional Test". Observe vacuum gauge. If vacuum pulses are above and below 5 in. Hg, proceed to next step. If pulses are always below 5 in. Hg, proceed to step **12)**. If pulses are above 5 in. Hg, proceed to next step.

2) Reconnect hose to TAB. Disconnect hose at TAD valve and connect vacuum gauge. Start engine and raise speed above 2500 RPM to start "Functional Test". Observe vacuum readings. If above and below 5 in. Hg, go to next step. If always above 5 in. Hg, go to next step. If pulses are always below 5 in. Hg, go to step **18)**.

3) Reconnect hose to TAD valve. Remove upstream air hose at TAD valve. Start engine and raise speed above 2500 RPM to activate "Functional Test" and maintain speed. Check for air at TAD nipple 20 seconds after initialization (air will last for about 6 seconds). If air is present, proceed with test. If air is not present at TAD outlet, check air pump and hoses.

4) Turn engine off and reconnect air hose. Disconnect harness from oxygen sensor and jumper harness to ground. Start engine, increase speed to initiate Self-Test (2 or 3 pulses on VOM connected to diagnostic connector).

5) Maintain speed until diagnostic codes are received (ignore any pulses longer than 1 second). If code 41 is read on voltmeter, check choke system, then go to next step. If code 44 is received, replace MCU module.

CAUTION: For the next step, a DVOM must be used which has an input impedance of at least 10 megohms.

6) Turn ignition off. Remove jumper wire from oxygen sensor harness wire. Connect a DVOM between ground and oxygen sensor harness wire. If voltage is greater than 0.4 volts, service or repair wire. If reading is less than 0.4 volts, proceed with test.

7) Connect DVOM between oxygen sensor and ground. Start engine and run at 2000 RPM for 1 minute to warm up sensor. Turn engine off and immediately check DVOM. If voltage is less than 0.4 volts, check carburetor (too rich). If voltage is greater than 0.4 volts, go to next step.

8) Immediately purge exhaust system. Disconnect coil "horseshoe" connector and crank engine for 10 seconds with throttle wide open. If voltage is greater than 0.4 volts, replace oxygen sensor. If voltage is less than 0.4 volts, check carburetor (too rich).

9) Disconnect MCU connector, then connectors at TAD and TAB solenoids. Check continuity between MCU connector pin 20 and TAD solenoid, then between pin 9 and TAB solenoid. If less than 5 ohms resistance, go to next step. If greater than 5 ohms resistance is measured, repair wiring.

10) Measure resistance of TAB solenoid. If between 50-110 ohms, go to next step. If not within 50-110 ohms, replace TAB solenoid.

11) Check at TAB solenoid output to be sure vacuum is not present when solenoid is energized (12 volts applied). If vacuum is present, replace TAB solenoid. If no vacuum, replace MCU module.

12) Check vacuum hose between TAB valve and TAB solenoid, then between source and TAB solenoid. Repair as necessary. If hoses are okay, go to next step.

13) Check thermal vacuum switch (TVS) and retard delay valve (RDV) for proper installation and operation. Check vacuum schematic for usage and location. Service valves if necessary, otherwise go to next step.

14) Check at TAB solenoid output to be sure vacuum is present when the solenoid is energized (12 volts applied). If vacuum is not present, replace TAB solenoid. If vacuum is present, go to next step.

15) Disconnect TAB solenoid connectors and MCU connector. Measure resistance between pin 20 and TAB connector, then pin 9 and TAB connector. If resistance is less than 5 ohms, replace MCU module. If higher than 5 ohms, repair circuits.

16) Disconnect MCU connector. Measure resistance from pin 10 to ground. If greater than 1000 ohms, go to next step. If less than 1000 ohms, repair short to ground.

17) Check at TAD solenoid to be sure vacuum is not present when solenoid is deactivated. If vacuum is present, replace TAD solenoid. If vacuum is not present, replace MCU module.

18) Check vacuum hoses between TAD valve and TAD solenoid, then between TAD solenoid and vacuum source. Repair if necessary. If vacuum source and hoses are okay, go to next step.

19) Check retard delay valve (RDV) for proper installation and operation. Check thermal vacuum switch (TVS) for proper installation and operation (if equipped). Replace if necessary. If okay, go to next step.

20) Measure resistance of TAD solenoid. If not between 50-110 ohms, replace solenoid. If resistance is okay, go to next step.

21) Check at TAD solenoid to be sure vacuum is present when solenoid is energized (12 volts applied). If vacuum is not present, replace solenoid. If vacuum is present, go to next step.

22) Disconnect wiring at TAD solenoid and MCU. Measure between MCU pin 20 and TAD solenoid, then between pin 10 and solenoid. If resistance is greater than 5 ohms, repair wiring. If less than 5 ohms, replace MCU module.

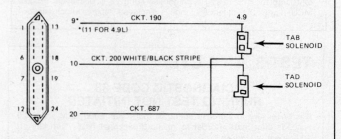

TEST 7 — 6-CYL.

DIAGNOSTIC CODE 45
THERMACTOR AIR DIVERTER

1) Remove vacuum hose from TAD valve and connect vacuum gauge to hose. Start engine and raise speed to 2500 RPM to begin "Functional Test". Observe gauge during initial pulses. If pulses are above and below 5 in. Hg or constantly below 5 in. Hg, MCU is okay, check Thermactor pump. If pulses are always above 5 in. Hg, go to next step.

2) Check vacuum hoses between vacuum source, TAD solenoid, and TAD valve. If vacuum source or hoses are faulty, repair. If okay, go to next step.

3) Measure resistance of TAD solenoid. If within 50-110 ohms, go to next step. If not, replace TAD solenoid.

4) Check at TAD solenoid output for vacuum when solenoid is energized (12 volts applied). If no vacuum is present, replace solenoid. If vacuum is present, go to next step.

5) Disconnect MCU connector and TAD connector. Measure resistance between MCU pin 10 and TAD connector, then between pin 20 and TAD connector. If resistance is less than 5 ohms, replace MCU module. If resistance is greater than 5 ohms, repair circuit.

6) Check at TAD solenoid output to ensure vacuum is not present when solenoid is deactivated. If vacuum is present, replace solenoid. If no vacuum, go to next step.

7) Measure resistance between MCU pin 10 and ground. If resistance is less than 1000 ohms, repair short circuit to ground. If resistance is more than 1000 ohms, replace MCU module.

TEST 8 — 6-CYL.

DIAGNOSTIC CODE 46
THERMACTOR AIR BY-PASS

1) Remove vacuum hose at TAB valve and connect gauge to hose. Start engine and raise speed above 2500 RPM to start "Functional Test". Observe gauge during initial pulses.

2) If pulses are above and below or consistently below 5 in. Hg, MCU is okay, check thermactor pump. If pulses are always above 5 in. Hg, go to next step.

3) Check vacuum hoses between vacuum source, TAB solenoid, and TAB valve for leaks or blockage. Repair if necessary. If hoses are okay, go to next step.

4) Check at TAB solenoid output to be sure vacuum is present when solenoid is deactivated. If no vacuum is present, replace solenoid. If vacuum is present, go to next step.

5) Disconnect MCU and TAB solenoid connectors. Measure resistance between ground and MCU pin 9. If resistance is less than 1000 ohms, repair short to ground. If resistance is greater than 1000 ohms, replace MCU module.

6) Check TAB solenoid output to make sure vacuum is not present when solenoid is deactivated. If vacuum is present, replace solenoid. If vacuum is not present, go to next step.

7) Disconnect MCU and TAB solenoid connectors. Measure resistance between ground and MCU pin 11. If resistance is less than 1000 ohms, repair short to ground. If greater than 1000 ohms, replace MCU module.

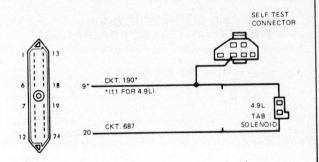

TEST 9 — 6-CYL.

DIAGNOSTIC CODE 53
LOW TEMPERATURE SWITCH

1) Ensure that coolant temperature was above 128°F (53°C) during "Functional Test" when code was observed.

2) Check contacts of midtemperature switch (should be closed above 128°F/53°C). If resistance measures less than 5 ohms, go to step **3)**. If above 5 ohms, replace midtemperature switch.

3) Measure resistance in wiring between MCU (pins 5 & 14) and midtemperature switch. If resistance is less than 5 ohms, proceed with test. If greater than 5 ohms, repair wiring.

4) Disconnect harness from midtemperature switch and measure resistance between wire leading to MCU pin 14 and ground. If resistance is less than 1000 ohms, repair wire leading to MCU pin 14. If resistance is greater than 1000 ohms, replace MCU.

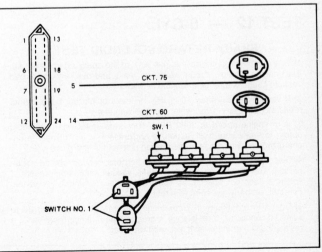

TEST 10 — 6-CYL.

DIAGNOSTIC CODES 52, 54, 55, 62, 64 & 65 VACUUM SWITCHES

1) Verify switches are open when correct amount of vacuum is present at switch (use vacuum gauge). At least 13 in. Hg should be present at high vacuum switch.

2) All other switches require 8 in. Hg. If switches are not open, check vacuum lines for leakage and blockage. If switches operate properly, go to next step.

3) Check switch contacts. Continuity should be present without vacuum. If resistance is greater than 5 ohms, replace vacuum switch. If less than 5 ohms, go to next step.

4) Check switch contacts with vacuum applied to switch (at least 20 in. Hg). If resistance is less than 5 ohms, replace switch. If greater than 5 ohms, go to next step.

5) Check continuity from pin 14 in MCU connector to connector at vacuum switches (circuit 60). If resistance is less than 5 ohms, go to next step. If greater than 5 ohms, repair wiring.

6) Check continuity of switch circuits from MCU connector to switch. Use MCU pin 7, 13 and 17; and appropriate switch connector pin. If resistance is greater than 5 ohms, repair circuit. If less than 5 ohms, go to next step.

7) Check same circuit for short to ground. Measure between MCU pin 7 and ground. If resistance is less than 1000 ohms, repair short in circuit. If greater than 1000 ohms, MCU module must be replaced.

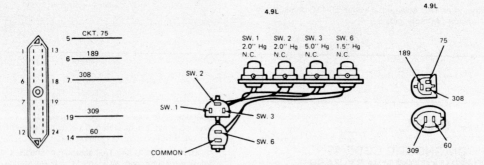

TEST 11 — 6-CYL.

NO DIAGNOSTIC CODE FUNCTIONAL TEST NOT OPERATING

1) Ensure that test connections, jumper wires, and voltmeter were all correctly hooked up.

2) Disconnect MCU connector. With ignition on, battery voltage should be present at pin 20. If not, check fuse. With ignition off, pin 14 should have continuity to ground. If not, repair. If wiring is okay, go to next step.

3) Check for continuity between Self-Test connector and MCU. See wiring diagram at end of this test for wire connections. Check to ensure circuit from MCU to TAD solenoid is not shorted to ground.

4) Measure TAB solenoid resistance. If within 50-110 ohms, replace MCU module. If not within 50-110 ohms, replace solenoid. Repeat "Functional Test".

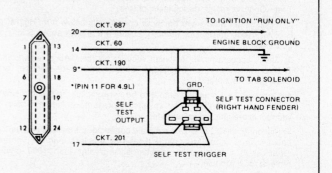

TEST 12 — 6-CYL.

SPARK RETARD SOLENOID TEST

1) Tee a vacuum gauge to the inlet side of the spark retard solenoid. Start engine. Check vacuum hoses for leaks and blockage, and read vacuum gauge with engine running at 2500 RPM.

2) If vacuum is less than 10 in. Hg, or leaks or blockage are found, repair as necessary. Otherwise, proceed with test.

3) With engine speed at 2000 RPM, check the spark retard solenoid output to make sure that vacuum is not present when solenoid is de-energized and vacuum is present when solenoid is energized.

4) Disconnect solenoid connector from harness, vacuum should not be present. Reconnect solenoid to harness, vacuum should be present. If solenoid does not operate as specified, replace solenoid. If solenoid operates properly, proceed with test.

5) Check for continuity in wires leading from MCU pins 9 and 20 to solenoid connector. If resistance is greater than 5 ohms, repair wire. If resistance is 5 ohms or less, proceed with test.

6) Connect an ohmmeter between ground and MCU connector pin 9. Measure resistance. If resistance is less than 1000 ohms, repair short to ground. If resistance is greater than 1000 ohms, replace MCU module.

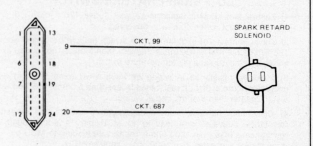

FORD EEC-III SYSTEM

5.0L Calif. Light Duty Models, 5.8L Bronco, F150, F250 & High Alt. F250 HD

DESCRIPTION

The EEC system consists of an Electronic Control Assembly (ECA), several sensors located on the engine or in the various engine systems, special actuators governed by the ECA, and various connecting electrical and vacuum lines. This system adjusts the engine to the best settings for various conditions of load, speed, temperature and altitude by controlling the following functions:

- Ignition Timing
- Carburetor Air/Fuel Ratio
- Engine Speed At Idle
- Exhaust Gas Recirculation (EGR) Flow Rate
- Secondary (Thermactor) Air Flow Rate
- Fuel Evaporation Canister Purging

OPERATION

ELECTRONIC CONTROL ASSEMBLY (ECA)

The ECA is a solid-state, micro-computer consisting of a processor assembly and a calibration assembly. This unit is located in the passenger compartment under the instrument panel, to the left of the steering column. The ECA is the "brain" of the EEC system.

Processor Assembly

The processor assembly is housed in an aluminum case and contains circuits designed to:

- Continuously sample input signals from the sensors.
- Calculate the proper spark advance, air/fuel ratio, EGR flow and thermactor air flow.
- Send out control signals to adjust spark timing, air/fuel ratio, EGR flow, thermactor air mode, evaporation canister purge and idle speed.

The processor assembly also provides a continuous reference voltage of 9 volts to the sensors.

Calibration Assembly

The calibration assembly is contained in a black plastic housing which is attached to the top of the processor assembly. It contains the "memory" and programming used by the processor assembly. The calibration assembly is capable of:

- Providing operating information for that particular vehicle, for use by the processor assembly.
- Recalling information from its memory when required.

Power Relay

Activated by the ignition switch to supply battery voltage to the EEC. The power relay is mounted under the hood on the left fender apron. Also protects ECA from possible damage due to reversed voltage polarity.

Fig. 1: EEC-III Component Locations

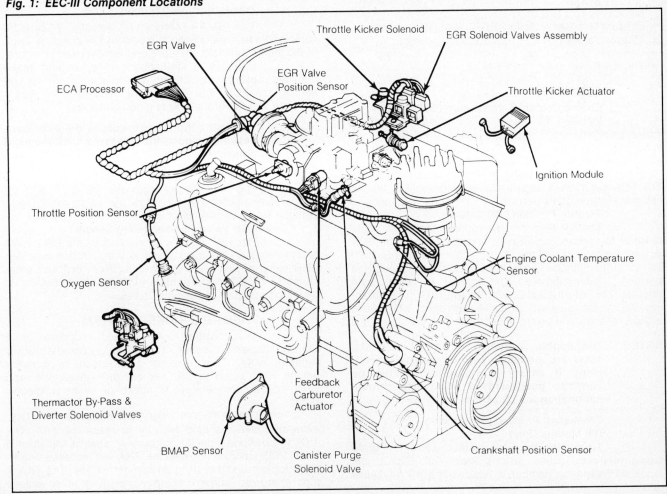

Fig. 2: EEC Electronic Control Assembly (ECA)

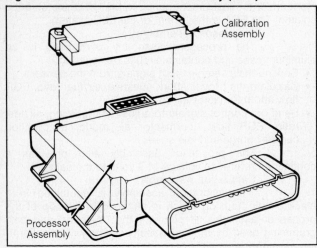

Calibration Assembly

Processor Assembly

LIMITED OPERATION STRATEGY (LOS) MODE

The LOS mode functions during engine start, or upon failure of the ECA detected by a "safeguard" circuit in the ECA. This mode allows continued vehicle operation (with reduced performance) until repairs can be made. In this mode the actuator functions are set as follows:

- Ignition Module Timing; Minimum spark advance (10° BTDC).
- Exhaust Gas Recirculation (EGR): No EGR.
- Thermactor Air (TAB): By-pass (dump) position.
- Canister Purge (CANP): Canister sealed, no purge.
- Throttle Kicker (TK): Low RPM idle.

SENSORS

Engine Coolant Temperature (ECT) Sensor

Installed in heater outlet fitting at front of intake manifold near right valve cover, the ECT sensor converts coolant temperature to an electrical signal for the ECA. The brass sensor housing contains a thermistor (resistor that changes value according to temperature). The ECA determines engine coolant temperature by the resistance value of the sensor.

Throttle Position (TP) Sensor

The TP sensor is a potentiometer. The resistance of the sensor varies with throttle opening. The ECA applies a reference voltage to the sensor and the resultant sensor output voltage allows the ECA to determine throttle position (closed throttle, part throttle or wide open throttle). This information is used by the ECA in determining the proper amount of spark advance, EGR flow, air/fuel ratio and the proper thermactor air mode.

NOTE: The throttle position (TP) sensor mounting holes are slotted to permit rotational adjustment. If sensor is replaced, it must be correctly positioned or misleading throttle information will be sent to the ECA.

Crankshaft Position (CP) Sensor (V8 Models Only)

To provide the EEC system with an accurate timing reference (when pistons reach 10° BTDC), the crankshaft vibration damper is fitted with a 4-lobe "pulse ring".

As the crankshaft rotates, the pulse ring interrupts a magnetic field at the tip of the CP sensor (mounted on right front of engine). When the field is interrupted, an output signal is generated and sent to the ECA.

The ECA uses these signals to determine the exact position of the crankshaft. From the pulse frequency, the ECA can determine engine RPM. By knowing these two factors, the ECA can determine amount of ignition timing advance required for best engine operation.

NOTE: Once the CP sensor is installed, no field adjustment is necessary.

Exhaust Gas Oxygen (EGO) Sensor

Installed in the exhaust manifold, the oxygen sensor provides the ECA with the oxygen concentration of the exhaust gas.

The oxygen sensor monitors the oxygen concentration of the exhaust gas and generates an output of .6 to 1.1 volts when detecting a rich exhaust gas mixture, and less than .2 volts when detecting a lean mixture. The constantly changing voltage signal is sent to the ECA for analysis.

CAUTION: The EGO sensor resistance CANNOT be measured by connecting an ohmmeter directly to its output lead. Sensor damage will result if this is attempted.

Barometric and Manifold Absolute Pressure (BMAP) Sensor

The BMAP sensor is actually 2 sensors combined into 1 assembly. It monitors the absolute value of the intake manifold pressure and atmospheric pressure.

Changes in atmospheric pressure and intake manifold pressure are converted into electrical signals and sent to the ECA. The signals are used to adjust spark advance and EGR rate to fit engine conditions.

NOTE: Manifold absolute pressure is the difference between barometric pressure and manifold pressure.

Air Charge Temperature (ACT) Sensor

The ACT sensor provides the ECA with air temperature readings which allow the computer to compensate for air density variations.

EGR Valve Position (EVP) Sensor

The EVP sensor is attached to the EGR valve and provides an electrical signal to the ECA that indicates EGR valve position. Using the input from this and other sensors, the ECA can regulate EGR flow by activating or deactivating a pair of solenoid valves.

THROTTLE KICKER SYSTEM

The throttle kicker system consists of a Throttle Kicker Solenoid (TKS) and a Throttle Kicker Actuator (TKA). The system is designed to increase engine RPM when the A/C is on, at high altitude, and when coolant temperature is above or below a specific range.

With A/C "ON", the ECA energizes the TKS, allowing intake manifold vacuum to reach the TKA. The TKA is positioned on the carburetor against the throttle lever. With vacuum applied, the TKA will increase engine RPM for increased cooling and smoother idle. The TKA is also energized during engine warm-up or if an engine overheat condition exists.

Fig. 3: Electronic Engine Control Sensors

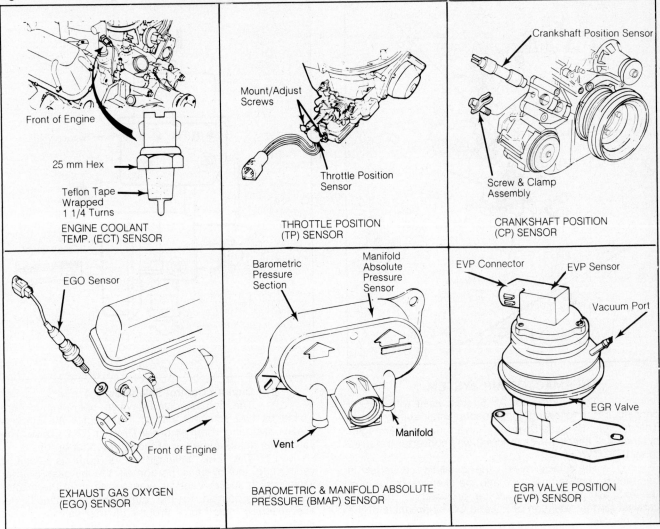

ENGINE COOLANT TEMP. (ECT) SENSOR

THROTTLE POSITION (TP) SENSOR

CRANKSHAFT POSITION (CP) SENSOR

EXHAUST GAS OXYGEN (EGO) SENSOR

BAROMETRIC & MANIFOLD ABSOLUTE PRESSURE (BMAP) SENSOR

EGR VALVE POSITION (EVP) SENSOR

EXHAUST GAS RECIRCULATION (EGR) SYSTEM

The EGR system used with EEC-III has 3 major components: an EGR valve and sensor assembly, an EGR cooler, and a 2-solenoid EGR control assembly.

Utilizing engine manifold vacuum to operate the EGR valve, the ECA controls EGR gas flow. When EGR valve is open, exhaust gas from exhaust manifold is directed into the intake manifold and becomes part of the combustion cycle, helping to reduce NOx emission levels.

EGR Valve and Sensor Assembly

The EGR valve is mounted to the intake manifold under the carburetor. The valve controls EGR flow through a pintle valve and seat. An EGR valve position sensor (EVP) is attached to the valve and provides an electrical signal to the ECA indicating EGR valve position.

The EGR valve, unlike standard EGR valves, has no opening to observe pintle valve movement. The EGR valve and position sensor are serviced as individual units.

Dual EGR Control Solenoids

EGR valve flow rate is controlled by two solenoid valves mounted on the left valve cover. Proper control of vacuum needed to operate the EGR valve requires two types of solenoid valves:

- A vent valve, which is normally open; that is, the outlet port is normally connected to the inlet port when the solenoid is not energized.
- A vacuum valve, which is normally open; that is, the outlet port is normally blocked when solenoid is not energized.

Utilizing input from the various sensors, the ECA directs the vacuum and vent solenoids to: (1) Increase EGR flow by applying vacuum to the EGR valve, (2) Maintain the EGR flow by trapping vacuum in the system, and (3) Decrease EGR flow by venting the system to the atmosphere.

EGR Cooler Assembly

An EGR gas cooler is used to reduce EGR gas temperature, thus providing improved flow characteristics, better engine operation and EGR valve durability.

1983 Computerized Engine Controls

FORD EEC-III SYSTEM (Cont.)

Fig. 4: Dual EGR Control Solenoids

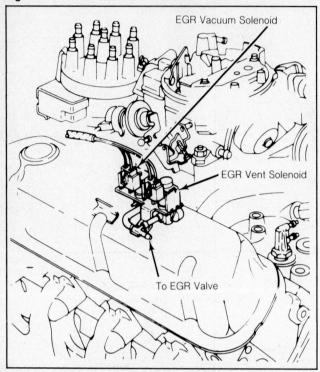

EGR Vacuum Solenoid

EGR Vent Solenoid

To EGR Valve

Fig. 5: Thermactor Air System By-Pass/Diverter Valve

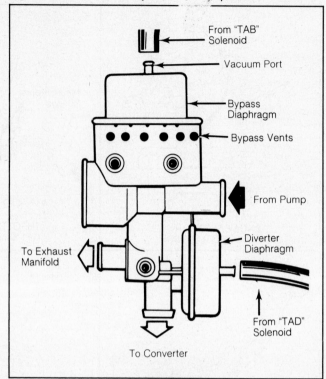

From "TAB" Solenoid

Vacuum Port

Bypass Diaphragm

Bypass Vents

From Pump

Diverter Diaphragm

To Exhaust Manifold

From "TAD" Solenoid

To Converter

THERMACTOR AIR SYSTEM

The Thermactor Air System used with EEC-III consists of the following components: an air supply pump, Thermactor By-pass/Diverter valve, dual Thermactor solenoids, 2 check valves, and a 3-way converter (referred to as COC/TWC).

The efficiency of the catalytic converter is dependent upon temperature and the chemical makeup of the exhaust gases. Air must be provided to the COC catalyst for the oxidation of HC and CO by-products of the TWC catalyst.

Air Supply Pump

This belt driven pump provides the source of air to be controlled by the by-pass/diverter valve as directed by the ECA. The air pump does not have a pressure relief valve, this function being controlled by the by-pass/diverter valve.

By-Pass/Diverter Valve

Air from the air pump has three possible routes through the by-pass/diverter valve:
- Downstream air (air injected into three-way catalyst).
- Upstream air (air injected into exhaust manifold).
- By-pass (air by-passed to atmosphere).

The proper routing for thermactor air is determined by the ECA based on engine coolant temperature versus time curve and other sensor data. During normal coolant temperature operation, the air is normally directed downstream.

The air is by-passed when the closed throttle time exceeds a preset time value. The air will also be by-passed during wide open throttle mode or during extended closed throttle operation.

During engine warm-up the thermactor air will be routed upstream. This is to help remove excessive amounts of HC and CO produced during the warm-up period.

Dual Air Control Solenoids

The by-pass/diverter valve operation is controlled by two solenoid valves: Thermactor Air By-pass (TAB) valve, and Thermactor Air Diverter (TAD) valve. The valves are mounted on top of the right fender apron.

The TAB solenoid valve controls manifold vacuum to the by-pass portion of the by-pass/diverter valve, which in turn controls whether air from thermactor pump is by-passed to the atmosphere (solenoid de-energized) or routed to control the diverter valve (solenoid energized).

The TAD solenoid valve controls manifold vacuum to the diverter portion of the by-pass/diverter valve, which in turn controls which direction (upstream or downstream) thermactor air is routed. When de-energized, air is routed downstream. When energized, air is routed upstream.

Exhaust Check Valve

Two exhaust check valves are used in the EEC III Thermactor system to prevent reverse flow of exhaust gases in the event of system malfunction. One check valve is located between the by-pass/diverter valve and the exhaust port drillings, and the other valve between the catalytic converter and the by-pass/diverter valve.

Three-Way Catalytic Converter (COC/TWC)

This is a dual catalytic converter consisting of two converters in one shell, with a mixing chamber between the two. Each converter is composed of a ceramic "honey-comb" coated with catalyst material.

The front, or "three-way catalyst" (TWC) converter acts on exhaust gases as they arrive from the engine. As gases flow from the TWC converter to the rear, or "conventional oxidation catalyst" (COC) converter, they mix with air from the thermactor pump injected into the mixing chamber. This air is required for proper oxidation of HC and CO in the COC converter.

FORD EEC-III SYSTEM (Cont.)

CANISTER PURGE SYSTEM

Canister Purge (CANP) Solenoid

This solenoid is a combination solenoid and valve. Located in the line between the intake manifold purge fitting and the carbon canister, the CANP solenoid controls the flow of vapors from the canister to the intake manifold during various engine operating modes. The valve is opened and closed by a signal from the ECA.

DURA-SPARK III IGNITION SYSTEM

The EEC-III system uses a Dura-Spark III module (Brown grommet where wires emerge) and a Dura-Spark II ignition coil. A resistance wire is also used in the primary circuit.

Distributor

The EEC distributor eliminates conventional mechanical and vacuum advance mechanisms. All timing is controlled by the ECA, which is capable of firing the spark plug at any point within a 50° range depending on calibration. This increased spark capability requires greater separation of adjacent distributor cap electrodes to prevent cross-fire.

Fig. 6: EEC III Ignition Distributor Assembly

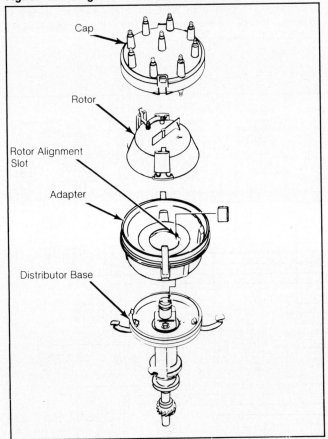

Cap

Rotor

Rotor Alignment Slot

Adapter

Distributor Base

DIAGNOSIS & TESTING

NOTE: Due to the complexity of the EEC III system, full testing cannot be done unless an EEC III tester (T79L-50-EEC-II or T80L-50-EEC-II, and T78L-50-DVOM or T79L-50-DVOM) is used. Instructions for testing come with the tester, which is available from Owatonna Tool Co. However, some checks can be made using regular shop equipment. These checks are outlined in the following procedures.

TESTING NOTES & CAUTIONS

NOTE: No repairs or adjustments can be made to the ECA components. If diagnosis shows Processor or Calibration units are not functioning properly, they must be replaced.

CAUTION: Shorting the wiring harness across a solenoid valve can burn out circuitry in the ECA that controls the solenoid valve actuator.

CAUTION: The EEC system contains transistors which CANNOT tolerate excessive voltage surges or transient voltage. Never try to jump-start the vehicle with 24 volts.

CAUTION: The oxygen sensor resistance CANNOT be measured by connecting an ohmmeter directly to its output lead. Sensor damage will result if this is attempted.

BASIC EEC TROUBLE SHOOTING

1) Perform basic fuel system and ignition system checks, to ensure there is gas and spark.

2) Remove air cleaner assembly and inspect all vacuum and pressure hoses for proper connection to fittings, or any broken, cracked or pinched conditions.

3) Inspect EEC sub-system harness for proper connections to EGR solenoid valves.

4) Check for any loose or detached connectors or broken or detached wires. Ensure all terminals are completely seated.

5) Repair items as required and replace air cleaner.

6) Check battery charge, cable connections and main electrical wiring.

7) Test resistance of all sensors and solenoids, using values given in COMPONENT RESISTANCE VALUES Chart. Be sure to disconnect component from circuit before checking resistance.

REMOVAL & INSTALLATION

BMAP SENSOR

Removal

Disconnect wiring harness from BMAP sensor. Disconnect vacuum hose, remove retaining nuts, and remove sensor.

Installation

Position sensor and tighten retaining nuts. Connect vacuum hose to "Manifold" port. Do not connect any hose to "Vent" port. Connect wiring harness.

CANISTER PURGE SOLENOID VALVE

Removal

Remove air cleaner. Disconnect 2-wire connector and 2 vacuum hoses from solenoid. Remove valve.

FORD EEC-III SYSTEM (Cont.)

Installation
Connect hose from manifold to nipple at end of valve. Connect hose from "T" to nipple toward middle of valve. Position valve so end with wires faces upward, then connect wiring and install air cleaner.

CRANKSHAFT POSITION (CP) SENSOR
Removal
Disconnect both sensor connectors. Remove sensor retaining clamp and pull sensor carefully out of holder.

Installation
Clean holder, then insert sensor fully (clamping surface about .025" from holder surface). Install retaining clamp and tighten to 70-100 INCH Lbs. (8-11 N.m). Route wires up water pump and under spark plug wires along manifold to right of carburetor.

ELECTRONIC CONTROL ASSEMBLY
Removal
1) Remove 10 mm retaining bolt and remove harness connector. Remove 2 bracket nuts, then remove gasket around connector.

2) From inside passenger compartment, remove 2 screws holding ECA to bracket. Slide out ECA and remove 2 screws to lift off calibration assembly.

Installation
1) Attach calibration assembly with 2 screws. Slide ECA into bracket, engaging clip in ECA flange.

Position connector surface through firewall, then install 2 mounting screws.

2) Install gasket carefully and replace bracket mounting nuts. Install connector and tighten retaining bolt to 40 INCH Lbs. (4.5 N.m).

OXYGEN SENSOR
Removal
Allow exhaust manifold to cool. Disconnect wiring and remove sensor with crow's foot socket or special tool (T79P-9472-A).

Installation
Clean mounting surface and install sensor with fingers. Use tool to tighten sensor until compression washer crushes, about 27-33 ft. lbs. (37-45 N.m), then connect wiring.

EGR VALVE POSITION SENSOR
Removal
Disconnect wiring connector. Remove 3 fasteners at perimeter of sensor. Lift sensor and "O" ring seal. Cover valve to prevent foreign material from entering.

Installation
Clean top of valve and "O" ring groove. Lubricate "O" ring with silicone grease, then install in groove. Install sensor and secure with 3 self-tapping screws. Connect wiring.

Fig. 7: Electronic Engine Control System Wiring Diagram

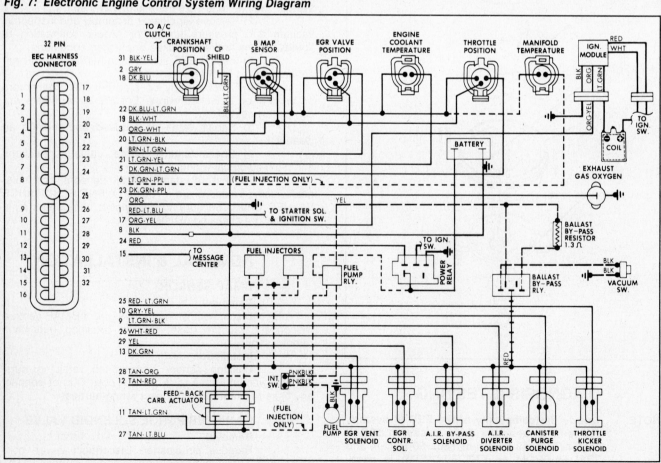

Also see chassis wiring in WIRING DIAGRAM Section.

FORD EEC-III SYSTEM (Cont.)

TAB/TAD SOLENOID ASSEMBLY

Removal

Remove wiring connector from solenoids. Remove vacuum source hose at "T" and disconnect both solenoid hoses. Remove bolts from underneath fender and remove valve assembly.

Installation

Install assembly and tighten screws. Connect vacuum source hose to "T". Connect air by-pass hose to TAB solenoid (toward front of engine), then connect air diverter hose to TAD solenoid (toward firewall). Install wiring connectors.

EEC III COMPONENT RESISTANCE VALUES

Component	Wire Colors	Resistance (Ohms)
Crankshaft Position (CP) Sensor	Gry - Dk Blue	100-640
Distributor Position (DP) Sensor	Gry - Dk Blue	300-800
Coolant (ECT) Sensor	Lt Green/Yellow - Black/White	1100-8000
Air Charge Temp (ACT) Sensor	Lt Green/Purple - Black/White	1700-60,000
Throttle Position (TP) Sensor		
Closed Throttle	Orange/White - Black/White	3000-5000
Closed Throttle	Dk Green/Lt Green - Black/White	550-1100
Wide Open Throttle	Dk Green/Lt Green - Black/White	More than 2100
EGR Control Solenoid	Red - Yellow	More than 30
EGR Vent Solenoid	Red - Dk Green	More than 30
TK Solenoid	Red - Red/Lt Green	More than 45
TAB Solenoid	Red - White/Red	45-90
TAD Solenoid	Red - Lt Green/Black	45-90
Fuel Pump Relay	Red - Tan/Lt Green	More than 40
By-Pass Ballast Resistor	.....	Less than 3

1983 Computerized Engine Controls

FORD EEC-IV SYSTEM

2.8L Bronco II, Ranger

DESCRIPTION

The center of the EEC-IV system is the Electronic Control Assembly (ECA). The ECA receives information from several sensors and other electronic devices. Based on information received and the operation program in the ECA's memory, the ECA generates output signals to control engine operation. The calibration module for EEC-IV systems is mounted inside the ECA. The ECA is located in the passenger compartment, under the center console.

The EEC-IV system controls 3 major areas of engine operation. These areas are, air/fuel mixture,

ignition, and emission control. Additionally the system controls A/C compressor clutch operation and provides self-diagnostic capabilities.

The air/fuel mixture control is accomplished by use of a feedback carburetor. The ignition system is controlled by the ECA through a Thick Film Ignition (TFI-IV) module. Ignition timing (advance or retard) and dwell are controlled with this system to improve ignition system performance.

Emission control components controlled by this system include the EGR system and the canister purge system. These systems are shut off until the engine and controls are ready to operate with the changed conditions presented by EGR and canister purge operation.

Fig. 1: EEC-IV System Inputs and Outputs

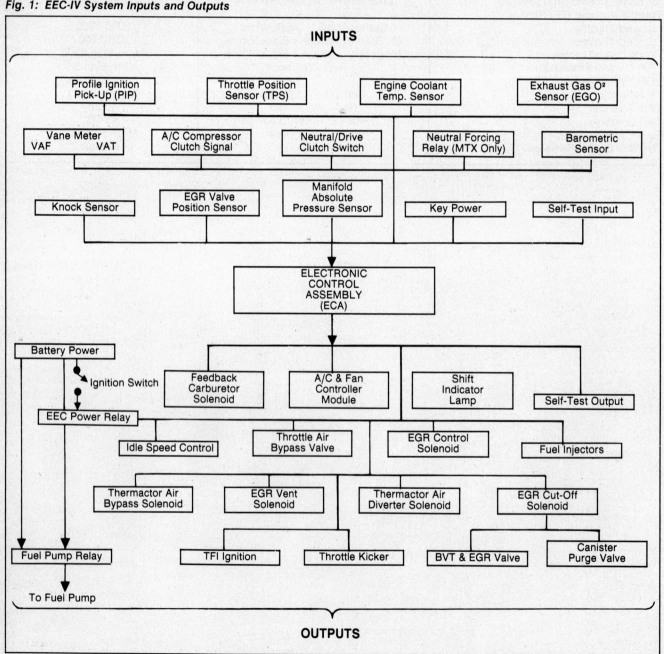

Not all inputs and outputs are used on all engines.

FORD EEC-IV SYSTEM (Cont.)

OPERATION

The engine control system consists of the ECA, sensors and switches, and actuators. In order for the ECA to properly perform its function, it must be kept constantly informed of engine operating conditions. It is the function of the engine sensors to supply the ECA, via electrical signal, with specific information as required to determine engine operating conditions. The ECA can then send out electrical signals of its own to control fuel flow (determining air/fuel ratio), emission controls and ignition timing. Individual component operation is as follows:

INPUTS

A/C Compressor Clutch Signal (ACC)

When battery voltage is applied to compressor clutch, a signal is sent to ECA. ECA uses signal to maintain engine idle speed, using throttle air bypass valve, to compensate for added load created by A/C compressor.

Barometric Pressure Sensor

Sensor is mounted on right inner fender and measures barometric pressure of atmospheric air. Signals are converted to electrical signals and sent to ECA.

Engine Coolant Temperature (ECT) Sensor

This sensor, threaded into heater supply tube, monitors and signals the ECA of engine coolant temperature. The ECA interprets this as either cold or normal operating temperature. This influences ECA control of fuel mixture enrichment, idle speed, ignition, and EGR operation.

Exhaust Gas Oxygen (EGO) Sensor

This sensor is threaded into exhaust manifold where it constantly monitors oxygen content of exhaust gases. A voltage signal is produced which varies according to difference in oxygen content between exhaust gases and surrounding atmosphere. This signal is sent to the ECA which translates exhaust gas oxygen content to air/fuel ratio. It then alters fuel delivery rate to aquire the ideal ratio for current engine operating conditions.

EGR Valve Position Sensor

Sensor located on top part of EGR valve. Sensor provides system with a signal indicating position of EGR valve.

Key Power

This is simply the test input for Quick Test using Key On, Engine Off routine. These tests are to detect hard faults only, not intermittent problems.

Manifold Absolute Pressure Sensor

Mounted on right inner fender, sensor measures absolute pressure of mixture in intake manifold and sends a signal to ECA that is proportional to absolute pressure in manifold.

Neutral Switch

Automatic transmission models use a neutral start switch. Switch indicates whether engine is loaded or unloaded and ensures that vehicle cannot be started in gear. ECA uses signal generated by these switches to maintain same idle speed whether engine is under a load or not.

Profile Ignition Pick-Up (PIP)

The PIP informs the ECA of crankshaft position and speed. PIP assembly is integral with distributor. PIP has an armature with 4 windows and 4 metal tabs that rotate past a stator assembly (Hall-Effect Switch).

When metal tab enters stator assembly, a signal to ECA indicates 10° BTDC crankshaft position.

ECA then calculates when to energize spark output signal to TFI module. When module receives a spark output signal, coil primary voltage is shut off resulting in coil secondary output.

Ignition distributor does not have any mechanical or vacuum advance. Distributor is adjustable for resetting base timing if necessary.

Self-Test Input

Self-test input is a wire in self-test connector used to start the self-test. Self-test procedures are built into EEC-IV control module so system can display continous self-test codes for diagnosis of intermittent problems.

Throttle Position Sensor (TPS)

The TPS is mounted on side of throttle body and connected directly to throttle shaft. The TPS senses throttle movement and position and transmits an electrical signal to the ECA. These signals keep the ECA informed of wide open throttle, closed throttle, or normal cruise conditions.

OUTPUTS

EGR Control Solenoid

Solenoid switches manifold vacuum to operate EGR valve on command from ECA. Vacuum opens EGR valve when solenoid is energized.

EGR Vent Solenoid

EGR vent solenoid is an electrically operated vacuum valve located between manifold vacuum source and EGR valve. This unit operates as a vacuum bleed.

Idle Speed Control (ISC) Motor

This is an electromechanical device used to alter or maintain throttle position to provide idle speed control according to signals from ECA.

Self-Test Output

Part of the self-test connector, service codes are transmitted on the output in the form of timed pulses to be read as diagnostic codes.

Thermactor Air Bypass Solenoid

Solenoid provides a vacuum signal to bypass valve, which then bypasses thermactor pump air to atmosphere.

Thermactor Air Diverter Solenoid

Solenoid provides a vacuum signal to diverter valve to divert thermactor pump air to either exhaust manifold or catalytic converter.

TFI Ignition Module

The TFI module triggers ignition coil and determines dwell. Module is mounted on side of distributor. ECA uses signal from Profile Ignition Pick-up to determine crankshaft position. Ignition timing is determined within ECA. ECA then signals TFI module when to fire coil.

Variable Voltage Choke (VVC)

The ECA controls the choke rate by controlling voltage on-time supplied to the choke. The voltage supplied to the choke is switched by the choke relay.

Temperature Compensated Accelerator Pump (TCP)

The ECA controls the TCP solenoid, which provides a vacuum signal to the carburetor. This vacuum signal is used to increase the accelerator pump shot when the engine is cold.

Canister Purge Solenoid (CANP)

This solenoid is mounted in-line with the canister purge hose. The ECA uses this solenoid to control canister vapor flow.

Feedback Carburetor Solenoid (FBC)

The FBC solenoid is mounted on the carburetor. The FBC solenoid is controlled by the ECA to meter the air/fuel mixture into the engine.

Ignition Module Signal

This is the signal sent from the ECA to the TFI module to determine spark advance.

TESTING & DIAGNOSIS

TEST EQUIPMENT

The following equipment is recommended to perform the Quick Tests and Pinpoint Tests on EEC-IV systems. Some equipment is REQUIRED to perform tests. DO NOT attempt to test this system without proper equipment. Damage to vehicle components will result if improper equipment is used.

- Self-Test Automatic Read-Out (STAR) Tester. This tool is recommended, but not required. It is specially built for the EEC-IV system and is used to display the two digit service codes that are programmed into the control module.
- Analog Volt-Ohmmeter with 0-20V DC range. This can be used as an alternate to the STAR tester.
- Jumper wire about 15" long.
- Vacuum Gauge with 0-30 in. Hg range, and resolution in the 1 in. Hg range.
- Tachometer with 0-6000 RPM range, accuracy plus/minus 40 RPM and resolution within 20 RPM.
- Vacuum Pump with 0-25 in. Hg range.
- Digital Volt-Ohmmeter (DVOM) with 10 megaohm minimum input impedance.
- Timing light.
- Spark tester. A modified spark plug with side electrode removed and alligator clip attached may be used.
- Breakout Box. This is a jumper wire assembly which connects between the vehicle harness and the processor assembly. The Breakout Box is REQUIRED to perform certain tests on the processor. Ford Motor Co. DOES NOT recommend using a DVOM to probe the processor pin connector as permanent damage to the pins will result.

PREPARATION

Correct test results for this system are dependent on the correct operation of several related non-EEC components and systems. All non-EEC problems should be corrected before attempting to diagnose the EEC system.

Before hooking up any equipment to diagnose the EEC system, make the following checks:

- Verify the condition of the air cleaner and air ducting.
- Check all vacuum hoses for leaks, restrictions and proper routing.
- Check the EEC system wiring harness electrical connections for loose or detached connectors, wires or terminals.
- Check the ECA, sensors and actuators for physical damage.
- Perform all necessary safety precautions to prevent personal injury or vehicle damage.
- Set parking brake and place shift lever in "Park" (Neutral for manual transmission). Do not move shift lever during testing unless specifically directed to do so.
- Turn off all lights and accesories, and make sure that vehicle doors are closed when making readings.
- Check coolant level and correct as necessary.
- Start engine and idle until upper radiator hose is hot and pressurized and throttle is off fast idle. Check for leaks around exhaust manifold, EGO sensor and vacuum connections
- Turn ignition key off.

NOTE: **If vehicle is towed in or is suspected of having intermittent problems, do not turn the ignition key off. Diagnostic codes may be stored in the continuous testing memory.**

QUICK TESTS

Reading Self-Test Codes

Service codes are transmitted on the Self-Test Output and are shown as voltage pulses on a Volt-Ohmmeter (VOM). Key On - Engine Off tests will show three groups of codes. The first group of codes is On Demand, the second group of codes is a Separator code and the third group of codes is the Continuous codes.

The On Demand code first digit is indicated by a pulse, then the needle drops to zero for 2 seconds, then the second digit of the code is displayed. Between service codes 4 seconds will elapse. At the end of the On Demand codes, 6 seconds will elapse. Then the Separator code will be displayed for 1/2 second. After 6 seconds, the first digit of the Continuous code will be displayed, the needle will drop to zero for 2 seconds, then the second digit of the Continuous code will display. At the end of the Continuous codes, all codes will be repeated. After codes have been repeated, Key Off - Engine On.

Engine Running tests will display codes in the same manner, except there will be an Engine ID code, a Dynamic Response Code and an the On Demand codes. The Engine ID code has no application in the field, and is for factory use only. The codes will be displayed in the same manner as Key On -Engine Off codes.

Equipment Hook-Up

With ignition key off, connect a jumper wire from the self-test input to pin 2 on the self-test connector. *See Fig. 2.* Set needle-type volt-ohmmeter (VOM) on DC 0-

Fig. 2: Meter Hook-Up for Reading Codes

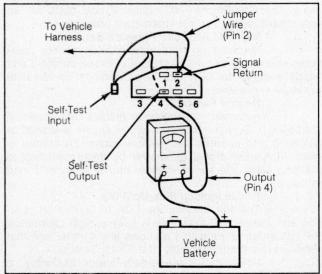

FORD EEC-IV SYSTEM (Cont.)

15 volt scale. Connect VOM from battery positive side to pin 4 on self-test connector.

Key On - Engine Off Test

Turn ignition switch on. Reconnect grounded jumper wire to self-test input terminal. Observe and record On Demand and Continuous codes. When more than 1 code is displayed, always repair problems in the order that codes were displayed. Do not depress throttle during test. Repair codes as follows:

KEY ON - ENGINE OFF TEST RESULTS

On Demand Codes	Continuous Codes	Proceed to Test
11	11	Timing Check
Any	11	See Code No.
Any	Any	See Code No.
11	Any	Timing Check
None	None	Test P
15		Replace processor, retest.
21		Test F
22		Test G
23		Test E
24		Test D
51		Test F
53		Test E
54		Test D
61		Test F
63		Test E
64		Test D
67		Test S
68		Test R
None	None	Test P

Timing Check

Engine Running Test must be activated while checking or adjusting timing. Connect timing light. Start engine and check timing for no longer than 25 seconds. Refer to vehicle emission decal for base timing specification. Timing is calculated as follows: Base timing plus 20°, plus or minus 3°, equals initial timing. Results are as follows:

- Timing is base, plus 20°, plus or minus 3°: Go to Engine Running Self-Test.
- Timing is not base, plus 20°, plus or minus 3°: Go to test Q, Spark Timing Check and check spark output circuit to TFI module.
- Vehicle does not start: go to test A: No Start Problem.
- Vehicle stalls during 25 second timing check: Go to test P: No Codes or Invalid Codes.

Engine Running Test

This test checks sensors under actual operating conditions. Fault must be present at time of test to be detected. This test will display an Engine ID Code, a Dynamic Response Code and an On Demand Service Code. After a Dynamic Response Code is received, quickly press and release accelerator once only. If test is not performed properly, a series 70 code (77, 76, 73, 72) will appear and the test will have to be repeated.

Start and run engine at more than 2000 RPM for 2 minutes. Ignore any output codes at this time. Turn engine off and wait 10 seconds. Verify test is activated. Start engine. Test will proceed with Engine ID Code, Dynamic Response code and Engine Running On Demand

service codes. If a 10 or 1 pulse occurs during Dynamic Response code, open throttle wide open momentarily. Record codes and proceed as follows:

ENGINE RUNNING TEST RESULTS

On Demand Codes	Continuous Codes	Proceed to Test
11	Any	Continuous Code
Any		See Code No.
None	None	Repeat self-test. [1]
12		Test N
13		Test N
21		Test F
22		Test G
23		Test E
24		Test D
25		Test K
31		Test H
32		Test H
33		Test H
34		Test H
35		Test H
41		Test J
42		Test J
43		Test J
44		Test L
45		Test L
46		Test L
47		Test J
55		Test Y
58		Test R
72		Test M
73		Test M
77		Test M
Invalid		Test P

[1] — If vehicle stalls in test, go to test P, and try to keep engine running during Engine Running test.

Continuous Test

1) Unless instructed to do so, do not disconnect any sensor with key on or service codes will be stored. Should Keep Alive Power pin 1 to processor be interrupted, all stored Continuous codes will be lost. If pin 1 fails, invalid codes may be received during test.

2) Correct method for clearing memory is to exit Key On - Engine Off Test during code output sequence. Exit test by removing self-test jumper. Before using stored information, first verify that previous tests indicated code 11.

3) If during tests an On Demand code is detected, this must be repaired first, since some hard failures also request a code in the continuous memory. Once On Demand testing is complete, clear memory of Continuous codes and operate vehicle to verify repair.

4) Before repairing any Continuous Test service codes, verify that a code 11 was received from both previous tests. Repair only those codes that are not repeated from previous tests.

5) With vehicle prepared as in Key On - Engine Off Test, record all Continuous codes. Perform Key On - Engine Off Test. When first service code is output, exit test by removing jumper from self-test input to signal return pin 2. This will erase any Continuous codes.

FORD EEC-IV SYSTEM (Cont.)

6) With test deactivated, key on and engine off, self-test output is checked. Wiggle system harness, connectors or sensors while observing VOM. A fault will be indicated by meter deflection of 10.5 volts or more, and a service code will be stored.

7) After checking all system components, perform Key On - Engine Off Test to retreive any codes stored during wiggle test. Remain in continuous monitor mode and service Continuous codes as follows:

NOTE: Record all service codes before removing or replacing processor. Codes will be erased from memory whenever processor is disconnected.

CONTINUOUS TEST CODES

Code	Proceed to Test
Code 11	[1]
21	Test U1
22	Test U2
31	Test U3
41	Test U4
51	Test U6
54	Test U7
61	Test U8
63	Test U9
64	Test U10

[1] — If no intermittent problems, test is complete. If intermittent problems exist, go to Test X, Invalid Codes-Continuous Test, and generate a fault in keep alive memory.

PINPOINT TESTS

Test Instructions

1) Do not run any test unless instructed to do so by the Quick Test. Make sure all non-EEC related faults are corrected. Do not replace any part unless directed to do so. When more than one service code is received, start with lowest code first.

2) Do not measure voltage or resistance at control module or connect any test lamps to it, unless specified. All measurements are made by probing the REAR of the connector. Isolate both ends of a circuit and turn key off whenever checking for shorts or continuity, unless specified.

3) Disconnect solenoids and switches from harness before measuring continuity, resistance or energizing with a 12 volt source. Follow each step in order until fault is found. After any repairs, check all component connections and repeat Quick Test.

Output State Test

1) The Output State Test is used to diagnose each actuator. Test is performed in the Key On - Engine Off Test mode after Continuous codes have been sent. Do not disable self-test but momentarily depress throttle and release. All auxiliary EEC outputs will be activated at this time. Another throttle depression will turn them off.

2) Connect VOM to self-test output pin 4. Initialize Key On - Engine Off On Demand Test. When Continuous codes are completed, VOM will read 0 volts. Depress accelerator to turn on actuators. VOM readings above 10.5 volts indicate actuators are on, readings below 2 volts indicate actuators are off.

3) Disconnect VOM from pin 4 and connect to appropriate actuator. Measure output state voltage of actuator. Each test will tell what action to take according to reading on VOM.

FORD EEC-IV SYSTEM (Cont.)

TEST A

NO START TEST

1) Try to start engine. If engine does not crank, problem is not EEC related. If engine cranks but does not start or stalls out, proceed with test.

2) Disconnect an ignition wire from spark plug and check for spark. If spark is present, problem is in ignition system. If spark is not present, proceed with test.

3) Remove coil wire from distributor and check for spark. If spark is present, problem is in ignition system. If spark is not present, proceed with test.

4) Turn ignition off and wait for 10 seconds. Disconnect processor and inspect both 60 pin connectors. Connect breakout box to hanrness and processor. Turn ignition on, engine off. Measure voltage from breakout box pin 37 to pin 40 and breakout box pin 57 to pin 60. If either reading is less than 10.5 volts, perform Battery Voltage Test. If both readings are 10.5 volts or more, proceed with test.

5) Turn ignition off and wait 10 seconds. Measure resistance from breakout box pin 16 to pin 40. If resistance is 5 ohms or more, repair ignition ground circuit wire. If resistance is 5 ohms or less, proceed with test.

6) Connect voltmeter positive lead to breakout box pin 56 and negative lead to pin 16. Observe voltage while cranking. If voltage is between 3 and 6 volts, proceed to step **9)**. If voltage is less than 3 volts or more than 6 volts, proceed to step **7)**.

7) Turn ignition off and wait for 10 seconds. Measure continuity from breakout box pin 56 to harness circuit 349 at TFI connector. If resistance is more than 5 ohms, repair open in circuit 349 and retest. If resistance is 5 ohms or less, proceed with test.

8) Turn ignition off and wait 10 seconds. Disconnect TFI connector and processor. Measure resistance from breakout box pin 56 to breakout box pins 26, 40, 46 and 57. If any resistance is less than 10,-000 ohms, repair short in circuit 349 and retest. If all resistances are more than 10,000 ohms, proceed with tests.

9) Turn ignition off and wait 10 seconds. Disconnect TFI connector and processor. Measure resistance from breakout box pin36 to breakout box pins 26, 40, 46 and 57. If any resistance is less than 10,-000 ohms, repair short in circuit 324 and retest. If all resistances are more than 10,000 ohms, proceed with test.

10) Reconnect TFI connector and leave processor disconnected. Try to start engine. If engine starts, replace processor and retest. If engine does not start, problem is not EEC related.

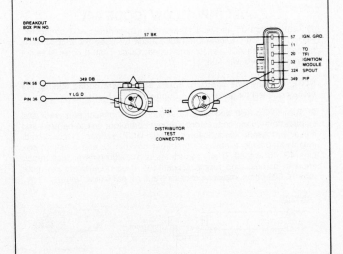

TEST B

BATTERY VOLTAGE TEST

1) Turn ignition on with engine off. Measure voltage across battery terminals. If voltage is 10.5 volts or less, service battery. If voltage is greater than 10.5 volts, proceed with test.

2) Measure voltage from battery negative post to signal return circuit 359 in self-test connector. If voltage reading is less than .5 volts, proceed to step **3)**. If voltage is .5 volts or more, proceed to step **4)**.

3) Turn ignition off and wait 10 seconds. Disconnect processor and inspect both 60 pin connectors. Connect breakout box to harness and processor. Turn ignition on with engine off. Measure voltage from battery positive post to breakout box pin 37 and then from positive post to pin 57. If both readings are less than .5 volts, perform Reference Voltage Test. If one or both readings are .5 volts or more, proceed to step **7)**.

4) Turn ignition off and wait 10 seconds. Disconnect processor and inspect both 60 pin connectors. Connect breakout box to harness and processor. Turn ignition on with engine off. Measure voltage from battery negative post to breakout box pin 40 and then from negative post to pin 60. If both readings are less than .5 volts, proceed to step **5)**. If one or both readings are .5 volts or more, high voltage indicates circuit with high resistance or open. Correct faulty ground circuit.

5) Turn ignition off and wait 10 seconds. Measure resistance from breakout box pin 46 to pin 40 and then from pin 46 to pin 60. If one or both readings are more than 5 ohms, disconnect processor and inspect for damaged or corroded connector pins. Repair or replace as necessary and retest. If fault is still present, replace processor. If both readings are less than 5 ohms, proceed with test.

6) Turn ignition off and reconnect processor. Measure resistance from breakout box pin 46 to harness circuit 359 in self-test connector. If resistance is 5 ohms or greater, repair or replace wire in circuit 359. If resistance is less than 5 ohms, system is ok, perform Quick Test.

7) With ignition on and engine off, connect negative lead of voltmeter to battery negative post and positive lead to circuit 37 at EEC power relay. Measure voltage. If voltage is 10.5 volts or less, check circuit 37 for opens. Before servicing, check circuits 37 and 361 for shorts to ground. Repair as necessary and repeat Quick Test. If voltage is greater than 10.5 volts, proceed with test.

NOTE: **If an open fusible link is found, check for shorts to ground before replacing fusible link.**

8) With ignition on, connect voltmeter negative lead to battery negative post and positive lead to circuit 640 at EEC power relay. Measure voltage. If voltage is 10.5 volts or less, check for blown fuses or opens in ignition circuits 16, 37 and 640. Repair as necessary and repeat Quick Test. If voltage is greater than 10.5 volts, proceed with test.

9) With ignition on, connect voltmeter negative lead to battery negative post and positive lead to circuit 57 at EEC power relay. Measure voltage. If voltage is greater than .5 volts, repair open or ground in circuit 57 and repeat Quick Test. If voltage is .5 volts or less, proceed with test.

10) With ignition on, connect voltmeter negative lead to battery negative post and positive lead to circuit 361 at EEC power relay. Measure voltage. If voltage is less than 10.5 volts, replace power relay and repeat Quick Test. If voltage is 10.5 volts or more, repair open in circuit 361 and repeat Quick Test.

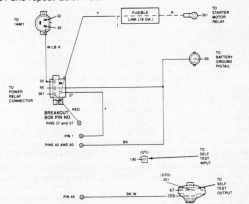

TEST C

REFERENCE VOLTAGE TEST

1) Turn ignition off and wait 10 seconds. Disconnect processor and inspect both 60 pin connectors. Connect breakout box to harness and processor. Turn ignition on with engine off. Connect voltmeter positive lead to breakout box pin 37 and negative lead to circuit 359 in self-test connector. Measure voltage. If voltage is greater than 10.5 volts, proceed with test. If voltage is 10.5 volts or less, perform Battery Voltage Test.

2) With ignition on, measure voltage from breakout box pin 26 to pin 46. If voltage is 6 volts or more, proceed to step **3)**. If voltage is 4 volts or less, proceed to step **5)**.

3) Turn ignition off and wait 10 seconds. Measure voltage from breakout box pin 26 to pin 46. If voltage is .5 volts or less, proceed with test. If voltage is more than .5 volts, repair short between battery power and reference voltage circuits. Repeat Quick Test.

4) Disconnect processor from breakout box. Turn ignition on. Measure voltage from breakout box pin 26 to pin 46. If voltage is .5 volts or less, replace processor and repeat Quick Test. If voltage is more than .5 volts, repair short between reference voltage circuit and battery power circuits in EEC harness.

5) Disconnect the throttle position sensor. With ignition on, measure voltage from breakout box pin 26 to pin 46. If voltage is 4 volts or less, proceed with test. If voltage is more than 4 volts, replace sensor and repeat Quick Test.

6) Disconnect the EGR valve position solenoid. With ignition on, measure voltage from breakout box pin 26 to pin 46. If voltage is 4 volts or less, proceed with test. If voltage is more than 4 volts, replace sensor, reconnect throttle and EGR sensors and repeat Quick Test.

7) Disconnect the MAP sensor. With ignition on, measure voltage from breakout box pin 26 to pin 46. If voltage is 4 volts or less, proceed

with test. If voltage is more than 4 volts, replace sensor, reconnect throttle and EGR sensors and repeat Quick Test.

8) Turn ignition off and wait 10 seconds. Disconnect processor, but leave breakout box connected to harness. Check continuity from breakout box pins 37 and 57 to circuit 37 on power relay. Check continuity from breakout box pins 40 and 60 to battery negative post. If any circuit reads more than 5 ohms, repair circuit and repeat Quick Test. If all circuits read less than 5 ohms, proceed with test.

9) Turn ignition off and wait 10 seconds. Disconnect MAP sensor, throttle sensor and EGR sensor. Disconnect processor and check for short circuits between breakout box pin 26 and pins 40, 46 or 57. If any circuit reads less than 100 ohms, repair short and repeat Quick Test. If all circuits read 100 ohms or more, replace processor assembly and repeat Quick Test.

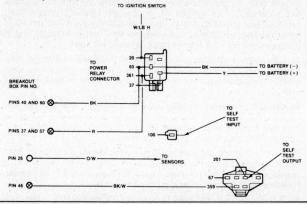

TEST D

AIR CLEANER TEMPERATURE (ACT) SENSOR TEST (CODE 24)

1) Check to verify that ACT sensor is seated in air cleaner. If installed properly, proceed with test. If not installed properly, correct and warm up engine before repeating Quick Test.

2) Disconnect ACT connector, connect voltmeter positive lead to harness circuit 357 and negative lead to circuit 359. Turn ignition on and measure voltage. If voltage is more than 6 volts, perform Reference Voltage Test. If voltage is less than 4 volts, proceed to step **5)**. If voltage is between 4 and 6 volts, proceed to step **3)**.

3) With ACT sensor disconnectted, measure resistance across ACT sensor pins. If resistance is less than 1,100 ohms or more than 58,000 ohms, check heat stove duct valve operation. If valve operates properly, replace ACT sensor and repeat Quick Test. If resistance is between 1,100 and 58,000 ohms, proceed with test.

4) With ACT sensor disconnected, run engine for 2 minutes and measure resistance across ACT sensor pins while engine is running. If resistance is less than 2,400 ohms or more than 29,000 ohms, check heat stove duct valve operation. If valve operates properly, replace ACT sensor and repeat Quick Test. If resistance is between 2,400 and 29,000 ohms, replace processor and repeat Quick Test.

5) Turn ignition off and wait 10 seconds. Disconnect processor and inspect both 60 pin connectors. Connect breakout box to harness. Leave processor disconnected. Measure continuity from circuit 357 to breakout box pin 25 and circuit 359 to breakout box pin 46. If either resistance is 5 ohms or more, repair wiring harness and repeat Quick Test. If both resistances are less than 5 ohms, proceed with test.

6) Turn ignition off and wait 10 seconds. Measure resistance between breakout box pin 25 and breakout box pins 40, 46 and 60. If any resistance is 10,000 ohms or less, repair short in harness and repeat Quick Test. If all resistances are more than 10,000 ohms, return to step **3)**.

5) Check continuity of wire from knock sensor to MCU harness connector pin 14. If resistance is more than 5 ohms, repair wire. If resistance is 5 ohms or less, reconnect MCU and proceed with test.

6) Reconnect the jumper wire to the self-test connector. Connect a test lamp to the positive terminal of the battery. Disconnect the knock sensor.

7) Repeat the "Engine Running Test" noting the following: When the initialization pulses occur, tap wire that leads to pin 14 of MCU with test lamp for 5 seconds. If diagnostic code 25 is displayed, replace MCU. If any other diagnostic code is displayed, replace knock sensor.

ACT INPUT HIGH (CODE 54)

1) Turn ignition off and wait 10 seconds. Disconnect ACT connector. Connect a jumper wire between harness circuits 357 and 359 at ACT connector. Perform Key On - Engine Off Test. Check for code 64. If code 64 is present, replace ACT sensor and repeat Quick Test. If code 64 is not present, proceed with test.

2) Turn ignition off and wait 10 seconds. Remove jumper wire. Disconnect processor and inspect both 60 pin connectors. Connect breakout box to harness and leave processor disconnected. Measure continuity from circuit 357 to breakout box pin 25 and circuit 359 to breakout box pin 46. If either resistance is 5 ohms or more, repair wiring harness and repeat Quick Test. If both resistances are less than 5 ohms, replace processor and repeat Quick Test.

ACT INPUT LOW (CODE 64)

1) Turn ignition off and wait 10 seconds. Disconnect ACT connector. Perform Key On - Engine Off Test. Check for code 54. If code 54 is present, replace ACT sensor and repeat Quick Test. If code 64 is not present, proceed with test.

NOTE: Any time shorts or opens are present during testing, the same code will be generated in Continuous Test.

2) Turn ignition off and wait 10 seconds. Disconnect processor and inspect both 60 pin connectors. Connect breakout box to harness and leave processor disconnected. With ACT sensor disconnected, measure resistance from breakout box pin 25 and breakout box pins 40, 46 and 60. If any resistance is 10,000 ohms or less, repair short in harness and repeat Quick Test. If all resistances are more than 10,000 ohms, replace processor and repeat Quick Test.

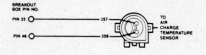

TEST E

THROTTLE POSITION (TP) SENSOR TEST (CODE 23)

NOTE: If code 23 was displayed during the Key On - Engine Off Test, start at step 1). If code 23 was displayed during the Engine Running Test, start at step 3).

1) Check for code 68. If code 68 is displayed during Quick Test, perform test for code 68 before proceeding. If code 68 is not displayed, proceed to step 2).

2) Perform Key On - Engine Off Test while attempting to completely close throttle. Check for service code 23. If code 23 is present, proceed to step 5). If code 23 is not present, TPS is slightly out of adjustment. Do not attempt to adjust. EEC system is functioning properly.

3) Check for code 58. If code 58 is displayed during Quick Test, perform test for code 58 before proceeding. If code 58 is not displayed, proceed to step 4).

4) Check for codes 31 or 41 present during Engine Running Test. If either or both codes are present, perform appropriate test. If codes 31 and 41 are not present, proceed with test.

5) Visually inspect carburetor and throttle linkages for binding or sticking. Check for throttle stuck on high cam. If no problems are found, proceed with test. If any problems are found, correct as necessary and repeat Quick Test.

6) Turn ignition off and wait 10 seconds. Disconnect TP sensor harness connector. Inspect both connectors. Connect voltmeter positive lead to TP harness circuit 351 and negative lead to circuit 359. Turn ignition on and observe voltage. If voltage is more than 6 volts, perform Reference Voltage Test. If voltage is less than 4 volts, repair open in harness circuit 359 and repeat Quick Test. If voltage is between 4 and 6 volts, proceed to step 7).

7) Turn ignition off and wait for 10 seconds. Disconnect TP sensor harness connector. Perform Key On - Engine Off Test. If code 63 is displayed, replace TP sensor and repeat Quick Test. If code 63 is not displayed, proceed to step 8).

8) Connect voltmeter positive lead to TP harness circuit 355 and negative lead to ground. Turn ignition on and observe voltage reading. If reading is higher than 2 volts, repair harness short and repeat Quick Test. If reading is 2 volts or less, replace processor and repeat Quick Test.

TP SIGNAL RETURN OPEN (CODE 53)

1) Turn ignition off and wait for 10 seconds. Disconnect TP sensor connector. Inspect for damaged pins, corrosion or loose wires. Repair as necessary. Connect voltmeter positive lead to battery positive post and negative lead to harness circuit 359. Observe voltage. If voltage is 10 volts or more, proceed to step 2). If voltage is less than 10 volts, proceed to step 4).

2) Connect voltmeter positive lead to circuit 355 and negative lead to circuit 359. Turn ignition on and observe voltage. If voltage is less than 4 volts, proceed to step 3). If voltage is 4 volts or more, proceed to step 5).

3) With TP sensor disconnected, perform Key On - Engine Off Test. Check for code 63. If code 63 is present, replace TP sensor and repeat Quick Test. If code 63 is not present, replace processor and repeat Quick Test.

4) Turn ignition off and wait 10 seconds. Connect breakout box and leave processor disconnected. Measure continuity of circuit 359 to breakout box pin 46. If resistance is 5 ohms or more, repair open circuit and repeat Quick Test. If resistance is less than 5 ohms, replace processor and repeat Quick Test.

5) Turn ignition off and wait 10 seconds. Connect breakout box and leave processor disconnected. Measure resistance of breakout box pin 47 to pins 26 and 57. If either resistance is 10,000 ohms or less, repair harness short and repeat Quick Test. If both resistances are 10,000 ohms or more, replace processor and repeat Quick Test.

TP SENSOR REFERENCE VOLTAGE TEST (CODE 63)

1) Turn ignition off and wait 10 seconds. Disconnect TP sensor. Inspect for damaged pins, corrosion or pins pushed out. Repair as necessary. Connect voltmeter positive lead to circuit 351 and negative lead to circuit 355. Turn ignition on and measure voltage. If voltage is 6 volts or more, perform Reference Voltage Test. If voltage is between 4 and 6 volts, proceed to step 2). If voltage is less than 4 volts, proceed to step 4).

2) Turn ignition off and wait for 10 seconds. Jumper circuit 351 to circuit 355. Perform Key On - Engine Off Test. Check for code 53. If code 53 is present, replace TP sensor and repeat Quick Test. If code 53 is not present, proceed to step 3).

3) Turn ignition off and wait 10 seconds. Disconnect processor 60 pin connector and inspect for damaged pins, corrosion or loose wires. Repair as necessary. Connect an ohmmeter between ground and harness circuit 355 at TP sensor connector. Measure resistance. If resistance is less than 10,000 ohms, repair short circuit and retest. If resistance is 10,000 ohms or more, proceed to step 4).

4) Turn ignition off and wait 10 seconds. Connect breakout box and leave processor disconnected. Check continuity of circuit 355 to breakout box pin 47 and circuit 351 to breakout box pin 26. If either resistance is 5 ohms or more, repair faulty circuit and repeat Quick Test. If both resistances are 5 ohms or less, replace processor and repeat Quick Test.

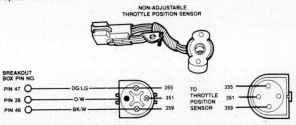

1983 Computerized Engine Controls

FORD EEC-IV SYSTEM (Cont.)

TEST F

ENGINE COOLANT TEMPERATURE (ECT) SENSOR TEST (CODE 21)

1) Start engine and run at 2000 RPM for 5 minutes. Check that upper radiator hose is hot and pressurized. Repeat Quick Test. If vehicle stalls, problem is not EEC related. If code 21 is not displayed, perform tests for other service codes (if any). If code 21 is still displayed, proceed with test.

2) Disconnect ECT and inspect both connectors. Connect voltmeter positive lead to harness circuit 354 and negative lead to circuit 359. Turn ignition on and observe voltage. If voltage is greater than 6 volts, perform Reference Voltage Test. If voltage is less than 4 volts, proceed to step **5)**. If voltage is between 4 and 6 volts, proceed to step **3)**.

3) Turn ignition off and wait 10 seconds. Measure resistance across ECT pins. If resistance is less than 1,300 ohms or more than 7,450 ohms, replace ECT sensor and repeat Quick Test. If resistance is between 1,300 and 7,450 ohms, proceed with test.

4) Turn ignition off and wait 10 seconds. Run engine for 2 minutes. Measure resistance across ECT pins. If resistance is less than 1,550 ohms or more than 4,250 ohms, replace ECT sensor and repeat Quick Test. If resistance is between 1,550 and 4,250 ohms, replace processor and repeat Quick Test.

5) Turn ignition off and wait 10 seconds. Disconnect processor and inspect both 60 pin connectors. Connect breakout box to harness and leave processor disconnected. Measure continuity of circuit 354 to breakout box pin 7 and circuit 359 to breakout box pin 46. If either resistance is more than 5 ohms, repair harness and repeat Quick Test. If both resistances are less than 5 ohms, proceed with test.

6) Turn ignition off and wait 10 seconds. Measure resistance from breakout box pin 7 to breakout box pins 40 and 60. If either reading is 10,000 ohms or less, repair short circuit and repeat Quick Test. If both readings are more than 10,000 ohms, return to step **3)**.

ECT INPUT HIGH (CODE 51)

1) Turn ignition off and wait 10 seconds. Disconnect ECT connector. Connect a jumper wire between harness circuits 354 and 359 at ACT connector. Perform Key On - Engine Off Test. Check for code 61. If code 61 is present, replace ECT sensor and repeat Quick Test. If code 61 is not present, proceed with test.

NOTE: Any time shorts or opens are present during testing, the same code will be generated in Continuous Test.

2) Turn ignition off and wait 10 seconds. Remove jumper wire. Disconnect processor and inspect both 60 pin connectors. Connect breakout box to harness and leave processor disconnected. Measure continuity from circuit 354 to breakout box pin 7 and circuit 359 to breakout box pin 46. If either resistance is 5 ohms or more, repair wiring harness and repeat Quick Test. If both resistances are less than 5 ohms, replace processor and repeat Quick Test.

ECT INPUT LOW (CODE 61)

1) Turn ignition off and wait 10 seconds. Disconnect ECT connector. Perform Key On - Engine Off Test. Check for code 51. If code 51 is present, replace ECT sensor and repeat Quick Test. If code 51 is not present, proceed with test.

NOTE: Any time shorts or opens are present during testing, the same code will be generated in Continuous Test.

2) Turn ignition off and wait 10 seconds. Disconnect processor and inspect both 60 pin connectors. Connect breakout box to harness and leave processor disconnected. With ACT sensor disconnected, measure resistance between breakout box pin 7 and breakout box pins 40 and 60. If any resistance is 10,000 ohms or less, repair short in harness and repeat Quick Test. If all resistances are more than 10,000 ohms, replace processor and repeat Quick Test.

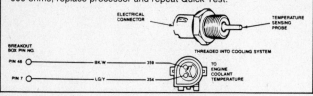

TEST G

MAP SENSOR TEST (CODE 22)

NOTE: If code 22 was displayed during the Key On -Engine Off Test, start at step 3). If code 22 was displayed during the Engine Running Test, start at step 1).

1) Verify that all accessories were off during Engine Running Test. Check vacuum line to MAP sensor for opens, kinks or restrictions. Check for vacuum leaks in engine system. Refer to Emission Control Decal for hose routing. If any faults or leaks are found, repair as necessary and repeat Quick Test. If no faults or leaks are found, proceed with test.

2) If codes 31 or 41 were present during Engine Running Test, perform appropriate test to repair code 31 and/or 41 before proceeding with test.

3) Disconnect vacuum line from MAP sensor and attach a vacuum pump to sensor. Apply 20 in. Hg of vacuum to sensor. If sensor does not hold vacuum, replace sensor, reconnect and repeat Quick Test. If sensor holds vacuum, proceed with test.

4) With MAP sensor disconnected, turn ignition on. Connect voltmeter positive lead to harness circuit 351 and negative lead to circuit 359. If voltage is greater than 6 volts, perform Reference Voltage Test. If voltage is less than 4 volts, proceed to step **6)**. If voltage is between 4 and 6 volts, proceed to step **5)**.

5) Turn ignition on. With MAP sensor disconnected, connect voltmeter positive lead to 356 and negative lead to circuit 359. If voltage is less than 4 volts, proceed to step **6)**. If voltage is 4 volts or more, proceed to step **8)**.

6) Turn ignition off and wait 10 seconds. Disconnect processor 60 pin connector and inspect for corrosion, damaged pins or loose wires. Connect breakout box to harness, but leave processor disconnected. Measure continuity of harness circuit 359 to breakout box pin 46, circuit 351 to pin 26, and circuit 356 to pin 45. If all resistances are 5 ohms or less, proceed to step **7)**. If any resistance is more than 5 ohms, repair faulty circuit in harness and repeat Quick Test.

7) Turn ignition off and wait 10 seconds. With processor disconnected, measure resistance from breakout box pin 26 to pins 40, 46 and 60. Measure resistance from breakout box pin 45 to pins 26, 40, 46 and 60. If any resistance is less than 100 ohms, repair short to ground and repeat Quick Test. If all resistances are 100 ohms or more, proceed to step **8)**.

8) Turn ignition off and wait 10 seconds. Disconnect processor 60 pin connector and inspect for corrosion, damaged pins or loose wires. Connect breakout box to harness, but leave processor disconnected. Disconnect MAP sensor. Measure resistance from breakout box pin 45 to pins 26, 37 and 57. If any resistance is less than 10,000 ohms, repair short circuit and repeat quick test. If all resistances are more than 10,000 ohms, proceed with test.

9) Plug in substitute MAP sensor and connect vacuum line. Repeat Quick Test. If code 22 is no longer present, permanently install sensor and repeat Quick Test. If code 22 is still present, replace processor, remove substitute sensor, and repeat Quick Test using original sensor.

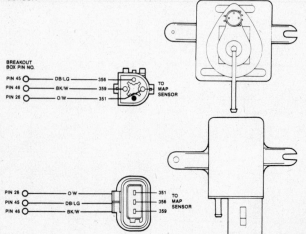

TEST H

EGR VALVE POSITION (EVP) SENSOR TEST (CODE 31)

1) Turn ignition off and wait for 10 seconds. Disconnect EGR vacuum line at EGR valve and cap vacuum line. Perform Engine Running Test and check for code 31. If code 31 is present, proceed to step 2). If code 31 is not present, but code 32 and/or 34 is present, perform EGR Control Valve Solenoid Test.

2) Turn ignition off and wait for 10 seconds. Disconnect EVP harness connector. Measure resistance from EVP sensor pin 1 to pin 2 and from pin 2 to pin 3. If either resistance is less than 100 ohms or more than 5,500 ohms, replace EVP sensor, reconnect EGR vacuum line, and repeat Quick Test. If both resistances are between 100 and 5,500 ohms, proceed with test.

3) Turn ignition off and wait for 10 seconds. Connect a vacuum pump to EGR valve. Measure resistance of EVP sensor between sensor pins 1 and 3 while gradually increasing vacuum to 10 in. Hg. If resistance is less than 100 ohms or more than 5,500 ohms, replace EVP sensor and repeat Quick Test. If EVP sensor reading does not decrease or does not hold vacuum, proceed to step 6) of EGR Control Valve Solenoid Test. If EVP resistance gradually decreases from 5,500 to 100 ohms, proceed with test.

4) Turn ignition on. Connect voltmeter positive lead to harness circuit 351 and negative lead to circuit 359. Measure voltage. If voltage is between 4 and 6 volts, proceed to step 5). If voltage is less than 4 volts, proceed to step 7). If voltage is more than 6 volts, perform Reference Voltage Test.

5) Turn ignition on. Connect voltmeter positive lead to harness circuit 351 and negative lead to circuit 352. Measure voltage. If voltage is between 4 and 6 volts, proceed to step 6). If voltage is less than 4 volts, proceed to step 7).

6) Turn ignition off and wait 10 seconds. Disconnect 60 pin processor connector and inspect both connectors. Measure resistance of harness circuit 352 to circuit 359 and then circuit 352 to ground. If either resistance is less than 10,000 ohms, repair short circuit and repeat Quick Test. If both resistance readings are 10,000 ohms or more, replace processor and repeat Quick Test.

7) Turn ignition off and wait 10 seconds. Disconnect 60 pin processor connector and inspect both connectors. Connect breakout box to harness, but leave processor disconnected. Measure continuity from breakout box pin 46 to harness circuit 359, pin 26 to circuit 351, and then pin 27 to circuit 352. If any reading is 5 ohms or more, repair faulty circuits and repeat Quick Test. If all resistances are less than 5 ohms, proceed to step 8).

8) Turn ignition off and wait 10 seconds. Disconnect EVP sensor. Measure resistance from breakout box pin 27 to pins 26 and 37. If either reading is 10,000 ohms or less, repair short circuit and repeat Quick Test. If both resistances are more than 10,000 ohms, replace processor and repeat Quick Test.

EGR CONTROL VALVE SOLENOID TEST (CODES 32, 33, 34)

1) Turn ignition off and wait for 10 seconds. Disconnect EGRC solenoid connector and measure solenoid resistance. Disconnect EGRV solenoid connector and measure solenoid resistance. If either solenoid resistance is less than 30 ohms or more than 70 ohms, replace EGR solenoid and repeat Quick Test. If both solenoids measure between 30 and 70 ohms, reconnect solenoids and proceed with test.

2) Turn ignition off and wait for 10 seconds. Connect voltmeter negative lead to self-test output connector and positive lead to battery positive post. Turn ignition on. Run Quick Test until the completion of the Continuous Codes. Voltmeter will read 0 volts. Depress and release throttle. Voltage reading should increase. If voltage is more than 10.5 volts, proceed with test. If voltage reading is 10.5 volts or less, depress and release throttle again. If voltage still does not increase, perform Output State Not Functioning Test.

3) Connect voltmeter negative lead to circuit 360 and positive lead to EGRV solenoid circuit 361. Depress and release throttle while observing voltmeter. Connect voltmeter negative lead to circuit 362 and positive lead to EGRC solenoid circuit 361. Depress and release throttle while observing voltmeter. If both outputs cycle on and off (high to low voltage), proceed to step 4). If either output does not cycle on and off, proceed to step 8).

4) Install vacuum pump to EGRC solenoid bottom port and connect a vacuum gauge to output tee. Disconnect vent vacuum line that goes to air cleaner. Apply and maintain a vacuum to solenoid with vacuum pump. While depressing and releasing throttle, observe vacuum gauge at output. If vacuum does not cycle on and off in less than 2 seconds, replace solenoid assembly and repeat Quick Test. If vacuum output cycles on and off in less than 2 seconds, proceed with test.

5) Turn ignition off and wait for 10 seconds. Check EGR vacuum supply line, vent vacuum line, and output vacuum line for presence of kinks, cracks, blockage, restrictions and leaks. If any problems are found, repair as necessary and repeat Quick Test. If all 3 vacuum lines are ok, proceed with test.

6) Turn ignition off and wait for 10 seconds. Connect a vacuum pump to EGR valve. Measure resistance of EVP sensor between sensor pins 1 and 3 while gradually increasing vacuum to 10 in. Hg. If EVP sensor reading does not decrease gradually to 100 ohms, proceed to step 7). If EVP resistance gradually decreases from 5,500 to 100 ohms, replace processor and repeat Quick Test.

7) Remove EVP sensor from EGR valve. Measure resistance of EVP sensor from pin 2 to pin 3 while gradually applying pressure to sensor shaft. Observe resistance as shaft is slowly pushed in, looking for sudden jumps in resistance readings. If EVP sensor reading does not decrease gradually, replace EGR valve assembly and repeat Quick Test. If EVP resistance gradually decreases from 5,500 to 100 ohms, replace EVP sensor and repeat Quick Test.

8) Turn ignition on. Connect voltmeter positive lead to circuit 361 at both solenoids and negative lead to ground. Measure voltage. If either reading is less than 10.5 volts, repair open in harness and repeat Quick Test. If both readings are more than 10.5 volts, proceed with test.

9) Turn ignition off and wait 10 seconds. Disconnect processor and inspect both 60 pin connectors. Connect breakout box to harness. Leave processor disconnected. Measure continuity from circuit 360 to breakout box pin 33 and circuit 362 to breakout box pin 52. If either resistance is 5 ohms or more, repair wiring harness and repeat Quick Test. If both resistances are less than 5 ohms, proceed with test.

10) Turn ignition off and wait 10 seconds. Disconnect EGR solenoid connectors. Measure resistance from breakout box pin 33 to pins 40, 46 and 57. Measure resistance from breakout box pin 52 to pins 40, 46 and 57. If all resistances are more than 10,000 ohms, replace processor and repeat Quick Test. If any resistance reading is less than 10,000 ohms, repair short circuit and repeat Quick Test.

RPM TOO LOW FOR EGR TEST (CODE 35)

1) Check for codes 12 and/or 13. If code 12 is present, perform EVP Sensor Test. If code 13 is present, perform RPM Not Returning To Normal Test. If no code 12 and/or 13 appears, proceed with test.

2) Turn ignition off and wait 10 seconds. Connect a tachometer to engine. Connect jumper wire to self-test input wire. Start engine and run at 1500 RPM. Record engine running service codes. Check for code 35. If code 35 is present, replace processor and repeat Quick Test. If code 35 is not present, repeat Quick Test and service codes as necessary.

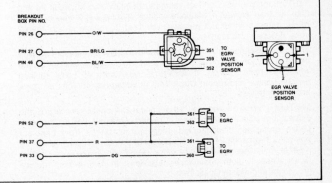

TEST J

FUEL MIXTURE TEST (CODE 41)

1) Verify that vehicle was running more than 2 minutes immediately before testing. If not, prepare vehicle and repeat Quick Test. If so, proceed with test.

2) Check that oxygen sensor lead is connected. Check oxygen sensor ground for proper connection and absence of corrosion. If any problems are found, repair as necessary and repeat Quick Test. Otherwise, proceed with test.

3) Disconnect oxygen sensor lead. Connect a DVOM between oxygen sensor lead and ground. Perform Engine Running Test and monitor oxygen sensor voltage for 14 seconds after start. If voltage reading is .45 volts or more, oxygen sensor is ok, proceed to step **14)**. If voltage reading is less than .45 volts, reconnect oxygen sensor and proceed with test.

4) Connect oxygen sensor. Disconnect thermactor air supply hose at the air pump and cap the hose to the manifold. Perform Engine Running Test. Check for code 41. If code 41 is not present, problem is not in EEC system. If code 41 is present, leave thermactor disconnected and proceed with test.

5) Turn ignition off and wait 10 seconds. Disconnect FBC solenoid connector. Start engine and perform Engine Running Test. Check for code 41. If code 41 is not present, proceed to step **8)**. If code 41 is present, leave FBC solenoid disconnected and proceed with test.

6) Run vehicle for 2 minutes at part throttle. After vehicle warm-up, hold choke plate 3/4 closed and perform Engine Running Test. Check for code 41. If code 41 is not present, fault is not in the EEC system, hook-up all disconnected parts and check fuel system for trouble. If code 41 is present, proceed with test.

7) Turn ignition off and wait 10 seconds. Disconnect jumper wire from self-test connector. Start engine. Alternate between 30 seconds of idle operation and 5 seconds of part-throttle operation for 3 minutes. Check engine idle quality. If engine idles rough or poorly, connect all disconnected components and check fuel system for trouble. If engine idles normally, proceed to step **10)**.

8) Turn ignition off and wait for 10 seconds. Measure resistance from each FBC solenoid terminal to ground. If either resistance is less than 1,000 ohms, replace FBC solenoid and repeat Quick Test. If both resistances are 1,000 ohms or more, proceed with test.

9) Turn ignition off and wait 10 seconds. Disconnect processor and inspect both 60 pin connectors. Connect breakout box to harness. Leave processor disconnected. With ignition on, connect voltmeter negative lead to harness circuit 97 and positive lead to battery positive post. If voltage is more than 2 volts, repair harness short in circuit 97 and repeat Quick Test. If voltage is 2 volts or less, replace processor and repeat Quick Test.

10) Turn ignition off and wait 10 seconds. Disconnect oxygen sensor connector. Measure resistance between harness circuit 94 and ground. If resistance is 10,000 ohms or less, proceed to step **11)**. If resistance is more than 10,000 ohms, proceed to step **12)**.

11) Turn ignition off and wait for 10 seconds. Disconnect 60-pin processor connector. Inspect for damaged pins, corrosion, frayed wires and pins pushed out. Correct as necessary. Measure resistance between harness circuit 94 and ground. If resistance is 10,000 ohms or less, repair short circuit, connect all disconnected components, and repeat Quick Test. If resistance is more than 10,000 ohms, replace processor, reconnect all disconnected components, and repeat Quick Test.

12) Turn ignition on. Connect voltmeter positive lead to circuit 94 and negative lead to ground. Measure voltage. If voltage is 2 volts or more, repair harness short and repeat Quick Test. If voltage is less than 2 volts, proceed with test.

13) Start vehicle and run for 2 minutes. Using DVOM measure voltage between oxygen sensor lead and ground. Hold choke plate 3/4 closed while observing voltage. If voltage is less than .45 volts, replace oxygen sensor and repeat Quick Test. If voltage is .45 volts or more, proceed with test.

14) Turn ignition off and wait 10 seconds. Disconnect processor and inspect both 60 pin connectors. Connect breakout box to harness. Leave processor disconnected. Measure resistance from breakout box pin 29 to circuit 94 and from breakout box pin 49 to pin 40 or 60. If either resistance is 5 ohms or more, repair faulty circuits and repeat Quick Test. If both resistances are less than 5 ohms, replace processor and repeat Quick Test.

VACUUM SWITCH TEST (CODE 42 & 47)

1) Check Vehicle Emission Control Decal to see if the vehicle is equipped with a 3-gang vacuum switch. If not, proceed to step **5)**. If so, proceed to step **2)**.

2) Turn ignition on and wait 10 seconds. Connect voltmeter positive lead to circuit 361 at FBC solenoid and negative lead to ground. Turn ignition on and observe voltage. If voltage reading is 10.5 volts or less, proceed to step **13)**. If voltage reading is more than 10.5 volts, proceed with test.

3) Turn ignition off and wait 10 seconds. With voltmeter still connected to circuit 361 and ground, perform Engine Running Test. Observe voltage. If voltage reading is 10.5 volts or less, proceed to step **4)**. If voltage reading is more than 10.5 volts, proceed to step **5)**.

4) Turn ignition off and wait 10 seconds. Tee a vacuum gauge into the manifold vacuum supply line at vacuum switch No. 3. Tee a second vacuum gauge into the spark port vacuum line at vacuum switch No. 1. Perform Engine Running Test while observing both vacuum gauges. If vacuum reading at switch No. 3 is less than 14.5 in. Hg, check both vacuum lines for restrictions or leaks; if ok, check engine manifold vacuum. If manifold vacuum is less than 14.5 in. Hg, determine and correct cause of low vacuum. If vacuum reading at switch No. 3 is greater than 14.5 in. Hg or if vacuum reading at switch No. 1 is greater than 2 in. Hg, replace vacuum switch assembly and repeat Quick Test.

5) Check for fully open choke plate. If not fully open, perform Variable Voltage Choke Test. If fully open, proceed with test.

6) Disconnect oxygen sensor. Perform Engine Running Test. Check for code 41. If code 41 is not present, proceed to step **12)**. If code 41 is present, proceed with test.

7) Turn ignition off and wait 10 seconds. Disconnect FBC solenoid connector and measure solenoid resistance. If resistance is less than 15 ohms or more than 30 ohms, replace FBC solenoid and repeat Quick Test. If resistance is between 15 and 30 ohms, reconnect FBC solenoid and proceed with test.

8) Turn ignition off and wait for 10 seconds. Connect voltmeter negative lead to self-test output connector and positive lead to battery positive post. Turn ignition on. Run Quick Test until the completion of the Continuous Codes. Voltmeter will read 0 volts. Depress and release throttle. Voltage reading should increase. If voltage increased, leave voltmeter connected and proceed with test. If voltage reading did not increase, depress and release throttle again. If voltage still does not increase, perform Output State Not Functioning Test.

9) Connect voltmeter negative lead to circuit 97 and positive lead to FBC solenoid circuit 361. Depress and release throttle while observing voltmeter. If FBC output cycles on and off (high to low voltage), problem is not in EEC system. If FBC output does not cycle on and off, proceed to step **10)**.

10) Connect voltmeter positive lead to harness circuit 361 and negative lead to ground. Turn ignition on and measure voltage. If voltage is less than 10 volts, repair open in power circuit and repeat Quick Test. If voltage is 10 volts or more, proceed with test.

11) Turn ignition off and wait 10 seconds. Disconnect processor and inspect both 60 pin connectors. Connect breakout box to harness. Leave processor disconnected. Measure continuity from circuit 97 to breakout box pin 58. If resistance is more than 5 ohms, repair wiring harness and repeat Quick Test. If resistance is 5 ohms or less, replace processor and repeat Quick Test.

12) Turn ignition off and wait 10 seconds. Disconnect processor and inspect both 60 pin connectors. Connect breakout box to harness. Leave processor disconnected. Measure resistance from breakout box pin 29 to breakout box pin 46. If resistance is more than 10,000 ohms, replace processor and repeat Quick Test. If resistance is 10,-000 ohms or less, isolate and repair short circuits then repeat Quick Test.

13) Turn ignition off and wait 10 seconds. Connect voltmeter positive lead to vacuum switch harness circuit 361A and negative lead to ground. Leave vacuum switch assembly connected to harness. Turn ignition on and measure voltage. If voltage is 10.5 volts or less, repair open in circuit 361 and repeat Quick Test. If voltage is more than 10.5 volts, proceed with test.

14) Turn ignition on. Connect voltmeter positive lead to vacuum switch circuit 361B and negative lead to ground. Leave vacuum switch assembly connected. Measure voltage. If voltage is more than 10.5 volts, repair open in harness to solenoid and repeat Quick Test. If voltage is 10.5 volts or less, replace vacuum switch assembly and repeat Quick Test.

TEST J (Cont.)

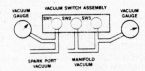

OXYGEN SENSOR TEST (CODE 43)

1) Disconnect jumper wire from self-test connector. Run vehicle at 2,000 RPM for 2 minutes. Perform Engine Running Test and record codes. Check for code 43. If code 43 is not present, repair other service codes as necessary. If code 43 is present, proceed with test.

2) Check for exhaust leaks. If any leaks are found, repair as necessary and repeat Quick Test. Otherwise, proceed with test.

3) If idle quality remains poor during and after the Engine Running Test, problem is not EEC related, check FBC solenoid for sticking and check fuel system operation. If idle quality improves during and after the Engine Running Test, replace oxygen sensor and repeat Quick Test.

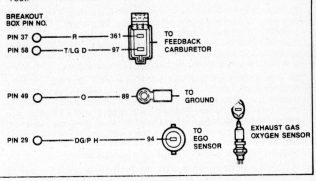

TEST K

KNOCK SENSOR TEST (CODE 25)

1) Prepare vehicle for Engine Running Test. Using a 4 oz. hammer, prepare to tap on driver's side exhaust manifold, directly above the knock sensor, when the Dynamic Response Signal is given. Perform Engine Running Test. Tap moderately on exhaust manifold when the meter indicates Dynamic Test is ready. After 15 seconds a code will be generated. If code 25 is not present, knock system is ok, repeat Engine Running Test and service codes as necessary. If code 25 is present, proceed with test.

2) Disconnect knock sensor connector and inspect. Connect voltmeter positive lead to harness circuit 310 and negative lead to circuit 359. Measure voltage. If voltage is less than 1 volt, proceed to step **3)**. If voltage is more than 4 volts, proceed to step **5)**. If voltage is between 1 and 4 volts, proceed to step **6)**.

3) Turn ignition off and wait 10 seconds. Disconnect processor and inspect both 60 pin connectors. Connect breakout box to harness. Leave processor disconnected. Measure continuity from circuit 310 to breakout box pin 23 and circuit 359 to breakout box pin 46. If either resistance is 5 ohms or more, repair wiring harness and repeat Quick Test. If both resistances are less than 5 ohms, proceed with test.

4) Turn ignition off and wait 10 seconds. Connect breakout box. Measure resistance from circuit 310 to pins 40, 46 and 60. If any resistance is less than 10,000 ohms, repair harness short and repeat Quick Test. If all resistances are 10,000 ohms or more, proceed with test.

5) Turn ignition off and wait 10 seconds. Disconnect processor and inspect both 60 pin connectors. Connect breakout box to harness. Leave processor disconnected. Turn ignition on. Connect voltmeter positive lead to breakout box pin 23 and negative lead to pin 40. Measure voltage. If voltage is more than .5 volts, repair harness short to power and repeat Quick Test. If voltage is less than .5 volts, proceed with test.

6) Plug a substitute knock sensor into harness (do not install). Perform Engine Running Test. Lightly tap knock sensor with 4 oz. hammer when Dynamic Test ready signal is given. After 15 seconds a code will be generated. If code 25 is not present, install new knock sensor and repeat Quick Test. If code 25 is present, replace processor and remove substitute knock sensor. Repeat Quick Test with original knock sensor.

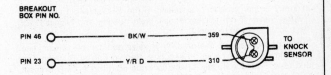

TEST L

AIR MANAGEMENT SYSTEM TEST (CODE 44)

1) Verify proper vacuum line routing to the TAB/TAD solenoids and to the bypass/diverter valve. Check for kinked, blocked or disconnected vacuum lines or air hoses. If any problems are found, repair as necessary and repeat Quick Test. Otherwise, proceed with test.

2) Turn ignition off and wait 10 seconds. Disconnect TAB solenoid connector and measure solenoid resistance. Disconnect TAD solenoid connector and measure solenoid resistance. If either resistance is less than 50 ohms or more than 110 ohms, replace TAB/TAD solenoid assembly and repeat Quick Test. If both resistances are between 50 and 110 ohms, reconnect solenoids and proceed with test.

3) Turn ignition off and wait for 10 seconds. Connect voltmeter negative lead to self-test output connector and positive lead to battery positive post. Turn ignition on. Run Quick Test until the completion of the Continuous Codes. Voltmeter will read 0 volts. Depress and release throttle. Voltage reading should increase. If voltage increased, leave voltmeter connected and proceed with test. If voltage reading did not increase, depress and release throttle again. If voltage still does not increase, perform Output State Not Functioning Test.

4) Connect voltmeter negative lead to circuit 190 and positive lead to TAB solenoid circuit 361. Depress and release throttle while observing voltmeter. Connect voltmeter negative lead to circuit 200 and positive lead to TAD solenoid circuit 361. Depress and release throttle while observing voltmeter. If both outputs cycle on and off (high to low voltage), proceed to step **5**). If either output does not cycle on and off, proceed to step **7**).

5) Install vacuum pump to TAB solenoid vacuum supply port and install a vacuum gauge to output port. Apply and maintain a vacuum at supply port. Observe vacuum gauge while depressing and releasing throttle. Repeat procedure for TAD solenoid. If either vacuum output does not cycle on and off, replace solenoid assembly and repeat Quick Test. If both vacuum outputs cycle on and off, proceed with test.

6) With vacuum lines to TAB/TAD solenoids disconnected, start engine and check for vacuum. If vacuum is present, EEC system is ok, check Thermactor pump. If no vacuum is present, repair vacuum source blockage or leak and repeat Quick Test.

7) Turn ignition on. Connect voltmeter positive lead to circuit 361 at TAB solenoid and negative lead to ground. Measure voltage. Repeat procedure at TAD solenoid. If either voltage is less than 10.5 volts, repair open circuit in harness and repeat Quick Test. If both voltage readings are more than 10.5 volts, proceed with test.

8) Turn ignition off and wait 10 seconds. Disconnect processor and inspect both 60 pin connectors. Connect breakout box to harness. Leave processor disconnected. Measure continuity from circuit 190 to breakout box pin 51 and circuit 200 to breakout box pin 11. If either resistance is 5 ohms or more, repair wiring harness and repeat Quick Test. If both resistances are less than 5 ohms, proceed with test.

9) Turn ignition on. With TAB/TAD solenoids disconnected, measure voltage from breakout box pin 51 to ground and from pin 11 to ground. If both voltages are less than 1 volt, replace processor and repeat Quick Test. If either voltage is 1 volt or more, repair short to power and repeat Quick Test. If code 44 is still present, replace processor.

TAD SYSTEM TEST (CODE 45)

1) Verify proper vacuum line routing to the TAD solenoid and to the diverter valve. If not correct, repair faulty routing and repeat Quick Test. If ok, proceed to step **2**).

2) Disconnect vacuum line on diverter valve and cap off vacuum line. Turn ignition off and wait 10 seconds. Repeat Engine Running Test and record service codes. Check for code 45. If code 45 is present, EEC system is ok, check Thermactor system. If code 45 is not present, proceed with test.

3) Turn ignition off and wait 10 seconds. Disconnect TAD solenoid connector and measure solenoid resistance. If resistance is less than 50 ohms or greater than 100 ohms, replace TAB/TAD solenoid assembly and repeat Quick Test. If resistance is between 50 and 100 ohms, reconnect solenoid and proceed with test.

4) Turn ignition off and wait for 10 seconds. Connect voltmeter negative lead to self-test output connector and positive lead to battery positive post. Turn ignition on. Run Quick Test until the completion of the Continuous Codes. Voltmeter will read 0 volts. Depress and release throttle. Voltage reading should increase. If voltage increased, leave voltmeter connected and proceed with test. If voltage reading did not increase, depress and release throttle again. If voltage still does not increase, perform Output State Not Functioning Test.

5) Disconnect TAD connector. Connect voltmeter negative lead to circuit 200 and positive lead to TAD solenoid circuit 361. Depress and release throttle while observing voltmeter. If output cycles on and off (high to low voltage), replace TAD solenoid and repeat Quick Test. If output does not cycle on and off, proceed to step **6**).

6) Turn ignition off and wait 10 seconds. Disconnect processor and inspect both 60 pin connectors. Measure resistance of harness circuit 200 to ground. If resistance is less than 10,000 ohms, repair harness short and repeat Quick Test. If resistance is 10,000 ohms or more, replace processor and repeat Quick Test.

TAB SYSTEM TEST (CODE 46)

1) Verify proper vacuum line routing to the TAB solenoid and to the bypass valve. If not correct, repair faulty routing and repeat Quick Test. If ok, proceed to step **2**).

2) Disconnect vacuum line on bypass valve and cap off vacuum line. Turn ignition off and wait 10 seconds. Repeat Engine Running Test and record service codes. Check for code 46. If code 46 is present, EEC system is ok, check Thermactor system. If code 46 is not present, proceed with test.

3) Turn ignition off and wait 10 seconds. Disconnect TAB solenoid connector and measure solenoid resistance. If resistance is less than 50 ohms or greater than 100 ohms, replace TAB/TAD solenoid assembly and repeat Quick Test. If resistance is between 50 and 100 ohms, reconnect solenoid and proceed with test.

4) Turn ignition off and wait for 10 seconds. Connect voltmeter negative lead to self-test output connector and positive lead to battery positive post. Turn ignition on. Run Quick Test until the completion of the Continuous Codes. Voltmeter will read 0 volts. Depress and release throttle. Voltage reading should increase. If voltage increased, leave voltmeter connected and proceed with test. If voltage reading did not increase, depress and release throttle again. If voltage still does not increase, perform Output State Not Functioning Test.

5) Disconnect TAB connector. Connect voltmeter negative lead to circuit 190 and positive lead to TAB solenoid circuit 361. Depress and release throttle while observing voltmeter. If output cycles on and off (high to low voltage), replace TAB solenoid and repeat Quick Test. If output does not cycle on and off, proceed to step **6**).

6) Turn ignition off and wait 10 seconds. Disconnect processor and inspect both 60 pin connectors. Measure resistance of harness circuit 190 to ground. If resistance is less than 10,000 ohms, repair harness short and repeat Quick Test. If resistance is 10,000 ohms or more, replace processor and repeat Quick Test.

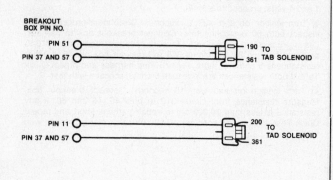

FORD EEC-IV SYSTEM (Cont.)

TEST M

INSUFFICIENT RPM DURING QUICK TEST (CODE 77)

Perform Engine Running Test. When Dynamic Response Signal is given, open throttle to the WOT position. Check for code 77. If code 77 is not present, service other codes as necessary. If code 77 is displayed, test was performed incorrectly. Repeat test.

INSUFFICIENT MAP SENSOR DYNAMIC RESPONSE (CODE 72)

1) Tee a vacuum gauge into the intake manifold vacuum line to MAP sensor. Perform Engine Running Test while observing vacuum gauge. Record Engine Running service codes. Check to see if vacuum decreased by more than 9 in. Hg during the Dynamic Response Test. Check for code 72. If vacuum changed more than 9 in. Hg and code 72 did not appear during test, disconnect vacuum gauge and service other codes as necessary. If vacuum changed by more than 9 in. Hg and code 72 was displayed, replace MAP sensor and repeat test. If vacuum decrease was 9 in. Hg or less, proceed with test.

2) Check vacuum lines for proper routing. Check MAP vacuum line for kinks or blockage. If any problems are found, correct as necessary and return to step **1)**. If no problems are found, fault is not in EEC system, check vacuum source for trouble.

INSUFFICIENT TP SENSOR DYNAMIC RESPONSE (CODE 73)

1) Disconnect TP sensor. Connect ohmmeter across outside terminals of TP sensor. Observe resistance while moving throttle to WOT. If resistance increases by 1,000 ohms or less, replace TP sensor and repeat Quick Test. If resistance increases by more than 1,000 ohms, proceed with test.

2) Reconnect TP sensor. Perform Engine Running Test. Open the throttle to the WOT position when the Dynamic Response Signal is given. Check for codes 23 or 73. If code 23 is present, perform TP Sensor Test. If code 73 is present, replace TP sensor and repeat Quick Test. If neither code 23 nor 73 is present, service other codes as necessary.

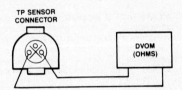

TEST N

RPM TEST (CODE 12)

1) If codes 31, 41 and/or 58 are present, perform appropriate tests before proceeding.

2) Check throttle plates and linkages for binding. Check speed control (if equipped) for binding. If any trouble is found, correct as necessary and repeat Quick Test. If no trouble is found, proceed with test.

3) Turn ignition off and wait 10 seconds. Disconnect processor and inspect both 60 pin connectors. Connect breakout box to harness and processor. Disconnect ISC connector. Measure continuity from circuit 95 to breakout box pin 41 and circuit 96 to breakout box pin 21. If either resistance is 5 ohms or more, repair wiring harness and repeat Quick Test. If both resistances are less than 5 ohms, proceed with test.

4) Disconnect processor. Turn ignition on. Measure voltage from breakout box pin 41 to pins 40 and 60. Measure voltage from breakout box pin 21 to pins 40 and 60. If any voltage reading is 1 volt or more, repair short to power circuit and repeat Quick Test. If code 12 is still present, replace processor. If all voltage readings are less than 1 volt, proceed with test.

5) Disconnect processor. Measure resistance from breakout box pin 41 to pins 40, 46 and 60. Measure resistance from breakout box pin 21 to pins 40, 46 and 60. If any resistance reading is 10,000 ohms or less, repair faulty circuit and repeat Quick Test. If code 12 is still present, replace processor. If all resistance readings are more than 10,000 ohms, proceed with test.

6) Disconnect processor. Turn ignition off and wait 10 seconds. Connect voltmeter positive lead to breakout box pin 1 and negative lead to ground. If voltage is less than 10.5 volts, repair open circuit and repeat step **6)** if code 12 is still present. If voltage is 10.5 volts or more, proceed with test.

7) Turn ignition off and wait 10 seconds. Reconnect ISC motor. Jumper breakout box pin 21 to pin 1 and pin 41 to ground. Check ISC motor for extension of shaft. If motor shaft extends less than 2", replace ISC motor and repeat Quick Test. If shaft extends 2" or more, proceed with test.

8) Turn ignition off and wait 10 seconds. Jumper breakout box pin 41 to pin 1 and pin 21 to ground. Check ISC motor for retraction. If shaft does not retract, replace ISC motor and repeat Quick Test. If shaft retracts, proceed with test.

9) Turn ignition off and wait 10 seconds. Jumper breakout box pin 21 to pin 1 and pin 41 to ground. Check ISC motor for extension of shaft. If motor shaft does not extend, replace ISC motor and repeat Quick Test. If shaft extends, replace processor and repeat Quick Test.

RPM NOT RETURNING TO NORMAL TEST (CODE 13)

1) Prepare system for normal engine operation. Disconnect the jumper wire from the self-test input connector. Turn A/C off. Run engine, alternating between 30 seconds at idle and 5 seconds at part throttle for a total of 3 minutes. Return engine to idle and note idle quality. If idle speed is erratic or oscillating, check for the following: vacuum leaks; codes 22, 31, 41 or 58. Repair codes as necessary before continuing. If idle speed is ok, proceed with test.

2) Connect equipment for Quick Test. Perform Engine Running Test. Check for code 13. If code 13 is not present, service other codes as necessary. If code 13 is present, proceed with test.

3) Inspect throttle and choke mechanisms for sticking or binding. Check for throttle stuck on high cam. If any problems are found, repair as necessary and repeat Quick Test. If no problems are found, proceed with test.

4) Perform Key On - Engine Off Test. Record the On Demand codes. Check for code 68. If code 68 is present, perform appropriate Idle Tracking Switch Test. If code 68 is not present, proceed with test.

5) Disconnect jumper wire from self-test connector. Disconnect ISC motor connector. Connect tachometer. Check anti-diesel idle speed against specifications. If idle speed is within specifications, perform RPM Test. If idle speed is not within specifications, adjust as necessary.

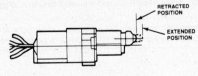

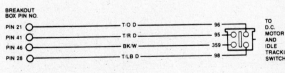

1983 Computerized Engine Controls
FORD EEC-IV SYSTEM (Cont.)

TEST P

NO CODES CODES DISPLAYED

1) Turn ignition off and wait 10 seconds. Connect voltmeter positive lead to EGR vent solenoid circuit 361 and negative lead to ground. Measure voltage. If voltage is 1 volt or more, isolate short to power and repair. If voltage is less than 1 volt, repeat Quick Test. If still no codes, proceed with test.

2) Disconnect MAP sensor. Connect voltmeter positive lead to MAP harness connector circuit 351 and negative lead to ground. Turn ignition on. If voltage is more than 6 volts, perforn Reference Voltage Test. If voltage is less than 4 volts, proceed to step **6)**. If voltage is between 4 and 6 volts, proceed to step **3)**.

3) Turn ignition off and wait 10 seconds. Disconnect MAP sensor. Perform Key On - Engine Off Test. If any codes are present, replace MAP sensor and repeat Quick Test. If no codes are present, proceed with test.

4) Turn ignition off and wait 10 seconds. Disconnect processor and inspect both 60 pin connectors. Connect breakout box to harness and processor. Measure continuity from circuit 100 to breakout box pin 48, circuit 359 at self test connector to breakout box pin 46 and circuit 201 to pin 17. If any resistance is 5 ohms or more, repair wiring harness and repeat Quick Test. If all resistances are less than 5 ohms, proceed with test.

5) Turn ignition off and wait 10 seconds. Disconnect processor. Measure resistance from breakout box pin 17 to pin 40 or 60. If resistance is less than 10,000 ohms, repair short circuit and repeat Quick Test. If resistance is 10,000 ohms or more, replace processor and repeat Quick Test.

6) Turn ignition off and wait 10 seconds. Disconnect MAP sensor. Perform Key On - Engine Off Test. If any codes are present, proceed to step **7)**. If no codes are present, proceed to step **8)**.

7) Turn ignition off and wait 10 seconds. Disconnect processor and inspect both 60 pin connectors. Connect breakout box to harness. Leave processor disconnected. Measure continuity from circuit 351 to breakout box pin 26. If resistance is more than 5 ohms, repair wiring harness and repeat Quick Test. If resistance is less than 5 ohms, replace processor and repeat Quick Test.

8) Turn ignition off and wait 10 seconds. Disconnect processor and inspect both 60 pin connectors. Connect breakout box to harness. Leave processor disconnected. Turn ignition on. Connect voltmeter positive lead to breakout box pin 37 and negative lead to pin 40. Measure voltage. If voltage is 10.5 volts or more, perform Reference Voltage Test. If voltage is less than 10.5 volts, perform Battery Voltage Test.

INVALID CODES DISPLAYED

1) Check automatic transmission equipped models to ensure that shift lever is fully seated in "P". If not, correct and repeat Quick Test. If ok, proceed with test.

2) Turn ignition off and wait 10 seconds. Connect voltmeter positive lead to EGR vent solenoid circuit 361 and negative lead to ground. Measure voltage. If voltage is 1 volt or more, isolate short to power and repair. If voltage is less than 1 volt, repeat Quick Test. If still no codes, proceed with test.

3) Turn ignition off and wait 10 seconds. Disconnect processor and inspect both 60 pin connectors. Connect breakout box to harness and processor. Turn ignition on. Connect voltmeter positive lead to breakout box pin 1 and negative lead to pin 40 or 60. Measure voltage. If voltage is 10.5 volts or more, proceed with test. If voltage is less than 10.5 volts, repair open in harness circuit and repeat Quick Test.

4) Turn ignition off and wait 10 seconds. Disconnect MAP sensor. Perform Engine Running Test. If any codes are present, perform MAP

Sensor Test. If no codes are present, replace processor and repeat Quick Test. If problem still exists, EEC is not at fault.

VEHICLE STALLS DURING QUICK TEST

1) Turn ignition off and wait 10 seconds. Install tachometer. Perform Engine Running Test and try to maintain engine speed of 2,000 RPM. If engine stalls, problem is not in EEC system. If engine does not stall, record Engine Running Test service codes and proceed with test.

2) Check for vacuum leaks and correct as necessary. Check for codes 31, 33, 41 and 58. Ignore any other codes at this time. If no codes are displayed, perform the No Codes Displayed Test. If codes 31 and/or 33 are displayed, perform appropriate EGR Test. If code 41 is displayed, proceed to step **4)**. If code 58 is displayed, proceed to step **3)**.

3) Disconnect jumper wire from self-test connector. Start engine and run engine for 15 seconds. Turn ignition off and wait 10 seconds. Inspect ISC motor for full extension. If motor shaft is extended 2" or more, problem is not in EEC system, perform normal engine diagnosis. If motor shaft is extended less than 2", perform RPM Test.

4) Turn ignition off and wait 10 seconds. Disconnect FBC solenoid connector. Disconnect jumper wire from self-test connector. Start and run engine at 2,000 RPM for 2 minutes. Activate Engine Running Test. Check for code 41. If code 41 is not present, perform Fuel Mixture Test. If code 41 is present, check for vacuum leaks and correct as necessary.

OUTPUT STATE NOT FUNCTIONING TEST

1) Turn ignition off and wait 10 seconds. Perform Key On - Engine Off Test. Leave ignition on to enter output state check. Check for codes 23, 53, 63 and/or 68 during the On Demand Test results. If any of the codes are displayed, service as necessary according to the On Demand instructions of the Key On - Engine Off Test. If none of the listed codes are displayed, leave ignition on and proceed with test.

2) Connect voltmeter negative lead to self-test output connector and positive lead to battery positive post. Depress throttle wide open and release. Apply slight pressure to throttle lever. Measure voltage. If voltage is 10 volts or less, replace TP sensor and repeat Quick Test. If voltage is more than 10 volts, check throttle linkages for sticking or binding, repair as necessary, and repeat Quick Test.

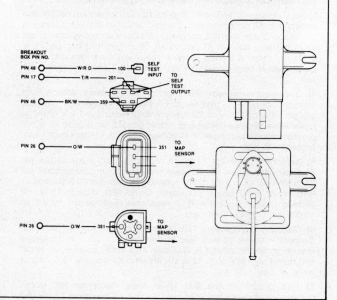

FORD EEC-IV SYSTEM (Cont.)

TEST Q

SPARK TIMING CHECK

1) Check to ensure that jumper wire was connected to self-test connector during Engine Running Test. Check timing during Engine Running Test within 25 seconds of engine start-up. If base timing is 17-23°, repeat Engine Running Test. If timing is not within 17-23°, proceed to step 2).

2) Locate and disconnect distributor spark output test connector. Connect a jumper wire to ground. Start engine. Connect jumper wire to distributor test connector. If vehicle stalls, proceed to step 3). If vehicle does not stall, check for open in circuit 324. If no opens are found, problem is in ignition system.

3) Disconnect jumper wire. Leave distributor test connector disconnected. Start engine and check base timing. If timing is within 3° of base timing (20°), proceed to step 4). If timing is off by more than 3°, correct timing as necessary.

4) Turn ignition off and wait 10 seconds. Disconnect processor and inspect both 60 pin connectors. Connect breakout box to harness. Leave processor disconnected. Measure continuity from circuit 324 to breakout box pin 36. If resistance is 5 ohms or less, replace processor and check timing as in step 1). If resistance is more than 5 ohms, repair open circuit and reconnect distributor test connector. Check timing as in step 1). If problem is still present, perform ignition system diagnosis.

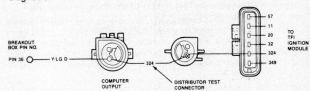

TEST R

IDLE TRACKING SWITCH TEST (CODE 58)

1) Press ISC motor shaft to simulate throttle contact. With force pushing on motor shaft, perform Key On - Engine Off Test. If code 68 is present, proceed to RPM Test. If code 68 is not present, go to next step.

2) Disconnect ISC motor. Perform Key On - Engine Off Test. If code 68 is present, replace ISC motor and repeat Quick Test. If code 68 is not present, go to next step.

3) Turn ignition off and wait 10 seconds. Disconnect processor 60 pin connector and check for corrosion or bent pins. Connect breakout box, leaving processor disconnected. Disconnect ISC motor. Measure resistance of breakout box pin 28 to breakout box pins 26, 40, 46 and 60. If resistance on any pin is 10,000 ohms or less, repair short to ground. Repeat Quick Test. If all resistances are 10,000 ohms or over, replace processor and repeat Quick Test.

IDLE TRACKING SWITCH TEST (CODE 68)

1) Move throttle away from ISC motor shaft. Perform Key On - Engine Off Test. Check for code 68. If code 68 is present, go to next step. If code 68 is not present, proceed to RPM Test.

2) Turn ignition off and wait 10 seconds. Disconnect ISC motor. Connect a jumper between pins 3 and 4. Perform Key On - Engine Off Test. Check for code 68. If code 68 is present, go to next step. If code 68 is not present, replace ISC motor and repeat Quick Test.

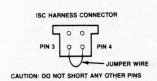

3) Turn ignition off and wait 10 seconds. Disconnect processor and inspect both 60 pin connectors. Connect breakout box to harness. Leave processor disconnected. Measure continuity of pin 46 to circuit 359 and pin 28 to circuit 98. If either resistance is over 5 ohms, repair faulty circuit and repeat Quick Test. If both resistances are under 5 ohms, replace processor and repeat Quick Test.

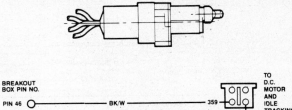

TEST S

NEUTRAL DRIVE SWITCH (CODE 67)

1) Ensure A/C was off during Quick Test. If A/C was on, turn to off and repeat Quick Test. If A/C was off, continue with test.

2) Check type of transmission. If transmission is automatic, go to next step. If transmission is manual, proceed to step 5).

3) Check shift selector position. If selector is not in Park or Neutral, engage selector in Park position. Repeat Quick Test. If selector is in Park or Neutral position, continue with test.

4) Check if engine will crank. If engine will not crank, proceed to No Start Test. If engine will crank, continue with test.

5) Disconnect processor 60 pin connector and inspect connectors. Connect breakout box with processor and harness connected. Connect jumper breakout box pin 30 to breakout box pin 46. Perform Key On - Engine Off Test. Record service codes. If code 67 is present, remove jumper and continue with test. If code 67 is not present, repair open circuit. Repeat Quick Test.

6) Turn ignition on. Connect DVOM positive test lead to breakout box pin 10 and negative test lead to pin 46. Check DVOM reading. If voltage is greater than 1 volt, verify A/C is off. Isolate short to power circuit or short to reference voltage circuit and repair. Repeat Quick Test. If voltage is 1 volt or less, replace processor and repeat Quick Test.

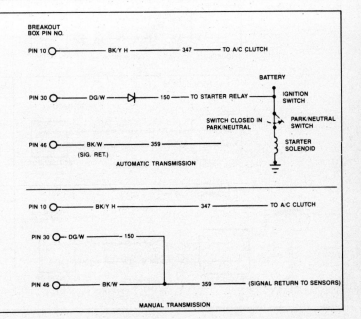

TEST U

WIGGLE TEST

1) Service Code 21. Turn ignition off and wait 10 seconds. Disconnect all self-test equipment. Drive vehicle and attempt to simulate complaint. After completing drive test, perform Key On - Engine Off Test. If code 21 appears, check thermostat operation. If okay, replace ECT sensor and repeat Quick Test. If no code 21, testing is complete.

2) Service Code 22. Connect vacuum pump to MAP sensor. Slowly apply 25 in. Hg. vacuum to sensor. Slowly bleed off vacuum. Lightly tap on sensor, and wiggle connector. Refer to fig. U2. If a service code is indicated (high VOM deflection), disconnect and inspect connectors. If good, replace MAP sensor and repeat Quick Test. If no code, go to step **11)**.

3) Service Code 31. Connect vacuum pump to EGR valve. Slowly apply 10 in. Hg to valve, then bleed off vacuum. Lightly tap on EVP sensor, and wiggle connector. Refer to fig. U3. If a service code is indicated (high VOM deflection), disconnect and inspect connectors. If good, replace EVP sensor and repeat Quick Test. If no codes, go to step **11)**.

4) Service Code 41. Turn ignition off and wait 10 seconds. Disconnect all self-test equipment. Drive vehicle and attempt to simulate complaint. After completing drive test, perform Key On - Engine Off Test. If code 41 appears, go to step **5)**. If no code 41, testing complete.

5) Turn ignition off and wait 10 seconds. Perform Engine Running Test. If code 41 is present, proceed to Fuel Mixture Test, step **2)**. If no code 41, problem is not CEC related. Check fuel system.

6) Service Code 51. Lightly tap on ECT sensor, and wiggle connector. If a service code is indicated (high VOM deflection), disconnect and inspect connectors. Refer to fig. U6. If good, replace ECT sensor and repeat Quick Test. If no codes, go to step **11)**.

7) Service Code 54. Observe voltmeter. Lightly tap on ACT sensor and wiggle connector. Refer to fig. U7. If a service code is indicated (high VOM deflection), disconnect and inspect connectors. If good, replace ACT sensor and repeat Quick Test. If no codes, go to step **11)**.

8) Service Code 61. Perform same test as step **6)**. Refer to fig. U8. Results are the same.

9) Service Code 63. Move throttle slowly to wide open position. Release throttle slowly to closed position. Lightly tap on TP sensor and wiggle connectors. Refer to fig. U9. If a service code is indicated, disconnect and inspect connectors. If good, replace TP sensor and repeat Quick Test. If no codes, go to step **11)**.

10) Service Code 64. Perform same test as in step **7)**. Refer to fig. U10. Results are the same.

11) Observe voltmeter. Using figure number from step that brought you here, grasp harness as close to sensor connector as possible. Wiggle, shake or bend a small section of CEC system harness while working toward bulkhead. Do same to harness from bulkhead to processor. If a service code is indicated, isolate fault and make necessary repairs. Repeat Quick Test. If no codes, go to next step.

12) Turn ignition off and wait 10 seconds. Disconnect processor 60 pin connector. Inspect connector for damage, corrosion, etc. Repair as required and repeat Quick Test. If unable to duplicate fault, but problem still exists, drive vehicle and check for continuous codes. Repair as required and repeat Quick Test.

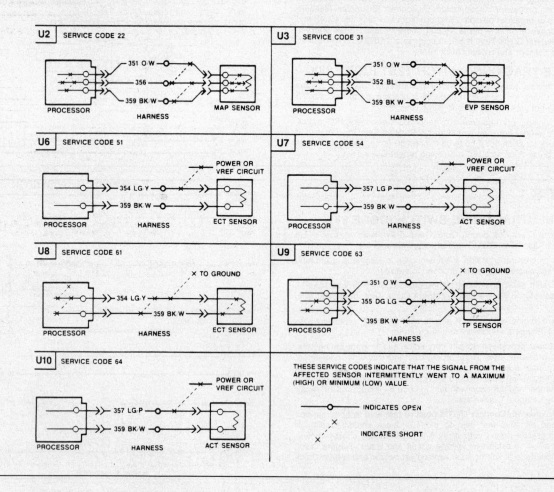

FORD EEC-IV SYSTEM (Cont.)

TEST X

INVALID CODES DURING CONTINUOUS TEST

1) Check if any EEC components are routed too close to high electrical energy components. If so, reroute them.

2) Turn ignition on. Perform Key On - Engine Off Test until first code is output, then deactivate Test. This will erase continuous codes. Turn ignition off. Perform Key On - Engine Off Test and record any codes. Valid codes are 11, 22, 31, 51, 54, 61, 63 and 64. If any codes are invalid, go to step **3)**. If all codes are valid, go back to Continuous Test portion of Quick Test.

3) Turn ignition off. Deactivate test. Disconnect ECT sensor. Turn ignition on and wait 15 seconds. Turn ignition off. Connect ECT sensor. Activate test. Turn ignition on and record codes. If code 51 is present, Keep Alive Memory is functional. Repeat Quick Test. If no code 51, go to next step.

4) Check power circuit to Keep Alive Memory for voltage. Turn ignition off. Disconnect processor and inspect 60 pin connectors. Connect breakout box to harness, with processor connected. Connect voltmeter positive lead to breakout box pin 1 and negative lead to pin 46. Turn ignition on. If less than 10 volts, repair open to power circuit and repeat Quick Test. If more than 10 volts, replace processor and repeat Quick Test.

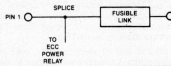

TEST Y

POWER INPUT TEST (CODE 55)

1) Turn ignition off and wait 10 seconds. Deactivate Key On - Engine Off Test. Disconnect processor 60 pin connector and inspect connectors. Connect breakout box to processor and harness. Connect voltmeter positive lead to breakout box pin 5 and negative lead to pin 40. Measure voltage with engine running. If voltage is over 13.5, continue with test. If voltage is between 10.5 volts and 13.5 volts, problem is not in EEC system, check charging system. If voltage is less than 10.5 volts, turn engine off, repair circuit 20 and repeat Quick Test.

2) Perform Engine Running Test. If code 55 is present, replace processor and repeat Quick Test. If no code 55, refer to system wiring diagram to isolate intermittent problem.

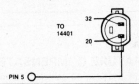

TEST Z

VARIABLE VOLTAGE CHOKE

1) Perform Engine Running Test. If choke voltage is greater than 10.5 volts, EEC system is ok. Check choke plates for binding and sticking. If no problem is found, check fuel system. If voltage is 10.5 or less, go to next step.

2) Turn ignition off and wait 10 seconds. Connect voltmeter negative lead to self-test output connector and positive lead to positive battery cable. Connect jumper wire to self-test input connector. Perform Key On - Engine Off Test until Continuous Test codes are completed. At this point voltmeter will indicate 0 volts. Depress and release throttle. If voltmeter reading changed to a high voltage, go to next step. If voltmeter reading did not change to a high voltage, depress throttle to wide open position and release. If self-test output connector voltage does not increase, proceed to Output State Not Functioning Test.

3) Connect voltmeter positive lead to circuit 361 on VVC relay and negative lead to VVC ouput circuit 462. While observing voltage, depress and release throttle several times to cycle output on and off. If VVC output cycles on and off, go to next step. If VVC output does not cycle on and off, go to step **5)**.

4) Turn ignition off and wait 10 seconds. Measure continuity from ground to pin 1 of relay connector and relay pin 3 to choke harness connector. If either resistance is more than 5 ohms, repair harness circuit and repeat Quick Test. If both resistances are 5 ohms or less, replace choke relay and repeat Quick Test.

5) Connect voltmeter positive lead to positive battery terminal. While observing voltage reading, depress and release throttle several times to cycle output on and off. If VVC output cycles on and off, repair open in choke power circuit 361 or 37 and repeat Quick Test. If VVC output voltage is low, go to next step. If VVC output voltage is high, go to step **7)**.

6) Turn ignition off and wait 10 seconds. Disconnect processor and inspect both 60 pin connectors. Connect breakout box to harness. Leave processor disconnected. Measure continuity of breakout box pin 55 to harness circuit 462. If resistance is 5 ohms or more, repair harness circuit 462 and repeat Quick Test. If resistance is less than 5 ohms, replace processor and repeat Quick Test.

7) Turn ignition off and wait 10 seconds. Disconnect processor and inspect both 60 pin connectors. Connect breakout box to harness leaving processor disconnected. Measure resistance of breakout box pin 55 to breakout box pins 40, 46 and 60. If any resistance reading is less than 10,000 ohms, go to next step. If all resistance readings are 10,000 ohms or more, replace processor and repeat Quick Test.

8) Turn ignition off and wait 10 seconds. Disconnect VVC relay. Measure resistance of breakout box pin 55 to breakout box pins 40, 46 and 60. If all resistance readings are 10,000 ohms or more, replace choke relay and repeat Quick Test. If any resistance readings are less than 10,000 ohms, repair harness short and repeat Quick Test.

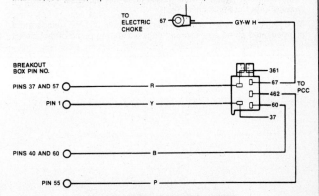

CANISTER PURGE TEST

1) Turn ignition off and wait 10 seconds. Disconnect canister purge solenoid connector and measure solenoid resistance. Disconnect solenoid connector. If solenoid resistance is between 40 and 90 ohms, connect canister purge solenoid and go to next step. If resistance is less than 40 ohms or more than 90 ohms, replace canister purge solenoid and repeat Quick Test.

2) Turn ignition off and wait 10 seconds. Connect voltmeter negative lead to self-test output connector and positive lead to positive battery cable. Connect jumper wire to self-test input connector. Perform Key On - Engine Off Test until Continuous Test codes are completed. At this point, voltmeter will indicate 0 volts. Depress and release throttle. If voltage changes to high reading, go to next step. If voltage does not change to high reading, depress throttle to wide open position and release. If self-test output voltage does not increase, proceed to Output State Not Functioning Test.

TEST Z (Cont.)

3) Connect voltmeter positive lead to circuit 361 on canister purge solenoid and negative lead to canister purge output circuit 101. While observing voltage, depress and release throttle several times. If canister purge output cycles on and off, EEC system is OK. Check solenoid for proper operation. If canister purge output voltage is low, go to next step. If canister purge output voltage is high, go to step **5)**.

4) Turn ignition on. Measure voltage from harness circuit 361 at canister purge solenoid to ground. If voltage is less than 10.5 volts, repair harness open in circuit 361 and repeat Quick Test. If voltage reading is 10.5 volts or more, go to next step.

5) Turn ignition off and wait 10 seconds. Disconnect processor and inspect pin 60 connectors. Connect breakout box to harness. Leave processor disconnected. Measure continuity of breakout box pin 35 to harness circuit 101 at canister purge connector. If resistance is greater than 5 ohms, repair open circuit 101 and repeat Quick Test. If resistance is 5 ohms or less, replace processor and repeat Quick Test.

BREAKOUT
BOX PIN NO.

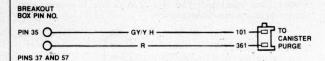

TEMPERATURE COMPENSATED PUMP

1) Turn ignition off and wait 10 seconds. Disconnect temperature compensated pump solenoid connector. Measure solenoid resistance. If solenoid resistance is between 50-110 ohms, connect solenoid and go to next step. If resistance is less than 50 ohms or more than 110 ohms, replace solenoid.

2) Turn ignition off and wait 10 seconds. Connect voltmeter negative lead to self-test output connector and positive test lead to battery positive post. Connect jumper wire to self-test input connector. Perform Key On - Engine Off Test until Continuous Test codes are completed. Voltmeter should now indicate 0 volts. Depress and release throttle. If voltmeter reading changed to high voltage, go to next step. If reading did not change to high voltage, depress and release throttle again. If voltage still does not increase, proceed to Output State Not Functioning Test.

3) Connect voltmeter positive lead to circuit 361 on temperature compensated pump solenoid and negative lead to pump output circuit

256. While observing voltmeter, depress and release throttle several times to cycle output on and off. If temperature compensated pump output cycles on and off, go to next step. If pump output does not cycle on and off, go to step **5)**.

4) Install vacuum pump to temperature compensated pump solenoid vacuum supply port and install vacuum gauge to output port. Apply a minimum of 6 in. Hg. of vacuum. Depress and release throttle to cycle output on and off. If vacuum output cycles on and off, go to next step. If vacuum output does not cycle on and off, replace solenoid and repeat Quick Test.

5) Check that temperature compensated pump vacuum lines are free of leaks, blockage and kinks. Verify vacuum line routing is correct. Repair vacuum lines as necessary and repeat Quick Test. If vacuum lines are OK, check fuel system.

6) Turn ignition on. Connect voltmeter positive lead to circuit 361 and negative lead to ground. If voltage on temperature compensated pump solenoid circuit 361 is more than 10.5 volts, go to step **8)**. If voltage reading is 10.5 volts or less, repair open in circuit 361 and repeat Quick Test.

7) Turn ignition off and wait 10 seconds. Disconnect processor and inspect both 60 pin connectors. Connect breakout box to harness, leaving processor disconnected. Measure continuity of breakout box pin 54 to harness circuit 256. If resistance reading is less than 5 ohms, replace processor and repeat Quick Test. If resistance reading is 5 ohms or more, repair open in circuit 256 and repeat Quick Test.

8) Turn ignition off and wait 10 seconds. Disconnect processor and inspect both 60 pin connectors. Connect breakout box to harness leaving processor disconnected. Measure resistance of breakout box pin 54 to breakout box pins 40, 46 and 60. If any resistance readings are less than 10,000 ohms, repair harness short in circuit 256 and repeat Quick Test. If all resistance readings are 10,000 ohms or more, replace processor and repeat Quick Test.

BREAKOUT
BOX PIN NO.

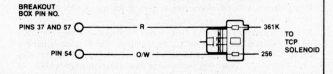

FORD EEC-IV SYSTEM (Cont.)

Fig. 3: EEC-IV System Wiring Diagram (Manual Transmission)

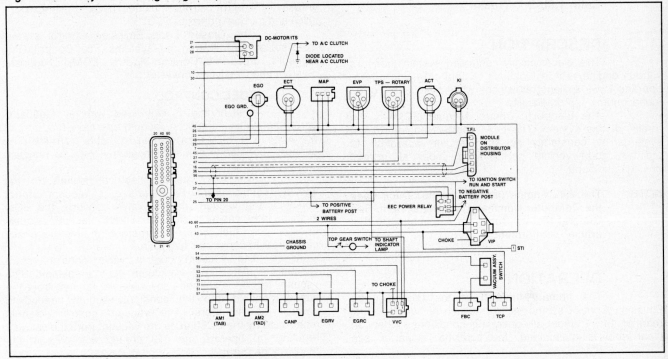

Also see chassis wiring in WIRING DIAGRAM Section

Fig. 4: EEC-IV System Wiring Diagram (Automatic Transmission)

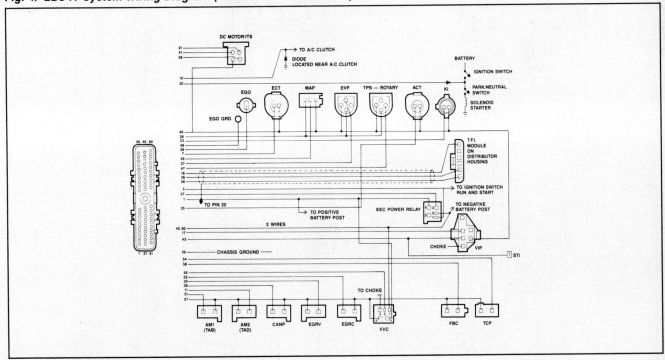

Also see chassis wiring in WIRING DIAGRAM Section

1983 Computerized Engine Controls
GENERAL MOTORS CLOSED LOOP EMISSION CONTROL SYSTEM

Calif. 1.9L S/T-Trucks

DESCRIPTION

This electronically controlled system monitors various engine/vehicle functions to control engine operation and lower exhaust emissions while maintaining good fuel economy and driveability.

The Electronic Control Module (ECM) is the "brain" of this system. The ECM controls engine-related systems by constantly adjusting engine operation to maintain good vehicle performance under all normal driving conditions.

NOTE: **The 2.8L engine used in the "S" truck uses the Computer Command Control system. See General Motors Computer Command Control article for information.**

OPERATION

The primary function of the Closed Loop Emission Control system is to maintain an ideal air/fuel ratio of 14.7:1 under all operating conditions. When an ideal ratio is maintained, the catalytic converter can effectively control nitrogen oxides (NOx), hydrocarbons (HC) and carbon monoxide (CO).

The Closed Loop Emission Control system consists of the following sub-systems: Fuel Control, Data Sensors, Electronic Control Module (ECM), Diagnostic System and Catalytic Converter.

FUEL CONTROL

The engine is equipped with a "feedback" carburetor which contains vacuum-operated fuel control actuators. The ECM, responding to inputs from the data sensors, constantly adjusts the air/fuel ratio to maintain engine performance.

The ECM sends electrical signals to the vacuum control valve. By means of a vacuum control solenoid, the vacuum control valve converts the ECM signals into vacuum signals. These vacuum signals operate the fuel control actuators in the feedback carbuertor to control air fuel ratio.

The vacuum control valve consists of a vacuum regulator and a vacuum control solenoid. The vacuum regulator changes the variable vacuum from the intake manifold into the constant vacuum needed to control the actuators. The vacuum control solenoid (controlled by the ECM) uses the vacuum from the vacuum regulator to operate the fuel control actuators in the feedback carburetor.

Fig. 1: 1.9L Engine Closed Loop Emission Control System Schematic

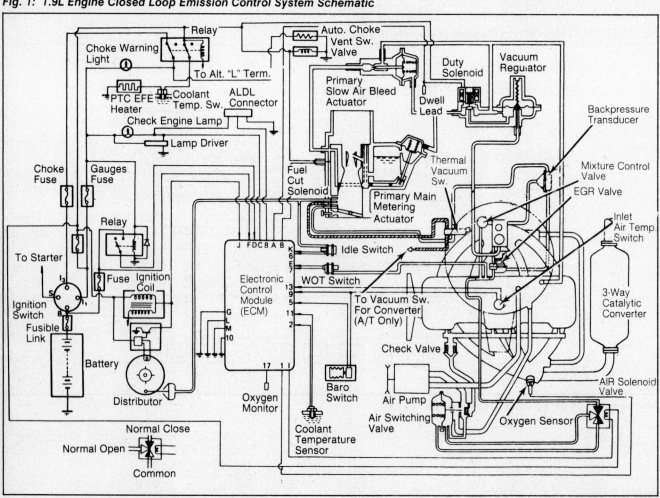

GENERAL MOTORS CLOSED LOOP
EMISSION CONTROL SYSTEM (Cont.)

When the ECM adjusts fuel mixture based upon signals received from the oxygen sensor, the system is in closed loop operation. Under certain operating conditions, the ECM may ignore inputs from various data sensors and use a pre-programmed calibration control to operate the engine. For instance, during cold engine starts, the vacuum control solenoid is turned off by the ECM to provide a rich fuel mixture. Various operating conditions which cause the ECM to ignore oxygen sensor signals, cause the system to operate in the open loop mode.

Although not a major component of the fuel control system, a vacuum-operated mixture control (M/C) valve is used to prevent backfiring in the exhaust system during deceleration. To perform this function, the M/C valve admits air from the air pump into the intake manifold, when the throttle valve is suddenly closed. Under normal operating conditions, the M/C valve is closed. However, when vacuum in the intake manifold increases rapidly (as in deceleration), the valve opens and allows air from the air pump to be admitted into the intake manifold.

DATA SENSORS

Each sensor furnishes information to the ECM. Based on sensor information, the ECM computes the fuel mixture ratio necessary to maintain proper engine operation. The function of each sensor is closely related to that of the other sensors. The operation of each sensor follows:

Oxygen Sensor

This sensor is mounted in the exhaust manifold. It supplies a low voltage signal when fuel mixture is lean (too much oxygen) and a higher voltage signal when fuel mixture is rich (not enough oxygen). Oxygen sensor must be heated to over 600°F (315°C) to function properly. The oxygen sensor measures quantity of oxygen in the exhaust gas stream only.

No attempt should be made to measure oxygen sensor voltage output. Current drain of conventional voltmeters could permanently damage sensor, shift sensor calibration range and/or render sensor unusable.

Do not connect jumper wire, test leads or other electrical connectors to sensor. Use these devices only on ECM side of harness after disconnecting from sensor.

Coolant Temperature Sensor (CTS)

The CTS is located in the engine coolant stream to supply coolant temperature information to ECM. This information is used by the ECM to determine when the system is ready to go into closed loop and to determine operation of the secondary air injection system.

Idle Position Switch

The idle position switch is vacuum-controlled. It is mounted on a bracket on right side of engine compartment (next to coil). This switch senses intake manifold vacuum and sends an electrical signal to the ECM in relation to the amount of manifold vacuum. The ECM uses this information to distinguish between closed throttle (idle) and open throttle positions.

Wide Open Throttle (WOT) Switch

This switch is mounted on the same bracket as the idle position switch. Like the idle position switch, this switch senses intake manifold vacuum and sends an electrical signal to the ECM when the engine is at WOT. This information is used by the ECM to distinguish between closed throttle (idle) and wide open throttle positions.

ELECTRONIC CONTROL MODULE (ECM)

The ECM is located in the passenger compartment (behind glove compartment) and controls all functions of the Closed Loop Emission Control system. The ECM sends an electrical signal to the vacuum control solenoid, which controls the air/fuel mixture by vacuum signals. This control signal is constantly cycling the solenoid between "on" and "off" time (duty cycle) as a function of the input voltages from the data sensors.

The control signal generated by the ECM is selected from 4 operational modes. These modes include: Inhibit Mode, Enrichment Mode, Open Loop Mode and Closed Loop Mode. A brief description of each mode follows:

Fig. 2: Engine Compartment Component Locations

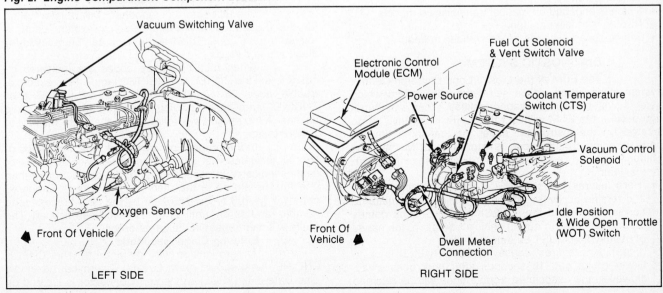

1983 Computerized Engine Controls
GENERAL MOTORS CLOSED LOOP
EMISSION CONTROL SYSTEM (Cont.)

- **Inhibit Mode**
  No electrical signals are sent to the vacuum control solenoid by the ECM in this mode.
- **Enrichment Mode**
  In this mode, a fixed pre-programmed duty cycle electrical signal is sent to the vacuum control solenoid by the ECM. This signal is sent to the solenoid when fuel enrichment is necessary for cold engine starts or sudden acceleration.
- **Open Loop Mode**
  In this mode the ECM sends electrical signals to the vacuum control solenoid based upon stored information within the ECM. This information has been calculated and is used by the ECM to operate the engine at optimum efficiency for that particular operating condition of the engine, without any input from the data sensors. Open loop mode is used when the engine has not reached operating temperature.
- **Closed Loop Mode**
  In this mode the ECM sends an electrical signal to the vacuum control solenoid based upon input from the oxygen sensor and other data sensors. In closed loop, the air/fuel mixture is controlled directly by the ECM in response to oxygen sensor signals.

During any operating mode, the ECM maintains the current duty cycle being used within its memory; for either idle or off-idle operation. When the ECM receives a change in idle position, as signaled by the idle position switch or WOT switch, the ECM retrieves data from its memory to operate the engine at the duty cycle last recorded for optimum operation. After the initial change in idle position, the ECM then controls the system in 1 of the 4 operational modes.

The ECM also controls operation of the fuel cut solenoid valve incorporated within the carburetor. When the ECM senses a coasting condition (based upon signals received from the transmission gear position switch, clutch pedal position awitch and idle position switch), it opens the circuit to the fuel cut solenoid. The circuit to the fuel cut solenoid valve is cut off only when the following 4 conditions exist at the same time:

- Transmission is not in Neutral (man. trans.) or in "N" or "P" (auto. trans.).
- Clutch is engaged on manual transmission models.
- Throttle is at idle position.
- Engine speed exceeds predetermined speed.

DIAGNOSTIC SYSTEM

The ECM of the Closed Loop Emission Control system is equipped with a self-diagnostic system which detects system failures or abnormalities. When a malfunction occurs, the ECM will light the "CHECK ENGINE" lamp located on the instrument panel. At the same time, a corresponding trouble code is stored in ECM memory. Malfunctions are recorded as "hard failures" or "intermittent failures".

- "Hard failures" cause "CHECK ENGINE" lamp to glow and remain on (while engine is running) until malfunction is repaired. If the "CHECK ENGINE" lamp comes on and remains on during vehicle operation, the cause of malfunction MUST be determined.
- "Intermittent failures" cause "CHECK ENGINE" lamp to flicker or go out, 10 seconds after fault goes away. However, the associated trouble code will be retained

in ECM memory. "Intermittent failures" may be sensor related. If a sensor fails, ECM will use a substitute value in its calculations to continue engine operation. In this condition, service is not mandatory, but loss of driveability may result.

As a bulb and system check, the "CHECK ENGINE" lamp will glow when ignition switch is turned "ON" and engine is not running. When engine is started, the lamp should go out after 1-4 seconds. If not, a malfunction has been detected in the Closed Loop Emission Control system.

NOTE: **Trouble codes will be recorded at various operating times. Some codes require operation of that sensor or switch for 5 seconds; others require operation for 5 minutes or longer.**

Diagnose the Closed Loop Emission Control system in the following order:

1) Ensure all engine systems NOT related to the system are fully operational. Do not proceed with testing unless all other problems have been corrected. Ensure that all electrical and vacuum connections are correct and in good condition.

2) Enter diagnostic mode and record trouble codes flashed by "CHECK ENGINE" lamp. Exit diagnostic mode.

3) Distinguish between "hard" and "intermittent" trouble codes.

4) If trouble codes were displayed, go to Diagnostic Circuit Check chart. Follow instructions given there.

5) If no trouble codes were recorded, go to Driver Complaint chart and follow instructions given there.

6) After any repairs are made, perform System Performance Check. Clear any trouble codes.

DIAGNOSIS & TESTING

DIAGNOSTIC PROCEDURE

The ECM stores component failure information for the Closed Loop Emission Control system under a related trouble code. This trouble code can be recalled for diagnosis and repair.

When recalled, these codes are indicated by flashes of the "CHECK ENGINE" lamp. For example, trouble code 23 would be indicated by the "CHECK ENGINE" lamp flashing twice, a short pause, then three flashes. A long pause will follow, then the cycle will repeat 2 more times.

In the preceeding paragraph, the first series of flashes indicates first digit of the code; second series of flashes indicates the second digit of the code. If more than one fault is stored in the memory, the lowest numbered code will flash 3 times, followed by the next highest code number, and so on, until all faults have been flashed. The faults will then repeat in the same order.

Entering Diagnostic Mode

1) Turn ignition "ON" (engine off). The "CHECK ENGINE" lamp should glow. Locate 12-terminal Assembly Line Data Link (ALDL) connector. Connector is located on

Fig. 3: ALDL Connector

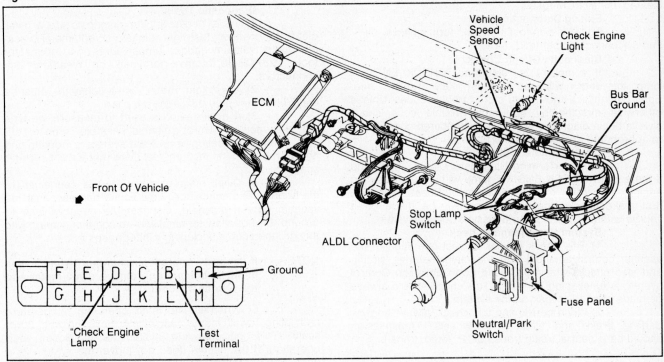

ECM is mounted behind glove compartment.

underside of instrument panel center portion. A trouble code test terminal is located in the ALDL connector and a ground terminal is located next to it. *See Fig. 3.* Jumper the test terminal to ground.

2) The "CHECK ENGINE" lamp should flash code "12". Code "12" consists of one flash, a short pause, then 2 flashes. A longer pause will follow, then Code "12" will repeat 2 more times. Code "12" is not a trouble code. This check indicates that the self-diagnostic system is working.

3) If any trouble codes are stored in ECM memory, the "CHECK ENGINE" lamp will flash 2-digit codes. If more than one fault is stored in the ECM memory, the lowest number code will flash 3 times, followed by the next highest code number, until all faults have been displayed (flashed). The faults will then repeat in the same order.

4) A trouble code indicates a fault in a given circuit. The "CHECK ENGINE" lamp will only be on if the malfunction exists under conditions listed in ECM Trouble Code Identification chart.

5) If the malfunction clears, the lamp will go out and a trouble code will be set in the ECM. If the lamp comes on intermittently, but no code is stored, go to the Driver Comment section. Any codes stored will be erased if no fault reoccurs within 50 engine starts.

6) Faults indicated by trouble codes "13", "31", "44" and "45" require that the engine be operated at part throttle for up to 5 minutes after engine warm-up, before the "CHECK ENGINE" lamp will come on and store a trouble code. The fault indicated by trouble code "15" takes 5 minutes of engine operation before it will display. Remove ground from test terminal before starting engine.

ECM TROUBLE CODE IDENTIFICATION

Trouble Code	Malfunction
12	No ignition reference pulses to ECM (Not Stored in Memory)
13	Oxygen Sensor Circuit
14	Shorted Coolant Sensor Circuit
15	Open Coolant Sensor Circuit
21	Idle Switch or WOT Switch Circuit Open or Shorted
22	Fuel Cut Solenoid Circuit Open or Grounded
23	Vacuum Control Solenoid Circuit Open or Grounded
25	Air Switching Solenoid Circuit Open or Grounded
31	No Ignition Reference Pulses to ECM (Stored in Memory)
44	Lean Oxygen Sensor Indication
45	Rich Oxygen Sensor Indication
51	Shorted Fuel Cut Solenoid Circuit
52	Faulty ECM (RAM Error)
53	Shorted Air Switching Solenoid and/or Faulty ECM
54	Shorted Vacuum Control Solenoid and/or Faulty ECM
55	Faulty ECM

Clearing Trouble Codes

The trouble code memory is continuously fed 12 volts even when the key is "OFF". To clear memory of trouble codes after a fault has been corrected, remove the

GENERAL MOTORS CLOSED LOOP EMISSION CONTROL SYSTEM (Cont.)

ECM fuse for 10 seconds. Any stored codes will be cleared. Install ECM fuse.

Exiting Diagnostic Mode

To exit diagnostic mode, turn ignition "OFF" and disconnect jumper lead.

Diagnostic Circuit Check

If complaint is related to "CHECK ENGINE" lamp, this check will lead to most likely problem area. Enter diagnostics and record stored trouble codes. Unless otherwise directed by applicable trouble code chart, always begin diagnosis with lowest numbered code. Refer to appropriate trouble code chart.

Driver Comment Sheet

After performing Diagnostic Circuit Check and if there is no "CHECK ENGINE" lamp with a warm running engine, then refer to Driver Comment Sheet. However, first make checks that would normally be made on a vehicle without Closed Loop Emission Control system.

System Performance Check

1) This check verifies correct operation of the vacuum control solenoid and the main metering circuit, and also checks that the Closed Loop Emission Control system is functioning correctly. This check should always be made after any repair on the system.

2) When performing this check, always engage parking brake and block drive wheels. Transmission should be in neutral (man. trans.) or "P" (auto. trans.).

TOOLS REQUIRED

Diagnostic Tools

1) Tools necessary for diagnosis are a dwell meter, tachometer, test light, digital volt/ohmmeter, vacuum pump, vacuum gauge, jumper wires, and connector tool (J-28742) to remove terminals on Weather Pack connectors.

2) A test light, rather than a voltmeter, must be used when indicated by diagnostic chart.

3) A dwell meter is used to measure the time that the vacuum control solenoid solenoid is on or off. This gives an indication of how the system is working and how rich or lean the mixture. Set dwell meter for 4-cylinder scale.

4) Dwell meter positive lead is connected to the bright green connector in the wiring harness, near the vacuum control solenoid. Connect the negative lead to ground. Do not allow terminal wire to come in contact with any ground source, including rubber hoses.

NOTE: If engine operation changes when dwell meter is connected, remove dwell meter and try another model.

5) When engine is at operating temperature and idling, dwell meter needle will move up and down scale. This indicates the system is in closed loop operation. If the needle does not move, the system is in open loop operation.

Fig. 4: Electronic Control Module Terminal Identification

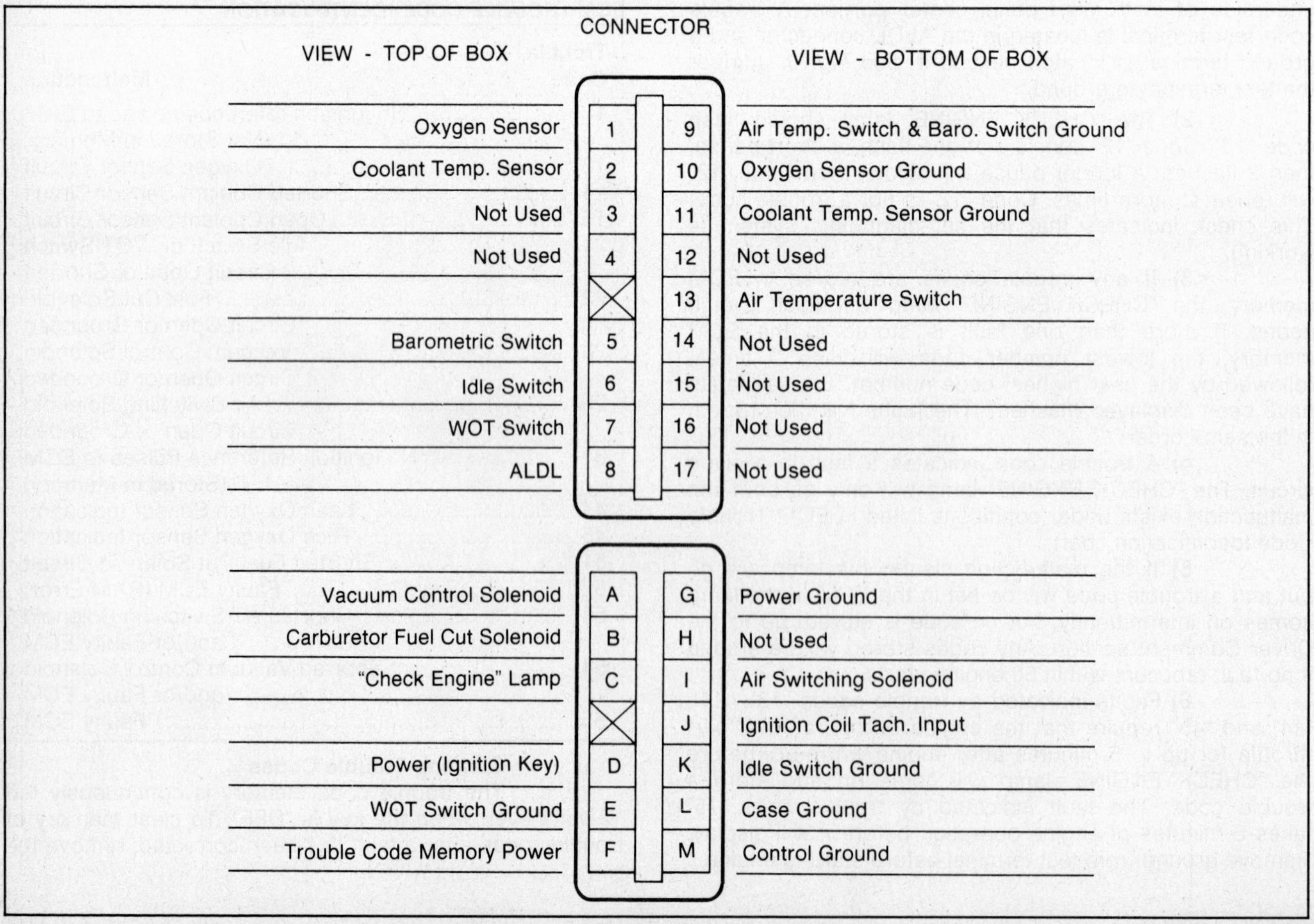

CONNECTOR

VIEW - TOP OF BOX			VIEW - BOTTOM OF BOX
Oxygen Sensor	1	9	Air Temp. Switch & Baro. Switch Ground
Coolant Temp. Sensor	2	10	Oxygen Sensor Ground
Not Used	3	11	Coolant Temp. Sensor Ground
Not Used	4	12	Not Used
	⊠	13	Air Temperature Switch
Barometric Switch	5	14	Not Used
Idle Switch	6	15	Not Used
WOT Switch	7	16	Not Used
ALDL	8	17	Not Used

Vacuum Control Solenoid	A	G	Power Ground
Carburetor Fuel Cut Solenoid	B	H	Not Used
"Check Engine" Lamp	C	I	Air Switching Solenoid
	⊠	J	Ignition Coil Tach. Input
Power (Ignition Key)	D	K	Idle Switch Ground
WOT Switch Ground	E	L	Case Ground
Trouble Code Memory Power	F	M	Control Ground

GENERAL MOTORS CLOSED LOOP
EMISSION CONTROL SYSTEM (Cont.)

DIAGNOSTIC PROCEDURE CHART

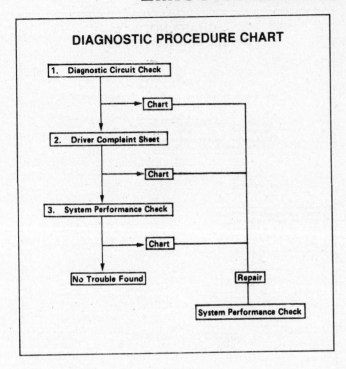

1. **Diagnostic Circuit Check**
   → Chart
2. **Driver Complaint Sheet**
   → Chart
3. **System Performance Check**
   → Chart

No Trouble Found — **Repair**

System Performance Check

DRIVER COMPLAINT SHEET

ENGINE PERFORMANCE CONDITION (ODOR, SURGE, FUEL ECONOMY...) EMISSION SYSTEM CONDITION.

IF THE "CHECK ENGINE" LIGHT IS NOT ON, NORMAL CHECKS THAT WOULD BE PERFORMED ON CARS WITHOUT CLOSED LOOP EMISSION CONTROL SYSTEM SHOULD BE DONE FIRST.

IF GENERATOR OR COOLANT LIGHT IS ON WITH THE "CHECK ENGINE" LIGHT, THEY SHOULD BE DIAGNOSED FIRST.

INSPECT FOR POOR CONNECTIONS AT COOLANT SENSOR, V/C SOLENOID, ETC., AND POOR OR LOOSE VACUUM HOSES AND CONNECTIONS. REPAIR AS NECESSARY.

- INTERMITTENT CHECK ENGINE LIGHT BUT NO TROUBLE CODE STORED.

    IF FOR ANY REASON ENGINE RPM DROPS BELOW 200, THE CHECK ENGINE LIGHT WILL COME ON UNTIL RPM EXCEEDS 200 AND FOR 4 SEC. AFTER RPM EXCEEDS 200.
- CHECK FOR INTERMITTENT CONNECTION IN CIRCUIT FROM:
    - DISTRIBUTOR TO ECM TERMINAL "J"
    - BATTERY TO ECM TERMINAL "F"
    - ECM TERMINAL "G" TO ENGINE GROUND
    - ECM TERMINAL "C" TO LAMP DRIVER
    - ECM TERMINAL "D" TO BATTERY (INCLUDING ECM RELAY CIRCUIT)

- LOW BATTERY VOLTAGE (UNDER 9 VOLTS) AT ECM
- LOSS OF TROUBLE CODE MEMORY
    MOMENTARILY GROUNDING DWELL LEAD WITH ENGINE IDLING SHOULD GIVE CODE 23 WHICH SHOULD BE RETAINED AFTER ENGINE IS STOPPED AND IGNITION TURNED TO "ON" POSITION. IF VOLTAGE IS PRESENT AT ECM TERM "F" BUT NO CODE IS STORED. ECM IS FAULTY.

- STALLING, ROUGH IDLE OR IMPROPER IDLE SPEED
    CHECK IDLE SPEED ADJUSTMENT
    CHECK - VACUUM CONTROL VALVE
- DETONATION
    CHECK - EGR OPERATION AND VACUUM SWITCH ENRICHMENT CIRCUIT (CHART #4).
- SURGE
    SEE - IDLE AND HOT SWITCHES ASM. CHECK.
- POOR PERFORMANCE AND/OR FUEL ECONOMY
    SEE - VACUUM CONTROL VALVE CHECK.
- POOR FULL THROTTLE PERFORMANCE
    SEE CHART #4 - VACUUM SWITCH ENRICHMENT CIRCUIT CHECK.
    SEE - VACUUM CONTROL VALVE CHECK.
- ALL OTHER COMMENTS
    MAKE "SYSTEM PERFORMANCE CHECK" ON WARM ENGINE (UPPER RADIATOR HOSE HOT).

THE "SYSTEM PERFORMANCE CHECK" SHOULD BE PERFORMED AFTER ANY REPAIRS TO THE "SYSTEM" HAVE BEEN MADE.

DIAGNOSTIC CIRCUIT CHECK

VACUUM HOSE ROUTING, CONNECTIONS AND HARNESS CONNECTOR CONNECTIONS SHOULD BE CHECKED BEFORE THIS CHECK.

- KEY "ON", ENGINE STOPPED, "TEST" TERM. UNGROUNDED.
- NOTE "CHECK ENGINE" LIGHT.

LIGHT "OFF" → SEE CHART #5

LIGHT "ON" STEADY → GROUND "TEST" TERM. AND NOTE "CHECK ENGINE" LIGHT.

LIGHT FLASHES (INTERMITTENTLY OR A CODE.) → CHECK FOR GN'DED WIRE TO ECM TERM. "B" IF NOT GN'DED, IT IS FAULTY ECM.

DOES NOT FLASH CODE 12 → SEE CHART #6

FLASHES CODE 12 (THIS IS NOT A "TROUBLE CODE 12")

NOTE AND RECORD ANY ADDITIONAL CODES.

CODE 52 OR 55 → REPLACE ECM

NO CODE 52 OR 55:
- TURN IGNITION "OFF" AND CLEAR CODE(S).
- REMOVE "TEST" TERM. GROUND.
- SET PARKING BRAKE WITH TRANS. IN "PARK" (A.T.), "NEUTRAL" (M.T.), AND BLOCK DRIVE WHEELS.
- RUN WARM ENGINE AT SPECIFIED CURB IDLE FOR TWO(2) MINUTES AND NOTE "CHECK ENGINE" LIGHT.

LIGHT "OFF" → REFER TO THE ADDITIONAL CODES RECORDED ABOVE.

LIGHT "ON" → GROUND "TEST" TERM. AND NOTE CODES.

NO ADDITIONAL CODES → ALL OTHERS

ADDITIONAL CODES → CODES 13, 15, 21, 22, 31, 44, 45

FLASHES CODE

FLASHES BUT NO CODE → REPLACE ECM

TROUBLE IS INTERMITTENT SO CODE CHARTS CANNOT BE USED. MAKE PHYSICAL CHECK OF CIRCUIT INDICATED BY TROUBLE CODE.

- SEE APPLICABLE TROUBLE CODE CHART(S).
- IF MORE THAN ONE CODE IS STORED, START WITH LOWEST CODE.

SEE DRIVER COMMENT

UNDER DASH CONNECTOR

F E D C B A → GROUND
G H J K L M

"CHECK ENGINE" LIGHT   "TEST" TERMINAL

THE SYSTEM PERFORMANCE CHECK SHOULD BE PERFORMED AFTER ANY REPAIRS TO THE "SYSTEM" HAVE BEEN MADE.

SYSTEM PERFORMANCE CHECK

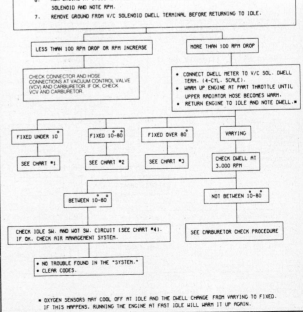

1. SET PARKING BRAKE WITH TRANS. IN "PARK" (A.T.), "NEUTRAL" (M.T.), AND BLOCK DRIVE WHEELS.
2. START ENGINE.
3. DISCONNECT PURGE HOSE FROM CANISTER AND PLUG IT.
4. CONNECT TACHOMETER.
5. DISCONNECT VACUUM CONTROL (V/C) SOLENOID AND GROUND V/C SOLENOID DWELL TERMINAL.
6. RUN ENGINE AT 3,000 RPM AND, WHILE KEEPING THROTTLE CONSTANT, RECONNECT V/C SOLENOID AND NOTE RPM.
7. REMOVE GROUND FROM V/C SOLENOID DWELL TERMINAL BEFORE RETURNING TO IDLE.

LESS THAN 100 RPM DROP OR RPM INCREASE
CHECK CONNECTOR AND HOSE CONNECTIONS AT VACUUM CONTROL VALVE (VCV) AND CARBURETOR. IF OK, CHECK VCV AND CARBURETOR.

MORE THAN 100 RPM DROP
- CONNECT DWELL METER TO V/C SOL. DWELL TERM. (4-CYL. SCALE)
- WARM UP ENGINE AT PART THROTTLE UNTIL UPPER RADIATOR HOSE BECOMES WARM.
- RETURN ENGINE TO IDLE AND NOTE DWELL.■

FIXED UNDER 10° → SEE CHART #1

FIXED 10-80° → SEE CHART #2

FIXED OVER 80° → SEE CHART #3

VARYING → CHECK DWELL AT 3,000 RPM

BETWEEN 10-80° → CHECK IDLE SW. AND HOT SW. CIRCUIT (SEE CHART #4). IF OK, CHECK AIR MANAGEMENT SYSTEM.

NOT BETWEEN 10-80° → SEE CARBURETOR CHECK PROCEDURE

- NO TROUBLE FOUND IN THE "SYSTEM."
- CLEAR CODES.

■ OXYGEN SENSORS MAY COOL OFF AT IDLE AND THE DWELL CHANGE FROM VARYING TO FIXED. IF THIS HAPPENS, RUNNING THE ENGINE AT FAST IDLE WILL WARM IT UP AGAIN.

GENERAL MOTORS CLOSED LOOP
EMISSION CONTROL SYSTEM (Cont.)

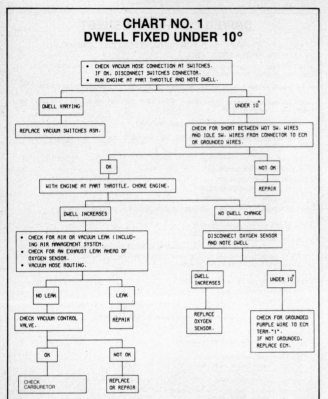

CHART NO. 1
DWELL FIXED UNDER 10°

- CHECK VACUUM HOSE CONNECTION AT SWITCHES. IF OK, DISCONNECT SWITCHES CONNECTOR.
- RUN ENGINE AT PART THROTTLE AND NOTE DWELL.

DWELL VARYING → REPLACE VACUUM SWITCHES ASM.

UNDER 10° → CHECK FOR SHORT BETWEEN WOT SW. WIRES AND IDLE SW. WIRES FROM CONNECTOR TO ECM OR GROUNDED WIRES.

OK → WITH ENGINE AT PART THROTTLE, CHOKE ENGINE.

NOT OK → REPAIR

DWELL INCREASES:
- CHECK FOR AIR OR VACUUM LEAK (INCLUDING AIR MANAGEMENT SYSTEM).
- CHECK FOR AN EXHAUST LEAK AHEAD OF OXYGEN SENSOR.
- VACUUM HOSE ROUTING.

NO DWELL CHANGE → DISCONNECT OXYGEN SENSOR AND NOTE DWELL

NO LEAK → CHECK VACUUM CONTROL VALVE.

LEAK → REPAIR

OK → CHECK CARBURETOR

NOT OK → REPLACE OR REPAIR

DWELL INCREASES → REPLACE OXYGEN SENSOR.

UNDER 10° → CHECK FOR GROUNDED PURPLE WIRE TO ECM TERM. "1". IF NOT GROUNDED, REPLACE ECM.

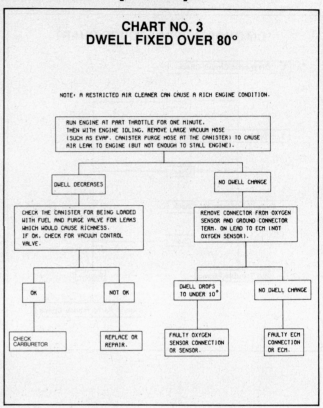

CHART NO. 3
DWELL FIXED OVER 80°

NOTE: A RESTRICTED AIR CLEANER CAN CAUSE A RICH ENGINE CONDITION.

RUN ENGINE AT PART THROTTLE FOR ONE MINUTE, THEN WITH ENGINE IDLING, REMOVE LARGE VACUUM HOSE (SUCH AS EVAP. CANISTER PURGE HOSE AT THE CANISTER) TO CAUSE AIR LEAK TO ENGINE (BUT NOT ENOUGH TO STALL ENGINE).

DWELL DECREASES → CHECK THE CANISTER FOR BEING LOADED WITH FUEL AND PURGE VALVE FOR LEAKS WHICH WOULD CAUSE RICHNESS. IF OK, CHECK FOR VACUUM CONTROL VALVE.

NO DWELL CHANGE → REMOVE CONNECTOR FROM OXYGEN SENSOR AND GROUND CONNECTOR TERM. ON LEAD TO ECM (NOT OXYGEN SENSOR).

OK → CHECK CARBURETOR

NOT OK → REPLACE OR REPAIR.

DWELL DROPS TO UNDER 10° → FAULTY OXYGEN SENSOR CONNECTION OR SENSOR.

NO DWELL CHANGE → FAULTY ECM CONNECTION OR ECM.

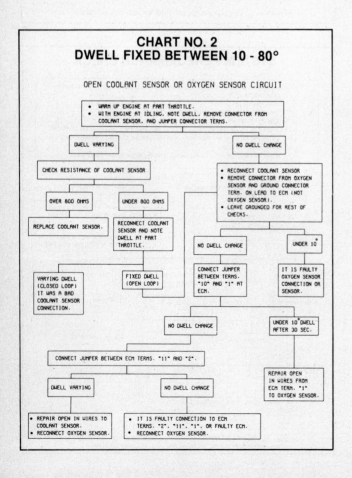

CHART NO. 2
DWELL FIXED BETWEEN 10 - 80°

OPEN COOLANT SENSOR OR OXYGEN SENSOR CIRCUIT

- WARM UP ENGINE AT PART THROTTLE.
- WITH ENGINE AT IDLING, NOTE DWELL. REMOVE CONNECTOR FROM COOLANT SENSOR, AND JUMPER CONNECTOR TERMS.

DWELL VARYING → CHECK RESISTANCE OF COOLANT SENSOR.

NO DWELL CHANGE:
- RECONNECT COOLANT SENSOR
- REMOVE CONNECTOR FROM OXYGEN SENSOR AND GROUND CONNECTOR TERM. ON LEAD TO ECM (NOT OXYGEN SENSOR).
- LEAVE GROUNDED FOR REST OF CHECKS.

OVER 800 OHMS → REPLACE COOLANT SENSOR.

UNDER 800 OHMS → RECONNECT COOLANT SENSOR AND NOTE DWELL AT PART THROTTLE.

VARYING DWELL (CLOSED LOOP) IT WAS A BAD COOLANT SENSOR CONNECTION.

FIXED DWELL (OPEN LOOP)

NO DWELL CHANGE → CONNECT JUMPER BETWEEN TERMS. "10" AND "1" AT ECM.

UNDER 10° → IT IS FAULTY OXYGEN SENSOR CONNECTION OR SENSOR.

NO DWELL CHANGE → CONNECT JUMPER BETWEEN ECM TERMS. "11" AND "2".

UNDER 10° DWELL AFTER 30 SEC. → REPAIR OPEN IN WIRES FROM ECM TERM. "1" TO OXYGEN SENSOR.

DWELL VARYING:
- REPAIR OPEN IN WIRES TO COOLANT SENSOR.
- RECONNECT OXYGEN SENSOR.

NO DWELL CHANGE:
- IT IS FAULTY CONNECTION TO ECM TERMS. "2", "11", "1", OR FAULTY ECM.
- RECONNECT OXYGEN SENSOR.

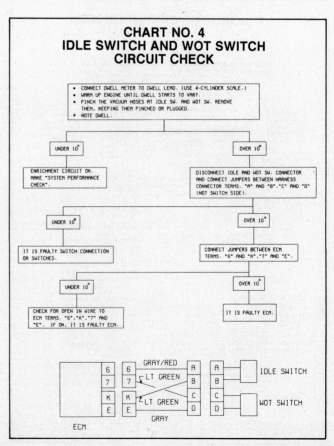

CHART NO. 4
IDLE SWITCH AND WOT SWITCH CIRCUIT CHECK

- CONNECT DWELL METER TO DWELL LEAD. (USE 4-CYLINDER SCALE.)
- WARM UP ENGINE UNTIL DWELL STARTS TO VARY.
- PINCH THE VACUUM HOSES AT IDLE SW. AND WOT SW. REMOVE THEM, KEEPING THEM PINCHED OR PLUGGED.
- NOTE DWELL.

UNDER 10° → ENRICHMENT CIRCUIT OK. MAKE "SYSTEM PERFORMANCE CHECK".

OVER 10° → DISCONNECT IDLE AND WOT SW. CONNECTOR AND CONNECT JUMPERS BETWEEN HARNESS CONNECTOR TERMS. "A" AND "B", "C" AND "D" (NOT SWITCH SIDE).

UNDER 10° → IT IS FAULTY SWITCH CONNECTION OR SWITCHES.

OVER 10° → CONNECT JUMPERS BETWEEN ECM TERMS. "6" AND "K", "7" AND "E".

UNDER 10° → CHECK FOR OPEN IN WIRE TO ECM TERMS. "6", "K", "7" AND "E". IF OK, IT IS FAULTY ECM.

OVER 10° → IT IS FAULTY ECM.

ECM — GRAY/RED — LT GREEN — LT GREEN — GRAY — IDLE SWITCH — WOT SWITCH

GENERAL MOTORS CLOSED LOOP
EMISSION CONTROL SYSTEM (Cont.)

CHART NO. 5
NO "CHECK ENGINE" LAMP

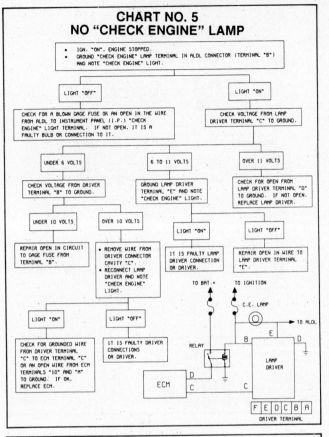

TROUBLE CODE 12

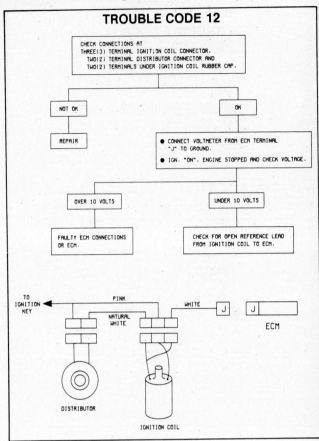

CHART NO. 6
WON'T FLASH CODE 12

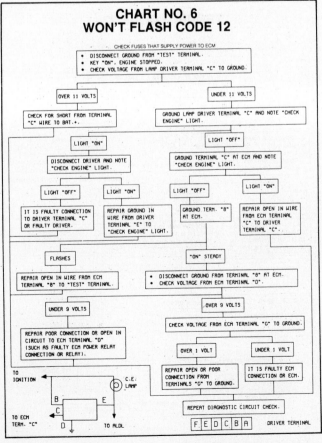

TROUBLE CODE 13

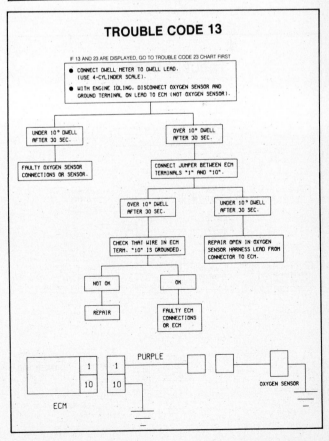

1983 Computerized Engine Controls
GENERAL MOTORS CLOSED LOOP
EMISSION CONTROL SYSTEM (Cont.)

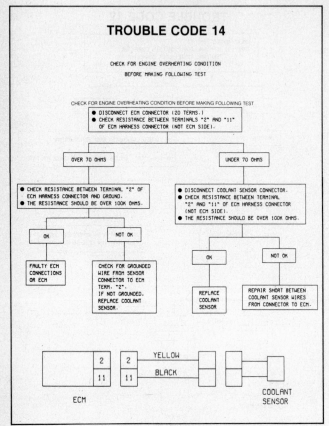

TROUBLE CODE 14

CHECK FOR ENGINE OVERHEATING CONDITION
BEFORE MAKING FOLLOWING TEST

CHECK FOR ENGINE OVERHEATING CONDITION BEFORE MAKING FOLLOWING TEST

- DISCONNECT ECM CONNECTOR (20 TERMS.)
- CHECK RESISTANCE BETWEEN TERMINALS "2" AND "11" OF ECM HARNESS CONNECTOR (NOT ECM SIDE).

OVER 70 OHMS

- CHECK RESISTANCE BETWEEN TERMINAL "2" OF ECM HARNESS CONNECTOR AND GROUND.
- THE RESISTANCE SHOULD BE OVER 100K OHMS.

OK → FAULTY ECM CONNECTIONS OR ECM.

NOT OK → CHECK FOR GROUNDED WIRE FROM SENSOR CONNECTOR TO ECM TERM. "2". IF NOT GROUNDED, REPLACE COOLANT SENSOR.

UNDER 70 OHMS

- DISCONNECT COOLANT SENSOR CONNECTOR.
- CHECK RESISTANCE BETWEEN TERMINAL "2" AND "11" OF ECM HARNESS CONNECTOR (NOT ECM SIDE).
- THE RESISTANCE SHOULD BE OVER 100K OHMS.

OK → REPLACE COOLANT SENSOR.

NOT OK → REPAIR SHORT BETWEEN COOLANT SENSOR WIRES FROM CONNECTOR TO ECM.

ECM | 2 | 11 | YELLOW | BLACK | COOLANT SENSOR

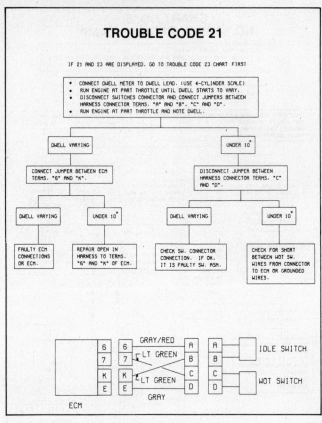

TROUBLE CODE 21

IF 21 AND 23 ARE DISPLAYED, GO TO TROUBLE CODE 23 CHART FIRST

- CONNECT DWELL METER TO DWELL LEAD. (USE 4-CYLINDER SCALE)
- RUN ENGINE AT PART THROTTLE UNTIL DWELL STARTS TO VARY.
- DISCONNECT SWITCHES CONNECTOR AND CONNECT JUMPERS BETWEEN HARNESS CONNECTOR TERMS. "A" AND "B", "C" AND "D".
- RUN ENGINE AT PART THROTTLE AND NOTE DWELL.

DWELL VARYING

CONNECT JUMPER BETWEEN ECM TERMS. "6" AND "K".

DWELL VARYING → FAULTY ECM CONNECTIONS OR ECM.

UNDER 10° → REPAIR OPEN IN HARNESS TO TERMS. "6" AND "K" OF ECM.

UNDER 10°

DISCONNECT JUMPER BETWEEN HARNESS CONNECTOR TERMS. "C" AND "D".

DWELL VARYING → CHECK SW. CONNECTOR CONNECTION. IF OK, IT IS FAULTY SW. ASM.

UNDER 10° → CHECK FOR SHORT BETWEEN WOT SW. WIRES FROM CONNECTOR TO ECM OR GROUNDED WIRES.

ECM | 6 | 7 | K | E | 6 | 7 | K | E | GRAY/RED | LT GREEN | LT GREEN | GRAY | A | B | C | D | A | B | C | D | IDLE SWITCH | WOT SWITCH

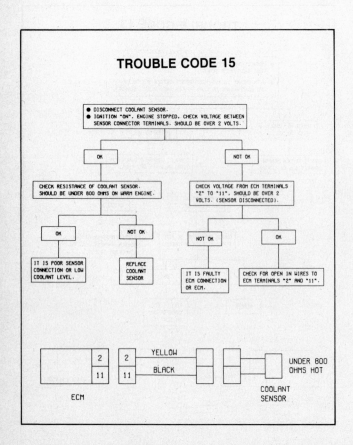

TROUBLE CODE 15

- DISCONNECT COOLANT SENSOR.
- IGNITION "ON". ENGINE STOPPED. CHECK VOLTAGE BETWEEN SENSOR CONNECTOR TERMINALS. SHOULD BE OVER 2 VOLTS.

OK

CHECK RESISTANCE OF COOLANT SENSOR. SHOULD BE UNDER 800 OHMS ON WARM ENGINE.

OK → IT IS POOR SENSOR CONNECTION OR LOW COOLANT LEVEL.

NOT OK → REPLACE COOLANT SENSOR.

NOT OK

CHECK VOLTAGE FROM ECM TERMINALS "2" TO "11". SHOULD BE OVER 2 VOLTS. (SENSOR DISCONNECTED).

NOT OK → IT IS FAULTY ECM CONNECTION OR ECM.

OK → CHECK FOR OPEN IN WIRES TO ECM TERMINALS "2" AND "11".

ECM | 2 | 11 | YELLOW | BLACK | COOLANT SENSOR | UNDER 800 OHMS HOT

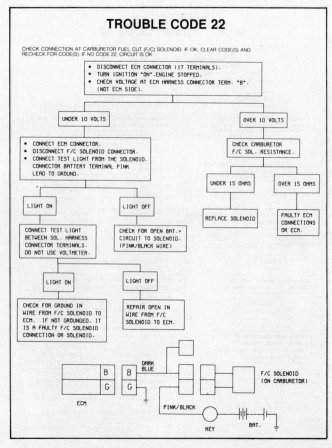

TROUBLE CODE 22

CHECK CONNECTION AT CARBURETOR FUEL CUT (F/C) SOLENOID. IF OK, CLEAR CODE(S) AND RECHECK FOR CODE(S). IF NO CODE 22, CIRCUIT IS OK.

- DISCONNECT ECM CONNECTOR (17 TERMINALS).
- TURN IGNITION "ON". ENGINE STOPPED.
- CHECK VOLTAGE AT ECM HARNESS CONNECTOR TERM. "B". (NOT ECM SIDE).

UNDER 10 VOLTS

- CONNECT ECM CONNECTOR.
- DISCONNECT F/C SOLENOID CONNECTOR.
- CONNECT TEST LIGHT FROM THE SOLENOID. CONNECTOR BATTERY TERMINAL PINK LEAD TO GROUND.

LIGHT ON

CONNECT TEST LIGHT BETWEEN SOL. HARNESS CONNECTOR TERMINALS. DO NOT USE VOLTMETER.

LIGHT ON → CHECK FOR GROUND IN WIRE FROM F/C SOLENOID TO ECM. IF NOT GROUNDED, IT IS A FAULTY F/C SOLENOID CONNECTION OR SOLENOID.

LIGHT OFF → REPAIR OPEN IN WIRE FROM F/C SOLENOID TO ECM.

LIGHT OFF → CHECK FOR OPEN BAT.+ CIRCUIT TO SOLENOID. (PINK/BLACK WIRE)

OVER 10 VOLTS

CHECK CARBURETOR F/C SOL. RESISTANCE.

UNDER 15 OHMS → REPLACE SOLENOID

OVER 15 OHMS → FAULTY ECM CONNECTIONS OR ECM.

ECM | B | G | B | G | DARK BLUE | F/C SOLENOID (ON CARBURETOR) | PINK/BLACK | KEY | BAT.

GENERAL MOTORS CLOSED LOOP
EMISSION CONTROL SYSTEM (Cont.)

TROUBLE CODE 23

CHECK CONNECTIONS AT VACUUM CONTROL (V/C) SOLENOID. IF OK, CLEAR CODE(S) AND RECHECK FOR CODE(S). IF NO CODE 23, CIRCUIT IS OK

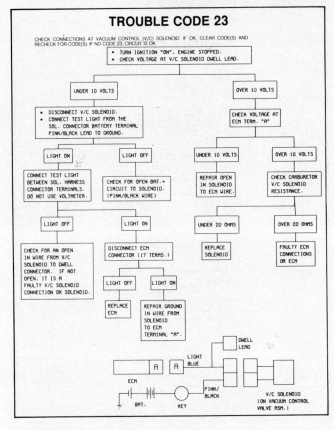

TROUBLE CODE 31

CHECK CONNECTIONS AT
THREE (3) TERMINAL IGNITION COIL CONNECTOR,
TWO (2) TERMINAL DISTRIBUTOR CONNECTOR,
TWO (2) TERMINALS UNDER IGNITION COIL RUBBER CAP
AND FOUR (4) TERMINAL VACUUM SWITCHES CONNECTOR.

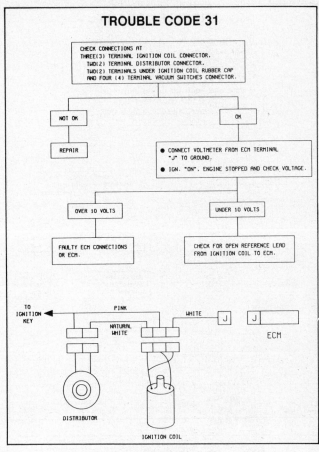

TROUBLE CODE 25

CHECK CONNECTIONS AT AIR SWITCHING (A/S) SOLENOID. IF OK, CLEAR CODE(S) AND RECHECK FOR CODE(S). IF NO CODE 25, CIRCUIT IS OK.

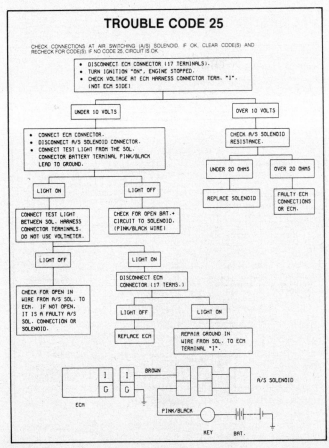

TROUBLE CODE 44

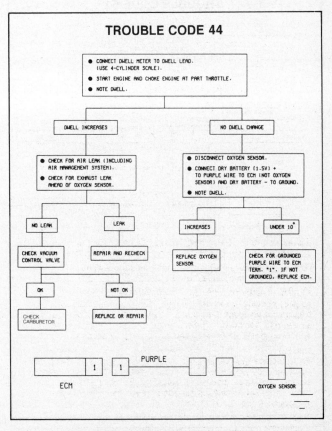

1983 Computerized Engine Controls
GENERAL MOTORS CLOSED LOOP
EMISSION CONTROL SYSTEM (Cont.)

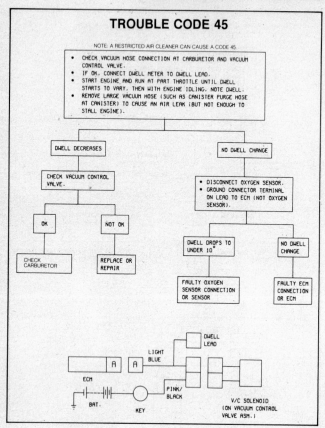

TROUBLE CODE 45

NOTE: A RESTRICTED AIR CLEANER CAN CAUSE A CODE 45

- CHECK VACUUM HOSE CONNECTION AT CARBURETOR AND VACUUM CONTROL VALVE.
- IF OK, CONNECT DWELL METER TO DWELL LEAD.
- START ENGINE AND RUN AT PART THROTTLE UNTIL DWELL STARTS TO VARY, THEN WITH ENGINE IDLING, NOTE DWELL.
- REMOVE LARGE VACUUM HOSE (SUCH AS CANISTER PURGE HOSE AT CANISTER) TO CAUSE AN AIR LEAK (BUT NOT ENOUGH TO STALL ENGINE).

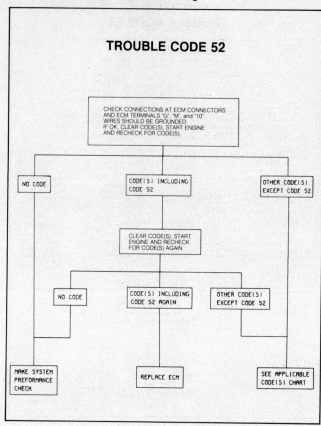

TROUBLE CODE 52

CHECK CONNECTIONS AT ECM CONNECTORS AND ECM TERMINALS "G", "M", and "10". WIRES SHOULD BE GROUNDED. IF OK, CLEAR CODE(S), START ENGINE AND RECHECK FOR CODE(S).

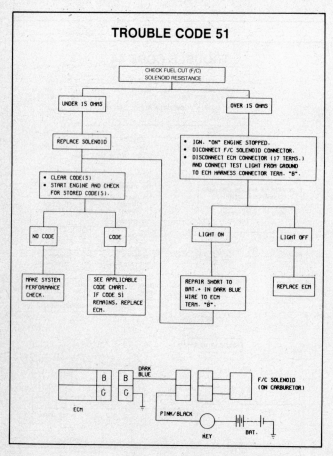

TROUBLE CODE 51

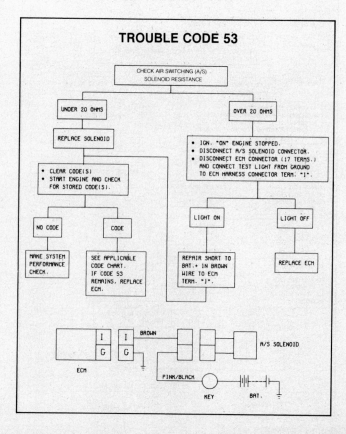

TROUBLE CODE 53

GENERAL MOTORS CLOSED LOOP
EMISSION CONTROL SYSTEM (Cont.)

TROUBLE CODE 54

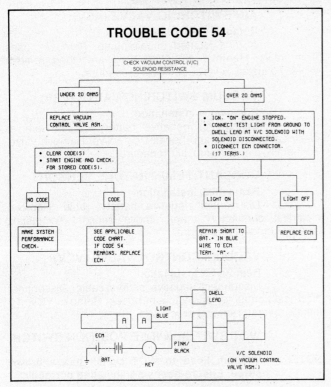

AIR MANAGEMENT CHECK

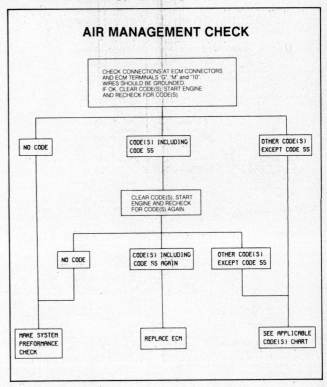

TROUBLE CODE 55

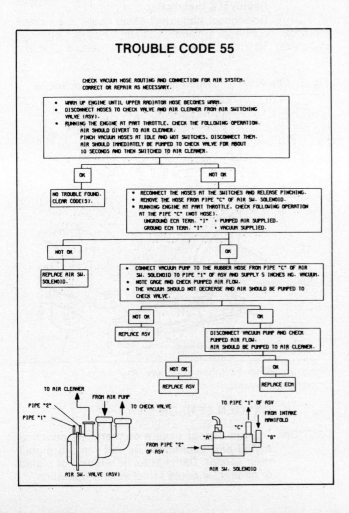

IDLE & WOT SWITCH ASM. CHECK

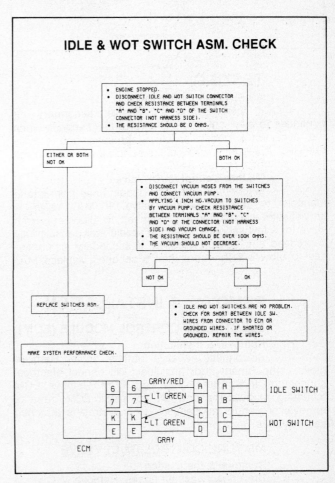

1983 Computerized Engine Controls

GENERAL MOTORS CLOSED LOOP EMISSION CONTROL SYSTEM (Cont.)

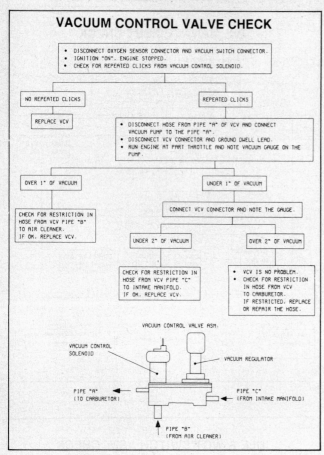

VACUUM CONTROL VALVE CHECK

- DISCONNECT OXYGEN SENSOR CONNECTOR AND VACUUM SWITCH CONNECTOR.
- IGNITION "ON". ENGINE STOPPED.
- CHECK FOR REPEATED CLICKS FROM VACUUM CONTROL SOLENOID.

NO REPEATED CLICKS → REPLACE VCV

REPEATED CLICKS
- DISCONNECT HOSE FROM PIPE "A" OF VCV AND CONNECT VACUUM PUMP TO THE PIPE "A".
- DISCONNECT VCV CONNECTOR AND GROUND DWELL LEAD.
- RUN ENGINE AT PART THROTTLE AND NOTE VACUUM GAUGE ON THE PUMP.

OVER 1" OF VACUUM
CHECK FOR RESTRICTION IN HOSE FROM VCV PIPE "B" TO AIR CLEANER. IF OK, REPLACE VCV.

UNDER 1" OF VACUUM
CONNECT VCV CONNECTOR AND NOTE THE GAUGE.

UNDER 2" OF VACUUM
CHECK FOR RESTRICTION IN HOSE FROM VCV PIPE "C" TO INTAKE MANIFOLD. IF OK, REPLACE VCV.

OVER 2" OF VACUUM
- VCV IS NO PROBLEM.
- CHECK FOR RESTRICTION IN HOSE FROM VCV TO CARBURETOR. IF RESTRICTED, REPLACE OR REPAIR THE HOSE.

VACUUM CONTROL VALVE ASM.

VACUUM CONTROL SOLENOID

VACUUM REGULATOR

PIPE "A" (TO CARBURETOR)

PIPE "C" (FROM INTAKE MANIFOLD)

PIPE "B" (FROM AIR CLEANER)

TESTING

Air Switching Valve (ASV)

If the ASV is serviceable, secondary air continues to blow out from valve for a few seconds when the accelerator pedal is fully depressed and quickly released. If secondary air continues to blow out for more than 5 seconds, replace ASV.

Mixture Control (M/C) Valve

Disconnect and plug vacuum hose from intake manifold to mixture control valve. If M/C valve is serviceable, secondary air continues to blow out from valve for a few seconds when the accelerator pedal is fully depressed and quickly released. If secondary air continues to blow out for more than 5 seconds, replace M/C valve.

REMOVAL & INSTALLATION

ELECTRONIC CONTROL MODULE (ECM)

Removal & Installation

Disconnect negative battery cable. Remove glove compartment door and liner. Disconnect electrical connectors and ground strap from ECM. Remove ECM mounting hardware and ECM. To install ECM, reverse removal procedure and ensure ground strap is attached securely. See Fig. 3.

MIXTURE CONTROL (M/C) VALVE

Removal & Installation

Disconnect vacuum hoses. Remove M/C valve from clamp bracket. To install, reverse removal procedure.

AIR SWITCHING VALVE (ASV)

Removal & Installation

ASV is located on air pump. Remove hoses from valve. Remove mounting hardware, then remove valve. To install, reverse removal procedure.

VACUUM SWITCHING VALVE (VSV)

Removal & Installation

Disconnect negative battery cable. Remove electrical connector and hoses from valve. Remove valve. To install, reverse removal procedure.

COOLANT TEMPERATURE SENSOR

Removal & Installation

Disconnect negative battery cable. Remove electrical connector, then remove sensor. To install, reverse removal procedure.

VACUUM CONTROL VALVE (VCV)

Removal & Installation

Disconnect negative battery cable. Disconnect electrical connector and vacuum hoses. Remove VCV. To install, reverse removal procedure.

WOT SWITCH & IDLE POSITION SWITCH

NOTE: **Vacuum hose to WOT switch has a brown stripe. Ensure hoses are installed correctly.**

Removal & Installation

Disconnect negative battery cable. Disconnect electrical connectors and vacuum hoses. Remove switch(es). To install, reverse removal procedure. See Fig. 5.

Fig. 5: Idle Position Switch and WOT Switch Locations.

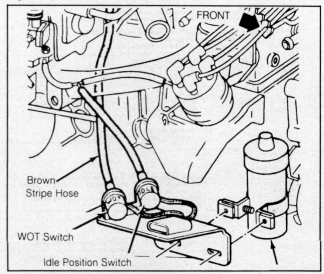

FRONT

Brown Stripe Hose

WOT Switch

Idle Position Switch

When installing switches, be sure that vacuum lines are properly connected.

OXYGEN SENSOR

CAUTION: **Oxygen sensor uses a permanently attached pigtail and connector. Do not remove pigtail from sensor. Damage to, or removal of pigtail or connector could affect sensor operation.**

GENERAL MOTORS CLOSED LOOP
EMISSION CONTROL SYSTEM (Cont.)

CAUTION: Oxygen sensor may be difficult to remove when engine temperature is below 120°F (50°C). To avoid damage to threads in exhaust manifold, DO NOT use excessive force to remove sensor.

Removal

When handling oxygen sensor, use care to keep connector and louvered end free of grease or other contaminants. Do not use cleaning solvents of any type. Disconnect negative battery cable. Disconnect electrical connector and any attaching hardware. Carefully remove oxygen sensor. *See Fig. 6.*

Installation

A new oxygen sensor is pre-coated with anti-seize compound. If same oxygen sensor is being installed, coat threads with anti-seize compound. Install oxygen sensor and torque to 30 ft. lbs. (41 N.m). Reconnect electrical connector and any attaching hardware.

Fig. 6: Oxygen Sensor Location

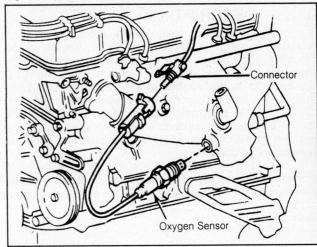

Fig. 7: Electronic Control Module Wiring Diagram

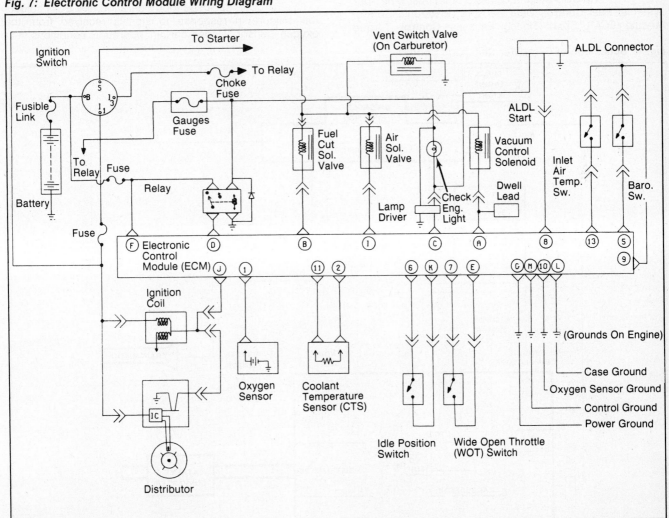

Also see chassis wiring in WIRING DIAGRAM Section.

1983 Computerized Engine Controls

GENERAL MOTORS COMPUTER COMMAND CONTROL

Calif. 2.8L, 4.1L, 5.0L & 5.7L

DESCRIPTION

CCC is an electronically controlled exhaust emission system. It monitors several engine/vehicle functions and controls various operations, including the transmission torque converter clutch (TCC). The CCC system aids in the control of exhaust emissions while maintaining good fuel economy and driveability.

The Electronic Control Module (ECM) is the "brain" of the CCC system. The ECM controls engine systems to maintain good vehicle performance under all normal driving conditions.

The primary objective of the system is to maintain an ideal air/fuel ratio of 14.7:1. With this ratio maintained, the catalytic converter can effectively control nitrogen oxides (NOx), hydrocarbons (HC) and carbon monoxide (CO).

OPERATION

The CCC system consists of the following subsystems: Fuel Control, Data Sensors, Electronic Control Module (ECM), Spark Timing, Emission Control, Torque Converter Clutch (TCC), Diagnostic System and Catalytic Converter.

FUEL CONTROL

California vehicles are equipped with "feedback" carburetors. These carburetors contain an electrically operated mixture control (M/C) solenoid. The M/C solenoid operates single or dual metering rods in the float bowl of the carburetor.

A metering rod supplements fuel supply to idle and main systems, varying air/fuel ratio within a precalibrated range. The M/C solenoid also controls air/fuel ratio through use of an idle air bleed circuit that operates in conjunction with the metering rod(s).

The ECM reacts to input from data sensors by constantly adjusting air/fuel mixture to maintain efficient engine performance. ECM controls M/C solenoid by providing a ground for solenoid.

When solenoid is energized, fuel flow through carburetor is reduced, providing a leaner mixture. When solenoid is de-energized, fuel flow through carburetor is increased, providing a richer mixture. The solenoid cycles (turns on and off) 10 times per second.

During closed loop operation, the ECM adjusts fuel mixture in response to signals received from the oxygen sensor. Under certain operating conditions, the

Fig. 1: Schematic of Computer Command Control

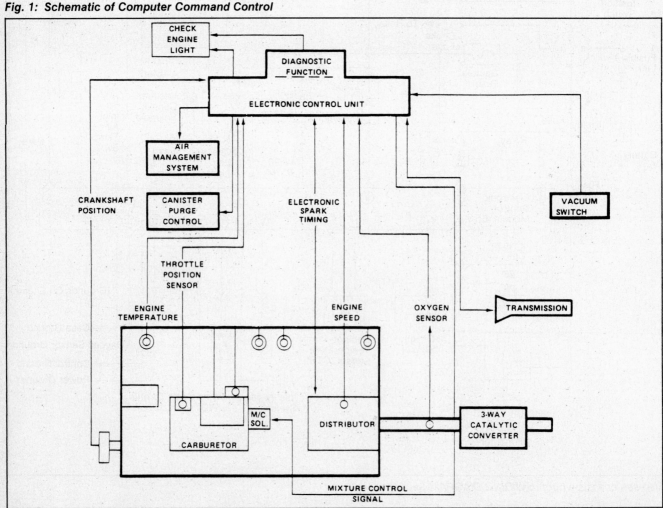

All components shown are not used on all engines.

GENERAL MOTORS COMPUTER COMMAND CONTROL (Cont.)

ECM may ignore inputs from some sensors and substitute pre-programmed data to operate the engine.

During cold engine starts (engine speed below 200 RPM), M/C solenoid is turned off by the ECM. This provides a rich mixture to the engine. Under certain operating conditions, the ECM ignores oxygen sensor signals. When these conditions exist, the CCC system then operates in open loop mode.

DATA SENSORS

Each sensor sends electrical impulses to ECM. The ECM computes ideal spark timing and fuel mixture ratio based on these signals. The function of each sensor is closely related to that of the other sensors. Operation of each sensor is as follows:

Oxygen Sensor

The oxygen sensor is mounted in the engine exhaust stream. It supplies a low voltage (under .2 volt) when fuel mixture is lean (high oxygen content). When the fuel mixture is rich (low oxygen content), a higher voltage (up to 1 volt) will be supplied to the ECM. Oxygen sensor temperature must be over 600°F (316°C) to function properly.

Oxygen sensor measures quantity of oxygen only. On occasion, the oxygen sensor may cool off during idle, causing the CCC system to go into open loop mode. Running the engine at fast idle will warm up the oxygen sensor. Proper operation of the oxygen sensor requires the use of unleaded fuel only.

Oxygen sensor voltage output should not be measured. Current drain from voltmeter can cause permanent damage to sensor, shift sensor calibration range, and/or render sensor unusable. Do not connect jumper wire, test leads or other electrical connectors to sensor. Use these devices on ECM side of harness only, after disconnecting harness from sensor.

Coolant Temperature Sensor (CTS)

The CTS is located in the engine coolant stream. It supplies coolant temperature information to the ECM. The sensor has a high resistance (around 100,000 ohms) when coolant temperature is cold and a low resistance (under 1,000 ohms) when the coolant is warm.

The sensor sends engine temperature information to the ECM. This information is used to accomplish the following:

- To vary air/fuel ratio as the coolant temperature varies with time during a cold start.
- To accomplish various switching functions at different temperatures on Early Fuel Evaporation (EFE), AIR Management Systems and Torque Converter Clutch (TCC).
- To vary spark advance.

Vacuum Sensor

The vacuum sensor is mounted in the engine compartment. This sensor signals the ECM of changes in manifold pressure (vacuum). The ECM uses these signals to adjust air/fuel mixture and spark timing.

Throttle Position Sensor (TPS)

This sensor is mounted on the carburetor. It is actuated by the accelerator pump linkage. The TPS is a variable resistor, similar to a fuel tank sending unit. It signals the ECM of changes in throttle blade position from closed to wide open throttle.

Vehicle Speed Sensor (VSS)

This sensor is used on "S" series trucks with automatic transmissions. It is mounted behind the speedometer in the instrument cluster. It provides a series of electrical pulses to the ECM, indicating vehicle speed.

Park/Neutral (P/N) Switch

This switch is connected to transmission gear selector. It is closed when selector is in "P" or "N" positions and open when selector is in gear.

ELECTRONIC CONTROL MODULE (ECM)

The ECM is located under the passenger seat on "G" series models (vans). On all other models, the ECM is located inside the instrument panel, near the glove box. It controls the CCC system by constantly monitoring and adjusting engine operation. The ECM also monitors distributor reference pulses to measure engine RPM and to determine spark timing.

Information concerning cooling system temperature, crankshaft RPM, throttle blade position, manifold pressure and amount of oxygen in exhaust gases is continuously fed into the ECM while the engine is running. The ECM is designed to process this data sensor information, and programmed to send the electrical responses necessary to control the CCC system.

The ECM contains an engine calibration unit called a PROM. The PROM is located under an access cover within the ECM. The PROM contains specific instructions to tailor each ECM to individual vehicle design. Information such as vehicle size and weight, transmission, engine and final drive ratio are contained within the PROM. A PROM that is programmed for a particular vehicle cannot be used on another vehicle that does not have the same standards.

ELECTRONIC SPARK TIMING

The Electronic Spark Timing (EST) system uses an HEI distributor with a 7-terminal HEI module. The distributor has no provision for vacuum or centrifugal advance. The HEI distributor communicates a reference pulse (indicating engine RPM) to the ECM via a 4-terminal connector. The ECM determines the proper spark advance for engine operating conditions, then sends an "EST" pulse to the distributor.

The ECM controls spark advance under normal operating conditions. Under certain operating conditions such as cranking, or when setting base timing, the distributor can operate without ECM control. This operating condition is called the by-pass mode. It is determined by the by-pass lead from the ECM to the distributor. When the by-pass lead is 5 volts, the ECM will control the spark. When the by-pass lead is grounded or open-circuited, the HEI module will control the spark.

Disconnecting the 4-terminal EST connector causes the engine to operate in the by-pass mode. It will also cause trouble code 41 to be set in the memory. Use the by-pass mode when setting base timing. After setting base timing, be sure to clear trouble code 41 from the memory.

EMISSION CONTROL

The ECM electrically controls the following emission systems: AIR Management (AIR), Early Fuel Evaporation (EFE), and Exhaust Gas Recirculation (EGR). A brief description of each system follows:

AIR Management System

This system helps to reduce HC and CO content in exhaust gases and to quickly heat up catalytic converter and oxygen sensor during cold engine opera-

GENERAL MOTORS COMPUTER COMMAND CONTROL (Cont.)

tion. This is accomplished by injecting air into exhaust port of each cylinder.

The ECM energizes an air control solenoid which permits air flow to air switching valve, directing air to exhaust ports. During warm engine (closed loop) operation, the ECM de-energizes air switching valve. This directs air to dual-bed converter, which lowers HC and CO emissions.

If air control valve detects rapid increase in manifold vacuum (deceleration condition), or ECM detects any failure in CCC system, air is diverted to air cleaner or dumped into atmosphere.

Early Fuel Evaporation (EFE)

The ECM controls the electric EFE system on the "S" series truck. The system uses a ceramic heater grid (EFE heater). The grid is located under the primary carburetor bore and is part of the carburetor insulator gasket.

The ECM applies voltage to the EFE relay when the ignition is turned "ON" and coolant temperature is low. With the EFE relay energized, voltage is applied to the EFE heater to heat the air/fuel mixture. As coolant temperature increases, the ECM discontinues voltage to the EFE relay, which shuts off the EFE heater.

Exhaust Gas Recirculation (EGR)

The ECM controls ported vacuum to EGR valve with an electrically operated EGR bleed solenoid. When engine is cold, solenoid is energized, blocking vacuum to EGR valve. When engine is warm, solenoid is de-energized and EGR operation is allowed. The solenoid decreases ported vacuum to the EGR valve when the torque converter clutch is applied.

CATALYTIC CONVERTER

Proper emission control is accomplished with a special 3-way catalytic converter which converts all 3 major pollutants. The converter is a dual-bed type. The "upstream" section of the converter contains a reducing-/oxidizing bed to reduce NOx while at the same time oxidizing HC and CO.

An air supply pipe from the AIR system introduces air between the dual beds (during closed loop operation) so the second bed can oxidize any remaining HC and CO with a high conversion efficiency, to minimize overall emissions.

TORQUE CONVERTER CLUTCH (TCC)

The ECM controls a solenoid (mounted on automatic transmission) which allows torque converter to directly connect engine to transmission. When vehicle speed is high enough, within specified engine temperature, load and at relatively constant throttle, ECM energizes TCC solenoid and engine is mechanically coupled to transmission.

When operating conditions indicate that transmission should operate as a normal fluid-coupled transmission, (during rapid acceleration or deceleration), solenoid is de-energized. The transmission also returns to normal automatic operation when brake pedal is depressed.

On 4-wheel drive models, a relay is installed between the torque converter clutch solenoid and the ECM. When the vehicle is in 4-wheel drive, the relay opens and the transmission will operate as a fluid coupled transmission through 2nd and 3rd gear operation. In 4th gear, the torque converter mechanically couples.

DIAGNOSTIC SYSTEM

The ECM of the CCC system is equipped with a self-diagnosis system which detects system failures. When a malfunction occurs, the amber "CHECK ENGINE" light on the instrument panel comes on and a corresponding trouble code is stored in ECM memory. Malfunctions are recorded as either "hard failures" or "intermittent failures".

"Hard failures" cause "CHECK ENGINE" light to come on, and stay on, until malfunction is repaired. When "CHECK ENGINE" light remains on during vehicle operation, cause of malfunction MUST be determined.

"Intermittent failures" cause light to flicker and/or go out, 10 seconds after fault goes away. However, associated trouble code will be retained in ECM memory. "Intermittent failures" may be sensor related. If a sensor fails, ECM will use a substitute value in its calculations to continue engine operation.

In this condition, service is not mandatory, but driveability may suffer. If same or similar fault does not repeat within 50 ignition cycles, related trouble code will be erased from ECM memory.

As a bulb and system check, the "CHECK ENGINE" light will glow with ignition switch "ON" and engine not running. When engine is started, light should go out within 4 seconds. If not, a malfunction has been detected in CCC system.

NOTE: **Different codes require different time intervals to set. Some codes set in as little as 5 seconds, while others may require that the related sensor or switch operate for 5 minutes or longer.**

DIAGNOSIS & TESTING

CCC system diagnosis should be done in the following order:

1) Ensure that all engine systems NOT related to CCC are fully operational. Do not proceed with testing until all other systems have been checked and/or repaired as needed.

2) Enter diagnostic mode and record trouble codes flashed by "CHECK ENGINE" light. Exit diagnostic mode.

3) Distinguish between "hard" and "intermittent" trouble codes.

4) If trouble codes were displayed, go to Diagnostic Circuit Check chart. Follow instructions given there.

5) If no trouble codes were recorded, go to Driver Complaint Sheet and follow instructions given there.

6) After any repairs are made, perform System Performance Check. Clear any trouble codes.

RECALLING TROUBLE CODES

The ECM stores component failure information under related trouble codes which can be recalled for diagnosis and repair. When recalled, these codes will be displayed by flashes of the "CHECK ENGINE" light. Codes are displayed starting with the lowest numbered code. Only codes in which a related malfunction has occurred will be displayed.

GENERAL MOTORS COMPUTER COMMAND CONTROL (Cont.)

Codes are called out by flashes of the "CHECK ENGINE" light. For example, "FLASH", "FLASH", "FLASH", pause, "FLASH", "FLASH", followed by a longer pause, identifies trouble code "32". First series of flashes indicates first digit of trouble code; second series of flashes indicates second digit of trouble code.

Entering Diagnostic Mode

1) Turn ignition switch to "ON" position. "CHECK ENGINE" light should come on. Locate Assembly Line Data Link (ALDL) connector attached to ECM wiring harness under instrument panel. Connector is located under center of instrument panel on "S" series trucks, and on left side of instrument panel on all other models. *See Fig. 2.* Insert jumper wire from terminal "A" to "B" (12-pin ALDL) or terminal "D" to "E" (5-pin ALDL).

2) "CHECK ENGINE" light should flash code "12". Code "12" consists of a "FLASH", pause, "FLASH", "FLASH". A longer pause will follow, then code "12" will repeat 2 more times. This check indicates that the self-diagnostic system is working. After code "12" displays 3 times, any other trouble codes stored in the ECM memory will be displayed.

3) If more than one code is stored, they will be displayed from the lowest numbered code to the highest. Each code will flash 3 times. After all codes have been displayed, the complete cycle will repeat. Repetition of cycle continues as long as the "TEST" terminal of ALDL connector is grounded.

CAUTION: DO NOT start engine or turn ignition switch "OFF" without first removing ground from "TEST" terminal.

Clearing Trouble Codes

To clear memory of trouble codes, turn ignition "OFF" and remove "ECM" fuse for 10 seconds. On "S" series trucks, fuse is located in engine compartment, at center of vehicle. On all other models, fuse is located at upper right corner of fuse block.

Fig. 2: ALDL Connector Terminal Locations

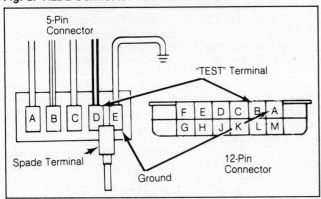

Jumper test terminal to ground terminal.

Fig. 3: ECM Terminal Identification

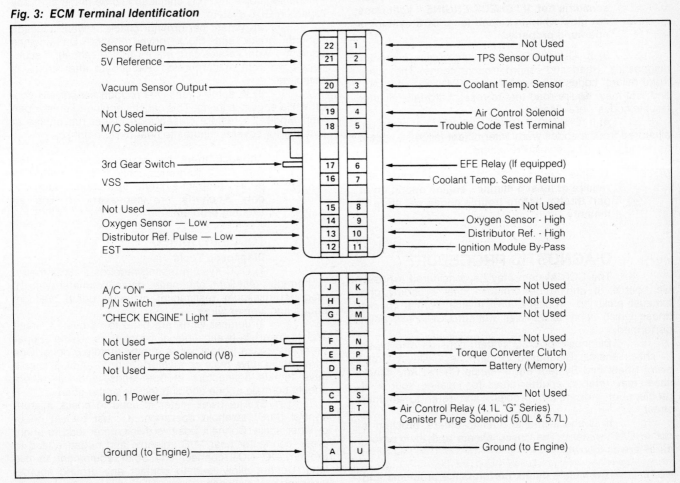

All terminals are not used in all applications.

GENERAL MOTORS COMPUTER COMMAND CONTROL (Cont.)

Exiting Diagnostic Mode

To exit diagnostic mode, turn ignition "OFF", then remove jumper wire from ALDL connector.

NOTE: The terms "enter diagnostics" and "exit diagnostics" will be used periodically throughout this section. Follow appropriate procedure for entering and exiting diagnostic mode when instructed to do so.

FAILURE CODE DETERMINATION

During any diagnostic procedure, "hard failure" codes MUST be distinguished from "intermittent failure" codes. Diagnostic charts CANNOT be used to analyze "intermittent failure" codes, except as noted under Diagnostic Procedure. To determine "hard failure" codes and "intermittent failure" codes, proceed as follows:

1) Turn ignition "ON" and enter diagnostics. Read and record all stored trouble codes. Exit diagnostics and clear trouble codes.

2) Apply parking brake and place manual transmission in neutral, or automatic transmission in "P" (park). Block drive wheels. Start engine. "CHECK ENGINE" light should go out. Run warm engine at specified curb idle for 5 minutes and note "CHECK ENGINE" light.

NOTE: Grounding "TEST" terminal with engine running will force engine to operate in closed loop mode if engine is warm and oxygen sensor is hot. If "CHECK ENGINE " light does not glow while in closed loop, CCC system is operating properly.

3) If "CHECK ENGINE" light comes on, enter diagnostics. Read and record trouble codes. These are "hard failure" codes. Codes "13", "15", "24", "35", "44", "45" and "55" may require road test to reset "hard failure" after trouble codes were cleared.

4) If "CHECK ENGINE" light does not come on, all stored trouble codes were "intermittent failures", except as noted under Diagnostic Procedure.

NOTE: Trouble codes "13", "24", "44" and "45" require at least 5 minutes engine operation at part throttle before trouble codes will store in memory.

DIAGNOSTIC PROCEDURE

The CCC system may be considered a possible source of engine performance, fuel economy and exhaust emission problems, ONLY after normal checks (those which apply to vehicles without CCC) have been performed.

Diagnosis of CCC system consists of 3 types of check sheets: Diagnostic Circuit Check, Driver Complaint Sheet and System Performance Check. Any check sheet may refer to another chart for locating source of problem, or indicate no problem and refer to another sheet.

If all check sheets refer to others, problem is not in CCC system. The check sheets and their procedures are as follows:

NOTE: If vehicle exhibits performance problems and no codes are set, refer to System Perfor-

mance Chart. Components recorded by trouble codes are generally not the source of performance problems when no codes are stored in ECM memory.

SYSTEM CHECKS

Diagnostic Circuit Check

This check ensures that the self-diagnostic system is working, determines that the trouble codes will display and guides diagnosis to other problem areas. Use this test if complaint is "CHECK ENGINE" light related, while noting the following:

- If code "51" is displayed, refer to PROM removal and installation in this article for diagnosis of code.
- If codes "51," "54" or "55" are displayed in addition to other codes, refer to diagnostic chart for "50" series code first, then go to lowest numbered code.

Driver Complaint Sheet

1) If complaint is not "CHECK ENGINE" light related, this check will lead to most likely problem area. However, before beginning procedure, make checks that would normally be made for a similar complaint on a vehicle without CCC system.

2) Follow instructions in diagnostic chart and repair malfunction. After repair, perform System Performance Check.

System Performance Check

1) This check verifies that CCC system is functioning correctly. This check should be made after any repair on CCC system.

2) When performing check, always engage parking brake and block drive wheels. On engines equipped with Varajet carburetors (E2SE model), disconnect bowl vent at carburetor. Reconnect after check is complete.

3) In some cases, the oxygen sensor will cool off while engine is idling. This causes engine to enter open loop mode. To restore closed loop mode, run engine at fast idle for several minutes to heat oxygen sensor.

NOTE: Although there are many charts connected with CCC diagnosis, only 2 are needed to prove proper system operation. Normally, only 3 charts are necessary to find an existing problem.

TOOLS REQUIRED

Diagnostic Tools

1) CCC system testing requires a dwell meter, tachometer, test light, ohmmeter, digital voltmeter (with 10 megohm minimum resistance), vacuum pump, vacuum gauge and jumper wires.

2) Jumper wires are used to by-pass a circuit and to insert between special connectors. Using proper terminals, make jumper wires approximately 6" long. One wire should have male connectors at both ends, 2 should have female connectors at both ends, and the others should be male at one end and female at the other.

3) The dwell meter is used to check mixture control (M/C) solenoid operation. It must be set on 6-cylinder scale. Connect positive dwell meter lead to bright green connector near M/C solenoid and negative lead to ground. DO NOT connect any other equipment to this lead. Do not allow lead to contact any ground source, including rubber hoses.

GENERAL MOTORS COMPUTER COMMAND CONTROL (Cont.)

NOTE: If engine operation changes when dwell meter is connected, remove it and try a different meter. Some brands of meters affect system operation.

4) When engine is at operating temperature and idling, dwell meter needle will fluctuate between 10° and 50°. This indicates closed loop operation. If the needle does not move, open loop operation is indicated.

ECM TROUBLE CODE IDENTIFICATION

Trouble Code	Circuit Malfunction
12	No distributor reference pulse to ECM
13	Oxygen sensor circuit
14	Shorted coolant sensor circuit
15	Open coolant sensor circuit
21	Throttle position sensor circuit
23	Open or grounded M/C solenoid circuit
24 [1]	Vehicle speed sensor
34	Vacuum sensor circuit
41	No distributor reference pulses at specified engine vacuum
42	EST or EST bypass circuit grounded or open
44	Lean oxygen sensor value
44 & 45	Faulty oxygen sensor circuit
45	Rich oxygen sensor value
51	Faulty PROM or improper PROM installation
54	Shorted M/C or faulty ECM
55	Grounded voltage reference, high voltage on oxygen sensor circuit or ECM

[1] — Applies to "S" series truck.

GENERAL MOTORS COMPUTER COMMAND CONTROL (Cont.)

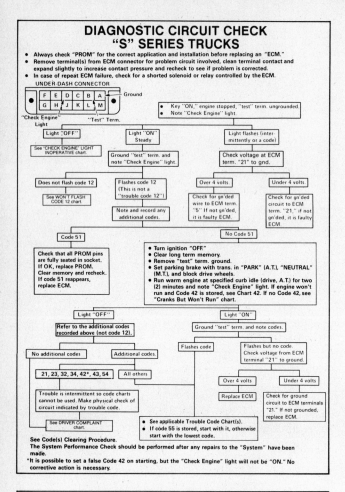

DIAGNOSTIC CIRCUIT CHECK "S" SERIES TRUCKS

- Always check "PROM" for the correct application and installation before replacing an "ECM."
- Remove terminal(s) from ECM connector for problem circuit involved, clean terminal contact and expand slightly to increase contact pressure and recheck to see if problem is corrected.
- In case of repeat ECM failure, check for a shorted solenoid or relay controlled by the ECM.

See Code(s) Clearing Procedure.
The System Performance Check should be performed after any repairs to the "System" have been made.
*It is possible to set a false Code 42 on starting, but the "Check Engine" light will not be "ON." No corrective action is necessary.

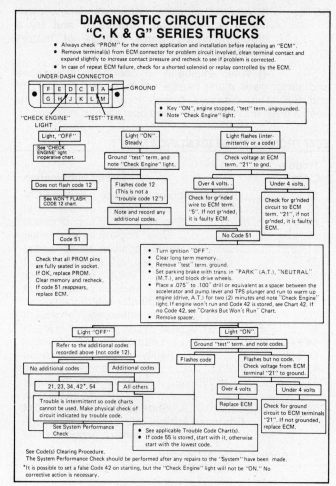

DIAGNOSTIC CIRCUIT CHECK "C, K & G" SERIES TRUCKS

- Always check "PROM" for the correct application and installation before replacing an "ECM."
- Remove terminal(s) from ECM connector for problem circuit involved, clean terminal contact and expand slightly to increase contact pressure and recheck to see if problem is corrected.
- In case of repeat ECM failure, check for a shorted solenoid or replay controlled by the ECM.

See Code(s) Clearing Procedure.
The System Performance Check should be performed after any repairs to the "System" have been made.
*It is possible to set a false Code 42 on starting, but the "Check Engine" light will not be "ON." No corrective action is necessary.

DRIVER COMPLAINT SHEET

ENGINE PERFORMANCE PROBLEM (ODOR, SURGE, FUEL ECONOMY . . .)
EMISSION PROBLEM

IF THE "CHECK ENGINE" LIGHT IS NOT ON, NORMAL CHECKS THAT WOULD BE PERFORMED ON VEHICLE WITHOUT THE SYSTEM SHOULD BE DONE FIRST.

IF GENERATOR OR COOLANT LIGHT IS ON WITH THE "CHECK ENGINE" LIGHT, THEY SHOULD BE DIAGNOSED FIRST.

INSPECT FOR POOR CONNECTIONS AT COOLANT SENSOR, M/C SOLENOID, ETC., AND POOR OR LOOSE VACUUM HOSES AND CONNECTIONS. REPAIR AS NECESSARY.

- Intermittent "Check Engine" light but no trouble code stored.
  - Check for intermittent connection in circuit from:
    - Ignition coil to ground and arcing at spark plug wires or plugs.
    - Bat. to ECM Terms. 'C' and 'R.'
    - ECM Terms. 'A' and 'U' to engine ground.
  - Loss of trouble code (long-term) memory.
    Grounding lead for 10 seconds with "test" lead ungrounded should give Code 23 which should be retained after engine is stopped and ignition turned to "RUN" position.
    If it is not, ECM is defective.
  - EST wires should be kept away from spark plug wires, distributor housing, coil and generator. Wires from ECM Term. 13 to dist. and the shield (if used) around EST wires should be a good ground.
  - Open diode across A/C compressor clutch.

- Stalling, Rough Idle, Dieseling or Improper Idle Speed.
  See Idle Speed Control (ISC) Check.

- Detonation (spark knock)
  Check: ESC System Check, if applicable.
  MAP or Vacuum Sensor Output
  EGR Check.
  TPS Enrichment Operation.
  HEI Operation.

- Poor Performance and/or Fuel Economy.
  See EST Performance Check.
  See ESC System Check if applicable.

- Poor Full Throttle Performance
  Check TPS Enrichment Operation.

- Intermittent No-start
  - Incorrect pick-up coil or ignition coil. See "Cranks, But Won't Run" chart.
  - Intermittent ground connections on ECM.

- ALL OTHER COMPLAINTS
  Make System Peformance Check on warm engine
  (upper radiator hose hot).

The System Performance Check should be performed after any repairs to the system have been made.

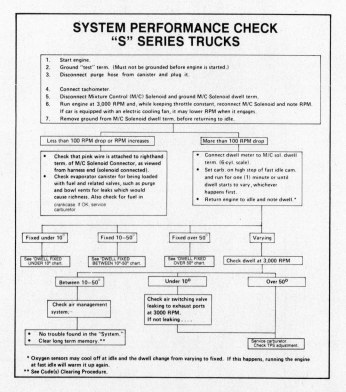

SYSTEM PERFORMANCE CHECK "S" SERIES TRUCKS

1. Start engine.
2. Ground "test" term. (Must not be grounded before engine is started.)
3. Disconnect purge hose from canister and plug it.
4. Connect tachometer.
5. Disconnect Mixture Control (M/C) Solenoid and ground M/C Solenoid dwell term.
6. Run engine at 3,000 RPM and, while keeping throttle constant, reconnect M/C Solenoid and note RPM. If car is equipped with an electric cooling fan, it may lower RPM when it engages.
7. Remove ground from M/C Solenoid dwell term. before returning to idle.

* Oxygen sensors may cool off at idle and the dwell change from varying to fixed. If this happens, running the engine at fast idle will warm it up again.
** See Code(s) Clearing Procedure.

GENERAL MOTORS COMPUTER COMMAND CONTROL (Cont.)

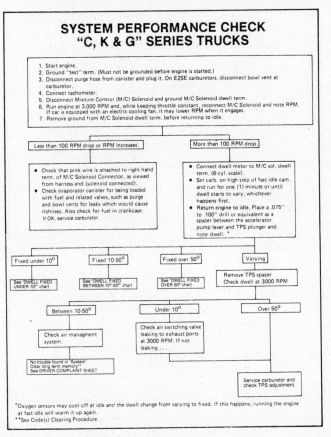

SYSTEM PERFORMANCE CHECK "C, K & G" SERIES TRUCKS

1. Start engine.
2. Ground "test" term. (Must not be grounded before engine is started.)
3. Disconnect purge hose from canister and plug it. On E2SE carburetors, disconnect bowl vent at carburetor.
4. Connect tachometer.
5. Disconnect Mixture Control (M/C) Solenoid and ground M/C Solenoid dwell term.
6. Run engine at 3,000 RPM and, while keeping throttle constant, reconnect M/C Solenoid and note RPM. If car is equipped with an electric cooling fan, it may lower RPM when it engages.
7. Remove ground from M/C Solenoid dwell term. before returning to idle.

*Oxygen sensors may cool off at idle and the dwell change from varying to fixed. If this happens, running the engine at fast idle will warm it up again.
* See Code(s) Clearing Procedure.

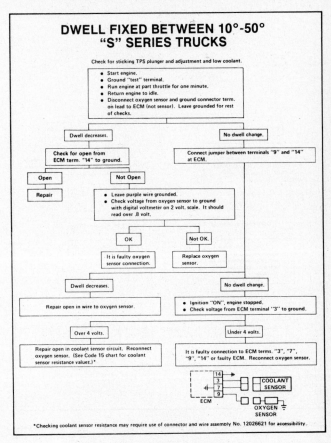

DWELL FIXED BETWEEN 10°-50° "S" SERIES TRUCKS

Check for sticking TPS plunger and adjustment and low coolant.

- Start engine.
- Ground "test" terminal.
- Run engine at part throttle for one minute.
- Return engine to idle.
- Disconnect oxygen sensor and ground connector term. on lead to ECM (not sensor). Leave grounded for rest of checks.

*Checking coolant sensor resistance may require use of connector and wire assembly No. 12026621 for accessibility.

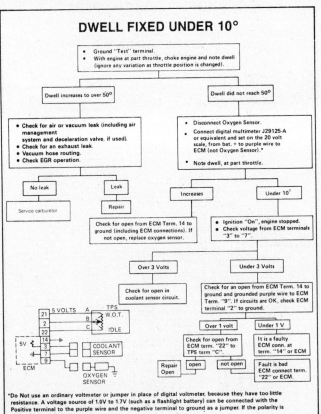

DWELL FIXED UNDER 10°

- Ground "Test" terminal.
- With engine at part throttle, choke engine and note dwell (ignore any variation as throttle position is changed).

*Do Not use an ordinary voltmeter or jumper in place of digital voltmeter, because they have too little resistance. A voltage source of 1.0V to 1.7V (such as a flashlight battery) can be connected with the Positive terminal to the purple wire and the negative terminal to ground as a jumper. If the polarity is reversed, it won't work.

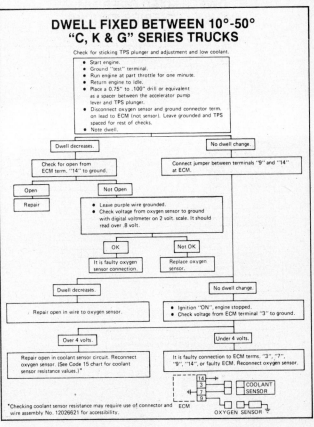

DWELL FIXED BETWEEN 10°-50° "C, K & G" SERIES TRUCKS

Check for sticking TPS plunger and adjustment and low coolant.

- Start engine.
- Ground "test" terminal.
- Run engine at part throttle for one minute.
- Return engine to idle.
- Place a 0.75" to .100" drill or equivalent as a spacer between the accelerator pump lever and TPS plunger.
- Disconnect oxygen sensor and ground connector term. on lead to ECM (not sensor). Leave grounded and TPS spaced for rest of checks.
- Note dwell.

*Checking coolant sensor resistance may require use of connector and wire assembly No. 12026621 for accessibility.

GENERAL MOTORS COMPUTER COMMAND CONTROL (Cont.)

DWELL FIXED OVER 50° "S" SERIES TRUCKS

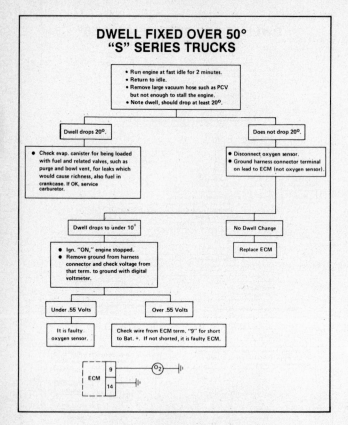

- Run engine at fast idle for 2 minutes.
- Return to idle.
- Remove large vacuum hose such as PCV but not enough to stall the engine.
- Note dwell, should drop at least 20°.

Dwell drops 20°.

- Check evap. canister for being loaded with fuel and related valves, such as purge and bowl vent, for leaks which would cause richness, also fuel in crankcase. If OK, service carburetor.

Dwell drops to under 10°

- Ign. "ON," engine stopped.
- Remove ground from harness connector and check voltage from that term. to ground with digital voltmeter.

Under .55 Volts — It is faulty oxygen sensor.

Over .55 Volts — Check wire from ECM term. "9" for short to Bat. +. If not shorted, it is faulty ECM.

Does not drop 20°.

- Disconnect oxygen sensor.
- Ground harness connector terminal on lead to ECM (not oxygen sensor).

No Dwell Change — Replace ECM

TPS ENRICHMENT CHECK

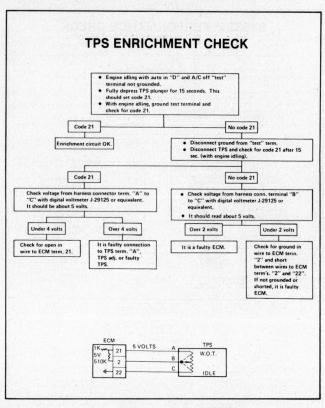

- Engine idling with auto in "D" and A/C off "test" terminal not grounded.
- Fully depress TPS plunger for 15 seconds. This should set code 21.
- With engine idling, ground test terminal and check for code 21.

Code 21 — Enrichment circuit OK.

No code 21
- Disconnect ground from "test" term.
- Disconnect TPS and check for code 21 after 15 sec. (with engine idling).

Code 21 — Check voltage from harness connector term. "A" to "C" with digital voltmeter J-29125 or equivalent. It should be about 5 volts.

Under 4 volts — Check for open in wire to ECM term. 21.

Over 4 volts — It is faulty connection to TPS term. "A", TPS adj. or faulty TPS.

No code 21 — Check voltage from harness conn. terminal "B" to "C" with digital voltmeter J-29125 or equivalent.
- It should read about 5 volts.

Over 2 volts — It is a faulty ECM.

Under 2 volts — Check for ground in wire to ECM term. "2" and short between wires to ECM term's. "2" and "22". If not grounded or shorted, it is faulty ECM.

DWELL FIXED OVER 50° "C, K & G" SERIES TRUCKS

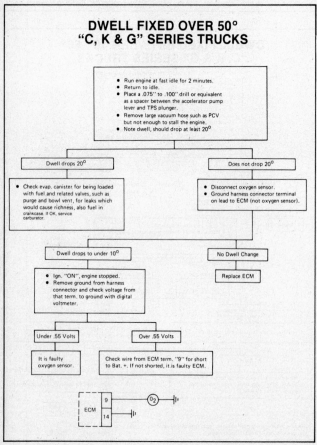

- Run engine at fast idle for 2 minutes.
- Return to idle.
- Place a .075" to .100" drill or equivalent as a spacer between the accelerator pump lever and TPS plunger.
- Remove large vacuum hose such as PCV but not enough to stall the engine.
- Note dwell, should drop at least 20°

Dwell drops 20°

- Check evap. canister for being loaded with fuel and related valves, such as purge and bowl vent, for leaks which would cause richness, also fuel in crankcase. If OK, service carburetor.

Dwell drops to under 10°

- Ign. "ON", engine stopped.
- Remove ground from harness connector and check voltage from that term. to ground with digital voltmeter.

Under .55 Volts — It is faulty oxygen sensor.

Over .55 Volts — Check wire from ECM term. "9" for short to Bat. +. If not shorted, it is faulty ECM.

Does not drop 20°

- Disconnect oxygen sensor.
- Ground harness connector terminal on lead to ECM (not oxygen sensor).

No Dwell Change — Replace ECM

"CHECK ENGINE" LIGHT INOPERATIVE

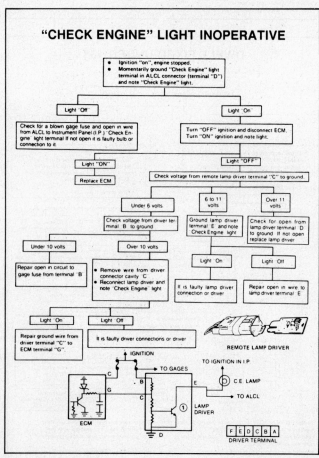

- Ignition "on", engine stopped.
- Momentarily ground "Check Engine" light terminal in ALCL connector (terminal "D") and note "Check Engine" light.

Light "Off" — Check for a blown gage fuse and open in wire from ALCL to Instrument Panel (I.P.) "Check Engine" light terminal. If not open it is faulty bulb or connection to it.

Light "ON" — Replace ECM

Light "On" — Turn "OFF" ignition and disconnect ECM. Turn "ON" ignition and note light.

Light "OFF" — Check voltage from remote lamp driver terminal "C" to ground.

Under 6 volts — Check voltage from driver terminal "B" to ground.

Under 10 volts — Repair open in circuit to gage fuse from terminal "B".

Over 10 volts
- Remove wire from driver connector cavity "C".
- Reconnect lamp driver and note "Check Engine" light.

Light "On" — Repair ground wire from driver terminal "C" to ECM terminal "G".

Light "Off" — It is faulty driver connections or driver.

6 to 11 volts — Ground lamp driver terminal "E" and note Check Engine light.

Light On — It is faulty lamp driver connection or driver

Light Off — Repair open in wire to lamp driver terminal E

Over 11 volts — Check for open from lamp driver terminal "D" to ground. If not open replace lamp driver

REMOTE LAMP DRIVER

GENERAL MOTORS COMPUTER COMMAND CONTROL (Cont.)

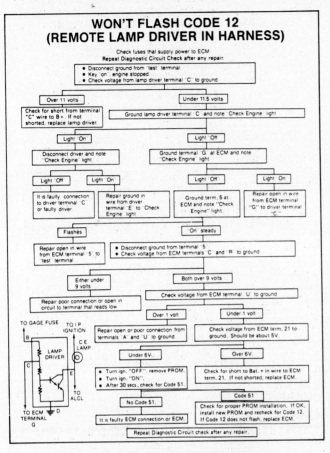

WON'T FLASH CODE 12 (REMOTE LAMP DRIVER IN HARNESS)

Check fuses that supply power to ECM
Repeat Diagnostic Circuit Check after any repair.

- Disconnect ground from "test" terminal
- Key "on", engine stopped.
- Check voltage from lamp driver terminal "C" to ground

Over 11 volts → Check for short from terminal "C" wire to B+. If not shorted, replace lamp driver.

Under 11.5 volts → Ground lamp driver terminal "C" and note "Check Engine light"

Light "On" → Disconnect driver and note "Check Engine" light.

Light "Off" → It is faulty connection to driver terminal "C" or faulty driver

Light "On" → Repair ground in wire from driver terminal "E" to "Check Engine" light.

Light "Off" → Ground terminal "G" at ECM and note "Check Engine" light.

Light "Off" → Ground term. 5 at ECM and note "Check Engine" light.

Light "On" → Repair open in wire from ECM terminal "G" to driver terminal "C".

Flashes → Repair open in wire from ECM terminal "5" to "test" terminal.

'On' steady →
- Disconnect ground from terminal "5"
- Check voltage from ECM terminals "C" and "R" to ground

Either under 9 volts → Repair poor connection or open in circuit to terminal that reads low

Both over 9 volts → Check voltage from ECM terminal "U" to ground

Over 1 volt → Repair open or poor connection from terminals "A" and "U" to ground

Under 1 volt → Check voltage from ECM terminal, 21 to ground. Should be about 5V.

Under 6V. →
- Turn ign. "OFF", remove PROM.
- Turn ign. "ON".
- After 30 secs., check for Code 51.

Over 6V. → Check for short to Bat. + in wire to ECM term. 21. If not shorted, replace ECM.

No Code 51. → It is faulty ECM connection or ECM.

Code 51 → Check for proper PROM installation. If OK, install new PROM and recheck for Code 12. If Code 12 does not flash, replace ECM.

Repeat Diagnostic Circuit check after any repair.

TO GAGE FUSE / TO I.P IGNITION — LAMP DRIVER — TO ALCL — TO ECM TERMINAL G

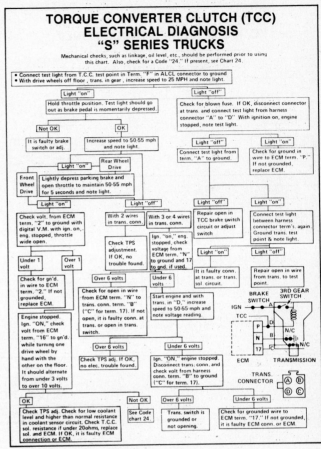

TORQUE CONVERTER CLUTCH (TCC) ELECTRICAL DIAGNOSIS "S" SERIES TRUCKS

Mechanical checks, such as linkage, oil level, etc., should be performed prior to using this chart. Also, check for a Code "24." If present, see Chart 24.

- Connect test light from T.C.C. test point in Term. "F" in ALCL connector to ground
- With drive wheels off floor, trans. in gear, increase speed to 25 MPH and note light.

Light "on" → Hold throttle position. Test light should go out as brake pedal is momentarily depressed.

Light "off" → Check for blown fuse. If OK, disconnect connector at trans. and connect test light from harness connector "A" to "D." With ignition on, engine stopped, note test light.

...

ELECTRIC DIVERTER VALVE (EDV) CHECK, EXCEPT MODELS WITH MECHANICAL DIVERT VALVE

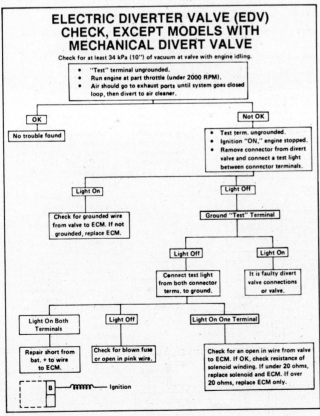

Check for at least 34 kPa (10") of vacuum at valve with engine idling.

- "Test" terminal ungrounded.
- Run engine at part throttle (under 2000 RPM).
- Air should go to exhaust ports until system goes closed loop, then divert to air cleaner.

OK → No trouble found

Not OK →
- Test term. ungrounded.
- Ignition "ON," engine stopped.
- Remove connector from divert valve and connect a test light between connector terminals.

Light On → Check for grounded wire from valve to ECM. If not grounded, replace ECM.

Light Off → Ground "Test" Terminal

Light Off → Connect test light from both connector terms. to ground.

Light On → It is faulty divert valve connections or valve.

Light On Both Terminals → Repair short from bat. + to wire to ECM.

Light Off → Check for blown fuse or open in pink wire.

Light On One Terminal → Check for an open in wire from valve to ECM. If OK, check resistance of solenoid winding. If under 20 ohms, replace solenoid and ECM. If over 20 ohms, replace ECM only.

B — Ignition

EFE (ELECTRICALLY HEATED) CHECK "S" SERIES TRUCKS ONLY

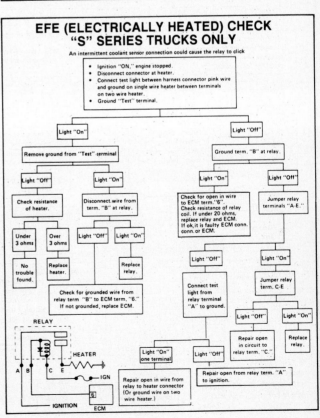

An intermittent coolant sensor connection could cause the relay to click

- Ignition "ON," engine stopped.
- Disconnect connector at heater.
- Connect test light between harness connector pink wire and ground on single wire heater between terminals on two wire heater.
- Ground "Test" terminal.

Light "On" → Remove ground from "Test" terminal

Light "Off" → Ground term. "B" at relay.

...

GENERAL MOTORS COMPUTER COMMAND CONTROL (Cont.)

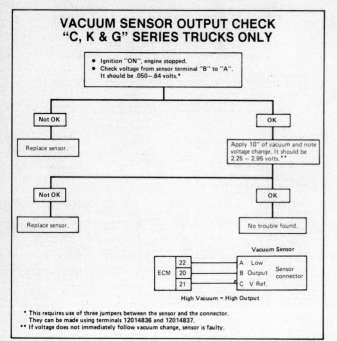

VACUUM SENSOR OUTPUT CHECK "C, K & G" SERIES TRUCKS ONLY

- Ignition "ON", engine stopped.
- Check voltage from sensor terminal "B" to "A". It should be .050—.64 volts.*

Not OK → Replace sensor.

OK → Apply 10" of vacuum and note voltage change. It should be 2.25 — 2.95 volts.**

Not OK → Replace sensor.

OK → No trouble found.

Vacuum Sensor

ECM	22	A	Low
	20	B	Output
	21	C	V Ref.

Sensor connector

High Vacuum = High Output

* This requires use of three jumpers between the sensor and the connector. They can be made using terminals 12014836 and 12014837.
** If voltage does not immediately follow vacuum change, sensor is faulty.

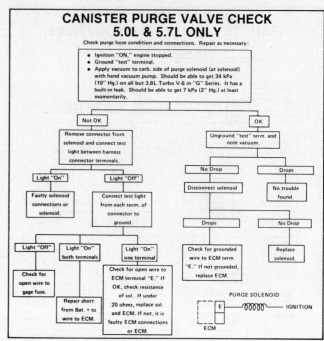

CANISTER PURGE VALVE CHECK 5.0L & 5.7L ONLY
Check purge hose condition and connections. Repair as necessary:

- Ignition "ON," engine stopped.
- Ground "test" terminal.
- Apply vacuum to carb. side of purge solenoid (at solenoid) with hand vacuum pump. Should be able to get 34 kPa (10" Hg.) on all but 3.8L Turbo V-6 in "G" Series. It has a built-in leak. Should be able to get 7 kPa (2" Hg.) at least momentarily.

Not OK → Remove connector from solenoid and connect test light between harness connector terminals.

- **Light "On"** → Faulty solenoid connections or solenoid.
- **Light "Off"** → Connect test light from each term. of connector to ground.
  - **Light "Off" both terminals** → Check for open wire to gage fuse.
  - **Light "On" both terminals** → Repair short from Bat. + to wire to ECM.
  - **Light "On" one terminal** → Check for open wire to ECM terminal "E." If OK, check resistance of sol. If under 20 ohms, replace sol. and ECM. If not, it is faulty ECM connections or ECM.

OK → Unground "test" term. and note vacuum.

- **No Drop** → Disconnect solenoid.
  - **Drops** → Check for grounded wire to ECM term. "E." If not grounded, replace ECM.
  - **No Drop** → Replace solenoid.
- **Drops** → No trouble found.

PURGE SOLENOID

E ——/0000\—— IGNITION

ECM

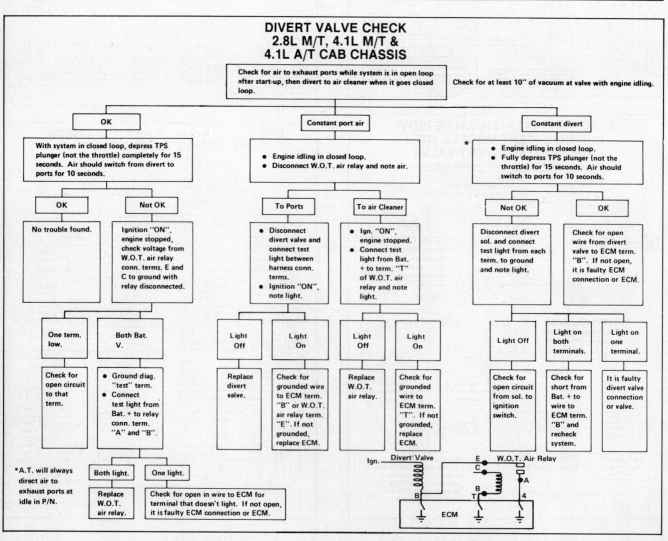

DIVERT VALVE CHECK 2.8L M/T, 4.1L M/T & 4.1L A/T CAB CHASSIS

Check for air to exhaust ports while system is in open loop after start-up, then divert to air cleaner when it goes closed loop.

Check for at least 10" of vacuum at valve with engine idling.

OK → With system in closed loop, depress TPS plunger (not the throttle) completely for 15 seconds. Air should switch from divert to ports for 10 seconds.

- **OK** → No trouble found.
- **Not OK** → Ignition "ON", engine stopped, check voltage from W.O.T. air relay conn. terms. E and C to ground with relay disconnected.
  - **One term. low.** → Check for open circuit to that term.
  - **Both Bat. V.** → • Ground diag. "test" term. • Connect test light from Bat. + to relay conn. term. "A" and "B".
    - **Both light.** → Replace W.O.T. air relay.
    - **One light.** → Check for open in wire to ECM for terminal that doesn't light. If not open, it is faulty ECM connection or ECM.

*A.T. will always direct air to exhaust ports at idle in P/N.

Constant port air
- Engine idling in closed loop.
- Disconnect W.O.T. air relay and note air.

- **To Ports** → • Disconnect divert valve and connect test light between harness conn. terms. • Ignition "ON", note light.
  - **Light Off** → Replace divert valve.
  - **Light On** → Check for grounded wire to ECM term. "B" or W.O.T. air relay term. "E". If not grounded, replace ECM.
- **To air Cleaner** → • Ign. "ON", engine stopped. • Connect test light from Bat. + to term. "T" of W.O.T. air relay and note light.
  - **Light Off** → Replace W.O.T. air relay.
  - **Light On** → Check for grounded wire to ECM term. "T". If not grounded, replace ECM.

Constant divert
- Engine idling in closed loop.
- Fully depress TPS plunger (not the throttle) for 15 seconds. Air should switch to ports for 10 seconds.

- **Not OK** → Disconnect divert sol. and connect test light from each term. to ground and note light.
  - **Light Off** → Check for open circuit from sol. to ignition switch.
  - **Light on both terminals.** → Check for short from Bat. + to wire to ECM term. "B" and recheck system.
  - **Light on one terminal.** → It is faulty divert valve connection or valve.
- **OK** → Check for open wire from divert valve to ECM term. "B". If not open, it is faulty ECM connection or ECM.

Ign. **Divert Valve** — E **W.O.T. Air Relay**
C
B — A
B T 4
ECM

TORQUE CONVERTER CLUTCH (TCC) ELECTRICAL DIAGNOSIS "C, K & G" SERIES TRUCKS

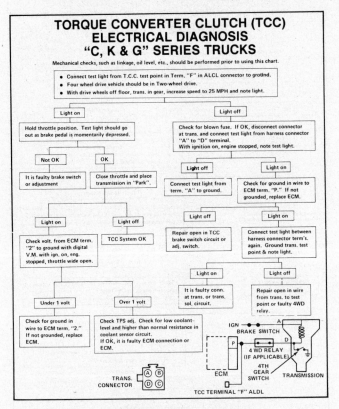

Mechanical checks, such as linkage, oil level, etc., should be performed prior to using this chart.

- Connect test light from T.C.C. test point in Term. "F" in ALCL connector to ground.
- Four wheel drive vehicle should be in Two-wheel drive.
- With drive wheels off floor, trans. in gear, increase speed to 25 MPH and note light.

EST PERFORMANCE CHECK

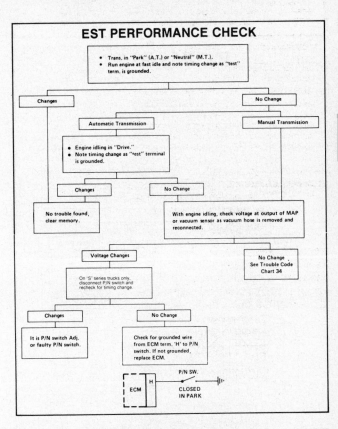

- Trans. in "Park" (A.T.) or "Neutral" (M.T.).
- Run engine at fast idle and note timing change as "test" term. is grounded.

ENGINE CRANKS, BUT WILL NOT RUN (WITH INTEGRAL COIL)

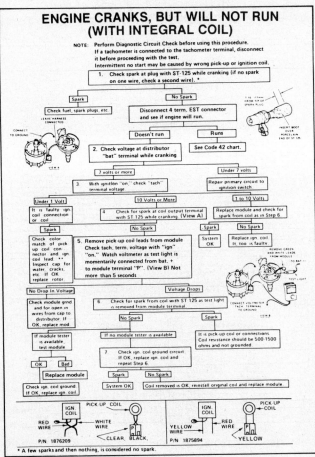

NOTE: Perform Diagnostic Circuit Check before using this procedure. If a tachometer is connected to the tachometer terminal, disconnect it before proceeding with the test. Intermittent no start may be caused by wrong pick-up or ignition coil.

* A few sparks and then nothing, is considered no spark.

ENGINE CRANKS, BUT WILL NOT RUN (WITH REMOTE COIL)

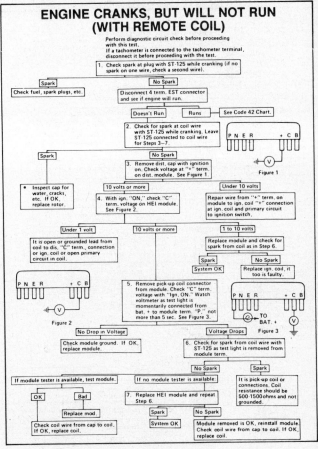

Perform diagnostic circuit check before proceeding with this test. If a tachometer is connected to the tachometer terminal, disconnect it before proceeding with the test.

GENERAL MOTORS COMPUTER COMMAND CONTROL (Cont.)

TROUBLE CODE 12

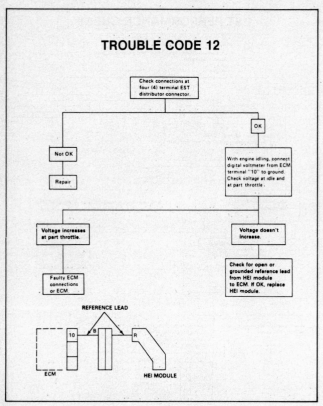

TROUBLE CODE 13

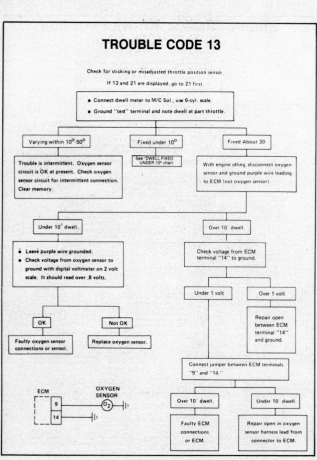

TROUBLE CODE 14

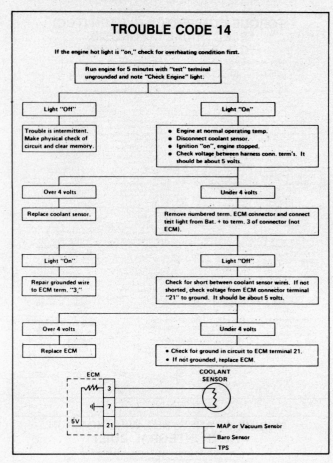

TROUBLE CODE 15

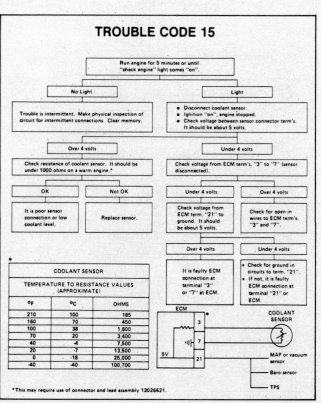

GENERAL MOTORS COMPUTER COMMAND CONTROL (Cont.)

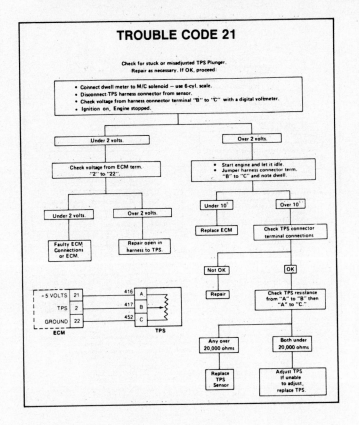

TROUBLE CODE 21

Check for stuck or misadjusted TPS Plunger.
Repair as necessary. If OK, proceed:

- Connect dwell meter to M/C solenoid — use 6-cyl. scale.
- Disconnect TPS harness connector from sensor.
- Check voltage from harness connector terminal "B" to "C" with a digital voltmeter.
- Ignition on, Engine stopped.

Under 2 volts.
- Check voltage from ECM term. "2" to "22".
  - **Under 2 volts.** → Faulty ECM Connections or ECM.
  - **Over 2 volts.** → Repair open in harness to TPS.

Over 2 volts.
- Start engine and let it idle.
- Jumper harness connector term. "B" to "C" and note dwell.
  - **Under 10°** → Replace ECM
  - **Over 10°** → Check TPS connector terminal connections
    - **Not OK** → Repair
    - **OK** → Check TPS resistance from "A" to "B" then "A" to "C."
      - **Any over 20,000 ohms** → Replace TPS Sensor
      - **Both under 20,000 ohms** → Adjust TPS if unable to adjust, replace TPS.

ECM:
- +5 VOLTS 21 — 416 — A
- TPS 2 — 417 — B
- GROUND 22 — 452 — C
- TPS

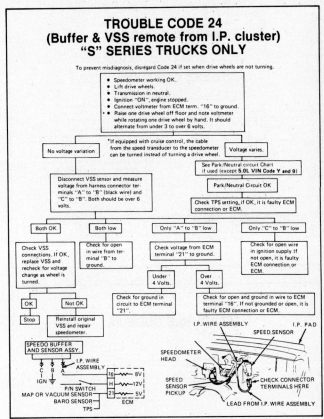

TROUBLE CODE 24
(Buffer & VSS remote from I.P. cluster)
"S" SERIES TRUCKS ONLY

To prevent misdiagnosis, disregard Code 24 if set when drive wheels are not turning.

- Speedometer working OK.
- Lift drive wheels.
- Transmission in neutral.
- Ignition "ON", engine stopped.
- Connect voltmeter from ECM term. "16" to ground.
- Raise one drive wheel off floor and note voltmeter while rotating one drive wheel by hand. It should alternate from under 3 to over 6 volts.

No voltage variation
- *If equipped with cruise control, the cable from the speed transducer to the speedometer can be turned instead of turning a drive wheel.
- Disconnect VSS sensor and measure voltage from harness connector terminals "A" to "B" (black wire) and "C" to "B". Both should be over 6 volts.
  - **Both OK** → Check VSS connections. If OK, replace VSS and recheck for voltage change as wheel is turned.
    - **OK** → Stop
    - **Not OK** → Reinstall original VSS and repair speedometer.
  - **Both low** → Check for open in wire from terminal "B" to ground.
  - **Only "A" to "B" low** → Check voltage from ECM terminal "21" to ground.
    - **Under 4 Volts.** → Check for ground in circuit to ECM terminal "21".
    - **Over 4 Volts.** → Check for open and ground in wire to ECM terminal "16". If not grounded or open, it is faulty ECM connection or ECM.
  - **Only "C" to "B" low** → Check for open wire in ignition supply. If not open, it is faulty ECM connection or ECM.

Voltage varies.
- See Park/Neutral circuit Chart if used (except 5.0L VIN Code Y and 9)
- Park/Neutral Circuit OK
- Check TPS setting. If OK, it is faulty ECM connection or ECM.

SPEEDO BUFFER AND SENSOR ASSY.
C B A — I.P. WIRE ASSEMBLY
IGN — P/N SWITCH
MAP OR VACUUM SENSOR
BARO SENSOR
TPS
ECM: 16 — 8V; H — 12V; 21 — 5V

I.P. WIRE ASSEMBLY — I.P. PAD
SPEED SENSOR
SPEEDOMETER HEAD
SPEED SENSOR PICKUP
CHECK CONNECTOR TERMINALS HERE
LEAD FROM I.P. WIRE ASSEMBLY

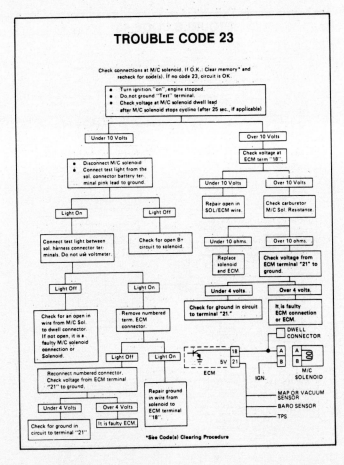

TROUBLE CODE 23

Check connections at M/C solenoid. If O.K.: Clear memory* and recheck for code(s). If no code 23, circuit is OK.

- Turn ignition "on", engine stopped.
- Do not ground "Test" terminal.
- Check voltage at M/C solenoid dwell lead after M/C solenoid stops cycling (after 25 sec., if applicable)

Under 10 Volts
- Disconnect M/C solenoid.
- Connect test light from the sol. connector battery terminal pink lead to ground.
  - **Light On** → Connect test light between sol. harness connector terminals. Do not use voltmeter.
    - **Light Off** → Check for an open in wire from M/C Sol. to dwell connector. If not open, it is a faulty M/C solenoid connection or Solenoid.
    - **Light On** → Remove numbered term. ECM connector.
      - **Light Off** → Reconnect numbered connector. Check voltage from ECM terminal "21" to ground.
        - **Under 4 Volts** → Check for ground in circuit to terminal "21"
        - **Over 4 Volts** → It is faulty ECM.
      - **Light On** → Repair ground in wire from solenoid to ECM terminal "18".
  - **Light Off** → Check for open B+ circuit to solenoid.

Over 10 Volts
- Check voltage at ECM term "18".
  - **Under 10 Volts** → Repair open in SOL/ECM wire.
  - **Over 10 Volts** → Check carburetor M/C Sol. Resistance.
    - **Under 10 ohms** → Replace solenoid and ECM.
    - **Over 10 ohms** → Check voltage from ECM terminal "21" to ground.
      - **Under 4 volts.** → Check for ground in circuit to terminal "21."
      - **Over 4 volts.** → It is faulty ECM connection or ECM.

DWELL CONNECTOR
ECM: 18, 21 — 5V — IGN — A B / A B — M/C SOLENOID
MAP OR VACUUM SENSOR
BARO SENSOR
TPS

*See Code(s) Clearing Procedure

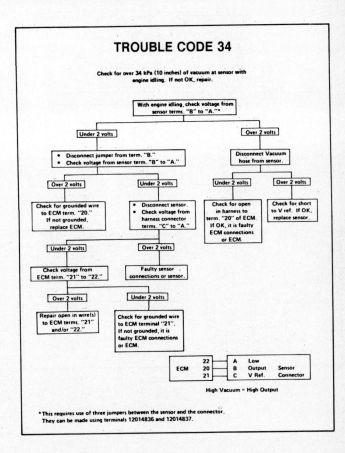

TROUBLE CODE 34

Check for over 34 kPa (10 inches) of vacuum at sensor with engine idling. If not OK, repair.

With engine idling, check voltage from sensor terms. "B" to "A."*

Under 2 volts
- Disconnect jumper from term. "B."
- Check voltage from sensor term. "B" to "A."
  - **Over 2 volts** → Check for grounded wire to ECM term. "20." If not grounded, replace ECM.
    - **Under 2 volts** → Check voltage from ECM term. "21" to "22."
      - **Over 2 volts** → Repair open in wire(s) to ECM terms. "21" and/or "22."
  - **Under 2 volts** → Disconnect sensor. Check voltage from harness connector terms. "C" to "A."
    - **Over 2 volts** → Faulty sensor connections or sensor.
      - **Under 2 volts** → Check for grounded wire to ECM terminal "21". If not grounded, it is faulty ECM connections or ECM.

Over 2 volts
- Disconnect Vacuum hose from sensor.
  - **Under 2 volts** → Check for open in harness to term. "20" of ECM. If OK, it is faulty ECM connections or ECM.
  - **Over 2 volts** → Check for short to V ref. If OK, replace sensor.

ECM: 22 — A — Low; 20 — B — Output Sensor; 21 — C — V Ref. — Connector

High Vacuum = High Output

* This requires use of three jumpers between the sensor and the connector. They can be made using terminals 12014836 and 12014837.

GENERAL MOTORS COMPUTER COMMAND CONTROL (Cont.)

TROUBLE CODE 41

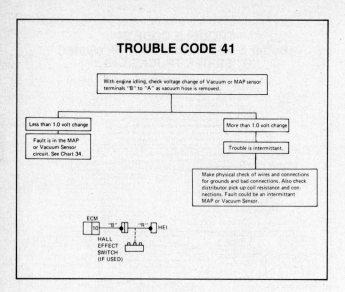

With engine idling, check voltage change of Vacuum or MAP sensor terminals "B" to "A" as vacuum hose is removed.

Less than 1.0 volt change

Fault is in the MAP or Vacuum Sensor circuit. See Chart 34.

More than 1.0 volt change

Trouble is intermittant.

Make physical check of wires and connections for grounds and bad connections. Also check distributor pick-up coil resistance and connections. Fault could be an intermittent MAP or Vacuum Sensor.

```
ECM
10  "B"    "R"    HEI
    HALL
    EFFECT
    SWITCH
    (IF USED)
```

TROUBLE CODE 42

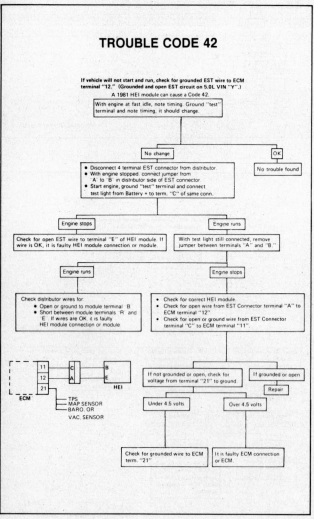

If vehicle will not start and run, check for grounded EST wire to ECM terminal "12." (Grounded and open EST circuit on 5.0L VIN "Y".)

A 1981 HEI module can cause a Code 42.

With engine at fast idle, note timing. Ground "test" terminal and note timing, it should change.

No change | **OK**

OK → No trouble found

No change:
- Disconnect 4 terminal EST connector from distributor.
- With engine stopped, connect jumper from "A" to "B" in distributor side of EST connector.
- Start engine, ground "test" terminal and connect test light from Battery + to term. "C" of same conn.

Engine stops | **Engine runs**

Engine stops: Check for open EST wire to terminal "E" of HEI module. If wire is OK, it is faulty HEI module connection or module.

Engine runs: With test light still connected, remove jumper between terminals "A" and "B".

Engine runs | **Engine stops**

Engine runs: Check distributor wires for:
- Open or ground to module terminal "B"
- Short between module terminals "R" and "E". If wires are OK, it is faulty HEI module connection or module.

Engine stops:
- Check for correct HEI module.
- Check for open wire from EST Connector terminal "A" to ECM terminal "12"
- Check for open or ground wire from EST Connector terminal "C" to ECM terminal "11".

```
    11    C    B
    12    A    E
    21         HEI
ECM
    TPS
    MAP SENSOR
    BARO. OR
    VAC. SENSOR
```

If not grounded or open, check for voltage from terminal "21" to ground.

If grounded or open → Repair

Under 4.5 volts | **Over 4.5 volts**

Under 4.5 volts → Check for grounded wire to ECM term. "21"

Over 4.5 volts → It is faulty ECM connection or ECM.

TROUBLE CODE 44

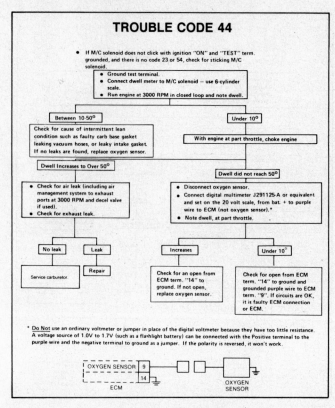

- If M/C solenoid does not click with ignition "ON" and "TEST" term. grounded, and there is no code 23 or 54, check for sticking M/C solenoid.
  - Ground test terminal.
  - Connect dwell meter to M/C solenoid — use 6-cylinder scale.
  - Run engine at 3000 RPM in closed loop and note dwell.

Between 10-50° | **Under 10°**

Between 10-50°: Check for cause of intermittent lean condition such as faulty carb base gasket leaking vacuum hoses, or leaky intake gasket. If no leaks are found, replace oxygen sensor.

Under 10°: With engine at part throttle, choke engine

Dwell increases to Over 50° | **Dwell did not reach 50°**

Dwell increases to Over 50°:
- Check for air leak (including air management system to exhaust ports at 3000 RPM and decel valve if used).
- Check for exhaust leak.

Dwell did not reach 50°:
- Disconnect oxygen sensor.
- Connect digital multimeter J291125-A or equivalent and set on the 20 volt scale, from bat. + to purple wire to ECM (not oxygen sensor).*
- Note dwell, at part throttle.

No leak | **Leak** | **Increases** | **Under 10°**

No leak → Service carburetor.

Leak → Repair

Increases → Check for an open from ECM term. "14" to ground. If not open, replace oxygen sensor.

Under 10° → Check for open from ECM term. "14" to ground and grounded purple wire to ECM term. "9". If circuits are OK, it is faulty ECM connection or ECM.

*Do Not use an ordinary voltmeter or jumper in place of the digital voltmeter because they have too little resistance. A voltage source of 1.0V to 1.7V (such as a flashlight battery) can be connected with the Positive terminal to the purple wire and the negative terminal to ground as a jumper. If the polarity is reversed, it won't work.

```
OXYGEN SENSOR  9
               14              OXYGEN
ECM                            SENSOR
```

TROUBLE CODE 45

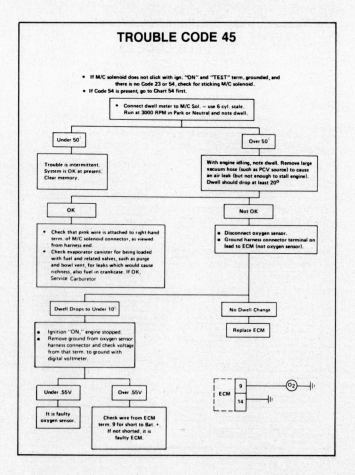

- If M/C solenoid does not click with ign. "ON" and "TEST" term. grounded, and there is no Code 23 or 54, check for sticking M/C solenoid.
- If Code 54 is present, go to Chart 54 first.

- Connect dwell meter to M/C Sol. — use 6 cyl. scale. Run at 3000 RPM in Park or Neutral and note dwell.

Under 50° | **Over 50°**

Under 50°: Trouble is intermittent. System is OK at present. Clear memory.

Over 50°: With engine idling, note dwell. Remove large vacuum hose (such as PCV source) to cause an air leak (but not enough to stall engine). Dwell should drop at least 20°.

OK | **Not OK**

OK:
- Check that pink wire is attached to right-hand term. of M/C solenoid connector, as viewed from harness end.
- Check evaporator canister for being loaded with fuel and related valves, such as purge and bowl vent, for leaks which would cause richness, also fuel in crankcase. If OK, Service Carburetor

Not OK:
- Disconnect oxygen sensor.
- Ground harness connector terminal on lead to ECM (not oxygen sensor).

Dwell Drops to Under 10° | **No Dwell Change**

Dwell Drops to Under 10°:
- Ignition "ON," engine stopped.
- Remove ground from oxygen sensor harness connector and check voltage from that term. to ground with digital voltmeter.

No Dwell Change → Replace ECM

Under .55V | **Over .55V**

Under .55V → It is faulty oxygen sensor.

Over .55V → Check wire from ECM term. 9 for short to Bat. +. If not shorted, it is faulty ECM.

```
ECM  9        O₂
     14
```

GENERAL MOTORS COMPUTER COMMAND CONTROL (Cont.)

TROUBLE CODE 51

PROM is either installed incorrectly, defective, or wrong part number. Check for proper installation and application. If ok, replace PROM.

TROUBLE CODE 54
"C, K & G" SERIES TRUCKS ONLY

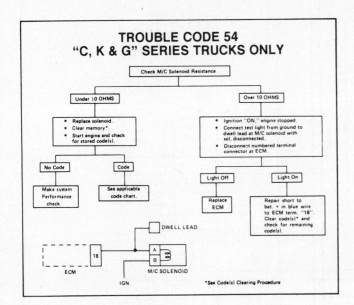

TROUBLE CODE 55

Check for corrosion at ECM edgeboard connectors and terms. If present, check for coolant sensor, windshield or heater core leaks. Repair leak, clean connector terms. and replace ECM. Also, check for 4 term. EST harness being too close to electrical signals, such as spark plug wires, distributor housing, generator, etc.

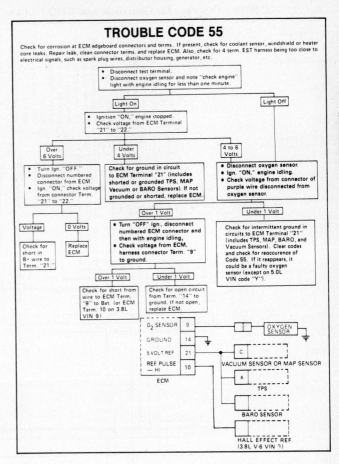

Fig. 4: "S" Series Truck Component Locations

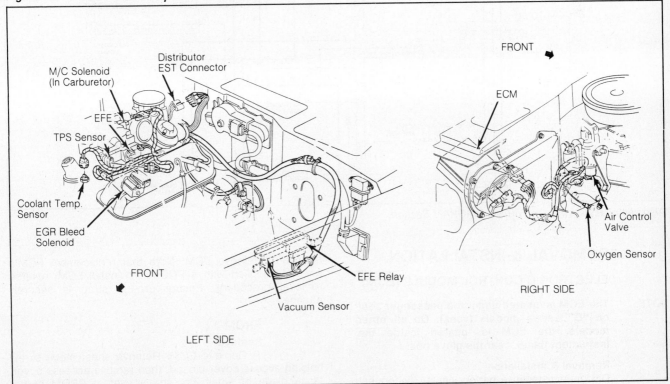

1983 Computerized Engine Controls

GENERAL MOTORS COMPUTER COMMAND CONTROL (Cont.)

Fig. 5: CCC Wiring Diagram for Chevrolet and GMC Trucks

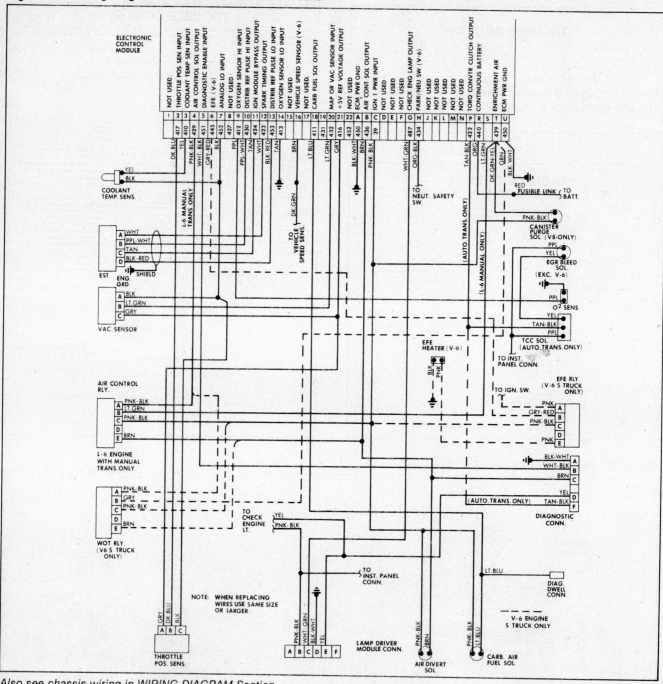

Also see chassis wiring in WIRING DIAGRAM Section.

REMOVAL & INSTALLATION

ELECTRONIC CONTROL MODULE (ECM)

NOTE: The ECM is located under the passenger seat on "G" series models (vans). On all other models, the ECM is located inside the instrument panel, near the glove box.

Removal & Installation

Disconnect negative battery cable. Disconnect electrical connectors from ECM. Remove ECM mounting hardware. Remove ECM. Note that replacement ECM's are not supplied with a PROM. To install ECM, reverse removal procedure. Ensure ground strap is securely attached.

PROM

Removal

1) Remove ECM. Remove sheet metal screw holding access cover closed, then remove access cover. Place blade of small, flat screwdriver at PROM carrier reference end between edge of opening in case and

GENERAL MOTORS COMPUTER COMMAND CONTROL (Cont.)

underside of protruding lip of carrier. Pry up side of carrier as far as possible.

2) Repeat procedure on other reference end lip. Grasp carrier with thumb and forefinger. Gently rock carrier from side to side while applying upward force and remove PROM.

Fig. 6: Replacing PROM in Electronic Control Module

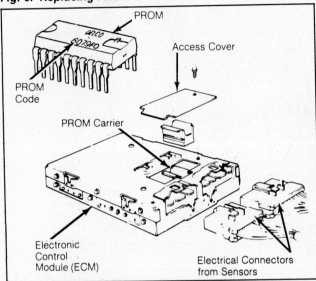

The PROM will be destroyed if it is installed backwards and the ignition switch is turned "ON".

Installation

1) Before installing new PROM, ensure part number agrees with that of removed PROM. Molded "half-round" depression of PROM must be installed at same end as "squared-off" symmetrical end of carrier. Make sure that PROM is centered in carrier.

2) Position carrier squarely over PROM socket with "squared-off" symmetrical end of carrier aligned with small notch in socket. Press down firmly on top of carrier while pressing down on body of PROM with narrow, blunt

tool. Squarely seat PROM in socket by alternately pressing down on either end of PROM.

3) Replace access cover and install ECM. Reconnect electrical connectors and start engine. Enter diagnostics and check for trouble code "51". If trouble code "51" does not appear, PROM is correctly installed.

4) If code "51" does appear, PROM is not fully seated, is installed backwards, has bent pins, or is defective. Remove ECM and fully seat PROM. If pins are bent, remove PROM, straighten pins and reinstall. If pins break or crack during straightening process, replace PROM. If PROM is installed backwards, it must be replaced.

OXYGEN SENSOR

CAUTION: Oxygen sensor uses a permanently attached pigtail and connector. Do not remove pigtail from sensor. Damage to, or removal of pigtail or connector could affect sensor operation.

CAUTION: Oxygen sensor may be difficult to remove when engine temperature is below 120°F (50°C). To avoid damage to threads in exhaust manifold, DO NOT use excessive force to remove sensor.

Removal

When handling oxygen sensor, use care to keep connector and louvered end free of grease or other contaminants. Do not use cleaning solvents of any type. Disconnect negative battery cable. Disconnect electrical connector and any attaching hardware. Carefully remove oxygen sensor.

Installation

A new oxygen sensor is pre-coated with anti-seize compound. If same oxygen sensor is being installed, coat threads with anti-seize compound. Install oxygen sensor and torque to 30 ft. lbs. (41 N.m). Reconnect electrical connector and any attaching hardware.

Fig. 7: Component Locations for "G" Series Trucks With 4.1L Engine

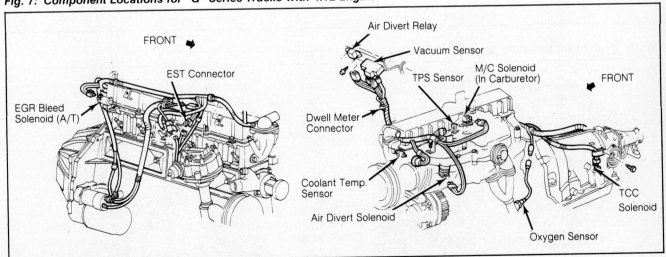

GENERAL MOTORS COMPUTER COMMAND CONTROL (Cont.)

Fig. 8: *Component Locations for "G" Series Trucks With V8 Engines*

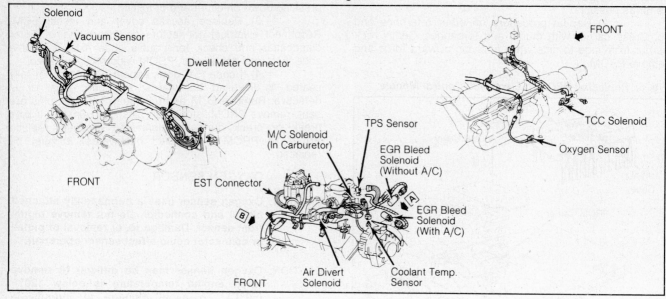

Fig. 9: *Component Locations for "C/K" Series Trucks With 4.1L Engine*

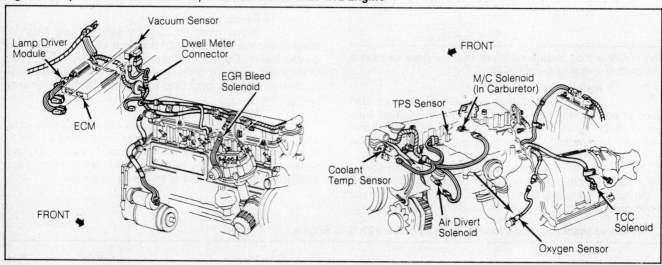

Fig. 10: *Component Locations for "C/K" Series Trucks With V8 Engines*

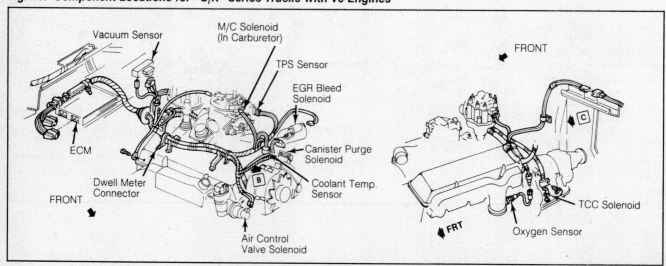

GENERAL MOTORS COMPUTER COMMAND CONTROL (Cont.)

VACUUM SENSOR

Removal & Installation

Vacuum sensor is located in engine compartment. *See Figs. 5, 7, 8, 9, and 10.* Locate sensor. Remove electrical connector, then remove sensor. To install sensor, reverse removal procedure.

COOLANT TEMPERATURE SENSOR

Removal & Installation

Partially drain radiator until coolant level is below sensor. Disconnect electrical connector from sensor. Remove sensor from block. Reverse removal procedure to install.

VEHICLE SPEED SENSOR (VSS)

Removal & Installation

Remove speedometer cluster and disconnect VSS connector. Remove mounting hardware and sensor. To install, reverse removal procedure.

1983 Computerized Engine Controls
JEEP COMPUTERIZED EMISSION CONTROL
4-CYLINDER

DESCRIPTION

The Computerized Emission Control (CEC) system is an electronically controlled system that closely controls air/fuel ratio. This close control of the air/fuel ratio is needed to lower exhaust emissions while maintaining good fuel economy and performance.

The primary objective of the CEC system is to maintain the ideal air/fuel mixture ratio of 14.7:1 under all operating conditions. When the ideal air/fuel ratio is maintained, the catalytic converter can effectively control nitrogen oxides (NOx), hydrocarbons (HC) and carbon monoxide (CO).

Fig. 1: Jeep 4-Cyl. CEC System

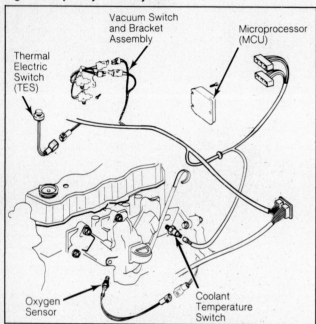

Carburetor (not shown) is controlled by this system.

OPERATION

The CEC system consists of 4 sub-systems: Fuel control, data sensors, Microcomputer Control Unit (MCU) and catalytic converter.

FUEL CONTROL

All models are equipped with a feedback carburetor which contains an electro-mechanically operated mixture control (M/C) solenoid. The M/C solenoid regulates the air/fuel mixture according to commands from the MCU. One terminal of the M/C solenoid is connected to battery voltage (12 volts) and the other terminal is connected to the MCU.

The MCU functions as a switch that either provides a ground for current flow to energize the M/C solenoid or an open circuit to de-energize the M/C solenoid. The MCU switches the M/C solenoid on and off about 10 times per second.

When the M/C solenoid is energized, a needle is inserted into the jet resulting in a lean air/fuel mixture. When the solenoid is de-energized, the needle is withdrawn from the jet resulting in a rich air/fuel mixture.

DATA SENSORS

Oxygen Sensor

The oxygen sensor, located in the exhaust manifold, is used by the MCU to determine oxygen content of exhaust gases. The sensor sends a voltage signal to the MCU that is proportional to the oxygen content of exhaust gases.

When higher amounts of oxygen are detected in the exhaust gases (lean mixture indicated), the electrical signal generated by the sensor drops in voltage. A lower oxygen content (rich mixture indicated) causes an increase in voltage signal output.

10 in. Hg (Adaptive Mode) Vacuum Switch

This switch is mounted on a bracket attached to the right inner fender panel. The 10 in. Hg switch is closed during engine idle and partial throttle operation. The switch opens when manifold vacuum decreases to 10 in. Hg and below.

4 in. Hg (Wide Open Throttle) Vacuum Switch

The 4 in. Hg vacuum switch is used to sense a full throttle condition. A full throttle condition is detected by the switch when manifold vacuum drops below 4 in. Hg, closing the switch. This results in the M/C solenoid being regulated to provide a rich air/fuel mixture.

Open Loop Coolant Temperature Switch

The coolant temperature switch operates in conjunction with the 4 in. Hg vacuum switch. Depending on temperature (above or below 100°F/38°C) when engine is at full throttle operation, the M/C solenoid richens the air/fuel mixture as required for increased air flow during wide open throttle operation.

Thermal Electric Switch (TES)

The TES is attached to the inside of the air cleaner. This sensor provides both a ground circuit for the MCU, for cold weather start-up (below 55°F/13°C) or an open circuit to indicate normal start-up (above 65°F/18°C).

Engine RPM Voltage

This voltage signal is supplied to the MCU from the tach terminal on the distributor. The M/C solenoid is de-energized until a voltage, equivalent to a predetermined RPM, is received by the MCU. This causes the system to remain in the open loop mode of operation. The result is a rich air/fuel mixture for engine starting.

NOTE: **All switching temperatures and vacuum levels are average values. The actual switching temperature or vacuum level will vary slightly from switch to switch.**

MICROCOMPUTER CONTROL UNIT (MCU)

The MCU is a microprocessor unit that monitors oxygen sensor voltage and, based upon the mode of engine operation, generates an output control signal for the M/C solenoid. In this manner, the MCU provides the correct air/fuel ratio for all engine operating conditions.

Engine operating conditions are relayed to the MCU by the data sensors. From this information, the MCU determines the operating mode for the engine (open loop or closed loop).

Open Loop Mode

When the engine is in the open loop mode of operation, the air/fuel mixture ratio will be based on a value that is established for each of the following engine

JEEP COMPUTERIZED EMISSION CONTROL
4-CYLINDER (Cont.)

operating conditions: cold weather start-up and operation (below 55°F/13°C), cold engine at or near WOT operation (below 100°F/38°C & below 4 in. Hg), warm engine at or near WOT operation (above 100°F/38°C & below 4 in. Hg), adaptive operation (at idle speed, accelerating from idle speed, or decelerating to idle speed).

Closed Loop Mode

This mode of operation occurs when none of the open loop engine operating conditions exist. In this mode, the MCU regulates the M/C solenoid to adjust the air/fuel mixture according to voltage signals from the oxygen sensor.

The oxygen sensor only measures oxygen content in the exhaust. Because of this, air leakage anywhere between the carburetor and the oxygen sensor can cause incorrect operation during the closed loop mode.

Closed loop operation is characterized by constant variation of the air/fuel mixture. This is because the MCU is forced to constantly make small changes in order to maintain an optimum air/fuel mixture ratio.

CATALYTIC CONVERTER

A 3-way catalytic converter and a conventional oxidizing catalyst are combined to form a dual bed converter. The dual bed converter has the ability to convert the following gases:

- Carbon monoxide (CO) and hydrocarbons (HC) to water vapor (H_2O) and carbon dioxide (CO_2).
- Nitrogen oxide (NOx) and carbon monoxide (CO) to nitrogen (N_2) and carbon dioxide (CO_2).

DIAGNOSIS & TESTING

The CEC system should be considered as a possible source of trouble for engine performance, fuel economy and exhaust emission problems only after normal tests and inspections are performed. Normal tests and inspections are those that would apply to a vehicle without the CEC system (ignition system, carburetor, etc.).

The steps listed in the following charts will provide a systematic evaluation of each component that could cause a malfunction. After completing a repair, repeat the test to ensure that the malfunction has been corrected.

TESTING INFORMATION

The following tools will be needed to perform the diagnostic tests: Dwell meter, digital volt-ohmmeter, tachometer, vacuum gauge and jumper wire.

NOTE: **Although most dwell meters should be acceptable, if one causes a change in engine operation when connected to the test location, it should not be used.**

To determine air/fuel mixture the dwell meter should be set on the 6-cylinder scale and connected to a pigtail wire test connector leading from the mixture control solenoid or diagnostic connector pin 14. When the dwell meter is connected, do not allow the connector terminal to contact any engine component that is connected to engine ground. This includes hoses that may be electrically conductive.

With a normally operating engine, at partial throttle, the dwell will be between 10 and 50 degrees and will be varying. Varying means the pointer continually moves back and forth across the scale. The amount it varies is not important, only the fact that it does vary. This indicates closed loop operation, indicating that the mixture is being varied according to oxygen sensor input to the MCU.

During idle, WOT, and/or cold operation, the mixture is predetermined by the MCU so the meter pointer will vary only slightly. This is open loop operation, indicating that the oxygen sensor output has no effect on air/fuel mixture.

If there is any question as to whether the system is in open or closed loop operation, richening or leaning out the air/fuel mixture will cause the dwell meter reading to vary more during closed loop operation.

NOTE: **The "System Operational Test" should be performed after all repairs on the CEC system have been completed.**

SYSTEM TEST CHARTS

Chart No.	Test
No. 1	System Operational Test
No. 2	Coolant Temperature Switch Circuit Test
No. 3	Vacuum Switch Circuit Test
No. 4	Thermal Electric Switch Circuit Test
No. 5	Engine RPM (TACH) Voltage Test
No. 6	Mixture Control Solenoid Test

Fig. 2: Diagnostic Connector Pin Location

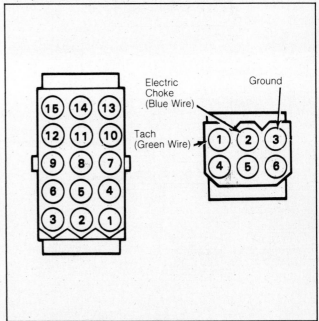

Connect meter to these terminals as directed by test charts.

1983 Computerized Engine Controls
JEEP COMPUTERIZED EMISSION CONTROL
4-CYLINDER (Cont.)

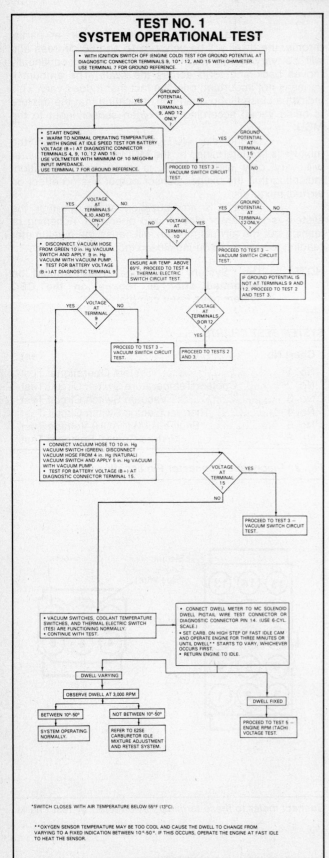

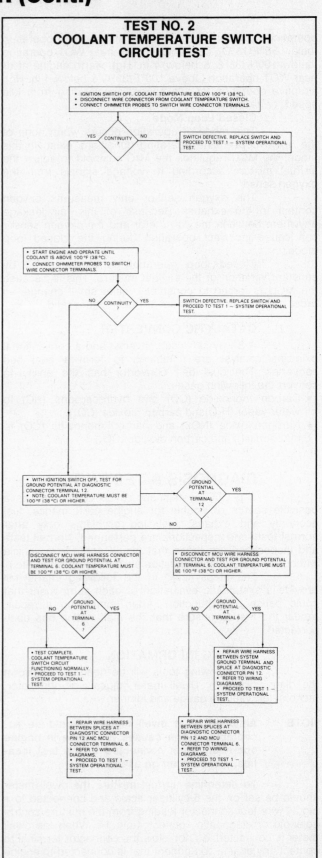

TEST NO. 3
VACUUM SWITCH CIRCUIT TEST

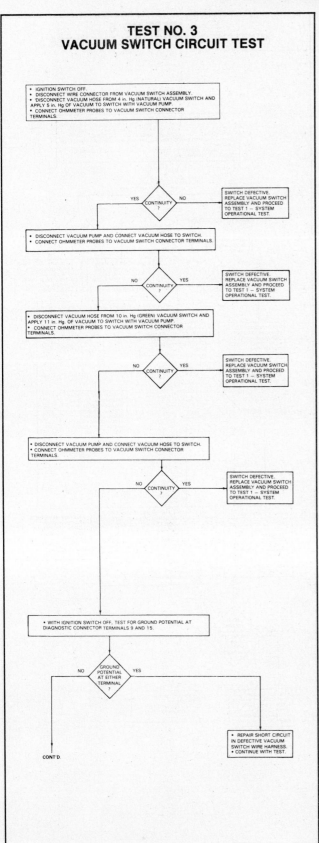

- IGNITION SWITCH OFF.
- DISCONNECT WIRE CONNECTOR FROM VACUUM SWITCH ASSEMBLY.
- DISCONNECT VACUUM HOSE FROM 4 in. Hg (NATURAL) VACUUM SWITCH AND APPLY 5 in. Hg OF VACUUM TO SWITCH WITH VACUUM PUMP.
- CONNECT OHMMETER PROBES TO VACUUM SWITCH CONNECTOR TERMINALS.

CONTINUITY?

YES → NO → SWITCH DEFECTIVE. REPLACE VACUUM SWITCH ASSEMBLY AND PROCEED TO TEST 1 — SYSTEM OPERATIONAL TEST.

- DISCONNECT VACUUM PUMP AND CONNECT VACUUM HOSE TO SWITCH.
- CONNECT OHMMETER PROBES TO VACUUM SWITCH CONNECTOR TERMINALS.

CONTINUITY?

NO → YES → SWITCH DEFECTIVE. REPLACE VACUUM SWITCH ASSEMBLY AND PROCEED TO TEST 1 — SYSTEM OPERATIONAL TEST.

- DISCONNECT VACUUM HOSE FROM 10 in. Hg (GREEN) VACUUM SWITCH AND APPLY 11 in. Hg. OF VACUUM TO SWITCH WITH VACUUM PUMP.
- CONNECT OHMMETER PROBES TO VACUUM SWITCH CONNECTOR TERMINALS.

CONTINUITY?

NO → YES → SWITCH DEFECTIVE. REPLACE VACUUM SWITCH ASSEMBLY AND PROCEED TO TEST 1 — SYSTEM OPERATIONAL TEST.

- DISCONNECT VACUUM PUMP AND CONNECT VACUUM HOSE TO SWITCH.
- CONNECT OHMMETER PROBES TO VACUUM SWITCH CONNECTOR TERMINALS.

CONTINUITY?

NO → YES → SWITCH DEFECTIVE. REPLACE VACUUM SWITCH ASSEMBLY AND PROCEED TO TEST 1 — SYSTEM OPERATIONAL TEST.

- WITH IGNITION SWITCH OFF, TEST FOR GROUND POTENTIAL AT DIAGNOSTIC CONNECTOR TERMINALS 9 AND 15.

GROUND POTENTIAL AT EITHER TERMINAL?

NO → YES → REPAIR SHORT CIRCUIT IN DEFECTIVE VACUUM SWITCH WIRE HARNESS.
- CONTINUE WITH TEST.

CONT'D.

TEST NO. 3 (Cont.)

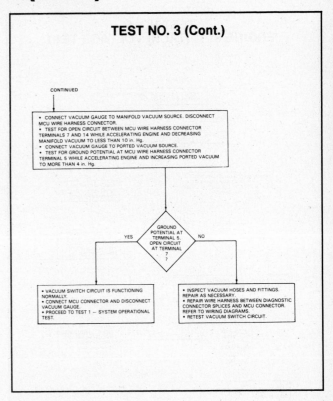

CONTINUED

- CONNECT VACUUM GAUGE TO MANIFOLD VACUUM SOURCE. DISCONNECT MCU WIRE HARNESS CONNECTOR.
- TEST FOR OPEN CIRCUIT BETWEEN MCU WIRE HARNESS CONNECTOR TERMINALS 7 AND 14 WHILE ACCELERATING ENGINE AND DECREASING MANIFOLD VACUUM TO LESS THAN 10 in. Hg.
- CONNECT VACUUM GAUGE TO PORTED VACUUM SOURCE.
- TEST FOR GROUND POTENTIAL AT MCU WIRE HARNESS CONNECTOR TERMINAL 5 WHILE ACCELERATING ENGINE AND INCREASING PORTED VACUUM TO MORE THAN 4 in. Hg.

GROUND POTENTIAL AT TERMINAL 5. OPEN CIRCUIT AT TERMINAL 7?

YES → NO

- VACUUM SWITCH CIRCUIT IS FUNCTIONING NORMALLY.
- CONNECT MCU CONNECTOR AND DISCONNECT VACUUM GAUGE.
- PROCEED TO TEST 1 — SYSTEM OPERATIONAL TEST.

- INSPECT VACUUM HOSES AND FITTINGS. REPAIR AS NECESSARY.
- REPAIR WIRE HARNESS BETWEEN DIAGNOSTIC CONNECTOR SPLICES AND MCU CONNECTOR. REFER TO WIRING DIAGRAMS.
- RETEST VACUUM SWITCH CIRCUIT.

TEST NO. 4
THERMAL ELECTRIC SWITCH CIRCUIT

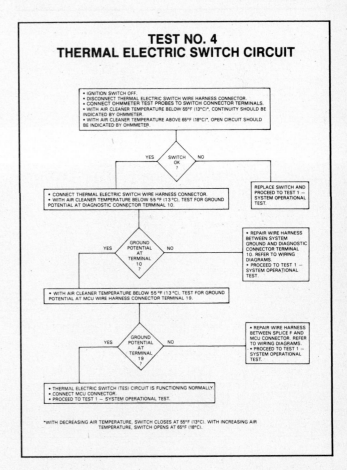

- IGNITION SWITCH OFF.
- DISCONNECT THERMAL ELECTRIC SWITCH WIRE HARNESS CONNECTOR.
- CONNECT OHMMETER TEST PROBES TO SWITCH CONNECTOR TERMINALS.
- WITH AIR CLEANER TEMPERATURE BELOW 55°F (13°C)*, CONTINUITY SHOULD BE INDICATED BY OHMMETER.
- WITH AIR CLEANER TEMPERATURE ABOVE 65°F (18°C)*, OPEN CIRCUIT SHOULD BE INDICATED BY OHMMETER.

SWITCH OK?

YES → NO → REPLACE SWITCH AND PROCEED TO TEST 1 — SYSTEM OPERATIONAL TEST.

- CONNECT THERMAL ELECTRIC SWITCH WIRE HARNESS CONNECTOR.
- WITH AIR CLEANER TEMPERATURE BELOW 55°F (13°C), TEST FOR GROUND POTENTIAL AT DIAGNOSTIC CONNECTOR TERMINAL 10.

GROUND POTENTIAL AT TERMINAL 10?

YES → NO → - REPAIR WIRE HARNESS BETWEEN SYSTEM GROUND AND DIAGNOSTIC CONNECTOR TERMINAL 10. REFER TO WIRING DIAGRAMS.
- PROCEED TO TEST 1 — SYSTEM OPERATIONAL TEST.

- WITH AIR CLEANER TEMPERATURE BELOW 55°F (13°C), TEST FOR GROUND POTENTIAL AT MCU WIRE HARNESS CONNECTOR TERMINAL 19.

GROUND POTENTIAL AT TERMINAL 19?

YES → NO → - REPAIR WIRE HARNESS BETWEEN SPLICE F AND MCU CONNECTOR. REFER TO WIRING DIAGRAMS.
- PROCEED TO TEST 1 — SYSTEM OPERATIONAL TEST.

- THERMAL ELECTRIC SWITCH (TES) CIRCUIT IS FUNCTIONING NORMALLY.
- CONNECT MCU CONNECTOR.
- PROCEED TO TEST 1 — SYSTEM OPERATIONAL TEST.

*WITH DECREASING AIR TEMPERATURE, SWITCH CLOSES AT 55°F (13°C). WITH INCREASING AIR TEMPERATURE, SWITCH OPENS AT 65°F (18°C).

1a-88

1983 Computerized Engine Controls
JEEP COMPUTERIZED EMISSION CONTROL
4-CYLINDER (Cont.)

TEST NO. 5
ENGINE RPM (TACH) VOLTAGE TEST

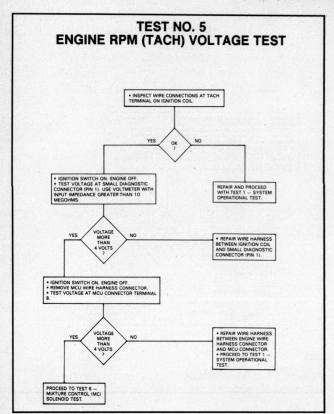

TEST NO. 6
MIXTURE CONTROL SOLENOID TEST

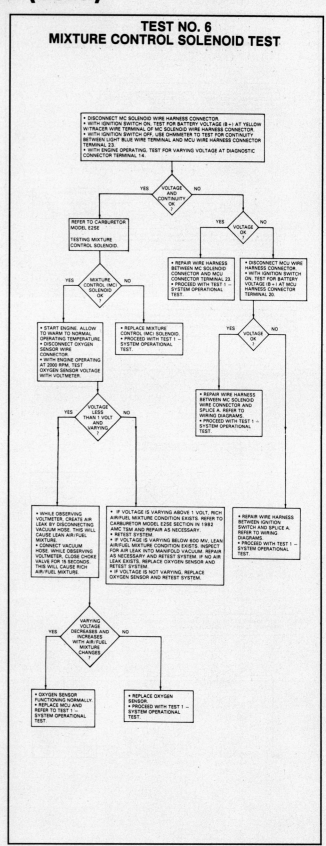

Fig. 3: Jeep 4-Cyl. CEC System Wiring Diagram

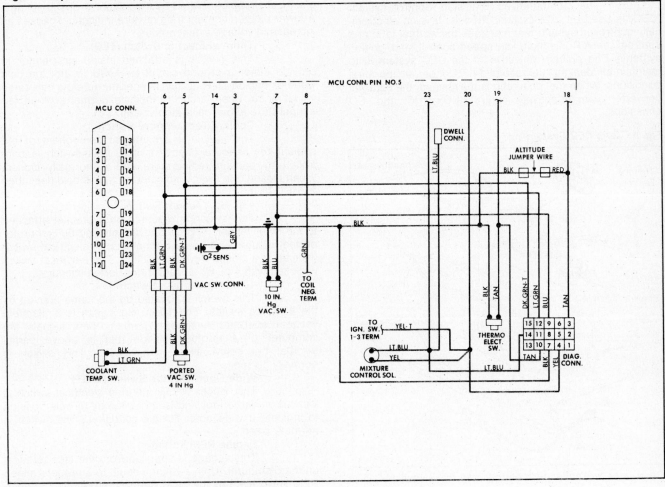

Also see chassis wiring in WIRING DIAGRAM Section.

REMOVAL & INSTALLATION

OXYGEN SENSOR

Removal & Installation

Disconnect wire connector from oxygen sensor. Remove sensor from exhaust manifold using sensor wrench (J-29533). Clean threads in manifold. Coat threads of replacement sensor with anti-seize compound. Install new sensor in exhaust manifold and tighten to 20-25 ft. lbs. (27-34 N.m). Reconnect wire connector.

MCU

Removal & Installation

The MCU is located behind the right front kick panel. Remove MCU mounting bolts and disconnect wiring harness connector. Do not bend connector pins when removing. Reconnect harness to MCU and replace mounting bolts.

MIXTURE CONTROL SOLENOID

Removal & Installation

Remove air cleaner and disconnect solenoid harness connector. Remove retaining screws and remove

solenoid from carburetor. Coat rubber seal, on end of solenoid stem, with silicone grease or light engine oil prior to reinsertion. Using a new gasket, replace solenoid. Reconnect wiring harness and replace air cleaner.

1983 Computerized Engine Controls
JEEP COMPUTERIZED EMISSION CONTROL
6-CYLINDER

DESCRIPTION

The Computerized Emission Control system (CEC) is used on all 6-cylinder models. It is an electronically controlled system that manages the air/fuel ratio and controls the AIR injection, idle speed control, and ignition systems. The primary objective of the CEC system is to maintain an ideal air/fuel ratio of 14.7:1 under all operating conditions. When the ideal ratio is maintained, the catalytic converter can effectively control NOx, HC and CO emissions.

Fig. 1: Jeep CEC System

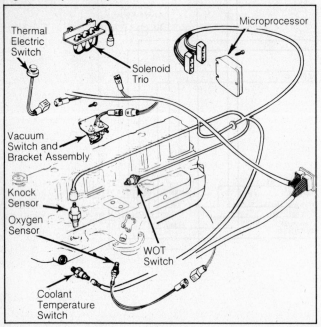

Carburetor (not shown) is controlled by this system.

OPERATION

The CEC system consists of 7 sub-systems: fuel control, data sensors, Microcomputer Control Unit (MCU), catalytic converter, idle speed control, air injection control, and ignition advance control.

FUEL CONTROL

All models are equipped with feedback carburetors which contain an electronically operated stepper motor. The stepper motor controls metering pins which vary the size of idle and main air bleed orifices in carburetor body.

The stepper motor moves the pins in and out of the orifices in steps, in response to signals received from MCU. The motor has a range of 100 steps, but normally operates in the middle of its range.

When the metering pins are stepped into the orifices, the air/fuel mixture becomes richer. When the pins are stepped out of the orifices, the mixture becomes leaner.

DATA SENSORS
Oxygen Sensor

The oxygen sensor is located in the exhaust manifold to measure oxygen content of exhaust gases. As more oxygen is sensed (lean mixture indication), the electrical signal generated by the sensor drops in voltage. A lower oxygen content (rich mixture indication) causes an increase in voltage signal output.

Thermal Electric Switch (TES)

This switch is attached inside air cleaner to provide either a ground circuit for MCU to indicate cold weather engine start-up (air temperature below calibrated value) or an open circuit to indicate normal start-up (air temperature above calibrated value).

Coolant Temperature Switch

This switch is an integral component of the coolant temperature control switch. This switch is controlled by coolant temperature and is normally closed. When closed, the switch indicates engine is cold (less than 135°F/57°C).

4 in. Hg Vacuum Switch

This switch is mounted on a bracket attached to the inner fender. This switch is controlled by carburetor ported vacuum and has a normally open electrical switch (indicating a closed throttle position). The electrical switch is closed with 4 in. Hg of carburetor ported vacuum.

10 in. Hg Vacuum Switch

This switch is located on the same bracket as the 4 in. Hg switch. The 10 in. Hg switch is a manifold vacuum operated switch that, when open, signals the computer of a throttle position that is above partial throttle, but below wide open throttle. This switch is normally closed.

Wide Open Throttle Switch (WOT)

This mechanically operated electrical switch is located on carburetor and is controlled by throttle position to indicate a wide open throttle condition. This switch is normally open.

Engine RPM Voltage

This voltage is supplied from the tach terminal on the distributor. Until a voltage equal to a predetermined RPM is received by the MCU, the system remains in open loop mode of operation. The result is a fixed rich air/fuel mixture for engine starting.

Timer

The timer is activated whenever system is operating in open loop 2 mode (wide open throttle). This timer remains active for a preset period of time. If a "lean limit" condition (altitude jumper wire installed) occurs, the timer becomes inoperative. The timer has multi-function abilities; in addition to OL2 mode, it is used as a WOT timer and start-up timer.

MICROCOMPUTER CONTROL UNIT

The MCU is located in passenger compartment, behind right-hand kick panel. The MCU monitors the CEC system data sensors and, based upon mode of operation, generates an output control signal to the stepper motor mounted in carburetor. The MCU allows the following 3 modes of operation:

Initialization

This function occurs when ignition switch is turned on. This sets initial air bleed metering rod position by signaling the stepper motor to drive them first to a full rich position (fully toward front of vehicle) and then, by a pre-programmed number of steps, in lean direction (toward rear of vehicle). This serves as a starting point of mixture control operation.

Open Loop

In this mode, the MCU determines the air/fuel mixture based upon engine operation rather than oxygen sensor input signals. There are 5 open loop modes of operation and each has a specific metering pin position.

However, because more than one condition may exist at any time, the MCU is programmed with a priority ranking for each operation. The MCU complies with the highest priority. The open loop priorities (listed from highest to lowest) are as follows: Cold Weather Start-Up, Open Loop 2 (Wide Open Throttle), Open Loop 4 (Low Manifold Vacuum), Open Loop 3 (Low Ported Vacuum), Open Loop 1 (Cold Engine Operation).

NOTE: **With each engine start-up, a start-up timer is activated. During this interval, if engine operating condition would otherwise trigger normal closed loop operation, OL1 mode is selected.**

Closed Loop

When all input data and engine operation meet programmed criteria (when OL1, OL2, OL3, OL4 and cold start modes are not selected and start-up timer has deactivated), the CEC system goes into closed loop operation. In this mode, oxygen sensor input signals are accepted by MCU to determine proper air/fuel mixture based upon oxygen content of exhaust gases. Air injection is routed "downstream" during this mode for partial or wide open throttle conditions and both "upstream" and "downstream" for all other throttle positions.

NOTE: **Closed loop operation is characterized by constant movement of the metering pins. The MCU is constantly making small corrections in air/fuel ratio in an attempt to create the ideal air/fuel ratio.**

CATALYTIC CONVERTER

Proper emission control is accomplished with the special catalytic converter used with the CEC system. All models use a dual bed monolithic-type converter with "downstream" air injection. The injection of air between the 2 beds allows more complete oxidation of HC and CO in the closed loop mode. In order for these converters to be effective, precise control of the oxygen content of exhaust gases entering the converter is necessary; thus the need for the oxygen sensor, MCU and feedback carburetor.

IDLE SPEED CONTROL

The idle speed control system is operated by vacuum signals and the MCU. The idle speed system raises and/or maintains the engine idle whenever high electrical loads or air conditioning compressor loads are present. The idle speed control system consists of a sole-vac (throttle positioner), an idle vacuum switching solenoid, and an idle speed relay.

AIR INJECTION CONTROL

The air injection system is switched from upstream to downstream injection (or both) by the MCU. Two electrically operated vacuum valves supply operating vacuum to the upstream air injection valve and the downstream air injection valve. This allows the MCU to control catalyst operation and thereby reduce exhaust emissions.

IGNITION ADVANCE CONTROL

A vacuum operated electrical switch is used to electronically retard the ignition timing advance during certain phases of engine operation.

TESTING

The steps listed in the following charts will provide a systematic evaluation of each component that could cause the malfunction. After completing a repair, repeat the test to ensure the malfunction has been eliminated.

Before performing any of the tests, make sure that the following related systems are operating properly:
- Basic carburetor adjustments.
- Mechanical engine operation (plugs, valves, rings, etc.).
- Ignition system.
- Intake manifold, carburetor or base plate gaskets.
- Loose vacuum hoses or fittings.

TEST EQUIPMENT

1) The equipment required for testing includes: tachometer, hand vacuum pump, digital volt-ohmmeter (minimum 10 megohm impedance) and a jumper wire.

2) Before beginning any of the tests, a clear air cleaner cover must be fabricated from clear plastic at least .25" thick. This is secured with air cleaner wing nut after top of air cleaner has been removed to observe operation and position of metering pins. *See Fig. 2.*

NOTE: **The metering pins operate in tandem. Only the upper pin is visible.**

Fig. 2: Air Cleaner Cover Dimensions

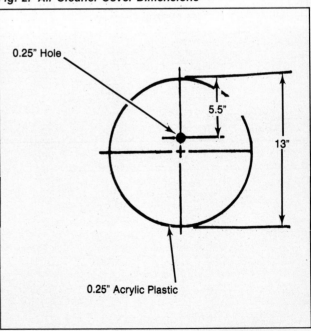

0.25" Hole

5.5"

13"

0.25" Acrylic Plastic

Fabricate cover to allow observation of metering pins.

1983 Computerized Engine Controls
JEEP COMPUTERIZED EMISSION CONTROL
6-CYLINDER (Cont.)

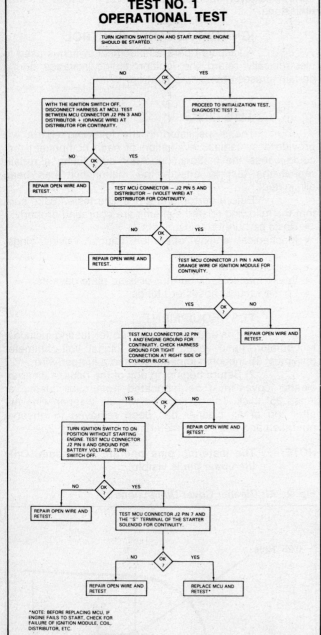

TEST NO. 1
OPERATIONAL TEST

TEST NO. 2
INITIALIZATION TEST

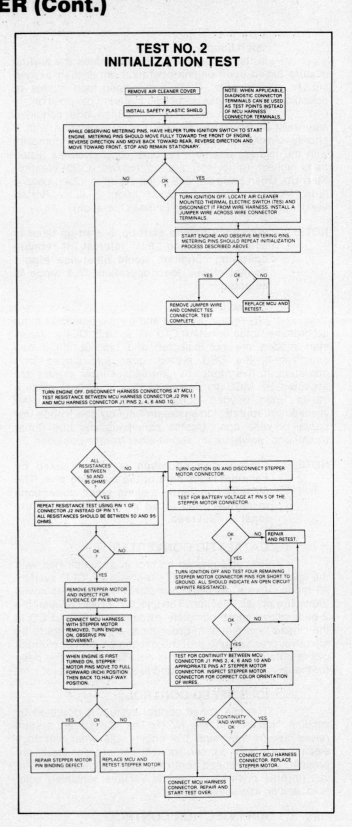

TEST NO. 3
OPEN LOOP SWITCH TEST

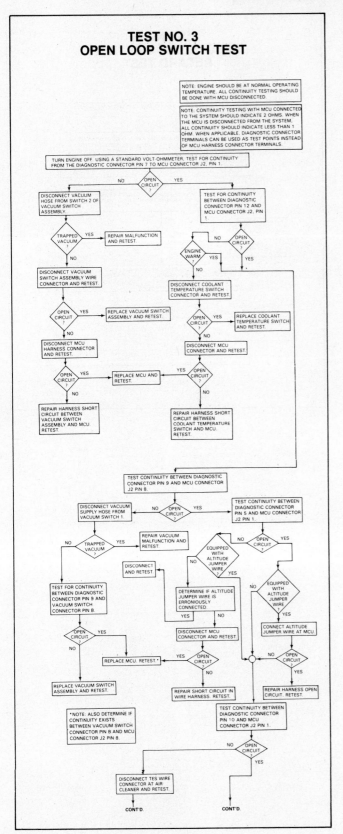

TEST NO. 3 (Cont.)

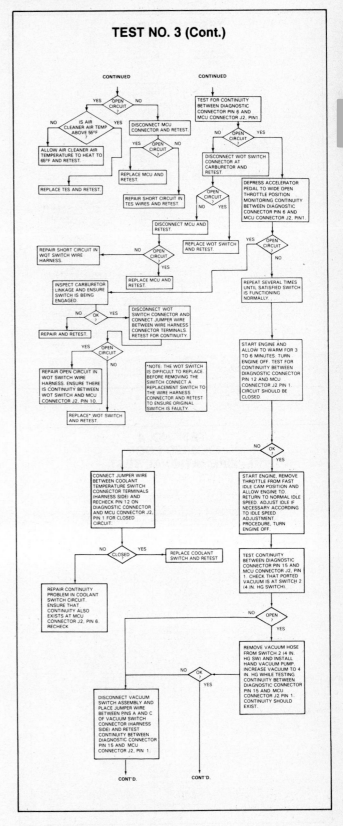

1a-94

1983 Computerized Engine Controls
JEEP COMPUTERIZED EMISSION CONTROL
6-CYLINDER (Cont.)

TEST NO. 3 (Cont.)

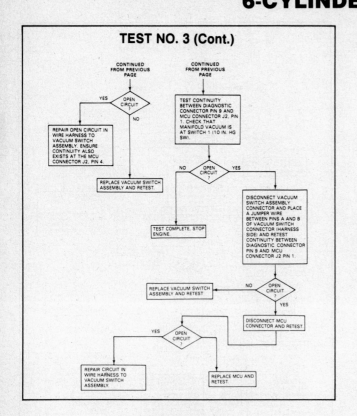

TEST NO. 5
ELECTRONIC IGNITION
RETARD TEST

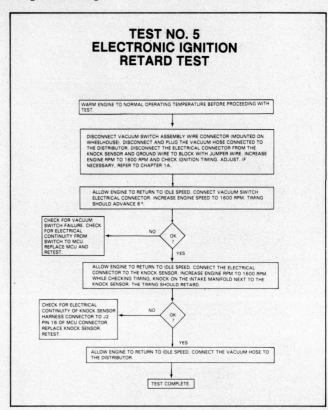

TEST NO. 4
CLOSED LOOP
OPERATIONAL TEST

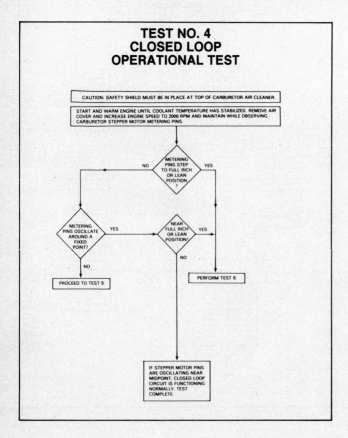

JEEP COMPUTERIZED EMISSION CONTROL
6-CYLINDER (Cont.)

TEST NO. 6
OXYGEN SENSOR AND
CLOSED LOOP TEST

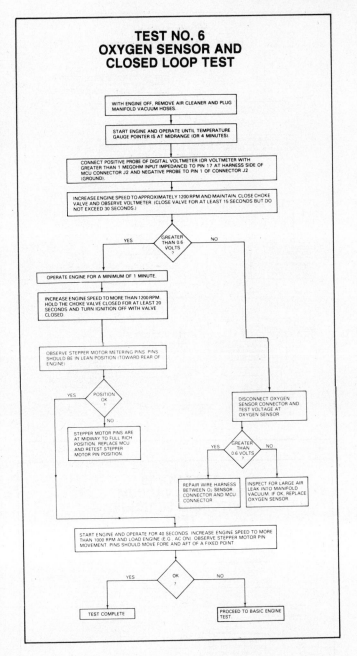

TEST NO. 7
DOWNSTREAM SOLENOID
TEST

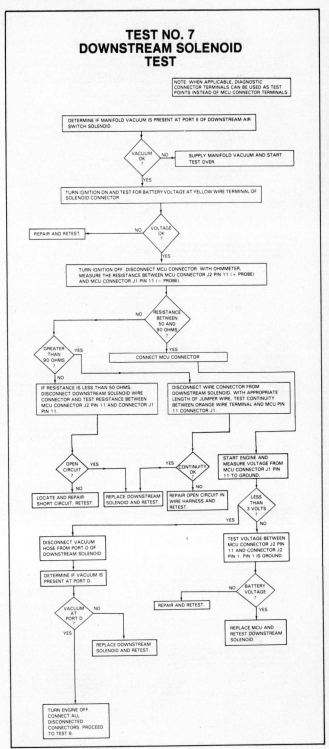

TEST NO. 8
UPSTREAM SOLENOID TEST

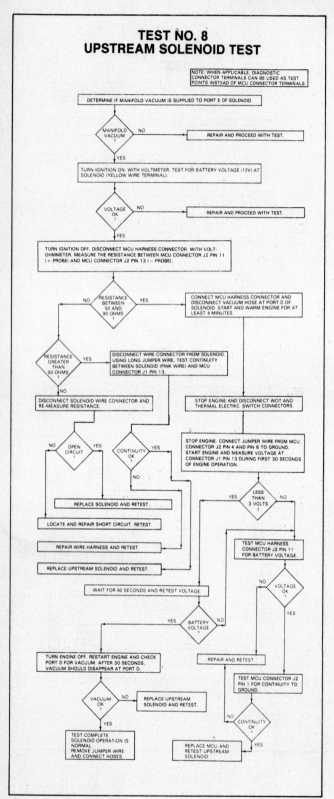

TEST NO. 9
IDLE SPEED CONTROL
SYSTEM TEST

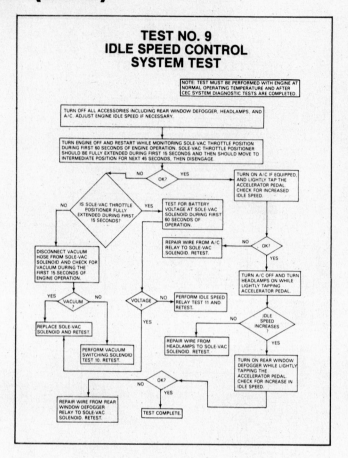

TEST NO. 10
SOLE-VAC VACUUM
SWITCHING SOLENOID
TEST

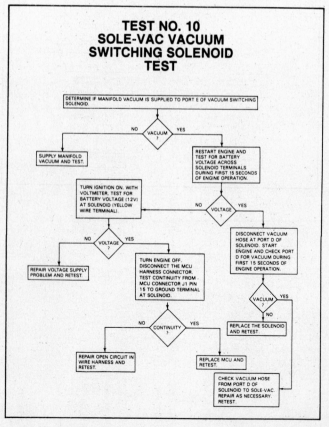

JEEP COMPUTERIZED EMISSION CONTROL
6-CYLINDER (Cont.)

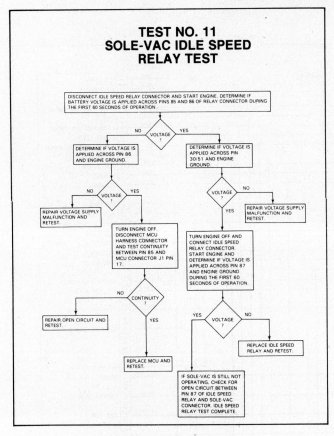

TEST NO. 11
SOLE-VAC IDLE SPEED RELAY TEST

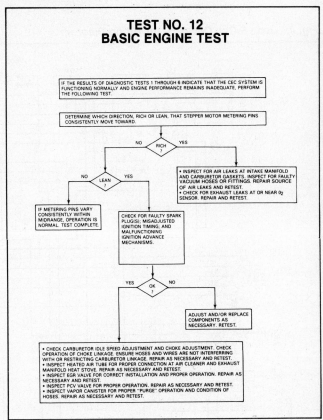

TEST NO. 12
BASIC ENGINE TEST

REMOVAL & INSTALLATION

MICROCOMPUTER CONTROL UNIT (MCU)

Removal & Installation

Remove MCU attaching bolts. Disconnect electrical plug connector. To install MCU, reverse removal procedure and ensure terminal ends are not forced out of position when connecting plug.

STEPPER MOTOR

CAUTION: Do not drop metering pins and spring when removing stepper motor.

Removal & Installation

Remove air cleaner and disconnect motor connector. Remove retaining screw and unit from carburetor. To install, reverse removal procedure and tighten screw to 25 INCH Lbs. (2.8 N.m).

OXYGEN SENSOR

Removal & Installation

Disconnect electrical lead and remove sensor from manifold. Clean threads of manifold. To install, coat threads of new oxygen sensor with anti-seize compound and carefully install sensor. Tighten sensor to 31 ft. lbs. (42 N.m). Reconnect electrical lead.

NOTE: Do not push rubber boot down on sensor body more than 1/2" above base. Also, oxygen sensor pigtail wires cannot be spliced or soldered. If broken, replace sensor.

Fig. 3: Stepper Motor Connector Terminal Identification

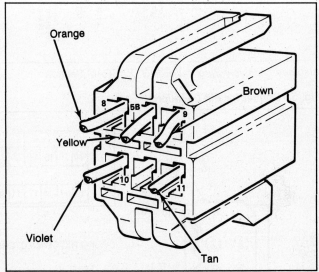

1983 Computerized Engine Controls
JEEP COMPUTERIZED EMISSION CONTROL
6-CYLINDER (Cont.)

Fig. 4: Jeep 6-Cyl. CEC System Wiring Diagram

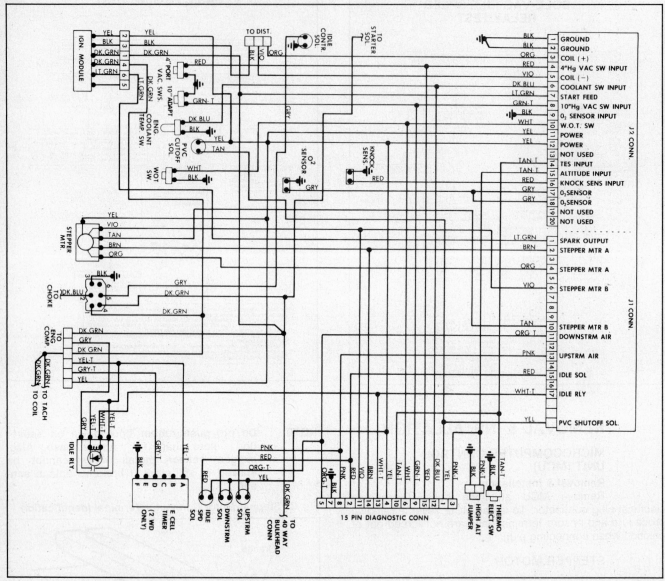

Also see chassis wiring in WIRING DIAGRAM Section.

Fig. 5: Connector Pin Locations

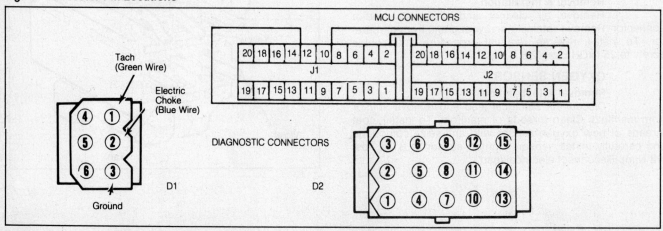

Perform tests on circuits as required by connecting meter to appropriate connector pins.

CONTENTS

SECTION 2

FUEL SYSTEMS

NOTE: ALSO SEE GENERAL INDEX.

IMPORTANT: Because of the many model names used by vehicle manufacturers, accurate identification of models is important. See Model Identification at the front of this publication.

1983 Fuel Systems

CARBURETOR TROUBLE SHOOTING

CONDITION	POSSIBLE CAUSE	CORRECTION
Engine Won't Start	Choke not closing	Check choke operation, see FUEL
	Choke linkage bent	Check linkage, see FUEL
Engine Starts, Then Dies	Choke vacuum kick setting too wide	Check setting and adjust, see FUEL
	Fast idle RPM too low	Reset RPM to specification, see TUNE-UP
	Fast idle cam index incorrect	Reset fast idle cam index, see FUEL
	Vacuum leak	Inspect vacuum system for leaks
	Low fuel pump outlet	Repair or replace pump, see FUEL
	Low carburetor fuel level	Check float setting, see FUEL
Engine Quits Under Load	Choke vacuum kick setting incorrect	Reset vacuum kick setting, see FUEL
	Fast idle cam index incorrect	Reset fast idle cam index, see FUEL
	Incorrect hot fast idle speed RPM	Reset fast idle RPM, see TUNE-UP
Engine Starts, Runs Up, Then Idles Slowly With Black Smoke	Choke vacuum kick set too narrow	Reset vacuum kick, see FUEL
	Fast idle cam index incorrect	Reset fast idle cam index, see FUEL
	Hot fast idle RPM too low	Reset fast idle RPM, see TUNE-UP

HOT STARTING SYMPTOMS

Engine Won't Start	Engine flooded	Allow fuel to evaporate

COLD ENGINE DRIVEABILITY SYMPTOMS

Engine Stalls in Gear	Choke vacuum kick setting incorrect	Reset choke vacuum kick, see FUEL
	Fast idle RPM incorrect	Reset fast idle RPM, see TUNE-UP
	Fast idle cam index incorrect	Reset fast idle cam index, see FUEL
Acceleration Sag or Stall	Defective choke control switch	Replace choke control switch
	Choke vacuum kick setting incorrect	Reset choke vacuum kick, see FUEL
	Float level incorrect (too low)	Adjust float level, see FUEL
	Accelerator pump defective	Repair or replace pump, see FUEL
	Secondary throttles not closed	Inspect lockout adjustment, see FUEL
Sag or Stall After Warmup	Defective choke control switch	Replace choke control switch, see FUEL
	Defective accelerator pump (low output)	Replace pump, see FUEL
	Float level incorrect (too low)	Adjust float level, see FUEL
Backfiring & Black Smoke	Plugged heat crossover system	Remove restriction

WARM ENGINE DRIVEABILITY SYMPTOM

Hesitation With Small Amount of Gas Pedal Movement	Vacuum leak	Inspect vacuum lines
	Accelerator pump weak or inoperable	Replace pump, see FUEL
	Float level setting too low	Reset float level, see FUEL
	Metering rods sticking or binding	Inspect and/or replace rods, see FUEL
	Carburetor idle or transfer system plugged	Inspect system and remove restrictions
	Frozen or binding heated air inlet	Inspect heated air door for binding
Hesitation With Heavy Gas Pedal Movement	Defective accelerator pump	Replace pump, see FUEL
	Metering rod carrier sticking or binding	Remove restriction
	Large vacuum leak	Inspect vacuum system and repair leak
	Float level setting too low	Reset float level, see FUEL
	Defective fuel pump, lines or filter	Inspect pump, lines and filter
	Air door setting incorrect	Adjust air door setting, see FUEL

NOTE: For additional carburetor trouble shooting information, see the appropriate article in COMPUTERIZED ENGINE CONTROLS Section. Information is provided there for diagnosing fuel system problems on vehicles with feedback carburetors.

NOTE: For GASOLINE FUEL INJECTION TROUBLE SHOOTING, see the appropriate article under the individual manufacturer in this section. Also see the appropriate article in COMPUTERIZED ENGINE CONTROLS Section.

DIESEL FUEL INJECTION TROUBLE SHOOTING

CONDITION	POSSIBLE CAUSE	CORRECTION
Engine Won't Start	No voltage to fuel solenoid	Check electrical connections
	Faulty glow plugs or glow plug controls	Check and/or replace glow plugs or controller
	Plugged fuel return system	Remove restrictions
	No fuel to nozzles	Inspect fuel delivery system
	No fuel to injecton pump	Inspect fuel delivery system
	Clogged fuel tank filter	Replace filter, see FUEL
	Incorrect or contaminated fuel	Remove and replace fuel
	Incorrect pump timing	Reset pump timing, see FUEL
Engine Stalls at Idle	Incorrect slow idle adjustment	Reset idle adjustment, see TUNE-UP
	Faulty fast idle solenoid	Replace solenoid, see FUEL
	Plugged fuel return system	Remove restrictions
	Glow plugs turn off too soon	Check glow plug system, see FUEL
	Incorrect pump timing	Check and reset timing, see FUEL
	Limited fuel to injection pump	Check fuel delivery system
	Air in injection lines to nozzles	Check line fittings
	Incorrect or contaminated fuel	Remove and replace fuel
	Faulty injection pump	Remove and replace pump, see FUEL
	Fuel solenoid closes in RUN position	Check solenoid operation, see FUEL
Engine Starts, Idles Rough WITHOUT Unusual Noise or Smoke	Incorrect slow idle adjustment	Reset slow idle adjustment, see TUNE-UP
	Leaking injection line	Check fittings and/or replace line
	Plugged fuel return line	Remove restrictions
	Air in lines to nozzles	Check line fittings
	Air in injection pump	Check pump fittings and pump operation
	Faulty nozzle	Replace nozzle, see FUEL
	Improper or contaminated fuel	Remove and replace fuel
	Uneven fuel distribution	Check fuel delivery system
Engine Starts and Idles WITH Excessive Noise and/or Smoke	Incorrect pump timing	Reset injection pump timing, see FUEL
	Air in injection lines to nozzles	Check fittings on lines
	Faulty nozzle	Replace nozzle, see FUEL
	Improperly installed high pressure lines	Remove and reinstall properly
Engine Idles Okay but Misfires Above Idle	Plugged fuel filter	Remove restrictions and/or replace filter
	Incorrect pump timing	Reset injection pump timing, see FUEL
	Incorrect or contaminated fuel	Remove and replace fuel
Engine Will Not Idle	Linkage binding or misadjusted	Remove binding and readjust linkage
	Defective injection pump	Replace injection pump, see FUEL
Fuel Leaks With No Other Engine Malfunction	Loose or broken fuel line or connection	Check all fuel line fittings and correct
	Internal seal leak in injection pump	Remove and replace injection pump
Low Engine Power	Restricted air intake	Remove restrictions
	Plugged fuel filter	Remove restriction and/or replace filter
	Restricted fuel return system	Remove restrictions
	Restricted tank-to-pump fuel supply	Check fuel delivery system
	Incorrect or contaminated fuel	Remove and replace fuel
	Restricted fuel tank filter	Replace filter
	Nozzle or glow plug compression leaks	Check fittings and replace as required
	Plugged nozzle	Remove restriction and/or replace nozzle
"Rapping" Noise From One or More Cylinders	Air in fuel system	Check fuel delivery system for leaks
	Air in high pressure lines	Check fittings for leaks
	Nozzle sticking in open position	Inspect nozzle and/or replace
	Low nozzle opening pressure	Check nozzle operation, see FUEL
	Filter in nozzle broken or loose	Remove and replace filter, see FUEL
Excessive Combustion Noise With Black Smoke	Incorrect pump timing	Reset injection pump timing, see FUEL
	Incorrect pump housing pressure	Check pump for internal leaks, FUEL
	Defective injection pump	Replace injection pump, see FUEL
Engine Will Not Shut Off With Key	Injection pump fuel solenoid does not return to off position	Check solenoid operation, see FUEL

1983 Carter Carburetors

CARTER YFA & YFA FEEDBACK SINGLE BARREL

CARBURETOR APPLICATION

FORD MOTOR CO. (CARTER) CARBURETOR NO.

Application	Man. Trans.	Auto. Trans.
2.0L 4-Cyl.		
Federal	E27E-CB	
	E27E-CC	
	E27E-GB	
	E37E-EA	
	E37E-FA	
2.3L 4-Cyl.		
Federal	E27E-BB	
	E37E-BA	
	E37E-LA	
California	E27E-FB	E27E-HA
	E37E-FA	E27E-HB
	E37E-LA	E37E-BA
	E37E-NA	
High Altitude	E27E-BB	E27E-EB
	E37E-RA	E37E-TA
4.9L 6-Cyl.		
Federal	E3TE-AGA	E3TE-AAA
	E3TE-AHA	E3TE-AFA
	E3TE-AJA	E3TE-ANA
	E3TE-AMA	E3TE-ARA
	E3TE-APA	
	E3TE-ASA	
	E3TE-BDA	
	E3TE-BNA	
	E3TE-YA	
California	E3TE-BDA	E3TE-ALA
	E3TE-GA	E3TE-BKA
		E3TE-FA
High Altitude	E3TE-ZA	E3TE-ABA
		E3TE-AKA
		E3TE-BRA

CARBURETOR IDENTIFICATION

A carburetor identification tag is attached to carburetor. Tag contains part number prefix and suffix, design change code, if any, and assembly date code, including year, month and day. To obtain replacement parts, it is necessary to know identification number prefix and suffix, and in some instances, the design change code.

DESCRIPTION

Carter YFA and YFA Feedback carburetors are made up of three main assemblies: Air horn, main body and throttle body. YFA carburetors have an adjustment limiting vacuum diaphragm type automatic choke with an electric assist choke cap.

The electric choke adds a high mileage economy application to the carburetor. The main body contains a temperature compensated accelerator pump which has a thermostatic disc designed to open and close within a specified range.

The YFA Feedback carburetor differs from the YFA in its addition of a feedback solenoid attached to the air horn assembly. This solenoid is used to meter air into both the idle and main circuits for improved engine performance.

A Microprocessor Control Unit (MCU) senses various engine needs and supplies feedback fuel as required by forcing air into fuel bowl, and in turn, more fuel into carburetor air stream.

ADJUSTMENT

NOTE: **For all on vehicle adjustments, see TUNE-UP SERVICE PROCEDURES.**

FLOAT LEVEL

1) Remove air cleaner assembly. Remove air horn and gasket from top of carburetor.

2) Turn air horn assembly upside-down. Measure distance between top of float at free end and gasket surface of air horn.

NOTE: **Do not apply pressure against needle when adjusting float.**

3) Bend float arm as necessary to obtain correct clearance. DO NOT bend tab at end of float arm as this will stop float travel to bottom of fuel bowl when empty.

4) When adjustment is completed, reinstall air horn and new gasket. Start engine and check for fuel leaks. Install air cleaner.

Fig. 1: Ford Motor Co. Carburetor Identification Tag

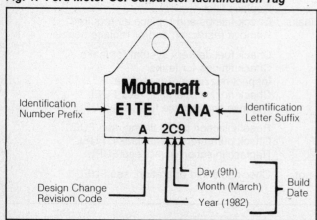

Identification tag is attached to top of carburetor.

Fig. 2: Float Level Clearance Adjustment

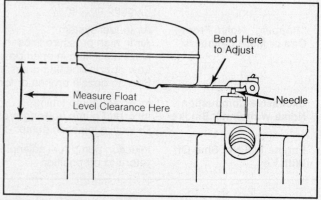

Float arm should rest gently on needle.

CARTER YFA & YFA FEEDBACK SINGLE BARREL (Cont.)

FLOAT DROP

1) Remove air cleaner, carburetor air horn and gasket from top of carburetor.

2) Hold air horn in upright position. Allow float to hang free. Measure minimum clearance from tip of float to bottom of air horn casting with a suitable gauge. *See Fig. 3.*

3) Bend tab at end of float arm to adjust. After completing adjustment, install air horn and a new gasket on carburetor. Start engine and check for fuel leaks. Install air cleaner.

Fig. 3: Float Drop Clearance Adjustment

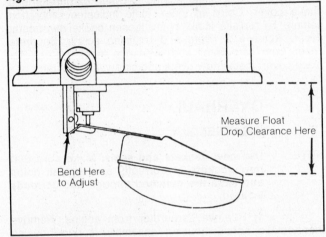

Bend tab at end of float arm.

METERING ROD

1) Remove air cleaner, air horn and gasket from carburetor.

2) Back out idle speed adjusting screw until throttle plate is tightly closed in throttle bore.

3) Press down on end of pump diaphragm shaft until assembly bottoms. While holding diaphragm assembly in this position, turn rod adjustment screw counterclockwise until metering rod gently bottoms in body casting. *See Fig. 4.*

Fig. 4: Metering Rod Adjustment

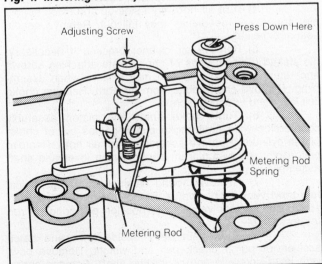

Before adjusting, press down on pump diaphragm shaft.

4) Now turn metering rod adjustment screw clockwise (IN) one turn for final adjustment.

5) Install air horn and new gasket on carburetor. Start engine and check for fuel leaks. Install air cleaner.

CHOKE UNLOADER (DECHOKE)

1) Remove air cleaner. Hold throttle valve in fully open position and press choke valve toward closed position.

2) Measure clearance between lower edge of choke valve and air horn wall.

3) Adjust by bending arm on choke lever of throttle lever. *See Fig. 5.*

4) Bend arm upward to increase clearance; bend downward, away from fast idle cam, to decrease clearance.

5) Operate throttle to check for binding or clearance interference. Install air cleaner.

Fig. 5: Choke Unloader (Dechoke) Adjustment

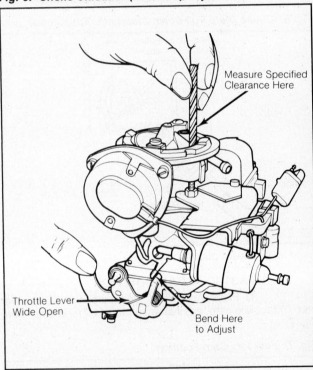

Adjust by bending choke lever arm of throttle lever.

CHOKE VALVE PULL-DOWN CLEARANCE (YFA MODEL)

Piston Type Choke

1) Remove air cleaner. Remove choke thermostatic spring housing and heat baffle from carburetor.

2) Bend a .026" diameter wire gauge at a 90° angle approximately 1/8" from one end. Insert the bent end of the wire gauge between choke piston slot and right hand slot in the choke housing.

3) Rotate choke piston counterclockwise until gauge is snug in slot. Hold pressure against lever to keep gauge in place.

4) Measure choke valve pull-down specified clearance between lower edge of choke valve and air horn wall.

CARTER YFA & YFA FEEDBACK SINGLE BARREL (Cont.)

5) To adjust, bend choke lever. Bend lever toward piston to decrease clearance; bend lever away from piston to increase clearance.

NOTE: Do not distort piston link while adjusting or erratic choke operation will result.

CHOKE PLATE PULL-DOWN CLEARANCE (YFA FEEDBACK MODEL)
Diaphragm Type Choke

1) Remove air cleaner. Remove choke thermostatic spring housing and heat baffle from carburetor.

2) Temporarily rotate choke housing to rich setting to lightly close choke plate, then increase an additional 90°.

3) Activate pull-down motor by applying an external vacuum source. Check clearance between lower edge of choke valve and air horn wall.

4) To adjust, bend choke diaphragm link as required. Reinstall choke thermostat housing using two No. 6-32 screws in place of rivets. Replace air cleaner.

Fig. 6: Choke Plate Pull-Down Clearance Adjustment

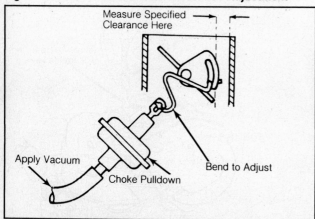

Bend lever toward piston to decrease clearance.

FAST IDLE CAM POSITION

1) Place fast idle speed screw on kickdown step of fast idle cam, against shoulder of highest step. *See Fig. 7.*

Fig. 7: Fast Idle Cam Position

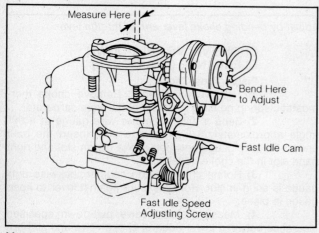

Measure clearance between choke valve and air horn wall.

2) Measure specified clearance between lower edge of choke valve and air horn wall.

3) If clearance is not to specification, adjust by bending fast idle cam link.

AUTOMATIC CHOKE

NOTE: Although automatic choke is of tamper-proof design, these steps are used if automatic choke is damaged or when carburetor is rebuilt.

Choke housing is non-adjustable. Setting is fixed by an index plate located between carburetor and choke cover. Color of index plate indicates calibration setting. To replace index plate, loosen choke thermostat cover. Remove 2 rivets and retaining screw. Separate cover from carburetor and exchange index plates. Replace cover. Install new rivets and screw, and tighten.

OVERHAUL

DISASSEMBLY

NOTE: Use new gaskets and seals. Make sure that new gaskets fit correctly and that all holes and slots are punched through and correctly located.

1) Remove carburetor from engine. Remove thermostatic spring housing assembly, spring housing gasket, index plate, choke over center spring, if equipped and fast idle link. Remove EGR WOT dump valve and bracket. If equipped, remove front mounted solenoid and bracket.

2) On Feedback carburetor, remove pull-down diaphragm adjustment limiting shield. Remove 2 retaining screws; disconnect choke pull-down link and remove pull-down motor assembly. Disengage link from choke shaft lever.

3) Remove air horn assembly screws and dashpot. On YFA Feedback model, remove feedback solenoid and bracket assembly. Lift air horn away from main body and remove gasket. Turn air horn upside-down and remove float pin, float and lever assembly.

4) Turn air horn right-side-up and catch needle pin, spring and needle as they fall out. Remove needle seat and gasket.

5) Remove air cleaner bracket. If necessary, file staked (burred) ends of choke plate attaching screws and remove. Be sure to use new screws when assembling. Remove choke plate from air horn. Remove choke link lever and attaching screw.

6) Turn choke shaft and piston assembly counterclockwise until choke piston comes out of choke piston cylinder. Remove assembly from air horn. Remove piston pin and piston from choke piston lever and shaft assembly.

7) Remove spring retainer from mechanical fuel bowl vent flapper valve. Remove vent shaft rod and spring and flapper valve. Note position of spring on rod for reassembly.

8) Turn main body upside-down and catch accelerator pump check ball and weight. Remove bowl vent lever screw in end of throttle shaft. Remove spring washer, actuating lever, operating lever and clip.

CARTER YFA & YFA FEEDBACK SINGLE BARREL (Cont.)

Fig. 8: Exploded View of Carter Model YFA 1-Barrel Feedback Carburetor (YFA Similar)

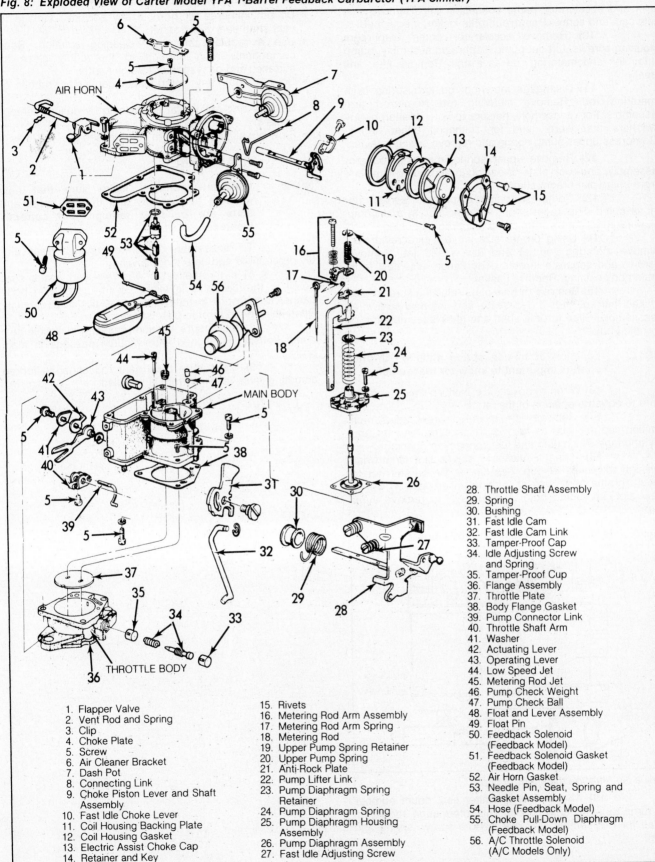

1. Flapper Valve
2. Vent Rod and Spring
3. Clip
4. Choke Plate
5. Screw
6. Air Cleaner Bracket
7. Dash Pot
8. Connecting Link
9. Choke Piston Lever and Shaft Assembly
10. Fast Idle Choke Lever
11. Coil Housing Backing Plate
12. Coil Housing Gasket
13. Electric Assist Choke Cap
14. Retainer and Key
15. Rivets
16. Metering Rod Arm Assembly
17. Metering Rod Arm Spring
18. Metering Rod
19. Upper Pump Spring Retainer
20. Upper Pump Spring
21. Anti-Rock Plate
22. Pump Lifter Link
23. Pump Diaphragm Spring Retainer
24. Pump Diaphragm Spring
25. Pump Diaphragm Housing Assembly
26. Pump Diaphragm Assembly
27. Fast Idle Adjusting Screw
28. Throttle Shaft Assembly
29. Spring
30. Bushing
31. Fast Idle Cam
32. Fast Idle Cam Link
33. Tamper-Proof Cap
34. Idle Adjusting Screw and Spring
35. Tamper-Proof Cup
36. Flange Assembly
37. Throttle Plate
38. Body Flange Gasket
39. Pump Connector Link
40. Throttle Shaft Arm
41. Washer
42. Actuating Lever
43. Operating Lever
44. Low Speed Jet
45. Metering Rod Jet
46. Pump Check Weight
47. Pump Check Ball
48. Float and Lever Assembly
49. Float Pin
50. Feedback Solenoid (Feedback Model)
51. Feedback Solenoid Gasket (Feedback Model)
52. Air Horn Gasket
53. Needle Pin, Seat, Spring and Gasket Assembly
54. Hose (Feedback Model)
55. Choke Pull-Down Diaphragm (Feedback Model)
56. A/C Throttle Solenoid (A/C Models Only)

CARTER YFA & YFA FEEDBACK SINGLE BARREL (Cont.)

9) Loosen throttle shaft arm screw. Remove arm and accelerator pump connector link. Remove fast idle cam and screw. Remove throttle kicker, if equipped.

10) Remove accelerator pump diaphragm housing screws. Lift out pump diaphragm assembly, pump lifter link and metering rod as a unit. Remove lifter link seal.

11) Disengage metering rod arm spring from metering rod. Remove metering rod from rod arm assembly. For reassembly, be sure to note location of any washers that were used for shimming either spring. Compress upper pump spring and remove spring retainer.

12) Remove upper spring, metering rod arm assembly, anti-rock plate, if equipped and pump lifter link from pump diaphragm shaft.

13) Compress pump diaphragm spring, remove pump diaphragm spring retainer, spring and pump diaphragm assembly from pump diaphragm housing.

14) Using proper size jet tool or screwdriver, remove metering rod jet and low speed jet. Remove screws and separate throttle body flange assembly from main body casting. Remove gasket.

15) Remove throttle plate retaining screws. File staked (burred) ends if necessary, and use new screws at reassembly. Slide throttle shaft and lever assembly out of throttle body.

NOTE: **Location of torsion spring ends on throttle shaft is important to know for reassembly.**

16) When removing idle mixture limiter cap, be sure to note the position of the tab.

17) Remove idle mixture screw adjustment limiting cap and cup as follows: Invert carburetor assembly and tape all vacuum and fuel connection openings.

18) Using a hacksaw, saw a slot lengthwise through thickness of cup. *See Fig. 9.* Be careful not to touch throttle body with saw blade. Insert screwdriver in new slot, spreading outer cup enough to remove inner cap.

Fig. 9: Idle Mixture Screw Limiter Cap Removal

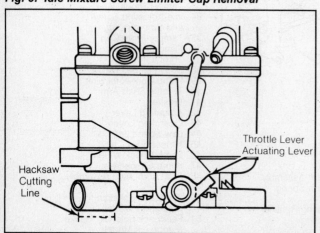

Saw a slot through thickness of cup.

19) After removing limiter cap, count number of turns to lightly seat needle. This information should be used for reassembly. Remove mixture screw, spring and cup.

CLEANING & INSPECTION

- Do not immerse air horn in any solvent. Damage to vent shaft seal could result.
- Use a regular carburetor cleaning solution. Soak components long enough to thoroughly clean all surfaces and passages of foreign matter.
- Do not soak any components containing rubber or leather.
- Remove any residue after cleaning by rinsing components in a suitable solvent.
- Blow out all passages with compressed air.

REASSEMBLY

NOTE: **Use new gaskets. Make sure that new gaskets fit correctly and that all holes and slots are punched through and correctly located.**

To reassemble carburetor, reverse disassembly procedures and note the following:

1) If throttle valve was removed, make sure notch in throttle valve is aligned with idle port in body flange. Make sure throttle plate does not bind or stick. Restake or peen throttle plate screws.

2) Make sure vacuum passage in accelerator pump housing is aligned with vacuum passage in main body.

3) Make sure bowl vent rod engages forked actuating lever when air horn is installed.

CARTER YFA & YFA FEEDBACK SINGLE BARREL (Cont.)

CARBURETOR ADJUSTMENT SPECIFICATIONS

Application	Float Level	Choke Unloader	Choke Pull-Down	Fast Idle	Auto. Choke [1]
E2TE-ANA	.780"	.280"	.300"	.140"	Red
E27E-BB	.650"	.220"	.320"	.140"	Yellow
E27E-CB	.650"	.220"	.320"	.140"	Yellow
E27E-CC	.650"	.220"	.320"	.140"	Orange
E27E-EB	.650"	.220"	.320"	.140"	Black
E27E-FB	.650"	.220"	.320"	.140"	Yellow
E27E-GB	.650"	.220"	.320"	.140"	Yellow
E27E-HA	.650"	.270"	.320"	.140"	Black
E27E-HB	.650"	.270"	.320"	.140"	Black
E3TE-AAA	.780"	.280"	.300"	.140"	Red
E3TE-ABA	.780"	.280"	.300"	.140"	White
E3TE-AFA	.780"	.280"	.270"	.140"	Red
E3TE-AGA	.780"	.280"	.270"	.140"	Red
E3TE-AHA	.780"	.280"	.270"	.140"	Red
E3TE-AJA	.780"	.280"	.300"	.140"	Red
E3TE-AKA	.780"	.280"	.270"	.140"	White
E3TE-ALA	.780"	.330"	.320"	.140"	Red
E3TE-AMA	.780"	.280"	.270"	.140"	Red
E3TE-ANA	.780"	.280"	.300"	.140"	Red
E3TE-APA	.780"	.280"	.270"	.140"	Red
E3TE-ARA	.780"	.280"	.300"	.140"	Red
E3TE-ASA	.780"	.280"	.270"	.140"	Red
E3TE-BDA	.780"	.330"	.320"	.140"	Red
E3TE-BKA	.780"	.330"	.320"	.140"	Red
E3TE-BNA	.780"	.330"	.320"	.140"	White
E3TE-BRA	.780"	.280"	.300"	.140"	Red
E3TE-FA	.780"	.330"	.320"	.140"	Red
E3TE-GA	.780"	.330"	.320"	.140"	Red
E3TE-YA	.780"	.280"	.270"	.140"	White
E3TE-ZA	.780"	.280"	.300"	.140"	Yellow
E37E-BA	.650"	.270"	.320"	.140"	Orange
E37E-EA	.650"	.270"	.320"	.140"	Gray [2]
E37E-FA	.650"	.270"	.320"	.140"	Gray
E37E-LA	.650"	.270"	.320"	.140"	Gray
E37E-NA	.650"	.270"	.320"	.140"	Gray
E37E-RA	.650"	.270"	.320"	.140"	Gray
E37E-TA	.650"	.270"	.320"	.140"	

[1] — Choke setting is fixed by index plate of specified color.
[2] — 2.0L Gray, 2.3L Yellow.

CARTER BBD 2-BARREL

CARBURETOR APPLICATION

CHRYSLER CORP. (CARTER) CARBURETOR NO.

Application	Man. Trans.	Auto. Trans.
3.7L 6-Cylinder		
Federal	BBD-8371S	
5.2L V8		
Federal		BBD-8359S
Calif.	BBD-8358S	
High Alt.	BBD-8374S	BBD-8374S

JEEP (CARTER) CARBURETOR NO.

Application	Man. Trans.	Auto.Trans.
4.2L 6-Cylinder		
Federal	8367	8362
Calif.	8364	8360

CARBURETOR IDENTIFICATION

Carter carburetors are identified by a code number and build date. Both numbers are stamped on a tag attached to carburetor by an air horn screw. Each carburetor build month is coded alphabetically beginning with letter "A" (for January), and ending with "M" (for December). Letter "I" is not used.

Second number on tag is year in which carburetor was built. Third and fourth numbers are for build day. There may be a revision letter following build day numbers if needed.

Fig. 1: Carter Model BBD I.D. Tag

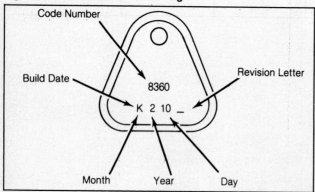

DESCRIPTION

The Carter model BBD is a 2-barrel downdraft carburetor. The BBD has 4 basic fuel metering systems: float (fuel inlet) system, idle (low speed) system, accelerator pump system, and the main (high speed) system.

The float system maintains fuel level. The idle system is used for idle and initial part-throttle operation. The main system is used for part-throttle and cruising operation. The pump system provides additional fuel for acceleration.

An electric choke with a choke diaphragm is used. The carburetor is equipped with a stepper motor to control air flow in metered air bleeds in the main fuel metering circuit. All Jeep vehicles use a vacuum solenoid called a Solevac to keep idle speed constant when load is placed on engine.

ADJUSTMENT

NOTE: For all on vehicle adjustments, see TUNE-UP SERVICE PROCEDURES.

FLOAT LEVEL (BENCH ADJUSTMENT)
Chrysler Corp.

1) Separate air horn from main body of carburetor. Turn main body upside-down and catch pump intake check ball as it falls out. Weight of floats should be gently forcing inlet needle against its seat. See Fig. 2.

NOTE: Do not allow float lip to press against the needle. Needle has a synthetic rubber tip which is easily damaged.

2) Hold finger against retainer to fully seat fulcrum pin. Using a straightedge, check float setting. Measure from float bowl surface to crown of each float.

3) If adjustment is required, gently hold floats on bottom of bowl. Bend float lip toward or away from needle as needed. Recheck setting after bending.

4) Reassemble carburetor using new gasket.

Fig. 2: Adjusting Float Level on Chrysler Corp. Models

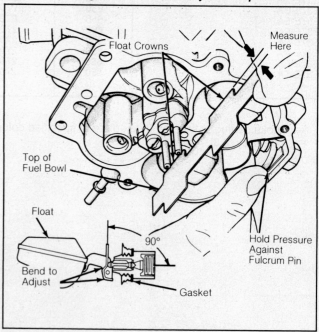

Hold finger against fulcrum pin retainer.

Jeep

1) Remove air horn. Hold float lip gently against needle. See Fig. 3.

2) Using a straightedge, place across float bowl to measure float level. If adjustment is needed, release float and then bend float tip to obtain correct clearance. Reinstall air horn.

NOTE: To avoid damaging synthetic rubber tip, do not bend lip while float is resting against needle.

CARTER BBD 2-BARREL (Cont.)

Fig. 3: *Adjusting Float Level on Jeep Models*

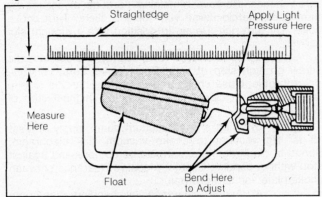

Hold finger against fulcrum pin retainer.

VACUUM STEP-UP PISTON GAP QUALIFICATION

NOTE: **This adjustment is required if step-up piston is removed or if piston lifter position is changed on actuating rod. This adjustment (qualification) places piston in a centered "mean" position.**

1) Remove step-up piston cover plate and gasket. Remove lifter lock screw and remove piston step-up assembly.

2) Measure piston gap. *See Fig. 4.* If not to specification, adjust by turning Allen head screw on top of piston.

3) Record number of turns and direction to obtain proper dimension. This must be reset to its original position after vacuum step-up piston adjustment has been made.

Fig. 4: *Vacuum Step-Up Piston Gap Qualification*

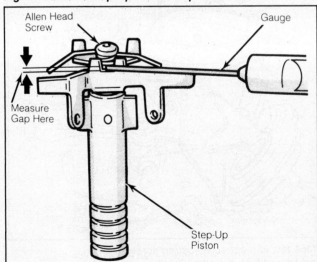

Record number of turns and direction.

VACUUM STEP-UP PISTON ADJUSTMENT

NOTE: **Perform Vacuum Step-Up Piston Gap Qualification adjustment before adjusting vacuum step-up piston.**

1) With vacuum piston installed, back off idle speed screw until throttle valves are completely closed. Count number of turns so screw can be returned to its original position. *See Fig. 5.*

Fig. 5: *Adjusting Step-Up Piston*

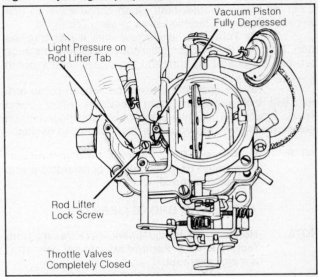

If this adjustment is changed, the step-up piston must be re-qualified.

2) Fully depress step-up piston while holding moderate pressure on rod lifter tab. While in this position, tighten rod lifter lock screw.

3) Release piston and rod lifter. Return idle speed set screw to its original position.

4) Reset Allen head calibration screw on top of step-up piston to its original position as recorded under Vacuum Step-Up Piston Gap Qualification. If this adjustment is changed, the step-up piston must be requalified.

Fig. 6: *Adjusting Accelerator Pump Stroke*

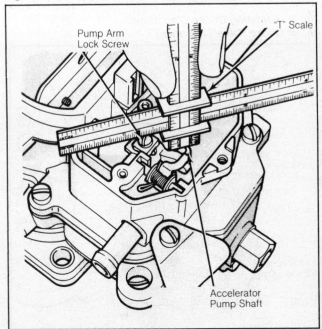

Fast idle cam must be in open position.

1983 Carter Carburetors

CARTER BBD 2-BARREL (Cont.)

ACCELERATOR PUMP STROKE ADJUSTMENT

1) Remove step-up piston cover plate and gasket. Back off curb idle screw to fully close throttle valves. Fast idle cam must be in open position. On Chrysler Corp. vehicles, if pump arm has 2 holes ensure pump "S" link is in outer hole. Open choke valve so that fast idle cam allows throttle valves to seat. *See Fig. 6.*

2) Turn curb idle screw until it just touches stop. Continue 2 more complete turns. Measure distance between surface of air horn and top of accelerator pump shaft.

3) If adjustment is required, loosen pump arm adjusting lock screw and turn sleeve to adjust pump travel. When correct measurement is obtained, tighten lock screw. Install step-up piston cover plate and gasket.

NOTE: On Chrysler Corp. vehicles, bowl vent adjustment must be performed if accelerator pump stroke is changed.

AUTOMATIC CHOKE (JEEP ONLY)

NOTE: Normally, no readjustment is necessary from factory setting. Perform adjustment only after a major overhaul.

1) Loosen choke thermostat cover retaining screws.

2) Rotate cover in "Rich" or "Lean" direction to align reference mark on cover with specified scale graduation on choke housing. Tighten retaining screws.

VACUUM KICK (INITIAL CHOKE VALVE CLEARANCE)

NOTE: All carburetors incorporate tamper-proof choke, choke pull-off, and idle adjusting screws. Adjustments given are for after major overhaul, or if carburetor components have been damaged.

Fig. 7: Adjusting Choke Diaghragm (Initial Choke Valve Clearance)

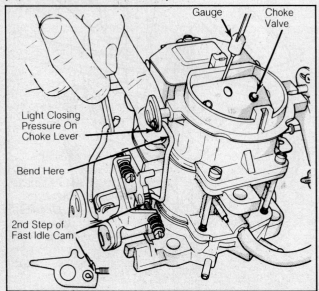

Place fast idle screw on high step of cam.

1) On Jeep vehicles, grind off torque-head screw heads. Remove remaining portions of screws by turning counterclockwise with locking pliers. Turn choke cover 1/4 turn rich. Retain in position with 1 straight slot screw.

2) Open throttle valve slightly to place fast idle screw on high step of cam. On Chrysler Corp. vehicles, open throttle, close choke and then close throttle to trap fast idle cam at closed choke position (highest step of cam). *See Fig. 7.*

3) Using a hand vacuum pump, apply at least 15 in. Hg vacuum to choke vacuum kick diaphragm. Spring in diaphragm stem should be compressed against stop without bending linkage. Measure clearance between choke plate and air horn wall.

4) Adjust clearance by bending diaphragm connecting link at "U" bend. On Jeep vehicles, remove straight slot screw and adjust cover index to specified notch. Install replacement torque-head screws.

FAST IDLE CAM POSITION

NOTE: All carburetors incorporate tamper-proof choke, choke pull-off, and idle adjusting screws. The following adjustments are for after major carburetor overhaul, or if carburetor components are damaged.

1) On Jeep vehicles, remove torque-head screws and position choke cover 1/4 turn rich. Retain with 1 straight-slot screw to hold choke cover in position. On all models, place fast idle adjusting screw on 2nd step of fast idle cam. *See Fig. 8.*

Fig. 8: Adjusting Fast Idle Cam Position

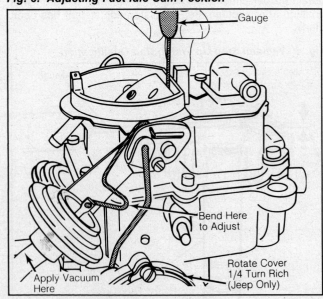

Place fast idle speed adjusting screw on 2nd step of fast idle cam.

2) With specified drill or pin gauge, measure clearance between upper edge of choke valve and air horn wall. To adjust, bend fast idle connecting rod down to increase measurement or up to decrease measurement.

3) On Jeep vehicles, loosen housing cover screw and reset choke to specified index position. Install replacement torque-head screws.

CARTER BBD 2-BARREL (Cont.)

CHOKE UNLOADER

1) Hold throttle valves wide open. Apply light closing pressure to choke valve lever. *See Fig. 9.*

Fig. 9: Adjusting Choke Unloader

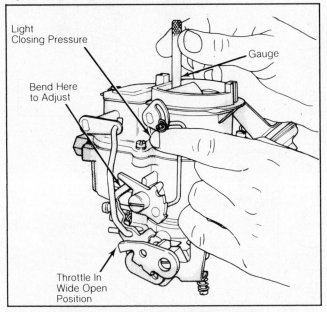

Light Closing Pressure

Gauge

Bend Here to Adjust

Throttle In Wide Open Position

Throttle valves should be in wide open position.

2) Measure choke unloader specified clearance between upper edge of choke valve and air horn wall. Clearance can be checked using a specified drill or pin gauge.

3) To adjust, bend choke unloader tang. Make sure tang does not interfere with other components after it is adjusted.

OVERHAUL

DISASSEMBLY

All Models

1) Place carburetor on a repair stand, and remove stepper motor if equipped. Remove retaining clip from accelerator pump arm link and remove link.

2) Remove cover and gasket from top of air horn. Remove screws and locks from accelerator pump arm and vacuum piston rod lifter. Slide pump lever out of air horn. Remove pump arm and rod lifter.

3) Lift vacuum piston and step-up rods up and out of air horn as an assembly. Remove the vacuum piston spring. Remove choke vacuum diaphragm hose. Disconnect clips and remove link from choke housing lever and choke lever.

4) Remove screw and lever from choke shaft. Remove choke diaphragm, linkage, and bracket assembly. Remove fast idle cam retaining screw. Remove fast idle cam, choke link, and clip. On Jeep vehicles, grind heads off of torque-head screws. Remove choke cover assembly and housing from throttle body. Remove remaining portion of screws with locking pliers.

5) Remove screws securing air horn and lift air horn up and away from main body. Discard gasket. Turn air horn upside-down and compress accelerator pump drive spring. Remove "S" link from pump shaft. Remove pump assembly.

6) Remove fuel inlet needle valve, seat and gasket from main body. Carefully lift out float fulcrum pin retainer and baffle. Lift out floats and fulcrum pin. Remove the main metering jets.

7) Remove venturi cluster screws. Lift cluster and gaskets away from main body and discard gaskets. DO NOT remove idle orifice tubes or main vent tubes from cluster as they can be cleaned with solvent and dried with compressed air while assembled.

8) Turn carburetor upside-down and catch accelerator pump discharge and intake check balls as they fall out.

9) On Jeep vehicles, turn idle limiter caps to stop. Remove plastic caps from idle air mixture screws. Be sure to count number of turns it takes to seat screws to ease reassembly adjustment.

10) On Chrysler vehicles, center punch the side of idle screw housing 5/16" (8 mm) from end. Using a 3/16" drill bit, drill at a 90° angle into side of housing. Insert a punch through hole and pry out idle screw plug. On all vehicles, remove screws and springs from throttle body.

11) Remove screws and separate throttle body from main body. Discard gasket. Check choke plate in air horn for freedom of movement. If any sticking or binding is evident, clean thoroughly.

CLEANING & INSPECTION

NOTE: **Do not apply compressed air to diaphragm. Do not use wire or drill to clean jets or passageways.**

- Use a regular carburetor cleaning solution. Soak components long enough to thoroughly clean all surfaces and passages of foreign matter.
- Do not soak any components containing rubber, leather or plastic.
- Remove any residue after cleaning by rinsing components in a suitable solvent.
- Blow out all passages with dry compressed air.

REASSEMBLY

Use all new gaskets and reverse disassembly procedures while noting the following:

Idle Mixture Screw Installation

1) Install idle mixture screws and springs in body. Tapered portion must be straight and smooth. If tapered portion is grooved or ridged, use a new screw. DO NOT use a screwdriver for installation.

2) Turn screws lightly against their seats with fingers. Back off 2 turns (Chrysler) or number of turns counted at disassembly (Jeep). On Jeep vehicles install new plastic caps with tab against stop.

Accelerator Pump Check Ball Installation

Accelerator pump intake and discharge check balls are different sizes. Make sure large check ball is installed in float bowl. *See Fig. 11.*

Accelerator Pump Assembly

1) Check operation as follows: Pour clean unleaded gasoline into carburetor bowl approximately 1/2" deep. Operate accelerator pump plunger several times to expel air from pump passage. Using a small brass rod, hold discharge check ball down firmly on its seat. *See Fig. 12.*

1983 Carter Carburetors

CARTER BBD 2-BARREL (Cont.)

Fig. 10: *Exploded View of Carter Model BBD 2-Barrel Carburetor*

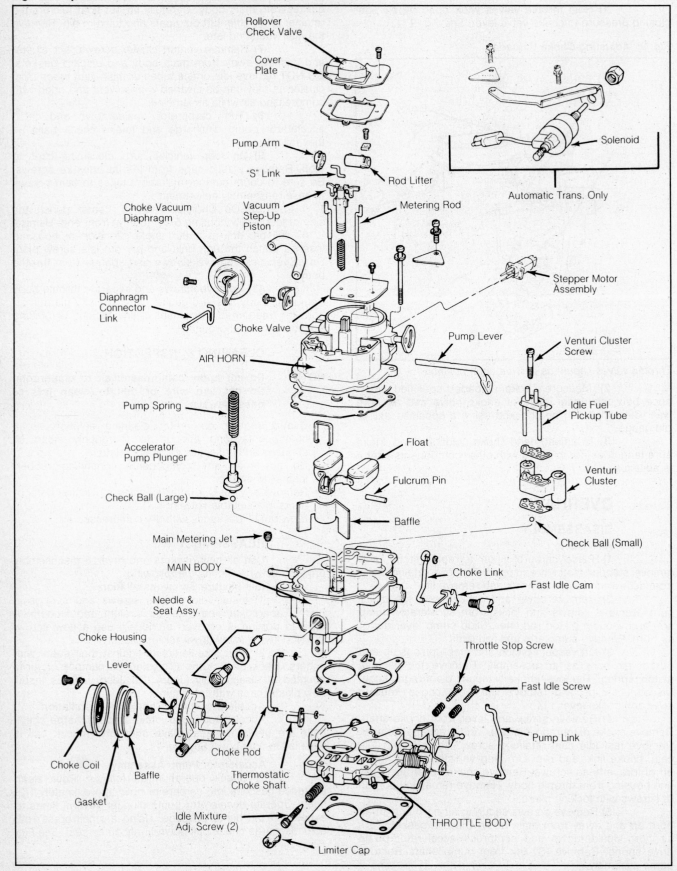

CARTER BBD 2-BARREL (Cont.)

Fig. 11: *Installing Accelerator Pump Intake and Discharge Check Balls*

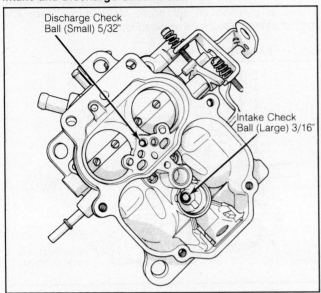

Large check ball is installed in float bowl.

Fig. 12: *Testing Accelerator Pump Intake and Discharge*

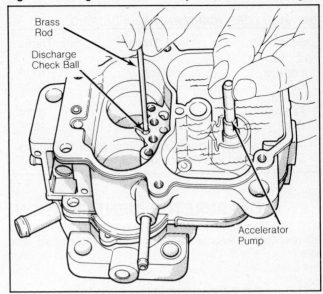

Hold discharge check ball down on its seat.

2) Again raise plunger and press downward. No fuel should be emitted from either intake or discharge passage. If fuel does escape from either passage, check that ball seat is not damaged or dirty. Clean passages and retest.

3) If leakage is still present, attempt to form a new seat. This is accomplished by installing a discharge check ball in leaking seat. Place a piece of drill rod on top of check ball and tap it lightly with a hammer to form a new seat. Remove check ball and discard. Install a new check ball and retest as described above. If service does not correct problem, carburetor replacement is necessary.

Step-Up Piston & Rod Assembly

Be sure step-up rods move freely each side of vertical position. Carefully guide step-up rods into main metering jets.

CARBURETOR ADJUSTMENT SPECIFICATIONS

Application	Float Level	Vacuum Piston Gap	Accelerator Pump Stroke	Fast Idle Cam	Choke Vacuum Kick	Choke Unloader	Auto. Choke
Chrysler	1/4"	.035"	.470"	.070"	.130"	.280"	.....
Jeep	1/4"	.035"	.520"	.095"	.140"	.280"	1 Rich

1983 Carter Carburetors

CARTER THERMO-QUAD 4-BARREL

CARBURETOR APPLICATION

CHRYSLER CORP. (CARTER) CARBURETOR NO. [1]

Application	Man. Trans.	Auto. Trans.
5.2L V8		
Federal	9342	9342
Calif.	9375	9375
5.9L V8		
Federal	9379	9379
Calif.	9376	9376

[1] — Carburetor numbers are preceded by the letters "TQ", and followed by the letter "S".

CARBURETOR IDENTIFICATION

Carburetor identification number is stamped on left rear foot of throttle body on vertical surface near bolt hole.

DESCRIPTION

Thermo-Quad carburetors have 3 main parts; the air horn, main body, and throttle body. Air horn houses choke valve, air valve for secondaries, fuel inlet system (2 floats, inlet needles and seats), and accelerator pump system.

Also housed in air horn are primary boost venturis, vacuum controlled step-up piston and metering rods, and high and low speed fuel metering system (secondary jets, fuel discharge nozzles, and air bleeds).

Main body houses primary jets and is constructed of phenolic resin for cooler fuel temperatures. Throttle body houses throttle valves and linkage.

All Thermo-Quad carburetors installed on vehicles equipped with an EGR system have a venturi vacuum port on the side of the carburetor. This is the only vacuum port located in the main body. All other vacuum pick-up points are located in the throttle body.

ADJUSTMENT

NOTE: For all on vehicle adjustments, see TUNE-UP SERVICE PROCEDURES.

Thermo-Quad carburetors have unique features which require extra caution during adjustment. The vacuum kick diaphragm provides 2 separate functions. It provides for vacuum kick and also controls the secondary air valve.

Because of the separate nature of these functions, separate but interrelated adjustments are necessary. These adjustments must be performed in proper sequence.

NOTE: All carburetors incorporate tamper-proof choke, choke pull-off, and air/fuel mixture adjusting screws. Adjustments are to be performed only after a major overhaul, or if carburetor has received component damage.

FLOAT LEVEL (BENCH ADJUSTMENT)

1) Turn air horn upside-down. Place air horn gasket in position on air horn. Make sure floats are against seated needle valve. See Fig. 1.

Fig. 1: Adjusting Float Level

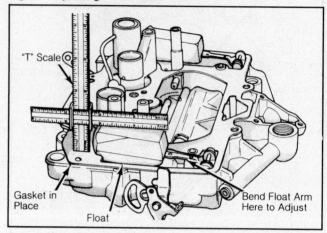

Do not allow lip of float lever to press against needle.

2) Measure float level specified clearance from bottom side of float to gasket surface. To adjust, bend float lever. Do not allow lip of float lever to press against needle when adjusting. This will damage needle and cause carburetor flooding and incorrect float level.

SECONDARY THROTTLE LINKAGE

1) Hold fast idle lever in curb idle position. Turn carburetor upside-down. Open throttle valves wide open. See Fig. 2.

Fig. 2: Adjusting Secondary Throttle Linkage

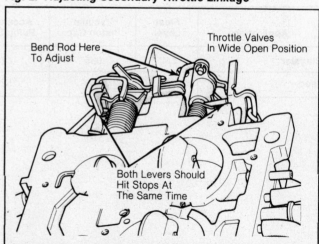

Primary and secondary levers both touch stops at same time.

2) Primary and secondary levers should both contact stops at the same time. To adjust, bend secondary throttle operating rod at point shown in illustration. Check linkage for interference and smooth movement after bending linkage rod.

CARTER THERMO-QUAD 4-BARREL (Cont.)

SECONDARY AIR VALVE ALIGNMENT

1) While performing alignment, observe carburetor from directly above. *See Fig. 3.*

Fig. 3: Checking Secondary Air Valve Alignment

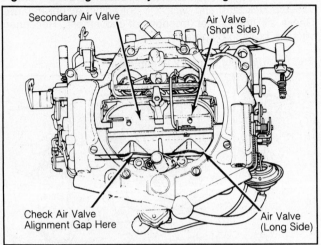

Secondary air valve closed during measurement.

2) With air valve in closed position, gap between air valve and air horn wall must be at its maximum and parallel with air horn gasket.

SECONDARY AIR VALVE OPENING

1) Hold secondary air valve wide open. Measure specified gap between raised edge (short side) of air valve and air horn wall. *See Fig. 4.*

Fig. 4: Adjusting Secondary Air Valve Opening

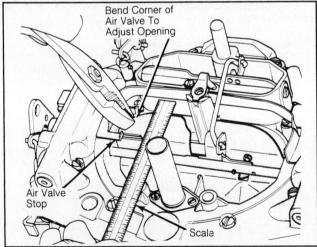

Corner of air valve is notched to aid in adjustment.

2) To adjust, bend short side of air valve with pliers until specified gap is obtained. Corner of air valve is notched to aid in adjustment.

SECONDARY AIR VALVE SPRING TENSION

CAUTION: When performing this adjustment, hold air valve adjustment plug with screwdriver when loosening lock plug. If not, spring may snap out of position. This would require taking the carburetor apart to get the spring out.

1) Loosen air valve lock plug. Turn air valve adjustment plug clockwise. This allows air valve to move to wide open position. *See Fig. 5.*

Fig. 5: Adjusting Secondary Air Valve Spring Tension

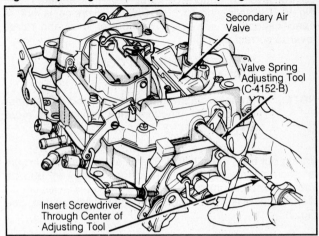

Hold air valve adjustment plug with screwdriver when loosening lock plug.

2) Insert a long slender screwdriver through center of special valve spring adjustment tool (C-4152-B or equivalent).

3) With adjusting tool positioned on air valve lock plug, turn adjustment plug counterclockwise until air valve lightly touches stop.

4) Lightly press air valve against stop with finger. Now turn adjustment plug additional amount of specified turn(s) counterclockwise. Hold adjustment plug with screwdriver and tighten lock plug with adjusting tool.

CHOKE CONTROL LEVER ADJUSTMENT

NOTE: If choke control lever adjustment is changed, the vacuum kick, fast idle cam position and choke unloader adjustment must be reset.

Fig. 6: Choke Control Lever Adjustment

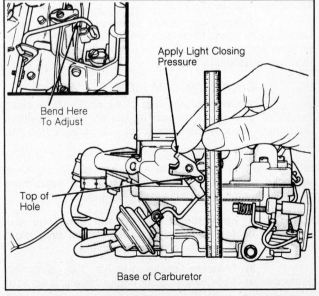

Choke lever should be 3 3/8" above bottom of carburetor.

1983 Carter Carburetors

CARTER THERMO-QUAD 4-BARREL (Cont.)

1) Remove tamper-resistant cover by drilling out 2 blind rivets. Place carburetor on flat surface. Close choke by pushing on choke lever with throttle partly open.

2) Measure distance from top of hole in choke control lever to bottom of carburetor (flat surface). *See Fig. 6.* Distance should be 3 3/8". If distance is not to specifications, loosen screw on control lever and rotate lever to correct position.

CHOKE DIAPHRAGM CONNECTOR ROD ADJUSTMENT

NOTE: If choke diaphragm connector rod adjustment is changed, vacuum kick adjustment must also be reset.

1) Remove tamper-proof choke cover by drilling out blind rivets with 1/8" drill. Make sure diaphragm is securely mounted to carburetor. Using an outside vacuum source, apply at least 15 in. Hg of vacuum to diaphragm. Make sure diaphragm stem is fully seated. *See Fig. 7.*

Fig. 7: Adjusting Choke Diaphragm Connector Rod

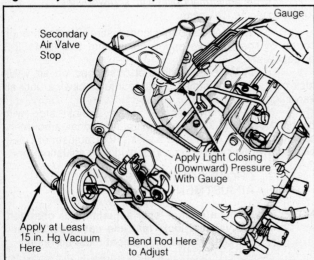

If adjustment is changed, vacuum kick adjustment must be reset.

2) Apply light opening (downward pressure) on secondary air valve. Measure specified clearance between air valve and stop. To adjust, bend connector rod at point shown in illustration.

CHOKE VACUUM KICK

1) Open throttle and close choke. Now close throttle to trap fast idle cam at closed choke position. Disconnect vacuum hose from choke diaphragm. *See Fig. 8.*

2) Apply an outside vacuum source of at least 15 in. Hg to choke diaphragm. Apply enough closing force on choke control lever to move vacuum kick adjustment tang against stop without distorting linkage.

NOTE: A weak torsion spring will easily be deflected. Vacuum kick adjustment tang must be at stop for proper adjustment.

3) Measure choke vacuum kick specified clearance between lower edge of choke valve and air horn

wall at throttle lever side. Measurement can be checked using a specified drill or pin gauge. Make sure clearance does not change as drill or pin gauge is inserted or removed.

4) To adjust, insert screwdriver in slot in vacuum kick tang and twist. Do not adjust diaphragm rod. Check all linkage for freedom of movement. Reconnect vacuum hose to diaphragm.

Fig. 8: Adjusting Choke Vacuum Kick

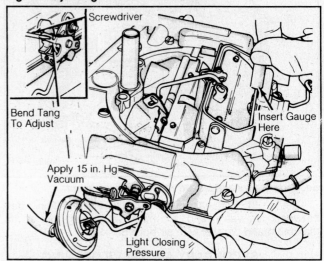

The vacuum kick adjustment tang must be at stop for proper adjustment.

CHOKE UNLOADER

1) Hold throttle valves wide open. Apply light closing pressure on fast idle control lever to close choke valve. *See Fig. 9.*

Fig. 9: Adjusting Choke Unloader

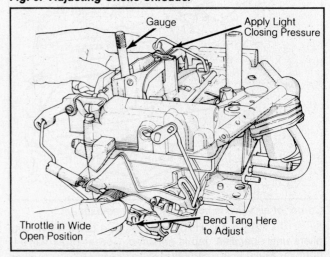

Throttle valves in wide open position.

2) Measure specified clearance between lower edge of choke valve and air horn wall at throttle lever side. Measurement can be checked using specified drill or pin gauge. Make sure clearance does not change as drill or pin gauge is inserted or removed.

3) To adjust, bend tang on fast idle lever until specified clearance is obtained.

CARTER THERMO-QUAD 4-BARREL (Cont.)

FAST IDLE CAM POSITION

NOTE: **If fast idle cam position adjustment is changed, choke unloader and secondary throttle lockout adjustments must also be reset.**

1) Place fast idle speed adjusting screw on 2nd highest step of fast idle cam. Move choke valve toward closed position using light pressure on fast idle control lever. *See Fig. 10.*

Fig. 10: Adjusting Fast Idle Cam Position

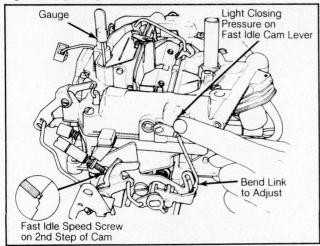

Fast idle speed adjusting screw on 2nd highest step of fast idle cam.

2) Measure clearance by inserting specified drill or pin gauge between bottom of choke valve and air horn wall at throttle lever side. Make sure clearance does not change as drill or pin gauge is inserted or removed.

3) To adjust, bend fast idle cam connector rod at point shown until correct valve opening is obtained.

SECONDARY THROTTLE LOCKOUT

1) Move fast idle control lever to open choke position. Measure specified clearance between lockout lever and stop. Clearance can be checked using specified drill or pin gauge. *See Fig. 11.*

Fig. 11: Adjusting Secondary Throttle Lockout

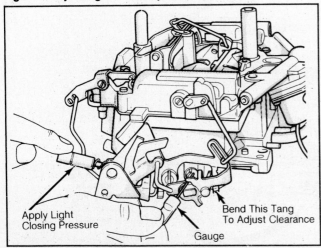

Measure between lockout lever and stop.

2) To adjust, bend tang on lower end of fast idle control lever until specified clearance is obtained.

ACCELERATOR PUMP STROKE

NOTE: **Accelerator pump stroke is determined by measurement of accelerator pump plunger height above air horn surface AT CURB IDLE.**

1) Be sure throttle connector rod is in specified hole of pump arm.

2) To check first stage of pump, use a scale to measure height of accelerator pump plunger stem (from stem top to air horn surface) at curb idle.

3) Adjust plunger height by bending throttle connector rod. *See Fig. 12.* To check second stage of pump, open choke and then throttle until secondary lockout latch is just applied. Using scale, measure height to top of plunger. If second stage setting is not to specifications, bend throttle connector rod to adjust.

Fig. 12: Adjusting Accelerator Pump Stroke

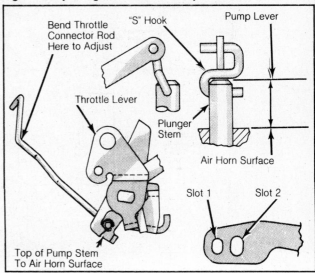

Adjustment is made at curb idle.

OVERHAUL

DISASSEMBLY

1) Place carburetor on a repair stand to protect throttle valves. Remove idle enrichment valve assembly.

2) Remove rod retainers that hold throttle connector rod to accelerator pump arm and throttle lever. Remove connector rod from carburetor.

3) Remove accelerator pump arm screw. Disengage pump arm from "S" link and remove pump arm. Leave "S" link connected to pump rod.

4) Remove choke countershaft fast idle lever attaching screw while holding lever. Remove lever from countershaft. Swing fast idle connector rod in an arc to disengage it from fast idle operating lever.

5) Remove retainers and washers holding choke diaphragm connecter rod to vacuum diaphragm and air valve lever. Remove retainer holding rod to choke countershaft. Disengage rod and swing rod in an arc to disengage choke shaft lever assembly.

6) Remove step-up piston cover plate and metering rod cover plate. Remove step-up piston and link

1983 Carter Carburetors

CARTER THERMO-QUAD 4-BARREL (Cont.)

Fig. 13: Exploded View of Carter Thermo-Quad 4-Barrel Carburetor

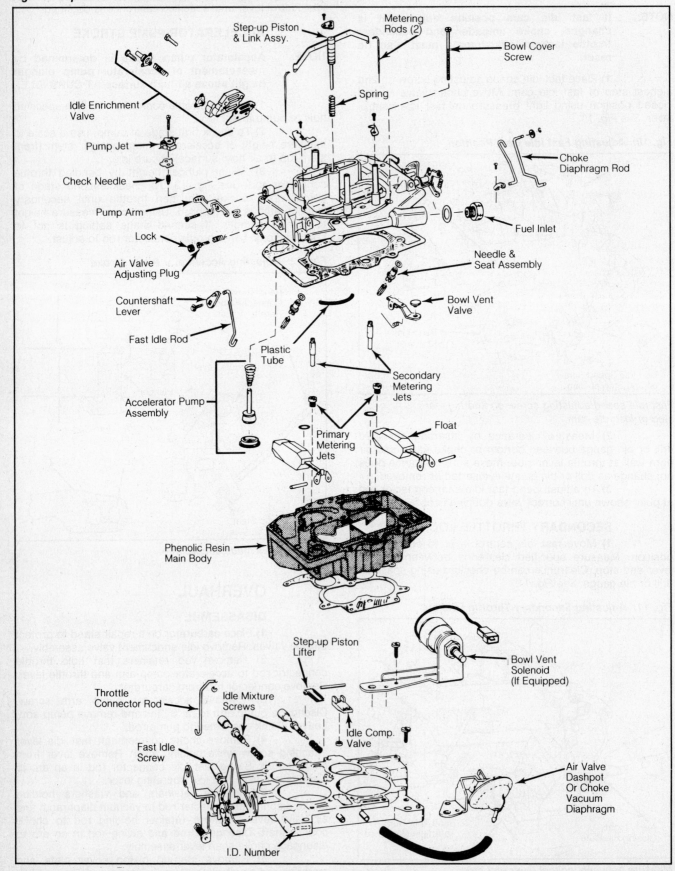

Step-up Piston & Link Assy.

Metering Rods (2)

Bowl Cover Screw

Spring

Idle Enrichment Valve

Choke Diaphragm Rod

Pump Jet

Check Needle

Pump Arm

Fuel Inlet

Lock

Needle & Seat Assembly

Air Valve Adjusting Plug

Bowl Vent Valve

Countershaft Lever

Fast Idle Rod

Plastic Tube

Secondary Metering Jets

Accelerator Pump Assembly

Float

Primary Metering Jets

Phenolic Resin Main Body

Step-up Piston Lifter

Bowl Vent Solenoid (If Equipped)

Throttle Connector Rod

Idle Mixture Screws

Fast Idle Screw

Idle Comp. Valve

Air Valve Dashpot Or Choke Vacuum Diaphragm

I.D. Number

CARTER THERMO-QUAD 4-BARREL (Cont.)

assembly with step-up rods. Remove step-up piston spring.

7) Remove discharge pump nozzle housing and gasket. Invert carburetor and remove discharge check needle. Needle should drop out when carburetor is inverted.

8) Remove 10 air horn (bowl cover) screws. Two of these screws are located between choke valve and air horn wall. Remove air horn with floats. Separate float bowl from throttle body.

Bowl Cover

1) Remove float lever pins and lift out float assembly. Mark floats so they can be installed in original locations.

2) Remove 2 needle valves from seats, marking them for reassembly in original location. Using a wide blade screwdriver, remove needle valve seats. Mark seats for reassembly in original location.

3) Remove secondary metering jets. Remove plastic accelerator pump passage tube. Remove bowl cover gasket.

4) Remove pump rod "S" link. Carefully remove accelerator pump plunger assembly by tapping lightly on upper end of plunger shaft. Care must be taken not to damage plunger shaft hole in cover. Catch intake check seat, plunger and spring.

NOTE: **Always install a new check seat and plunger when carburetor is reassembled.**

5) If equipped, note position of bowl vent actuating lever. Remove retainer clip from lever. Remove lever from bowl vent operating arm. Remove seal from arm. Remove fuel inlet fitting and gasket.

Throttle Body

1) Remove step-up actuating lever. Remove choke diaphragm and bracket assembly with hose. Do not place this assembly in carburetor cleaning solvent.

NOTE: **The carburetor vacuum fitting contains a small vacuum passage restriction. Clean with compressed air only.**

2) Locate and center punch 1/4" from end of mixture housing. Mark should be at the 10 o'clock position on the right bank and at the 2 o'clock position on the left bank. Using a 3/16" drill bit, drill through screw housing a a 90° angle to screw bore.

3) Pry out plug using a small drift punch through hole. Remove idle mixture screws and springs. Be sure to count number of turns it takes to seat screws so they may be installed in their original positions.

NOTE: **Manufacturer does not recommend removal of throttle shafts or valves unless absolutely necessary. These parts are precisely adjusted at factory. The slightest misalignment upon reassembly would adversely affect carburetor operation between curb idle and about 30 mph.**

Main Body

1) Remove and discard primary "O" ring seals. Remove primary metering jets.

2) It is not necessary to remove baffle plate from main body.

NOTE: **No further disassembly is recommended. Do not leave main body in carburetor solvent for a prolonged period of time.**

CLEANING & INSPECTION

- Do not soak choke diaphragm or plastic parts in solvent. Do not leave main body in solvent for too long a time.
- Rinse parts with HOT water after using solvent. Blow dry with compressed air.
- Do not use wire, drill or any hard parts to clean passages.
- Be sure gasket holes match up and all parts are clean and ready for installation.

REASSEMBLY

To reassemble carburetor, reverse disassembly procedures, using new gaskets and seals. Make sure gaskets fit correctly and that all holes are punched through and correctly located. Also, note the following:

1) Install pump discharge check needle with point toward base of carburetor.

2) Install upper pump plunger spring in cylinder with large end first. Lubricate and install plunger, pushing stem through hole in casting. Install "S" link with lower open end toward choke valve.

3) Install pump arm and screw before installing pump intake check valve assembly. Install 10 bowl cover screws and tighten to 35 INCH lbs. (4 N.m).

CARBURETOR ADJUSTMENT SPECIFICATIONS

Application	Float Level Setting	Secondary Air Valve		Choke Diaphragm Rod Setting	Choke Vacuum Kick	Fast Idle Cam Setting	Choke Unloader Setting	Secondary Throttle Lockout	Accel. Pump Hole	Accel. Pump Stroke [2]
		Opening Setting	Spring Tension [1]							
TQ-9342-S	29/32"	27/64"	2 1/2	.040"	.130"	.100"	.310"	.060"	#1	.340"
TQ-9375-S	29/32"	3/8"	2 1/2	.040"	.130"	.130"	.310"	.060"	#1	.340"
TQ-9376-S	29/32"	3/8"	2	.040"	.180"	.100"	.310"	.060"	#1	.340"
TQ-9379-S	29/32"	7/16"	2	.040"	.130"	.130"	.310"	.060"	#1	.340"

[1] — Specification is number of turns CCW after air valve contacts stop.
[2] — First stage shown, second stage is .190".

1983 Hitachi Carburetors

HITACHI DCH 340 2-BARREL

CARBURETOR APPLICATION

CHEVROLET & GMC CARBURETOR NO.

Application	Man. Trans.	Auto. Trans.
1.9L 4-Cyl.		
"S" Truck (2WD)		
Federal	8942273760	
Calif.	8942505970	8942505980
"T" Truck (4WD)		
Federal	8942273760	
Calif.	8942545850	

DESCRIPTION

Carburetor is a 2-barrel downdraft type with piston type accelerator pump. Carburetor consists of low speed (primary) barrel and high speed (secondary) barrel integrated into a single unit with a common fuel bowl.

Secondary throttle is actuated by a vacuum diaphragm when primary throttle is opened a pre-determined amount. Additional equipment includes a slow cut solenoid (all models), power valve (Federal models) and main and slow actuators (Calif. models).

The main and slow actuators on Calif. models are operated by a vacuum control solenoid. The vacuum control solenoid is controlled by an electronic control module (computer). The main and slow actuators receive vacuum signals from the vacuum control solenoid, in response to the computer. In this manner, the air/fuel ratio can be maintained close to 14.7:1.

ADJUSTMENT

NOTE: For all on vehicle adjustments, see TUNE-UP SERVICE PROCEDURES.

FLOAT LEVEL

1) Fuel bowl is equipped with a sight glass (Federal models). Line on sight glass indicates proper fuel level. If adjustment must be made to correct improper level, use following procedure.

Fig. 1: Float Level Adjustment

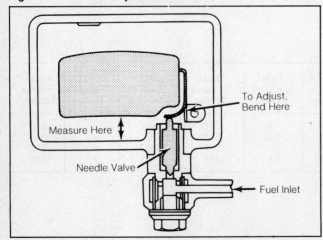

Perform adjustment only if fuel level is not at line on sight glass.

2) With float bowl removed and held upright, bend float tang until float is parallel with top of float bowl.

FLOAT DROP

1) With sight glass removed and carburetor main body inverted, fully raise float. Measure clearance between float seat and needle valve stem. Needle valve should be bottomed in bore. *See Fig. 2.*

2) If clearance is not as specified, adjust by bending float stopper.

Fig. 2: Float Drop Adjustment

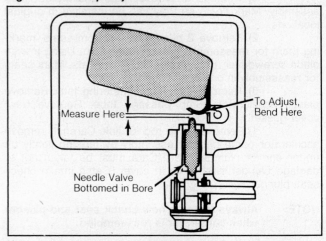

Raise float to measure clearance.

PRIMARY THROTTLE OPENING

1) Check the primary throttle valve angle with the choke all the way closed. Adjust throttle angle by turning the fast idle screw.

Fig. 3: Primary Throttle Valve Adjustment

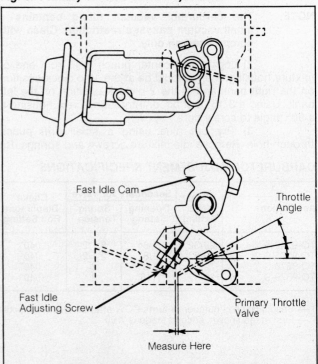

Close choke fully when adjusting.

HITACHI DCH 340 2-BARREL (Cont.)

2) With choke closed, check clearance between throttle valve and throttle bore at center of throttle plate. Primary throttle valve clearance should be at specification when throttle angle is properly set. *See Fig. 3.*

SECONDARY THROTTLE INITIAL OPENING

1) When primary throttle valve opens 47°, primary throttle lever tang contacts secondary throttle lockout. Any further opening of throttle valve will force secondary throttle lockout lever to actuate secondary throttle lever. Secondary throttle valve will begin to open. Check and adjust as follows:

2) Open primary throttle valve until secondary is just beginning to open. Hold throttle in this position. Measure clearance between center of primary throttle valve and throttle bore. If clearance is not to specification, adjust by bending primary throttle tang. *See Fig. 4.*

Fig. 4: Secondary Throttle Initial Opening Adjustment

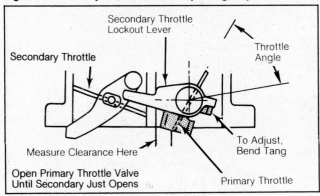

Measure clearance between center of primary throttle valve and throttle bore.

SECONDARY LOCKOUT

1) Close primary throttle valve by turning throttle adjusting screw out.

2) With throttle valve completely closed, loosen lock nut on lockout lever screw. Turn screw until it contacts return plate. Tighten lock nut. *See Fig. 5.*

Fig. 5: Secondary Lockout Adjustment

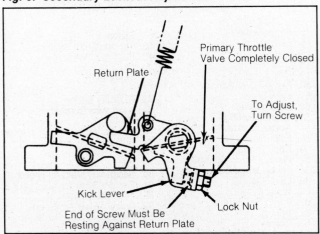

Perform adjustment with primary throttle valve completely closed.

OVERHAUL

DISASSEMBLY

1) With carburetor removed, remove main and assist throttle return springs. Disconnect accelerator pump lever.

2) Remove harness connector hanger from carburetor and disconnect automatic choke lead wire from the connector. Remove fuel nipple and strainer.

3) Disconnect vent valve switch wire from the connector. Remove circlip connecting choke connecting rod to counter lever. Disconnect choke connecting rod.

4) Disconnect automatic choke vacuum hose. Remove 4 choke-to-air horn screws. Remove choke assembly. Remove circlip connecting vacuum break diaphragm to secondary throttle lever. Remove vacuum break diaphragm.

5) Separate main body from throttle body. Remove slow actuator.

6) Remove accelerator pump plunger assembly. Remove float needle valve assembly.

7) On Federal models, remove 3 float level cover screws. Remove cover, gasket and float assembly. Do not damage rubber seal or lose float collar.

8) On Calif. models, remove 4 main actuator screws. Carefully remove actuator and float. Do not damage rubber seal or lose float collar.

9) On all models, remove diaphragm cover retaining screws. Separate diaphragm cover, spring and diaphragm. Do not lose ball and spring.

10) Remove check ball plugs. Invert air horn assembly and catch weight, ball and spring (Calif. models) in hand. Remove all jets from upper part of main body. Remove power jet. *See Fig. 6.*

11) Remove main jet plugs and primary and secondary main jets. Remove primary slow air bleed from air horn.

12) Further disassembly is not required. Primary and secondary throttle valves, and choke valve screws are staked in position. No attempt should be made to remove screws.

Fig. 6: Location of Jets in Main Body

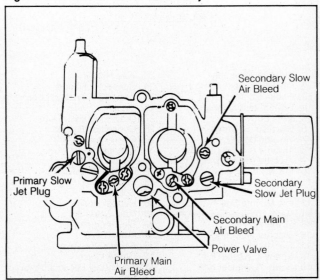

Make sure jet wrench or screwdriver fits securely in slots of jets.

1983 Hitachi Carburetors

HITACHI DCH 340 2-BARREL (Cont.)

Fig 7: Exploded View of Hitachi DCH Carburetor Assembly

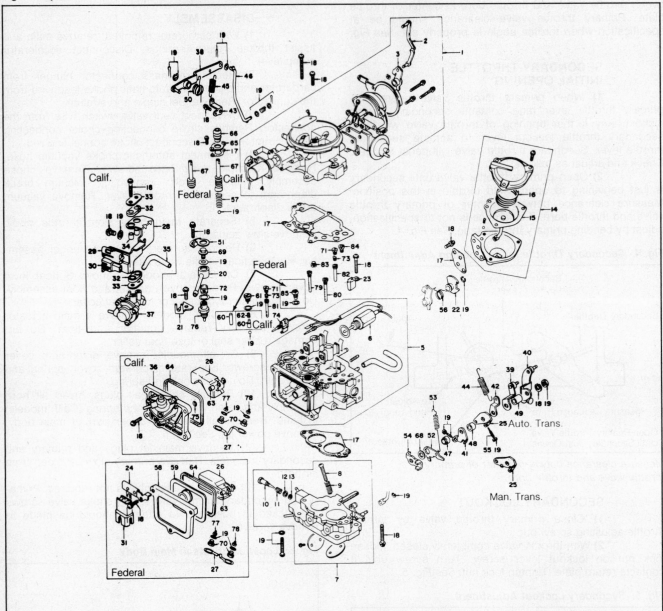

1. Air Horn Assembly	23. Wire Holder	45. Assist Spring	67. Piston
2. Choke Connecting Rod	24. Connector Hanger	46. Pump Rod	68. Throttle Shaft Washer
3. Choke Counter Lever	25. Fast Idle Adjusting Lever	47. Sleeve	69. Fuel Inlet Set Screw
4. Switch Vent Solenoid	26. Float	48. Collar	70. Drain Plug
5. Main Body	27. Drain Plug Lock Plate	49. Collar	71. Taper Plug
6. Slow Cut Solenoid	28. Connector Hanger	50. Pump Lever Spring	72. Filter
7. Throttle Body	29. Connector	51. Lock Lever	73. Slow Jet Spring
8. Throttle Adjusting Screw	30. Connector	52. Return Plate	74. Lead Wire Connector
9. Throttle Adjusting Spring	31. Connector	53. Throttle Spring	75. "O" Ring
10. Idle Mixture Screw	32. Rubber Mount	54. Adjusting Lever	76. Needle Valve
11. Idle Mixture Spring	33. Plate	55. Fast Idle Screw	77. Primary Main Jet
12. Idle Mixture Washer	34. Collar	56. Cam Spring	78. Secondary Main Jet
13. Idle Mixture Seal	35. Rubber Hose	57. Piston Return Spring	79. Primary Main Air Bleed
14. Vacuum Break Diaphragm	36. Main Actuator	58. Level Gauge Cover	80. Secondary Main Air Bleed
15. Diaphragm	37. Slow Actuator	59. Level Gauge	81. Primary Slow Jet
16. Diaphragm Spring	38. Pump Lever	60. Weight	82. Secondary Slow Jet
17. Gasket Kit	39. Accelerator Lever	61. Pump Set Screw	83. Primary Slow Air Bleed
18. Screw & Washer Kit	40. Cruise Lever	62. Spring	84. Secondary Slow Air Bleed
19. Screw & Washer Kit	41. Secondary Lockout Lever	63. Collar	85. Power Valve
20. Fuel Inlet	42. Spring Hanger	64. Seal	
21. Stop Plate	43. Spring Hanger	65. Plate	
22. Fast Idle Cam	44. Main Spring	66. Dust Cover	

HITACHI DCH 340 2-BARREL (Cont.)

INSPECTION

Air Horn

1) Inspect air horn for cracks and damage. Pay particular attention to mating surfaces. Check shaft holes for wear. Check choke valve for smooth operation.

2) On Federal models, check vacuum piston for smooth operation.

Main Body

1) Inspect and remove carbon deposits from inside main body. Inspect for cracks and damage, particularly on mating surfaces. Inspect threaded portion and head slots of jets for damage.

2) On Federal models, check power valve for leaks. Check power valve rod for bending and smooth operation.

3) On all models, inspect accelerator pump plunger for damage and distortion. Check for smooth plunger movement within cylinder bore.

Throttle Body

1) Check all ports for clogging. Inspect throttle valves for carbon deposits and wear. Check throttle shaft holes for wear.

2) Check mixture adjusting screw seating face for step wear. Check vacuum break diaphragm for deterioration and damage.

REASSEMBLY

Reverse disassembly procedures and note the following:

1) On Federal models, be careful not to bend rod when installing power jet valve.

2) On California models, apply grease to main actuator "O" ring during assembly. Carefully tighten the screws to prevent cracking "O" ring.

3) On all models, fill accelerator pump cavity with fuel after assembly. Depress accelerator pump and ensure fuel is injected smoothly. Do not bend piston connecting rod during assembly.

CARBURETOR ADJUSTMENT SPECIFICATIONS

Application	Float Level	Float Drop	Primary Throttle Angle	Primary Throttle Clearance	Secondary Throttle Opening	Secondary Throttle Lockout
8942273760	[1]	.059"	16°	.050-.059"	.240-.300"	[2]
8942505970	[1]	.059"	16°	.050-.059"	.240-.300"	[2]
8942545850	[1]	.059"	16°	.050-.059"	.240-.300"	[2]
8942505980	[1]	.059"	18°	.059-.069"	.240-.300"	[2]

[1] — Float parallel with top of bowl.
[2] — Adjusting screw contacting return plate with throttle closed.

1983 Holley Carburetors

HOLLEY 1945 SINGLE BARREL

CARBURETOR APPLICATION

CHRYSLER CORP. (HOLLEY) CARBURETOR NO.

Application	Man. Trans.	Auto. Trans.
3.7L 6-Cylinder Federal	R-40055-A	R-40056-A

CARBURETOR IDENTIFICATION

Carburetor is identified by a part number stamped into main body, or by tag attached to carburetor top.

DESCRIPTION

Holley 1945 is single venturi of concentric downdraft design. Internally, fuel bowl completely surrounds venturi. Carburetor consists of 3 main parts: bowl cover, main body, and throttle body. Carburetor includes 4 basic fuel metering systems: idle and transfer, main metering system, accelerating system and electric assist choke systems.

ADJUSTMENT

NOTE: For all on vehicle adjustments, see TUNE-UP SERVICE PROCEDURES.

FLOAT LEVEL

1) With air horn removed, turn main body upside-down with gasket installed. Using a straightedge, check that ends of floats furthest away from the fuel inlet just contact straightedge. *See Fig. 1.*

Fig. 1: Adjusting Float Level

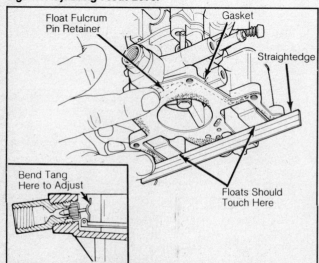

Measure at ends of floats furthest away from fuel inlet.

2) To adjust, bend float tang on float arm that contacts fuel inlet needle.

CHOKE VACUUM KICK

1) Open throttle and close choke. Close throttle to trap fast idle cam in closed choke position. *See Fig. 2.*

Fig. 2: Adjusting Choke Vacuum Kick

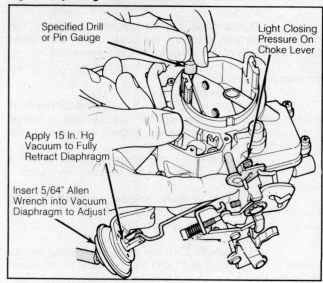

Spring in diaphragm stem must be compressed during adjustment.

2) Disconnect vacuum hose from choke vacuum diaphragm. Connect hand vacuum pump to diaphragm and apply at least 15 in. Hg. Apply light finger pressure on choke shaft lever to compress spring in diaphragm stem without distorting linkage. Diaphragm stem reaches a stop as spring is compressed.

3) Measure choke vacuum kick specified clearance between upper edge of choke valve and air horn wall. Clearance can be measured using a specified drill or pin gauge.

4) To adjust, insert a 5/64" Allen wrench into choke vacuum diaphragm. Turn adjusting screw to obtain specified clearance. Check all linkage for freedom of movement. Remove vacuum pump and install vacuum hose on diaphragm.

FAST IDLE CAM POSITION

1) Position fast idle speed screw on 2nd step of fast idle cam. Apply light finger pressure on choke shaft lever to close choke valve. *See Fig. 3.*

Fig. 3: Adjusting Fast Idle Cam Position

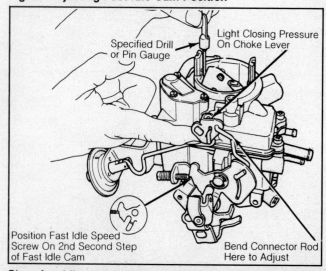

Place fast idle speed screw on 2nd step of fast idle cam.

HOLLEY 1945 SINGLE BARREL (Cont.)

2) Measure fast idle cam specified clearance between top of choke valve and air horn wall at throttle lever side. Measure clearance using a drill or pin gauge of specified clearance.

3) To adjust, bend fast idle cam connector rod until specified valve opening is obtained.

CHOKE UNLOADER

1) Hold throttle valves in wide open position. Apply light finger pressure on the choke shaft lever to close choke valve. *See Fig. 4.*

Fig. 4: Adjusting Choke Unloader

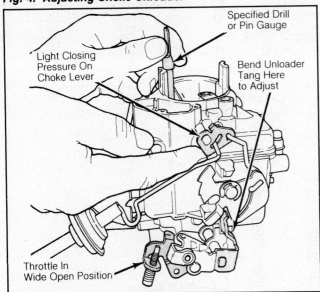

Measure with throttle valves wide open.

2) Measure choke unloader specified clearance between top edge of choke valve and air horn wall at throttle lever side. Clearance can be checked using a specified drill or pin gauge.

3) To adjust, bend choke unloader tang on throttle lever until specified clearance is obtained.

Fig. 5: Adjusting Accelerator Pump Stroke

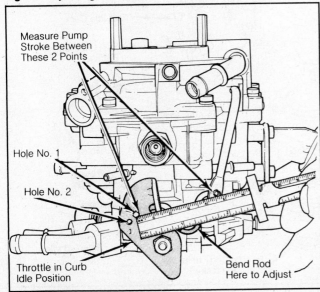

Ensure pump rod link is installed in correct hole.

ACCELERATOR PUMP STROKE

1) Place throttle lever in curb idle position. Make sure accelerator pump rod link is installed in correct hole in throttle lever. *See Fig. 5.*

2) Measure accelerator pump stroke specified distance between center of rod in throttle lever and center of rod in accelerator pump arm.

3) To adjust, bend the accelerator pump rod at existing "U" bend.

OVERHAUL

DISASSEMBLY

1) Place carburetor on a repair stand for disassembly to prevent damage to throttle valves. Remove wire retainer and bowl vent solenoid. Remove solenoid idle stop (SIS).

2) Remove fast idle cam retaining clip, fast idle cam and connector rod. Remove rod from fast idle cam.

3) Remove choke vacuum diaphragm, link and bracket assembly. Disconnect diaphragm rod from slot in choke lever. Place diaphragm aside to avoid cleaning with carburetor cleaner.

4) Remove nut and washer from throttle shaft. Remove throttle lever and link, noting hole position of lever. Remove air horn screws. Separate air horn from main body by lifting straight up until vacuum piston, accelerator pump and main well tube clears main body.

NOTE: **Do not pry cover off with screwdriver. If necessary, tap with a plastic hammer.**

5) Remove air horn gasket. Remove accelerator pump rod retainer screw and retainer. Remove accelerator pump retainer screw and accelerator pump.

NOTE: **Do not scrape any remaining gasket material from air horn or carburetor surfaces with a metal scraper. Use nylon or hard plastic scraper to prevent damage to components.**

6) Rotate and remove accelerator pump operating rod. Remove pump operating rod grommet from air horn. Remove 3 screws and power valve diaphragm assembly. Do not attempt to remove main well tube from air horn. Main well tube must be carefully blown out from both sides of cover.

7) Remove fuel inlet fitting from main body and separate gaskets. Remove float pin retainer, float pin and float assembly. Turn main body upside-down and catch accelerator pump discharge check ball and weight.

8) Remove main jet using a screwdriver with a blade at least 3/8" wide. Ensure screwdriver has a good square blade.

9) Carefully depress power valve needle with a 3/8" wide screwdriver until screwdriver blade fits into slot in top of valve. Remove valve assembly. Power valve assembly consists of needle, seat and spring. All of these components of service valve should be used if replacement is required.

10) Remove 3 throttle body screws and separate throttle body from main body. Remove throttle body gasket. Remove idle speed screw from throttle body. Center punch idle mixture screw housing 1/4" from end at the 2 o'clock position.

11) Using a 3/16" drill bit, drill through outer section of mixture screw housing at the center punch

1983 Holley Carburetors

HOLLEY 1945 SINGLE BARREL (Cont.)

Fig. 6: *Exploded View of Holley Model 1945 Single Barrel Carburetor*

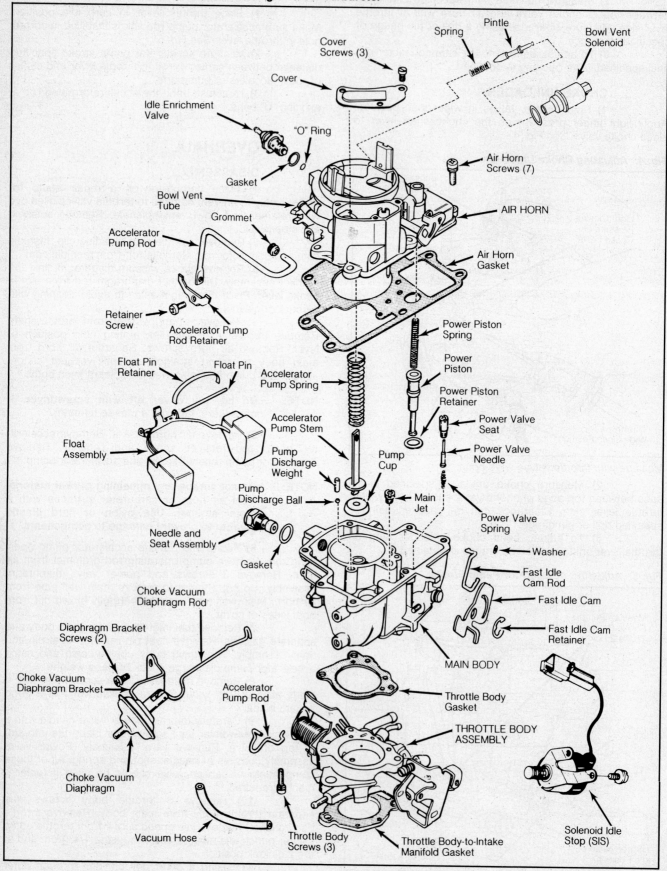

HOLLEY 1945 SINGLE BARREL (Cont.)

mark. Pry plug out using small drift punch through hole. Remove mixture screw and spring, noting number of turns required to seat screw.

CLEANING & INSPECTION

- Use a regular carburetor cleaning solution. Soak components long enough to thoroughly clean all surfaces and passages of foreign matter.
- Do not soak any components containing rubber, leather or plastic.
- Remove any residue after cleaning by rinsing components in a suitable solvent.
- Blow out all passages with dry, compressed air.

REASSEMBLY

To reassemble carburetor, reverse disassembly procedures, using new gaskets and seals. Make sure gaskets fit correctly and that all holes and slots are punched through and correctly located. Also, note the following:

1) Install idle mixture screw and spring in throttle body. Ensure tapered portion is straight and smooth.

2) Install a new throttle body gasket on main body. Place throttle body in position and tighten 3 retaining screws to 30 INCH lbs. (3 N.m).

3) Install accelerator pump discharge check ball and weight. Fill fuel bowl with clean fuel to check ball and seat operation.

4) Hold ball and weight down with a brass rod. Place accelerator pump assembly in well and operate by hand. If no resistance is felt, check ball is leaking.

5) Remove weight and leave check ball in place. Using a small drift punch, lightly tap ball against seat to form a new seal. Remove old check ball and discard. Install a new check ball and weight.

6) Perform fuel leak test again. If there is still no resistance felt, main body must be replaced. If resistance is felt, check ball is seating correctly. Remove check ball and weight.

7) Install accelerator pump, pump rod and rod retainer in air horn.

8) Install power valve assembly in bottom of fuel bowl. Tighten securely. Ensure needle valve operates freely. Install main jet in main body.

9) Install float pin in main body. Place float assembly in float shaft cradle. Install float pin retainer. Check float alignment to make sure it does not bind against main body casting.

10) Install a new gasket on fuel inlet fitting. Install fitting in main body. Tighten securely. Check float level.

11) Insert check ball and weight into accelerator pump discharge well. Position air horn gasket on air horn. Carefully install air horn on main body. Make sure accelerator pump cup is not damaged.

12) Install 7 air horn screws and tighten alternately in steps to 30 INCH lbs. (3 N.m). Install fast idle cam and link.

13) Install choke vacuum diaphragm, solenoid idle stop (SIS), and bowl vent solenoid.

CARBURETOR ADJUSTMENT SPECIFICATIONS

| Application | Float Level | Accelerator Pump | | Fast Idle Cam | Choke Unloader | Choke Vacuum Kick |
		Hole	Stroke			
R-40055-A	Flush [1]	#2	1.70"	.080"	.250"	.130"
R-40056-A	Flush [1]	#2	1.61"	.080"	.250"	.130"

[1] — Setting is flush with top of casting to .050" above.

1983 Holley Carburetors

HOLLEY 6145 SINGLE BARREL

CARBURETOR APPLICATION

CHRYSLER CORP. (HOLLEY) CARBURETOR NO.

Application	Man. Trans.	Auto. Trans.
3.7L 6-Cyl. Calif.	R-40029-A	R-40030-A

CARBURETOR IDENTIFICATION

Part number is stamped on main body or on tag attached to carburetor.

DESCRIPTION

The Holley model 6145 is an "Electronic Feedback" type carburetor. The carburetor is designed to maintain an air/fuel ratio within specified limits to allow the catalytic converter to operate effectively. The carburetor is controlled by the Spark Control Computer.

The carburetor includes 4 basic fuel metering systems: idle system, main metering system, accelerator system and power enrichment system. In addition to these 4 basic systems, there is a fuel inlet system and choke system.

ADJUSTMENTS

NOTE: For all on-vehicle adjustments, see TUNE-UP SERVICE PROCEDURES.

FLOAT LEVEL

1) With air horn removed, install float shaft and position assembly in float shaft cradle. Install retaining spring and place air horn gasket on top of the fuel bowl.

2) Turn carburetor upside down and hold air horn gasket in place. Place a straightedge across air horn gasket surface and toes of both floats. *See Fig. 1.*

Fig. 1: Float Level Adjustment

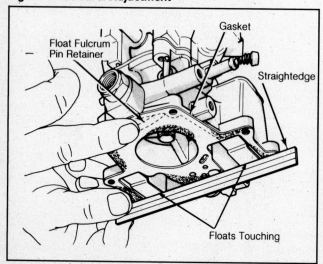

Bend float tang to adjust.

3) To adjust, bend float tang. Make sure floats are correctly aligned with walls of float bowl and that they move freely through full travel.

CHOKE VACUUM KICK (CHOKE PULLDOWN)

1) Open throttle then close choke. Now close throttle to trap fast idle cam at closed choke position. *See Fig. 2.*

Fig. 2: Choke Vacuum Kick (Choke Pulldown) Adjustment

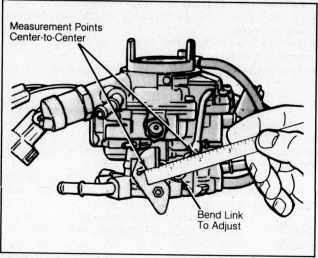

Bend link to adjust.

2) Disconnect vacuum hose from carburetor. Connect an outside vacuum source of at least 15 in. Hg to choke vacuum diaphragm. Apply enough closing pressure on choke valve to compress spring in diaphragm without distorting linkage.

3) Insert a 5/64" Allen wrench into diaphragm and turn to adjust choke vacuum kick. Check for free movement between open and adjusted positions. Correct binding by rebending link and readjusting.

FAST IDLE CAM POSITION

1) Position the fast idle speed screw on second step of the fast idle cam. Hold choke valve toward closed position with light pressure on choke shaft lever. *See Fig. 3.*

Fig. 3: Fast Idle Cam Position Adjustment

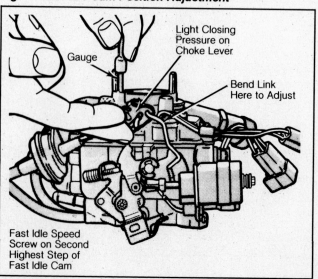

Bend fast idle cam connector rod to adjust.

HOLLEY 6145 SINGLE BARREL (Cont.)

2) Using specified drill or pin gauge, measure fast idle cam specified clearance between upper edge of choke valve and air horn wall. To adjust, bend fast idle connector rod at angle.

CHOKE UNLOADER

1) Hold throttle valves in wide open position. Hold choke valve toward closed choke position by applying light closing pressure to choke lever. *See Fig. 4.*

Fig. 4: Choke Unloader Adjustment

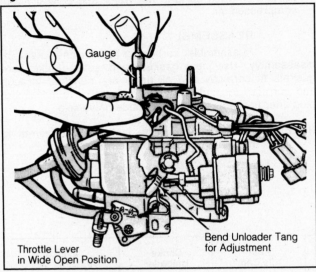

Bend tang on throttle lever to adjust.

2) Using specified drill or pin gauge, measure clearance between top of choke valve and air horn wall at throttle lever side. To adjust, bend tang on throttle lever.

ACCELERATOR PUMP

1) Place throttle lever in curb idle position. Make sure accelerator pump rod is in correct hole.

2) Measure accelerator pump distance between inner side of tab to outer side of radius. *See Fig. 5.* To adjust, bend accelerator pump operating link.

Fig. 5: Accelerator Pump Adjustment

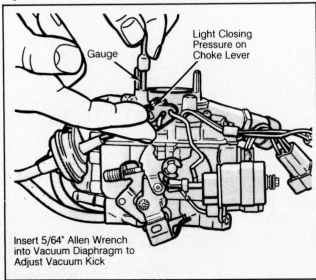

Bend accelerator pump operating link to adjust.

OVERHAUL

DISASSEMBLY

Air Horn

1) Place carburetor on repair stand. Remove wire retainer and bowl vent assembly. Remove Solenoid Idle Stop (SIS). Remove fast idle cam retaining clip, fast idle cam and link. Disconnect link.

2) Remove choke vacuum diaphragm, link and bracket assembly. Disengage link from slot in choke lever. Place diaphragm to one side and clean as special items.

3) Remove nut and washer from throttle shaft. Remove throttle lever and link. Note hole position of lever. Remove screws and duty cycle solenoid. Remove air horn screws.

4) Separate air horn from carburetor body by tapping with a plastic hammer or screwdriver handle. DO NOT pry off. Lift air horn straight up until vacuum piston stem, accelerator pump and main well tube are clear of main body.

5) Remove air horn gasket and clean gasket surface with cleaner. DO NOT use a metal scraper. Remove accelerating pump operating rod retainer screw and retainer.

6) Remove accelerator pump assembly retaining screw and pump assembly. Rotate pump operating rod and remove from air horn. Remove pump operating rod grommet.

7) Carefully remove power piston assembly retaining ring staking with a sharp tool. Remove vacuum piston from air horn by depressing piston and allowing it to snap up against retaining ring.

NOTE: **Main well tube cannot be removed and must be carefully blown out from both sides of cover with compressed air.**

Fig. 6: Holley Model 6145 Carburetor Assembly

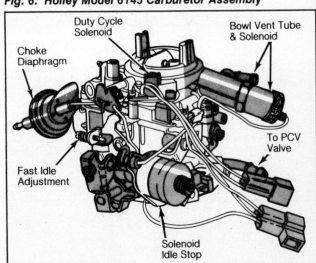

Main Body

1) Remove fuel inlet fitting valve assembly. Remove and discard old gaskets. Remove float shaft retainer, shaft and float assembly. Turn main body upside down and catch pump discharge weight and ball as they fall out.

2) Remove main metering jet with jet wrench or 3/8" wide flat screwdriver. Remove power enrichment valve needle with 3/8" wide screwdriver.

1983 Holley Carburetors

HOLLEY 6145 SINGLE BARREL (Cont.)

NOTE: Screwdriver should be modified by cutting a 1/16" wide and 3/8" deep slot in center of blade. This provides clearance for valve stem.

3) Remove 3 main body-to-throttle body screws and separate assemblies. Remove and discard gasket. Remove low idle speed (TSP Off) adjusting screw and spring, and remove solenoid.

Throttle Body

1) Remove curb idle adjusting screw. Remove fast idle speed adjusting screw and spring.

NOTE: Manufacturers do not recommend removal of throttle plate or shaft. If damage or wear is evident, replace throttle body assembly.

2) Locate and center punch a mark 1/4" from end of mixture screw housing. Punch mark should be indexed at 2 o'clock position.

3) Drill through outer section of housing using a 3/16" drill bit. Mixture screw plug should drop out. If not, use small drift to remove plug.

4) Turn mixture screw clockwise until it lightly seats, recording number of turns for reassembly reference. Remove mixture screw and spring.

CLEANING & INSPECTION
- Inspect all gasket mating surfaces for nicks, burrs or any damage that would prevent gasket sealing.
- Do not place choke cover, pulldown diaphragm, bowl vent assembly or pump plunger in cleaning solvent.
- Inspect idle mixture screw tip. If grooved or worn, replace with new needle.
- Ensure all new gaskets match gaskets removed in placement of holes and slots. Use new gaskets only.
- Ensure all parts are clean and free of solvent before assembly. Wash parts in hot water and blow dry with compressed air.

REASSEMBLY
Reassemble carburetor in reverse order of disassembly. Use new gaskets and seals. Make sure gaskets fit correctly and all holes are punched through and correctly located. Install mixture screw concealment plug after final adjustments are made on vehicle.

NOTE: Choke cap must be installed with rivets to maintain tamper-proof requirement.

CARBURETOR ADJUSTMENT SPECIFICATIONS

Application	Float Level	Accelerator Pump		Fast Idle Cam	Choke Unloader	Choke Vacuum Kick
		Hole	Stroke			
R-40029-A	Flush	#2	1.70"	.090"	.250"	.150"
R-40030-A	Flush	#2	1.61"	.090"	.250"	.150"

HOLLEY 2280 2-BARREL

CARBURETOR APPLICATION

CHRYSLER CORP. (HOLLEY) CARBURETOR NO.

Application	Man. Trans.	Auto. Trans.
5.2L V8		
Federal	R-9951-A	R-9951-A
		R-9949-A

CARBURETOR IDENTIFICATION

Carburetor part number is stamped on main body flange. It is in front of the lever, controlled by throttle position transducer, under the choke vacuum diaphragm.

DESCRIPTION

The Holley model 2280 2 barrel carburetor uses 4 basic fuel metering systems: basic idle system, accelerator pump system, main metering and power enrichment systems.

The basic idle system provides mixture at idle and low speed engine operation. The accelerator pump system provides additional fuel for acceleration. The main metering system provides an economical mixture for normal cruising.

The power enrichment system provides a richer mixture when high power output is required (full throttle operation).

ADJUSTMENT

NOTE: For all on-vehicle adjustments, see TUNE-UP SERVICE PROCEDURES.

FLOAT LEVEL

1) With air horn removed, turn main body upside-down. Catch pump intake check ball as it falls out. Hold retainer in place with finger to fully seat float pin in cradle.

2) Using a "T" scale, measure float level specified clearance from air horn gasket surface on main body to toe of each float. See Fig. 1.

Fig. 1: Adjusting Float Level

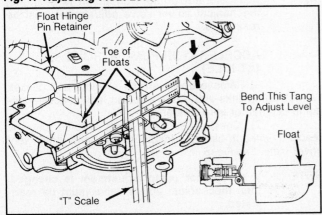

Measure from air horn gasket surface to toe of each float.

3) To adjust, bend float tang. If necessary, bend either float arm to equalize float positions.

CHOKE VACUUM KICK

1) Open throttle and close choke. Now close throttle to trap fast idle cam in closed choke position. See Fig. 2.

Fig. 2: Adjusting Choke Vacuum Kick

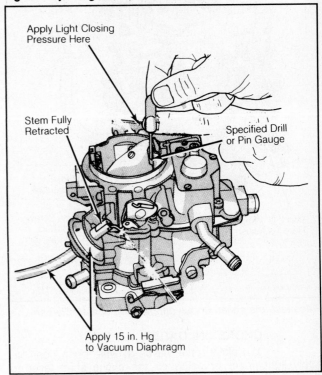

Spring in diaphragm stem must be compressed during adjustment.

2) Disconnect vacuum hose from choke vacuum diaphragm. Connect hand vacuum pump to diaphragm, and apply at least 15 in. Hg vacuum. Apply light finger pressure on choke shaft lever to compress spring in diaphragm stem without distorting linkage. Diaphragm stem reaches a stop as spring is compressed.

3) Measure choke vacuum kick specified clearance between upper edge of choke valve and air horn wall. Clearance can be measured using a specified drill or pin gauge.

4) To adjust, insert a 5/64" Allen wrench into choke vacuum diaphragm. Turn adjusting screw to obtain specified clearance. Check all linkage for freedom of movement. Remove vacuum pump, and install vacuum hose on diaphragm.

FAST IDLE CAM POSITION

1) Position fast idle speed screw on 2nd step of fast idle cam. Apply light finger pressure on choke shaft lever to close choke valve. See Fig. 3.

2) Measure fast idle cam specified clearance, between upper edge of choke valve and air horn wall. Clearance can be measured using a specified drill or pin gauge.

3) To adjust, bend fast idle cam connector rod at existing "U" bend until specified clearance is obtained.

HOLLEY 2280 2-BARREL (Cont.)

Fig. 3: Adjusting Fast Idle Cam Position

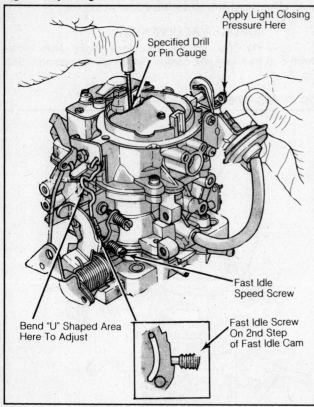

Apply Light Closing Pressure Here

Specified Drill or Pin Gauge

Fast Idle Speed Screw

Bend "U" Shaped Area Here To Adjust

Fast Idle Screw On 2nd Step of Fast Idle Cam

Place fast idle speed screw on 2nd step of fast idle cam.

CHOKE UNLOADER

1) Hold throttle valves in wide open position. Apply light finger pressure on the choke shaft lever to close choke valve. *See Fig. 4.*

Fig. 4: Adjusting Choke Unloader

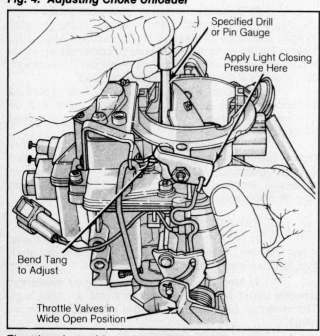

Specified Drill or Pin Gauge

Apply Light Closing Pressure Here

Bend Tang to Adjust

Throttle Valves in Wide Open Position

Throttle valves wide open to adjust choke unloader.

2) Measure choke unloader specified clearance between upper edge of choke valve and air horn wall. Clearance can be checked, using a specified drill or pin gauge.

3) To adjust, bend choke unloader tang on accelerator pump lever until specified clearance is obtained.

MECHANICAL POWER VALVE

1) Remove bowl vent valve cover, and hold throttle lever in wide open position. *See Fig. 5.*

Fig. 5: Adjusting Mechanical Power Valve

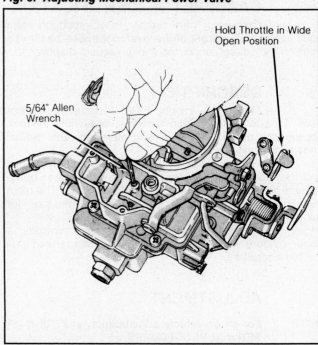

Hold Throttle in Wide Open Position

5/64" Allen Wrench

This adjustment must be reset if accelerator pump adjustment is changed.

2) Insert a 5/64" Allen wrench in mechanical power valve adjustment screw. Push down on screw, then release to determine if there is any clearance. If so, turn screw clockwise until there is no clearance.

3) To make final adjustment, turn screw counterclockwise 1 full turn from zero clearance. Install bowl vent valve cover plate and gasket.

NOTE: If accelerator pump adjustment is changed, mechanical power valve adjustment must be reset also.

ACCELERATOR PUMP STROKE (AT IDLE)

1) Remove bowl vent cover plate and gasket. With all pump links and levers installed, adjust accelerator pump cap nut for zero clearance.

2) Check that wide open throttle can be reached without binding. Install gasket and bowl vent cover plate. *See Fig. 6.*

NOTE: If accelerator pump adjustment is changed, then mechanical power valve must be readjusted.

HOLLEY 2280 2-BARREL (Cont.)

Fig. 6: Adjusting Accelerator Pump Stroke

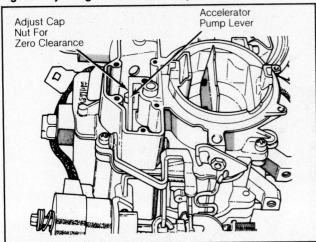

Adjust Cap Nut For Zero Clearance

Accelerator Pump Lever

If this adjustment is changed, mechanical power valve must be reset.

OVERHAUL

DISASSEMBLY

1) Position carburetor on a repair stand for disassembly to prevent damage to throttle valves. Remove air cleaner bolt and retainer. Remove accelerator pump link arm.

2) Remove bowl vent cover plate and bowl vent solenoid assembly. Remove choke vacuum diaphragm, linkage, and bracket. Remove electronic throttle control.

3) Remove nut and washer securing fast idle cam lever to choke shaft. Disconnect fast idle cam rod from lever and fast idle cam. Disconnect and remove accelerator operating link.

4) Remove 6 air horn screws. Lift air horn straight up from main body. Remove and discard air horn gasket. Remove bowl vent valve seal. Disconnect spring and lift valve lever, spring and pin out of air horn.

5) Remove accelerator pump operating shaft retaining clip. Pull shaft out straight. Remove accelerator pump arm and internal pump lever. Using a wrench, remove accelerator pump plunger cap nut. Remove accelerator pump plunger.

6) Gently pry up vacuum piston retaining ring tangs. Remove vacuum power valve piston. Remove mechanical power valve push rod and spring assembly by gently prying off plastic cap and removing clip.

7) Remove fuel inlet fitting and gasket. Discard gasket. Remove float hinge pin retainer, hinge pin, float baffle and float assembly. Using a screwdriver, remove main metering jets.

8) Using special tool (C-4231) remove vacuum power valve and mechanical power valve. Make sure blade of tool is squarely seated in slots of valves to avoid damage.

NOTE: **Do not interchange the mechanical and vacuum power valve assemblies. Mechanical power valve needle is about .050" longer than vacuum power valve needle. The vacuum power valve needle has an undercut**

groove just above the needle stop. Mechanical power valve is located on choke side of carburetor. **Do not mix up valve seats. Assemblies must be reinstalled in original locations, and must be kept with their respective needle and spring assembly.**

9) Remove venturi cluster screws. Lift cluster and gasket up and away from main body. Do not remove idle well tubes. Turn main body upside-down and catch accelerator pump weight and check ball.

10) Remove 4 throttle body screws. Separate throttle body from main body, and discard gasket. Remove clip securing fast idle cam, and slide cam off stub shaft.

11) Locate and center punch 1/4" from end of each mixture screw housing. Using a 3/16" drill through each screw housing at a 45° angle to housing. Pry plugs out using a small drift punch. Remove mixture screws and springs from throttle body.

CLEANING & INSPECTION

- Do not soak choke diaphragm or plastic parts in solvent.
- Rinse all metal parts with HOT water after using solvent. Blow dry with compressed air.
- Do not use wire, drill or any hard parts to clean passages and orifices in carburetor.
- Be sure gasket holes match up, and that all parts are clean and ready for installation.
- Test freedom of choke mechanism in air horn. Choke shaft must float freely to operate correctly. If movement is not free, thorough cleaning is required.

REASSEMBLY

Throttle Body

Install idle mixture screws and springs. Gently seat both mixture screws by hand. Now back out 1 full turn as a preliminary idle mixture adjustment.

Main Body

1) Install fast idle cam on stub shaft with steps facing fast idle speed screw. Install retaining clip.

2) Turn main body upside-down. Place throttle body gasket in position. Position throttle body on main body. Install 4 attaching screws, and tighten to 30 INCH lbs. (3 N.m).

3) Install accelerator pump discharge check ball and weight. Fill fuel bowl with clean fuel, and check ball and seat operation. Hold ball and weight down with a small brass rod. Place accelerator pump plunger in well, and operate by hand. If no resistance is felt, check ball is leaking.

4) Remove weight and leave check ball in place. Use a small drift punch, and lightly tap ball against seat to form a new seal. Remove old check ball and discard. Install a new ball and weight.

5) Perform fuel leak test again. If there is still no resistance felt, main body must be replaced. If resistance is felt, check ball is seating correctly.

6) Install new venturi cluster gaskets. Install venturi cluster in position in main body. Install screws and tighten securely.

7) Install main metering jets. Using the same tool as used during disassembly, install mechanical and vacuum power valves. Use care not to damage power

1983 Holley Carburetors

HOLLEY 2280 2-BARREL (Cont.)

Fig. 7: Exploded View of Holley Model 2280 2-Barrel Carburetor

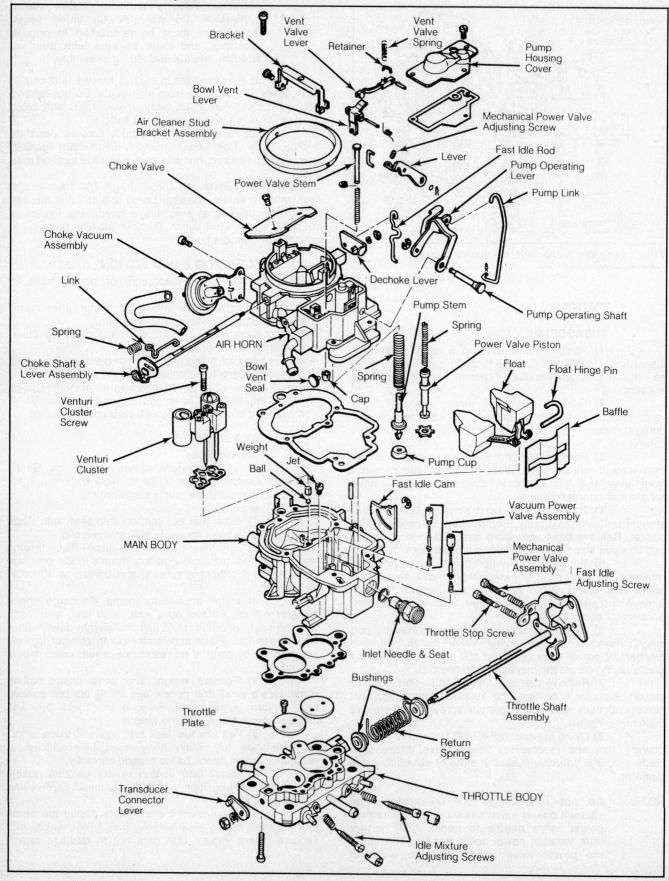

HOLLEY 2280 2-BARREL (Cont.)

valve needles. Ensure valves are installed in original locations as noted during disassembly.

8) Install hinge pin in float. Insert hinge pin through slot in float baffle. Tabs on baffle should point down. Place assembly in pin cradle in main body. Install hinge pin retainer.

9) Install fuel inlet fitting with new gasket. Perform float level adjustment.

Air Horn

1) Install vacuum power piston spring and piston. Install retaining ring over piston and carefully seat in place. Check piston operation for binding or sticking. If piston binds or sticks enough to prevent smooth operation, install new piston.

2) Install mechanical power valve push rod spring, rod and retaining clip. Install plastic cap on push rod.

3) Install accelerator pump assembly through air horn and install cap nut.

4) Install new air horn gasket. Carefully lower air horn into position on main body, guiding accelerator pump plunger into its cylinder. Use care not to damage accelerator pump plunger.

5) Install air horn screws. Starting from center and working out, tighten screws to 25 INCH lbs. (2.8 N.m).

6) With pump override spring retainer contacting air horn boss, adjust cap nut for a clearance of .310" (8 mm) between housing surface and cap nut. Install accelerator pump lever and operating shaft.

7) Connect plain end of fast idle cam connector rod to slot in fast idle cam from inside of cam. Engage other end of rod in choke lever. Place choke valve in wide open position. Align flats, and slide choke lever onto choke shaft. Install lock washer and tighten nut.

8) Connect choke vacuum break diaphragm rod to slot in choke lever. Install diaphragm assembly and tighten screws. Install electronic throttle control.

9) Install bowl vent assembly. Using a new gasket, fit bowl vent cover plate to air horn. Install accelerator pump lever, using a new cotter pin. Install air cleaner bolt and retainer.

CARBURETOR ADJUSTMENT SPECIFICATIONS

Application	Float Level	Accel. Pump	Choke Unloader	Choke Vac. Kick	Fast Idle Cam
R-9949-A	9/32"	Flush [1]	.200"	.140"	.052"
R-9951-A	9/32"	Flush [1]	.200"	.140"	.052"

[1] — Flush with top of bowl vent casting.

1983 Holley Carburetors

HOLLEY 4180-C 4-BARREL

CARBURETOR APPLICATION

FORD CARBURETOR NO.

Application	Man. Trans.	Auto. Trans.
7.5L V8		
Federal	E1TE-PC	E1TE-RC
Calif.	E1TE-TB	E1TE-SB

CARBURETOR IDENTIFICATION

Identification tag is attached to carburetor. Tag contains part number prefix and suffix. Basic part number for all carburetors is 9510. A design change code (if any) is stamped on the tag. An assembly date code (year, month and day) is also stamped on the tag. *See Fig. 1.*

Fig. 1: Ford Motor Co. Carburetor Identification Tag

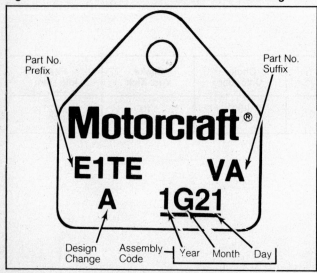

Identification tag is attached to carburetor.

DESCRIPTION

The Holley 4180-C 4-Barrel is a downdraft 2 stage carburetor. It can be considered as 2 separate carburetors: one supplying air/fuel mixture throughout entire range of engine operation (primary stage); the other functioning only when a greater supply of air/fuel is needed (secondary stage).

The primary stage (front section) of carburetor contains a fuel bowl, metering block, and accelerator pump assembly. The secondary (rear) section of carburetor contains a fuel bowl, metering body, and secondary throttle operating diaphragm assembly.

This model carburetor has a modulated power valve system. The system ensures power valve opening when manifold vacuum increases (during full acceleration) beyond the point where power valve would start to close. Vacuum will bleed off whenever throttle valve opening is 50° or more.

Vehicles over 8500 lbs. GVW use a decel throttle modulator which keeps throttle plates from closing on deceleration for improved emission control. All models use a hot air operated automatic choke system.

ADJUSTMENT

NOTE: For all on-vehicle adjustments, see TUNE-UP SERVICE PROCEDURES.

FLOAT LEVEL (DRY SETTING)

1) Remove float bowl. Hold upside-down. Float is adjusted correctly if top of float is parallel with float bowl. *See Fig. 2.*

Fig. 2: Float Level Adjustment (Dry Setting)

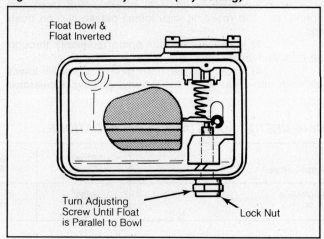

Float is adjusted correctly if top of float is parallel with float bowl when turned upside-down.

2) To adjust, loosen lock nut and turn adjusting screw until float is parallel.

ACCELERATOR PUMP LEVER

1) Place throttle valves in wide open position. Using a feeler gauge, measure specified clearance between the lever adjustment screw head and pump arm with the pump arm manually open. *See Fig. 3.*

Fig. 3: Accelerator Pump Lever Adjustment

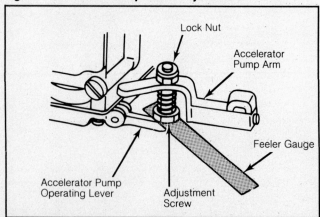

Each 1/2 turn of adjustment screw equals .015".

2) To adjust, loosen adjustment screw lock nut. Turn adjusting screw in to increase clearance and out to decrease clearance. Each 1/2 turn of adjustment screw equals .015". Tighten lock nut.

HOLLEY 4180-C 4-BARREL (Cont.)

ACCELERATOR PUMP STROKE

NOTE: Accelerator pump stroke has been preset at factory. Setting should not be changed. If original setting has been changed, adjust as follows:

1) Check that plastic accelerator pump cam is aligned with correct hole (top or bottom) in throttle lever. Plastic accelerator pump cam is located behind throttle lever.

2) If not aligned with correct hole, remove screw. Reposition in correct hole. Install and tighten screw.

SECONDARY THROTTLE VALVES

1) Hold secondary throttle valves closed. Turn secondary throttle valve stop screw out until secondary throttle valves seat in throttle bores.

2) Turn screw in until it just contacts secondary throttle valve lever. Then turn screw in an additional 1/4 turn.

CHOKE PULLDOWN

1) Remove choke thermostat housing, gasket and retainer. Insert a .026" wire gauge into choke piston bore. This moves choke piston down against stop screw. See Fig. 4.

Fig. 4: Choke Pulldown Adjustment

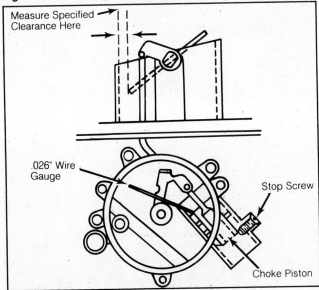

Use .026" wire gauge to hold choke piston down against stop screw.

2) Hold choke valve toward closed position. Measure specified choke pulldown clearance between lower edge of choke valve and air horn wall.

3) If adjustment is required, remove putty covering stop screw. Turn screw clockwise to decrease clearance and counterclockwise to increase clearance.

FAST IDLE CAM POSITION

1) Loosen choke thermostat housing screws. Rotate housing 45° counterclockwise (rich) to close choke valve. Tighten choke housing screws. See Fig. 5.

Fig. 5: Adjusting Fast Idle Cam Position

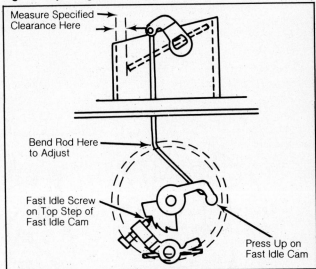

Fast idle speed screw must be on high step of fast idle cam for adjustment.

2) Open and then close throttle. This will position fast idle speed screw on top step of fast idle cam. Insert specified gauge between lower edge of choke valve and air horn wall. Open and close throttle to allow fast idle cam to drop.

3) Press up on fast idle cam. There should be little or no movement. This indicates that fast idle screw is on 2nd (kickdown) step of cam, against first step.

4) To adjust, bend choke control rod until fast idle screw is in correct position on fast idle cam. Readjust automatic choke to correct setting and tighten screws.

CHOKE UNLOADER

1) Hold throttle valves wide open. Apply light closing pressure on choke valve. See Fig. 6.

Fig. 6: Choke Unloader Adjustment

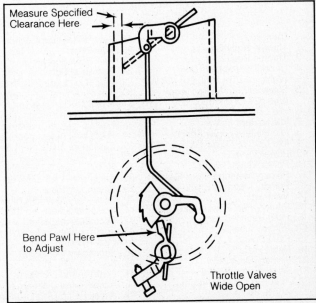

Throttle valves must be in wide open position.

1983 Holley Carburetors

HOLLEY 4180-C 4-BARREL (Cont.)

Fig. 7: Exploded View of Holley Model 4180-C 4-Barrel Carburetor

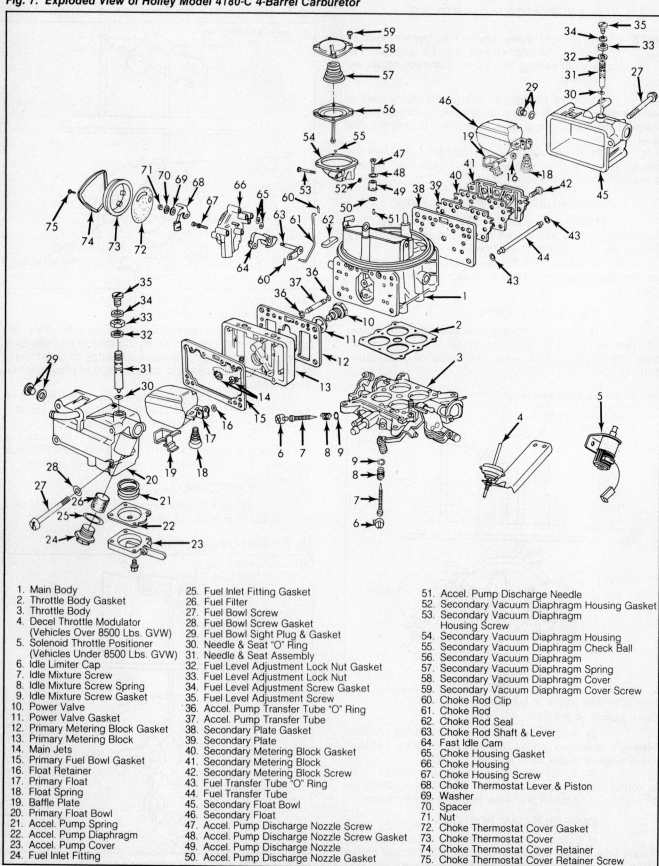

1. Main Body
2. Throttle Body Gasket
3. Throttle Body
4. Decel Throttle Modulator (Vehicles Over 8500 Lbs. GVW)
5. Solenoid Throttle Positioner (Vehicles Under 8500 Lbs. GVW)
6. Idle Limiter Cap
7. Idle Mixture Screw
8. Idle Mixture Screw Spring
9. Idle Mixture Screw Gasket
10. Power Valve
11. Power Valve Gasket
12. Primary Metering Block Gasket
13. Primary Metering Block
14. Main Jets
15. Primary Fuel Bowl Gasket
16. Float Retainer
17. Primary Float
18. Float Spring
19. Baffle Plate
20. Primary Float Bowl
21. Accel. Pump Spring
22. Accel. Pump Diaphragm
23. Accel. Pump Cover
24. Fuel Inlet Fitting

25. Fuel Inlet Fitting Gasket
26. Fuel Filter
27. Fuel Bowl Screw
28. Fuel Bowl Screw Gasket
29. Fuel Bowl Sight Plug & Gasket
30. Needle & Seat "O" Ring
31. Needle & Seat Assembly
32. Fuel Level Adjustment Lock Nut Gasket
33. Fuel Level Adjustment Lock Nut
34. Fuel Level Adjustment Screw Gasket
35. Fuel Level Adjustment Screw
36. Accel. Pump Transfer Tube "O" Ring
37. Accel. Pump Transfer Tube
38. Secondary Plate Gasket
39. Secondary Plate
40. Secondary Metering Block Gasket
41. Secondary Metering Block
42. Secondary Metering Block Screw
43. Fuel Transfer Tube "O" Ring
44. Fuel Transfer Tube
45. Secondary Float Bowl
46. Secondary Float
47. Accel. Pump Discharge Nozzle Screw
48. Accel. Pump Discharge Nozzle Screw Gasket
49. Accel. Pump Discharge Nozzle
50. Accel. Pump Discharge Nozzle Gasket

51. Accel. Pump Discharge Needle
52. Secondary Vacuum Diaphragm Housing Gasket
53. Secondary Vacuum Diaphragm Housing Screw
54. Secondary Vacuum Diaphragm Housing
55. Secondary Vacuum Diaphragm Check Ball
56. Secondary Vacuum Diaphragm
57. Secondary Vacuum Diaphragm Spring
58. Secondary Vacuum Diaphragm Cover
59. Secondary Vacuum Diaphragm Cover Screw
60. Choke Rod Clip
61. Choke Rod
62. Choke Rod Seal
63. Choke Rod Shaft & Lever
64. Fast Idle Cam
65. Choke Housing Gasket
66. Choke Housing
67. Choke Housing Screw
68. Choke Thermostat Lever & Piston
69. Washer
70. Spacer
71. Nut
72. Choke Thermostat Cover Gasket
73. Choke Thermostat Cover
74. Choke Thermostat Cover Retainer
75. Choke Thermostat Cover Retainer Screw

HOLLEY 4180-C 4-BARREL (Cont.)

2) Measure specified choke unloader clearance between lower edge of choke valve and air horn wall. To adjust, bend pawl on fast idle cam lever.

AUTOMATIC CHOKE

Loosen choke thermostat cover retaining screws. Rotate cover assembly in "Rich" or "Lean" direction to align reference mark on cover with specified scale graduation in housing. Tighten cover screws.

OVERHAUL

DISASSEMBLY

Primary Fuel Bowl & Metering Block

1) Remove primary fuel bowl and gasket. Remove metering block and gasket. Discard gaskets.

2) Remove pump transfer tube and "O" rings from main body if it was not removed with metering block. Remove fuel line tube and "O" rings. Discard "O" rings.

3) Using a jet wrench, remove main jets from metering block. Using a socket wrench, remove power valve and gasket.

4) Remove fuel level adjustment screw and gasket. Turn lock nut counterclockwise and remove nut and gasket. Remove fuel inlet needle and seat assembly. Do not disassemble needle and seat, they are replaced as an assembly.

5) Using needle nose pliers, remove float shaft retainer clip. Slide float off shaft and remove spring from float. Remove baffle plate from fuel bowl. Remove fuel level sight plug and gasket.

6) Remove fuel inlet fitting, gasket and filter. Invert fuel bowl and remove accelerator pump cover, diaphragm and spring. Do not remove accelerator pump inlet check ball. Check ball is not serviced separately.

Secondary Fuel Bowl & Metering Block

Remove fuel bowl. Using a clutch type screwdriver, remove metering block screws. Remove metering block, plate and gaskets. Discard gaskets. Disassemble fuel bowl by following steps 4) and 5) in Primary Fuel Bowl and Metering Block.

Main Body

1) Remove air cleaner stud. Remove secondary diaphragm link retainer. Invert carburetor and remove throttle body retaining screws and lock washers. Lift off throttle body and discard throttle body gasket.

2) Remove choke rod cotter pin from choke housing shaft and lever assembly. Remove choke cover,

thermostatic spring and gasket. Remove choke main housing and gaskets from main body.

3) Remove choke housing shaft nut, lock washer and spacer. Remove shaft and fast idle cam. Remove choke piston and lever assembly.

4) If it is necessary to remove choke valve and shaft, tips of choke valve screws may have to be filed because they are staked into shaft. After removing screws, remove valve and slide out choke shaft.

5) Remove secondary diaphragm housing and gasket. Secondary diaphragm housing must be removed before attempting to remove cover. Remove diaphragm housing cover, spring diaphragm and vacuum check ball.

6) Remove accelerator pump discharge nozzle screw. Lift off discharge nozzle and gaskets. Invert main body and catch accelerator pump discharge needle as it falls out of bore in main body.

Throttle Body

Components of throttle body are matched to meet emission control standards. Manufacturer does not recommend disassembly of throttle body.

CLEANING & INSPECTION

- Use a regular carburetor cleaning solution. Soak components long enough to thoroughly clean all surfaces and passages of foreign matter.
- Do not soak any components containing rubber, leather or plastic.
- Do not use wire, drill or any hard parts to clean passages and orifices in carburetor.
- Remove any residue after cleaning by rinsing components in suitable solvent.
- Blow out all passages with dry compressed air.

REASSEMBLY

Use new gaskets and seals. Make sure that new gaskets fit correctly and that all holes and slots are punched through and correctly located. To reassemble carburetor, reverse disassembly procedure and note the following:

1) Apply petroleum jelly to all "O" rings before installation.

2) Make sure projection on the choke rod is positioned under the fast idle cam. This will ensure that fast idle cam will be raised up when the choke valve closes.

3) It will be necessary to install the secondary diaphragm housing cover and all 4 screws before diaphragm housing is installed onto main body.

CARBURETOR ADJUSTMENT SPECIFICATIONS

Application	Accelerator Pump		Choke Pulldown Setting	Fast Idle Cam Setting	Choke Unloader Setting	Auto. Choke Setting
	Lever (Clearance)	Stroke (Hole No.)				
E1UE-PC, RC, SB & TB	.015"	#1	.210-.230"	.....	.300-330"	3 Rich

1983 Motorcraft Carburetors
MOTORCRAFT 2150 2-BARREL

CARBURETOR APPLICATION

FORD (MOTORCRAFT) CARBURETOR NO.

Application	Man. Trans.	Auto. Trans.
2.8L V6		
Federal	E37E-ABA	E37E-AAA
California	E37E-ADA	E37E-ADA
3.8L V6		
Federal	E3TE-BCA	E3TE-BBA
	E3TE-BFA	E3TE-BGA
5.0L V8		
Federal	E3TE-AUA	E3TE-AVA
		E3TE-AYA
		E3TE-BSA
California		E3TE-BJA
		E3TE-BLA
		E3TE-BPA
High Altitude	E3TE-BHA	E3TE-BEA
	E3TE-BMA	E3TE-BMA
		E3TE-BTA
5.8L V8		
Federal		E2UE-FA
		E3UE-CA
California		E2UE-KA
		E3UE-BA

JEEP CARBURETOR NO.

Application	Man. Trans.	Auto. Trans.
4.2L 6-Cylinder		
Nationwide	1RHM2	1RHA2
High Altitude	1RHM2	2RHA2

CARBURETOR IDENTIFICATION
Ford

A carburetor identification tag is attached to carburetor. The tag contains part number prefix and suffix. Basic part number for all carburetors is 9510.

A design change code (if any) is also stamped on the tag. An assembly date code (year, month and day) is also stamped on the tag. See Fig. 1.

Fig. 1: Ford Carburetor Identification Tag

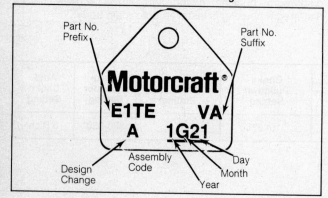

Jeep
A carburetor identification tag is attached to carburetor. The tag contains the Jeep carburetor list

number. An assembly date code (year, month and day) is also stamped on the tag. See Fig. 2.

Fig. 2: Jeep Carburetor Identification Tag

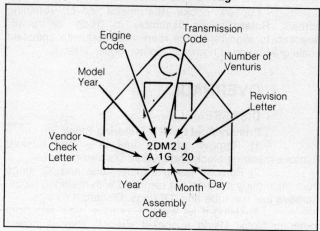

DESCRIPTION

The Motorcraft 2150 carburetor has 2 main assemblies: the air horn and main body.

The air horn contains choke plate, fuel bowl vent, and hot idle compensator. The main body houses throttle plate, accelerator pump assembly, float assembly, power valve, fuel bowl and duty cycle solenoid on feedback models.

Each bore contains main and boost venturis, main fuel discharge, accelerator pump discharge, idle fuel discharge and throttle plate.

On some applications, booster venturis contain variable high speed bleed control system. This system allows control of air/fuel mixture for improved high speed operation and low speed responses. Feedback models use a duty cycle solenoid to control air/fuel mixture. The duty cycle solenoid is operated by an Electronic Control Assembly.

Vehicles sold for high altitude use (above 4000 ft. or 1219 m) contain an altitude compensator. This circuit compensates for thinner air by metering an additional amount of air into the air/fuel mixture, preventing an over-rich situation. An aneroid (automatic device) reacts to atmospheric pressure and overrides the compensation feature at lower altitudes.

ADJUSTMENT

NOTE: **For all on-vehicle adjustments, see TUNE-UP SERVICE PROCEDURES.**

         FLOAT LEVEL (DRY SETTING)

NOTE: **Dry float setting is a preliminary adjustment only. Final adjustment (wet setting) must be made after carburetor is installed on vehicle.**

Remove float bowl. Hold upside-down. Float is adjusted correctly if top of float is specified distance from top of float bowl. See Fig. 3.

MOTORCRAFT 2150 2-BARREL (Cont.)

Fig. 3: Float Level Adjustment (Dry Setting)

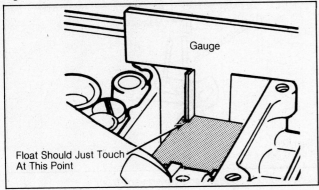

This is a preliminary setting; final adjustment must be made with carburetor installed on engine.

ACCELERATOR PUMP STROKE

NOTE: **Accelerator pump stroke has been preset at factory. Setting should not be changed. If original setting has been changed, adjust as follows.**

Support accelerator pump cover and drive out pump lever roll pin. Rotate pump lever and rod until key on rod lines up with keyway on over-travel lever. Remove rod and reposition in proper hole of over-travel lever. Reinstall pump lever and roll pin. *See Fig. 4.*

Fig. 4: Accelerator Pump Stroke Adjustment

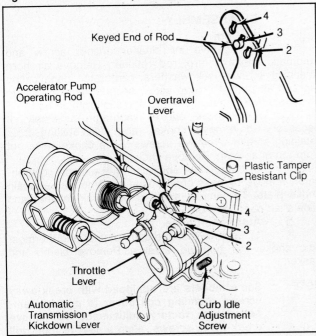

Ensure connecting rod is installed in correct hole of overtravel lever.

CHOKE PULL-DOWN

NOTE: **Most applications have a tamper-proof choke, incorporating a sealed pull-down motor and break-away choke cap screws. Adjustments given are used when a major**

overhaul is performed or if components are damaged.

1) Loosen choke cover retainers. Open throttle and rotate choke cover until choke valve is held closed. Tighten choke cover.

2) Using an external vacuum source, apply vacuum to hold choke diaphragm against set screw. Do not apply pressure to linkage.

NOTE: **If vacuum is applied to choke diaphragm with a hand vacuum pump, an air leak may be detected. This is normal.**

3) Using a specified drill or pin gauge, measure clearance between lower edge of choke valve and air horn.

4) If adjustment is required, file a 1/8" (3 mm) deep recessed groove 1/4" (6 mm) behind edge of adjusting screw end of diaphragm.

5) Using an awl angled toward plug, drive plug out. Turn adjusting screw until specified clearance is obtained. *See Fig. 5.*

Fig. 5: Adjusting Choke Pull-Down Clearance

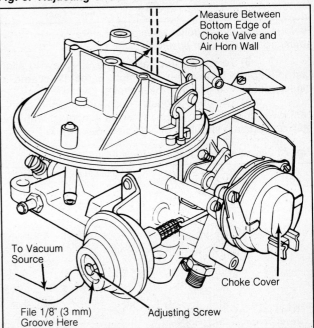

If adjustment is changed, fast idle cam position must be checked.

6) After adjustment, reinstall plug and seal with epoxy. If adjustment was changed, check fast idle cam position.

FAST IDLE CAM POSITION

NOTE: **Check choke vacuum pull-down adjustment before adjusting fast idle cam position.**

1) Perform steps **1)** and **2)** of Choke Pull-Down adjustment.

2) On Ford models, open and close throttle. Fast idle cam should drop to 2nd (kickdown) step. Fast idle screw should be opposite "V" notch on cam. *See Fig. 6.*

NOTE: On models equipped with an idle speed control motor, the fast idle screw does not actually touch fast idle cam. However, the screw should still line up with the "V" notch on the cam.

Fig. 6: Ford Fast Idle Cam Position Adjustment

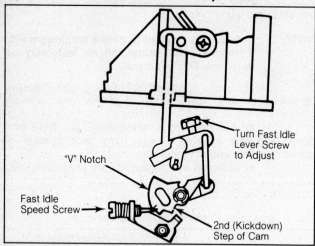

Perform vacuum pull-down adjustment before adjusting fast idle cam position.

3) To adjust, turn fast idle lever screw to align fast idle speed screw with "V" notch. Screw is located in plastic fast idle cam lever. Reset choke.

4) On Jeep models, push down on fast idle cam lever until fast idle speed screw is in contact with 2nd step and against shoulder of high step. *See Fig. 7.*

Fig. 7: Jeep Fast Idle Cam Position Adjustment

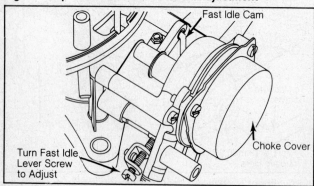

Perform vacuum pull-down adjustment before adjusting fast idle cam position.

5) To adjust, turn fast idle lever screw. Reset choke to proper adjustment notch.

CHOKE UNLOADER

1) Hold throttle fully open, and lightly press choke valve toward closed position. Using a specified drill or pin gauge, measure specified choke unloader clearance between lower edge of choke valve and air horn wall.

2) To adjust, bend choke unloader tang that contacts fast idle cam. Bend tang toward cam to increase clearance and away from cam to decrease clearance. Do not bend unloader tang downward from a horizontal plane. *See Fig. 8.*

Fig. 8: Choke Unloader Adjustment

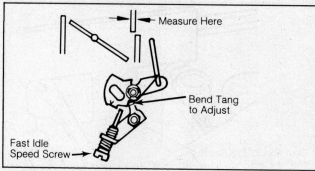

Do not bend unloader tang downward from a horizontal plane.

3) After correct adjustment is obtained on Jeep models, open throttle until unloader tang is directly under fast idle cam pivot. Make sure there is .070" (1.78 mm) clearance, between unloader tang and fast idle cam.

4) On all models, operate throttle after adjustment. Make sure that tang does not stick or bind against any portion of the linkage or carburetor casting.

AUTOMATIC CHOKE

Loosen choke thermostat cover retaining screws. Rotate cover assembly in "Rich" or "Lean" direction to align reference marks. Tighten cover screws.

OVERHAUL

DISASSEMBLY

Air Horn

1) Remove air cleaner anchor screw and automatic choke control rod retainer. Remove air horn attaching screws, lock washers, carburetor identification tag and air horn. Remove screw securing choke lever to choke shaft. Remove choke rod and seal from air horn.

2) Remove choke diaphragm assembly. If necessary to remove choke valve, file staking from retaining screws. Remove screws. Slide choke valve out from top of air horn. Remove choke shaft.

3) On models equipped with altitude compensator, remove by-pass choke plate in same way as main choke plate. To remove shaft, remove link retainer and slide shaft out of air horn.

Automatic Choke

1) Remove fast idle cam retainer and thermostatic choke coil housing screws. Remove clamp and gasket.

NOTE: **Some models are equipped with break-away screws retaining coil cover to prevent tampering with factory adjustment. To remove break-away screws, align a 1/4" (6 mm) drill on head, and drill only enough to remove head. Using an 1/8" (3 mm) punch, drive remaining portion of screw from housing. Repeat for remaining break-away screws.**

2) Remove choke housing screws, choke housing, gasket and fast idle cam rod from cam lever. Remove choke lever retaining screw and washer. Remove choke lever and fast idle cam lever.

MOTORCRAFT 2150 2-BARREL (Cont.)

Fig. 9: Exploded View of Motorcraft Model 2150 2-Barrel Carburetor

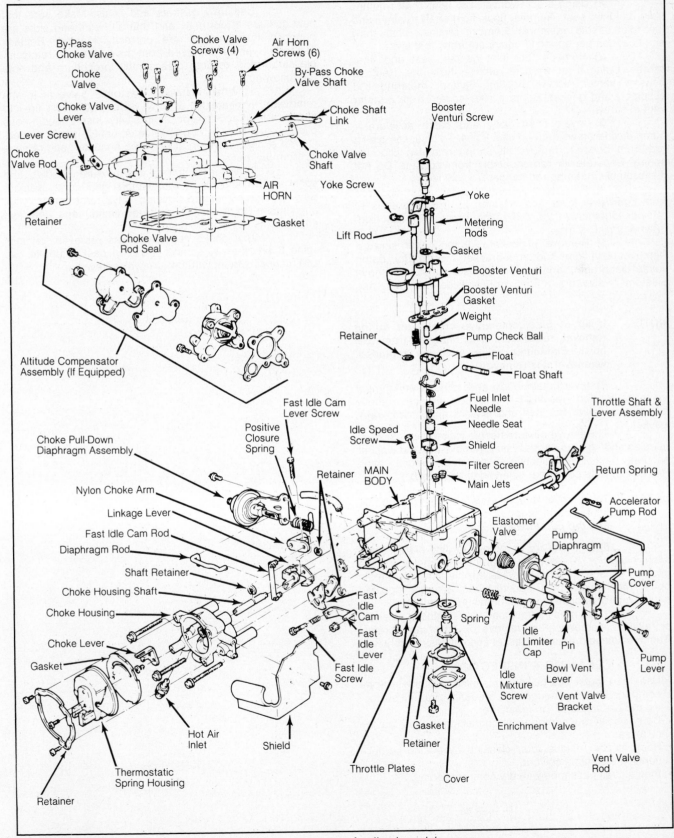

Duty cycle solenoid is used in place of altitude compensator on feedback models.

MOTORCRAFT 2150 2-BARREL (Cont.)

Main Body

1) Using a screwdriver, pry float shaft retainer from fuel inlet seat. Remove float, float shaft retainer and fuel inlet needle assembly. Remove retainer, float shaft and float damper spring (if equipped) from float lever.

2) Remove fuel inlet needle, seat and filter screen. Using a jet wrench, remove main jets. Remove booster venturi screw, booster venturi, metering rod assembly and gasket. Remove filter screen from booster venturi screw.

3) Invert main body and catch accelerator pump discharge weight and check ball. To disassemble lift rod from booster, remove lift spring retaining clip and spring. Separate lift rod assembly from booster. Do not disassemble metering rod hanger from lift rod.

4) Remove accelerator pump operating rod from overtravel lever and retainer, by pressing ends of retainer together. At the same time, press rod away from retainer until it is free.

5) Remove accelerator pump cover screws. Remove bowl vent rod and bracket, accelerator pump cover diaphragm, and spring. If necessary to remove Elastomer valve, grasp firmly from outside main body and pull out.

NOTE: If tip of Elastomer valve breaks off during removal, make sure it is removed from fuel bowl. Elastomer valve must be replaced, whenever it is removed.

6) Invert main body and remove enrichment valve cover and gasket. Using a box wrench, remove enrichment valve. Remove and discard enrichment valve gasket.

7) Remove mixture needle limiter caps, mixture needles and springs. If necessary, remove nut and washer securing fast idle adjusting lever, and remove lever. Remove throttle positioner solenoid (if equipped).

NOTE: To remove tamper-resistant mixture needle limiter caps, support area under limiter plug and tap cap forward.

8) If necessary to remove throttle plates, mark each plate for reassembly reference. Remove throttle position sensor if equipped. Slide throttle shaft from main body. Mechanical high speed bleed actuator (located between throttle plates in main body) will drop out.

9) On models equipped with feedback solenoid or altitude compensator, remove 3 attaching screws. Remove solenoid/aneroid, gasket and valve assembly.

CLEANING & INSPECTION

- Use a regular carburetor cleaning solution. Soak components long enough to thoroughly clean all surfaces and passages of foreign matter.
- Do not soak any components containing rubber, leather or plastic.
- Remove any residue after cleaning by rinsing components in a suitable solvent.
- Blow out all passages with dry compressed air.

REASSEMBLY

Use new gaskets and seals. Make sure that new gaskets fit correctly and that all holes and slots are punched through and are correctly located. Replace Elastomer valve if removed from main body. To reassemble carburetor, reverse disassembly procedure and note the following:

1) When installing Elastomer valve (if it was removed), lubricate tip of new valve, and insert tip into center hole of accelerator pump cavity. Insert needle nose pliers in fuel bowl, and pull valve in, until it is fully seated. Cut off excess valve tip at retaining shoulder, and remove tip from fuel bowl.

2) When installing idle mixture needles and springs, turn screws in with fingers until lightly seated. Back screws off seated position 1 1/2 turns for an initial adjustment. Do not install idle screw limiter caps, until final adjustments have been made.

3) If choke coil cover was removed, reinstall using 3 break-away screws. Position gasket, choke cap and retainer. Mount with break-away screws.

1983 Motorcraft Carburetors

MOTORCRAFT 2150 2-BARREL (Cont.)

CARBURETOR ADJUSTMENT SPECIFICATIONS

Application	Float Level (Dry Setting)	Accel. Pump	Choke Pull-Down	Fast Idle Cam	Choke Unloader	Auto. Choke	Bowl Vent Valve [1]
Ford							
E2UE-FA	31/64"	#3	.120"	V-Notch	.200"	V-Notch	3/8"
E2UE-KA	31/64"	#2	.120"	V-Notch	.200"	V-Notch	3/8"
E3TE-AUA	7/16"	#3	.142"	V-Notch	.200"	V-Notch	3/8"
E3TE-AVA	7/16"	#3	.149"	V-Notch	.250"	V-Notch	3/8"
E3TE-AYA	7/16"	#4	.137"	V-Notch	.250"	V-Notch	3/8"
E3TE-BBA	7/16"	#3	.125"	V-Notch	.250"	V-Notch	3/8"
E3TE-BCA	7/16"	#3	.125"	V-Notch	.250"	V-Notch	3/8"
E3TE-BEA	7/16"	#3	.149"	V-Notch	.200"	V-Notch	3/8"
E3TE-BFA	7/16"	#3	.125"	V-Notch	.250"	V-Notch	3/8"
E3TE-BGA	7/16"	#3	.125"	V-Notch	.250"	V-Notch	3/8"
E3TE-BHA	7/16"	#3	.152"	V-Notch	.200"	V-Notch	3/8"
E3TE-BJA	7/16"	#4	.157"	V-Notch	.200"	V-Notch	3/8"
E3TE-BLA	7/16"	#3	.157"	V-Notch	.200"	V-Notch	3/8"
E3TE-BMA	7/16"	#4	.150"	V-Notch	.200"	V-Notch	3/8"
E3TE-BPA	7/16"	#3	.157"	V-Notch	.200"	V-Notch	3/8"
E3TE-BSA	7/16"	#4	.137"	V-Notch	.250"	V-Notch	3/8"
E3TE-BTA	7/16"	#4	.150"	V-Notch	.200"	V-Notch	3/8"
E3UE-BA	31/64"	#2	.120"	V-Notch	.200"	V-Notch	3/8"
E3UE-CA	31/64"	#3	.120"	V-Notch	.200"	V-Notch	3/8"
E37E-AAA	7/16"	#4	.136"	V-Notch	.250"	V-Notch	3/8"
E37E-ABA	7/16"	#4	.136"	V-Notch	.250"	V-Notch	3/8"
E37E-ADA	7/16"	#4	.136"	V-Notch	.250"	V-Notch	3/8"
Jeep							
1RHA2	21/64"	#3	.113"	.086"	.350"	2 Rich	.120"
1RHM2	21/64"	#3	.104"	.081"	.348"	2 Rich	.120"
2RHA2	21/64"	#3	.116"	.076"	.420"	1 Rich	.120"

[1] — Size of fuel bowl vent tube.

1983 Motorcraft Carburetors

MOTORCRAFT 7200 VV 2-BARREL

CARBURETOR APPLICATION

FORD CARBURETOR NO.

Application	Man. Trans.	Auto. Trans.
5.8L V8	E2TE-CDB	E2TE-CCB
	E2TE-CDD	E2TE-CCC

CARBURETOR IDENTIFICATION

Carburetor part number identification is stamped on left side of the upper throttle body. Stamped number also contains part number prefix and suffix. Basic part number for all carburetors is 9510. A design change code (if any) is included on the stamped number. An assembly date code (year, month and day) is also included on the stamped number. *See Fig. 1.*

Fig. 1: Ford Motor Co. Carburetor Identification Stamp

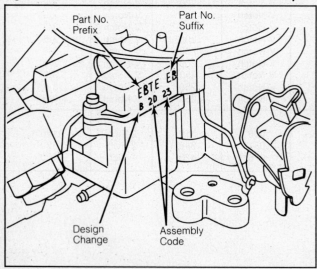

Identification is stamped on left side of the upper throttle body.

DESCRIPTION

Motorcraft model 7200 variable venturi carburetor differs from other standard type carburetors. It has the ability to change the area of the venturi for varying engine speed and load conditions.

This is accomplished by dual venturi valves, controlled by engine vacuum and throttle position. Depending upon engine speed and load conditions, the position of the venturi valves change (move in and out of the air stream) to determine the air flow to the 2 carburetor throats.

The venturi valves are connected to 2 tapered main metering rods, which ride in the main metering jets. When the venturi valve position changes, the metering rods vary the amount of fuel flow through the carburetor.

Systems on the 7200 carburetor include: fuel inlet, main metering, control vacuum, cold enrichment, accelerator pump system and an all-electric dual-stage choke.

The 7200 carburetor is equipped with a feedback control system. This system works in conjunction with an on-board electronic control module. The air bleed feedback system uses a stepper motor to regulate bleed air admitted into main metering system. This provides a more precise metering of the air/fuel ratio, as dictated by the module through a series of sensors.

ADJUSTMENT

NOTE: For all on-vehicle adjustments, see TUNE-UP SERVICE PROCEDURES.

FLOAT LEVEL

1) Remove upper body assembly. Remove and discard upper body gasket. Construct a gauge to specified float level setting.

2) Turn upper body assembly upside-down. Using gauge, measure distance from cast surface of upper body to bottom of float. *See Fig. 2.*

Fig. 2: Float Level Adjustment

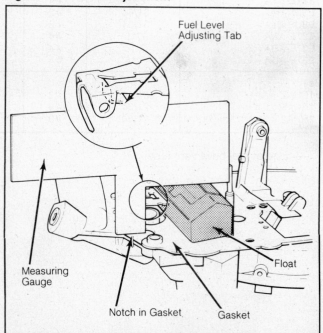

Construct a gauge to specified float level setting.

3) To adjust, bend adjusting tab on float arm. Bend away from inlet needle to decrease setting and toward inlet needle to increase setting.

FLOAT DROP

1) With upper body and gasket removed, hold upper body in upright position and allow float to hang. *See Fig. 3.*

2) Construct a gauge to specified float drop setting. Using gauge, measure distance from cast surface of upper body to bottom of float. *See Fig. 3.*

3) To adjust, bend float lever stop tab on float arm. Bend away from hinge pin to increase setting and toward hinge pin to decrease setting.

MOTORCRAFT 7200 VV 2-BARREL (Cont.)

Fig. 3: Float Drop Adjustment

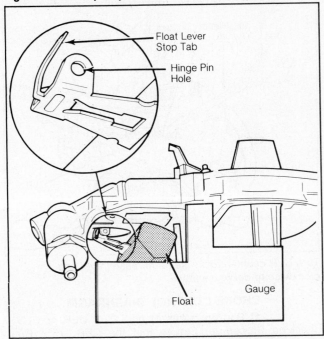

Place gauge against cast surface, not gasket surface.

ACCELERATOR PUMP LEVER LASH

1) Make sure curb idle speed is correctly adjusted. Using a feeler gauge, measure clearance between accelerator pump stem and pump operating link. *See Fig. 4.*

Fig. 4: Accelerator Pump Lever Lash Adjustment

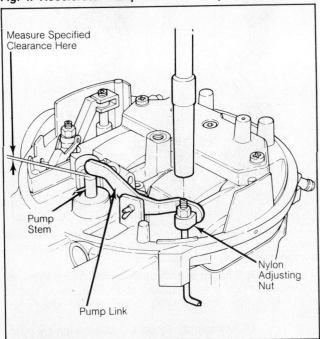

This adjustment must be checked whenever curb idle speed is adjusted.

2) If clearance is not to specification, tighten or loosen nut on end of link to obtain specified clearance.

COLD ENRICHMENT METERING ROD (CER) & CONTROL VACUUM REGULATOR (CVR)

Checking Procedure

1) Perform steps **1)** and **2)** of Automatic Choke adjustment procedure. Position dial indicator on carburetor, with indicator stem on top surface of enrichment rod.

2) Install choke weight (T77L-9848-A7 or equivalent) on choke bimetal lever. With cold enrichment metering rod (CER) seated, install dial indicator with tip on CER top surface. Zero dial indicator. *See Fig. 5.*

Fig. 5: Cold Enrichment Metering Rod (CER) Adjustment

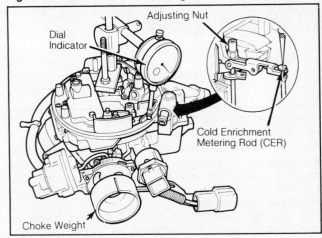

This is the initial set-up procedure.

3) Free fast idle cam from fast idle lever interference. Install stator cap. Rotate cap to index position. Dial indicator reading should be within the CER "75°F Run" specification. *See Fig. 6.*

Fig. 6: Cold Enrichment Metering Rod (CER) "75°F Run" Adjustment

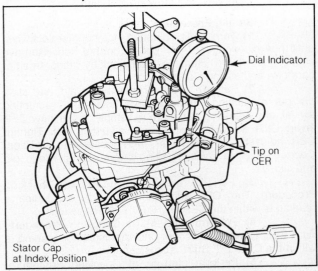

Stator cap mounted and rotated to index position.

4) Do not remove or zero dial indicator. Remove stator cap. Rotate thermostat lever clockwise, until CER travel stop screw is bottomed on upper body. Dial indicator reading should be within the CER "0°F Start" specification. *See Fig. 7.*

1983 Motorcraft Carburetors

MOTORCRAFT 7200 VV 2-BARREL (Cont.)

Fig. 7: Cold Enrichment Metering Rod (CER) "0°F Start" Adjustment

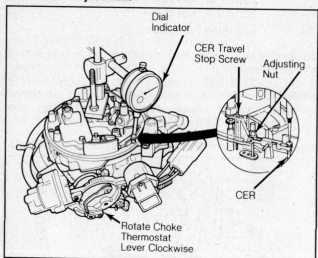

Choke thermostat lever rotated clockwise to bottom CER travel stop screw on upper body.

5) Do not remove or zero dial indicator. Using the stator cap as a weight, push down on control vacuum regulator rod (CVR) until it bottoms against seat. Dial indicator reading should be within the "Control Vacuum Regulator" specification.

6) If any 1 of these 3 settings is out of specification, reset to specifications following Setting Procedure.

NOTE: Adjusting nuts are filled with epoxy sealer after final adjustment is made by manufacturer. To adjust, new parts must be installed. Also, choke control rod has undercut groove designed to break at 10 INCH. lbs. (1 N.m) torque. If rod breaks during setting procedure, new rod must be installed.

Setting Procedure

1) Turn CER adjusting nut counterclockwise, until nut disengages from choke control rod. Remove choke control rod. Remove dust seal by lifting retainer carefully, and sliding seal out.

2) Remove clip on choke hinge pin, and slide pin out of casting. Remove CER lever, CVR adjusting swivel, and adjusting nut as an assembly. Install new CER lever, CVR adjusting swivel, and adjusting nut. Tighten CER adjusting nut to lower, and locate into position. Connect lever to CVR adjusting swivel. Install hinge pin and clip.

3) Perform steps **2)** and **3)** of Checking Procedure. Turn CER adjustment nut until dial indicator reading is within the CER "75°F Run" specification.

4) Perform step **4)** of Checking Procedure. Turn CER travel stop screw, until dial indicator reading is within the CER "0°F Start" specification.

5) Perform step **5)** of Checking Procedure. Hold CVR nut with a 3/8" wrench. Using a 3/32" Allen wrench, turn CVR counterclockwise to increase travel and clockwise to decrease travel. *See Fig. 8.*

6) Apply epoxy to nuts and stop screw. Replace choke cap following steps **3)** and **4)** of Automatic Choke adjustment procedure.

Fig. 8: Control Vacuum Regulator (CVR) Adjustment

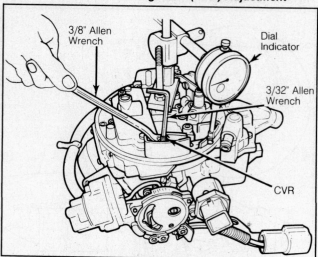

Turn CVR counterclockwise to increase travel and clockwise to decrease travel.

CHOKE CONTROL DIAPHRAGM

1) Perform steps **1)** and **2)** of CER and CVR Checking Procedure. Ensure that the CER "75°F Run" adjustment is set to specification.

2) Remove diaphragm cover. Using finger pressure, seat diaphragm. Dial indicator reading should be within the CER "75°F Run" specification. *See Fig. 9.*

Fig. 9: Choke Control Diaphragm Adjustment at CER "75°F Start" Position

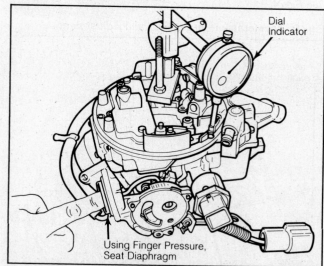

Ensure CER "75°F Run" adjustment is set to specification prior to performing this adjustment.

3) If not to specification, rotate diaphragm until dial indicator reads within specification. Turn diaphragm to align diaphragm and casting holes. Install diaphragm cover.

4) Depress choke control diaphragm by pushing in diaphragm rod until diaphragm bottoms out. Rotate thermostat lever clockwise, until choke shaft lever pin touches fast idle intermediate lever. Dial indicator reading should be within the CER "0°F Run" specification. *See Fig. 10.*

MOTORCRAFT 7200 VV 2-BARREL (Cont.)

Fig. 10: Choke Control Diaphragm Adjustment at CER "0°F Run" Position

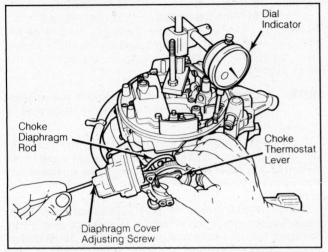

Hold thermostat lever in position so choke shaft lever pin is touching fast idle intermediate lever.

5) If dial indicator reading is not to specification, remove lead ball covering choke control diaphragm cover adjusting screw. Turn adjusting screw clockwise to increase height and counterclockwise to decrease height. Install a new lead ball over adjusting screw.

NOTE: **If lead ball is not removable, install a new, unplugged cover.**

6) After adjustment, install lead ball. Using steps 3) and 4) of Automatic Choke adjustment, install diaphragm cover and choke cap assembly.

FAST IDLE CAM POSITION

Standard Procedure

1) Before making adjustment, perform steps 1) and 2) of Automatic Choke adjustment procedure. Position fast idle lever in corner of specified step of fast idle cam. Highest step is considered 1st step. Hold throttle lightly closed with a rubber band to secure fast idle cam in position. *See Fig. 11.*

Fig. 11: Fast Idle Cam Position Adjustment (Standard Procedure)

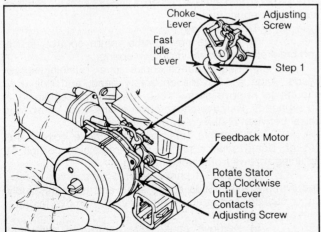

Highest step is considered 1st step.

2) Install stator cap T77L-9848-A (or equivalent) in place of choke cover. Rotate stator cap clockwise, until fast idle speed screw contacts lever. Choke cap should be on specified notch.

3) Remove sealer from fast idle cam adjusting screw. Adjust fast idle cam adjusting screw, until index mark on stator cap aligns with specified notch on choke housing. Remove stator cap and install choke cover.

4) Adjust choke cover to specified setting. When adjustment is completed, perform steps 3) and 4) of Automatic Choke adjustment procedure to complete this adjustment.

Alternate Procedure

1) Perform steps 1) and 2) of CER and CVR Checking Procedure. Ensure that the CER "75°F Run" adjustment is set to specification.

2) Hold throttle slightly open to allow free linkage movement. Position fast idle cam lever on specified step of fast idle cam. Rotate choke bimetal lever, until choke shaft lever contacts fast idle cam screw.

3) Dial indicator reading should be as specified. To adjust, turn adjusting screw clockwise to increase reading and counterclockwise to decrease reading.

NOTE: **Turning adjusting screw in clockwise direction turns cam in counterclockwise direction.**

4) When adjustment is completed, perform steps 3) and 4) of Automatic Choke adjustment procedure to complete this adjustment.

AUTOMATIC CHOKE

1) Center punch choke cover retaining screw heads. Align a 1/4" drill on screw head, and drill only enough to remove screw head. Repeat for remaining 2 screw heads. Remove choke cover by inserting sharp, flat chisel between choke cover gasket layers.

2) Using small pliers, remove remaining portion of retaining screws from choke housing. Carefully clean epoxy and gasket from choke cover and housing using gasket scraper. Remove choke cover carefully. Choke cover and gasket are sealed to housing with epoxy sealer.

3) Apply 1/2" bead of epoxy sealer to each side of choke cover gasket, adjacent to the 3 screw bosses. Install gasket and choke cover using new break-away screws.

4) Rotate cover assembly in "Rich" or "Lean" direction to align reference mark on choke cover with specified scale graduation on housing. Tighten each break-away screw until head of screw breaks off. Ensure that bimetal spring tab is engaged in slotted choke shaft lever.

VENTURI VALVE WIDE OPEN THROTTLE (WOT) OPENING

1) Center punch expansion plug covering venturi valve (WOT) stop adjustment screw. Center punch until loose. Plug is located at rear of main body on throttle side of carburetor.

2) Using a 5/32" Allen wrench, remove adjustment screw. Hold throttle valves wide open. Apply light closing pressure on venturi valve.

3) Measure venturi valve closing gap clearance between venturi valve and air horn wall. Using a 5/64" Allen wrench, turn venturi valve limiter adjustment screw on venturi valve arm to set closing gap clearance.

1983 Motorcraft Carburetors

MOTORCRAFT 7200 VV 2-BARREL (Cont.)

4) Using a 5/32" Allen wrench, install adjustment screw and spring. Recheck specified clearance.

5) Hold throttle plates wide open. Apply light closing pressure on venturi valve. Measure maximum opening clearance, between venturi valve and venturi opening wall.

6) Using a 3/32" Allen wrench, turn throttle (WOT) stop adjustment screw until maximum opening clearance is within specification.

7) Install a new expansion plug in access hole.

Fig. 12: Venturi Valve Wide Open Throttle (WOT) Opening Adjustment

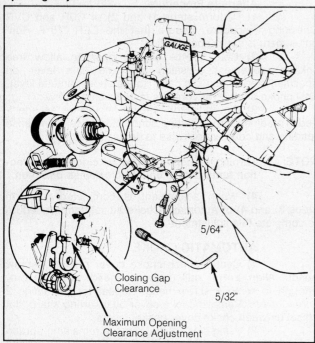

Use a 5/64" Allen wrench to adjust closing gap clearance and a 3/32" Allen wrench to adjust maximum opening clearance.

OVERHAUL

DISASSEMBLY

Upper Body

1) Mount carburetor in a holding fixture. Remove fuel inlet fitting, filter, gasket and spring. Remove clips from accelerator pump and choke control rods. Disconnect rods.

2) Remove air cleaner stud. Remove 7 screws and upper body. Note position of long screw for reassembly reference. Place upper body upside-down on a clean surface. Remove float hinge pin and float assembly. Remove upper body gasket.

3) Remove fuel inlet valve, seat and gasket. Remove accelerator pump link and nut, accelerator pump adjusting nut, and pump link. Remove accelerator pump overtravel spring, clip, and washer. Remove pump rod and dust seal.

4) Remove cold enrichment rod (CER) adjusting nut by turning counterclockwise. Adjusting nuts are filled with epoxy sealer after final adjustment is made by manufacturer. Sealer may cause breakage of choke

control rod. Undercut design of choke control rod allows it to break at 10 INCH lbs. (1 N.m). If breakage occurs, new assembly must be installed.

5) Remove choke control rod. Carefully lift retainer, and slide out dust seal. Remove choke hinge pin clip, and slide pin out. Remove cold enrichment rod nut, lever, swivel, control vacuum regulator, and adjusting nut as an assembly.

NOTE: **Disassembly of cold enrichment rod assembly is only required if parts replacement is necessary.**

6) Slide cold enrichment rod from casting. Remove 2 Torx-head screws, securing venturi valve cover plate. Holding cover in place, turn carburetor upside-down and remove cover, gasket, and roller bearings as an assembly.

7) Using remover (T77L-9928-A or equivalent), press tapered plugs out of venturi valve pivot pins. Push pivot pins out, and slide venturi valve rearward until free of casting. Remove pivot pin bushings.

8) Remove metering rod pivot pins (on outer side of venturi valve), metering rods, and springs. Mark rods "throttle" or "choke" for reassembly reference.

9) Block venturi valve wide open. Using jet plug removal tool (T77L-9533-B or equivalent), remove main jet cup plugs, recessed in upper body casting. Using a jet wrench (T77L-9533-A or equivalent), turn each metering jet clockwise, counting number of turns required to seat them in bottom of casting. Record number of turns to nearest 1/4 turn.

10) Turn jet assemblies counterclockwise to remove. Remove "O" rings. Mark or identify main metering jets as to choke or throttle side for reassembly reference. Remove accelerator pump plunger assembly.

11) Remove venturi valve limiter adjusting screw from throttle side of venturi valve. If necessary for cleaning, remove 1/8" pipe plug in fuel inlet casting boss.

Main Body

1) Remove venturi valve diaphragm cover, spring guide and spring. Carefully loosen diaphragm and slide out of main body. Place hand under carburetor to catch accelerator pump check ball and weight as it is turned upside-down. Place carburetor upside-down on a clean surface.

2) Remove 5 throttle body screws. Remove throttle body and gasket. Using a 1 5/8" socket, remove feedback stepper motor.

Throttle Body

1) Remove any throttle return control device and bracket. Disconnect kickdown spring.

2) Center punch choke cover retaining screw heads. Align a 1/4" drill on screw head, and drill only enough to remove screw head. Repeat for remaining 2 screw heads. Remove choke cover by inserting sharp, flat chisel between choke cover gasket layers.

3) Remove retaining ring, choke cover, and gasket. Using small pliers, remove remaining portion of retaining screws from choke housing.

4) Remove choke thermostatic lever screw, and remove lever. Slide choke shaft and lever assembly out of casting, and remove fast idle cam. Remove fast idle cam adjusting screw.

5) Remove choke diaphragm rod clip, and remove the fast idle intermediate lever. Center punch

MOTORCRAFT 7200 VV 2-BARREL (Cont.)

choke control diaphragm cover retaining screw heads. Align a 1/4" drill on screw head, and drill only enough to remove screw head.

6) Repeat for remaining screw head. Remove choke control diaphragm cover and spring. Remove choke control diaphragm and rod. Disconnect rod from diaphragm.

7) If necessary to remove choke housing bushing, file off staking from around bushing. Carefully press bushing out, while supporting casting.

8) Remove choke heat tube fitting. Remove off idle (TSP) adjusting screw. Remove throttle shaft retaining nut. Remove fast idle adjusting lever, fast idle lever and adjusting screw.

9) Remove large throttle position sensor retaining clip. Scribe a mark across throttle position sensor and throttle body for reassembly reference. Remove 2 retaining screws, throttle position sensor and roll pin.

10) If necessary to remove throttle valves, scribe alignment mark along shaft. Identify throttle valves as to choke side or throttle side. Throttle valve screws are staked in place. Staking must be removed before removing screws. Remove screws and throttle valves.

11) To remove throttle shaft, drive limiter lever stop pin down until it is flush with shaft. Remove clip next to venturi valve limiter screw. Slide throttle shaft out of casting. Remove transmission kickdown adjustment screw. Remove venturi valve limiter lever and bushing assembly.

REASSEMBLY
Throttle Body

1) Support throttle shaft assembly, and drive out venturi valve limiter stop pin. Discard pin. Position venturi valve limiter assembly in throttle body and slide throttle shaft into place. Install clip.

2) Place throttle valves in correct position (noted during disassembly). Install new screws, and tighten until just snug. Close throttle, and lightly tap plates to center. Tighten throttle plate screws, and stake into position.

3) Drive venturi valve limiter stop pin into shaft. Leave 1/8" (3 mm) of pin exposed. Install throttle position sensor roll pin. Slide throttle position sensor over shaft. Engage roll pin with socket. Hold firmly, and rotate throttle position sensor clockwise to align marks made during disassembly. Install screws and large clip.

4) Install fast idle lever, adjusting lever, and fast idle adjusting screw. Install and tighten throttle shaft nut. Install off idle (TSP) adjusting screw. Install choke heat tube fitting. Install choke shaft bushing in housing. Support housing when installing bushing. Stake into position.

5) Install fast idle intermediate lever, large clip, fast idle cam, and adjusting screw. Install choke control diaphragm and rod. Connect rod to lever.

6) Install choke shaft and lever assembly. Install choke thermostatic lever in position. Install and tighten lever screw.

7) Install choke control diaphragm spring, cover, and new break-away cover screws. Apply 1/2" bead of epoxy sealer to each side of choke cover gasket, adjacent to the 3 screw bosses. Install gasket, choke cover, and retaining ring using new break-away screws. Install throttle control device and bracket

Main Body

1) Position throttle body gasket on main body. Assemble main body to throttle body. Install screws and tighten securely. Drop accelerator pump check ball and weight into position in main body.

NOTE: **Do not install venturi valve limiter stop screw and plug at this time. They are installed after carburetor is assembled and venturi valve limiter is adjusted.**

2) Slide venturi valve diaphragm into position. Install diaphragm spring, spring guide, cover and cover screws. Install venturi valve diaphragm adjustment screw. Install pintle spring, gasket pintle valve, and feedback stepper motor.

Upper Body

1) Install 1/8" pipe plug in fuel inlet boss. Install venturi valve limiter adjustment screw in venturi valve. Lubricate "O" rings with mild soapy solution. Install "O" rings on main metering jets.

2) Using jet wrench used during disassembly, install main metering jets in correct holes. Turn jets clockwise until they are lightly seated in casting. Turn each jet counterclockwise number of turns recorded during disassembly.

3) Using plug driver (T77L-9533-C or equivalent), drive main jet plugs into casting recesses. Tap lightly on tool until plugs bottom in casting. Install metering rods and springs on venturi valve, in position noted during disassembly. Install metering rod pivot pins.

4) Install venturi valve, carefully guiding metering rods into jets. If springs are correctly installed, metering rods will spring back up when depressed. Install venturi valve bushings and pivot pins. Install tapered plugs in pivot pins using tool used to remove plugs during disassembly.

5) Install venturi valve cover plate roller bearings, gasket, and cover plate. Install and tighten screws. Install accelerator pump operating rod and dust seal. Attach clip and washer. Slide accelerator pump overtravel spring on to rod.

6) Install accelerator pump lever and swivel assembly into pump link. Install accelerator pump link screw and nut. Install accelerator pump adjusting nut.

7) Install fuel inlet valve seat gasket, seat and valve. Install float bowl gasket. Place float in position and install hinge pin. Install accelerator pump return spring, cup, plunger, internal vent valve and retainer. Place pump piston assembly in position in hole in upper body.

8) If choke control rod broke during disassembly, install new rod. Install upper body on main body. Guide accelerator pump piston assembly into cavity in main body. Make sure venturi valve diaphragm stem engages venturi valve.

9) Install fuel filter spring, filter, inlet fitting gasket, and inlet fitting. Install air cleaner stud. Install choke control rod dust seal. Tap seal gently to straighten retainer.

10) Slide cold enrichment rod into upper body. Assemble cold enrichment rod adjusting nut, lever, swivel, control vacuum regulator, and adjusting nut. Install assembly on carburetor, and tighten nut enough to seat assembly.

11) Install choke hinge pin and retaining clip. Install choke control rod. Perform Cold Enrichment Rod adjustment. Adjust fast idle cam.

1983 Motorcraft Carburetors

MOTORCRAFT 7200 VV 2-BARREL (Cont.)

Fig. 13: Exploded View of Motorcraft Model 7200 VV 2-Barrel Carburetor

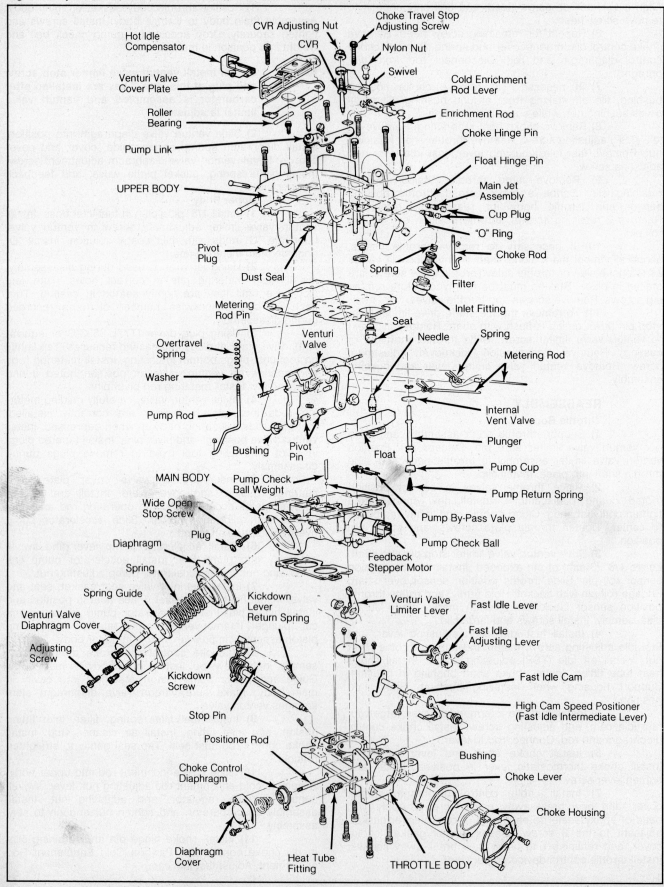

MOTORCRAFT 7200 VV 2-BARREL (Cont.)

12) Install choke thermostat gasket, housing, and retainer using 3 break-away screws. Adjust choke cap. Tighten screws until heads break off.

13) Connect accelerator pump operating rod and choke control rod. Install retaining clips. Install venturi valve limiter stop screw. Perform Venturi Valve Wide Open Throttle (WOT) Opening adjustment. Install plug after adjustment. Adjust accelerator pump lash.

CARBURETOR ADJUSTMENT SPECIFICATIONS

Application	Accel. Pump Lever Lash [1]	Fuel Level Setting	Float Drop Setting	Cold Enrichment Rod Specifications				Control Vacuum Regulator Setting	Fast Idle Cam		Choke Cover Setting	Venturi Limiter	
				0°F Start	0°F Run	75°F Start	75°F Run		Setting	Stop		Maximum Open	Closing Gap Clearance
E2TE-CCB	.010"	1-3/64"	1-15/32"	.525"	.350"	.475"	.125"	.250"	.360"	.....	Index	1.00"	.500"
E2TE-CCC	.010"	1-3/64"	1-15/32"	.525"	.350"	.475"	.125"	.250"	.360"	.....	Index	1.00"	.500"
E2TE-CDB	.010"	1-3/64"	1-15/32"	.525"	.350"	.445"	.125"	.250"	.360"	.....	Index	1.00"	.500"
E2TE-CDD	.010"	1-3/64"	1-15/32"	.525"	.350"	.445"	.125"	.250"	.360"	.....	Index	1.00"	.500"

[1] — Plus 1 turn counterclockwise.

1983 Rochester Carburetors

ROCHESTER 1ME SINGLE BARREL

NOTE: SERIES IDENTIFICATION: The vehicle numbers used in this article have been abbreviated for common reference to both Chevrolet and GMC models. Chevrolet models use numerical designations as listed; GMC models are identified as follows: 10 = 1500; 20 = 2500; 30 = 3500.

CARBURETOR APPLICATION

CHEVROLET & GMC (ROCHESTER) CARBURETOR NO.

Application	Man. Trans.	Auto. Trans.
4.8L 6-Cylinder		
Federal		
C, K, & P20	17081009	17081009
Calif.		
C & K20	17081309	17081309
P30	17081329	17081329

CARBURETOR IDENTIFICATION

The carburetor model identification is stamped on a vertical portion of the float bowl, adjacent to the fuel inlet nut. If replacing float bowl, follow manufacturer's instructions contained in service package so that the identification number can be transferred to the new float bowl. *See Fig. 1.*

Fig. 1: Rochester 1ME Carburetor Identification Location

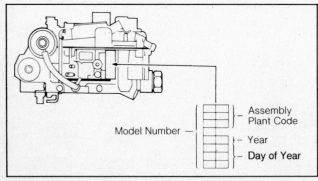

If float bowl is replaced, transfer identification number to new float bowl.

DESCRIPTION

The Rochester model 1ME carburetor is a single bore downdraft type carburetor. The 1ME uses a triple venturi in conjunction with a plain tube nozzle. This carburetor incorporates an electrically activated integral automatic choke system.

The choke vacuum diaphragm is mounted externally to carburetor air horn and is connected to thermostatic coil lever through a connector link. An electrically actuated idle stop solenoid and dual throttle return springs are used on all models.

ADJUSTMENT

NOTE: For all on vehicle adjustments, see TUNE-UP SERVICE PROCEDURES.

FLOAT LEVEL

1) Remove air horn. Hold float pin firmly in place. Push down on end of float arm against top of float needle. *See Fig. 2.*

Fig. 2: Adjusting Float Level

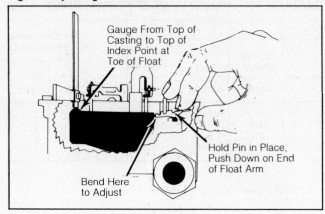

Measure distance with gasket removed.

2) With gasket removed, use a depth gauge or "T" scale to measure distance from top of casting to index point at toe of float.

3) To adjust, gently bend float arm up or down. Do not force needle against needle seat to avoid damage.

METERING ROD ADJUSTMENT

1) To remove metering rod, hold throttle valve wide open. Push down on metering rod against spring tension. Slide metering rod out of slot in holder and remove from main metering jet.

2) Hold throttle valve fully closed and back out idle stop solenoid. Hold power piston down. Swing metering rod holder over flat surface of bowl casting next to carburetor bore with gasket removed.

3) Measure specified clearance between rod holder and carburetor surface. Measurement can be made using a specified drill or pin gauge. Clearance should be a "slide" fit. *See Fig. 3.*

Fig. 3: Adjusting Metering Rod

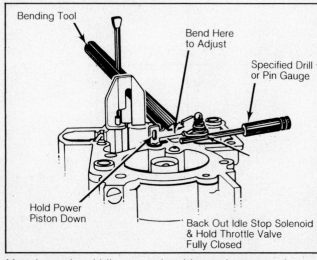

Metering rod and idle stop solenoid must be removed prior to performing adjustment.

ROCHESTER 1ME SINGLE BARREL (Cont.)

4) To adjust, gently bend holder arm up or down. Recheck clearance. Reassemble carburetor and install new air horn gasket.

CHOKE COIL LEVER

1) Place fast idle cam follower on HIGHEST step of fast idle cam. Hold choke valve closed. *See Fig. 4.*

Fig. 4: Adjusting Choke Coil Lever

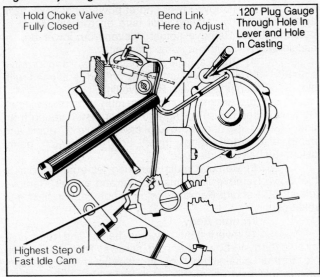

Fast idle cam follower must be on highest step of fast idle cam.

2) If adjustment is correct, specified plug gauge should pass through hole in lever and enter hole in casting. To adjust, bend connector link.

FAST IDLE CAM POSITION (CHOKE ROD)

1) Make sure fast idle speed is correctly set. Hold fast idle cam follower on 2nd step of fast idle cam, against HIGHEST step. *See Fig. 5.*

Fig. 5: Adjusting Fast Idle Cam Position (Choke Rod)

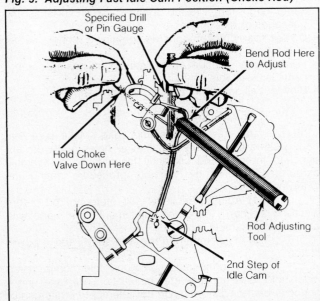

2) Apply light closing pressure to choke valve. Measure specified clearance between lower edge of choke valve (center) and air horn wall. Measurement can be made with a specified drill or pin gauge. To adjust, bend fast idle cam rod.

AUTOMATIC CHOKE

NOTE: Choke coil cover uses rivets in place of retaining screws. If necessary to remove choke coil cover, refer to Disassembly and Reassembly procedures in this article.

VACUUM BREAK

1) Place fast idle cam follower on HIGHEST step of fast idle cam. Using an outside vacuum source, apply enough vacuum to seat diaphragm. Push down on choke valve. Diaphragm plunger should be seated and bucking spring compressed (if used). *See Fig. 6.*

Fig. 6: Adjusting Vacuum Break

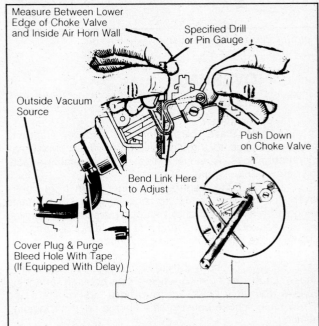

Fast idle cam follower on highest step of cam.

2) Measure clearance between lower edge of choke valve and inside air horn wall with specified drill or pin gauge. On models equipped with delay feature, cover plug and purge bleed hole in vacuum break end cover with masking tape.

3) To adjust, bend "U" shaped portion of vacuum diaphragm connector link. Remove masking tape. Check linkage for binding and freedom of movement.

CHOKE UNLOADER

1) Install choke coil in housing, and index properly. If choke is warm, cool down to point where choke valve will fully close.

2) Hold throttle valve wide open. Measure clearance, between lower edge of choke valve and inside air horn wall, using specified drill or pin gauge. To adjust, bend choke unloader tang to achieve specified clearance. *See Fig. 7.*

Fig. 7: Adjusting Choke Unloader

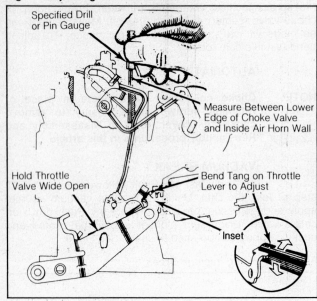

Hold throttle valve wide open.

OVERHAUL

DISASSEMBLY

Air Horn

1) Place carburetor on suitable stand to prevent damage to throttle valve. Pull off vacuum break diaphragm hose. Remove 2 diaphragm assembly attaching screws and diaphram assembly.

2) Slide diaphragm plunger stem from choke lever link. Do not attempt to remove screw that retains vacuum break lever to choke shaft. This screw is installed with thread-locking compound and should not be removed unless choke shaft replacement is required.

3) Remove fast idle cam attaching screw and cam. Remove choke rod from choke coil lever on end of choke shaft. Remove 3 choke coil housing attaching screws from float bowl; 2 screws have lock washers and screw facing choke housing has tapered head for locating housing.

4) If necessary to remove choke coil cover, drill rivet heads from cover retainer using a .159" (No. 21) drill. Using a drift and small hammer, drive remainder of rivets out of choke housing. Remove 3 retainers and cover from housing.

5) Remove 4 remaining air horn-to-float bowl screws (3 long and 1 short) and lock washers. Carefully remove air horn by lifting and twisting back toward choke housing. Disengage choke coil lever link from choke coil lever at choke housing.

6) Turn air horn upside-down. If required, remove choke valve and choke shaft by removing screw retaining vacuum break lever to choke shaft. Screw is retained with thread-locking compound; use care when removing. Remove 2 choke valve attaching screws. Remove choke valve and shaft from air horn.

NOTE: Choke valve screws are staked in place. File off staking for removal and restake during reassembly. Use care not to bend choke shaft when staking screws.

Float Bowl

1) Remove air horn gasket. Lift up on float hinge pin to remove float assembly from bowl. Remove hinge pin from float arm. Withdraw float needle from seat.

2) Disconnect accelerator pump and power piston actuator lever from end of throttle shaft by removing lever attaching screw. Hold power piston down while removing lever. Remove power piston spring and metering rod assembly.

3) Remove lower end of power piston link from actuator lever by rotating until tang on rod slides out of notch in lever. Remove actuator lever from lower end of accelerator pump link in same manner.

4) Push accelerator pump down and remove actuator link by rotating until tang on rod is aligned with slot on pump plunger lever. Remove link.

5) Remove pump assembly from float bowl. Remove pump return spring and power piston spring from float bowl. Using needle nose pliers, remove "T" guide and pump discharge spring. Invert bowl and catch pump discharge ball and idle tube.

6) Remove main metering jet from bottom of fuel bowl. Remove float needle seat and gasket. Remove idle stop solenoid. Remove fuel inlet nut, gasket, filter and relief spring.

Throttle Body

1) Invert float bowl on bench and remove 2 throttle body-to-bowl attaching screws. Remove gasket. No further disassembly of throttle body is necessary unless idle mixture needle is damaged or idle channels need cleaning.

2) If necessary to remove idle mixture needle, cut tang from plastic limiter cap. Do not install replacement. Due to close tolerance fit of throttle valve in bore of throttle body, do not remove throttle valve or shaft.

3) California models have seals built into float bowl to seal the power piston drive rod and pump lever to prevent escape of fuel vapors to the atmosphere. Remove seals and retainer prior to immersing float bowl in carburetor cleaner.

CLEANING & INSPECTION

- Use regular carburetor cleaning solution. Soak components long enough to thoroughly clean all surfaces and passages of foreign matter.
- Do not soak any components containing rubber, leather or plastic.
- Remove any residue after cleaning by rinsing components in a suitable solvent.
- Blow out all passages with dry compressed air.

REASSEMBLY

Use new gaskets and seals. Make sure that new gaskets fit correctly and that all holes and slots are punched through and correctly located. To reassemble carburetor, reverse disassembly procedure noting the following:

1) Adjust float level and metering rod before installing air horn. All other adjustments are made with carburetor assembled.

2) Install metering rod with spring above power piston.

3) Thermostatic spring in idle compensator must hold valve closed after installation. Replace unit if spring is bent or distorted. Do not attempt to straighten or adjust spring.

1983 Rochester Carburetors
ROCHESTER 1ME SINGLE BARREL (Cont.)

Fig. 8: *Exploded View of Rochester Model 1 ME Single Barrel Carburetor*

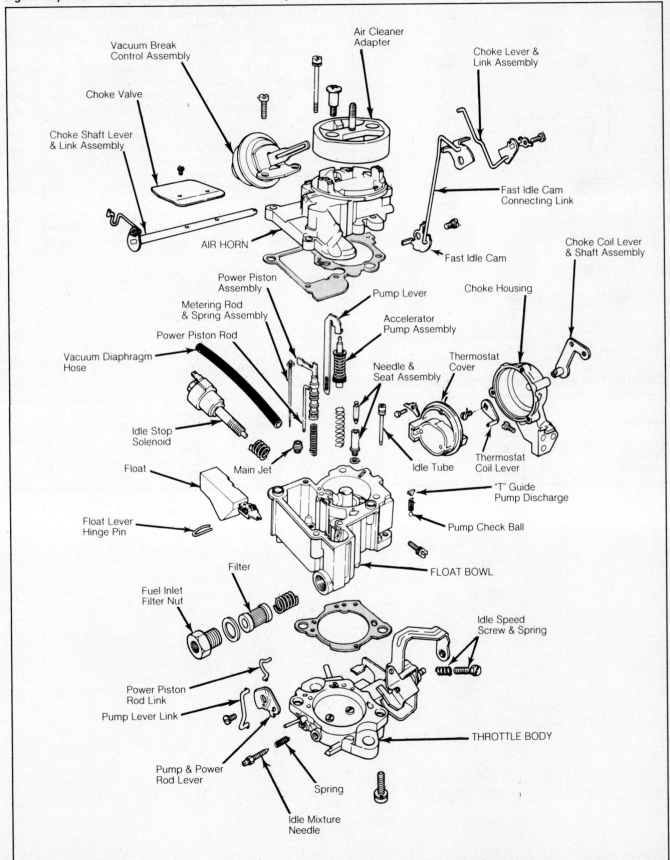

1983 Rochester Carburetors

ROCHESTER 1ME SINGLE BARREL (Cont.)

Fig. 9: *Air Horn Tightening Sequence*

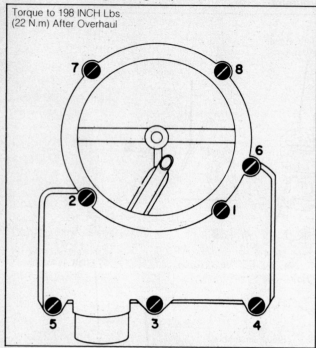

Torque to 198 INCH Lbs. (22 N.m) After Overhaul

Tighten bolts in clockwise direction.

4) Install seals in float bowl on California models to seal power piston drive rod and pump lever. These seals prevent the escape of fuel vapors.

5) Use 2 tapered head screws for mounting and locating diaphragm bracket. Install and tighten air horn screws evenly and in sequence. *See Fig. 9.*

6) If choke coil cover was removed, it will be necessary to install replacement rivets supplied in service kit. Do not use a gasket between choke housing and cover; direct contact is needed to ground electric coil housing.

7) Place fast idle screw on high step of fast idle cam. Install choke coil cover, aligning notch in cover with raised boss on housing cover flange. Install self-tapping screws and tighten.

8) Install vacuum diaphragm hose to diaphragm tube and connect to vacuum extension on bowl.

9) When installing carburetor on intake manifold, install insulator, then carburetor. Tighten nuts alternately to 37 INCH lbs. (4 N.m) and then tighten to 16 ft. lbs. (22 N.m).

CARBURETOR ADJUSTMENT SPECIFICATIONS

Application	Float Level	Metering Rod	Choke Coil Lever	Auto. Choke	Choke Coil Rod	Vacuum Break	Auto. Unloader
17081009	11/32"	.090"	.120"	.....	.275"	.400"	.520"
17081309	11/32"	.090"	.120"	.....	.275"	.400"	.520"
17081329	11/32"	.090"	.120"	.....	.275"	.400"	.520"

ROCHESTER 2SE & E2SE 2-BARREL

NOTE: SERIES IDENTIFICATION: The vehicle numbers used in this article have been abbreviated for common reference to both Chevrolet and GMC models. Chevrolet models use numerical designations as listed; GMC models are identified as follows: 10 = 1500; 20 = 2500; 30 = 3500. References to the Chrevrolet S10 also apply to the GMC S15.

CARBURETOR APPLICATION

CHEVROLET & GMC (ROCHESTER) CARBURETOR NO.

Application	Man. Trans.	Auto. Trans.
2.0L 4-Cyl.		
Federal		
Without A/C	17083391	17083390
With A/C	17083393	17083392
High Alt.		
Without A/C	17083395	17083394
With A/C	17083397	17083396
2.8L V6		
Federal		
Without A/C	17083349	17083348
		17083360
With A/C	17083351	17083350
		17083362
Calif.		
Without A/C	17083357	17083356
With A/C	17083359	17083358
High Alt.		
Without A/C	17083353	17083352
		17083364
With A/C	17083355	17083354
		17083366
4.1L 6-Cyl.		
Federal		
Without A/C		
C 10	17083411	17083410
	17083417	
	17083425	
G 10	17083419	17083414
	17083425	
K 10	17083415	17083414
	17083417	
	17083425	
C 20	17083415	
G 30	17083423	
With A/C		
C 10	17083413	17083412
	17083427	
G 10	17083421	17083416
	17083427	
K 10	17083427	17083416
G 30	17083429	
Calif.		
Without A/C	17083431	17083430
With A/C	17083435	17083430
High Alt.		
C 10	17083565	17083560
		17083562
G 10	17083569	17083560
K 10	17083565	17083562

JEEP (ROCHESTER) CARBURETOR NO.

Application	Man. Trans.	Auto. Trans.
2.5L 4-Cyl.		
Federal (2SE)	17082380	
Calif. (E2SE)	17083385	

CARBURETOR IDENTIFICATION

The Rochester 2SE and E2SE carburetor numbers are stamped vertically on the float bowl, next to the vacuum tube. If float bowl is replaced, follow manufacturer's instructions contained in service package to transfer part number to new float bowl. See Fig. 1.

Fig. 1: Carburetor Part Number Location

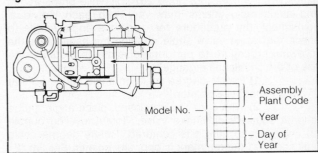

Model No. — Assembly Plant Code / Year / Day of Year

If float bowl is replaced, transfer part number to new float bowl.

DESCRIPTION

The Rochester 2SE and E2SE are 2-stage, 2-barrel downdraft carburetors. The primary stage consists of a triple venturi with a 35 mm bore.

The secondary stage has a 46 mm bore and is equipped with an air valve with a single tapered metering rod. Both are equipped with integral electronically-activated chokes, a choke vacuum break diaphragm, and an idle speed solenoid.

The E2SE model is used in conjunction with the Jeep Computerized Emission Control (CEC) system and the Chevrolet/GMC Computer Command Control (CCC) system.

The E2SE model is equipped with an electrically-actuated mixture control solenoid mounted in the air horn. Fuel metering is controlled by the mixture control solenoid plunger, which opens and closes in response to signals from the on-board computer.

This opening and closing action causes a variable restriction of fuel to the main metering circuit, changing air/fuel ratio. Also, air metered to the idle system is controlled by the movement of the mixture control solenoid plunger.

The solenoid is activated by an electronic signal from the Electronic Control Module (ECM). The ECM responds to a signal from the oxygen sensor in the exhaust. When energized, the solenoid moves the plunger down to a lean position. When de-energized, the solenoid moves the plunger up to a rich position.

Air metered (by the solenoid plunger) to the idle system is controlled by an idle air bleed valve located in the air horn. This valve follows movement of the mixture control solenoid.

1983 Rochester Carburetors

ROCHESTER 2SE & E2SE 2-BARREL (Cont.)

On E2SE models, a Throttle Position Sensor (TPS) is used to signal the ECM of throttle position changes as they occur. When throttle position is changed, a tang on the pump lever moves the TPS plunger. This signals the ECM to hold the last known air/fuel ratio to aid in throttle response.

ADJUSTMENT

NOTE: For all on-vehicle adjustments, see TUNE-UP SERVICE PROCEDURES.

ANGLE GAUGE ADJUSTMENT TOOL

Manufacturer recommends that some carburetor adjustments be performed using a choke valve angle gauge (Kent-Moore tool no. J-26701). While preparations and actual adjustments may vary with each individual adjustment, the procedure for using the angle gauge to check the choke valve angle remains the same. Use the following procedure to perform adjustments requiring the use of the choke angle gauge.

1) Rotate degree scale on angle gauge so that 0° mark is opposite pointer.

2) With choke valve closed, place angle gauge magnet squarely on choke valve. Rotate leveling bubble on angle gauge until it is centered. Rotate degree scale until specified degree mark is opposite pointer. See Fig. 2.

Fig. 2: Choke Valve Angle Gauge

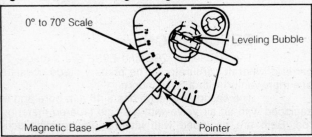

This gauge must be used to perform certain adjustments.

3) Perform individual adjustment preparations as outlined in the following carburetor adjustments requiring angle gauge. If bubble is centered, adjustment is correct. If not, adjust carburetor as outlined.

Fig. 3: Float Level Adjustment

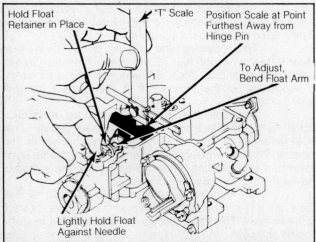

Measure distance from float bowl casting to float.

FLOAT LEVEL

1) Remove air horn and gasket from float bowl. Hold float retainer down firmly, while lightly pushing float down against needle. See Fig. 3.

2) Position a "T" scale over toe of float at point furthest away from float hinge. Measure distance from float bowl casting to float.

3) To adjust, remove float, and bend float arm. Check to make sure float is correctly aligned after adjustment.

CHOKE COIL LEVER

NOTE: Choke coil cover is retained on housing with rivets to prevent tampering with adjustment. If necessary to remove cover, refer to Overhaul procedures in this article. If rivets and cover are removed, a choke cover retainer kit is required for reassembly.

1) Remove choke thermostatic cover from choke housing. Place fast idle speed screw on high step of fast idle cam. Push on intermediate choke lever until choke valve is fully closed.

2) Insert specified drill or pin gauge in hole provided in choke housing. Edge of choke lever (inside housing) should just touch drill or pin gauge. See Fig. 4.

Fig. 4: Choke Coil Lever Adjustment

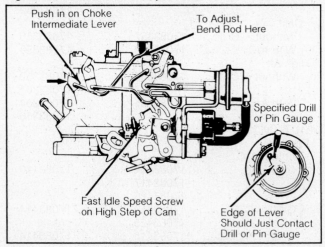

Push in on intermediate choke lever until choke valve is fully closed.

3) To adjust, bend intermediate choke rod at point shown in Fig. 4. Reinstall choke cover, and adjust.

CHOKE ROD (FAST IDLE CAM)

NOTE: Before adjusting choke rod, choke coil lever adjustment must be correct and fast idle adjustment must be made. Use angle gauge adjustment tool to perform adjustments. See Angle Gauge Adjustment Tool at beginning of Adjustments.

1) Place fast idle speed screw on 2nd step of fast idle cam, against shoulder of highest step.

2) Close choke valve by lightly pushing on intermediate choke lever. Hold in place with rubber band. Push vacuum break lever toward open choke position, until lever is against rear tang on choke lever. See Fig. 5.

ROCHESTER 2SE & E2SE 2-BARREL (Cont.)

Fig. 5: Choke Rod (Fast Idle Cam) Adjustment

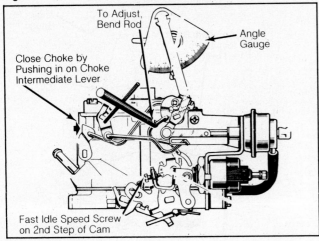

Close choke valve by lightly pushing on intermediate choke lever.

3) Bubble on choke angle gauge should be centered, with specified degree mark opposite pointer.

4) To adjust, bend fast idle cam rod at point shown in *Fig. 5* until bubble is centered in angle gauge.

Fig. 6: Air Valve Rod Adjustment

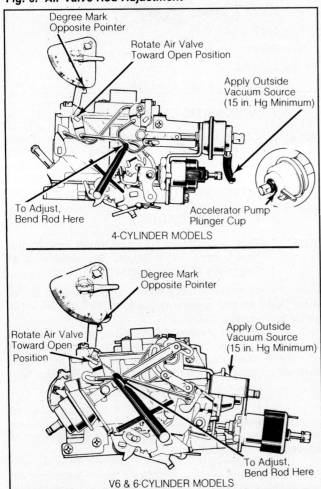

If equipped with purge bleed hole, cover hole with masking tape or accelerator pump plunger cup.

AIR VALVE ROD

NOTE: This adjustment is made by using the choke valve angle gauge. See procedure at beginning of Adjustments.

1) Using an outside vacuum source of at least 15 in. Hg, seat primary choke vacuum break diaphragm. If purge bleed hole is used, plug end cover with masking tape or accelerator pump plunger cup. Close air valve, then mount and adjust angle gauge. *See Fig. 6.*

2) Apply light opening pressure to air valve shaft. Set to specified angle by bending air valve rod until angle gauge bubble is centered. Remove masking tape, if used.

AIR VALVE SPRING

1) Using an Allen wrench, loosen lock screw. Turn tension adjusting screw clockwise until air valve partially opens. *See Fig. 7.*

Fig. 7: Air Valve Spring Adjustment

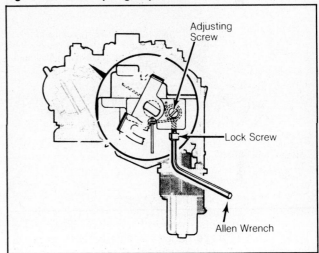

2) Turn tension adjusting screw counterclockwise, until air valve just closes. Turn screw counterclockwise 1 (1 1/4 turns on 2.0L carburetors or 1/2 turn on carburetor No. 17083650) additional turn. Tighten lock screw.

3) Lubricate contact area of air valve shaft pin and closing spring with lithium base grease.

PRIMARY VACUUM BREAK

NOTE: This adjustment is performed using the choke valve angle gauge. See procedure at beginning of Adjustments.

1) Attach a rubber band to intermediate choke lever. Open throttle to allow choke valve to close. Set up angle gauge and set to specification. Using an outside vacuum source of at least 18 in. Hg, seat primary choke vacuum break diaphragm. On models with air bleed, plug air bleed hole to maintain vacuum.

2) Air valve rod must not restrict plunger from retracting fully. If necessary, bend air valve rod to permit full plunger travel. If equipped with bucking spring, plunger stem must be at full extent of travel to compress spring. Bubble on choke valve angle gauge should be centered with specified degree mark opposite pointer. *See Fig. 8.*

1983 Rochester Carburetors

ROCHESTER 2SE & E2SE 2-BARREL (Cont.)

Fig. 8: Primary Vacuum Break Adjustment

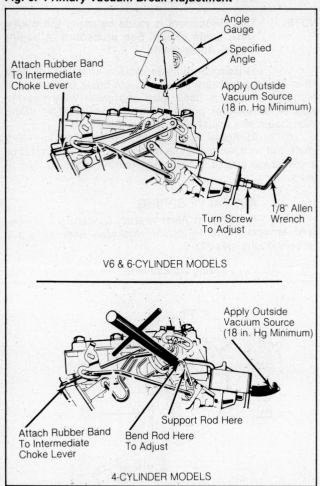

V6 & 6-CYLINDER MODELS

4-CYLINDER MODELS

Fig. 9: Secondary Vacuum Break Adjustment

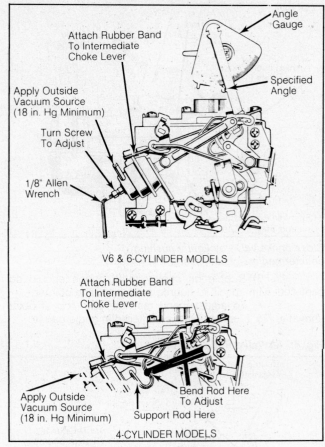

V6 & 6-CYLINDER MODELS

4-CYLINDER MODELS

3) To adjust, bend rod at location shown in *Fig. 8* until bubble of angle gauge is centered OR use a 1/8" Allen wrench to turn diaphragm screw in or out until bubble of angle gauge is centered. Perform either adjustment with vacuum still applied. Apply a bead of sealer over screw to seal adjustment.

SECONDARY VACUUM BREAK

NOTE: This adjustment is made using the choke valve angle gauge. See procedure at beginning of Adjustments.

1) Attach a rubber band to intermediate choke lever. Open throttle to allow choke valve to close. Set up angle gauge and set to specification. Using an outside vacuum source of at least 18 in. Hg, seat primary choke vacuum break diaphragm. On models with air bleed, plug air bleed hole to maintain vacuum.

2) If equipped with bucking spring, plunger stem must be at full extent of travel to compress spring. Bubble on choke valve angle gauge should be centered with specified degree mark opposite pointer. *See Fig. 9.*

3) To adjust, bend rod at location shown in *Fig. 9* until bubble of angle gauge is centered OR use a 1/8" Allen wrench to turn diaphragm screw in or out until bubble of angle gauge is centered. Perform either adjustment with vacuum still applied. Apply a bead of sealer over screw to seal adjustment.

AUTOMATIC CHOKE

NOTE: Choke coil cover is retained on housing with rivets to prevent tampering with factory adjustment. If necessary to remove cover, refer to Disassembly and Reassembly procedures in this Section.

CHOKE UNLOADER

NOTE: This adjustment is performed using the choke valve angle gauge. See procedure at beginning of Adjustments.

1) Attach a rubber band to intermediate choke lever. Open throttle to allow choke to close fully. Set angle gauge to specifications.

2) Hold primary throttle valve wide open. Push on choke shaft lever to open choke and to make contact with Black closing tang. To adjust, bend tang on throttle lever until bubble in angle gauge is centered. See Fig. 10.

SECONDARY LOCKOUT

1) Hold choke valve wide open by pushing counterclockwise on choke intermediate lever. Open throttle valves until end of secondary actuating lever is opposite toe of lockout lever.

2) Measure specified clearance between end of actuating lever and toe of lockout lever. Measurement can be checked using a drill or pin gauge of specified size. To adjust, bend lockout lever tang contacting fast idle cam. See Fig. 11.

ROCHESTER 2SE & E2SE 2-BARREL (Cont.)

Fig. 10: Choke Unloader Adjustment

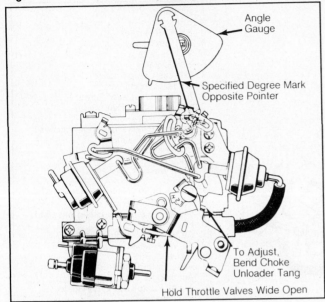

Hold primary throttle valve wide open.

Fig. 11: Secondary Throttle Lockout Adjustment

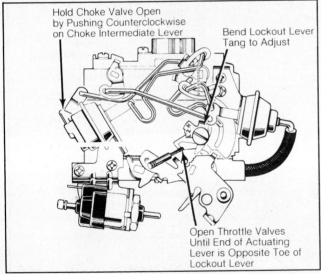

Measure clearance between end of actuating lever and toe of lockout lever.

OVERHAUL

DISASSEMBLY

NOTE: Before disassembling carburetor, mount unit in a suitable holding fixture to prevent damage to throttle valves or linkage.

Air Horn

1) Remove hose from vacuum break assembly or assemblies. Remove vacuum break and idle speed solenoid bracket attaching screws from air horn. Rotate vacuum break and bracket assembly to disengage vacu-um break link (T-pin) from slot in vacuum break lever, and air valve rod from slot in air valve lever.

2) Remove secondary vacuum break bracket assembly attaching screws from throttle body (if equipped). Rotate bracket to remove vacuum break link from vacuum break lever slot. Remove clip from hole in accelerator pump rod.

NOTE: Do not remove pump lever retaining screw. Pump lever and washer must not be removed from air horn assembly.

3) If necessary to remove air valve rod from vacuum break, remove and discard retaining clip from end of air valve. New retaining clip must be used on reassembly. Plastic bushing used on rod may be reused.

4) Remove and discard retaining clip from intermediate choke rod at choke lever. Use a new retaining clip at reassembly. Remove plastic choke rod and bushing from choke lever. Bushing may be reused.

5) If equipped, remove hot idle compensator valve screws. Remove valve and seal from air horn, discard seal. Valve removal is necessary to gain access to short air horn-to-bowl attaching screw.

6) On E2SE models, remove 3 mixture control solenoid screws, and remove mixture control solenoid using a light twisting motion. Remove and discard solenoid gasket, plunger seal and plunger seal retainer. Retain spacer for use during reassembly.

7) Remove air horn-to-float bowl screws and lock washers. Remove vent and screen assembly. Rotate fast idle cam to full "UP" (12 o'clock) position. Remove air horn assembly by tilting to disengage fast idle cam rod from slot in fast idle cam and pump rod from hole in pump lever.

8) Disconnect fast idle cam rod from choke lever by aligning tang on rod with slot in lever. Remove from air horn assembly.

9) On E2SE models, remove TPS plunger by pushing through seal in air horn. Remove seal retainer and seal. Remove accelerator pump plunger seal from air horn.

NOTE: To prevent damage to sealing surface, use fingers only (no tools) when removing plunger. To prevent damage to air horn, use care in removing plunger seal retainer and plunger stem seal retainer. Discard seals and retainers.

10) It is not necessary to remove choke valve and shaft unless they are bent or damaged. Choke valve screws are staked in place. Staking must be removed before screws are removed.

NOTE: Do not remove plugs covering idle air bleed screw during routine service. This adjustment is factory-set, and no attempt should be made to change the adjustment, unless air horn or float bowl is replaced.

Float Bowl

1) Remove air horn gasket. Remove pump plunger and pump spring from pump well. Remove plastic filler block from float valve. Remove float assembly and float valve by pulling up on retaining pin.

2) Remove float needle seat, gasket and extended metering jet from float bowl. Use a jet tool (J-

1983 Rochester Carburetors

ROCHESTER 2SE & E2SE 2-BARREL (Cont.)

Fig. 12: Exploded View of Rochester Model 2SE Carburetor

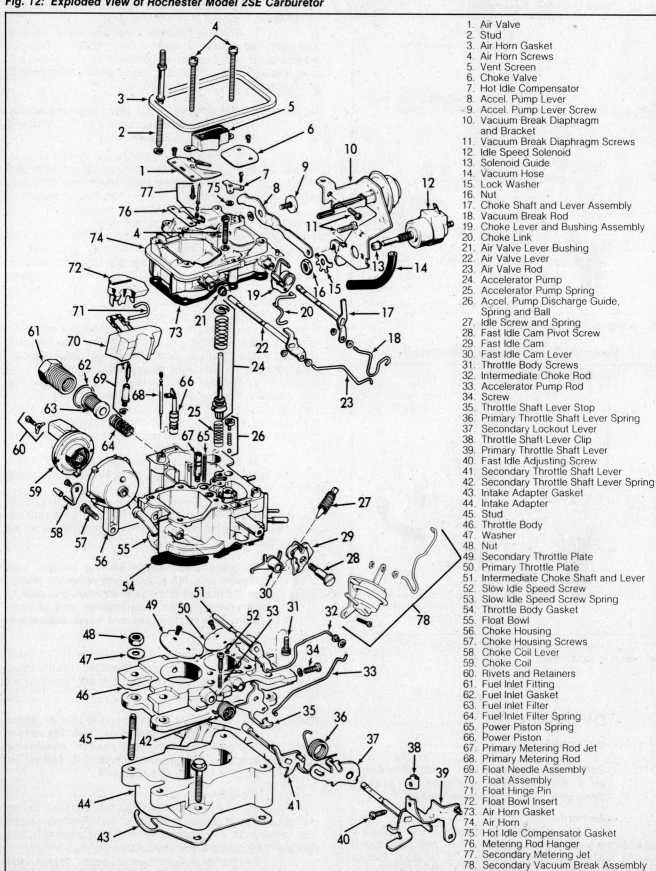

1. Air Valve
2. Stud
3. Air Horn Gasket
4. Air Horn Screws
5. Vent Screen
6. Choke Valve
7. Hot Idle Compensator
8. Accel. Pump Lever
9. Accel. Pump Lever Screw
10. Vacuum Break Diaphragm and Bracket
11. Vacuum Break Diaphragm Screws
12. Idle Speed Solenoid
13. Solenoid Guide
14. Vacuum Hose
15. Lock Washer
16. Nut
17. Choke Shaft and Lever Assembly
18. Vacuum Break Rod
19. Choke Lever and Bushing Assembly
20. Choke Link
21. Air Valve Lever Bushing
22. Air Valve Lever
23. Air Valve Rod
24. Accelerator Pump
25. Accelerator Pump Spring
26. Accel. Pump Discharge Guide, Spring and Ball
27. Idle Screw and Spring
28. Fast Idle Cam Pivot Screw
29. Fast Idle Cam
30. Fast Idle Cam Lever
31. Throttle Body Screws
32. Intermediate Choke Rod
33. Accelerator Pump Rod
34. Screw
35. Throttle Shaft Lever Stop
36. Primary Throttle Shaft Lever Spring
37. Secondary Lockout Lever
38. Throttle Shaft Lever Clip
39. Primary Throttle Shaft Lever
40. Fast Idle Adjusting Screw
41. Secondary Throttle Shaft Lever
42. Secondary Throttle Shaft Lever Spring
43. Intake Adapter Gasket
44. Intake Adapter
45. Stud
46. Throttle Body
47. Washer
48. Nut
49. Secondary Throttle Plate
50. Primary Throttle Plate
51. Intermediate Choke Shaft and Lever
52. Slow Idle Speed Screw
53. Slow Idle Speed Screw Spring
54. Throttle Body Gasket
55. Float Bowl
56. Choke Housing
57. Choke Housing Screws
58. Choke Coil Lever
59. Choke Coil
60. Rivets and Retainers
61. Fuel Inlet Fitting
62. Fuel Inlet Gasket
63. Fuel Inlet Filter
64. Fuel Inlet Filter Spring
65. Power Piston Spring
66. Power Piston
67. Primary Metering Rod Jet
68. Primary Metering Rod
69. Float Needle Assembly
70. Float Assembly
71. Float Hinge Pin
72. Float Bowl Insert
73. Air Horn Gasket
74. Air Horn
75. Hot Idle Compensator Gasket
76. Metering Rod Hanger
77. Secondary Metering Jet
78. Secondary Vacuum Break Assembly

ROCHESTER 2SE & E2SE 2-BARREL (Cont.)

Fig. 13: Exploded View of Rochester Model E2SE Carburetor

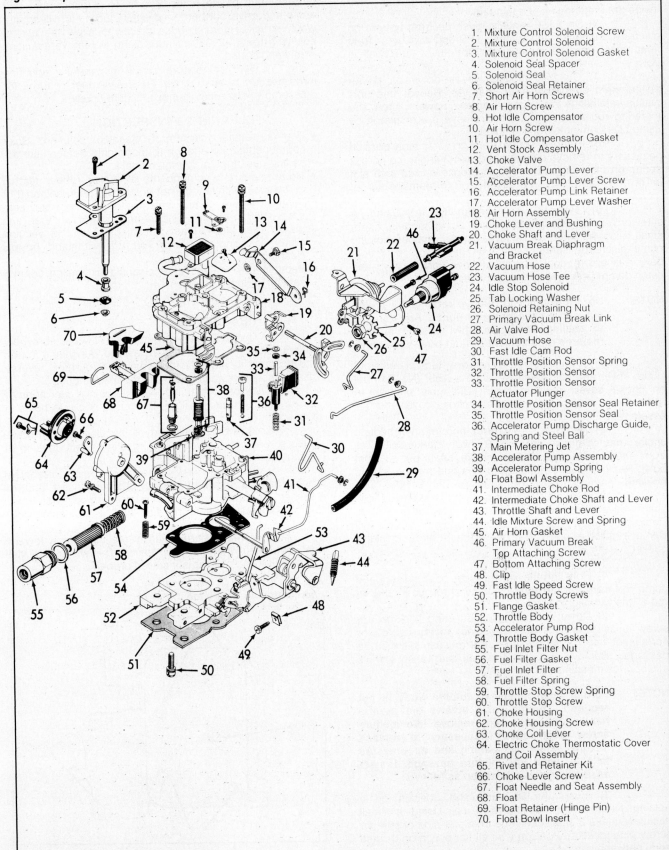

1. Mixture Control Solenoid Screw
2. Mixture Control Solenoid
3. Mixture Control Solenoid Gasket
4. Solenoid Seal Spacer
5. Solenoid Seal
6. Solenoid Seal Retainer
7. Short Air Horn Screws
8. Air Horn Screw
9. Hot Idle Compensator
10. Air Horn Screw
11. Hot Idle Compensator Gasket
12. Vent Stock Assembly
13. Choke Valve
14. Accelerator Pump Lever
15. Accelerator Pump Lever Screw
16. Accelerator Pump Link Retainer
17. Accelerator Pump Lever Washer
18. Air Horn Assembly
19. Choke Lever and Bushing
20. Choke Shaft and Lever
21. Vacuum Break Diaphragm and Bracket
22. Vacuum Hose
23. Vacuum Hose Tee
24. Idle Stop Solenoid
25. Tab Locking Washer
26. Solenoid Retaining Nut
27. Primary Vacuum Break Link
28. Air Valve Rod
29. Vacuum Hose
30. Fast Idle Cam Rod
31. Throttle Position Sensor Spring
32. Throttle Position Sensor
33. Throttle Position Sensor Actuator Plunger
34. Throttle Position Sensor Seal Retainer
35. Throttle Position Sensor Seal
36. Accelerator Pump Discharge Guide, Spring and Steel Ball
37. Main Metering Jet
38. Accelerator Pump Assembly
39. Accelerator Pump Spring
40. Float Bowl Assembly
41. Intermediate Choke Rod
42. Intermediate Choke Shaft and Lever
43. Throttle Shaft and Lever
44. Idle Mixture Screw and Spring
45. Air Horn Gasket
46. Primary Vacuum Break Top Attaching Screw
47. Bottom Attaching Screw
48. Clip
49. Fast Idle Speed Screw
50. Throttle Body Screws
51. Flange Gasket
52. Throttle Body
53. Accelerator Pump Rod
54. Throttle Body Gasket
55. Fuel Inlet Filter Nut
56. Fuel Filter Gasket
57. Fuel Inlet Filter
58. Fuel Filter Spring
59. Throttle Stop Screw Spring
60. Throttle Stop Screw
61. Choke Housing
62. Choke Housing Screw
63. Choke Coil Lever
64. Electric Choke Thermostatic Cover and Coil Assembly
65. Rivet and Retainer Kit
66. Choke Lever Screw
67. Float Needle and Seat Assembly
68. Float
69. Float Retainer (Hinge Pin)
70. Float Bowl Insert

1983 Rochester Carburetors

ROCHESTER 2SE & E2SE 2-BARREL (Cont.)

22769) or screwdriver that fully fits slot in top of jet. Do not remove or change adjustment of screw located deep inside the metering jet (if equipped).

3) On E2SE models, push up from bottom on electrical connector and remove TPS and connector from float bowl. Remove spring from bottom of TPS well in bowl.

4) On 2SE models, press down on power piston stem and allow it to snap up. Repeat this until plastic retainer is dislodged. Remove power piston and metering rod assembly. Do not remove power piston by using pliers on metering rod holder.

5) Remove spring from power piston bore. If necessary to remove metering rod from hanger, compress spring on metering rod and align groove on rod with slot in holder. Care must be taken not to damage tip of metering rod.

6) Remove main metering jet using a screwdriver that fits tight in groove. On all models, use a small slide hammer to remove plastic retainer holding pump discharge spring and check ball in place in float bowl. Discard retainer. Turn float bowl upside-down and catch pump discharge spring and check ball.

NOTE: Do not attempt to remove retainer by prying out with a screwdriver or punch. Any damage to sealing beads on bowl casting surface requires replacement of float bowl assembly.

7) If necessary to remove tamper-resistant choke cover and coil assembly, align a .159" (No. 21) drill on choke cover retaining rivets. Drill only enough to remove rivet heads. Remove rivets, choke cover and coil assembly.

8) Remove screw from end of intermediate choke shaft in choke housing. Remove choke coil lever from shaft. Slide intermediate choke shaft out of float bowl. Remove choke housing screws and remove choke housing.

9) Remove fuel inlet nut with gasket. Remove check valve/filter and spring. Discard gasket and filter. Remove 4 screws securing throttle body to float bowl. Remove throttle body. Remove throttle body insulator gasket.

Throttle Body

1) Hold throttle valves wide open. Disengage pump rod from throttle lever by rotating rod until tang on rod aligns with slot in lever.

2) Do not remove plug covering idle mixture screw unless it is necessary to replace mixture screw or normal soaking and air pressure fails to clean idle mixture passages. Remove curb idle and fast idle speed screws and springs if necessary.

NOTE: Further disassembly of throttle body is not required. Throttle valve screws are permanently staked. Do not remove idle mixture screw plug unless necessary to replace mixture screw or cleaning and air pressure fails to clean idle mixture passage. If necessary to remove, proceed as follows:

3) Invert throttle body and position on a holding fixture with manifold side up. Using a small hacksaw, make 2 small cuts, one on either side of mixture screw plug location. Position a small flat punch on throttle body between cuts.

4) Drive punch down and break out portion of throttle body between the 2 cuts. Hold punch at a 45° angle and drive out hardened steel plug. Plug will shatter when struck. Remove loose pieces to allow the use of adjusting tool (J-29030 or equivalent) to remove adjusting screw and spring.

5) Turn mixture screw in carefully, counting turns needed to seat screw. Record number of turns for reassembly reference. Remove mixture screw.

CLEANING & INSPECTION

- Use a regular carburetor cleaning solution. Soak components long enough to thoroughly clean all surfaces and passages of foreign matter.
- Do not soak any components containing rubber, leather or plastic. Definitely do not soak idle speed solenoid or control mixture control solenoid, throttle position sensor, electric choke, diaphragms, pump plunger and plastic filler block. Plastic bushings in end of vacuum break link and air valve rod will withstand normal cleaning.
- Remove any residue after cleaning by rinsing components in a suitable solvent.
- Blow out all passages with dry compressed air.

REASSEMBLY

Use new gaskets and seals. Make sure new gaskets fit correctly and all holes are punched through and properly located. To reassemble carburetor, reverse disassembly procedure and note the following:

1) Install fuel inlet needle pull clip over edge of flat on float arm facing float. Do not hook clip in holes in float arm.

2) After throttle body is installed on float bowl, make sure secondary lockout tang is in correct position to engage secondary lockout lever.

3) Install new accelerator pump discharge check ball, spring and plastic retainer. Insert end of retainer in spring and place in position in float bowl. Lightly tap retainer into position until it is flush in float bowl.

4) Make sure holes in fuel filter face toward fuel inlet fitting when filter is installed. This will ensure that check valve end of filter is installed properly.

Fig. 14: Air Horn Screw Location and Tightening Sequence

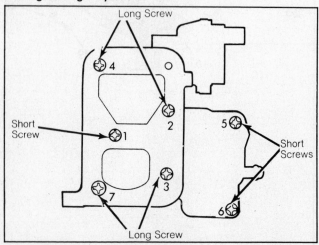

Ensure screws are properly located.

ROCHESTER 2SE & E2SE 2-BARREL (Cont.)

5) Some linkage retaining clips are dished. Make sure portion of clip that bends outward is toward end of rod. Make sure clip makes full contact with rod.

6) Place fast idle screw on high step of fast idle cam. Install choke coil cover, aligning notch in cover with raised boss on housing cover flange. If choke cover and coil assembly was removed from housing, a service rivet kit must be used to restore tamper-resistant feature.

7) On E2SE models, be sure coil pick-up lever is located inside choke coil tang. On electric chokes, the ground contact is provided by a metal plate at rear of choke cover assembly. Do not install a choke cover gasket between electric choke assembly and choke housing.

8) Install air horn screws, noting location and type of screw for correct installation. Tighten all screws evenly, securely and in sequence. *See Fig. 14.*

9) On E2SE models, install mixture control solenoid seal on solenoid stem. Using a 3/16" socket and hammer, lightly tap retainer in place on stem. Leave a slight clearance between retainer and seal. Apply silicone grease to seal before installation of solenoid.

1983 Rochester Carburetors

ROCHESTER 2SE & E2SE 2-BARREL (Cont.)

CARBURETOR ADJUSTMENT SPECIFICATIONS

Application	Float Level	Accel. Pump	Choke Coil Lever	Choke Rod	Air Valve Rod	Vacuum Break Primary	Vacuum Break Secondary	Auto. Choke	Choke Unloader	Secondary Lockout
GM (2SE)										
17083348	7/16"	TR	.085"	22°	1°	30°	32°	TR	40°	.025"
17083349	7/16"	TR	.085"	22°	1°	30°	32°	TR	40°	.025"
17083350	7/16"	TR	.085"	22°	1°	30°	32°	TR	40°	.025"
17083351	7/16"	TR	.085"	22°	1°	30°	32°	TR	40°	.025"
17083352	7/16"	TR	.085"	22°	1°	30°	35°	TR	40°	.025"
17083353	7/16"	TR	.085"	22°	1°	30°	35°	TR	40°	.025"
17083354	7/16"	TR	.085"	22°	1°	30°	35°	TR	40°	.025"
17083355	7/16"	TR	.085"	22°	1°	30°	35°	TR	40°	.025"
17083360	7/16"	TR	.085"	22°	1°	30°	32°	TR	40°	.025"
17083361	7/16"	TR	.085"	22°	1°	28°	32°	TR	40°	.025"
17083362	7/16"	TR	.085"	22°	1°	30°	32°	TR	40°	.025"
17083363	7/16"	TR	.085"	22°	1°	28°	32°	TR	40°	.025"
17083364	7/16"	TR	.085"	22°	1°	30°	35°	TR	40°	.025"
17083365	7/16"	TR	.085"	22°	1°	30°	35°	TR	40°	.025"
17083366	7/16"	TR	.085"	22°	1°	30°	35°	TR	40°	.025"
17083367	7/16"	TR	.085"	22°	1°	30°	35°	TR	40°	.025"
17083390	13/32"	TR	.085"	28°	1°	30°	35°	TR	38°	.025"
17083391	13/32"	TR	.085"	28°	1°	30°	35°	TR	38°	.025"
17083392	13/32"	TR	.085"	28°	1°	30°	35°	TR	38°	.025"
17083393	13/32"	TR	.085"	28°	1°	30°	35°	TR	38°	.025"
17083394	13/32"	TR	.085"	28°	1°	30°	35°	TR	38°	.025"
17083395	13/32"	TR	.085"	28°	1°	30°	35°	TR	38°	.025"
17083396	13/32"	TR	.085"	28°	1°	30°	35°	TR	38°	.025"
17083397	13/32"	TR	.085"	28°	1°	30°	35°	TR	38°	.025"
17083410	3/16"	TR	.085"	15°	1°	23°	38°	TR	42°	.025"
17083411	3/16"	TR	.085"	15°	1°	26°	38°	TR	42°	.025"
17083412	3/16"	TR	.085"	15°	1°	23°	38°	TR	42°	.025"
17083413	3/16"	TR	.085"	15°	1°	26°	38°	TR	42°	.025"
17083414	3/16"	TR	.085"	15°	1°	23°	38°	TR	42°	.025"
17083415	3/16"	TR	.085"	15°	1°	26°	38°	TR	42°	.025"
17083416	3/16"	TR	.085"	15°	1°	23°	38°	TR	42°	.025"
17083417	3/16"	TR	.085"	15°	1°	26°	38°	TR	42°	.025"
17083419	3/16"	TR	.085"	15°	1°	26°	38°	TR	42°	.025"
17083421	3/16"	TR	.085"	15°	1°	26°	38°	TR	42°	.025"
17083423	3/16"	TR	.085"	15°	1°	28°	38°	TR	42°	.025"
17083425	3/16"	TR	.085"	15°	1°	26°	38°	TR	42°	.025"
17083427	3/16"	TR	.085"	15°	1°	26°	38°	TR	42°	.025"
17083429	3/16"	TR	.085"	15°	1°	28°	38°	TR	42°	.025"
17083560	3/16"	TR	.085"	15°	1°	28°	38°	TR	42°	.025"
17083562	3/16"	TR	.085"	15°	1°	28°	38°	TR	42°	.025"
17083565	3/16"	TR	.085"	15°	1°	28°	38°	TR	42°	.025"
17083569	3/16"	TR	.085"	15°	1°	28°	38°	TR	42°	.025"
GM (E2SE)										
17083356	13/32"	TR	.085"	22°	1°	25°	35°	TR	30°	.025"
17083357	13/32"	TR	.085"	22°	1°	25°	35°	TR	30°	.025"
17083358	13/32"	TR	.085"	22°	1°	25°	35°	TR	30°	.025"
17083359	13/32"	TR	.085"	22°	1°	25°	35°	TR	30°	.025"
17083368	1/8"	TR	.085"	22°	1°	25°	35°	TR	30°	.025"
17083370	1/8"	TR	.085"	22°	1°	25°	35°	TR	30°	.025"
17083430	11/32"	TR	.085"	15°	1°	26°	38°	TR	42°	.025"
17083431	11/32"	TR	.085"	15°	1°	26°	38°	TR	42°	.025"
17083434	11/32"	TR	.085"	15°	1°	26°	38°	TR	42°	.025"
17083435	11/32"	TR	.085"	15°	1°	26°	38°	TR	42°	.025"
17083450	1/8"	TR	.085"	28°	1°	27°	35°	TR	45°	.025"
17083451	1/4"	TR	.085"	28°	1°	27°	35°	TR	45°	.025"
17083452	1/8"	TR	.085"	28°	1°	27°	35°	TR	45°	.025"
17083453	1/4"	TR	.085"	28°	1°	27°	35°	TR	45°	.025"
17083454	1/8"	TR	.085"	28°	1°	27°	35°	TR	45°	.025"
17083455	1/4"	TR	.085"	28°	1°	27°	35°	TR	45°	.025"
17083456	1/8"	TR	.085"	28°	1°	27°	35°	TR	45°	.025"
17083630	1/4"	TR	.085"	28°	1°	27°	35°	TR	45°	.025"
17083631	1/4"	TR	.085"	28°	1°	27°	35°	TR	45°	.025"
17083632	1/4"	TR	.085"	28°	1°	27°	35°	TR	45°	.025"
17083633	1/4"	TR	.085"	28°	1°	27°	35°	TR	45°	.025"
17083634	1/4"	TR	.085"	28°	1°	27°	35°	TR	45°	.025"
17083635	1/4"	TR	.085"	28°	1°	27°	35°	TR	45°	.025"
17083636	1/4"	TR	.085"	28°	1°	27°	35°	TR	45°	.025"
17083650	1/8"	TR	.085"	28°	1°	27°	35°	TR	45°	.025"
JEEP (2SE)										
17082380	7/32"	.128"	.085"	18°	2°	21°	.....	TR	34°	.065"
JEEP (E2SE)										
17083385	9/64"	.128"	.085"	18°	2°	19°	.....	TR	34°	.065"

ROCHESTER E4ME 4-BARREL

CARBURETOR APPLICATION

GENERAL MOTORS (ROCHESTER) CARBURETOR NO.

Application	Man. Trans.	Auto. Trans.
5.0L V8		
Without A/C	17083524	17083524
With A/C	17083526	17083526
5.7L V8		
Without A/C	17083506	17083506
With A/C	17083508	17083508

CARBURETOR IDENTIFICATION

The Rochester E4ME carburetor number is stamped vertically on the float bowl, near secondary throttle. If float bowl is replaced, follow manufacturer's instructions contained in service package to transfer part number to new float bowl. Some models have machined pump wells to reduce the pump well taper.

The E4ME Quadrajet carburetor is used nationwide with the Computer Command Control (CCC) system. The first letter "E" indicates the carburetor is a part of the CCC system. The final letter, if "E", indicates the carburetor is equipped with an electric choke.

Fig. 1: Carburetor Identification Label

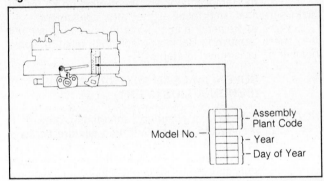

Original part number must be transfered from old float bowl if new float bowl is installed.

DESCRIPTION

The E4ME carburetor is a 2-stage, downdraft design. Each bore has a triple venturi system. The secondary side is composed of 2 large throttle bores, using the air valve principle, in which fuel is metered in direct proportion to the amount of air passing through the secondary throttle bores. A baffle is attached to the secondary side of the air horn, above the main well bleed tubes. This deflects incoming air to improve secondary nozzle operation on heavy acceleration.

The E4ME uses an electrically-actuated choke assembly. All E4ME models have 2 vacuum break diaphragm assemblies, the front and rear.

The E4ME model is used in conjunction with the Computer Command Control (CCC) System. The carburetor is equipped with an electrically-actuated mixture control solenoid mounted in the float bowl. Fuel metering is controlled by stepped metering rods that operate in removable jets.

All models include tamper-resistant factory settings of the mixture control solenoid rich mixture stop screw and lean mixture screw, idle air bleed valve, TPS, ISC, ISS and idle mixture screws. No attempt should be made to adjust these except during major overhaul or replacement of air horn, float bowl or throttle body. Both electric and hot air chokes have riveted covers which must not be removed except for major overhaul.

The carburetor may be equipped with an Idle Speed Control (ISC) on the fuel bowl. Controlled by the ECM, the ISC controls the normal curb idle speed and acts as a dashpot on deceleration and throttle closing. On vehicles without an ISC, but with air conditioning, an Idle Speed Solenoid (ISS) maintains a specific idle speed during A/C operation.

TESTING

ELECTRIC CHOKE

NOTE: **This test should be performed when air temperature is 60-80°F (15-27°C).**

1) Allow choke to cool to permit full closing of choke blade when throttle is opened slightly. Start engine and time the interval required for choke blade to reach full open position. (Start timing when engine starts). If choke blade does not fully open within 3 1/2 minutes, proceed with test.

2) With engine running, check voltage at choke heater connection. If voltage is about 12-15 volts, replace electric choke unit. If voltage is low or zero, check all wires and connections and repair as required. Power for choke unit is through the oil pressure switch. Ensure switch circuitry is good.

3) If procedure in step 2) does not correct the problem, replace oil pressure switch.

ADJUSTMENTS

NOTE: **For all on-vehicle adjustments not covered in this article, see appropriate TUNE-UP article.**

ANGLE GAUGE ADJUSTMENT TOOL

Manufacturer recommends that some carburetor adjustments be performed using a choke valve angle gauge (Kent-Moore tool No. J-26701). While preparations and actual adjustment may vary with each individual adjustment, the procedure for using the angle gauge to check the choke valve angle remains the same. Use the following procedure to perform adjustments requiring the use of the choke valve angle gauge.

Fig. 2: Choke Valve Angle Gauge

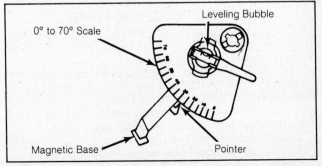

This gauge must be used to perform some adjustments.

1983 Rochester Carburetors

ROCHESTER E4ME 4-BARREL (Cont.)

1) Rotate degree scale on angle gauge so that 0° mark is opposite pointer.

2) With choke valve closed, place angle gauge magnet squarely on choke valve.

3) Rotate leveling bubble on angle gauge until it is centered.

4) Rotate degree scale until specified degree mark is opposite pointer.

5) Now perform individual adjustment preparation as outlined in the following carburetor adjustments requiring an angle gauge.

6) If bubble is centered, adjustment is correct. If not, adjust carburetor as outlined in adjustment procedure.

FLOAT LEVEL (WET SETTING)

NOTE: **This is an on-vehicle adjustment.**

1) With engine running at idle and choke wide open, carefully insert float gauge into vent slot or vent hole (next to air cleaner mounting stud) in air horn. Allow gauge to float freely. See Fig. 3.

NOTE: **Pressing down on float gauge could result in float damage or carburetor flooding.**

Fig. 3: Wet Float Level Adjustment

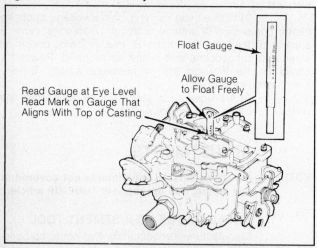

Allow float gauge to float freely.

2) With gauge floating freely, observe mark on gauge which aligns with top of casting (at eye level). Reading should be within 1/16" of specified float level. Incorrect fuel pressure will affect fuel level.

3) If reading is not within 1/16" of specified float level, remove carburetor. Remove air horn and perform Float Level (Dry Setting) adjustment.

FLOAT LEVEL (DRY SETTING)

1) Remove air horn and gasket from float bowl. Hold float retainer down firmly. Lightly push float down against needle. See Fig. 4.

2) Position a "T" scale over toe of float at a point 3/16" from end of float toe. Measure distance from top of float bowl casting to top of float.

3) If float level setting varies more than 1/16" from specified setting, proceed as follows:

Float Level Too High

a) Hold float retainer clip firmly in place.

Fig. 4: Dry Float Level Adjustment

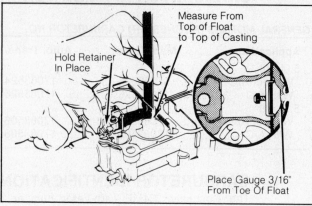

Follow procedures to properly adjust float level.

b) Push down on center of float pontoon until correct float level setting is obtained.

Float Level Too Low

a) Lift out metering rods. Remove solenoid connector screws.

b) Turn lean mixture solenoid screw clockwise, counting and recording number of turns required to lightly seat screw in float bowl.

c) Turn screw counterclockwise and remove. Lift solenoid and connector from float bowl.

d) Remove float and bend arm up to adjust. Make sure float is correctly aligned after adjustment.

e) Reinstall components in reverse order that they were removed. Back out solenoid mixture screw number of turns noted in step **b)**.

SOLENOID LEAN MIXTURE SCREW (BENCH ADJUSTMENT)

NOTE: **This is a preliminary adjustment only. It is required to ensure that lean mixture screw is set close to specifications prior to final adjustment. Final adjustment must be made with carburetor installed and engine running. See appropriate TUNE-UP article.**

1) Install plastic aneroid cavity insert beneath mixture control solenoid connector in float bowl, if used. Ensure insert is installed with inset aligned with recess of bowl cavity and seated flush with bowl casting surface. Tang on upper lip of insert goes in deep slot in bowl closest to fuel inlet nut.

2) Install mixture control solenoid screw tension spring between raised bosses next to float hanger pin. Carefully install mixture control solenoid in float chamber. Align pin on end of solenoid with hole in raised boss at bottom of bowl. Align connector wires to fit in slot in bowl or plastic insert, if used.

3) Install solenoid lean mixture screw through hole in solenoid bracket and tension spring in float bowl. The first 6 threads of the mixture screw should be engaged to assure proper installation.

4) Install mixture control solenoid gauging tool over throttle side metering jet rod guide. Temporarily install solenoid plunger. See Fig. 5.

5) Hold solenoid plunger against solenoid stop. Using a "double D" wrench, slowly turn lean mixture screw clockwise until solenoid plunger just contacts gauging tool. See Fig. 5.

ROCHESTER E4ME 4-BARREL (Cont.)

Fig. 5: *Solenoid Lean Mixture Screw Bench Adjustment*

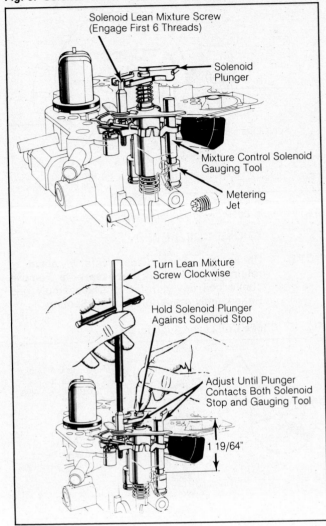

Lean mixture screw should be installed with first 6 threads engaged in float bowl.

6) Adjustment is correct when solenoid plunger is contacting BOTH the solenoid stop and gauging tool. Remove solenoid plunger and gauging tool.

SOLENOID RICH MIXTURE STOP SCREW (BENCH ADJUSTMENT)

NOTE: This is a preliminary adjustment only. It is required to ensure that rich mixture stop screw is set close to specifications prior to final adjustment. Final adjustment must be made with carburetor installed and engine running. See appropriate TUNE-UP article.

1) With solenoid lean mixture screw properly set and air horn installed, insert plastic float gauge in vertical "D" shaped vent hole in air horn casting.

2) With float gauge installed, read mark (in inches) on gauge that lines up with top of air horn casting at eye level. Record reading. Lightly depress float gauge and again read mark on gauge that lines up with top of casting. Record reading.

3) Subtract the 2 readings taken in step 2). This difference is the total solenoid travel. Using a "double

Fig. 6: *Solenoid Rich Mixture Stop Screw Bench Adjustment*

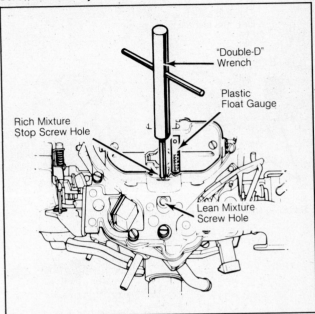

Air horn must be properly installed prior to adjustment.

D" wrench, turn rich mixture stop screw until total solenoid travel (difference between readings) is 4/32". *See Fig. 6.*

4) After adjustment, install lean mixture screw plug and rich mixture stop screw plug. Plugs must be installed to seal settings and to prevent fuel vapor loss. *See Fig. 7.*

Fig. 7: *Installing Lean Mixture Screw Plug and Rich Mixture Stop Screw Plug*

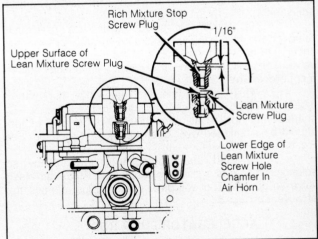

Plugs seal settings and prevent loss of fuel vapor.

IDLE MIXTURE (BENCH ADJUSTMENT)

NOTE: This is a preliminary adjustment only. It is required to ensure that mixture screws and idle air bleed valve are set close to specifications prior to final adjustment. Final adjustment must be made with carburetor installed and engine running. See appropriate TUNE-UP article.

Fig. 8: Idle Mixture Bench Adjustment

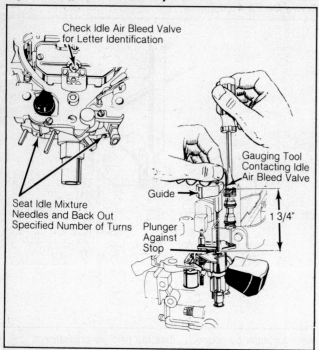

Fig. 9: Air Valve Spring Adjustment

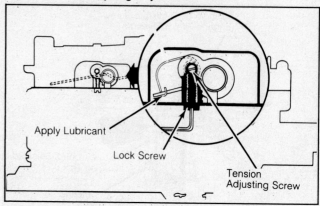

Apply lithium base grease to lubricate contact area.

CHOKE COIL LEVER

NOTE: Choke coil cover uses rivets in place of retaining screws. If necessary to remove choke coil cover, refer to Disassembly and Reassembly procedures in this Section.

Fig. 10: Choke Coil Lever Adjustment

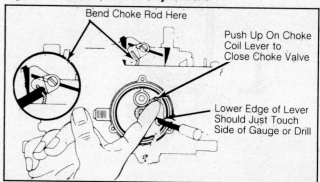

Bend choke rod to adjust.

Final adjustments must be performed with carburetor installed and engine running.

1) With air horn properly installed, lightly seat mixture screws. Back out 3 turns.

2) The idle air bleed valve is sealed with a riveted cover. This cover should not be removed unless required for cleaning, part replacement, improper dwell readings, or if Computer Command Control System Performance Check indicates that carburetor requires adjustment.

3) If idle air bleed cover was previously removed, or if conditions described in step 2) are met, check idle air bleed valve for a letter inscribed on top of valve. This will determine the correct on-vehicle adjustment procedure.

4) To adjust idle air bleed valve, if required, insert air bleed valve gauging tool in throttle side "D" shaped vent hole in air horn casting. Upper end of tool should be positioned over open cavity next to valve. *See Fig. 8.*

5) Hold the gauging tool down lightly so solenoid plunger is against solenoid stop. Adjust air bleed valve so gauging tool will pivot over and just contact top of valve. *See Fig. 8..*

ACCELERATOR PUMP ROD

No pump adjustment is required on carburetors for the Computer Command Control system.

AIR VALVE SPRING

1) Use hex wrench to loosen lock screw. Turn tension adjusting screw counterclockwise until air valve opens part way.

2) Turn tension adjusting screw clockwise until air valve just closes. Then turn adjusting screw clockwise specified number of turns. *See Fig. 9.*

3) Hold adjusting screw and tighten lock screw. Apply lithium base grease to lubricate contact area.

1) Remove retaining rivets. Remove choke cover and coil assembly from choke housing. *See Fig. 10.*

2) Position fast idle speed cam follower on high step of fast idle cam.

3) Push up (counterclockwise) on choke coil tang to close choke valve.

4) Insert specified drill or pin gauge in hole provided in choke housing. Lower edge of choke lever inside housing should just touch drill or pin gauge.

5) To adjust, bend choke rod. *See Fig. 10.*

NOTE: Electric choke units do not use a gasket between choke cover and choke housing.

CHOKE ROD (FAST IDLE CAM)

NOTE: Choke coil lever adjustment must be correct before performing this adjustment. Fast idle speed adjustment must be performed using the Emission Control Tune-Up Decal with carburetor installed and vehicle running. Adjustment is performed with choke valve angle gauge. See procedure at beginning of Adjustments. Do not remove rivets and choke cover to perform this adjustment.

ROCHESTER E4ME 4-BARREL (Cont.)

Fig. 11: Choke Rod (Fast Idle Cam) Adjustment

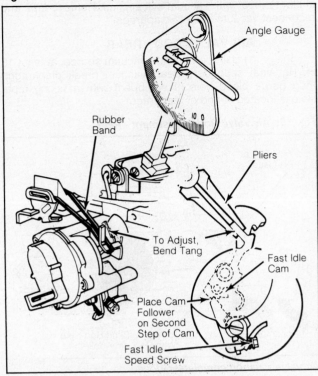

Bend tang on fast idle cam to adjust.

1) Attach rubber band to Green tang of intermediate choke shaft. Open throttle to allow choke valve to close. Set up angle gauge.

2) Place fast idle speed cam follower on second step of fast idle cam against shoulder of highest step. If cam follower does not contact cam, turn in fast idle speed screw additional turns. *See Fig. 11.*

3) Bubble on choke angle gauge should be centered with specified angle mark opposite pointer.

4) To adjust, bend tang on fast idle cam until bubble of choke valve angle gauge is centered.

PRIMARY (FRONT) VACUUM BREAK

NOTE: **Choke coil lever and choke rod (fast idle cam) adjustments must be correct before performing this adjustment. Adjustment is performed with choke valve angle gauge. See procedure at beginning of Adjustments. Do not remove rivets and choke cover to perform this adjustment.**

1) Attach rubber band to Green tang of intermediate choke shaft. Open throttle to allow choke valve to close. Set up angle gauge.

2) Using an outside vacuum source of at least 18 in. Hg, seat primary (front) vacuum break diaphragm. If air valve rod restricts vacuum break plunger from being seated, bend rod to allow full plunger travel. Be sure leaf bucking spring is seated against lever, if equipped. *See Fig. 12.*

NOTE: **On models equipped with air bleed, remove rubber cover from filter and plug vacuum tube with a piece of tape. If bleed hole is in end of diaphragm, plug hole in end of diaphragm**

Fig. 12: Primary (Front) Vacuum Break Adjustment

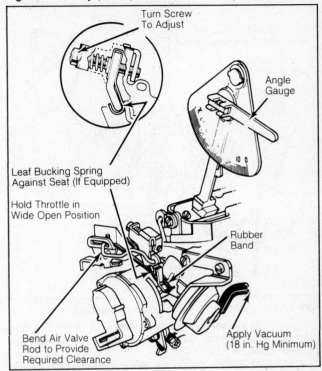

Turn vacuum break adjustment screw to adjust.

with a piece of tape. Remove tape after completing adjustment.

3) Bubble on choke valve angle gauge should be centered with specified degree mark opposite pointer.

4) To adjust, turn vacuum break adjustment screw with vacuum still applied. Adjustment is correct when bubble of choke valve angle gauge is centered.

SECONDARY (REAR) VACUUM BREAK

NOTE: **Choke coil lever and choke rod (fast idle cam) adjustments must be correct before performing this adjustment. Adjustment is performed with choke valve angle gauge. See procedure at beginning of Adjustments. Do not remove rivets and choke cover to perform this adjustment.**

1) Attach rubber band to Green tang of intermediate choke shaft. Open throttle to allow choke valve to close. Set up angle gauge.

2) Using an outside vacuum source of at least 18 in. Hg, seat secondary (rear) vacuum break diaphragm. If air valve rod restricts vacuum break plunger from being seated, bend rod to allow full plunger travel. Be sure leaf bucking spring is compressed, if equipped. *See Fig. 13.*

NOTE: **On models equipped with air bleed, remove rubber cover from filter and plug vacuum tube with a piece of tape. If bleed hole is in end of diaphragm, plug hole in end of diaphragm with tape. On delay models with air bleed, plug end cover with an accelerator pump plunger cup. Remove tape or cup after completion of adjustment.**

1983 Rochester Carburetors

ROCHESTER E4ME 4-BARREL (Cont.)

Fig. 13: Secondary (Rear) Vacuum Break Adjustment

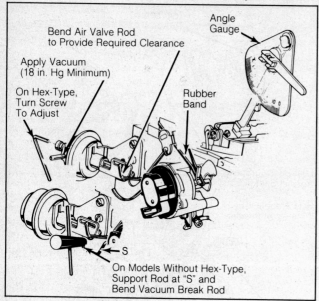

Turn screw or bend vacuum break rod to adjust.

    3) Close choke by pushing up on choke coil lever or vacuum break lever tang. Hold choke closed with a rubber band.

    4) Bubble on choke valve angle gauge should be centered with specified degree mark opposite pointer.

    5) To adjust on models equipped with hex adjustment, use a 1/8" hex wrench to turn adjustment screw in rear cover of vacuum break with vacuum still applied.

    6) To adjust on models without hex adjustment, support rod at "S" and bend vacuum break rod with vacuum still applied. Adjustment is correct when bubble of choke valve angle gauge is centered.

AIR VALVE ROD - FRONT

    1) Using an outside vacuum source, at least 18 in. Hg, seat primary (front) vacuum break diaphragm. Plug purge bleed hole (if equipped) with masking tape. Hole is located in end of diaphragm. *See Fig. 14.*

Fig. 14: Air Valve Rod Adjustment - Front

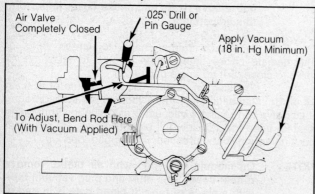

Air valve must be completely closed.

    2) Make sure air valve is completely closed. Measure clearance between rod and end of slot in lever. Clearance can be checked using a specified drill or pin gauge. *See Fig. 14.*

    3) Bend rod at point shown to adjust clearance in slot to .025" with vacuum still applied. Remove tape and reconnect vacuum hose to diaphragm.

AIR VALVE ROD - REAR

    1) Using an outside vacuum source, at least 18 in. Hg, seat secondary (rear) vacuum break diaphragm. Plug purge bleed hole (if equipped) with masking tape. Hole is located in end of diaphragm.

Fig. 15: Air Valve Rod Adjustment - Rear

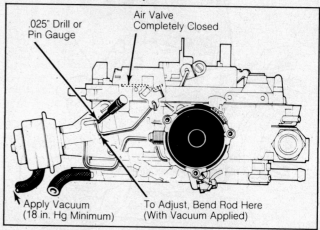

Air valve must be completely closed.

    2) Make sure air valve is completely closed. Measure clearance between rod and end of slot in lever. Clearance can be checked using a specified drill or pin gauge. *See Fig. 15.*

    3) Bend rod at point shown to adjust clearance in slot to .025" with vacuum still applied. Remove tape and reconnect vacuum hose to diaphragm.

AUTOMATIC CHOKE

NOTE: **Choke coil cover is retained in place with rivets. No adjustment is required. If necessary to remove choke coil cover, refer to Disassembly and Reassembly procedures in this Section. Only remove choke cover if major overhaul is required or if choke cover requires replacement.**

CHOKE UNLOADER

NOTE: **Choke coil lever and choke rod (fast idle cam) adjustments must be correct before performing this adjustment. Adjustment is performed with choke valve angle gauge. See procedure at beginning of Adjustments. Do not remove rivets and choke cover to perform this adjustment.**

    1) Attach rubber band to Green tang of intermediate choke shaft. Open throttle to allow choke valve to close. Set up angle gauge. Hold secondary lockout lever away from pin. *See Fig. 16.*

    2) Hold throttle lever in wide open position. Bubble on choke valve angle gauge should be centered with specified degree mark opposite pointer.

    3) To adjust, bend choke unloader tang on fast idle lever until bubble of choke valve angle gauge is centered. Remove gauge.

ROCHESTER E4ME 4-BARREL (Cont.)

Fig. 16: Choke Unloader Adjustment

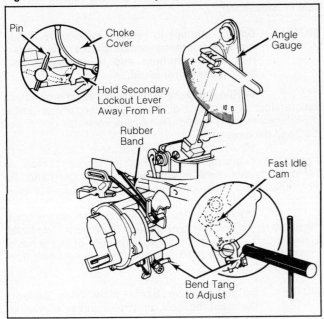

Bend tang to adjust.

SECONDARY THROTTLE VALVE LOCKOUT

Lockout Lever Side Clearance

1) Hold choke valve and throttle valves completely closed. *See Fig. 17.*

Fig. 17: Secondary Throttle Valve Lockout Adjustment

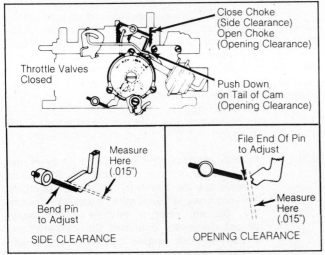

2) Measure secondary throttle valve lockout specified side clearance between pin and lockout lever.

3) Specified lockout lever side clearance is .015". To adjust, bend pin.

Lockout Lever Opening Clearance

1) Push down on tail of fast idle cam and open choke valve completely.

2) Measure secondary throttle valve lockout specified opening clearance between end of pin and toe of lockout lever.

3) Specified clearance is .015". To adjust, file end of lock out pin. Make sure all burrs are removed.

OVERHAUL

DISASSEMBLY

NOTE: Before performing any service on carburetor, it is essential that carburetor be placed on a holding fixture (J-9789-118) to prevent damage to throttle valves.

Air Horn

1) Remove ISC or ISS attaching screws, bracket and assembly. Remove upper choke lever from end of choke shaft by removing retaining screw. Rotate upper choke lever to remove choke rod from slot in lever. Remove choke rod from lower lever inside float bowl casting. Remove rod by holding lower lever outward with small screwdriver and twisting rod counterclockwise.

2) Remove secondary metering rods by removing small screw in top of metering rod hanger. Lift up on metering rod hanger until secondary metering rods clear air horn. Metering rods may be disassembled from hanger by rotating ends out of holes in end of hanger.

3) Using a small drift punch, drive pump lever pivot pin (roll pin) inward until pin is against air cleaner locating boss on air horn casting. Disconnect pump rod from pump lever. Remove vacuum hose from front vacuum break unit and note location for reassembly reference. Remove 11 air horn-to-float bowl screws. Remove 2 countersunk screws located near venturi.

CAUTION: Be careful when removing roll pin to avoid damage to pump lever bosses.

4) Remove secondary air baffle deflector (if equipped) from beneath 2 center air horn screws. Remove air horn from float bowl by lifting straight up. Air horn gasket should remain on float bowl.

NOTE: Use care not to damage mixture control solenoid connector, TPS adjustment lever, and small tubes protruding from air horn. Do not attempt to remove small tubes.

5) Remove primary (front) vacuum break diaphragm. Remove air valve rod from vacuum break and air valve lever. Using fingers only, remove TPS plunger by pushing plunger up through air horn seal. If air horn is removed, lean mixture screw plug and rich mixture stop screw plug must be removed from air horn. Drive plugs out from bottom side. Discard plugs.

6) Remove TPS seal by inverting air horn and remove staking from around seal retainer with a small screwdriver. Remove and discard retainer and seal. Use care removing retainer and seal to prevent damage to air horn casting.

7) Further disassembly of air horn assembly is not required for cleaning purposes. Choke valve and choke valve screws, air valve and air valve shaft should not be removed. Instructions for replacing the air valve closing spring and plastic cam are included in service kit.

8) The air horn has an idle air bleed valve which is preset and sealed at the factory. The idle air bleed valve should not be removed unless "System Performance Check" of Computer Command Control system indicates need for adjustment or repair.

1983 Rochester Carburetors

ROCHESTER E4ME 4-BARREL (Cont.)

NOTE: Air horn assembly, with idle air bleed valve installed, should be cleaned only in low volatile cleaning solvent. Do not place air horn (with idle air bleed valve) in carburetor cleaner. No tamper-resistant plug should be removed during normal carburetor cleaning and servicing unless carburetor or mixture control solenoid has been diagnosed as cause of poor engine performance.

9) If necessary to replace idle air bleed valve or disassemble air horn for immersion in carburetor cleaner, cover internal bowl vents and air inlets to bleed valve with tape. Drill off rivet heads of bleed valve cover with a .110" (No. 35) drill. Drive remainder of rivet out of tower with drift and small hammer. Lift out cover over valve and remove remaining rivet pieces from inside tower.

10) After removing cover, check for letter identification on top of idle air bleed valve. This will determine the necessary adjustment procedure after reassembly. Turn valve counterclockwise and remove from air horn. Remove and discard "O" ring seals from air bleed valve. Air bleed valve is serviced as a complete assembly only.

NOTE: A missing air valve cover indicates that idle air bleed valve setting has been changed from original factory setting.

Float Bowl

1) Remove solenoid metering rod plunger by lifting straight upward. Remove air horn gasket by lifting off of dowel locating pins. Discard gasket.

2) Remove pump plunger and return spring from pump well. Remove staking holding TPS in bowl. To do so, protect gasket surface by laying a flat piece of metal across casting.

3) Using a small screwdriver, lightly depress and hold TPS down against spring tension. Carefully remove staking from around TPS by prying upward with a small chisel against the metal piece (not bowl casting).

4) Push up from bottom on electrical connector and remove TPS and connector assembly from bowl. Use care not to damage sensor during removal. Remove spring from bottom of TPS well. Remove plastic filler block from float valve.

5) Carefully remove each metering rod from metering jet. Make sure return spring is removed with each rod. Remove return spring by sliding it off metering rod.

6) Remove screws connecting mixture control solenoid connector to float bowl. Do not remove connector from float bowl at this time. Using adjusting tool (J-28696), remove lean mixture screw. Carefully lift solenoid and connector assembly from bowl.

NOTE: Do not remove plunger return spring or connector from solenoid body. Solenoid and connector are serviced as an assembly.

7) Remove plastic insert from solenoid connector cavity in float bowl (if used). Remove solenoid screw tension spring (next to float hanger clip). Remove float assembly and needle valve by lifting straight up. Remove needle valve seat and gasket.

8) Remove large mixture control solenoid tension spring from boss on bottom of float bowl located between metering jets. Remove primary main metering jets (if necessary).

NOTE: Do not attempt to remove secondary metering jets (metering orifice plates). Secondary jets are permanent and if damaged, float bowl must be replaced.

9) Remove accelerator pump discharge check ball retainer and check ball. Remove secondary air baffle, if replacement is required. Remove accelerator pump well baffle (if necessary).

10) If equipped, remove rear vacuum break hose and retaining screws. Rotate vacuum break to remove vacuum break link from slot in plunger head. Do not remove non-adjustable vacuum break link until after removal of choke assembly from float bowl.

11) Align a .159" (No. 21) drill on choke cover retaining rivets and drill only enough to remove rivet head. Using a drift and hammer, drive remainder of rivets out of choke housing. Remove 3 retainers and choke cover from choke housing.

NOTE: Do not remove baffle plate from beneath thermostatic coil on choke cover of hot air type chokes.

12) Remove retaining screw and washer from inside choke housing. Slide choke housing from float bowl. Remove rear vacuum break link from intermediate choke lever.

13) Remove secondary throttle valve lockout lever from float bowl. Remove lower choke lever from inside float bowl cavity by turning float bowl upside down. Remove coil lever retaining screw from end of intermediate choke shaft and remove lever.

14) Slide intermediate choke shaft from choke housing. Remove fast idle cam from intermediate choke shaft.

15) Remove intermediate choke shaft cup seal from float bowl insert. Do not remove insert. Remove fuel inlet nut, gasket and filter. Remove 3 throttle body-to-float bowl screws and throttle body.

Throttle Body

1) Remove accelerator pump rod from throttle lever by rotating rod until tang aligns with slot in lever.

NOTE: Further disassembly of throttle body is not required for normal cleaning. Throttle valve screws are permanently staked in position. Throttle body is serviced as complete assembly. Do not remove mixture screw plugs unless diagnosis indicates the carburetor is cause of poor engine performance or idle mixture needles or throttle body must be replaced. If necessary to remove plugs, continue as follows:

2) Turn throttle body over, and position on a holding fixture with manifold side up. Make 2 parallel cuts in throttle body using small hacksaw, cutting on each side of idle mixture needle plug. Cuts should reach down to steel plug, but no more than 1/8" beyond locator points. Distance between saw marks will depend upon size of punch used.

3) Place a flat punch at a point near ends of saw marks. Hold punch at 45° angle and drive it into

ROCHESTER E4ME 4-BARREL (Cont.)

Fig. 18: *Exploded View of Rochester Model E4ME 4-Barrel Carburetor*

1. Air Horn Assembly
2. Air Horn Gasket
3. Pump Actuating Lever
4. Pump Lever Hinge Pin
5. Long Air Horn Screws (2)
6. Short Air Horn Screws
7. Air Horn Countersunk Screws (2)
8. Solenoid Connector-to-Air Horn Gasket
9. Secondary Metering Rods (2)
10. Secondary Metering Rod Holder and Screw
11. Secondary Air Baffle
12. Idle Air Bleed Valve
13. Thick "O" Ring
14. Thin "O" Ring
15. TPS Actuator Plunger
16. TPS Plunger Seal
17. TPS Seal Retainer
18. TPS Adjusting Screw
19. TPS Screw Plug
20. Pump Plunger Seal
21. Pump Seal Retainer
22. Solenoid Rich Mixture Stop Screw
23. Solenoid Rich Mixture Stop Screw Plug
24. Solenoid Lean Mixture Screw Plug
25. Front (Primary) Vacuum Break
26. Vacuum Break Attaching Screws
27. Vacuum Hose
28. Air Valve Rod
29. Upper Choke Rod Lever
30. Choke Lever Screw
31. Choke Rod
32. Lower Choke Rod Lever
33. Intermediate Choke Shaft Seal
34. Secondary Lockout Lever
35. Rear (Secondary) Vacuum Break Link
36. Intermediate Choke Shaft and Lever
37. Fast Idle Cam
38. Hot Air Choke Housing-to-Bowl Seal
39. Choke Housing
40. Choke Housing-to-Bowl Screw
41. Hot Air Choke Intermediate Choke Shaft Seal
42. Choke Coil Lever
43. Choke Coil Lever Screw
44. Hot Air Choke Thermostatic Cover Gasket
45. Hot Air Choke Cover and Coil Assembly
46. Electric Choke Cover and Coil Assembly
47. Rivet Service Kit
48. Rear Vacuum Break
49. Rear Vacuum Break Screws
50. Float Bowl Assembly
51. Primary Metering Jets (2)
52. Pump Discharge Ball
53. Pump Discharge Ball Retainer
54. Pump Well Baffle
55. Needle and Seat Assembly
56. Float Assembly
57. Float Assembly Hinge Pin
58. Primary Metering Rod (2)
59. Primary Metering Rod Springs
60. Float Bowl Insert
61. Bowl Cavity Insert
62. Connector Attaching Screw
63. Mixture Control Solenoid and Plunger Assembly
64. Solenoid Tension Spring
65. Solenoid Lean Mixture Screw
66. Solenoid Adj. Screw Spring
67. Pump Return Spring
68. Pump Assembly
69. Pump Link
70. Secondary Bore Baffle
71. Throttle Position Sensor (TPS)
72. TPS Tension Spring
73. Fuel Inlet Filter Nut
74. Filter Nut Gasket
75. Fuel Inlet Filter
76. Fuel Filter Spring
77. Idle Stop Screw
78. Idle Stop Screw Spring
79. Idle Speed Solenoid (If Equipped)
80. Throttle Return Spring Bracket
81. Idle Load Compensator (ILC) (If Equipped)
82. Idle Speed Control (ISC) (If Equipped)
83. Attaching Screws
84. Throttle Body Assembly
85. Throttle Body Gasket
86. Throttle Body Screw
87. Idle Needle and Springs (2)
88. Fast Idle Adjusting Screw
89. Fast Idle Screw Spring
90. Vacuum Hose "T"
91. Flange Gasket

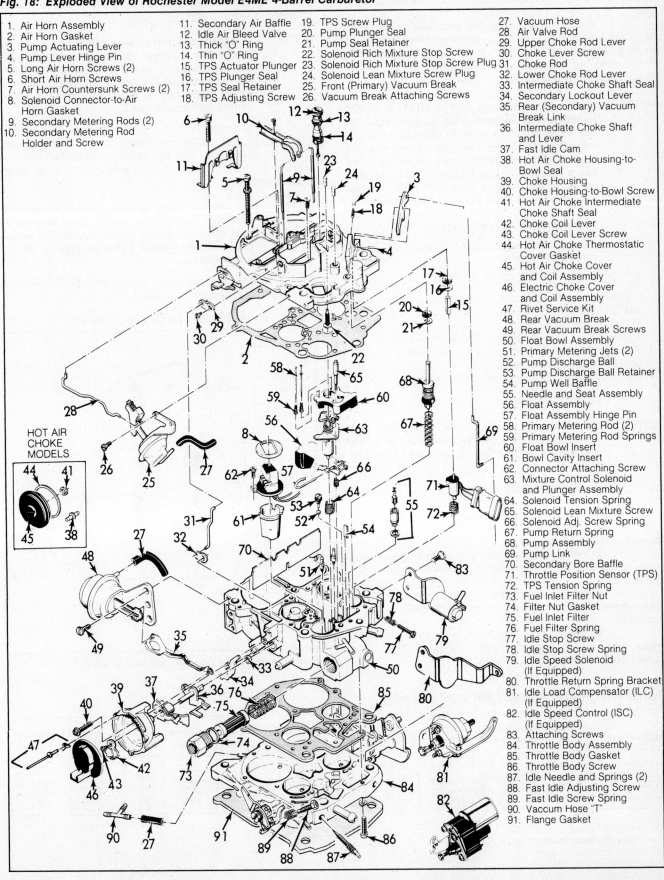

HOT AIR CHOKE MODELS

1983 Rochester Carburetors

ROCHESTER E4ME 4-BARREL (Cont.)

throttle body until casting breaks away, exposing steel plug.

    4) Hold punch vertically and drive it into steel plug. Then hold punch at 45° angle and drive plug out of casting. Repeat process for remaining mixture needle. When removing or installing needles, refer to Idle Mixture (Bench Adjustment) procedure in this article.

NOTE: **Hardened steel plug will shatter. It is not necessary to remove plug completely. Remove just enough pieces to allow idle mixture adjusting tool to be used to remove mixture screws and springs. Idle mixture screw head has a "double-D" configuration and can also be removed using a piece of 7/32" copper tubing that has been partially flattened.**

CLEANING & INSPECTION

- Use a regular carburetor cleaning solution. Soak components long enough to thoroughly clean all surfaces and passages of foreign matter.
- Do not soak any components containing rubber, leather or plastic. Particularly do not soak air horn with idle air bleed valve installed, electric choke, ISS, ISC, TPS, thermostatic choke cover and coil, vacuum break diaphragms, pump plunger and other such parts.
- Remove any residue after cleaning by rinsing components in a suitable solvent.
- Blow out all passages with dry compressed air.

REASSEMBLY

NOTE: **Use new gaskets and seals. Make sure that new gaskets fit correctly and that all holes and slots are punched through and correctly located.**

    Reassemble carburetor in reverse order of disassembly, noting the following:

    1) The intermediate choke shaft lever and fast idle cam are assembled correctly when tang on lever is beneath fast idle cam.

    2) When installing float and retaining pin, make sure open end of float retaining pin faces accelerator pump well.

    3) When installing fuel inlet valve, hook pull clip over edge of flat on float arm. Do not hook clip in holes in float arm.

    4) When installing mixture control solenoid, make sure pin on end of solenoid aligns with hole in raised boss at bottom of float bowl.

    5) Install, adjust and plug all screws to restore tamper-resistant design.

NOTE: **If choke coil cover was removed, it will be necessary to install service rivet retaining kit. Before installing cover, place fast idle screw on high step of fast idle cam. Align notch in cover with raised boss on housing cover flange and install rivets.**

    6) Place fast idle screw on high step of fast idle cam. Install choke coil cover if removed, aligning notch in cover with tab on cover retainer (supplied in service kit). Be sure coil tang engages pick-up lever. Install blind rivets.

NOTE: **On E4ME models, ground contact for electric choke is provided by metal plate located at rear of choke cover assembly. Do not install choke cover gasket between electric choke and housing.**

    7) Install air horn screws and tighten evenly, securely and in sequence shown in *Fig. 19*.

Fig. 19: Air Horn Screw Tightening Sequence

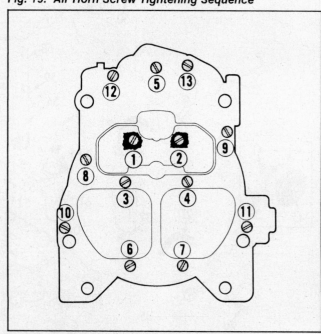

Screws 1 and 2 are countersunk next to venturi.

CARBURETOR ADJUSTMENT SPECIFICATIONS

Application	Float Level	Accel. Pump	Idle Air Bleed	Air Valve Spring [1]	Choke Coil Lever	Choke Rod	Vacuum Break		Air Valve Rod	Auto. Choke	Choke Unloader	Secondary Lockout
							Primary	Secondary				
17083506	7/16	TR	1 3/4	7/8	.120"	20°	27°	36°	.025"	TR	36°	.015"
17083508	7/16	TR	1 3/4	7/8	.120"	20°	27°	36°	.025"	TR	36°	.015"
17083524	7/16	TR	1 3/4	7/8	.120"	20°	25°	36°	.025"	TR	36°	.015"
17083526	7/16	TR	1 3/4	7/8	.120"	20°	25°	36°	.025"	TR	36°	.015"

[1] — Specification is number of turns.

ROCHESTER M4MC & M4ME 4-BARREL

CARBURETOR APPLICATION

CHEVROLET & GMC (ROCHESTER) CARBURETOR NO.

Application	Man. Trans.	Auto. Trans.
5.0L V8		
C 10		
Federal		
Without A/C	17083223	17083222
With A/C	17083225	17083224
C, G & K 10		
Federal		
Without A/C	17083220	17083226
With A/C	17083221	17083226
High Alt.	17083231	17083230
5.7L V8		
C, G & K 10		
Federal		
Without A/C		17083290
With A/C		17083292
High Alt.		17083234
C & K 20		
Federal		17082213
G 30		
Federal		17083298
Calif.		17083507
K 10		
Federal		
Without A/C	17083291	
With A/C	17083293	
High Alt.	17083235	
C, K & P 20/30 [1]		
Federal		17080213
Calif.	17080513	
7.4L V8		
C, K & P 20/30 [1]		
Federal		17080212
Calif.	17080512	

[1] — P 20 not available in California.

CARBURETOR IDENTIFICATION

The Rochester M4MC and M4ME carburetor numbers are stamped vertically on the float bowl, near the secondary throttle. If float bowl is replaced, follow manufacturer's instructions contained in service package to transfer part number to new float bowl. See Fig. 1.

Fig. 1: Carburetor Part Number Location

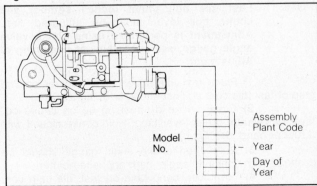

If float bowl is replaced, transfer part number.

DESCRIPTION

The M4MC carburetor is a 2-stage downdraft design. The primary side has a triple venturi system. The secondary side is composed of 2 large bores using the air valve principle (fuel is metered in direct proportion to amount of air passing through secondary bores).

A baffle is attached to secondary side of the air horn above main well bleed tubes. This baffle deflects incoming air to improve secondary nozzle operation during heavy acceleration. The M4MC uses a bowl-mounted choke housing with thermostatic control assembly.

Model M4ME is used for light duty emission vehicles. The M4ME is basically the same carburetor as the M4MC. The M4ME does not have an aneroid cavity and is equipped with an electric rather than hot air choke.

ADJUSTMENT

NOTE: **For all on vehicle adjustments, see TUNE-UP SERVICE PROCEDURES.**

ANGLE GAUGE ADJUSTMENT TOOL

Manufacturer recommends that some carburetor adjustments be performed using a choke valve angle gauge (Kent-Moore tool no. J-26701). While preparations and actual adjustments may vary with each individual adjustment, the procedure for using the angle gauge to check the choke valve angle remains the same. Use the following procedure to perform adjustments requiring the use of the choke angle gauge.

1) Rotate degree scale on angle gauge so that 0° mark is opposite pointer.

2) With choke valve closed, place angle gauge magnet squarely on choke valve. Rotate leveling bubble on angle gauge until it is centered. Rotate degree scale until specified degree mark is opposite pointer. See Fig. 2.

3) Perform individual adjustment preparations as outlined in the following carburetor adjustments requiring angle gauge. If bubble is centered, adjustment is correct. If not, adjust carburetor as outlined.

Fig. 2: Choke Valve Angle Gauge

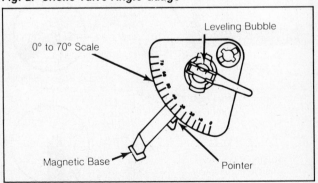

This gauge must be used to perform certain adjustments.

FLOAT LEVEL

1) Remove air horn. Remove gasket from main body casting. Hold float retainer firmly in place.

2) Using light finger pressure, gently push float against needle. Using a "T" scale, measure distance from

ROCHESTER M4MC & M4ME 4-BARREL (Cont.)

top of casting to top of float. Gauging point should be 3/16" back from end of float at toe. *See Fig. 3.*

3) If adjustment is needed, remove float from main body of carburetor. Bend float arm up or down. Install float and recheck float level.

4) Be sure to check float alignment after adjusting operation. Install new gasket and reinstall air horn.

Fig. 3: Float Level Adjustment

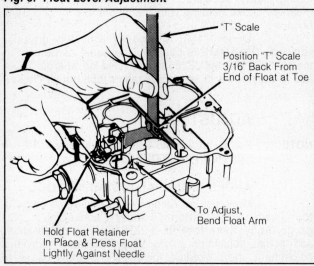

Measure distance from float bowl casting to float.

ACCELERATOR PUMP

1) Close throttle valves completely. Make sure fast idle cam follower is off fast idle cam steps. Bend secondary throttle closing tang to fully close primary throttle valves. Readjust after accelerator pump adjustment.

Fig. 4: Accelerator Pump Adjustment

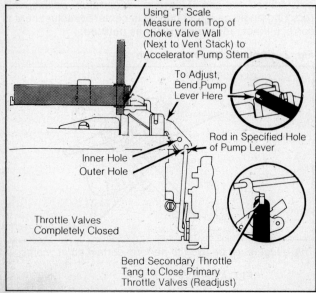

Make sure fast idle cam follower is off fast idle cam steps.

2) Make sure accelerator pump rod is in specified hole (inner or outer) of accelerator pump lever.

3) Using a "T" scale, measure specified distance from top of choke valve wall (next to vent stack) to top of pump stem.

4) To adjust, bend accelerator pump lever at point shown in *Fig. 4.*

CHOKE COIL LEVER

NOTE: **Choke coil cover is retained on housing with rivets to prevent tampering with factory adjustment. If necessary to remove cover, refer to Disassembly and Reassembly procedures in this article. If rivets and cover are removed, a choke thermostat cover retainer kit is required for reassembly.**

1) Remove choke thermostatic cover from choke housing. Place fast idle speed screw on high step of fast idle cam. Push up on thermostatic coil tang (counterclockwise) until choke valve is fully closed.

2) Insert specified drill or pin gauge in hole provided in choke housing. Lower edge of choke lever (inside housing) should just touch drill or pin gauge. *See Fig. 5.*

Fig. 5: Choke Coil Lever Adjustment

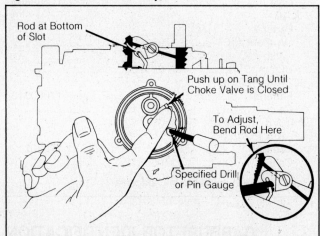

Place fast idle speed screw on high step of fast idle cam.

3) To adjust, bend choke rod at point shown in *Fig. 5.* Reinstall choke cover and adjust.

CHOKE ROD (FAST IDLE CAM)

NOTE: **Fast idle adjustment (bench setting) and choke coil lever must be adjusted first. Adjustment is performed using choke valve angle gauge, see procedure at beginning of Adjustment.**

1) Place fast idle speed cam follower on 2nd step of fast idle cam against shoulder of highest step.

2) Close choke by pushing up on choke coil lever or vacuum break lever tang. Hold choke closed with a rubber band. *See Fig. 6.*

3) Bubble on choke angle gauge should be centered with specified angle mark opposite pointer.

4) To adjust, bend tang on fast idle cam until bubble of choke valve angle gauge is centered.

ROCHESTER M4MC & M4ME 4-BARREL (Cont.)

Fig. 6: Choke Rod (Fast Idle Cam) Adjustment

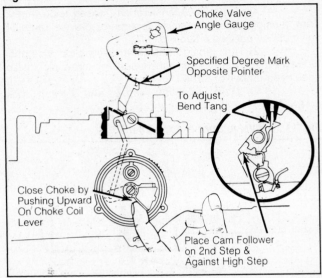

Hold choke closed with a rubber band.

FRONT AIR VALVE ROD

1) Using an outside vacuum source, seat primary (front) choke vacuum break diaphragm. Plug purge bleed hole (if equipped) with masking tape. Hole is found in end of diaphragm.

2) Make sure air valve is completely closed. Insert a .025" drill or pin gauge between rod and end of slot in lever. *See Fig. 7.*

Fig. 7: Front Air Valve Rod Adjustment

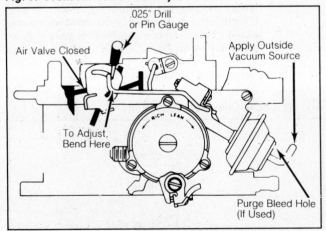

Place drill or pin gauge between rod and end of slot in lever.

3) Bend rod at point shown in *Fig. 7* to adjust clearance in slot. Remove tape and reconnect vacuum hose to diaphragm.

REAR AIR VALVE ROD
Federal M4ME Only

1) Using an outside vacuum source, seat secondary (rear) choke vacuum break diaphragm.

2) Make sure air valve is completely closed. Insert a .025" drill or pin gauge between rod and end of slot in lever. *See Fig. 8.*

3) Bend rod at point shown in *Fig. 8* to adjust clearance in slot. Reconnect vacuum hose to diaphragm.

Fig. 8: Rear Air Valve Rod Adjustment

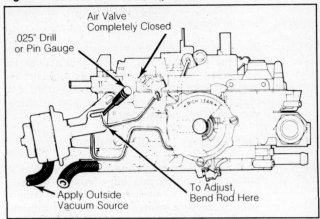

This adjustment is performed on Federal M4ME models only.

PRIMARY VACUUM BREAK

NOTE: Choke coil lever adjustment must be correct before performing this adjustment. This adjustment is performed using the choke angle gauge, see procedure at beginning of Adjustment.

1) Using an outside vacuum source of at least 15 in. Hg, seat primary vacuum break diaphragm. Plug purge bleed hole (if equipped) with masking tape. Hole is found in end of diaphragm.

2) Air valve rod must not keep vacuum unit from fully retracting. If necessary, bend air valve rod at air valve lever to provide clearance for proper adjustment. Adjust final air rod clearance after setting primary vacuum break adjustment.

3) Lightly close choke by pushing up on choke coil lever or vacuum break lever tang. Hold choke closed with a rubber band. Make sure bucking spring on diaphragm plunger (if equipped) is compressed and seated. Bubble on angle gauge should be centered with specified degree mark opposite pointer. *See Fig. 9.*

Fig. 9: Primary Vacuum Break Adjustment

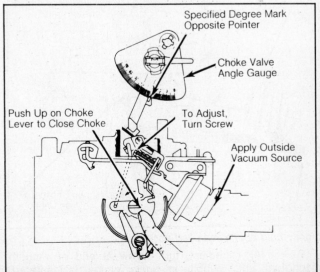

Lightly hold choke in closed position.

1983 Rochester Carburetors

ROCHESTER M4MC & M4ME 4-BARREL (Cont.)

4) To adjust, turn vacuum break adjustment screw in until bubble of choke valve angle gauge is centered. Remove gauge.

NOTE: Some models will have tamper-proof plugs over the adjustment screw. To gain access to adjustment screw, remove vacuum break bracket from carburetor. Carefully grind off plugs over adjustment screw and replace vacuum break diaphragm.

SECONDARY VACUUM BREAK

NOTE: Choke coil lever adjustment must be correct before performing this adjustment. This adjustment is performed using the choke angle gauge, see procedure at beginning of Adjustment.

1) Using an outside vacuum source of at least 15 in. Hg, seat secondary vacuum break diaphragm. Plug purge bleed hole (if equipped) with masking tape. Hole is found in end of diaphragm.

2) Air valve rod must not keep vacuum unit from fully retracting. If necessary, bend air valve rod at air valve lever to provide clearance for proper adjustment. Adjust final air rod clearance after setting secondary vacuum break adjustment.

3) Lightly close choke valve by pushing up on choke coil lever or vacuum break lever tang. Hold in position with a rubber band. Make sure bucking spring on diaphragm plunger (if equipped) is compressed and seated. Bubble on choke valve angle gauge should be centered with specified degree mark opposite pointer. *See Fig. 10.*

Fig. 10: Secondary Vacuum Break Adjustment

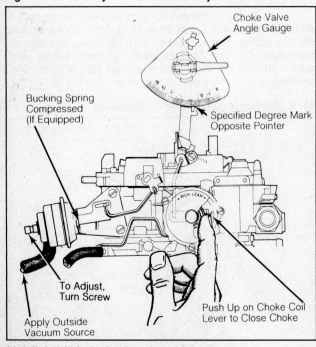

Lightly hold choke in closed position.

4) To adjust, turn screw at end of vacuum diaphragm until bubble in angle gauge is centered. Remove gauge.

AIR VALVE SPRING

1) Using an Allen wrench, loosen lock screw. Turn tension adjusting screw counterclockwise until air valve opens part way. *See Fig. 11.*

2) Turn tension adjusting screw clockwise until air valve just closes. Then turn adjusting screw clockwise specified number of turns.

3) Hold adjusting screw and tighten lock screw.

Fig. 11: Air Valve Spring Adjustment

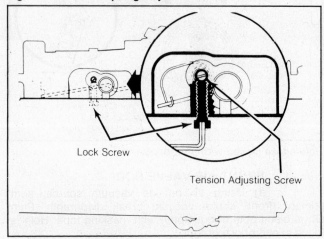

Tighten adjusting screw specified number of turns.

AUTOMATIC CHOKE

NOTE: Choke coil cover is retained on housing by rivets to prevent tampering with factory adjustment. If necessary to remove cover, refer to Disassembly and Reassembly procedures in this article.

CHOKE UNLOADER

Fig. 12: Choke Unloader Adjustment

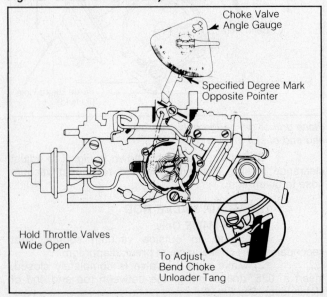

Choke thermostatic cover and coil must be installed prior to performing adjustment.

ROCHESTER M4MC & M4ME 4-BARREL (Cont.)

NOTE: This adjustment is performed using the choke valve angle gauge. See procedure at beginning of Adjustments. Choke coil lever must be adjusted correctly, and fast idle adjustment must be set before proceeding.

1) If removed, install choke thermostatic cover and coil. Close choke by pushing up on tang on vacuum break lever. Hold in position with a rubber band. Hold primary throttle valves wide open. See Fig. 12.

2) Bubble on choke valve angle gauge should be centered with specified degree mark opposite pointer.

3) To adjust, bend choke unloader tang on throttle lever until bubble of choke valve angle gauge is centered.

SECONDARY THROTTLE VALVE LOCKOUT

Lockout Lever Side Clearance

1) Hold choke valve and throttle valves closed.

2) Measure secondary throttle valve lockout lever side clearance between pin and lockout lever. Bend pin to obtain clearance of .015". See Fig. 13.

Lockout Lever Opening Clearance

1) Push down on tail of fast idle cam to completely open choke valve.

2) Measure secondary throttle valve lockout lever opening clearance between end of pin and toe of lockout lever. See Fig. 13.

3) File end of lockout pin to obtain clearance of .015". Make sure all burrs are removed.

Fig. 13: Secondary Throttle Valve Lockout Adjustments

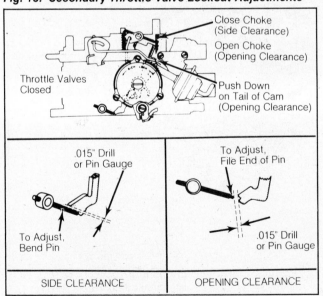

Both steps must be done to perform adjustment.

OVERHAUL

DISASSEMBLY

NOTE: Before performing any service on carburetor, it is essential that carburetor is placed on a holding fixture (J-9789-118 or equivalent) to prevent damage to throttle valves.

Idle Speed Solenoid

If equipped with idle speed solenoid, remove screws securing solenoid and bracket to float bowl. Remove assembly.

Air Horn

1) Remove upper choke lever from end of choke shaft by removing retaining screw. Rotate upper choke lever to remove choke rod from slot in lever. Remove choke rod from lower (inner) lever inside float bowl casting. Remove rod by holding lower lever outward with small screwdriver and twisting rod counterclockwise.

2) Remove vacuum hose from primary vacuum break unit. Remove secondary metering rods by removing small screw in top of metering rod hanger. Lift upward on metering rod hanger until secondary metering rods are completely out of air horn. Metering rods may be disassembled from hanger by rotating ends out of holes in end of hanger.

3) Drive pump lever pivot pin inward until pump lever can be removed. Disconnect pump rod from pump lever. Note location of pump rod for reassembly reference.

4) Remove air horn-to-float bowl attaching screws. Countersunk screws (2) are located next to venturi. Remove secondary air baffle deflector (if equipped) from beneath 2 center attaching screws. Remove air horn from float bowl by lifting straight up. Gasket should remain on float bowl for later removal.

5) Remove primary vacuum break attaching screws and vacuum break diaphragm. Disconnect diaphragm from air valve rod and remove rod from air valve lever.

6) Invert air horn to remove pump plunger stem seal (if used). Using a small screwdriver, remove staking holding seal retainer in position. Remove and discard retainer and seal. Use care removing pump plunger stem seal from air horn to prevent damage to air horn casting.

7) It is not necessary to remove choke valve and shaft unless bent or damaged. Choke valve screws are staked in position. Staking must be removed before screws are removed.

8) Further disassembly of air horn is not required. Air valve screws are permanently staked in position. However, a repair kit is available for air valve closing spring and center plastic eccentric cam.

Float Bowl

1) Remove air horn gasket by lifting out of dowel locating pins. Lift tab of gasket from beneath power piston hanger, being careful not to distort springs holding main metering rods.

2) Remove pump plunger and return spring from pump well. Remove power piston and metering rods by depressing piston stem and allowing it to snap free. Repeat until piston force dislodges retainer. Do not use pliers on metering rod hanger to remove power piston. Remove power piston spring from well.

NOTE: The adjustable part throttle (APT) metering rod adjustment screw is located in a well next to power piston well. The APT is preset at the factory and no attempt should be made to alter its setting. If a new float bowl is required, it will contain a preset APT screw.

3) Remove metering rods from power piston by disconnecting tension spring from top of each rod. Rotate rods out of hanger.

1983 Rochester Carburetors

ROCHESTER M4MC & M4ME 4-BARREL (Cont.)

Fig. 14: Exploded View of Rochester Model M4MC and M4ME 4-Barrel Carburetor

1. Air Horn
2. Air Horn Gasket
3. Pump Lever
4. Pump Lever Hinge Pin
5. Long Air Horn Screw (2)
6. Short Air Horn Screw
7. Countersunk Air Horn Screw
8. Secondary Metering Rod (2)
9. Secondary Metering Rod Holder and Screw
10. Secondary Air Baffle
11. Pump Plunger Seal
12. Pump Seal Retainer
13. Primary Vacuum Break Assembly
14. Primary Vacuum Break Screw
15. Vacuum Hose
16. Air Valve Rod
17. Upper Choke Rod Lever
18. Choke Lever Screw
19. Choke Rod
20. Lower Choke Rod Lever
21. Intermediate Choke Shaft Seal
22. Secondary Lockout Lever
23. Secondary Vacuum Break Link
24. Intermediate Choke Shaft and Lever Assembly
25. Fast Idle Cam
26. Choke Housing-to-Bowl Seal (M4MC Models Only)
27. Choke Housing Kit
28. Choke Housing-to-Bowl Screw
29. Intermediate Choke Shaft Seal (M4MC Models Only)
30. Choke Coil Lever
31. Choke Coil Lever Screw
32. Thermostatic Cover Gasket (M4MC Models Only)
33. Thermostatic Cover and Coil Assembly (M4MC Models Only)
34. Thermostatic Cover and Coil Assembly (M4ME Models Only)
35. Thermostatic Cover Kit
36. Secondary Vacuum Break Assy.
37. Secondary Vacuum Break Screw
38. Float Bowl
39. Primary Metering Jet (2)
40. Pump Discharge Ball
41. Pump Discharge Ball Retainer
42. Aneriod Cavity
43. Needle and Seat Assembly
44. Float Assembly
45. Float Hinge Pin
46. Power Piston Assembly

47. Power Piston Spring
48. Primary Metering Rod (2)
49. Metering Rod Retainer Spring
50. Float Bowl Insert
51. Bowl Cavity Insert
52. Pump Return Spring
53. Pump Assembly
54. Pump Rod
55. Secondary Bore Baffle
56. Idle Compensator Assembly
57. Idle Compensator Seal
58. Idle Compensator Cover
59. Idle Comp. Cover Screw
60. Fuel Inlet Filter Nut
61. Filter Nut Gasket
62. Fuel Inlet Filter
63. Fuel Filter Spring
64. Idle Stop Screw

65. Idle Stop Screw Spring
66. Idle Speed Solenoid Assy.
67. Idle Load Compensator Assy.
68. Throttle Return Spring Bracket
69. Throttle Lever Actuator
70. Throttle Lever Actuator Bracket
71. Actuator Nut Washer
72. Actuator Nut
73. Screw
74. Throttle Body
75. Throttle Body Gasket
76. Throttle Body Screw (3)
77. Idle Mixture Needle and Spring Assembly (2)
78. Fast Idle Adjusting Screw
79. Fast Idle Screw Spring
80. Vacuum Hose Tee
81. Flange Gasket

Electric Choke Models

ROCHESTER M4MC & M4ME 4-BARREL (Cont.)

4) Remove plastic filler block located over float valve. Remove float assembly and fuel inlet needle by pulling up on retaining pin. Remove inlet seat and gasket. Remove aneroid cavity from float bowl, if equipped.

5) Remove primary main metering jets. Remove pump discharge check ball retainer and check ball. Do not remove secondary metering jets. These jets are fixed in place, and if damaged, float bowl must be replaced.

6) Remove secondary air baffle, if replacement is required. Remove pump well baffle. Remove secondary vacuum break attaching screws. Rotate vacuum break assembly to remove vacuum break rod from slot in plunger head. On M4ME models, do not remove the non-adjustable vacuum break link at this time.

7) Align a .159" (No. 21) drill on choke cover retaining rivet and drill only enough to remove rivet head. Repeat for remaining 2 rivets. Drive remainder of rivets out of choke housing. Remove choke cover and coil assembly.

8) Remove choke housing retaining screw located inside choke housing. Slide complete choke assembly from float bowl. Remove plastic tube seal from choke housing (M4MC models). On M4MC models, do not remove baffle plate from below coil on choke cover.

9) On M4ME models, remove non-adjustable vacuum break link. On all models, remove secondary throttle valve lockout lever from float bowl. Remove lower (inside) choke lever from inside float bowl cavity.

10) Remove choke coil lever retaining screw at end of intermediate choke shaft. Remove lever. Slide intermediate choke shaft from choke housing. Remove fast idle cam from intermediate choke shaft. On M4MC models, remove and discard cup seal from from inside choke housing shaft hole.

11) On all models, remove cup seal (intermediate choke shaft) from float bowl insert for bowl cleaning. Do not attempt to remove plastic insert.

12) Remove fuel inlet nut, gasket and filter. Remove throttle body-to-float bowl attaching screws and throttle body. Remove throttle body-to-float bowl insulator gasket.

Throttle Body

1) Remove accelerator pump rod from throttle lever by rotating rod until tang on rod aligns with slot in lever.

2) It is not necessary to disassemble throttle body any further. Do not remove idle mixture screw plugs unless it is necessary to replace mixture screws or cleaning and air pressure fails to clean idle mixture passages.

3) If necessary to remove idle mixture plugs, proceed as follows: Invert throttle body and position on a holding fixture with manifold side up. Position a punch in between 2 locator points on manifold side of throttle body. There are 2 locator points adjacent to each mixture screw.

4) Using a hammer, drive punch against throttle body to break out portion of throttle body to gain access to idle mixture screw plugs. Drive out hardened steel plugs.

5) Hardened steel plugs will shatter. It is not necessary to remove plug completely. Remove just enough pieces to allow idle mixture adjusting tool (J-28706) or a thin-walled 3/16" deep socket to be used to remove mixture screws and spring.

CLEANING & INSPECTION

- Use a regular carburetor cleaning solution. Soak components long enough to thoroughly clean all surfaces and passages of foreign matter.
- Remove any residue after cleaning by rinsing components in a suitable solvent.
- Do not soak any components containing rubber, leather or plastic.
- Blow out all passages with dry compressed air.

REASSEMBLY

1) Use new gaskets and seals. Make sure that new gaskets fit correctly. Make sure that all holes and slots are punched through and correctly located. To reassemble carburetor, reverse disassembly procedure and note the following:

2) Install fuel inlet needle pull clip over edge of flat on float arm facing float. Do not hook clip in holes in float arm.

3) Install plastic float bowl filler block after float level adjustment and before metering rod installation.

4) The intermediate choke shaft lever and fast idle cam are installed correctly when tang on lever is beneath fast idle cam. Make choke coil lever adjustments before installing choke coil cover.

5) If choke coil cover was removed, it will be necessary to install replacement rivets supplied in service kit. Do not install choke coil cover until completion of adjustments. Do not use a gasket between choke housing and choke coil cover on M4ME models. Surface contact is needed to provide a ground for electric choke.

6) Place fast idle screw on high step of fast idle cam. Install choke coil cover, aligning notch in cover with tab on cover retainer (supplied in service kit). Install retainer with tab into screw hole in housing nearest front of carburetor. Install remaining self-tapping screws and tighten.

7) When installing air horn screws, note that 2 long screws are installed with lock washers. Countersunk screws (2) are installed next to venturi area. Install secondary air baffle under screws No. 2 and 4. Tighten air horn screws evenly and in sequence. *See Fig. 15.*

Fig. 15: Air Horn Screw Location and Tightening Sequence

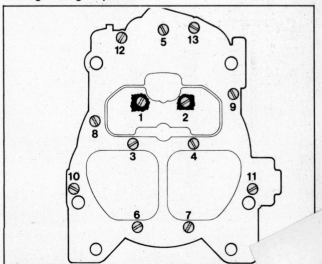

Make sure countersunk screws are installed next to venturi area.

1983 Rochester Carburetors

ROCHESTER M4MC & M4ME 4-BARREL (Cont.)

CARBURETOR ADJUSTMENT SPECIFICATIONS

| Application | Float Level | Accelerator Pump | | Choke Coil Lever | Choke Rod | Vacuum Break | | Air Valve Spring [1] | Auto. Choke | Choke Unloader |
		Stem	Hole			Primary	Secondary			
17080201	15/32"	9/32"	Inner	.120"	46°	.....	23°	7/8	TR	42°
17080205	15/32"	9/32"	Inner	.120"	46°	.....	23°	7/8	TR	42°
17080206	15/32"	9/32"	Inner	.120"	46°	.....	23°	7/8	TR	42°
17080212	3/8"	9/32"	Inner	.120"	46°	24°	30°	3/4	TR	40°
17080213	3/8"	9/32"	Inner	.120"	37°	23°	30°	1	TR	40°
17080290	15/32"	9/32"	Inner	.120"	46°	.....	26°	7/8	TR	42°
17080291	15/32"	9/32"	Inner	.120"	46°	.....	26°	7/8	TR	42°
17080292	15/32"	9/32"	Inner	.120"	46°	.....	26°	7/8	TR	42°
17080298	3/8"	9/32"	Inner	.120"	37°	23°	30°	1	TR	40°
17080507	3/8"	9/32"	Inner	.120"	37°	23°	30°	1	TR	40°
17080512	3/8"	9/32"	Inner	.120"	46°	24°	30°	3/4	TR	40°
17080513	3/8"	9/32"	Inner	.120"	37°	23°	30°	1	TR	40°
17082213	3/8"	9/32"	Inner	.120"	37°	23°	30°	1	TR	40°
17082513	3/8"	9/32"	Inner	.120"	37°	23°	30°	1	TR	40°
17083220	13/32"	9/32"	Inner	.120"	46°	.....	24°	7/8	TR	39°
17083222	13/32"	9/32"	Inner	.120"	46°	.....	24°	7/8	TR	39°
17083223	13/32"	9/32"	Inner	.120"	46°	.....	24°	7/8	TR	39°
17083224	13/32"	9/32"	Inner	.120"	46°	.....	24°	7/8	TR	39°
17083225	13/32"	9/32"	Inner	.120"	46°	.....	24°	7/8	TR	39°
17083226	13/32"	9/32"	Inner	.120"	46°	.....	24°	7/8	TR	39°
17083227	13/32"	9/32"	Inner	.120"	46°	.....	24°	7/8	TR	39°
17083230	13/32"	9/32"	Inner	.120"	46°	.....	26°	7/8	TR	39°
17083231	13/32"	9/32"	Inner	.120"	46°	.....	26°	7/8	TR	39°
17083234	13/32"	9/32"	Inner	.120"	46°	.....	26°	7/8	TR	39°
17083235	13/32"	9/32"	Inner	.120"	46°	.....	26°	7/8	TR	39°
17083290	13/32"	9/32"	Inner	.120"	46°	.....	24°	7/8	TR	39°
17083291	13/32"	9/32"	Inner	.120"	46°	.....	24°	7/8	TR	39°
17083292	13/32"	9/32"	Inner	.120"	46°	.....	24°	7/8	TR	39°
17083293	13/32"	9/32"	Inner	.120"	46°	.....	24°	7/8	TR	39°

[1] — Specification is amount of turns.
TR — Tamper Resistant.

DIESEL KIKI — FORD

Ranger

DESCRIPTION

The Ranger diesel pickup fuel injection system consists of a combination injection pump and fuel distributor, 4 fuel injection nozzles, a fuel filter with an integral priming pump, a water separator, fuel lines and the fuel tank. The injection system is also tied in with a quick start (glow plug) system.

The injection pump is a vane type pump and is driven by the engine timing gears. An altitude compensator and a cold start device are installed on the pump to modify injection duration as necessary. The distributor portion of the pump contains a fuel cut solenoid to stop fuel flow to the injectors after the ignition switch is turned off. *See Fig. 1.*

The injectors use a needle type valve at the end of the nozzle. Injector opening pressure can be changed by adding or subtracting adjusting shim thickness. The adjusting shim is located just above the needle valve return spring in the injector.

The quick start system consists of a glow plug in each cylinder, 2 relays, a ballast resistor, a glow plug control unit as well as various switches and warning lights.

OPERATION

FUEL INJECTION PUMP

The Diesel Kiki single plunger mechanical injection pump contains a low pressure vane-type fuel pump, a high pressure distributor-type injection pump, a centrifugal governor and an injection timing advance mechanism.

The vane pump output pressure (sometimes referred to as injection pump body pressure) averages 50-100 psi (3.5-7.0 kg/cm²) depending upon engine speed and application. The plunger injection pump boosts the fuel pressure to about 2000 psi (140 kg/cm²). The pump assembly is also equipped with an electric fuel shut-off valve.

INJECTORS

The injection nozzles spray fuel into a prechamber as each compression stroke occurs. Nozzles can be disassembled, cleaned and adjusted to correct improper spray patterns.

Injector opening pressure is adjusted with a shim on top of the needle valve return spring. *See Fig. 3.* The injector receives a high pressure pulse of fuel which forces open the needle valve allowing the fuel to pass into the prechamber.

Fig. 1: Diesel Kiki Diesel Fuel Injection Pump

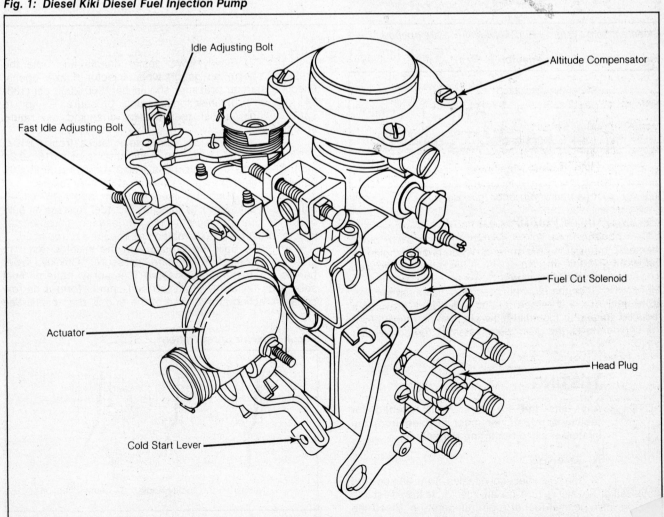

Shop disassembly of injection pump is not recommended.

1983 Diesel Fuel Injection
DIESEL KIKI — FORD (Cont.)

Fig. 2: Ranger Diesel Fuel System

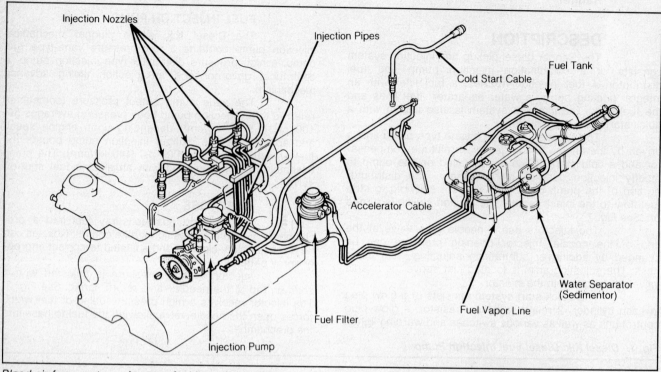

Bleed air from system whenever fuel lines are opened.

Fig. 3: Ranger Diesel Injector

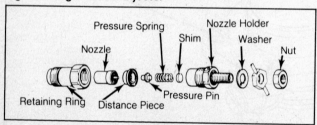

Injector must be free of dirt prior to reassembly.

GLOW PLUGS

The glow plug system uses 4 glow plugs (heaters) to assist in cold starting. When engine coolant is below 86°F (30°C), the No. 2 glow plug relay is energized to quickly heat the glow plugs.

When the glow plug reaches maximum temperature, relay No. 1 is turned off and relay No. 2 provides a reduced voltage to maintain glow plug temperature. When the engine starts, the glow plug system is turned off. *See Fig. 5.*

TESTING

NOTE: Any time the fuel system is opened for testing or repair, air must be bled from the system prior to restarting the engine.

INJECTORS

1) Remove injection nozzles from engine and install each nozzle in turn on an injector tester. Test the injectors using diesel fuel at room temperature. Bleed the air out of the tester by pumping the handle several times.

2) Slowly lower tester handle and note the pressure shown on gauge when injector nozzle opens. Injection starting pressure should be 1960-2030 psi (138-143 kg/cm²). If injection starting pressure is not to specifications, adjust pressure by changing the return spring shim.

3) Shims are available in sizes from 0.0197" (0.5 mm) to 0.06" (1.54 mm) in increments of 0.016" (0.04 mm). Changing shim thickness 1 size should result in a 68 psi (4.8 kg/cm²) change in injection starting pressure.

4) Using the injector tester, apply 1676-1746 psi (118-123 kg/cm²) to injector. No fuel leakage should occur at this pressure range. If leakage does occur, injector must be disassembled and repaired or replaced.

5) Build up pressure in the injector tester to just below injection starting pressure. Quickly lower handle on tester and observe fuel spray pattern. Fuel should be uniformly atomized and should form a narrow cone projecting straight out of the end of the nozzle. *See Fig. 4.*

Fig. 4: Injector Spray Pattern

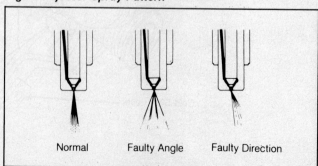

Injector must not drip when needle valve is closed.

DIESEL KIKI — FORD (Cont.)

Fig. 5: *Ranger Diesel Quick Start System Schematic Diagram*

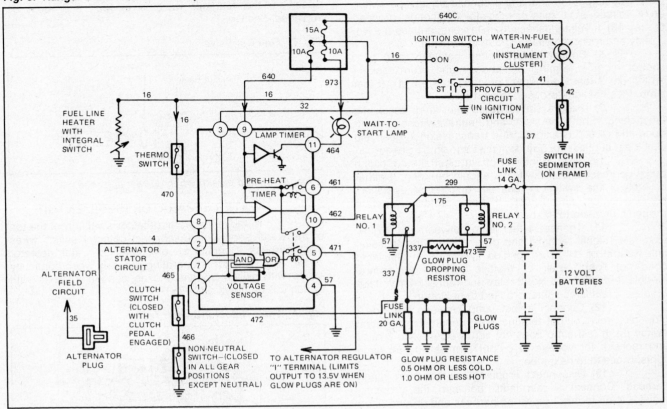

GLOW PLUG SYSTEM

1) Place transmission in neutral. If engine coolant temperature is above 86°F (30°C), jumper the connections at the coolant thermoswitch. Turn ignition on. Using a voltmeter, check voltage at each glow plug lead. Voltage should be at least 11 volts at each lead for 6 seconds, then drop to 4.2-5.3 volts.

2) If voltage is ok, remove jumper from thermoswitch and proceed to step **16)**. If voltage is present at 1 or more glow plugs, but not all glow plugs, replace glow plug harness and retest. If voltage drops to 0 volts after 6 seconds, proceed to step **7)**. If voltage is not present at any glow plug lead, proceed to next step.

3) Disconnect glow plug harness from engine harness and glow plugs. Connect a self-powered test lamp between glow plug harness connector and each glow plug terminal. If test lamp does not light, repair or replace glow plug harness and retest. If test lamp lights, reconnect both ends of glow plug harness and proceed to next step.

4) Connect a 12 volt test lamp between glow plug control module terminal 9 and ground. Turn ignition switch on. If test lamp does not light, repair and/or replace ignition switch and/or wiring and retest. If test lamp lights, proceed to next step.

5) Connect a test lamp between glow plug control module terminal 6 and ground. Turn ignition switch on. If test lamp does not light, replace control unit and recheck voltage at terminal 6. If test lamp lights for 6 seconds, proceed to next step.

6) Connect a test lamp between the No. 1 glow plug relay signal terminal and ground. Turn ignition switch on. If test lamp does not light, repair or replace wiring

Fig. 6: *Glow Plug Control Module Terminals*

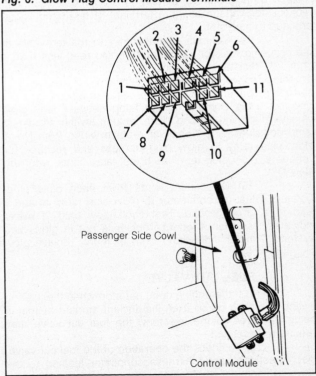

Module is located behind kick-panel on passenger side.

from relay to control module terminal 6 and then recheck for voltage at relay. If test lamp lights for 6 seconds, proceed to next step.

DIESEL KIKI — FORD (Cont.)

7) Connect a voltmeter between No. 1 glow plug relay output terminal and ground. Turn ignition switch on. If voltage is 11 volts or more for 6 seconds, proceed to step **15)**. If voltage is less than 11 volts, replace the No. 1 relay and recheck voltage at output terminal.

8) Connect a test lamp between glow plug control module terminal 10 and ground. Turn ignition switch on. If test lamp lights, proceed to step **11)**. If test lamp does not light, proceed to next step.

9) Using a self-powered test lamp, check the functioning of both the clutch and neutral switches in both open and closed positions. With transmission in gear and clutch pedal released, both switches should be closed.

10) With transmission in neutral and clutch pedal depressed, both switches should be open. If either or both of the switches does not operate as specified, replace switch and retest. If both switches operate properly, proceed to next step.

11) Connect a test lamp between No. 2 glow plug relay signal terminal and ground. Shift transmission into Neutral or "N". Turn ignition switch on. If test lamp does not light, repair or replace wiring from control module terminal 10 to No. 2 relay and recheck for voltage at relay. If test lamp lights, proceed to next step.

12) Connect a test lamp between the No. 2 glow plug relay output terminal and ground. Turn ignition switch on. If test lamp does not light, replace No. 2 relay and recheck for voltage at output terminal. If test lamp lights, proceed to next step.

13) Disconnect dropping resistor from wiring harness. Connect a test lamp between the dropping resistor input terminal on wiring harness and ground. Turn ignition switch on. If test lamp does not light, repair or replace wiring from No. 2 relay to dropping resistor and recheck for voltage at input terminal. If test lamp lights, proceed to next step.

14) Connect an ohmmeter to the terminals of the dropping resistor. Ohmmeter should read less than 1 ohm. If resistance is not to specifications, replace dropping resistor and recheck resistance. If resistance is correct, reconnect resistor and proceed to next step.

15) Connect a test lamp between any glow plug terminal and ground. Turn ignition switch on. If test lamp does not light. Repair or replace wiring from No. 1 glow plug relay to glow plug harness and recheck for voltage at glow plug terminal. If test lamp lights, return to step **1)**.

16) Disconnect leads from each glow plug. Connect 1 lead of ohmmeter to glow plug terminal and 1 lead to a good ground. Test each glow plug. If meter indicates less than 1 ohm, problem is not in glow plug system. If meter indicates 1 ohm or more, replace glow plug and retest.

FUEL CUT VALVE

1) If the engine does not stop when the ignition switch is turned off or if an insufficient amount of fuel is being delivered to the injectors, the fuel cut valve may require replacement.

2) To check the operation of the fuel cut valve, disconnect the wiring harness connector leading to the valve and connect a voltmeter.

3) Voltage should be present at the connector when the ignition switch is on and should drop to zero immediately after turning the ignition switch off.

4) If the voltage at the connector is as specified, the fuel cut valve is at fault and must be replaced. *See Fig. 7.*

Fig. 7: Fuel Cut Valve

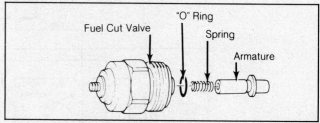

Armature should extend when current is turned off.

WATER SEPARATOR (SEDIMENTOR)

Remove the water detector switch from the top of the water separator. Disconnect detector switch wires from harness. Connect an ohmmeter to water detector switch. The detector is operating properly when continuity exists with switch upright and no continuity exists with switch upside down. *See Fig. 7.*

Fig. 8: Water Detector Switch Test

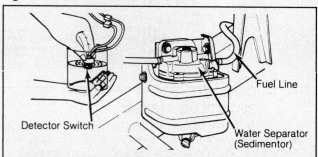

Continuity should only exist when switch is upright.

REMOVAL & INSTALLATION

FUEL INJECTION PUMP

Removal

1) Remove hood. Remove accessory drive belt and idler pulley. Scribe an alignment mark on injection pump mounting flange and timing gear housing for reassembly reference. Disconnect battery negative cable, accelerator cable, cold start device cable, cruise control cable and the fuel cut valve connector. Remove radiator fan and shroud.

2) Remove the fuel injection pipes and fuel hoses from the fuel pump. Remove the injection pump drive gear cover. Cap all openings in fuel lines to prevent contamination. Remove the injection pump drive gear lock nut and spring washer, taking care not to drop the spring washer into the timing gear case. If necessary use a steel wire to remove spring washer.

3) Remove the lock plate from the drive gear. Rotate the engine until the injection pump shaft key groove is facing up. Disconnect the air intake hose from the air cleaner and intake manifold. Remove the injection pump attaching nuts and bolt.

4) Using the injection pump extractor tool (T83T-6306-A) or similar tool, remove the injection pump.

DIESEL KIKI — FORD (Cont.)

Take care when withdrawing the pump from the timing gear case so as not to drop the pump shaft key into the timing gear case. *See Fig. 9.*

Fig. 9: Injection Pump Removal

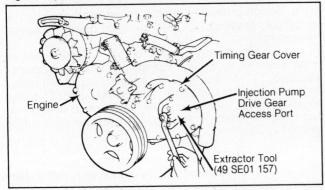

Use care to avoid dropping lock nut, spring washer or shaft key into timing gear housing.

Installation

To install, reverse removal procedure and note the following:

- Before installing the pump shaft key onto the shaft, tap the key groove in the shaft with a hammer to insure a tight fit for the key.
- After installing the injection pump, evacuate any air present from the pump.
- Tighten the pump drive gear lock nut to 29-52 ft. lbs. (39-71 N.m).

ADJUSTMENTS

INJECTION PUMP TIMING

1) Disconnect ground cables from both batteries. Disconnect fuel injection pipes from fuel injection pump. Remove the hydraulic head plug from the pump. Align the timing mark (2° ATDC) on the crankshaft pulley with the indicator pin by turning the crankshaft.

2) Mount the injection timing measuring device (14-030349 & D82L-4201-A) into the hydraulic head plug hole. With the tip of the measuring tool firmly against the pump plunger, set the dial indicator to read about 0.08" (2 mm). *See Fig. 10.*

Fig. 10: Injection Pump Timing

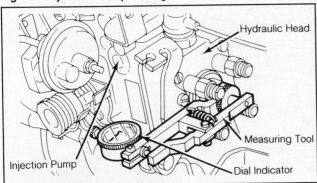

Dial indicator should read about 0.04" (1 mm) when timing mark is aligned with pointer.

3) Turn the crankshaft pulley slowly counterclockwise (in reverse direction of engine rotation) about 30-50°. Make sure the dial indicator pointer stops.

4) Set the dial indicator pointer to zero. Turn the crankshaft slightly left and right to make sure that the indicator pointer does not move from zero.

5) Turn the crankshaft pulley clockwise (in direction of engine rotation) to align timing mark with indicator pin. If timing is adjusted correctly dial indicator will read 0.04" ±0.0008" (1 mm ±0.02 mm) when the timing mark is aligned with the indicator pin.

6) If timing is not to specifications, loosen injection pump attaching nuts and bolt. Turn injection pump housing past correct position and then back until dial indicator reading is correct.

COLD START SYSTEM

Attach a tachometer to engine. Pull cold start knob out to the full extent of its travel. Turn the cold start lever adjusting screw (on injection pump) until engine speed is 1150-1250 RPM.

IDLE SPEED

1) Start and run engine to normal operating temperature. Connect a tachometer to engine and check idle speed. Idle speed should be 780-830 RPM.

2) To adjust idle speed loosen the lock nut on the idle stop screw and adjust idle stop screw until idle meets specifications. After completing adjustment, race the engine 2 or 3 times to ensure that the accelerator cable is returning properly.

MAINTENANCE

WATER SEPARATOR

1) When the water level in the water separator reaches a maximum level, a warning lamp on the dash will light up. The warning lamp will also light up whenever the key is in the "Start" position. When the warning lamp is lit, it is necessary to drain water from the separator.

2) Stop vehicle and shut off engine. Pull up on the remote control drain handle (located behind driver's seat) and hold valve open until about 45 seconds after light goes out. Release remote handle.

3) Restart the engine and check the warning lamp. If the warning lamp is still lit, fuel system needs to be checked or repaired. The only servicable item on the separator is the water level sensor.

1983 Diesel Fuel Injection
FORD 6.9L

DESCRIPTION

In this diesel system, a mechanical high pressure rotary pump is gear driven at camshaft speed. Through this method the pump injects a precisely metered amount of fuel into each cylinder at the proper time. The pump is mounted on top of the engine and provides necessary timing advance under all operating conditions.

Eight high pressure fuel pipes carry fuel from pump to an injection nozzle in each cylinder. All 8 pipes are exactly the same length to ensure that there is no variance in timing. Engine RPM is controlled by a rotary fuel metering valve. As the accelerator pedal is pushed down, a throttle cable opens the metering valve and allows increased fuel delivery. A mechanical fuel pump located on the right side of the engine, draws fuel from the fuel tank and delivers it to the injection pump via a fuel filter.

The fuel filter is located between the mechanical pump and injection pump (mounted on side of engine block). Any excess fuel in the supply system is returned to the tank by a fuel return system. A water separator is located in the fuel line between the tank and the mechanical fuel pump. The separator collects water out of the fuel system. When the separator becomes about 1/3 full, a warning lamp on the dash will light up. When the warning lamp lights up, water should be drained from the separator. The warning lamp will also light when the key is in the "START" position to serve as a lamp test.

An electrical glow plug system is used to assist in engine starting and cold operation. A glow plug is located in the pre-chamber for each cylinder. Glow plug current is controlled by a temperature switch, a power relay and an after glow relay.

OPERATION

FUEL INJECTION PUMP

The Stanadyne DB-2 twin plunger mechanical injection pump contains a low pressure vane-type transfer pump, a high pressure distributor-type injection pump, a centrifugal governor and an injection timing advance mechanism.

The transfer pump output pressure (sometimes referred to as injection pump housing pressure) averages 50-100 psi (3.5-7.0 kg/cm²) depending upon engine speed and application. The plunger injection pump boosts the fuel pressure to about 2000 psi (140 kg/cm²). The pump assembly is also equipped with an electric fuel shut-off valve.

INJECTORS

The injection nozzles spray fuel into a pre-chamber as each compression stroke occurs. Nozzles can be disassembled, cleaned and adjusted to correct improper spray patterns.

Injector opening pressure is adjusted with a shim on top of the needle valve return spring. *See Fig. 3.* The injector receives a high pressure pulse of fuel which forces open the needle valve allowing the fuel to pass into the prechamber.

FUEL SUPPLY SYSTEM

Diesel fuel is drawn through a water separator from the fuel tank by an engine mounted mechanical fuel pump. This pump is driven by an eccentric cam mounted on the crankshaft and puts out about 3 psi to the injection pump. A small screen type filter is located in the fuel tank

Fig. 1: Stanadyne DB-2 Diesel Fuel Injection Pump

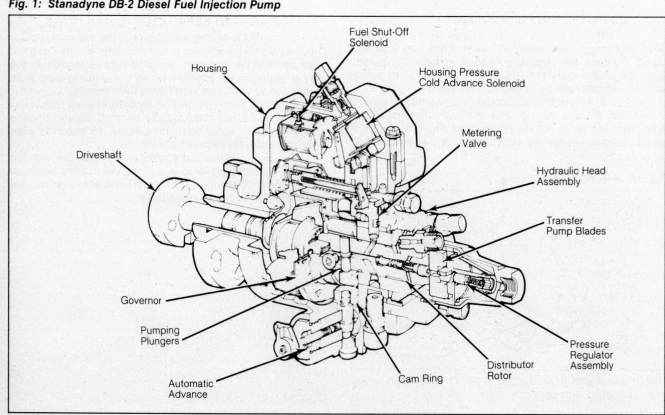

Disassembly of pump should only be performed by an authorized calibration shop.

Fig. 2: Ford Diesel Fuel System

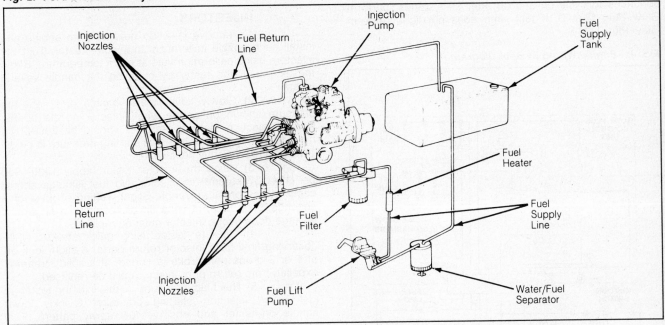

Bleed air from system whenever fuel lines are opened.

Fig. 3: Ford Diesel Injector

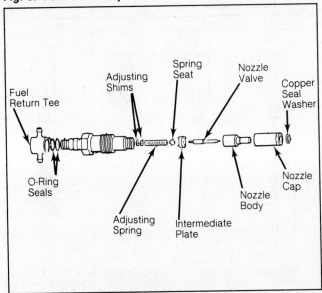

Injector must be free of dirt prior to reassembly.

at the pickup. Diesel fuel arrives at the center inlet fitting on the injection pump after leaving the filter. A fuel return line is provided to return any excess fuel to the tank.

FUEL INJECTION LINES

Eight high pressure fuel injection lines are routed from injection pump to an injector in each cylinder. The lines are of equal length but are bent differently to maintain equal length, prevent any difference in timing from cylinder-to-cylinder and aid installation. Lines are not interchangeable and are pre-bent by the manufacturer.

GLOW PLUGS

Glow plugs are threaded into each cylinder combustion chamber. Glow plugs are small heaters that assist in cold starting. The glow plug controller and relay cycle 12 volts to these 6 volt heaters, which causes them to heat rapidly. After the engine starts, the glow plugs remain on for short time then shut off.

TROUBLE SHOOTING

FUEL INJECTION SYSTEM

Before suspecting the fuel injection system as a possible source of engine trouble, other engine systems should be checked. The exhaust system should not be restricted, the fuel supply system should supply an adequate amount of clean fuel to the injection pump, and the air intake system should not be restricted. If after checking the other systems and making the necessary repairs a problem still exists, perform the following test:

1) Check fuel lines to injectors for kinks or restrictions. Repair as necessary.

2) Run the engine at the RPM where the problem was most pronounced.

3) Momentarily loosen (1/2-1 turn) the fuel line on 1 injector. Then tighten fuel line to specification.

4) Repeat step **2)** for each cylinder.

5) If one or more nozzles are found where loosening the fuel line makes no difference in operation, the nozzle should be removed and tested.

GLOW PLUG SYSTEM

1) Connect a 12 volt test lamp between the glow plug power relay output and ground. Turn ignition on. Test lamp should light, stay lit for 4 to 10 seconds, then cycle on and off. If so, proceed to step **2)**. If test lamp does not light, perform Glow Plug Test C. If test lamp stays on continuously, perform Glow Plug Test B. If test lamp lights for 4-10 seconds and then goes out, perform Glow Plug Test E.

2) With test lamp still connected, start engine. Test lamp should cycle on and off for 20 to 90 seconds then turn off. If so, perform Glow Plug Test A. If test lamp continues to cycle on and off after 90 seconds, perform Glow Plug Test D. If test lamp does not light, perform Glow Plug Test E.

Fig. 4: Engine Wiring System Diagram

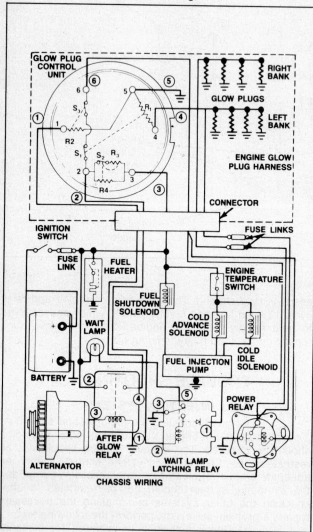

Also see chassis wiring in WIRING DIAGRAM Section.

WAIT-TO-START LAMP

1) Turn ignition on. Wait-To-Start lamp should light for 4-10 seconds, depending on engine temperature, and then go out. If lamp lights for 4-10 seconds, Wait-To-Start lamp system is okay. Perform Glow Plug Trouble Shooting. If lamp lights and does not turn off, proceed to step **2)**. If lamp does not light and engine is at or near operating temperature, allow engine to cool down and retest. If lamp still does not light, proceed to step **2)**.

2) Perform Glow Plug Trouble Shooting. If test lamp functioned as required and Wait-To-Start lamp did not light in step **1)**, perform Wait-To-Start Lamp Test A. If test lamp functioned as required and Wait-To-Start lamp did not turn off in step **1)**, perform Wait-To-Start Test B. If test lamp did not function as required, glow plug system is faulty. Proceed as directed by Glow Plug Trouble Shooting.

TESTING

INJECTORS

1) Remove injection nozzles from engine and install each nozzle in turn on an injector tester. Test the injectors using calibration fluid at room temperature. Bleed the air out of the tester by pumping the handle several times.

2) Slowly lower tester handle and note the pressure shown on gauge when injector nozzle opens. Normal injection starting pressure should be 2000-2150 psi (140-151 kg/cm²). If injection starting pressure is below 1600 psi (112 kg/cm²), replace injector.

3) Using the injector tester, apply 1900-1950 psi (134-137 kg/cm²) to injector. No fuel leakage should occur at this pressure range. Slight wetting of tip after 5 seconds is ok. Do not wipe tip of nozzle with fingers. If leakage does occur, injector must be replaced.

4) Operate tester using quick strokes while observing flow from injector return ports. A slight leak-off of 1 or 2 drops per stroke is normal. If a solid stream is expelled from return port, injector must be replaced.

5) Build up pressure in the injector tester to just below injection starting pressure. Quickly lower handle on tester and observe fuel spray pattern. Fuel should be uniformly atomized and should form a narrow cone projecting straight out of the end of the nozzle. See Fig. 5.

Fig. 5: Injector Spray Pattern

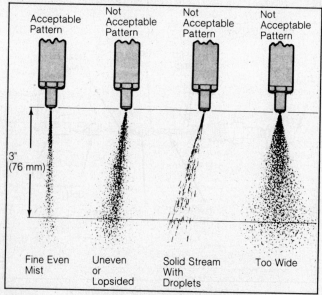

Injector must not drip when needle valve is closed.

TRANSFER PUMP (HOUSING) PRESSURE

Remove screw from transfer pressure port. See Fig. 6. Install a gauge adapter (T83T-9000-A or equivalent) into transfer pressure port. Connect a gauge to adapter. Run engine at 3,300 RPM, under no load, with transmission in Neutral. Pressure should be 95-110 psi (7-8 kg/cm²). If pressure is not to specifications, replace pump and retest. If performance problem still exists, check and adjust timing.

Fig. 6: *Transfer Pressure Test Connection*

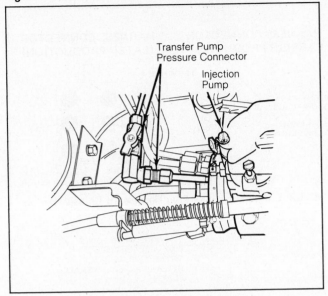

Transfer Pump
Pressure Connector

Injection
Pump

GLOW PLUG TEST A
TEST LAMP SIGNAL CORRECT

1) Remove all leads from glow plugs. Connect a test lamp between glow plug power relay output and ground. Turn ignition on. Measure voltage at each glow plug lead whenever test lamp is lit. Voltage should be at least 11 volts. If voltage is ok at all leads, proceed to step **4)**. If voltage is not ok at 1 or more leads, proceed to step **2)**.

2) Turn ignition off. Disconnect fusible links from chassis harness and engine glow plug harness. Check continuity of fusible links with an ohmmeter. If 1 or both fusible links are open, replace fusible link and repeat step **1)**. If both fusible links are ok, proceed to step **3)**.

3) Turn ignition off. Disconnect engine harness from chassis connector and all glow plugs. Check resistance between chassis connector left and right bank glow plug terminals and each glow plug lead. If any resistance is 1 ohm or more, replace engine harness and recheck vehicle operation. If resistance is more than 1 ohm, proceed to step **4)**.

4) Turn ignition off. Remove test lamp from power relay. Check resistance between glow plug terminal and metal case of glow plug. If resistance is less than 2 ohms at all glow plugs, glow plug system is ok, problem is engine related. If resistance is more than 2 ohms at any glow plug(s), replace glow plug(s), reconnect harness and check vehicle operation.

GLOW PLUG TEST B
TEST LAMP ON CONTINUOUSLY

1) Disconnect all leads from glow plugs and do not reconnect until after system has been checked for proper operation. Connect a 12 volt test lamp to glow plug power relay output and ground. Turn ignition on, but do not start engine. Disconnect harness plug from control switch. If test lamp turns off, replace control switch and repeat Glow Plug Trouble Shooting. If test lamp does not turn off, proceed to step **2)**.

2) With test lamp still connected, turn ignition on. Disconnect engine harness from chassis harness. If test lamp goes out, replace engine harness and proceed to step **6)**. If test lamp does not go out, proceed to step **3)**.

3) Turn ignition off. Disconnect signal lead from power relay. Turn ignition off. If test lamp does not go out, replace power relay and proceed with test. If test lamp goes out, repair or replace chassis wiring harness and proceed with test.

4) Turn ignition off and remove test lamp from relay. Leave glow plug leads and power relay output lead disconnected. Check continuity between each glow plug lead and power relay output lead. If all resistances are less then 1 ohm, proceed to step **6)**. If 1 or more resistances are 1 ohm or more, proceed to step **5)**.

5) With ignition off, disconnect engine harness from chassis harness. Disconnect chassis harness fusible links from chassis harness. Check resistance of fusible links. If resistance is less than 1 ohm, replace engine wiring harness and proceed to step **6)**. If resistance is 1 ohm or more, replace fusible link(s) as necessary and return to step **4)**.

6) With ignition off and all glow plugs disconnected, check resistance between each glow plug terminal and metal shell of glow plug. If all resistances are less than 2 ohms, glow plug system is ok. Reconnect harness and repeat trouble shooting procedure. If 1 or more resistance is 2 ohms or more, replace affected glow plugs. Reconnect harness and repeat trouble shooting procedure.

GLOW PLUG TEST C
TEST LAMP DOES NOT LIGHT

1) Connect a test lamp between glow plug power relay output and ground. Turn ignition on, but do not start engine. If test lamp lights, perform Glow Plug Test E. If test lamp does not light, for coolant temperatures of 140° F (60° C) or above, condition is normal. For coolant temperatures below 140° F (60°C), turn ignition off, wait 5 minutes, and turn ignition back on. If lamp lights, perform Glow Plug Test E. If lamp does not light, proceed to step **2)**.

2) Check batteries for sufficient state of charge. Batteries should be able to crank engine. If charge is ok, proceed to step **3)**. If charge is insufficient, charge or replace batteries as necessary and repeat trouble shooting procedure.

3) Check fusible link from ignition switch to control switch. If fusible link is ok, proceed to step **8)**. If fusible link is not ok, proceed to step **4)**.

4) Replace fusible link and repeat trouble shooting procedure. If fuse blows, proceed to step **5)**. If fuse does not blow and system operates correctly, testing is complete. If fuse does not blow and system still does not operate correctly, proceed to step **8)**.

5) Remove signal lead from power relay. Replace fusible link. Turn ignition on and then off. If fuse blows, proceed to step **6)**. If fuse does not blow, replace power relay and repeat trouble shooting procedure.

6) Disconnect chassis harness from engine harness. Replace fusible link. Turn ignition on and then off. If fuse blows, repair chassis wiring harness and repeat trouble shooting procedure. If fuse does not blow, proceed to step **7)**.

7) Disconnect harness connector at latching relay. Check resistance between relay terminals 1 and 2 by connecting red probe of meter to pin 2 and black probe to pin 1. If resistance is 45 ohms or greater, replace

1983 Diesel Fuel Injection

FORD 6.9L (Cont.)

Fig. 7: Glow Plug & Wait Lamp System Test Connections

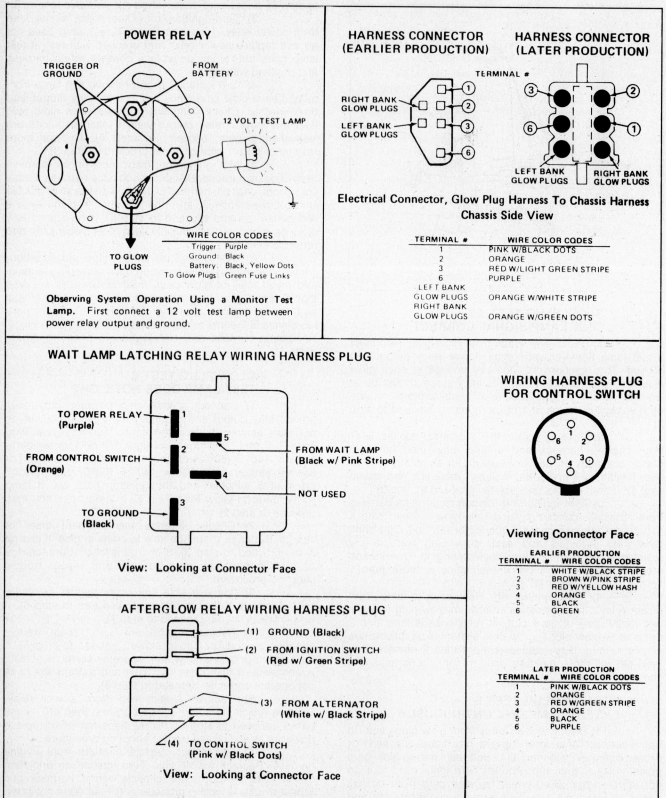

POWER RELAY

TRIGGER OR GROUND

FROM BATTERY

12 VOLT TEST LAMP

TO GLOW PLUGS

WIRE COLOR CODES
Trigger: Purple
Ground: Black
Battery: Black, Yellow Dots
To Glow Plugs: Green Fuse Links

Observing System Operation Using a Monitor Test Lamp. First connect a 12 volt test lamp between power relay output and ground.

HARNESS CONNECTOR (EARLIER PRODUCTION)

TERMINAL #

RIGHT BANK GLOW PLUGS

LEFT BANK GLOW PLUGS

HARNESS CONNECTOR (LATER PRODUCTION)

LEFT BANK GLOW PLUGS

RIGHT BANK GLOW PLUGS

Electrical Connector, Glow Plug Harness To Chassis Harness Chassis Side View

TERMINAL #	WIRE COLOR CODES
1	PINK W/BLACK DOTS
2	ORANGE
3	RED W/LIGHT GREEN STRIPE
6	PURPLE
LEFT BANK GLOW PLUGS	ORANGE W/WHITE STRIPE
RIGHT BANK GLOW PLUGS	ORANGE W/GREEN DOTS

WAIT LAMP LATCHING RELAY WIRING HARNESS PLUG

TO POWER RELAY (Purple)

FROM CONTROL SWITCH (Orange)

TO GROUND (Black)

FROM WAIT LAMP (Black w/ Pink Stripe)

NOT USED

View: Looking at Connector Face

WIRING HARNESS PLUG FOR CONTROL SWITCH

Viewing Connector Face

EARLIER PRODUCTION	
TERMINAL #	WIRE COLOR CODES
1	WHITE W/BLACK STRIPE
2	BROWN W/PINK STRIPE
3	RED W/YELLOW HASH
4	ORANGE
5	BLACK
6	GREEN

LATER PRODUCTION	
TERMINAL #	WIRE COLOR CODES
1	PINK W/BLACK DOTS
2	ORANGE
3	RED W/GREEN STRIPE
4	ORANGE
5	BLACK
6	PURPLE

AFTERGLOW RELAY WIRING HARNESS PLUG

(1) GROUND (Black)

(2) FROM IGNITION SWITCH (Red w/ Green Stripe)

(3) FROM ALTERNATOR (White w/ Black Stripe)

(4) TO CONTROL SWITCH (Pink w/ Black Dots)

View: Looking at Connector Face

FORD 6.9L (Cont.)

engine harness and repeat trouble shooting procedure. If resistance is less than 45 ohms, replace latching relay and repeat trouble shooting procedure.

8) Turn ignition off. Connect a voltmeter between power relay input terminal and ground. If voltage is 11 volts or more, proceed to step **9)**. If voltage is less than 11 volts, charge or replace batteries as necessary and/or repair wiring from batteries to power relay. Repeat trouble shooting procedure.

9) Disconnect wiring harness connector from control switch. Turn ignition on. Check voltage between control switch harness connector pin 3 and ground. If voltage is 11 volts or more, proceed to step **11)**. If voltage is less than 11 volts, proceed to step **10)**.

10) Turn ignition off. Disconnect chassis harness from engine harness. Turn ignition on. Check voltage at pin 3 on chassis side of connector. If voltage is 11 volts or more, replace engine harness and repeat trouble shooting procedure. If voltage is less than 11 volts, repair or replace chassis wiring as necessary and repeat trouble shooting procedure.

11) Turn ignition off. Disconnect power relay signal lead. Disconnect wiring harness from control switch. Check resistance between control switch harness connector pin 6 and power relay signal lead. If resistance is less than 1 ohm, proceed to step **13)**. If resistance is 1 ohm or more, proceed to step **12)**.

12) Turn ignition off. Disconnect chassis harness from engine harness. Disconnect power relay signal lead. Check resistance between power relay signal lead and chassis side of harness connector pin 2 or 6. If resistance is less than 1 ohm, replace engine harness and repeat trouble shooting procedure. If resistance is 1 ohm or more, repair or replace chassis wiring and repeat trouble shooting procedure.

13) Turn ignition off. Reconnect all leads except power relay signal lead. Wait 5 minutes and then turn ignition on. Check voltage between relay signal lead and ground. Voltage should be at least 11 volts for each cycle. If ok, repair power relay ground connection or replace power relay and repeat trouble shooting procedure. If not ok, proceed to step **14)**.

14) Disconnect harness from control switch. Turn ignition on. Check for voltage between control switch harness pin 1 and ground. If no voltage is detected, replace control switch and repeat trouble shooting procedure. If voltage is detected, repair alternator and replace after-glow relay as necessary. Repeat trouble shooting procedure.

GLOW PLUG TEST D
TEST LAMP CYCLES CONTINUOUSLY

1) Remove engine harness connector at control switch. Start engine. Check for voltage between control switch connector pin 1 and ground. If voltage is 11 volts or more, turn engine off, replace control switch and repeat trouble shooting procedure. If voltage is less than 11 volts, proceed to step **2)**.

2) With ignition off, disconnect harness connector from after-glow relay. Check for ground at connector terminal 1. If not grounded, repair or replace ground wiring as necessary and repeat trouble shooting procedure. If grounded, proceed to step **3)**.

3) Turn ignition on. Check for voltage between after-glow relay connector terminal 2 and ground. If voltage is less than 11 volts, repair or replace wiring as

necessary and repeat trouble shooting procedure. If voltage is 11 volts or more, proceed to step **4)**.

4) Start engine. Check for voltage between relay connector terminal 3 and ground. Voltage should be 6.5-7.5 volts. If so, proceed to step **5)**. If not, turn engine off, repair or replace wiring as necessary and repeat trouble shooting procedure.

5) Turn ignition off. Remove harness connector at control switch. Check resistance between relay connector terminal 4 and control switch connector pin 1. If resistance is less than 1 ohm, replace after-glow relay and repeat trouble shooting procedure. If resistance is 1 ohm or more, proceed to step **6)**.

6) Turn ignition off. Disconnect chassis harness from engine harness. Check resistance between relay connector terminal 4 and chassis connector pin 1 or 5. If resistance is less than 1 ohm, replace engine harness and repeat trouble shooting procedure. If resistance is 1 ohm or more, repair chassis harness and repeat trouble shooting procedure.

GLOW PLUG TEST E
TEST LAMP DOES NOT CYCLE

1) Connect a test lamp between glow plug power relay output and ground. Turn ignition on, but do not start engine. If test lamp lights, proceed to step **2)**. If test lamp does not light, for coolant temperatures of 140° F (60° C) or above, condition is normal. For coolant temperatures below 140° F (60°C), turn ignition off, wait 5 minutes, and turn ignition back on. If lamp lights, proceed to step **2)**. If lamp does not light, perform Glow Plug Test C.

2) Turn ignition off. Disconnect engine harness from control switch and all glow plugs. Check resistance between control switch connector pin 4 and power relay output connector. If resistance is less than 1 ohm, proceed to step **4)**. If resistance is 1 ohm or more, proceed to step **3)**.

3) Turn ignition off. Disconnect chassis harness from engine harness. Disconnect fusible links from chassis harness. Check resistance of the fusible links. If resistance is less than 1 ohm, replace engine harness and repeat trouble shooting procedure. If resistance is 1 ohm or more, replace fusible link(s) and repeat trouble shooting procedure.

4) Turn ignition off. Check resistance between control switch connector pin 5 and ground. If resistance is less than 1 ohm, proceed to step **5)**. If resistance is 1 ohm or more, repair or replace harness ground connections as necessary and repeat trouble shooting procedure.

5) Turn ignition off. Disconnect wiring harness from latching relay. Check resistance across latching relay terminals 1 and 2 using positive probe on terminal 2 and negative probe on terminal 1. Resistance should be 45 ohms or greater. Reverse ohmmeter leads. Resistance should be greater than 1 megohm. If resistance is not as specified, replace latching relay and repeat trouble shooting procedure. If resistance is ok, proceed to step **6)**.

6) Turn ignition off. Disconnect wiring harness at control switch. Connect all other leads. Check resistance between control switch connector pin 6 and ground. If resistance is less than 2.5 ohms, replace power relay and repeat trouble shooting procedure. If resistance is 2.5 ohms or more, proceed to step **7)**.

7) Disconnect wiring harness from control switch. Turn ignition on, but do not start engine. Check for

1983 Diesel Fuel Injection

FORD 6.9L (Cont.)

voltage between switch harness connector pin 1 and ground. If voltage is detected, turn ignition off and proceed to step **8)**. If no voltage is not detected, turn ignition off, replace control switch, and repeat trouble shooting procedure.

8) Leave harness disconnected at control switch. Disconnect engine harness from chassis harness. Turn ignition on. Check for voltage at chassis harness connector pin 1 or 5. If voltage is detected, proceed to step **9)**. If no voltage is detected, replace engine harness and repeat trouble shooting procedure.

9) Disconnect engine harness at control switch and chassis connector. Turn ignition on. Remove connector from after-glow relay. Check for voltage at chassis connector pin 1 or 5. If no voltage is detected, turn ignition off, replace after-glow relay and proceed to step **10)**. If voltage is detected, turn ignition off, repair or replace chassis wiring from relay to engine harness connector and repeat trouble shooting procedure.

10) Disconnect engine harness at control switch and chassis connector. Reconnect after-glow relay. Turn ignition on. Check for voltage at chassis side of chassis connector pins 1 and 5. If voltage is detected, repair or replace wiring and/or alternator as necessary, then repeat trouble shooting procedure. If no voltage is detected, problem is solved. Repeat trouble shooting procedure.

WAIT-TO-START LAMP TEST A
LAMP DOES NOT LIGHT

1) Remove bulb from Wait-To-Start indicator and test bulb. If bulb is not ok, replace bulb and repeat Wait-To-Start Lamp Trouble Shooting. If bulb is ok, reinstall bulb and proceed with test.

2) Disconnect harness from lamp latching relay. Install jumper wire between connector pin 5 and ground. Turn ignition on. If lamp does not light, turn ignition off and repair wiring between ignition switch and lamp or between lamp and latching relay, then repeat trouble shooting procedure. If lamp lights, proceed with test.

3) Install between latching relay connector terminals 5 and 3. Turn ignition on. If lamp does not light, turn key off, repair latching relay ground connection and repeat trouble shooting procedure. If lamp lights, replace latching relay and repeat trouble shooting procedure.

WAIT-TO-START LAMP TEST B
LAMP STAYS LIT WITH KEY ON

1) Turn ignition on. Disconnect latching relay. If lamp does not turn off, turn ignition off and repair grounded wiring between lamp and relay, then repeat Wait-To-Start Lamp Trouble Shooting. If lamp turns off, proceed with test.

2) With relay disconnected, turn ignition on. Check voltage between relay connector pin 2 and ground. If voltage is 11 volts or more, proceed to step **3)**. If voltage is less than 11 volts, proceed to step **4)**.

3) With relay disconnected, turn ignition off. Check resistance between relay connector pin 1 and ground. If resistance is 5 ohms or less, replace latching relay and repeat trouble shooting procedure. If resistance is more than 5 ohms, repair or replace wiring from latching relay to power relay and repeat trouble shooting procedure.

4) With harness disconnected at latching relay and control switch, turn ignition off. Check harness resistance between relay connector pin 2 and switch connector pin 2. If resistance is less than 1 ohm, replace control switch and repeat trouble shooting procedure. If resistance is 1 ohm or more, repair or replace wiring from control switch to latching relay and repeat trouble shooting procedure.

REMOVAL & INSTALLATION

INJECTION PUMP
Removal

1) Open hood. Disconnect battery ground cables from both batteries. Remove engine oil filler neck. Remove bolts attaching injection pump to drive gear. Disconnect electrical connectors from injection pump. Disconnect accelerator cable and cruise control cable from throttle lever.

2) Remove air cleaner and cover air intake. Remove accelerator cable bracket, with cables attached, and position out of the way. Remove fuel line from injection pump inlet and cap both fittings. Remove and cap injection pump fitting adapter.

3) Remove fuel return line from injection pump, rotate out of the way and cap both fittings. Loosen injector line fittings at the pump. Disconnect injector lines from injector nozzles and cap all fittings.

4) Remove 3 injection pump retaining nuts. If injection pump is to be replaced, remove injector lines from pump and cap all fittings. Remove injection pump from engine compartment.

Installation

Install new "O" ring on drive gear end of injection pump. Reverse removal procedure to complete installation. Purge injector lines by loosening connector 1/2 to 1 turn and cranking engine until a solid stream of fuel flows from connector. Check and adjust injection pump timing as necessary.

INJECTOR NOZZLES
Removal

1) Before removing nozzles, clean nozzle, surrounding area and piping connections with clean fuel or solvent to prevent contamination. Blow area dry with compressed air. Remove fuel line retaining clamps from the lines being removed.

2) Disconnect fuel lines and return lines and support out of way. Cap all open connections. Unscrew nozzle and remove nozzle and copper washer from engine.

3) Do not strike nozzle tip against any hard surface during removal. Cap both ends of nozzle and store in a rack such that the nozzles may be reinstalled in their original cylinders.

Installation

1) Clean nozzle bore in cylinder head thoroughly before reinstalling nozzle. Remove protective cap from nozzle tip. Coat nozzle threads with anti-seize compound. Install a new copper gasket on nozzle using a small amount of grease to retain gasket on nozzle.

2) Install nozzle into cylinder head bore and tighten to specifications. Remove caps from fuel lines and nozzle fittings. Install 2 new "O" rings on each fuel return

FORD 6.9L (Cont.)

tee. Install return tee onto nozzle and connect fuel line to nozzle.

3) Install fuel line retainer clamps and tighten to specification. Purge injector lines by loosening connector 1/2 to 1 turn and cranking engine until a solid stream of fuel flows from connector. Run engine and check for fuel line leakage.

ADJUSTMENTS

NOTE: **For vacuum regulator valve adjustment procedure, see TUNE-UP SERVICE PROCEDURES.**

INJECTION PUMP TIMING

1) Loosen 3 nuts retaining injection pump to gear housing slightly to allow pump rotation. Align timing mark on pump with timing mark on housing.

2) Tighten retaining nuts slightly to prevent pump rotation. Start and run engine until it reaches normal operating temperature. Stop engine and connect a luminosity probe timing meter to engine. Connect magnetic pick-up to receptacle on timing pointer and install luminosity probe in the No. 1 glow plug hole. Set timing meter offset to -20°.

3) With transmission in Neutral and rear wheels raised off the ground, start engine. Raise engine speed to 1400 RPM with no accessory load. Observe injection timing on meter. Timing should be 4-6° ATDC (+ 1° for altitudes over 3,000 ft.).

4) If timing is not to specifications, stop engine and loosen pump retaining nuts. As viewed from front of vehicle, rotate top of pump to right to retard timing or to the left to advance timing. Moving the timing mark .030" (.75 mm) is equal to 2° of timing. Retighten retaining nuts.

5) Recheck timing using meter. If still not to specifications, repeat step **4)**. When timing is correct, tighten retaining nuts to specifications. Remove timing meter. Reinstall glow plug using anti-seize compound on the threads.

Fig. 8: Timing Mark Alignment

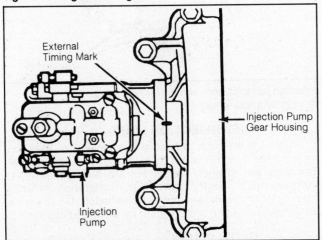

CURB IDLE SPEED

1) Start and run engine until it reaches normal operating temperature. Idle speed is measured with man. trans. in Neutral or auto. trans. in "D". Adjust idle speed to 750 RPM using curb idle screw on side of pump.

2) Shift transmission out of gear and rev engine momentarily. Shift back into specified gear and recheck idle speed. Readjust if necessary.

FAST IDLE SPEED

1) Start and run engine until it reaches normal operating temperature. Disconnect wiring harness from fast idle solenoid. Apply battery voltage to solenoid to activate it. Rev engine momentarily to set solenoid plunger. Fast idle speed should be 875 RPM.

2) Adjust fast idle speed if necessary by turning solenoid plunger. Rev engine and recheck fast idle speed. Readjust if necessary. Remove battery voltage from solenoid and reconnect harness.

Fig. 9: Throttle Adjustment Locations

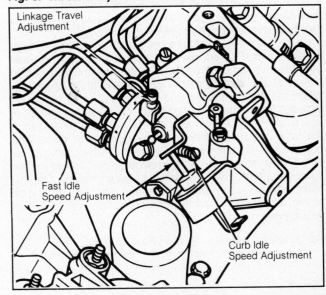

ACCELERATOR LINKAGE ADJUSTMENT

With engine off, check that throttle lever contacts injection pump stop at full accelerator depression. Adjust stop screw on throttle lever if necessary.

MAINTENANCE

WATER SEPARATOR

1) When the water level in the water separator reaches a maximum level, a warning lamp on the dash will light up. When the warning lamp is lit, it is necessary to drain water from the separator.

2) Stop vehicle and shut off engine. On F-series models, unscrew the vent (located on top of separator) 2 1/2-3 turns. Unscrew the drain (located on the bottom of separator) 1-1 1/2 turns. Drain water into a container. Close vent and drain.

3) On E-series models, locate the water separator drain knob on the left side of the firewall under the hood. Place a container under the separator, located behind the left front wheel. Pull the knob out and hold for 45 seconds. Release knob and remove container.

4) On all models, restart the engine and check the warning lamp. If the warning lamp is still lit, fuel system needs to be checked or repaired. The only servicable item on the separator is the water level sensor.

1983 Diesel Fuel Injection

GENERAL MOTORS

DESCRIPTION

Diesel mechanical fuel injection systems differ greatly from electronic fuel injection systems. In this diesel system, a mechanical high pressure rotary pump is gear driven by the camshaft at camshaft speed. Through this method the pump injects a precisely metered amount of fuel into each cylinder at the proper time. The pump is mounted on top of the engine and provides necessary timing advance under all operating conditions.

Eight high pressure fuel pipes carry fuel from pump to an injection nozzle in each cylinder. All 8 pipes are exactly the same length to ensure that there is no variance in timing. Engine RPM is controlled by a rotary fuel metering valve. As the accelerator pedal is pushed down, a throttle cable opens the metering valve and allows increased fuel delivery. A mechanical fuel pump located on the right side of the engine, draws fuel from the fuel tank and delivers it to the injection pump.

Three fuel filters are used to remove foreign material which could damage injection pump. The fuel tank filter screens out water from the fuel and allows it to collect at the bottom of the tank below the fuel pickup. When the water reaches a level where it could be drawn into the fuel supply, a dash-mounted warning lamp is energized. When the lamp is energized, water collected in the tank can be siphoned off at the shut off point. The primary fuel filter is located between the mechanical fuel pump and the fuel tank (mounted on firewall). The secondary fuel filter is located between the mechanical pump and injection pump (mounted on side of engine block). Any excess fuel is returned to the tank by a fuel return system.

Fig. 1: Diesel Injection System Fuel Circuit

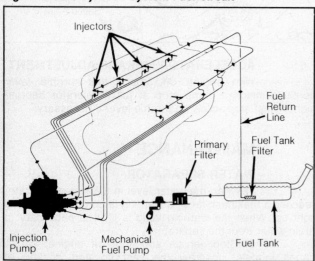

Secondary fuel filter is mounted on side of engine block.

OPERATION

AIR INDUCTION SYSTEM

The intake manifold is always open to atmospheric pressure. The intake manifold has a single inlet for drawing air through an air filter assembly mounted above. The manifold consists of 8 branches, one leading to each cylinder.

FUEL TANK-TO-PUMP SYSTEM

Diesel fuel is drawn from the fuel tank by an engine mounted mechanical fuel pump. This pump is driven by an eccentric cam mounted on the crankshaft and puts out about 5 1/2-6 1/2 psi to the injection pump. A small screen type filter is located in the fuel tank at the pickup. Diesel fuel arrives at the center inlet fitting on the injection pump after leaving the filter. A fuel return line is provided to return any excess fuel to the tank.

DIESEL INJECTION PUMP

The high pressure diesel injection pump is mounted to the top of the engine below the intake manifold. The pump is cam driven at speed equal to the camshaft. Because of this, the pump can precisely govern time and amount of fuel injection.

A built-in fuel pressure regulator and transfer pump picks up fuel at the pump inlet, and pushes it through a passage to the pump head. The pump head distributes fuel, still at transfer pump pressure (8-12 psi), to metering valve, governor and automatic advance mechanisms. Fuel then passes to the rotary fuel metering valve and into a charging passage. As the pump shaft rotates, fuel is fired, under high pressure, through each delivery pipe to an injector. The pump is not serviceable and must be exchanged in case of a malfunction.

Fig. 2: Diesel Injection Pump

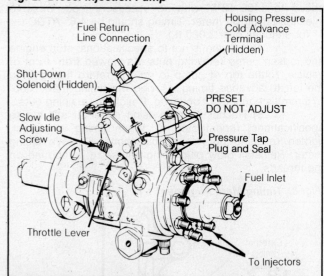

Injection pump is not serviceable; exchange in case of malfunction.

FUEL INJECTION LINES

Eight high pressure fuel injection lines are routed from injection pump to an injector in each cylinder. The lines are of equal length but are bent differently to maintain equal length, prevent any difference in timing from cylinder-to-cylinder and aid installation. Lines are not interchangeable and are pre-bent by the manufacturer.

GLOW PLUGS

Glow plugs are threaded into each cylinder combustion chamber. Glow plugs are small heaters that assist in cold starting. The glow plug controller and relay cycle 12 volts to these 6 volt heaters, which causes them

GENERAL MOTORS (Cont.)

to heat rapidly. After the engine starts, the glow plugs remain on for short time then shut off.

Controller failure, as in the case of prolonged preheat (more than 9 seconds of initial glow plug activation), would cause a circuit breaker to open in the controller. When this takes place, glow plug circuit fails to operate completely.

NOTE: Any attempt to by-pass relay with jumper wire or rewire for manual control may result in glow plug failure.

INJECTION NOZZLES

Each engine cylinder combustion chamber is equipped with 1 injection nozzle. The injection nozzle has a single fuel inlet fitting and 2 fuel return fittings (1 on each side of fuel inlet fitting). The nozzle is threaded into the cylinder head. Injection nozzles are spring loaded and calibrated to open at a specified fuel line pressure. The combustion chamber end of the nozzle has a replaceable compression seal and carbon stop seal.

Fig. 3: Injection Nozzle Installation

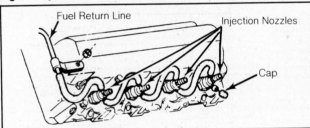

Last nozzle on cylinder bank has 1 fuel return fitting plugged.

VACUUM PUMP

Vacuum to operate accessory systems on diesel vehicles is provided by a vacuum pump which is located at the rear of the block and driven by the cam. The engine should never be operated without the vacuum pump in place as it is also the oil pump drive.

HOUSING PRESSURE COLD ADVANCE (HPCA)

The HPCA circuit is used to improve cold starting and aid emission control. The circuit is controlled by a temperature switch located on right rear head bolt. The circuit advances injection timing about 4° when the engine is cold.

When engine temperature is below 125°F (45°C), the circuit decreases housing pressure from 10 psi to zero. At the same time, the fast idle solenoid is activated. When the temperature switch opens, the HPCA circuit is de-energized and housing pressure rises, retarding pump timing. The temperature switch will close again when engine temperature falls below 95°F (35°C).

DIESEL FUEL HEATER

This option is used to heat the fuel during low temperature operation, below 20°F (−5°C). This prevents wax crystals from building up and blocking the fuel filters. The heater is located along the right side of the intake manifold and uses a resistance wire spiralled around the fuel line.

ADJUSTMENT

NOTE: For all on-vehicle adjustments, see TUNE-UP SERVICE PROCEDURES.

TROUBLE SHOOTING

NOTE: Trouble shooting charts should be used only after ensuring that the glow plug system is properly installed. Check that all connectors are properly installed and that all connections are clean and tight.

THERMAL CONTROLLER CHECK

With connector removed from controller the controller heater circuits may be checked using a high impedance ohmeter. However, this check will not determine shorted switches within the controller.

Pin 3 – Pin 2 .40 to .75 Ω   Pin 5 – Pin 1   130 Ω ± 10%

Pin 4 – Pin 5 27 Ω ± 3 Ω   Pin 2 – Pin 6 Continuity ("O" ohms)

"GLOW PLUGS" LAMP CYCLES ON & OFF WITH WARM ENGINE

This condition can be caused by an open circuit in 25 circuit from generator telltale output to pin 1 of controller, or by generator output failure. Check generator operation.

ENGINE CONTINUES TO RUN WITH IGNITION OFF

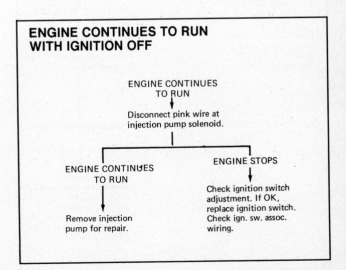

ENGINE DOES NOT START COLD

- "Glow Plugs" lamp may or may not come on.
- Fuel system okay.
- Battery voltage is 12.4 volts or more with ignition off.
- Cranking speed okay (100 RPM or more).

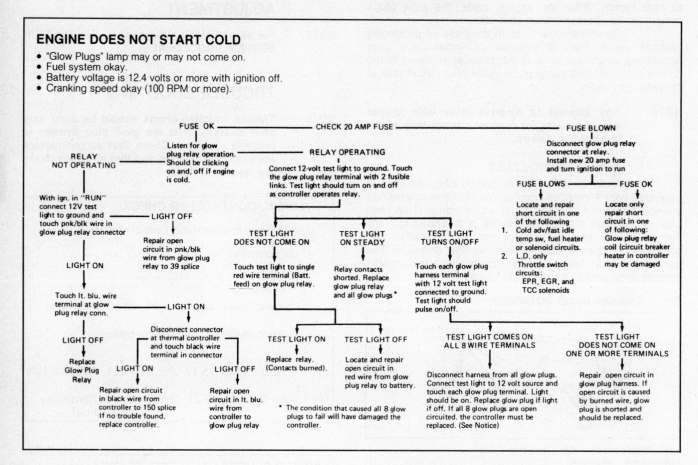

ENGINE REMAINS ON FAST IDLE

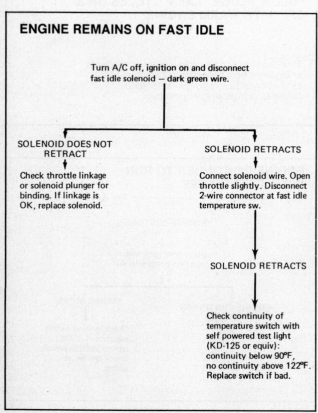

ENGINE RUNS ROUGH ON COLD START GLOW PLUGS NOT CYCLING ON & OFF AFTER ENGINE STARTS (20 AMP FUSE OKAY)

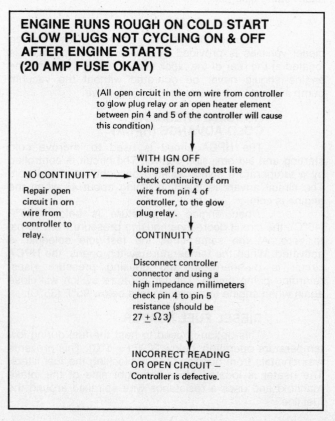

NO "GLOW PLUGS LAMP"

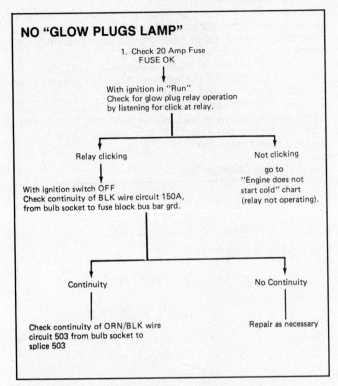

1. Check 20 Amp Fuse
FUSE OK

With ignition in "Run"
Check for glow plug relay operation
by listening for click at relay.

Relay clicking

Not clicking

go to
"Engine does not
start cold" chart
(relay not operating).

With ignition switch OFF
Check continuity of BLK wire circuit 150A,
from bulb socket to fuse block bus bar grd.

Continuity

No Continuity

Check continuity of ORN/BLK wire
circuit 503 from bulb socket to
splice 503

Repair as necessary

NO FAST IDLE WITH COLD ENGINE (TEMPERATURE BELOW 90°F) (20 AMP FUSE OKAY)

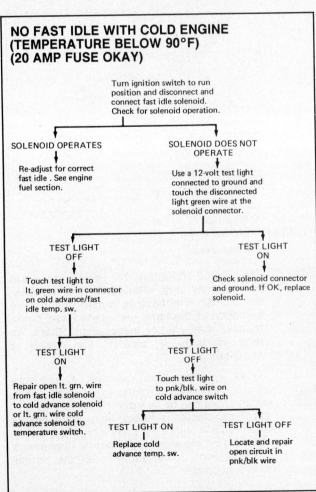

Turn ignition switch to run
position and disconnect and
connect fast idle solenoid.
Check for solenoid operation.

SOLENOID OPERATES

Re-adjust for correct
fast idle . See engine
fuel section.

**SOLENOID DOES NOT
OPERATE**

Use a 12-volt test light
connected to ground and
touch the disconnected
light green wire at the
solenoid connector.

**TEST LIGHT
OFF**

Touch test light to
lt. green wire in connector
on cold advance/fast
idle temp. sw.

**TEST LIGHT
ON**

Check solenoid connector
and ground. If OK, replace
solenoid.

**TEST LIGHT
ON**

Repair open lt. grn. wire
from fast idle solenoid
to cold advance solenoid
or lt. grn. wire cold
advance solenoid to
temperature switch.

**TEST LIGHT
OFF**

Touch test light
to pnk/blk. wire on
cold advance switch

TEST LIGHT ON

Replace cold
advance temp. sw.

TEST LIGHT OFF

Locate and repair
open circuit in
pnk/blk wire

NO COLD ADVANCE ON COLD ENGINE

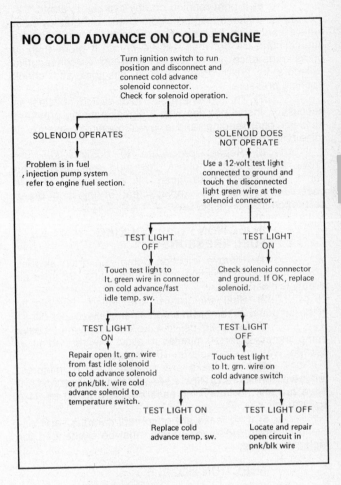

Turn ignition switch to run
position and disconnect and
connect cold advance
solenoid connector.
Check for solenoid operation.

SOLENOID OPERATES

Problem is in fuel
, injection pump system
refer to engine fuel section.

**SOLENOID DOES
NOT OPERATE**

Use a 12-volt test light
connected to ground and
touch the disconnected
light green wire at the
solenoid connector.

**TEST LIGHT
OFF**

Touch test light to
lt. green wire in connector
on cold advance/fast
idle temp. sw.

**TEST LIGHT
ON**

Check solenoid connector
and ground. If OK, replace
solenoid.

**TEST LIGHT
ON**

Repair open lt. grn. wire
from fast idle solenoid
to cold advance solenoid
or pnk/blk. wire cold
advance solenoid to
temperature switch.

**TEST LIGHT
OFF**

Touch test light
to lt. grn. wire on
cold advance switch

TEST LIGHT ON

Replace cold
advance temp. sw.

TEST LIGHT OFF

Locate and repair
open circuit in
pnk/blk wire

TESTING

GLOW PLUG RESISTANCE TEST

CAUTION: The following test requires a high impedance ohmmeter (J-29125 or equivalent). Select scale values as follows: Left-hand switch - "OHMS" position; Right-hand switch - fully counterclockwise (200 ohms); Slide center switch - left position ("DC-LOW")

1) Start engine, turn on heater and allow engine to warm up. Remove all electrical feed wires at glow plugs.

2) Using a magnetic pickup tachometer (Mag-Tach J-26925 or equivalent), adjust engine speed. Turn idle speed screw on side of injection pump until engine idle is at roughest speed. About 860 RPM is desirable, but do not exceed 900 RPM.

3) Allow engine to run for 1 minute at roughest idle. Thermostat must be open and upper radiator hose hot.

4) Attach jumper wire between voltmeter ground lead and engine lift point on left side of intake manifold. DO NOT use any other point for ground connection. This ground wire must remain in position until all tests have been completed.

5) Check resistance by touching positive lead of voltmeter to glow plug terminal (with engine running). Record value obtained in firing order sequence (1-8-7-2-6-5-4-3).

6) If ohm reading on any cylinder is about 1.2-1.3 ohms, make a compression check on that cylinder before continuing fuel injection diagnosis. Most cylinders should measure between 1.8-3.4 ohms. If more than .3 ohms difference is observed between 2 consecutive cylinders in firing order, remove injectors and check opening pressure.

7) To improve rough idle, switch nozzles as necessary. Install nozzles with a higher opening pressure to lower ohm reading, and a lower opening pressure to raise ohm reading.

8) Repeat procedure to confirm idle improvement. Be sure to check glow plug resistance at the same idle speed both times. If no improvement is observed, injection line replacement or injection pump calibration may be necessary.

INJECTION PUMP HOUSING FUEL PRESSURE

1) Remove injection pump and drain all fuel. Connect an air supply line to fuel inlet fitting. Be sure air supply is clean and dry.

2) Seal the return line fitting. Completely immerse pump assembly in a container of clean test oil.

3) Apply 20 psi (1.4 kg/cm²) to pump. Leave pump immersed for 10 minutes to allow any trapped air to escape. Watch for leaks after 10 minutes.

4) If no leaks are noticed after 10 minutes, reduce air pressure to 2 psi (.14 kg/cm²) for 30 seconds. If there are still no leaks, increase pressure to 20 psi (1.4 kg/cm²) again.

5) If no leaks are observed, pump is serviceable. If leaks are observed, pump must be exchanged for replacement unit.

INJECTION NOZZLE

CAUTION: When testing nozzles, keep spray contained to avoid serious injury. DO NOT allow injector to release line pressure on hands, arms or any part of body. Pressure of atomized test spray has sufficient penetrating power to puncture flesh.

Test Preparation

1) Remove injection nozzle from engine. Clean carbon from tip area of nozzle with soft brass brush. Do not use steel brush or motorized brush to clean nozzle tip. Damage to nozzle tip may result.

2) Connect nozzle assembly to injection nozzle tester. Close tester shut off valve to pressure gauge. Fill tester with test fluid. Fill and flush nozzle assembly with test oil by operating tester lever briskly and repeatedly. This purges air from nozzle and coats all parts with test fluid.

Opening Pressure Test

1) Open tester shut off valve to pressure gauge 1/4 turn. Slowly depress tester lever and observe pressure gauge. Note pressure at which needle stopped, indicating pressure increase (nozzle does not chatter) or at which pressure the pressure dropped substantially (nozzle chatters).

2) The maximum pressure is the opening pressure. Lowest acceptable pressure is 1500 psi (105 kg/cm²). Replace any nozzle which does not meet lowest acceptable pressure. Release tester pressure.

Leakage Test

1) Open tester shut off valve to pressure gauge an additional 1/2 to 1 1/2 turns. Blow dry nozzle tip. Connect a short piece of clear plastic tubing to each fuel return fitting on nozzle.

2) Slowly depress tester lever until pressure gauge reads 1400 psi (98 kg/cm²). Maintain pressure for 10 seconds and observe nozzle tip.

3) Replace nozzle assembly if drop of test fluid drops from tip within 10 seconds. A drop may form but not drop off within the specified time period. *See Fig. 4.* Release tester pressure.

Fig. 4: Nozzle Leakage Test

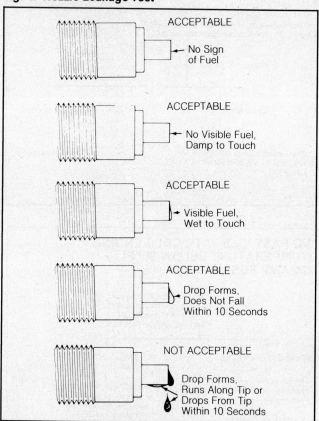

A drop of test fluid may form but not drop off within 10 seconds.

Chatter Test

NOTE: **The sound (chatter) for new and used nozzles may vary. With some used nozzles, the chatter is difficult to detect during slow actuation of the hand test stand lever. Some nozzles may chatter louder than others. As long as there is chatter, the nozzle is acceptable.**

1) Close tester shut off lever at pressure gauge. Slowly depress lever of manual test stand noting whether chatter noises can be heard.

2) If no chatter is heard, increase speed of lever movement until it reaches a point where the nozzle chatters. At fast lever movement, the nozzle may emit a "hissing" or "squealing" sound rather than the normal chatter. This is acceptable.

3) These sounds indicate that the nozzle needle moves freely and that the nozzle seat, guide and pintle have no mechanical defects.

4) Replace any nozzle assembly which does not chatter. Release tester pressure.

Spray Pattern Test

This nozzle features a longer nozzle overlap, greater pintle to body clearance and greater needle to body clearance. This assembly also features an internal wave washer between the nozzle nut and nozzle. Because of these features, testing is difficult. A pop tester will not deliver fuel with the velocity necessary to obtain proper spray pattern analysis. Based on the above, this type nozzle should not be rejected for spray pattern.

REMOVAL & INSTALLATION

NOTE: Manufacturer does not recommend disassembly of pump. However, the following seals can be replaced with the injection pump installed on the engine. For problems not covered in this article, pump must be removed and taken to an authorized repair station.

INJECTION PUMP SEAL REPLACEMENT

Pump Cover Seal & Guide Stud Seal

1) Disconnect ground cables from both batteries. Remove air cleaner and intake manifold. Install screens (J-29664) in cylinder heads to prevent entrance of dirt. Disconnect fuel return line and wiring from injection pump.

2) Remove throttle cable and return springs. Remove top fast idle solenoid attaching bolt. Loosen lower bolt and move solenoid aside. Clean injection pump cover and area around throttle rod and guide stud. Place rags in engine valley to catch fuel. Remove injection pump cover and remove screws from cover.

NOTE: After removing injection pump cover, extreme care must be exercised to prevent entrance of foreign material.

Fig. 5: Guide Stud Seal Replacement

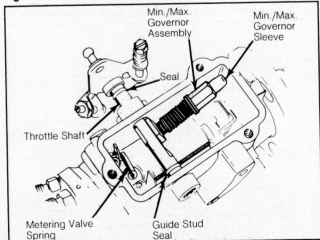

Metering valve spring must be installed in original position over guide stud.

3) Observe position of metering valve spring over top of guide stud. This position must be exactly duplicated during reassembly. Before removing guide stud and washer, note location. Remove guide stud and washer. *See Fig. 5.*

4) Install guide stud with new washer. Make sure that upper extension of metering valve spring rides on top of guide stud. Carefully tighten guide stud.

5) Hold throttle in idle position. Install new pump cover seal. Make sure cover screws are removed from cover. Position cover about 1/4" forward (toward shaft end) and about 1/8" above pump. *See Fig. 6.*

Fig. 6: Injection Pump Cover Installation

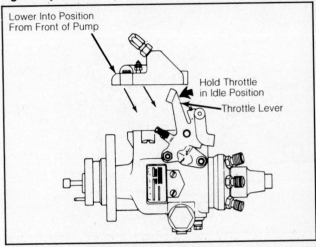

Screws must be removed from cover before installing cover to prevent screws from falling into pump.

6) Using care not to cut seal, move cover rearward and downward into position. Install cover screws with flat washer against cover. Use care not to drop lock washers or flat washers into pump. Tighten screws.

7) Reconnect negative battery cables to both batteries. Turn ignition switch to "run" position. Momentarily touch Pink solenoid wire to solenoid. A clicking noise should be heard as the wire is connected and disconnected at solenoid. If clicking noise is heard, go to step **10)**. If not, go to step **8)**.

8) If clicking noise is not heard, the linkage may be jammed in a wide open throttle position. Engine MUST NOT be started. Remove cover.

9) Ground solenoid lead (opposite "hot" lead) and connect Pink wire. With ignition switch in "run" position, solenoid in cover should move the linkage. If not, replace solenoid and cover. Repeat steps **5)** through **7)**. Minimum voltage across solenoid terminals should be 12 volts.

10) If clicking noise is heard, connect the pump solenoid and HPCA wires. Install fuel return line, throttle cable and return springs. Reposition fast idle solenoid.

11) Start engine and check for leaks. Idle roughness may occur due to air in the fuel system. Allow plenty of time for air to be purged from system. Engine may have to be stopped to allow air in injection pump to rise to top of pump for purging.

12) Remove cylinder head screens. Install intake manifold and air cleaner.

Throttle Shaft Seal

1) Disconnect ground cables from both batteries. Remove air cleaner and intake manifold. Install screens (J-29664) in cylinder heads to prevent entrance of dirt. Disconnect fuel return line and wiring from injection pump.

2) Remove throttle position switch (TPS) or vacuum regulator valve. Remove throttle rod and return springs. Loosen fast idle solenoid and move aside. Remove throttle cable bracket.

3) Install advance cam tool (J-29601) over throttle shaft with slots of tool engaging pin. Place spring clip over throttle shaft advance cam and tighten wing nut. Without loosening wing nut, pull tool off throttle shaft to provide alignment for reassembly. *See Fig. 7.*

Fig. 7: *Advance Cam Tool Installed on Injection Pump*

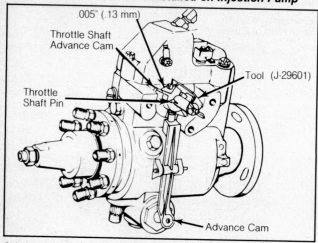

Advance cam tool provides proper alignment of throttle shaft advance cam for reassembly.

4) Drive pin from throttle shaft. Remove throttle shaft advance cam and fiber washer. Remove any burrs from throttle shaft after removing cam. Clean injection pump cover, upper portion of pump, throttle shaft and guide stud area. Remove injection pump cover and remove screws from cover.

NOTE: **Do not allow any dirt or foreign objects to drop into injection pump after cover is removed. Engine damage may result.**

5) Note position of metering valve spring over top of guide stud for reassembly reference. Note position of guide stud and washer. Remove guide stud and washer. *See Fig. 5.*

6) Rotate min./max. governor assembly up to provide clearance and remove from throttle shaft. If idle governor spring becomes disengaged from throttle block, reinstall with tightly wound coils toward throttle block.

7) Remove throttle shaft and inspect. If damaged or worn, replace. Inspect throttle shaft bushings for damage, wear or leaks. If bushing replacement is required, pump must be sent to authorized repair station.

8) Remove throttle shaft seals. Do not cut seals for removal. A nick on shaft will cause leakage. Lightly coat new seals with grease. Install seals on shaft without cutting seals on sharp edges of shaft.

9) Carefully slide shaft into pump until min./max. governor assembly will slip onto throttle shaft. Rotate governor downward and hold in position. Slide shaft and governor into place.

10) Install new fiber washer, throttle shaft advance cam (do not tighten cam screw) and throttle shaft

drive pin. Align advance cam so advance cam tool can be reinstalled over throttle shaft. Install pin in slots and spring clip over advance cam.

11) Insert a .005" (.13 mm) feeler gauge between white washer on throttle shaft and pump housing. Squeeze throttle shaft and tighten cam screw. Remove advance cam tool.

12) Install guide stud with new washer. Ensure that upper extension of metering valve spring rides on top of guide stud. Tighten guide stud.

13) Hold throttle in idle position. Install new pump cover seal. Make sure cover screws are removed from cover. Position cover about 1/4" forward (toward shaft end) and about 1/8" above pump. *See Fig. 6.*

14) Using care not to cut seal, move cover rearward and downward into position. Install cover screws with flat washer against cover. Use care not to drop lock washers or flat washers into pump. Tighten screws. Install vacuum regulator or TPS.

15) Reconnect negative battery cables to both batteries. Turn ignition switch to "run" position. Momentarily touch Pink solenoid wire to solenoid. A clicking noise should be heard as the wire is connected and disconnected at solenoid. If clicking noise is heard, go to step **18)**. If not, go to step **16)**.

16) If clicking noise is not heard, the linkage may be jammed in a wide open throttle position. Engine MUST NOT be started. Remove cover.

17) Ground solenoid lead (opposite "hot" lead) and connect Pink wire. With ignition switch in "run" position, solenoid in cover should move the linkage. If not, replace solenoid and cover, and repeat step **15)**. Minimum voltage across solenoid terminals should be 12 volts.

18) If clicking noise is heard, connect the pump solenoid and HPCA wires. Install fuel return line, throttle cable, throttle cable bracket and return springs. Reposition fast idle solenoid.

19) Start engine and check for leaks. Idle roughness may occur due to air in the fuel system. Allow plenty of time for air to be purged from system. Engine may have to be stopped to allow air in injection pump to rise to top of pump for purging.

20) Remove cylinder head screens. Install intake manifold and air cleaner. Perform on-vehicle adjustments.

Fig. 8: *Exploded View of Automatic Advance Assembly*

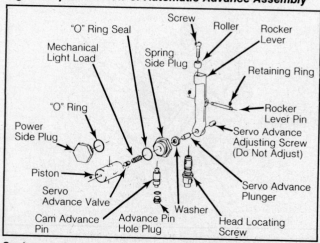

Seals must be replaced with injection pump removed from engine.

GENERAL MOTORS (Cont.)

NOTE: The following seals must be replaced with the injection pump removed from the engine. For problems not covered in this article, pump must be removed and taken to an authorized repair station.

Advance Pin Hole Plug Seal

1) Tap advance pin hole plug lightly with a hammer to loosen. Remove plug. Remove and discard seal. *See Fig. 8.*

2) Lubricate and install new seal. Install and tighten plug.

Automatic Advance Seals

1) Remove advance pin hole plug as previously described. Remove spring side advance piston hole plug. Remove plug, piston, spring and washer.

2) Remove power side advance piston hole plug. Remove plug, piston and washer. Disassemble plugs and pistons. Discard seals.

3) Lubricate and install new seals. Reverse removal procedure and tighten plugs. *See Fig. 8.*

Hydraulic Head Seal

1) Remove throttle shaft and seals as previously described. Remove metering valve. Remove housing vent screw assembly. Remove advance pin hole plug and advance pin.

2) Install pump in holding fixture so that rear of pump is tilted downward. Remove hydraulic head locating screw. Remove 2 hydraulic head locking screws and discard seals.

3) Using a twisting motion, remove hydraulic head from pump assembly. Remove and discard "O" ring seal.

4) Lubricate and install new seal. Install hydraulic head into pump assembly. Lubricate and install 2 locking screw seals. Install locating screw. Install and tighten locking screws.

Fig. 9: Injection Pump Hydraulic Head Components Location

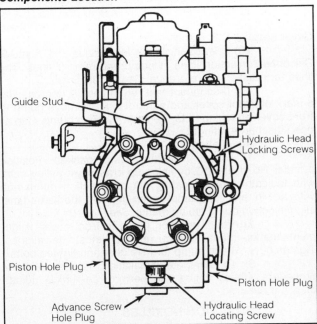

Pump assembly must be mounted in holding fixture to remove hydraulic head assembly.

5) Install advance pin, advance pin seal and advance pin hole plug. Position pump so cover opening is up, and install metering valve. Install throttle shaft, seals and pump cover.

Drive Shaft Seal

1) Mount pump in holding fixture (J-29692-B) and tilt pump slightly towards you. Remove fast idle solenoid bracket.

2) Clean upper portion of pump. Remove 3 governor cover hold down screws and governor cover. Discard cover gasket.

NOTE: Do not allow any dirt or foreign objects to drop into injection pump after cover is removed. Engine damage may result.

3) Note position of metering valve spring over top of guide stud for reassembly reference. Remove guide stud and washer. Discard washer.

4) Remove min./max. governor by rotating throttle shaft. Rotate drive shaft until hump on retaining clip is visible.

5) Using removal tool (J-9553-01), pull drive shaft retaining clip off of the drive shaft and discard retaining clip. With alignment pin at top, remove drive shaft. Remove and discard seals.

6) Lubricate seal installer tool (J-29745-A) with Skynkut oil (J-33198) or equivalent. Install one Black seal. Install Red seal and last Black seal relubricating seal installer each time.

7) Install new retaining clip on drive shaft. DO NOT spread clip so large that it becomes loose in the drive shaft retaining clip slot.

8) Install min./max. governor, guide stud and new washer. Ensure guide is under metering valve spring. Using new gasket, install governor cover. Install fast idle solenoid bracket.

FUEL INJECTION LINES

Removal (Pickup)

1) Disconnect negative battery cables. Disconnect air cleaner bracket from valve cover. Remove crankcase vent bracket and move aside. Disconnect secondary filter lines. Remove secondary filter adapter.

2) Loosen vacuum pump hold-down clamp. Rotate pump to gain access to intake manifold bolt. Remove intake manifold. Install screens (J-29664) in cylinder heads.

3) Remove injection line clamps. Remove injection lines at injection nozzles. Remove lines at pump. Tag lines for reassembly reference. Cap open lines.

Installation

1) Remove caps from lines and loosely install injection lines. Ensure lines are properly positioned.

2) Reverse removal procedures to complete installation. After installation, start engine and check for leaks.

Removal (Van)

1) Disconnect negative battery cables. Remove engine cover and air cleaner. Disconnect necessary wires and hoses. Remove EGR/EPR switches.

2) Remove crankcase depression regulator valve hoses from intake manifold. Remove rear A/C compressor bracket (if equipped).

3) Remove fuel filter to intake manifold bracket. Remove vacuum pump. Place a rag or cover over hole

to prevent foreign material from entering engine. Remove intake mainfold bolts and fuel line clips. Remove intake manifold.

4) Install screens (J-29664) in cylinder heads. Remove injection line clips at loom brackets. Raise left side of vehicle.

5) Remove injection lines at injection nozzles. Lower vehicle. Remove lines at pump. Tag lines for reassembly reference. Cap open lines.

Installation

1) Remove caps from lines and loosely install injection lines. Ensure lines are properly positioned. Raise and lower left side of vehicle as necessary.

2) Reverse removal procedures to complete installation. After installation, start engine and check for leaks.

INJECTION PUMP

Removal (Pickup)

1) Disconnect negative battery cables. Remove fan, shroud, air cleaner and intake manifold. Install screens in cylinder heads. Remove fuel injection lines as previously described.

2) Disconnect throttle cable, return springs and detent cable (if equipped). Disconnect wires, fuel return line, fuel supply line and fuel injection lines at pump. Cap all fuel lines.

3) Remove oil filler tube and PCV vent hose assembly. Remove A/C hose retainer bracket, if equipped. Remove grommet. Scribe or paint an alignment mark on front cover and injection pump.

4) Rotate engine to remove injection pump retaining bolts that are accessible through oil filler neck hole. Remove injection pump-to-front cover bolts. Remove injection pump and gasket.

Fig. 10: Injection Pump Timing Mark Locations

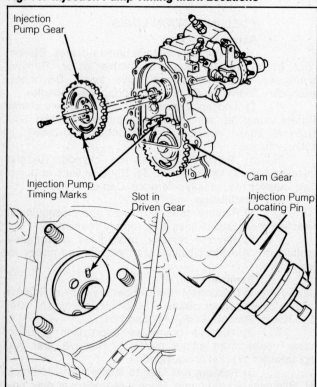

Injection Pump Gear

Injection Pump Timing Marks

Slot in Driven Gear

Cam Gear

Injection Pump Locating Pin

Cylinder No. 1 must be set at TDC.

Installation

1) Install injection pump gasket. Position cylinder No. 1 at TDC by lining up crankshaft pulley mark with indicator. Align locating pin on injection pump hub with slot in injection pump driven gear. At the same time, align injection pump timing marks. *See Fig. 10.*

2) Attach injection pump to front cover. Alignment marks made during removal must be aligned. Tighten nuts. Attach pump to drive gear and tighten bolts.

3) To complete installation, reverse removal procedure. Check timing and perform on-vehicle adjustments, if required.

Removal (Van)

1) Disconnect negative battery cables. Remove engine cover and air cleaner. Disconnect necessary wires and hoses. Remove EGR/EPR switches.

2) Remove crankcase depression regulator valve hoses from intake manifold. Remove rear A/C compressor bracket (if equipped).

3) Remove fuel filter to intake manifold bracket. Remove vacuum pump. Place a rag or cover over hole to prevent foreign material from entering engine. Remove intake mainfold bolts and fuel line clips. Remove intake manifold.

4) Rotate snorkel of air cleaner inlet hose up. Remove hood latch, disconnect cable and move aside.

5) Remove windshield washer bottle, fan shroud bolts and upper shroud. Disconnect rubber hose from oil fill tube. Disconnect oil fill tube attaching nuts and remove oil fill tube.

6) Remove oil fill tube grommet. Rotate engine as necessary and remove drive gear to pump bolts. Remove fuel filter and bracket including line to injection pump.

7) Disconnect wire looms from injection lines and injection lines at brackets. Disconnect oil pan dipstick tube at left cylinder head.

8) Disconnect electrical connections at injection pump. If equipped with automatic transmission, disconnect TV cable. Disconnect accelerator cable.

9) Disconnect injection lines at nozzles 2, 4, 5, 6, 7 and 8. Raise vehicle and disconnect remaining lines. Cover nozzles 1, 3, 5 and 7.

10) Lower vehicle. Cover nozzles 2, 4, 6 and 8. Disconnect injection lines at pump and remove lines. Tag lines for reassembly reference. Cap all fuel lines.

11) Disconnect fuel return line. Scribe or paint a mark on front cover and pump flange. Remove pump to front cover attaching nuts. Remove injection pump. Cap all open discharge fittings.

Installation

1) Install injection pump gasket. Position cylinder No. 1 at TDC by lining up crankshaft pulley mark with indicator. Align locating pin on injection pump hub with slot in injection pump driven gear. At the same time, align injection pump timing marks. *See Fig. 10.*

2) Attach injection pump to front cover. Alignment marks made during removal must be aligned. Tighten nuts. Attach pump to drive gear and tighten bolts.

3) To complete installation, reverse removal procedure. Check timing and perform on-vehicle adjustments, if required.

INJECTION NOZZLES

Removal

1) Disconnect negative battery cables. Remove fuel line clip. Remove fuel return line from nozzle without bending line out of the way. Remove fuel injection line.

    2) Using injector tool (J-29873), remove injection nozzle. Always remove injector by placing remover on the 30 mm hex flats of injector body to prevent damage to injector body. Cap injector and lines.

Installation

    1) Use new compression seal and install nozzle. Tighten nozzle with injector tool.

    2) Install fuel injection line. Install fuel return line. Start engine and check for leaks.

TIGHTENING SPECIFICATIONS

Application	Ft. Lbs. (N.m)
Injection Pump-to-Front Cover Nuts	30 (40)
Fuel Injection Lines	20 (27)
Inj. Pump Hydraulic Head Bolts	15-18 (20-24)
	INCH Lbs. (N.m)
Injection Pump Guide Stud	85 (9)
Inj. Pump Auto. Advance Plugs	75-100 (8-11)

SECTION 3

EMISSION CONTROL

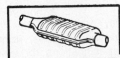

CONTENTS

NOTE: ALSO SEE GENERAL INDEX.

IMPORTANT: Because of the many model names used by vehicle manufacturers, accurate identification of models is important. See Model Identification at the front of this publication.

1983 Exhaust Emission Systems

EMISSION STANDARDS & TUNE-UPS

MANUFACTURING STANDARDS

Federal and state governments have established air quality standards during the past 20 years. Automobile manufacturers design their vehicles to conform to standards where the vehicle will be sold. These standards cover carbon monoxide (CO), hydrocarbons (HC) and oxides of nitrogen (NOx).

Federal and California standards which must be met by manufacturers are specified in units easily measured in a testing laboratory. Since 1970, these standards have been in "grams per mile". This means no vehicle, whether 2-cylinder or V8, may emit more than a set weight (in grams) of pollutants for each mile it travels. Since large engines burn more fuel per mile than smaller ones, they must be "cleaner" per gallon burned if they are to meet these standards.

When manufacturers certify vehicles, the cars are placed on a dynamometer and the exhaust gases are collected in a bag. After the vehicle runs for a specified time, the gases are analyzed and weighed. Engines and emission systems are designed so the weight of emissions will be less than the specified grams per mile.

Infra-red exhaust analyzers are commonly used in automotive test stations. They use a test probe placed in the exhaust stream, and measure the percentage of CO in the exhaust gas, or parts per million of HC. These are not the same units used by the manufacturer when the car is certified. (NOx emissions can be measured only in a laboratory.)

TUNE-UP STANDARDS

When a tune-up is performed, the mechanic must have specifications to use when adjusting the vehicle. The first few years of emission-regulated vehicles were adjusted using carbon monoxide percentage or hydrocarbon parts per million. These are the units measured by an exhaust gas analyzer.

In the past few years, manufacturers have made their vehicles much cleaner (measured in grams per mile). The CO% and HC ppm have become very low, especially when measured AFTER a catalytic converter. It has become hard to accurately measure the effect of turning the idle mixture screws.

One solution to this problem requires the use of artifically-enriched propane adjustments. The added propane boosts the emissions by a known amount, and makes the effect of turning the mixture screws easily measureable. However, CO and HC can only be accurately measured while the propane is being added.

As computer-controlled systems were developed, it became possible for the vehicle to adjust its own mixture throughout the entire engine operating range, not just at idle. These "feedback" systems use oxygen sensors to measure how much unburned oxygen is left in the exhaust. The computer can then determine when the air/fuel mixture is too rich or too lean, and correct it as necessary. Even if a mechanic incorrectly adjusts the mixture, most computers can compensate enough so the vehicle will still run clean. In fact, newer cars burn fuel so completely that changes in the pollutant levels after the catalytic converter are hard to measure accurately.

New vehicles are now adjusted by measuring the percentage of time that the computer-controlled system is adding fuel versus the time fuel is shut off. The mechanic checks this percentage with a dwell meter (normally used to measure the time a set of points is open/closed), then adjusts the fuel system until the percentage is correct.

Although many shops have exhaust gas analyzers which measure tailpipe emissions, computer-controlled engines normally do NOT have CO or HC specifications for tuning. These specifications would be neither useful or possible for adjusting new vehicles. This manual provides procedures and specifications given by the manufacturers and does not necessarily list CO or HC specifications.

STATE TEST STANDARDS

Some states have established standards for testing used vehicles to see if they are still running clean. Generally speaking, these standards are given in CO% and HC ppm. They can be checked with an exhaust gas analyzer. Typical standards for newer cars would be less than 2.0% CO (non-catalyst) or 0.5% CO (with catalyst) and less than 200 ppm of HC. If vehicle emissions are below these levels, the vehicle passes inspection. The important thing to remember is that these specifications are NOT to be used for TUNING. They are only for testing to see if the vehicle is functioning properly. If it isn't, it must be tuned using the manufacturer's procedures and specifications, then tested again.

Test standards change each year and vary from state to state, and even by county within each state. It is not possible to provide an accurate and up-to-date list in this manual. Specifications can be obtained from your local county or state government. Remember that these standards are ONLY for test purposes. The manufacturer's adjustment procedures and specifications MUST be used when actually tuning a vehicle.

1983 EMISSION CONTROL SYSTEMS & DEVICES

1983 CHRYSLER CORP.

Engine	Emission Control Systems & Devices	Remarks
Light Duty Emission 3.7L 6-Cyl.	AIR, APDV, APREVLV [1], ASV [2], CAT, CCEGR, CCEVS [2], ChVLV, EAC, ECS, EGR, EGR-CTS, EGR-DV [3], ESA, MHCV, MCU, OSAC [3], PCV, TAC	[1] — Federal only. [2] — Calif. Only. [3] — Some models. [4] — With A/C.
5.2L V8	AAS, AIR, APDV [2], APREVLV [1], CAT, CCEGR, CCEVS [2], ChVLV, EAC, ECS, EGR, EGR-CTS, EGR-DV [3], MHCV, MCU, OSAC [3], PCV, TAC	
Heavy Duty Emissions 5.2L V8	AIR, APDV [2], APREVLV [1], CAT, CCEGR, CCEVS [2], ChVLV, ECS, EGR, EGR-DV [3], MHCV, PCV, TAC, TIDC [4], VTP	
5.9L V8	AIR, APDV [2], APREVLV [1], CAT [2], CCEGR, CCEVS [2], ChVLV, ECS, EGR, EGR-DV [3], MHCV, MCU, OSAC, PCV, TAC, TIDC, VTP	

Light Duty Emissions: Vehicles up to 8500 GVW. **Heavy Duty Emissions:** Vehicles over 8500 GVW.

AAS — Aspirator Air System
AIR — Air Injection Reactor
APDV — Air Pump Diverter Valve
APREVLV — Air Pump Relief Valve
ASV — Air Switching Valve
CAT — Catalytic Converter
CCEGR — Coolant Controlled
    Exhaust Gas Recirculation
CCEVS — Coolant Controlled
    Engine Vacuum Switch

ChVLV — Check Valve
EAC — Electric Assist Choke
ECS — Emission Control System
EGR — Exhaust Gas Recirculation
EGR-CTS — Exhaust Gas Recirculation
    Charge Temperature Switch
EGR-DV — Exhaust Gas Recirculation
    Delay Valve
ESA — Electronic Spark Advance
MHCV — Manifold Heat Control Valve

MCU — Micro Computer Unit
OSAC — Orifice Spark Advance Control
PCV — Positive Crankcase Ventilation
TAC — Thermostatic Air Cleaner
TIDC — Thermostatic Ignition
    Distributor Control
VTP — Vacuum Throttle Positioner

1983 JEEP

Engine	Emission Control Systems & Devices	Remarks
2.5L 4-Cyl.	CAT, CEC, DC-VLV [2], DLV, EGR, EGR-CTO, EGR-TVS, HDVA-CTO [3], MCU [2], PCV, RDV, TSD, VA-CTO, VSA [2]	[1] — Federal only. [2] — Calif. only. [3] — Heavy duty. [4] — Some Models. [5] — Some Federal, all Calif.
4.2L 6-Cyl.	ACV [1], ASV [2], CAT, CEC [5], DLV, DVTRV, EGR, EGR-CTO, EGR-FDLV [4], EGR-TVS, HDSP-CTO [3], HDVA-CTO [3] MCU [5], NLRV [1], PAIR, PCV, RDV, SLV, VA-CTO, VSA [5]	
6.0L V8	ACV, AIR, CAT, CEC, DLV, DVTRV, EGR, EGR-CTO, EGR-TVS, HDVA-CTO [3], MCU [2], NLRV [1], PCV, RDV, VA-CTO, VSA [2]	

Light Duty Emissions: Vehicles up to 8500 GVW. **Heavy Duty Emissions:** Vehicles over 8500 GVW.

ACV — Air Control Valve
AIR — Air Injection System
ASV — Air Switching Valve
CAT — Catalytic Converter
CEC — Computerized Emission Control
DC-VLV — Deceleration Valve
DLV — Delay Valve
DVTRV — Diverter Valve
EGR — Exhaust Gas Recirculation

EGR-CTO — Exhaust Gas Recirculation
    Coolant Temperature Override
EGR-FDLV — Exhaust Gas Recirculation
    Forward Delay Valve
EGR-TVS — Exhaust Gas Recirculation
    Thermal Vacuum Switch
HDSP-CTO [3] — Heavy Duty Spark Coolant
    Temperature Override
HDVA-CTO [3] — Heavy Duty Vacuum Advance
    Coolant Temperature Override

MCU — Micro Computer Unit
NLRV — Non-Linear Valve
PAIR — Pulse-Air Injection
PCV — Positive Crankcase Ventilation
RDV — Reverse Delay Valve
SLV — Solevac
TSD — Throttle Solenoid
VA-CTO — Vacuum Advance
    Coolant Temperature Override
VSA — Vacuum Switch Assembly

1983 EMISSION CONTROL SYSTEMS & DEVICES (Cont.)

1983 FORD

Engine	Emission Control Systems & Devices	Remarks
Light Duty Emissions 2.0L 4-Cyl.	A/CL-BMS, A/CL-TSOV, A/CL-VCD, A/CL-VCV, A/CL-VM, ACV, AIR, AIR-BPV, AIR-ChV, AIR-IVV, CAT, DMV, DRCV, DVCV, EGR, EGR-BPTV, EGR-RSR, EGR-VCV, EGR-VSOL, EVCR, FCS, FVEC, OS, PCV, TAC, V-RSR, V-RST	[1] — Calif. only. [2] — High alt. only. [3] — Man. trans. only. [4] — Some models.
2.3L 4-Cyl.	A/CL-BMS, A/CL-TSOV, A/CL-VCD, A/CL-VCV, A/CL-VM, ACV, AIR, AIR-BPV, AIR-ChV, AIR-IVV, BPS, CAT, DMV, DRCV, DVCV, EGR, EGR-BPTV, EGR-RSR, EGR-VCV, EGR-VSOL, EVCR, FVEC, MCU, OS, PCV, TAC, V-RSR, V-RST,	
4.9L 6-Cyl.	A/CL-BMS, A/CL-TSOV, A/CL-VCD, A/CL-VCV, A/CL-VM, ACV [1], AIR, AIR-BPV, AIR-ChV, BPS [2], CAT, DMV [1], DRCV, DVCV, EGR, EGR-BPTV, EGR-VCV, EGR-VSOL [1], FCS [1], FVEC, ITVS, MCU [1], OS [1], PCV, TAC, V-RSR, V-RST [1]	
2.8L V6	A/CL-BMS, A/CL-VCD, A/CL-VM, ACV, AIR, AIR-BPV, AIR-ChV, BMAPS, CAT, DRCV, EEC, EGR, EGR-EPV, EGR-RSR, EGR-VSOL, FVEC, OS, PCV, TAC, V-RSR	
3.8L V6	A/CL-BMS, A/CL-VCD, A/CL-VM, AIR, AIR-BPV, AIR-ChV, AIR-IVV, CAT, DRCV, DVCV, EGR, EGR-BPTV, EGR-VCV, EGR-VSOL, FVEC, ITVS [3], PCV, TAC, V-RSR	
5.0L V8	A/CL-BMS, A/CL-TSOV [4], A/CL-VCD, A/CL-VCV, A/CL-VM, ACV [1], AIR, AIR-BPV, AIR-ChV, AIR-IVV, BMAPS [4], BPS [2 3], CAT [4], CTS [4], DVCV, DRCV, DMV, EEC [1], EGR, EGR-BPTV, EGR-CLR [1], EGR-EPV [1], EGR-VCV, EGR-VSOL [1], EVCR [4], FCS [1], FVEC, HIC, ITVS, OS [1], PCV, TAC, TP, V-RSR, V-RST	
5.8L V8	A/CL-BMS, A/CL-VCD, A/CL-VCV, A/CL-VM, ACV [4], AIR, AIR-BPV, AIR-ChV, BMAPS [1 4], CAT [4], CTS [4], DVCV, EEC [4], EGR, EGR-BPTV, EGR-CLR [4], EGR-EPV [4], EGR-VCV, EGR-VSOL [4], FCS [4], FVEC, HIC, ITVS, OS [4], PCV, TAC, TP, V-RSR, V-RST	
Heavy Duty Emissions 4.9L 6-Cyl.	A/CL-BMS, A/CL-TSOV, A/CL-VCV, A/CL-VM, AIR, AIR-BPV, DVCV, EGR, EGR-RSR, EGR-VCV, EGR-VSOL, FVEC, PCV, TAC	
5.8L V8	A/CL-BMS, A/CL-VM, AIR, AIR-BPV, DVCV, EGR, EGR-VCV, EGR-VSOL, FVEC, PCV, TAC, TP, V-RST	
7.5L V8	A/CL-BMS, A/CL-VM, AIR, AIR-BPV, DVCV, EGR, EGR-RSR, EGR-VCV, EGR-VSOL, FVEC, HIC, PCV, TAC, TP, V-RST	

Light Duty Emissions: Vehicles up to 8500 GVW. **Heavy Duty Emissions:** Vehicles over 8500 GVW.

A/CL-BMS — Air Cleaner Bi-Metal Sensor
A/CL-TSOV — Air Cleaner Temperature Sensor Override Valve
A/CL-VCD — Air Cleaner Vacuum Control Delay
A/CL-VCV — Air Cleaner Vacuum Control Valve
A/CL-VM — Air Cleaner Vacuum Motor
ACV — Air Control Valve
AIR — Air Injection System
AIR-BPV — Air By-Pass Valve
AIR-ChV — Air Check Valve
AIR-IVV — Air Idle Vacuum Valve
BMAPS — Barometric/Manifold Absolute Pressure Sensor

BPS — Barometric Pressure Switch
CAT — Catalytic Converter
CTS — Coolant Temperature Sensor
DMV — Distributor Modulator Valve
DRCV — Distributor Retard Control Valve
DVCV — Distributor Vacuum Control Valve
EEC — Electronic Engine Control
EGR — Exhaust Gas Recirculation
EGR-BPTV — EGR Back Pressure Transducer Valve
EGR-CLR — EGR Cooler
EGR-EPV — EGR External Pressure Valve
EGR-RSR — EGR Reservoir

EGR-VCV — EGR Vacuum Control Valve
EGR-VSOL — EGR Vacuum Solenoid
EVCR — Emission Vacuum Control Regulator
FCS — Fuel Control System
FVEC — Fuel Vapor Emission Control
HIC — Hot Idle Compensator
ITVS — Ignition Timing Vacuum Switch
MCU — Micro Computer Unit
OS — Oxygen Sensor
PCV — Positive Crankcase Ventilation
TAC — Thermostatic Air Cleaner
TP — Throttle Positioner
V-RSR — Vacuum Reservoir
V-RST — Vacuum Restrictor

1983 EMISSION CONTROL SYSTEMS & DEVICES (Cont.)

1983 CHEVROLET & GMC

Engine	Emission Control Systems & Devices	Remarks
Light Duty Emissions 1.9L 4-Cyl.	ABAV [1], A/CL-BMS, A/CL-VM, AIR, AIR-DVLV, CAT, DCM/C-VLV, EEC, EGR, EGR-BPTV, EGR-TVS, HIC, IS [1], PCV, TAC, TCVS [2], VCV [1], VSV [1], WOT-SW [1]	[1] — Calif. only. [2] — Auto. trans. only. [3] — Some models. [4] — High alt. only.
2.0L 4-Cyl.	A/CL-BMS, A/CL-VM, ACV, AIR, CP-TVS, DCM/C-VLV, EGR, EGR-BldSOL, EGR-DVLV, EGR-TVS, PCV, PVBrk, SADV-TVS, SVBrk, SVBrk-TVS, TCVS	
4.1L 6-Cyl.	A/CL-BMS, A/CL-VM, AIR [3], AIR-DVLV [3], CAT, DC-VLV DCP-TVS, EEC, EFE, EFE-TVS, EGR, EGR-BldSOL [4], EGR-TVS, PAIR [3], PCV, SRD-VLV, SVBrk, SVBrk-TVS TAC, TC-DVLV [2], TC-TVS [2], TCVS [2], VRV [3]	
2.8L V6	A/CL-BMS, A/CL-VM, ACV, AIR, CAT, CP-TVS, DC-VLV, DD-VLV [3], DVRV [4], DV-TVS [4], EEC, EGR, EGR/TC-TVS [2], EGR-TVS, MVS, PCV, PVBrk, SVBrk, SVBrK-TVS, TAC, TC-DVLV [2], TCVS [2]	
5.0L V8	A/CL-BMS, A/CL-VM, AIR [3], AIR-DVLV [3], CAT, ChVLV, DC-VLV [3], DD-VLV, EEC, EFE, EFE-TVS, EGR, EGR-BldSOL [3], EGR-TVS, PCV, PTVS, SVBrk [3], SVBrK-TVS [3], TAC, TC-DVLV [2], TC-TVS [2], TCVS [2]	
5.7L V8	A/CL-BMS, A/CL-VM, AIR, AIR-DVLV [3], CAT, ChVLV, DC-VLV [3], DD-VLV, EEC, EFE, EFE-TVS, EGR, EGR-BldSOL [3], EGR-TVS, PCV, SVBrk [1], SVBrk-TVS [1], TAC, TC-DVLV [2], TC-TVS [2], TCVS [2]	
Heavy Duty Emissions 4.8L 6-Cyl.	A/CL-BMS, A/CL-VM, AIR, AIR-DVLV, DD-VLV, DV-TVS, TLA, TRC-VLV	
5.7L V8	A/CL-BMS, A/CL-VM, AIR, AIR-DVLV, ChVLV [3], EEC [3], EFE, EFE-TVS, PCV, SADV-TVS, SVBrk, SVBrK-TVS, TAC, TC-DVLV [2], TC-TVS [2], TCVS [2], TLA, TRC-SOL, VDVLV	
6.2L V8	CD-REGVLV, EGR [3], EGR-SOL [3], EPR-SOL [3], EPR-VLV [3], VACP [3]	
7.4L V8	A/CL-BMS, A/CL-VM, AIR, AIR-DVLV, ChVLV, EEC [1] EFE, EFE-TVS, PCV, SADV-TVS, SVBrk, SVBrk-TVS, TAC, TLA, TRC-SOL	

Light Duty Emissions: Vehicles up to 8500 GVW. **Heavy Duty Emissions:** Vehicles over 8500 GVW.

ABAV — Air Bleed Actuator Valve
A/CL-BMS — Air Cleaner Bi-Metal Sensor
A/CL-VM — Air Cleaner Vacuum Motor
ACV — Air Control Valve
AIR — Air Injection Reactor
AIR-DVLV — AIR Diverter Valve
CAT — Catalytic Converter
CD-REGVLV — Crankcase Depression
    Regulator Valve
ChVLV — Check Valve
CP-TVS — Canister Purge Thermal
    Vacuum Switch
DC-VLV — Deceleration Valve
DCM/C-VLV — Deceleration Mixture Control Valve
DCP-TVS — Distributor and Canister Purge
    Thermal Vacuum Switch
DD-VLV — Distributor Delay Valve
DVRV — Distributor Vacuum Regulator Valve
DV-TVS — Distributor Vacuum Thermal
    Vacuum Switch
EEC — Evaporative Emission Control

EFE — Early Fuel Evaporation
EFE-TVS — EFE Thermal Vacuum Switch
EGR — Exhaust Gas Recirculation
EGR-BldSOL — EGR Bleed Solenoid
EGR-BPTV — EGR Backpressure Transducer
    Valve
EGR-DVLV — EGR Delay Valve
EGR-RST — EGR Restrictor
EGR-SOL — EGR Solenoid
EGR/TC-TVS — EGR/Torque Converter
    Thermal Vacuum Switch
EGR-TVS — EGR Thermal Vacuum Switch
EPR-SOL — Exhaust Pressure Regulator Solenoid
EPR-VLV — Exhaust Pressure Regulator Valve
HIC — Hot Idle Compensator
IS — Idle Switch
MVS — Manifold Vacuum Switch
PAIR — Pulse Air Injection System
PCV — Positive Crankcase Ventilation
PTVS — Purge Thermal Vacuum Switch
PVBrk — Primary Vacuum Break

SADV-TVS — Spark Advance Thermal
    Vacuum Switch
SRD-VLV — Spark Retard Delay Valve
SVBrk — Secondary Vacuum Break
SVBrK-TVS — Secondary Vacuum Break
    Thermal Vacuum Switch
TAC — Thermostatic Air Cleaner
TC-DVLV — Torque Converter Delay Valve
TC-TVS — Torque Converter Thermal
    Vacuum Switch
TCVS — Torque Converter Vacuum Switch
TLA — Throttle Lever Actuator
TRC-SOL — Throttle Return Control Solenoid
TRC-VLV — Throttle Return Control Valve
VACP — Vacuum Pump
VCV — Vacuum Control Valve
VDVLV — Vacuum Delay Valve
VRV — Vacuum Regulator Valve
VSV — Vacuum Switching Valve
WOT-SW — Wide Open Throttle Switch

1983 Exhaust Emission Systems

POSITIVE CRANKCASE VENTILATION SYSTEMS

All Models

DESCRIPTION

The crankcase ventilation system is designed to prevent contaminating hydrocarbons from escaping to the atmosphere. This is accomplished by routing the vapors from the crankcase through a vacuum-controlled ventilating valve (PCV Valve) into the intake manifold. There, they mix with the air/fuel mixture and are burned in the combustion process.

OPERATION

Air is supplied to the crankcase ventilation system through a crankcase ventilating filter assembly, located in the carburetor or on rocker arm cover.

When the engine is operating, fresh air enters the positive crankcase ventilation system through the air cleaner and filter.

The air then flows into the rocker arm cover and valve compartment. It combines with blow-by gas and unburned air/fuel mixture and burns in combustion chamber. *See Fig. 1.*

Fig. 1: Typical Crankcase Ventilation System

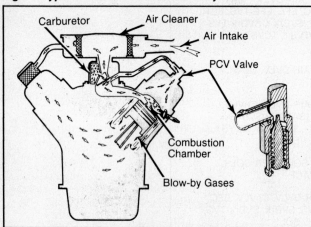

Air mixes with blow-by gases and air/fuel mixture, and burns in combustion chamber.

The ventilator valve is constructed so it is held closed by spring pressure when engine is not running. *See Fig. 2.* This prevents an accumulation of hydrocarbon fumes from collecting in the intake manifold, which could result in hard starting.

Fig. 2: Typical PCV Valve & Airflow

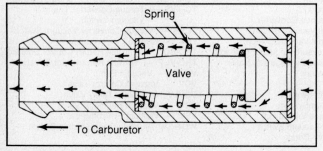

Air flows through valve when engine is running.

As the engine is started, manifold vacuum pulls the valve open against spring pressure. As long as there is engine vacuum, the valve floats, permitting crankcase fumes to enter the intake manifold.

A baffle in the rocker arm prevents oil from being drawn into the intake manifold through the ventilator valve.

In the event of an engine backfire through the intake manifold, the ventilator valve shuts, preventing any flow through it. This action prevents the ignition of fumes in the crankcase.

During certain engine operations, more blow-by is created than the ventilator valve can handle. The excess amount is returned to the air cleaner and carburetor through the rocker arm cover and breather assembly. It is then burned in the engine.

The breather assembly acts as a separator to keep oil from being drawn into the air cleaner during this operation.

TESTING

ALL MODELS

To test crankcase ventilation system, start engine and allow it to reach normal operating temperature. Make sure engine is idling at normal curb idle, and perform the following checks:

1) Remove PCV valve from its mounting. If valve is functioning properly, a hissing noise will be heard as air passes through it. A strong vacuum should be felt when your finger is placed over valve inlet. While finger is over inlet, check for presence of vacuum leaks in hose line and at all connections.

2) Re-install PCV valve, and then remove crankcase air inlet hose at air cleaner.

3) Loosely hold a piece of stiff paper over opening at end of inlet hose. Paper should be sucked against hose opening with a noticeable force after sufficient time has elapsed for crankcase pressure to lower (usually about a minute). As a final check, stop engine, remove PCV valve and shake it, A metallic clicking noise should be heard, indicating valve is free.

4) If system passes both the engine running and stopped tests, it is functioning properly. No further tests are required. If it has failed either test, replace appropriate components and retest. If it does not pass on second try, clean system.

MAINTENANCE

An engine may idle slow or rough due to a clogged ventilator valve or system. Therefore never adjust the carburetor idle without first checking the valve and system.

If the ventilator valve or system becomes clogged, all crankcase ventilation will stop, and serious engine damage could result.

Although the following manufacturers' service procedures give specific intervals, it is recommended the crankcase ventilation system be checked more frequently if vehicles are operated under severe conditions (extreme dust, prolonged idling, trailer hauling or short trips in cold weather).

POSITIVE CRANKCASE VENTILATION SYSTEMS (Cont.)

CHRYSLER CORP.

PCV Valve

On Light Duty Emission models (up to 8500 lbs. GVW), check every 15,000 miles and replace every 30,000 miles. On Heavy Duty Emission models (over 8500 lbs. GVW), check every 12,000 miles and replace every 24,000 miles.

Filter Element

On Light Duty Emission models, clean crankcase inlet air cleaner every 30,000 miles. On Heavy Duty Emission models, clean every 12,000 miles.

FORD

PCV Valve

Valve is located on rocker covers. On all models replace every 30,000 miles. Under extreme conditions service will be more frequent.

Filter Element

Filter is located in air cleaner housing. Replace crankcase filter on 6-cylinder engines every 30,000 miles. On V8 engines for E350 and F350 models, replace every 30,000 miles. Replacement is not required on other models.

GENERAL MOTORS

PCV Valve

Check every 15,000 miles and replace every 30,000 miles on Light Duty Emission models (up to 8500 lbs. GVW). Check every 12,000 miles and replace every 24,000 miles on Heavy Duty Emission models (over 8500 lbs. GVW). Valve is located on rocker cover.

Filter Element

Replace every 30,000 miles on Light Duty Emission models; every 24,000 miles on Heavy Duty Emission models. Filter is located in carburetor.

JEEP

PCV Valve

Replace every 30,000 miles. Valve is located on rocker arm cover of 4- and 6-cylinder models; on intake manifold of V8 models.

Filter Element

Clean every 30,000 miles. Filter is located inside air cleaner of 4-and 6-cylinder models; in oil filler cap of V8 models.

1983 Fuel Evaporation Systems

CHRYSLER CORP.

DESCRIPTION

The evaporation control system prevents gasoline vapors from the fuel tank and carburetor from escaping into the atmosphere. The systems are all dual canister types.

Fig. 1: Typical Dual Canister Mounting on Chrysler "D" & "W" Models

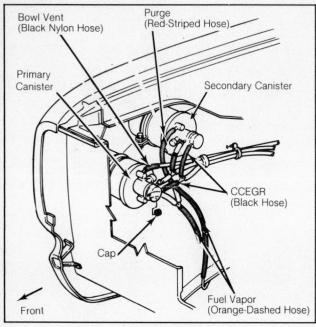

Canisters are mounted on right front fender.

OPERATION

When fuel evaporates in the carburetor float chamber or fuel tank, vapors pass through vent hoses or tubes to the charcoal canister.

Fuel vapors are held on the activated charcoal surface until they are drawn into the intake manifold (when the engine is running). A vacuum port in the carburetor base controls vapor flow to the engine.

On the 2-canister system, fuel vapors from the primary canister are purged through the carburetor port. Vapors from the secondary canister are purged through the PCV hose to the carburetor, using a distributor vacuum signal, applied to the purge switch.

Fig. 2: Typical Vapor Hose Routing for Dual Canister Chrysler "B" & "PB" Models

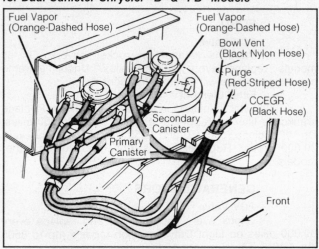

MAINTENANCE

There is no service required on the fuel evaporation control system, except replacement of the filter element in the charcoal canister. Replace filters every 18,000 miles on Heavy Duty Emission models (over 8,500 lbs. GVW). On all other models replace filter every 30,000 miles.

Fig. 3: Typical Evaporation Control System Hose Routing for Chrysler "D" & "W" Models

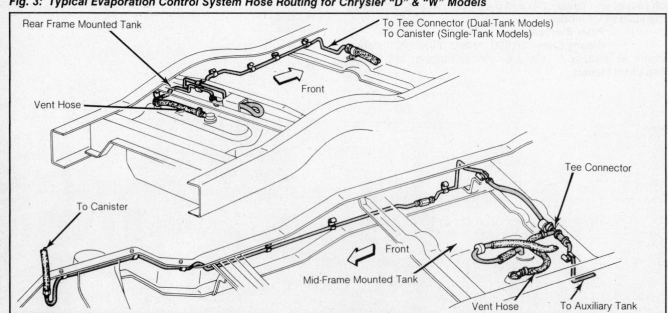

1983 Fuel Evaporation Systems

FORD

DESCRIPTION

All models are equipped with fuel evaporation emission control systems. This closed system is designed to limit the amount of fuel vapor released to the atmosphere. The system consists of a special fuel filler cap, a specially designed fuel tank, a carbon-filled canister, an orifice valve and necessary fuel vent vapor lines. All 6-cylinder models with dual fuel tanks and all V8 models use 2 carbon canisters.

FUEL FILLER CAP

The fuel filler cap has a one-way vent. This prevents tank collapse, by allowing air to enter the tank as fuel is consumed.

FUEL TANK

In most installations, the fuel tank is constructed with a dome in the top. Fuel vapors rise and tend to gather in this dome.

ORIFICE VALVE

On all vehicles, liquid fuel is prevented from entering the vapor lines by restricted orifices. Orifices usually take the form of a .050" (1.27 mm) orifice valve, located in emission control valve in fuel tank dome.

CARBON CANISTER

The carbon-filled canister acts as a storage system for fuel vapors vented from the fuel tank and carburetor. The outlet of the canister is connected to the carburetor bowl vent.

OPERATION

Fuel vapors, trapped in the sealed fuel tank, are vented through the orifice vapor separator assembly in the top of the tank.

Vapors then leave the separator through a single vapor line, and continue to the carbon canister in the engine compartment.

There, they are absorbed by carbon granules, until they are purged from the canister by carburetor vacuum once the engine is started.

MAINTENANCE

No regular replacement of components is required with this system. Periodically inspect components for proper functioning.

Fig. 1: Ford Evaporation Emission Control System (F100/250 Reg. Cab Shown, Others Similar)

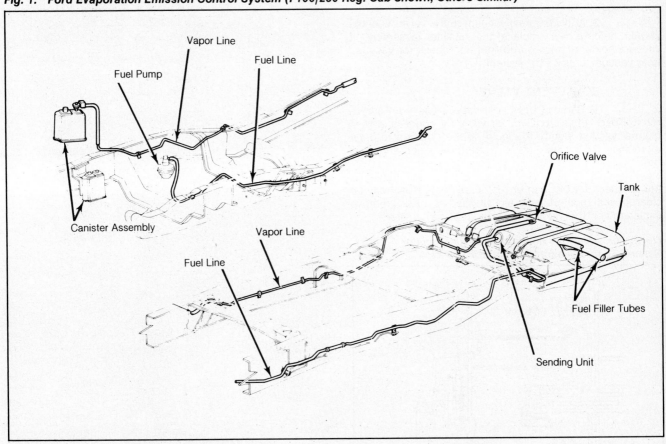

Canister must be at lowest point in system.

1983 Fuel Evaporation Systems

GENERAL MOTORS

DESCRIPTION

All Light and some Heavy Duty Emissions models are equipped with an Evaporative Control System (ECS), designed to prevent raw fuel vapors from escaping to the atmosphere. System consists of a special fuel tank with an expansion section, a venting system which allows only vaporous fuel to be drawn into the system, a pressure-vacuum relief valve in the gas cap to control tank pressure, and a vapor-storing charcoal canister.

OPERATION

During periods of engine operation, vapors are drawn through the system vent lines and into the intake manifold of the engine for burning. When engine is off, fuel vapors are stored in the charcoal of the vapor storage canister. Vapors are then drawn into the intake manifold when engine is running again.

TESTING

PURGE VALVE (ON CANISTER)

1) Remove purge valve control vacuum line. Check for vacuum at line with engine running at approximately 1500 RPM. If there is no vacuum present, check EGR system.

2) Apply external vacuum to the valve. Vacuum should hold. If not, replace the canister assembly. If vacuum holds, remove purge line, and check for vacuum. If no vacuum, check PCV system.

BOWL VENT VALVE

1) Remove bowl vent vapor hose from carburetor. Check open condition of valve by connecting to a manual vacuum pump. It should not be possible to draw more than 0.5 in. Hg if valve is open (as when engine is off).

2) If high resistance or plugged system is found, check for plugged or restricted hose. Hose may be cleared with compressed air. If hose is clear, remove canister filter. If restriction persists, replace canister.

Fig. 1: Vacuum Hose Routing for Single-Canister General Motors Evaporative Control System

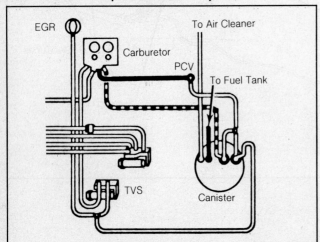

Canister must be lowest point in system.

3) To check valve closed position, run engine at idle. Manifold vacuum will be applied to valve through control line. Bowl vent line should exhibit a plugged condition.

4) If valve is not closed, remove control vacuum line, and check for vacuum. If no vacuum, check for hose restriction or leak. Replace hose if required. If vacuum is present, replace canister assembly.

MAINTENANCE

The charcoal canister is the only serviceable item. It should be replaced every 24 months or 30,000 miles on Light Duty Emission models and every 24 months or 24,000 miles on Heavy Duty Emission models. If operated in severe conditions, more frequent replacement may be required.

JEEP

DESCRIPTION

The fuel evaporation control system is used on all models. It is designed to retain raw fuel vapors, which would normally escape to the atmosphere, and transferring them to the intake manifold for burning. System consists of a special fuel tank, sealed gas cap, rollover check valve, charcoal canister, and connecting lines and hoses.

OPERATION

During periods of non-operation, raw vapors from the fuel tank and carburetor are channeled to the charcoal canister, where they are stored. When engine is running, canister is purged of these vapors, which are then taken into the intake manifold and burned. The rollover valve prevents fuel flow from tank in the event of vehicle rollover.

ROLLOVER VALVE

Valve consists of a plunger and a stainless steel ball. When valve is inverted, the stainless steel ball pushes the plunger against its seat, blocking fuel flow through valve.

Fig. 1: Typical Charcoal Canister Connections

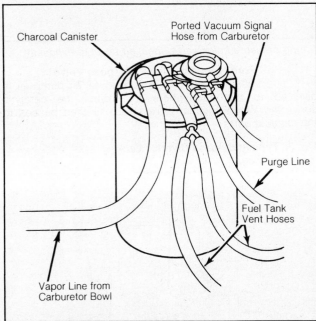

Vapors are stored in canister until engine is started.

CHARCOAL CANISTER

All models are equipped with a dual-purge type canister. Two inlets are provided: 1 for the carburetor fuel bowl vapors and 1 for the fuel tank vapors. The outlet is connected to intake manifold vacuum. The 4th nipple (secondary purge) connects to the carburetor spark port.

When the engine is running, manifold vacuum draws fresh air through the inlet filter in the bottom of the canister and purges stored vapors. When ported vacuum reaches 12 in. Hg, the secondary purge circuit is opened, and canister is purged at a much higher rate.

CARBURETOR BOWL VENT

The carburetor bowl vent used on all models provides an outlet for fuel vapors when the engine is not running. When the engine is running, the fuel bowl is vented to the inside of the air cleaner. The bowl is automatically closed by a mechanical link to the throttle when the engine is started.

MAINTENANCE

No adjustments are required with this system. The air inlet filter in bottom of charcoal canister should be replaced every 30,000 miles. A regular inspection of system components should be made and defective components replaced as necessary.

Fig. 2: Typical Jeep Evaporation Control System

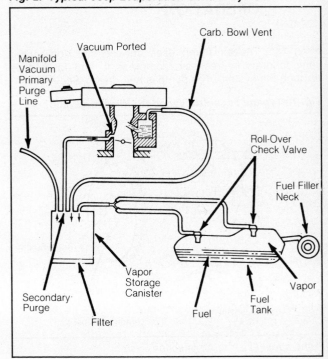

1983 Exhaust Emission Systems

AIR INJECTION SYSTEMS — AIR PUMP TYPE

All Models

DESCRIPTION

The air injection systems, used in many applications (may vary according to engine and equipment), are designed to reduce carbon monoxide and hydrocarbon emissions. This is done by injecting fresh air at critical points in the exhaust manifold to burn those gases which passed through the combustion cycle.

System consists of an air pump with integral filter, diverter/by-pass valve, check valve(s), external or internal injection tubing and connecting hoses. Some Ford and all Chrysler models use additional valves, depending on applications. These valves are explained below.

OPERATION

AIR PUMP

The air pump uses an eccentric (off-center) vane to draw in fresh air, compress it, and force it on through the system. The pump is belt-driven. *See Fig. 1.*

Fig. 1: Typical Eccentric Vaned Air Injection Pump

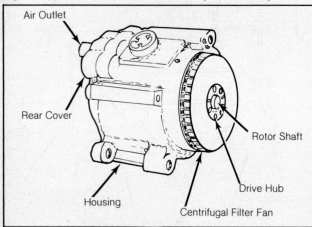

Pump supplies air to Air Injection System.

DIVERTER VALVE

The air flows from the air pump into the diverter valve. This valve prevents backfiring, by stopping air injection flow during periods of high increase in manifold vacuum (such as during deceleration). The diverter valve dumps the air supply to the atmosphere for the first few seconds of deceleration.

Most diverter valves also have a built-in pressure relief valve, which bleeds off excessive air pump pressure to prevent damage to the system. Most diverter valves are similar. *See Fig. 2 & 3.*

Ford & Jeep Timed By-pass Valve

This is a normally-open valve. During normal operation, vacuum is equalized on both sides of the diaphragm. Spring pressure holds the valve open, allowing fresh air to the exhaust.

On deceleration, manifold vacuum pulls the diaphragm, and air is directed to the atmosphere. A small orifice in the diaphragm will allow the pressure to quickly equalize again. *See Fig. 3.*

Fig. 2: Typical Diverter Valve for Chevrolet, Chrysler Corp. & GMC

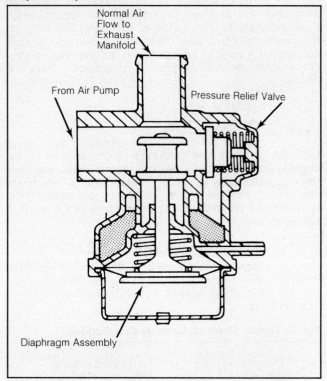

Spring pressure holds valve open; air flows to exhaust.

Ford Normally-Closed By-pass Valve

When no vacuum is applied, all air pump air is diverted to the atmosphere to protect the catalytic converter. When vacuum is received, air then passes to the exhaust ports.

Fig. 3: Typical By-pass Diverter Valve for Ford & Jeep

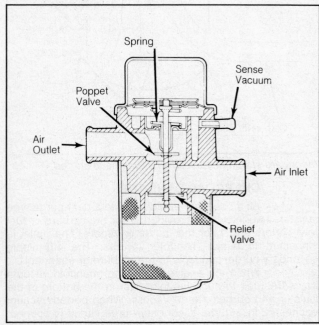

Zero vacuum pressure diverts air to atmosphere.

AIR INJECTION SYSTEMS — AIR PUMP TYPE (Cont.)

Ford & Jeep Timed & Vented By-pass Valve

Valve operation is similar to that of the timed valve described earlier. When vacuum signal is 8 in. Hg or more, the valve will continuously vent air pump air to the atmosphere. *See Fig. 5.*

AIR SWITCHING VALVE (CHRYSLER CORP. ONLY)

This valve is used to switch the injection air from the exhaust ports to a point downstream after engine warm-up. A bleed hole in the switching valve allows a small portion of the air to be injected at the exhaust ports at all times to assist in reducing emissions.

POWER HEAT CONTROL VALVE (CHRYSLER CORP. ONLY)

This vacuum-operated valve is located between the right exhaust manifold and exhaust pipe. It directs a majority of the exhaust gas flow through the left side exhaust manifold, until engine temperature reaches a pre-determined point. After that temperature is reached, gas flows through both manifolds.

INJECTION MANIFOLD

The injection manifold in many applications is an external tubing system, mounted to the exhaust manifold with air delivery ports for each exhaust port. It is through this manifold that air pump air reaches the exhaust system. Some applications have an internal air injection system, consisting of specially drilled passages in the intake manifold, which carry the air pump air to the exhaust ports. External tubing is eliminated.

CHECK VALVE

The check valve is a 1-way flow valve. It prevents exhaust manifold air from backing up through the system and reaching the air pump. The check valve will be found either in the tubing, leading to the injection manifold or as an integral part of the manifold.

Fig. 5: Ford & Jeep Timed & Vented By-pass Valve (Diverter Valve)

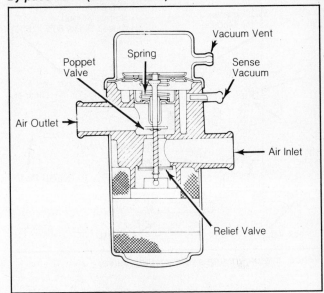

Apply 8 in. Hg or more, to operate valve.

IDLE VACUUM VALVE (FORD ONLY W/CAT. CONVERTER)

This valve is used on Ford models which have a catalytic converter. The air injection system on these models is also tied into the EGR system. *See Fig. 6.*

Operating in conjunction with a vacuum delay valve, the idle vacuum valve provides backfire control, full-time idle air dump, cold temperature catalyst protection and cold EGR lockout.

On long idle, the air dump prevents high underbody temperatures in the exhaust system.

During cold engine operation, the valve prevents air injection and EGR operation until the catalyst and engine are warm.

Fig. 4: Three Different Types of Air Injection Systems Used on V8 Engines

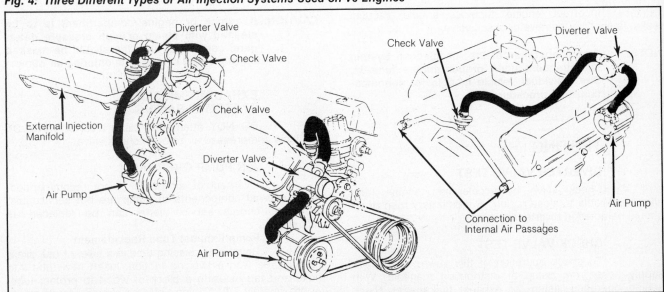

Air Injection Systems may vary according to equipment.

1983 Exhaust Emission Systems

AIR INJECTION SYSTEMS — AIR PUMP TYPE (Cont.)

Fig. 6: Schematic of Typical Ford Air Injection System

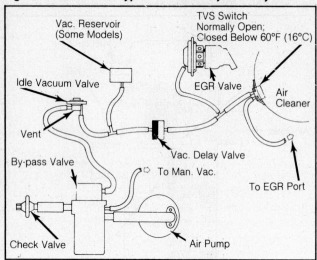

Notice, system includes idle vacuum valve.

TROUBLE SHOOTING

EXCESSIVE BELT NOISE

Loose pump drive belt or seized pump.

EXCESSIVE PUMP NOISE

Leak in hose or loose hose. Hose touching other engine parts. Diverter valve or by-pass valve failure. Check for valve failure, pump mounting loose, pump or impeller damaged.

NO AIR SUPPLY

Loose drive belt, leak in hose or hose fitting. Diverter valve or by-pass valve failure. Check for valve failure or pump failure.

EXHAUST BACKFIRE

Incorrect engine tune-up, engine vacuum leaks, faulty diverter valve or check valve.

NOTE: Proper operation of the Air Injection System is dependent upon proper engine tune-up. See individual vehicle models for specifications and procedures.

TESTING

DIVERTER VALVE TEST

Check valve by accelerating engine, and allowing throttle to close rapidly. A momentary rush of air should be noted at diverter air outlet.

CHECK VALVE TEST

To check operation of this valve, remove air supply hose from pump at distribution manifold. With engine operating, listen for exhaust leakage at check valve, which is connected to distribution manifold.

MAINTENANCE

Approximately every 15,000 miles, air injection system components should be checked for proper operation and condition. No regular parts replacement schedule is required. Service is limited to replacement of air pump filter, if it becomes clogged.

CENTRIFUGAL FAN FILTER

To replace, remove drive belt, pulley mounting bolts, and pulley. Break off remaining portions of centrifugal fan filter from pump hub. Use care that fragments do not enter air intake hole. Install new filter by drawing it on with the pulley and pulley bolts. Do not attempt to hammer or press filter on shaft.

Fig. 7: Removing Centrifugal Fan Filter from Air Injection Pump with Pulley Removed

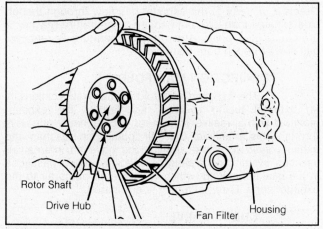

Be careful that fragments do not enter air intake hole.

NOTE: After new filter is installed, it may squeal during operation, until its outside diameter has worn in. This may require 20 to 30 miles of operation.

CAUTION: If engine or engine compartment is to be cleaned with steam or high pressure detergent, centrifugal filter fan should be masked off to prevent liquids from entering air pump.

EXHAUST EMISSION SYSTEM CLEANING

DO NOT attempt to clean diverter valve. Do not blow compressed air through check valve.

AIR PUMP OVERHAUL

Overhaul of air pump is not recommended, since internal components of pump are not serviceable. However, certain service items can be replaced as follows:

Pump Exhaust Tube Replacement

Remove by placing tube in a vise, or use pliers to pull tube with a twisting motion. Insert new tube into hole, and tap in using a block of wood to protect tube. Approximately 7/8" (22 mm) of tube should extend above cover.

CATALYTIC CONVERTERS

All Light Duty Emission Models

NOTE: Light Duty Emission vehicles are those vehicles whose Gross Vehicle Weight (GVW) does not exceed 8500 lbs.

DESCRIPTION & OPERATION

The catalytic converter(s) is installed in the exhaust system in front of the muffler, so that all exhaust gas must pass through the converter(s). The converter is a stainless steel muffler-shaped device that reduces exhaust emissions.

The catalyst reduces hydrocarbons (HC) and carbon monoxide (CO) emissions. The material inside the converter is 1 of 2 types: a coated 1-piece honeycombed block (monolithic type), or small beads of catalyst-coated material.

Fig. 1: Cross Section of Monolithic Catalytic Converter

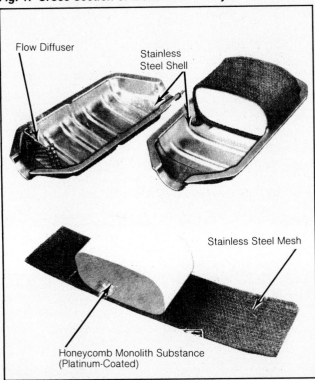

Flow Diffuser

Stainless Steel Shell

Stainless Steel Mesh

Honeycomb Monolith Substance (Platinum-Coated)

Chrysler Corp. models shown; Ford models similar.

NOTE: Use ONLY unleaded fuel in vehicles using catalytic converters. If leaded fuel is used, the Tetra Eythel Lead will coat the palladium, platinum and rhodium, rendering these catalysts inoperative. If this happens, the converter must be replaced.

HEAT SHIELDS

The combustion reaction, which is furthered by the converter, releases additional heat. Temperature in the catalytic converter can reach 1600°F (871°C) under normal conditions. Special heat shields are used to protect underbody and components from this extreme heat.

Fig. 2: Cutaway View of Bead-Type Catalytic Converter

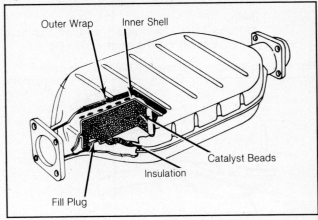

Outer Wrap

Inner Shell

Catalyst Beads

Insulation

Fill Plug

Beads may be replaced in General Motors & Jeep models.

SERVICE

MAINTENANCE

There is no scheduled maintenance required for catalytic converters. However, on General Motors and Jeep models with bead-type converters, bead removal and replacement is possible.

BOTTOM COVER REPLACEMENT (GENERAL MOTORS ONLY)

1) Using a hand or power tool, remove bottom cover by making a shallow, close cut to bottom outside edge.

Fig. 3: Removal of Converter Bottom Cover (General Motors Vehicles Only)

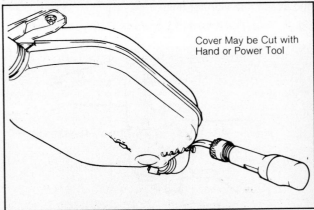

Cover May be Cut with Hand or Power Tool

Make a shallow cut; avoid damage to inner shell.

2) Remove insulation and check inner shell for damage. If damage is found, entire converter must be replaced.

3) If no damage is found, position new insulation into replacement cover. Apply sealer (8998245 or equivalent) around edge of cover, using extra sealer at front and rear pipe openings.

4) Install replacement cover on converter, and position retaining channel along edges. Complete the installation by attaching clamps (provided with replacement cover) to both ends of converter.

CATALYTIC CONVERTERS (Cont.)

CATALYST REPLACEMENT
Jeep
1) Raise vehicle, and attach vacuum aspirator (J-25077-01 or equivalent) to exhaust pipe. *See Fig. 4.*

Fig. 4: Jeep Vacuum Aspirator (J-25077-01) Installed

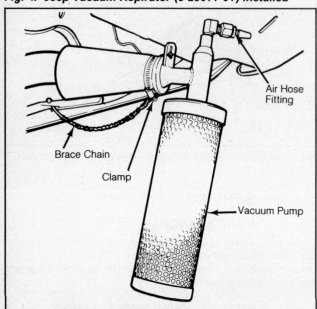

Apply minimum of 80 lbs. (36 kg) of air pressure to hold beads in place.

2) Apply enough air pressure, minimum 80 lbs. (36 kg) to hold catalyst beads in place while converter fill plug is removed.

3) Clamp on vibrator and catalyst receptacle. *See Fig. 5.* Disconnect air supply from vacuum aspirator, and attach it to vibrator unit.

Fig. 5: Jeep Placement of Vibrator & Catalyst Container

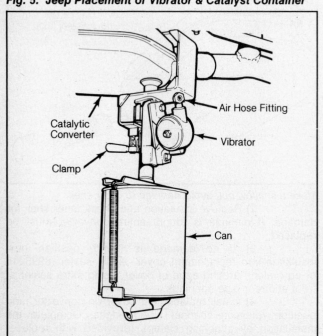

Using air pressure & vibrator operate for 10 minutes.

4) Using air pressure, vibrator should operate and empty the converter of the catalytic beads in about 10 minutes.

5) When all catalyst material is removed, disconnect air supply, and remove container from converter. Discard beads.

6) Fill container with approved replacement catalyst, and install a fill tube fixture to the vibrator device.

7) Attach air supply to both vibrator and aspirator. With container attached to fill tube, catalyst will begin to move into converter.

8) When catalyst stops flowing, disconnect air supply to vibrator, and note level of catalyst. It should be even with fill plug. Add more catalyst, if required.

9) Apply nickle-base, anti-seize compound to fill plug. Install plug and tighten to 60 ft. lbs. (82 N.m). If equipped with press-type fill plug, install "bridge-and-bolt" type service plug and torque to 28 ft. lbs. (37 N.m).

CHRYSLER CORP. SYSTEMS

DESCRIPTION

Control of exhaust emission is accomplished by a combination of engine modifications and special system components. Component usage varies according to model, engine, states, and emissions cycle application.

NOTE: There are 2 light duty truck emission control standards classifications: Light Duty and Heavy Duty. Light Duty refers to vehicles up through 8,500 lbs. GVW; Heavy Duty refers to vehicles over 8,500 lbs. GVW.

CHRYSLER VACUUM DIAGRAMS NO LONGER PROVIDED

NOTE: Chrysler Corp. vehicles use a new type of vacuum harness with connectors at each end. This harness prevents incorrect routing, so Chrysler Corp. no longer provides vacuum hose diagrams.

THERMOSTATIC AIR CLEANER (TAC)

System provides heated air to carburetor (from stove on exhaust manifold) in combination with underhood air. This maintains a constant intake air temperature for more efficient combustion and emission control.

AIR INJECTION

System consists of an air pump, diverter valve, check valves and various air distribution lines. Injection of fresh air adjacent to the exhaust valves creates an afterburn effect, which results in lower emission levels. *For additional information, see "Air Injection Systems — Air Pump Type" in this section.*

ASPIRATOR AIR SYSTEM

System is used to reduce carbon monoxide and hydrocarbon emissions by drawing fresh air from the air cleaner, and allowing it to mix with exhaust gases. System consists of an aspirator air valve and connecting tubes to the air cleaner and exhaust manifold.

EXHAUST GAS RECIRCULATION (EGR)

System allows a predetermined amount of hot exhaust gas to recirculate and dilute air/fuel mixture. This aids combustion and reduces NOx emissions.

ELECTRONIC FUEL CONTROL

The Electronic Fuel Control (EFC) system is an electronically controlled system that closely manages air/fuel ratio and ignition timing. The Spark Control Computer (SCC) is the heart of the system.

This computer provides the capability of igniting a lean air/fuel mixture according to different modes of engine operation; plus, during closed loop operation, the computer maintains the air/fuel mixture close to the ideal ratio of 14.7:1. *For additional information, see appropriate article in Computerized Engine Control section.*

ELECTRIC ASSIST CHOKE

System is designed to give faster choke openings at temperatures above 60°F (16°C) and slower choke openings below 60°F (16°C).

ORIFICE SPARK ADVANCE CONTROL (OSAC)

System is used on some Light Duty Emission engines to aid in control of oxides of nitrogen (NOx). It controls vacuum to distributor vacuum advance unit in response to changes in throttle position.

IDLE ENRICHMENT SYSTEM

System is used on some Light Duty Emission models with automatic transmission to reduce cold engine stalling. During cold or semi-cold operation, system enriches carburetor mixture at curb idle and fast idle.

VACUUM THROTTLE POSITIONER

System is used on Heavy Duty Emission vehicles. Throttle positioner prevents unburned hydrocarbons from entering atmosphere. It does so by preventing full throttle closure during deceleration from high engine speeds.

CATALYTIC CONVERTER

Converter brings about combustion-type reaction to further consume unburned elements in the engine exhaust. Converter is located in exhaust system ahead of muffler. Vehicles equipped with catalytic converters must use unleaded fuel only. *For additional information, see Catalytic Converter article in this section.*

POSITIVE CRANKCASE VENTILATION (PCV)

System is used on all cars to eliminate fumes and vapors from crankcase. It does so by directing them back through the combustion chamber to be burned. *For additional information, see Crankcase Ventilation article in this section.*

EVAPORATION CONTROL SYSTEM

The dual canister evaporation control system is used on all vehicles. The system routes fuel vapors from fuel tank through filter canisters to engine for burning. This closed system prevents vapors from venting to the atmosphere. *For additional information see appropriate Fuel Evaporation System article in this section.*

1983 Exhaust Emission Systems

CHRYSLER CORP. THERMOSTATIC AIR CLEANER

All Models

DESCRIPTION

All Chrysler Light Duty Truck models use a heated air inlet system, as part of the air cleaner. The system controls the temperature, permitting the carburetor to be calibrated leaner to control hydrocarbon (HC) emissions and improve warm-up characteristics.

The system consists of an air cleaner assembly, a temperature sensor, an air control valve, a vacuum diaphragm, a duct system and a shroud on the exhaust manifold.

OPERATION

When the ambient air temperature is less than 50°F (10°C), carburetor intake air flows through the shroud, into a flexible connector, through the vacuum diaphragm and into the carburetor.

When the temperature rises to operating temperature, the vacuum diaphragm shuts off the air coming from the shroud, and allows fresh air to enter the carburetor. When the temperature is between the minimum and maximum, the air will flow through both circuits.

TESTING

1) Ensure that all vacuum hoses, flexible duct hose and air cleaner duct are in good condition. With engine cold, the heat control door in the air cleaner snorkel should be up, in the heat on position.

2) With engine running at normal operating temperature, the door should be in the down, or heat off position.

3) Turn off engine and allow it to cool to 50°F (10°C). Remove air cleaner. Using an external vacuum source, apply 20 in. Hg vacuum to the temperature sensor. The door should be in the up position. If not, check vacuum diaphragm for proper operation.

4) Apply 20 in. Hg vacuum to diaphragm. The diaphragm should not bleed down more than 10 in. Hg, in 5 minutes. The door should not lift off the bottom at less than 5 in. Hg, and should be in the full up position at no more than 8.5 in. Hg.

5) If vacuum diaphragm does not meet specifications, replace it and repeat steps **1)** and **2)**. If diaphragm performs as specified, but proper temperature is not maintained, replace temperature sensor and repeat temperature checks.

Fig. 1: Chrysler Corp. Thermostatic Air Cleaner

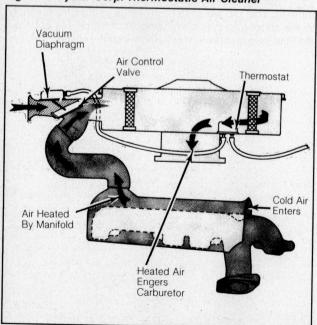

Vacuum Diaphragm

Air Control Valve

Thermostat

Air Heated By Manifold

Cold Air Enters

Heated Air Engers Carburetor

All Chrysler light trucks use a heated air inlet system.

CHRYSLER CORP. ASPIRATOR AIR SYSTEM

DESCRIPTION

The aspirator air system consists of an aspirator valve and an aspirator tube assembly. The valve uses exhaust pressure pulsation to draw air into the exhaust system, reducing carbon monoxide (CO), and hydrocarbon (HC) emissions.

The tube assembly connects the aspirator valve to the air cleaner at one end, and the exhaust manifold at the other end.

Fig. 1: Chrysler Corp. Aspirator Valve Air Flow

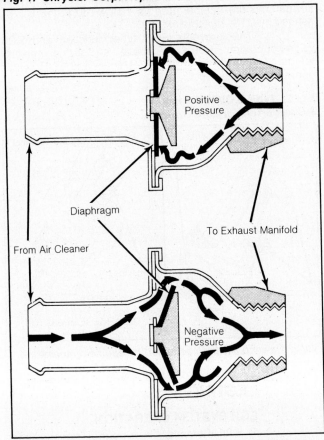

Aspirator is used when Air Injection Pump is not necessary.

OPERATION

The aspirator valve draws fresh air from the "clean" side of the air cleaner, past a 1-way, spring-loaded rubber diaphragm. The diaphragm opens to allow fresh air to mix with the exhaust gases during negative pressure (vacuum) pulses, which occur at the exhaust ports and manifold passages.

If the pressure is positive, the diaphragm closes, and no exhaust gas is allowed to flow past the valve into the "clean" side of the air cleaner.

The valve works best at idle and slightly off-idle, when the negative pulses are at maximum. At higher engine speeds the valve remains closed.

TESTING

The aspirator valve is not repairable. If the valve fails, it must be replaced. Check all connections for proper assembly. If leakage is noted at any joints, repair before testing valve.

To test aspirator valve, disconnect hose from aspirator inlet. With engine idling in neutral, vacuum exhaust pulses should be felt at the aspirator inlet. If hot exhaust gas is escaping from the inlet, the valve is defective and must be replaced.

Fig. 2: Chrysler Corp. Aspirator Air System Assembly

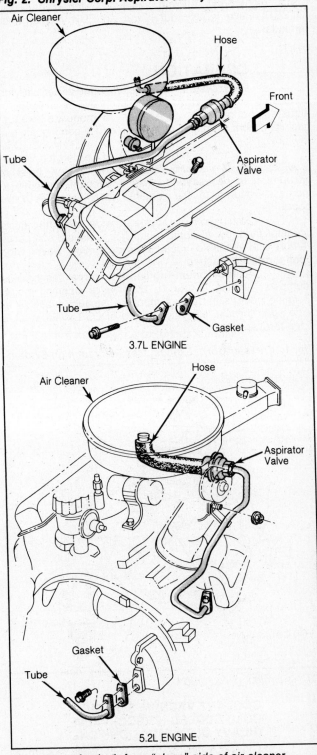

Valve draws fresh air from "clean" side of air cleaner.

1983 Exhaust Emission Systems

CHRYSLER CORP. EXHAUST GAS RECIRCULATION

DESCRIPTION

Exhaust Gas Recirculation (EGR) allows a predetermined amount of hot exhaust gas to recirculate and dilute the incoming air/fuel mixture. This reduces peak flame temperature during combustion, thereby reducing NOx emission.

System consists of an EGR valve, timer, vacuum solenoid, vacuum amplifier, charge temperature switch (light duty), coolant vacuum switch cold closed (CVSCC) valve (heavy duty) and an EGR maintenance reminder.

OPERATION

EGR system controls vacuum under varying conditions to EGR valve. The EGR valve is a vacuum-actuated, poppet-type valve, used to modulate exhaust gas flow from manifold crossover into incoming air/fuel mixture.

A vacuum tap at throat of carburetor venturi provides control vacuum. Because of the low level of vacuum, it is necessary to use a vacuum amplifier to increase vacuum to the required level for EGR valve operation.

Elimination of recycle at wide open throttle is accomplished by a dump diaphragm, which compares venturi and manifold vacuum to determine when wide open throttle is reached.

At wide open throttle, the internal reservoir is "dumped", limiting output to EGR valve opening point. Opening point is set above manifold vacuum available at wide open throttle, allowing closure of EGR valve at wide open throttle.

Fig. 1: Chrysler Corp. Exhaust Gas Recirculation System

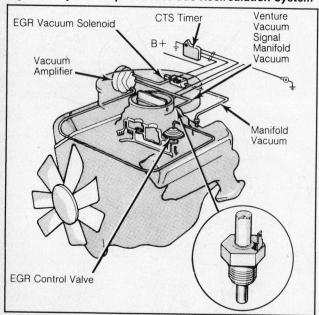

CTS is circled in illustration.

COOLANT VACUUM SWITCH COLD CLOSED (CVSCC) VALVE (HEAVY DUTY EMISSIONS ONLY)

CVSCC valve is used with EGR system to delay EGR operation until engine warm-up is achieved.

Valve location and opening temperature varies according to vehicle model and engine type.

On models with CVSCC valve in the radiator tank, opening temperature is 59°F (15°C). On models with valve in thermostat housing, opening temperature is 108-115°F (42-52°C).

CHARGE TEMPERATURE SWITCH (CTS) (LIGHT DUTY EMISSIONS ONLY)

A Charge Temperature Switch (CTS) is installed on a branch of engine intake manifold. When air/fuel mixture temperature is below 60°F (16°C), as sensed by CTS, switch closes.

This prevents EGR timer function and EGR valve operation. However, above an air/fuel mixture temperature of 60°F (16°C), EGR timer and EGR switch operation are allowed.

Fig. 2: Typical CVSCC Valve & Charge Temperature Switch

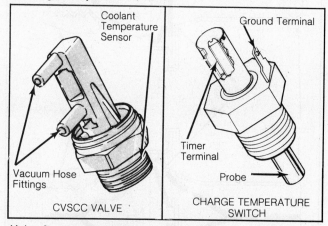

Valve & switch are both activated by engine temperature.

TESTING

EGR SYSTEM OPERATION

1) With transmission in neutral, parking brake on, and engine at normal operating temperature, allow engine to idle with throttle closed. Then, quickly accelerate engine to approximately 2000 RPM, while watching EGR valve stem. Stem should move when engine is accelerated. If not, refer to "Trouble Shooting" in this article.

2) Once EGR valve movement has been obtained, verify that EGR is actually taking place. On CVSCC systems, disconnect EGR valve-to-CVSCC valve hose at CVSCC valve. On CTS systems, disconnect hose from EGR valve-to-CTS valve. On either CVSCC or CTS systems, disconnect air cleaner-to-carburetor hose at carburetor.

3) With engine idling at normal operating temperature, hold free end of EGR valve hose tightly against opening of carburetor connector (from which air cleaner hose was removed). With hose on connector, engine idle speed should drop about 150 RPM and engine may stall. This shows that EGR is taking place.

4) If speed does not change or change is less than minimum, exhaust deposits are in EGR valve or intake manifold passages. Remove, inspect and clean valve. Inspect and manifold passages.

CHRYSLER CORP. EXHAUST GAS RECIRCULATION (Cont.)

NOTE: When cleaning valve, do not allow solvents on diaphragm. Do not push on diaphragm to operate valve; use vacuum only.

EGR DELAY SYSTEM TEST

1) If equipped with Delay System, stop engine, then restart. Immediately open throttle to approximately 1000 RPM, and watch EGR valve stem for movement. *See Fig. 3.*

2) If it moves during first 30 seconds after starting, EGR time delay system is defective.

3) Check hose connections to time delay solenoid valve. If okay, detach electrical plug from solenoid valve. Energize valve by grounding either terminal, and connecting the other terminal to the positive battery post.

4) If EGR valve stem moves on this test, solenoid valve is defective and must be replaced.

5) If EGR valve stem did not move, EGR timer control should be replaced. If this does not correct the problem, check wiring for proper connections.

TROUBLE SHOOTING

EGR VALVE STEM DOES NOT MOVE ON SYSTEM TEST

1) Check for correct hose connections, and leak check to confirm all hoses are in good condition.

2) Check EGR valve for ruptured diaphragm or frozen valve stem. Connect an external vacuum source of 10 in. Hg or greater to valve diaphragm. If no valve movement occurs, replace valve.

3) If valve opens 1/8" (3 mm), pinch off supply hose to check for diaphragm leakage. Valve should remain open 30 seconds or longer. If leakage occurs, replace valve.

EGR VALVE STEM DOES NOT MOVE ON TEST; OPERATES OKAY WITH EXTERNAL VACUUM APPLIED

1) Follow this procedure to check system for a defective CVSCC valve or CTS:

- On CVSCC systems, by-pass CVSCC valve and connect vacuum amplified directly to EGR valve. If EGR valve operates normally, replace CVSCC valve.
- On CTS systems, by-pass EGR solenoid and connect vacuum amplifier directly to EGR valve. If EGR valve operates normally, reconnect EGR solenoid hoses, and remove wire from timer terminal of CTS. If EGR valve operates within 90 seconds, replace CTS.

2) In Venturi Vacuum Control System, remove venturi vacuum hose from carburetor nipple. With engine at idle, apply 2 in. Hg vacuum to hose. Engine speed should drop 150 RPM or more, and EGR valve stem should move 1/8" (3 mm) or more. If this does not occur, replace vacuum control valve.

3) If vacuum control amplifier operated normally in previous test, plugged vacuum tap to carburetor is indicated. Use carburetor solvent to remove deposits from passage, and clear with light air pressure.

NOTE: Do not use drills or wires to clear carburetor control passages for either control system.

Calibration of precision orifices could be altered, resulting in unsatisfactory vehicle operation.

ROUGH IDLE, SLOW IDLE, OR STALL ON RETURN TO IDLE

1) Disconnect hose from EGR valve and plug hose. Recheck idle. If satisfactory, replace vacuum control amplifier.

2) If vacuum hose removal does not correct problem, remove EGR valve and inspect to insure poppet is seated. Clean poppet seat, or replace if poppet does not seat correctly.

POOR COLD DRIVEABILITY, ROUGH IDLE OR STALLS ON RETURN TO IDLE

CVSCC valve or EGR control valve could be leaking. Check by performing leak test, and replace valves as necessary.

WEAK PERFORMANCE AT WIDE OPEN THROTTLE

Disconnect hose from EGR valve and plug hose. Road test vehicle, if performance is restored, replace vacuum control amplifier.

Fig. 3: Chrysler Corp. Vacuum-Actuated EGR Valve

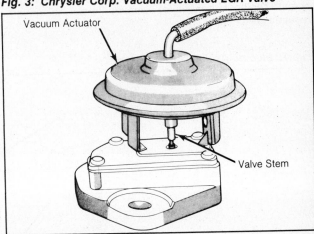

Watch for EGR valve stem movement during tests.

1983 Exhaust Emission Systems

CHRYSLER CORP. ELECTRIC ASSIST CHOKE

DESCRIPTION

All Light Duty Emission models are equipped with an electric assist choke system. This system helps to control hydrocarbon (HC) and carbon monoxide (CO) emissions and to shorten warm-up time.

The electric assist choke system consists of an electric heating element, a bimetal spring, a thermostatic choke coil and connecting linkage.

OPERATION

The choke thermostatic coil spring reacts to engine temperature. However, an electric heating element (located next to a bimetal spring inside the choke well) assists engine heat during both summer and winter operations to shorten choke "on-time."

This single-stage electric assist choke is designed to give a more rapid choke opening at temperatures above 60°F (16°C), and slower choke opening below this temperature.

A wire from the choke heater is connected to an electrical control switch. Above 60°F (16°C), the control switch energizes the choke heater.

Since the heater control switch is mounted on the engine, some cold weather operation may energize the choke heater. This could occur after the choke has opened without benefit of electric heat. No adverse reaction will occur.

TESTING

CONTROL SWITCH TEST

1) Before starting test, check test light by connecting it to battery terminals. Note light intensity.

2) Before starting engine, detach ignition harness electrical connector from heater control switch.

3) Connect test light to load (choke) terminal of control switch and to ground.

4) Start engine and allow it to reach normal operating temperature.

5) Apply 12 volts to ignition harness terminal of control switch. If test light does not light or have the same original intensity, replace defective control switch.

CHOKE HEATING ELEMENT TEST

1) Disconnect only the B+ wire at the control switch. Connect an ohmmeter lead to the choke housing or choke retainer screw.

2) Touch other meter lead to a bare portion of choke wire connector at switch (not B+ terminal). A meter reading of 4 to 12 ohms indicates heater is electrically functional. If circuit is open or shorted, install a new choke assembly.

NOTE: Never immerse heater element in any fluid, as an electrical short to the choke heater is also a short circuit to the ignition system.

Fig. 1: Electric Assist Choke System

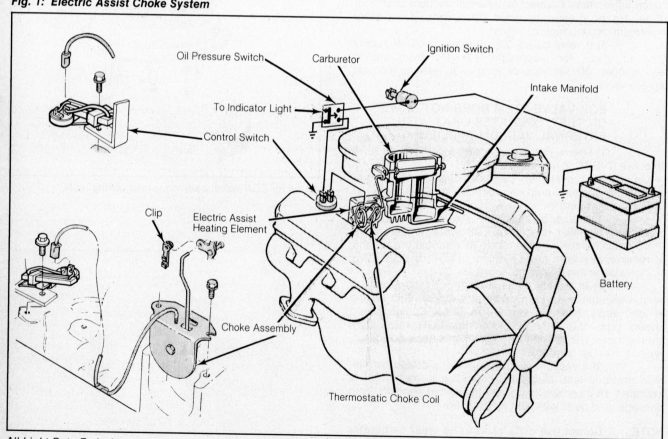

All Light Duty Emission models are equipped with an electric assist choke system.

CHRYSLER CORP. OSAC VALVE

DESCRIPTION

The Orifice Spark Advance System (OSAC) is used on most Light Duty Emission models to aid in control of oxides of nitrogen (NOx). It controls vacuum to the vacuum advance actuator of the distributor.

A tiny orifice incorporated in the OSAC valve delays change in ported vacuum to distributor by about 17 seconds (27 seconds on some models), when going from idle to part throttle. When going from part throttle to idle, change in ported vacuum to distributor will be instantaneous.

Fig. 1: Chrysler Corp. OSAC Valve Hose Routing

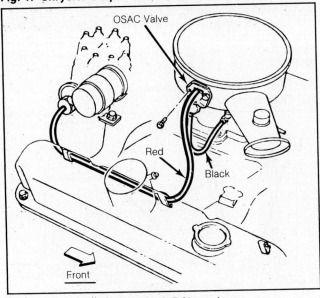

Typical hose routing for 5.2L & 5.9L engines.

OPERATION

Vacuum is obtained by a vacuum tap just above throttle valves of carburetor. This type of tap

Fig. 2: Chrysler Corp. OSAC Valve

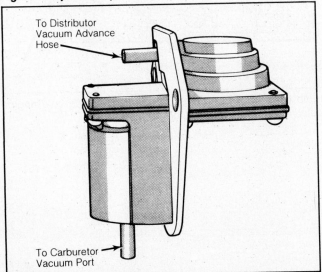

Controls vacuum to distributor's vacuum advance actuator.

provides no vacuum at idle, but provides manifold vacuum as soon as throttle valves are opened slightly. Proper operation requires airtight fittings.

TESTING

1) Inspect all hoses for leakage or damage. Replace as necessary.

2) Warm engine to normal operating temperature. Tee a vacuum gauge into red hose at OSAC valve leading to distributor.

3) Set parking brake and run engine at 2000 RPM in neutral.

4) Vacuum should increase gradually (about 20 seconds) to a stable level. Time will vary with different engines.

5) If vacuum rises immediately to same level as manifold vacuum, OSAC valve is not operating properly, and must be replaced. If there is NO increase in vacuum, OSAC valve is defective and must be replaced.

1983 Exhaust Emission Systems

CHRYSLER CORP. IDLE ENRICHMENT SYSTEM

DESCRIPTION

Idle Enrichment System is designed to reduce cold engine stalling, by use of a metering system related to the basic carburetor instead of the choke. It is used on some vehicles with automatic transmissions and Light Duty Emissions.

System enriches carburetor mixtures in curb idle and fast idle area during cold or semi-cold operation. It consists of a vacuum idle enrichment valve and a coolant vacuum switch (or a solenoid vacuum switch and electric timer combination).

OPERATION

When vacuum is applied to enrichment valve diaphragm, idle air is reduced. As a result of less idle air, air/fuel mixture is enriched.

With coolant vacuum switch, when engine is cold, the switch is open and vacuum is applied to enrichment valve. When engine warms to 98°F (37°C), switch closes and engine returns to normal lean mixture condition.

With solenoid vacuum switch, the switch receives its vacuum signal from a solenoid valve, operated by an electric timer. Enrichment duration is approximately 35 seconds after engine start, or until switch closes at 150°F (66°C); or 98°F (37°C) on some models. All switches open approximately 12°F below closing temperature.

TESTING

SYSTEM TEST

1) With engine at normal operating temperature, remove air cleaner. DO NOT cap any vacuum fittings opened by hose removal (leakage needed for test).

2) Disconnect hose to idle enrichment valve at plastic connector. Connector has a filtered bleed which will interfere with test, so it must be removed. Start engine, and place fast idle screw on slowest step of fast idle cam. Connect 3-4' (1-1.3 m) length of hose to enrichment valve.

3) Using a hand pump, apply vacuum to end of hose and listen for engine speed change. If engine speed can be controlled by vacuum, diaphragm and air valve are operating correctly. If speed cannot be controlled by vacuum, replace valve assembly on Holley carburetors. Proceed to next step for Carter carburetors.

4) Place finger on the other plug, over air inlet passage. Listen for engine speed change. If speed can be controlled, diaphragm is leaking or air valve is stuck open. If speed cannot be controlled, air valve is stuck closed. Clean air valve or replace diaphragm, as necessary.

TIME DELAY TEST

NOTE: On some vehicles, timing module and solenoid valve serve a dual function of controlling both EGR delay and idle enrichment duration.

1) With ignition switch off, remove wiring connector from time delay solenoid valve. Place a test light across connector terminals.

2) Start engine. Test light should come on, and stay on for approximately 60 seconds after engine starts. If light does not come on, or stays on indefinitely, replace timer.

NOTE: Test light current should not exceed .5 amps. or damage to timer may occur.

COOLANT VACUUM SWITCH

1) Disconnect molded connector from valve, and attach a 1/8" (3 mm) I.D. hose to bottom port of valve. With radiator top tank warm to the touch, no warmer than 75°F (31°C), blow through hose. If air cannot be blown through valve, replace it.

2) Bring engine to normal operating temperature. Attach a vacuum pump and gauge to bottom port of valve. Apply 10 in. Hg. If in 15 seconds, vacuum level drops more than 1 in., replace valve.

Fig. 1: Cutaway of Chrysler Corp. Idle Enrichment System

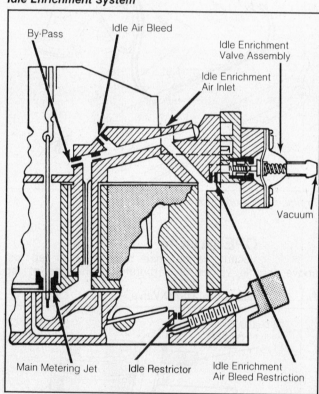

Idle enrichment system is designed to reduce cold engine stalling without using a choke.

CHRYSLER CORP. VACUUM THROTTLE POSITIONER

DESCRIPTION

Some Heavy Duty Emission models have a carburetor equipped with a vacuum throttle positioner. This system prevents unburned hydrocarbon (HC) emissions, during periods of rapid deceleration from high engine speeds.

System consists of an electronic speed switch, a vacuum solenoid valve and a vacuum throttle positioner.

OPERATION

The electronic speed switch receives an ignition pulse through the ballast resistor, which is connected to electronic ignition control unit. It then senses when engine speed is above 2000 RPM, and energizes throttle positioner.

When energized, throttle positioner plunger extends slightly, holding throttle blades open at 1750 RPM upon sudden deceleration. This prevents an overly rich mixture from flowing into carburetor.

When speed switch senses that engine RPM has dropped below 2000 RPM, it de-energizes positioner and throttle blades return to normal idle position.

ADJUSTMENT

1) Start engine and accelerate to about 2000 RPM. Verify throttle positioner operation. Throttle positioner must withstand hand pressure. Manually open throttle, until engine speed reaches approximately 2000 RPM. Loosen lock nut, and adjust throttle positioner until it just contacts throttle lever.

2) Release throttle lever. Then, slowly adjust positioner until a sudden drop in speed occurs (over 1000 RPM). At this point, continue adjusting positioner in a decreasing direction for an additional 1/4 of a turn, and tighten lock nut. Accelerate engine to approximately 2300 RPM and release throttle. Engine should return to normal idle speed.

TESTING

1) Check all wiring and hose connections in system. Repair or replace as necessary.

2) Apply vacuum from an external source to vacuum throttle positioner. If positioner does not extend, replace it. If it does, pinch off vacuum hose and observe plunger. If it remains extended for 1 minute or more, unit is okay.

3) Apply external vacuum to manifold supply hose connection on solenoid valve. Disconnect wiring harness from solenoid, and ground 1 terminal of solenoid. Connect 12 volt source to the other terminal, while observing throttle positioner.

4) If plunger does not cycle as voltage is applied, replace solenoid. If it does, replace speed switch.

Fig. 1: Schematic of Vacuum Throttle Positioner System

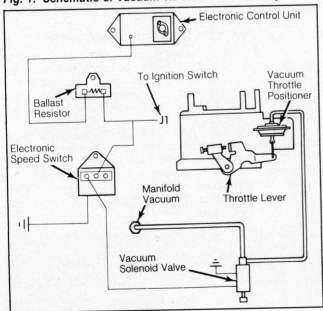

System prevents unburned hydrocarbon emissions during deceleration.

1983 Exhaust Emission Systems

FORD SYSTEMS

DESCRIPTION

Several systems are used to control emission of pollutants. System usage depends on model and engine-transmission combinations. Each system is designed to control a particular vehicle emission. In addition, specially calibrated carburetors, distributors and modified combustion chambers are used with these systems.

NOTE: **There are 2 light duty truck emission standards classifications: Light Duty and Heavy Duty Emissions. Light Duty refers to vehicles up through 8,500 lbs. GVW; Heavy Duty refers to vehicles over 8,500 lbs. GVW.**

THERMOSTATIC AIR CLEANER

Regardless of the type of thermostatic air cleaner used, air valve or thermostat, the function is the same. The system provides hot air from exhaust manifold shroud to carburetor during warm-up conditions..

AIR INJECTION

Air injection system consists of an air pump, diverter valve, check valve, and various air distribution lines for injecting fresh air adjacent to exhaust valves or into converter. Such injection creates an afterburn, which further consumes unburned material in the engine's exhaust. *For additional information, see "Air Injection Systems — Air Pump Type" in this section.*

EXHAUST GAS RECIRCULATION

Exhaust Gas Recirculation (EGR) system uses a vacuum-operated EGR valve to introduce metered amounts of exhaust gas into engine's combustion chambers. This lowers peak combustion chamber temperatures and also reduces NOx formation.

ELECTRONIC ENGINE CONTROL SYSTEM (EEC-III)

This system is used on light duty models with 5.0L and 5.8L engines. Sensors monitor crankshaft position, EGR valve position, throttle position, manifold and barometric pressure, engine coolant temperature and exhaust gas oxygen. Information is sent to the Electronic Control Assembly (ECA) where it is analyzed.

The ECA then computes correct engine operating modes and signals other components to adjust timing, air/fuel ratio, EGR flow rate, thermactor air flow, canister vapor flow and idle speed. *For additional information, see appropriate article in Computerized Engine Control section.*

MICROPROCESSOR CONTROL UNIT (MCU) SYSTEM

Used on models with 2.3L and 4.9L engines, this system is named for and commanded by a microcomputer. Computer is located in the engine compartment, and is capable of controlling engine air/fuel ratios, air injection, and on some models, canister purge, spark retard and idle speed. *For additional information, see appropriate article in Computerized Engine Control section.*

ELECTRONIC ENGINE CONTROL SYSTEM (EEC-IV)

The EEC-IV system is used on Bronco II models with 2.8L V6 engines. The center of the EEC-IV system is the Electronic Control Assembly (ECA). The ECA receives information from several sensors and other electronic devices. Based on information received and the operation program in the ECA's memory, the ECA generates output signals to control engine operation. The calibration module for EEC-IV systems is mounted inside the ECA.

The EEC-IV system controls 3 major areas of engine operation. These areas are, air/fuel mixture, ignition, and emission control. Additionally the system controls A/C compressor clutch operation and provides self-diagnostic capabilities. *For additional information, see appropriate article in Computerized Engine Control section.*

ELECTRIC CHOKE

The electric choke can be either an all electric choke or an electric assist choke. Depending on application, choke voltage is supplied by the battery positive terminal or the alternator stator terminal. The all electric choke uses a resistance heating element to warm up the choke bimetal. The electric assist choke uses a heating element and a heated air inlet to heat the choke bimetal.

DECEL THROTTLE MODULATOR

This unit holds the throttle partly open during deceleration, reducing emissions of hydrocarbons (HC).

CATALYTIC CONVERTER

This unit is used on all light duty emission models. It is connected into the exhaust system so exhaust gasses pass through the converter. Inside the converter, a chemical reaction takes place which reduces exhaust emissions. *For additional information, see Catalytic Converter article in this section.*

POSITIVE CRANKCASE VENTILATION

Positive Crankcase Ventilation (PCV) system controls crankcase blow-by gasses. This system takes blow-by gasses from the crankcase and recirculates them back into the combustion chamber for reburning. Key device in PCV system is vacuum controlled PCV valve. *For additional information, see Crankcase Ventilation article in this section.*

EVAPORATIVE EMISSION CONTROL

Fuel evaporative control system consists of a special fuel tank, a liquid vapor separator, a non-vented filler cap, a charcoal filled storage canister located in the engine compartment, and hoses necessary for routing the vapors from the fuel tank to the charcoal canister for storage.

With this system, fuel vapors are not allowed to evaporate from the carburetor or the fuel tank. Instead they are routed to the charcoal canister for storage. Carburetor vacuum later purges canister of stored fuel vapors. For additional information, see appropriate Fuel Evaporation System article in this section.

FORD THERMOSTATIC AIR CLEANER

All Models

DESCRIPTION

Fresh air or heated air is made available to the engine by a system of ducting which directs air into air cleaner assembly. Air temperature is controlled by a temperature-sensitive vacuum system that operates duct valve.

The vacuum-operated duct can select cool air from outside through a pickup tube, or warm air from a shroud around the exhaust manifold. The system consists of the shroud, an air cleaner assembly with a vacuum motor, a duct and valve assembly, a temperature sensor, and a cold-weather modulator (some models). *See Fig. 1.*

OPERATION

When engine is cold, air is selected from exhaust manifold shroud, because the heat sensor in air cleaner is cold. In the "open" position, vacuum applied to vacuum motor operates duct valve. *See Fig. 2.* Duct valve shuts off fresh air supply and opens, allowing heated air to enter air cleaner.

As engine warms up, the sensor operates, preventing vacuum from being applied to vacuum motor. In this "closed" position, the duct valve closes off supply of heated air, and allows air from outside to flow through pickup tube into air cleaner. *See Fig. 2.*

A cold-weather modulator on some models, controls operation of duct valve under certain air temperature conditions for improved emission control.

Fig. 2: Open & Closed Operation of Duct Valve

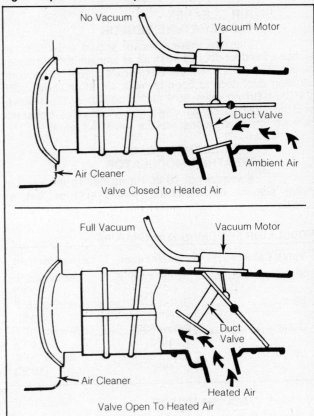

Fig. 1: Vacuum-Operated Air Cleaner Assembly — Typical V8 Assembly Shown (Others Similar)

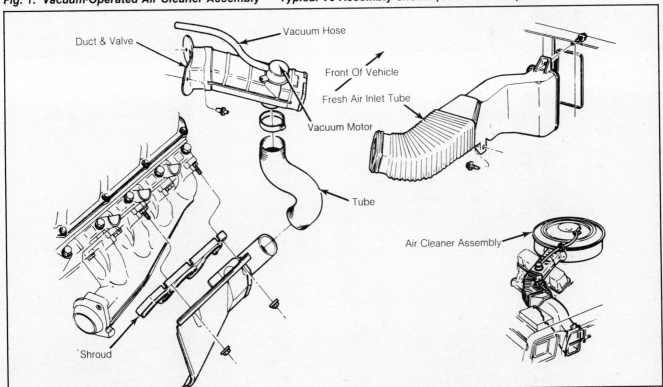

Duct valve switches from heated air to fresh air.

FORD THERMOSTATIC AIR CLEANER (Cont.)

TESTING

AIR CLEANER TEMPERATURE SENSOR

The temperature sensor should allow vacuum to close the duct door to fresh air at ambient temperatures below 75°F (24°C). The sensor should bleed off vacuum, allowing duct door to open to fresh air, at or above 75°F (24°C) on Brown valve, 90°F (32°C) on Pink or Black valve, or 105°F (41°C) on all other colors. If valve does not perform to specifications, replace valve and retest.

AIR CLEANER COLD WEATHER MODULATOR

A vacuum of 16 in. Hg applied to the vacuum motor side of the modulator should hold or leak as follows:

MODULATOR SWITCHING TEMPERATURE

Valve Color	Holds Vacuum	Leaks Vacuum
Black	Below 20°F (-7°C)	Above 35°F (2°C)
Blue	Below 40°F (4°C)	Above 55°F (13°C)
Green	Below 50°F (10°C)	Above 76°F (24°C)
Yellow	Above 65°F (18°C)	Below 50°F (10°C)

VACUUM MOTOR

Disconnect vacuum hose from vacuum motor connector tube. Apply 16 in. Hg vacuum and trap. Vacuum motor should remain closed for 60 seconds. If not, replace duct and valve assembly.

FORD EXHAUST GAS RECIRCULATION

DESCRIPTION

The Exhaust Gas Recirculation (EGR) system is used to reduce NOx emissions. This is accomplished by recycling exhaust gases back into the intake manifold, resulting in cooler combustion temperatures and controlled NOx emissions.

Fig. 1: Typical Ford EGR System for V8 Engines

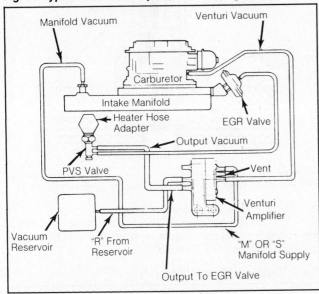

Lowers emissions by reducing combustion temperatures.

The EGR system used by Ford consists of an EGR valve, a vacuum amplifier, a vacuum reservoir, ported vacuum switch (PVS) and connecting lines and hoses.

Fig. 2: Cutaway View of EGR Valve Without Back Pressure Transducer

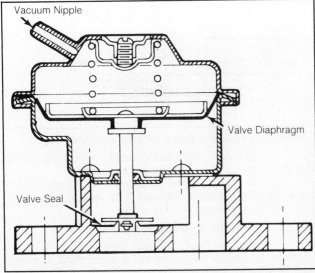

When testing, apply 8 in. Hg to EGR Valve and hold it for at least 30 seconds.

OPERATION

EGR system is controlled by EGR valve. When valve is open, exhaust gas enters manifold passages.

When closed, no gas is allowed to enter intake manifold. Vacuum signals control opening and closing of EGR valve.

Light Duty Emissions EGR systems use a back pressure transducer to aid in controlling exhaust gas recirculation. This unit senses exhaust gas back pressure and modulates vacuum signal to EGR valve in response to amount of back pressure. Back pressure is used to provide information on engine operation modes. The back pressure transducer is integral with EGR valve.

TESTING

EGR VALVE WITHOUT BACK PRESSURE TRANSDUCER

1) Check that all vacuum lines are properly routed, all connections are secure, and that vacuum hoses are not cracked, crimped or broken. When the engine is cold there should be no vacuum to operate the valve. If there is vacuum, check PVS function and replace if necessary. There should be no vacuum to the valve at warm curb idle.

2) Vacuum should be available at or above part throttle with engine at operating temperature. If vacuum is not available, check PVS function and replace as necessary.

3) With engine at idle, apply 8 in. Hg vacuum to EGR valve. The valve stem should move to open the valve and engine idle should roughen. If valve stem moves but idle does not roughen, remove valve and clean inlet and outlet ports with a wire brush.

4) With engine at idle, trap 4 in. Hg vacuum in EGR valve and hold. Vacuum should not drop more than 1 in. Hg in 30 seconds.

5) If vacuum drops, replace valve. To test valve seat, insert a blocking gasket (no flow holes) between valve and mounting base, then retighten valve. If idle improves, replace valve and remove blocking gasket. If idle does not improve, problem is not in EGR system.

Fig. 3: Integral Back Pressure Transducer & EGR Valve

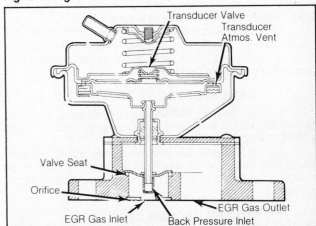

Valve cannot be opened by vacuum, until bleed hole is closed by exhaust back pressure.

EGR VALVE WITH INTEGRAL BACK PRESSURE TRANSDUCER

1) Check that all vacuum lines are properly routed, all connections are secure, and that vacuum hoses are not cracked, crimped or broken. Disconnect vacuum

FORD EXHAUST GAS RECIRCULATION (Cont.)

line to EGR valve and plug line. Connect a vacuum pump to EGR valve. Apply vacuum to the valve. Vacuum (6 in. Hg) should bleed off and valve should not operate. If vacuum holds and valve stays open, replace valve.

2) When the engine is cold there should be no vacuum to operate the valve. If there is vacuum, check PVS function and replace if necessary. There should be no vacuum to the valve at idle under any conditions.

3) Vacuum should be available at or above part throttle with engine at operating temperature. If vacuum is not available, check PVS function and replace as necessary.

4) Clamp a drive socket wrench into the tailpipe. Socket outside diameter should be about 1/16" less than tailpipe inside diameter. Socket drive hole should be covered and socket should be inserted into tailpipe with open end facing out to ensure proper back pressure.

5) Do not block tailpipe fully or run engine faster than idle for prolonged periods of time. Be sure to remove socket from tailpipe at end of test.

6) Idle engine and apply vacuum to EGR valve gradually. EGR valve diaphragm should move smoothly and idle should roughen. Trap 6 in. Hg vacuum in EGR valve and hold. Vacuum should drop more than 1 in. Hg in 30 seconds.

7) If vacuum does not drop or diaphragm does not move, replace valve. If diaphragm moves but idle does not roughen, remove valve and clean inlet and outlet ports with a wire brush.

8) If valve is suspected of sticking, remove valve from engine and cycle valve by pressing carefully with fingers against the lower transducer plate. If valve sticks open when fingers are released, replace valve. If valve does not stick and correct vacuum signal is present at valve, check valve for carbon deposits and clean as necessary.

9) If engine has less than 6000 miles on it, is idling rough, and the valve is suspected of being open, remove valve and check valve for foreign material. Tap base of valve on table while holding valve open with fingers. If foreign material falls from valve, make sure valve closes and return valve to engine.

10) Reconnect vacuum line and check for rough idle. If rough idle continues and valve is still sticking, replace valve. If valve is not sticking, rough idle problem is not in EGR system.

CARBURETOR EGR PORT

1) Attach vacuum gauge directly to EGR carburetor port, using hose. Start engine, quickly open throttle to halfway position and close.

2) Observe vacuum gauge for quick rise and fall as throttle is opened and closed. If definite vacuum is evident, port is okay. If not, port is clogged and must be cleaned.

PORTED VACUUM SWITCH
PVS with 2 Connections

1) Detach both vacuum hoses from PVS, and connect a vacuum gauge to top port on PVS. Connect other PVS nipple to manifold vacuum or external vacuum supply of at least 10 in. Hg. *See Fig. 4.*

2) Start engine and warm until engine operating temperature is reached. If no vacuum reading is noted, PVS should be replaced. If vacuum is present, PVS is okay.

Fig. 4: Cutaway View of 2-Port PVS

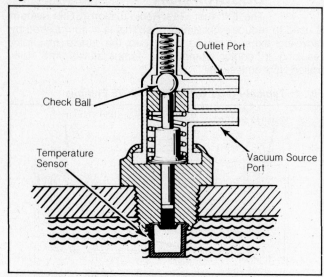

PVS will open when engine reaches operating temperature.

PVS with 3 Connections

1) Disconnect EGR vacuum hose from PVS and connect manifold vacuum or external vacuum source to lowest port on PVS. *See Fig. 5.*

Fig. 5: Cutaway View of 3-Port PVS

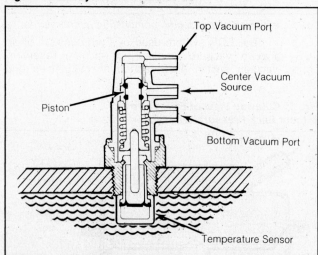

Warm engine should indicate vacuum at center PVS port.

2) Detach distributor supply hose from center port, and attach vacuum gauge to center port.

3) Start engine and warm up until engine operating temperature is reached. If no vacuum is present, replace PVS. If present, PVS is okay.

PVS with 4 Connections

1) Disconnect vacuum hoses at PVS valve. Connect a vacuum gauge to top port of PVS. Connect external vacuum source to 2nd port. *See Fig. 6.*

2) Start engine and warm up until engine operating temperature is reached. If no vacuum, this portion of PVS is damaged and valve should be replaced. If vacuum is present, proceed to next step.

3) Connect gauge to 3rd port and vacuum supply to the bottom port. If vacuum is noted, PVS is okay. If no vacuum, replace PVS.

FORD EXHAUST GAS RECIRCULATION (Cont.)

Fig. 6: Cutaway View of 4-Port PVS

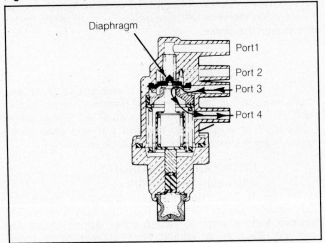

Connect vacuum gauge to 1st & 3rd port to check PVS.

VENTURI VACUUM AMPLIFIER

NOTE: **Amplifiers have built-in calibrations, and no external adjustments are required. If an amplifier bias test reveals malfunction, replace amplifier. Always check venturi vacuum amplifier last, after checking all other basic EGR components.**

1) With engine at normal operating temperature, curb idle set and adequate manifold vacuum supplied to system, connect a vacuum gauge to the hose at amplifier port "O". The gauge may read as much as 2 in. Hg at idle.

2) Disconnect the venturi hose (amplifier port "V") at carburetor and increase engine speed to 2000-3000 RPM. Vacuum should not change.

3) While maintaining high engine speed, connect venturi hose. Vacuum should increase to 4 in. Hg. Return to idle. Gauge should return to initial reading. If amplifier does not perform as specified, replace amplifier.

Fig. 7: Testing Ford Venturi Vacuum Amplifier

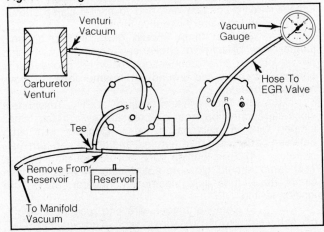

Amplifiers do not require external adjustments.

VACUUM AMPLIFIER RESERVOIR

When charged with 15-20 in. Hg vacuum, vacuum loss should not exceed .5 in. Hg in 60 seconds. If it does, replace reservoir.

FORD ALL-ELECTRIC & ELECTRIC ASSIST CHOKES

DESCRIPTION

NOTE: If the choke housing has no inlet air connection, either from the external heat stove or from the thermactor air system, the vehicle is equipped with an all-electric choke. However, if the housing has an air inlet connection, it can still include an all-electric or electric assist choke.

ALL-ELECTRIC CHOKE
12-Volt System

This 12-volt choke system is controlled by an engine "RUN" signal from a 3-terminal oil pressure switch. Vehicles without all-electric choke systems have a 1-terminal oil pressure switch or sender.

The 3-terminal switch has 2 sets of contacts. The 2 outside terminals are for the ungrounded, normally open contacts, which actuate the choke. These contacts complete the circuit to ground when they are closed. This permits the choke heater to operate, when the ignition switch is in the "RUN" position.

The center terminal is for the case-grounded, normally closed contacts, which actuate the oil pressure or engine light.

7.2-Volt System

This choke system operates in much the same manner, but receives its power from the stator terminal (center tap) of the alternator.

ELECTRIC ASSIST CHOKE

Many Light Duty emission models use a hot air choke with electric assist. An electrically-heated choke thermostat spring housing acts as an aid to fast choke release.

The heater receives its voltage either from the stator terminal on the alternator or from the battery through the oil sensor switch. The heater only operates when the engine is actually running.

The electric assist choke system consists of a choke cap, thermostatic spring, a bimetal temperature sensing disc and a positive temperature coefficient (PTC) ceramic heater. *See Fig. 1.*

OPERATION

ELECTRIC ASSIST CHOKE

Current is constantly supplied to the temperature sensing switch. The system is grounded through a ground strap connected to the carburetor body. At temperatures below about 54°F (12°C), the switch is open. No current is supplied to the ceramic heater located within the thermostatic spring, allowing normal choking action to occur.

At temperatures from 54-74°F (12-24°C), depending on engine requirements, switch will remain open or will close to supply current to the ceramic heater. The switch will always be closed at temperatures above 74°F (24°C). As the heater warms, it causes the thermostatic spring to pull the choke plate open within 1 to 1.5 minutes.

ALL-ELECTRIC CHOKES

Although several different all-electric chokes are used on Ford Light Duty trucks, they operate similarly to the electric assist chokes. Temperature ranges may vary, however, between models. A ceramic heater is used to act upon the bimetal thermostatic spring, which opens and closes the choke.

TESTING

Remove air cleaner, check choke plate and choke linkage for free operation. Remove hot air supply tube at choke housing, and install a choke tester (LRE34618 or equivalent). Perform hot and cold choke function per instructions contained in tester kit.

CHOKE CAP CONTINUITY
Alternator-Powered Choke

1) Disconnect electrical lead from choke cap. Turn ignition switch "OFF". Connect one test lamp lead to positive battery terminal. Attach other lead to choke cap terminal. Test lamp should light. If test lamp lights, proceed to step 3). If test lamp does not light, use a jumper wire to connect one end to choke clamp shroud and other end to battery negative terminal.

2) Test lamp should glow. If not, connect jumper wire directly to choke cap ground pin; if lamp glows, correct poor connections between choke clamp shroud and choke cap ground pin. If lamp does not glow, replace choke cap.

3) Leave test lamp connected and remove jumper wire. Test lamp should glow. If not, locate and repair open in ground circuit. Reconnect electrical lead to choke cap.

4) Connect test lamp between choke cap shroud and battery negative terminal. Start engine. Test lamp should glow. If not, locate and repair open circuit between choke cap and alternator stator terminal. If no open circuit is found, check alternator output and service as required. Stop engine and remove test equipment.

Battery-Powered Choke

1) Disconnect electrical lead from choke cap. Turn ignition switch "OFF". Connect one test lamp lead to positive battery terminal. Attach other lead to choke cap terminal. Test lamp should light. If test lamp lights, proceed to step 3). If test lamp does not light, use a jumper wire to connect one end to choke clamp shroud and other end to battery negative terminal.

2) Test lamp should glow. If not, connect jumper wire directly to choke cap ground pin; if lamp glows, correct poor connections between choke clamp shroud and choke cap ground pin. If lamp does not glow, replace choke cap.

3) Turn ignition switch "OFF". Disconnect electrical connection from oil pressure switch and install jumper wire in electrical harness. Connect test lamp between battery negative terminal and choke cap terminal.

4) Turn ignition "ON" but do not start engine. Test lamp should glow. If not, locate and repair open circuit (fuse, fuse link, electrical connector, etc.). Turn ignition switch "OFF".

5) Remove jumper wire and reconnect electrical connector to oil pressure switch. Turn ignition "ON", but do not start engine. Test lamp should not glow. If lamp glows, replace oil pressure switch.

6) With test lamp still connected, start engine. Test lamp should glow. If not, replace oil pressure switch.

FORD ALL-ELECTRIC & ELECTRIC ASSIST CHOKES (Cont.)

CHOKE CAP RESISTANCE

1) Heat choke with choke tester for 3-5 minutes. Disconnect electrical connector from choke cap terminal. Connect an ohmmeter between choke cap terminal and choke cap ground.

2) Ensure metal-to-metal contact, not metal oxide-to-metal contact. Ohmmeter reading should be under 30 ohms; but more than 0 ohms. If not to specifications, repeat test. If specifications are not met after second test, replace choke cap.

3) On 7200 VV carburetors, disconnect ohmmeter and reconnect choke cap terminal connector. Remove air cleaner and plug vacuum hoses. Start engine and run it for 3 minutes. If engine was warm prior to start, cold enrichment rod (CER) should remain seated. If engine was cold prior to start, CER should slowly lower to seat. Turn engine off.

4) If CER does not operate as described, make a note and continue test. Replace air cleaner and reconnect vacuum lines. Choke cap should be quite warm. Reconnect ohmmeter as described in step **1)**.

5) On all models, use a choke tester and cool the cap by directing cold air towards oval insulator (not case) around cap terminal. Ohmmeter reading should gradually vary and then register a sudden increase. Stop cooling.

6) The sudden increase should occur within 10 minutes after cooling began (choke tester used at maximum capacity and held close to cap). If sudden increase does not occur within 10 minutes, replace choke cap. If change does occur, warm oval insulator with choke tester.

7) Ohmmeter reading should again vary and then register a sudden decrease. Stop warming cap. Sudden decrease should occur within 10 minutes after warming began (choke tester used at maximum capacity and held close to cap).

8) If sudden decrease does not occur within 10 minutes, replace choke cap. If change occurs, choke cap is operating properly. If CER did not operate as described in step **3)**, check linkage and correct the problem.

Fig. 1: Ford Electric Assist Choke Assembly

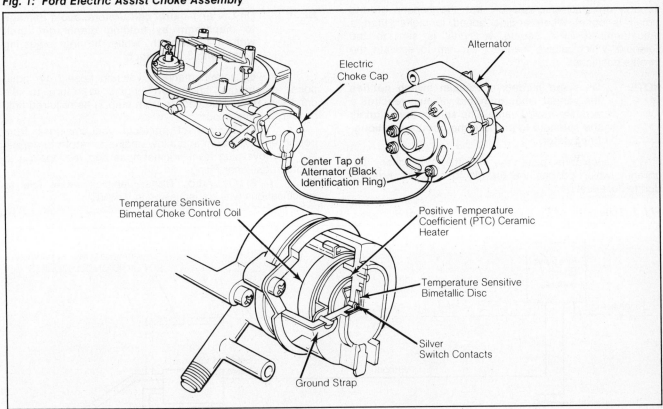

Alternator

Electric Choke Cap

Center Tap of Alternator (Black Identification Ring)

Temperature Sensitive Bimetal Choke Control Coil

Positive Temperature Coefficient (PTC) Ceramic Heater

Temperature Sensitive Bimetallic Disc

Silver Switch Contacts

Ground Strap

All-electric chokes are similar.

1983 Exhaust Emission Systems

FORD DECEL THROTTLE CONTROL SYSTEM

DESCRIPTION

The decel throttle control (modulator) system keeps the throttle valves open slightly during sudden deceleration to help reduce hydrocarbon and carbon monoxide emissions.

System consists of a governor module or speed sensor, a ported vacuum switch (some models), solenoid vacuum valve, throttle positioner (modulator) on throttle linkage, and electrical wiring and vacuum hoses. *See Fig. 1.*

Some systems also utilize a vacuum switch that notifies the module or speed sensor when manifold vacuum is at a predetermined level. The system is electrically connected to the ignition switch and to the "TACH" terminal of ignition coil.

OPERATION

Manifold vacuum is routed through a solenoid vacuum valve, which is normally closed, to the vacuum throttle positioner (modulator).

Power is available to solenoid vacuum valve through an electronic sensor, but the sensor ground circuit is open. When engine speed is higher than a predetermined RPM setting, a signal is sent to the solenoid, which allows manifold vacuum to activate the throttle positioner.

NOTE: **On some models a vacuum switch notifies the sensor when manifold vacuum reaches a predetermined value. The sensor then signals the solenoid to activate the throttle positioner (modulator).**

Vacuum pulls the throttle positioner diaphragm, which pushes the throttle to high idle position during deceleration.

ADJUSTMENT

NOTE: **This adjustment is to be performed when replacing components found defective during "Testing" sequence.**

1) With engine at normal operating temperature, set transmission in neutral (all transmissions).

2) Adjust carburetor to specified curb idle speed. On Auto. Trans. vehicles, this will be set to 150 RPM higher than specified curb idle speed (which is set with transmission in "DRIVE"), although transmission will remain in neutral. This is to keep minimum load on engine.

3) Disconnect system vacuum hose from throttle positioner diaphragm, and plug hose. Using a "slave" hose, connect manifold vacuum source to diaphragm.

4) Allow one minute for engine speed to stabilize. If engine speed is within specifications, the modulator is properly set. Go to step 7).

5) If RPM was not within specification, adjust throttle positioner by loosening lock nut and turning it until speed is within limits. Retighten lock nut.

NOTE: **On Carter 1-barrel carburetors, avoid damage to diaphragm by holding diaphragm shaft with 1/4" wrench while turning adjusting screw with 3/8" wrench.**

6) Detach manifold vacuum hose from positioner diaphragm, and allow engine to return to idle condition. Repeat procedure from step 2) as required until proper function occurs.

7) Disconnect manifold vacuum hose from positioner diaphragm and allow engine to return to normal idle. Remove plug from original hose and reconnect it to throttle positioner fitting.

8) On Auto. Trans. vehicles, reset idle to specifications with transmission in "DRIVE".

Fig. 1 Schematic of Ford Decel Throttle Control System

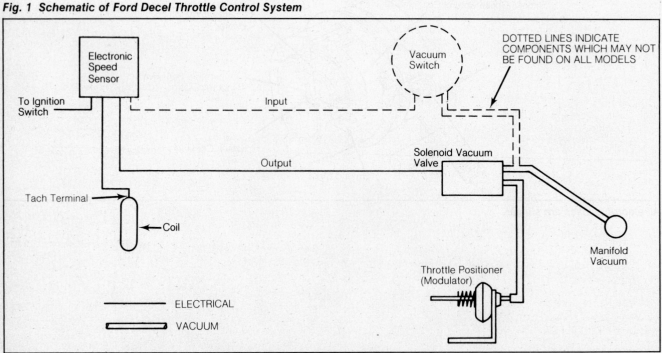

Components indicated with dotted lines may not be found on all models.

FORD DECEL THROTTLE CONTROL SYSTEM (Cont.)

9) On all vehicles, stop engine. Install air cleaner assembly.

TESTING

PRE-TEST SET-UP

1) If vehicle is equipped with vacuum delay valves, test for proper operation as instructed in *Ford Vacuum Delay Valve article in this section.*

2) All tests should be made with engine at operating temperature and all accessories off. Remove air cleaner and plug vacuum line. Check primary and secondary throttle linkage and choke linkage for freedom of movement. Connect tachometer to engine.

SYSTEM QUICK CHECK

1) With engine at idle, accelerate to 2000 RPM or more, and then let it return to idle. Manifold vacuum should exceed 20.6 in. Hg since the system includes a vacuum solenoid valve.

2) If vacuum diaphragm plunger extends and retracts, system is functioning properly. If not, continue with tests in sequence given.

THROTTLE POSITIONER (MODULATOR) DIAPHRAGM CHECK

1) Disconnect vacuum line from diaphragm. Connect external vacuum source to diaphragm. Apply and trap 19 in. Hg.

2) If diaphragm does not respond, or will not hold vacuum, replace the diaphragm. If diaphragm responds and holds vacuum, proceed with testing.

3) Remove external vacuum source. If the diaphragm does not return within 5 seconds, replace the defective diaphragm. Reconnect vacuum line. If diaphragm returns in 5 seconds, it is not at fault.

PORTED VACUUM SWITCH TEST

NOTE: This switch may not be found on all models.

1) Disconnect hose from PVS to solenoid vacuum valve, and connect external vacuum source.

2) Start engine and let it idle long enough to reach normal operating temperature. At normal temperature, there should be vacuum indicated on gauge.

3) If no vacuum is present, check vacuum hose for leaks. If hose is not leaking, replace the PVS. Reconnect vacuum line.

VACUUM SOLENOID VALVE TEST

1) With engine at normal operating temperature, engine idling and transmission in neutral, make sure choke plate is fully open.

2) Turn off air conditioner, power take-off (if equipped), and all accessories. Disconnect vacuum supply hose at solenoid valve and check for vacuum. If no vacuum is present, clean or replace hose as required.

3) If a vacuum delay valve is used, remove valve and install a straight connector. Disconnect wires to solenoid valve. With a jumper wire, apply battery voltage to one of the solenoid terminals. The engine speed should not increase. If it does, replace the solenoid valve.

4) With battery voltage on one terminal, use a second jumper wire to ground the other terminal of the valve. The engine speed should increase, if not, replace the valve.

5) Remove the ground jumper wire. The engine should return to idle within 15 seconds. If not, replace the solenoid valve.

VACUUM SENSING SWITCH TEST

1) On models with vacuum sensing switch, check continuity between terminals while applying vacuum less than 19.4 in. Hg.

2) If switch shows continuity (switch closed), replace switch. If not, apply more than 20.6 in. Hg to switch, and recheck continuity. If no continuity now exists, replace switch.

NOTE: Between 19.4 and 20.6 in. Hg, switch may be either open or closed.

ELECTRONIC SPEED SENSOR MODULE TEST

1) Number harness terminals from 1 to 6 (or 8), starting with terminal 1 nearest the locator key. With ignition switch "ON", connect negative voltmeter lead to ground and touch positive lead, in turn, to terminals 1, 4, and 6. Battery voltage should be indicated at terminals 1 and 4. Terminal 6 should be 6-8 volts.

2) If voltage is less than specified, service harness as necessary. If all tests are satisfactory, and problem still remains, replace electronic speed sensor module.

ELECTRONIC GOVERNOR MODULE CHECK

1) Check the harness as follows: Number the harness terminals from 1 to 8, with No. 1 being nearest the locator key.

2) With engine running, connect tachometer to terminals 1 and 2. Engine RPM should be indicated. Next, turn ignition switch "ON", and connect positive lead of voltmeter to terminal 1 and negative lead to terminal 8. Battery voltage should be indicated.

3) Turn ignition switch "OFF". Connect one lead of ohmmeter to terminal 4 and the other lead to terminal 6. Ohmmeter should read continuity. Repeat same test between terminals 5 and 7. Continuity should again be indicated.

4) If any of the terminals fail any of the tests, repair the wiring harness as required. If harness meets all specifications, replace the electronic governor module.

1983 Exhaust Emission Systems

FORD VACUUM DELAY VALVES

DESCRIPTION & OPERATION

Vacuum Delay Valves (VDV) are used on various parts of the engine to provide for gradual application or release of vacuum to engine or emission-related devices.

These valves may be one-way or two-way delay valves, depending upon application. Although each valve is named for a given system, it may be used elsewere.

NOTE: Be sure valve is installed in correct direction, or engine will run rough, ping or use excessive fuel.

TESTING

1) Connect a hand vacuum pump and hose to valve to be tested. Valves with both sides the same color are good, if vacuum can be built up in both directions before bleeding off.

2) Valves with one side Black or White and the other side colored are good if vacuum can be built up in one direction only before bleeding off.

NOTE: Use care to prevent oil or dirt from entering valves during testing.

Fig. 1: Four Types of Vacuum Delay Valves

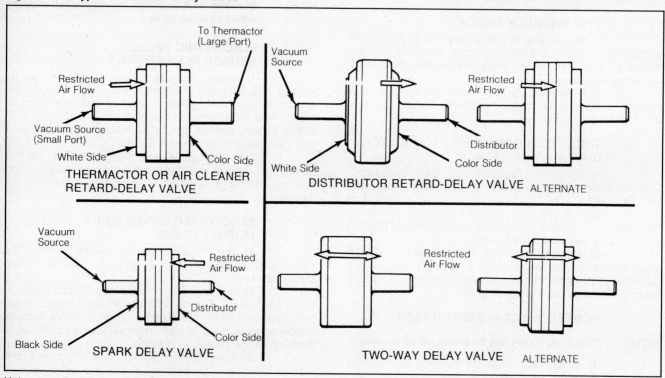

Valves can best be tested with a vacuum pump.

1982 FORD VACUUM DIAGRAMS

INSTRUCTIONS

Located on the front of the engine, there is an Engine Code Information label containing the engine calibration. The label may be any of several different styles. *See fig. 1.* Using the calibration number and the Vacuum Diagram Index, determine which vacuum diagram to use for the vehicle being serviced.

Fig. 1: Engine Code Information Label

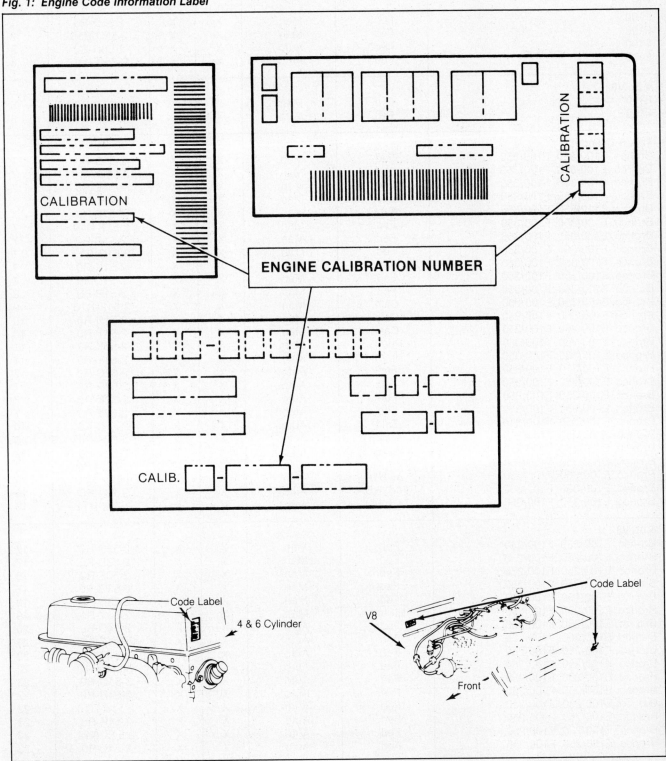

1982 Exhaust Emission Systems

1982 FORD VACUUM DIAGRAMS (Cont.)

1982 FORD MOTOR CO. VACUUM DIAGRAM INDEX

Engine & Model	Application	Transmission	A/C	Non A/C	Calibration	Fig. No.
3.8L V6						
F100	Fed.	Man.	X	X	2-55D-R0	1
F100	Fed.	Man.	X	X	2-55D-R10	2
F100	Fed.	Auto.	X	X	2-56D-R0	3
F100	Fed.	Auto.	X	X	2-56D-R10	4
4.2L V8						
F100	Fed.	Man.	X	X	2-57G-R0	5
F100	Fed.	Auto.	X	X	2-58H-R0	6
4.9L 6-Cylinder						
Bronco, E100/350, F100/350	Fed.	Man.	X	X	2-51D-R0	7
Bronco, E100/350, F100/350	Fed.	Man.	X	X	2-51D-R10	7
Bronco, E100/350, F100/350	Fed.	Man.	X	X	2-51E-R0	7
Bronco, E100/350, F100/350	Fed.	Man.	X	X	2-51E-R10	7
Bronco, E100/350, F100/350	Fed.	Man.	X	X	2-51F-R0	7
Bronco, E100/350, F100/350	Fed.	Man.	X	X	2-51F-R10	7
Bronco, E100/350, F100/350	Fed.	Man.	X	X	2-51G-R0	7
Bronco, E100/350, F100/350	Fed.	Man.	X	X	2-51G-R10	7
Bronco, E100/350, F100/350	Fed.	Man.	X	X	2-51K-R0	7
Bronco, E100/350, F100/350	Fed.	Man.	X	X	2-51L-R0	7
Bronco, E100/350, F100/350	Fed.	Man.	X	X	2-51P-R0	8
Bronco, E100/350, F100/350	Calif.	Man.	X	X	2-51P-R10	9
Bronco, E100/350, F100/350	Calif.	Man.	X	X	2-51S-R0	10
Bronco, E100/350, F100/350	Calif.	Man.	X	X	2-51T-R0	10
Bronco, E100/350, F100/350	Hi. Alt.	Man.	X	X	2-51X-R0	11
Bronco, E100/350, F100/350	Hi. Alt.	Man.	X	X	2-51Y-R0	11
Bronco, E100/350, F100/350	Fed.	Auto.	X	X	2-52G-R0	7
Bronco, E100/350, F100/350	Fed.	Auto.	X	X	2-52H-R0	7
Bronco, E100/350, F100/350	Fed.	Auto.	X	X	2-52K-R0	7
Bronco, E100/350, F100/350	Fed.	Auto.	X	X	2-52L-R0	7
Bronco, E100/350, F100/350	Calif.	Auto.	X	X	2-52S-R0	10
Bronco, E100/350, F100/350	Calif.	Auto.	X	X	2-52T-R0	10
Bronco, E100/350, F100/350	Hi. Alt.	Auto.	X	X	2-52Y-R0	12
Bronco, E100/350, F100/350	Fed. HD	Man.	X	X	9-77J-R12	13
Bronco, E100/350, F100/350	All HD	Man.	X	X	9-77S-R10	14
Bronco, E100/350, F100/350	Fed. HD	Auto.	X	X	9-78J-R0	15
Bronco, E100/350, F100/350	Fed. HD	Auto.	X	X	9-78J-R11	16
5.0L V8						
Bronco, E100/250, F100/250	Fed.	Man.	X	X	2-53D-R0	17
Bronco, E100/250, F100/250	Fed.	Man.	X	X	2-53D-R0	17
Bronco, E100/250, F100/250	Fed.	Man.	X	X	2-53F-R0	18
Bronco, E100/250, F100/250	Fed.	Man.	X	X	2-53G-R0	17
Bronco, E100/250, F100/250	Fed.	Man.	X	X	2-53H-R0	18
Bronco, E100/250, F100/250	Hi. Alt.	Man.	X	X	2-53X-R1	19
Bronco, E100/250, F100/250	Fed.	Auto.	X	X	2-54D-R0	20
Bronco, E100/250, F100/250	Fed.	Auto.	X	X	2-54D-R10	21
Bronco, E100/250, F100/250	Fed.	Auto.	X	X	2-54F-R0	22
Bronco, E100/250, F100/250	Fed.	Auto.	X	X	2-54F-R10	22
Bronco, E100/250, F100/250	Fed.	Auto.	X	X	2-54G-R0	23
Bronco, E100/250, F100/250	Fed.	Auto.	X	X	2-54H-R0	22
Bronco, E100/250, F100/250	Fed.	Auto.	X	X	2-54H-R10	22
Bronco, E100/250, F100/250	Fed.	Auto.	X	X	2-54K-R0	23
Bronco, E100/250, F100/250	Fed.	Auto.	X	X	2-54K-R12	23
Bronco, E100/250, F100/250	Fed.	Auto.	X	X	2-54L-R0	23

1982 FORD VACUUM DIAGRAMS (Cont.)

1982 FORD MOTOR CO. VACUUM DIAGRAM INDEX

Engine & Model	Application	Transmission	A/C	Non A/C	Calibration	Fig. No.
5.0L V8 (Cont.)						
Bronco, E100/250, F100/250	Calif.	Auto.	X	X	2-54P-R0	24
Bronco, E100/250, F100/250	Calif.	Auto.	X	X	2-54P-R10	24
Bronco, E100/250, F100/250	Calif.	Auto.	X	X	2-54P-R11	25
Bronco, E100/250, F100/250	Calif.	Auto.	X	X	2-54R-R0	24
Bronco, E100/250, F100/250	Calif.	Auto.	X	X	2-54R-R10	24
Bronco, E100/250, F100/250	Calif.	Auto.	X	X	2-54R-R11	25
Bronco, E100/250, F100/250	Hi. Alt.	Auto.	X	X	2-54X-R1	26
Bronco, E100/250, F100/250	Hi. Alt.	Auto.	X	X	2-54X-R10	27
5.8L V8						
Bronco, E100/350, F150/350	Fed.	Man.	X	X	1-63T-R0	28
Bronco, E100/350, F150/350	Fed.	Man.	X	X	1-63T-R10	28
Bronco, E100/350, F150/350	Fed.	Man.	X	X	1-63T-R11	28
Bronco, E100/350, F150/350	Fed.	Man.	X	X	1-63T-R12	28
Bronco, E100/350, F150/350	Fed.	Auto.	X	X	1-64H-R2	29
Bronco, E100/350, F150/350	Calif.	Auto.	X	X	1-64R-R1	30
Bronco, E100/350, F150/350	Calif.	Auto.	X	X	1-64R-R10	30
Bronco, E100/350, F150/350	Fed.	Auto.	X	X	1-64S-R0	28
Bronco, E100/350, F150/350	Fed.	Auto.	X	X	1-64S-R10	28
Bronco, E100/350, F150/350	Fed.	Auto.	X	X	1-64T-R0	28
Bronco, E100/350, F150/350	All	Auto.	X	X	1-64T-R10	31
Bronco, E100/350, F150/350	All	Auto.	X	X	1-64T-R11	31
Bronco, E100/350, F150/350	All	Auto.	X	X	1-64T-R12	31
Bronco, E100/350, F150/350	Hi. Alt.	Man.	X	X	2-63Y-R10	32
Bronco, E100/350, F150/350	Hi. Alt.	Man.	X	X	2-63Y-R11	32
Bronco, E100/350, F150/350	Hi. Alt.	Auto.	X	X	2-64X-R0	33
Bronco, E100/350, F150/350	Hi. Alt.	Auto.	X	X	2-64Y-R0	32
Bronco, E100/350, F150/350	Hi. Alt.	Auto.	X	X	2-64Y-R11	32
Bronco, E100/350, F150/350	Fed. HD	All	X	X	2-75J-R18	34
Bronco, E100/350, F150/350	Fed. HD	All	X	X	2-75J-R20	34
Bronco, E100/350, F150/350	Fed. HD	All	X	X	2-76J-R18	34
Bronco, E100/350, F150/350	Fed. HD	All	X	X	2-76J-R20	34
Bronco, E100/350, F150/350	All HD	Man.	X	X	7-75J-R14	35
Bronco, E100/350, F150/350	Fed. HD	Auto.	X	X	7-76J-R11	36
Bronco, E100/350, F150/350	All HD	Auto.	X	X	7-76J-R13	35
Bronco, E100/350, F150/350	All HD	Auto.	X	X	7-76J-R14	35
Bronco, E100/350, F150/350	Fed. HD	Auto.	X	X	7-76J-R15	36
6.6L V8						
E250/350, F350	All HD	Man.	X	X	9-73J-R11	37
E250/350, F350	All HD	Man.	X	X	9-73J-R12	37
E250/350, F350	Fed. HD	Man.	X	X	9-73J-R13	38
E250/350, F350	All HD	Man.	X	X	9-73J-R14	37
E250/350, F350	All HD	Auto.	X	X	9-74J-R11	37
E250/350, F350	All HD	Auto.	X	X	9-74J-R12	37
E250/350, F350	Fed. HD	Auto.	X	X	9-74J-R13	38
E250/350, F350	All HD	Auto.	X	X	9-74J-R14	37
7.5L V8						
E250/350	Fed. HD	Auto.	X	X	9-97J-R12	39

EMISSION CONTROL DEVICE ABBREVIATIONS

A/CL-BI MET — Air Cleaner Bi-Metal Sensor
A/CL-DV — Air Cleaner Duct Valve
A/CL-CWM — Air Cleaner Cold Weather Modulator
ACV — Air Control Valve
AIR-BPV — Air By-Pass Valve
EGR — Exhaust Gas Recirculation

BPT — EGR Back Pressure Transducer
PCV — Positive Crankcase Ventilation
SOLV — Vacuum Solenoid Valve
VCV — Vacuum Control Valve
VCS — Vacuum Control Switch
VRESER — Vacuum Reservoir
V-REST — Vacuum Restrictor

1982 Exhaust Emission Systems

1982 FORD VACUUM DIAGRAMS (Cont.)

Fig. 1: 3.8L V6
Calibration 2-55D-R0

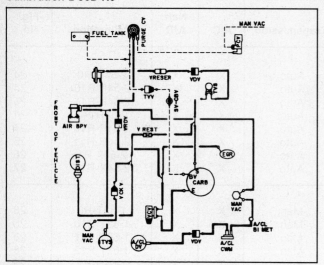

Fig. 4: 3.8L V6
Calibration 2-56D-R10

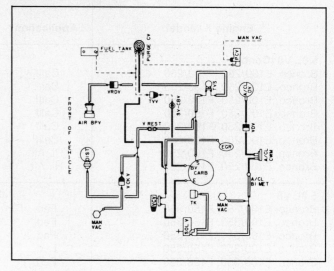

Fig. 2: 3.8L V6
Calibration 2-55D-R10

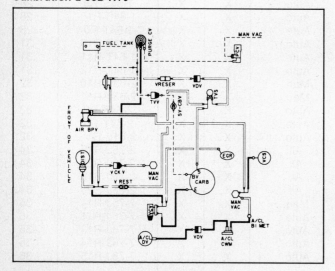

Fig. 5: 4.2L V8
Calibration 2-57G-R0

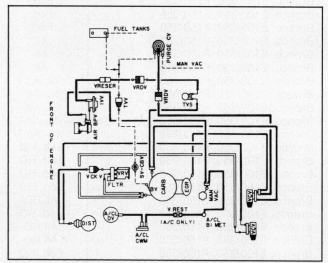

Fig. 3: 3.8L V6
Calibration 2-56D-R0

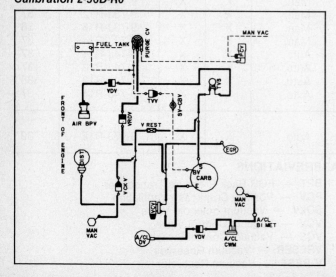

Fig. 6: 4.2L V8
Calibration 2-58H-R0

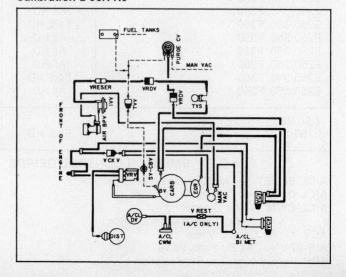

1982 FORD VACUUM DIAGRAMS (Cont.)

Fig. 7: 4.9L 6-Cylinder
(See Index for Calibration Numbers)

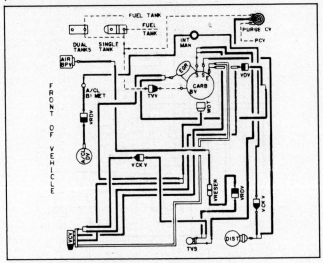

Fig. 10: 4.9L 6-Cylinder
(See Index for Calibration Numbers)

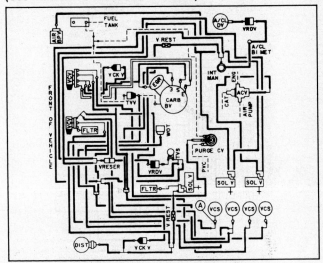

Fig. 8: 4.9L 6-Cylinder
Calibration 2-51P-R0

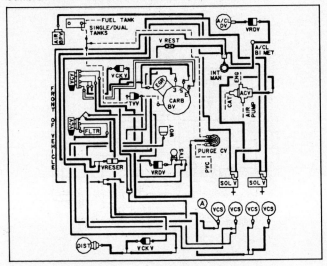

Fig. 11: 4.9L 6-Cylinder
Calibration 2-51X-R0 & 2-51Y-R0

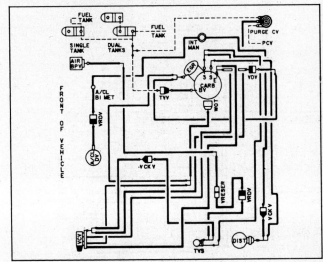

Fig. 9: 4.9L 6-Cylinder
Calibration 2-51P-R10

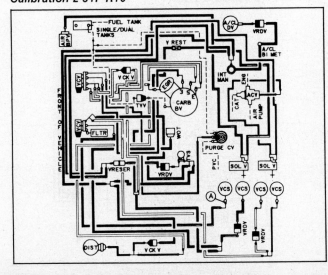

Fig. 12: 4.9L 6-Cylinder
Calibration 2-52Y-R0

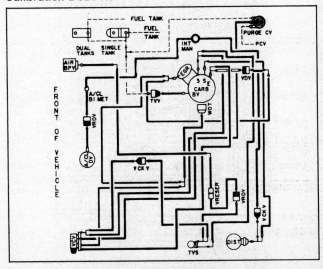

1982 Exhaust Emission Systems

1982 FORD VACUUM DIAGRAMS (Cont.)

**Fig. 13: 4.9L 6-Cylinder
Calibration 9-77J-R12**

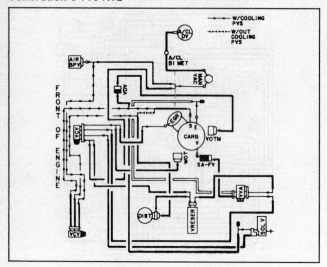

**Fig. 16: 4.9L 6-Cylinder
Calibration 9-78J-R11**

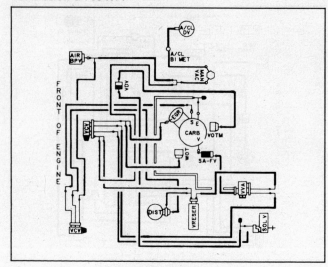

**Fig. 14: 4.9L 6-Cylinder
Calibration 9-77S-R10**

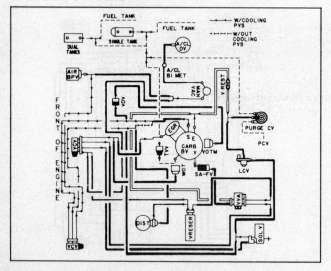

**Fig. 17: 5.0L V8
(See Index for Calibration Numbers)**

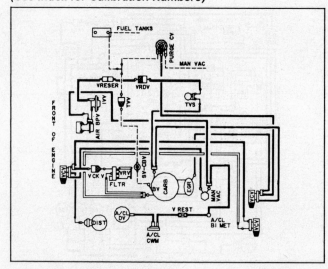

**Fig. 15: 4.9L 6-Cylinder
Calibration 9-78J-R0**

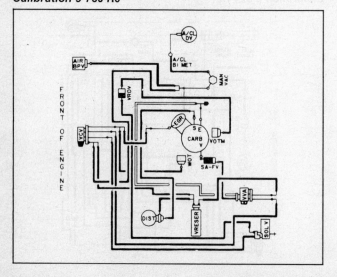

**Fig. 18: 5.0L V8
Calibration 2-53F-R0 & 2-53H-R0**

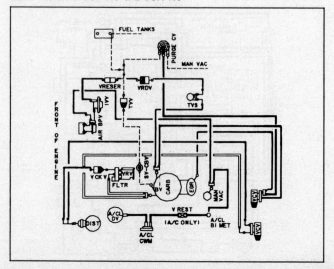

1982 FORD VACUUM DIAGRAMS (Cont.)

Fig. 19: 5.0L V8
Calibration 2-53X-R1

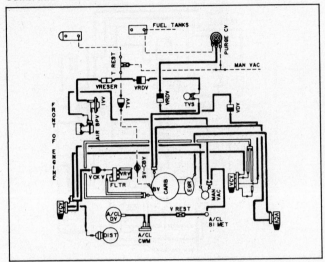

Fig. 22: 5.0L V8
(See Index for Calibration Numbers)

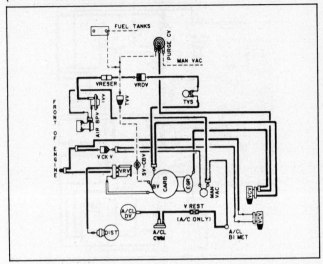

Fig. 20: 5.0L V8
Calibration 2-54D-R0

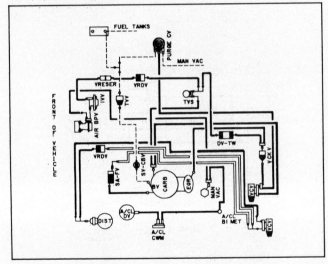

Fig. 23: 5.0L V8
(See Index for Calibration Numbers)

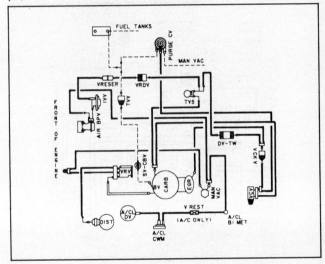

Fig. 21: 5.0L V8
Calibration 2-54D-R10

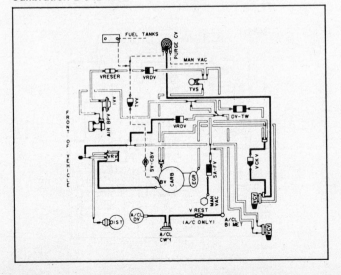

Fig. 24: 5.0L V8
(See Index for Calibration Numbers)

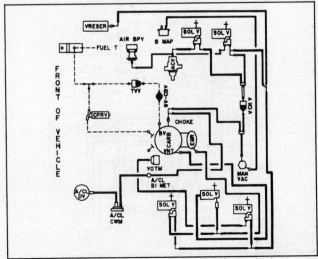

1982 Exhaust Emission Systems

1982 FORD VACUUM DIAGRAMS (Cont.)

Fig. 25: 5.0L V8
Calibration 2-54P-R11 & 2-54R-R11

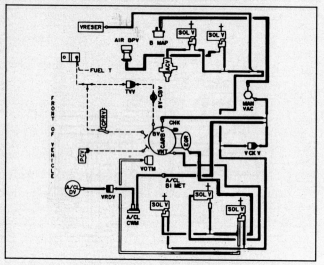

Fig. 28: 5.8L V8
(See Index for Calibration Numbers)

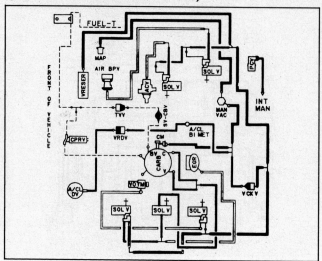

Fig. 26: 5.0L V8
Calibration 2-54X-R1

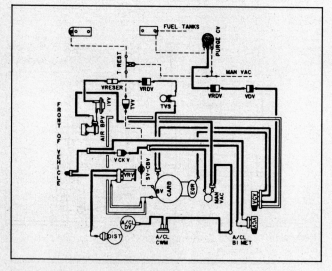

Fig. 29: 5.8L V8
Calibration 1-64H-R2

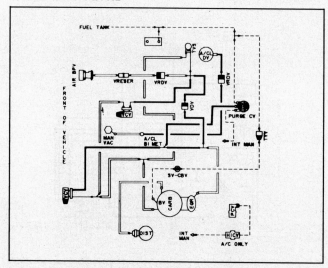

Fig. 27: 5.0L V8
Calibration 2-54X-R10

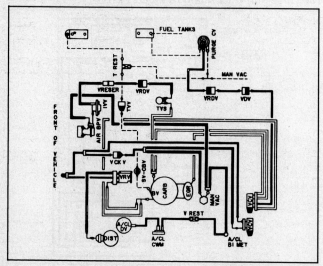

Fig. 30: 5.8L V8
Calibration 1-64R-R1 & 1-64R-R10

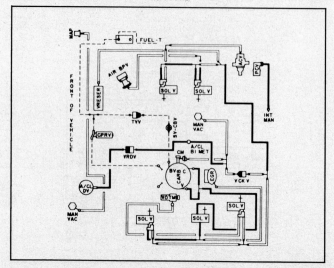

1982 FORD VACUUM DIAGRAMS (Cont.)

Fig. 31: 5.8L V8
(See Index for Calibration Numbers)

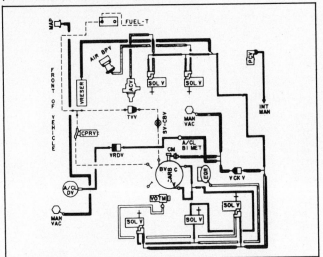

Fig. 32: 5.8L V8
(See Index for Calibration Numbers)

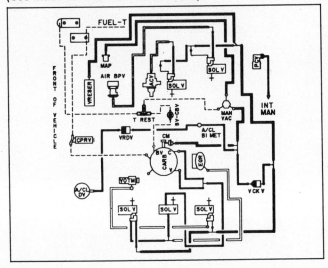

Fig. 33: 5.8L V8
Calibration 2-64X-R0

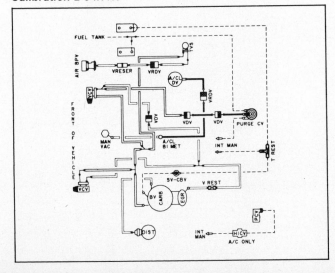

Fig. 34: 5.8L V8
(See Index for Calibration Numbers)

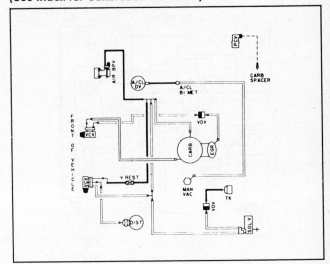

Fig. 35: 5.8L V8
(See Index for Calibration Numbers)

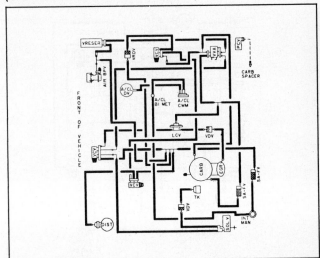

Fig. 36: 5.8L V8
Calibration 7-76J-R11 & 7-76J-R15

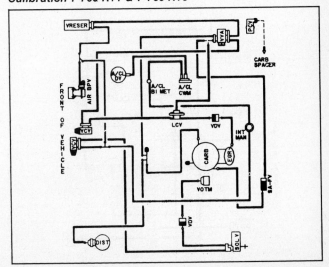

1982 Exhaust Emission Systems

1982 FORD VACUUM DIAGRAMS (Cont.)

Fig. 37: 6.6L V8
(See Index for Calibration Numbers)

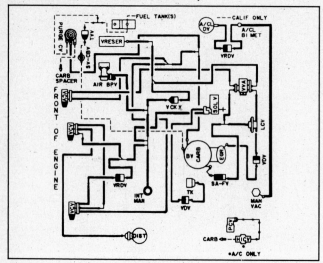

Fig. 38: 6.6L V8
Calibration 9-73J-R13 & 9-74J-R13

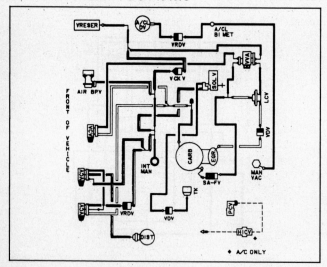

Fig. 39: 7.5L V8
Calibration 9-97J-R12

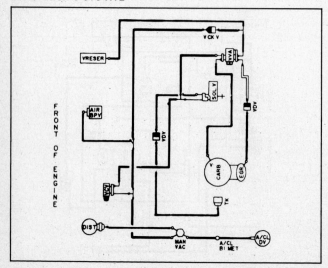

1983 FORD VACUUM DIAGRAMS

INSTRUCTIONS

Located on the front of the engine, there is an Engine Code Information label containing the engine calibration. The label may be any of several different styles. *See fig. 1.* Using the calibration number and the Vacuum Diagram Index, determine which vacuum diagram to use for the vehicle being serviced.

Fig. 1: Engine Code Information Label

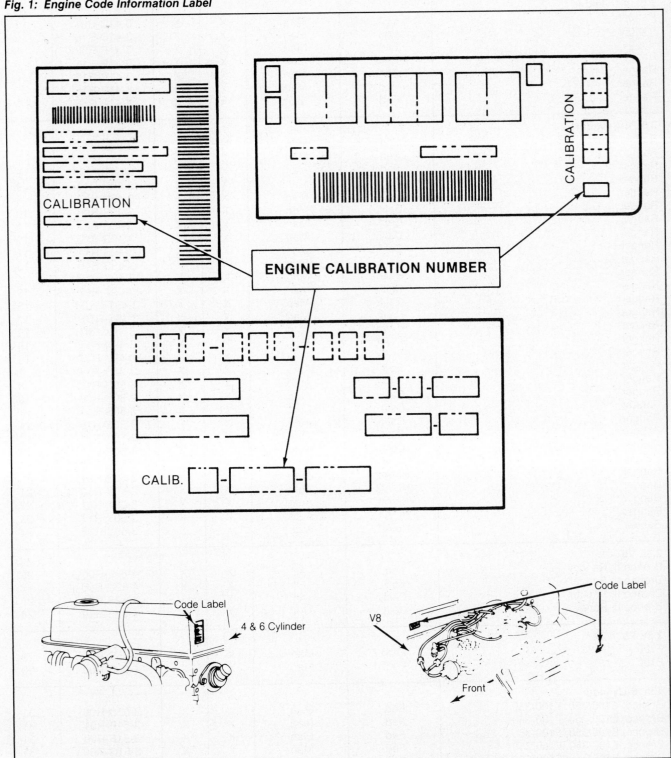

1983 Exhaust Emission Systems
1983 FORD VACUUM DIAGRAMS (Cont.)

1983 FORD MOTOR CO. VACUUM DIAGRAM INDEX

Engine & Model	Application	Transmission	A/C	Non A/C	Calibration	Fig. No.
2.0L 4-Cylinder						
Ranger	Fed.	Man.	X	X	3-41D-R01	1
Ranger	Fed.	Man.	X	X	3-41D-R10	2
Ranger	Fed.	Man.	X	X	3-41P-R02	3
Ranger	Fed.	Man.	X	X	3-41P-R11	4
Ranger	Fed.	Man.	X	X	3-41P-R12	4
Ranger	Fed.	Man.	X	X	3-41P-R15	5
Ranger	Fed.	Man.	X	X	3-41P-R16	5
2.3L 4-Cylinder						
Ranger	Fed.	Man.	X	X	3-49G-R17	6
Ranger	Fed.	Man.	X	X	3-49G-R20 [1]	7
Ranger	Fed.	Man.	X	X	3-49G-R20 [2]	8
Ranger	Fed.	Man.	X	X	3-49H-R16	9
Ranger	Fed.	Man.	X	X	3-49H-R17	8
Ranger	Calif.	Man.	X	X	3-49S-R00	10
Ranger	Calif.	Man.	X	X	3-49S-R01	11
Ranger	Calif.	Man.	X	X	3-49S-R10	12
Ranger	Calif.	Man.	X	X	3-49S-R11	12
Ranger	Calif.	Man.	X	X	3-49S-R15	13
Ranger	Calif.	Man.	X	X	3-49S-R16	14
Ranger	Calif.	Man.	X	X	3-49T-R17	15
Ranger	Calif.	Man.	X	X	3-49T-R20 [2]	16
Ranger	Calif.	Man.	X	X	3-49T-R20 [1]	17
Ranger	Hi. Alt.	Man.	X	X	3-49X-R01	18
Ranger	Hi. Alt.	Man.	X	X	3-49X-R11	18
Ranger	Hi. Alt.	Man.	X	X	3-49Y-R17	19
Ranger	Fed.	Auto.	X	X	3-50H-R17	9
Ranger	Fed.	Auto.	X	X	3-50H-R18	8
Ranger	Calif.	Auto.	X	X	3-50S-R00	10
Ranger	Calif.	Auto.	X	X	3-50S-R01	11
Ranger	Calif.	Auto.	X	X	3-50S-R10	11
Ranger	Calif.	Auto.	X	X	3-50S-R11	12
Ranger	Calif.	Auto.	X	X	3-50S-R17	13
Ranger	Calif.	Auto.	X	X	3-50S-R18	14
Ranger	Hi. Alt.	Auto.	X	X	3-50X-R01	21
Ranger	Hi. Alt.	Auto.	X	X	3-50X-R10	21
Ranger	Hi. Alt.	Auto.	X	X	3-50X-R11	22
Ranger	Hi. Alt.	Auto.	X	X	3-50Y-R17	23
Ranger	Hi. Alt.	Auto.	X	X	3-50Y-R18	24
2.8L V6						
Bronco II, Ranger	Fed.	All	X	X		25
Bronco II, Ranger	Fed.	All	X	X	4-61F-R00	26
Bronco II, Ranger	Calif.	All	X	X	4-62D-R00	27
Bronco II, Ranger	Calif.	All	X	X	4-62S-R01	28
					4-62S-R10	
3.8L V6						
F100	Fed.	Man.	X	X	4-55D-R00	29
F100	Fed.	Auto.	X	X	4-56D-R00	30
4.9L 6-Cylinder						
Bronco, E100/350, F100/350	Fed	Man	X	X	3-51D-R00	31
Bronco, E100/350, F100/350	Fed	Man	X	X	3-51E-R01	31
Bronco, E100/350, F100/350	Fed	Man	X	X	3-51F-R00	31
Bronco, E100/350, F100/350	Fed	Man	X	X	3-51G-R00	31
Bronco, E100/350, F100/350	Fed	Man	X	X	3-51H-R00	31
Bronco, E100/350, F100/350	Fed	Man	X	X	3-51K-R00	31

1983 FORD VACUUM DIAGRAMS (Cont.)

1983 FORD MOTOR CO. VACUUM DIAGRAM INDEX

Engine & Model	Application	Transmission	A/C	Non A/C	Calibration	Fig. No.
4.9L 6-Cylinder (Cont.)						
Bronco, E100/350, F100/350	Fed	Man	X	X	3-51L-R00	31
Bronco, E100/350, F100/350	Fed	Man	X	X	3-51P-R00	32
Bronco, E100/350, F100/350	Calif	Man	X	X	3-51R-R00	33
Bronco, E100/350, F100/350	Calif	Man	X	X	3-51R-R10	33
Bronco, E100/350, F100/350	Calif	Man	X	X	3-51S-R00	33
Bronco, E100/350, F100/350	Calif	Man	X	X	3-51S-R10	33
Bronco, E100/350, F100/350	Calif	Man	X	X	3-51T-R00	33
Bronco, E100/350, F100/350	Fed	Man	X	X	3-51T-R10	34
Bronco, E100/350, F100/350	Hi. Alt	Man	X	X	3-51V-R00	35
Bronco, E100/350, F100/350	Hi. Alt	Man	X	X	3-51X-R00	35
Bronco, E100/350, F100/350	Hi. Alt	Man	X	X	3-51Z-R00	35
Bronco, E100/350, F100/350	Fed	Auto	X	X	3-52E-R00	31
Bronco, E100/350, F100/350	Fed	Auto	X	X	3-52F-R00	31
Bronco, E100/350, F100/350	Fed	Auto	X	X	3-52G-R00	31
Bronco, E100/350, F100/350	Fed	Auto	X	X	3-52K-R00	31
Bronco, E100/350, F100/350	Fed	Auto	X	X	3-52L-R00	31
Bronco, E100/350, F100/350	Calif	Auto	X	X	3-52R-R00	33
Bronco, E100/350, F100/350	Calif	Auto	X	X	3-52R-R10	33
Bronco, E100/350, F100/350	Calif	Auto	X	X	3-52S-R00	33
Bronco, E100/350, F100/350	Calif	Auto	X	X	3-52S-R10	33
Bronco, E100/350, F100/350	Calif	Auto	X	X	3-52T-R00	33
Bronco, E100/350, F100/350	Calif	Auto	X	X	3-52T-R10	33
Bronco, E100/350, F100/350	Hi. Alt	Auto	X	X	3-52V-R00	35
Bronco, E100/350, F100/350	Hi. Alt	Auto	X	X	3-52Y-R00	35
Bronco, E100/350, F100/350	Hi. Alt	Auto	X	X	3-52Z-R00	35
Bronco, E100/350, F100/350	All HD	Man	X	X	9-77J-R12	36
Bronco, E100/350, F100/350	All HD	Man	X	X	9-77S-R10	37
Bronco, E100/350, F100/350	All HD	Auto	X	X	9-78J-R00	38
Bronco, E100/350, F100/350	All HD	Auto	X	X	9-78J-R11	36
5.0L V8						
Bronco, E100/250, F100/250	Fed.	Man.	X	X	3-53F-R00	39
Bronco, E100/250, F100/250	Fed.	Man.	X	X	3-53G-R00	39
Bronco, E100/250, F100/250	Fed.	Man.	X	X	3-53K-R00	39
Bronco, E100/250, F100/250	Fed.	Man.	X	X	3-53L-R00	39
Bronco, E100/250, F100/250	Hi. Alt.	Man.	X	X	3-53W-R00	40
Bronco, E100/250, F100/250	Hi. Alt.	Man.	X	X	3-53Y-R00	40
Bronco, E100/250, F100/250	Hi. Alt.	Man.	X	X	3-53Z-R00	40
Bronco, E100/250, F100/250	Fed.	Auto.	X	X	3-54E-R00	41
Bronco, E100/250, F100/250	Fed.	Auto.	X	X	3-54E-R10	41
Bronco, E100/250, F100/250	Fed.	Auto.	X	X	3-54F-R00	41
Bronco, E100/250, F100/250	Fed.	Auto.	X	X	3-54J-R00	41
Bronco, E100/250, F100/250	Fed.	Auto.	X	X	3-54J-R10	41
Bronco, E100/250, F100/250	Fed.	Auto.	X	X	3-54L-R00	42
Bronco, E100/250, F100/250	Calif.	Auto.	X	X	3-54P-R00	43
Bronco, E100/250, F100/250	Calif.	Auto.	X	X	3-54R-R00	43
Bronco, E100/250, F100/250	Calif.	Auto.	X	X	3-54T-R00	43
Bronco, E100/250, F100/250	Hi. Alt.	Auto.	X	X	3-54W-R00	44
Bronco, E100/250, F100/250	Hi. Alt.	Auto.	X	X	3-54Y-R00	44
Bronco, E100/250, F100/250	Hi. Alt.	Auto.	X	X	3-54Y-R10	45
Bronco, E100/250, F100/250	Hi. Alt.	Auto.	X	X	3-54Z-R00	44
Bronco, E100/250, F100/250	Hi. Alt.	Auto.	X	X	3-54Z-R10	45
5.8L V8						
Bronco, E100/350, F150/350	Fed.	Man.	X	X	1-63T-R12	46
Bronco, E100/350, F150/350	Fed.	Man.	X	X	1-63T-R13	46
Bronco, E100/350, F150/350	Fed.	Man.	X	X	1-63T-R15B	47

1983 Exhaust Emission Systems

1983 FORD VACUUM DIAGRAMS (Cont.)

1983 FORD MOTOR CO. VACUUM DIAGRAM INDEX

Engine & Model	Application	Transmission	A/C	Non A/C	Calibration	Fig. No.
5.8L V8 (Cont.)						
Bronco, E100/350, F150/350	Fed.	Auto.	X	X	1-64H-R02	48
Bronco, E100/350, F150/350	Fed.	Auto.	X	X	1-64T-R12	46
Bronco, E100/350, F150/350	Fed.	Auto.	X	X	1-64T-R13	46
Bronco, E100/350, F150/350	All	Auto.	X	X	1-64T-R15B	49
Bronco, E100/350, F150/350	Hi. Alt.	Man.	X	X	2-63Y-R11	50
Bronco, E100/350, F150/350	Hi. Alt.	Man.	X	X	2-63Y-R12	50
Bronco, E100/350, F150/350	Hi. Alt.	Man.	X	X	2-63Y-R14B	51
Bronco, E100/350, F150/350	Hi. Alt.	Auto.	X	X	2-64X-R00	52
Bronco, E100/350, F150/350	Hi. Alt.	Auto.	X	X	2-64Y-R11	53
Bronco, E100/350, F150/350	Hi. Alt.	Auto.	X	X	2-64Y-R12	53
Bronco, E100/350, F150/350	Hi. Alt.	Auto.	X	X	2-64Y-R14B	51
Bronco, E100/350, F150/350	All HD	All	X	X	2-75J-R20	54
Bronco, E100/350, F150/350	All HD	All	X	X	2-76J-R20	54
7.5L V8						
E250/350, F250 HD/350	Fed. HD	All	X	X	9-97J-R13	55
E250/350, F250 HD/350	All HD	All	X	X	3-98S-R00	56

¹ — 4WD models.
² — 2WD models.

EMISSION CONTROL DEVICE ABBREVIATIONS

A/CL-BI MET — Air Cleaner Bi-Metal Sensor
A/CL-DV — Air Cleaner Duct Valve
A/CL-CWM — Air Cleaner Cold Weather Modulator
ACV — Air Control Valve
AIR-BPV — Air By-Pass Valve
EGR — Exhaust Gas Recirculation

BPT — EGR Back Pressure Transducer
PCV — Positive Crankcase Ventilation
SOLV — Vacuum Solenoid Valve
VCV — Vacuum Control Valve
VCS — Vacuum Control Switch
VRESER — Vacuum Reservoir
V-REST — Vacuum Restrictor

1983 FORD VACUUM DIAGRAMS (Cont.)

Fig. 1: 2.0L 4-Cylinder
Calibration 3-41D-R01

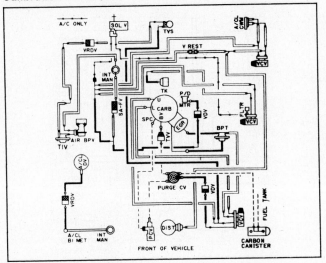

Fig. 4: 2.0L 4-Cylinder
Calibration 3-41P-R11 & 3-41P-R12

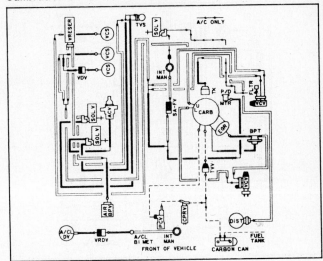

Fig. 2: 2.0L 4-Cylinder
Calibration 3-41D-R10

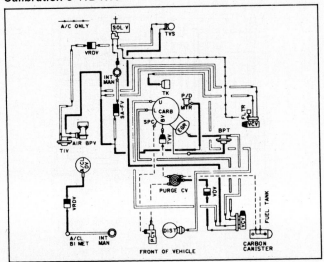

Fig. 5: 2.0L 4-Cylinder
Calibration 3-41P-R15 & 3-41S-R16

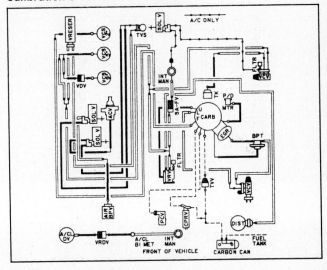

Fig. 3: 2.0L 4-Cylinder
Calibration 3-41P-R02

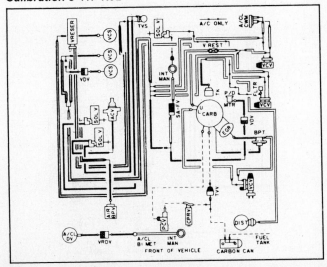

Fig. 6: 2.3L 4-Cylinder
Calibration 3-49G-R17

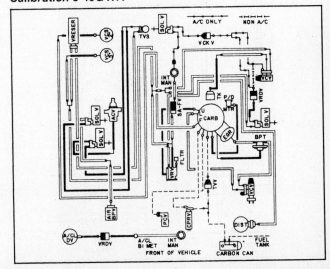

1983 Exhaust Emission Systems

1983 FORD VACUUM DIAGRAMS (Cont.)

Fig. 7: 2.3L 4-Cylinder
Calibration 3-49G-R20 (4WD)

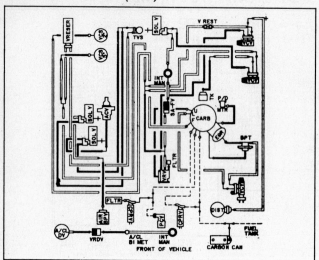

Fig. 8: 2.3L 4-Cylinder
(See Index for Calibration Numbers)

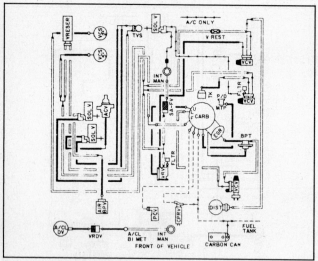

Fig. 9: 2.3L 4-Cylinder
Calibration 3-49H-R16 & 3-50H-R17

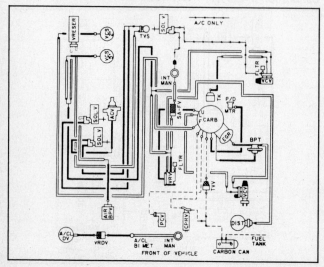

Fig. 10: 2.3L 4-Cylinder
Calibration 3-49S-R00 & 3-50S-R00

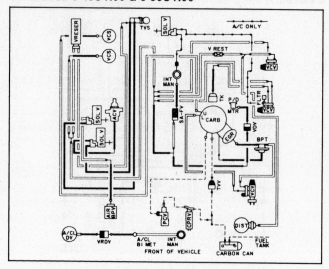

Fig. 11: 2.3L 4-Cylinder
(See Index for Calibration Numbers)

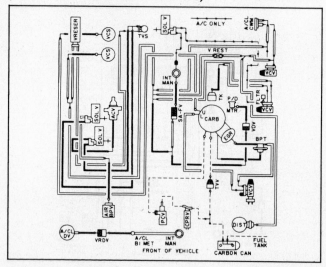

Fig. 12: 2.3L 4-Cylinder
(See Index for Calibration Numbers)

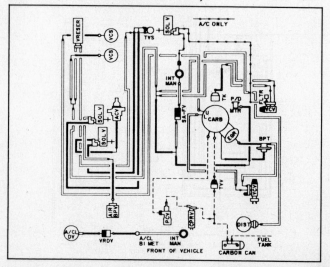

1983 FORD VACUUM DIAGRAMS (Cont.)

Fig. 13: 2.3L 4-Cylinder
Calibration 3-49S-R15 & 3-50S-R17

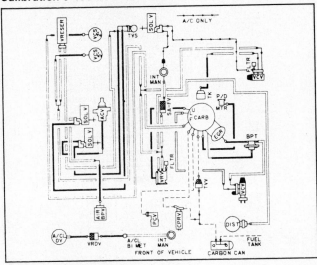

Fig. 16: 2.3L 4-Cylinder
Calibration 3-49T-R20 (2WD)

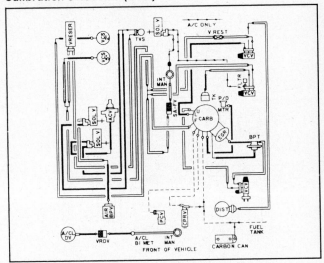

Fig. 14: 2.3L 4-Cylinder
Calibration 3-49S-R16 & 3-50S-R18

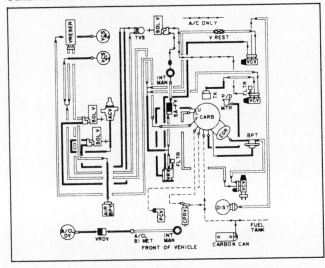

Fig. 17: 2.3L 4-Cylinder
Calibration 3-49T-R20 (4WD)

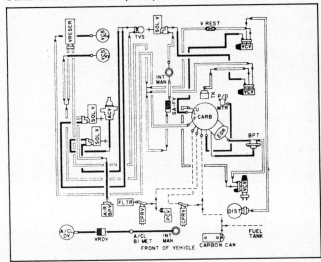

Fig. 15: 2.3L 4-Cylinder
Calibration 3-49T-R17

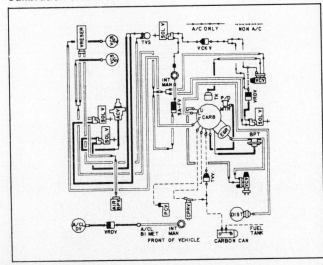

Fig. 18: 2.3L 4-Cylinder
Calibration 3-49X-R01 & 3-49X-R11

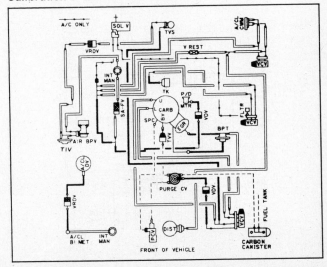

1983 Exhaust Emission Systems

1983 FORD VACUUM DIAGRAMS (Cont.)

Fig. 19: 2.3L 4-Cylinder
Calibration 3-49Y-R17

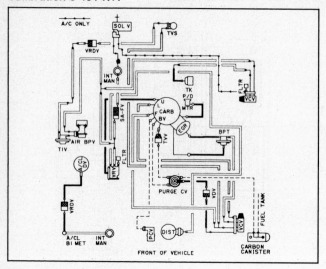

Fig. 20: 2.3L 4-Cylinder
Calibration 3-49Y-R19

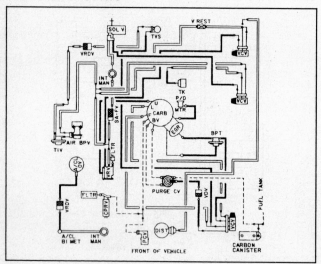

Fig. 21: 2.3L 4-Cylinder
Calibration 3-50X-R01 & 3-50X-R10

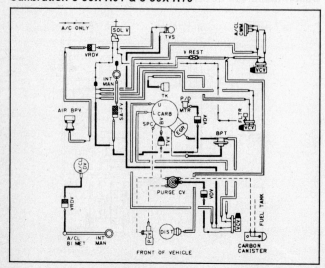

Fig. 22: 2.3L 4-Cylinder
Calibration 3-50X-R11

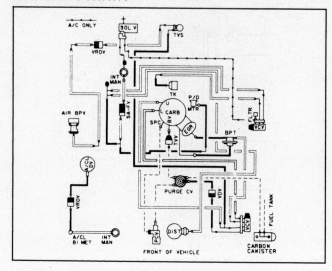

Fig. 23: 2.3L 4-Cylinder
Calibration 3-50Y-R17

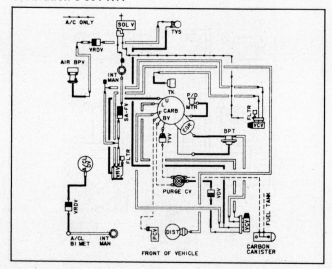

Fig. 24: 2.3L 4-Cylinder
Calibration 3-50Y-R18

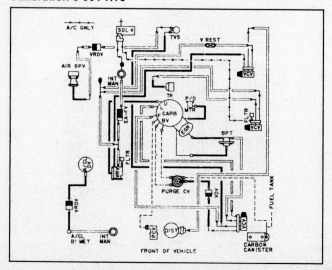

1983 FORD VACUUM DIAGRAMS (Cont.)

Fig. 25: 2.8L V6
Calibration 4-61F-R00

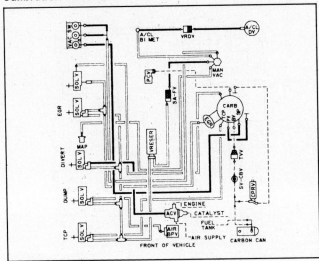

Fig. 26: 2.8L V6
Calibration 4-62D-R00

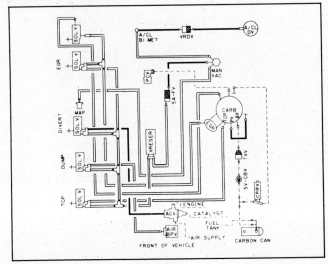

Fig. 27: 2.8L V6
Calibration 4-62S-R01

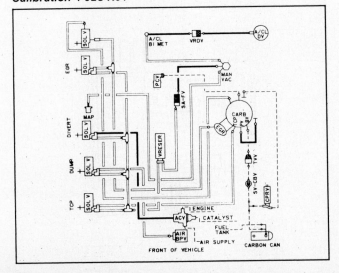

Fig. 28: 2.8L V6
Calibration 4-62S-R10

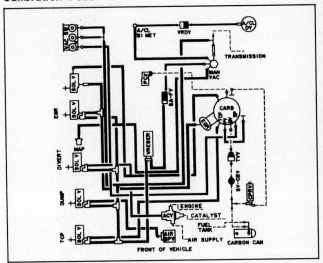

Fig. 29: 3.8L V6
Calibration 3-55D-R00

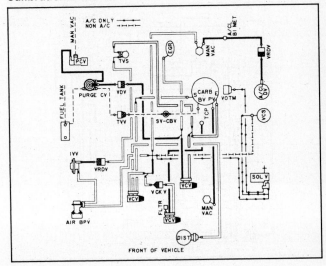

Fig. 30: 3.8L V6
Calibration 3-56D-R00

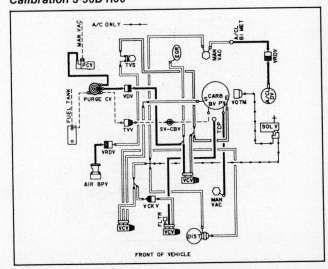

1983 Exhaust Emission Systems
1983 FORD VACUUM DIAGRAMS (Cont.)

Fig. 31: 4.9L 6-Cylinder
(See Index for Calibration Numbers)

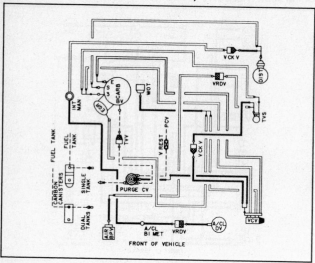

Fig. 34: 4.9L 6-Cylinder
Calibration 3-51T-R10

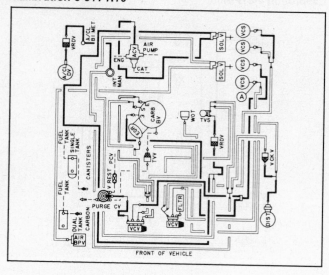

Fig. 32: 4.9L 6-Cylinder
Calibration 3-51P-R00

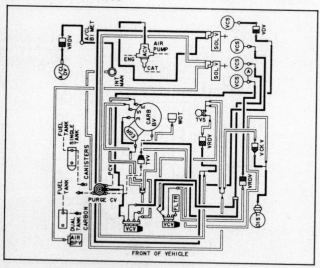

Fig. 35: 4.9L 6-Cylinder
(See Index for Calibration Numbers)

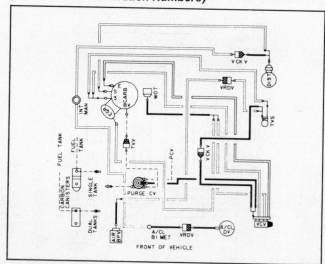

Fig. 33: 4.9L 6-Cylinder
(See Index for Calibration Numbers)

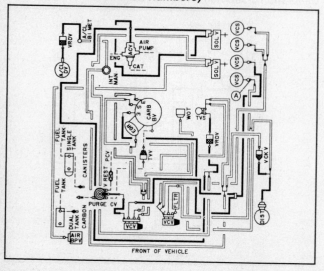

Fig. 36: 4.9L 6-Cylinder
Calibration 9-77J-R12 & 9-78J-R11

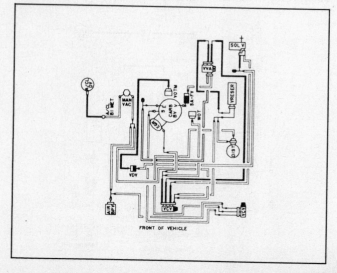

1983 FORD VACUUM DIAGRAMS (Cont.)

Fig. 37: 4.9L 6-Cylinder
Calibration 9-77S-R10

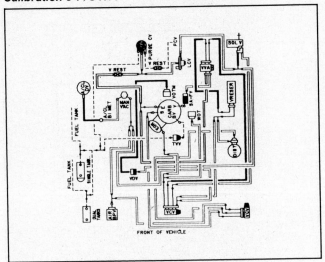

Fig. 40: 5.0L V8
(See Index for Calibration Numbers)

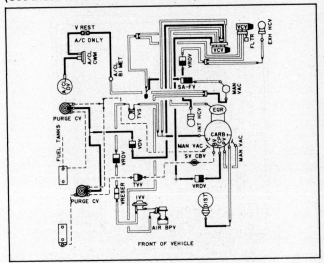

Fig. 38: 4.9L 6-Cylinder
Calibration 9-78J-R00

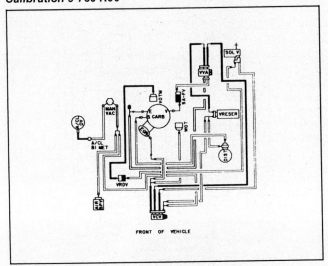

Fig. 41: 5.0L V8
(See Index for Calibration Numbers)

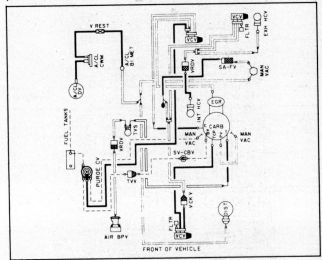

Fig. 39: 5.0L V8
(See Index for Calibration Numbers)

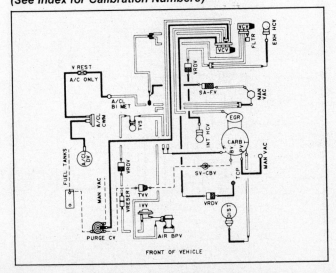

Fig. 42: 5.0L V8
Calibration 3-54L-R00

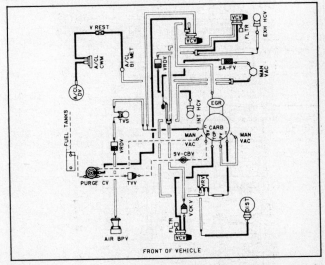

1983 Exhaust Emission Systems

1983 FORD VACUUM DIAGRAMS (Cont.)

Fig. 43: 5.0L V8
(See Index for Calibration Numbers)

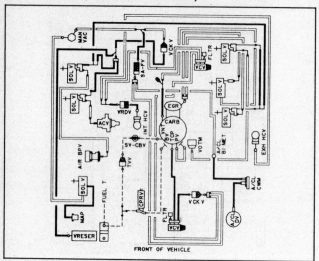

Fig. 46: 5.8L V8
(See Index for Calibration Numbers)

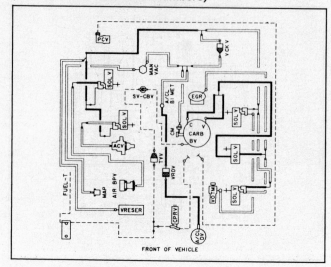

Fig. 44: 5.0L V8
(See Index for Calibration Numbers)

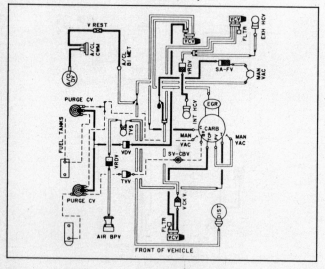

Fig. 47: 5.8L V8
Calibration 1-63T-R15B

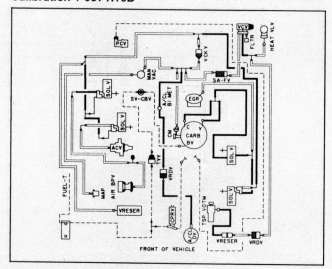

Fig. 45: 5.0L V8
Calibration 3-54Y-R10 & 3-54Z-R10

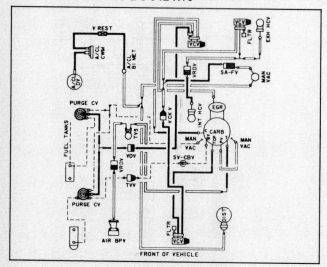

Fig. 48: 5.8L V8
Calibration 1-64H-R02

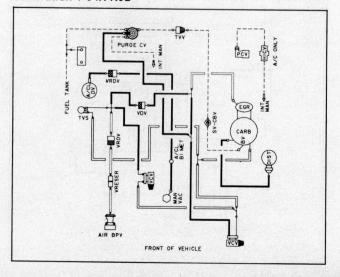

1983 FORD VACUUM DIAGRAMS (Cont.)

Fig. 49: 5.8L V8
Calibration 1-64T-R15B

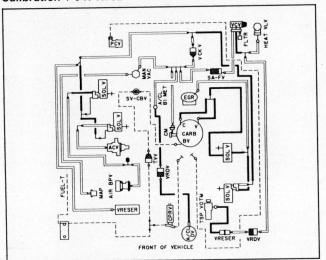

Fig. 52: 5.8L V8
Calibration 2-64X-R00

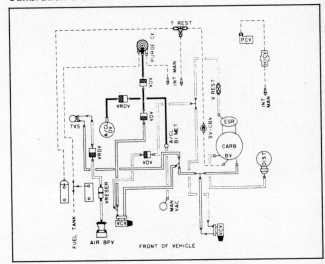

Fig. 50: 5.8L V8
Calibration 2-63Y-R11 & 2-63Y-R12

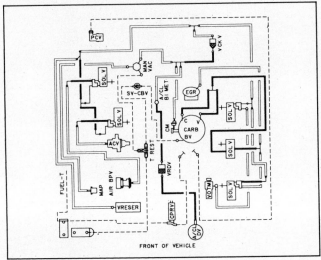

Fig. 53: 5.8L V8
Calibration 2-64Y-R11 & 2-64Y-R12

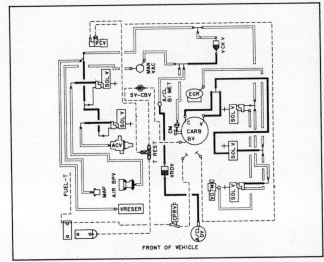

Fig. 51: 5.8L V8
Calibration 2-63Y-R14B & 2-64Y-R14B

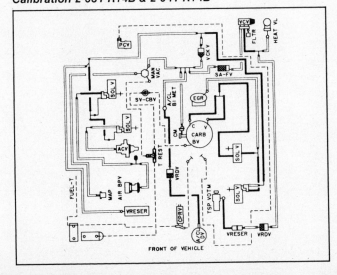

Fig. 54: 5.8L V8
Calibration 2-75J-R20 & 2-76J-R20

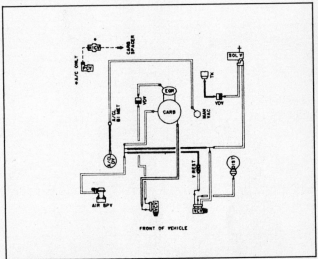

1983 FORD VACUUM DIAGRAMS (Cont.)

Fig. 55: 7.5L V8
Calibration 9-97J-R13

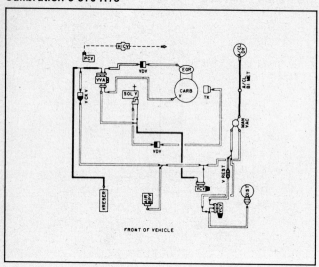

Fig. 56: 7.5L V8
Calibration 3-98S-R00

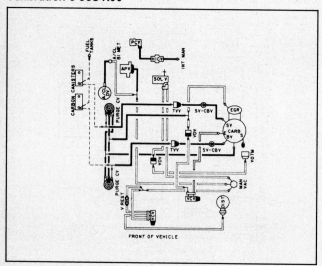

GENERAL MOTORS SYSTEMS

DESCRIPTION

Several systems are used to control emission of pollutants. System usage depends on model, engine and transmission combination. Each system is designed to control a particular vehicle emission.

NOTE: There are 2 light duty truck emission control standard classifications: Light Duty and Heavy Duty. Light Duty refers to vehicles up through 8500 lbs. GVW; Heavy Duty refers to vehicles over 8500 lbs. GVW.

THERMAC AIR CLEANER (TAC)

Used on all models, this unit is designed to aid engine in more complete burning of air/fuel mixture and to provide smoother operation. It does this by controlling temperature of intake air. Heated or cooled portions of air are fed into air cleaner assembly as temperature sensor regulates.

AIR INJECTION REACTOR (AIR)

This system, uses an air pump to supply additional fresh air to exhaust ports, further burning exhaust gases before they reach exhaust system. This reduces hydrocarbon (HC) and carbon monoxide (CO) emissions. *For additional information, see "Air Injection Systems — Air Pump Type" article in this section.*

PULSE AIR INJECTION REACTOR (PAIR)

This PAIR system, used on 4.1L 6-cylinder models, allows additional fresh air into exhaust system without using an air pump. A special set of check valves is used. These respond to exhaust system pulses, drawing in fresh air. As with the A.I.R. system, HC and CO emissions are reduced.

EXHAUST GAS RECIRCULATION (EGR)

This system recirculates exhaust gases into the intake manifold and combustion chambers. This has the effect of lowering combustion temperatures, thereby lowering NOx emissions.

COMPUTER COMMAND CONTROL (CCC)

CCC is an electronically controlled exhaust emission system. It monitors several engine/vehicle functions and controls various operations, including the transmission torque converter clutch (TCC). The CCC system aids in the control of exhaust emissions while maintaining good fuel economy and driveability.

The Electronic Control Module (ECM) is the "brain" of the CCC system. The ECM controls engine systems to maintain good vehicle performance under all normal driving conditions.

The primary objective of the system is to maintain an ideal air/fuel ratio of 14.7:1. With this ratio maintained, the catalytic converter can effectively control nitrogen oxides (NOx), hydrocarbons (HC) and carbon monoxide (CO). *For additional information, see appropriate article in Computerized Engine Control section.*

CLOSED LOOP EMISSION CONTROL

This electronically controlled system monitors various engine/vehicle functions to control engine operation and lower exhaust emissions while maintaining good fuel economy and driveability.

The Electronic Control Module (ECM) is the "brain" of this system. The ECM controls engine-related systems by constantly adjusting engine operation to maintain good vehicle performance under all normal driving conditions. *For additional information, see appropriate article in Computerized Engine Control section.*

VACUUM ADVANCE SPARK CONTROL

Used on all models, this system provides increased spark advance during cold engine operation. When engine coolant temperature is below 100°F (38°C), the thermal vacuum switch (TVS) closes. Manifold vacuum is supplied to distributor through a delay valve, which holds vacuum at high levels during acceleration. Above 100°F (38°C), TVS opens, causing manifold vacuum to by-pass delay valve.

EARLY FUEL EVAPORATION (EFE)

Used on all Light Duty and some Heavy Duty Emission models. During cold engine operation, system uses exhaust gases or an electric heater at base of carburetor to raise temperature of incoming mixture. This improves driveability while reducing exhaust emissions.

THROTTLE RETURN CONTROL (TRC)

Used on all Heavy Duty Emission models. Upon deceleration, system opens throttle slightly, thus reducing hydrocarbons during coastdown.

CATALYTIC CONVERTER (CAT)

Used on all Light Duty Emission models, this unit is connected into exhaust system so exhaust gas passes through converter. Inside converter, a chemical reaction takes place which reduces exhaust emissions. *For additonal information, see "Catalytic Converter" article in this section.*

POSITIVE CRANKCASE VENTILATION (PCV)

System removes engine crankcase vapors which result from normal combustion. Vapors are drawn through a metered PCV valve, and routed back to intake manifold where they are reburned in combustion chamber. *For additional information, see "Crankcase Ventilation" article in this section.*

EVAPORATIVE EMISSION CONTROL (EEC)

This system, used on all except Federal Heavy Duty Emissions models, is designed to keep fuel system vapors from escaping to atmosphere. This sealed system separates fuel vapors and routes them to engine to be burned, while retaining liquid fuel in tank. A carbon canister stores vapors until engine draws them off for burning. *For additional information, see appropriate "Fuel Evaporation System" article in this section.*

1983 Exhaust Emission Systems

GENERAL MOTORS THERMOSTATIC AIR CLEANER

All Models

DESCRIPTION

All models use a system for preheating air entering carburetor. A vacuum motor, part of the air cleaner, maintains the air temperature at a point where the carburetor can be calibrated much leaner to reduce hydrocarbon (HC) emissions while also improving warm-up operations and reducing carburetor icing.

System consists of an air cleaner assembly, integral air control door, vacuum control temperature sensor, vacuum motor, heat shroud (on exhaust manifold) with connecting pipe and vacuum hoses. Some models use additional controls, such as vacuum traps and cold weather modulators.

Fig. 1: General Motors V8 Engine Air Cleaner Assembly

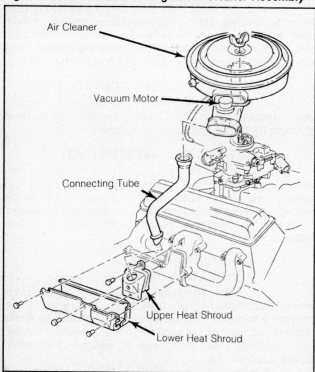

All Light Duty Emission vehicles use preheated air to warm carburetor.

OPERATION

When temperature of air entering air cleaner is less than setting of temperature sensor, sensor closes. This allows engine vacuum to operate vacuum motor, which closes damper assembly to outside air. Heated air is then drawn from around exhaust manifold, through heat shroud and into air cleaner.

As air inside air cleaner warms, sensor valve begins to open. This bleeds off vacuum to vacuum motor. As vacuum to vacuum motor drops, air control door begins to open. This allows outside air to enter air cleaner. When air entering air cleaner reaches a specified temperature, air control door opens completely, thus closing off the supply of heated air from around exhaust manifold.

TESTING

VACUUM CONTROL TEMPERATURE SENSOR TEST

1) With engine cold, check damper door. It should be in open snorkel position. Place thermometer inside air cleaner, near the sensor.

2) With engine temperature below 80°F (27°C), start engine and run at idle. Damper door should be in closed snorkel position. When door starts to open, read thermometer in air cleaner. Temperature should be 100-140°F (38-59°C). If door does not begin to open at this temperature, replace sensor.

VACUUM MOTOR TEST

1) Check all hoses and connections for proper hook-up. With engine off, observe damper door through snorkel opening. Door should be open to outside air.

2) With an external vacuum unit, apply 7 in. Hg vacuum to diaphragm assembly, through hose disconnected at sensor. Damper door should close when vacuum is applied. If not, check for vacuum leak, or binding linkage.

3) With vacuum applied, bend hose to trap vacuum in diaphragm assembly. Damper door should remain closed. If not, replace diaphragm assembly.

GENERAL MOTORS PULSE AIR INJECTION

4.1L 6-Cyl. Engine

DESCRIPTION

Pulse Air Injection Reaction (Pair) system is used on General Motors models with 4.1L 6-cylinder engines. It is a non-pump type air injection system, which uses engine exhaust pulses to draw fresh air into exhaust system. This helps to lower HC and CO emissions. System consists of a grouping of check valves in 2 plenum chambers (located on valve covers) and related tubing.

OPERATION

Each of the check valves in the plenum chambers is connected to an exhaust port. Firing of the engine creates a pulsating flow of exhaust gases. When positive exhaust pressure is felt, check valve will be forced closed.

No exhaust gas will flow past valve into fresh air supply line. With negative exhaust pressure (vacuum), check valve will open. Fresh air will be drawn and mixed with exhaust gases. During high engine RPM, such as under heavy acceleration, check valve will remain closed.

TESTING

FUNCTIONAL TEST

1) Remove air cleaner-to-plenum pipe hose from plenum pipe. Slide a length of tight-fitting 3/4" (19 mm) hose onto plenum pipe. Using an adapter, connect a hand vacuum pump to hose.

2) Apply 17 in. Hg vacuum. Note time required for vacuum level to drop from 17 in. Hg to 6 in. Hg. If less than 2 seconds, remove check valves and test individually. Replace check valve(s) which fail leak-down test.

NOTE: **If system fails leak-down test, ensure that failure is not due to a leaking test hose or connection.**

TROUBLE SHOOTING

FAILURE DIAGNOSIS

Short Hissing Noise
May indicate a defective check valve or improper torque at manifold. Inspect check valves.

Surge or Poor Performance
May be caused by failure of 1 or more check valves. Exhaust gas will enter carburetor through air cleaner and cause poor driveability.

Excessive Heat;
Paint Burned Off of Valve
Exhaust gas passing through pulse air valve, sending heat to valve body. Rubber hose will also be damaged. A short hissing noise may also be noticed. Repair plenum chamber-to-valve cover seals, and replace grommets and hose as required.

Poor Driveability
Rubber hose deteriorated. Hose particles entering carburetor causing poor driveability. Clean carburetor, and remove particles from plenum chambers and connecting pipe.

Fig. 1: General Motors Pulse Air Injection Reactor (PAIR) System Components

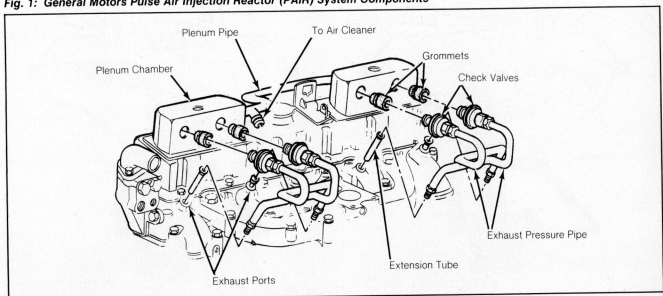

System functions without need of a mechanical pump.

1983 Exhaust Emission Systems

GENERAL MOTORS EXHAUST GAS RECIRCULATION

DESCRIPTION

Exhaust Gas Recirculation (EGR) is used on all Light Duty Emission models to reduce oxides of nitrogen (NOx) emissions. This process is accomplished by lowering combustion temperatures of burning gases. Recirculated and metered amounts of exhaust gases are reintroduced into engine through the intake manifold, where they are mixed with air/fuel mixture.

The vacuum modulated system regulates exhaust gas recirculation according to manifold vacuum. The back pressure modulated system regulates timed vacuum according to exhaust back pressure level. A special control valve within the EGR valve housing responds as a pressure regulator.

OPERATION

VACUUM MODULATED
EGR SYSTEM

With this system, the amount of exhaust gas admitted into the intake manifold depends on a vacuum signal (ported vacuum), controlled by throttle position.

When the throttle is closed (at idle or deceleration), there is no vacuum signal to the EGR valve because the EGR vacuum port is above the closed throttle valve. As the throttle valve is opened, a ported vacuum signal is supplied to the EGR valve, admitting exhaust gas into the intake manifold.

BACK PRESSURE EGR SYSTEM

Two types of back pressure type EGR valves are used by General Motors: a Positive Back Pressure

EGR valve (used on Federal V8 models) and a Negative Back Pressure EGR valve (used on some 6-cylinder and most California V8 models).

Operation of the positive and negative back pressure systems is explained as follows:

Positive Back Pressure EGR Valve

A small diaphragm control valve inside EGR valve assembly acts as a pressure regulator. Control valve receives an exhaust back pressure signal through a hollow shaft, which exerts a force on bottom of control valve diaphragm, opposed by a light spring. A metal deflector plate prevents hot exhaust gases from flowing directly onto diaphragm. *See Fig. 1.*

Vacuum is applied to EGR valve assembly from carburetor spark port, to assure no exhaust gas recirculation at idle. During off-idle operation, manifold vacuum is applied to vacuum chamber through a restriction in signal tube.

When engine load is light, and back pressure is low, control valve is open. This allows air to flow from 6 bleeds in diaphragm plate, through control valve orifice, into vacuum chamber. Air bleeds off vacuum, decreasing signal trying to open EGR valve. Therefore, if back pressure does not close control valve, sealing off air flow, there will be no vacuum built up to open EGR valve for exhaust gas recirculation.

When power demands are made on engine, and exhaust gas recirculation is needed, exhaust gas back pressure increases, closing control valve. This shuts off air flow through valve. Vacuum builds up in vacuum chamber, until spring force holding EGR valve closed is overcome.

Fig. 1: Sectional View of Positive Back Pressure EGR Valve

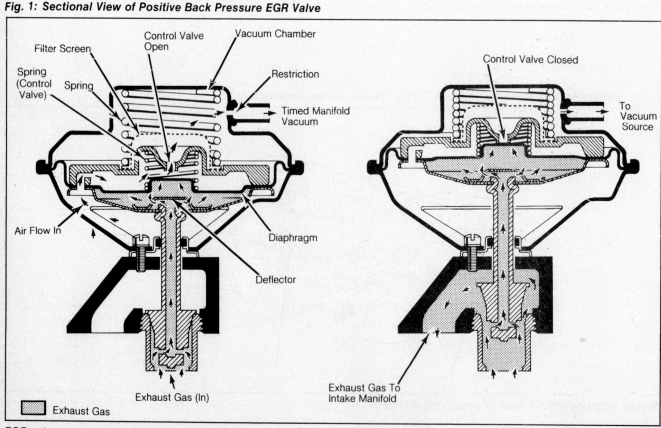

EGR valve sends metered amounts of exhaust gases back through intake manifold.

GENERAL MOTORS EXHAUST GAS RECIRCULATION (Cont.)

Once EGR valve opens, exhaust pressure decreases, because some of the exhaust gas is flowing into intake manifold through EGR passage. In actual operation, system will reach a balanced condition, providing optimum EGR operation.

Any increase in engine load will momentarily increase exhaust signal, causing control valve to close. This allows a stronger vacuum signal. The system will then stabilize at a greater EGR flow.

At maximum engine load, when manifold vacuum is nearly zero, momentarily, there will be no EGR operation. This is because of insufficient vacuum to pull valve open, even though high exhaust back pressure has closed control valve.

Negative Transducer Back Pressure EGR Valve

The negative transducer back pressure EGR valve assembly has the same function as positive back pressure EGR valve except transducer is designed to allow valve to open with negative exhaust back pressure.

Flow of valve is controlled by manifold vacuum, negative exhaust back pressure and carburetor ported vacuum signal. Control valve spring in transducer is placed on bottom side of diaphragm.

When carburetor ported vacuum signal is applied to main vacuum chamber partially opening valve, vacuum signal from manifold side (reduced by exhaust back pressure) is transmitted up the hollow stem of valve. This enables signal to act on diaphragm, opening bleed and causing transducer to modulate providing a specific valve flow. Thus flow of valve is a constant percentage of engine air flow.

Fig. 2: Sectional View of Negative Back Pressure EGR Valve

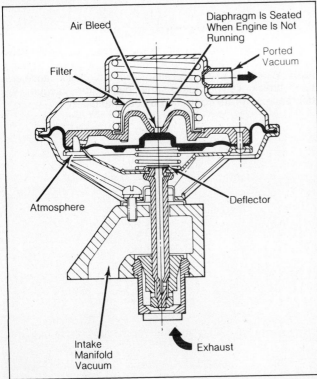

Vacuum modulated EGR valve is of similar design, but without air bleeds.

EGR THERMAL VACUUM SWITCH

EGR TVS, used on all models, closes to prevent EGR operations when engine coolant temperature is below 85°F (29°C). This improves cold engine driveability. When coolant temperature rises above 85°F (29°C), TVS opens to allow vacuum to be directed to EGR valve.

TESTING

FUNCTIONAL TESTS
**Vacuum Modulated &
Negative Back Pressure Types**

1) Check for proper hose routing, according to appropriate diagrams. *See "General Motors Vacuum Diagrams" in this Section.* Check EGR signal tube orifice for obstructions.

2) Hook vacuum gauge between EGR valve and carburetor and check vacuum with engine running at normal operating temperature. With engine at 3,000 RPM, there should be at least 5 in. Hg.

3) Manually depress valve diaphragm. While depressed, hold finger over source tube and release diaphragm.

4) Check for diaphragm and seat movement. Valve is okay if it takes over 20 seconds for diaphragm to move to seated position. If less, replace EGR valve. Check operation of Thermal Vacuum Switch.

Positive Back Pressure Type

1) Check for proper hose routing, according to appropriate diagrams. *See "General Motors Vacuum Diagrams" in this Section.* Check EGR signal tube orifice for obstructions. Check operation of Thermal Vacuum Switch. Remove valve from engine. Apply external vacuum of 10 in. Hg or more to EGR valve signal tube.

NOTE: A constant vacuum supply must be used.

2) Valve should not open. If it does, transducer control valve is stuck closed and EGR valve must be replaced.

3) With vacuum still applied, apply a stream of air from a low pressure source 15 psi (1.05 kg/cm²) into EGR valve exhaust gas intake passage. Valve should open completely. If it does not open at all, transducer control valve is stuck open or exhaust passages are plugged. Replace EGR valve.

4) If EGR valve and control valve are both functioning properly, clean mounting surfaces. Using a new gasket, install valve on engine. Reconnect vacuum hose.

EGR-TVS Test (Hot)

1) Remove EGR valve vacuum hose at EGR valve and connect hose to a vacuum gauge. Start engine. With transmission in Park or Neutral, open throttle partially. As throttle is opened, vacuum gauge should respond with an increase in vacuum reading. If operation is satisfactory, remove gauge and reconnect hose to EGR valve. If gauge does not respond to throttle opening, proceed to step **2)**.

2) Remove carburetor-to-TVS hose from switch and connect hose to vacuum gauge. Start engine. With transmission in Park or Neutral, open throttle partially. If vacuum gauge responds to throttle opening, switch is defective. Remove switch and replace with new

GENERAL MOTORS EXHAUST GAS RECIRCULATION (Cont.)

part. If gauge does not respond to throttle opening, check for plugged hose or defective carburetor.

EGR-TVS Test (Cold)

1) Engine coolant must be below 85°F (29°C). Drain coolant to below level of switch. Disconnect vacuum lines and remove switch. Inspect switch to make sure it is in good condition.

2) Connect a vacuum hose to lower nipple of switch, marked "C" or "CARB". Connect a vacuum gauge to upper nipple, marked "E" or "EGR". Place switch in water at 75°F (24°C) and submerge completely for 2 minutes while agitating water thoroughly. Apply 12 in. Hg to hose on lower nipple of switch. Under this condition, switch should be closed.

NOTE: Leakage of up to 2 in. Hg in 2 minutes is allowable and does not mean a defective switch.

3) If operation is satisfactory, reinstall switch. If switch is defective, replace with a new part. Replace coolant and check level.

MAINTENANCE

EGR PASSAGE CLEANING

If inspection of EGR passages in intake manifold indicates excessive build up of exhaust deposits, passages should be cleaned. Care should be taken to ensure that all loose particles are completely removed to prevent them from clogging EGR valve or from being ingested into engine.

GENERAL MOTORS VACUUM ADVANCE SPARK CONTROL

DESCRIPTION

TRAPPED VACUUM SPARK

Trapped vacuum spark is used on all models. A thermal vacuum switch (TVS) is mounted in cylinder head and used to sense engine coolant temperature. A vacuum check valve is mounted between manifold vacuum, distributor and thermal vacuum switch. The system maintains high vacuum levels to distributor during cold engine operation and cold engine acceleration.

SPARK VACUUM DELAY

The spark vacuum delay is used on 5.7L V8 engines with Heavy Duty Emissions. It is installed between TVS check valve and distributor.

OPERATION

TRAPPED VACUUM SPARK

When engine temperature is below a pre-set specified value, manifold vacuum signal is routed through check valve to distributor. Ports on TVS are blocked. The check valve will keep distributor vacuum at levels higher than manifold depression during vehicle acceleration.

A small sintered iron bleed orifice is provided in check valve to allow for a leak-down to enable engine to be restarted if it stalls. (This applies to all models except: Light Duty California and High Altitude Emissions; 5.7L V8 with Heavy Duty Emissions; all 7.4L V8 engines.)

When engine temperature is above pre-set value, TVS ports will be open to allow manifold vacuum to distributor. During this mode of operation, check valve will act as a connector.

SPARK VACUUM DELAY

As manifold vacuum increases, check valve opens and allows distributor vacuum to increase to same level. When vacuum decreases during vehicle acceleration, check valve closes and distributor vacuum will decrease at a rate controlled by internal bleed.

GENERAL MOTORS EARLY FUEL EVAPORATION

DESCRIPTION

Two Early Fuel Evaporation (EFE) systems are used on General Motors light and heavy duty trucks. The EFE systems are used to provide heat to the engine induction system during cold driveaway. Engines may be equipped with either an electric heater type (4-cyl.) or a vacuum operated exhaust heat riser valve type (all others) EFE system.

Both the vacuum type and the electric type systems provide rapid heating, resulting in faster fuel evaporation and more uniform fuel distribution. This also helps reduce choke "on" time by warming the engine faster.

Fig. 1: General Motors EFE System for 6-Cylinder Engines

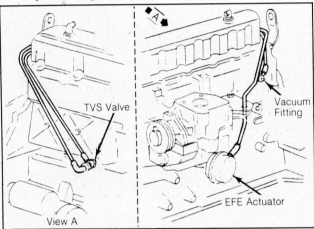

6-Cylinder engine EFE is controlled by oil temperature.

Fig. 2: General Motors EFE System for V8 Engines

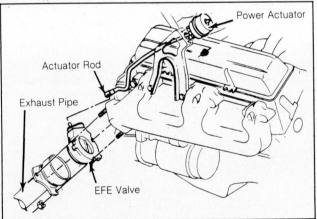

V8 engine EFE is controlled by water temperature.

OPERATION

4-CYLINDER ENGINES

The electrical heater type system uses a ceramic heater grid under the primary bore of the carburetor as an integral part of the carburetor insulator and gasket. When the engine coolant temperature is below a given value, electrical current is supplied to the heater through a relay.

6-CYLINDER ENGINES

Thermal vacuum switch is a normally closed switch which is sensitive to oil temperature. With a cold engine, below 150°F (66°), TVS is closed which allows manifold vacuum to actuator valve. Vacuum pulls diaphragm in actuator, closing EFE Valve.

This causes hot exhaust gases to be routed to base of carburetor. When oil temperature is above 150°F (66°C), thermal vacuum switch opens. This stops vacuum to actuator. Without vacuum, a spring pushes actuator diaphragm to its at rest position and opens EFE valve.

V8 ENGINES

On V8 engines TVS is located in coolant outlet housing and directly controls vacuum. With coolant temperatues below 180°F (82°C), manifold vacuum is applied to actuator which closes EFE valve. This routes hot exhaust gases to base of carburetor. When temperatures reach 180°F (82°C), vacuum to actuator is stopped. This allows a spring to return actuator to its at rest position, opening EFE valve.

Fig. 3: General Motors EFE System for 4-Cylinder Engines

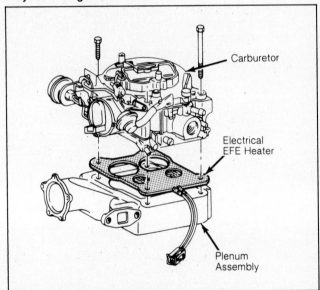

Heater grid warms incoming fuel mixture.

TESTING

VACUUM OPERATED TYPE

1) With engine cold, position transmission in "Neutral" or "PARK" and apply parking brake. Start engine and observe movement of actuator rod and exhaust heat valve. Valve should move to its closed position.

2) If valve does not close, disconnect hose from actuator and apply 10 in. Hg vacuum to actuator. Valve should close and stay closed for at least 20 seconds. If valve does not stay closed for 20 seconds, replace actuator. Check valve rod and valve for proper operation. Repair as necessary.

3) When coolant temperature reaches 180°F (82°C) on V8 or oil temperature reaches 150°F (66°C) 6-cylinder engines, exhaust heat valve should move to open position.

GENERAL MOTORS EARLY FUEL EVAPORATION (Cont.)

4) If valve does not open, disconnect hose at actuator and check for vacuum. If there is vacuum, replace TVS. If no vacuum is present, replace actuator.

ELECTRIC HEATER TYPE

With ignition on, engine off and engine temperature below 140°F (60°C), battery voltage should be available at EFE heater. If not, check EFE temperature switch and wiring back to ignition switch and ground. Repair as necessary.

MAINTENANCE

Periodically inspect vacuum hoses for damage, actuator for proper operation, linkage for binding and EFE valve for smooth operation.

GENERAL MOTORS THROTTLE RETURN CONTROL SYSTEM

DESCRIPTION

A Throttle Return Control (TRC) system is used on all Heavy Duty Emission models. Upon deceleration, system opens throttle slightly to reduce hydrocarbon emissions. System consists of a throttle lever actuator, a solenoid vacuum control valve and an electronic speed sensor.

OPERATION

Manifold vacuum is routed through solenoid vacuum valve, which is normally closed, to throttle lever actuator. Upon vehicle deceleration, electronic speed sensor signals solenoid vacuum valve to open when engine speed is above a preset RPM.

When valve opens, manifold vacuum is directed to throttle lever acuator, which extends to open throttle slightly. When engine speed drops below preset RPM, solenoid valve closes, retracting throttle lever actuator and returning throttle to curb idle position.

TESTING AND ADJUSTMENT

SYSTEM OPERATION

1) Connect a tachometer (accurate to within 10 RPM). Start engine and open throttle until tachometer reads 1890 RPM. Throttle lever actuator should be extended at this speed. Decrease engine speed to 1700 RPM. Throttle actuator should be retracted at this speed.

2) If throttle actuator operates at specified engine speeds, system is functioning. If actuator operates outside of RPM limits, replace speed sensor. If actuator does not operate at any speed, proceed with the following steps:

3) Using a voltmeter, check for battery voltage at voltage wire terminal on solenoid valve and speed sensor. If voltage is present at one component only, repair wiring harness as required. If no voltage at both components, check engine harness connections at distributor and bulkhead connector and repair as required.

Fig. 1: Schematic of Throttle Return Control (TRC) System

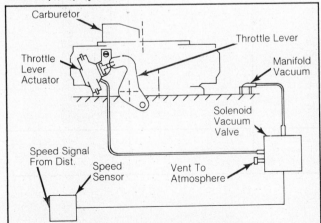

Throttle return control (TRC) system is used on all Heavy Duty Emission models.

4) If battery voltage is present at solenoid valve and speed sensor, start engine and use a jumper wire to ground solenoid-to-speed sensor connecting wire terminal at speed sensor. Throttle actuator should extend.

• If actuator did not extend, remove throttle actuator hose from solenoid and check solenoid orifice for blockage. If orifice is plugged, clean as required. If orifice is clear, replace solenoid.

• If actuator did extend, ground solenoid-to-switch wire terminal at speed switch. If actuator does not extend, repair speed switch-to-solenoid wire. If it extends, ensure speed switch ground wire reads ground with engine running and check speed switch-to-distributor wire connections. If actuator still does not extend with all wires properly connected and engine speed above 1890 RPM, replace speed sensor.

5) If throttle actuator remains extended at all speeds, remove electrical connector from solenoid.

• If actuator remains extended, check actuator vacuum orifice on solenoid valve for blockage. Clean orifice, and reconnect system. If actuator again remains extended, remove solenoid connector. If actuator does not retract, replace solenoid valve.

• If actuator retracts with connector removed, reconnect and then remove speed switch connector. If actuator retracts, replace speed switch. If actuator does not retract, solenoid-to-switch wire is shorted to ground in harness. Repair wire.

THROTTLE LEVER ACTUATOR

1) Disconnect valve-to-actuator hose at valve and connect to an external vacuum supply, with a vacuum gauge intalled near actuator.

2) Apply 20 in. Hg vacuum to actuator and seal off vacuum source. If vacuum gauge reading drops, actuator is leaking and must be replaced.

3) To check actuator for proper operation, first ensure throttle lever, shaft and linkage work without binding. Start engine and run to normal operating temperature. Turn off air conditioner and note idle RPM.

4) Apply 20 in. Hg vacuum to actuator. Manually open throttle slightly and allow it to close against extended actuator plunger. Note engine RPM.

5) Release throttle and reapply 20 in. Hg vacuum to actuator and note RPM to which engine speed increases (do not assist actuator).

6) If RPM as just noted is not within 150 RPM of speed noted in Step 4), actuator plunger is binding. Clean around plunger to see if condition can be corrected. If not, replace actuator.

7) Release vacuum from actuator and engine speed should return to within 50 RPM of idle speed noted in Step 3). If not, plunger may be binding and should be cleaned. If problem cannot be corrected, replace actuator.

8) If engine RPM noted in Step 4) is not to specified TRC speed, actuator must be adjusted.

9) To adjust actuator, apply 20 in. Hg vacuum to actuator. Manually open throttle slightly and allow it to close against extended actuator plunger. Turn hex-end of plunger to obtain specified speed.

NOTE: **See Emission Control Tune-Up decal for throttle lever actuator adjustment speeds.**

1983 Exhaust Emission Systems

GENERAL MOTORS VACUUM DIAGRAMS

MODEL IDENTIFICATION

Truck models, listed in tables, are identified using manufacturers letter and number designations. The letters identify the vehicle model series (i.e., "C" is conventional chassis, including Pickup, Blazer and Suburban). The number reference identifies the vehicles load capacity. Refer to following charts for actual letter and number designations.

VEHICLE LOAD CAPACITY

Chevrolet Number	GMC Number	Ton Capacity
10	15	1/2
10	1500	1/2
20	2500	3/4
30	3500	1

VEHICLE SERIES IDENTIFICATION

Vehicle Series	I.D. Letter
Conventional Chassis (2WD)	C
Conventional Chassis (2WD)	S
Conventional Chassis (4WD)	K
Conventional Chassis (4WD)	T
Conventional Van Chassis	G
Forward Control/Stepvan Chassis	P

GENERAL MOTORS VACUUM DIAGRAM REFERENCE CHART

Vehicle Model, Series & Engine	Application	Transmission	Equipment	Fig. No.
1.9L 4-Cylinder				
S10/15 & T10/15	Fed.	Man.		1
S10/15 & T10/15	Fed.	Man.	Optional Tank	2
S10/15 & T10/15	Calif.	Auto.		3
S10/15 & T10/15	Calif.	Man.	Optional Tank	4
S10/15 & T10/15	Calif.	Man.		5
S10/15 & T10/15	Calif.	Man.	Optional Tank	6
S10/15 & T10/15	Hi. Alt.	Man.		7
S10/15 & T10/15	Hi. Alt.	Man.	Optional Tank	8
2.0L 4-Cylinder				
S10/15 & T10/15	Fed.	Auto.		9
S10/15 & T10/15	Fed.	Man.		10
S10/15 & T10/15	Fed.	Man.	Optional Tank	11
S10/15 & T10/15	Hi. Alt.	Man.		12
S10/15 & T10/15	Hi. Alt.	Man.	Optional Tank	13
2.8L V6				
S10/15 & T10/15	Fed.	Auto.		14
S10/15 & T10/15	Fed.	Auto.	Optional Tank	15
S10/15 & T10/15	Fed.	Man.		16
S10/15 & T10/15	Fed.	Man.	Optional Tank	17
S10/15 & T10/15	Calif.	All		18
S10/15 & T10/15	Calif.	All	Optional Tank	19
4.1L 6-Cylinder				
C10	Fed.	Auto.		20
C10	Calif.	Auto.		21
C10	Calif.	Man.		22
C10/20 & K10	Fed.	Man.	PAIR	23
C10/20 & K10	Fed. & Hi. Alt.	Auto.		24
C10/20 & K10	Fed. & Hi. Alt.	Man.	AIR	25
G10/20/30	Fed.	Man.	AIR	26
G10/20/30	Fed. & Hi. Alt.	Auto.		27
G10/20/30	Fed. & Hi. Alt.	Man.	AIR	28
G10/20/30	Calif.	Auto.		29
G10/20/30	Calif.	Man.		30
4.8L 6-Cylinder				
All	Fed.	All		31
All	Calif.	All		32

GENERAL MOTORS VACUUM DIAGRAMS (Cont.)

GENERAL MOTORS VACUUM DIAGRAM REFERENCE CHART

Vehicle Model, Series & Engine	Application	Transmission	Equipment	Fig. No.
5.0L V8				
C10	Fed.	Auto.		33
C10	Fed.	Auto.	Dual Tanks	34
C10	Fed.	Man.		35
C10	Fed.	Man.	Dual Tanks	36
C10	Calif.	Auto.		37
C10/20 & K10	Fed. & Hi. Alt.	Auto.		38
C10/20 & K10	Fed. & Hi. Alt.	Man.		39
G10/20	Fed.	Man.	No AIR	40
G10/20	Fed. & Hi. Alt.	Auto.		41
G10/20	Fed. & Hi. Alt.	Man.	AIR	42
G10/20	Calif.	Auto.		43
5.7L V8 Light Duty				
C10/20 & K10	Fed. & Hi. Alt.	Auto.		44
C10/20 & K10	Calif.	Auto.		45
G10/20/30	Fed. & Hi. Alt.	Auto.		46
G10/20	Calif.	Auto.		47
K10/20	Hi. Alt.	Man.		48
5.7L V8 Heavy Duty				
All	Fed.	All		49
All	Fed.	All	Chassis	50
All	Fed.	Auto.		51
C20 & K20/30	Calif.	All		52
C20 & K20/30	Calif.	Auto.		53
G30	Calif.	All		54
G30	Calif.	Auto.		55
6.2L V8 Diesel				
All	All LD/Calif. MD	All		56
All	All HD	All		57
7.4L V8				
All	Fed.	All		58
All	Calif.	All		59
All	Calif.	Auto.		60

EMISSION CONTROL DEVICE ABBREVIATIONS

AIR — Air Injection Reactor
DVTR — Diverter Valve
EFE — Early Fuel Evaporation
EGR — Exhaust Gas Recirculation
PCV — Positive Crankcase Ventilation
TRC — Throttle Return Control
TVS — Thermal Vacuum Switch

1983 Exhaust Emission Systems
GENERAL MOTORS VACUUM DIAGRAMS (Cont.)

Fig. 1: 1.9L 4-Cyl. S10/15 & T10/15 Federal Manual Trans.

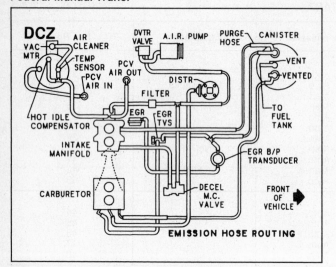

Fig. 2: 1.9L 4-Cyl. S10/15 & T10/15 Federal Manual Trans.

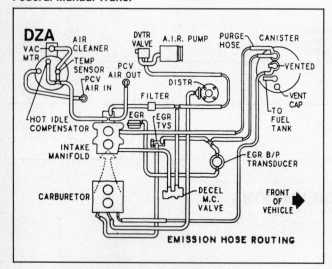

Fig. 3: 1.9L 4-Cyl. S10/15 & T10/15 California Automatic Trans.

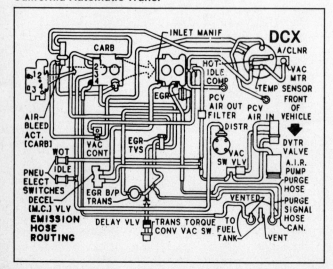

Fig. 4: 1.9L 4-Cyl. S10/15 & T10/15 California Manual Trans.

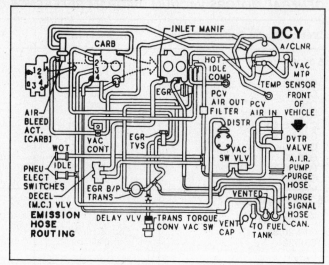

Fig. 5: 1.9L 4-Cyl. S10/15 & T10/15 California Manual Trans.

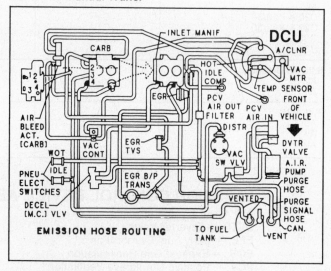

Fig. 6: 1.9L 4-Cyl. S10/15 & T10/15 California Manual Trans.

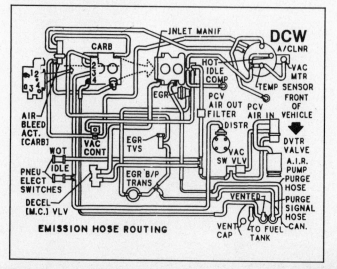

GENERAL MOTORS VACUUM DIAGRAMS

Fig. 7: 1.9L 4-Cyl. S10/15 & T10/15
High Altitude Manual Trans.

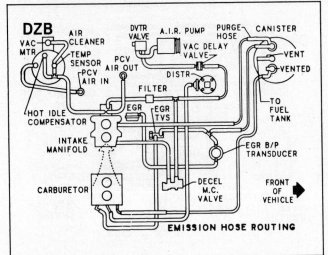

Fig. 10: 2.0L 4-Cyl. S10/15 & T10/15
Federal Manual Trans.

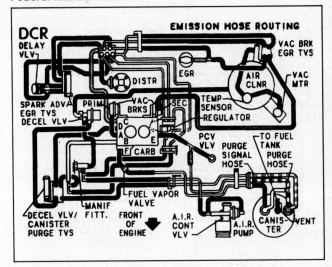

Fig. 8: 1.9L 4-Cyl. S10/15 & T10/15
High Altitude Manual Trans.

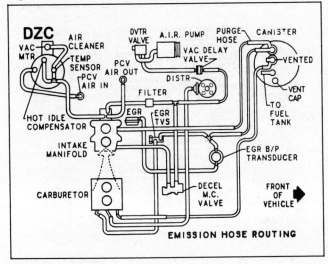

Fig. 11: 2.0L 4-Cyl. S10/15 & T10/15
Federal Manual Trans.

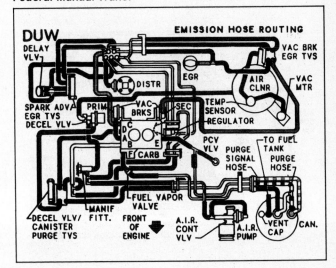

Fig. 9: 2.0L 4-Cyl. S10/15 & T10/15
Federal Automatic Trans.

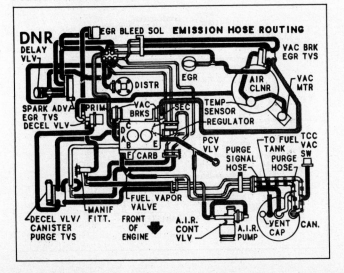

Fig. 12: 2.0L 4-Cyl. S10/15 & T10/15
High Altitude Manual Trans.

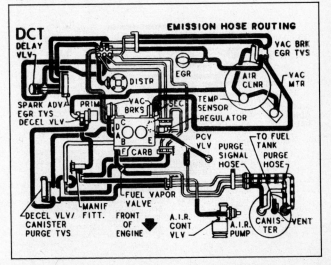

1983 Exhaust Emission Systems

GENERAL MOTORS VACUUM DIAGRAMS (Cont.)

Fig. 13: 2.0L 4-Cyl. S10/15 & T10/15
High Altitude Manual Trans.

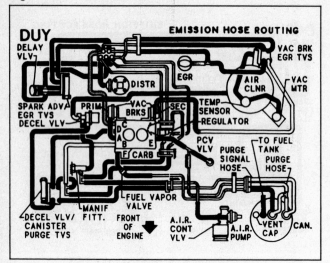

Fig. 16: 2.8L V6 S10/15 & T10/15
Federal Manual Trans.

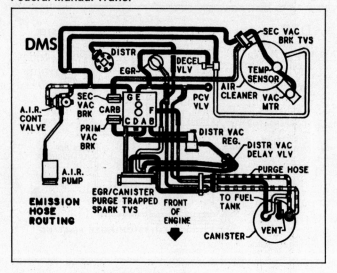

Fig. 14: 2.8L V6 S10/15 & T10/15
Federal Automatic Trans.

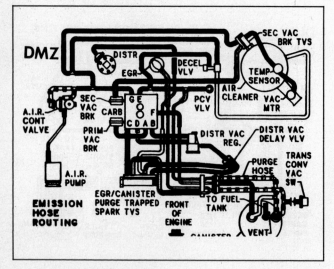

Fig. 17: 2.8L V6 S10/15 & T10/15
Federal Manual Trans.

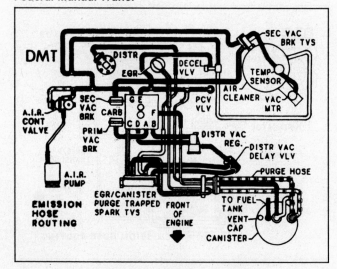

Fig. 15: 2.8L V6 S10/15 & T10/15
Federal Automatic Trans.

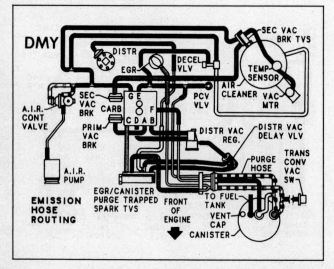

Fig. 18: 2.8L V6 S10/15 & T10/15 California

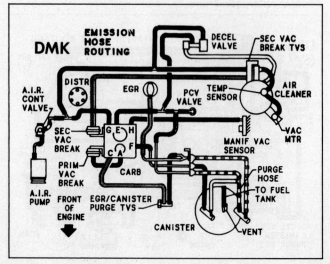

GENERAL MOTORS VACUUM DIAGRAMS (Cont.)

Fig. 19: 2.8L V6 S10/15 & T10/15 California

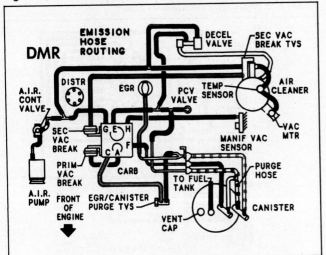

Fig. 22: 4.1L 6-Cyl. C10 California Manual Trans.

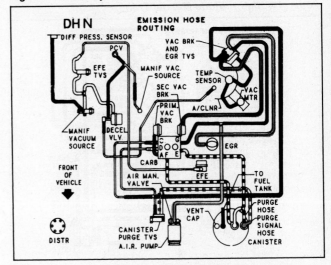

Fig. 20: 4.1L 6-Cyl. C10 Federal Automatic Trans.

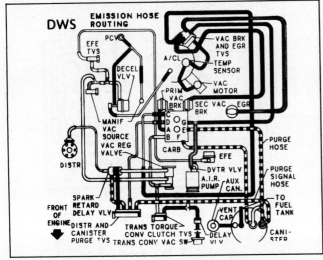

Fig. 23: 4.1L 6-Cyl. C10/20 & K10 Federal Manual Trans.

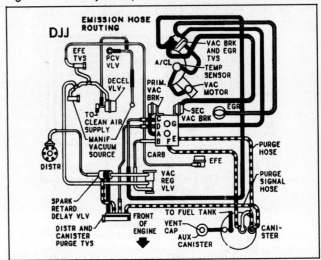

Fig. 21: 4.1L 6-Cyl. C10 California Automatic Trans.

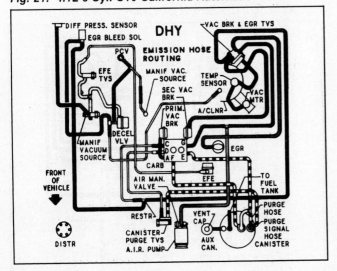

Fig. 24: 4.1L 6-Cyl. C10/20 & K10 Federal & High Altitude Automatic Trans.

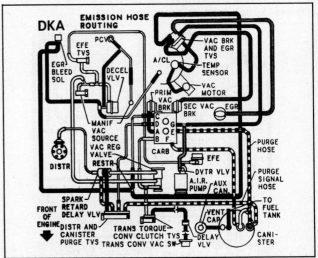

1983 Exhaust Emission Systems

GENERAL MOTORS VACUUM DIAGRAMS (Cont.)

Fig. 25: 4.1L 6-Cyl. C10/20 & K10
Federal & High Altitude Manual Trans.

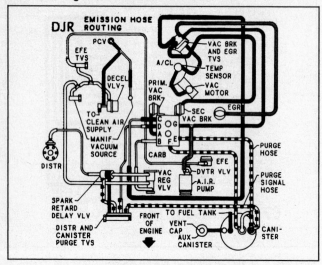

Fig. 26: 4.1L 6-Cyl. G10/20/30 *Federal Manual Trans.*

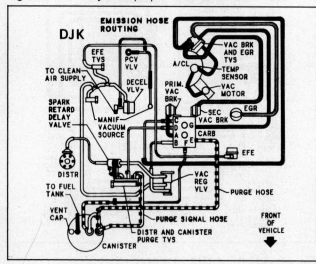

Fig. 27: 4.1L 6-Cyl. G10/20/30
Federal & High Altitude Automatic Trans.

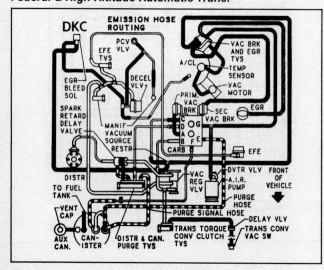

Fig. 28: 4.1L 6-Cyl. G10/20/30
Federal & High Altitude Manual Trans.

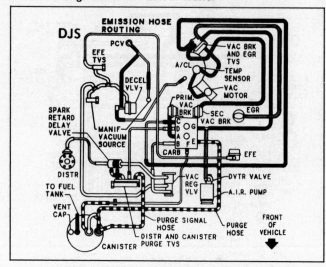

Fig. 29: 4.1L 6-Cyl. G10/20/30 *California Automatic Trans.*

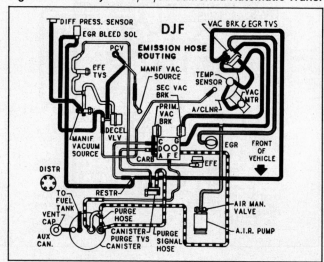

Fig. 30: 4.1L 6-Cyl. G10/20/30 *California Manual Trans.*

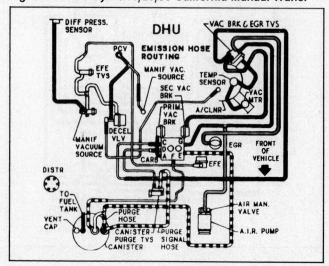

GENERAL MOTORS VACUUM DIAGRAMS (Cont.)

Fig. 31: 4.8L 6-Cyl. Federal

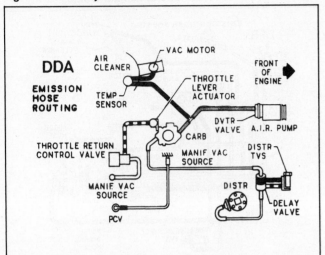

Fig. 34: 5.0L V8 C10 Federal Automatic Trans.

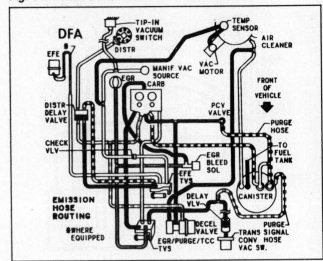

Fig. 32: 4.8L 6-Cyl. California

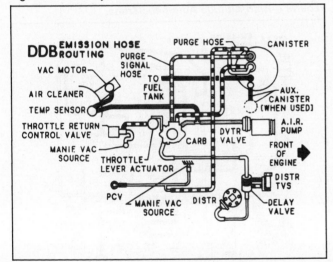

Fig. 35: 5.0L V8 C10 Federal Manual Trans.

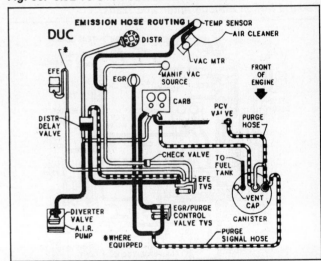

Fig. 33: 5.0L V8 C10 Federal Automatic Trans.

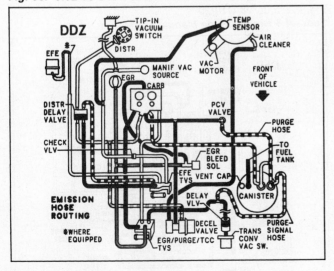

Fig. 36: 5.0L V8 C10 Federal Manual Trans.

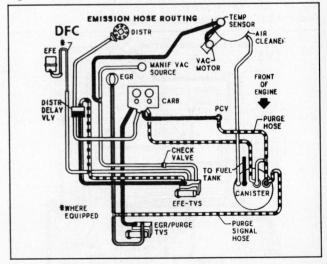

1983 Exhaust Emission Systems

GENERAL MOTORS VACUUM DIAGRAMS (Cont.)

Fig. 37: 5.0L V8 C10 California Automatic Trans.

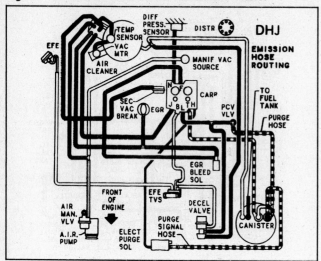

**Fig. 38: 5.0L V8 C10/20 & K10
Federal & High Altitude Automatic Trans.**

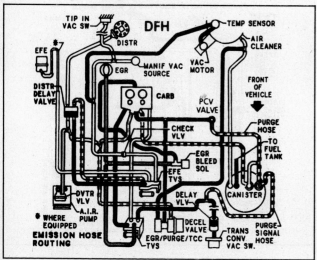

**Fig. 39: 5.0L V8 C10/20 & K10
Federal & High Altitude Manual Trans.**

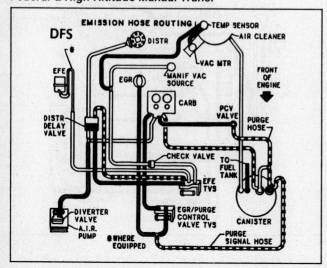

Fig. 40: 5.0L V8 G10/20 Federal Manual Trans.

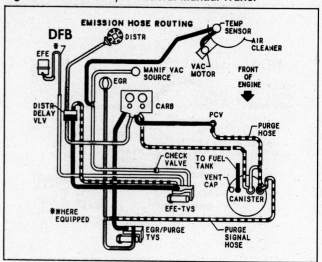

**Fig. 41: 5.0L V8 G10/20
Federal & High Altitude Automatic Trans.**

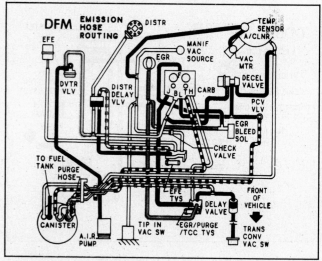

**Fig. 42: 5.0L V8 G10/20
Federal & High Altitude Manual Trans.**

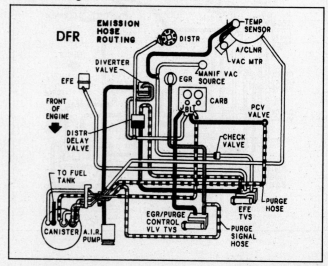

GENERAL MOTORS VACUUM DIAGRAMS (Cont.)

Fig. 43: 5.0L V8 G10/20 California Automatic Trans.

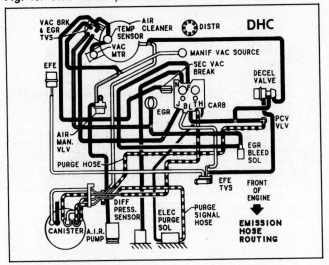

Fig. 46: 5.7L V8 G10/20/30
Federal & High Altitude Automatic Trans.

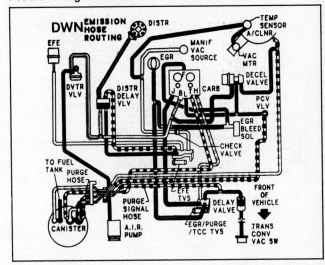

Fig. 44: 5.7L V8 C10/20 & K10
Federal & High Altitude Automatic Trans.

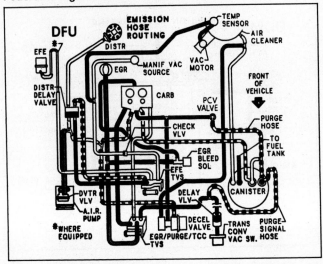

Fig. 47: 5.7L V8 G10/20 California Automatic Trans.

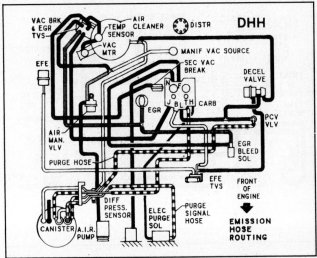

Fig. 45: 5.7L V8 C10/20 & K10
California Automatic Trans.

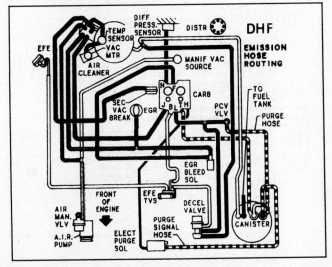

Fig. 48: 5.7L V8 K10/20 High Altitude Manual Trans.

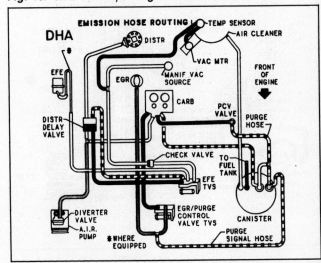

1983 Exhaust Emission Systems

GENERAL MOTORS VACUUM DIAGRAMS (Cont.)

Fig. 49: *5.7L V8 Federal*

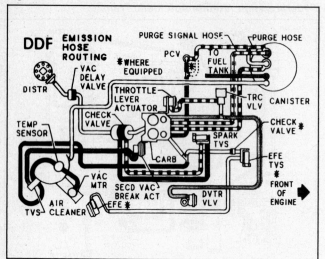

Fig. 52: *5.7L V8 C20 & K20/30 California All Trans.*

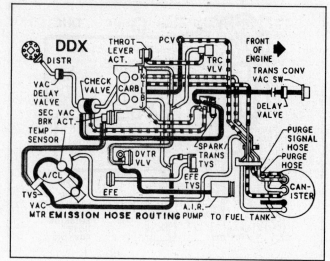

Fig. 50: *5.7L V8 Federal*

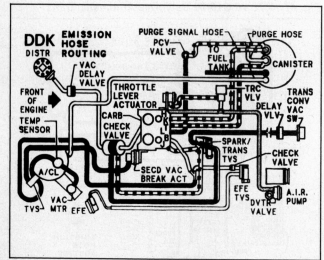

Fig. 53: *5.7L V8 C20 & K20/30 California Automatic Trans.*

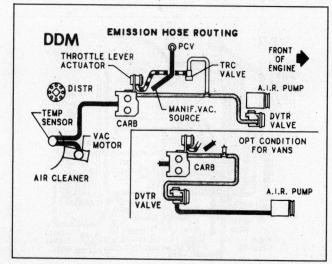

Fig. 51: *5.7L V8 Federal Automatic Trans.*

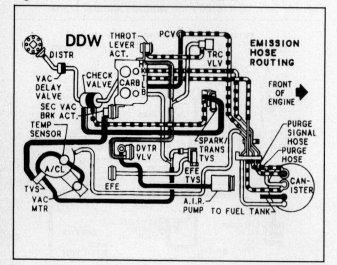

Fig. 54: *5.7L V8 G30 California All Trans.*

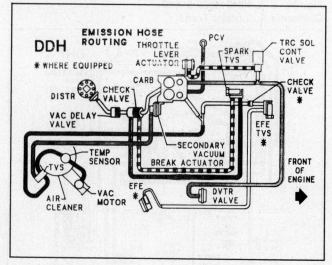

GENERAL MOTORS VACUUM DIAGRAMS (Cont.)

Fig. 55: 5.7L V8 G30 California Automatic Trans.

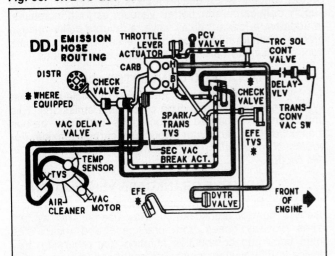

Fig. 58: 7.4L V8 Federal

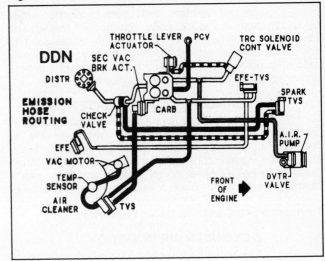

Fig. 56: 6.2L V8 Diesel Light & Medium Duty

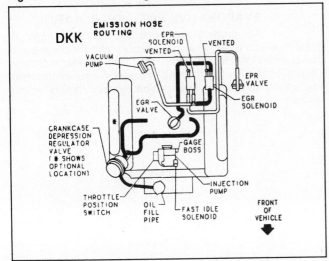

Fig. 59: 7.4L V8 California

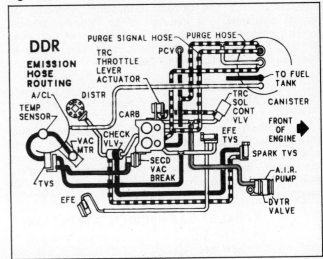

Fig. 57: 6.2L V8 Diesel Heavy Duty

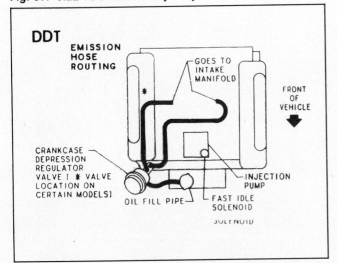

Fig. 60: 7.4L V8 California Automatic Trans.

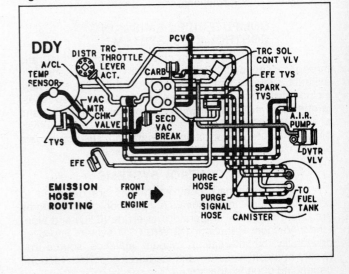

JEEP SYSTEMS

DESCRIPTION

Several systems are used to control emissions. System usage depends on model, engine and transmission combinations. Each system is designed to control a particular vehicle emission. In addition, specially calibrated carburetors, distributors and modified combustion chambers are used with these systems.

THERMOSTATIC AIR CLEANER (TAC)

TAC assembly is used to keep incoming air in carburetor at a stable temperature which is able to promote complete combustion (resulting in fewer emissions). The system consists of a heat shroud at exhaust manifold, a hot air hose, an air cleaner assembly with a thermal sensor, an air door, a vacuum motor and a delay valve on all models. *For additional information, see "Jeep Thermostatic Air Cleaner" article in this section.*

6-CYLINDER AIR INJECTION

The pulse-air air injection system consists of check valves, control valves, control valve solenoids and various lines and hoses. Air is injected either at the front exhaust pipe or the catalytic converter depending on engine operation. The injection of air into the exhaust system helps to complete the combustion of unburned gasses. *For additional information, see "Jeep Pulse-Air Injection System" article in this section.*

V8 AIR INJECTION

Air injection system consists of an air pump, diverter valve, check valve, and various air distribution lines necessary to inject fresh air adjacent to exhaust valves. Injection of fresh air adjacent to exhaust valves creates an afterburn which further consumes unburned material in engine's exhaust. *For additional information, see "Air Injection Systems — Air Pump Type" article in this section.*

EXHAUST GAS RECIRCULATION (EGR)

EGR system uses a vacuum operated EGR valve to introduce metered amounts of exhaust gas into engine's combustion chambers. This introduction of inert exhaust gas lowers peak combustion temperatures and thus lowers NOx formations.

COMPUTERIZED EMISSION CONTROL (CEC) SYSTEM

The CEC system closely controls air/fuel ratio through a feedback system from an oxygen sensor in exhaust system. The major components of this system include an exhaust gas oxygen sensor, vacuum switches, temperature switches, a Micro Computer Unit (MCU) and a special carburetor with a stepper motor that controls air/fuel mixture. *For additional information, see appropriate article in Computerized Engine Control section.*

SPARK CONTROL SYSTEMS

Jeep spark control systems are designed to control vacuum spark advance operation. Two systems are used: Coolant Temperature Override (CTO) and Non-Linear Vacuum Regulator (NLVR). CTO system improves driveability by alternating vacuum advance source between manifold vacuum and carburetor ported vacuum, depending upon temperature.

NLVR system supplies vacuum advance unit with a regulated combination of manifold and carburetor ported vacuum when engine load is low and switches to supply only carburetor ported vacuum as load increases. In addition, a forward delay valve, a reverse delay valve, a thermal vacuum spark control valve and a vacuum spark control delay valve are used with various applications.

CATALYTIC CONVERTER (CAT)

The converter is installed in vehicle's exhaust system to aid in the reduction of exhaust emissions. This unit changes unburned hydrocarbons (HC) and carbon monoxide (CO) into water vapor and carbon dioxide. *For additional information, see "Catalytic Converter" article in this section.*

POSITIVE CRANKCASE VENTILATION

Positive Crankcase Ventilation (PCV) system is used to control crankcase blow-by gases. This system takes blow-by gases from crankcase and recirculates them back into combustion chamber for reburning. Key device in PCV system is vacuum-controlled PCV valve. *For additional information, see "Crankcase Ventilation" article in this section.*

EVAPORATIVE EMISSION CONTROL

All models use this closed tank (sealed) system, which returns raw fuel vapors and routes them to intake manifold for burning. A carbon canister stores vapors until they are burned. *For additional information, see appropriate "Fuel Evaporation System" article in this section.*

JEEP THERMOSTATIC AIR CLEANER

All Models

DESCRIPTION

All Jeep vehicles use a system for pre-heating air entering carburetor. This system is part of the air cleaner and maintains air temperature at a point where carburetor can be calibrated at a leaner setting to reduce hydrocarbon emissions and improve engine performance during warm-up.

Jeep systems are vacuum operated and consist of a heat shroud on exhaust manifold, hot air duct, thermal sensor switch, vacuum motor, air valve assembly and reverse delay valve.

Fig. 1: Jeep Thermostatic Air Cleaner (TAC) Assembly

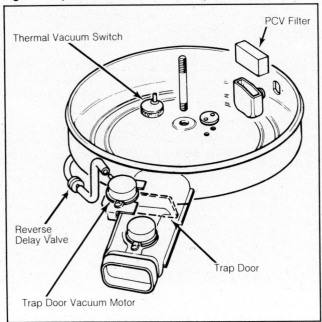

All Jeep vehicles use a system for pre-heating air entering carburetor.

OPERATION

During engine warm-up, temperature sensor switch applies vacuum to vacuum motor. Air diverter valve is held in the "ON" position. Exhaust manifold heated air flows to air cleaner. As temperature of incoming air increases to 90°F (32°C), temperature sensor opens vacuum line to atmosphere allowing spring pressure to push valve to "OFF" position. Air now flows from outside, through air cleaner duct to carburetor.

AIR CLEANER TRAP DOOR

On California vehicles, a spring-loaded trap door is built-in to air cleaner to close off air cleaner when engine is shut-off. Door is vacuum operated.

REVERSE DELAY VALVE

A reverse delay valve is installed in vacuum line in some vehicles to prevent trap door from closing during low engine vacuum periods. Valve provides about 9 seconds delay before allowing trap door to close.

Fig. 2: Cutaway View of Jeep Thermostatic Air Cleaner Assembly

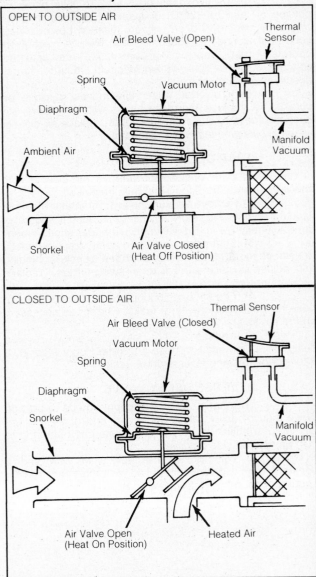

During warm-up, temperature sensor switch applies vacuum to vacuum motor.

TESTING

VACUUM MOTOR & TEMPERATURE SENSOR

1) Remove air cleaner assembly from vehicle and allow to cool to room temperature. Sight through air cleaner duct and observe position of air diverter valve. It should be fully open to outside air.

2) Reinstall assembly on carburetor and connect hot air duct and manifold vacuum hose. Start engine and observe position of air diverter valve. It should be fully closed to outside air.

3) Move throttle lever rapidly to 1/2 to 3/4 opening and release. Air diverter valve should open and then close again. Allow engine to warm to operating

1983 Exhaust Emission Systems

JEEP THERMOSTATIC AIR CLEANER (Cont.)

temperature and observe position of air diverter valve. It should be fully open to outside air.

4) If valve does not move to fully close off outside air at 83°F (28°C) or less with vacuum applied, check for binding of duct, vacuum leaks in hose connections or disconnected vacuum motor. If valve mechanism operates freely and no vacuum leaks are detected, connect a hose from intake manifold vacuum source directly to vacuum motor.

5) If diverter valve now moves to close off outside air, replace thermal sensor switch. If valve still does not move to close off outside air, replace air cleaner assembly and vacuum motor assembly.

TRAP DOOR

1) With engine off, remove air cleaner and check position of trap door. It should be closed.

2) Remove vacuum hose from intake manifold vacuum source and apply an external vacuum source of approximately 2-4 in. Hg vacuum. Trap door should open.

3) If door does not open apply vacuum directly to vacuum motor. If door does not open, check for binding and adjust as necessary. If door swings freely, replace vacuum motor.

4) If door opens during step **3)**, check vacuum hose for blockage, cracks or leaks. Correct as necessary and retest as specified in step **2)**.

5) If hoses are not defective, remove reverse delay valve, join vacuum hose and retest from step **2)**. If door opens, replace reverse delay valve.

REVERSE DELAY VALVE

1) Connect external vacuum source to port on White side of delay valve. Connect 1 end of 24" (.61 m) section of rubber hose to vacuum gauge and other end to port on colored side of valve.

2) With clock, time device in view and a constant 10 in. Hg vacuum applied, note time required for gauge pointer to move from 0-8 in. Hg.

JEEP PULSE AIR INJECTION SYSTEM

6-Cylinder Engines

DESCRIPTION

The pulse air injection system is used to inject fresh air into the exhaust system. When fresh air is injected into the hot exhaust gasses, combustion takes place. This reduces the amount of unburned fuel that escapes to the atmosphere.

The system consists of check valves, control valves, control valve solenoids, a vacuum reservoir, vacuum lines and air lines. The pulse air system is capable of injecting air at both the catalytic converter (downstream) or the front exhaust pipe.

OPERATION

The pulse air system uses the alternating positive and negative pressure pulsations in the exhaust system to draw in fresh air through the air cleaner. Check valves are used to allow fresh air into the exhaust, but prevent exhaust from flowing back into the intake system.

Air is switched between upstream and downstream injection by 2 vacuum operated control valves. Each control valve is switched by an electrically operated vacuum solenoid.

The vacuum solenoids are switched on and off by the MCU according to engine operating conditions. A vacuum storage tank maintains the vacuum supply to the switching solenoids.

DIAGNOSIS & TESTING

1) Check condition of all hoses and lines in system. Reroute any kinked or restricted hoses. Repair or replace any cracked or broken hoses. To check system operation, feel for suction in injection hoses at air cleaner.

2) If a problem exists, check to see if vacuum is being supplied to the valve. If vacuum is not present at the valve(s) perform appropriate test(s). *See appropriate article in Computerized Engine Control section.*

Fig. 1: Jeep Pulse Air Injection System

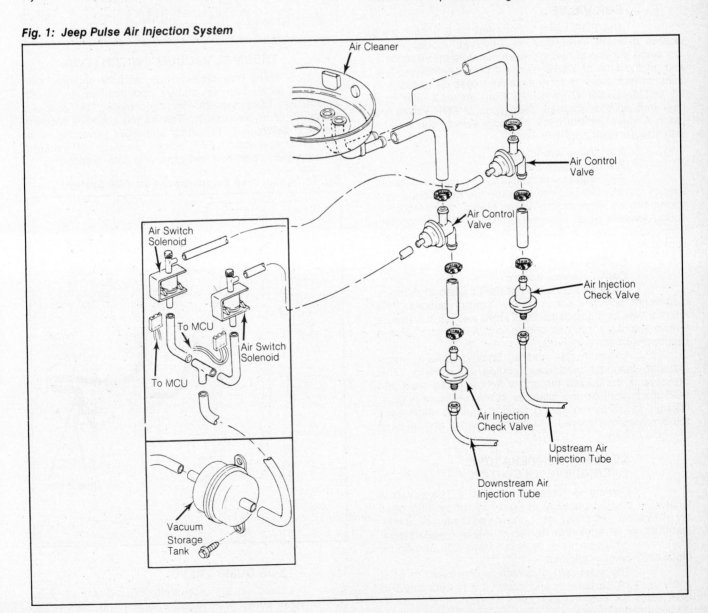

1983 Exhaust Emission Systems

JEEP EXHAUST GAS RECIRCULATION

DESCRIPTION

The purpose of the Exhaust Gas Recirculation (EGR) system is to limit formation of oxides of nitrogen (NOx) emissions. This is done by reducing high peak combustion temperatures at which NOx is formed. By reintroducing some exhaust gas back into combustion chamber, high temperatures are avoided and thus NOx emissions formation is reduced.

System consists of a vacuum-operated EGR valve and a coolant temperature override (CTO) switch. In addition, some models are equipped with an air cleaner-mounted thermal vacuum switch (TVS), and some models are equipped with an EGR vacuum dump valve.

OPERATION

When EGR valve receives a vacuum signal from carburetor, through CTO switch, EGR valve opens and meters gases from exhaust manifold into intake manifold. Individual component operation is as follows:

EGR VALVE

The EGR valve is mounted on a spacer plate located beneath carburetor on 4-cylinder models, on a machined surface at rear of intake manifold on V8 models, and on the side of intake manifold on 6-cylinder models. Exhaust gas is drawn from exhaust crossover passage in V8 and 4-cylinder engines and from an area near heat riser in 6-cylinder engines. Two types of EGR valves are used: A valve without back pressure sensor and a valve with integral back pressure sensor.

EGR Valve w/o Integral Back Pressure Sensor

EGR valves are calibrated by use of different shapes of valve pintles. Valve is normally held closed by a spring (above diaphragm). Valve opens by overcoming spring tension when vacuum is sensed through coolant temperature override switch (CTO) and back pressure sensor (if used).

EGR Valve w/Integral Back Pressure Sensor

Calibration is accomplished by use of different diaphragm spring loads and flow control orifices. This integral type unit combines EGR valve and back pressure sensor functions into one component. A restrictor plate is required with some engines.

Exhaust gas exerts back pressure inside exhaust manifold whenever engine is running. This pressure is conducted through a hollow pintle stem into EGR diaphragm control chamber. If this pressure is great enough to overcome spring tension against diaphragm, the diaphragm is moved against bleed valve and exhaust gas flow begins.

COOLANT TEMPERATURE OVERRIDE (CTO) SWITCH

Coolant temperature override (CTO) switch is located in coolant passage at right rear of cylinder head on 4-cylinder engines, at coolant passage of intake manifold, or at right rear corner of intake manifold near EGR valve on V8 engines, or at left front side of cylinder block on 6-cylinder engines.

The inner port of switch is connected to EGR spark port on carburetor and outer port is connected to EGR valve, or TVS. Switch opens at 100°F (38°C) for 4-

cylinder engines, or 115°F (46°C) for 6-cylinder and V8 engines. Below these temperatures, no EGR is possible.

Fig. 1: Typical Jeep V8 Engine EGR System

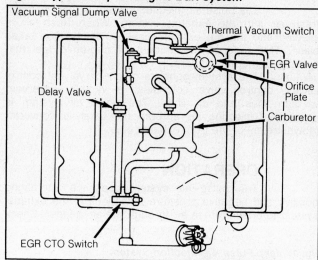

THERMAL VACUUM SWITCH (TVS)

Used only on 6-cylinder and V8 engines, this switch is located in air cleaner and acts as an on-off switch for EGR system. It is controlled by ambient temperature in air cleaner. The switch controls vacuum passage between CTO switch and EGR valve. Below a pre-set temperature, TVS blocks passage of vacuum delaying EGR operation and improving cold driveability.

Fig. 2: Typical Jeep 6-Cylinder Engine EGR System

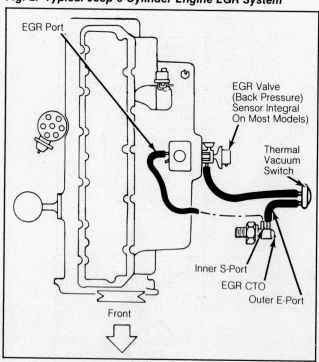

EGR DUMP VALVE

Used on some models, EGR dump valve is connected in series with vacuum source and EGR valve.

JEEP EXHAUST GAS RECIRCULATION (Cont.)

Valve is used to eliminate EGR function at low vacuum levels. When vacuum drops below a predetermined level, valve "dumps" vacuum rather than allowing it to flow to EGR valve.

FORWARD DELAY VALVE

The forward delay valve is located between EGR CTO switch and EGR valve. It modifies the initial vacuum signal applied to EGR valve by delaying full vacuum force.

TESTING

EGR VALVE

Valve Opening Test

1) With engine at normal operating temperature and at curb idle, rapidly open and close throttle. Open throttle sufficiently to obtain at least 1500 RPM. A definite movement should be noticed in EGR diaphragm.

2) If diaphragm does not move, probable causes are: Faulty vacuum signal to EGR; defective EGR diaphragm or defective back pressure sensor diaphragm (if equipped); or leaks in vacuum lines or connections.

Valve Closing Test

1) With engine at normal operating temperature and at curb idle, manually depress EGR valve diaphragm. This should cause an immediate engine speed drop, indicating that EGR valve had been properly cutting off exhaust gas flow at idle.

2) If there is no change in RPM and engine is idling properly, exhaust gases are not reaching combustion chamber. There is probably a plugged passage between EGR valve and intake manifold.

3) If engine idles poorly and RPM is not greatly affected by moving diaphragm, EGR valve is not closing off exhaust gas flow. Defective hoses, hose routing, or EGR valve is problem.

COOLANT TEMPERATURE OVERRIDE (CTO) SWITCH

NOTE: **Engine coolant temperature must be below 100°F (38°C) to perform this test.**

1) Check vacuum lines for leaks and correct routing. Disconnect vacuum line at back pressue sensor (if equipped) or at EGR valve, and attach this line to a vacuum gauge.

2) Operate engine at 1500 RPM. No vacuum should be indicated on gauge. If vacuum is shown, replace CTO switch.

3) Idle engine until coolant temperature exceeds 100°F (38°C) on 4-cylinder engines, or 115°F (46°C) on 6-cylinder and V8 engines.

4) Accelerate engine to 1500 RPM. Carburetor ported vacuum should be shown on gauge. If not, replace CTO switch.

DUMP VALVE

1) With engine at normal operating temperature, remove dump valve vacuum hose from manifold and plug manifold connection.

2) Accelerate engine to 2000 RPM. Vacuum should be present at exhaust ports on bottom of valve. If not, replace valve.

3) Reconnect vacuum hose to manifold and accelerate engine to 2000 RPM. No vacuum should be felt at exhaust ports on bottom of valve. If vacuum is present, replace valve.

THERMAL VACUUM SWITCH

1) With air cleaner temperature below 40°F (-4°C), disconnect vacuum hoses from TVS and connect vacuum source to large outlet.

2) Apply vacuum to TVS. Vacuum should be held. If not, replace TVS.

3) Start engine and warm air cleaner to 55°F (13°C), or above. Vacuum should not be held. If it is held, replace TVS.

1983 Exhaust Emission Systems

JEEP SPARK CONTROL SYSTEMS

DESCRIPTION

Jeep vehicles use spark control devices to assist ignition system in controlling exhaust emissions. They are Spark Control Temperature Override (CTO) valve, Non-Linear Vacuum Regulator (NLVR) valve, Forward Delay Valve, Reverse Delay Valve, and on 4-cylinder engines, a Vacuum Spark Control Delay Valve. System application depends upon engine size, emissions category and vehicle model.

SPARK COOLANT TEMPERATURE OVERRIDE (CTO) SYSTEM

This system alternates distributor vacuum advance vacuum source between carburetor ported vacuum or delayed manifold vacuum and normal manifold vacuum, depending upon coolant temperature. Two types of CTO switch are used: a single-function switch for models with standard cooling systems, and a single-function switch for heavy duty cooling systems.

CTO switch is threaded into left rear of block on 6-cylinder engines, and into thermostat housing on 4-cylinder and V8 engines. On some models, this system is used in conjunction with NLVR valve.

Fig. 1: Cutaway View of Single-Function CTO Switch

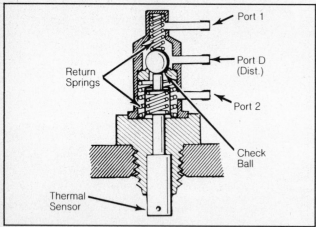

CTO alternates distributor vacuum between carburetor ported vacuum or delayed manifold vacuum and manifold vacuum.

Fig. 2: Jeep Non-Linear Vacuum Regulator Valve

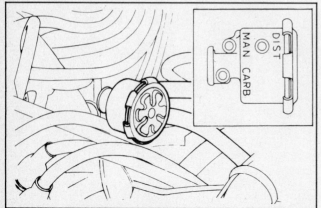

NLVR valve performs different functions depending upon engine loads.

NON-LINEAR VACUUM REGULATOR VALVE

NLVR valve is used on some models. This valve supplies vacuum advance unit with a regulated combination of manifold and carburetor ported vacuum when engine load is low and switches to supply only carburetor ported vacuum as load increases.

OPERATION

SPARK COOLANT TEMPERATURE OVERRIDE SWITCH

Single-Function for Standard Cooling

When coolant temperature is below 155°F (68°C) on 6-cylinder and V8 engines, or 120°F (49°C) on 4-cylinder engines, check ball is held against inner seat by spring tension. Manifold vacuum enters through port "1" and is applied through port "D". See Fig. 1.

When temperature goes above specified limits, check ball is moved up in valve and manifold vacuum is applied from port "2" to port "D", bypassing delay valve, on 4-cylinder engines, or carburetor ported vacuum is applied from port "2" to port "D" on 6-cylinder and V8 engines.

Single-Function for Heavy-Duty Cooling

Valve is used to prevent engine overheating at high ambient temperatures. When coolant temperature is below 220°F (104°C), carburetor ported vacuum enters port "1" and is applied through port "D".

This allows full ported vacuum to distributor. Above 220°F (104°C), port "1" is blocked and manifold vacuum enters through port "2" and connectors to port "D". Manifold vacuum then controls spark advance. See Fig. 1.

NON-LINEAR VACUUM REGULATOR VALVE

There are 2 input ports on NLVR: intake manifold vacuum and carburetor ported vacuum. One outlet port connects to distributor vacuum unit. At curb idle, regulated vacuum is supplied to advance unit, when manifold vacuum is high and ported vacuum is very low. See Fig. 2.

NLVR regulates vacuum signal so it is between these 2 vacuum source levels at idle. As engine load increases and vacuum signal is above 7.5 in. Hg vacuum, regulator valve switches to ported vacuum output.

FORWARD DELAY VALVE

Some engines use this valve to improve driveability and reduce hydrocarbon emissions. The valve functions to delay effects of sudden increases in vacuum. This prevents sudden spark advance during deceleration.

REVERSE DELAY VALVE

Some engines use this valve to improve cold driveability and reduce hydrocarbon emissions. The valve is installed in vacuum line to delay effects of manifold vacuum decrease causing retarded ignition timing.

VACUUM ADVANCE CONTROL DELAY VALVE

This valve is used on 4-cylinder engines to improve driveability when engine is cold. It is located in vacuum advance circuit. When vacuum is greater at port

JEEP SPARK CONTROL SYSTEMS (Cont.)

"4" than at port "1", air must flow through orifice to equalize pressure. This creates a momentary delay that prevents a sudden decrease in spark advance. When vacuum is greater at port "1" than at port "4", air flows freely through check valve and pressure is instantly equalized. See Fig. 3.

MAINTENANCE

Periodic maintenance is not normally required; should any switch or valve fail to function properly it should be replaced.

TESTING

SPARK COOLANT TEMPERATURE OVERRIDE SWITCH

Single-Function For Standard Cooling (6-Cylinder & V8 Engine)

Connect a vacuum gauge to center port "D" of CTO switch. When coolant is below 155°F (68°C), manifold vacuum should register. Above 155°F (68°C), carburetor ported vacuum should register. If valve does not meet these requirements, it must be replaced. See Fig. 1.

Fig. 3: Jeep Vacuum Spark Control Delay Valve (4-Cylinder Engines)

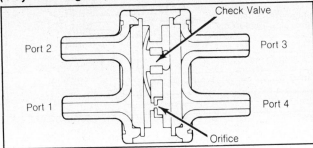

When testing disconnect vacuum hose from port "4".

Single-Function for Standard Cooling (4-Cylinder)

Disconnect vacuum hose from distributor vacuum advance mechanism and connect a vacuum gauge to hose. Start engine. With coolant temperature below 120°F (49°C), manifold vacuum should register. Disconnect vacuum hose from port "4" of delay valve and cap. Manifold vacuum should not register until coolant temperature reaches about 120°F (49°C). If valve fails these tests it must be replaced. See Fig. 3.

NOTE: Ported vacuum is not available with throttle closed. Ported vacuum is available at part throttle (equivalent of 1000 RPM).

Single-Function for Heavy-Duty Cooling

Connect a vacuum gauge to center port "D" of CTO switch. When coolant is below 220°F (104°C), carburetor ported vacuum should register. Above 220°F (104°C), manifold vacuum should be indicated.

NON-LINEAR VACUUM REGULATOR VALVE

Connect vacuum gauge to distributor port "DIST" on NLVR. With engine at idle speed, a vacuum

reading of 7 in. Hg vacuum should be shown. As throttle is opened and engine speed increases, ported vacuum level should be indicated. If not, replace NLVR. See Fig. 2.

FORWARD DELAY VALVE

1) Connect an external vacuum source to port on Black (or Red) side of delay valve. Connect 1 end of a section of rubber hose to vacuum gauge and other end to port on colored side of valve.

2) With elapsed time device in view and a constant 10 in. Hg vacuum applied, note time required for gauge pointer to move from 0-8 in. Hg.

3) If valve fails to meet time limits, replace valve. If valve meets specifications, install so that Black (or Red) side is toward vacuum source.

FORWARD DELAY VALVE TIME LIMITS [1]

Valve Color	Min. Time	Max Time
Black/Purple	3.2	4.8
Black/Gray	8	12
Black/Brown	16	24
Black/Orange	1.5	2.5
Black/White	50	77
Black/Yellow	80	120
Black/Green	160	240

[1] — Time in seconds.

REVERSE DELAY VALVE

1) Connect external vacuum source to port on White side of delay valve. Connect 1 end of a section of rubber hose to vacuum gauge and other end to port on colored (non-White) side of valve.

2) With elapsed time device in view and a constant 10 in. Hg vacuum applied, note time required for gauge pointer to move from 0-8 in. Hg.

3) If valve fails to meet time limits, replace valve. If valve meets specifications, install with non-White side toward vacuum source.

Reverse Delay Valve Time Limits [1]

Valve Color	Min. Time	Max. Time
White/Purple	3.2	4.8
White/Gray	8	12
White/Gold	12	18
White/Brown	16	24
White/Yellow	80	120
White/Red	300	450
White/Orange	1.5	2.5

[1] — Time in seconds.

VACUUM SPARK CONTROL DELAY VALVE

1) Connect a tee fitting at ports "1" and "4". Connect vacuum gauge to each fitting. Start engine. Vacuum should be equal at both ports. See Fig. 3.

2) When throttle is suddenly depressed, vacuum at port "1" will instantly decrease and vacuum at port "4" should be maintained momentarily. If valve fails these tests, replace valve.

1983 Exhaust Emission Systems

JEEP SPARK CONTROL SYSTEMS (Cont.)

Fig. 4: Jeep (California) 4-Cylinder Spark Control System

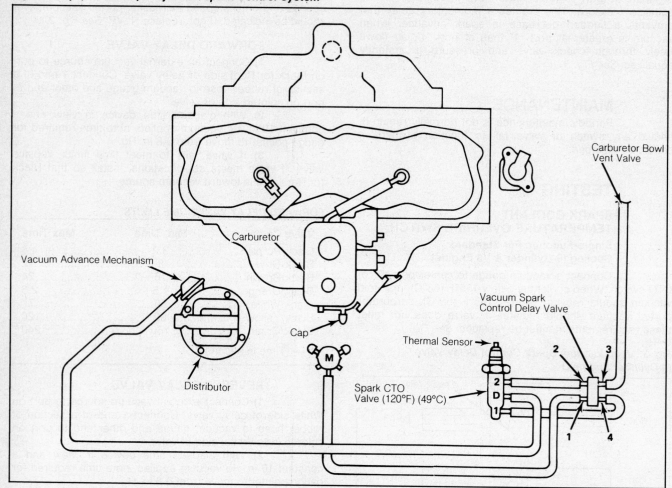

JEEP VACUUM DIAGRAMS

JEEP VACUUM DIAGRAM ABBREVIATIONS

CTO — Coolant Temperature Override; **EGR** — Exhaust Gas Recirculation; **HDC CTO** — Heavy Duty Cooling, Coolant Temperature Override; **PCV** — Positive Crankcase Ventilation; **TAC** — Thermostatic Air Cleaner; **VSD** —Vacuum Signal Dump

Fig. 1: 2.5L 4-Cyl. California Man. Trans. CJ5, CJ7 & Scrambler

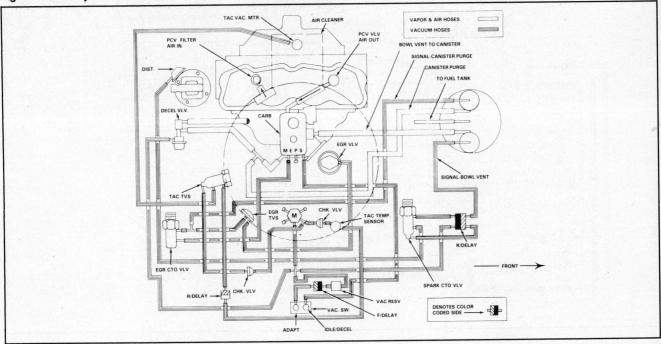

Fig. 2: 2.5L 4-Cyl. Federal & High Altitude Man. Trans. CJ5, CJ7 & Scrambler

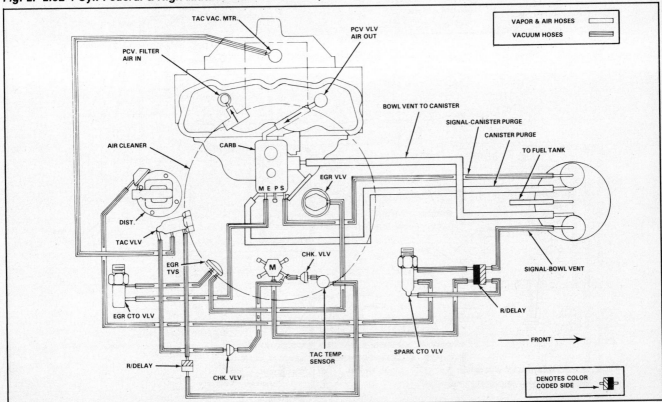

1983 Exhaust Emission Systems

JEEP VACUUM DIAGRAMS (Cont.)

Fig. 3: 4.2L 6-Cyl. California Man. Trans. CJ5, CJ7 & Scrambler

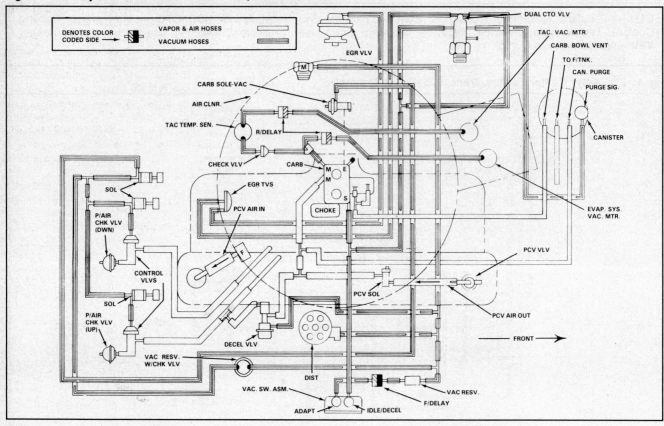

Fig. 4: 4.2L 6-Cyl. California Auto. Trans. CJ7 & Scrambler

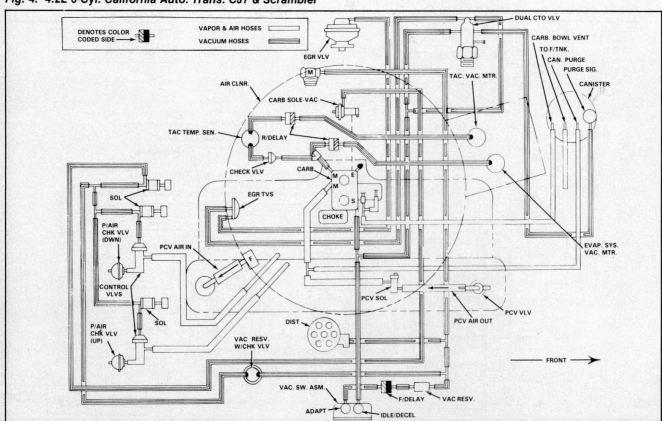

JEEP VACUUM DIAGRAMS (Cont.)

Fig. 5: 4.2L 6-Cyl. California Man. Trans. Cherokee, J10 & Wagoneer

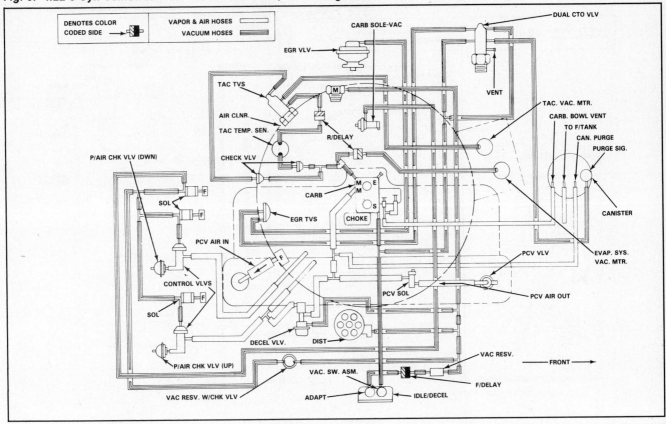

Fig. 6: 4.2L 6-Cyl. California Auto. Trans. Cherokee, J10 & Wagoneer

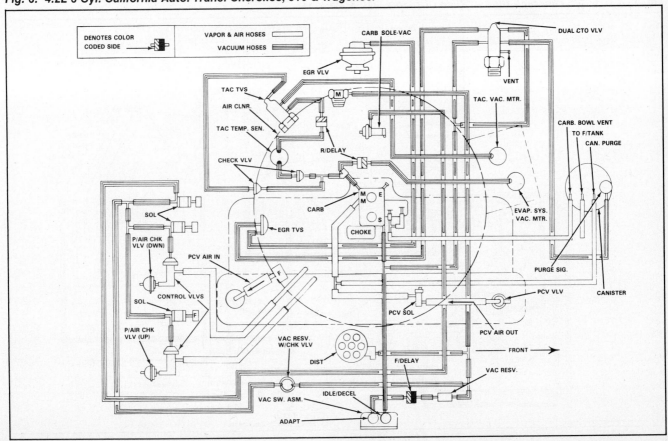

1983 Exhaust Emission Systems

JEEP VACUUM DIAGRAMS (Cont.)

Fig. 7: 4.2L 6-Cyl. Federal & High Altitude CJ5, CJ7 & Scrambler

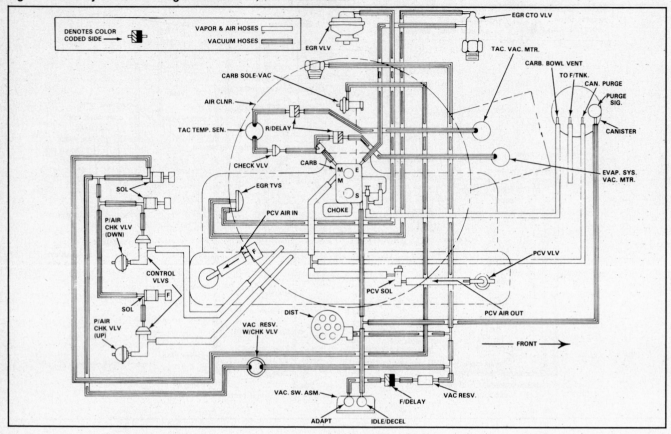

Fig. 8: 4.2L 6-Cyl. Federal & High Altitude Cherokee, J10 & Wagoneer

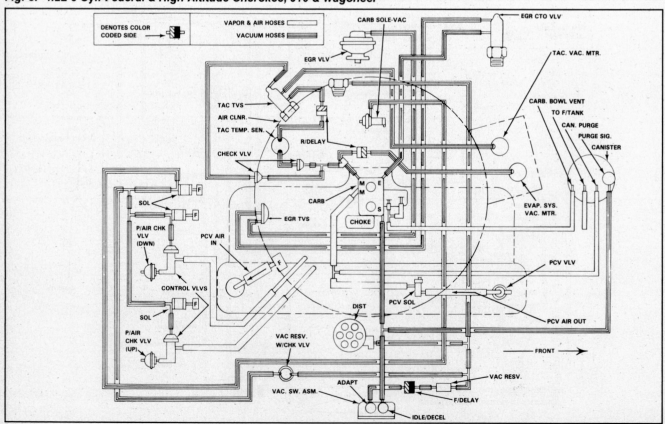

JEEP VACUUM DIAGRAMS (Cont.)

Fig. 9: 6.0L 8-Cyl. Federal & High Altitude Cherokee, J10/20 & Wagoneer W/H.D. Cooling

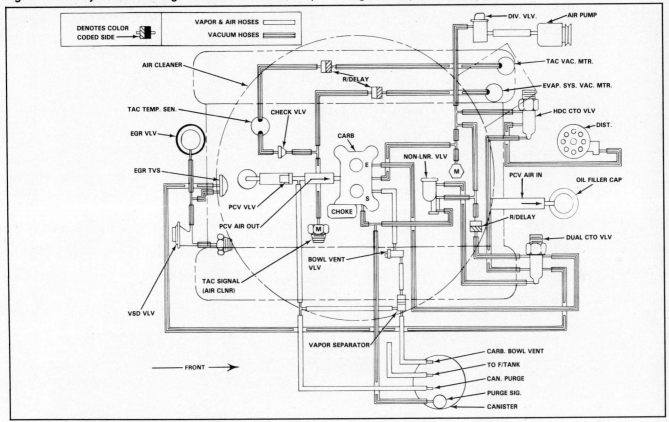

Fig. 10: 6.0L 8-Cyl. Federal & High Altitude Cherokee, J10/20 & Wagoneer W/O H.D. Cooling

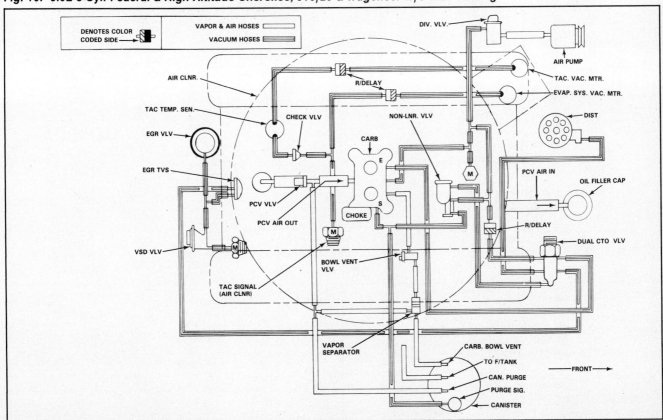

SECTION 4

ELECTRICAL

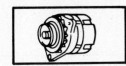

CONTENTS

NOTE: ALSO SEE GENERAL INDEX.

IMPORTANT: Because of the many model names used by vehicle manufacturers, accurate identification of models is important. See Model Identification at the front of this publication.

Ignition Systems

IGNITION SECONDARY QUICK CHECK CHART

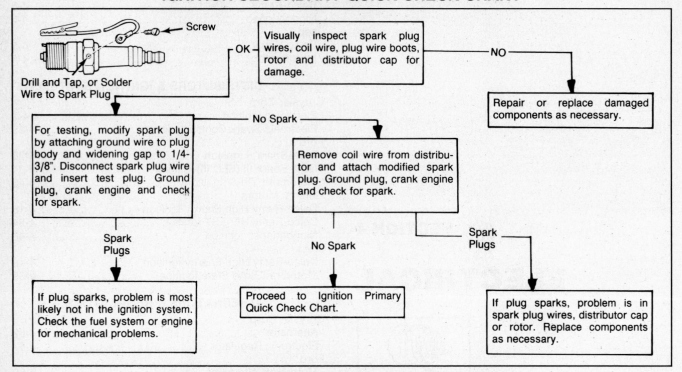

Screw

Drill and Tap, or Solder
Wire to Spark Plug

OK

Visually inspect spark plug wires, coil wire, plug wire boots, rotor and distributor cap for damage.

NO

Repair or replace damaged components as necessary.

For testing, modify spark plug by attaching ground wire to plug body and widening gap to 1/4-3/8". Disconnect spark plug wire and insert test plug. Ground plug, crank engine and check for spark.

No Spark

Remove coil wire from distributor and attach modified spark plug. Ground plug, crank engine and check for spark.

Spark Plugs

If plug sparks, problem is most likely not in the ignition system. Check the fuel system or engine for mechanical problems.

No Spark

Proceed to Ignition Primary Quick Check Chart.

Spark Plugs

If plug sparks, problem is in spark plug wires, distributor cap or rotor. Replace components as necessary.

IGNITION PRIMARY QUICK CHECK CHART

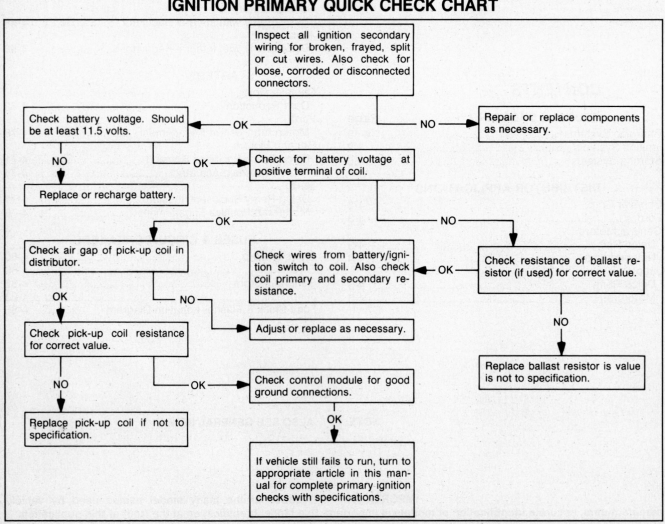

Inspect all ignition secondary wiring for broken, frayed, split or cut wires. Also check for loose, corroded or disconnected connectors.

OK

NO

Repair or replace components as necessary.

Check battery voltage. Should be at least 11.5 volts.

NO

Replace or recharge battery.

OK

Check for battery voltage at positive terminal of coil.

OK

NO

Check air gap of pick-up coil in distributor.

OK

Check pick-up coil resistance for correct value.

NO

Replace pick-up coil if not to specification.

NO

Check wires from battery/ignition switch to coil. Also check coil primary and secondary resistance.

Adjust or replace as necessary.

OK

Check control module for good ground connections.

OK

If vehicle still fails to run, turn to appropriate article in this manual for complete primary ignition checks with specifications.

OK

Check resistance of ballast resistor (if used) for correct value.

NO

Replace ballast resistor is value is not to specification.

ALL MANUFACTURERS

CHRYSLER CORP.

DODGE & PLYMOUTH

Application	Part No.
3.7L 6-Cylinder	4145751
5.2L 2-Bbl. V8	
W/Dual Pickup	4145753
W/O Dual Pickup	4111950
5.2L 4-Bbl. V8	
Federal	
Light Duty	4145602
Heavy Duty	4091661
Calif.	
W/Dual Pickup	4111501
W/O Dual Pickup	4111950
5.9L V8	
Federal	4091661
Calif.	4111950

[1] — "Light Duty" and "Heavy Duty" refer to emission control standards classifications. "Light Duty" refers to vehicles of 8500 lbs. GVW or less. Vehicles over this weight are referred to as "Heavy Duty".

DELCO-REMY

NOTE: SERIES IDENTIFICATION: The vehicle numbers used in this section have been abbreviated for common reference to both Chevrolet and GMC models. Chevrolet models use numerical designations as listed; GMC models are identified as follows: 10 = 1500, 20 = 2500, 30 = 3500 and S10 = S15.

CHEVROLET & GMC [1]

Application	Part No.
2.0L 4-Cylinder	
Man. Trans.	1103536
Auto. Trans.	1103441
2.8L V6	
Federal	
Man. Trans.	1103520
Auto. Trans.	1103521
Calif.	1103519
4.1L 6-Cylinder	
Federal	
Man. Trans.	
C10	1103482
C20	1103481
G10/30	1103483
K10	
Overdrive	1103482
Saginaw	
3.42:1 Rear Axle	1103481
3.73:1 Rear Axle	1103488
Auto. Trans.	1103483
Calif.	1103480
High Altitude	
Man. Trans.	1103532
Auto. Trans.	1111388
4.8L 6-Cylinder	1110753

DELCO-REMY (Cont.)

CHEVROLET & GMC [1] (Cont.)

Application	Part No.
5.0L V8 (VIN F)	1103460
5.0L V8 (VIN H)	1103465
5.7L V8 (VIN L)	
Federal	1103436
Calif.	1103460
5.7L V8 (VIN M)	
Federal	1103375
Calif.	1103420
7.4L V8	1103376

[1] — For 1.9L 4-cylinder engines, see NIPPONDENSO DISTRIBUTORS.

JEEP [1]

Application	Part No.
2.5L 4-Cylinder	
Federal	1110598
Calif.	1103527

[1] — For Jeep distributors for 6-cylinder and V8 engines, see MOTORCRAFT DISTRIBUTORS.

MOTORCRAFT

JEEP [1]

Application	Part No.
4.2L 6-Cylinder	3242409
5.0L V8	3233174

[1] — For Jeep distributors for 4-cylinder engines, see DELCO-REMY DISTRIBUTORS.

FORD

Application	Part No.
2.0L 4-Cylinder	E27E-BA, E27E-GA
2.3L 4-Cylinder	E27E-AA, E27E-BA, E27E-FA
2.8L V6	E37E-EA
3.8L V6	
Man. Trans.	E3TE-PA
Auto. Trans.	E3TE-YA
4.9L 6-Cylinder	
Bronco	
Man. Trans.	
Federal	E3TE-TA, E3TE-VA
Calif.	E3TE-TA
Auto. Trans.	E3TE-UA
E100/150	
Man. Trans.	
Federal	E3UE-HA, E3UE-JA, E3UE-GA
Calif.	E3UE-HA
Auto. Trans.	
AOT	
Federal	E3TE-KA, E3TE-RA
Calif.	E3TE-RA
C-6	E1TE-FA, E1TE-GA

Distributor Applications

ALL MANUFACTURERS (Cont.)

MOTORCRAFT (Cont.)

FORD (Cont.)

Application	Part No.
E250	
Man. Trans.	D9TE-AEA, E3UE-GA, E3UE-HA
Auto. Trans.	
AOT	E3TE-RA
C-6	D9TE-ADA
E350	
Man. Trans.	D9TE-AEA
Auto. Trans.	D9TE-ADA
F100/150	
2WD	
Man. Trans.	
Federal	E2TE-FA, E2TE-RA
	E3TE-TA, E3TE-VA
Calif.	E3TE-NA
Auto. Trans.	
AOT	
Federal	E3TE-KA, E3TE-RA
Calif.	E3TE-RA
C-6	E3TE-UA
4WD	
Man. Trans	
Federal	E3TE-TA, E3TE-VA
Calif.	E3TE-TA
Auto. Trans.	E3TE-UA
F250	
Under 8500 Lbs. GVW	
Man. Trans.	E3TE-TA
Auto. Trans.	E3TE-UA
Over 8500 Lbs. GVW	
Man. Trans.	D9TE-AEA
Auto. Trans	D9TE-ADA
5.0L V8	
Bronco	
Man. Trans.	E3TE-JA, E3TE-ZA
Auto. Trans.	
Federal	E2TE-MA, E2TE-TA, E3TE-AAA
Calif.	E2AE-GA
E100/250	
Man. Trans.	E3TE-ZA
Auto. Trans.	
Federal	E3UE-EA
Calif.	E2AE-GA
F100/150	
2WD	
Man. Trans.	E3TE-ZA
Auto. Trans.	
Federal	E3TE-HA, E3TE-SA
Calif.	E2AE-GA
4WD	
Man. Trans.	E3TE-JA, E3TE-ZA
Auto. Trans.	
Federal	E2TE-TA, E3TE-AAA
Calif.	E2AE-GA
F250	
Man. Trans.	E3TE-JA, E3TE-ZA
Auto. Trans.	
Federal	
AOT	E3TE-HA, E3TE-SA
C-6	E2TE-MA, E2TE-TA
Calif.	E2AE-GA

MOTORCRAFT (Cont.)

FORD (Cont.)

Application	Part No.
5.8L V8	
Bronco	E1AE-LA
E100/250	E1UE-GA, E2TE-UA
E350	E2TE-UA
F150	E1AE-LA
F250	
Under 8500 Lbs. GVW	E1AE-LA
Over 8500 Lbs. GVW	E2TE-UA
7.5L V8	
Federal	D7TE-APA
Calif.	E3UE-DA

¹ — Basic part number is 12127. Table gives prefix and suffix only.

NIPPONDENSO

CHEVROLET & GMC

Application	Part No.
1.9L 4-Cylinder	
Federal	94240905
Calif.	
2WD	
Man. Trans.	94230979
Auto. Trans.	94230990
4WD	94230990

CHRYSLER CORP. DISTRIBUTOR ADVANCE SPECIFICATIONS
FOR DISTRIBUTOR RPM AND DEGREES, DIVIDE SPECIFICATIONS BY 2

Distributor Part No.	Rot.[1]	Automatic Advance (Engine Degrees & RPM)						Vacuum Advance (Engine Deg. & In. of Hg)			
		Deg.	RPM	Deg.	RPM	Deg.	RPM	Deg.	In. Hg	Deg.	In. Hg
4091661	C	3-6	1100	11-15	1700	22-26	4000	1-4	14	12-16	30
4111501	C	1-3	1400	3-7	1800	15-20	4400	2-5	14	20-24	30
4111950	C	1-5	1300	5-9	1800	16-20	4400	2-5	14	20-24	30
4145602	C	1-5	1800	5-7	2400	11-15	4400	0-2	12	20-24	26
4145751	C	Electronic Spark Advance									
4145753	C	Electronic Spark Advance									

[1] — C=Clockwise, as viewed from rotor end.

DELCO-REMY (GMC) DISTRIBUTOR ADVANCE SPECIFICATIONS
FOR DISTRIBUTOR RPM AND DEGREES, DIVIDE SPECIFICATIONS BY 2

Distributor Part No.	Rot.[1]	AUTOMATIC ADVANCE (Engine Degrees & RPM)						VACUUM ADVANCE (Engine Deg.)			
		Deg.	RPM	Deg.	RPM	Deg.	RPM	Deg.	In. Hg	Deg.	In. Hg
1103375	CC	0-6	1400	14-18	2800	20-24	4200	0	3-6	10	7-9
1103376	CC	0-6	1400	12-16	2800	18-22	4200	0	7-10	10	13-14
1103420	CC	0-6	2000	.....	.....	22-26	4000	0	9-11	10	12-14
1103436	CC	0-8	1300	14-18	2400	20-24	4600	0	2-4	20	6-9
1103441	CC	0-6	1400	12-18	2200	20-26	6000	0	2-4	12	7-10
1103460 [2]	CC	.....	.....	.....	.....	18-22	.....	.....	.....	.....	.....
1103465	CC	0-4	1400	6-10	2000	18-22	4200	0	2-4	20	6-9
1103480 [2]	CC	.....	.....	.....	.....	.....	.....	.....	.....	.....	.....
1103481	CC	0-4	1400	6-10	2000	18-22	4200	0	2-4	18	5-7
1103482	CC	0-4	1400	6-10	2000	18-22	4200	0	2-4	24	7-9
1103483	CC	0-4	1400	6-10	2000	18-22	4200	0	2-4	20	6-9
1103488	CC	0-4	1400	6-10	2000	18-22	4200	0	3-5	14	7-9
1103519 [2]	CC	.....	.....	.....	.....	.....	.....	.....	.....	.....	.....
1103520	CC	0-6	1200	12-18	2200	18-24	6000	0	2-4	10	5-7
1103521	CC	0-4	1400	8-12	2200	16-20	4800	0	2-4	10	5-7
1103532	CC	0-6	1300	12-16	2400	22-26	4100	0	2-4	24	7-10
1103536	CC	0-6	1600	10-16	2400	24-28	5200	0	2-4	12	7-10
1110753	CC	0-6	1300	12-16	2400	22-26	4100	0	3-6	10	7-10
1111388	CC	0-6	1300	12-16	2400	22-26	4100	0	2-4	20	6-9

[1] — CC=Counterclockwise, as viewed from rotor end.
[2] — HEI-EST distributor does not use vacuum or centrifugal advance mechanisms.

DELCO-REMY (JEEP) DISTRIBUTOR ADVANCE SPECIFICATIONS
FOR DISTRIBUTOR RPM AND DEGREES, DIVIDE SPECIFICATIONS BY 2

Distributor Part No.	Rot.[1]	AUTOMATIC ADVANCE (Engine Degrees & RPM)						VACUUM ADVANCE (Engine Deg.)			
		Deg.	RPM	Deg.	RPM	Deg.	RPM	Deg.	In. Hg	Deg.	In. Hg
1103527	CC	0-4	1600	6-10	2600	12-18	4000	0	3-5	20	10-12
1110598	CC	0-4	1600	4-10	2400	12-16	4000	0	2-4	20	7-9

[1] — CC=Counterclockwise, as viewed from rotor end.

MOTORCRAFT (JEEP) DISTRIBUTOR ADVANCE SPECIFICATIONS
FOR DISTRIBUTOR RPM AND DEGREES, DIVIDE SPECIFICATIONS BY 2

Distributor Part No.[1]	Rot.[2]	AUTOMATIC ADVANCE (Engine Degrees & RPM)						VACUUM ADVANCE (Engine Deg.)			
		Deg.	RPM	Deg.	RPM	Deg.	RPM	Deg.	In. Hg	Deg.	In. Hg
3233174	C	0-3	1000	6-10	2000	12-16	4000	0-1	1-2	24	13-16
3242409	C	0-1	800	7-12	2000	6-10	4000	0-1	1-3	20	18-24

[1] — For Jeep specifications on 2.5L 4-cylinder engine, see Delco-Remy Distributor Advance Specifications.
[2] — C=Clockwise, as viewed from rotor end.

1983 Distributor Specifications

MOTORCRAFT (FORD) DISTRIBUTOR ADVANCE SPECIFICATIONS
FOR DISTRIBUTOR RPM & DEGREES, DIVIDE SPECIFICATIONS BY 2

Distributor Part Number (Basic Part No. is 12127)	Initial Ignition Timing (Degrees BTDC)	Total Advance @ 2500 Engine RPM (Including Initial Advance)	
		Hose Disconnected (Degrees BTDC)	Hose Connected (Degrees BTDC)
D7TE-APA	8	18-24	36-46
D9TE-ADA	12	18-23	24-34
D9TE-AEA [2]	12	18-23	24-34
E1TE-FA	10	13-19	39-49
E1TE-GA	14	19-24	40-51
E1UE-GA [3]	10	10-15	35-46
E2TE-FA	6	13-18	42-53
E2TE-MA	8	14-19	28-37
E2TE-RA	10	17-22	42-53
E2TE-TA	12	18-22	36-45
E2TE-UA	8	12-18	17-29
E27E-AA [4]	10	17-21	38-49
E27E-BA [5]	6	16-21	37-48
E3TE-AAA	8	16-21	33-44
E3TE-HA	8	13-18	39-48
E3TE-JA	8	16-22	34-44
E3TE-KA	10	15-20	44-55
E3TE-NA	6	14-19	39-52
E3TE-PA	2	13-17	42-56
E3TE-RA [6]	10	14-19	40-52
E3TE-SA	12	17-21	40-52
E3TE-TA	6	15-20	38-50
E3TE-UA [7]	10	15-20	40-52
E3TE-VA	6	13-18	39-53
E3TE-YA	10	14-19	38-49
E3TE-ZA [8]	8	15-20	32-43
E3UE-DA	6	18-23	28-37
E3UE-EA	8	13-17	30-40
E3UE-GA [9]	6	13-18	38-50
E3UE-HA	6	14-19	41-54
E3UE-JA	6	13-18	41-53
E37E-FA	6	16-21	33-45

[1] — Part throttle advance hose at distributor diaphragm. If hose is disconnected, plug hose.
[2] — Calibration No. 9-77S-R10 is 10 initial timing, 16-21 disconnected, and 22-32 connected.
[3] — Calibration No. 2-64X-R00 is 14 initial timing, 14-19 disconnected, and 39-50 connected.
[4] — Calibration Nos. 3-50S-R00, 3-50S-R01, 3-50S-R10, 3-50S-R11, 3-50X-R10 are 8 initial timing, 15-20 disconnected, and 36-47 connected; calibration no. 3-49T-R17 is 6 initial timing, 13-18 disconnected, and 34-45 connected.
[5] — Calibration No. 3-41P-R15 is 8 initial timing, 18-23 disconnected, and 39-50 connected.
[6] — Calibration No. 3-52V-R00 is 14 initial timing, 18-23 disconnected, and 44-56 connected.
[7] — Calibration No. 3-52Z-R00 is 14 initial timing, 19-24 disconnected, and 44-56 connected.
[8] — Calibration Nos. 3-53W-R00, 3-53Y-R00, 3-53Z-R00 are 12 initial timing, 19-24 disconnected, and 36-47 connected.
[9] — Calibration No. 3-51V-R00 is 10 initial timing, 17-22 disconnected, and 42-54 connected.

NIPPONDENSO DISTRIBUTOR ADVANCE SPECIFICATIONS
FOR DISTRIBUTOR RPM AND DEGREES, DIVIDE SPECIFICATIONS BY 2

Distributor Part No.	Rot.[1]	Automatic Advance (Engine Degrees & RPM)						Vacuum Advance (Engine Deg. & In. of Hg)			
		Deg.	RPM	Deg.	RPM	Deg.	RPM	Deg.	In. Hg	Deg.	In. Hg
94230979	CC	2	1600	10	2600	16	3900	2	3-4	18	8-11
94230990	CC	2	1600	10	2600	16	3900	2	3-4	12	6-8
94240905	CC	2	1600	10	2600	16	3900	2	2-4	18	6-9

[1] — CC=Counterclockwise, as viewed from rotor end.

CHRYSLER CORP. ELECTRONIC IGNITION

Dodge & Plymouth, All V8 Models

DESCRIPTION

All models with V8 engines use Chrysler Corp. Electronic Ignition. This system consists of an electronic control unit, ignition switch, ignition coil, a 1.2 ohm ballast resistor. The distributor has vacuum and centrifugal advance mechanisms, pickup coil assemblies and a reluctor. *See Fig. 1 and 2.*

Fig. 1: Electronic Ignition Wiring Diagram for V8 Engines with Single Pick-Up Coil

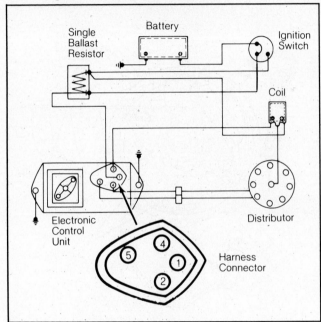

Note there is no terminal No. 3.

Fig. 2: Electronic Ignition Wiring Diagram for V8 Engines with Dual Pick-up Coil

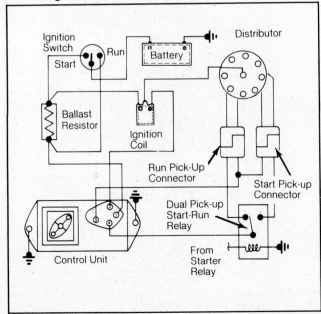

Note there is no terminal No. 3.

Distributors may vary between models, as most models have a reluctor and single pick-up coil assembly. All Trucks and Vans with V8 engines and automatic transmissions have a reluctor and 2 pick-up coil assemblies.

Models with dual pick-up coil assemblies also have a dual pick-up start-run relay, located between the electronic control unit and the distributor.

The dual pick-up start-run relay permits use of a dual pick-up distributor without electronic spark advance. This results in improved timing and increased fuel economy.

The control unit is connected to the rest of the system through a 4-wire connector. The distributor is connected to the control unit by a 2-wire or by two 2-wire connectors (dual pick-up models).

NOTE: There is no terminal 3 on the control unit.

OPERATION

DISTRIBUTOR

Single Pick-Up Models

The distributor has a toothed wheel, called a reluctor, having one tooth for each of the engine's 8 cylinders. *See Fig. 3.* As the reluctor rotates with the distributor shaft, its teeth approach, become aligned with, and pass the center pole piece of the pick-up coil.

Fig. 3: Exploded View of Distributor Used on Dual Pick-Up System for V8 Engines

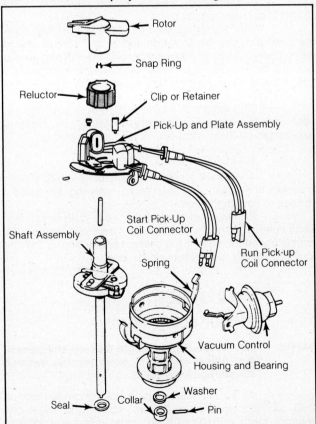

Reluctor has one tooth for each cylinder.

Distributors & Ignition Systems

CHRYSLER CORP. ELECTRONIC IGNITION (Cont.)

This interruption of the magnetic field around the pick-up coil(s) creates an electronic signal. This signal is transmitted to the control until, which shuts off current flow to the primary circuit of the ignition coil as each signal is received.

Dual Pick-Up Models

This system operates identically to single pick-up models with one exception. Signals are sent by different pick-up coils during cranking and normal running conditions.

When cranking, the system operates through the start pick-up circuit of the dual pick-up start-run relay. Once the engine begins to run, the relay switches back to the run pick-up circuit. Only one pick-up coil operates at a time.

Distributor pick-up coil connectors can be identified by their terminals. Run pick-up connectors have one male and one female terminal; start pick-up connectors have 2 male terminals.

ELECTRONIC CONTROL UNIT

The electronic control unit is located in a metal housing on the firewall. A switching transistor is exposed on top for more efficient cooling.

The control unit is connected to the rest of the system by a wiring harness and a 4-wire connector. The control unit functions whenever the ignition switch is turned to the "START" or "RUN" positions.

The control unit furnishes current to the distributor pick-up coil directly on single pick-up models. On dual pick-up models, current flows through the dual pick-up start-run relay to either the start or run pick-up assembly, depending on whether ignition switch is in the "START" or "RUN" position.

The signal created, as the reluctor teeth pass the "live" pick-up coil, is transmited by the control unit to the primary circuit of the ignition coil. As current to the primary is cut off, the magnetic field there collapses, causing a voltage surge in the secondary windings. This fires the spark plugs.

The length of time that current is permitted to flow through the coil's primary circuit (dwell time) is determined by the control unit and is not adjustable.

BALLAST RESISTOR

A single 2-pin ballast resistor is used. During cranking, the resistor is by-passed, allowing full battery voltage to flow to the coil.

In low speed operation, the ballast resistor limits voltage to the coil, protecting it from overheating. As engine speed increases, the ballast resistor allows the coil to charge faster to prevent voltage loss.

ADJUSTMENT

PICK-UP COIL AIR GAP

NOTE: On models with a single pick-up coil assembly, adjust air gap in same manner outlined for start pick-up coils.

1) To set **start** pick-up coil (or single pick-up coil) air gap, loosen hold-down screw and align one reluctor tooth with pick-up coil pole. Insert a .006" (.15

mm) non-magnetic feeler gauge between reluctor tooth and pick-up coil pole. *See Figs. 4 and 5.*

2) Move pick-up coil assembly until contact is made between pick-up coil pole, feeler gauge and reluctor tooth. Tighten hold-down screw and remove feeler gauge. Gauge should not require force during removal.

3) Check air gap of **start** pick-up coil (or single pick-up coil) using an .008" (.20 mm) non-magnegic feeler gauge. It should not fit in gap. Do not force it to fit. Apply vacuum to vacuum unit and rotate distributor shaft.

Fig. 4: Checking Air Gap of Dual Pick-Up Distributor Start Pick-Up Coil

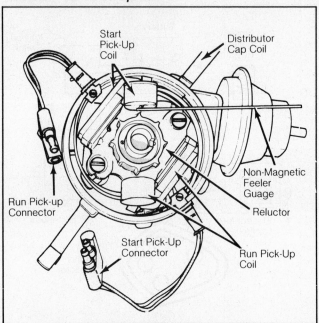

Run pick-up is checked similarly.

Fig 5: Checking Air Gap of Single Pick-Up Distributor Pick-Up Coil

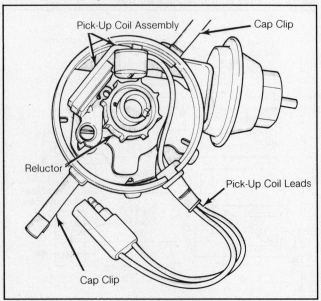

Use non-magnetic feeler gauges.

CHRYSLER CORP. ELECTRONIC IGNITION (Cont.)

4) Pick-up coil pole should not strike reluctor teeth. If so, gap is incorrectly set. If pick-up coil pole strikes teeth only on one side, distributor shaft is probably bent, requiring replacement.

5) To adjust **run** pick-up coil air gap, use same procedure as for start pick-up coil, except set gap with a .012" (.31 mm) feeler gauge and check it with a .014" (.36 mm) gauge.

TESTING

NOTE: If tester (C-4166 with adapter C-4166-1 or C-4166A, or tester C-4503 with adapter C-4503-3) is available, use tester and follow manufacturer's instructions. If tester is not available, proceed as follows:

CAUTION: When removing or installing wiring connector, ignition switch must be in "OFF" position.

1) Check that all secondary cables, primary wire at coil, and ballast resistor are not loose and not cracked excessively. Use a voltmeter with a 20,000 ohm/volt rating and an ohmmeter which uses a 9 volt battery for its operation.

2) Check calibration of both meters. Check and record battery voltage reading using volt meter. Proceed with following tests.

DUAL PICK-UP START-RUN RELAY

NOTE: Only models equipped with dual pick-up coils have this relay.

1) Turn ignition switch "OFF". Remove 2-wire connector from dual pick-up start-run relay terminals 4 and 5. Using an ohmmeter, connect leads to terminals 4 and 5 of start-run relay. *See Fig. 6.*

2) Resistance reading should be 20-30 ohms. If not to specifications, replace dual pick-up start-run relay.

Fig 6: Dual Pick-Up Start-Run Relay

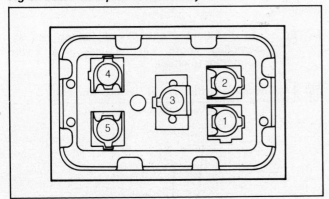

Note relay terminal locations.

SYSTEM VOLTAGE CHECK

1) Remove coil secondary wire from distributor cap. Turn ignition switch "ON". Connect a special jumper wire momentarily from ignition coil negative terminal to ground, while holding secondary wire 1/4" from engine ground. *See Fig. 7.* A spark should jump to ground.

Fig. 7: Special Jumper Wire with Capacitor

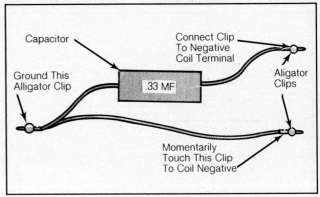

Capacitor

Connect Clip To Negative Coil Terminal

Ground This Alligator Clip

.33 MF

Aligator Clips

Momentarily Touch This Clip To Coil Negative

Wire is used for checking system voltage.

2) If spark was present, proceed to "Wiring Harness and Connector." If no spark was obtained, turn ignition switch "OFF". Disconnect 4-wire harness connector from electronic control unit.

3) Turn ignition switch "ON". Repeat step **1)**. If spark now results with connector removed, replace electronic control unit.

4) If no spark was obtained in step **3)**, measure voltage at coil positive terminal. It should be within 1 volt of battery voltage. If so, check for battery voltage at coil negative terminal. If battery voltage is indicated, but no spark was noted in step **3)**, replace ignition coil.

5) If no battery voltage was present at ignition coil positive terminal in step **4)**, replace starter relay, and check wiring between battery positive terminal and coil positive terminal. If continuity does not exist, replace ballast resistor and repeat step **4)**.

WIRING HARNESS & CONNECTOR

1) Measure voltage across battery terminals, record this measurement. Turn ignition switch "OFF", then disconnect harness connector from control unit. Connect voltmeter negative lead to a good ground and then turn ignition "ON". Make the following checks.

2) Connect voltmeter positive lead to control unit harness connector cavity 1. Reading should be battery voltage. If not, check and repair wires and components from harness connector cavity 1 back to battery. *See Figs. 8 and 9.*

Fig. 8: Checking Voltage at Cavity No. 1

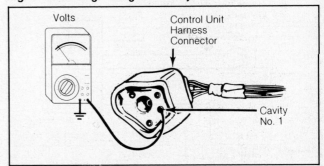

Volts

Control Unit Harness Connector

Cavity No. 1

Testing is at harness connector.

3) With voltmeter negative lead still connected to ground, connect positive lead to harness connector cavity 2. Voltmeter should again read battery voltage.

Fig. 9: Circuitry Checked if Cavity No. 1 Reading is Not to Specifications

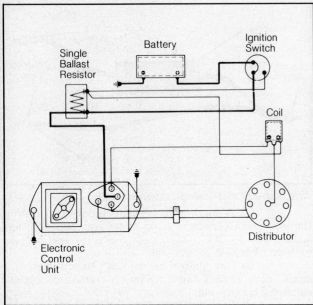

Check circuit outlined in heavy lines.

4) If reading is not to specification, check voltage at each connection (coil negative terminal, coil positive terminal, ballast resistor, ignition switch, etc.) back to battery. Repair wiring or replace components as necessary. *See Figs. 10 and 11.*

Fig. 10: Checking Voltage at Cavity No. 2

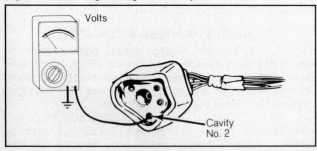

Fig. 11: Circuitry Checked if Cavity No. 2 Reading is Not to Specifications

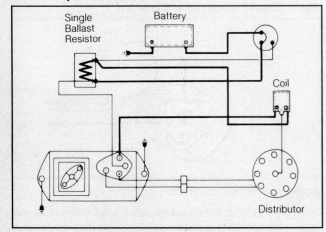

Check circuit outlined in heavy lines.

5) If reading jumped to battery voltage on positive side of ignition coil, check coil primary and secondary resistance. If coil is bad, replace it.

6) Check ballast resistor by disconnecting wires from resistor, and then taking an ohmmeter reading across its 2 terminals. Resistance should be 1.12-1.38 ohms. If reading is not to specifications replace ballast resistor. *See Fig. 12.*

Fig. 12: Checking Ballast Resistor Resistance

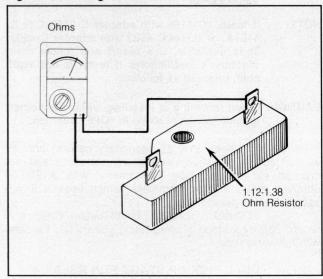

Connect ohmmeter leads to 2 terminals.

DISTRIBUTOR PICK-UP COILS

1) Turn ignition switch "OFF". Disconnect control unit harness connector. Connect ohmmeter leads to cavities 4 and 5 of harness connector. *See Fig. 13.* Ohmmeter reading should be 150-900 ohms.

2) If reading is not to specifications, make same check at 2-wire connector(s) leading to distributor. If readings at pick-up coils are now correct, start-run relay or harness from control until to distributor is defective. If readings are still not correct, replace faulty pick-up coil assembly.

NOTE: On distributors with single pick-up coil assemblies, there will be only one 2-wire connector to check.

Fig. 13: Checking Resistance at Cavities No. 4 and 5

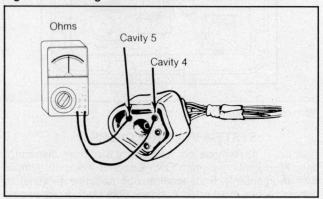

Pick-Up coil resistance will be read.

CHRYSLER CORP. ELECTRONIC IGNITION (Cont.)

3) Connect one ohmmeter lead to a good ground (distributor housing). Connect other lead to either terminal of start pick-up coil distributor connector, then to either terminal of run pick-up coil connector. If ohmmeter shows a reading for either test, replace faulty pick-up coil and adjust air gap.

ELECTRONIC CONTROL UNIT GROUND CIRCUIT

1) Connect one ohmmeter lead to a good ground and other lead to control unit connector pin 5 (not cavity 5 of harness connector). Ohmmeter should show full continuity.

2) If not, make sure control unit is making good contact with ground at hold-down bolts. If contact with ground is good, replace control unit.

CENTRIFUGAL ADVANCE CURVE

1) Install distributor in test stand. It is important that appropriate adapter for checking electronic type distributors be used. Adjust tester speed control to operate distributor at speeds called for in distributor tables.

2) If advance is not according to specifications, replace distributor shaft assembly (shaft, reluctor sleeve, governor weights).

IGNITION COIL RESISTANCE

1) Coil is designed to operate with an external ballast resistor. When testing ignition coil for output and resistance, also make ballast resistor tests. *See Fig. 12.* Inspect coil for external cracks and arcing at same time.

2) To check coil primary resistance, isolate coil from rest of system. Connect ohmmeter leads to positive and negative primary terminals. To check secondary resistance, connect ohmmeter leads to coil negative terminal and coil tower.

3) If resistance readings are not to specifications, replace ignition coil.

RESISTANCE SPECIFICATIONS

Application	Ohms@70-80°F (21-27°C)
Primary Resistance	
Prestolite	1.60-1.79
Essex	1.34-1.55
Secondary Resistance	
Prestolite	9400-11,700
Essex	9000-12,200
Single Ballast Resistor	
Resistor Resistance	1.2

OVERHAUL

DISASSEMBLY

1) Remove distributor cap, rotor and vacuum control unit. Remove reluctor. Some reluctors may be pulled off with fingers. If this is impossible, pry up from bottom with 2 screwdrivers. Be careful not to distort reluctor teeth.

2) Remove screws attaching lower plate to housing, and lift out lower plate, upper plate, and pick-up coils as an assembly. Do not attempt to remove distributor cap clamp springs.

3) Remove distributor drive collar retaining pin, and slide collar off end of shaft. Use a file to clean burrs from around pin hole in shaft, and remove lower thrust washer. Push shaft up, and remove it through top of distributor housing.

REASSEMBLY

1) Test operation of governor weights and inspect the weight springs for distortion. Lubricate governor weights. Inspect all bearing surfaces and pivot pins for roughness, binding, or looseness. Lubricate and install upper thrust washer on shaft and slide shaft into distributor housing.

2) Install lower thrust washer and original collar on lower end of shaft, and install retaining pin. If collar is not in good condition, replace it.

3) Install lower plate, upper plate, and dual pick-up coil assembly. Attach vacuum advance unit arm to pick-up plate, and install attaching screws.

4) Position reluctor keeper pin into place on reluctor sleeve. Slide reluctor down reluctor sleeve, and press firmly into place. Make sure keeper pin is in place. Lubricate felt pad in top of reluctor sleeve, and install rotor.

Distributors & Ignition Systems

CHRYSLER CORP. ELECTRONIC SPARK CONTROL SYSTEM

**Dodge & Plymouth
All 6-Cylinder Engines**

DESCRIPTION

The Electronic Spark Control (ESC) system is governed by a Spark Control Computer (SCC). This system includes up to 6 engine sensors, a specially calibrated carburetor, and a dual pick-up distributor. The ESC system is designed to burn a lean air/fuel mixture, with a minimum of emissions. *See Fig. 1.*

SPARK CONTROL COMPUTER

The Spark Control Computer (SCC), mounted on the air cleaner, is the heart of the entire system. It gives the system the capability of igniting a lean fuel mixture according to different modes of engine operation by delivering an infinite number of variable advance curves.

The computer determines the exact instant when ignition is required, then signals the ignition coil to produce the spark required to fire the spark plugs.

The computer is basically an electronic printed circuit board, which receives signals from all the sensors. Within milliseconds, it computes the signals so that proper advance or retard is immediately achieved.

SENSORS

The electronic Spark Control Computer uses up to 6 engine sensors to determine when to fire the spark plugs. *See Fig. 2.*

These include 2 magnetic distributor pick-up coils (start and run), a coolant temperature sensor,

carburetor switch, vacuum transducer, and a charge temperature switch. Sensor signals are processed by a microprocessor in the computer. Sensor functions are as follows:

Fig. 2: Electronic Spark Control Computer

Vacuum transducer is mounted on computer housing.

Magnetic Pick-Up Assembly

The pick-up coil assembly is located in the distributor. The start pick-up coil supplies a signal to the computer, which will cause the spark plugs to fire at a fixed amount of advance during cranking only.

Once the engine begins to run, the run pick-up coil takes over, supplying advance information to the computer. The computer then modifies advance information to reflect other engine operating conditions supplied by the remaining sensors.

Coolant Temperature Sensor

The coolant sensor is located in the cylinder head. It informs the computer when the engine has reached a predetermined temperature. This information is

Fig. 1: Wiring Diagram for Chrysler Corp. Electronic Spark Control System

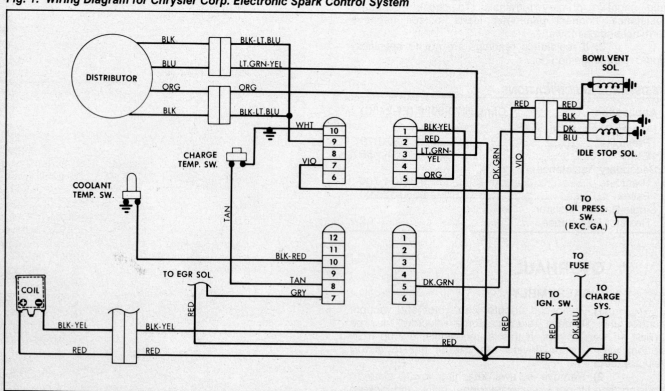

This system is used on all Chrysler Corp. Light Trucks with 3.7L 6-Cylinder Engines.

CHRYSLER CORP. ELECTRONIC SPARK CONTROL SYSTEM (Cont.)

necessary to determine correct spark advance in accordance with engine operating temperature.

Vacuum Transducer

This sensor, located on the spark control computer, signals the computer to inform it of engine operating vacuum. Vacuum is one of the factors used to determine how much the computer will advance or retard ignition timing.

Carburetor Switch

Located on the end of idle stop, the carburetor switch informs the computer when the engine is at idle. When carburetor switch contacts throttle lever ground, the computer will cancel spark advance and prevent air/fuel ratio from being adjusted.

Charge Temperature Switch

This sensor is located in the No. 6 branch runner of the intake manifold. The switch will be closed whenever intake charge (air/fuel mixture) is below 60°F (16°C).This permits no EGR timer function and no EGR valve operation. When temperature is above 60°F (16°C), the switch is open, allowing EGR timer to time out and EGR valve to operate.

OPERATION

The Spark Control Computer has 2 functional modes, "Start" and "Run". The "Start" mode operates while cranking and starting only. The "Run" mode operates after engine has started and during normal engine operation.

The two modes never operate at the same time. When cranking and starting, the pick-up coil sends a signal to the computer which is in the "Start" mode, the "Run" mode is by-passed.

During the "start" mode a fixed advance is used. Advance is determined by distributor position (basic timing). After engine starts, the pick-up coil continues to send a signal to the computer. The computer is now in "Run" mode and "Start" mode is by-passed. The amount of timing advance is now controlled by the computer, based upon information received from the engine sensors.

The amount of spark advance is determined by 2 factors, engine speed and engine vacuum. At what point it occurs, depends upon computer programming. Advance from **vacuum** will be provided when carburetor switch is open.

The spark advance programmed into the computer is proportional to the amount of vacuum and engine RPM. Advance from **speed** will be given by the computer when the carburetor switch is open and is programmed to engine RPM.

If for some reason, there is a failure of the "Run" mode of the computer, the "Start" mode will come back into service. This is called the "Limp-in" mode, it allows the vehicle to be driven. Performance and economy will be greatly reduced because of the fixed timing.

If the pick-up coil in the distributor fails (both coils in dual coil distributors) or the "Start" mode in the computer fails, the engine will not start or run.

TESTING

IGNITION SYSTEM STARTING TEST

1) Turn ignition switch "ON". Remove coil wire from distributor cap. Hold end of wire 1/4" from engine ground. Using a special jumper, intermittently ground coil negative terminal. Watch for spark at coil wire. If there is spark, it must be constant and bright blue. *See Fig. 3.*

Fig. 3: Special Jumper Wire with Capacitor

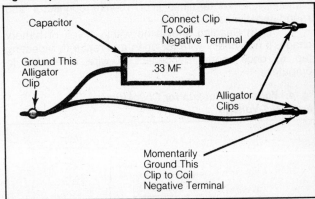

Use for "Ignition System Starting Test".

2) If spark is good, continue to intermittently ground coil negative terminal, while slowly moving coil wire away from ground. Check for arcing at coil tower. If arcing occurs, replace ignition coil.

3) If spark is weak or not constant, or if there is no spark, proceed to "Failure to Start Test."

4) If spark is good and there is no arcing at coil tower, ignition system is producing necessary high secondary voltage. Make sure spark is getting to plugs by checking distributor rotor, cap, spark plugs, and plug wires.

5) If all this checks out, but engine still will not start, ignition system is not the problem. It will be necessary to check fuel system and engine mechanical components.

FAILURE TO START TEST

NOTE: Perform "Ignition System Starting Test" first. If a good spark is obtained in this test, proceed to step 6). Failure to do so may result in lost diagnostic time or incorrect test results.

1) Turn ignition switch "OFF", and disconnect 10-wire connector from spark control computer. Repeat "Ignition System Starting Test", step **1)**. If spark results, replace spark control computer.

2) If no spark is obtained, check voltage at coil positive terminal. Turn ignition switch "ON". Connect positive voltmeter lead to coil positive terminal and ground negative lead. Reading should be within 1 volt of battery voltage. If not, check wiring between battery and coil positive terminal.

3) If voltage at positive coil terminal was correct, connect positive voltmeter lead to coil negative terminal and ground negative meter lead. Again, voltage should be within 1 volt of battery voltage. If not, replace ignition coil.

NOTE: You may wish to check coil primary and secondary resistance before replacing ignition coil. However, if you have battery voltage on positive side, but not on negative side, ignition coil normally requires replacement.

CHRYSLER CORP. ELECTRONIC SPARK CONTROL SYSTEM (Cont.)

4) If voltage was correct at negative coil terminal, but no spark resulted in "Ignition System Starting Test", step **1)**, replace ignition coil.

5) If spark results, but engine will not start, turn ignition switch to the "RUN" position. Connect positive voltmeter lead to terminal 1 of 10-wire connector and ground negative lead. *See Fig. 4.*

6) Reading should be within 1 volt of battery voltage. If not, check wire for open and repair it, repeating step **6)** once more. Reconnect 10-wire connector to computer.

Fig. 4: Voltmeter Hookup for Checking Terminal 1 Voltage

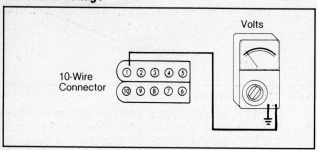

Insert positive lead into connector cavity.

7) If battery voltage was recorded in step **5)**, place a thin insulator (piece of paper) between curb idle adusting screw and carburetor switch or make sure screw does not touch switch. *See Fig. 5.* Ground negative lead of voltmeter.

8) Turn ignition switch to "RUN" position, and touch positive voltmeter lead to carburetor switch terminal. Reading should be approximately 5 volts. If so, proceed to step **13)**.

Fig. 5: Checking Voltage at Carburetor Switch

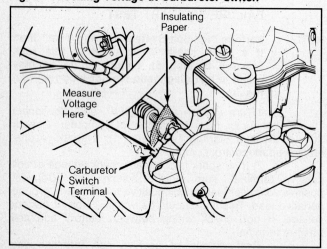

Insert insulator between contacts.

9) If voltage was not at least 5 volts, turn ignition switch "OFF". Disconnect 10-wire connector from computer. Turn ignition switch back to "RUN" position. Connect positive voltmeter lead to terminal 2 of 10-wire connector and negative lead to ground. *See Fig. 6.*

10) Voltage reading should again be within 1 volt of battery voltage. If not correct, check wiring between terminal 2 and ignition switch for opens, shorts or poor connections.

Fig. 6: Voltmeter Hookup for Checking Terminal 2 Voltage

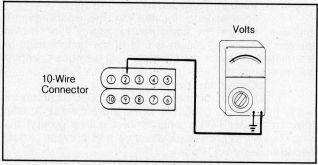

Insert positive lead into connector cavity.

11) If voltage at terminal 2 was correct, turn ignition switch "OFF". Using an ohmmeter, check continuity between terminal 7 of 10-wire connector and carburetor switch terminal. *See Fig. 7.* Continuity should exist. If not, check wire between connections for opens, shorts, or poor connections.

Fig. 7: Ohmmeter Hookup for Checking Carburetor Switch Wiring Harness

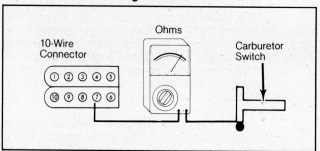

Insert ohmmeter lead into connector cavity.

12) If continuity is present, use an ohmmeter with leads attached to terminal 10 and engine ground to check continuity of ground circuit. *See Fig. 8.* If there is continuity, replace computer. If there is no continuity, check wire from terminal 10 to ground. If engine fails to start, proceed to next step.

Fig. 8: Ohmmeter Hookup for Checking Computer Ground Circuit

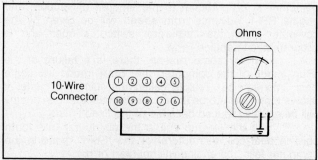

Insert ohmmeter lead into connector cavity.

13) Turn ignition switch "OFF". Attach ohmmeter leads to terminals 5 and 9 of 10-wire harness connector to check run pick-up coil resistance and to terminals 3 and 9 to check start pick-up coil resistance. *See Fig. 9.* Resistance should be 150-900 ohms. If so, proceed to step **15)**.

CHRYSLER CORP. ELECTRONIC SPARK CONTROL SYSTEM (Cont.)

Fig. 9: Ohmmeter Hookup for Checking Pick-Up Coil Resistance

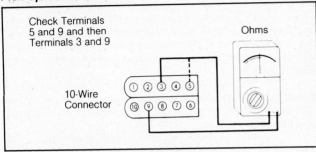

Resistance should be 150-900 ohms for each pick-up coil.

14) If not, disconnect distributor connectors, and attach ohmmeter leads to run pick-up coil leads and then to start pick-up coil leads coming from distributor. If resistance is now okay, wiring harness between computer and distributor is defective. If resistance is still not 150-900 ohms, replace pick-up coils, as necessary.

15) Next, connect one lead of an ohmmeter to engine ground and touch other lead to each terminal of 2 leads coming from each of the 2 distributor pick-up coils. There should be no continuity. If continuity is indicated, replace pick-up coils as necessary.

16) Remove distributor cap and check each reluctor-to-pick-up coil air gap. When setting **start** pick-up coil gap, use a .006" non-magnetic feeler gauge. Check gap using an .008" gauge. When setting **run** pick-up gap, set with .012" gauge and check with .014" gauge. Larger gauges should not fit in gap. *See Fig. 10.*

Fig. 10: Checking Distributor Pick-Up Air Gap

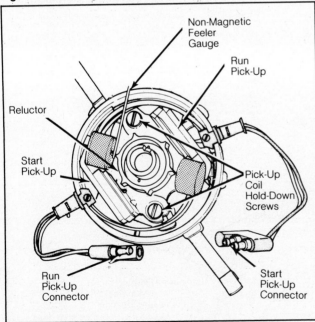

Use non-magnetic feeler gauge.

NOTE: To adjust gap, loosen pick-up coil hold-down screws, move pick-up coil against feeler gauge resting against reluctor tooth. Tighten hold-down screw, remove feeler gauge, and recheck gap.

17) Install distributor cap, and reinstall all wiring. If engine fails to start, replace spark control computer. If it still fails to start, install original computer and retest.

IGNITION COIL RESISTANCE CHECKS

1) If ignition coil is suspected, connect ohmmeter leads to positive and negative primary terminals. Ignition switch should be "OFF" and primary coil wires removed. Primary reistance should read 1.60-1.79 ohms for Prestolite coils; 1.34 to 1.55 ohms for Essex coils.

2) Then move ohmmeter leads to coil negative terminal and coil tower. Ohmmeter resistance reading should be 9400-11,700 for Prestolite coils, 9000-12,200 ohms for Essex coils.

3) Replace ignition coil if either specification is not obtained.

POOR PERFORMANCE TEST

Basic Advance Timing Test

1) Connect an adjustable timing light to engine so that total timing advance at crankshaft can be checked. Connect a jumper wire between carburetor switch and ground.

2) Be sure vacuum line is connected to vacuum transducer on computer. Observe timing mark on crankshaft damper immediately after engine starts to run. Adjust timing light so basic timing signal is seen at timing plate.

3) The meter on timing light should then show amount of advance, as indicated on vehicle emission control label.

Spark Advance of Computer

1) Set basic timing. Start engine and allow it to warm to normal operating temperature. Put transmission in neutral and set parking brake.

NOTE: The Spark Control Computer has various spark advance schedules incorporated into its microprocessor for operation at differing engine temperatures. Be sure engine is at normal operating temperature before testing.

2) Place a thin insulator (piece of paper) between curb idle adjusting screw and carburetor switch, make sure screw is not touching switch. *See Fig. 5.* Remove and plug vacuum line at vacuum transducer.

CAUTION: Use a metal exhaust tube for step 3), as high temperatures could cause rubber hose to catch fire.

3) Connect an auxiliary vacuum supply to vacuum transducer. Set to 10 in. Hg for 3.7L engines and 16 in. Hg for 5.2L engines. Increase engine speed to 2000 RPM, wait 1 minute for specified accumulator clock up time, and then check specifications. Advance specifications are in addition to basic advance.

4) If computer fails to obtain specified settings, replace computer.

CARBURETOR SWITCH TEST

1) Grounding the carburetor switch eliminates all spark advance on most systems. Turn key off, and disconnect 10-wire harness connector from computer.

2) With throttle completely closed, check continuity between terminal 7 and ground. If no continuity

CHRYSLER CORP. ELECTRONIC SPARK CONTROL SYSTEM (Cont.)

is indicated, check wire and carburetor switch. Recheck basic timing.

3) With throttle opened, check continuity between terminal 7 and ground. There should be no continuity.

CHARGE TEMPERATURE & COOLANT SWITCH

1) Turn ignition switch "OFF", and disconnect wire from charge temperature switch. Connect one lead of ohmmeter to engine ground (or to switch's ground terminal). Connect other lead to center terminal of coolant switch. Check for continuity.

2) For a cold engine, continuity should be present (resistance less than 100 ohms). If not, replace the switch. The charge temperature switch must be cooler than 60°F to obtain this reading.

3) For an engine at normal operating temperature, the terminal should show no continuity. If it does, replace coolant switch.

COOLANT SENSOR

1) Resistance of sensor changes continually with engine temperature. This device is not a switch. Connect ohmmeter leads to coolant sensor terminals. Check resistance with engine cold and at operating temperature.

2) Resistance with engine cold should be 500-1100 ohms. Resistance at operating temperature should be more than 1300 ohms.

3) If resistance is outside of specifications, replace sensor.

ELECTRONIC EGR SYSTEM TEST

The Spark Control Computer incorporates an electronic EGR control system. Check that engine temperature sensors are working properly, and proceed as follows:

1) With engine cold and ignition switch turned off, connect voltmeter positive lead to EGR solenoid Gray wire and negative lead to ground. Start engine.

2) Voltage should be less than 1 volt, remaining 1 volt until engine reaches normal operating temperature and electronic EGR schedule has timed out. Solenoid will then de-energize, and voltmeter should read charging system voltage.

3) If not to specification, replace solenoid and repeat test. If voltmeter indicates charging voltage before EGR schedule is complete, replace computer or externally mounted timer.

4) If an engine is started with engine hot, EGR solenoid will be energized for the length of time delay schedule only. It will then de-energize.

ELECTRONIC THROTTLE CONTROL SYSTEM TEST

The Spark Control Computer also incorporates an electronic throttle system on Federal 6-cylinder models. A solenoid, mounted on the carburetor, is energized when the A/C, heater, electronic backlite, or electronic timers are activated.

The 2 timers, incorporated in the ignition system, operate when throttle is closed, plus a time delay of 2 seconds, or after an engine start condition (EGR time delay).

1) To test system, connect a tachometer to engine. Start engine. Depress accelerator and let it up. A higher than curb idle speed should be seen for the length of EGR schedule.

2) If vehicle is equipped with A/C or electronic backlite, turn system on and depress accelerator for a brief period. A higher than curb idle speed should result. Turn system off and normal idle speed should return.

Fig. 11: Distributor for 6-Cylinder Vehicles

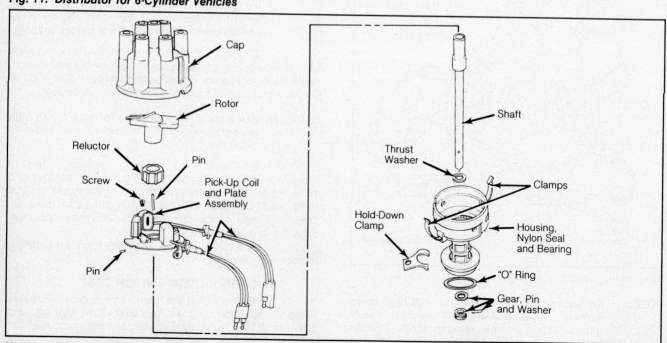

Notice difference between start and run pick-up coil connectors.

CHRYSLER CORP. ELECTRONIC SPARK CONTROL SYSTEM (Cont.)

NOTE: A/C clutch will cycle as it is running. This should not be mistaken as part of electronic control.

3) If speed increases do not occur, disconnect 3-way connector at carburetor. Check solenoid with ohmmeter, measuring resistance from terminal that contained Black wire to ground. Resistance should read 15-35 ohms. If not, replace solenoid.

4) Start vehicle and before delay has timed out, measure voltage of Black wire at 3-way connector. Charging voltage should be observed. If not, replace computer or Gray start timer.

5) After time delay, turn A/C or backlite on. Charging voltage should be read. If not, check wiring back to instrument panel for an open circuit.

OVERHAUL

Disassembly

1) Remove distributor cap. Using 2 screwdrivers, pry off rotor from shaft. Remove reluctor by prying up from bottom of reluctor using 2 pry bars or screwdrivers with a maximum width of 7/16". Be careful not to distort or damage reluctor teeth.

2) Remove 2 screws and lock washers attaching lower plate to housing, and lift out lower plate and pick-up coils as an assembly. Do not attempt to remove distributor cap clamps, as they are peened in place.

3) If distributor has excessive shaft side play (more than .006"), replace housing shaft and reluctor sleeve by removing shaft, retaining pin and sliding drive gear off end of shaft.

NOTE: Prior to removing shaft, scribe a line on end of shaft from center of shaft to edge. Line should align with space between 2 gear teeth.

4) Use a file to clean burrs from around pin hole in shaft, and remove lower thrust washer. Push shaft up, and remove shaft through top of distributor housing.

Reassembly

To assemble, reverse disassembly procedure

Distributors & Ignition Systems

DELCO-REMY HIGH ENERGY IGNITION (HEI)

**Chevrolet & GMC, Except Calif. S10
Pickups with V6 Engines
Jeep Models with 4-Cylinder Engines**

DESCRIPTION

NOTE: **Some Chevrolet and GMC light truck models with 5.0L 4-Bbl. (VIN LE9) engines are equipped with Electronic Spark Control to combat detonation. ESC models have 5-terminal electronic modules in the distributor, non-ESC models have 4-terminal modules.**

The Delco-Remy High Energy Ignition system consists of a battery, ignition switch, ignition coil, spark plugs, primary and secondary wiring, and a special distributor assembly.

The distributor housing and cap contain vacuum and centrifugal advance mechanisms, an electronic control module, pick-up coil, pole piece (with internal teeth), timer core (with external teeth), rotor, distributor shaft and a capacitor for radio noise suppression. Some distributor models also include an integral ignition coil.

Fig. 1: Exploded View of HEI Distributor

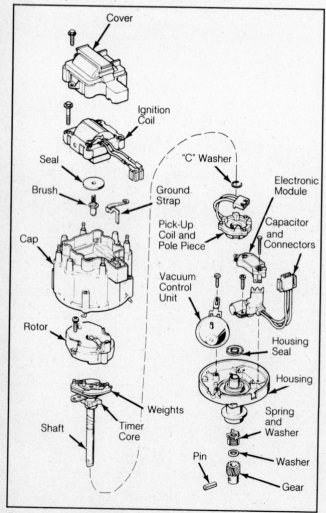

The timer core and pick-up coil pole piece have one tooth per cylinder.

Full battery voltage is present at the battery terminal of the distributor in either the "START" or "RUN" position, as no ballast resistance wire is used.

OPERATION

The pick-up coil assembly consists of a permanent magnet, a pole piece, and a pick-up coil. The pick-up coil assembly is stationary, unless it is shifted by the vacuum control unit. The timer core position can also be shifted by the centrifugal weights.

The timer core, mounted on the distributor shaft, rotates with the shaft inside the pole piece portion of the pick-up coil assembly.

When the external teeth of the timer core line up with the internal teeth of the pole piece, a voltage is induced in the pick-up coil. This signals the electronic module inside the distributor, which opens the ignition coil primary circuit. *See Fig. 2.*

Fig. 2: Delco-Remy HEI System Wiring Diagram

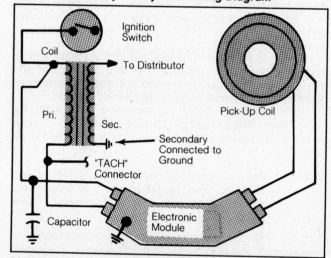

Module terminal letters may vary by model.

The magnetic field in the ignition coil primary circuit collapses, inducing high voltage in the coil's secondary circuit. This travels through the distributor cap contact, rotor and secondary wires to fire the spark plugs.

The electronic module automatically controls dwell period, stretching it with increasing engine speed. Dwell is not adjustable, and periodic checks of dwell are unnecessary. The HEI system features a longer spark duration, which is desirable for firing lean and EGR diluted mixtures.

TESTING

CAUTION: **During testing procedures, the following precautions must be observed. Do not ground tachometer terminal of distributor connector. Disconnect ignition switch connector at distributor before making compression checks.**

NOTE: **To remove plug wires, twist boot 1/2 turn and pull on boot (not on wire). When using a timing light, connect at plug end of number 1 spark plug wire (do not pierce plug boot).**

DELCO-REMY HIGH ENERGY IGNITION (HEI) (Cont.)

Check that wiring connector is properly attached to connector at side of distributor cap, and that spark plug leads are properly connected at both ends before continuing with test procedures.

ENGINE WILL NOT START

NOTE: **If engine is difficult to start or misses, check position of battery terminal connector at distributor cap. Terminal must be inserted on side of connector opposite hold-down clip.**

1) Connect voltmeter between battery terminal lead on distributor connector and ground. Turn ignition switch on. If voltage is zero, check system for open circuit.

2) If reading is battery voltage, connect a modified spark plug (plug that has ground electrode cut off) to center brush contact in distributor cap.

3) Crank engine. If spark occurs, trouble is not in ignition system. Check fuel system, spark plugs and wires for trouble. If sparking does not occur, follow procedures under *System Testing or Component Testing*. See Fig. 3.

Fig. 3: Modifying Spark Plug for Testing

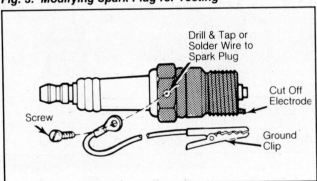

A commercial spark tester may also be used.

ENGINE STARTS BUT RUNS ROUGH

1) Check for proper fuel delivery to carburetor, vacuum hoses for leakage, ignition timing, centrifugal advance for proper operation, spark plugs for defects, and visually inspect and listen for sparks jumping to ground or to other wires.

2) If no defects are found or condition continues after correction, follow procedures under *System Testing or Component Testing*.

SYSTEM TESTING

1) Connect voltmeter positive lead to distributor battery terminal and negative lead to ground. Crank engine. If voltage is under 7 volts, repair or replace wiring or components back to battery, including ignition switch and all connections.

2) If voltmeter reading in step 1) was 7 volts or more, connect positive lead of voltmeter to "TACH" terminal of distributor, while leaving negative lead attached to ground. If voltmeter reading is 10 volts or more, proceed to step 4).

3) If reading in step 2) was under 1 volt, replace ignition coil. If reading was 1-10 volts, replace electronic HEI module in distributor, and check for spark as instructed in step 9). If spark results, system is OK. If

no spark results, replace ignition coil in addition to the module.

4) If reading in step 2) was 10 volts or more, remove distributor cap, but leave wiring harness attached to cap connector. Connect spark tester (ST-125) or modified spark plug so terminal touches center contact of cap. Ground tester ground wire, and crank engine. See Fig. 4.

Fig. 4: Checking for Spark at Ignition Coil Output Terminal

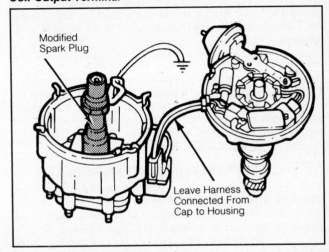

Integral coil model is illustrated.

5) If spark occurs, inspect cap for water, cracks, or other defects. If cap is OK, replace rotor. If no spark occurred in step 4), remove pick-up coil leads (Green and White wires) from module. Again, check voltage at "TACH" terminal of distributor cap.

6) Attach voltmeter positive lead to "TACH" terminal and negative lead to ground. See Fig. 5. Turn ignition switch on. Attach test light to battery positive terminal.

Fig. 5: Checking Distributor Components with Voltmeter and Test Light

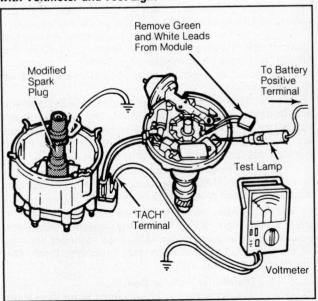

Integral coil model is illustrated.

DELCO-REMY HIGH ENERGY IGNITION (HEI) (Cont.)

7) Perform next test with test light still connected to battery positive terminal and Green and White wires still disconnected from module. Momentarily touch other test light lead to module terminal P. This is the small terminal. Touch light to module for no more than 5 seconds. Observe voltmeter reading.

8) If voltage did not drop, check module ground. Also check for open in wires for distributor to cap. If OK, replace HEI module.

9) If voltage dropped in step **5)** when test light was connected, or if 1-10 volts was recorded in step **2)**, check for spark at coil center contact (using spark tester as before) as test light is removed from module's "P" terminal.

10) If spark results, replace pick-up coil assembly. If no spark appears, use module tester to test HEI module. If OK, check ignition coil ground. If ground is OK, replace ignition coil. If module is defective, replace it.

11) If no module tester is available, check ignition coil ground circuit. If OK, replace ignition coil and repeat step **9)**. If spark results, system is OK. If no spark results, original coil is OK. Replace module.

INTERMITTENT SYSTEM PROBLEMS

1) Using a spark tester or modified spark plug, check for spark at 2 spark plug wires. If no spark results, see *System Testing*. If spark is noted on one or both wires, check for dwell increase from low to high RPM.

2) Check pick-up coil with ohmmeter leads attached to Green and White wires, removed from HEI module. If reading does not indicate between 500-1500 ohms, replace pick-up coil. If pick-up coil reading was satisfactory, and dwell did not increase, replace electronic module.

3) If pick-up coil was satisfactory, but dwell increased, check fuel, spark plug wires, distributor cap, rotor or spark plugs.

COMPONENT TESTING

Distributor Cap & Coil Testing

1) Remove distributor cap and coil assembly by removing wiring harness connector, battery lead, and cap-to-housing latches. Inspect rotor, cap, and coil assembly for arc-over. Replace parts as necessary.

2) To test coil primary resistance on **integral** ignition coil, connect ohmmeter leads to battery and "TACH" terminals on distributor cap. See Fig. 6. Ohmmeter reading should be zero or nearly zero. Replace coil if not to specifications.

3) Connect ohmmeter leads to "TACH" terminal and ground, and note reading. Next, test coil secondary resistance by connecting ohmmeter leads to coil secondary contact (cap button) and "TACH" terminal. See Fig. 6. Replace coil only if both readings are infinity.

4) On **external** coils, connect ohmmeter leads to battery and "TACH" terminals. See Fig. 7. Primary resistance should read zero or nearly zero.

5) Now connect leads to battery terminal and ground. On high scale, an infinity reading should be indicated. For secondary coil resistance, connect ohmmeter leads to "TACH" and secondary terminals. Ohmmeter should read less than infinite.

Distributor Pick-Up Coil

1) Connect external vacuum source to vacuum advance unit. If vacuum advance unit is inoperative,

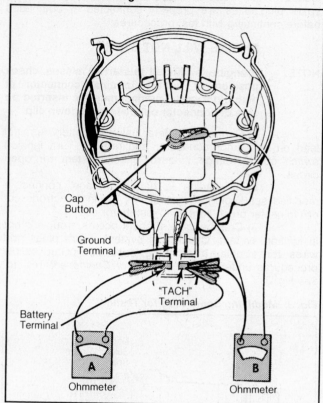

Fig. 6: HEI Distributor Cap and Coil Testing Connections with Integral Coil

Cap Button

Ground Terminal

"TACH" Terminal

Battery Terminal

Ohmmeter A

Ohmmeter B

Be sure leads contact proper connections.

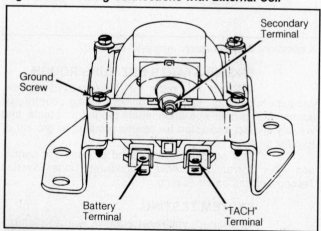

Fig. 7: Coil Testing Connections with External Coil

Secondary Terminal

Ground Screw

Battery Terminal

"TACH" Terminal

Touch coil mounting screw for ground.

replace unit. To check pick-up coil for shorts, connect ohmmeter leads as *shown by meter "A" in Fig. 8.*

2) Set on middle scale of meter. Operate vacuum advance through range. Reading should be infinite at all times. If not, replace pick-up coil.

3) To check pick-up coil resistance, connect ohmmeter leads as *shown by meter "B" in Fig. 8.* Again use the middle scale. Operate vacuum advance through its range. Ohmmeter reading should be 500-1500 ohms in all advance positions. If readings are not as specified, replace pick-up coil.

DELCO-REMY HIGH ENERGY IGNITION (HEI) (Cont.)

Fig. 8: Distributor Pick-Up Coil Testing Connections

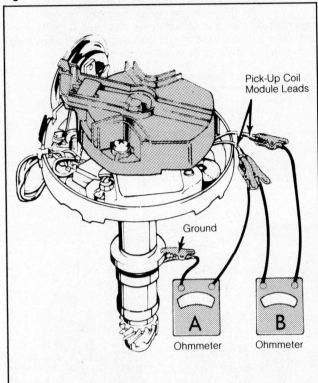

Fig. 9: Wiring Diagram for HEI System with Electronic Spark Control (ESC)

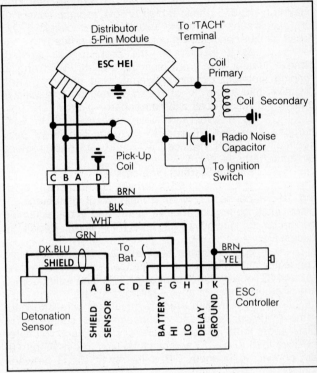

Capacitor

Set ohmmeter in x1000 scale. Disconnect capacitor. Touch ohmmeter leads to capacitor terminal and to ground. The needle should move slightly, but very quickly, and return to infinity. Any continuous reading other than infinity indicates defective capacitor.

HEI Distributor Electronic Module

If engine operation remains rough after preceding test procedures are completed, replace the distributor electronic module.

NOTE: When installing a new HEI module, use silicone lubricant on back of module and on housing under module.

ELECTRONIC SPARK CONTROL (ESC) TESTING

NOTE: Electronic Spark Control (ESC) is used on some Chevrolet and GMC models using the 5.0L 4-Bbl. (VIN H) engine.

Detonation Problems

1) With engine running at fast idle speed and transmission in Neutral or Park, tap exhaust manifold lightly and repeatedly. Check for spark timing retard with a timing light. If retard is noted, check other engine detonation causes.

2) If no retard occurs, disconnect 10-pin connector from ESC controller in passenger compartment. Connect voltmeter leads between pins "B" and "K" of connector. Voltage should read 80 millivolts (.08 volts). If so, proceed to step **4)**.

3) If voltage reading was lower than 80 millivolts, disconnect detonation sensor wire. Measure

voltage from sensor wire to ground. Reading should be more than 80 millivolts.

4) If low, replace sensor. If OK, check wires from pins "A", "B", and "K" of 10-pin connector for opens or shorts. If OK, repair sensor connector. If not OK, replace or repair wiring harness.

5) If resistance reading in step **2)** was OK, try to start engine with 10-pin connector disconnected. If it starts, replace distributor's HEI module.

6) If engine will not start, reconnect 10-pin connector to controller. Disconnect sensor wire from sensor, and insert a jumper wire into sensor wire connector. With engine running at fast idle speed, lay wire on top of distributor over ignition coil. If spark timing retard occurs, replace sensor.

7) If no spark retard occurs, connect voltmeter positive lead to pin "H" of 10-pin connector and negative lead to pin "K". With ignition switch "ON", voltage should read more than 0.2 volt. If voltage is more than 0.2 volt, replace ESC controller. If less than 0.2 volt, repair open wire from pin "H" in ESC harness.

Poor Engine Performance Problems

1) Disconnect 4-pin connector at distributor, and install a jumper wire between pins "A" and "C" of distributor connector. If problem remains, check other causes of poor engine performance.

2) If problem disappeared, remove jumper wire and reconnect 4-pin connector. Without disconnecting 10-pin ESC connector, attach jumper wire from pin "A" to pin "K". If problem remains, proceed to step **5)**.

3) If problem disappeared in step **2)**, remove jumper wire and disconnect sensor wire. Measure voltage from sensor terminal to ground. Minimum reading is 80 millivolts. If OK, check for engine noises other than detonation that might cause input to sensor.

DELCO-REMY HIGH ENERGY IGNITION (HEI) (Cont.)

4) If resistance reading was either high or low in the previous step, disconnect wire from sensor. Measure resistance from terminal to ground, checking again for 175-375 ohms. If high or low, replace sensor. If OK, check sensor wire and shield for open circuit. If OK, repair sensor connector. If not OK, repair harness.

5) If in step 2), the problem still existed, remove jumper wire from pins "A" and "K". With engine running, connect positive voltmeter lead to pin "F" and negative lead to pin "K" of 10-pin connector. If reading is under 11.6 volts, repair alternator charging circuit.

6) If over 11.6 volts, check wires in ESC harness from pins "H" and "K" for open circuits or poor connections. If OK, replace ESC controller; if not, replace or repair harness.

Engine Starting Problems

1) Check all ESC harness connections, including 10-pin connector, 4-pin connector at distributor, 2-blade male connector to distributor, and 2-blade female connector to ignition switch lead (Pink wire). Repair as necessary.

2) If all connections are OK, disconnect 4-pin connector at distributor. Install jumper wire between pins "A" and "C" of distributor connector. If engine will not start, check other causes of engine failing to start.

3) If engine starts with jumper wire attached, remove jumper wire and reconnect 4-pin connector to distributor. With ignition switch "ON", connect voltmeter positive lead to pin "F" and negative lead to pin "K" on 10-pin connector. If under 7.0 volts, repair circuit between ignition switch and pin "F".

4) If over 7.0 volts are read, check wires in ESC harness from pins "G", "H", "J" and "K" of 10-pin connector for opens or shorts. If harness is OK, replace ESC controller.

OVERHAUL

DISASSEMBLY

1) Disconnect wiring harness from cap. Disconnect coil wire. Remove distributor cap and disconnect vacuum hose from vacuum advance unit. *See Fig. 10.*

2) Mark rotor-to-distributor housing position and distributor housing-to-engine position for reassembly reference. Remove hold-down bolt and remove distributor housing from engine.

3) Remove rotor, two advance springs, weight retainer and advance weights. Mark distributor shaft and gear so they may be assembled in same position. Drive out roll pin from drive gear while supporting gear so no damage will occur to distributor shaft.

4) Remove gear, shim and tanged washer from distributor shaft, and clean any burrs from shaft. Remove distributor shaft from housing.

NOTE: **Do not attempt to service shaft bushings in housing.**

5) Remove 2 attaching screws holding module to housing, and position module to disconnect pick-up coil and wiring harness connectors. Remove "C" washer from housing, and lift pick-up coil assembly from advance unit and distributor shaft.

6) Remove 2 attaching screws, and remove vacuum advance mechanism. Disconnect capacitor lead,

and remove attaching screw and capacitor. Remove wiring harness from position in distributor housing.

7) For integral coils, remove 3 coil cover attaching screws and lift off cover. Remove 4 ignition coil attaching screws, disconnect coil leads, and remove coil from cap. Remove ignition coil arc seal.

Fig. 10: *Internal Components of HEI Distributor*

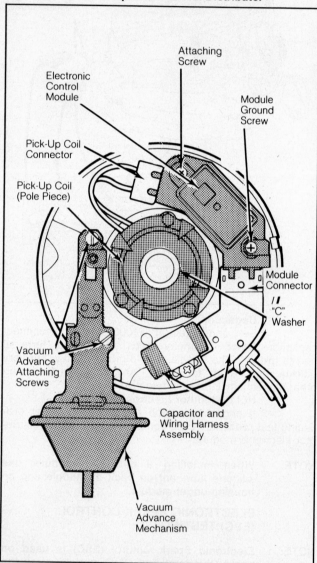

Number of module terminals will vary between regular and ESC systems.

REASSEMBLY

1) Reverse disassembly procedures, while noting the following: Ensure there is special silicone lubricant between module and distributor base to provide heat transfer for module cooling. Lubricate felt washer with a few drops of engine oil.

2) After installation of distributor shaft, rotate to check for even clearance between external timer core teeth and internal pole piece teeth. Notch on side of rotor must engage tab on cam weight base.

DELCO-REMY HIGH ENERGY IGNITION (HEI) (Cont.)

TYPICAL DELCO-REMY HEI OSCILLOSCOPE PATTERNS

TYPICAL PRIMARY PATTERNS
Scope Instructions for Primary Parade Only:

NOTE: **Also refer to instructions furnished by scope manufacturer.**

1) Scope secondary pick-up cannot be connected on integral coils, because coil center terminal is inside distributor .
2) Connect pick-up to No. 1 spark plug wire.
3) Connect primary pick-up to "TACH" terminal at distributor connector plug. *See Fig. 11.*
Reading Scope Primary Pattern:
A) Spark Zone — spark plug arcing.
B) Coil and Condenser Zone
B1) Firing Zone - no plug arc.
C) Dwell Zone - displays current through coil primary with module turned on.

TYPICAL SECONDARY PATTERNS

NOTE: **A special adapter placed on top of the coil cap assembly may be used with some scopes to view the secondary pattern. The output voltage will read low with the adapter; this is normal. Refer to the scope manufacturers' instructions.**

Secondary Voltage Patterns:
It is normal if dwell time varies from cylinder to cylinder. A 40 to 60 percent variation is shown below. It could be more, or it could be less. The voltage ripple shown may or may not appear; either is normal. Variation in dwell time or voltage ripple, as shown, does not necessarily indicate a bad module. *See Fig. 11.*

Fig. 11: *Typical Primary and Secondary Oscilloscope Patterns*

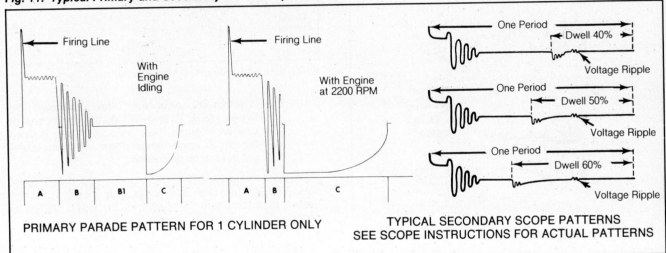

PRIMARY PARADE PATTERN FOR 1 CYLINDER ONLY

TYPICAL SECONDARY SCOPE PATTERNS
SEE SCOPE INSTRUCTIONS FOR ACTUAL PATTERNS

Refer to instructions furnished by scope manufacturer.

Distributors & Ignition Systems

DELCO-REMY HEI-EST IGNITION SYSTEM

**Chevrolet & GMC Calif. S10 Pickups
with V6 Engines**

DESCRIPTION

The Delco-Remy HEI-EST system, a part of all General Motors Computor Command Control (CCC) systems, is designed to provide optimum performance through electronic control of air/fuel ratios, spark timing, air management and idle speed.

The system consists of an electronic control module (ECM), an HEI-EST distributor, an external ignition coil, and necessary wiring. The distributor has neither vacuum nor centrifugal advance mechanisms. *See Figs. 1 and 2.*

The distributor contains a 7-terminal HEI-EST electronic module, a timer core, pole piece, pick-up coil, and a radio noise suppression capacitor.

Fig. 1: Disassembled View of EST Distributor

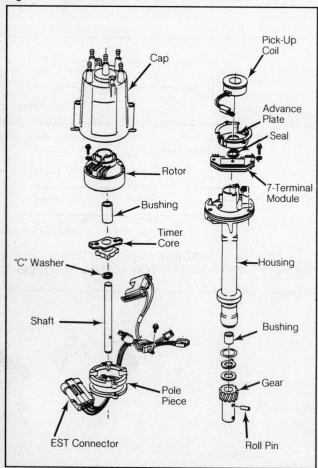

Distributor works with an external ignition coil.

The distributor is connected to the EST system by means of a 4-wire connector, leading to the CCC system's electronic control module (ECM).

The ECM (not the distributor HEI-EST module) receives voltage signals from a number of sensors. A typical system could be provided signals from oxygen, engine coolant temperature, throttle position, barometric pressure and manifold absolute pressure sensors, as well as, the distributor pick-up coil.

Fig. 2: Components of an HEI-EST Distributor

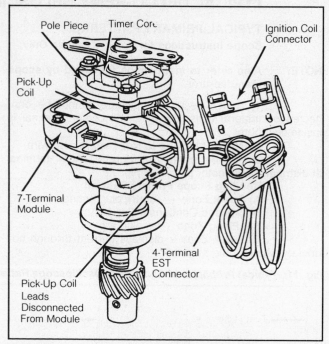

Timer core and pole piece have 4 teeth each.

CAUTION: Few components are interchangeable between HEI-EST and HEI distributors used on various engines. Be sure correct part is used, as similar appearance does not mean identical design or operation.

The HEI-EST distributor module has 7 terminals. The ignition coil battery terminal (positive) is connected to the module "+" terminal; the coil's "TACH" or negative terminal to the "C" terminal. *See Fig. 3.*

Terminals "N" and "P" are attached to the pick-up coil. HEI-EST module terminal "R" connects through the EST connector "B" to ECM terminal 10 (Distributor Reference Pulse Hi). Terminal "B" connects through terminal "C" to ECM terminal 11 (Ignition Module By-Pass).

Terminal "E" connects through connector "A" to ECM terminal 12 (EST). ECM terminal 13 (Distributor Reference Pulse Lo) connects to connector "D" and then to HEI-EST module ground.

OPERATION

During cranking or in event of EST ECM failure, a by-pass signal from ECM terminal 11 to HEI-EST module terminal "B" is either absent or low. *See Fig. 3.*

This notifies the HEI-EST module to take over control of spark advance and to ignore any EST information coming from the ECM. During this period, poor engine performance may result under some conditions, but the diagnostic "CHECK ENGINE" light will not come on.

The HEI-EST module will then convert pick-up coil RPM signals, and transmit them through the by-pass switch and terminal "C" directly to the negative "TACH" terminal of the ignition coil. These signals turn the coil primary circuit on and off, causing a surge in the secondary that fires the spark plugs.

DELCO-REMY HEI-EST IGNITION SYSTEM (Cont.)

Fig. 3: Schematic of HEI-EST Ignition System, Including Relationship To Computer Command Control ECM

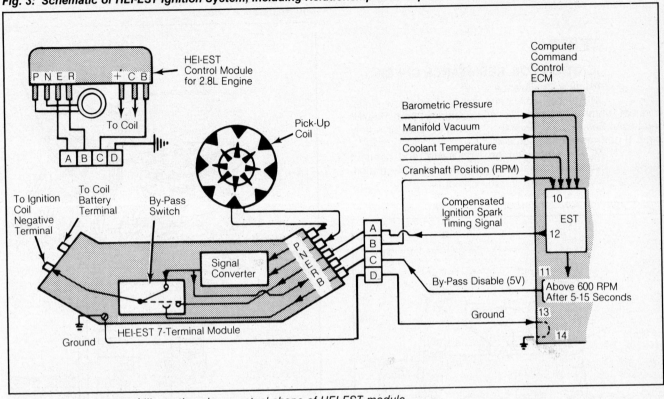

Upper left-hand corner of illustration shows actual shape of HEI-EST module.

When engine speed reaches 600 RPM or more (about 5-15 seconds after starting), the ECM transmits a constant 5-volt signal to the distributor HEI-EST module. This signal changes the position of the by-pass switch.

As a result, the pick-up coil's RPM signals can no longer flow directly to the ignition coil, as this circuit is now open. Instead, the signals are converted in the distributor module and routed through terminal "R" to ECM terminal 10.

The PROM (Programmed Read Only Memory) portion of the ECM carries the basic spark advance curve based on engine RPM. Spark timing is calculated by the ECM whenever an ignition pulse is present, however, spark advance information is only SENT TO the distributor when the engine is running (not during cranking).

Engine sensor values are used by the ECM to modify the PROM information, increasing or decreasing spark advance to achieve maximum performance with minimum emissions.

The coolant temperature sensor advances spark on a cold engine, and reduces advance as engine reaches normal operating temperature. If engine is too hot, spark is retarded to prevent detonation.

During light throttle operation, the throttle switch allows for additional advance. Additional adjustment by the ECM results from input from coolant temperature, engine RPM and manifold absolute pressure (MAP) sensors. When MAP is low, spark is at maximum advance.

As load increases and pressure increases, spark timing is retarded to allow the engine to maintain its performance and emission level.

After computation of all information from the various sensors, a compensated ignition spark timing signal is sent back to the distributor through the HEI-EST module's "E" terminal to the by-pass switch, "C" terminal, and ignition coil negative terminal.

Each time the signal is flashed on and off, the coil's primary circuit is turned on and off. As this occurs, a voltage surge is created in the secondary that fires the spark plugs.

The ECM is continually computing sensor information to maintain efficient engine performance with low emission levels, doing so under varying engine conditions.

PRE-TESTING DIAGNOSIS

If the reference or EST signals are interrupted due to open wires or a faulty ECM, the vehicle will still run. The HEI-EST module will provide a timing signal based on engine RPM.

If the by-pass signal is lost, the ECM cannot control spark timing, as the by-pass switch will permit direct flow of information to the ignition coil rather than to the ECM.

Normally, 5-15 seconds after starting a warm engine, the by-pass signal electronically operates a by-pass switch in the HEI-EST module. The HEI-EST module's RPM-controlled timing signal no longer can flow directly to the ignition coil, but is diverted to the ECM for modification by information from engine sensors.

Loss of the EST signal with the by-pass signal "ON", however, will stop the engine, because the HEI-EST module is no longer sending signals directly to the ignition coil, but to the ECM.

Any loss of the EST signal cuts all flow to the coil. If an attempt is made to restart the vehicle, the engine

DELCO-REMY HEI-EST IGNITION SYSTEM (Cont.)

will run for a few seconds and then stop when the by-pass signal comes back on.

TESTING

IGNITION COIL RESISTANCE CHECK
Primary Resistance

    1) Remove coil connector. Using the low scale, connect ohmmeter leads to coil's battery and "TACH" terminals. *See Fig. 4.* Resistance should be zero or nearly zero. If not, replace ignition coil.

    2) Set ohmmeter on high scale, and connect leads to battery terminal and a good ground on coil. Reading should be infinity. If not, replace coil.

Fig. 4: Ignition Coil Resistance Test Points

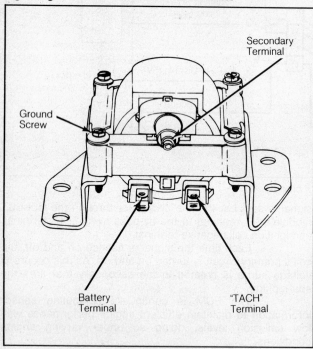

Coil primary wires must be removed for testing.

Secondary Resistance

    With ohmmeter set in high range, connect leads to "TACH" terminal and to secondary terminal. Reading should be less than infinite (approximately 6,000 to 30,000 ohms). If reading is infinity, replace coil.

DISTRIBUTOR PICK-UP COIL SHORT AND RESISTANCE CHECKS

    1) Disconnect pick-up coil leads from HEI-EST module "N" and "P" terminals (usually a Green and a White wire). To check for shorted pick-up coil, set ohmmeter in middle range.

    2) Connect an ohmmeter lead to either pick-up coil wire terminal. Connect other lead to distributor housing. *See Fig. 5.* Reading should be infinite. If not, replace pick-up coil.

    3) Connect ohmmeter leads to both pick-up coil leads, while flexing wires and connectors to locate intermittent opens. *See Fig. 5.* Resistance should read a constant unchanging value between 500 and 1500 ohms. If not, replace pick-up coil.

Fig. 5: Distributor Pick-Up Coil Short and Resistance Checks

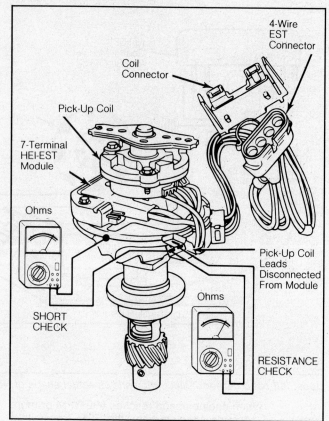

Notice ohmmeter test points.

IGNITION SYSTEM CHECK

NOTE: **Before making the following tests, secure an ignition spark tester. If tachometer is connected to ignition coil "TACH" terminal, disconnect it before performing tests. Use a digital voltmeter with 10 megohms impedance or larger.**

    1) Remove spark plug wire and attach spark tester to wire. Crank engine and check for spark at tester gap. If there is no spark, check a second wire in same manner. If sparks result, ignition system is not at fault. Suspect fuel system or spark plugs.

    2) If no spark resulted in step **1)**, attach ignition tester to ignition coil secondary wire. Crank engine and recheck for spark at tester cap. If spark occurs, inspect distributor cap for water, cracks, or carbon tracking. If cap is OK, replace rotor.

    3) If no spark occurred in either step **1)** or **2)**, remove distributor cap. Turn ignition system "ON". Check voltage at battery feed terminal (+) of HEI-EST module. Attach positive voltmeter lead to "+" terminal and negative lead to ground. Check for voltage while cranking engine.

    4) If reading is less than 10 volts, repair primary circuit back to ignition switch. If 10 volts or more, turn ignition "ON". Move positive voltmeter lead from HEI-EST "+" terminal to module "C" terminal. Leave negative lead grounded.

    5) If reading is under 1 volt, problem lies with open wire to ignition coil negative terminal, ignition coil

DELCO-REMY HEI-EST IGNITION SYSTEM (Cont.)

connection or primary circuit of ignition coil. Repair or replace as necessary. If 10 volts or more is registered on voltmeter, proceed to step **7)**.

6) If voltage reading on "C" terminal was 1-10 volts, replace distributor HEI-EST module and check for spark, following procedure outlined in steps **7)** through **10)**. However, if a spark results in step **10)**, ignition system is OK following module replacement. If there is still no spark, replace ignition coil also, as it too is defective.

7) If in step **5)**, 10 volts or more were read on module "C" terminal, remove pick-up coil connector from module. Turn ignition "ON". Check voltage again at module "C" terminal. Watch voltmeter as a test light is momentarily (not more than 5 seconds) connected to battery positive terminal to module "P" terminal.

8) If no drop in voltage occurs, check HEI-EST module ground. Also check for open in wires from distributor cap (coil) to distributor. If OK, replace HEI-EST module.

9) If voltage dropped, check for spark at tester gap (still attached to coil secondary terminal) when test light is removed from module "P" terminal. If spark occurs, either pick-up coil or its connections are defective.

NOTE: **Perform Distributor Pick-Up Coil Short and Resistance Check if not done previously. Resistance should be 500-1500 ohms.**

10) If no spark occurs and distributor module tester is available, check HEI-EST module. If OK, check ignition coil ground and coil-to-distributor wiring. If OK, replace ignition coil. If module is defective, replace.

11) If no module tester is available, replace HEI-EST module and repeat step **9)**. If spark results, system is OK. If no spark results, original module is OK. Reinstall module and replace coil.

INTERMITTENT OPERATION CHECK

1) Connect spark tester to 2 different spark plug wires, and crank engine. If no spark, perform Ignition System Check. If spark occurs at either or both wires, check for dwell increase from low to high RPM.

2) Check pick-up coil. Replace, if faulty. If pick-up coil is good and dwell did not increase, replace HEI-EST module. If good, but dwell increased, check fuel system spark plug wires, distributor cap and plugs.

EST EMISSION SYSTEM CHECK

1) With shift lever in "PARK" (auto. trans.) or "NEUTRAL" (man. trans.), run engine at fast idle and note timing change as test terminal is grounded. If timing changes, system is operating properly. Clear memory.

2) If timing does not change on vehicles equipped with manual transmissions, proceed to step **3)**. If timing does not change on vehicles equipped with automatic transmission, let engine return to idle and place transmission in "DRIVE". Note timing change as test terminal is grounded. If timing changes, system is operating properly. Clear memory.

3) If no change in timing occurs, check voltage at output of MAP (Manifold Absolute Pressure) sensor or vacuum sensor as vacuum hose is removed and re-installed. If no change occurs, problem is in the vacuum or MAP sensor circuit. If voltage output changes, proceed to next step.

4) Disconnect park/neutral switch and recheck for timing change. If timing changes, problem is either an improperly adjusted or faulty park/neutral switch. If timing does not change, check for grounded wire from terminal "H" of ECM to park/neutral switch. If wire is not grounded, replace ECM.

OVERHAUL
Disassembly

1) Remove coil connector and disconnect 4-wire EST connector. Turn 2 latches and lift off distributor cap.

2) Remove rotor and disconnect pick-up coil leads from HEI-EST module. *See Fig. 1.* Mark distributor shaft and gear for later reassembly. Drive out roll pin and remove distributor shaft from housing.

3) Remove retaining "C" washer, pick-up coil, magnet and pole piece. Remove 2 module attaching screws and capacitor screw. Lift module, capacitor and harness assembly from distributor housing. Disconnect wiring harness from module.

Reassembly

Assemble in reverse order, noting the following. Wipe distributor housing and module clean, and apply silicone grease between module and housing. Spin shaft to be sure timer core external teeth do not strike pole piece internal teeth.

Distributors & Ignition Systems

MOTORCRAFT DURA-SPARK II IGNITION SYSTEM

Ford, All Except Models Equipped with Electronic Engine Control (EEC)

DESCRIPTION

Dura-Spark II is a solid-state ignition system, consisting of a breakerless distributor, electronic control module, ignition coil, battery, ignition switch, secondary wires and various wiring harnesses. *See Figs. 1 and 3.*

Most models use a large rotor, a distributor cap and adapter, secondary wires, and wide gap spark plugs to take advantage of higher energy produced in the Dura-Spark II ignition system. The Dura-Spark II system can be identified by the module's 2-wire and 4-wire connectors. *See Figs. 1 and 2.* Depending on calibration, some models use the Universal Ignition Module (UIM). This module has three connectors.

OPERATION

As the engine cranks, the distributor shaft turns. A reluctor (armature) on the distributor shaft rotates past a pick-up coil (stator).

The reluctor has the same number of teeth as the engine has cylinders. As the teeth rotate past the pick-up coil, a signal is sent to the electronic control module.

Based on this signal, the module then determines when to turn current off and on in the primary windings of the ignition coil. This current collapse in the primary, causes a high voltage surge in the secondary.

This high voltage is routed to the spark plugs through the rotor, distributor cap and spark plug wires. A discussion of system components follows.

ELECTRONIC CONTROL MODULE

Each Dura-Spark II module has 6 wires (a 2-wire and a 4-wire connector). *See Figs. 1 and 2.* The Red and White wires are the ignition feed wires. The White wire is for cranking, and the Red wire is for operation after the engine is running.

The Red wire circuit contains a 1.1 ohm resistance wire. The current to the primary circuit of the ignition coil is turned off and on through the Green wire.

The Orange and Purple wires transmit signals to the electronic control module from the reluctor (armature) and pick-up coil (stator) in the distributor.

The Black wire is used to ground the electronic control module through the distributor housing.

Electronic control modules of the UIM type, having the third connector, provide for additonal spark timing control. This connector recieves a signal from the Ingition Barometric Switch, Ignition Timing Vacuum Switch, or the MCU module depending on engine calibration.

DISTRIBUTOR

Distributors on 6-cylinder models rotate clockwise, those of V8 models, counterclockwise.

A reluctor, containing the same number of teeth as the engine has cylinders, turns with the distributor shaft. The pick-up coil contains a permanent magnet, causing a magnetic field around the pick-up coil.

As the teeth of the reluctor approach and pass the pick-up coil, the magnetic field builds and collapses. This causes a signal to be sent to the electronic control module.

In turn, the control module turns the ignition coil primary off and on, causing a high voltage surge in the secondary.

Dura-Spark II systems have an adapter between the distributor housing and cap. *See Fig. 3.* Distributor caps are larger than for conventional distributors, and have male terminals. Dura-Spark II distributors have both centrifugal and vacuum advance mechanisms.

On single diaphragm vacuum units, increased vacuum causes the movable pick-up coil to pivot on the lower plate assembly, advancing spark timing.

On dual diaphragm units, the outer (primary) diaphragm operates from carburetor vacuum to provide timing advance during normal idle off driving conditions. It is connected to the pick-up coil assembly.

The inner (secondary) diaphragm operates from intake manifold vacuum and acts to retard ignition timing. The inner diaphragm is connected to the outer diaphragm rod by means of sliding linkage. Stronger intake manifold vacuum can override carburetor vacuum during closed throttle operation, retarding spark timing.

Fig. 1: Dura-Spark II Ignition System Wiring Diagram

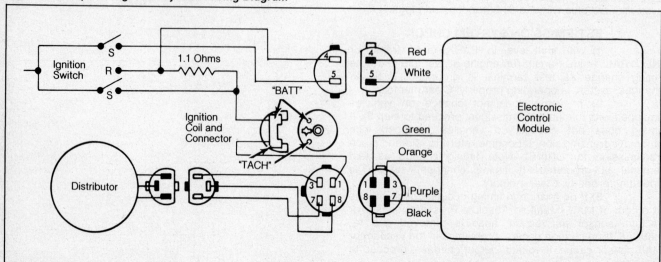

Electronic control module has a 2-wire and 4-wire connector.

MOTORCRAFT DURA-SPARK II IGNITION SYSTEM (Cont.)

Fig. 2: Control Module and Distributor Connectors for Dura-Spark II System

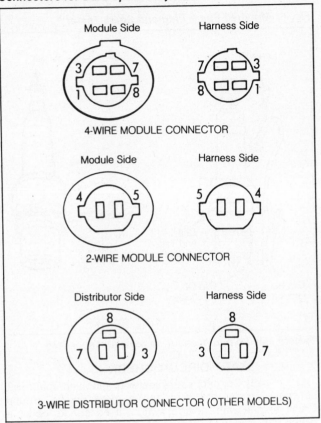

Compare terminal location to shape.

IGNITION COIL

Coils are oil-filled, and are energized whenever the ignition switch is in the "ON" or "START" position. They contain a positive "BATT" terminal, a negative "TACH" (sometimes called "DEC") terminal, and a single secondary terminal.

NOTE: "DEC" refers to Distributor Electronic Control. This terminal is also referred to as the "Tach Test" terminal.

A special connector attaches the Green wire from the control module to the negative terminal ("TACH") and the wire from the ignition switch to the positive terminal ("BATT").

RESISTANCE WIRE

The special ignition resistance wire in the Red wire circuit must be of specified length and diameter to reduce operating voltage.

CAUTION: Under no circumstances should it be replaced by any other wire other than correct service resistance wire.

When new wire is installed, old wire should be removed from system. Resistance value of wire is 1.0-1.1 ohms.

SYSTEM PROTECTION

Dura-Spark systems are protected against electrical currents produced or used by any other vehicle component during normal operation. However, damage to the ignition system can occur if proper testing procedures are not followed.

DURA-SPARK II SYSTEM PRECAUTIONS

Since the electronic control module and ignition coil are "ON" whenever the ignition switch is in the "ON" or "START" position, the system will generate a spark whenever the ignition switch is turned "OFF". This

Fig. 3: Schematic of Dura-Spark II Ignition System

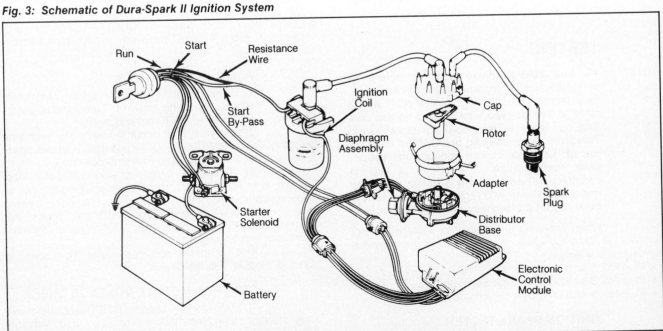

Illustration shows relationship of components to each other.

MOTORCRAFT DURA-SPARK II IGNITION SYSTEM (Cont.)

feature may be used as a diagnostic tool to check for continuity of circuit, coil and ignition switch. Some testing precautions follow:

CAUTION: Since a spark may occur if distributor cap is removed with switch "ON", keep switch "OFF" during underhood operations, unless you plan to start the engine or perform a test requiring the switch to be "ON". This will prevent accidental engine rotation during service or test procedures.

NOTE: Silicone dielectric grease must be applied to all insulating areas at distributor (not on cap or rotor, if vehicle is equipped with FM radio), coil and spark plug boots.

NOTE: A 3/4" clearance must be maintained at distributor cap mounting edge, spark plug wire terminals, and coil tower to prevent high voltage arc to ground.

NOTE: When replacing spark plug wires, insure wire made of the same material is used for a replacement. Silicone/Silicone wire can be identified by the letters "SS" appearing on the wire in WHITE lettering. Silicone/EPDM wire can be identified by the letters "SE" appearing on the wire in BLACK lettering. The "SS" wire is used on cylinders subject to very high engine temperatures.

NOTE: When removing distributor cap and adapter, always remove the distributor cap first, then the adapter.

ADJUSTMENTS

No adjustments are to be made to the ignition system except initial engine timing and spark plug gap.

TESTING

NOTE: All wire colors shown refer to colors of electronic control module wires. For example, "the Green wire leading to the coil" would refer to any colored wire leading to the coil, that connects to the module's Green wire. Therefore, when making tests, wires must be traced back to control module for proper color identification. Also, when a test is completed and a problem is found, make the necessary repair and repeat the failed test to be sure that the problem has been corrected.

When checking the secondary voltage, do not remove the following spark plug wires while the engine is running or cranking:
• Plug No. 1 or 8 on V8 engines.
• Plug No. 3 or 5 on 6 Cylinder engines.
• Plug No. 1 or 3 on 4 Cylinder engines.

IGNITION SPARK TESTER

Either use an ignition spark tester, or modify a spark plug for use in testing ignition system. To modify

plug, cut off side terminal, and install spring clip for grounding plug housing. *See Fig. 4.*

Fig. 4: Modified Spark Plug and Spark Tester

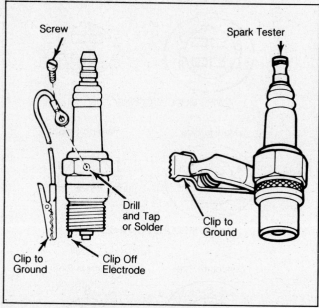

Testers may be purchased from most tool suppliers.

START CIRCUIT CHECK

1) Connect spark tester or modified spark plug between ignition coil wire and a good engine ground. Crank engine with ignition switch. If no sparks occur at tester gap, proceed to step **2)**. If sparks occur at tester gap, proceed to "Run Circuits Check".

2) If no sparks occurred in step **1)**, remove coil wire from distributor cap and ignition coil. Connect ohmmeter leads to both ends of coil wire, and measure resistance.

3) If resistance is more than 5,000 ohms per inch, replace coil wire. Also, inspect ignition coil for damage or carbon tracking. Crank engine to verify distributor rotation and proceed to "Voltage Supply Circuits Check".

RUN CIRCUITS CHECK

1) Remove ignition coil wire from distributor cap, and install spark tester on wire. Turn ignition switch from "OFF" to "RUN" to "OFF" several times.

2) Sparks should occur at tester gap each time switch goes from "RUN" to "OFF" position. Remove spark tester and reconnect coil wire to distributor cap.

3) If sparks occur, check distributor cap, adapter, and rotor for cracks, carbon tracking or lack of silicone compound. Also check for roll pin retaining reluctor to sleeve in distributor shaft and check that Orange and Purple wires are not crossed between distributor and control module.

4) If no sparks occurred in step **1)**, proceed to "Control Module Voltage Check".

CONTROL MODULE VOLTAGE CHECK

1) With ignition switch "OFF", carefully insert small straight pin in Red module wire. *See Fig. 5.* Measure battery voltage at battery. Attach negative voltmeter lead to distributor base and positive lead to straight pin.

MOTORCRAFT DURA-SPARK II IGNITION SYSTEM (Cont.)

Fig. 5: Checking Control Module Run and Start Circuits with Voltmeter

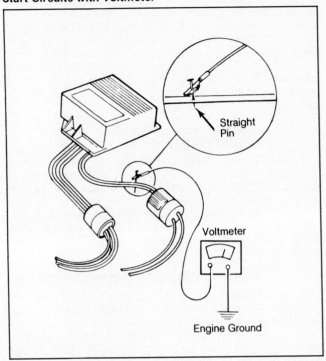

Do not let straight pin touch a ground.

2) Turn ignition switch to "RUN" position. Measure voltage at straight pin in Red wire. After reading voltmeter, turn ignition switch "OFF" and remove straight pin.

3) Voltage at pin should read at least 90 percent of battery voltage. If so, proceed to "Resistance Wire Check".

4) If reading was less than 90 percent of battery voltage, check wiring harness between control module and ignition switch. Also check for a worn or damaged ignition switch.

RESISTANCE WIRE CHECK

1) Disconnect control module 2-wire connector and remove coil connector from coil. Connect ohmmeter leads to "BATT" terminal of coil connector and to harness connector terminal mating with Red control module wire. Read ohmmeter, then reconnect all connectors.

2) If resistance is 0.8-1.6 ohms, problem is either intermittent or not in ignition system. If resistance was less than 0.8 or more than 1.6 ohms, replace resistance wire.

VOLTAGE SUPPLY CIRCUITS CHECK

1) If starter relay has an "I" terminal, disconnect cable between relay and starter motor at starter relay. If starter relay does not have an "I" terminal, disconnect wire to "S" terminal of starter relay. Insert small straight pins in Red and White control module wires.

CAUTION: Do not allow straight pins to contact an electrical ground.

2) Measure battery voltage at battery. Connect negative voltmeter lead to distributor base, and note voltmeter reading in each of the following situations:

- Positive voltmeter lead connected to pin in White wire, with ignition switch in "START" position.
- Positive voltmeter lead connected to "BATT" terminal of ignition coil, with ignition switch in "START" position. *See Fig. 6.*

Fig. 6: Checking for Battery Voltage at Ignition Coil Positive ("BATT") Terminal

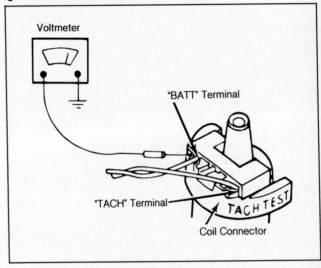

3) Turn ignition switch "OFF". Reconnect any wires disconnected from starter relay. Remove voltmeter leads, and remove straight pins from wires.

4) If voltage readings were at least 90 percent of battery voltage, test result is OK; proceed to "Ignition Coil Voltage Supply Check". If reading was less than 90 percent of battery voltage, check for faulty wiring harness/connectors or damaged ignition switch.

IGNITION COIL VOLTAGE SUPPLY CHECK

1) Connect negative lead of voltmeter to distributor base and positive lead to "BATT" terminal of ignition coil. *See Fig. 6.* Turn ignition switch to "RUN" position, and read voltmeter. Turn ignition switch "OFF".

2) If voltage was 6-8 volts, proceed to "Pick-Up Coil & Distributor Wiring Harness Check". If voltage was less than 6 volts or more than 8 volts, proceed to "Ignition Coil Primary Resistance Check".

PICK-UP COIL & DISTRIBUTOR WIRING HARNESS CHECK

1) Disconnect control module 4-wire connector, and inspect for dirt, corrosion or damage. Connect ohmmeter leads to harness connector terminals that mate with Orange and Purple control module wires.

2) Resistance should be 400-1300 ohms. If so, proceed to "Control Module to Distributor Wiring Harness Check". If resistance is not to specifications, proceed to "Pick-Up Coil Resistance Check".

CONTROL MODULE TO DISTRIBUTOR WIRING HARNESS CHECK

1) Disconnect 4-wire control module connector. Connect an ohmmeter lead to distributor base. Alternately, connect the other ohmmeter lead to wiring harness connector terminals that mate with Orange and Purple wires of control module connector.

MOTORCRAFT DURA-SPARK II IGNITION SYSTEM (Cont.)

2) If resistance is greater than 70,000 ohms, test result is OK. Proceed to "Ignition Coil Secondary Resistance Check". If resistance was less than 70,000 ohms, check wiring harness between control module connector and distributor, including distributor grommet.

IGNITION COIL SECONDARY RESISTANCE CHECK

1) Disconnect ignition coil secondary wire and ignition coil connector from coil. Connect ohmmeter leads to ignition coil "BATT" terminal and to high voltage terminal. Measure resistance and reconnect wire and connector.

2) If resistance is 7700-10,500 ohms, coil is OK, proceed to "Module-to-Coil Wire Check". If resistance is less than 7700 or greater than 10,500 ohms, replace ignition coil.

MODULE-TO-COIL WIRE RESISTANCE CHECK

1) Disconnect ignition coil connector from ignition coil, and disconnect ignition module 4-wire connector. Connect ohmmeter leads to engine ground and "TACH" terminal of ignition coil connector.

2) Measure resistance. Remove ohmmeter leads, reconnect ignition module and coil connectors.

3) If resistance was greater than 1 ohm, replace ignition module. If resistance was 1 ohm or less, inspect wiring harness between ignition module and ignition coil.

PICK-UP COIL RESISTANCE CHECK

1) Disconnect distributor connector from wiring harness. Connect ohmmeter leads to distributor connector terminals that mate with Orange and Purple wires of control module. Measure resistance of pick-up coil. Reconnect distributor connector to wiring harness.

2) Resistance should be 400-1000 ohms. If resistance is within this range, pick-up coil is OK. If resistance is not within specified range, replace pick-up coil assembly.

IGNITION COIL PRIMARY RESISTANCE CHECK

1) Disconnect ignition coil connector. Connect ohmmeter leads to "BATT" and "TACH" terminals of ignition coil. Measure resistance, and reconnect ignition coil connector.

2) If resistance is 0.8-1.6 ohms, coil is OK. Proceed to "Primary Circuit Continuity Check". If resistance is less than 0.8 or greater than 1.6 ohms, replace ignition coil.

PRIMARY CIRCUIT CONTINUITY CHECK

1) Insert a small straight pin in control module Green wire. Connect negative voltmeter lead to distributor base, and positive lead to pin in Green wire.

2) With ignition switch in "RUN" position, measure voltage. Turn ignition switch "OFF" and remove straight pin from Green wire.

Fig. 7: Components of Dura-Spark II Distributor

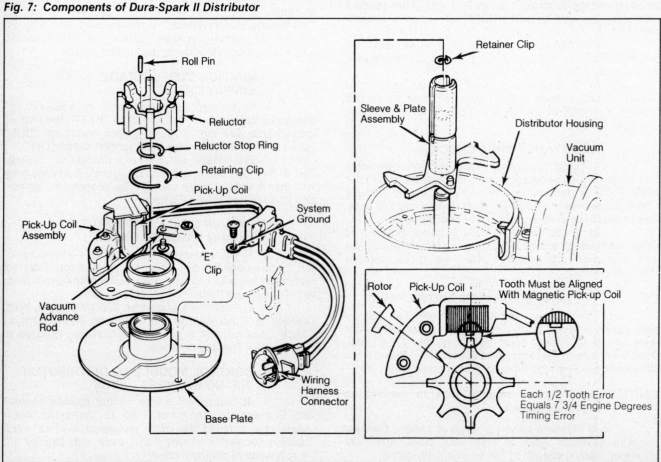

MOTORCRAFT DURA-SPARK II IGNITION SYSTEM (Cont.)

3) If voltage reading was greater than 1.5 volts, proceed to "Ground Circuit Continuity Check''. If voltage reading was 1.5 volts or less, inspect wiring between module and coil.

GROUND CIRCUIT CONTINUITY CHECK

1) Insert a small straight pin in control module Black wire. Connect negative lead of voltmeter to distributor base, and positive lead to straight pin in Black wire. With ignition switch in "RUN" position, measure voltage. Turn ignition switch "OFF", and remove straight pin.

2) If voltage reading was greater than 0.5 volt, proceed to "Distributor Ground Circuit Continuity Check". If voltage was 0.5 volt or less, replace control module.

DISTRIBUTOR GROUND CIRCUIT CONTINUITY CHECK

1) Disconnect distributor connector from wiring harness. Connect ohmmeter leads to distributor base, and to Black wire terminal in distributor connector. Measure resistance, then reconnect distributor connector to wiring harness.

2) If resistance was less than 1 ohm, circuit is OK. If resistance was greater than 1 ohm, check ground screw in distributor housing.

SPARK PLUG WIRE RESISTANCE CHECK

1) Remove distributor cap, and disconnect spark plug end of suspected wire or wires. Connect ohmmeter leads to spark plug terminal and terminal inside distributor cap (each end of wire).

CAUTION: **Never puncture a spark plug wire when measuring resistance.**

2) If resistance is less than 5000 ohms per inch, visually inspect wires for damage and remove spark plug for inspection and/or replacement. If resistance is greater than 5000 ohms per inch, disconnect suspected wire from distributor cap and again connect leads to each end of wire.

3) If resistance is now less than 5000 ohms per inch, inspect distributor cap and spark plug wire terminals for damage. Repair as necessary. If resistance is still greater than 5000 ohms per inch, replace wire(s).

OVERHAUL

DISASSEMBLY

1) Remove distributor cap, adapter, and rotor. Disconnect distributor wiring harness plug. Using a small gear puller or two screwdrivers, carefully pry armature from sleeve and plate assembly. Remove roll pin.

CAUTION: **Do not pinch stator wires when removing armature.**

2) On V8 engines, remove large wire retaining clip from base plate annular groove. Remove ground screw base, and pull up to remove rubber grommet from base.

3) Remove "E" clip securing diaphragm rod advance link to stator assembly. Lift diaphragm rod off post on stator assembly, and move it out against housing. Remove stator assembly.

4) On 6-cylinder models, remove "E" clip washer and wave washer, securing stator assembly to lower plate. Remove stator assembly ground screw and lift assembly from distributor.

REASSEMBLY

Reverse disassembly procedure. Using new roll pin, install roll pin in different groove, 180° from original groove.

MOTORCRAFT DURA-SPARK III IGNITION SYSTEM (EEC III)

**Ford Light Duty Emission Models
All Models With EEC III**

DESCRIPTION

The ignition portion of the EEC III system is referred to as Dura-Spark III. It is a solid state system, which provides power switching of the ignition coil. Dura-Spark III input signals are controlled by the EEC system.

Unlike Dura-Spark II, the Dura-Spark III distributor has no centrifugal or vacuum advance, armature (reluctor) or stator (pick-up coil). *See Fig. 2* The functions of these components are performed by the EEC module. All engines with EEC III use this except the 3.8L V6 engine, which uses a modified Dura-Spark II distributor. Secondary wires and spark plugs are the same in Dura-Spark II and III systems.

Although control modules appear similar, they must not be interchanged. Dura-Spark III control modules have no Purple wire, and can also be identified by a Brown grommet. Dura-Spark II modules have a Blue grommet. Universal Ignition Modules (UIM) used in Dura-Spark II systems have a Yellow grommet and a third connector.

Ignition timing is determined by the EEC control module based on information received from crankshaft position (CP) sensor and other engine sensors. These sensors feed information to the EEC III system Electronic Control Assembly (ECA) through a special 32-pin connector. For further information on these sensors and the electronic control assembly, *see Ford Electronic Engine Control III article in EMISSION CONTROL SECTION.*

Unlike conventional distributors that are restricted to approximately 20° advance, the EEC system permits up to 50° distributor advance. Both distributor cap and rotor have upper and lower electrode levels.

As the rotor turns, one of the high voltage electrode pick-up arms is aligned with one arm of the distributor cap center electrode plate. This allows high voltage to pass from the center plate arms through the rotor, distributor cap, and spark plug wire to the appropriate spark plug.

OPERATION

With the ignition switch turned "ON", the primary circuit is on and the ignition coil is energized. *See Fig. 1.* The EEC system provides a signal telling the ignition module to turn off the coil primary circuit for all models except 3.8L V6.

Fig. 2: Exploded View of Dura-Spark III Distributor

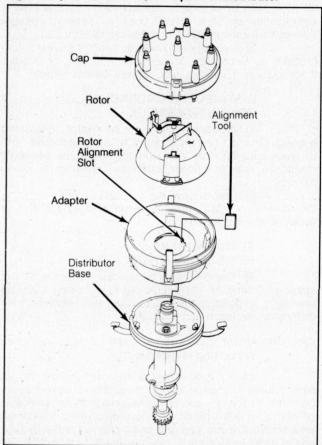

No vacuum or centrifugal advance units are used.

Fig. 1: Wiring Schematic of Dura-Spark III Ignition System

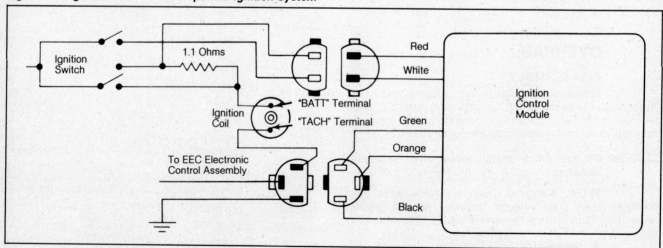

Dura-Spark III modules have a 2-wire and 3-wire connector.

MOTORCRAFT DURA-SPARK III IGNITION SYSTEM (EEC III) (Cont.)

The length of time the primary circuit is turned on or off is controlled by the EEC Electronic Control Assembly (ECA). *See Fig. 3.* When the current is on, it flows from the battery through the ignition switch, primary windings of ignition coil, and ignition module circuits to ground.

Fig. 3: EEC III Electronic Control Assembly

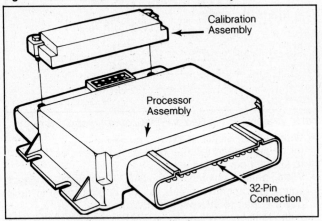

ECA is located on left front inner fender well.

When current is turned off, the magnetic field, which is built up in the ignition coil collapses, inducing high voltage to the secondary windings of the coil.

This high voltage, produced each time the magnetic field builds and collapses, is transmitted by the coil to the distributor cap, rotor and to individual spark plugs.

Fig. 4: Spark Tester & Modified Spark Plug

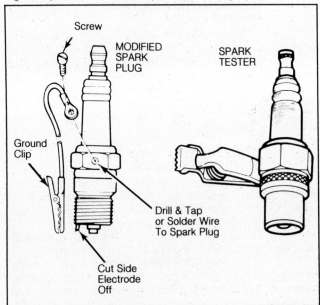

Modify spark plug by cutting off side terminal, and installing spring clip.

TESTING

NOTE: **Before beginning test procedures, visually inspect the engine compartment to ensure all vacuum hoses and spark plug wires are properly routed and connected. Check all wiring harnesses and connectors for damage. Be sure that battery is fully charged.**

NOTE: **All wire colors referred to are colors of ignition module wires. When test requires inspection of wiring harness, both visual and continuity checks should be performed. Also, when making measurements on a wiring harness or connector, wiggle the wires while measuring.**

SPARK TESTER

Use either an ignition spark tester or modify a spark plug (cut off side terminal, and install spring clip for grounding plug housing) for use in testing ignition system. *See Fig. 4.*

RUN CIRCUIT CHECK

1) Disconnect ignition module 3-wire connector, and install ignition diagnostic test adapter (T79P-12127-A or equivalent) as shown in *Fig. 5.* Disconnect ignition coil wire from distributor, and connect spark tester to coil wire and engine ground.

Fig. 5: Ignition Diagnostic Test Adapter and Spark Tester Hook-Up for Run Circuits Check

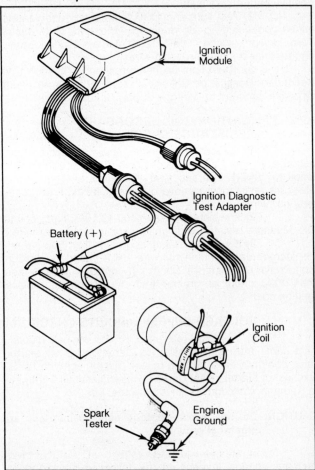

Spark should occur at tester, when lead is touched to battery positive terminal.

Distributors & Ignition Systems

MOTORCRAFT DURA-SPARK III IGNITION SYSTEM (EEC III) (Cont.)

2) Turn ignition switch to "RUN" position, and touch diagnostic adapter lead to positive battery terminal. Sparks should occur at tester gap each time lead touches battery terminal. Turn ignition switch "OFF", remove spark tester, and remove ignition diagnostic test adapter. Reconnect all wires.

3) If sparks occurred at tester gap, proceed to "Start Circuits Check". If no sparks occurred at tester gap, proceed to "Ignition Coil Primary Circuit Switching Check".

START CIRCUIT CHECK

1) Disconnect ignition coil wire from distributor cap, and attach spark tester to wire and engine ground. Crank engine, using ignition switch. Disconnect spark tester, and reconnect coil wire to distributor.

2) If spark occurred at tester gap, inspect distributor cap, adapter and rotor for cracks, carbon tracking, rotor alignment or lack of silicone compound. If sparks did not occur at tester gap, proceed to "Voltage Supply Circuits Check".

IGNITION COIL PRIMARY CIRCUIT SWITCHING CHECK

1) Disconnect ignition module 3-wire connector and install diagnostic adapter (T79P-12127-A or equivalent). Connect a test light between "TACH" terminal of ignition coil and an engine ground. With ignition switch in "RUN" position, touch diagnostic adapter test lead to positive battery terminal.

2) Test light should flash each time test lead is either connected to or removed from battery terminal. Turn ignition switch "OFF", remove diagnostic adapter, and reconnect ignition module wires.

3) If test light flashes, proceed to "Ignition Coil Secondary Resistance Check". If test light does not flash or is dim, proceed to "Voltage Supply Circuits Check".

IGNITION COIL SECONDARY RESISTANCE CHECK

1) Disconnect ignition coil connector and secondary wire from ignition coil. Connect ohmmeter leads to "TACH" and secondary terminals of ignition coil. Measure resistance, remove ohmmeter leads, and reconnect coil wires.

2) If resistance was 7700-10,500 ohms, coil is OK. Measure resistance of ignition coil-to-distributor wire.

3) If wire resistance is greater than 5000 ohms per inch, replace ignition coil wire and proceed to "Ignition Coil Primary Resistance Check". If coil resistance is less than 7000 ohms or greater than 10,500 ohms, replace ignition coil.

VOLTAGE SUPPLY CIRCUITS CHECK

1) If starter relay has an "I" terminal, disconnect cable from starter relay to starter motor. If starter relay does not have an "I" terminal, disconnect wire to "S" terminal of starter relay. Carefully insert small straight pins in Red and White ignition module wires. *See Fig. 6.*

CAUTION: Do not allow straight pins to contact an electrical ground.

2) Measure battery voltage at battery, then measure voltage in each of the following situations at points indicated:

Fig. 6: Checking Voltage Supply Circuits

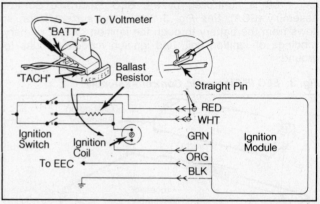

Install straight pins in Red & White control module wires.

- With ignition switch in "RUN" position, connect voltmeter negative lead to an engine ground and positive lead to straight pin in Red wire.
- With ignition switch in "START" position, connect voltmeter negative lead to an engine ground and positive lead to straight pin in White wire.
- With ignition switch in "START" position, connect voltmeter negative lead to an engine ground and positive lead to ignition coil "BATT" terminal.

3) Turn ignition switch "OFF", remove voltmeter and straight pins, and reconnect starter relay cables. If voltage was at least 90 percent of battery voltage, proceed to "Ignition Coil Voltage Supply Check".

4) If voltage was less than 90 percent of battery voltage, inspect wiring harness/connectors or damaged ignition switch.

IGNITION COIL VOLTAGE SUPPLY CHECK

1) Attach negative lead of voltmeter to engine ground, and positive lead of voltmeter to "BATT" terminal of ignition coil. Turn ignition switch to "RUN" position and measure voltage. Turn ignition switch "OFF".

2) If voltage was 6-8 volts, proceed to "Module-to-Coil Wire Resistance Check". If voltage was less than 6 volts or greater than 8 volts, proceed to "Ignition Coil Primary Resistance Check".

MODULE-TO-COIL WIRE RESISTANCE CHECK

1) Disconnect ignition coil connector from ignition coil, and disconnect ignition module 3-wire connector. Connect ohmmeter leads to engine ground and "TACH" terminal of ignition coil connector.

2) Measure resistance. Remove ohmmeter leads, reconnect ignition module and coil connectors.

3) If resistance was greater than 1 ohm, replace ignition module. If resistance was 1 ohm or less, inspect wiring harness between ignition module and ignition coil.

IGNITION COIL PRIMARY RESISTANCE CHECK

1) Disconnect ignition coil connector. Connect ohmmeter leads to "BATT" and "TACH" terminals of ignition coil. Measure resistance, remove ohmmeter leads, and reconnect ignition coil connector.

MOTORCRAFT DURA-SPARK III IGNITION SYSTEM (EEC III) (Cont.)

2) If resistance was 0.8-1.6 ohms, proceed to "Module-to-Coil Wire Voltage Check". If resistance was less than 0.8 ohm or greater than 1.6 ohms replace ignition coil.

MODULE-TO-COIL WIRE VOLTAGE CHECK

1) Carefully insert a small straight pin in Green ignition module wire. Turn ignition switch to "RUN" position.

2) Attach negative lead of voltmeter to engine ground, and positive lead to straight pin in Green wire. Observe reading. Move positive lead to "TACH" terminal of ignition coil, observe reading. Turn ignition switch "OFF", remove pin from wire.

3) If the difference in voltage readings was less than 0.5 volt, proceed to "Primary Circuit Continuity Check". If difference in voltage readings was greater than 0.5 volt, inspect wiring harness between ignition module and ignition coil.

PRIMARY CIRCUIT CONTINUITY CHECK

1) Carefully insert a small straight pin in Green ignition module wire. Connect negative voltmeter lead to engine ground and positive voltmeter lead to pin in Green wire.

2) Turn ignition switch to "RUN" position, and measure voltage. Turn ignition switch "OFF", remove voltmeter and straight pin.

3) If voltage was greater than 1.5 volts, proceed to "Ground Circuit Continuity Check". If voltage was 1.5 volts or less, proceed to "Ballast Resistor Check".

BALLAST RESISTOR CHECK

1) Disconnect ignition module 2-wire connector. Disconnect ignition coil connector from ignition coil.

2) Connect ohmmeter leads to "BATT" terminal of ignition coil connector and to wiring harness terminal that mates with Red module wire. Measure resistance. Reconnect ignition coil and ignition module connectors.

3) If resistance was 0.8-1.6 ohms, replace ignition module. If resistance was less than 0.8 ohm or greater than 1.6 ohms, replace ballast resistor.

GROUND CIRCUIT CONTINUITY CHECK

1) Carefully insert a small straight pin in ignition module Black wire. Attach negative voltmeter lead to ground. Attach positive voltmeter lead to straight pin.

2) Turn ignition switch to "RUN" position, measure voltage. Turn ignition switch "OFF", remove straight pin.

3) If voltage was more than 0.5 volt, proceed to "Wiring Harness Ground Circuit Check". If voltage was less than 0.5 volt, replace ignition module.

WIRING HARNESS GROUND CIRCUIT CHECK

1) Disconnect ignition module 3-wire connector. Connect ohmmeter leads to engine ground and terminal in wiring harness connector that mates with Black wire of ignition module.

2) Measure resistance. Reconnect ignition module 3-wire connector.

3) If resistance was less than 1 ohm; inspect Black wire, ignition module connector and wiring harness. If resistance was greater than 1 ohm, inspect wiring harness/connectors between ignition module and ground.

SPARK PLUG WIRE CHECK

1) Disconnect spark plug end of suspected wire or wires. Remove distributor cap. Measure resistance of spark plug wires by touching ohmmeter probes to each end of wire. Measure from inside distributor cap. If resistance is less than 5000 ohms per inch, wire is OK.

2) If resistance is more than 5000 ohms per inch, remove wire from cap and measure resistance of wire only.

3) If resistance is less than 5000 ohms per inch, wire is OK. Check distributor cap and spark plug terminal for corrosion. If resistance is more than 5000 ohms, replace spark plug wire.

Fig. 7: Rotor and Adapter for Dura-Spark III Distributor

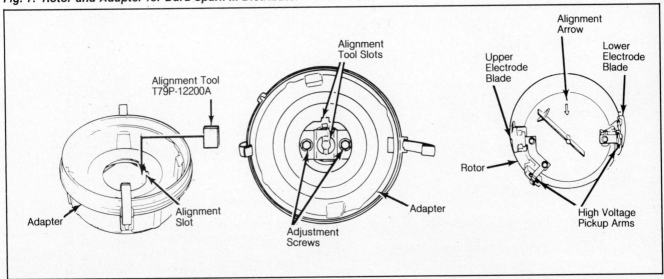

Notice rotor and adapter-to-distributor shaft alignment.

Distributors & Ignition Systems

MOTORCRAFT DURA-SPARK III IGNITION SYSTEM (EEC III) (Cont.)

OVERHAUL

ROTOR

Removal

Remove distributor cap. Remove rotor by pulling up on rotor pull tab. Rotor is held in place by a spring clip.

NOTE: Rotor removal is only necessary when replacing rotor or adapter or when checking rotor condition. No adjustment to distributor is needed when rotor is replaced.

Installation

1) Coat rotor lower electrode blade only (not upper blades) using silicone grease. Coat all 4 distributor cap center blade arms to a 1/32" thickness.

2) To check rotor alignment set No. 1 piston on compression stroke. Rotate crankshaft until rotor alignment tool (T79P-12200-A) can be inserted into alignment slots in rotor and center of shaft. *See Fig. 7.*

3) Read timing mark on damper that is aligned with pointer. If timing mark is within 4° of specification, do not reset rotor alignment. EEC models should be adjusted to TDC.

4) If alignment is not within 4° of specified timing when installing rotor, remove alignment tool. Position crankshaft at proper timing mark. Loosen 2 sleeve assembly adjustment screws.

5) Rotate sleeve until alignment tool fits into alignment slots. Tighten adjustment screws and remove alignment tool.

6) Align arrow, molded into top of rotor, with large key way slot in distributor sleeve. Press down on rotor until retaining spring snaps into place.

NOTE: Since EEC distributors have no vacuum or centrifugal advance mechanisms, overhaul is limited to removal, inspection, and alignment of rotor or removal and inspection of cap.

MOTORCRAFT SOLID STATE IGNITION (SSI)

Jeep 6-Cylinder & V8 Models

DESCRIPTION

The Solid State Ignition (SSI) system features a solid state distributor, an electronic control unit (ECU), an ignition coil, and conventional distributor cap, rotor, spark plug wires and spark plugs.

Other components include the battery, ignition switch, starter solenoid and primary resistance wires.

ELECTRONIC CONTROL UNIT

The electronic control unit (ECU) has 6 wires that lead to 2-wire and 4-wire connectors.

The White and Red wires leading to the 2-wire connector are ignition feed circuits — the White wire for cranking, the Red wire for engine running.

The electronic control unit uses the Green wire to turn power to the ignition coil off and on. The Orange and Violet wires are used to transmit signals from the distributor's sensor to the control unit. The Black wire supplies the distributor ground circuit.

NOTE: **The ECU is sealed to resist moisture, vibration, dirt and atmospheric conditions. It is not repairable and must be serviced as a complete unit.**

DISTRIBUTOR

Components are divided into 3 groups, the sensor and trigger wheel, the spark advance, and the cap and rotor. The trigger wheel which has 6 or 8 teeth (1 per cylinder), rotates with the distributor shaft. The sensor is a coil of fine wire mounted around a permanent magnet.

There are no contacting surfaces between the trigger wheel and sensor. Dwell is not adjustable and is controlled electronically.

Centrifugal advance is controlled by engine speed. Vacuum spark advance is controlled by carburetor ported vacuum, supplied to the distributor's vacuum unit. Distributor cap and rotor are of conventional design.

IGNITION COIL

Coil is oil-filled and sealed, and contains a primary and secondary circuit. Its basic function is to convert battery voltage applied to the primary circuit into high secondary voltage for firing the spark plugs.

The coil has positive and negative primary terminals and a single secondary terminal. A special coil connector slides over the primary terminals.

RESISTANCE WIRE

A wire with 1.3-1.4 ohms resistance is provided in the Red wire (engine running) circuit to supply less than battery voltage to the coil.

This resistance wire is by-passed during starting, so that full battery voltage may be applied to the coil. The by-pass is accomplished through the "I" terminal of the starter solenoid.

SYSTEM PROTECTION

The ECU unit has built-in reverse polarity and transient voltage protection. System can be damaged, however, if proper testing procedures are not followed.

OPERATION

The ECU and ignition coil are turned on whenever the ignition switch is in the "START" or "ON" position. When the engine begins turning the distributor shaft, the trigger wheel rotates with it.

Fig. 1: Jeep Solid State Ignition (SSI) System Wiring Diagram, 6 Cyl. Engine.

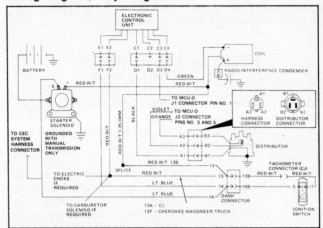

Fig. 2: Jeep Solid State Ignition (SSI) System Wiring Diagram, 8 Cyl. Engine.

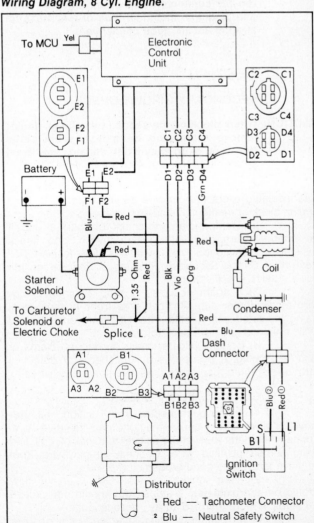

Distributors & Ignition Systems

MOTORCRAFT SOLID STATE IGNITION (SSI) (Cont.)

As each tooth passes the sensor, it interrupts the magnetic field around the sensor. This continual build-up and collapse of the field provides a signal to the ECU.

The ECU receives this signal and turns the power to the ignition coil's primary circuit off and on as each tooth passes the sensor.

The collapse of the magnetic field in the ignition coil primary circuit induces a high voltage surge in secondary. This current flows from the coil to the distributor, rotor, cap and spark plug wires.

SOLID STATE IGNITION (SSI) SYSTEM NOTES

NOTE: When disconnecting wire from spark plug or distributor cap, twist rubber boot slightly to loosen. Grasp boot (not wire) and pull off with steady, even force.

NOTE: When disconnecting control unit connectors, pull with firm, straight pull. Do not attempt to pry apart with screwdriver. When connecting, press together firmly to overcome hydraulic pressure of grease. If connector locking tabs weaken or break off, it is unnecessary to replace connector. Just press together firmly and bind with electrical tape or a harness tie strap to assure good connection.

TESTING

SECONDARY CIRCUIT CHECK

CAUTION: When checking the secondary voltage, do not remove spark plug wires from spark plugs No. 1 or 5 on 6-cylinder engines nor from spark plugs No. 3 or 4 on V8 Engines.

1) Disconnect coil wire from distributor cap. Use insulated pliers to hold wire approximately 1/2" from engine block or intake manifold.

2) Crank engine and check for spark at gap. If no spark occurs, turn off ignition switch, and check resistance of secondary coil windings. *See Ignition Coil Resistance Check, Secondary Resistance.* Replace ignition coil if outside specifications.

3) If spark occurred in step **2)**, connect coil wire to distributor cap. Remove wire from 1 spark plug. Using insulated pliers, hold wire 1/2" from engine head while cranking engine. Check for spark.

4) If spark occurs, check for fuel problems or incorrect timing. If no sparks occur, check for defective rotor or distributor cap or for defective spark plug wires.

CURRENT FLOW CHECK

1) Remove connector from ignition coil. Remove positive wire from connector, then negative wire. Connect ammeter between positive terminal of coil and disconnected positive wire. Connect jumper wire from negative terminal to good ground.

2) Turn ignition switch "ON". Current flow should be approximately 7 amps., but should not exceed 7.6 amps. If more than 7.6 amps., replace ignition coil.

3) With ammeter still connected to coil positive terminal, remove jumper wire from negative terminal.

Connect coil Green wire to negative terminal. Current flow should be approximately 4 amps.

4) If less than 3.5 amps., check for poor connections in 4-wire and 3-wire connectors or for poor ground at distributor ground screw.

5) If current flow is greater than 5 amps., the control unit is defective and must be replaced. Start engine. Normal current flow with engine running is 2.0-2.4 amps. If outside of specifications, replace control unit.

COIL OUTPUT CHECK

1) Connect oscilloscope to engine. Start engine and observe secondary winding spark voltage. Remove 1 spark plug wire (not wire No. 1 or 5 on 6-cylinder engine nor wire No. 3 or 4 on V8 engines) from distributor cap. Run engine at 1000 RPM.

2) Observe voltage on oscilloscope. This voltage, referred to as open circuit voltage, should be 24,-000 volts minimum.

NOTE: Do not operate engine with spark plug disconnected for more than 30 seconds or damage may result to catalytic converter.

SPARK PLUG REQUIRED VOLTAGE

1) Attach secondary voltage pick-up over coil high tension wire. Run engine at approximately 1000 RPM. Firing voltage should be relatively even and between 5000-16,000 volts.

Fig. 3: Solid State Ignition Connectors

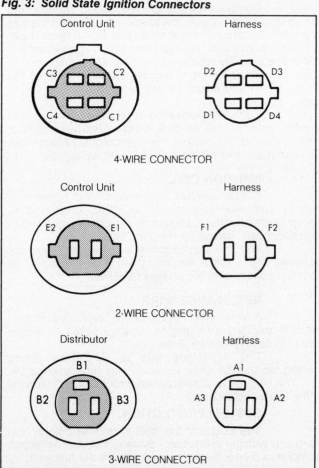

Terminals are identified for testing purposes.

MOTORCRAFT SOLID STATE IGNITION (SSI) (Cont.)

2) If firing voltage is bad, check each cylinder. Maximum variation between cylinders is 3000 to 5000 volts.

IGNITION COIL RESISTANCE CHECK

Primary Resistance

1) Remove connector from positive and negative coil terminals. Be sure ignition switch is "OFF". Set an ohmmeter on low scale and connect ohmmeter leads to positive and negative terminals.

2) Ohmmeter reading should be 1.13-1.23 ohms at 75°F (24°C). With coil temperature at 200°F (93°C), a 1.5 ohm reading is acceptable.

Secondary Resistance

1) Turn ignition switch "OFF". Set ohmmeter to high scale (x1000 scale). Connect one lead to coil negative terminal and other lead to coil tower (remove coil secondary wire).

2) Ohmmeter reading should be 7700-9300 ohms with coil temperature at 75°F (24°C). With coil temperature at 200°F (93°C) or above, a maximum reading of 12,000 ohms is acceptable.

COIL PRIMARY CIRCUIT CHECK

1) Connect voltmeter positive lead to coil positive terminal and negative lead to ground. Turn ignition switch to "ON" position. Reading should be 5.5-6.5 volts. If voltage is too high (battery voltage), proceed to step **4)**. If voltage is too low (below 5.5 volts), disconnect condenser lead. If voltage is now correct, replace condenser. If voltage is still low, proceed to step **7)**.

2) If voltage was 5.5-6.5 volts in step **1)**, turn ignition switch to "START" position. Voltage should be the same as battery cranking voltage. If correct, check other systems (fuel, mechanical, etc.) for problems. If voltage is not correct proceed to next step.

3) Check wire connected to starter solenoid "I" terminal for shorts or opens. If wire is OK, check for defective starter solenoid. Replace solenoid if necessary.

4) With ignition switch in "ON" position and voltmeter still connected to coil positive terminal, disconnect wire connected to starter solenoid "I" terminal. If voltage drops to 5.5-6.5 volts, replace starter solenoid.

5) If voltage remains high, connect a jumper wire from coil negative terminal to ground. If voltage drops to 5.5-6.5 volt range, proceed to step **6)**. If voltage does not drop, resistance wire is defective. Replace resistance wire and retest, beginning with step **2)**.

6) With ignition switch "OFF", connect an ohmmeter lead to the coil negative terminal and the other lead to the Green wire terminal "D4" of the 4-wire harness connector. Also check from Black wire terminal "D1" to ground. If continuity is OK, replace the control unit. If no continuity is present, repair wire in harness and retest beginning at step **2)**.

7) With ignition switch "OFF", connect ohmmeter leads between coil positive terminal and dash connector "AV" (Red wire). If resistance is not 1.3-1.4 ohms, replace resistance wire. If ohmmeter reading is to specifications, proceed to next step.

8) With ignition switch still "OFF", connect ohmmeter leads between dash connector "AV" (Red wire) and ignition switch terminal "L1". Resistance should be less than 0.1 ohm. If reading is to specifications, repair feed wire or replace ignition switch.

9) If resistance is more than 0.1 ohm, check for opens in wire or for poor connections at connectors. Repair or replace as necessary.

CONTROL UNIT & SENSOR CHECK

1) Disconnect high tension coil wire from distributor cap. Attach a modified spark plug to coil wire (side electrode of plug cut off and ground wire attached to side of plug casing). If plug is not available, hold coil wire 1/2" from engine block, using insulated pliers.

2) Turn ignition switch "ON" and disconnect 4-wire connector from control unit. Watch for spark at modified spark plug, as connector is disconnected. If sparking occurs, proceed with next step. If no sparking occurs, proceed to step **6)**.

3) Turn ignition switch "OFF", and disconnect 4-wire connector at control unit. Connect an ohmmeter between the Orange and Violet wire terminals "D2" and "D3" of harness connector. Ohmmeter reading should be 400-800 ohms. If reading is correct, proceed to step **8)**. If reading is not correct, proceed to next step.

4) Disconnect and reconnect the 3-wire connector at the distributor. If ohmmeter reading is now correct, proceed to step **8)**. If reading is still not correct, proceed to next step.

5) Disconnect 3-wire connector at the distributor and connect ohmmeter leads between the Orange and Violet wire terminals "B2" and "B3" of distributor connector. If reading is now 400-800 ohms, repair harness between 3-wire and 4-wire connectors. If reading is still out of specifications, replace sensor in distributor.

6) With ignition switch "OFF" and 4-wire connector disconnected, connect ohmmeter leads to battery negative terminal (ground) and Black wire terminal "D1" in harness connector. Ohmmeter reading should be nearly zero (less than .002 ohms).

7) If ohmmeter reading is OK, recheck system starting at step **3)**. If reading is above specifications, check for the source of the bad ground, (ground cable resistance, distributor-to-engine block resistance, or ground screw in distributor to black wire terminal "D1").

8) With ignition switch "ON" and voltmeter connected to harness side of 4-wire connector Orange and Violet wire terminals "D2" and "D3", crank engine. Voltmeter reading should fluctuate.

9) If no voltage fluctuation occurs, check for defective trigger wheel, distributor shaft not turning, or missing trigger wheel retaining pin (shaft turning but not trigger wheel).

CONTROL UNIT POWER FEED CHECK

NOTE: **Before making this check, always check ignition coil primary circuit first.**

1) Disconnect 2-wire connector at control unit. Connect voltmeter negative lead to ground and positive lead to Red wire harness connector terminal "F2". Turn ignition switch "ON". Voltage reading should be battery voltage (within 0.2 volts). If reading is correct, replace control unit. If not, proceed to next step.

2) Locate and repair cause of voltage reduction (corroded connectors, defective ignition switch, etc.). If connectors are repaired and there is spark at coil wire, start engine. If connectors are repaired and there is no spark at coil wire, replace control unit.

3) Connect voltmeter negative lead to ground and positive lead to Light Blue wire at harness connector terminal "F1" in 2-wire connector. Crank engine. Voltmeter reading should be within 1 volt of battery cranking voltage. If not, check for bad connections, ignition switch or starter solenoid.

Distributors & Ignition Systems

MOTORCRAFT SOLID STATE IGNITION (SSI) (Cont.)

Fig. 4: Exploded View of Jeep SSI Distributor

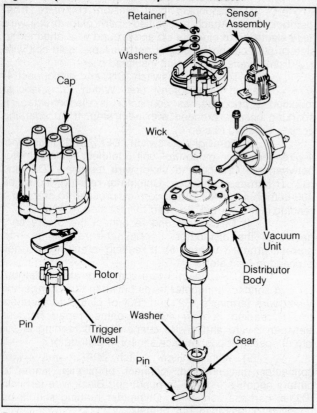

Reluctors have 1 tooth for each cylinder.

4) Turn ignition switch "OFF", connect 2-wire connector and disconnect 4-wire connector. Connect an ammeter to ground and to Black wire terminal "C1" of control unit (not harness) connector. Turn ignition switch "ON". Reading should be 0.9-1.1 amps. If reading is higher or lower than specified, replace control unit.

OVERHAUL

DISTRIBUTOR

Disassembly

1) Remove distributor cap and rotor. Using suitable gear puller (J-28509), remove trigger wheel (2 screwdrivers can be used to pry trigger wheel upward). Remove pin.

2) On 6-cylinder engines, remove sensor retainer and washers from pivot pin on base plate. On V8 engines, remove sensor snap ring from shaft. Remove retainer from vacuum unit-to-sensor drive pin and move vacuum lever aside.

3) Remove ground screw from harness tab. Lift sensor assembly from distributor housing. Only remove vacuum unit if it is to be replaced.

Reassembly

Reverse disassembly procedure, being sure to coat brass surface of rotor with silicone grease. If sensor or vacuum unit was replaced, check ignition timing.

TYPICAL MOTORCRAFT IGNITION OSCILLOSCOPE PATTERNS

To analyze the Solid State (SSI) and Dura-Spark Ignition Systems using an oscilloscope, follow the procedures recommended by the manufacturer of the scope.

The electrical display patterns will appear similar to patterns of conventional breaker type ignition systems except as shown. *See Fig. 5.*

Fig. 5: Normal Oscilloscope Patterns Shown for Solid State Ignition (SSI) Systems

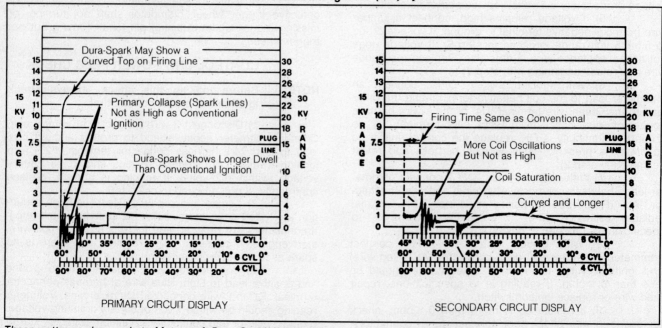

These patterns also apply to Motorcraft Dura-Spark II systems.

Distributors & Ignition Systems

MOTORCRAFT TFI-IV IGNITION

Ford Motor Co. 2.8L V6 Bronco II & Ranger

DESCRIPTION

The TFI (Thick Film Integrated) ignition system is used on all vehicles equipped with a 2.8L V6 engine.

In the TFI-IV ignition systems, the small Blue plastic TFI ignition module replaces the bulky and much larger Dura-Spark module. The TFI ignition module is mounted on the distributor housing and is retained with 2 screws. It is electrically connected to the distributor pick-up coil assembly without the use of a wiring harness between the ignition module and the pick-up coil assembly.

The TFI ignition system consists of a distributor, a TFI ignition module, E-Core ignition coil, ignition switch, battery, and primary and secondary wiring.

The distributor contains the following components: Pick-up coil assembly with internal teeth, distributor shaft, reluctor with external teeth (mounted on distributor shaft), TFI ignition module (mounted on outside of distributor housing), octane rod, rotor and distributor cap (with male terminals). *See Fig. 1*

Vehicles equipped with the TFI-IV ignition system also use an E-Core ignition coil. The E-Core ignition coil is unlike any other Ford coil. It is encased in laminated plastic rather than being encased in an oil filled case, as most other coils are. This ignition coil has a very low primary resistance and is used without a ballast resistor in the electrical system. There are the usual primary connections on this coil.

The ignition module sends the pulse signal to the electronic control assembly (ECA) for modifications of the timing signal. Then, a modified spark timing signal is returned to the ignition module. This signals the ignition module when to turn the ignition coil primary circuit on and off. This causes a high voltage surge in the secondary which fires the spark plugs.

After initial ignition timing has been set on TFI-IV models, adjustments for octane concerns can be made by installing the appropriate octane link in the distributor.

NOTE: **Changing the timing by the use of octane rods can only be by Technical Service Bulletin authorization.**

Fig. 2: TFI-IV Ignition System Wiring Diagram

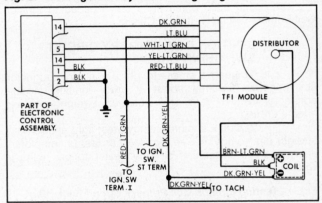

Also see chassis wiring in WIRING DIAGRAM Section.

TESTING

NOTE: **When a test requires the inspection of a wiring harness, both a visual inspection and a continuity test should be performed. When making measurements of a wire or connector, it is a good idea to wiggle the wires while measuring.**

Fig. 3: Modified Spark Plug and Spark Tester

Fig. 1: Exploded View of TFI-IV Distributor

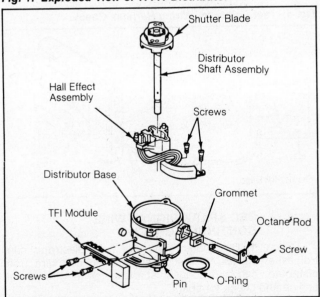

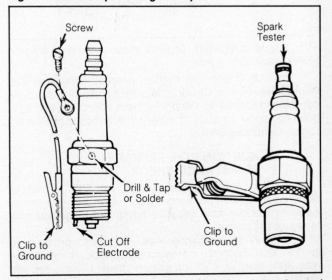

Modify spark plug by cutting off side electrode and installing spring clip.

OPERATION

Each time the teeth on the reluctor pass the teeth on the pick-up coil, the magnetic field around the pick-up coil builds and collapses. As this occurs, a pulse is generated in the pick-up coil and sent to the TFI ignition module. The ignition module then turns the ignition coil primary circuit off and on causing a high voltage surge in the secondary which fires the spark plugs.

Distributors & Ignition Systems

MOTORCRAFT TFI-IV IGNITION (Cont.)

TEST SPARK PLUG

Use either a spark tester tool or modify a spark plug (cut off side terminal and install spring clip for grounding plug housing) for use in testing ignition system. *See Fig. 3.*

IGNITION COIL SECONDARY VOLTAGE CHECK

1) Disconnect ignition coil secondary wire from distributor cap and attach spark tester to wire. Crank engine. Disconnect spark tester and reconnect secondary wire to distributor cap.

2) If sparks occurred at tester gap, inspect distributor cap and rotor for damage or carbon tracking. Crank engine to verify reluctor rotation. If no sparks occurred, measure resistance of ignition coil wire. Replace if greater than 5000 ohms per inch. Proceed to Ignition Coil Primary Circuit Switching Check.

IGNITION COIL PRIMARY CIRCUIT SWITCHING CHECK

1) Insert a small straight pin in wire to ignition coil negative terminal about 1" from ignition module connector. Attach test light between straight pin and engine ground.

2) Crank engine. Remove test light and remove straight pin from wire. *See Fig. 4.* After test is completed, apply a small amount of silicone sealer to pin holes in wire.

Fig. 4: Testing Ignition Coil Primary Circuit Switching

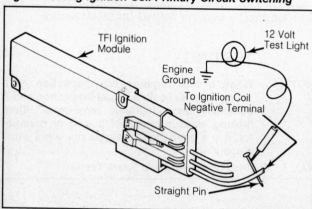

After test is completed, apply a small amount of silicone sealer to pin hole in wire.

3) If test light flashes, proceed to Ignition Coil Primary Resistance Check. If test light comes on but does not flash, proceed to Wiring Harness Check. If test light does not come on at all or is very dim, proceed to Primary Circuit Continuity Check.

IGNITION COIL PRIMARY RESISTANCE CHECK

1) With ignition switch in "OFF" position, disconnect ignition coil connector. Connect ohmmeter leads to positive and negative terminals of ignition coil. Measure resistance.

2) If resistance was .3-1 ohm, proceed to Ignition Coil Secondary Resistance Check. If resistance was less than .3 ohm or greater than 1 ohm, replace ignition coil.

IGNITION COIL SECONDARY RESISTANCE CHECK

1) With ignition switch in "OFF" position, disconnect ignition coil connector and secondary wire from ignition coil. Connect ohmmeter leads to ignition coil's negative and secondary terminals. Measure resistance.

2) If resistance was 8000-11,500 ohms, proceed to Wiring Harness Check. If resistance was less than 8000 ohms or greater than 11,500 ohms, replace ignition coil.

WIRING HARNESS CHECK

1) Disconnect ignition module connector from ignition module. Disconnect wire at "S" terminal of starter relay. Attach negative lead of voltmeter to distributor base and measure battery voltage at battery. With negative lead of voltmeter still connected to distributor base, check voltage in each of the following situations:

- Positive voltmeter lead connected to terminal 2 of ignition module connector with ignition switch in "RUN" position. *See Fig. 5.*
- Positive voltmeter lead connected to terminal 3 of ignition module connector with ignition switch in "RUN" position. *See Fig. 5.*
- Positive voltmeter lead connected to terminal 4 of ignition module connector with ignition switch in "START" position. *See Fig. 5.*

2) If reading was 90 percent of battery voltage or more, proceed to EEC Spark Signal Wire Continuity Check. If reading was less than 90 percent of battery voltage, inspect wiring harness and ignition switch.

Fig. 5: Test Points for Wiring Harness Check

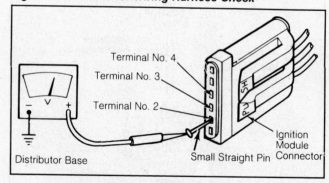

EEC SPARK SIGNAL WIRE CONTINUITY CHECK

1) Disconnect connector from electronic control assembly (ECA). Disconnect ignition coil wire from distributor cap and connect spark tester to wire. Crank engine and check for spark.

2) If sparks did not occur, proceed to Distributor and Module Check. If sparks did occur, disconnect ignition module connector and check for continuity in Dark Green wire between ignition module connector and terminal of ECA.

3) If no continuity exists, repair wire or connectors as necessary. If continuity exists, proceed to testing procedures in *Ford Motor Co. EEC-IV System article* in *ELECTRONIC ENGINE CONTROL Section.*

MOTORCRAFT TFI-IV IGNITION (Cont.)

DISTRIBUTOR & TFI-IV MODULE CHECK

1) Remove distributor from engine with secondary coil wire still connected to distributor. Remove module from distributor. Install new module on the distributor.

2) Connect jumper lead from the distributor base to a good engine ground. Connect vehicle harness to module. Connect spark tester to end of coil wire. Rotate distributor by hand and check for spark.

3) If sparks occur, reinstall distributor with new module. If no sparks occur, install new distributor using original module.

IGNITION COIL PRIMARY VOLTAGE CHECK

1) Attach negative lead of voltmeter to distributor base and measure battery voltage. Turn ignition switch to "RUN" position. Connect positive lead of voltmeter to coil connector negative terminal (connector still connected to coil). Measure voltage. Turn ignition switch to "OFF" position.

2) If reading was 90 percent of battery voltage or more, inspect wiring harness between ignition module and ignition coil negative terminal. If reading was less than 90 percent of battery voltage, inspect wiring harness between ignition module and ignition coil negative terminal and proceed to Ignition Coil Voltage Supply Check.

IGNITION COIL VOLTAGE SUPPLY CHECK

1) Attach negative lead of voltmeter to distributor base. Measure battery voltage. Turn ignition switch to "RUN" position.

2) Connect positive voltmeter lead to positive terminal of ignition coil connector (connector still connected to ignition coil). Read voltmeter and turn ignition switch "OFF".

3) If reading was at least 90 percent of battery voltage, inspect ignition coil and ignition coil connector for dirt, corrosion or damage. Replace ignition coil if necessary.

4) If reading was less than 90 percent of battery voltage, repair wiring between ignition coil and ignition switch, check for damaged ignition switch.

OVERHAUL

NOTE: **On models equipped with TFI-IV ignition systems, only the distributor cap, rotor, TFI module, distributor shaft O-ring and octane rod can be replaced. If any other component is found to be defective, the entire distributor assembly must be replaced.**

TFI IGNITION MODULE
Removal

1) Disconnect wiring harness connector from ignition module. Remove distributor cap with secondary wiring connected and position out of way. Remove distributor hold down bolt and remove distributor from engine. Engine may be equipped with security hold-down bolt for distributor. To remove bolt, use Distributor Hold-Down Wrench, tool T82L-12270-A.

2) With distributor on work bench, remove 2 screws retaining ignition module. Pull the right side of the ignition module down to the distributor mounting flange. Push ignition module back up and ignition module terminals will disengage from connector in distributor. Pull ignition module down and away from distributor to remove.

CAUTION: **Do not attempt to lift module from mounting surface prior to moving entire TFI module toward distributor flange. You will break the pins at the distributor/module connector.**

Installation
Reverse removal procedures and note the following: Coat the metal base plate of ignition module with about 1/32" of silicone grease before installing. Be sure that ignition module terminals are fully engaged in distributor connector. Tighten the 2 ignition module retaining screws to 9-16 INCH Lbs. (1.1-1.8 N.m).

OCTANE ROD
Removal & Installation

1) Remove distributor cap and rotor for visual access. Remove screw that retains octane rod to distributor housing.

2) Slide the octane rod and grommet out to a point at which the rod end can be disengaged from the pick-up coil retaining post.

3) Install grommet on new octane rod. Reinstall rod in distributor, making sure that rod is engaged with pick-up coil retaining post. Reinstall retaining screw, rotor and distributor cap.

DISTRIBUTOR
Disassembly

1) Remove distributor cap and rotor. Using a small screwdriver or ice pick remove drive coupling spring. Using compressed air, blow any dirt or oil from drive end of distributor.

2) Put a small paint dot on drive coupling and distributor shaft for reassembly reference. Line up drive pin with slot in base of distributor housing. Support distributor in a vise and remove pin from distributor shaft using a 1/8" drift punch and hammer.

3) Remove distributor from vise. Remove drive coupling from distributor shaft. Before removing shaft from distributor housing, remove any burrs from end of shaft. After all burrs have been removed, carefully remove shaft from distributor base.

4) Remove 2 screws retaining pick-up coil connector to housing. If TFI module has not been removed, remove pick-up coil connector from top of TFI module. Remove TFI module. Remove pick-up coil retainer from pick-up coil assembly. Remove pick-up coil assembly from distributor housing.

Reassembly
Reassemble distributor in reverse order of disassembly while noting the following: Be sure to align paint dots, made during disassembly, on housing and shaft. Apply a light coat of oil to distributor shaft before installing in housing. Be sure that connectors are securely connected to TFI module.

Distributors & Ignition Systems

NIPPONDENSO ELECTRONIC IGNITION SYSTEM

**Chevrolet & GMC S10 Pickups with 1.9L
4-Cylinder Engines**

DESCRIPTION

Two variations of electronic ignition are used with the 1.9L 4-cylinder engine, both making use of a Nippondenso distributor.

California models feature a computer, in addition to other ignition components. The computer is a part of the computerized engine control system. Federal models incorporate an engine speed sensor into the system, but have no computer.

The distributor has both vacuum and centrifugal advance mechanisms. It also houses a reluctor, stator, magnet set, and a pick-up coil and control module assembly. *See Figs. 1 and 2.* The system makes use of a conventional ignition coil with positive, negative, and secondary terminals.

Fig. 1: Distributor Breaker Plate Assembly

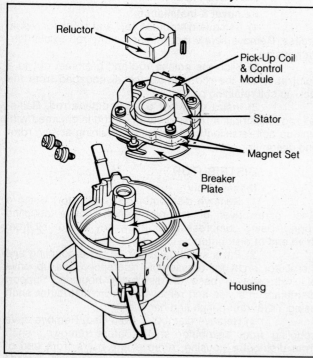

Note stator-to-pick-up coil and module relationship.

OPERATION

As the engine cranks, the distributor shaft turns, carrying with it the rotor shaft assembly. A reluctor (toothed wheel), mounted on the rotor shaft, turns inside a 2-pronged stator, which is attached to the magnet set.

As each reluctor tooth approaches and passes the stator upright prong, the magnetic field around the prong is broken. The pick-up coil and control module assembly is mounted inside the distributor, next to the magnet set and stator. Components are attached to the breaker plate assembly. *See Fig. 1.*

The build-up and collapse of the magnetic field causes the pick-up coil to send a signal to the control module. The module, in response, opens and closes the ignition coil primary circuit. Each time this occurs, a voltage surge occurs in the coil secondary circuit, firing the spark plugs.

On California models, the computer monitors the ignition system along with other engine sensors. The computer then makes calculations and adjusts the air/fuel ratio. No ballast resistors or resistance wires are used with the system.

ADJUSTMENT

PICK-UP COIL AIR GAP

1) Using a feeler gauge, measure air gap between each tooth of the reluctor and stator prongs.

2) Air gap should read .012-.020" (.30-.50 mm). If not to specifications, loosen 2 screws and adjust position of stator and magnets until gap is correct. Tighten screws and recheck air gap.

TESTING

NOTE: **When testing the ignition system, use either an ignition spark tester or modified spark plug (case grounded, with side electrode cut off).**

IGNITION SYSTEM NO-START CHECK

1) Remove spark plug wire, and attach ignition tester to its end. Crank engine. If no spark, check a second spark plug wire in similar manner.

2) If spark resulted at either wire, ignition system is not at fault. Check fuel system, mechanical condition, and spark plugs. If no spark resulted at either wire, connect negative voltmeter lead to ground. In turn, touch positive lead to battery terminals of ignition coil and distributor, while cranking engine.

3) If voltage is below 7 volts, repair primary circuit (from battery terminals back to ignition switch and battery positive terminal. If voltage is above 7 volts, proceed to next step.

4) Turn ignition switch "OFF". Connect the ohmmeter leads to positive and negative terminals of ignition coil. Check for an open circuit in the coil. If open, replace ignition coil.

5) If ignition coil is not open, turn ignition switch "ON". Connect voltmeter negative lead to ground, and touch positive lead to ignition coil negative terminal. If voltage is below 5 volts, replace ignition coil.

6) If voltage is above 5 volts at negative terminal of coil, remove secondary wire from top of distributor. Attach ignition spark tester to end of coil wire. Crank engine and check for spark at tester.

7) If spark results, check distributor cap. If cap is okay, replace rotor. If there is no spark, check distributor pick-up coil air gap. Clearance should be .012-.020" (.30-.50 mm) minimum on one side. If OK, replace rotor with a new one.

8) If no spark results at coil wire, check air gap at distributor pick-up coil. Clearance should be .012-.020" (.30-.50 mm) minimum on one side.

9) If gap is incorrect, adjust as necessary. If correct, replace control module (part of pick-up coil assembly). Repeat steps 1) through 5).

10) If spark results at tester, no-start problem has been corrected. If no spark results, original module

NIPPONDENSO ELECTRONIC IGNITION SYSTEM Cont.)

was not defective. Install original module, and replace ignition coil. Again, repeat steps **1)** through **5)**. Spark should result at tester.

IGNITION SYSTEM CHECK WHEN ENGINE RUNS ROUGH

1) Remove spark plug wire from spark plug. Attach ignition spark tester to end of spark plug wire. Crank engine and watch for spark at tester.

2) If there is no spark, refer to Ignition System No-Start Check. If spark occurs, check ignition timing. If necessary, adjust to correct. If timing is to specifications, check to see if dwell angle increased. If so, problem is not with ignition system. Check fuel system and spark plugs.

3) If dwell angle did not increase, check distributor pick-up coil air gap. See Pick-Up Coil Air Gap under Adjustments. Adjust if necessary. If air gap is normal, replace control module.

IGNITION COIL PRIMARY RESISTANCE CHECK

1) Remove primary wires from ignition coil. Set ohmmeter in low range. Connect ohmmeter leads to coil positive and negative terminals (Leads may be touched to Red and White wire terminals in ignition coil harness connector).

2) Primary resistance should be .90-1.40 ohms. If not within specified range, replace ignition coil.

IGNITION COIL SECONDARY RESISTANCE CHECK

1) Remove primary wires and secondary wire from ignition coil. Set ohmmeter in high range. Connect ohmmeter leads to secondary tower and to either primary terminal (or White wire terminal in ignition coil harness connector).

2) Secondary resistance should measure 7,300-11,100 ohms. If not, replace ignition coil.

IGNITION COIL INSULATION RESISTANCE CHECK

1) Set ohmmeter in highest range. Connect ignition coil harness to coil primary terminals, if previously removed. Connect ohmmeter leads to Red wire terminal in coil harness and to coil outer shell.

2) Insulation resistance should be 10 megohms or more. Even if tester needle deflects slightly, ignition coil is poorly insulated and must be replaced.

SPARK PLUG AND COIL WIRE RESISTANCE

1) Examine wires for broken insulation, terminals, corrosion, or other damage. Replace if necessary.

2) Set ohmmeter to high range. Connect ohmmeter leads to each end of spark plug and coil secondary wires. Resistance should be 31,500-73,500 ohms per foot.

OVERHAUL

DISASSEMBLY

1) Remove the cap, rotor, and packing. Remove cover. Remove screws attaching vacuum unit, and lift out vacuum unit from housing. *See Fig. 2.*

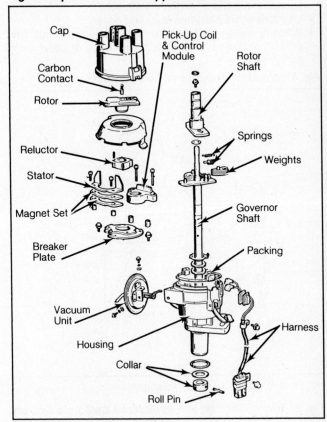

Fig. 2: Exploded View of Nippondenso Distributor

Pick-up coil is built into control module.

2) Remove screw attaching harness assembly. Disconnect connectors (Pink and White wires) from control unit. Remove harness assembly from housing. Using 2 screwdrivers to pry upward on reluctor, remove reluctor from rotor shaft.

3) Remove 2 screws securing breaker plate assembly, and lift assembly from housing. Remove pick-up coil and control module assembly. Remove governor shaft assembly, packing, and screw attaching rotor shaft assembly.

NOTE: **End of governor shaft is offset. To maintain original relationship of 2 shafts, scribe mark across rotor shaft and governor shaft before removal.**

4) Remove rotor shaft from governor shaft. Remove governor weights and springs.

INSPECTION

1) Wash and clean disassembled parts. Do not wash inner face of vacuum unit. Check parts for wear or damage, correcting as necessary.

2) Check distributor cap and rotor head for cracks and carbon tracking. Check center carbon contact for wear.

REASSEMBLY

To reassemble, reverse disassembly procedures, noting the following points:

• Governor springs should be fitted to spring hanger pin of governor shaft assembly with smaller hook end downward.

Distributors & Ignition Systems

NIPPONDENSO ELECTRONIC IGNITION SYSTEM Cont.)

- Correctly align rotor and governor shafts, according to scribe marks made during installation.
- Use a new roll pin when installing collar.
- When installing breaker assembly, the edge at cutaway portion of base must be flush with edge of base fixing screw slot.

- Roll pin should be installed so that slot is parallel with cutaway portion of reluctor, as viewed from above.
- Harness terminal should be connected to pick-up coil and control module assembly. *See Fig. 3.* Install gasket after setting cover to housing.

Fig. 3: Attaching Harness to Control Module

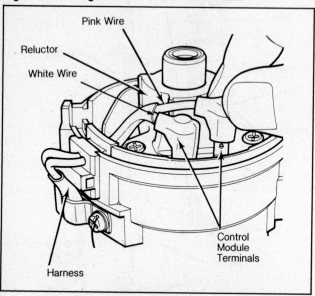

Notice wire colors and their location.

Fig. 4: Wiring Diagram of Nippondenso Federal System

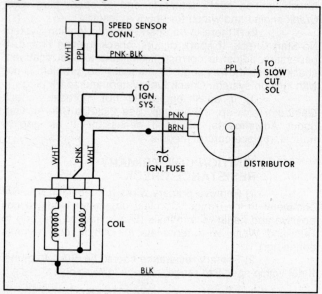

Federal models have no computer.

Fig. 5: Wiring Diagram of Nippondenso California System

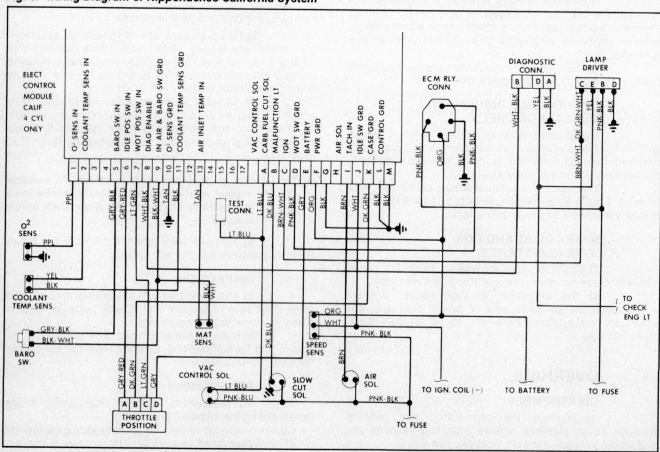

California models have computerized engine control.

Charging Systems

TROUBLE SHOOTING

CONDITION	POSSIBLE CAUSE	CORRECTION
Vehicle Will Not Start	Dead battery	Check battery cells, alternator belt tension and alternator output
	Loose or corroded battery connections	Check that all charging system connections are tight and clean
	Ignition switch malfunction	Check and replace ignition switch as necessary
Alternator Light Stays ON With Engine Running	Loose or worn alternator drive belt	Check alternator drive belt tension and condition. See Belt Adjustment in TUNE-UP
	Loose alternator wiring connections	Check all charging system connections
	Short in alternator light wiring	See Indicator Warning Lights in SWITCHES, GAUGES & INSTRUMENT PANELS
	Defective alternator stator or diodes	See Bench Tests in ALTERNATORS & REGULATORS
	Defective regulator	See Regulator Check in ALTERNATORS & REGULATORS
Alternator Light Stays OFF With Ignition Switch ON	Blown fuse	See FUSES & CIRCUIT BREAKERS
	Defective alternator	See Testing in ALTERNATORS & REGULATORS
	Defective indicator light bulb or socket	See Indicator Warning Lights in SWITCHES, GAUGES & INSTRUMENT PANELS
Alternator Light Stays ON With Ignition Switch OFF	Short in alternator wiring	See On Vehicle Tests in ALTERNATORS & REGULATORS
	Defective rectifier bridge	See Bench Tests in ALTERNATORS & REGULATORS
Lights or Fuses Burn Out Frequently	Defective alternator wiring	See On Vehicle Tests in ALTERNATORS & REGULATORS
	Defective regulator	See Regulator Check in ALTERNATORS & REGULATORS
	Defective battery	Check and replace as necessary
Ammeter Gauge Shows Discharge	Loose or worn drive belt	Check alternator drive belt tension and condition. See Belt Adjustment in TUNE-UP
	Defective wiring	Check all wires and wire connections
	Defective alternator or regulator	See Bench Tests and On Vehicle Tests in ALTERNATORS & REGULATORS
	Defective ammeter, or improper ammeter wiring connections	See Testing in SWITCHES, GAUGES & INSTRUMENT PANELS
Noisy Alternator	Loose drive pulley	Tighten drive pulley attaching nut
	Loose mounting bolts	Tighten all alternator mounting bolts
	Worn or dirty bearings	See Bearing Replacement in ALTERNATORS & REGULATORS
	Defective diodes or stator	See Bench Tests in ALTERNATORS & REGULATORS
Battery Does Not Stay Charged	Loose or worn drive belt	Check alternator drive belt tension and condition. See Belt Adjustment in TUNE-UP
	Loose or corroded battery connections	Check that all charging system connections are tight and clean
	Loose alternator connections	Check all charging system connections
	Defective alternator or battery	See On Vehicle Tests and Bench Tests in ALTERNATORS & REGULATORS
	Defective alternator stator or diodes	See Bench Tests in ALTERNATORS & REGULATORS
	Add-on electrical accessories exceeding alternator capacity	Install larger capacity alternator
Battery Overcharged - Uses Too Much Water	Defective battery	Check alternator output and repair as necessary
	Defective alternator	See On Vehicle Tests and Bench Tests in ALTERNATORS & REGULATORS
	Excessive alternator voltage.	Check alternator output and repair as necessary

Starting Systems
TROUBLE SHOOTING

CONDITION	POSSIBLE CAUSE	CORRECTION
Starter Fails to Operate	Dead battery or bad connections between starter and battery	Check battery charge and all wires and connections to starter
	Ignition switch faulty or misadjusted	Adjust or replace ignition switch
	Open circuit between starter switch and ignition terminal on starter relay	Check and repair wires and connections as necessary
	Starter relay or starter defective	See Testing in STARTERS
	Open solenoid pull-in wire	See Testing in STARTERS
Starter Does Not Operate and Headlights Dim	Weak battery or dead battery cell	Charge or replace battery as necessary
	Loose or corroded battery connections	Check that battery connection are clean and tight
	Internal ground in starter windings	See Testing in STARTERS
	Grounded starter fields	See Testing in STARTERS
	Armature rubbing on pole shoes	See Overhaul in STARTERS
Starter Turns but Engine Does Not Rotate	Starter clutch slipping	See Overhaul in STARTERS
	Broken clutch housing	See Overhaul in STARTERS
	Pinion shaft rusted or dry	See Overhaul in STARTERS
	Engine basic timing incorrect	See Ignition Timing in TUNE-UP
	Broken teeth on engine flywheel	Replace flywheel and check for starter pinion gear damage
Starter Will Not Crank Engine	Faulty overrunning clutch	See Overhaul in STARTERS
	Broken clutch housing	See Overhaul in STARTERS
	Broken flywheel teeth	Replace flywheel and check for starter pinion gear damage
	Armature shaft sheared or reduction gear teeth stripped	See Overhaul in STARTERS
	Weak battery	Charge or replace battery as necessary
	Faulty solenoid	See On Vehicle Tests in STARTERS
	Poor grounds	Check all ground connections for tight and clean connections
	Ignition switch faulty or misadjusted	Adjust or replace ignition switch as necessary
Starter Cranks Engine Slowly	Battery weak or defective	Charge or replace battery as necessary
	Engine overheated	See ENGINE COOLING SYSTEMS
	Engine oil too heavy	Check that proper viscosity oil is used
	Poor battery-to-starter connections	Check that all connections between battery and starter are clean and tight
	Current draw too low or too high	See Bench Tests in STARTERS
	Bent armature, loose pole shoe screws or worn bearings	See Overhaul in STARTERS
	Burned solenoid contacts	Replace solenoid
	Faulty starter	Replace starter
Starter Engages Engine Only Momentarily	Engine timing too far advanced	See Ignition Timing In TUNE-UP
	Overrunning clutch not operating	Replace overrunning clutch. See Overhaul in STARTERS
	Broken starter clutch housing	See Overhaul in STARTERS
	Broken teeth on engine flywheel	Replace flywheel and check starter pinion gear for damage
	Weak drive assembly thrust spring	See Overhaul in STARTERS
	Weak hold-in coil	See Bench Tests in STARTERS
Starter Drive Will Not Engage	Defective point assembly	See Testing in STARTERS
	Poor point assembly ground	See Testing in STARTERS
	Defective pull-in coil	Replace starter solenoid
Starter Relay Does Not Close	Dead battery	Charge or replace battery as necessary
	Faulty wiring	Check all wiring and connections leading to relay
	Neutral safety switch faulty	Replace neutral safety switch
	Starter relay faulty	Replace starter relay

Starting Systems

TROUBLE SHOOTING (Cont.)

CONDITION	POSSIBLE CAUSE	CORRECTION
Starter Drive Will Not Disengage	Starter motor loose on mountings	Tighten starter attaching bolts
	Worn drive end bushing	See Overhaul in STARTERS
	Damaged engine flywheel teeth	Replace flywheel and check starter pinion gear for damage
	Drive yolk return spring broken or missing	Replace return spring
	Faulty ignition switch	Replace ignition switch
	Solenoid contact switch plunger stuck	Replace starter solenoid
	Faulty starter relay	Replace starter relay
	Insufficient clearance between winding leads to solenoid terminal and main contact in solenoid	Replace starter solenoid
	Starter clutch not disengaging	Replace starter clutch
	Ignition starter switch contacts sticking	Replace ignition switch
Starter Relay Operates but Solenoid Does Not	Faulty solenoid switch, switch connections or switch wiring	Check all wiring between relay and solenoid or replace relay or solenoid as necessary
	Broken lead or loose soldered connections	Repair wire or wire connections as necessary
Solenoid Plunger Vibrates When Switch is Engaged	Weak battery	Charge or replace battery as necessary
	Solenoid contacts corroded	Clean contacts or replace solenoid
	Faulty wiring	Check all wiring leading to solenoid
	Broken connections inside switch cover	Repair connections or replace solenoid
	Open hold-in wire	Replace solenoid
Low Current Draw	Worn brushes or weak brush springs	Replace brushes or brush springs as necessary
High Pitched Whine During Cranking Before Engine Fires but Engine Fires and Cranks Normally	Distance too great between starter pinion and flywheel	Align starter or check that correct starter and flywheel are being used
High Pitched Whine After Engine Fires With Key Released. Engine Fires and Cranks Normally	Distance too small between starter pinion and flywheel. Flywheel runout contributes to the intermittent nature	Align starter or check that correct starter and flywheel are being used

Alternators & Regulators
CHRYSLER CORP. ALTERNATORS

Dodge, Plymouth

DESCRIPTION

The main components of the alternator are the stator, rotor, rectifiers, end shields and drive pulley. The built-in silicon rectifiers convert A.C. current (alternating current) into D.C. output current (direct current). The 117 amp. model has 12 silicon rectifiers while all other models have 6 rectifiers.

IDENTIFICATION

CHRYSLER CORP. ALTERNATOR IDENTIFICATION

Part No.	Tag Color	Rated Amp. Output
4091563	Violet	41
4111226	Yellow	60
4091460	Yellow	117

SPECIFICATIONS

CHRYSLER CORP. SPECIFICATIONS

Rated Amp. Output	[1] Minimum Amp. Output
41	40@15 Volts
60	57@15 Volts
117	72@13 Volts

[1] — At 900 engine RPM for 117 amp. alternator; 1250 RPM for all others. Voltage measured at the alternator.

OTHER SPECIFICATIONS

Rotation — Clockwise at drive end.
Field Coil Current Draw — 4.5-6.5 amps. at 12 volts while rotating by hand.
Capacitor Capacity — .50 mfd. plus or minus 20%.

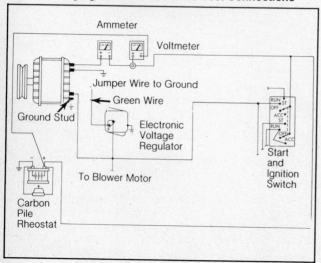

Fig. 1: Charging Circuit Resistance Test Connections

Diagram shows ammeter & voltmeter attaching points.

ON-VEHICLE TESTS

CHARGING CIRCUIT RESISTANCE

NOTE: Before making test connections, disconnect negative battery cable at battery to avoid accidental shorting of charging or field circuits.

1) Disconnect "BAT" lead at alternator. Connect a 0-150 ampere scale D.C. ammeter in series between alternator "BAT" terminal and disconnected "BAT" lead wire. Connect positive lead of voltmeter to disconnected "BAT" lead wire. Connect negative lead of voltmeter to positive post on battery.

2) Disconnect Green regulator field lead from alternator. Connect a jumper lead from alternator field terminal to ground. Connect a tachometer, and reattach battery ground cable. Connect a variable carbon pile to battery terminals (set in open or off position). *See Fig. 1.*

3) Start engine, and immediately reduce engine speed to idle. Adjust engine speed and set carbon pile to obtain 20 amps. flowing in circuit. Voltmeter reading should not exceed 0.7 volts. If a high voltage drop is indicated, inspect, clean and tighten all connections in charging circuit.

NOTE: If necessary, test voltage drop at each connection to locate connection with excessive resistance.

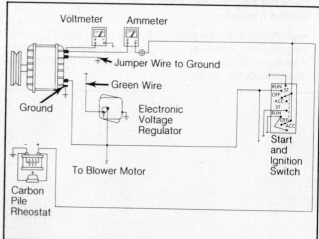

Fig. 2: Alternator Current Output Test Connections

Hookup ammeter & voltmeter as shown.

CURRENT OUTPUT

1) Disconnect "BAT" lead at alternator. Connect a 0-150 ampere scale D.C. ammeter in series between alternator "BAT" terminal and disconnected "BAT" lead wire. Connect positive lead of voltmeter to "BAT" terminal. Connect negative lead of voltmeter to a good ground. Disconnect Green field wire to alternator. *See Fig. 2.*

2) Connect a jumper wire from alternator field terminal to ground. Connect a tachometer to engine and reconnect negative battery cable. Connect a variable carbon pile between battery terminals (set in open or off position). *See Fig. 2.* Start engine, and operate at idle speed immediately after starting.

CHRYSLER CORP. ALTERNATORS (Cont.)

3) Adjust engine speed and carbon pile until a speed of 900 RPM (117 amp.) or 1250 RPM (all others) and a voltmeter reading of 13 volts (117 amp.) or 15 volts (all others) is obtained. Do not allow voltage to exceed 16 volts. Observe ammeter. Current output should be within specifications. If output is less than specified, remove the alternator from the vehicle and proceed to "BENCH TESTING".

BENCH TESTING

FIELD COIL CURRENT DRAW

1) Connect a jumper wire between 1 field terminal of alternator and negative terminal of a fully-charged battery. Connect ammeter positive lead to the other field terminal of alternator. Connect ammeter negative lead to battery positive terminal.

2) Connect a jumper wire from negative terminal of battery to alternator end shield. *See Fig. 3.* Slowly rotate alternator by hand. Observe ammeter reading. Field coil draw should be 4.5-6.5 amps. at 12 volts.

3) A low coil draw is an indication of high resistance in field coil (brushes, slip rings or rotor coil). A high coil draw indicates possible shorted rotor coil or grounded rotor. No reading indicates an open rotor or defective brushes.

Fig. 3: Connections for Field Coil Current Draw Test

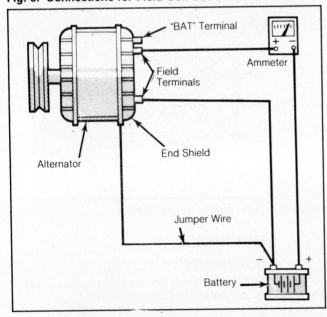

RECTIFIER (DIODE) TESTS

NOTE: Do not break plastic cases of diodes, as they protect against corrosion. Always touch test probe to metal strap nearest diode. Rectifier diodes may be tested with a test lamp or tester C-3829A.

Test Lamp Method

1) With rectifier end shield and stator assembly separated, test rectifiers with a 12V battery and suitable test lamp (No. 67 bulb, 4 candle power). Connect test lamp to battery positive terminal and to 1 test probe. Touch

other test probe to negative battery terminal. Measure rectifier continuity with probes touching heat sink and rectifier top strap.

2) Now reverse probes. If lamp lights with current flow in one direction only, rectifier is satisfactory. If lamp lights with probes either way, rectifier is shorted. If lamp does not light at all, rectifier is open. Test each rectifier in both assemblies in same manner. Replace rectifier and heat sink assemblies, which have shorted or open rectifiers.

Fig. 4: View of Rectifier End Shield

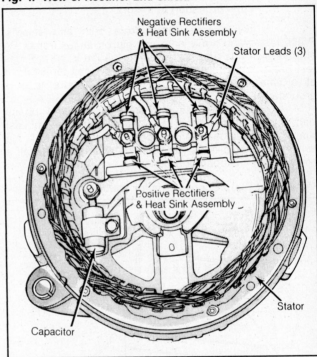

Note location of rectifiers and heat sink assemblies.

Tool C-3829A Method (Positive Rectifiers)

1) Remove alternator brushes and through bolts. Separate rectifier end housing and stator from drive end housing and rotor. With alternator on an insulated surface, connect test lead clip to alternator "BAT" output terminal. Plug tool into 110 volt A.C. power supply.

2) Touch the metal strap of each positive rectifier with test probe. Reading for satisfactory rectifiers will be 1 3/4 amperes or more and should be approximately the same for each rectifier. When 2 rectifiers are good and 1 is shorted, reading taken at good rectifiers will be low and reading at shorted rectifier will be zero.

3) Disconnect lead to rectifier reading zero, and retest. Reading of good rectifiers will now be within satisfactory range. When 1 rectifier is open, it will read approximately 1 ampere, while the 2 good rectifiers will read within satisfactory range.

Tool C-3829A Method (Negative Rectifiers)

1) Remove alternator brushes and through bolts. Separate rectifier end housing and stator from drive end housing and rotor. Connect test lead clip to rectifier end housing. Touch metal strap of each negative rectifier with test probe.

2) Test specifications and results will be approximately the same as for positive rectifiers, except meter will read on opposite side of scale. If a negative

CHRYSLER CORP. ALTERNATORS (Cont.)

rectifier shows shorted condition, remove stator from rectifier end shield and retest. Stator winding could be grounded to stator laminations or rectifier end shield, indicating a shorted negative rectifier.

STATOR TEST

NOTE: **On 117 amp. alternators, stator windings are "Delta" wound, and cannot be checked for opens and shorts with common shop equipment. If stator is not grounded, and all other components check correctly, suspect an open or a short in stator.**

1) Separate stator from both end shields. Press test probe firmly onto any pin on stator frame. Be sure varnish has been removed so the pin is bare. Press test probe firmly to each of the 3 phase lead terminals, 1 at a time. *See Fig. 5.* If lamp lights, stator lead is grounded.

2) Now press test probe firmly on 1 phase lead, and contact each of the other 2 stator leads. Test lamp should light when probe contacts each of the terminals. If lamp does not light, stator is open. Install a new stator if it is open or grounded.

Fig. 5: Test Lamp Connections for Stator Ground Test

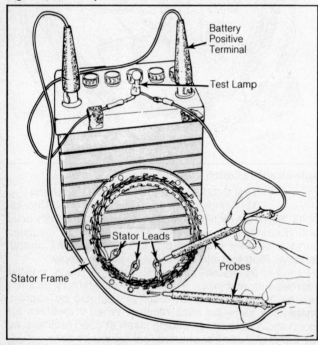

Battery Positive Terminal

Test Lamp

Stator Leads

Stator Frame

Probes

Touch test lamp probes to stator frame and stator leads.

ROTOR TEST

1) Test rotor for grounded, open or shorted field coils, using an ohmmeter. *See Figs. 6 and 7.* Test for grounds between each slip ring and rotor shaft. No continuity should exist.

2) Check for open field by connecting ohmmeter leads across slip rings. Normal resistance reading with rotor at room temperature is 1.7-2.1 ohms for 117 amp. alternator and 1.5-2.0 ohms for all other models.

3) Readings between 2.5 and 3.0 ohms would result from rotors operating at high engine compartment

temperatures. Readings above 3.5 ohms indicate high resistance, possibly requiring rotor replacement. If reading is below 1.7 ohms (117 amp. alternator) or 1.5 ohms (all other models), the field coil is shorted.

Fig 6: Ohmmeter Probe Connections for Rotor Ground Test

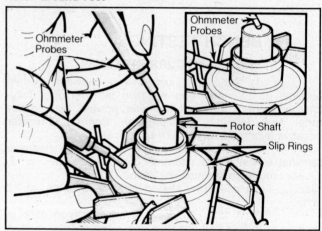

Ohmmeter Probes

Ohmmeter Probes

Rotor Shaft

Slip Rings

Touch one ohmmeter probe to shaft; touch other probe to each slip ring.

Fig. 7: Ohmmeter Probe Connections for Open or Short Tests

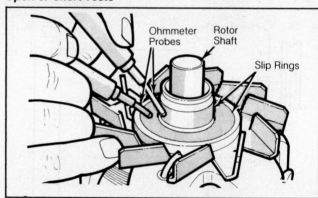

Ohmmeter Probes

Rotor Shaft

Slip Rings

Touch ohmmeter probes to slip rings.

OVERHAUL

DISASSEMBLY

1) Remove brush screws and insulating washers, and lift brush assemblies from end shield.

CAUTION: Stator is laminated. Do not burr stator or end shield.

2) Remove through bolts, and pry between stator and drive end shield with blade of screwdriver, using slot provided. Carefully separate drive end shield, pulley and rotor assembly away from stator and rectifier end shield assembly. If negative heat sink diode straps are on top of positive heat sink straps, remove 4 hex head screws on negative rectifier and heat sink assembly. Remove heat sink assembly.

3) On all except 117 amp. alternators, remove nut, washer and insulator from output ("BAT") terminal on outside of end shield. Turn end shield over, and remove

CHRYSLER CORP. ALTERNATORS (Cont.)

capacitor, insulated washer and positive heat sink assembly. Remove insulator from "BAT" terminal hole.

4) On 117 amp. alternators, reach inside end shield. Remove nut and insulator, attaching positive heat sink to end shield. Remove capacitor screw, capacitor and insulator.

5) From outside end shield, remove nut and insulator, attaching positive heat sink to end shield. Remove screws attaching negative heat sink to end shield. Remove positive and negative heat sink assemblies, noting location of insulators. Remove terminal block attaching screws and terminal block.

6) On all except 117 amp. alternators, remove mica insulator from end shield and loosen four hex head screws on negative rectifier and heat sink assembly. Remove two outer screws and remove heat sink assembly.

Fig. 8: Installing Drive End Shield Bearing

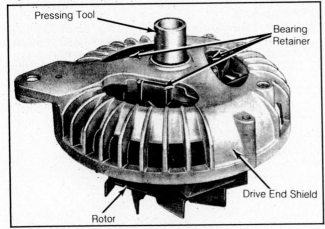

Support rotor shaft base, while pressing bearing into end shield.

7) Using a puller (C-4068 or C-4333; C-4467 on 117 amp. models), remove drive pulley from shaft. Remove screws attaching bearing retainer to drive end shield on 117 amp. alternators. Separate bearing retainer

from end shield. Support end shield and tap rotor shaft with plastic hammer to separate rotor from end shield.

8) Using puller, remove drive end ball bearing. If needle roller bearing in rectifier end shield must be replaced, it can be pressed out of end shield using an end shield support tool (C-3925) and press tool (C-3770A).

SLIP RING REPLACEMENT

NOTE: Slip rings are not serviced as a separate item, only as part of the rotor assembly.

REASSEMBLY

EXCEPT 117 AMP. ALTERNATOR

1) Place grease retainer on rotor shaft, and press retainer onto shaft with installer tool (C-3921). Press until grease retainer bottoms on rotor shaft. Position rectifier end shield bearing on base of needle bearing installer tool (C-4201-1). Place end shield on top of bearing so it is properly aligned. With top part of bearing press tool (C-4201-2) placed on end shield, press into place until it bottoms.

NOTE: New bearings are pre-lubricated and should require no additional lubrication.

2) Insert drive end bearing in drive end shield. Install retainer plate to hold bearing in place. A metal spacer is supplied with replacement rotors and ball bearings (but is not a part of original alternator assembly). Place spacer on pulley end of rotor shaft first. Position bearing and drive end shield on rotor shaft. Support base of rotor shaft. Press bearing end shield into position on rotor shaft with an arbor press and adapter (C-3858).

CAUTION: Ensure bearing is installed squarely to avoid damage to bearing and rotor shaft.

3) Install pulley on rotor shaft. Shaft of rotor must be supported, so all pressing force is on pulley hub and rotor shaft, (not on bearings). Do not hammer pulley on or apply more than 6800 lbs. (3084 kg).

Fig. 9: Exploded View of Typical Chrysler Corp. Alternator

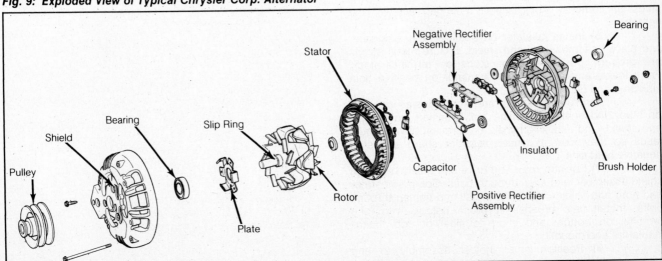

4) If removed, install output terminal stud and insulator through end shield. Be sure mica insulators are in place and undamaged. Install positive heat sink assembly over studs. Guide rectifier straps over studs on terminal block. Install capacitor. Slide negative rectifier and heat sink assembly into place. Position straps and install screws.

5) Position stator over rectifier end shield, and install winding terminals on terminal block. Press stator pins into each end shield. Route leads so they cannot contact rotor or sharp edge of negative heat sink. Position rotor and drive end shield over stator and rectifier end shield. Install through bolts. Compress both ends, and tighten through bolts evenly.

6) Install field brushes in insulated holders. Position vertical and horizontal field brushes properly in rectifier end shield. Place an insulating washer on each field brush terminal. Install lock washers. Be sure brushes are not grounded. Rotate pulley slowly by hand to ensure rotor blades do not hit stator leads.

117 AMP. ALTERNATOR ONLY

1) Position rectifier end shield bearing on base of support tool (C-4330-1-3). Place end shield on top of bearing, so that it is properly aligned. With bearing installer tool (C-4330-2) placed on end shield, press into place until end shield touches base of press.

NOTE: **New bearings are prelubricated and require no additional lubrication.**

2) Insert drive end bearing in end shield. Position retainer, and tighten mounting screws, ensuring rotor spacer is in position. Place bearing and drive end shield on rotor shaft. Press end shield into position with arbor press and tool C-3858.

3) Install pulley on rotor shaft. Support shaft so that pressing force is on pulley hub. Press pulley on shaft until it contacts inner race of drive end bearing. Do not hammer pulley on or exceed 6800 lbs. (3084 kg) of force. Position insulator and capacitor on positive heat sink mounting stub, and tighten attaching screw.

4) Position terminal block in rectifier end shield, and tighten screws. Position negative heat sink in end shield, ensuring that metal straps are placed over studs on terminal block. Install mounting screws and tighten.

5) Install insulator on positive heat sink stud, and place assembly into end shield. Ensure metal straps are properly positioned over studs on terminal block. From inside end shield, install insulator on positive heat sink stud and tighten nut.

6) From outside of end shield, install insulator on stud, and tighten mounting bolt. Position stator over end shield, and install terminals on terminal block. Route leads so they cannot contact rotor or sharp edges of negative heat sink.

7) Position rotor and drive end shield over end shield assembly, and align through bolts. Compress stator and both end shields manually. Install and tighten through bolts. Install field brushes in brush holder, with long terminal on bottom and short terminal on top. Install insulators and mounting screw.

8) Position brush holder assembly to end shield, making sure it is properly seated, and tighten

mounting screw. Rotate pulley by hand to ensure rotor poles do not hit stator winding leads.

TIGHTENING SPECIFICATIONS

Application	INCH Lbs. (N.m)
Capacitor Bracket Screws	30-40 (3.4-4.5)
End Bearing Mount Screws	
117 Amp.	19-29 (2.1-3.3)
Field Brush Screws	
All Exc. 117 Amp.	15-35 (1.7-4.0)
117 Amp.	30-40 (3.4-4.5)
Negative Heat Sink Mount Screw	
All Exc. 117 Amp.	19-29 (2.1-3.3)
117 Amp.	30-40 (3.4-4.5)
Plastic Insulator Nut	30-50 (3.4-5.6)
Positive Heat Sink Stud Nut	20-30 (2.3-3.4)
Terminal Block Mount Screws	
117 Amp. Only	30-40 (3.4-4.5)
Through Bolts	
All Exc. 117 Amp.	25-55 (2.8-6.2)
117 Amp.	40-60 (4.5-6.8)
Winding Terminal Nut	11-17 (1.2-1.9)

CHRYSLER CORP. ELECTRONIC REGULATOR

Dodge, Plymouth

DESCRIPTION

The electronic voltage regulator regulates electrical system voltage by limiting voltage generated by alternator. This is accomplished by controlling amount of current that is allowed to pass through alternator field winding. Regulator has no moving parts and requires no adjustment after it is set at factory.

Unit contains several semiconductor components, transistors and diodes plus some resistors and a capacitor. A large transistor is placed in series with alternator field winding and a control circuit which senses system voltage and turns transistor on and off as required.

As alternator speed and electrical system load conditions change, control circuit is turning transistor on and off many times per second most of the time engine is in operation.

The only time transistor is not turning on and off rapidly is during low engine speed operation when high electrical loads are present. This requires the alternator field to be in the "ON" state continuously. Electronic regulator control circuit can also vary the regulated system voltage up or down as temperatures change.

TESTING

NOTE: Battery specific gravity should be above 1.220 for a properly regulated voltage check. Charge battery or use a good test battery before testing regulator.

NOTE: Where tester (C-4133) is available, use an adapter (C-4341) to switch circuit of regulator to be tested. The adapter has a 3-position switch to select regulator part number or regulator installed. Follow manufacturer's test procedure.

1) Connect positive lead of a voltmeter to positive post on battery. Connect negative lead of voltmeter to a good ground. Start and run vehicle at 1250 RPM with all lights and accessories turned off. Check voltmeter reading. Regulator is working properly if voltage readings are within specifications.

Voltage Regulator Specifications

Ambient Temperature [1]	Voltage Range
—20°F (—29°C)	14.9-15.9
80°F (27°C)	13.9-14.6
140°F (60°C)	13.3-13.9
Above 140°F (60°C)	Less than 13.6

[1] — Ambient temperature is measured ¼" (6.35 mm) from regulator.

2) If voltage is not within limits or is fluctuating, check that regulator has a good ground. With engine off, disconnect regulator terminals. Turn ignition "ON", but do not start engine.

3) Battery voltage should be present at both regulator harness terminals. If so, replace regulator and repeat test.

ADJUSTMENT

The Electronic Voltage Regulator cannot be adjusted. If specifications are not obtained and investigation has shown the rest of electrical system to be satisfactory, then regulator must be replaced.

Fig. 1: Chrysler Corp. Test Connections for Voltage Regulator Test

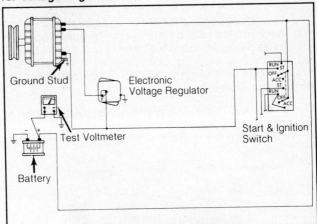

Be sure all connections are clean and tight.

Alternators & Regulators

DELCO-REMY WITH INTEGRAL REGULATOR

Chevrolet, GMC, Jeep

DESCRIPTION

Delco 10SI, 12SI, 15SI and 27SI Integral regulator alternators feature a solid state regulator mounted inside alternator. These alternators are available with different outputs at idle and different maximum outputs.

Delcotrons consist of 2 separate housings (end frame assemblies), a rotor, stator, brushes, slip rings and diodes. Rotor is supported in drive end frames by ball bearings and in slip ring end frame by roller bearings. Bearings contain enough lubrication to eliminate need for periodic lubrication.

Fig. 1: Cutaway View Showing Internal Components of Delcotron Integral Regulator Alternator

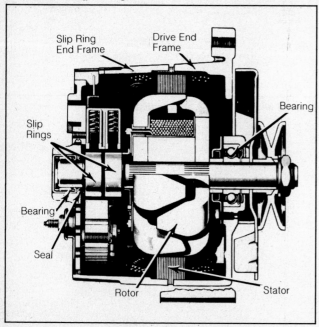

Illustration applies to Chevrolet, GMC & Jeep.

IDENTIFICATION

Alternator rated ampere output is stamped on alternator case. Alternators for Chevrolet and GMC are available in 37, 42, 61, 63, and 80 ampere ratings. Jeep models are rated at 42, 55 and 85 amperes.

OPERATION

Two brushes carry current through slip rings to and from field coil mounted on rotor. Stator windings are assembled on the inside of a laminated core that forms part of the alternator frame.

A rectifier bridge, connected to stator windings, contains 6 diodes (3 positives and 3 negatives) molded into an assembly. This rectifier bridge changes stator A.C. voltage into D.C. voltage, which appears at output terminal.

The blocking action of the diodes prevents battery discharge back through alternator. Because of the blocking action, the need for a cutout relay is eliminated.

Alternator field current is supplied through a diode trio which is also connected to stator windings.

A capacitor is mounted in end frame, protecting rectifier bridge and diodes from high voltage and suppressing radio interference noise. Some vehicles are equipped with ammeters, others with voltmeters.

ADJUSTMENT

No periodic adjustments or maintenance of any kind is required on alternator assembly. Regulator voltage is preset, and no adjustment is possible.

CAUTION: Do not attempt to polarize alternator. Do not short or ground any terminals except as instructed. Never operate alternator with battery out of circuit or output terminal open. Alternator and battery must share same ground polarity.

TESTING

NOTE: Before making electrical checks, visually inspect all terminals for clean and tight connections. Check alternator mounting bolts and drive belt tension. Do not ground No. 2 lead wire. Battery must be in good condition to test charging system.

UNDERCHARGED BATTERY

1) With ignition switch "ON", connect a voltmeter from alternator "BAT" terminal to ground, then from No. 1 terminal to ground, and last, No. 2 terminal to ground. A zero reading indicates an open between connection and battery.

2) Opens in the No. 2 lead may be between terminals at the crimp between harness wire and terminal, or in wire. *See Fig. 2.*

NOTE: If preceding test is satisfactory, continue to next step.

3) Disconnect battery ground cable. Connect an ammeter in circuit at "BAT" terminal of alternator.

4) Reconnect battery ground cable. Turn on all available accessories. Connect a carbon pile across battery. Operate engine at moderate speed and adjust carbon pile as required to obtain maximum current output.

5) If ampere output is within 10 amps of rated output as stamped on alternator case, alternator is good.

6) If output is not within 10 amps of rated output, ground field winding by inserting a screwdriver into test hole. *See Fig. 2.*

CAUTION: Tab is within 3/4" (19 mm) of casting surface. Do not force screwdriver deeper than 1" (25 mm) into end frame. If test hole is not accessible, proceed to "Testing (On Bench)" as described under Overhaul.

7) Operate engine at moderate speed as required and adjust carbon pile for maximum output.

8) If output is now within 10 amps of rated output with fields grounded, regulator is defective and requires replacement.

DELCO-REMY WITH INTEGRAL REGULATOR (Cont.)

**Fig. 2: Identification of Delcotron Terminal
Locations All Models**

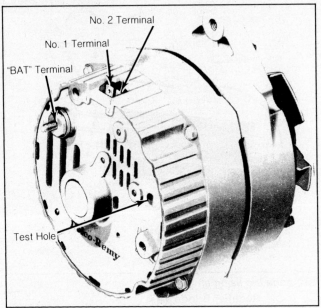

*Visually inspect all terminals for clean
and tight connections.*

9) If output is still not within 10 amps of rated output, check field winding, diode trio, rectifier bridge, and stator.

OVERCHARGED BATTERY

Connect a voltmeter from alternator terminal No. 2 to ground. If reading is zero, No. 2 lead circuit is open. If battery and No. 2 lead circuit check out good, alternator will have to be disassembled for further checks. *See Overhaul.*

OVERHAUL

DISASSEMBLY

1) Scribe marks on housings for reassembly reference. Remove through bolts connecting housings. Separate front and rear housings by prying apart with screwdriver.

2) Place a piece of tape over slip ring end frame bearing to prevent entry of dirt. At this point brushes may drop onto rotor shaft and become contaminated with bearing lubricant. Clean brushes as soon as possible with a cleaner (acetone) to keep them from becoming grease soaked.

3) Place rotor in vise and tighten vise only enough to permit removal of shaft nut. Remove shaft nut, washer, pulley, fan and collar. Separate front housing from rotor shaft. Remove 3 stator lead attaching nuts and remove stator leads from bridge terminal.

4) Separate stator from rear housing. Remove diode trio lead clip attaching screw, and remove diode trio. Remove capacitor attaching screw and remove capacitor lead from bridge rectifier.

5) Remove bridge rectifier and battery terminal attaching screws and remove bridge rectifier. Remove 2 brush holder screws and 1 diode trio lead strap screw.

Remove brush holder and brushes. Note location of brushes for reassembly.

6) Remove voltage regulator. Remove front bearing retaining plate screws. Press front bearing out of housing with collar. Press out rear bearing from housing by inserting collar inside housing and pressing bearing toward the outside.

INSPECTION

Wash all metal parts except bearings, stator and rotor. Inspect rotor slip rings. They may be cleaned with 400 grain polishing cloth, while rotor is being rotated. Slip rings may be lathe turned to .002" (.051 mm) maximum indicator reading.

Slip rings are not replaceable. Excessive damage will require rotor replacement. Inspect brushes for wear, replacing them if more than 50% worn.

TESTING (ON BENCH)
Rotor Field Winding Test

1) Check rotor for grounds or an open circuit, using a 110-volt test lamp or an ohmmeter. *See Fig. 3.* To check for grounds, connect ohmmeter leads to shaft and slip ring (each ring in turn). No continuity should exist.

2) To test for open field, connect ohmmeter leads to each slip ring. Continuity should be indicated.

3) To test for shorts, connect a 12-volt battery and ammeter in series with both slip rings. Current draw is used for this test.

4) Resistance should be 2.5-3.0 ohms. Excessive amperage draw or low resistance indicates shorted windings. If rotor tests okay, but alternator output is low, continue with tests.

**Fig. 3: Bench Testing Rotor For Opens
or Grounds Using an Ohmmeter**

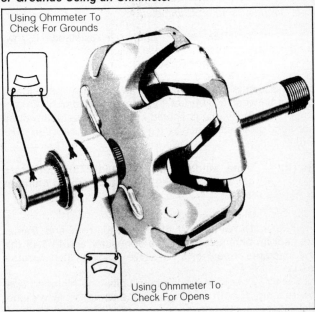

Check rotors using a 110-volt test lamp or an ohmmeter.

Stator Ground Test

1) Connect leads of 110-volt test lamp or an ohmmeter (x1000 scale) to any stator lead and to stator frame. Ohmmeter reading should be infinite. *See Fig. 4.*

Alternators & Regulators

DELCO-REMY WITH INTEGRAL REGULATOR (Cont.)

Fig. 4: Bench Testing Stator for Open or Grounded Circuits

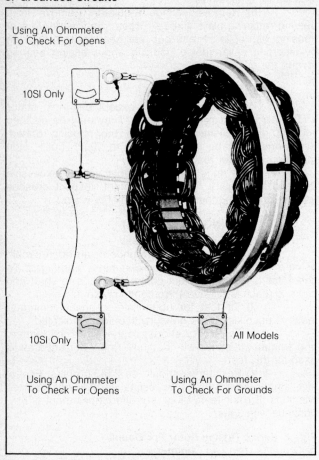

Test Circuits Using an Ohmmeter

2) If test lamp lights or if resistance is low, windings are grounded. Replace stator assembly.

Stator Open Test

1) Connect a 110-volt test lamp or an ohmmeter (x1 scale) with leads touching any 2 stator leads. Make checks between 2 different sets of stator leads.

2) Readings should be equal. If test lamp does not light or if resistance is high, windings are open. *See Fig. 4.*

NOTE: Delta windings on 15SI and 27SI alternators cannot be checked for open with an ohmmeter.

Diode Trio Test

1) With diode trio removed from end frame, connect an ohmmeter to single connector and to 1 of the 3 connectors. *See Fig. 5.* Observe reading, then reverse leads.

2) A good diode trio will give one high and one low reading. If both readings are the same, replace diode trio. Repeat tests between single connector and each of the 2 connectors.

NOTE: Before replacing diode trio, also check rectifier bridge. Do not use high voltage, such as 110-volt test lamp, when testing diode trio.

Fig. 5: Bench Testing Diode Trio

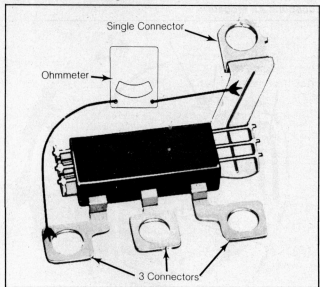

Test diode trio using an Ohmmeter

Rectifier Bridge Test

1) Connect an ohmmeter with one lead touching grounded heat sink and the other lead touching flat metal on 1 of the 3 terminals. Observe reading and reverse test lead connections. *See Fig. 6.*

2) If both readings are the same, replace rectifier bridge. A good bridge will give one high and one low reading. Repeat test on all terminals (6 tests with insulated heat sink).

3) Connect test leads to insulated heat sink and 1 edge of the 3 terminals. Observe reading and reverse connections. Repeat test on all terminals (6 tests with insulated heat sink).

4) When all 12 tests have been made, testing is complete. Do not use high voltage, such as 110-volt test lamp to check bridge. Do not replace diode trio or rectifier bridge unless at least 1 pair of readings is the same (with leads reversed).

Fig. 6: Bench Testing Rectifier Bridge and Identification of End Frame Components

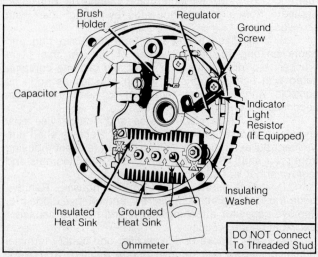

Observe reading and reverse test lead connections.

DELCO-REMY WITH INTEGRAL REGULATOR (Cont.)

Fig. 7: Exploded View of Delcotron Alternator Model 10SI

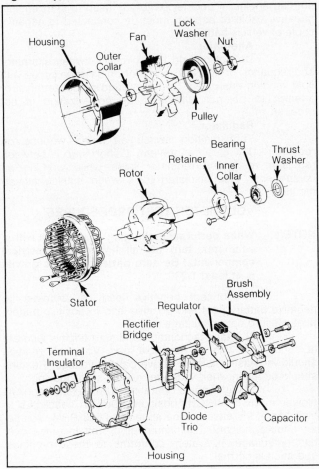

Used on Chevrolet, GMC and Jeep models.

REASSEMBLY

1) On early producton 15SI and 27SI, fill cavity between retainer plate and bearing 1/4 full with lubricant (Delco-Remy 1948791 or equivalent). Series 10SI, 12SI and late production 15SI and 27SI use a sealed bearing and no lubrication is required.

2) Assemble bearing and slinger (flat washer on some models) in front housing. Press bearing in with collar that fits over outer race. If bearing retainer plate felt seal is hardened, replace retainer plate.

3) Install retainer plate and screws. Press rotor into end frame. Assemble collar, fan, pulley, washer and nut. Torque nut to 40-60 ft. lbs. (54-82 N.m).

4) If rear bearing was removed, support inside of rear housing with hollow cylinder. On 10SI and 27SI models, place flat plate over bearing. Press bearing into housing from outside, until bearing is flush with end frame.

5) On 15SI models, use thin wall tube in space between grease cup and housing to push bearing in until flush with housing. Oil lip of replacement bearing seal, and press seal in with lip away from bearing.

6) Install springs and brushes in brush holder. Install wooden toothpick in hole at bottom of holder to retain brushes. Install voltage regulator. Attach brush holder into rear housing, noting stack-up of parts. Allow toothpick to protrude through hole in rear housing

7) Install diode trio lead strap attaching screw and washer. Tighten brush holder screws. Position bridge rectifier on rear housing with insulator between heat sink and rear housing.

8) Install bridge rectifier and battery terminal screws. Connect capacitor lead to bridge rectifier. Position diode trio on end housing. Install diode trio lead clip screw, making sure insulating washer is over top of diode connector.

9) Install stator on rear housing. Attach stator leads to bridge rectifier terminals. Remove tape covering bearing and join front and rear housings with scribe marks aligned. Install through bolts and tighten. Remove toothpick from brush holder assembly.

ALTERNATOR OUTPUT

Stamped Amperage	Amperage @14V	Rated Output (Engine RPM)
37	22	2000
42	25	2000
55	30	2000
61	30	2000
63	32	2000
70	55	2000
80	55	2000
85	[1]	[1]

[1] — Information not available from manufacturer. Police option.

Alternators & Regulators
MOTORCRAFT ALTERNATORS

Ford

DESCRIPTION

Ford light trucks use 2 similar alternators, a rear terminal model and a side terminal model. *See Figs. 1 and 2.* Rated outputs range from 40 to 100 amps. depending upon model used. Some models are equipped with indicator lights, others with ammeters.

Alternator is belt driven from engine. Current is supplied from Alternator-Regulator system to rotating field of alternator through 2 brushes to 2 slip rings. Power is produced in the form of alternating current which is rectified to direct current by 6 diodes. Alternator regulator automatically adjusts alternator field current to maintain alternator output voltage within prescribed limits to correctly charge battery. Charging systems are equipped with a fuse link between starter relay and alternator "BAT" terminal.

IDENTIFICATION & SPECIFICATIONS

Alternator is color-ink stamped with "Motorcraft" trademark. Color stamp is code for rated amperage output. Rated amperage is also stamped on end frame (40A, 60A, etc.). Color code is as follows:

ALTERNATOR OUTPUT

Application	Amperage @ 15V	Rated Output (Engine RPM)
Orange	40	2900
Green	60	2900
Green	65	2900
Black	70	[1] 1640
Red	100	[1] 2900

[1] — Rated cold output.

ALTERNATOR SPECIFICATIONS

Alternator	Specification
Field Current at 12 Volts (All)	4.0 Amps
Slip Rings (All)	
Minimum Diameter	1.22"
Maximum Runout	.0005"
Brush Length Wear Limit	
All Models	1/4"
Pulley Nut Torque (All)	60-100 ft. lbs. (8-136 N.m)

ADJUSTMENT

ALTERNATOR REGULATOR

An electronic regulator is used on all charging systems. It is factory calibrated and cannot be adjusted.

TESTING PRECAUTIONS

When testing or servicing alternator or regulator, take following precautions to avoid damage to components.

Battery

Do not reverse battery connections. Negative terminal must be connected to ground. When charging battery, cables must be disconnected from battery before connecting charger. Do not use charger as a booster for starting engine. If booster battery is used to start engine, negative cable of booster must be connected to negative cable of vehicle battery.

Alternator

Do not ground field circuit between alternator and regualtor, or operate alternator on an open circuit with field winding energized. Do not ground output terminal or attempt to polarize alternator as polzarization is not required.

Regulator

Turn ignition switch off when working on regulator. Use care to prevent a short circuit between regulator relay and regulator base while working on components. Use insulated tools when making adjustments.

VOLTMETER TEST PROCEDURES

NOTE: **When performing charging system test with a voltmeter, turn off all lights and electrical components. Be sure battery specific gravity is at least 1.230.**

1) Connect negative lead of voltmeter to negative battery post and positive lead to positive battery post. Record battery voltage.

2) Attach tachometer and start engine. Operate at 1500 RPM with no electrical load. Voltmeter reading should increase 1-2 volts above battery voltage. Reading should be taken when voltmeter needle stops moving.

3) With engine operating, turn on heater or A/C blower motor to "HIGH" position. Turn on headlights to high beam. Increase engine speed to 2000 RPM. Voltmeter should indicate a minimum of .5 volt increase over battery voltage. If system conforms to these readings, operation is normal.

Fig. 1: Rear View Showing Alternator Terminal Location on Rear Terminal Models

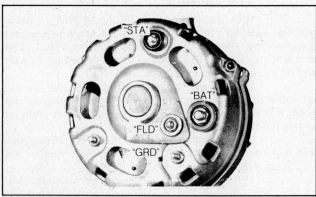

Do not ground field circuit between alternator and regulator.

TEST RESULTS

1) If voltmeter reading indicates over-voltage (more than 2 volts above battery voltage), shut off engine and check ground connections between regulator and alternator and/or regulator and engine. Clean and tighten connections and repeat test.

2) If over-voltage condition still exists, disconnect regulator wiring plug and repeat steps **2)** and **3)** of *"Voltmeter Test Procedures"*. If condition is corrected, replace regulator and repeat test.

MOTORCRAFT ALTERNATORS (Cont.)

Fig. 2: Side View Showing Alternator Terminal Location on Side Terminal Models

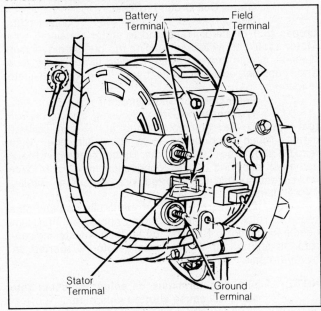

Connections must be clean and tight.

3) If over-voltage still exists with regulator disconnected, a short is indicated in wiring harness between alternator and regulator (Circuits "A" and "F"). Repair short circuit, and then reconnect regulator, repeating tests with regulator plug connected.

Fig. 3: Test Wiring Connections for Field Circuit Test

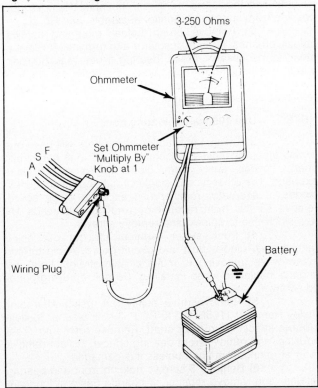

Field circuit should be checked with regulator wiring plug disconnected.

UNDER VOLTAGE & FIELD CIRCUIT TESTS

1) To determine if jumping procedure is safe, field circuit should be checked with regulator wiring plug disconnected and ohmmeter connected from "F" terminal of wiring plug to battery ground. Ohmmeter should indicate 3-250 ohms. *See Fig. 3.*

2) If load voltage did not increase 1/2 volt above base voltage, connect a jumper wire across "A" and "F" terminals of wiring plug and repeat test procedures.

3) If voltage is still under base voltage, remove jumper wire from wiring plug and leave plug disconnected from regulator. Connect jumper wire to "FLD" and "BAT" terminals on alternator and repeat test. If voltage increases more than 1/2 volt above battery voltage, repair wiring harness or replace regulator.

4) If voltmeter still indicates under voltage, stop engine and move positive voltmeter lead to "BAT" terminal. If voltmeter now indicates base voltage reading, repair alternator. If voltmeter indicates zero volts, repair "BAT" wire or replace fuse link.

Fig. 4: Internal View Showing Stator Lead Connections on Rear Terminal Models

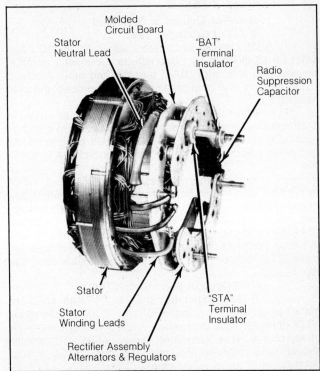

Be sure all connections are tight.

REGULATOR CIRCUIT TESTS

"S" Circuit With Ammeter

1) Connect positive voltmeter lead to regulator wiring plug "S" terminal position. Turn ignition "ON", but do not start engine.

2) Voltmeter should indicate battery voltage. If there is no voltage, "S" wire lead from ignition switch is open. Repair and retest system.

"S" & "I" Circuit With Indicator Light

1) Disconnect regulator wiring plug, and install a jumper wire between "A" and "F" terminals. With engine

Alternators & Regulators

MOTORCRAFT ALTERNATORS (Cont.)

idling, connect negative lead of voltmeter to ground. Connect positive voltmeter lead, in turn, to "S" and then "I" terminals of regulator wiring plug.

2) Voltage of "S" circuit should be about 1/2 that of "I" circuit. If no voltage is present, repair alternator or wiring circuit at fault. If circuit tests are satisfactory, install a new regulator. Remove jumper wire from regulator wiring plug, connect plug to regulator, and repeat *"Voltmeter Test Procedures"* No Load test.

DIODE TEST (ON VEHICLE)

1) Disconnect electric choke (if equipped) and voltage regulator plug. Connect jumper wire between "A" and "F" terminals of voltage regulator wiring plug. Connect voltmeter to battery posts, start and run engine at idle speed, record voltmeter reading.

2) Move positive voltmeter lead to "S" terminal of alternator and note voltmeter reading. If meter reads 1/2 of battery voltage, alternator has an open positive diode. If meter reads about 1.0-1.5 volts more than 1/2 battery voltage, alternator has an open negative diode. Reconnect electric choke (if equipped) back into circuit after test is completed.

BENCH TESTS

Rectifier Shorted or Grounded
& Stator Grounded Test

1) Use an ohmmeter, set knob at "10", and calibrate as directed by manufacturer. Connect 1 ohmmeter probe to alternator "BAT" terminal and other probe to "STA" terminal and note reading. Reverse probes and note reading.

2) A reading of 60 ohms should be observed in 1 direction and no movement with terminals reversed. A reading in both directions indicates a bad positive diode, grounded positive diode plate, or grounded "BAT" terminal.

3) Perform same test using "STA" and "GRD" terminals. Readings in both directions indicate either bad negative diode, grounded stator winding, grounded stator terminal, grounded positive diode plate, or grounded "BAT" terminal. Infinite reading (no needle movement) in all 4 probe positions in the preceeding tests indicates an open "STA" terminal lead connection inside alternator. *See Fig. 4.*

Field Open or Short Circuit Test

1) Set ohmmeter knob at "1" and calibrate meter as directed by manufacturer. Contact alternator "FLD" terminal with one probe and "GND" terminal with other probe, spin alternator pulley wheel. Ohmmeter should read between 2.4 and 100 ohms, and should fluctuate while pulley is spinning.

2) Infinite reading (no needle movement) indicates open brush lead, worn or stuck brushes, or bad rotor assembly. Meter reading of less than 2.4 ohms indicates grounded brush assembly, grounded field terminal, or bad rotor.

Diode Test

1) Remove rectifier assembly from alternator. Set ohmmeter knob at "10". Calibrate meter. To test 1 set of diodes, contact 1 probe to terminal bolt and contact each of 3 stator lead terminals with other probe. Reverse probes and repeat test.

2) All diodes should show readings of about 60 ohms in 1 direction, and infinite readings with probes reversed. Repeat test for other set of diodes, moving first

probe to other terminal screw. If meter readings are not as specified, replace rectifier assembly.

Stator Coil Grounded Test

Set ohmmeter knob at "1000". Contact meter probes to 1 of stator leads and to stator laminated core. Meter should show infinite reading (no needle movement). If meter needle moved, stator winding is shorted to core and must be replaced. Repeat test for each 1 of stator leads.

Rotor Open or Short Circuit Test

1) Disassemble front housing and rotor from rear housing. Set ohmmeter knob at "1" and calibrate meter. Touch each probe to a rotor slip ring. Meter reading should be 2.0-3.5 ohms. Higher reading indicates damaged slip ring solder connection or broken wire. Lower reading indicates shorted wire or slip ring. Replace rotor if damaged.

2) Contact 1 meter probe to slip ring and other probe to rotor shaft. Meter reading should be infinite (no needle deflection). Reading other than infinite indicates rotor is shorted to shaft. Replace rotor if shorted and beyond repair.

NOTE: **Slip ring terminals or solder touching rotor shaft will cause shorted condition.**

OVERHAUL

REAR TERMINAL MODELS

Disassembly

1) Mark both housings and stator with scribe for reassembly. Remove through bolts and separate front housing and rotor from stator and rear housing. Remove all nuts and insulators from rear housing. Remove rear housing from stator and rectifier assembly. *See Fig. 5.*

2) Remove brush holder mounting screws, holder, brushes, springs, insulator and terminal. If replacement is necessary, press bearing from rear housing, supporting housing on inner boss. If rectifier assembly is being replaced, unsolder stator leads from rectifier terminals and separate stator from rectifier assembly.

NOTE: **Use 100 watt soldering iron.**

3) Original production alternators will have one of two types of rectifier assembly boards; one has circuit board spaced away from diode plates with diodes exposed. The other type is single circuit board with built-in diodes. If alternator rectifier has exposed diode board, remove screws from rectifier by rotating bolt heads 1/4 turn clockwise to unlock, and remove screws.

4) Push stator terminal straight out on a rectifier with diodes built into circuit board. Avoid turning screw while removing to make certain straight knurl will engage insulators when installing. Do not remove grounded screw.

5) Remove drive pulley nut, using Alternator Pulley Remover (T65P-10300-B). Pull lock washer, pulley, fan and spacer from rotor shaft. Remove rotor from front housing, and remove front bearing spacer. Do not remove rotor stop ring from shaft unless it is damaged.

6) Remove 3 screws holding front end bearing retainer and remove retainer. If bearing has lost lubricant or is damaged, support housing close to bearing boss and press out old bearing.

MOTORCRAFT ALTERNATORS (Cont.)

Fig. 5: Exploded View of Motorcraft Rear Terminal Alternator Assembly

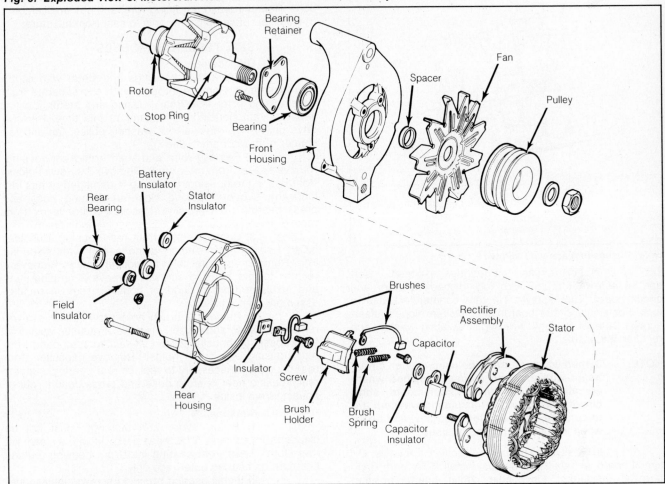

Fig. 6: Motorcraft Pulley Removal Procedure

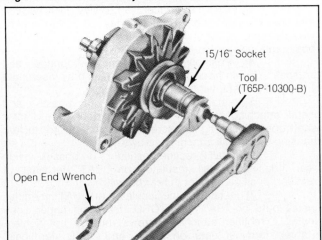

*Remove by using open end wrench, 15/16"
socket and puller (T65P-10300-B).*

Reassembly

1) Rotor, stator and bearing must not be cleaned with solvent. Wipe these parts off with a clean, lint free cloth. Press front bearing in front housing bearing boss, putting pressure on bearing outer race only.

2) Install bearing retainer. If stop-ring on rotor drive shaft is damaged, install new stop-ring. Push new ring on shaft and into groove.

NOTE: **Do not open ring with snap ring pliers, as permanent damage will result.**

3) Position bearing spacer on rotor shaft with recessed side against stop ring. Position front housing, fan spacer, fan, pulley and lock washer on rotor shaft and install retaining nut. Tighten nut.

4) If rear housing bearing was removed, support housing on inner boss and press a new bearing flush with outer end surface. Place brush springs, brushes, brush terminal and terminal insulator in brush holder.

5) Hold brushes in position by inserting small piece of stiff wire in brush holder. Position brush holder assembly in rear housing and install mounting screws. Position brush leads in holder. *See Figs. 7 & 8.*

6) Wrap 3 stator winding leads around rectifier terminals and solder using 100 watt soldering iron and resin core solder. On 65 amp models, push terminals of stator wires onto circuit board terminals and solder. Position stator neutral lead eyelet on stator terminal screw and install screw in rectifier assembly. *See Fig. 4.*

MOTORCRAFT ALTERNATORS (Cont.)

Fig. 7: Assembled View of Brush Holder Assembly

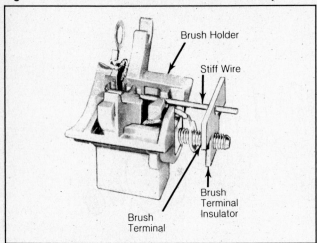

Hold brushes in place with stiff wire.

7) For rectifier with diodes exposed, insert special screws through wire lug, dished washers and circuit board. Turn screws 1/4 turn counterclockwise to lock. For single circuit boards with built-in diodes, insert screws straight through wire lug, insulating washer and rectifier, into insulator.

NOTE: Dished washers are to be used only on circuit board with exposed diodes. If dished washers are used on single circuit board, short circuit will occur. Flat insulating washers are to be used between stator terminal and board when single circuit board is used.

8) Position capacitor on rectifier terminals. On circuit board with exposed diodes, install "STA" and "BAT" terminal insulators. On single circuit board, position square stator terminal insulator in rectifier assembly.

9) Position "BAT" terminal insulator on "BAT" terminal. Position stator and rectifier assembly in rear housing. Make certain all terminal insulators are seated properly in appropriate recesses. Position "STA" (Black), "BAT" (Red), and "FLD" (Orange) isulators on terminal bolts and install retaining nuts.

10) Wipe rear end bearing of rotor shaft with clean, lint free cloth. Position rear housing and stator assembly over rotor and align scribe marks made during initial disassembly. Seat machined portion of stator core

Fig. 8: View Showing Motorcraft Brush Lead Wire Routing

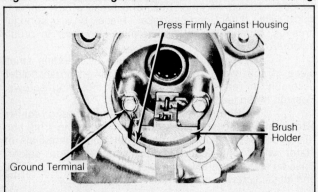

Wipe rear end bearing of rotor shaft with lint free cloth.

into step in both end housings. Install housing through bolts. Remove brush retracting wire, and put small amount of water-proof cement over hole to seal from moisture.

SIDE TERMINAL MODELS
Disassembly
1) Mark both housings and stator with scribe for reassembly. Remove through bolts and separate from housing and rotor from rear housing and stator. Do not separate rear housing from stator at this time. Remove drive pulley nut, remove lock washer, pulley, fan and fan spacer from rotor shaft. *See Fig. 9.*

2) Remove rotor and shaft from front housing, remove spacer from rotor shaft. Remove 3 screws holding front bearing to housing. If bearing is damaged or has lost lubricant, support housing close to bearing boss and press bearing from housing. Unsolder stator leads from rectifier assembly, using a 100 watt soldering iron.

3) Remove stator from rear housing. Unsolder brush holder from rectifier, using a 100 watt soldering iron. Remove capacitor lead-to-rectifier screw. Remove 4 rectifier-to-rear housing screws. Remove 2 terminal nuts and insulator from outside of housing, remove rectifier assembly from housing.

4) Remove 2 brush holder-to-housing screws, remove brushes and holder. Remove 2 rectifier insulators from bosses in housing. Clean all sealing compound from rear housing and brush holder. Remove capacitor from rear housing. If necessary to replace rear bearing, support rear housing near bearing boss and press bearing out of housing from inside.

Reassembly
1) Rotor, stator and bearings must not be cleaned with solvent. Wipe these parts off with a clean, lint free cloth. Press front bearing into front housing, putting pressure on bearing outer race only.

2) Install bearing retaining screws. Install inner space on rotor shaft and install shaft into front housing and bearing.

3) Install fan spacer, fan, pulley, lock washer, and nut onto rotor shaft. Tighten pulley nut. If rear bearing was removed, press new bearing in until it is flush with boss outer surface.

4) Position brush terminal, springs and brushes in brush holder and hold in position by inserting a small piece of stiff wire in brush holder.

5) Install brush holder to rear housing and install attaching screws. Push brush holder toward rotor shaft opening and tighten screws. Install capacitor to rear housing and install attaching screws.

6) Install 2 rectifier insulators on bosses, inside rear housing. Install insulator on "BAT" terminal of rectifier, position rectifier in rear housing.

7) Install outside insulator on "BAT" terminal, install nuts on "BAT" and "GRD" terminals finger tight. Install 4 rectifier attaching screws, but do not tighten. Tighten terminal nuts on "BAT" and "GRD" terminals, tighten 4 rectifier screws. Secure capacitor lead to rectifier. Press brush holder lead on rectifier pin and solder, using a 100 watt soldering iron.

8) Install stator in rear housing and align scribe marks. Press 3 stator leads onto rectifier pins and solder, using 100 watt soldering iron. Position rotor and front housing into stator and rear housing while aligning scribe marks.

MOTORCRAFT ALTERNATORS (Cont.)

9) Install 4 through bolts and tighten. Spin fan and pulley to ensure nothing is binding inside alternator. Remove brush retracting wire and put small amount of water-proof cement over hole to seal from moisture.

BRUSH REPLACEMENT

1) Mark both end housings and stator with a scribe. Remove 4 through bolts and separate front housing and rotor from rear housing and stator. Use a 100 watt soldering iron to detach brush holder lead from rectifier. Remove brush holder attaching screws and remove holder from rear housing. Remove any sealing compound.

2) To install, position holder to rear housing and insert wire, to retract brushes, through hole in rear housing. Install holder attaching screws, push holder toward rotor shaft and tighten screws. Press holder lead on rectifier pin and solder using a 200 watt soldering iron.

3) Install front housing and rotor to rear housing and stator while aligning scribe marks. Install 4 through bolts, spin fan and pulley to ensure nothing binds inside alternator. Remove wire, retracting brushes, and seal with a small amount of water-proof cement.

Fig. 9: Exploded View of Motorcraft Side Terminal Alternator Assembly (100 Amp. Shown)

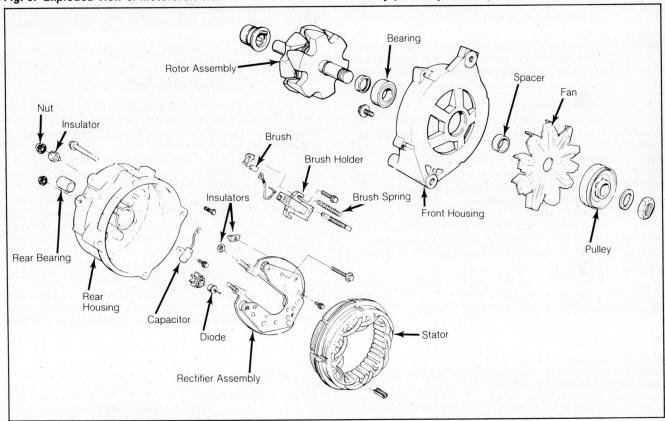

Starters

CHRYSLER CORP. GEAR REDUCTION

Dodge, Plymouth

DESCRIPTION

The starter motor consists of 4 series parallel fields, 4 brushes and a solenoid-shifted, overrunning clutch. The starter has a 2 to 1 reduction gear set, built into the starter assembly, and located in a die cast aluminum housing. The starter consists of 2 separate circuits: The supply circuit which provides the heavy current to motor and control circuit which activates solenoid.

TESTING

STARTER CONTROLS

NOTE: Test solenoid and relay in order as described. Before performing test, disconnect coil wire from distributor cap and secure to a good ground to prevent engine from starting.

Starter Solenoid

Connect a heavy jumper wire on starter relay between battery and solenoid terminals. If engine cranks, solenoid is good. Proceed to starter relay test. If engine does not crank or solenoid chatters, check wiring and connections from relay to starter for loose or corroded connections. Repeat test and if starter still fails to crank, starter must be removed for repairs.

Starter Relay

1) Position automatic transmission gear selector in "N" or "P" position and manual transmission in Neutral. Connect a jumper wire on starter relay between battery and ignition terminals.

2) If engine cranks, starter relay is good. If engine does not crank, connect a second jumper wire to starter relay ground terminal and a good ground. If engine still does not crank, replace starter relay.

3) If engine does crank, relay is functioning, transmission linkage is out of adjustment (automatic transmission) or neutral safety switch is defective (automatic transmission) or there is a poor ground between relay housing and its mounting surface.

CRANKING CIRCUIT RESISTANCE TEST

1) Make the following tests with engine cranking and all terminals connected. Connect a voltmeter at the following locations:
- Positive lead to battery positive post and negative lead to battery terminal on starter.
- Positive lead to starter housing and negative lead to negative post on battery.
- Positive lead to engine block and negative lead to battery ground cable.

2) Each of these 3 connections should show a voltmeter reading of .2 volt or less. If reading exceeds .2 volt, clean or repair cables and connections in circuit. Connect a voltmeter at the following locations:
- Positive lead to battery positive post and negative lead to cable clamp.
- Positive lead to battery negative post and negative lead to cable clamp.

3) If reading is other than zero on voltmeter, clean or repair cables and connections in circuit.

AMPERAGE DRAW TEST

NOTE: Engine should be up to operating temperature before performing this test. Heavy oil or a tight engine will increase starter draw amperage.

1) Connect a battery-starter tester and a remote starter jumper, both according to manufacturer's instructions. Turn variable resistor control knob to off or zero position. Crank engine long enough to read cranking voltage on voltmeter.

NOTE: Do not crank engine excessively, or starter may overheat.

2) Without cranking engine, turn variable resistor control knob on tester until voltmeter reads cranking voltage of previous test. With same voltmeter reading indicated, amperage reading will be equivalent to starter amperage draw test. See Starter Specifications.

SOLENOID WINDINGS

1) Connect solenoid to a 6 volt DC power supply with an ammeter in series. Connect positive lead of power supply to solenoid terminal and positive lead of ammeter to solenoid sleeve.

2) Connect negative lead of power supply to other ammeter terminal. Turn current on and check draw against hold-in specifications. Check pull-in coil the same way, except connect positive ammeter lead to solenoid lead terminal.

3) Check draw against specifications. If either winding does not meet specifications, or if winding looks burnt or damaged, replace solenoid assembly.

NO LOAD TEST (ON BENCH)

Connect a test ammeter and carbon pile rheostat in series with battery positive post and starter terminal. Connect a voltmeter across starter. Rotate carbon pile to full resistance position. Connect battery cable from battery negative post to starter frame. Adjust rheostat until battery voltage shown on voltmeter reads 11 volts. Amperage draw should be as shown in specifications.

LOCKED RESISTANCE TEST

Mount starter in test bench. Follow test equipment manufacturer's instructions. With battery voltage adjusted to 4 volts, amperage draw should be as shown in specifications.

STARTER SPECIFICATIONS

Application	Amps
Amperage Draw Test	
3.7L and 5.2L	165-180
5.9L	180-200
Solenoid Winding Test (6 Volts @ 77°F)	
Pull-In Circuit	13-15
Hold-In Circuit	8-9
No Load Test (11 Volts @ 3700 RPM Minimum)	90
Locked Resistance Test (4 Volts)	475-550

CHRYSLER CORP. GEAR REDUCTION (Cont.)

OVERHAUL

DISASSEMBLY

1) Remove through bolts and end head assembly. By pulling outward, remove armature from gear housing and field frame assembly. Carefully pull field frame assembly from gear housing just far enough to expose terminal screw. Remove terminal screw, completely remove field frame assembly.

2) Remove nuts and separate solenoid and brush plate assembly from gear housing. Remove nut, steel washer and sealing washer from solenoid terminal. Unwind solenoid lead wire from brush terminal. Remove screws attaching solenoid to brush plate. Remove solenoid from brush plate.

3) On brush plate, remove nut from battery terminal and remove terminal. From solenoid, remove solenoid contact and plunger assembly. Remove return spring from inside of solenoid moving core.

4) Remove dust cover from gear housing. Release retainer clip that positions driven gear on pinion shaft.

CAUTION: Retainer is under tension. Place cloth over assembly to catch it as it flies off.

5) Remove pinion shaft "C" clip. Push shaft toward rear of housing, remove retainer ring and thrust washers. Remove clutch and pinion assembly. Remove the 2 shift fork nylon actuators as an assembly.

6) Remove driven gear and friction washer. Pull shifting fork forward and remove solenoid moving core. Remove shifting fork retainer pin and shifting fork assembly.

Fig. 1: Chrysler Corp. Shift Fork & Clutch Assembly

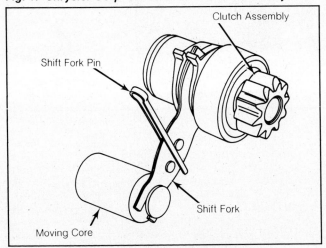

Remove shift fork assembly by removing retainer pin.

PARTS REPLACEMENT & TESTING

Brushes and Springs

Replace brushes if oil soaked or worn more than 1/2 length of new brushes. When soldering solenoid lead, use high temperature solder and resin flux. Measure spring tension with spring scale attached under spring near end. Pull on line parallel to edge of brush and note reading just as spring end leaves brush. Replace if tension is not within specifications.

SPRING TENSION

Application	Tension
All Models	32-36 ozs. (907-1021 g)

Starter Shaft Bushings

Inspect bearing surfaces for wear. Insert starter shaft into bushing and check for side play. Replace end head if its' bushing is worn. Replace other bushings, using a puller (C-3944). Service bushings are pre-sized and do not require burnishing or reaming.

Starter Clutch Unit

Pinion should rotate smoothly in 1 direction (not necessarily easy) and should not rotate in opposite direction. If not functioning properly, or if pinion is worn, chipped or burred, replace assembly.

CAUTION: Do not immerse in cleaning solvent, as the unit is pre-lubricated and lubricant will wash out.

Armature

Check for shorted armature coils in growler. Check for grounded coils by touching 1 test light probe to armature shaft and other probe to each commutator bar. Lamp should not light. If lamp lights, armature coils are grounded and armature must be replaced. Commutator should be smooth and clean, and runout must not exceed .004" (.10 mm). If runout is excessive, reface in a lathe.

Field Coil Assembly

With field frame removed from starter, drill out rivet attaching field coil lead and shunt coil lead to frame, Insulate leads from frame. Test for ground with 110V test lamp by touching 1 probe to field coil lead and other probe to field frame. Lamp should not light, if lamp lights, field coils are grounded. Replace field coils and field frame as an assembly.

CLEANING

Do not immerse parts in cleansing solvent. Clutch outer housing and pinion gear may be cleaned with a cloth moistened with cleaning solvent and then wiped dry. Clean all corrosion from solenoid assembly and inside of solenoid housing. Clean terminal contacts and contactor with crocus cloth.

REASSEMBLY

1) Ensure that shift fork plates have approximately 1/16" side movement. Lubricate sparingly between plates with SAE 10 engine oil. Position shift fork in housing, bend 1 tip of pin at a 15° angle away from housing. Fork and retainer pin must operate freely after tip of pin is bent. Install solenoid moving core and engage shifting fork.

2) Start pinion shaft into drive housing. Install friction washer and drive gear, clutch and pinion assembly, thrust washer, retaining ring and thrust washer. Shift fork must engage clutch actuators properly and friction washer must be positioned on shoulder of pinion shaft splines before driven gear is positioned.

3) Install driven gear, retainer clip, pinion shaft "C" clip and starter solenoid return spring into bore of movable core. Install solenoid contact plunger assembly into solenoid. Contact spring must be positioned on shaft of solenoid contact and plunger assembly.

CHRYSLER CORP. GEAR REDUCTION (Cont.)

4) Assemble battery terminal stud in brush holder. Position seal on brush holder plate. Start solenoid lead wire through hole in brush holder. Install solenoid stud, insulating washer, flat washer, and nut.

5) Wrap lead wire tightly around brush terminal post. Solder with high temperature resin core solder and resin flux. Install brush holder to solenoid attaching screws. Install solenoid coil and brush plate assembly into starter gear housing. Install and tighten nuts.

6) Install armature thrust washer in brushes with brushes resting on washer tabs (washer will hold brushes out and facilitate armature installation). Install brush terminal screw. Position field frame in correct position on gear housing and install armature in field frame and gear housing.

7) Carefully engage splines of shaft with reduction gear by rotating armature slightly. Install thrust washer on armature shaft. Position starter end head assembly and tighten through bolts securely.

Fig. 2: Exploded View of Reduction Gear Starter

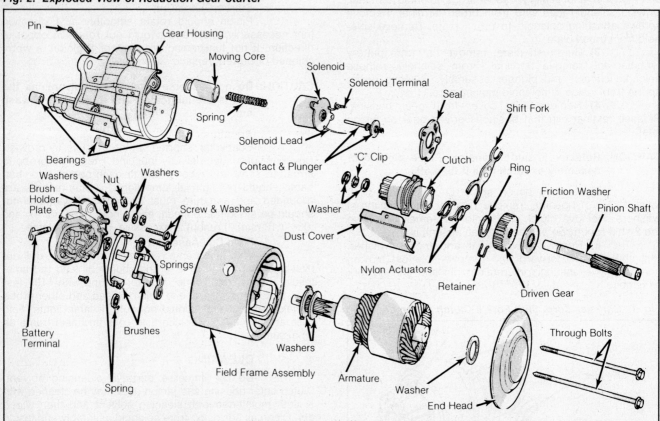

Starters

DELCO-REMY ENCLOSED HOUSING

Chevrolet, GMC, Jeep (4-Cyl.)

DESCRIPTION

Starter is a 12-volt, 4-pole unit of conventional design and has a solenoid pinion shaft (overrunning clutch) with entire mechanism enclosed within housing. Field assembly consists of 4 series coils or combination of series coils with 1 more shunt coil. Brush assemblies are completely enclosed within field frame at commutator end so entire starter and drive assembly is protected.

Starter solenoid is flange mounted on drive end housing and has a compression-type return spring located inside solenoid case. Jeep models use the 5MT starter. Diesel Chevrolet and GMC models use the 27MT starter, which differs only in that it uses a center bearing. All other models use the 10MT starter.

Jeep "CJ" and Scrambler models with 4-cylinder engine and automatic transmission have a starter motor relay, which is energized when ignition key is in "START" position and transmission selector lever is in either "NEUTRAL" or "PARK" position. Battery voltage is then applied to pull-in and hold-in windings.

TESTING

SOLENOID WINDINGS TEST

Tests are performed with all leads disconnected. Complete tests in minimum amount of time to prevent solenoid from overheating.

Hold-In Winding
All Models (Except Jeep)

Connect an ammeter, voltmeter and battery into starter circuit. See Fig. 1. Use a carbon pile to decrease battery voltage to 10 volts. Ammeter should read 14.5-16.5 amperes. If amperage is above 16.5, winding is shorted or grounded. If amperage draw is below 14.5 amperes, excessive resistance is indicated.

Fig. 1: All Models — Connections for Testing Solenoid Windings

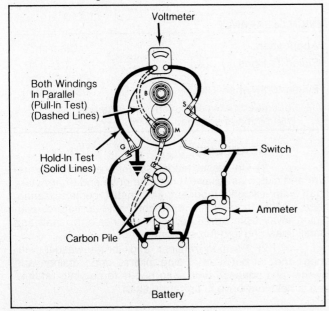

Compare current flow with value listed in Specifications.

Jeep 4-Cyl.

Specifications are 15-20 amps. at 10 volts for hold-in windings; 20-30 amps. at 5 volts for pull-in windings.

Both Windings in Parallel

Ground the "M" terminal and connect a 10 volt source (in series with ammeter) to solenoid switch terminal and ground. Current draw should be 40.5-47.5 amps.

STARTER NO LOAD TEST

To perform test, connect a tachometer, ammeter and voltmeter into start circuit. See Fig. 2. Adjust carbon pile to voltage indicated in Delco-Remy Starter Specifications. Read current draw and armature speed to ensure they are within specifications.

Do not apply voltage greater than specified, as excessive voltage may cause armature to throw windings due to excessive speed.

Low free speed and high current draw indicates too much friction, shorted armature, or grounded armature or fields. Failure to operate with high current draw indicates a direct ground in terminal or fields or frozen bearings.

Failure to operate with no current draw indicates an open field, open armature coils, or broken brush springs, worn brushes, or high commutator insulation. If no-load speed is low and there is low current draw, suspect high internal resistance due to poor connection, defective leads, or dirty commutator. A high free speed and high current draw usually indicates shorted fields.

Fig. 2: All Models — Connections for No Load Test

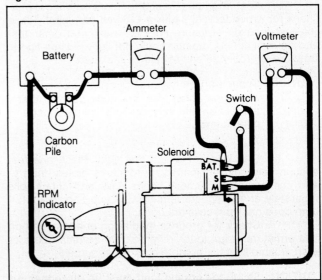

Use fully charged battery to make proper test.

DELCO-REMY STARTER SPECIFICATIONS [1]

Part No.	Amps. [2]	RPM
1109535	50-75	6000-11,900
1109563	120-210	9000-13,400
1998243	70-110	6500-10,700
1998397	70-110	6500-10,700

[1] — Starter requires 9 volts for test.
[2] — Includes the solenoid.

DELCO-REMY ENCLOSED HOUSING (Cont.)

OVERHAUL

DISASSEMBLY

1) Disconnect field coil connector from solenoid motor terminal. Remove solenoid mounting screws and rotate solenoid 90° and remove along with solenoid plunger spring.

2) Remove 2 through bolts, commutator end frame, field frame assembly and washer. On diesel models, remove insulator. On gasoline models, remove armature assembly from drive housing and thrust collar from armature shaft.

3) On diesel models, remove shift lever pivot bolt, center bearing screws and drive gear housing from armature shaft. Shift lever and plunger assembly will now fall away from starter clutch.

4) Slide a 5/8" deep socket over pinion shaft and with a hammer, strike socket against retainer to drive retainer off snap ring. Remove snap ring from groove in armature shaft.

5) On diesel models, remove retainer, clutch assembly, fiber washer and center bearing. Remove roll pin and remove shift lever and plunger. On gasoline models, roller clutches are serviced as an assembly only.

CLEANING

Clean all parts by wiping with clean cloth. Do not clean armature, field coils, or drive assembly in any type of grease dissolving solvent as this will damage insulation and wash lubricant out of drive assembly.

PARTS REPLACEMENT & TESTING

Armature

Test armature for shorted coils with a growler. Check for grounded coils with a 110 volt test lamp. Place one test lead on armature core or shaft, and other test lead on commutator. Lamp should not light. If lamp lights, armature is grounded and should be replaced.

CAUTION: Some starters have molded-type commutator, insulation must not be undercut on these models as this may cause serious damage to commutator.

Field Coils

Check with 110 volt test light. Place one test lead on field coil terminal strap, touch other test lead to field coil brush lead (check series coils and shunt coils separately at appropriate terminals). Lamp should light. If lamp does not light, coils are open.

Check for grounds by placing one test lead on field armature strap, touch other lead to armature core or shaft. If lamp lights, 1 or more coils are grounded.

CAUTION: Shunt coil ground lead must be disconnected and all field terminals insulated from frame when making this test.

Brushes, Springs, & Holders

Replace brushes if worn to 1/2 of original length, or if oil-soaked or pitted. Check brush spring tension and replace springs if weak or distorted. Deformed or bent brush holders can be replaced by service units which are installed with screws and nuts.

Drive & Pinion Assembly

Pinion should turn freely in overrun direction and should not slip in drive direction. Check spring for correct tension and drive collar for wear (these parts can be removed for replacement by forcing collar toward clutch and removing lock ring from end of tube). Replace drive assembly if pinion teeth are worn, chipped, or cracked.

Fig. 3: All Models (Except 5MT Starter) Brush Holder and Assembly

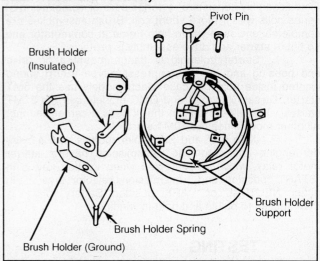

Replace brushes if worn to 1/2 of original length.

Pinion Clearance

Disconnect motor field coil connector and insulate it carefully. Connect a battery from solenoid switch terminal to solenoid frame. Momentarily flash a jumper lead from motor terminal to solenoid frame. This shifts pinion into cranking position. Push pinion back toward commutator end to eliminate slack.

Measure distance between pinion and pinion stop. When installing starter, check clearance between pinion and flywheel ring gear teeth. Insert gauge .020" (.6 mm) diameter wire, about 3" (76 mm) long, with a 1/4" to 1/2" 90° bend in end between pinion tooth and ring gear. Center pinion tooth between flywheel teeth when making measurement.

PINION CLEARANCE

Application	Clearance
Pinion-to-Housing	[1] .010-.140" (.25-3.56 mm)
Pinion-to-Flywheel Clearance	.020" (.6 mm)

[1] — Measured between pinion stop (retainer) with pinion in engaged position.

REASSEMBLY

1) On diesel model starters, assemble armature and clutch as follows: Lubricate drive end of armature shaft with silicone lubricant and install center bearing, fiber washer and clutch assembly onto armature, with pinion away from armature. Slide retainer onto shaft and install snap ring and thrust washer.

2) Position retainer and thrust washer with snap ring in between. Using pliers, grip retainer and washer and squeeze until snap ring is forced into retainer and is held in groove in armature shaft.

Starters

DELCO-REMY ENCLOSED HOUSING (Cont.)

Fig. 4: All Models — Checking Pinion-to-Housing Clearance

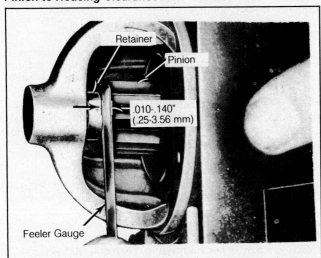

Force gear rearward to eliminate slack.

3) On all models, lubricate drive gear housing bushing with silicone lubricant. Engage shift lever yoke with clutch and slide complete assembly into drive gear housing.

4) Install center bearing screws and shift lever pivot bolt. Tighten securely. Install solenoid assembly on drive gear housing. Apply sealer (No. 1050026) to solenoid flange where it meets drive housing and field frame, using care not to damage brushes.

5) Position field frame against drive gear housing on alignment pin using care not to damage brushes. Lubricate commutator end frame bushing with silicone lubricant. Install washer on armature shaft and slide end frame onto shaft and install through bolts.

6) On diesel models, install insulator and then end frame onto shaft. Install through bolts, making sure they pass through bolt holes in insulator. Connect field coil connector to solenoid terminal. Check pinion clearance as outlined under *Parts Replacement and Testing in this article.*

Fig. 6: All Models — Exploded View of Shift Lever Assembly

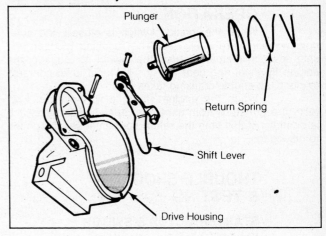

Fig. 5: Exploded View of Delco-Remy 27MT Starter Assembly.

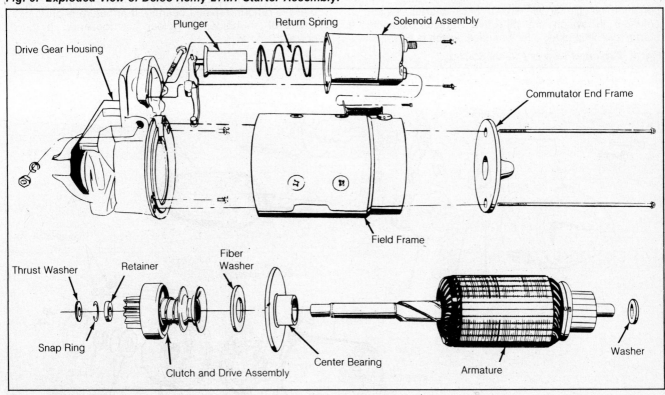

5MT & 10MT starters similar except they have no center bearing.

Starters

HITACHI SOLENOID-ACTUATED

General Motors "S" Model Pickups

DESCRIPTION

The starter is a 4 pole, 4 brush type direct current series wound motor. The engagement mechanism is integral with the starter, and controls switching on and off of the motor and shifting of the starter pinion.

Starter incorporates an overrunning clutch. The shift lever mechanisim and solenoid plunger are enclosed in the drive housing to protect them from exposure to dirt, icing conditions and splash.

OPERATION

When the ignition switch is closed, the solenoid windings are energized. The resulting plunger and shift lever movement cause the pinion to engage the engine flywheel ring gear and the solenoid main contacts to close, so engine cranking takes place.

When the engine starts, pinion overrun protects the armature from excessive speed until the switch is opened. At this time the return spring causes the pinion to disengage.

TROUBLE SHOOTING & TESTING

STARTER MOTOR & SWITCH

Engage Switch Does Not Work When Starter Switch is Turned "ON"

1) Check circuit. If circuit is faulty, correct condition. If circuit is okay, check starter switch. If contacts in switch are defective, replace contacts. If starter switch is okay, check engage switch coil.

2) If coil is open or burned, replace coil. If coil is okay, check plunger shaft. If shaft is bent or binding, repair or replace shaft.

Pinion Gear Does Not Properly Engage Ring Gear

1) Check battery. If charge is low, recharge. If battery is okay, check pinion and ring gear teeth. If teeth are worn or damaged, replace. If gear teeth are okay, check pinion gear movement.

2) If pinion return is incorrect, adjust. If pinion gear movement is okay, check armature shaft and bearing. Correct or replace as necessary. Check for foreign material on sliding portion of shaft.

Pinion Engages Ring Gear But Engine Will Not Turn Over

1) Check battery. If charge is low, recharge. If battery is okay, check brush contact with commutator face. If brush is in poor contact with face, correct or replace. If brush contact is okay, check pinion clutch.

2) If pinion clutch is slipping, replace. If pinion clutch is okay, check armature field coil. If field coil is open, correct or replace.

Starter Does Not Stop When Starter Switch Is Turned Off

Check engage switch contact point. If contact point is siezed, replace. If okay, check starter switch. Replace if defective.

Excessive Brush Sparking

1) Check brush contact with commutator face. If poor contact exists, correct. If contact is okay, check commutator. If commutator segment or phenol resin projects, correct or replace.

2) If soldering on commutator has loosened, correct. If commutator is okay, check armature shaft. If there is runout, replace bearing. If armature shaft is okay, check brush holder. If holder has loosened in mount, correct.

Fig. 1: Exploded View of Hitachi Starter

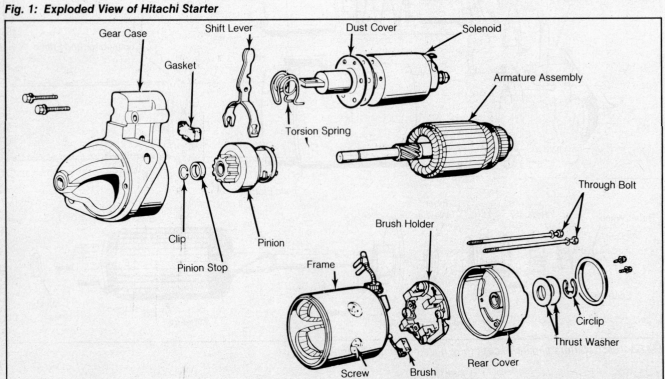

HITACHI SOLENOID-ACTUATED (Cont.)

OVERHAUL

DISASSEMBLY

1) Disconnect the lead from the "M" terminal of the solenoid. Remove the bolts attaching the solenoid. Remove the torsion spring from the solenoid. Remove the dust cover and remove the ring and thrust washer. *See Fig. 2.*

2) Remove the 2 screws and through bolts. Remove the rear cover assembly. Raise the brush spring, pull out the brush, and remove the brush holder assembly. Carefully remove the yoke from the gear case and remove the dust cover.

3) Remove the armature from the gear case toghether with shift lever and remove shift lever from the armature. Pull out the pinion stop clip and remove pinion stop. Remove pinion assembly.

PARTS INSPECTION & TESTING

Armature

1) Check the commutator face for roughness or burning and reface with fine sandpaper as necessary. If roughness or out of round is considerable, armature should be turned on a lathe. Mica insulators should be undercut to a depth of .020-.031" (.5-.8 mm).

2) Check for insulation between commutator coils and core using a growl tester. If the lamp of the tester comes on, coils are poorly insulated and must be replaced.

3) Make a continuity test between the segments of the commutator with growl tester. If lamp does not come on when tester leads are shorted across segments, coils are open and should be repaired or replaced.

4) Roll the armature on growl tester slowly while holding a strip of steel or a hacksaw blade over each segment of armature core. If the steel is pulled or vibrates, armature coils are shorted and must be repaired or replaced.

5) Check armature shaft for runout using a dial indicator. If beyond .0031" (.080 mm), replace. If clearance between shaft and bearing is more than .008" (.20 mm), replace bearing.

Field Coils

Measure resistance between field coils and yoke. Insulation should be 1 megohm or more. If the insulation is in poor condition, remove pole core set screws and locate parts grounded by removing the field coils one at a time. Make a continuity test between field coil terminals and correct or replace parts as necessary.

Brush and Brush Holder

1) Check brushes for wear, cracks or broken lead. Replace parts if defective. Minimum allowable brush length is .47" (12.0 mm). Standard length is .63" (16.0 mm). Check brush springs for rusting, distortion, weakening or breakage.

2) Spring tension should be 3.53 lbs. (1.6 kg). Clean brush holder and check insulation between brush holder and set plate.

Solenoid

1) Check the points in the magnetic switch for fouling or roughness. Dress with an oil stone if necessary. Make continuity test between "C" and "M" terminals and ground. If there is no continuity, the coil is open and magnetic switch should be replaced. *See Fig. 2.*

Fig. 2: Solenoid Test Connections

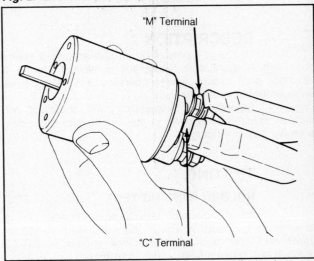

"M" Terminal

"C" Terminal

Apply 12 volts to test plunger action.

2) Apply 12 volts between "C" and "M" terminals of switch. Solenoid is okay when plunger is pulled when power is applied and returns smoothly when power is removed.

3) Check the gap between pinion and pinion stop when pinion is fully depressed due to action of the solenoid. Adjust if necessary by installing adjusting plate between magnetic switch and case. Standard gap is .012-.098" (.30-2.50 mm).

Pinion

Check pinion gear for wear or damage. Check sliding face of pinion for scuffs and replace if necessary. Check springs for damage or weakening. Check clutch for sticking or binding and replace if necessary.

REASSEMBLY

1) Apply new grease to bearings and sliding surfaces of parts before installation. Set the shift lever to the shift lever guide on the pinion. Do not turn the armature shaft after setting shift lever.

2) Install the yoke on the gear case and dust cover by aligning the groove in the joining portion of the yoke with the corresponding projection. Install the torsion spring with adjusting plate on the magnetic switch.

3) Insert end of the shift lever into the plunger fitting hole in the magnetic switch. Set the end of the torsion spring into the groove in the intermediate part of the shift lever. To complete reassembly, reverse disassembly procedure.

Starters

MOTORCRAFT POSITIVE ENGAGEMENT

Ford, Jeep 6-Cyl. & V8

DESCRIPTION

Unit is a 4-pole, 4-brush starter with 3 series coils and 1 shunt coil. Shunt coil is wound around a movable pole piece, which operates integral positive engagement drive mechanism.

Solenoids for Jeep vehicles with automatic and manual transmissions differ in their method of grounding solenoid pull-in windings.

TESTING

HOLD-IN WINDING TEST

Insert a piece of paper between contact points to serve as an insulator. Touch ohmmeter leads to starter frame and input terminal. Resistance should be 2.0-3.5 ohms. If not, replace field winding assembly.

PULL-IN WINDING TEST

1) Disconnect wire from solenoid "S" terminal. Connect ohmmeter test probes to "S" terminal and mounting bracket (ground terminal on Jeep vehicles with automatic transmission). *See Fig. 1.* If not to specifications, replace solenoid.

Fig. 1: Ford & Jeep Ohmmeter Test Connections for Solenoid.

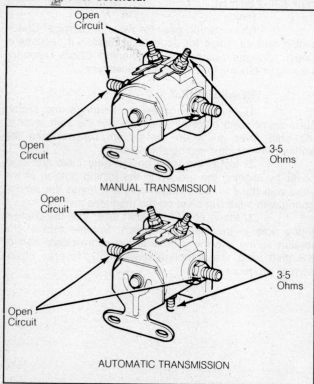

MANUAL TRANSMISSION

AUTOMATIC TRANSMISSION

Connections must be clean and tight to make proper test.

2) Check for a poor ground by connecting ohmmeter leads to battery negative terminal and "S" terminal. If reading is greater than results received between "S" terminal and mounting bracket, solenoid has poor ground.

STARTER CRANKING CIRCUIT TESTS

Before performing tests, remove and ground coil secondary wire (disconnect at distributor). Place transmission in "Neutral" or "PARK" and apply parking brake. Be sure battery is fully charged. When making voltmeter connections, be sure to connect leads to battery posts or threaded terminals and not just to cable ends.

Fig. 2: Connections for Cranking Circuit Test Ford & Jeep

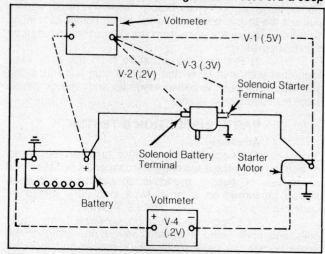

Voltages are shown for each connection.

Battery-to-Starter Motor Voltage Drop (V-1)

1) Connect voltmeter positive lead to battery positive post and negative lead to starter motor terminal. While cranking engine, note voltmeter reading. Reading should be .5 volts or less at specified load test amperage.

2) If reading is greater, move negative lead to starter cable at starter and retest. If voltage is now .5 volt or less, remove cable and clean connections, and retest at starter motor terminal. If voltage is still above specifications, test individual cables between battery and starter as follows:

Battery-to-Solenoid Voltage Drop (V-2)

1) Connect voltmeter positive lead to battery positive post and negative lead to battery terminal of solenoid. While cranking engine, note voltmeter reading. Reading should be .2 volt or less at specified load test amperage.

2) If just below or at specification, repair solenoid. If reading is greater, remove cable, clean connections, and retest. If reading is still above maximum .2 volt, replace cable.

Solenoid Voltage Drop (V-3)

1) Connect voltmeter positive lead to battery positive post and negative lead to starter CABLE at solenoid. While cranking engine, note voltmeter reading. Reading should be .3 volt or less at specified load test amperage.

2) If at or just below maximum reading, repair solenoid-to-starter cable. If reading is above maximum, move negative lead to starter TERMINAL at solenoid and retest.

3) If reading is now .3 volt or less, remove and clean cable connector, and retest. If still in excess of .3 volt, replace solenoid. If battery-to-starter circuit (V-1) reading is now greater than .5 volt, replace solenoid-to-starter cable.

Starters

MOTORCRAFT POSITIVE ENGAGEMENT (Cont.)

Starter Motor Ground Voltage Drop (V-4)

1) Connect voltmeter negative lead to starter motor housing and positive lead to battery negative post. While cranking engine, note voltmeter reading. Reading should be .2 volt or less at specified load test amperage.

2) If more, move positive lead to ground cable attaching bolt at engine and retest. If reading is now less than .2 volt, check starter motor for loose mounting bolts, corrosion or dirt on mounting surface. If reading is now more than .2 volt, examine ground cable for bad connections or bad cable.

STARTER LOAD TEST

1) Connect a tester and battery into starter circuit. *See Fig. 3.* Crank engine with ignition coil secondary wire grounded and note voltage on tester.

2) Stop cranking engine and turn load control knob until voltage reading is exactly the same as it was when engine was cranking. Read current draw on ammeter scale. If not within specifications, starter is defective and must be overhauled.

LOAD TEST SPECIFICATIONS

Application	Amperes
Ford	
4" Starter	150-200
4½" Starter	150-180
Jeep	
6-Cyl.	150-180
V8	160-210

Fig. 3: Ford & Jeep Connections for Load Test

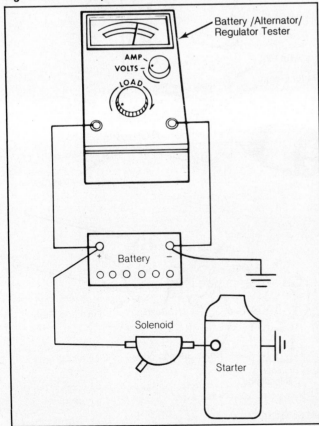

Take amperage draw reading with starter at maximum RPM.

STARTER NO-LOAD TEST

1) With tester and battery connected to starter, operate starter motor and note voltage reading and tachometer reading. *See Fig. 4.* Disconnect starter from battery. Turn load control knob until voltage reading is same as when starter is connected.

2) Read amperage draw, and if amperage reading is less than specifications, starter has high electrical resistance. If starter RPM is less than specifications, starter has high electrical resistance. If starter RPM is less than specifications starter has worn bushings or bent armature shaft.

NO-LOAD SPECIFICATIONS

Application	Specification
Voltage	12 Volts
Amperage	
Ford	
4" Starter	70 Amps.
4½" Starter	80 Amps.
Jeep	67 Amps.
RPM Range	7,380-9,356

Fig. 4: Ford & Jeep Connections for No-Load Test

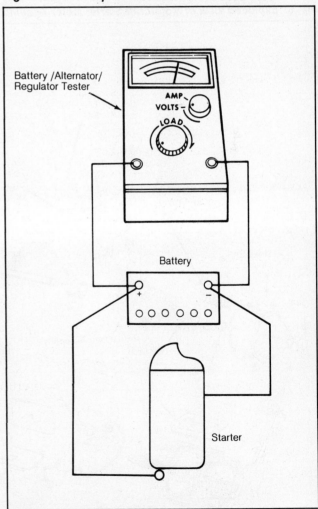

Test results will indicate faults such as open or shorted windings.

MOTORCRAFT POSITIVE ENGAGEMENT (Cont.)

OVERHAUL

DISASSEMBLY

1) Remove cover screw, cover, through bolts, starter drive end housing and starter drive plunger lever return spring. Remove pivot pin retaining plunger lever and remove plunger lever and armature.

2) Remove stop ring retainer, stop ring from starter drive gear and starter drive gear assembly. Remove brush end plate and insulator assembly. Remove brushes from brush holder and lift out brush holder. Note location of brush holder with respect to end terminal.

3) Remove ground brushes-to-frame retaining screws. On field coil which operates drive gear actuating lever, bend edges on retaining sleeve and remove sleeve and retainers.

4) Remove 3 coil retaining screws with Generator Pole Screw Wrench (10044-A) and an arbor press. Cut field coil connection at switch post lead and remove small diameter ground wire from upper tab riveted to frame.

5) Remove pole shoes and coils from frame. Cut positive brush leads from fields coils as close to field connection point as possible.

PARTS REPLACEMENT & TESTING

Brushes & Springs

1) Check brush holders for broken springs and insulated brush holders for shorts to ground. Tighten any

Fig. 5: Removing Pole Shoe Screw from Starter Housing.

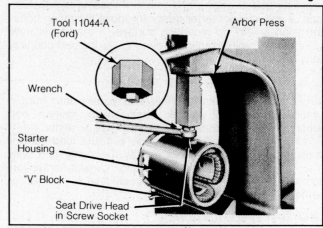

Use arbor press to hold generator pole screw wrench.

Fig. 6: Exploded View of Motorcraft Starter Motor Assembly Used On Ford & Jeep

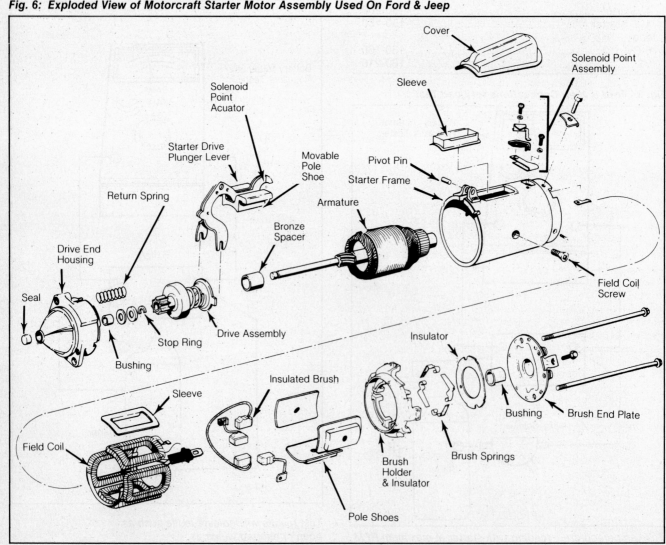

MOTORCRAFT POSITIVE ENGAGEMENT (Cont.)

loose rivets. Replace brushes if worn to 1/4" in length. Measure spring tension with spring scale hooked under spring near end.

2) Pull on line parallel to edge of brush and note reading just as spring end leaves brush. Spring tension should be 40 ozs. (1.134 kg) on 4" starters, 80 ozs. (2.263 kg) on 4 1/2" starters. If replacing brushes, use a 300 watt soldering iron and rosin core solder.

Field Coil Assembly

Inspect field coils for burned or broken insulation and continuity. Check field brush connections and lead insulation. Check for grounds in field coil windings.

Armature

1) Check armature for shorted coils with a growler and a test light. Touch 1 test lead to armature core and the other to each commutator bar 1 at a time. If light lights, armature is shorted to ground and must be replaced.

2) Place switch on growler in GROWLER position and hold steel blade parallel to and touching armature core. Rotate armature and if blade vibrates at any point, that area is shorted and armature must replaced.

3) Inspect armature shaft for excessive wear. Inspect windings for broken or burned insulation. If commutator is rough or more than .005" (.13 mm) out of round, turn down in a lathe, removing only enough material to provide a smooth, even surface.

REASSEMBLY

1) Position 3 coils and pole pieces and install attaching screws. As pole shoe screws are tightened, strike frame with a soft hammer to seat and align pole shoes, then stake screws.

2) Install remaining coil and retainer. Bend tabs to secure coil to frame. Position new field brush lead on field coil terminal. Install clip to hold brush lead to terminal. Solder lead, clip and terminal together with a 300 watt iron and rosin core solder.

3) Ground coil around retaining sleeve by placing small diameter wire from coil under copper tab which attaches contact to frame. Install ground brushes to frame with screws.

4) Lubricate armature shaft splines with Lubriplate (or equivalent). Install drive gear assembly on armature shaft. Install new retaining stop ring and stop retainer.

5) Install armature in frame. Partially fill drive end housing bearing bore with grease and position drive gear plunger lever to frame and starter drive assembly and install pivot pin.

6) Install plunger lever return spring and drive end housing to frame. Install brush holder, brushes and springs. Install brush holder insulator.

7) Position end plate to frame and align plate locator with frame slot. Install and tighten through bolts. DO NOT pinch brush leads when installing end plate. Position drive gear plunger lever cover on starter and tighten cover screw.

Fuses & Circuit Breakers

CHRYSLER CORP.

FUSE BLOCK

FUSE BLOCK LOCATION

On Pickup models, fuse block is located under instrument panel on driver's side of vehicle. On Van models, fuse block is located near glove compartment door.

Fig. 1: Fuse Block for Van Models

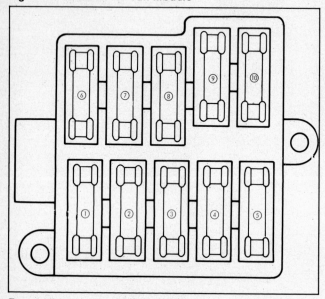

Fuse block located near glove box door.

FUSE BLOCK CIRCUITS

Van Models

1 - **5 Amp.** Instrument panel lights.
2 - **20 Amp.** Back-up lights, cruise control, turn signal lights and air conditioner clutch.
3 - **20 Amp.** Horn, heater, aux. heater and aux. air conditioning.
4 - **5 Amp.** Radio.
5 - **20 Amp.** Brake warning light, oil pressure warning light, gauges, clock, seat belt buzzer, power window relay and defogger relay.
6 - **20 Amp.** Tail, license, parking, side marker and instrument panel lights.
7 - **25 Amp.** Dome, stop, glove box and vanity mirror lights. Ignition time delay light, cigar lighter and clock.
8 - **20 Amp.** Hazard flashers.
9 - **30 Amp.** Air conditioning and heater blower motors.
10 - **25 Amp.** Heated rear window.

Pickup Models

1 - **30 Amp.** Heater and air conditioner.

2 - **5 Amp.** Instrument panel lights.
3 - **15 Amp.** Hazard flashers.
4 - **5 Amp.** Radio.
5 - **15 Amp.** Turn signal flasher and back-up lights.
6 - **20 Amp.** Speed control and air conditioner clutch.
7 - **20 Amp.** Trailer lights.
8 - **25 Amp.** Cigar lighter and exterior lights.
9 - **25 Amp.** Horn relay, cargo light and instrument panel lights.
10 - **30 Amp.** Window lift motor and door locks.
11 - **3 Amp.** Travel computer.
12 - **3 Amp.** Seat belt buzzer and gauges.
13 - Not used.
14 - Not used.
15 - Not used.

Fig. 2: Fuse Block for Pickup Models

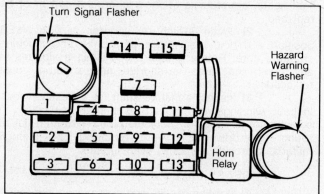

Fuse block under instrument panel on driver's side.

CIRCUIT BREAKERS

A 20 amp. circuit breaker is integral with headlight switch to protect headlight circuit. A 6 amp. circuit breaker is integral with windshield wiper switch to protect wiper circuit. A 20 amp. circuit breaker is located at rear of ammeter on Van models, or in fuse block on Pickup models, to protect trailer towing or camper options.

FUSIBLE LINKS

A fusible link is placed in the main charging circuit wiring to protect the alternator. On some applications, a link is placed in the wiring to protect the radio circuit.

FLASHER LOCATION

On Van models, the turn signal and hazard flashers are located to the right of the fuse block. On Pickup models, the flashers are located on the fuse block.

FORD

FUSE BLOCK

FUSE BLOCK LOCATION

On all models, fuse block is located under instrument panel to left of steering column.

FUSE BLOCK CIRCUITS

Van Models

1 - Not used.
2 - **3 Amp.** Instrument panel lights.
3 - **7.5 Amp.** Emission control and throttle solenoid.

FORD (Cont.)

4 - **7.5 Amp.** Seat belt warning and aux. fuel tank.
5 - **7.5 Amp. Circuit Breaker.** Windshield wipers.
6 - **35 Amp.** Air conditioner, aux. heater and air conditioner.
7 - Not used.
8 - **15 Amp.** Hazard warning and stop lights.
9 - **15 Amp.** Courtesy lights and cigar lighter.
10 - **20 Amp.** Speed control.
11 - **15 Amp.** Turn signal, back-up lights and windshield wipers.
12 - **7.5 Amp.** Radio.

Fig. 1: Fuse Block for Van Models

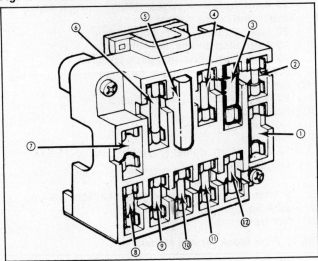

Fuse block under instrument panel at left side.

Fig. 2: Fuse Block for Bronco, Bronco II, "F" Pickup and Ranger Models

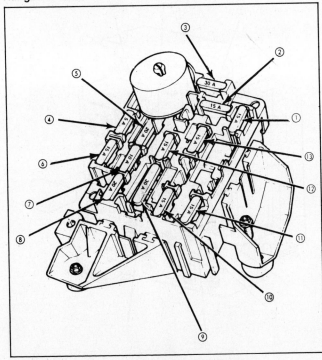

Fuse block under instrument panel at left side.

Bronco, Bronco II, "F" Pickups, & Ranger Models

1 - **15 Amp. Bronco & "F" Models, 20 Amp. Bronco II & Ranger.** Hazard and stop lights.
2 - **15 Amp.** Turn signals and back-up lights.
3 - **30 Amp.** Heater and air conditioning blower motor.
4 - **5 Amp.** Instrument panel lights, transmission indicator light.
5 - **20 Amp. Circuit Breaker "F" Models.** Power windows. **25 Amp. Circuit Breaker Bronco Models.** Power tailgate. Not used on Bronco II and Ranger.
6 - **15 Amp.** Warning lights, seat belt buzzer, carburetor circuits, tachometer, choke heater and transmission upshift light.
7 - **10 Amp.** Aux. fuel tank on pickups.
8 - **20 Amp.** Horn and cigar lighter.
9 - **30 Amp. Circuit Breaker.** Power door locks, tailgate and electric mirror. Not used on Bronco II and Ranger.
10 - **15 Amp.** Interior courtesy lights.
11 - **15 Amp.** Tail and parking lights. Trailer and camper option lights, instrument panel lights.
12 - **15 Amp. Bronco & "F" Models.** Radio. **10 Amp. Bronco II & Ranger.** Radio.
13 - **15 Amp.** Accessory feed and air conditioner clutch on Bronco II and Ranger. Accessories, windshield wipers, speed control, aux. battery and heater, and defogger on Bronco and "F" models.

CIRCUIT BREAKERS

Van Models

A 7.5 amp. circuit breaker in fuse panel protects windshield wipers. A 15 amp. circuit breaker in headlight switch protects the tail, license, parking and marker lights and horn. An 18 amp. circuit breaker in headlight switch protects the headlight circuit.

Bronco & "F" Pickup Models

A 22 amp circuit breaker in headlight switch protects the headlight circuit. A 6 amp. circuit breaker in wiper switch protects the windshield wiper circuit.

Bronco II & Ranger Models

An 18 amp. circuit breaker in headlight switch protects the headlight circuit. A 6 amp. circuit breaker in wiper switch protects the windshield wiper circuit.

FUSIBLE LINKS

Van Models

Separate links in the starter motor relay protect the air conditioner, alternator and dual battery circuit. Alternator is also protected by link located at electric choke.

Bronco & "F" Pickup Models

Separate links at starter motor relay protect the alternator, trailer towing circuits and electronic engine controls system. A link at the junction block protects the marker lights on Camper Special models and models with dual wheels. A link near auxiliary battery relay protects fog lights. Separate links near right hand fender apron protect the ignition switch, auxiliary battery and fuse block feed.

Bronco II & Ranger Models

Separate links at starter motor relay protect trailer lights and brakes and alternator. Separate links near left hand fender apron protect the headlight switch and ignition switch.

Fuses & Circuit Breakers

FORD (Cont.)

FLASHER LOCATION

Hazard Flasher

On Van models, flasher is taped to main wiring assembly in left corner of instrument panel. On all other models, flasher is mounted on fuse block.

Turn Signal Flasher

On Van models, flasher is attached to lower reinforcement of instrument panel on left side of steering column. On all other models, flasher is located on fuse block.

GENERAL MOTORS

FUSE BLOCK

FUSE BLOCK LOCATION

On all models, fuse block is located under instrument panel on driver's side of vehicle.

FUSE BLOCK CIRCUITS

Blazer, Pickup & Suburban Models

1 - **20 Amp.** Heater, air conditioning, alternator warning light.
2 - **15 Amp.** Converter clutch, radio and aux. battery.
3 - **20 Amp.** Cigar lighter, clock, dome and spot light and horn.
4 - Not used.
5 - **20 Amp.** Courtesy, tail, license, parking and side marker lights.
6 - **15 Amp.** Turn signals, stop and hazard lights.
7 - **15 Amp.** Back-up lights, front turn signals and side marker lights.
8 - **5 Amp.** Instrument panel lights and windshield wiper switch.
9 - **25 Amp.** Windshield wiper/washer.
10 - **20 Amp.** Choke heater.
11 - **30 Amp. Circuit Breaker.** Power windows. Power tailgate and defogger on Blazer and Suburban.
12 - **20 Amp.** Cruise control, gauges, seat belt warning, warning indicators, aux. fuel tank and idle stop solenoid.
13 - Not used.

"S" Models

1 - **20 Amp.** Choke.
2 - **15 Amp.** Radio, 4-wheel drive indicator.
3 - **25 Amp.** Heater and air conditioning.
4 - **20 Amp.** Ignition, gauges, defogger relay, converter clutch and cruise control.
5 - **20 Amp.** Courtesy lights and tail lights.
6 - **15 Amp.** Stop and hazard lights.
7 - **15 Amp.** Turn signal and back-up lights.
8 - **5 Amp.** Instrument lights, headlight warning, defogger switch light.
9 - **20 Amp.** Windshield wiper/washer.
10 - Not used.
11 - Not used.
12 - Not used.
13 - **20 Amp.** Horn, dome, glove box and courtesy lights. Liftgate release.

Van Models

1 - **5 Amp.** Instrument panel lights, headlight warning.
2 - **20 Amp.** Stop and hazard lights.
3 - Not Used.

Fig. 2: Fuse Block for Van Models

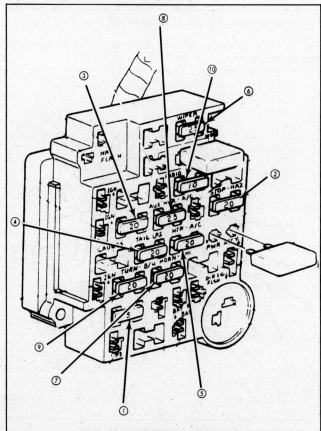

Fuse block under left side of instrument panel.

Fig. 1: Fuse Block for Blazer, Pickup, Suburban & "S" Models

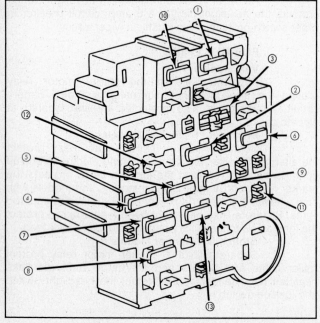

Fuse block located under left side of instrument panel.

GENERAL MOTORS (Cont.)

4 - **20 Amp.** License, parking, side marker and tail lights.
5 - **20 Amp.** Front heater and air conditioner.
6 - **25 Amp.** Windshield wiper.
7 - **20 Amp.** Cigar lighter, clock, dome light, horn and anti-theft system.
8 - **25 Amp.** Aux. heater and air conditioning.
9 - **20 Amp.** Turn signals and back-up lights.
10 - **10 Amp.** Radio and aux. battery.
11 - **20 Amp.** Gauges, cruise control and emission circuits.

"P" Models

NOTE: For location of fuses on "P" models, see fuse block located under instrument panel on driver's side. The following list details what size fuse protects which circuits.

5 Amp. Instrument panel lights.
10 Amp. Cruise control, gauges and warning indicators.
10 Amp. Radio.
15 Amp. Cigar lighter, clock, courtesy lights, dome light and horn.
15 Amp. Aux. battery, back-up lights, turn signals and stop lights.
15 Amp. Turn signals, stop and hazard lights.
20 Amp. Choke heater warning light.
20 Amp. License, parking, side marker and tail lights.
25 Amp. Air conditioner, heater and aux. heater.
25 Amp. Windshield wiper/washer.

CIRCUIT BREAKERS

All models except "S" have a 15 amp. circuit breaker in headlight switch to protect headlight and parking light circuit. "S" models have a 30 amp. circuit breaker in headlight switch to protect headlight circuit. "C" and "K" models each have two 30 amp. circuit breakers; one for tailgate window motor and other for power windows. All models have a circuit breaker in windshield wiper switch to protect windshield wipers. Van models have a 35 amp. circuit breaker under dashboard to protect rear air conditioner.

IN-LINE FUSES

In-line fuses protect engine compartment light and rear air conditioner circuits on "C," "K" and "S" models. Models with auxiliary heater also have a fuse in-line in heater circuit.

FUSIBLE LINKS

Fusible links are used to protect following circuits on all except "S" models: Horn, air conditioner high blower, ignition circuits and high beam indicator. "C" and "K" models also use fusible links to protect starter solenoid circuit.

FLASHER LOCATION

Hazard Flasher
Flasher is located on fuse block on all models.
Turn Signal Flasher
Flasher is located near fuse block on all models.

JEEP

FUSE BLOCK

FUSE BLOCK LOCATION
All Models
Fuse block is located under the instrument panel on driver's side of vehicle on all models.

FUSE BLOCK CIRCUITS
All Models

1 - **20 Amp. All except CJ and Scrambler.** Windshield wipers. **4.5 Amp. CJ and Scrambler.** Windshield wipers.
2 - **15 Amp.** Turn signals.
3 - **10 Amp.** Accessories.
4 - **3 Amp.** Instrument panel and accessory lights.
5 - **20 Amp.** Interior lights.
6 - **20 Amp.** Brake, tail and parking lights.
7 - **25 Amp.** Air conditioner, heater and electric fan.
8 - **3 Amp.** Instruments.
9 - **25 Amp. Pickups Only.** Seat belt warning and back-up lights. **10 Amp. CJ and Scrambler 6-cylinder only.** Seat belt warning and back-up lights. **20 Amp. CJ and Scrambler 4-cylinder only.** Seat belt warning and back-up lights.
10 - **20 Amp.** Hazard flasher, clock and stop lights.

CIRCUIT BREAKERS

A 24 amp. circuit breaker is located in the headlight switch to protect headlight circuit. Cherokee and

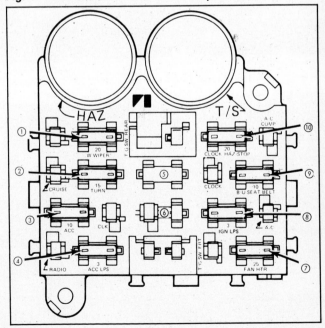

Fig. 1: Fuse Block Circuits for all Jeep Models

Wagoneer models have two 30 amp. circuit breakers located in fuse block to protect electric tailgate window. One circuit breaker protects the instrument panel switch, and the other protects the tailgate switch.

Fuses & Circuit Breakers

JEEP (Cont.)

IN-LINE FUSES

Six cylinder models have a 4 amp. in-line fuse protecting the cruise control. Models with V8 engines have a 1.5 amp. in-line fuse protecting the cruise control.

FUSIBLE LINKS

All models are equipped with fusible links in the engine compartment to protect the starting and charging circuits.

FLASHER LOCATIONS

Hazard & Turn Signal Flasher

Hazard and turn signal flashers are located on fuse panel on all models.

Fuses & Circuit Breakers

FUSE BLOCK & FLASHER LOCATIONS

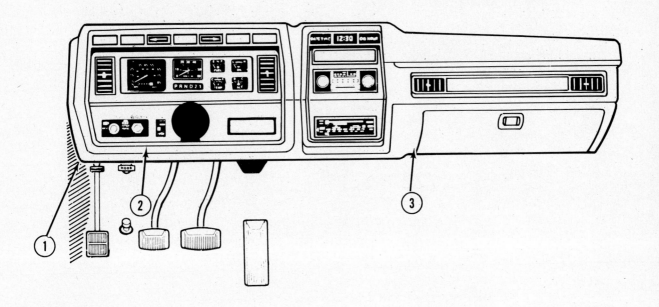

FUSE BLOCK & FLASHER LOCATIONS

Manufacturer & Model	Fuse Block	Hazard Flasher	Turn Signal Flasher
Chrysler Corp. Pickup Models Van Models	[2] Left of Steering Column [3] Near Glove Box	On Fuse Block Right of Fuse Block	On Fuse Block Right of Fuse Block
Ford Motor Co. Bronco & "F" Pickup Models Bronco II & Ranger Models Van Models	[2] Left of Steering Column [2] Left of Steering Column [2] Left of Steering Column	On Fuse Block On Fuse Block [1] Left Of Wiring Harness	On Fuse Block On Fuse Block Near Fuse Block
General Motors Blazer & Suburban Models Pickup Models "P" Models Van Models	[2] Left of Steering Column [2] Left of Steering Column [2] Left of Steering Column [2] Left of Steering Column	On Fuse Block On Fuse Block On Fuse Block On Fuse Block	Near Fuse Block Near Fuse Block Near Fuse Block Near Fuse Block
Jeep CJ, Cherokee, & Scrambler Models Wagoneer & Truck Models	[2] Left of Steering Column [2] Left of Steering Column	On Fuse Block On Fuse Block	On Fuse Block On Fuse Block

ARRANGEMENT OF DATA

Wiring diagrams on the following pages are arranged by manufacturer. Each manufacturer's diagrams are subdivided by vehicle models. Each group of similar models requires 4 pages of diagrams.

The first page includes the front lights and engine compartment. The additional pages work back from the engine compartment, including the fuse block, instrument panel, underdash area, accessories, rear lights and printed circuits. A heading appears on each page, indicating the portion of the vehicle covered by the diagram.

SECTION 5

WIRING DIAGRAMS

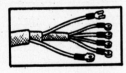

CONTENTS

NOTE: ALSO SEE GENERAL INDEX.

IMPORTANT: Because of the many model names used by vehicle manufacturers, accurate identification of models is important. See Model Identification at the front of this publication.

1983 Chrysler Corp.
CHASSIS CABS, PICKUPS & RAMCHARGER

ENGINE COMPARTMENT

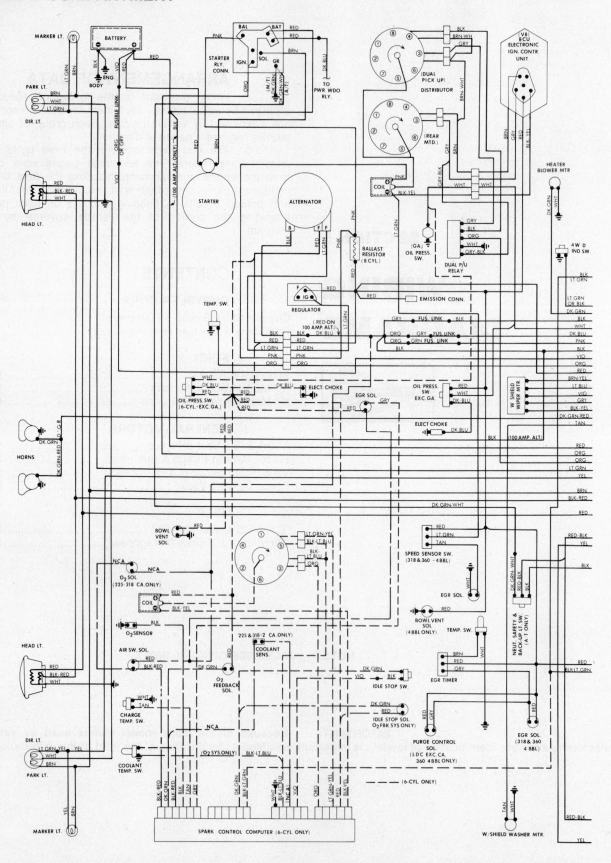

5-3

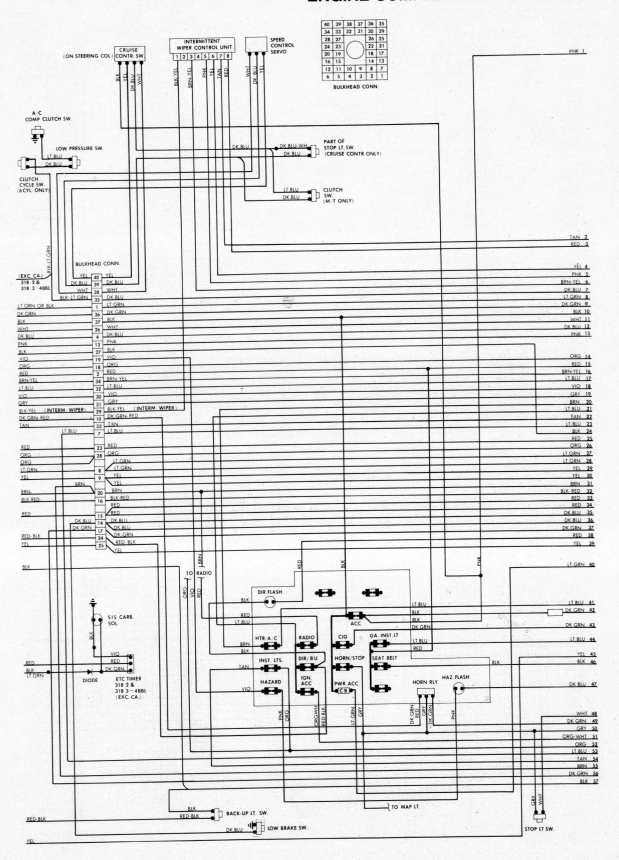

1983 Chrysler Corp.
CHASSIS CABS, PICKUPS & RAMCHARGER (Cont.)

UNDERDASH

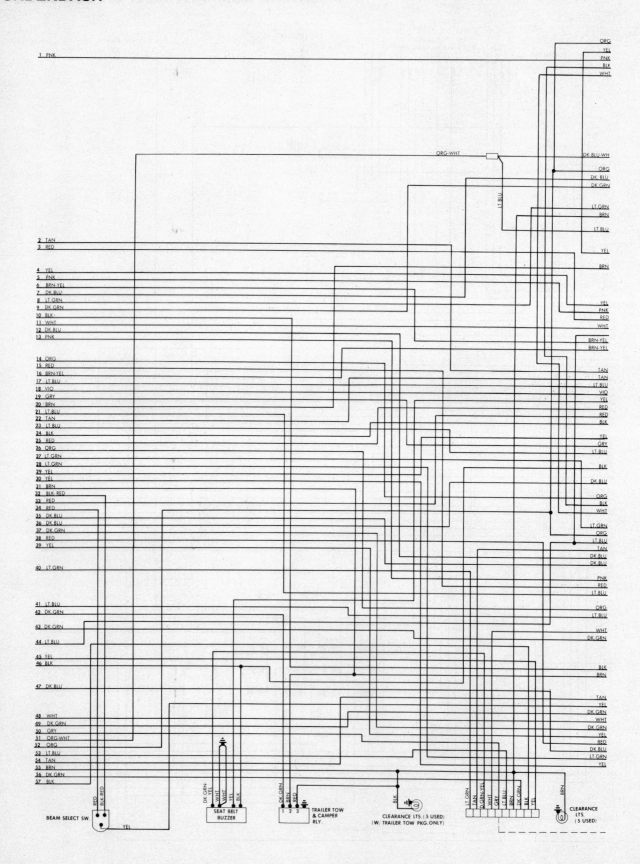

1983 Chrysler Corp.

CHASSIS CABS, PICKUPS & RAMCHARGER (Cont.)

REAR COMPARTMENT & ACCESSORIES

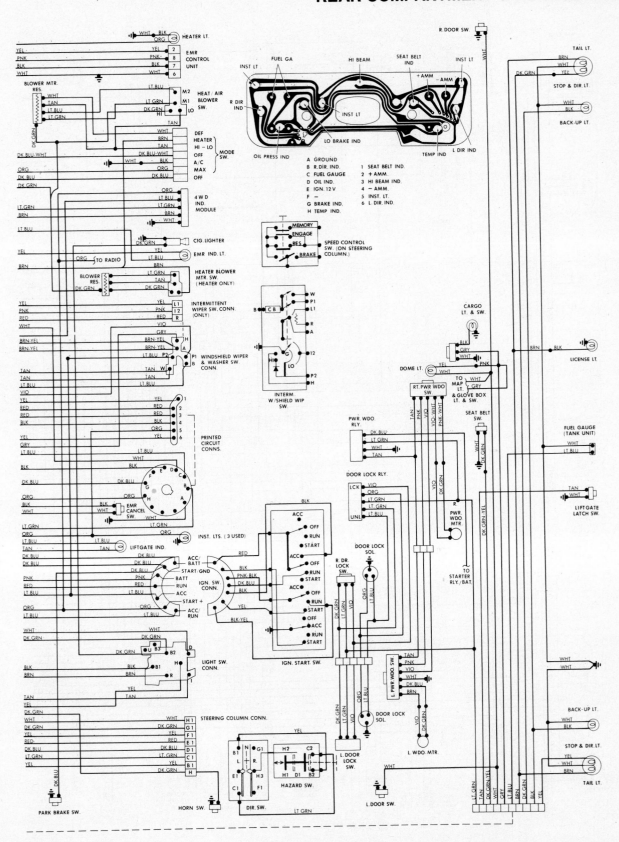

1983 Chrysler Corp.
RAM VANS & VOYAGER WAGONS

ENGINE COMPARTMENT

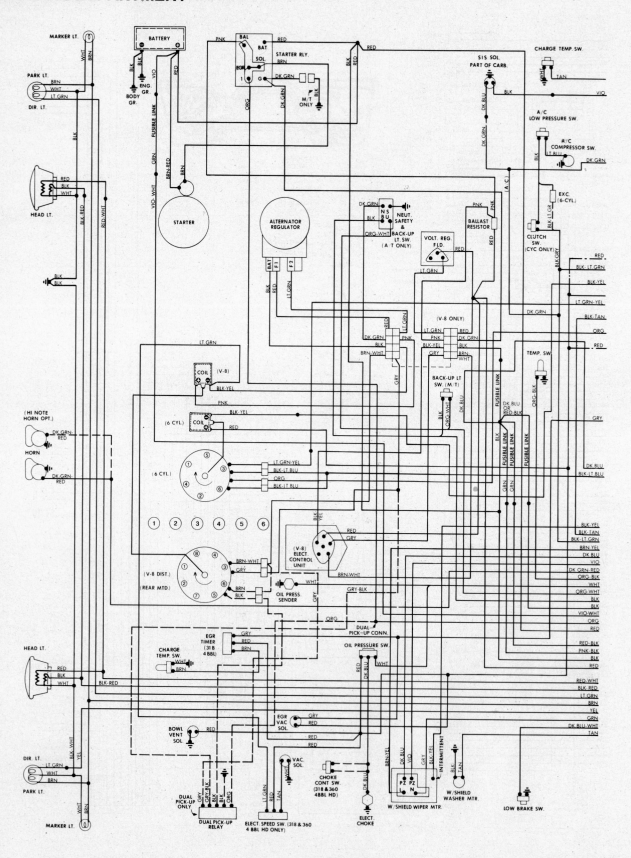

1983 Chrysler Corp.
RAM VANS & VOYAGER WAGONS (Cont.)
INSTRUMENT PANEL & FUSE BLOCK

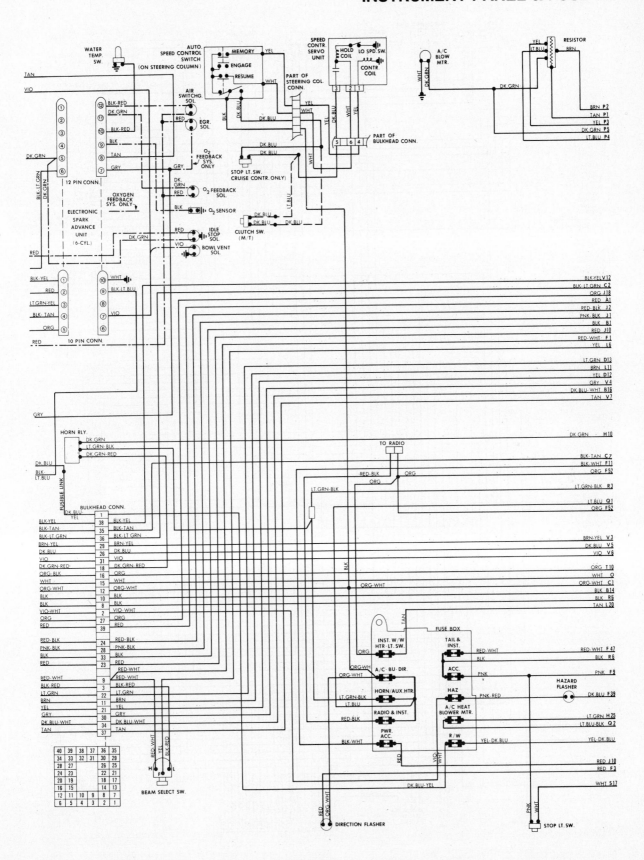

1983 Chrysler Corp.
RAM VANS & VOYAGER WAGONS (Cont.)

INSTRUMENT PANEL & UNDERDASH

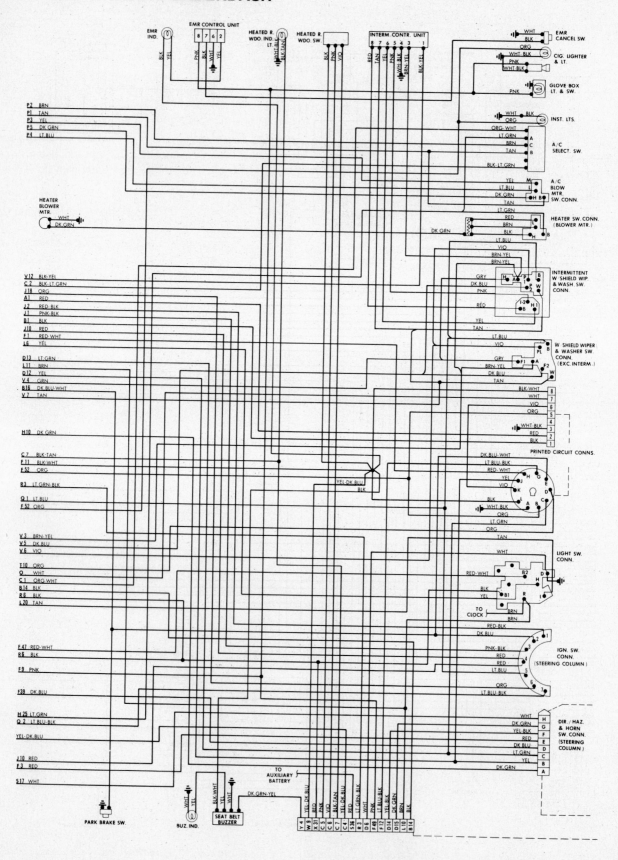

1983 Chrysler Corp.
RAM VANS & VOYAGER WAGONS (Cont.)

REAR COMPARTMENT & ACCESSORIES

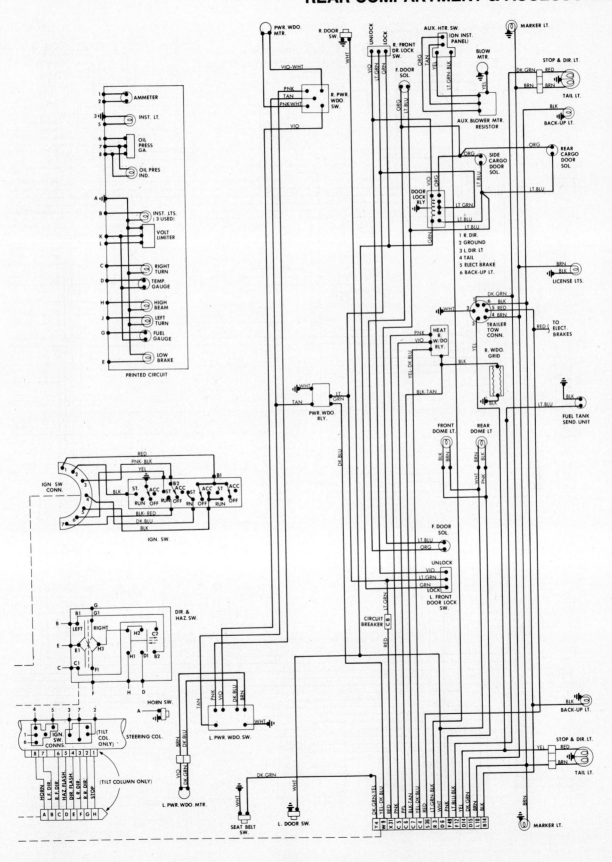

1983 Ford

BRONCO II & RANGER

ENGINE COMPARTMENT

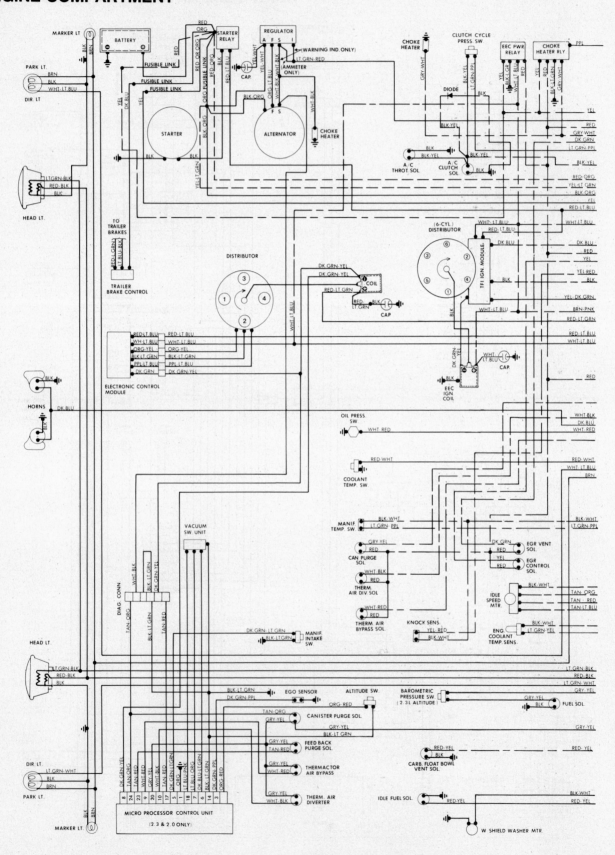

1983 Ford

BRONCO II & RANGER (Cont.)

FUSE BLOCK & UNDERDASH

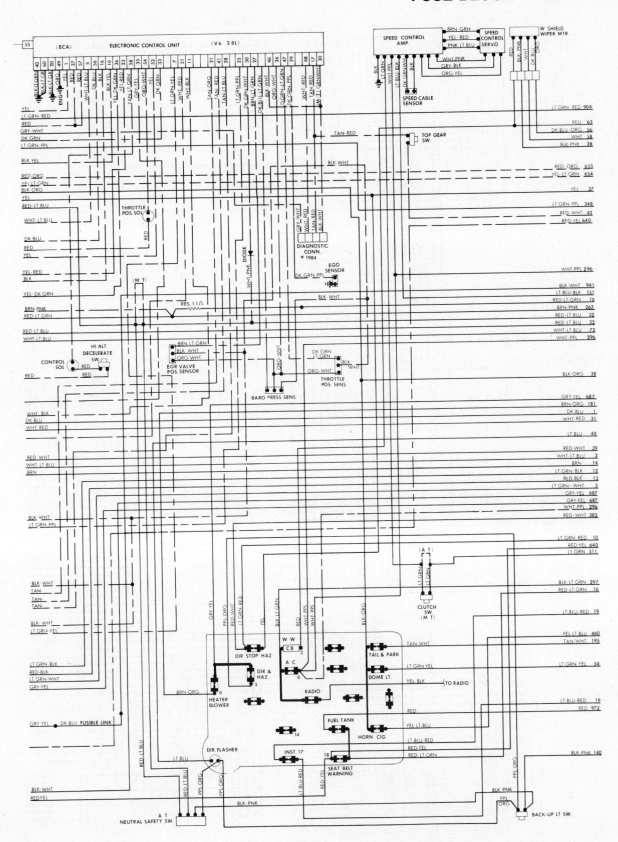

1983 Ford

BRONCO II & RANGER (Cont.)

UNDERDASH

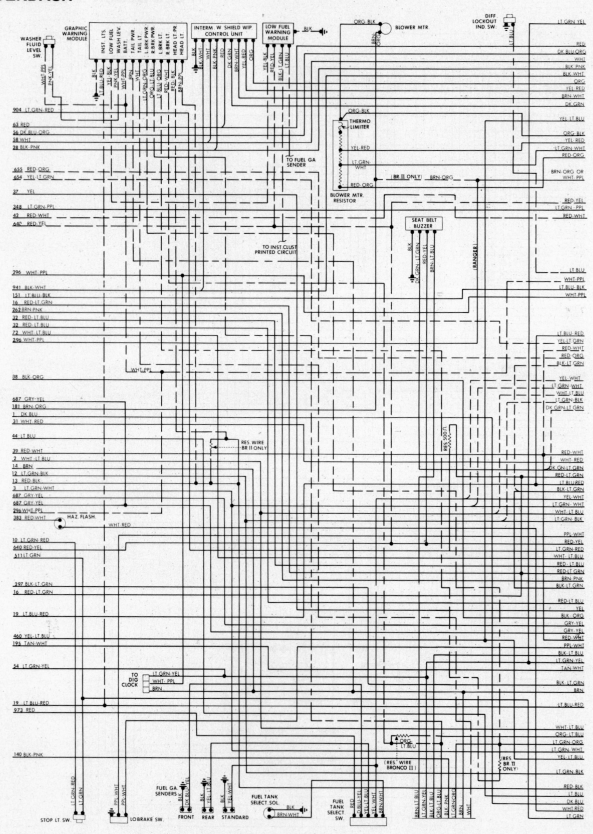

1983 Ford

BRONCO II & RANGER (Cont.)

UNDERDASH & REAR COMPARTMENT

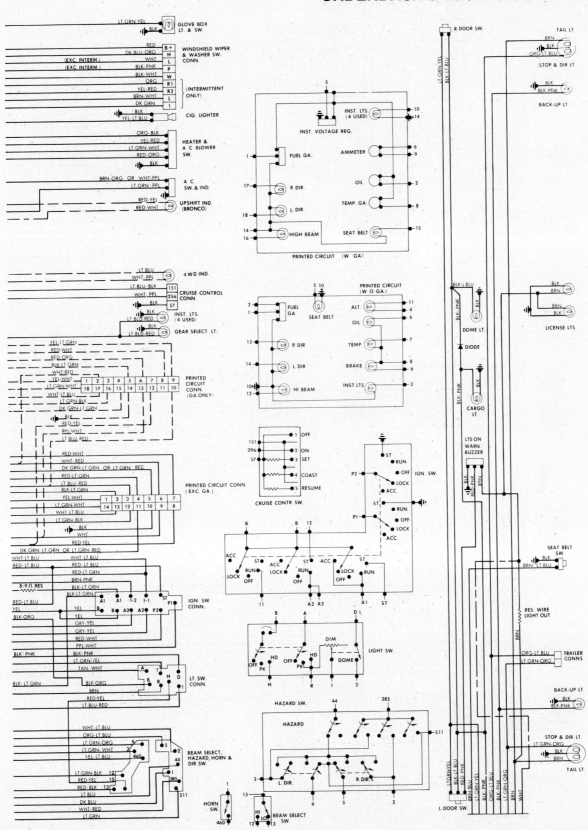

1983 Ford
E100/E350 ECONOLINE VANS & WAGONS

ENGINE COMPARTMENT

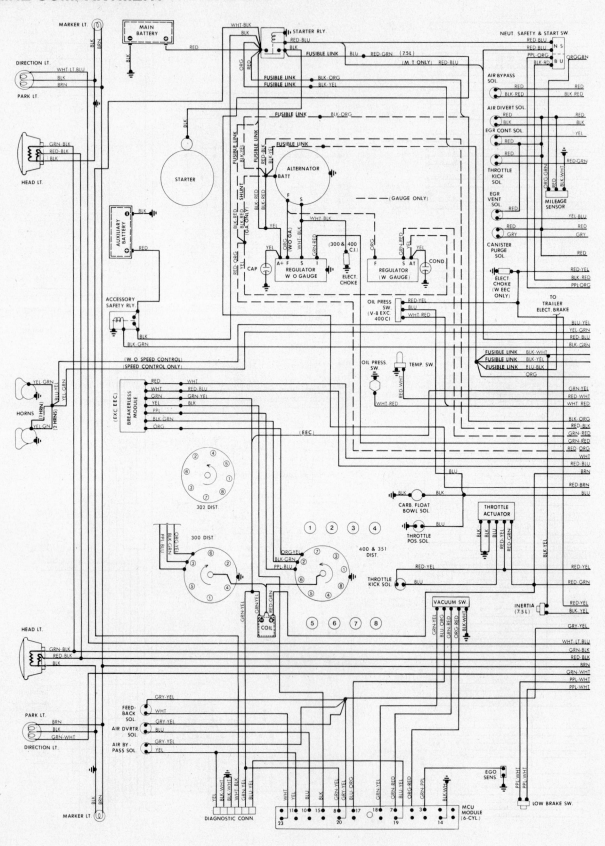

1983 Ford
E100/E350 ECONOLINE VANS & WAGONS (Cont.)

FUSE BLOCK & UNDERDASH

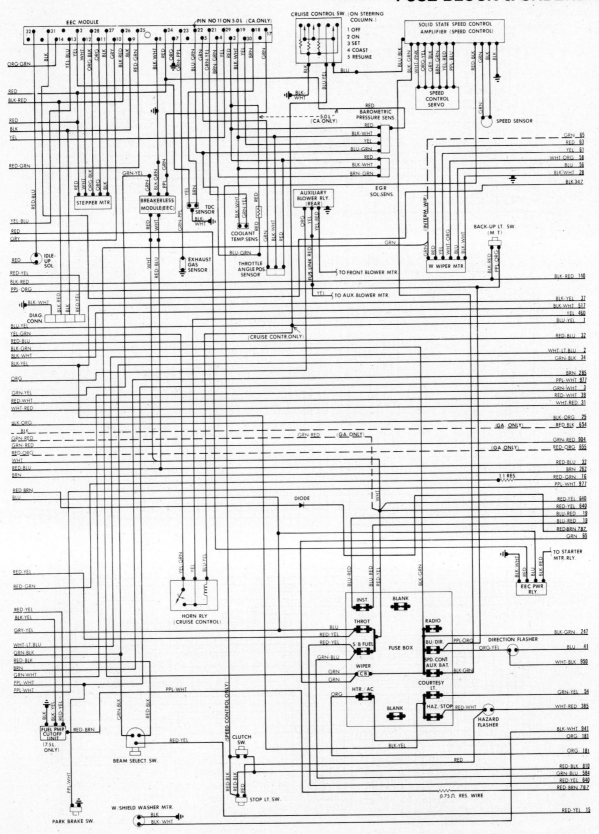

1983 Ford
E100/E350 ECONOLINE VANS & WAGONS (Cont.)

INSTRUMENT PANEL & UNDERDASH

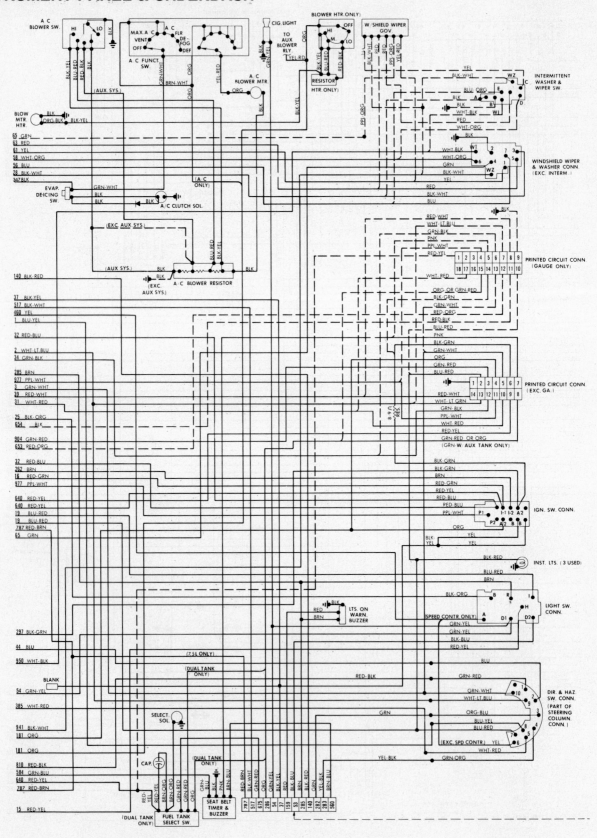

1983 Ford

E100/E350 ECONOLINE VANS & WAGONS (Cont.)

REAR COMPARTMENT & ACCESSORIES

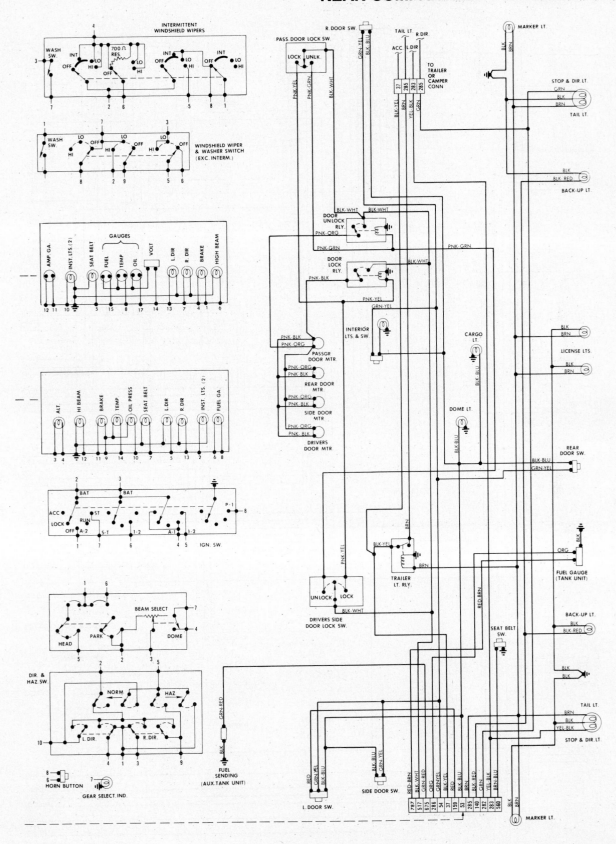

1983 Ford
BRONCO, F100/F350 PICKUPS & CHASSIS CABS

ENGINE COMPARTMENT

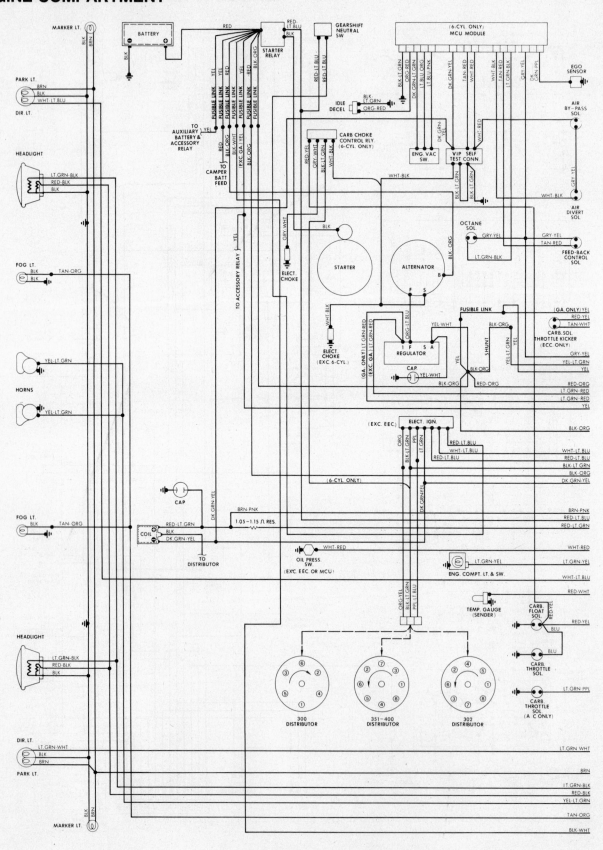

1983 Ford

BRONCO, F100/F350 PICKUPS & CHASSIS CABS (Cont.)

FUSE BLOCK & UNDERDASH

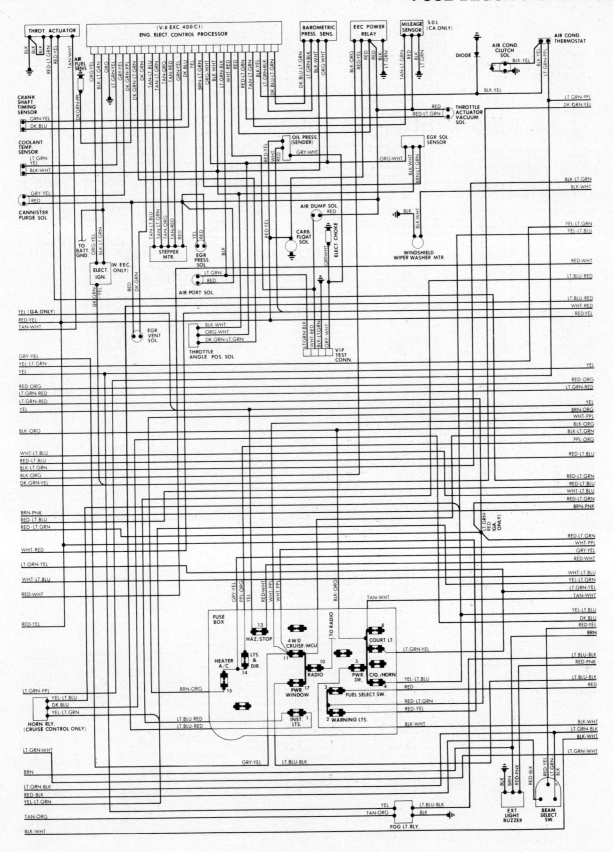

1983 Ford

BRONCO, F100/F350 PICKUPS & CHASSIS CABS (Cont.)

INSTRUMENT PANEL & UNDERDASH

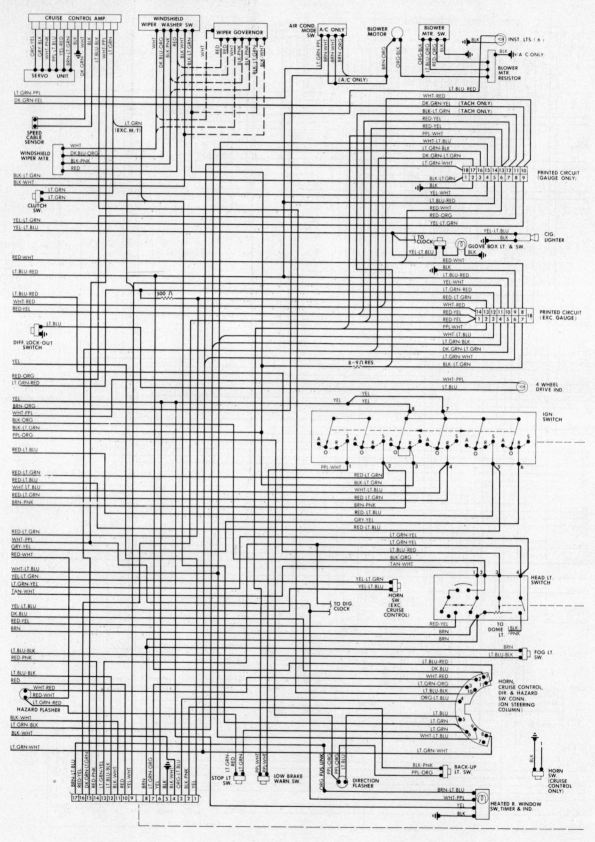

1983 Ford

BRONCO, F100/F350 PICKUPS & CHASSIS CABS (Cont.)

REAR COMPARTMENT & ACCESSORIES

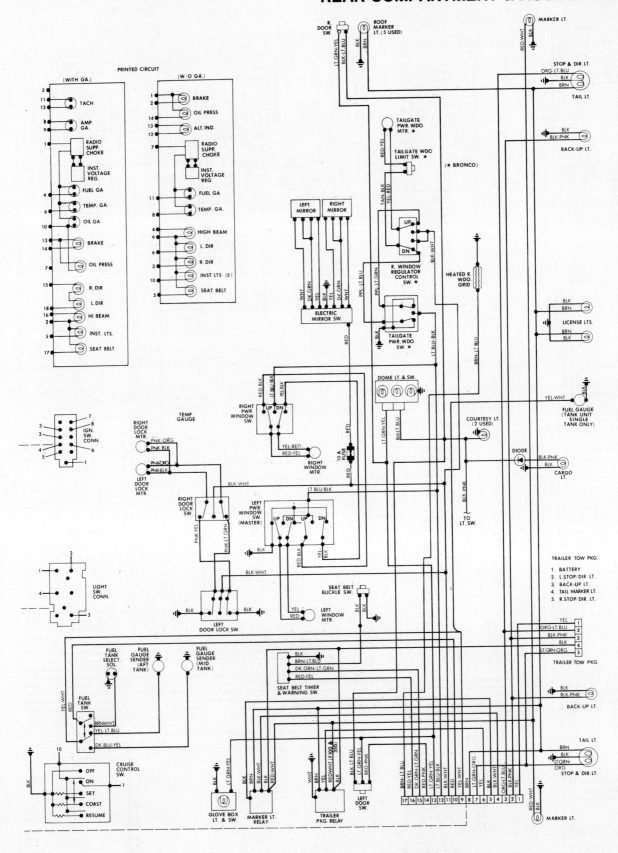

1983 General Motors
S10 & S15 Blazer & Pickup

ENGINE COMPARTMENT

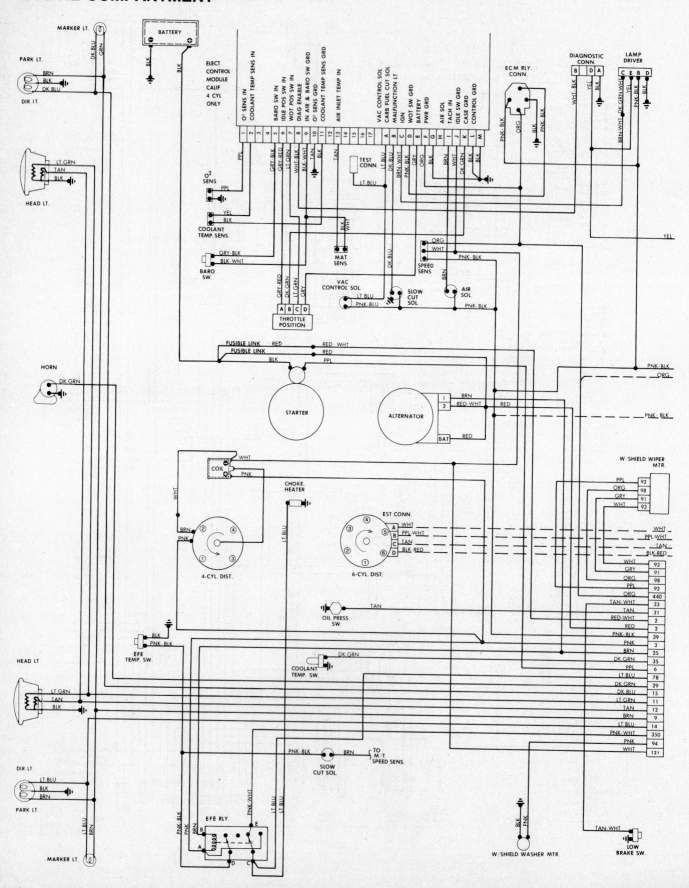

1983 General Motors
S10 & S15 BLAZER & PICKUP (Cont.)

FUSE BLOCK & UNDERDASH

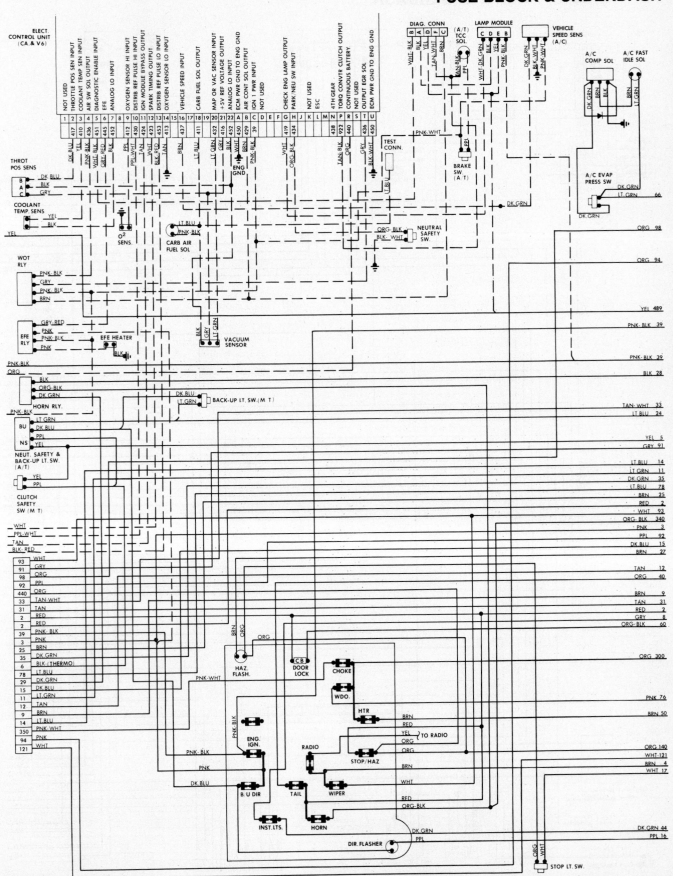

1983 General Motors
S10 & S-15 BLAZER & PICKUP (Cont.)

INSTRUMENT PANEL & UNDERDASH

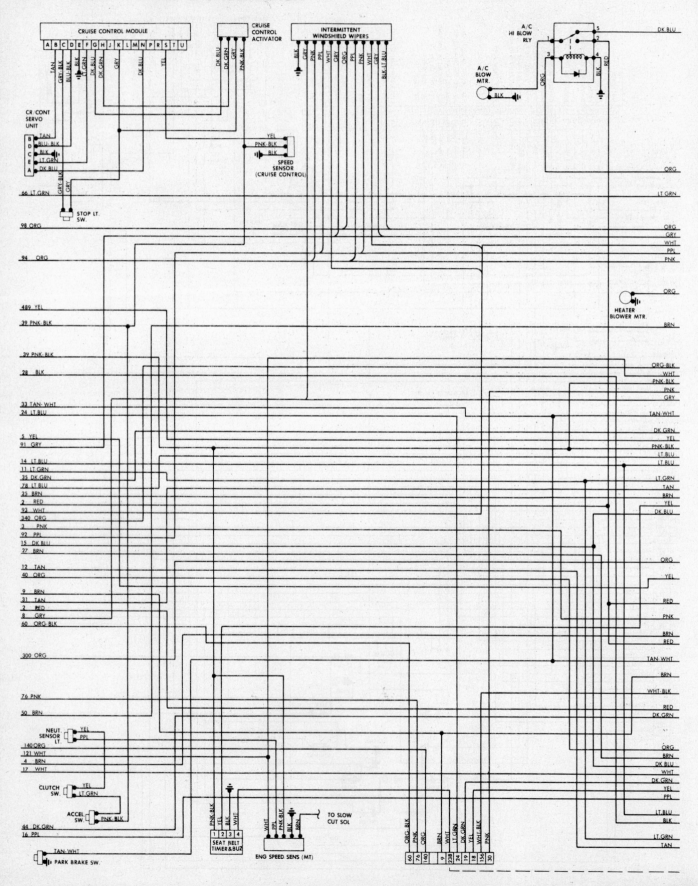

S10 & S15 BLAZER & PICKUP (Cont.)

REAR COMPARTMENT & ACCESSORIES

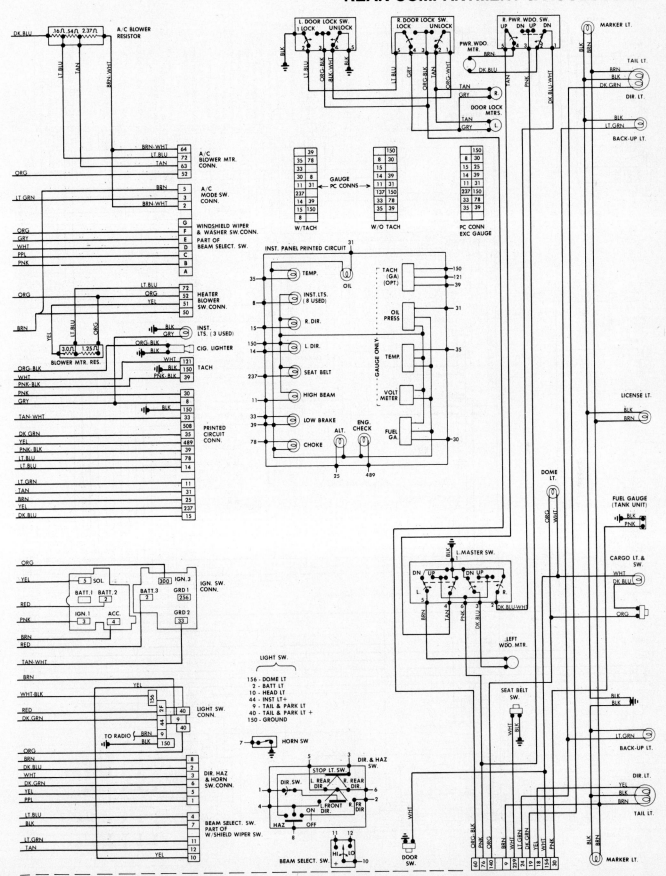

1983 General Motors

BLAZER, JIMMY, PICKUP & SUBURBAN

ENGINE COMPARTMENT

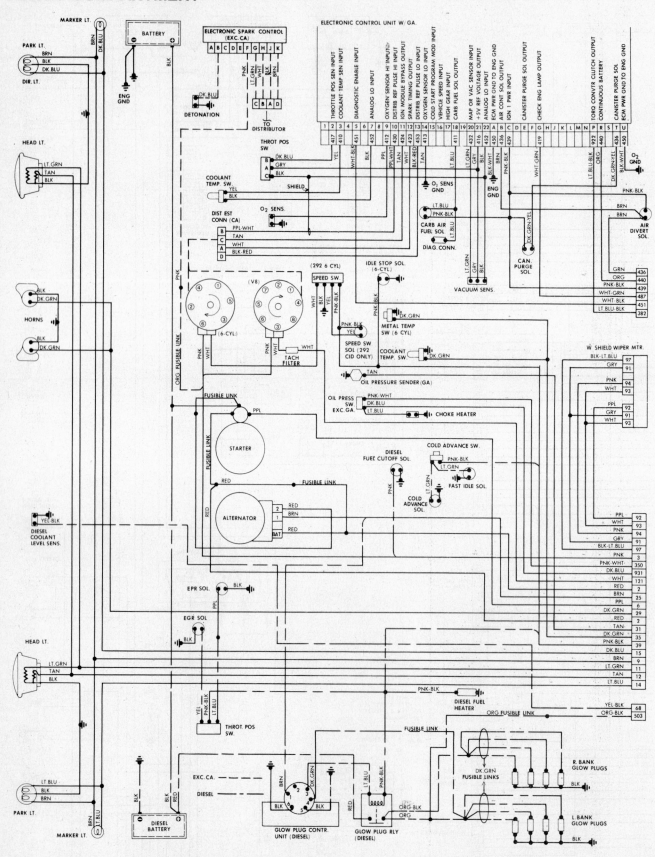

1983 General Motors
BLAZER, JIMMY, PICKUP & SUBURBAN (Cont.)

FUSE BLOCK & UNDERDASH

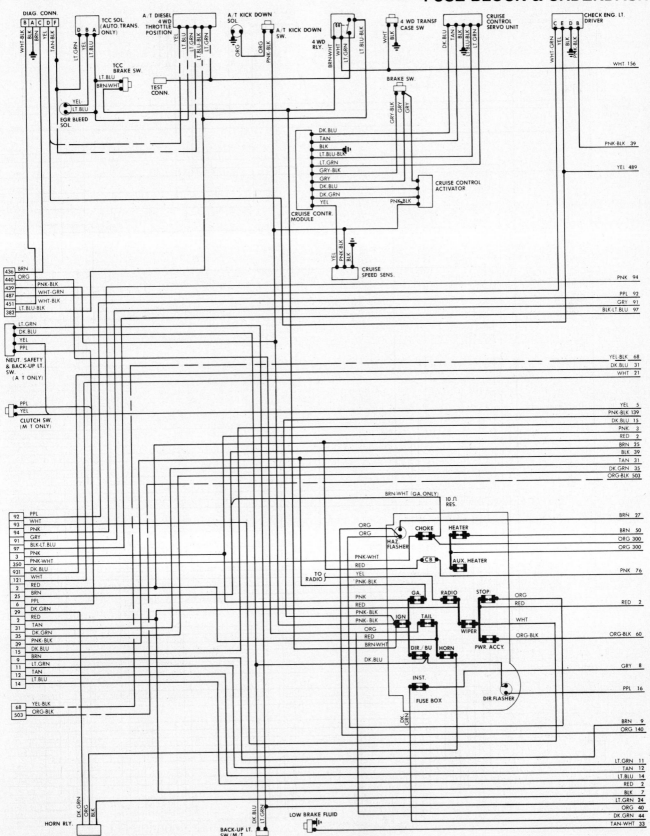

1983 General Motors
BLAZER, JIMMY, PICKUP & SUBURBAN (Cont.)

INSTRUMENT PANEL & UNDERDASH

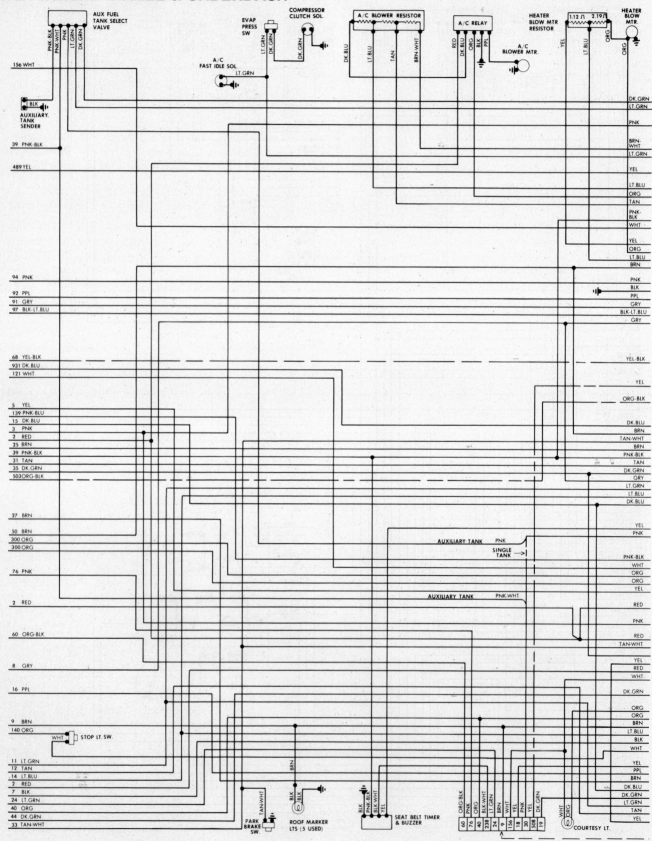

1983 General Motors
BLAZER, JIMMY, PICKUP & Suburban Cont.)

INSTRUMENT PANEL & REAR COMPARTMENT

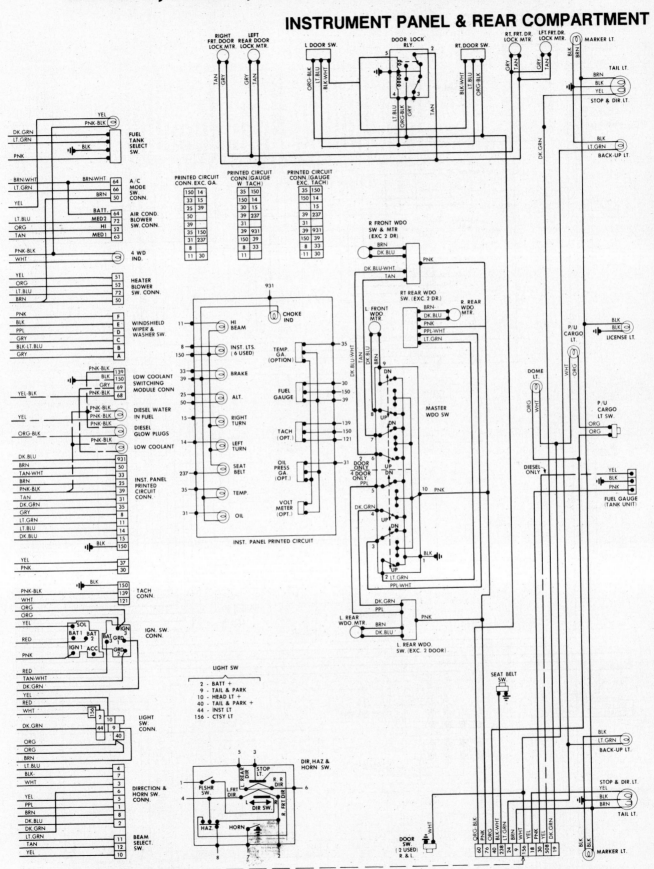

1983 General Motors
VANS, FRONT SECTIONS & HI-CUBES

ENGINE COMPARTMENT

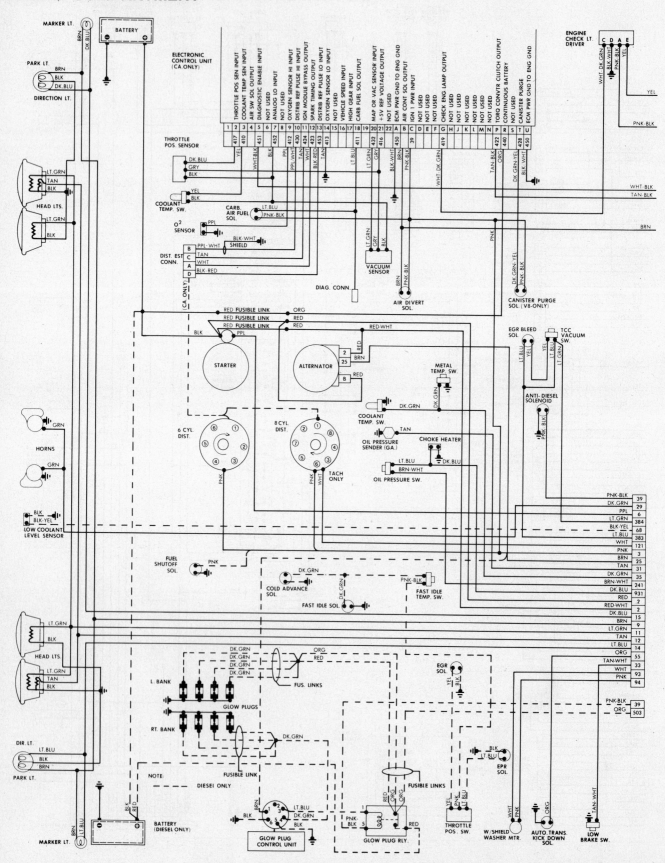

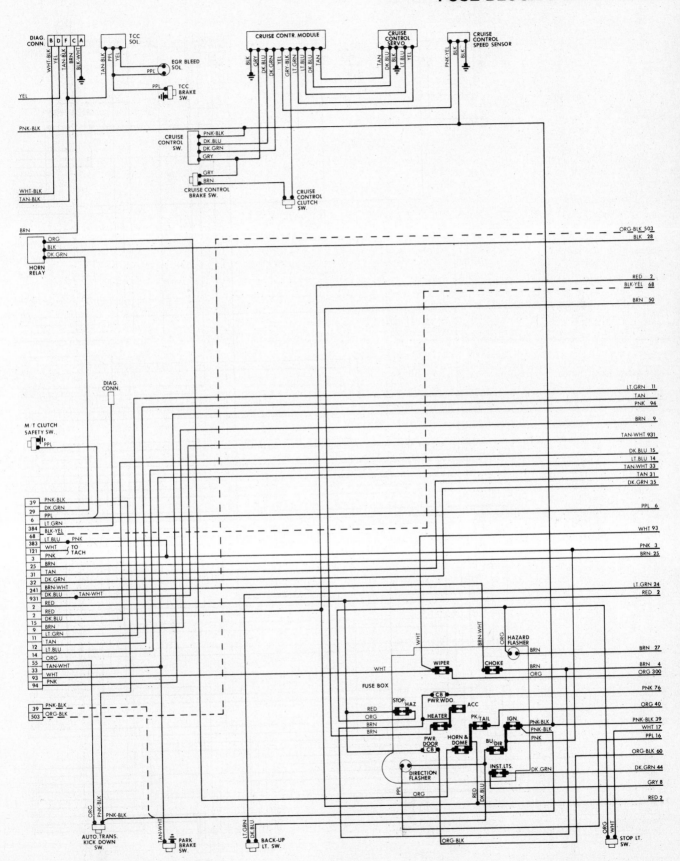

1983 General Motors
VANS, FRONT SECTIONS & HI-CUBES (Cont.)

INSTRUMENT PANEL & UNDERDASH

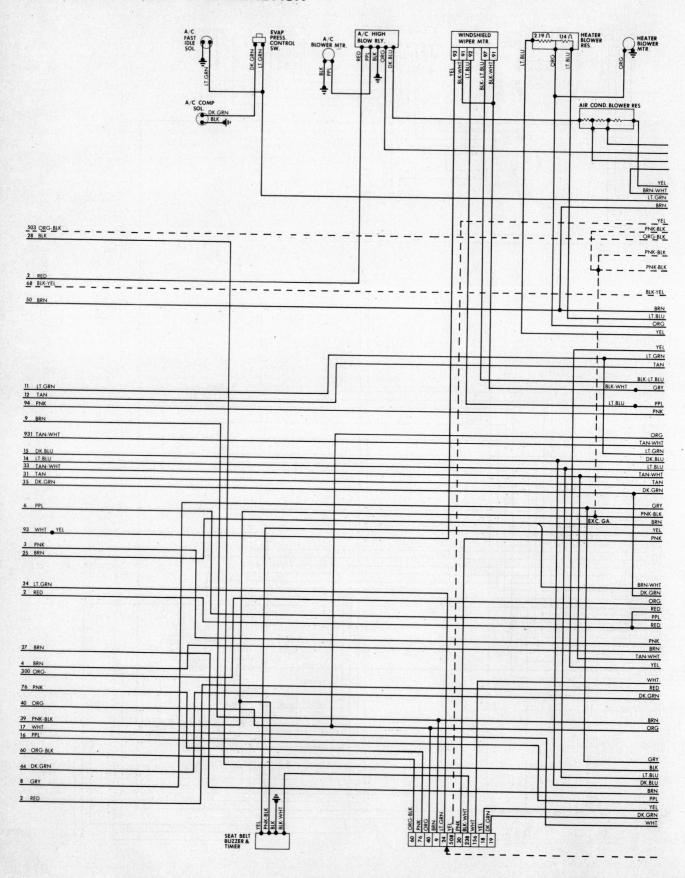

1983 General Motors
VANS, FRONT SECTIONS & HI-CUBES (Cont.)

UNDERDASH & REAR COMPARTMENT

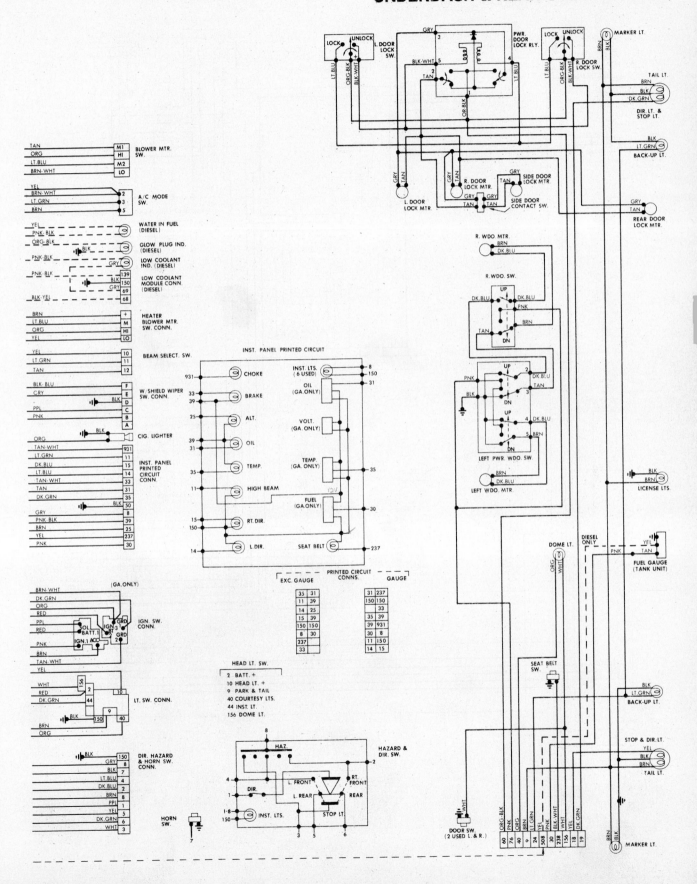

1983 General Motors
PARCEL DELIVERY VANS

ENGINE COMPARTMENT

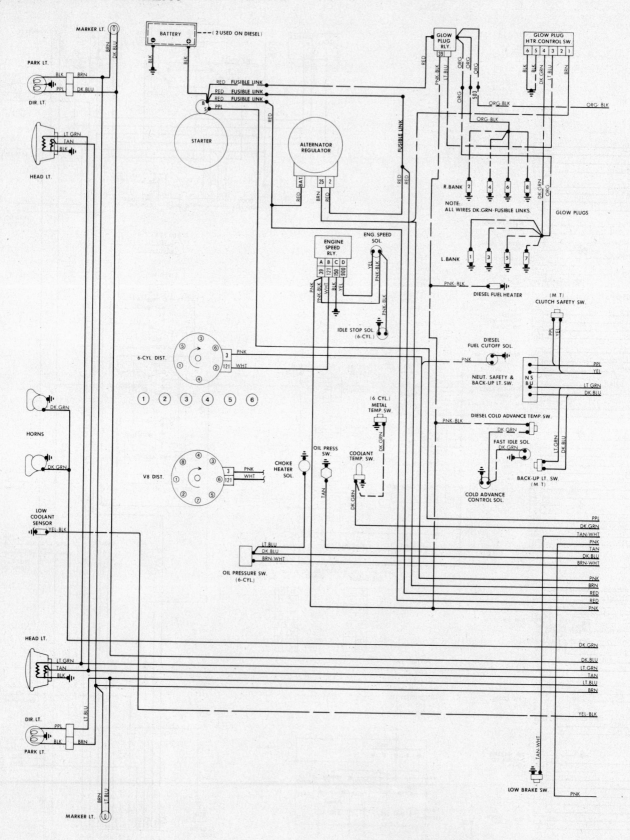

1983 General Motors
PARCEL DELIVERY VANS (Cont.)

Fuse Block & Underdash

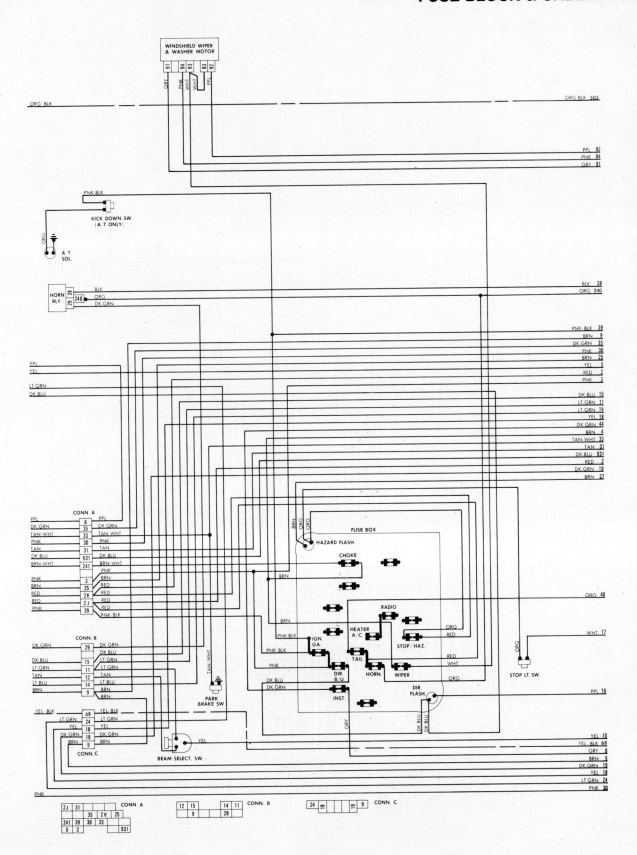

1983 General Motors
PARCEL DELIVERY VANS (Cont.)

INSTRUMENT PANEL & UNDERDASH

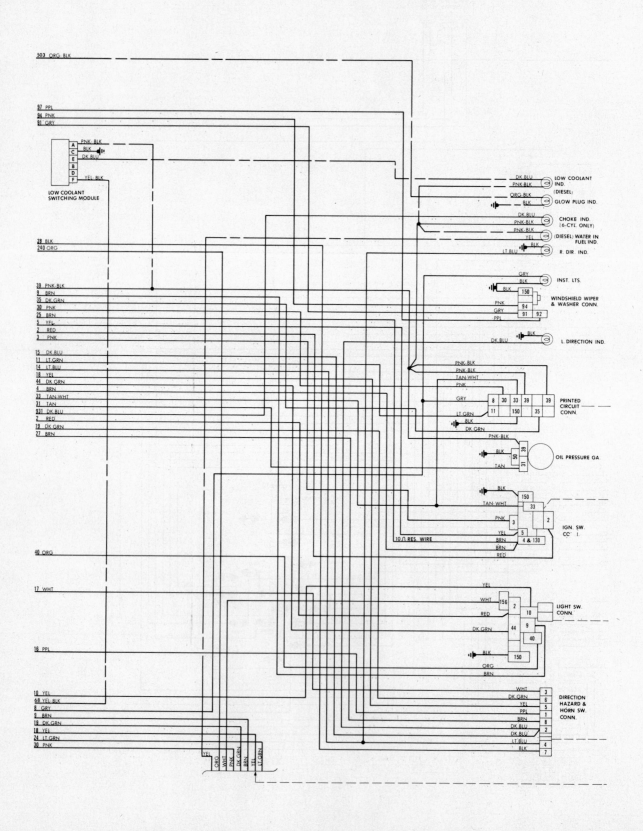

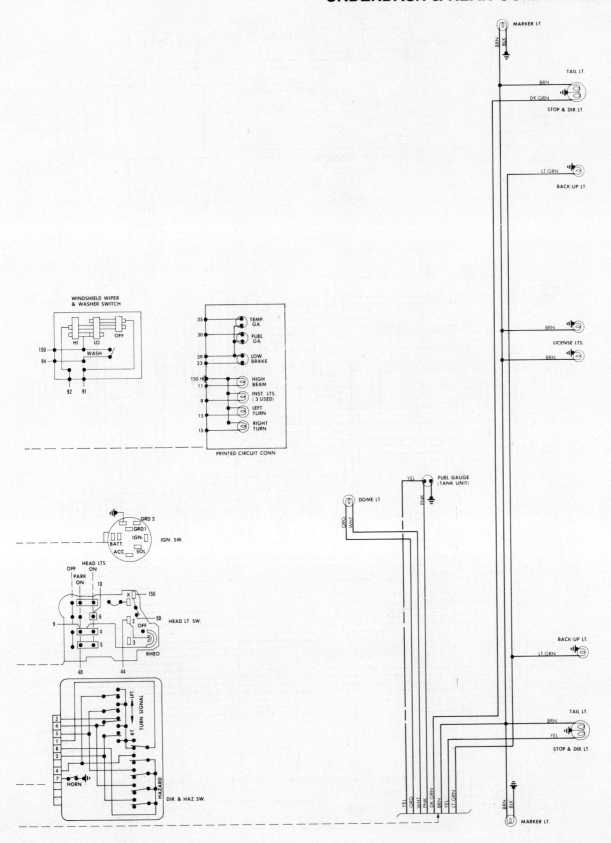

1983 Jeep
"CJ" & Scrambler

ENGINE COMPARTMENT

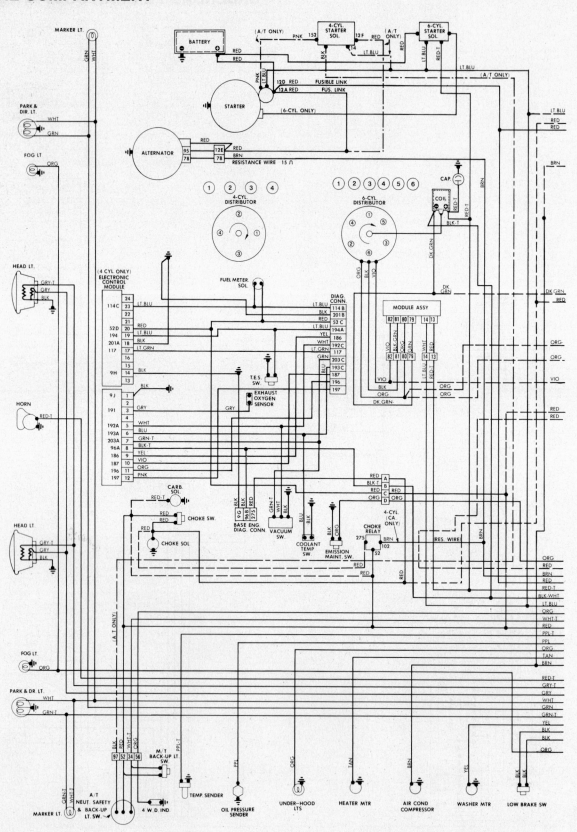

1983 Jeep
"CJ" & SCRAMBLER (Cont.)

ENGINE COMPARTMENT & FUSE BLOCK

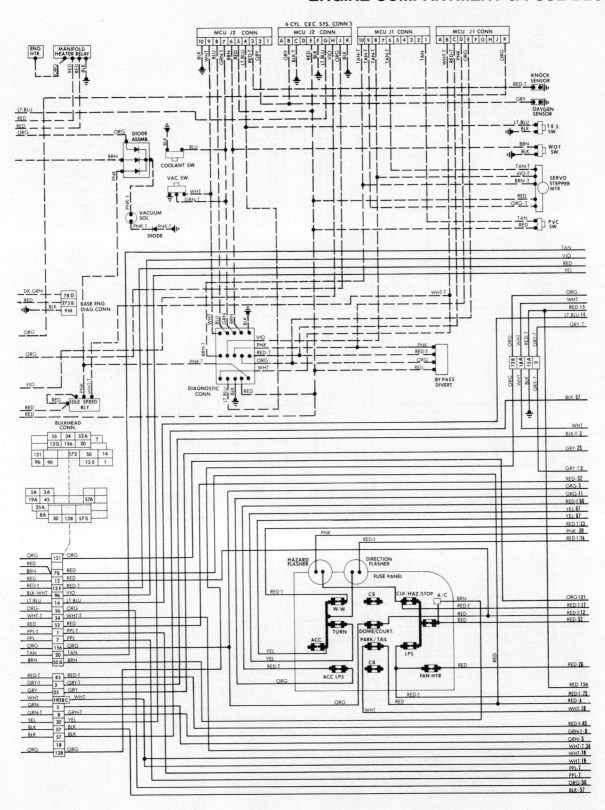

1983 Jeep
"CJ" & SCRAMBLER (Cont.)

INSTRUMENT PANEL & UNDERDASH

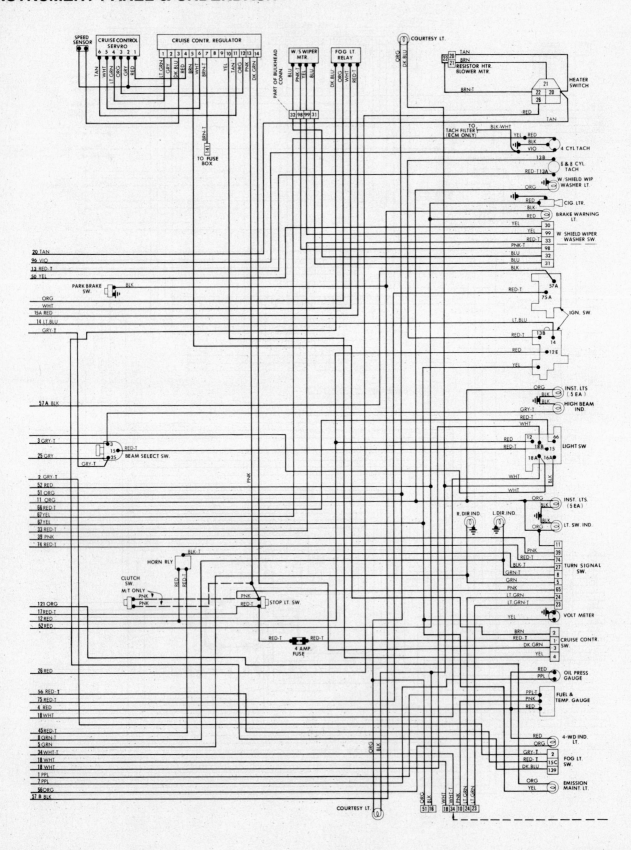

1983 Jeep
"CJ" & SCRAMBLER (Cont.)

REAR COMPARTMENT

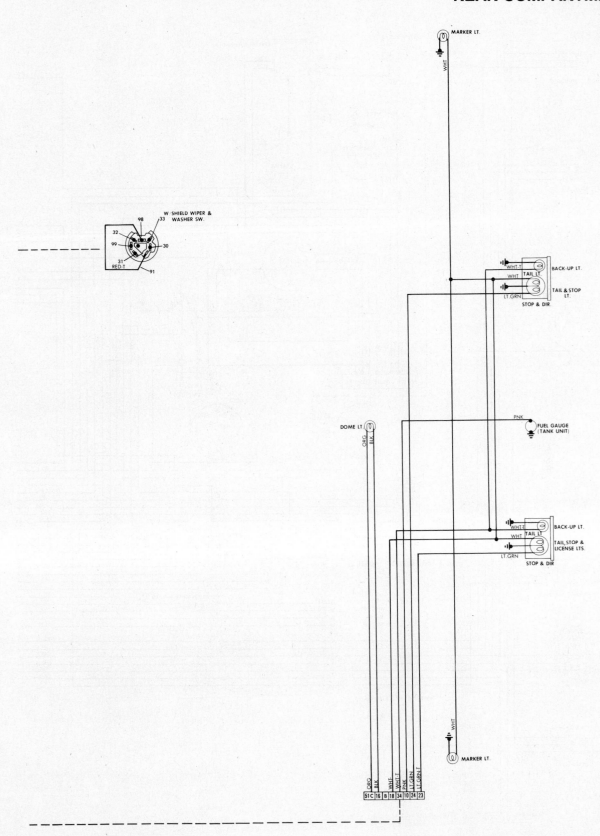

1983 Jeep
CHEROKEE, "J" TRUCKS & WAGONEER

ENGINE COMPARTMENT

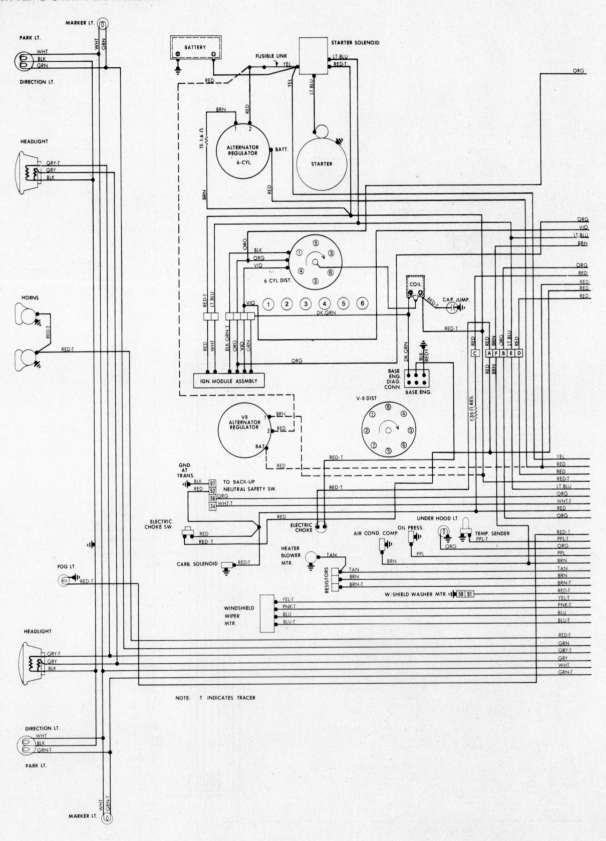

NOTE: T INDICATES TRACER

1983 Jeep

CHEROKEE, "J" TRUCKS & WAGONEER (Cont.)

FUSE BLOCK & UNDERDASH

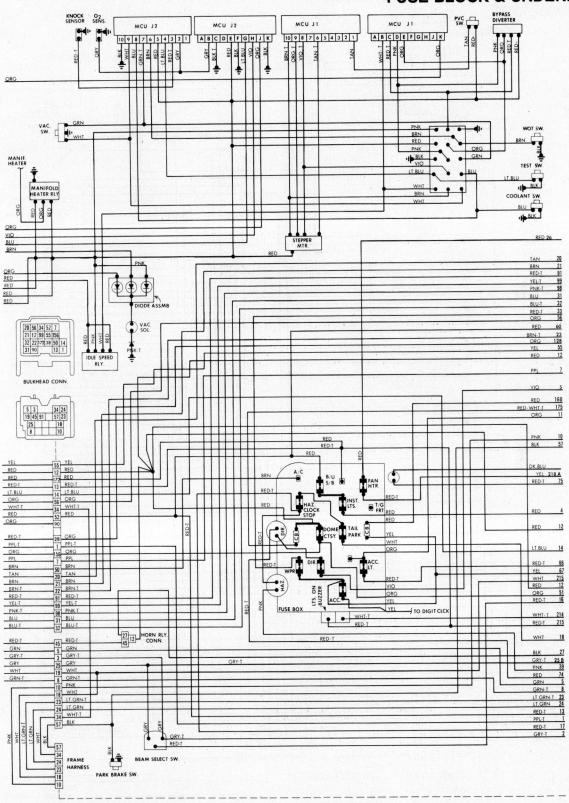

1983 Jeep
CHEROKEE, "J" TRUCKS & WAGONEER (Cont.)

INSTRUMENT PANEL & UNDERDASH

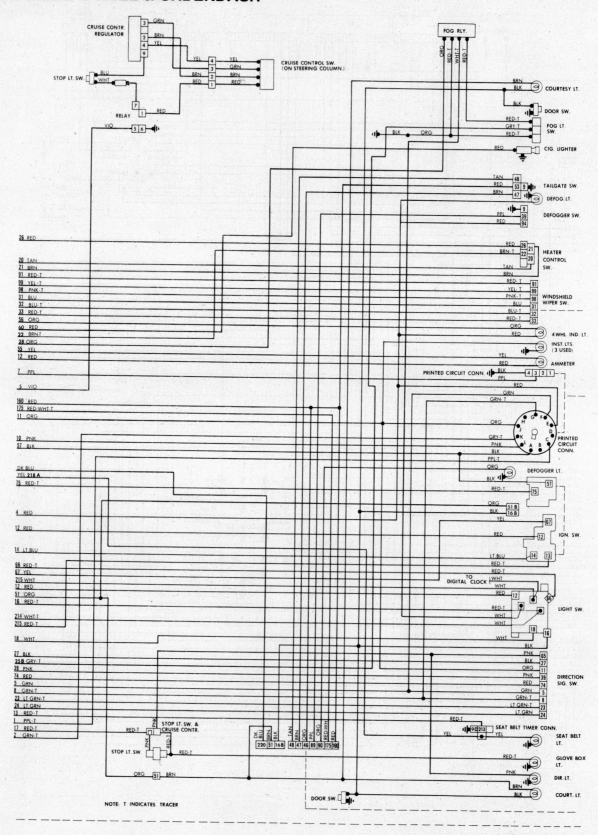

1983 Jeep
CHEROKEE, "J" TRUCKS & WAGONEER (Cont.)

REAR COMPARTMENT & ACCESSORIES

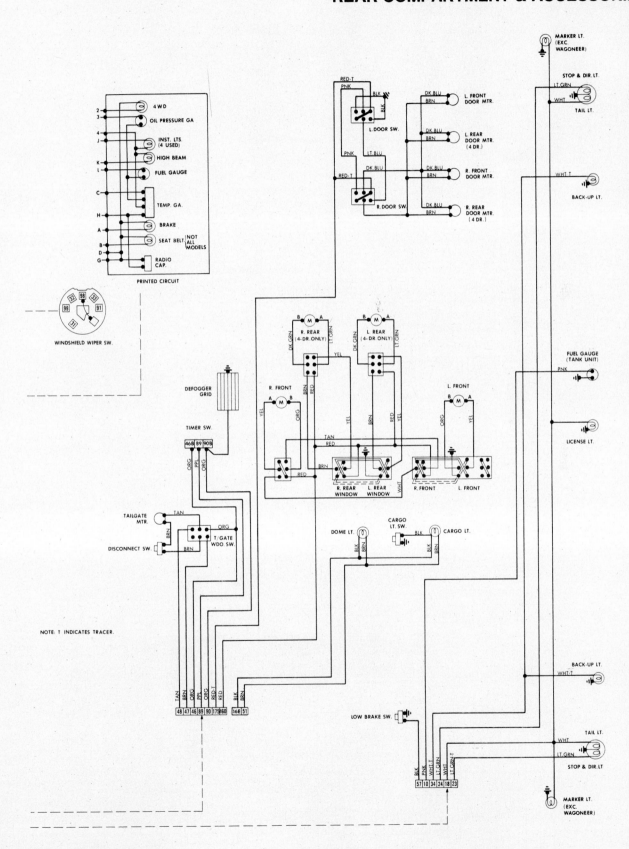

NOTE: T INDICATES TRACER.

SECTION 6

ACCESSORIES & EQUIPMENT

CONTENTS

NOTE: ALSO SEE GENERAL INDEX.

IMPORTANT: Because of the many model names used by vehicle manufacturers, accurate identification of models is important. See Model Identification at the front of this publication.

Air Conditioning Servicing

COMPRESSOR OIL CHECK

GENERAL NOTES
AIR TEMP, TECUMSEH & YORK COMPRESSORS

Oil level on these compressors may be checked with compressor mounted in vehicle. If these compressors are equipped with stem-type service valves, compressor may be "isolated", thereby avoiding necessity of discharging entire system. *See Compressor Isolating or related paragraphs in this Section.*

FRIGIDAIRE COMPRESSOR

When checking oil level on these compressors, it may be necessary to remove compressor from vehicle, as filler plug is located near bottom of compressor. After oil level is checked, system must be evacuated and recharged. *See Frigidaire Compressor in this Section.*

COMPRESSOR ISOLATING

On York and Tecumseh compressors with stem-type service valves (at compressor suction and discharge ports), it will not be necessary to discharge entire system in order to service compressor. *See York & Techumseh Compressors and Compressor Replacement in this Section.*

REFRIGERATION OIL

Only new, pure, moisture-free refrigeration oil should be used in the air conditioning system. This oil is highly refined with moisture content less than 10 parts per million.

Refrigeration oil container must be kept tightly closed at all times when not in use, or moisture will be absorbed and introduced into the refrigeration system.

AIR-TEMP COMPRESSOR

CHRYSLER CORP.

Oil capacity is 10-12 oz. in 2-cylinder compressors and 9-10 oz. in 6-cylinder compressors. Oil level need not be checked each time system is discharged, unless refrigerant charge has been lost or significant oil loss is indicated. Quantity of oil in compressor sump is measured using dipstick. *See Fig. 1.*

2-Cylinder (RV-2) Oil Level Check

1) Slowly discharge system. Near completion of discharge, oil dipstick should be flushed with freon to insure a clean dipstick.

2) Slowly remove compressor filler plug (some residual pressure will remain after discharge). Insert oil lever dipstick until it bottoms in sump. Oil lever on stick must be 3-3.4". If necessary, add recommended oil to bring level to specifications. Install filler plug and recharge system.

6-Cylinder (C-171) Oil Level Check

1) Slowly discharge system. Disconnect suction and discharge lines from compressor and remove compressor.

2) Drain oil from suction port and discard. Add 9 oz. of new refrigerant oil through suction port. Clean drain plug and put a light coat of sealant on threads. Install drain plug and tighten to 90-130 INCH lbs. (10-14.5 N.m).

3) Install compressor, connect suction and discharge lines and tighten. Use new gaskets to prevent leakage.

4) Evacuate system and recharge to specification.

Oil Level Check After Discharge

If using fast discharge method (with oil collector can attached to center discharge hose), measure amount of oil caught in can. Replace this amount with new oil. If following components are replaced, add specified additional amounts of oil:

AIR-TEMP OIL LEVELS

Application	Specification
Evaporator	2 oz.
Condenser	1 oz.
Receiver-Drier	1 oz.

NOTE: After adding oil, use standard dipstick method to determine exact oil level before recharging system.

Fig. 1: Air-Temp Compressor Oil Check Point and Dipstick for Chrysler

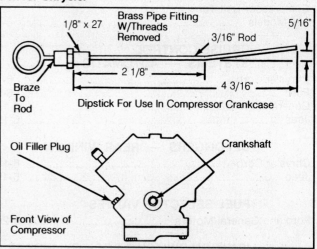

FRIGIDAIRE COMPRESSOR

GENERAL MOTORS
4 & 6-CYLINDER COMPRESSOR

A/C system with 6-cylinder compressor is fully charged with 10 oz. refrigerant oil. 4-cylinder compressor is fully charged with 6 oz. Optional overhead A/C system is fully charged with 13 oz. Adding additional oil is not required unless a definite oil loss has occurred.

NOTE: Do not reuse old oil.

On-Vehicle Checking After Minor Repairs

1) With compressor in installed position and system fully discharged, loosen oil plug far enough to determine if oil will run out. If oil starts to run out, do not add additional oil other than amount shown for component replacement.

COMPRESSOR OIL CHECK (Cont.)

2) If oil does not run out and there is visible evidence of considerable oil loss somewhere in the system, add 4 ounces of new oil to the compressor after compensating for component replacement.

3) If oil does not run out and there is no visible evidence of a large oil leak, add 2 ounces of new oil to the compressor after repairing leak and adding proper amount to replaced components.

4) Oil can be added without removing the compressor, by using a special oil injector (J-7605-03) or by using the A/C service station unit as recommended by the manufacturer. If these are not available, remove compressor and add oil.

Off-Car Checking After Major Repair

1) Before performing repairs, if system is operable, run A/C for several minutes to stabilize. Turn off air conditioner and engine, discharge system completely, and remove compressor. Slowly remove oil drain plug, then drain and measure oil from compressor. Replace amounts as outlined below.

2) If new compressor is being installed, drain and measure oil from old compressor and add new oil to replacement compressor using described method below. If compressor is being overhauled, add one additional ounce of oil to amount being replaced.

3) If quantity drained is less than 4 ounces, add 6 ounces of replacement oil. If quantity drained is between 4 and 6 ounces, oil is properly distributed throughout the system; add same amount as drained. If quantity drained is more than 6 ounces, add ONLY 6 ounces.

NOTE: A-6 system will have 6 oz. of oil in accumulator and/or compressor. This is why measurement is required.

4) If compressor is inoperable, use the following method: Remove compressor, drain, measure, and discard the oil. If amount drained is more than 1 1/2 ounces, and the system shows no sign of a major leak, add amount drained. If less than 1 1/2 ounces is drained and system appears to have lost excessive oil, add 6 ounces to replacement compressor, or 7 ounces if compressor is being overhauled.

5) When replacing components, add additional amounts of oil as specified:

FRIGIDAIRE OIL LEVELS

Application	Specification
Evaporator	3 oz.
Condenser	1 oz.
Receiver-Drier	1 oz.
Accumulator	1 oz.[1]

[1] — R-4 accumulator holds 2 oz. plus 1 oz. for desiccant.

NOTE: If oil drained contains metal chips or other foreign material, replace receiver-drier and flush or replace other components as necessary.

TECUMSEH & YORK COMPRESSORS

FORD W/SCHRADER SERVICE VALVES

1) Check compressor oil level only if any portion of refrigerant system is being replaced, or if system was discharged due to a leak. On horizontally mounted compressors, oil check hole is located on side of crankshaft which faces up.

Fig. 2: Checking Compressor Oil Level on Horizontally Mounted Unit

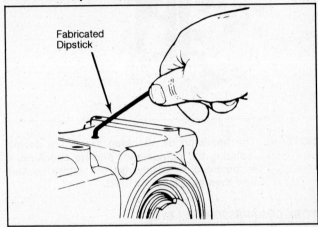

Fabricated Dipstick

2) On opposite or downward side there is a corresponding boss provided on inner wall as an alternate oil check hole, for different mounting. When checking oil level on such a compressor, angle the dipstick such that it bottoms against lower side of compressor and not against boss.

3) After system has been charged, operate for approximately 10 minutes, or until pressures have stabilized (with ambient temperature of 60°F or higher). Stop engine and discharge entire system using a suitable Schrader-Type service valve. Fabricate a suitable dipstick according to specifications. See Fig. 3.

4) Remove oil filler plug and insert dipstick until it bottoms. If necessary, slightly rotate compressor crankshaft by hand so that dipstick will clear. Level on dipstick must be within specifications.

TECUMSEH COMPRESSOR OIL LEVEL

Application	Measurement
Horizontal Mount	7/8-1 5/8"
Vertical Mount	7/8-1 3/8"

FORD & JEEP W/STEM TYPE SERVICE VALVES

Oil level should be checked whenever the system is discharged for service part replacement, or if system has self-discharged due to component malfunction. Oil level is checked with compressor in operating position.

It is important when checking oil level that system has been operated and car interior temperature has cooled to desired setting. This is necessary to stabilize amount of oil in the system.

Air Conditioning Servicing

COMPRESSOR OIL CHECK (Cont.)

Fig. 3: Checking Oil on Vertically Mounted York Compressor

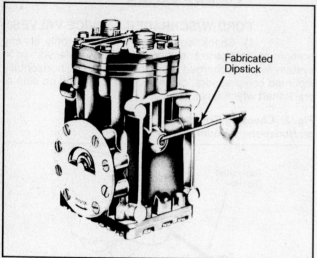

Fabricated Dipstick

NOTE: The following oil checking procedure details isolating the compressor prior to checking. It is possible to discharge the entire system and then check the oil level.

YORK COMPRESSOR OIL LEVEL

Application	Measurement
Ford	
Horizontal Mount	13/16"
Vertical Mount	7/8-1 1/8"
Jeep	
Horizontal Mount	13/16"
Vertical Mount	7/8-1 1/8"

1) Turn both the high and low pressure service valve clockwise as far as possible (front-seat position). Loosen cap on the high pressure service valve and bleed residual pressure from compressor.

CAUTION: Only loosen cap a small amount and DO NOT remove cap until pressure is totally relieved.

NOTE: Oil level check plugs are located on either side of compressor crankcase; use check plug which is most convenient.

2) Fabricate a suitable dipstick according to specifications. Check oil level. Add clean refrigerant oil if necessary. Install new "O" ring seal on filler plug.

3) When oil check is complete, compressor must be purged of air before operating the system. Refer to procedure under Component Replacement.

Fig. 4: Dimensions for Tecumseh Compressor Oil Level Dipstick

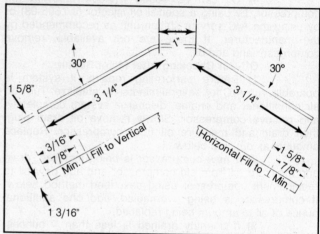

Fig. 5: Dimensions for York Compressor Oil Level Dipstick

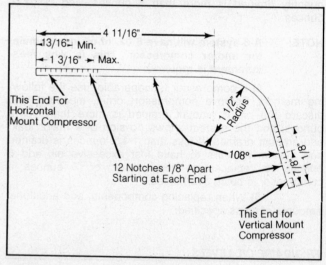

COMPONENT REPLACEMENT CAUTIONS

BEFORE OPENING THE SYSTEM

Before disconnecting any lines or fittings, the system must be completely discharged; however, if only the compressor is being removed and the compressor is equipped with stem-type service valves (York or Tecumseh), compressor may be isolated without discharging the system. Refer to Compressor Isolation Method.

DISCONNECTING LINES & FITTINGS

After system is discharged, carefully clean entire area around coupling nut to prevent dirt from entering the system. Always use two wrenches to avoid twisting or distorting lines and fittings (hold fitting with one wrench while loosening coupling nut with second wrench).

Cap or plug all LINES and FITTINGS immediately to prevent entry of air and moisture into system and do not remove these caps until connections are being made.

See following pages for removal and installation of each component. After replacement or repaired component is installed, connect lines as directed below.

COMPONENT REPLACEMENT CAUTIONS (Cont.)

COMPONENT REPLACEMENT

See following pages for removal and installation of each component. After replacement or repaired component installed, connect lines as directed below.

In addition to checking and adjusting the compressor oil level (see Compressor Oil Check), certain component replacement requires additional refrigeration oil. Add specified amounts of oil directly to the component prior to installation.

REFRIGERATION OIL ADDITION

Application	Amount
With Frigidaire Compressor	
Evaporator	3 oz.
Condenser	1 oz.
Receiver-Drier	1 oz.
With Air-Temp Compressor	
Evaporator	2 oz.
Condenser	1 oz.
Receiver-Drier	1 oz.

COMPRESSOR REPLACEMENT

CONNECTING LINES & FITTINGS

A new "O" ring should be used in all instances when connecting lines and fittings (dip "O" ring in clean refrigeration oil and make certain it is not twisted during installation). Always use two wrenches to avoid twisting or distorting lines and fittings, tighten coupling nuts securely.

PLACING SYSTEM IN OPERATION

After component replacement and/or system servicing has been completed and all connections have been made, proceed as follows:

1) Evacuate the system using a vacuum pump.

2) Charge the system with new R-12 (refrigerant) according to each individual vehicle manufacturers procedure as outlined in this Manual. *Also see Refrigerant Capacity in this Section.*

3) Leak test the system, with particular attention to all new connections and components.

4) Make a performance test of the system.

COMPRESSOR ISOLATION METHOD

On systems which have compressors equipped with stem-type service valves (York and some Tecumseh), it is possible to isolate the compressor for removal.

Isolating (Ford)

Turn both high and low pressure manual valves to extreme clockwise (front seat) position. Loosen cap on high pressure manual valve connection to compressor and allow gas to escape until compressor is relieved of pressure.

Isolating (Jeep)

1) Connect standard A/C pressure gauge and manifold assembly (J-23575). Close both gauge hand valves and mid-position both service valves. Start engine and operate A/C.

2) Turn suction service valve slowly clockwise toward front seat position. When suction pressure is reduced to zero or less, stop engine and compressor and quickly finish frontseating suction service valve.

3) Front-seat discharge service valve. Loosen oil check plug slowly to release any internal pressure in compressor. Compressor is now isolated from system.

Removal

1) Carefully remove service valves from compressor by unscrewing the mounting bolts. Do not disturb line connections and do not turn valve stems with valve assemblies disconnected from compressor (to prevent system discharge). Cap service valves and plug compressor openings to prevent entry of dirt and moisture.

2) If compressor clutch is to be removed (for installation on replacement compressor), energize compressor clutch with engine NOT running and remove clutch mounting bolt from end of compressor shaft, then install 5/8-11 bolt in driveshaft hold and tighten bolt to loosen clutch from shaft with clutch energized, disconnect clutch lead. Remove drive belt and clutch.

3) Remove service valve caps and shipping plugs from compressor valve ports and immediately install service valves on compressor using new "O" rings.

4) Remove compressor mounting bolts and lift compressor off engine. Remove clutch field assembly from compressor (on early compressors with rotating field, remove brush assembly).

Installation

1) Position compressor on engine, install compressor clutch using new retaining bolt and washer (energize clutch to hold shaft while tightening nut).

2) Make necessary compressor oil level check and add oil if necessary. *See Compressor Oil Check in this Section.*

3) Drain and measure compressor oil level. Retain measurement to make proper oil adjustment during installation.

4) Leak test compressor, and then evacuate it and connect it back into system. Recheck compressor oil level, adding or removing oil as necessary for correct oil level.

COMPRESSOR DISCHARGE METHOD

This procedure is to be used on vehicles which have compressor equipped with Schrader service valves. In these cases, the compressor cannot be isolated and the system must be discharged prior to compressor removal.

Removal (Chrysler Corp.)

1) Discharge system. Measure and record refrigerant level so that it can be refilled to exact level in replacement or repaired compressor. Disconnect suction and discharge lines and cap openings.

2) Disconnect magnetic clutch-to-control unit wire and on Air-Temp compressors, remove clutch assembly. Remove compressor-to-bracket attaching bolts and remove compressor. On C-171 compressors, drain oil from suction and discharge ports.

Installation (Chrysler Corp.)

1) Reverse removal procedures noting the following: On C-171 compressors, add oil to bring level to 5 ounces. On Air-Temp compressors, rotate crankshaft assembly by hand at least 2 revolutions to clear oil accumulation from compressor head before energizing clutch, or damage to reed valves will result.

Air Conditioning Servicing

COMPRESSOR REPLACEMENT (Cont.)

2) On all models, evacuate and charge air conditioning system.

Removal (General Motors "C", "K" & "S")

Discharge system. Remove connector attaching bolt. Remove connector and cap openings. Disconnect wiring to clutch actuating coil. Remove drive belt. Remove compressor mounting brackets and compressor. Drain and measure oil in compressor.

Installation (General Motors "C", "K" & "S")

Replace oil in compressor with exact amount drained. Reverse removal procedures, installing new "O" rings on connector. Evacuate and charge system. Check operation.

Removal (General Motors "G" Models)

1) Disconnect battery ground cable and compressor clutch connector. Purge system of refrigerant. Remove drive belt.

2) Remove 2 bolts and 2 clamps holding engine cover and remove engine cover. Remove air cleaner, fitting and muffler assembly. Cap openings.

3) Remove compressor-to-bracket bolts. Remove engine oil tube support bracket bolt and nut from compressor. Remove clutch ground wire and remove compressor. Drain and measure oil in compressor.

Installation (General Motors "G" Models)

Replace oil in compressor with same amount as that removed. Reverse removal procedures, installing new "O" rings on connectors. Evacuate and charge system.

GENERAL SERVICE SPECIFICATIONS

REFRIGERANT CAPACITY

O.E.M. REFRIGERANT TABLE

Application	Capacity (Lbs.)
Chrysler Corp.	
Van Models	
W/Standard System	3
W/Auxiliary Rear System	4
All Other Models	2 5/8
Ford	
Van Models	
W/Standard System	3 1/2
W/Auxiliary Rear System	4 1/4
All Other Models	3 1/2
General Motors	
Standard System	
"C" & "K" Models	3 3/4
"G" Models	3
"S" Models	2 1/2
Overhead System	
"C" & "K" Models	5 1/4
"G" Models	5
Jeep Corp.	
"CJ" & Scrambler Models	2 1/2
Cherokee, Truck & Wagoneer Models	2 1/4

COMPRESSOR BELT TENSION

BELT ADJUSTMENT TABLE (TENSION IN LBS.) [1]

Application	New Belt	Used Belt
Chrysler Corp. [2]	1/4-1/2"	1/4-5/16"
Ford		
Ranger	160-190	130-160
All Other Models		
5-Rib Belt	110-140	110-130
6-Rib Belt	140-170	140-160
General Motors		
"S" Models	145	65-100
All Others		
Gas Engines	145	65-100
Diesel Engine	175	55-100
Jeep	125-155	90-115

[1] — Using standard strand tension gauge unless otherwise indicated.

[2] — Chrysler Corp. recommends adjusting belt tension using the deflection method. Deflection is measured under a 10 pound load.

Cruise Control Systems

CHRYSLER CORP.

Dodge, Plymouth

DESCRIPTION

System is electrically-actuated and vacuum-operated. Turn signal lever on steering column incorporates a slide switch.

The switch has "OFF", "ON", and "RESUME SPEED" positions. A speed set button is located in the end of lever. System will not function under 30 MPH.

OPERATION

ENGAGING SYSTEM

Move slide switch to "ON" position, attain desired speed, and then momentarily depress and release speed set button.

Remove foot from accelerator, and speed will be maintained at selected level. Moving slide switch from "OFF" to "ON" while car is in motion establishes memory without system engagement at that speed.

DISENGAGING SYSTEM

Normal brake application or a soft tap on brake pedal will disengage control unit, without erasing speed memory. Moving slide switch to "OFF" or turning ignition off also disengages system, but also erases speed memory.

RESUMING SPEED

Move slide switch to "RESUME" position.

CHANGING SPEED SETTING

To increase speed, accelerate to desired speed, and momentarily depress and release speed set button. When unit is engaged, tapping button will increase speed in small amounts. To decrease speed, tap brake pedal lightly to disengage system.

When desired speed has been obtained, depress and release speed set button. Decrease in speed can also be obtained by holding set button depressed, until desired speed is attained. Releasing button engages system at that speed.

ACCELERATING FOR PASSING

Depress accelerator as necessary. When passing is completed, release accelerator. Vehicle will return to previous speed.

TROUBLE SHOOTING

NO SPEED CONTROL WHEN BUTTON IS PRESSED

Slide switch in "OFF" position. Fuse blown. Faulty electrical circuit. Vacuum leak. Insufficient brake switch clearance. Speed control throttle cable disconnected.

NO RESUME WHEN SLIDE SWITCH IS MOVED

Insufficient movement of slide switch. Faulty electrical circuit.

NO AUTOMATIC RELEASE WITH BRAKE PEDAL DEPRESSED

Speed control cable kinked or damaged. Improper adjustment of brake switch. Faulty electrical circuit.

SPEED CONTROL ENGAGES WITHOUT ACTUATING SPEED SET BUTTON

Faulty electrical circuit.

CARBURETOR DOES NOT RETURN TO NORMAL IDLE

Speed control cable kinked or damaged. Speed control cable improperly adjusted. Standard throttle linkage faulty.

SPEEDOMETER NOISE, EXCESSIVE NEEDLE FLUTTER OR ERRATIC SERVO LOCK-IN PERFORMANCE

Speedometer cable kinked or damaged. Cable core bent or too long. Cable ferrule nut loose at speedometer head, transmission, or speed control servo. No lubrication on speedometer cable or core. Noisy speedometer head assembly.

SPEED SETTING AFTER LOCK-IN TOO HIGH OR TOO LOW

Improper speed control throttle cable adjustment. Vacuum leak. Improper speed control lock-in adjustment.

UNIT DISENGAGES ON ROUGH ROAD

Insufficient brake switch clearance.

RESUME SPEED POSSIBLE BELOW 20 MPH

Faulty low speed inhibit switch in servo unit. Faulty electrical circuit.

Fig. 1: Wiring Diagram of Chrysler Corp. Speed Control System

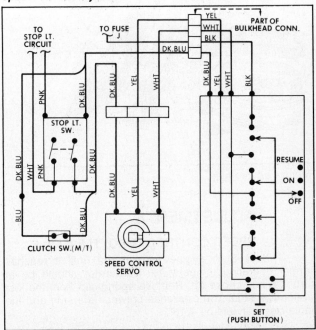

Cruise Control Systems
CHRYSLER CORP. (Cont.)

SPEED CONTROL ENGAGES WHEN ENGINE IS STARTED OR DOES NOT DISENGAGE WITH PEDAL DEPRESSED

Faulty electrical circuit.

TESTING

SPEED CONTROL SWITCH

1) Disconnect 4-wire connector at steering column. Connect a 12-volt positive source to Black wire terminal in speed control harness connector (male). With switch in "ON" position, connect a test lamp between connector Yellow wire and ground. Lamp should light, and then go out when "SPEED SET" button is depressed.

2) Move test lamp lead to connector Blue wire. Lamp should light with switch in "ON" position, and go out when switch is turned to "OFF" position. With switch in "ON" position, move test lamp lead to connector White wire. Lamp should light by either depressing "SPEED SET" button or by moving switch to "RESUME" position.

BRAKE SWITCH

1) Disconnect double connector at switch pigtail and connect a 12-volt source to either terminal, then connect a test lamp from other terminal to ground.

2) Test lamp should light with brake pedal in normal position. If switch is correctly adjusted, test lamp light should go out when brake pedal is depressed a maximum of 3/8" (10 mm).

Fig. 2: Adjusting Servo Throttle Cable

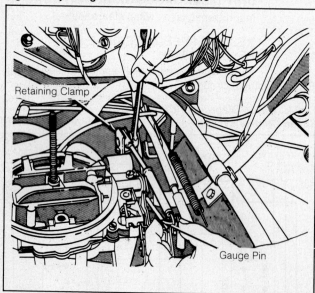

Remove all free play.

ADJUSTMENTS

SPEED CONTROL THROTTLE CABLE

1) Start engine and let run until it reaches normal operating temperature. Carburetor should be at curb idle and choke off. Remove spring clip from the lost motion link stud. The clearance between the stud and the cable clevis should be 1/16".

2) Insert a gauge pin between the cable clevis and stud. Loosen the clip at cable support bracket. Pull all slack out of the cable, but do not move away from curb idle position. Tighten clip at support bracket to 45 INCH lbs. Remove gauge pin and install spring clip in stud of lost motion link.

BRAKE LIGHT/SPEED CONTROLS SWITCH

1) Loosen switch mounting bracket. Insert .140" (3.6 mm) feeler gauge between brake push rod and switch, with brake pedal in fully released position.

2) Push switch bracket assembly toward brake push rod, until plunger is fully depressed and switch body contacts spacer. Tighten switch bracket bolt to 100 INCH lbs. (11 N.m). Remove feeler gauge.

SERVO UNIT LOCK-IN SCREW

NOTE: Lock-in accuracy will be affected by engine being out of tune, adverse power-to-weight ratio, and improper slack in throttle control cable.

1) If speed drops more than 2 to 3 MPH when speed control is activated, lock-in adjusting screws should be turned counterclockwise approximately 1/4 turn for each 1 MPH correction required.

2) If speed increases more than 2 to 3 MPH, turn screw clockwise approximately 1/4 turn for each 1 MPH correction required. If screw is loose, ensure a snug fit by staking side of servo housing adjacent to screw.

CAUTION: Screw should never be turned more than 2 turns in either direction or damage to servo unit may occur.

Fig. 3: Adjusting Lock-In Screw

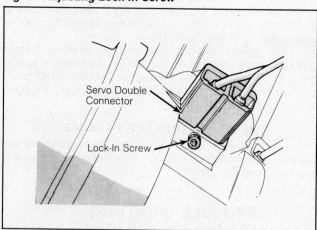

Do not adjust more than 2 turns in either direction.

FORD

DESCRIPTION

System consists of "ON-OFF", "SET-ACCEL", "COAST", and "RESUME" switches, servo assembly, speed control sensor, clutch position sensor switch (man. trans.), amplifier, wire harness, vacuum dump valve, and vacuum hoses to connect components.

The switches are located in steering wheel spokes. The amplifier is located under the instrument panel, and the servo assembly is attached to the engine intake manifold. The speed sensor is located on the left side of the dash panel.

OPERATION

This system is operational at speeds over 30 MPH. When "ON-OFF" switch is actuated to "ON" position and "SET-ACCEL" switch is activated, the vehicle speed will be maintained until a new speed is set, the brake pedal is depressed, the clutch pedal is depressed (man. trans.), or the system is turned off.

The clutch position sensor switch (man. trans.) disengages the speed control, preventing engine overspeed when the clutch pedal is depressed.

To decrease set speed, apply brake and reset speed, using the preceding method, or depress the "COAST" switch. When the vehicle has slowed to the desired speed, release switch. The new speed is set into system.

To increase set speed, accelerate until desired speed is reached, then depress and release the "SET-ACCEL" switch. Speed may also be increased by depressing "SET-ACCEL" switch and holding in that position while vehicle automatically increases in speed.

When desired speed is reached, release switch and new speed will be set into system. When the speed control system is deactivated by depressing brake pedal, vehicle speed before system deactivation may be resumed by depressing "RESUME" switch.

Cruise control memory of vehicle speed and "RESUME" switch will not function, however, if "OFF" switch is depressed, if ignition is turned off, or if vehicle speed drops below 30 MPH.

TESTING

NOTE: **Horn and/or speed control may operate intermittently if ground brush is missing.**

CONTROL SWITCH

Bronco II & Ranger

1) Check the main feed fuse and brake lamp fuse. Replace if necessary. Remove steering wheel cover. With ignition "OFF", connect ohmmeter to the Purple/Orange hash wire and the Black wire of switch connector at steering wheel. Depress the "ON" switch.

2) Ohmmeter should read 0-1 ohm. If reading is not correct, replace switch assembly. Clean brush assembly and slip rings with solvent and lubricate. Reinstall steering wheel. Depress remaining switches and check resistances against table.

3) If any values are not correct, replace switch assemblies. Turn ignition switch "OFF". Connect a voltmeter to the Blue/Black hash wire of connector at steering wheel. Turn ignition switch to "ON" or "ACC". Voltmeter should read about 7.8 volts. Depress "ON" switch.

CONTROL SWITCH RESISTANCES

Switch Position	Ohms
"OFF"	0-1
"SET ACCEL"	646-714
"COAST"	114-126
"RESUME"	2090-2310

4) Voltmeter should read approximately 12.0 volts. If voltages are correct, switches and wiring are okay. If either voltage is not read correctly, turn ignition "OFF". Disconnect ground brush assembly from wiring harness and connect ohmmeter to White/Purple hash wire and Black wire at brush assembly pigtail.

5) Depress "ON" switch. Ohmmeter should read 0-1 ohm. Turn the steering wheel while keeping the "ON" switch depressed. Check for fluctuations in reading. Connect the ohmmeter to the Light Blue/White hash and Black wire at brush assembly pigtail.

6) Check for resistance values as listed in Control Switch Resistances table. Turn steering wheel while testing and check for fluctuations. If fluctuations are noted, remove wheel and clean and lubricate brushes and slip rings. If no resistances are read, replace ground brush assembly.

7) If resistances are correct and no fluctuations occur, switches and ground brushes are okay. If replacement of switch assembly does not produce correct results, check slip ring for shorts. If necessary, replace entire wheel assembly.

All Other Models

1) Disconnect 6-way connector at amplifier. Check battery voltage at Light Blue/Black hash wire when "ON" switch is depressed. Battery voltage should be available from Light Blue/Black hash wire leading from control switches.

2) Connect an ohmmeter between Light Blue/Black hash wire and ground. Check wire for continuity to ground with "OFF" switch depressed. If resistance higher than 1 ohm is found, the wiring, slip rings or switch is at fault, or steering column may not be properly grounded.

3) To check steering column ground, connect an ohmmeter between a good body ground and steering column upper flange. Resistance should be less than 1/2 ohm. Rotate steering wheel, and check flexible coupling resistance. If resistance higher than 3 ohms is noted, clean horn brush contacts and ground brush.

4) A resistance less than 1 ohm must be obtained before performing the remaining tests. With ohmmeter connected between the Light Blue/Black hash wire and ground, depress the "SET-ACCEL" switch. A reading of approximately 680 ohms should be indicated on the ohmmeter.

5) Depress "COAST" switch and a reading of approximately 120 ohms should be indicated on ohmmeter. Depress and hold "RESUME" switch. A reading of approximately 2200 ohms should be indicated.

SPEED SENSOR

1) Disconnect sensor wires from amplifier, and connect an ohmmeter between wire connector terminals (Dark Green stripe and Black on Van models, Dark Green/White stripe and Black on all other models) at sensor end. A reading of about 40 ohms should be obtained.

2) A reading of "zero" ohms indicates a shorted coil. A maximum reading indicates an open coil. Replace sensor in either case. If reading is 40 ohms and speedometer operates properly, speed sensor is probably good. A new sensor can be substituted to check for proper operation.

SERVO ASSEMBLY

1) Disconnect ball chain from throttle linkage (if equipped). Separate 8-way connector at amplifier, then connect an ohmmeter between the Orange/Yellow hash wire and Gray/Black hash wire at the connector. A resistance of 40-125 ohms should be obtained.

2) Connect ohmmeter between Orange/Yellow hash wire and White/Pink hash wire at connector. A resistance of approximately 60-190 ohms should be obtained on Vans, and 60-90 on all other models. Reconnect the ball chain to carburetor. Start the engine with the servo-to-amplifier connector disconnected. Verify that engine vacuum exceeds 2.5 in. Hg.

3) Connect Orange/Yellow hash wire of servo to battery positive terminal. Connect White/Pink hash wire to ground, and then momentarily touch Gray/Black hash wire of servo to ground. Servo throttle actuator should tighten bead chain and open throttle.

4) Throttle should hold in that position or slowly release tension on chain. When White/Pink hash wire is removed from ground, servo should release bead chain tension immediately. If servo fails any of the preceding tests, replace the servo.

5) If Orange/Yellow hash wire is shorted to either White/Pink hash wire or Gray/Black hash wire, it may be necessary to replace amplifier.

Fig. 1: Typical Servo and Bracket Installation

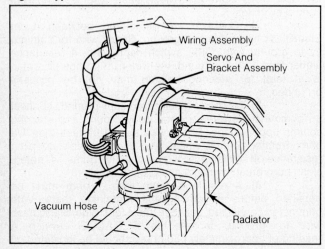

Wiring Assembly

Servo And Bracket Assembly

Vacuum Hose

Radiator

V8 with dual batteries shown, others similar.

AMPLIFIER

CAUTION: DO NOT use a test light to perform amplifier tests, as excessive current draw will damage electronic components. Use only a voltmeter of 5000 ohm/volt rating or higher.

"ON" Circuit Test
Bronco II & Ranger

1) Turn "ON" the ignition switch and connect a voltmeter between the White/Purple hash wire and ground in the 6-pin connector in the amplifier. Connect voltmeter between Light Blue/Black hash wire and ground in amplifier 6-pin connector.

2) The voltmeter should read battery voltage when the "ON" switch is depressed. If voltage is not available, perform control switch test. Release the "ON" switch. The voltmeter should read 7.8 volts. If meter reads 0, check ground on amplifier.

3) If there is no ground on the amplifier, check the system ground connection and wiring. Also check No. 1 and 6 fuses and/or temporarily install a known good amplifier and recheck for good "ON" circuit.

All Other Models

1) Turn ignition "ON", and connect a voltmeter between ground and Light Blue/Black hash wire at amplifier 6-way connector. Voltmeter should read 12 volts when "ON" switch in steering wheel is depressed and held. If no voltage is available, conduct Horn Relay Circuit Test and Control Switch Test.

2) Release "ON" button. A 7.8 volt reading should remain on voltmeter indicating the "ON" circuit is engaged. If voltage does not remain, check for ground at amplifier, fuse and/or circuit breaker. Insert a known good amplifier and recheck "ON" circuit if necessary.

"OFF" Circuit Test

1) With ignition "ON" and voltmeter connected to Light Blue/Black hash wire at amplifier 6-way connector, depress the "OFF" switch on steering wheel. Voltage should drop to zero indicating "ON" circuit is de-energized.

2) If voltage does not drop to zero, perform Control Switch Test. If switches test good, install a known good amplifier and retest.

"SET-ACC" Circuit Test

1) With ignition "ON" and voltmeter connected to Light Blue/Black hash wire at amplifier 6-way connector, depress the "ON" switch, then hold "SET-ACC" button on steering wheel.

2) Voltmeter should indicate approximately 4.5 volts. Rotate steering wheel, and watch voltmeter for variation. If voltage varies more than .5 volts, perform Control Switch Test.

"COAST" Circuit Test

1) With ignition "ON" and voltmeter connected to Light Blue/Black hash wire at amplifier 6-way connector, depress the "ON" switch and hold "COAST" button down on steering wheel.

2) Voltmeter should indicate about 1.5 volts. If all functions check good, perform Servo Assembly Test. Insert a known good amplifier, and recheck system if necessary.

NOTE: DO NOT substitute a new amplifier until actuator coils have been tested. See Servo Assembly Test.

"RESUME" Circuit Test

1) With ignition "ON" and voltmeter leads connected to ground and to Light Blue/Black hash wire at amplifier 6-way connector, depress and hold "RESUME" switch. Voltmeter should indicate approximately 6.5 volts.

2) If all functions check good, perform Servo Assembly Test. Insert a known good amplifier, and recheck system if necessary.

HORN RELAY CIRCUIT TEST

NOTE: Electrical connectors must remain connected during horn relay testing.

FORD (Cont.)

All Except Bronco II & Ranger

1) Locate Yellow wire on Vans or Yellow/Light Blue dot wire on Bronco and Pickups at connector "X". Check for battery voltage on pin side of connector. *See Fig. 2.*

2) Locate Blue/Yellow stripe wire on Vans or Dark Blue wire on Bronco and Pickups at connector "Y". Check for battery voltage on socket side of connector. With voltmeter still connected to socket, depress horn switch.

3) Horn should sound, but voltmeter should indicate zero volts. If voltmeter still indicates battery voltage when horn switch is depressed, check horn switch or steering column wiring for an open circuit.

4) To by-pass horn switch and check horn relay, momentarily ground Blue/Yellow stripe wire on Vans or Dark Blue wire on Bronco and Pickups on socket side of connector "Y".

5) If horn still does not sound, check Yellow/Green stripe wire on Vans or Yellow/Light green wire on Bronco and Pickups at connector "X" for battery voltage while relay is activated. If battery voltage is present when relay is activated, an open circuit is present between connector "X" and horn.

6) If battery voltage is present in step **1)** and horn relay failed to operate in step **3)**, replace relay.

CLUTCH SWITCH TEST
Bronco & Pickups With Man. Trans.

NOTE: **Switch operates magnetically. Do not use magnetized tools near switch. Use only a**

voltmeter of 5000 ohm/volt rating or higher to test switch. Test lamp will not indicate switch condition.

1) Check if clutch switch plunger is depressed (switch closed) when clutch pedal is released. Cruise control will not operate unless this condition exists.

2) Disconnect clutch switch connector from speed control harness connector, and connect an ohmmeter to switch connector terminals. With clutch pedal released in "full-up" position and switch plunger depressed (switch closed), resistance should be less than 5 ohms.

3) With clutch pedal depressed and switch plunger fully extended (switch open), resistance should be "infinity".

BRAKE STOP LIGHT SWITCH & CIRCUIT TEST

NOTE: **This test should be performed whenever brake application will not disengage speed control. If both stop lights are not working it will cause speed control malfunctions.**

1) Check for stop light operation with a maximum brake pedal effort of 6 lbs. (2.7 kg). Check brake pedal actuation and stop light switch if pedal effort required is excessive. If stop lights operate correctly, check battery voltage at Black/Green stripe wire at 6-way connector.

2) Depress pedal until stop lights are on, and check voltage at Red/Black stripe wire at 6-way connector. If voltage readings differ by more than 1.5 volts, high

Fig. 2: Wiring Diagram of Ford Cruise Control System

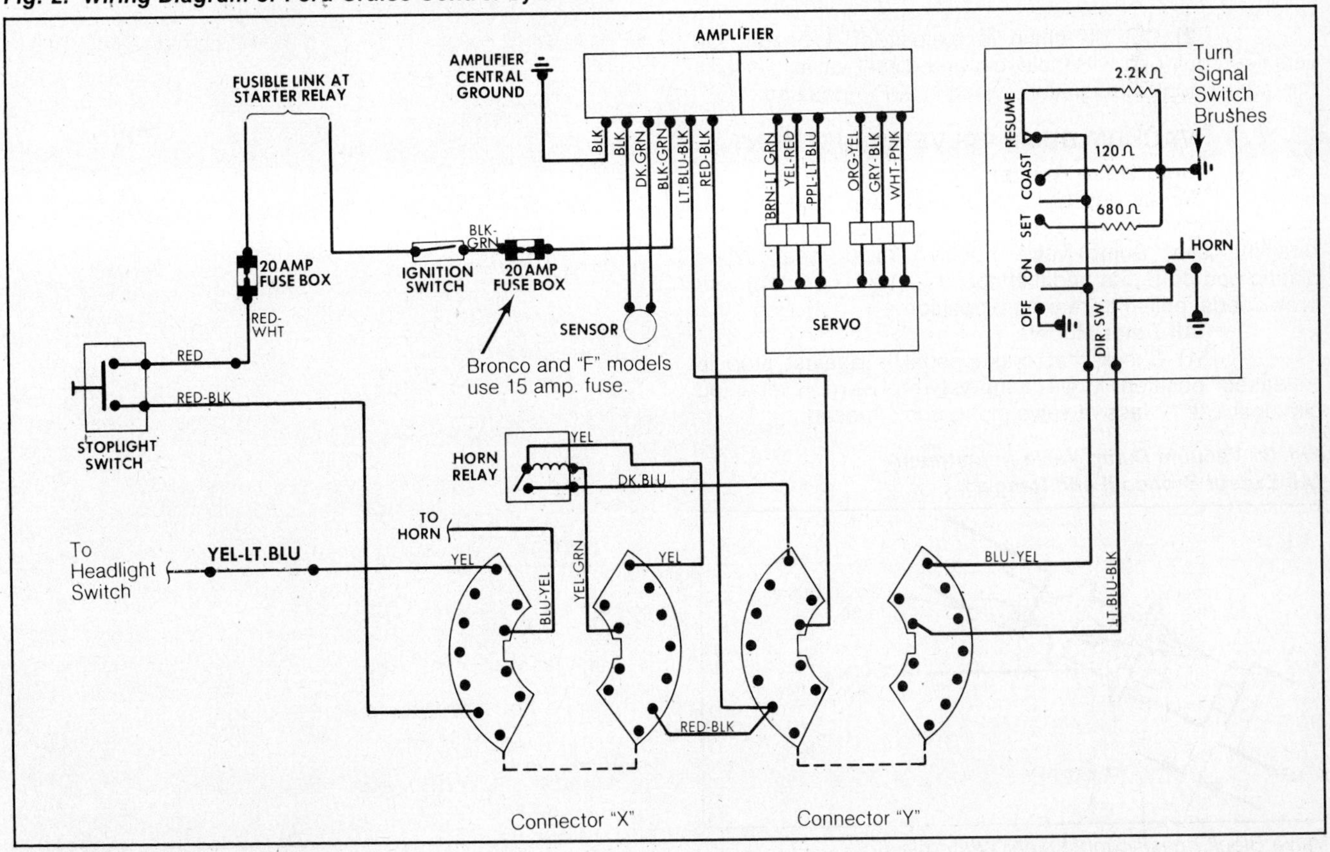

Van models diagram illustrated.

resistance exists in stop light circuit and must be corrected. If stop lights do not work, the stop light switch, supply circuit and bulbs must be checked for correct operation.

VACUUM DUMP VALVE TEST

1) Vacuum dump valve should be checked whenever brake application does not release speed control. Disconnect vacuum hose from the dump valve to the servo at the servo. Connect hand vacuum pump to hose and pump up a vacuum.

2) If vacuum cannot be obtained, the hose or dump valve leaks and should be replaced. Depress brake pedal. Vacuum should be released. If not, adjust or replace dump valve.

ADJUSTMENT

ACTUATOR CABLE

Bronco II & Ranger

Remove cable retaining clip. Disengage throttle positioner. Set carburetor at hot idle. Pull on actuator cable near servo to take up slack. Maintain light tension on cable. While holding cable, insert cable retaining clip and snap securely.

LINKAGE ADJUSTMENT

All Except Bronco II & Ranger

1) Adjust bead chain to obtain .06-.25" (1.6-6.4 mm) actuator arm free travel when engine is at hot idle. Adjustment should be made to eliminate as much slack as possible without restricting carburetor lever from returning to idle.

2) Cut off chain in excess of 4 beads. On vehicles equipped with solenoid anti-diesel valve, perform this adjustment with ignition switch in "OFF" position.

VACUUM DUMP VALVE ADJUSTMENT

Bronco II & Ranger

Firmly depress brake pedal and hold in position. Push in dump valve until valve collar bottoms against retaining clip. Dump valve housing must clear White plastic pad on brake pedal by .05-.10" (1.27-2.54 mm) with brake pedal pulled to rearmost position.

All Other Models

1) Check that brake pedal is against stop in "released" position. Move dump valve forward in retaining clip until 1/8" or less of valve plunger is exposed.

Fig. 3: Vacuum Dump Valve Adjustment (All Except Bronco II and Ranger)

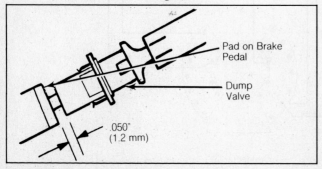

Valve Black housing must clear White plastic on brake pedal pad.

2) Tip of valve plunger should contact brake pedal adapter. Check again if brake pedal is against stop in "released" position. Step on brake pedal. If vacuum still does not release, replace vacuum dump valve.

Fig. 4: Wiring Diagram of Ford Cruise Control System

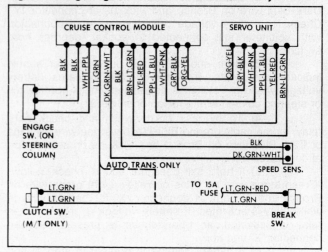

Bronco II and Ranger diagram illustrated.

GENERAL MOTORS CUSTOM CRUISE III

DESCRIPTION

System uses manifold vacuum to power a throttle servo unit. When speed adjustment is necessary, the servo moves the throttle by receiving a varying amount of controlled vacuum from a transducer.

The speedometer cable from transmission drives the transducer. A cable from the transducer drives instrument panel speedometer. There are 2 control switches operating speed control. The first is a "CRUISE" slide switch with "OFF", "ON" and "RESUME" positions.

The second is a "SET-COAST" button switch located on the end of turn signal lever. It controls engagement of transducer. Two brake release switches are provided.

An electric switch disengages transducer. A vacuum valve (switch) decreases vacuum in the servo unit to quickly return throttle to idle position when the brake pedal or clutch is depressed.

OPERATION

This system is designed to operate at speeds above 25 MPH. "CRUISE" switch must be in "ON" position to activate speed control system. Driver accelerates to desired speed, then partially depresses and slowly releases speed control "SET-COAST" switch button.

To change speed setting to higher speed, depress accelerator until desired speed is reached, then fully depress and slowly release "SET-COAST" switch.

To change speed setting to lower speed, depress "SET-COAST" switch fully. Hold in this position until vehicle has decelerated to new desired speed setting. Then, release "SET-COAST" switch slowly to re-engage speed control.

Speed control system is disengaged by applying brakes. To accelerate vehicle to previously set speed in memory, slide "CRUISE" switch to "RESUME" position.

Accelerator pedal may be depressed at any time to override speed control system. Release of accelerator returns speed to previous level. Sliding "SET-COAST" switch to "OFF" position or turning ignition "OFF" will also disengage the system and erase the "RESUME" memory.

PRELIMINARY INSPECTION

1) First make a visual inspection. Check the system to make sure there are no bare, broken or disconnected wires, or pinched, damaged or disconnected vacuum hoses.

2) The servo and throttle linkage should operate freely and smoothly. Servo linkage should be properly adjusted. If the visual inspection does not reveal any problems, further testing is required.

CRUISE SYSTEM INOPERATIVE

Disconnect brake and clutch switch. Check continuity with pedals in "free" position. If continuity shows an open, adjust or replace the brake/clutch switch as necessary. Check the vacuum release valve and the combination vacuum release valve/converter clutch switch for vacuum operation. If leaking, replace. If misadjusted, adjust.

SERVO CHECK

1) Disconnect the electrical connector at the servo. Make sure the connector and pins are free of corrosion. Check resistances. Resistances should be as follows. If not, replace servo unit.

SERVO PIN RESISTANCES

Pin Number	Ohms
A-C	10
E-C	10
B-D	5

2) Turn off ignition switch then disconnect the body harness connector from the Vehicle Speed Sensor buffer amplifier. Connect a Speedometer Signal Generator (J-33431) to amplifier connector. Disconnect the servo throttle linkage at the servo unit. Set the signal generator to 54 MPH and 30 Hertz square wave position. Start the engine and move mode switch slider to "ON" position.

3) Depress and release "SET/COAST" switch. Servo should pull to approximately 28-42% of servo position travel and hold. Move cruise lever and slider to "RESUME ACCEL" position and hold for 3 seconds. Servo will pull to the full stroke position and hold.

4) After releasing slider from the "RESUME ACCEL" position, the servo will return to 28-42% of the travel position. Momentarily move the CRUISE lever slider to "RESUME ACCEL" position. Servo will pull to the 28-42% position of travel and hold.

5) If tests in steps **3)** and **4)** do not perform as indicated, check the harness for defects, then make electrical and pneumatic tests as needed. If steps **3)** and **4)** do perform as indicated, a buffer amplifier or pulse modulator generator defect is indicated.

ELECTRICAL CHECK

Check fuse. Check chassis ground and harness. Perform continuity checks with ohmmeter between controller and servo. Check the Mode Control Switches by replacing with a known good switch or test for continuity as listed in Mode Control Switch Continuity table.

Fig. 1: Mode Control Switch Wire Identification

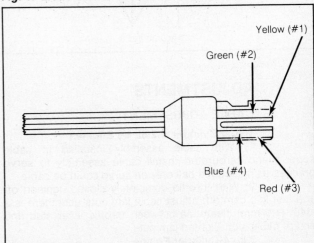

MODE CONTROL SWITCH CONTINUITY

SET/COAST SWITCH	POSITION SLIDER	1-2	1-3	1-4	2-3	2-4	3-4
Normal	Off	O	O	O	O	O	O
Normal	On	O	O	O	O	C	O
Normal	R/A	C	O	C	O	C	O
Depressed	Off	O	O	O	C	O	O
Depressed	On	O	O	O	C	C	C
Depressed	R/A	C	C	C	C	C	C

O = Open, C = Closed

PNEUMATIC CHECK

1) Disconnect bead chain or rod and electrical connector at the servo unit. Start the engine. Apply 12 volts between A and C. Apply 12 volts between E and C. Servo should move full stroke. If not, check the vacuum hoses to the vacuum supply. Remove voltage from E and C.

2) The servo should move a full stroke. If not, disconnect vacuum brake release at the servo and plug the servo. Momentarily apply 12 volts between E and C to allow the servo to full stroke. If the servo holds its position, adjust the brake vacuum release valve or replace the valve. If no defect is found in any of the tests, replace the electronic controller.

Fig. 2: Servo Terminal Lettering

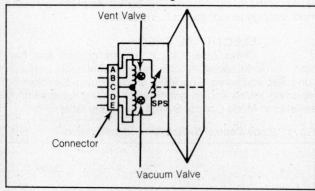

ADJUSTMENTS

CABLE ADJUSTMENT

1.9L 4-Cylinder & 2.8L V6 Engines

1) With cable assembly installed to cable support and carburetor, install cable assembly to servo bracket, using second ball only on servo chain on cable.

2) With throttle completely closed (ignition off and fast idle cam off) adjust cable jam nuts until there is a .040" (1.0 mm) clearance between throttle lever stud and end of cable slot. Tighten jam nuts.

2.0L 4-Cylinder Engine

1) With cable assembly installed to cable support and carburetor, install cable assembly to servo bracket, using second ball only on servo chain on cable.

2) With throttle completely closed (ignition off and fast idle cam off) adjust cable jam nuts until cable

sleeve at carburetor is tight but not holding throttle open. Tighten jam nuts.

4.0L 6-Cylinder Engine

Using third ball only on servo chain, and with throttle completely closed (ignition off and fast idle cam off) adjust cable jam nuts until there is a .040" (1.0 mm) clearance between stud pin and end of slot. Tighten jam nuts.

4.8L 6-Cylinder Engine

With cable assembly installed and using second ball only on servo chain, install servo assembly chain on cable assembly. With throttle completely closed, (ignition and fast idle cam off), adjust cable assembly jam nuts until there is .040" (1.0 mm) clearance between lever pin and end of cable assembly slot. Tighten cable assembly jam nuts.

SERVO ASSEMBLY TO CARBURETOR

All Gasoline V8 Engines

With ignition off and fast idle cam off (throttle completely closed), adjust length so that rod assembles over end of stud. Install retainer.

SERVO ASSEMBLY ROD LINK ADJUSTMENT

6.2L V8 Diesel Engine

With engine not running and idle screw against stop, assemble lower end of rod link to throttle lever and upper end to hole closest to servo which will provide a minimum of .040" (1.0 mm) slack.

Fig. 3: General Motors Custom Cruise III Wiring Diagram

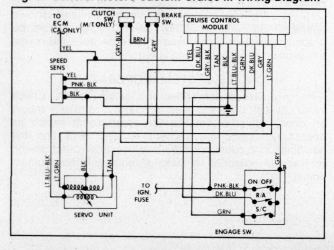

JEEP CRUISE COMMAND

All Models

DESCRIPTION

Jeep vehicles use an electro-mechanical servo system. The system consists of an electronic regulator, speed sensor, servo, control switch assembly, vacuum storage can, check valve and release system. Release system consists of a mechanical vacuum vent valve and brake and clutch (if equipped) switch.

OPERATION

Cruise Command control is an integral part of the directional switch lever and consists of 2 separate switches. The first is "ON-OFF" and "RESUME" slide switch located on the flat of directional switch lever.

Second is a push button switch located at the end of directional switch lever. To engage system, move slide switch to "ON" position and accelerate to desired speed. Depress and release button on end of switch lever. System will now maintain selected speed.

System will automatically disengage when brake pedal is depressed. It can be re-engaged to previously selected speed by accelerating to 30 MPH and moving slide switch to "RESUME" position, then releasing switch.

NOTE: **When slide switch is moved to "OFF" position, pre-set speed of "RESUME" function is canceled and must be reset when system is reactivated.**

A higher speed can be set by pressing on accelerator pedal until new speed is reached and then pushing control button. A lower speed can be achieved by lightly depressing brake pedal, allowing vehicle to slow to desired speed and then depressing and releasing push button. Operation of individual components is as follows:

ELECTRONIC REGULATOR

The electronic regulator receives an input voltage representing vehicle speed from the speed sensor, driven by the speedometer cable. The regulator has a low speed circuit that prevents operation at speeds below 30 mph.

SPEED SENSOR

The speed sensor is installed between the upper and lower speedometer cables. It converts speedometer revolutions into a voltage input for the regulator.

SERVO

The servo is controlled by the regulator and uses manifold vacuum to control the throttle. A bead-link chain connects the servo cable to the throttle linkage.

CONTROL SWITCH

The control switch assembly is an integral part of the turn signal switch lever.

RELEASE SYSTEM

The release system deactivates the Cruise Command system when the brake pedal or clutch pedal is depressed. Either a servo vent valve or a mechanical vacuum vent switch admits atmospheric pressure into the servo when the brake pedal is depressed.

TROUBLE SHOOTING

SYSTEM WILL NOT ENGAGE

Restricted vacuum hose or no vacuum. Control switch or regulator defective. Speed sensor defective. Brake light or brake light switch defective. Brake light switch wire defective. Open circuit between brake light switch and brake lights. Mechanical vent valve position improperly adjusted.

"RESUME" FEATURE INOPERATIVE

Defective servo ground connection. Control switch defective. Accelerate circuit in regulator inoperative. Defective control switch.

"ACCELERATE" FUNCTION INOPERATIVE

"ACCELERATE" circuit in regulator inoperative. Defective control switch.

SYSTEM RE-ENGAGES WHEN BRAKES OR CLUTCH RELEASED

Defective regulator. Mechanical vent valve not opening. Kink in mechanical vent valve hose. Brake light or clutch switch defective.

CARBURETOR THROTTLE DOES NOT RETURN TO IDLE POSITION

Improper linkage adjustment. Improper chain adjustment.

ROAD SPEED CHANGES MORE THAN 2 MPH WHEN SETTING SPEED

Centering screw adjustment set wrong.

Fig. 1: Wiring Diagram for Jeep Cruise Command

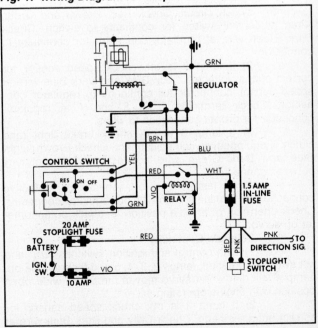

JEEP CRUISE COMMAND (Cont.)

SYSTEM DISENGAGES ON LEVEL ROAD WITHOUT APPLYING BRAKE OR CLUTCH

Loose wire connection. Loose vacuum hose connection. Servo linkage broken. Defective brake light or clutch switch.

ERRATIC OPERATION

Reverse polarity. Servo defective. Regulator is defective.

VEHICLE CONTINUES TO ACCELERATE WHEN "SET" BUTTON IS RELEASED

Servo or regulator defective.

SYSTEM ENGAGES BUT SLOWLY LOOSES SET SPEED

Air leak at vacuum hose. Air leak on vent valve on brake or clutch pedal.

TESTING

All tests of system should be performed as part of diagnosis of malfunction and to determine procedure(s) required for system repair.

CRUISE COMMAND SYSTEM TESTS

Testing is performed with Cruise Command System Tester (AM-PC-1-R). Remove wire harness connector from regulator. Connect Cruise Command System tester to wire harness connector. Perform the following tests. Various tester lamps are associated with specific components, circuits, etc.

Power Source Connection

With ignition switch and control switch "OFF", all test lamps should be off. If 1 or more lamps are on, remove brown wire at regulator connection from direct source of voltage or repair control switch.

System Continuity

1) With ignition and control switch "ON", lamps 1, 2, 3, and 4 should be on. Lamps 5 and 6 should be off. If lamp 1 is off, check for blown fuse in brake light switch to control switch circuit. Check Red, Brown and Green wires at control switch for continuity to switch. Check Dark Green wire at regulator connector for continuity to connector.

2) If lamp 2 is off, check speed sensor for correct output voltage. Check Grey and Dark Blue wire at speed sensor connector for continuity to regulator connector. Check terminals 2, 3, 5 and 7 at regulator connector for proper connection to wires.

3) If lamp 3 is off, check brake light (and clutch, if equipped) switch adjustment. Check Brown, Light Blue and Dark Green wire connections for continuity between connectors.

4) If lamp 4 is off, check for defective connection at terminals 2 and 11 on regulator connector. Check operation of throttle position feedback potentiometer on servo.

Solenoid Continuity

1) With control and ignition switches "ON" and set switch depressed, lamps 2, 3, 4, 5 and 6 should be on. Lamp 4 will dim when servo moves throttle to wide open position with engine operating.

2) If lamp 2 is off, check speed sensor for correct output voltage. Check Grey and Dark Blue wire at speed sensor connector for continuity to regulator con-

nector. Check terminals 2, 3, 5 and 7 at regulator connector for proper connection to wires.

3) If lamp 3 is off, check brake light (and clutch, if equipped) switch adjustment. Check Brown, Light Blue and Dark Green wire connections for continuity between connectors.

4) If lamp 4 is off, check for defective connection at terminals 2 and 11 on regulator connector. Check operation of throttle position feedback potentiometer on servo.

5) If lamp 5 is off, check for defective connections at terminals 6 and 12 on regulator connector. If necessary, replace defective servo.

6) If lamp 6 is off, check for defective connection at terminals 4 and 12 on regulator connector. If necessary, replace defective servo.

7) If all lamps are off after depressing set speed switch or moving control switch to "RESUME/ACCELERATION" position, check for blown fuse. Check for short circuits in Red, Pink and Brown wire circuits at control switch. If necessary, replace defective servo.

System Disengagement

1) With ignition and control switch "ON" and brake or clutch pedal depressed, lamps 1, 2 and 4 should be on. Lamps 3, 5 and 6 should be off. Lamp 3 should be on when brake or clutch pedal is released.

2) If lamp 2 is off, check speed sensor for correct output voltage. Check Grey and Dark Blue wire at speed sensor connector for continuity to regulator connector. Check terminals 2, 3, 5 and 7 at regulator connector for proper connection to wires.

3) If lamp 3 is off, check brake light (and clutch, if equipped) switch adjustment. Check Brown, Light Blue and Dark Green wire connections for continuity between connectors.

4) If lamp 4 is off, check for defective connection at terminals 2 and 11 on regulator connector. Check operation of throttle position feedback potentiometer on servo.

5) If lamp 3 is off when brake or clutch pedal is released, check brake light (and clutch, if equipped) switch adjustment. Check Brown, Light Blue and Dark Green wire connections for continuity between connectors.

"RESUME/ACCELERATION" Function

1) With ignition and control switchs "ON", move control switch to "RESUME/ACCELERATION" position. Note that when engine is running, servo will move throttle to wide open position.

2) If lamp 2 is off, check speed sensor for correct output voltage. Check Grey and Dark Blue wire at speed sensor connector for continuity to regulator connector. Check terminals 2, 3, 5 and 7 at regulator connector for proper connection to wires.

3) If lamp 3 is off, check brake light (and clutch, if equipped) switch adjustment. Check Brown, Light Blue and Dark Green wire connections for continuity between connectors.

4) If lamp 4 is off, check for defective connection at terminals 2 and 11 on regulator connector. Check operation of throttle position feedback potentiometer on servo.

5) If lamp 6 is off, check for defective connection at terminals 4 and 12 on regulator connector. If necessary, replace defective servo.

6) If all lamps are off after depressing set speed switch or moving control switch to "RESUME/ACCELERATION" position, check for blown fuse. Check for

short circuits in Red, Pink and Brown wire circuits at control switch. If necessary, replace defective servo.

SPEED SENSOR TEST

1) Disconnect wire harness connector at speed sensor. Connect a voltmeter set on low AC scale to wire terminals from speed sensor.

2) Raise front and rear wheels of vehicle off ground and support vehicle with safety stands. Operate engine (wheels spinning freely) at 30 mph and note voltage.

3) Voltage should be approximately 0.9 volts. Increases of 0.1 volts per each 10 mph increase in speed should also be noticed. Turn off engine and stop wheels. Lower vehicle. Connect speed sensor wire harness.

ADJUSTMENT

CENTERING SPRING

Cruise Command system is designed to maintain speed selected by driver, within 2 mph. System operation is checked at 50 mph. Speed adjustment is made by turning centering adjusting screw on regulator.

If speed control holds speed more than 2 mph above selected speed, turn centering screw counterclockwise a small amount. If engagement speed is 2 or more mph below selected speed, turn centering screw clockwise a small amount.

Fig. 2: Centering Screw Adjustment Location

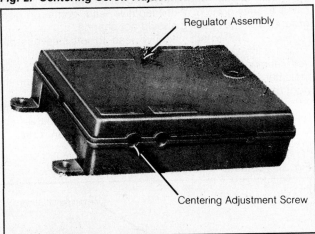

Regulator Assembly

Centering Adjustment Screw

Turn screw clockwise if engagment is too low, counterclockwise if engagement is too high.

VACUUM VENT VALVE

Depress brake or clutch pedal and hold in depressed position. Move vacuum vent valve toward bracket on pedal as far as possible. Release brake or clutch pedal.

CHRYSLER CORP. REAR WINDOW

Van Models

DESCRIPTION

Heated rear window system, available for van models, consists of 2 bus bars, heating elements baked on inside of glass, a control switch, 25-ampere fuse, and a continuous or timed relay.

OPERATION

With ignition and control switch turned "ON", continuous relay will remain on until ignition or switch is turned "OFF". Timed relay will operate 8 1/2 to 11 1/2 minutes. Relay is mounted to right of switch on lower dash panel. An indicator lamp on dash glows when system is in operation.

Fig. 1: Rear Window Defogger Wiring Diagram

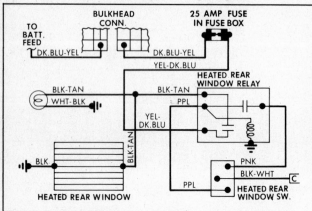

TESTING

CONTROL SWITCH CONTINUITY

For "NORMAL" switch position, there should be continuity between 2 terminals. For "ON" position, there should be continuity between all switch terminals. For "OFF" position, there should be no continuity between terminals.

INDICATOR LIGHT

Disconnect Black/Tan wire from indicator light. Connect jumper wire from "ACC" terminal to Black/Tan wire. Turn ignition to "ACC". Bulb should light.

RELAY

1) Remove relay. On continuous relay, ground housing. On timed relay, ground terminal "G". Connect jumper wire from terminal "B" (Yellow/Dark Blue wire) to terminal "Y" (Pink wire). Connect a 12-volt test lamp from terminal "L" (Black/Tan wire) of relay to ground.

2) Apply 12 volts to terminal "B" (Yellow/Dark Blue wire). Test lamp should not light. If lamp comes on, replace relay.

3) Short terminal "B" (Yellow/Dark Blue wire) and terminal "P" (Ground wire) for a few seconds. Lamp should light and stay on for 8 1/2 to 11 1/2 minutes on timed relays and until turned off on continuous relays. If lamp does not light, replace relay.

Fig. 2: Relay Terminals

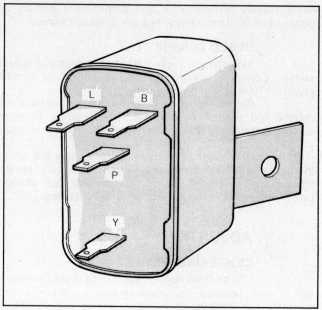

GRID

1) Using a DC voltmeter with a 0-15 volt range, contact bus bar connecting grid lines on right (Feed) side of glass with negative lead of voltmeter. Contact left bus bar with positive lead.

2) Turn ignition and control switches "ON". Voltmeter should read 10-14 volts. Lower voltage indicates a poor ground. With negative lead, contact a good ground. Voltage reading should not change.

3) Contact negative lead to left side bus bar. Touch each grid line at midpoint with positive lead. A 6-volt reading indicates line is good. A reading of 0 volts indicates a break in the line between the midpoint and the right bus bar.

4) A 10-14 volt reading indicates a break between midpoint and left bus bar. Move positive lead toward break and voltage will change when break is crossed.

Fig. 3: Voltmeter Connection for Grid Continuity

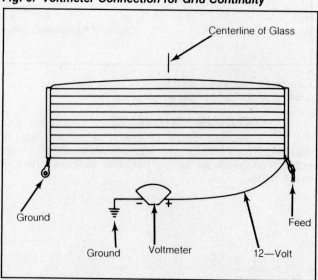

Defoggers

JEEP TAILGATE

Cherokee & Wagoneer

DESCRIPTION

A heated tailgate window defogger system is available on Cherokee and Wagoneer models. The system consists of 2 vertical bus bars and horizontal rows of heating elements fused to inside of glass, a control switch, indicator light, and timer relay.

Braided wire serves as the electrical feed and ground for the grid. The grid feed wire is attached to the timer relay located inside tailgate. The timer relay receives its power from the fuse panel power tailgate terminal. A 30-ampere circuit breaker protects the circuit.

OPERATION

A separate control circuit, connected to the heater control switch, operates the relay and timer. With the control switch on instrument panel and ignition switch "ON", the defogger relay contacts close.

A timer enclosed in the relay case will allow the defogger to operate for about 8 to 12 minutes, depending upon ambient temperature, or until the control switch or ignition switch is turned "OFF". An indicator light on the instrument panel is on when the system is in operation.

NOTE: The defogger switch and electric tailgate switch are serviced as an assembly.

Fig. 1: Wiring Diagram for Jeep Rear Window Defogger

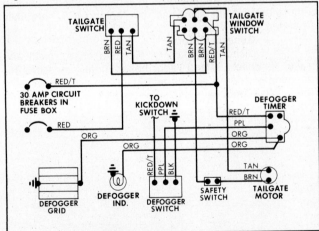

TESTING

CONTROL SWITCH

Turn ignition switch "ON", and press defogger switch. Separate wiring harness at connector under dash. Connect a 12-volt test lamp from Purple wire to ground. Test lamp should light. Turn defogger switch "OFF". Test lamp should not light.

INDICATOR LIGHT

Disconnect Orange wire from lamp. Connect jumper wire from accessory terminal to Orange wire. With ignition turned to "ACCESSORY", lamp should light.

RELAY

1) Attach negative lead of voltmeter to ground. Touch Red wire with voltmeter positive lead. Battery voltage should be indicated. If no voltage is indicated, operate tailgate window.

2) If window operates, the wire between the relay and window switch is open. Touch Orange wire with voltmeter positive lead. No voltage should be indicated. Turn ignition switch "ON". Voltmeter should indicate voltage. If not, relay is defective or not receiving voltage from Purple wire.

3) If relay operates properly, it should remain energized for 8 to 12 minutes before opening. If time period is too short or long, relay is defective. If relay did not energize, connect a jumper wire to a known good 12-volt source in tailgate and touch relay Purple terminal.

4) If relay clicks, trace Purple wire for open or short. If relay does not click, check relay ground. If ground is satisfactory, replace relay.

GRID

1) Use a 12-volt voltmeter, and connect positive lead to right (Feed) side of vertical element on inside of glass. Connect negative lead to left side of vertical element. Voltage should read 11 to 13 volts with ignition "ON".

2) Connect negative lead to ground, disconnect positive lead and touch each grid at center of window.

3) Voltage drop of 6 volts indicates good grid. Voltage drop of 12 volts at center indicates a break in grid between positive lead and ground. No voltage drop at center indicates break in grid between center and feed wire.

4) Exact location of break can be located by moving positive lead to left or right until an abrupt change in voltage is noticed. Repair to grid can then be made.

Fig. 2: Voltmeter Connections and Voltage Drop for Grid Continuity

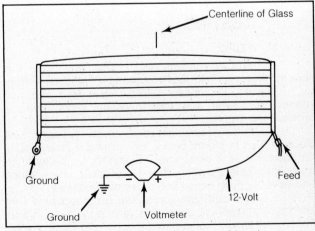

Abrupt voltage change indicates location of break.

DESCRIPTION

Fuel tank selector valves are used in conjunction with auxiliary fuel tanks on Ford Bronco, "F", and "E" models and General Motors "C" and "K" models.

Systems consist of a main and auxiliary fuel tank, a selector valve to route fuel from desired tank through fuel pump, a selector switch to choose tanks, necessary fuel lines, and electrical wiring.

OPERATION

FORD

The electrically-actuated fuel selector valve is spring-loaded. In the de-energized state, it feeds the fuel pump from the front tank on Bronco and "F" models and the rear tank on "E" models.

When activated by a minimum of 9.5 volts by the selector switch, the fuel feed transfers to the rear tank on Bronco and "F" models and to the front tank on "E" models.

GENERAL MOTORS

Two types of valves are used on General Motors trucks. Those models with a fuel return system use a 6-port valve, while those without a fuel return system use a 3-port valve.

Valve operation is the same for both valves. When the instrument panel switch is in the Auxiliary (left-hand) position, selector valve solenoid is energized. When switch is in Main (right-hand) position, selector valve solenoid is de-energized.

The dash switch is energized only when the ignition is "ON". When vehicle is operated in the Auxiliary switch position, fuel in the feed lines as well as return lines (if equipped) will always return to the main tank when ignition is turned off. Operation in the Auxiliary switch position with main tank full will result in overfilling of main tank.

TESTING

FORD

1) Turn ignition switch "ON", and place fuel selector switch on rear for Bronco and "F" models, or front for "E" models. Disconnect selector valve feed wire, and connect a 12-volt test light between wiring harness terminal and ground.

2) If light does not come on, check fuse at fuse block. If fuse is blown, check fuel valve circuit and valve for short. If fuse is okay, check switch for continuity. If no continuity, replace switch. If switch is okay, check wiring and valve for open circuit and repair as necessary.

3) If test light comes on, reconnect feed wire and place a paper clip on end of valve opposite port end. Paper clip should adhere to valve. If not, ground valve case to frame rail with a short piece of wire, and repeat paper clip test.

4) If paper clip does not adhere, replace valve and solenoid assembly. If paper clip adheres, remove valve mounting bolts, and clean mounting surface. Install new mounting bolts that are zinc or cadmium plated.

5) If the paper clip adhered in step **3)**, position selector switch on front for Bronco and "F" models, or rear for "E" models. Pinch off fuel hose from valve to main tank, remove fuel line from carburetor, and place end of fuel line in a container. Remove battery feed from coil, and crank engine.

6) If fuel flows continuously, remove and replace valve solenoid assembly. If no fuel flows into container, release fuel hose and crank engine to reestablish fuel flow.

7) Place selector switch on rear for Bronco and "F" models, or front for "E" models. Pinch off hose from valve to rear tank on Bronco and "F" models, or front tank on "E" models. Crank engine and observe fuel flow.

8) If fuel flows continuously, replace solenoid and valve assembly. If no fuel flows, system is operating correctly and problem has been misdiagnosed.

GENERAL MOTORS

NOTE: Testing procedures for General Motors vehicles were not available from manufacturer.

REMOVAL & INSTALLATION

SELECTOR VALVE

Ford

1) Disconnect fuel hoses from selector valve. Remove electrical connections. Remove nut and ground wire. Remove valve attaching bolts, and remove valve.

2) To install, reverse removal procedures, making sure to attach the ground wire. Specified mounting bolts must be installed, as the solenoid is internally grounded.

General Motors

Disconnect battery. Remove hose shield and brace. Remove fuel and vapor hoses, noting locations for reassembly reference. Remove 2 screws holding valve to frame, and remove valve. To install, reverse removal procedure.

ALL MANUFACTURERS

DESCRIPTION

Ignition switches are typically mounted on steering columns, and are actuated by ignition key locking cylinders.

SERVICING

Chrysler Corp. vehicles, with column-mounted ignition switches and lock cylinders, require that steering wheel and turn signal switch be removed before ignition components are accessible.

On General Motors and Jeep Corp. vehicles, steering column must be removed or lowered. Steering wheel and turn signal switch must be removed before ignition components are accessible.

CAUTION: Lock plate is under strong spring pressure. Do not remove snap ring without using compressor tool. If steering shaft has American threads, use compressor tool J-23653; if shaft has metric threads use Metric Forcing Screw J-23653-4.

Ford vehicles require that steering column be lowered before servicing the ignition switch or lock cylinder.

CAUTION: Some steering columns are collapsible. Special care must be taken to avoid bumping, jolting or hammering on steering shaft and gearshift tube of these columns.

REMOVAL & INSTALLATION

LOCK CYLINDER

Removal (Chrysler Corp.)

1) Remove 2 retaining screws and the lock lever guide plate to expose the lock cylinder release hole. Place cylinder in lock position and remove key.

2) Insert a small diameter screwdriver into lock cylinder release hole and push in to release spring loaded lock retainer. At the same time pull lock cylinder out of hole.

Fig. 1: Typical Column Type Ignition Switch Lock Cylinder Removal

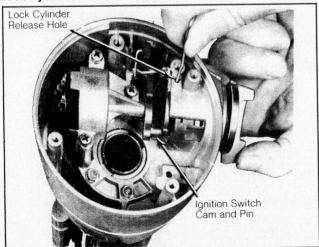

Lock Cylinder Release Hole

Ignition Switch Cam and Pin

On most models, push in to release lock retainer.

Installation

1) Place lock in "LOCK" position and remove key. Insert cylinder into housing. Press cylinder in far enough to contact switch acutator. Press inward, and move switch actuator rod up and down to align parts.

2) When aligned, cylinder will move inward and a spring loaded retainer will snap into place locking cylinder into housing.

Removal (Ford Bronco II & Ranger)

1) Disconnect battery ground. Remove the trim shroud. Remove electrical connector from the key warning switch. Turn the lock cylinder to "RUN" position.

2) Place a 1/8" diameter pin in the hole located in the outer edge of the lock cylinder housing. Depress the retaining pin, and pull out the lock cylinder.

Installation

1) Lubricate the cylinder cavity with Ford Lock Cylinder Lubricant. Turn the lock cylinder to the "RUN" position. Depress the retaining pin and insert it into the lock cylinder housing.

2) Make sure the cylinder is fully seated and aligned into the interlocking washer before turning the key to the "OFF" position. Use the key to rotate the cylinder to ensure correct mechanical operation in all positions.

3) Install with lock cylinder and switch in "LOCK" position, and engage actuator rod in switch. Position switch on column and install retaining nuts, but do not tighten. Move switch up and down along column to locate mid-position of rod lash, and then tighten nuts.

Removal (All Other Ford Models)

1) On non-tilt column models, remove steering wheel and trim pad. Place gear selector in "P" on automatic transmission models (any position on manual transmission models). On all models, insert key and turn cylinder to "ON" position.

2) Insert a 1/8" diameter pin in hole on outside of steering column casting near hazard warning button on tilt models. Insert pin in hole near base of lock cylinder on non-tilt models. On all models, depress pin and pull out on lock cylinder to remove.

Installation

Turn lock cylinder to "ON" position. Depress retaining pin and insert cylinder into housing. Make sure that cylinder is fully seated and aligned with interlocking washer. Turn key, and check operation of lock cylinder.

Removal (General Motors)

Place lock in "RUN" position. Remove lock plate, turn signal switch and buzzer switch. Remove lock retaining screws and lock cylinder.

Installation

Place lock in housing. Turn key to "RUN" position while holding cylinder. Align cylinder with keyway in housing. Push lock in and install retaining screw.

Removal (Jeep)

Place lock in "ON" position (manual transmission) or in "OFF-LOCK" position (automatic transmission). Insert thin tool (machinist's scale or knife blade) into lock cylinder slot. Push in to release spring-loaded lock retainer. Remove lock cylinder from housing.

Installation

1) Insert key in lock. Hold cylinder sleeve, and turn key clockwise until key stops. Align lock cylinder retaining tab with keyway in housing, and insert cylinder into column.

2) Push cylinder in until it contacts lock sector. Rotate cylinder to engage lock sector, and push in until cylinder retaining tab engages in housing groove.

Ignition Switch & Lock Cylinders

ALL MANUFACTURERS (Cont.)

IGNITION SWITCH
Removal (Chrysler Corp.)
Remove lock cylinder. Remove 3 retaining screws and ignition switch assembly.

Installation
To install, position ignition switch to "OFF" position. If vehicle has automatic transmission, place it in "PARK". On all models, feed wires down through space between housing and jacket. Position switch in jacket and tighten 3 mounting screws.

Removal (Ford Bronco II & Ranger)
1) Rotate lock cylinder key to "LOCK" position. Disconnect battery ground. On tilt columns, remove upper extension shroud by squeezing at the 6 and 10 o'clock positions and popping free of the retaining plate at the 3 o'clock position.

2) Remove 2 shroud halves by removing the 2 attaching screws. On all models, disconnect electrical connector from ignition switch. Drill out the 2 break-head bolts holding the ignition switch to lock cylinder with a 1/8" drill bit.

3) Using an easy-out, remove bolts. Disengage the ignition switch from the actuator pin and remove switch.

Installation
1) Rotate ignition key to the "RUN" position. Install switch by aligning the holes on switch casting base with the holes in the lock cylinder housing. Minor movement of the lock cylinder to align the actuator pin with slot in switch carrier may be required.

2) Install the new break-off head bolts and tighten until heads shear off. Connect the electrical connector to the ignition switch. To complete installation, reverse removal procedure.

Removal (All Other Ford Models)
Disconnect battery ground. Remove steering column shroud. Lower column. Disconnect switch wiring at multiple plug. Remove nuts securing switch to steering column. Lift switch vertically to disengage actuator, and remove switch.

Installation
With lock cylinder and switch in "LOCK" position, engage actuator rod in switch. Position switch on column and install retaining nuts, but do not tighten. Move switch up and down along column to locate mid-position of rod lash, and tighten retaining nuts.

Removal (General Motors "S" Series)
Remove attaching screws. Disconnect actuating rod and wiring from switch and remove switch from steering column.

Installation
To install, move switch slider to extreme left position and then 2 detents to the right on non key-release switches. On key release switches, move switch slider to the extreme left position. On all types, position rod in hole and install switch to steering column.

Removal (All Other General Motors Models)
Lower steering column, and support column to avoid causing damage. Remove lock cylinder. Pull switch-actuating rod up until there is a definite stop; then move rod down one detent to place lock in "LOCK" position. Remove 2 switch screws and switch assembly from vehicle.

Installation
Place lock and switch in "LOCK" position. Install actuating rod into switch, and install switch using

mounting screws. Tighten, making sure not to change switch position. To complete installation, reverse removal procedure.

Fig. 2: Rod-Actuated Ignition Switch

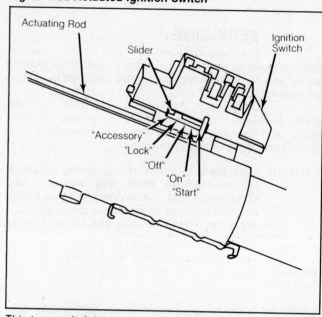

This type switch is common to all models.

Removal (Jeep)
Place lock in "OFF-UNLOCK" position, and remove 2 mounting screws. Disconnect switch from remote rod and harness connector. Remove switch.

Installation
Move switch slider to "ACC" position. Move switch slider back 2 clicks to "OFF-UNLOCK" position. Engage remote rod in switch slider, and position switch on column. Do not move slider. Install and tighten screws.

Power Door Locks

CHRYSLER CORP.

All Models

DESCRIPTION

The electric door lock system is solenoid-actuated at each door. It can be locked or unlocked electrically by operating either left or right front locking knobs.

When electrically-equipped, side and rear doors can be actuated by operation of front locking knobs. All doors must be closed before locking. They can be locked or unlocked manually with key or electrically as described.

The system combines a relay, circuit breaker, and "button" head terminals in door and post panels to combine all door wiring into 1 wiring harness. The relay and circuit breaker are mounted on the steering column support bracket on underside of dash. All components are serviced as complete assemblies.

ELECTRICAL TESTS

1) With battery in normal operating condition and solenoid adjusted properly, connect positive lead of voltmeter to buss bar on relay assembly. Connect negative lead to ground.

2) With no load, voltage should be approximately 12.5 volts. When locks are operated, voltage should be 11 volts. If no voltage is read at relay, test circuit breaker as follows.

3) Connect positive voltmeter lead to light green terminal of circuit breaker, and negative lead to ground. If reading of 12.5 volts is not obtained, connect positive lead to battery side of circuit breaker.

4) If 12.5 volts are now obtained, the circuit breaker is defective and should be replaced. If 12.5 volts are not obtained, check for broken feed wire or loose connection.

5) To check for faulty solenoids, disconnect the solenoid connectors one at a time, while operating the door lock switch. If none of the solenoids work, the problem may be a shorted solenoid or faulty relay.

6) If defective solenoid is found, disconnecting it will allow the remaining solenoids to operate, provided the relay is not damaged.

ADJUSTMENT

DOOR LOCK SOLENOID

Remove door trim panel. Loosen solenoid attaching screws. While pressing down on the lock knob, push up on the solenoid until the solenoid plunger bottoms out in the solenoid. Tighten screws, and test operation before installing trim panel.

REMOVAL & INSTALLATION

DOOR LOCK SOLENOID

1) Remove inside door release handle, window regulator handle and door trim panel.

2) Roll door water shield away from lower rear corner of door to reveal inside panel access opening.

3) Remove solenoid link at solenoid. Disconnect solenoid lead wires. Remove mounting bracket attaching screws, and remove solenoid from mounting.

4) To install, reverse removal procedure and adjust if necessary.

Fig. 2: Chrysler Corp. Light Truck Power Door Lock Wiring Diagram

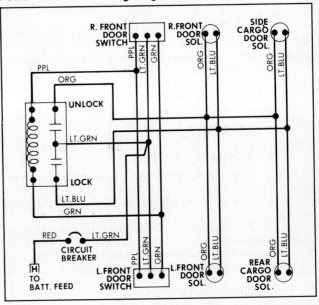

Fig. 1: Solenoid for Electric Door Lock

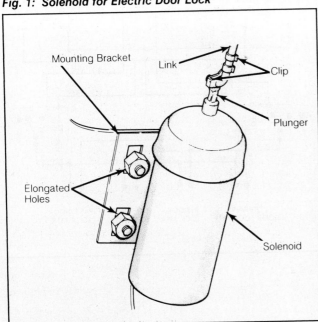

Adjust locks by solenoid position.

Power Door Locks

FORD

DESCRIPTION

The power door lock system uses electric switches, controlled by the front door lock push buttons. Relays direct the current to the door lock actuator motors to lock or unlock the doors.

The system includes contact buttons of the side cargo door and key-locked rear door. The buttons provide an electrical link for actuator motor operation in the remote doors.

REMOVAL & INSTALLATION

ACTUATOR MOTOR

Removal

Remove door trim panel. Disconnect actuator link from door latch. Remove actuator motor and swivel bracket from door by drilling out retaining rivet. Disconnect wiring at connector and remove motor.

Installation

To install, reverse removal procedure, noting that new pop rivet must retain actuator bracket securely.

DOOR LOCK CONTROL SWITCH

Removal & Installation (Bronco & Pickup)

1) To remove control switch, insert a small screwdriver into spring tab slot, located at top and bottom of switch housing. Apply pressure and assembly will pop out.

2) Disconnect housing from wiring connector by separating locking fingers. To install, reverse removal procedure.

Removal (Van)

1) Remove door trim panel. Detach switch from door latch and/or bellcrank. Disengage push button rod from latch.

2) Disengage wiring connector from switch by depressing tab on connector with screwdriver. Pry locking tab up from the flange of the connector, and pull apart.

Installation

To install, reverse removal procedures, making sure that switch is not binding with sheet metal or wires.

TESTING

ACTUATOR MOTOR

1) Apply 12 volts directly to one terminal of the actuator motor connector, and ground the other terminal. The motor should complete its travel in less than one second.

2) Reverse the connections for checking opposite travel. Measure current draw with an ammeter. Motor current draw should not exceed 6.2 amps. Reverse the power and ground leads, and retest opposite side.

WINDOW SWITCH

1) Using a self-powered test light, there should be no continuity between any terminals with the switch in its normal position. With the switch in the down (lock) position, continuity should exist between terminals A and B. See Fig. 2.

2) With the switch in the up (unlock) position, there should be continuity between terminals A and C.

RELAY

1) To perform relay tests, remove both relay connectors. The relays are located on the lower left side of the instrument panel reinforcer. Make sure that terminal 1 of the relay is grounded. If not, check relay case-to-ground screws for tightness.

2) If screws are tight, replace the relay. With a test light connected between terminals 1 and 2, apply power to terminals 2 and 4 of each relay. Do not leave light connected for more than 2 minutes. Test light should light. If not, replace the relay.

Fig. 1: Power Door Lock Relay Terminals

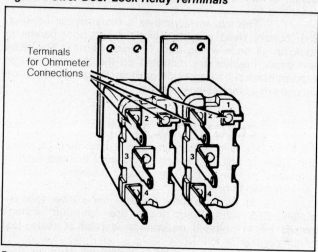

Do not leave test light connected for more than 2 minutes.

Fig. 2: Ford Power Door Lock Schematic

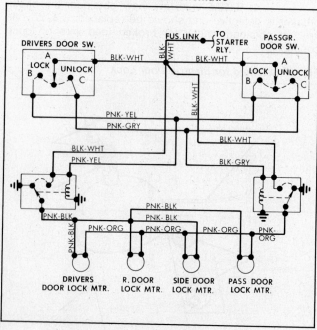

Power Door Locks
GENERAL MOTORS

Chevrolet, GMC

DESCRIPTION

The electric door lock system consists of a lock actuator assembly at each door, switches and a relay. All doors lock and unlock manually or from the door control switches. All components are serviced as complete assemblies.

The motor is a permanent magnet, 12 volt reversible type that is protected by an internal circuit breaker. Circuit breaker may require 1 to 3 minutes to reset. A 30 amp circuit breaker also protects the wiring from door lock feed circuit to relay.

The relay assembly is a double-pole, double-throw relay externally grounded to the body. It is located beneath the right side of the instrument panel behind glove compartment. The control switch is a 3-pin rocker type mounted on door armrests. The feed circuit to the lock switches is protected by a 20 amp fuse.

TROUBLE SHOOTING

DOOR LOCKS INOPERATIVE FROM BOTH CONTROL SWITCHES, COURTESY LIGHT FUSE BLOWN

Install new courtesy light fuse and press door lock switch to "Lock" position. If fuse blows, check for short in Light Blue wire between relay and switches. If system remains operative, check for short in Orange wire and in both Light Blue and Black wires between source and cross bar harness.

DOOR LOCKS INOPERATIVE, COURTESY LIGHT OPERATES

Ground test lamp. Check Orange/Black wire at relay connector. If lamp remains off, check circuit breaker and circuit to relay. With light on, press switch to lock position. If lamp remains off, check ground to the body. If grounded, replace relay.

DOORS WILL UNLOCK BUT WILL NOT LOCK

With a test lamp grounded, check Light Blue wire terminal at relay. Press switch to "Lock" position. If lamp comes on but system does not operate, replace relay. If lamp does not come on, check for short between relay and cross-body wiring harness.

DOORS WILL LOCK BUT WILL NOT UNLOCK

With a test lamp grounded, check Black wire at relay. Press switch to "Unlock" position. If lamp comes on but system does not operate, replace relay. If lamp does not come on, check for open in Black wire between relay and cross-body harness.

DOOR LOCKS OPERATE EXCEPT FOR ONE DOOR

Check for loose connection of Gray and Tan wires, or short in circuit. If both leads check to the actuator motor, replace the motor.

DOOR LOCKS OPERATE NORMALLY EXCEPT ONE DOOR WILL NOT UNLOCK/LOCK

Check ground. If correct, check for open in Light Blue wire between switch and cross-body harness.

DOOR LOCKS INOPERATIVE AND RELAY CLICKS WHEN ACTIVATED

Check Light Blue and Black wires between switch and relay.

DOOR LOCKS INOPERATIVE OR LOCKS PULSATE AND RELAY CHATTERS WHEN SWITCH IS ACTIVATED

Gray and Tan wires are making contact between relay and lock actuator motor.

REMOVAL & INSTALLATION

DOOR LOCK MOTOR

1) Disconnect battery cable, remove door trim panel and disconnect electrical connector from motor.

2) Remove screws attaching motor to door. Remove door lock lever from rubber mount at top of motor actuator and remove motor through access hole. To install, reverse removal procedure.

Fig. 1: General Motors Light Truck Power Door Lock Wiring Diagram

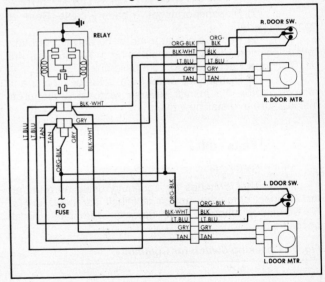

Power Door Locks
JEEP

All Models

DESCRIPTION

Jeep vehicles with power door locks use a battery-powered, motor-actuated lock system, controlled by 2 rocker switches. Pressing up on the switch unlocks doors. Pressing down on the switch locks the doors.

Power door locks are protected by a 30 amp. circuit breaker located in the fuse block. Two-door models have the wiring harness running from door-to-door and is secured at the instrument panel with retainers.

Four-door models have the wiring harness for the back doors connected to the front door harness of the side cowl panels.

REMOVAL & INSTALLATION

DOOR LOCK SWITCH

1) Disconnect negative battery cable. Remove door trim panel. Remove switch housing from inner door panel.

2) Disconnect wiring and remove switch assembly. To disconnect, pry clips holding connector up. Depress retainer clips through holes in switch housing, and remove switch.

3) To install, reverse removal procedures.

ACTUATOR MOTOR

1) Disconnect negative battery cable. Remove door trim panel.

2) Remove actuator motor by drilling out rivets (attaching motor to door panel) using a 1/4" (6 mm) drill bit. Disconnect acutator rod from bellcrank.

3) Disconnect wires from actuator motor, and remove motor. To install, reverse removal procedures, making sure to install new rivets.

TESTING

SWITCH

Test switches for continuity using an ohmmeter. Connect ohmmeter across terminals as shown in *Fig. 1*. Continuity should exist between terminals in all positions.

Fig. 1: Checking Switch for Continuity

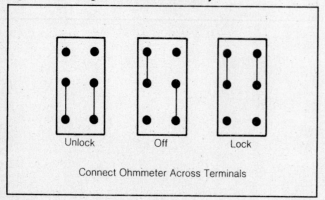

Continuity should exist at positions shown.

ACTUATOR MOTOR

Connect ammeter to motor terminals, and operate door switch. If current draw exceeds 8 amps. at room temperature or if actuator does not complete its travel within 1 second, replace actuator motor.

CIRCUIT BREAKER

1) Disconnect harness connector from fuse block. Test fuse block connection with test light. If light operates, battery voltage is present. If light stays off, remove circuit breaker, and test with ohmmeter.

2) If circuit breaker tests okay, check for battery voltage at circuit breaker connection at fuse block. If there is no battery voltage at connection, check for breakage of fusible link in engine compartment.

Fig. 2: Wiring Diagram for Jeep Power Door Locks

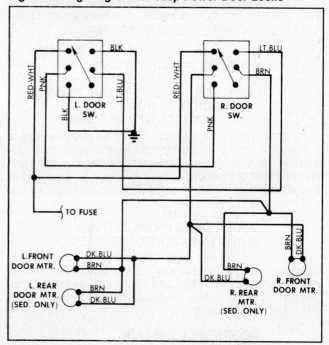

2-Door and 4-door models.

Power Mirrors

FORD

All Models

DESCRIPTION

Power rearview mirror assemblies consist of door-mounted mirrors with internal motor drive and backing plate. System includes a door panel switch and necessary wiring components.

TROUBLE SHOOTING & TESTING

ONE MIRROR DOES NOT FUNCTION

1) Working underneath mirror, remove head of plastic rivet, using a 1/4" (6 mm) drill. Remove rivet stem remnants. Remove screw from cover, remove cover, and disconnect plug. Check function of mirror by connecting 12 volts to terminals of wire plug.

2) Yellow and Green wires provide up-down movement; Blue and White wires, right-left movement. If mirror does not function, replace motor drive. See Motor Drive Removal.

3) If mirror functions when tested, but does not operate when connected to feed wire, remove left door panel. Test feed wire for continuity at switch plug. Then, apply 12 volts to feed wire. If mirror functions through feed wire, but fails to respond to switch operation, replace switch.

BOTH MIRRORS DO NOT FUNCTION

1) Remove left door inner trim panel. Unplug accessory feed wire (Black and Yellow with Red stripe), and check for voltage. On Van models, turn ignition switch to "ON" position.

2) If no voltage is observed, remove instrument panel on Van models or instrument panel pad on Pickup models. Check hot wire, in-line fuse, and ground connections. Repair as necessary. If voltage is present at accessory feed wire plug, reconnect wire and check mirror functions.

3) If satisfactory, install trim panel. If no voltage is observed, disconnect and check continuity of wiring, step-by-step, from hot wire lead to cowl/door harness connection, to switch wire feed connection, and to mirror feed wire connection. Replace or repair damaged wiring.

REMOVAL & INSTALLATION

MIRROR GLASS & MOTOR DRIVE
Removal

1) Break out, and remove center of mirror glass, exposing mounting screw attaching the backing plate to motor drive. *See Fig. 1.* Remove and discard mirror remnants and backing plate, saving 3 stabilizer bars.

2) Remove 4 screws attaching motor drive to mirror assembly. *See Fig. 1.* Unplug wires from motor drive by pushing connector retainer tab, separating connectors. Remove motor drive assembly.

Installation

1) Connect wiring connector to motor drive assembly. Insert stabilizer bars into motor drive. *See Fig.*

2. Install new backing plate to motor drive with center screw, and snap stabilizer ball joints in sockets of backing plate.

2) Install motor drive/backing plate assembly to bracket and tighten screws. Remove paper backing from new mirror replacement glass, and press firmly into backing plate.

Fig. 1: Electric Mirror Mounting Screws

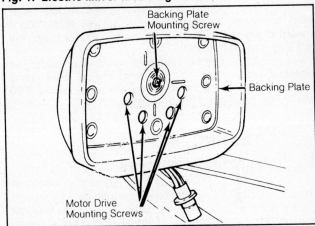

Mounting screws are located inside holes.

MIRROR ASSEMBLY
Removal

Using a 1/4" (6 mm) drill bit, remove head of plastic rivet securing cover on mirror assembly. Remove rivet stem remnants. Remove screw from cover, and remove cover. Disconnect electrical connector. Remove screws attaching mirror assembly to door, and remove mirror assembly.

Installation

To install, reverse removal procedure.

Fig. 2: Motor Drive Stabilizer Bars

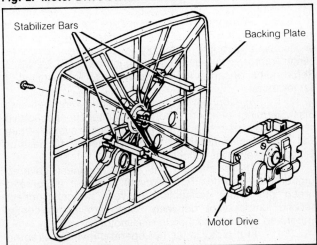

Save stabilizer bars when replacing glass.

NOTE: **Some Pickup models may use a snap-in bezel-switch assembly. Insert screwdriver in slots at bezel edge to release retention springs. Then, disconnect wiring harness from switch, loosen set screw, and remove switch.**

Power Seats

JEEP

Cherokee & Wagoneer

DESCRIPTION

Jeep power seats can be adjusted 6 ways; up, down, forward, backward, tilt forward and tilt backward. The control switch is located on the left lower side of the driver's seat.

The switch has 3 levers; the middle lever raises or lowers the complete seat, as well as moving it forward or rearward. The 2 side levers raise or lower the front and back of the seat.

A permanent magnet reversible motor is connected by cables to rack and pinion assemblies located in the seat tracks. The circuit is protected by a 30 amp. circuit breaker on the fuse block.

TESTING

ELECTRICAL CIRCUITS

1) With battery fully charged and all electrical connections cleaned and tightened, turn dome light on and operate seat switch. If dome light dims, seat may be jamming. Check for binding. If dome light does not dim, proceed with tests.

2) Disconnect wiring harness at connector under seat. Connect 12-volt test light between Red and Black wire in female connector. If lamp lights, harness to seat is good. If lamp doesn't light, check for blown circuit breaker, continuity in Red and Black wires at connector, and for proper ground.

3) Reconnect harness under seat. Remove switch from seat harness. To check rear motor of switch, connect a covered jumper wire between red terminal in center motor and either Light Blue or Orange connection in rear motor.

4) Connect a second jumper wire between Black terminal in center motor and open connection in front motor.

5) If motor does not operate, reverse jumpers in front motor. If motor still does not operate, the harness or complete 3-motor assembly is defective. To check center motor, connect a covered jumper wire between Red terminal of center motor and White or Tan terminal of center motor.

6) Connect a second jumper wire between Black terminal of center motor and open connection in center motor. If motor does not operate, reverse White and Tan wires. If motor still does not operate, harness or 3-motor assembly is defective.

7) To check front motor, connect covered jumper wire between Red terminal in center motor and Green or Yellow connection of rear motor. Connect second jumper wire between Black terminal of center motor and open connection in rear motor.

8) If motor does not operate, reverse wires on rear motor. If motor still does not operate, harness or 3-motor assembly is defective. If all motors and seat operate properly, the switch is bad and should be replaced.

REMOVAL & INSTALLATION

SEAT ASSEMBLY

1) Disconnect negative battery cable. Remove nuts attaching seat assembly to floorpan.

2) Tilt seat, and disconnect wiring harness. Remove seat assembly from vehicle. To install, reverse removal procedure.

MOTOR

NOTE: **Whenever the motor, cable, and housing assemblies are removed or serviced, they must be synchronized to ensure proper operation.**

1) Remove seat assembly as previously outlined. Lay seat assembly on its back on a clean surface.

2) Remove motor mounting screws. Disconnect housings and cables from motor assembly, and remove motor. To install, reverse removal procedures.

Fig. 1: Electrical Test Connections

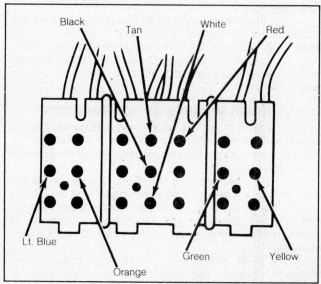

Power Windows

CHRYSLER CORP. SIDE WINDOWS

All Models

DESCRIPTION

The Chrysler Corp. electric window system consists of motors in each front door, switches to operate the motors, wiring harnesses and necessary connections. Window motors are permanent magnet type. Each motor is grounded through the master switch by a white wire.

REMOVAL & INSTALLATION

WINDOW REGULATOR
Removal

1) Raise window to full up position. Remove trim panel and watershield. Remove lower trim panel on stereo-equipped vehicles. Remove down stop bumper bracket.

2) Remove stereo speaker (if equipped). Remove vent wing. Disconnect wiring connector from harness. Disengage glass from regulator, and lower to door bottom. Drill out regulator rivets, and remove regulator through access hole.

Installation

1) Mount regulator to door panel with 1/4"-20 screws and nuts, tightened to 90 INCH Lbs. (10 N.m). Slide glass into regulator arms and into rear glass run. Install vent wing, and adjust. Raise glass to full up position.

2) Install stereo speaker (if equipped). Install down stop bumper bracket. Test regulator function. Install trim panel and watershield.

MOTORS
Removal

Remove regulator as previously described. Secure in a vise to prevent sector gear from rotating. Remove counterbalance spring. Remove 3 motor attaching screws and remove motor.

Installation

To install, reverse removal procedures, noting that counterbalance spring must be installed after motor is attached to regulator.

OVERHAUL

REGULATOR
Disassembly

1) Secure regulator in vise to prevent sector gear from rotating. Remove counterbalance spring.

2) Remove 3 screws holding motor to regulator, and remove motor.

Inspection

Check regulator sector gear for chipped or broken teeth, and for severe wear. Check that all sliders and rivets are securely attached. Parts must not be bent or cracked. Check that sector gear rotates freely.

Fig. 1: Connections for Motor Switch Tests

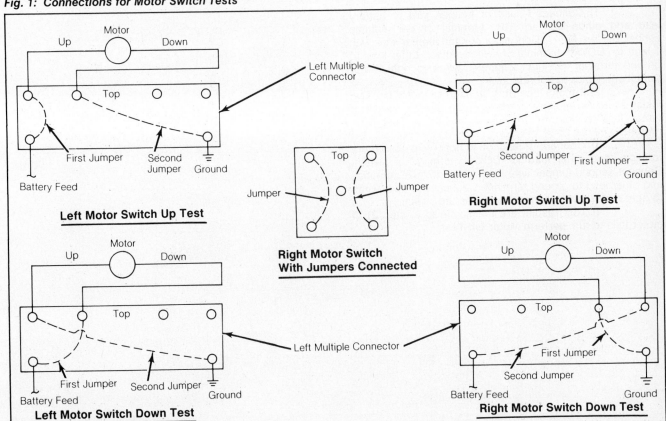

If motor does not run, perform Motor Lift Test.

Reassembly

To reassemble, reverse disassembly procedure, noting that counterbalance spring must be installed after motor is attached to regulator.

TESTING

MOTOR LIFT

1) Connect positive lead of test battery to either of the 2 terminals of motor. Connect other lead to remaining terminal. Motor should now rotate in 1 direction to move window up or down.

2) If window is in up position, and leads are connected so motor rotates in up direction, no movement should occur. The reverse holds true, if leads are connected so motor rotates in down direction, and window is already down.

3) Reverse battery leads. Window should now move in desired direction. If not, remove motor and replace. If motor moved window, reverse leads again and ensure that motor moves window in both directions.

SWITCH VOLTAGE

1) Remove switch from trim panel. Separate multiple terminal block on wiring harness from switch body. Connect 1 lead of test light to battery wire terminal. Connect other lead to ground wire terminal.

2) If test light comes on, wiring circuit is okay. If light does not light, check 30 amp. circuit breaker in fuse block for failure, check for broken wire or poor ground.

MOTOR SWITCH

1) Connect 1 lead of jumper wire to battery lead and other lead to "UP" terminal of left multiple connector. See Fig. 1. Connect a second jumper wire with 1 lead to "DOWN" terminal of switch. Attach other lead to ground terminal. Connect 2 jumper wires to right motor switch connector to operate switch.

2) If motor operates, voltage to motor is okay. Install switch to multiple connector and operate switch. If motor fails to operate, replace switch body. Test each switch.

3) Connect 1 lead of jumper wire to battery terminal, and other lead to "DOWN" terminal of switch. Connect second jumper wire with 1 lead to "UP" terminal, and other lead to ground terminal. Connect 2 jumper wires to right motor switch connector to operate switch.

4) Test results are the same as in step **2)**. If motor fails to run, perform Motor Lift Test.

Power Windows

FORD SIDE WINDOWS

Bronco, Pickups

DESCRIPTION

Ford power window system consists of reversible 12-volt motors in each front door, switches to operate motors, wiring harness and necessary connections. Driver's door has a multiple switch to control both windows.

REMOVAL & INSTALLATION

MOTORS

Removal

1) Disconnect battery ground. Remove door trim panel. Disconnect power window motor wire from harness connector. Using a 1/2" diameter drill bit, drill 2 holes in door inner panel at drill dimples, located opposite 2 unexposed motor drive retaining screws.

NOTE: Check before drilling to make sure no wires are in line with holes to be drilled.

2) Using 2 holes drilled in step 1) and existing access hole, remove 3 motor mount retainer screws. Push motor outward to disengage motor and drive from rectangular gear. After motor and drive are disengaged, prop window up. Remove motor and drive.

Installation

To install, reverse removal procedure. Tighten attaching screws to 50-85 INCH lbs. (5.6-9.6 N.m). Cover drilled holes with body tape. Ensure that door drain holes are open.

POWER WINDOW SWITCH

Removal

1) Insert a thin screwdriver between bezel and trim panel at either side of bezel. Carefully pry bezel from trim panel, and housing assembly will snap out.

2) On left side switch, remove 2 retaining screws from bottom side of connector. Unsnap right side connector from housing. Pry switch from connector with a small screwdriver.

Installation

To install, position switch in connector, and press firmly. Reverse removal procedure to complete installation.

SWITCH CONNECTOR WIRE

Removal

If replacement of a switch wire or switch connector is necessary, insert a needle-like tool into edge of pin hole and bend terminal in. Pull wire and terminal from connector.

Installation

To install terminal in connector, open terminal and insert it in connector.

TESTING

MOTOR

1) Remove door trim panel. Disconnect motor lead. Connect a power source (battery or power-pac) to motor with an ammeter in series. Operate motor and observe current draw.

2) Current draw should not fluctuate, and should not exceed 4 amps. Reverse motor wire connections to observe reversed motor rotation. Replace motor if current draw exceeds 4 amps.

MULTIPLE SWITCH

1) Remove switch from vehicle. Using an ohmmeter or test light, clip a test probe on pin No. 6, which is grounded. *See Fig. 1.* Place both switches in neutral position and test for continuity between pin No. 6 and pins No. 1 through 4.

Fig. 1: Multiple Switch Pin Location

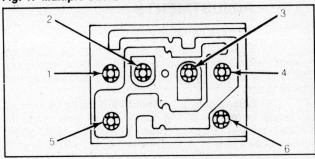

Use ohmmeter or test light for test.

2) Push both switches upward. Both No. 1 and No. 3 should lose continuity to pin No. 6. Push switches downward. No. 2 and No. 4 should lose continuity to pin No. 6.

3) Remove test probe from No. 6, and connect it to feed pin (No. 5). With both switches in neutral position, no continuity should exist at remaining terminals.

4) Push switches upward. No. 2 and No. 4 should show continuity with No. 5. If any switch does not test as indicated, replace complete switch assembly.

Fig. 2: Single Switch Pin Locations

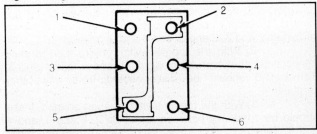

Use ohmmeter or test light for test.

SINGLE SWITCH

1) With the switch in the neutral position, use an ohmmeter to test switch. Continuity should exist between terminals No. 1, 2, 3, and 5. Continuity should also exist between No. 4 and 6. *See Fig. 2.*

2) With switch pushed downward, continuity should exist between terminals No. 2, 4 and 5. Continuity should also exist between No. 1 and 3. Terminal No. 6 should be disconnected from all other terminals.

3) With switch pushed upward, there should be continuity between terminals No. 2, 3, and 5; also No. 4 and 6. Terminal No. 1 should be disconnected from all other terminals. If switch does not operate as indicated in any test, replace switch.

Power Windows

FORD TAILGATE WINDOW

Bronco

DESCRIPTION

Power tailgate window system consists of a motor and regulator assembly inside the tailgate, a key-operated switch at the tailgate, an instrument panel switch, a limit switch to prevent window operation when tailgate is open, and necessary wiring and connections.

Circuit is protected by two 25 amp circuit breakers located in the fuse block. One circuit breaker protects the key switch.

ADJUSTMENTS

TAILGATE GLASS

Fore and aft adjustments can be made by opening tailgate and loosening back window side glass attaching screws. Adjust glass as required, and tighten attaching screws.

Side-to-side adjustments are made by removing inside cover panel and loosening window glass to window bracket screws. After positioning the glass, tighten screws to 6-11 ft. lbs. (9-14 N.m)

TESTING

TAILGATE WINDOW MOTOR

1) Remove tailgate trim panel. Disconnect motor lead. Supply power to the motor lead connector with an ammeter attached in series.

2) Operate the motor and observe the current draw. The current draw should not exceed 4 amps and should not fluctuate.

WINDOW SWITCH

1) Remove switch from vehicle. Use a self-powered test light or ohmmeter. With the switch in the neutral position, there should be continuity between terminals 1 and 3, 2 and 5, and 4 and 6. See Fig. 1.

2) With the toggle switch down, there should be continuity between terminals 2, 4, and 5, and 1 and 3. Terminal 6 should be disconnected from any other terminal.

3) With the toggle switch pushed upward, there should be continuity between terminals 2, 3 and 5, and 4 and 6. Terminal 1 should be disconnected from any other terminal. If the switch does not test as listed, replace switch.

Fig. 1: Tailgate Window Switch Pin Positions

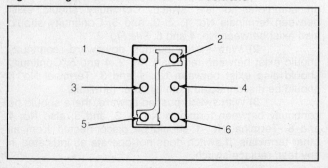

REMOVAL & INSTALLATION

REGULATOR SWITCH & MOTOR

Removal

1) Remove interior access cover from tailgate. Raise glass to full "UP" position.

2) Disconnect wiring harness from switch and/or motor. Remove clip attaching switch to lock cylinder, and remove switch. Remove motor mounting screws, and remove motor.

Installation

To install, reverse removal procedure. Check operation of switch and motor before replacing access cover.

WINDOW REGULATOR

Removal

1) Raise glass to full "UP" position. If glass cannot be raised, lower tailgate and remove interior access cover. Using fingers, locate and remove 4 glass attaching nuts and screws at bottom edge of access opening.

2) Slowly slide glass from tailgate. Remove regulator attaching screw and washer assemblies. Remove regulator.

Installation

To install, reverse removal procedure, tightening screws to 6-11 ft. lbs. (9-14 N.m).

Fig. 2: Ford Bronco Power Tailgate Window Wiring Diagram

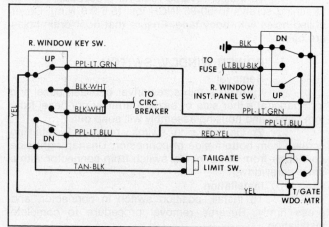

Power Windows

GENERAL MOTORS SIDE WINDOWS

Chevrolet, GMC

DESCRIPTION

DOOR WINDOWS

Window regulators are individually powered by a 12 volt reversible motor located in each door. The motor contains an internal circuit breaker requiring 1 to 3 minutes to reset.

The motor, bolted to the regulator assembly, utilizes a self-locking gear drive. A 2-way control switch is located on each door, with a master control switch located on left door. The window cannot be operated from the door control switches until the ignition is turned "ON".

CIRCUIT BREAKER

A 30 amp circuit breaker of the plug-in type is mounted on the fuse panel.

CONTROL SWITCHES

In addition to individual control switches adjacent to individual windows, a master control switch is mounted on the left door trim pad.

ACCESSORY JUNCTION BLOCK

Junction box is located on the reinforcement at the left shroud. It is used to supply current to power operated circuits. Current is supplied to junction block from the circuit breaker. The power window harness plugs into the junction block.

TROUBLE SHOOTING

WINDOWS WILL NOT OPERATE WITH IGNITION ON

Open circuit or short in power feed circuit. Switch defective.

RIGHT WINDOW OPERATES WITH MASTER SWITCH BUT WILL NOT OPERATE WITH RIGHT CONTROL SWITCH, LEFT WINDOW OPERATES

Open circuit or short in front harness power feed circuit.

TESTING

CIRCUIT BREAKER

Check power feed to circuit breaker. If no power is available, feed wire is open or shorted. Test breaker output terminal. If power fails, breaker is inoperative.

MASTER CONTROL SWITCH

Check power feed Pink wire at switch. If power fails, test wire between relay and master switch.

WINDOW CONTROL SWITCH

1) Connect 1 lead of test lamp to switch connector feed wire and ground other lamp lead. If lamp does not light, an open short circuit exists between switch and power source.

2) Insert 1 end of a jumper wire in switch connector and other end of jumper to motor lead in connector. Repeat procedure for motor lead terminal. If motor operates with jumper wire but does not operate with switch, replace switch.

WINDOW SWITCH TO WINDOW HARNESS

Disconnect harness connector from motor. Insert 1 end of a jumper wire in switch connector and other end of jumper to motor lead in connector. Using a test lamp, check for current at motor connector. If lamp does not light, switch to motor harness is shorted or has open circuit. Check other terminal using same procedure.

WINDOW MOTOR

Check power feed to motor terminals. If power is available, check motor ground. Inspect window regulator and channels for possible binding. Connect a jumper wire to the other motor terminal. Motor should operate window up and down. If not, replace motor.

Fig. 1: General Motors Light Truck Power Window Wiring Diagram

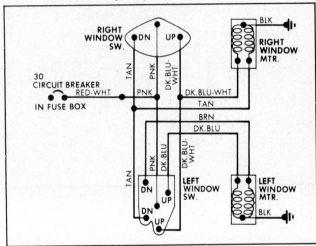

REMOVAL & INSTALLATION

WINDOW REGULATOR & MOTOR

CAUTION: Disconnect electrical connections before removing regulator assembly from window or injury may result.

1) Raise window to full "UP" position and tape glass to door frame to prevent it from falling. Disconnect negative battery cable and remove door trim panel.

2) Remove remote control bolts and place control assembly aside. Remove regulator-to-door panel attaching screws. Disconnect harness from regulator.

3) Slide regulator assembly rearward, disengaging rollers from sash panel. Remove regulator assembly.

CAUTION: Step 4) must be performed when regulator is removed from door. Serious injury can result if motor is removed without locking sector gear.

4) Drill a hole through sector gear and back plate. Do not drill closer than 1/2" (13 mm) to edge of sector gear or back plate. Install sheet metal screw or nut and bolt into hole to lock sector gear.

5) Remove motor-to-regulator attaching screws and remove regulator from motor.

6) To install, reverse removal procedures. Note that the motor drive gear and regulator sector gear should be lubricated with an approved lubricant that is effective down to -20°F. (-29°C).

Fig. 2: General Motors Power Window Regulator, Motor and Connector

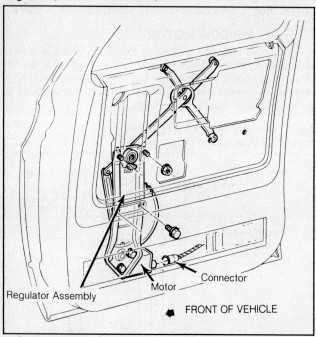

Regulator Assembly

Motor

Connector

FRONT OF VEHICLE

Power Windows

GENERAL MOTORS TAILGATE

Chevrolet, GMC

DESCRIPTION

Tailgate window system consists of a 12-volt reversible direction motor, internal regulator, and jackscrew type regulator. The internal circuit breaker may require 1 to 3 minutes to reset. Window is controlled by the jackscrew regulator.

The window is operated by an instrument panel switch when the ignition switch is in the "ON" position, or an external key switch located in the tailgate door. The window retracts into tailgate door.

A cut-out switch prevents operation of the window by either switch when the tailgate is open. Circuit is protected by a 30-ampere circuit breaker, located at fuse block.

Fig. 1: General Motors Tailgate Power Window Wiring Diagram

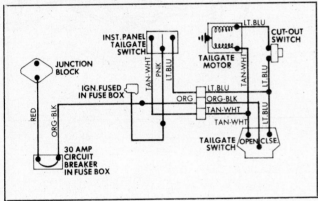

TESTING & TROUBLE SHOOTING

TAILGATE POWER WINDOW INOPERATIVE FROM PANEL OR TAILGATE KEY SWITCH

Check circuit breaker, and replace if bad. If good, check motor ground. If good, check the Tan/White and Lt. Blue wires for short. If not shorted, replace window motor.

TAILGATE POWER WINDOW INOPERATIVE FROM PANEL SWITCH, OPERATES FROM TAILGATE KEY SWITCH

1) If current from fuse block is good, ground 1 probe of 12-volt test lamp. Place tailgate panel switch in window "UP" position. Probe terminal for Lt. Blue wire at back of switch. If lamp does not light, replace switch.

2) If lamp lights, touch lamp probe to terminal for Tan/White wire at back of switch and press switch to "DOWN" position. If lamp does not light, replace switch. If lamp lights, check window motor ground to body and Lt. Blue and Tan/White wires between switch and motor.

NOTE: If switch operates from key switch, but not from panel switch, use same test procedure, replacing tailgate key switch if necessary.

TAILGATE WINDOW WILL NOT OPEN FROM PANEL SWITCH, OTHERWISE OPERATES

1) With ignition switch "ON" and tailgate open, place panel switch in "DOWN" position. Using a grounded 12-volt test lamp, probe Tan/White wire at panel switch.

2) If lamp does not light, replace switch. If lamp lights, probe Tan/White wire at window motor, with switch still in "DOWN" position. If lamp does not light now, check for open Tan/White wire between motor and panel switch. If lamp lights, system should operate normally.

TAILGATE WINDOW WILL NOT CLOSE FROM PANEL SWITCH, OTHERWISE OPERATES

1) With ignition switch "ON" and tailgate door open, place panel switch in "UP" position. Using a grounded 12-volt test lamp, probe terminal for Lt. Blue wire at back of switch. If lamp does not light, replace panel switch.

2) If lamp lights, probe terminal for Lt. Blue wire at cutout switch. If lamp does not light, check for open Lt. Blue wire between instrument panel and cutout switch. If lamp lights at cutout switch terminal, check Lt. Blue wire between cutout switch and motor. If wire is good, replace cutout switch.

TAILGATE WINDOW WILL NOT OPEN FROM TAILGATE KEY SWITCH, OTHERWISE OPERATES

1) With ignition switch "ON", open tailgate door. Turn tailgate key switch to "DOWN" position. Using a grounded 12-volt test lamp, probe Tan/White wire at key switch.

2) If lamp does not light, replace key switch. If lamp lights, check for open Tan/White wire between key switch and window motor.

TAILGATE WINDOW WILL NOT CLOSE FROM TAILGATE KEY SWITCH, OTHERWISE OPERATES

1) With ignition switch "ON" and tailgate door open, place key switch in "UP" position. Using a grounded 12-volt test lamp, probe Lt. Blue wire at key switch. If lamp does not light, replace key switch. If lamp lights, probe Lt. Blue wire at cutout switch.

2) If lamp does not light, check for open Lt. Blue wire between key switch and cutout switch. If lamp lights, check for open in Lt. Blue wire between cutout switch and window motor. If wire is okay, replace cutout switch.

REMOVAL & INSTALLATION

WINDOW MOTOR
Removal
1) Secure window regulator lift arms and remove window glass from lift arms. Drill a 1/8" hole through the sector gear and backplate. Install a sheet metal screw into the hole locking the sector gears in position.

2) Disconnect drive cable at regulator. Remove motor attaching screws and motor, and detach harness.

Installation

To install, reverse removal procedure.

CUT-OUT SWITCH

Removal

Disconnect left side remote control rod from center control by removing retaining clip. Remove side latch retaining screws and disconnect cut-out switch wiring. Remove side latch assembly and screws holding latch to switch.

Installation

To install, reverse removal procedures.

JACKSCREW REGULATOR

CAUTION: **If window glass is removed, or disengaged from regulator lift arms, the regulator lift arms must be secured before removing jackscrew. Regulator lift arms are under spring pressure and may cause injury if not secured.**

Removal

1) Drill a 1/8" hole through sector gear and backplate, and install a sheet metal screw in hole to secure sector gears in position.

2) Disconnect drive cable at jackscrew. Remove regulator jackscrew attaching screws and remove jackscrew assembly.

Installation

To install, reverse removal procedures.

Fig.2: Power Tailgate Window Components

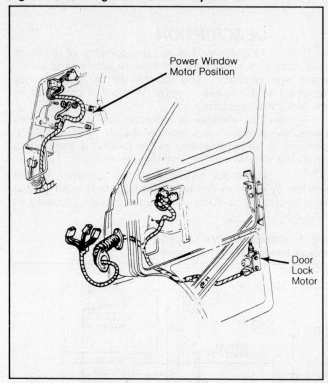

Power Windows

JEEP ELECTRIC WINDOWS

Cherokee, Wagoneer

DESCRIPTION

System consists of an electrically-operated tailgate window and individual motors at all side windows. Tailgate window operates on 2 circuits, from an instrument panel switch or an external key switch at the tailgate.

Side windows are operated by individual switches at each door, or by a complete set of control switches at the instrument panel. The electric tailgate window system consists of a safety switch, gearbox-type regulator, 12-volt DC motor, wiring, connections and a 30-ampere circuit breaker at the fuse block.

The electric side window system consists of regulator motors, switches, actuators and actuator rods, wiring and connections, and a 30-ampere circuit breaker located at the fuse block.

Fig. 1: Jeep Instrument Panel Tailgate Wiring Diagram

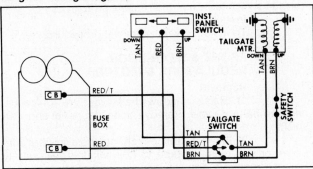

Fig. 2 : Jeep Power Window Wiring Diagram

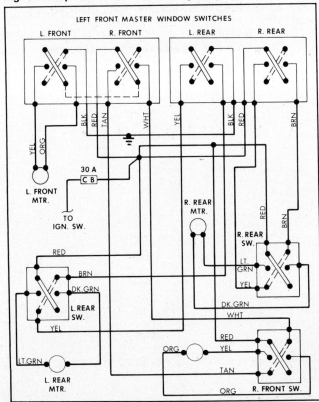

TESTING

INSTRUMENT PANEL & TAILGATE SWITCH

1) Turn ignition switch to "ON" position. Using a 12-volt test lamp or a voltmeter, connect one end of test equipment to ground and probe the Red lead. If voltage is not indicated, repair feed circuit.

2) If voltage is indicated, probe Brown lead with switch in "UP" position. If voltage is indicated, move switch to "DOWN" position and probe the Tan lead. If voltage is not indicated, replace switch. If voltage is indicated, check window switch in the tailgate using the same procedures.

NOTE: If vehicle is equipped with a tailgate window defogger, the defogger and tailgate switches are serviced as an assembly. Both switches must be replaced when either is defective.

TAILGATE WINDOW SAFETY SWITCH

1) Using a 12-volt test lamp or a voltmeter, place window switch in "UP" position. Probe Brown lead for voltage. If voltage is not indicated, repair feed circuits. If voltage is indicated, close safety switch, and check lead at motor.

2) If voltage is indicated, check motor ground. Motor is grounded through Black lead at instrument panel switch. If motor is properly grounded and system does not operate, replace motor. If voltage is not indicated, replace safety switch.

TAILGATE WINDOW MOTOR

1) Using a 12-volt test lamp or a voltmeter, connect one lead of test equipment to ground and probe Tan lead. Close safety switch and turn tailgate window switch to "DOWN" position. If voltage is not indicated, repair feed circuit.

2) Probe Brown wire at motor, close safety switch, and place switch in "UP" position. If voltage is not indicated, repair feed wire. If voltage is indicated in both tests but motor does not operate, replace motor.

MASTER SWITCH CIRCUITS

1) Remove escutcheon and housing from master switch. Separate terminal plate by releasing retainer hooks to expose terminal ends.

2) Turn ignition switch to "ON" position. Using a 12-volt test lamp, connect 1 lead to Black wire and other lead to Red terminal. Repeat test at second Black wire.

3) If lamp does not light in either test, remove Black lead and connect to chassis ground. If lamp lights, an open exists between master switch and ground. If lamp does not light, it indicates a defective circuit breaker or an opening in the Red wire from circuit breaker to master switch.

CONTROL SWITCH & MOTOR CIRCUITS

1) Connect test lamp between terminals of Orange and Yellow wires. Operate control switch "UP" and "DOWN".

2) If lamp lights in both switch positions, wires and door switch are not defective. Disconnect White and Green motor leads at terminal plate, and connect to Green and White leads.

3) Operate master switch. If window goes up and down, motor is okay, but switch is defective. If motor does not operate, check connections and leads to motor. If motor operates, switch is defective.

SIDE WINDOW MOTOR

Connect test battery positive lead to one of the motor terminals. Connect negative lead to other terminal. Motor should now rotate in one direction to go "UP" or "DOWN".

SWITCH VOLTAGE TEST

1) Connect a jumper wire between Red lead and switch "UP" terminal. Connect a second jumper wire between switch ground terminal and "DOWN" terminal. This will test "UP" operation of switch.

2) If motor runs, voltage is present to motor. Connect switch to multiple connector and operate switch. If motor fails to run, replace switch. Test all switches in this manner.

3) To test "DOWN" operation of switch, connect first jumper wire between Red lead and switch "DOWN" terminal, and second jumper wire between switch ground terminal and "UP" terminal. Repeat tests on all switches. Results are the same as "UP" test.

REMOVAL & INSTALLATION

TAILGATE WINDOW REGULATOR & MOTOR

Removal

1) Remove carpet and tailgate access cover plate. Remove retainers attaching regulator arms to channel. Disengage regulator arm pins from channel, and raise glass.

Fig. 3: Power Tailgate Motor and Regulator

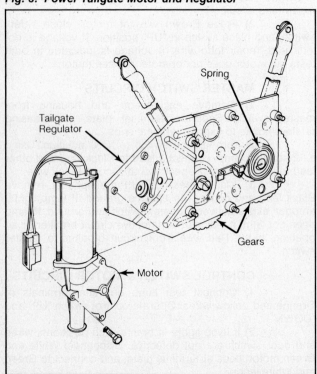

2) Carefully support glass in raised position. If regulator attaching screws are covered by sector gears, disconnect motor drive from gear regulator. Grasp regulator arm as far outboard as access hole will allow.

3) Push down on arm until holes in sector gears align with attaching screws and motor. Hold regulator in this position, and wedge a 1/4" screw between meshing teeth.

4) Remove regulator attaching screws, regulator, and motor. Release spring tension by using a large screwdriver to snap spring from under tension bracket.

Installation

To install, reverse removal procedure.

SIDE WINDOW MASTER SWITCH

Removal

1) Disconnect negative battery cable. Remove retaining screws and escutcheon. Remove switch housing screws.

2) Pull switch out to expose wires. Disconnect terminal plate from switch. Depress retainer clips through holes in switch housing, and remove switch.

Installation

To install, reverse removal procedure.

FRONT & REAR DOOR REGULATORS & MOTORS

Removal

1) Raise window half way up. Disconnect negative battery cable. Remove door trim panel and water shield.

2) Insert a drift punch into hole in door inner panel, or use masking tape to hold window half way up. Remove regulator arm retainer clip, and remove arm from bottom window channel.

3) Disconnect wires from motor. Remove inner door panel-to-regulator nuts and bolts. Remove regulator and motor assembly.

Installation

To install, reverse removal procedures.

FORD & GENERAL MOTORS

Ford, General Motors "C" & "K" Models

DESCRIPTION & OPERATION

If driver's seat belt is not buckled and ignition is turned to "ON" or "START" position, seat belt warning system will turn on "FASTEN SEAT BELTS" indicator light and sound buzzer for 4 to 8 seconds.

If the driver's belt is buckled after buzzer sounds, buzzer will remain on until timer turns it off. When ignition is turned to "ON" position, current is supplied through timer to buzzer circuit and indicator light circuit.

Light will always remain on until timer turns off current. Buzzer will only sound if single space driver's seat belt is not buckled before turning on ignition.

NOTE: Ford 2-point seat belt system does not have a warning system (lap belts only).

Fig. 1: General Motors Seat Belt Warning System Wiring Diagram

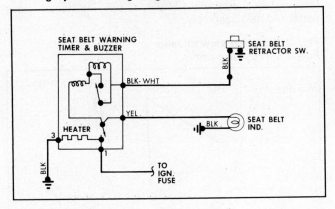

Fig. 2: Ford Seat Belt Warning System Wiring Diagram

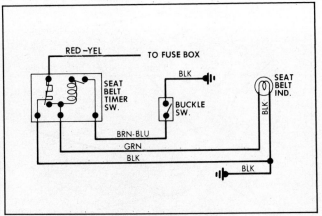

TROUBLE SHOOTING

BUZZER & INDICATOR LIGHT INOPERATIVE

Check fuse. Check for open circuit in timer feed wire. Check seat belt switch for good ground. Check for defective timer or ignition switch.

BUZZER INOPERATIVE

Check for defective buzzer, open circuit in seat belt switch or defective wire. Check connections at seat belt switch and buzzer. Check seat belt switch ground.

INDICATOR LIGHT INOPERATIVE

Check light and wiring for shorts, open circuits, or poor connections.

BUZZER & INDICATOR LIGHT REMAIN ON

Check for open circuit in timer ground lead. Check for a defective timer.

Sunroofs — Electric

JEEP

Cherokee, Wagoneer

DESCRIPTION

Jeep electric sunroof features a sliding glass panel operated by an electric motor, and a manually operated sun screen. System consists of sunroof assembly, electric motor mounted in the forward portion of the sunroof housing, a 2-position switch mounted in the windshield header and all necessary wiring.

Electrical feed is through air conditioning terminal of fuse block. Circuit is protected by air conditioning fuse and a 20 amp. in-line fuse located in the wiring harness just below the "A" pillar.

ADJUSTMENT

MOTOR CLUTCH

1) Remove motor cap to gain access to adjusting screw. Cap is located in headlining just above and at center of windshield.

2) Loosen clutch plate adjusting screw jam nut using a deep socket. Tighten adjusting screw to 50 INCH lbs. (5.6 N.m). Tighten jam nut and install motor cap.

GLASS PARALLEL ALIGNMENT

NOTE: Do not operate electric motor while the glass panel or cables are removed as cable damage could occur.

1) Open glass about 1/2". Determine how much out of line front edge of glass is in relation to forward edge of roof panel opening. Note variation.

2) Open panel about 8" to gain access to cable and drive gear mechanism. Remove cable front cover and drive gear plate. Remove cable from track.

3) Move one side of glass panel slightly forward or backward as required to obtain parallel alignment with roof edge. Install cable in front track and insert cable in drive gear teeth.

4) Install drive gear plate and cable front cover. Close glass to within 1/4" of roof panel edge. Check alignment. Repeat steps as necessary to obtain proper parallel alignment.

REMOVAL & INSTALLATION

HALO ASSEMBLY

Removal & Installation

1) Open glass panel partially and remove halo assembly attaching screws. *See Fig. 1.* Grasp center of halo assembly and pull assembly downward to disengage front tabs from track.

2) Close glass panel fully. Slide halo assembly forward and remove assembly from vehicle. To install, reverse removal procedures.

GLASS PANEL

Removal & Installation

1) With halo assembly removed, close glass panel and remove outboard screws from front guide shoe assemblies. Loosen inboard screws and rotate guide shoes to disengage slide portion from track.

2) Release rear slide tension springs by rotating them to inboard position. Remove screws attaching rear guide shoes and retainers to tabs in glass panel and remove retainers.

3) From outside of vehicle, raise front of glass panel and slide panel forward and out of vehicle. To install, reverse removal procedures noting that rear slide tension springs must be positioned under the spring lock roller.

SUNSCREEN

Removal

Remove halo assembly and glass panel. Open sunscreen fully. Working from outside of vehicle, pull sunscreen upward at center of screen and slide screen forward and upward to remove.

Installation

Working from outside of the vehicle, curve sunscreen upward at center of screen. Slide screen rearward and downward into roof opening. Install glass panel and halo assembly.

Fig. 1: Exploded View of Jeep Power Sunroof Assembly

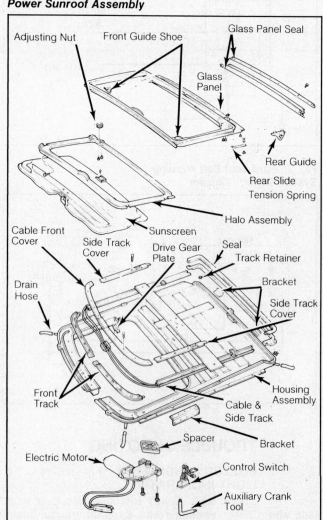

JEEP (Cont.)

CABLE & SIDE TRACK

Removal

1) Remove halo assembly, glass panel and sunscreen. Remove screws attaching cable front cover and remove cover.

2) Remove drive gear plate. Remove side track cover screws and remove side track cover.

3) Disengage cable from front track and motor gear and remove cable by pulling it up and out. Lift side track up and remove.

Installation

To install, reverse removal procedures. Make sure track retainer is seated in hole at rear of housing. If both cables have been removed, make sure rear guide shoes are in contact with side track covers before installing cables.

SUNROOF SWITCH

Removal & Installation

Pull switch straight down from windshield header and disconnect switch wires. To install, connect wires and install switch in opening.

SUNROOF MOTOR

Removal

1) Open glass panel fully, then disconnect negative battery cable. Remove sun visors, escutcheons, center support, windshield mouldings and end caps.

2) Remove sunroof switch and motor cap. Spray headliner release agent across headliner at windshield. Allow several minutes for agent to penetrate.

NOTE: **When removing headliner, use care to avoid separating foam backing from headliner. If backing begins to separate, apply more release agent.**

3) Pull front edge of headliner downward. Remove motor mounting screws and remove motor.

Installation

To install, reverse removal procedures. Mask off top of windshield and spray trim adhesive on roof panel along top of windshield and install headliner. Check sunroof operation and adjust motor clutch if necessary.

Fig. 2: Front Guide Shoe and Rear Tension Spring

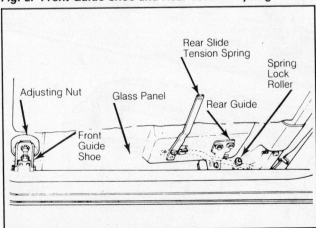

Rotate guide shoes to disengage slide portion from track.

Switches & Instrument Panels
CHRYSLER CORP.

Dodge, Plymouth

DESCRIPTION & OPERATION

Fuel, temperature and oil pressure gauges operate on the constant voltage principle through a common voltage limiter, which provides intermittent current to the gauge system.

FUEL LEVEL GAUGE

A hinged float arm in fuel tank raises or lowers, depending on fuel level. It contacts a variable resistor in the fuel gauge sending unit. This provides a change of resistance in the fuel gauge circuit. This resistance registers on the instrument panel gauge in the form of a level reading.

TEMPERATURE & OIL PRESSURE

The operation of the temperature and oil pressure indicating systems is identical in operation to the fuel system, with the exception of the method of varying resistance of the sending units.

For temperature, the resistance of the disc in the sending unit varies with a direct relation to coolant temperature. When coolant temperatures are high, resistance is low. When coolant temperatures are low, resistance is high.

For oil pressure, the sending unit resistance is controlled by a diaphragm. The diaphragm is actuated as oil pressure increases or decreases.

OIL PRESSURE WARNING LIGHT

The oil pressure switch is mounted on the engine (location depends on engine). When oil pressure is high, switch is held in the "OFF" or "OPEN" position.

This prevents current flow to the indicator light. When oil pressure is low, the switch is in the "ON" or "CLOSED" position, allowing current to flow to the indicator light.

ALTERNATOR INDICATOR SYSTEM

The alternator gauge is an ammeter, which senses the direction and rate of flow of electrical current to or from battery, thereby indicating whether battery is being charged or discharged.

TACHOMETER

The tachometer is a self-contained electronic unit connected to the ignition coil. The tachometer senses ignition firings and counts their number. This is shown on the face of the gauge. Gauge is marked off in RPM increments.

TESTING

VOLTAGE LIMITER

1) To quickly test voltage limiter in vehicle, connect one lead of a voltmeter or test light to temperature sending unit and other lead to a good ground.

2) Leave sending unit wire attached to sending unit. Turn ignition switch "ON". A fluctuating voltmeter or a flashing light indicates voltage limiter is operating.

FUEL GAUGE
With Tester

NOTE: Allow 2 minutes at each test point for gauge to settle. Tapping instrument cluster will help position needle.

1) Disconnect wire at fuel tank unit. Connect one lead of gauge tester (C-3826A) to wire terminal. Connect other lead to a good ground.

2) Turn ignition "ON", turn tester knob to "F" position, and observe instrument panel gauge. Gauge should read "FULL", plus 2 pointer widths or minus 1 pointer width.

3) Turn test knob to 1/2. Gauge should read 1/2 plus or minus 2 pointer widths. Turn knob to "E".

Fig. 1: Chrysler Corp. Instrument Cluster & Bezel

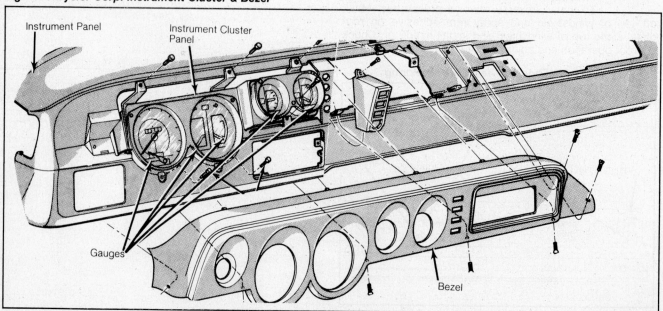

Van models shown.

CHRYSLER CORP. (Cont.)

Gauge should read "EMPTY", plus 1 pointer width or minus 2 pointer widths.

4) If panel gauge does not perform as described, continuity of circuit from tank sending unit to panel unit should be tested. Before replacing gauge, check printed circuit board for damage or defects.

5) If panel performs properly when tested but fails to operate properly when connected to vehicle system, inspect fuel tank sending unit ground strap for proper installation on fuel line. If ground continuity is good, remove tank unit for testing.

FUEL GAUGE

Without Tester

1) Disconnect wire from terminal on fuel tank sending unit. Attach wire to known good sending unit. Connect jumper wire between sending unit fuel pick up tube and a good ground. To check fuel gauge, allow at least 2 minutes at each test point for gauge to settle.

2) Clip float arm of sending unit to its empty stop, and turn ignition key to "ON" position. Gauge should read "EMPTY" plus 1 pointer width or minus 2 pointer widths. Move and clip sending unit float arm to full stop. Gauge should read "FULL" plus 2 pointer widths or minus 1 pointer width.

3) If fuel gauge does not perform as indicated, continuity of circuit from tank sending unit to panel should be tested, giving special attention to printed circuit board. Before replacing gauge, also check voltage limiter.

4) If panel gauge performs satisfactorily with tester (C-3826A) or known good sending unit, check fuel tank and original fuel gauge sending unit by removing sending unit from tank. Connect sending unit wire and jumper wire as in step 1). If fuel gauge now checks within specifications, original unit is electrically okay.

5) Check ground strap from sending unit to fuel line for continuity. Check for deformed sending unit, improper installation, deformed mounting flange on fuel tank, or deformed bottom of fuel tank. Then recheck sending unit.

TEMPERATURE GAUGE

1) Disconnect terminal from temperature sending unit or engine. Connect one test lead of tester (C-3826) to terminal and other lead to good ground. Turn ignition "ON", and turn tester knob to "E".

2) Temperature gauge should show "C", plus or minus 1/8". Turn tester knob to 1/2. Pointer should advance to driving range left of 1/2 position of dial.

3) Turn tester knob to "F". Gauge pointer should move to "H" position on dial. If gauge responds as stated, but does not operate with terminal attached to sending unit, replace sending unit.

4) If gauge does not respond, check for loose connections, broken wire, open printed circuit or faulty gauge.

AMMETER GAUGE

1) Turn ignition and headlights "ON" (do not start engine). Ammeter needle should move toward the "D" or discharge scale. If no movement of the needle is observed, check terminals for loose wires.

2) If terminals are secure, ammeter is defective. If needle moves toward the "C" or charge side, the connections are reversed.

OIL PRESSURE WARNING LIGHT

1) Check low oil pressure warning light system by turning key to "ON" position and observing pressure light. If light comes on, start engine. If light stays on, immediately turn off engine, and use direct pressure gauge to check oil pressure.

2) If pressure is to specifications, check for grounded wire or replace oil pressure sending unit. Turn ignition key to "ON" position. If light does not come on, disconnect lead of sending unit, and touch it to ground.

3) If bulb comes on, replace sending unit. If bulb does not come on, light bulb is burned out or bulb socket, wiring, or connections are faulty.

OIL PRESSURE GAUGE

1) Disconnect wire from oil pressure sending unit on engine. Connect one lead of tester (C-3826A) to removed wire and other lead to good ground. Place tester knob in "E" position and turn ignition "ON". Do not start engine.

2) Oil pressure gauge should read "L" plus or minus 1/8". Turn tester knob to 1/2 position, oil pressure gauge should advance to 1/2 position on dial. With tester knob in "F" position, gauge should also advance to "H" position.

3) Should gauge respond to above tests, but fail to operate when connected to vehicle system, indications are of a defective sending unit. Should gauge fail to respond to above tests, check for loose connection, broken wire or faulty gauge.

BRAKE WARNING LIGHT

1) Brake warning system light comes on when ignition switch is "ON" with parking brake applied, when 1 of the 2 service brake systems fails, or when ignition switch is positioned to "START".

2) Test system by hoisting vehicle with assistant inside. Observe warning light, as assistant depresses brake pedal. Light should come on when bleeder port on wheel cylinder is opened.

3) If light fails to operate, inspect for burned out bulb, disconnected socket, bad brake line switch, broken or disconnected wiring.

REMOVAL & INSTALLATION

SPEEDOMETER & GAUGES

Removal

Remove instrument panel cluster, lens plastic mounting clips, and lens. Remove mask and mounting nuts of gauge being serviced. Remove gauge through front of cluster.

Installation

To install, reverse removal procedure.

INSTRUMENT CLUSTER

Removal

1) Disconnect fusible link under hood, and remove screws fastening instrument panel hood and bezel assembly. Pull bezel off upper retaining clips, and remove cluster screws. On truck models, remove steering column cover and transmission select indicator (if equipped).

2) Loosen heater and air conditioner control, and pull rearward to clear cluster housing. On all cluster

Switches & Instrument Panels

CHRYSLER CORP. (Cont.)

models, carefully pull cluster out far enough to disconnect speedometer cable, circuit board connectors, and gauge wiring. Remove cluster assembly.

Installation
To install, reverse removal procedure.

PRINTED CIRCUITS

Removal
With instrument cluster removed, remove voltage limiter and radio capacitor. Remove all lamp socket assemblies and gauges except speedometer. Remove attaching screws and printed circuit board from vehicle.

Installation
To install, reverse removal procedure.

HEADLIGHT SWITCH

Removal
1) Disconnect fusible link in engine compartment. Remove left air conditioner and air outlet assembly

(if equipped). Reach under instrument panel, depress knob and stem release button located on switch housing, and at the same time pull knob and stem assembly out of switch housing located on front of instrument panel.

2) On truck models, remove wiper switch knob. On vans and wagons, remove instrument panel hood and bezel. Remove switch bezel mounting screws. On all models, remove spanner nut mounting switch to panel. Lower switch from behind panel and disconnect electrical leads. Remove switch from vehicle.

Installation
To install, reverse removal procedure.

Fig. 2: Chrysler Corp. Instrument Panel & Bezel

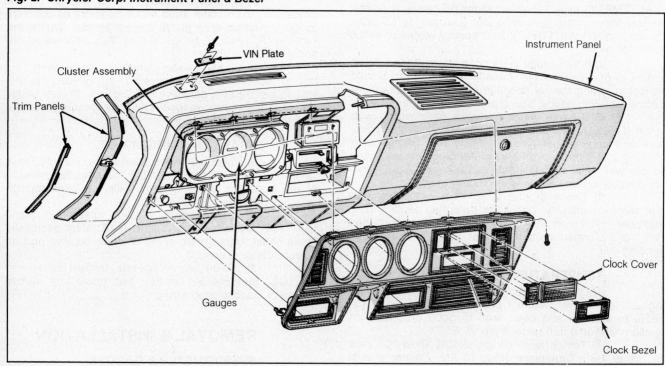

FORD

DESCRIPTION & OPERATION

AMMETER GAUGE

Gauge senses the direction and rate of flow of electrical current to or from the battery, indicating whether the battery is being charged or discharged. A shunt-type ammeter is used. Ammeters are non-adjustable and must be replaced as a unit.

FUEL GAUGE

Gauge pointer is operated by current flow heating a wire-wound bi-metal strip in gauge. Current flow is controlled by a variable resistor float type sending unit in the fuel tank.

As the amount of fuel decreases, more resistance is placed in the circuit, allowing less current flow and heat at the bi-metal strip. This causes the pointer to move a shorter distance.

INSTRUMENT VOLTAGE REGULATOR

Instrument Voltage Regulator (IVR) is used in conjunction with all gauges (except ammeter). It controls and maintains an average pulsating value of 5 volts at gauge. A supression choke is connected in series between printed circuit and IVR to prevent radio interference.

OIL PRESSURE GAUGE

Oil pressure gauge circuit consists of an IVR, oil pressure gauge and a pressure-operated sending unit. As oil pressure increases, resistance in sending unit decreases causing an increase in current flow and gauge pointer movement.

OIL PRESSURE INDICATOR LIGHT

The light is connected between the oil pressure switch unit on the engine and the coil terminal of the ignition switch. The light should come on when the ignition switch is first turned to the "R" or "RUN" position.

It should go out after engine is started, indicating oil pressure has reached a safe level. The light should also come on any time pressure drops below a safe level.

TEMPERATURE GAUGE

System consists of a variable resistance type sending unit and a gauge. As coolant temperature increases, resistance in sending unit decreases. This allows an increase of current flow and gauge pointer movement. It is possible, under certain driving conditions, for pointer to read at the top of the normal band and still have coolant temperature within limits.

TESTING

GAUGES

Oil Pressure Indicator Light

1) Turn ignition switch to "ON", but do not start engine. The indicator light should come on. Start engine and light should go out within seconds. To test oil pressure switch, turn ignition switch to "ON", but do not start engine.

2) If indicator light does not come on, disconnect wire from oil pressure switch terminal and touch to ground. If light now comes on, oil pressure switch is defective. If light does not come on, check for bad bulb or open circuits to bulb.

Oil Pressure Gauge

1) Disconnect connector from oil pressure sender unit and connect to matching terminals on tester (Rotunda 21-0015 or equivalent). Attach tester ground wire to vehicle frame. Turn vehicle ignition switch to "ACC" position.

2) Turn tester switch to IVR Check position. A flashing light indicates IVR and wiring are functional. Turn tester switch to either High or Low position. The center line of gauge pointer should be within the oil pressure White band of tester.

3) If center of pointer registers in White band, system is operating properly and oil pressure sending unit must be replaced. If pointer center line falls outside low band, replace gauge. If outside high band, replace IVR and repeat test. If still outside high band, replace gauge and reinstall original IVR.

Fig. 1: Testing IVR, Fuel, Oil or Temperature Gauge

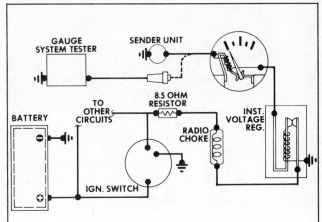

Use Rotunda tester 21-0015.

Ammeter

1) With engine off, turn headlights on. Meter pointer should move toward the "D" or discharge side of the gauge. If no pointer movement is noted, check connections at rear of meter housing, printed circuit connections and multiple connector at printed circuit.

2) If connections are good, replace ammeter. Should ammmeter pointer move toward "C" with lights on and engine off, ammeter connections are reversed.

Fuel Level Gauge

1) Using tester (Rotunda Instrument Gauge System Tester Model 21-0015 or equivalent), test fuel level gauge with instrument voltage regulator (IVR). Disconnect connnector from fuel sender and attach to tester. Turn ignition switch to "ACC" position.

2) Set tester switch to IVR Check position. If light flashes on and off, the IVR and wiring are functional. If IVR Check light is on steady, check IVR ground screw. If ground screw is secure, replace IVR. If IVR Check light does not come on, check for open circuit in gauge and/or circuit wiring.

3) With tester switch in either High or Low position, center line of gauge pointer should be within "F"

FORD (Cont.)

or "E" White band of tester. If so, fuel indicating system is working properly and replacement of fuel sender is necessary.

4) If pointer is outside the "E" White band, replace fuel gauge. If outside "F" White band, replace IVR and retest. If still outside, replace fuel gauge and reinstall original IVR.

Temperature Gauge
1) Disconnect connector from temperature sender and connect to tester (Rotunda 21-0015 or equivalent). Attach other tester lead to ground on vehicle. Turn vehicle ignition switch to "ACC" position. Turn tester switch to IVR Check position. A flashing light indicates IVR and wiring are functional.

2) Place tester switch in either High or Low position. Center line of pointer should be within White temperature level test band, indicating system is operating properly and that sending unit requires replacement. If center line is outside high White band, replace IVR and retest. If outside low White band, replace gauge and retest.

NOTE: If system still does not perform properly, check engine coolant level, proper operation of thermostat and fan belt tension.

REMOVAL & INSTALLATION
SPEEDOMETER & GAUGES
Removal & Installation (All Models)
Instrument cluster must be removed to allow any repair or replacement of speedometer or gauges.

INSTRUMENT CLUSTER
Removal (Bronco II & Ranger)
1) Disconnect battery ground. Remove the 2 screws attaching steering column shroud to panel. Remove shroud. Remove the lower instrument panel trim. Detach the cluster trim cover attaching screws and remove cover. Remove 4 screws attaching cluster to panel. Position cluster slightly away from panel.

Fig. 2: Exploded View of Van Instrument Cluster

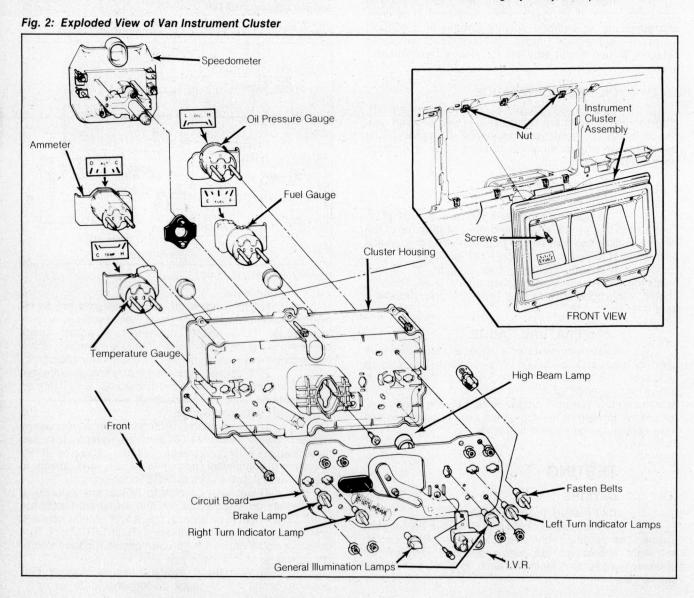

FORD (Cont.)

2) Disconnect speedometer cable at speedometer. If there is not enough room, detach cable at transmission. Disconnect the wiring harness connector from the printed circuit. Disconnect any light bulbs from sockets and remove instrument cluster.

Installation

To install, reverse removal procedure. Apply a 3/16" ball of silicon lubricant to the drive hole of the speedometer head.

Removal & Installation (Vans)

1) Disconnect battery ground and remove 7 screws retaining cluster to instrument panel. Position cluster part way out of panel for access to rear of cluster. At back of cluster, disconnect speedometer cable.

NOTE: **It may be necessary to remove 2 steering column shroud-to-panel retaining screws. Loosen bolts attaching column to Band C support to provide additional clearance for cluster removal. In some cases, it may prove necessary to remove speedometer cable at the transmission, pulling cable through cowl.**

2) Disconnect multiple feed plug from printed circuit board and remove the cluster assembly from instrument panel.

3) To install, reverse removal procedure. Apply approximately 3/16" diameter ball of silicone lubricant in drive hole of speedometer head.

Removal & Installation (Bronco & "F" Pickups)

1) Disconnect battery ground. Pull knobs from radio shafts (if equipped), fuel gauge switch knob, heater control knobs and wiper/washer knob. Use a hook tool to release each knob lock tab. Remove knob and shaft from light switch. Remove fog light switch knob (if equipped.)

2) Remove steering column shroud. On automatic transmission vehicles remove loop on selector indicator cable assembly from retainer pin. Open cable retaining clips with a hook tool. On all models, remove bracket screw from cable bracket and slide bracket out of slot in tube.

3) Remove cluster trim cover and 4 cluster attaching screws. Disconnect speedometer cable, wire connector from printed circuit and 4-wheel drive indicator light (if equipped). Remove instrument cluster. To install, reverse removal procedure.

INSTRUMENT VOLTAGE REGULATOR & PRINTED CIRCUIT

NOTE: **Removal and installation procedures were not available for Bronco and "F" Pickups.**

Removal (Bronco II & Ranger)

Remove the instrument cluster. Disconnect the printed circuit connector buttons from the instrument voltage regulator. Remove attaching screw and instrument voltage regulator. Remove all retaining nuts and lamp bulbs and remove printed circuit.

Installation

To install, carefully position circuit to back of cluster and engage with plastic locating pins. To complete installation, reverse removal procedure.

Removal (Vans)

1) Remove instrument panel cluster. Disconnect (snap off) printed circuit connector buttons from instrument voltage regulator.

Fig. 3: Exploded View of Bronco & "F" Pickups Instrument Cluster (Back View)

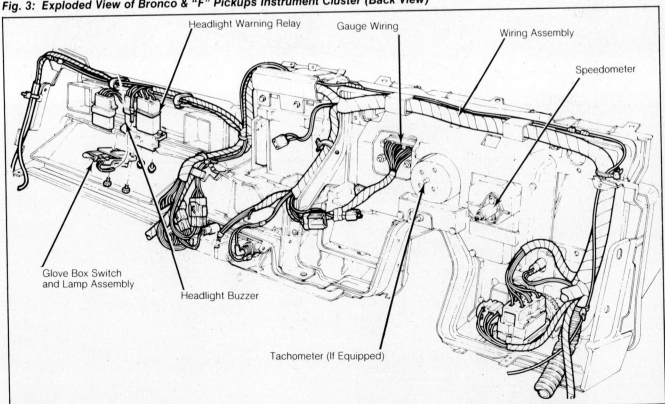

Headlight Warning Relay

Gauge Wiring

Wiring Assembly

Speedometer

Glove Box Switch and Lamp Assembly

Headlight Buzzer

Tachometer (If Equipped)

Switches & Instrument Panels

FORD (Cont.)

2) Disconnect multiple feed plug and remove the attaching screw, then remove the IVR from cluster assembly. Remove gauge retaining nuts, light bulbs, and printed circuit board from cluster.

Installation

To install, reverse removal procedure. Printed circuit board must be carefully positioned to back of cluster and engaged with the plastic locating pins.

HEADLIGHT SWITCH

Removal & Installation (Bronco II & Ranger)

Diconnect battery ground. Pull headlamp switch knob to "ON" position. Depress the shaft release button and remove knob and shaft assembly. Remove the instrument panel finish panel. Unscrew the mounting nut.

Remove switch from under instrument panel. and remove wiring from switch. To install, reverse removal procedure.

Removal (All Other Models)

1) Disconnect battery ground cable. On Bronco and "F" pickups, remove knob from switch shaft and remove center finish panel. Remove switch from back side of instrument panel.

2) On Van models, remove knob and shaft by pressing the knob release button switch housing, with knob in full "ON" position. Pull knob and shaft out of switch and unscrew mounting nut. Remove bezel and switch and then remove wiring connector.

Installation

To install, reverse removal procedure.

Fig. 4: Rear View of Bronco II and Ranger Instrument Panel

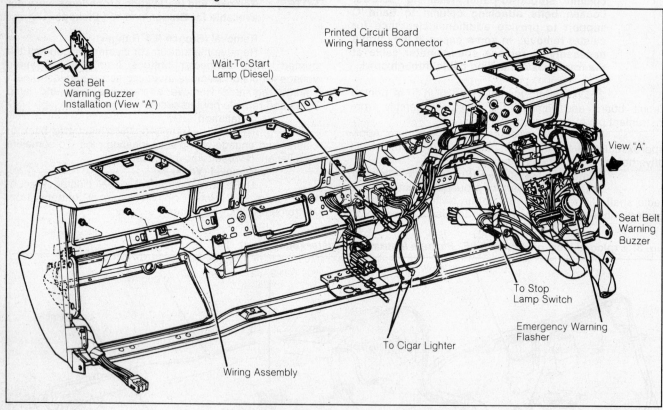

GENERAL MOTORS

Chevolet, GMC

DESCRIPTION

All instruments and gauges are installed in the instrument cluster. "C", "K" and "S" models can be serviced in the vehicle. "G" models require removal of the entire instrument cluster from the vehicle prior to servicing. Indicator lamps and illuminating bulbs may be replaced on all models without removing instrument cluster from vehicle.

TESTING & TROUBLE SHOOTING

INDICATOR WARNING LIGHTS

Oil Pressure Indicator

1) Indicator light is inoperative with ignition switch on and engine not running. Check for burned out bulb, open light circuit or defective oil pressure switch.

2) Indicator light is on and engine is running above idle speed. Indicates low oil pressure, defective oil pressure switch or ground condition between light and switch.

Fig. 1: General Motors "G" Models Instrument Cluster

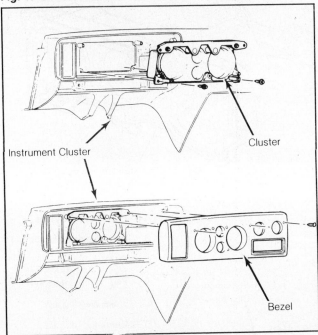

Instrument Cluster

Cluster

Bezel

Temperature Indicator

1) If "HOT" indicator light is inoperative when cranking engine, check for burned out light bulb, open light circuit or a defective ignition switch.

2) When light is on with engine running, check for coolant temperature above 258°F (125°C), grounded condition between light and switch, defective temperature sender or ignition switch.

Charging Indicator

1) If light is on with ignition "OFF", check for shorted positive diode. If light is not on with ignition "ON" and engine not running, check for burned out bulb, open in light circuit or open in field.

2) If light is on with engine running above idle speed, check for no alternator output, shorted negative diode or loose or broken alternator belt.

Fig. 2: General Motors "S" Models Instrument Cluster

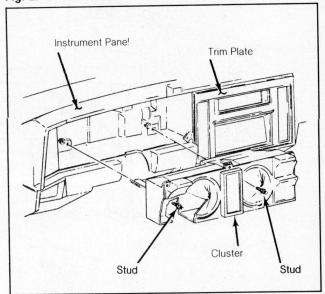

Instrument Panel

Trim Plate

Stud

Cluster

Stud

FUEL GAUGE

1) Use Fuel Gauge Tester (J-24538-A or equivalent). Disconnect feed wire from the fuel gauge tank terminal and connect one test lead to the wire and ground the other lead. Turn ignition "ON". If gauge responds but not accurately, proceed to step 2). If gauge does not respond, go to step 3). If gauge responds accurately, go to step 5).

2) Remove gauge and check for loose nuts at gauge terminals. If nuts are loose and gauge reads between 1/4 and 1/2 with 90 ohms from tester, tighten nuts and reinstall gauge. If gauge is inaccurate in other ways and/or nuts are tight, replace gauge.

3) Disconnect front body connector. Connect tester to lead going to gauge. If gauge responds accurately, check wiring between rear compartment and front body connector. If gauge does not respond, go to step 4).

4) Remove gauge. Check for bad connections at gauge terminal or instrument cluster connection. If connections are good, replace gauge. If bad, repair connections and replace gauge.

5) Check rear compartment connector and wires to sender. If okay, replace sender. If not, repair wire or connector.

OIL PRESSURE GAUGE

1) Disconnect oil gauge sender wire in rear compartment and connect tester (J-24538-A) to sender and ground. Turn ignition "ON". If gauge responds to tester accurately, replace sender. If gauge does not respond, go to step 2). If gauge responds but not accurately, go to step 4).

2) Disconnect oil gauge lead at wiring harness connector. Connect tester to lead that goes to gauge. If gauge responds to tester accurately, check wiring between sender connections and engine harness connector. If gauge does not respond, go to step 3).

Switches & Instrument Panels
GENERAL MOTORS (Cont.)

Fig. 3: General Motors "C" & "K" Models Instrument Cluster

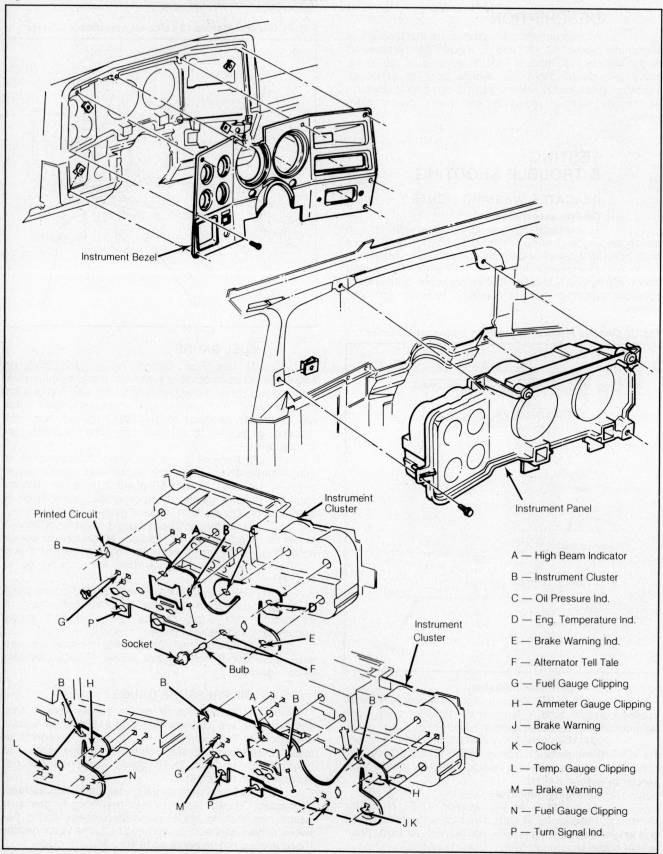

Instrument Bezel

Printed Circuit

Instrument Cluster

Instrument Panel

Socket

Bulb

Instrument Cluster

A — High Beam Indicator

B — Instrument Cluster

C — Oil Pressure Ind.

D — Eng. Temperature Ind.

E — Brake Warning Ind.

F — Alternator Tell Tale

G — Fuel Gauge Clipping

H — Ammeter Gauge Clipping

J — Brake Warning

K — Clock

L — Temp. Gauge Clipping

M — Brake Warning

N — Fuel Gauge Clipping

P — Turn Signal Ind.

GENERAL MOTORS (Cont.)

3) Remove gauge. Check for bad connections at gauge terminals or instrument cluster connector. If connections are good, replace gauge. If bad, repair connections and reinstall gauge.

4) Remove gauge and check for loose nuts at gauge terminals. If nuts are loose and gauge reads slightly below midscale with 90 ohms from tester, tighten nuts and reinstall gauge. If gauge is inaccurate in other ways and/or nuts are tight, replace gauge.

TEMPERATURE GAUGE

1) Disconnect temperature gauge sender wire in rear compartment and connect tester (J-24538-A) to sender and ground. Turn ignition "ON". If gauge responds to tester accurately, replace sender. If gauge does not respond, go to step **2)**. If gauge responds but not accurately, go to step **4)**.

2) Disconnect temperature gauge lead at wiring harness connector. Connect the tester to lead that goes to gauge. If gauge responds accurately, check wiring between sender connections and engine harness connector. If gauge does not respond, go to step **3)**.

3) Remove gauge. Check for bad connections at gauge terminals or instrument cluster connector. If connections are good, replace gauge. If bad, repair connections and reinstall gauge.

4) Remove gauge and check for loose nuts at gauge terminals or lack of ground connection to gauge. If connections are bad, repair connections and reinstall gauge. If connections are good, replace gauge.

AMMETER GAUGE

If gauge fails to read correctly, test charging system. *See Delco-Remy Alternators in ELECTRICAL Section for testing procedures.*

SPEEDOMETER

1) If speedometer is noisy, check for kinked, pinched or burnt casings. Check for bent cable tips, improper or insufficient lubrication of cable, or rough drive gear.

2) If speedometer whines, driven gear stem in transmission could be binding with adapter. If calibration is wrong, possible causes include wrong transmission adapter, wrong drive gear or sleeve, over or undersize tires, and faulty speedometer head.

REMOVAL & INSTALLATION

SPEEDOMETER & GAUGES

All Models

All instruments and gauges are installed in the instrument cluster. On "C" and "K" and "S" models they may be serviced in the vehicle. On "G" models, the entire cluster must be removed for service.

INSTRUMENT CLUSTER

"C" & "K" Models

1) Disconnect battery ground cable and remove headlight switch control knob and radio control knobs. Remove steering column cover, and 8 screws attaching bezel. Remove bezel.

2) Reach up under instrument panel cluster and disconnect speedometer by depressing tang on rear of speedometer head and pulling cable free.

3) Remove cluster from vehicle for further disassembly as required. To install, reverse removal procedure.

"G" Models

1) Disconnect battery ground cable. Reach up under instrument panel cluster and disconnect speedometer cable by depressing tang while pulling cable free.

2) Remove clock set stem knob. Remove bezel attaching screws and remove bezel. Remove lower cluster attaching screws. Pull top of cluster away from instrument panel and lift out bottom of cluster. Unplug harness connector from printed circuit and remove cluster.

3) To install, reverse removal procedure making sure that clips at top of cluster slip into instrument panel opening after bottom of cluster is installed.

"S" Models

1) Disconnect battery ground cable. Remove 5 screws and remove instrument cluster trim plate. Remove instrument panel face plate. Remove lens and speedometer cable.

2) Disconnect electrical connector from instrument cluster and remove cluster. To install, reverse removal procedure.

PRINTED CIRCUITS

All Models

1) Remove instrument cluster, all cluster light assemblies and printed circuit retaining screws.

2) On "G" Models, remove fuel, temperature and ammeter terminal nuts retaining printed circuits to rear of cluster. On all models, remove printed circuits from rear of cluster.

3) To install, reverse removal procedure while noting that retaining screws serve as ground for printed circuit. They must be properly installed to provide proper ground connection.

HEADLIGHT SWITCH

"C" & "K" Models

1) Disconnect battery ground cable. Reach up behind instrument cluster, depress shaft retaining button and remove switch knob and rod. Remove cluster bezel screws at left end, and pull out on bezel. Hold switch nut with wrench.

2) Disconnect multiple wiring connectors at switch terminals. To remove switch, turn while holding switch nut. To install, reverse removal procedure.

"G" Models

1) Disconnect battery ground cable. Reach up behind instrument panel and remove switch knob and shaft by depressing retaining button. Remove switch retaining nut from front of panel and push switch through panel opening.

2) Remove multiple electrical connector at switch terminals. To install, reverse removal procedure making sure ground ring is installed on switch.

"S" Models

1) Disconnect battery ground cable. Pull headlight switch to "ON" position. Reach up under instrument panel and depress switch shaft retainer button while pulling on the switch control shaft knob.

2) Remove 3 screws and remove switch trim plate. Use a large bladed screwdriver to remove light switch ferrule nut from front of instrument panel. Disconnect connector from bottom of light switch. To install, reverse removal procedure.

Switches & Instrument Panels

JEEP

All Models

DESCRIPTION

"CJ" & SCRAMBLER MODELS

Instrument panel is composed of speedometer housing, panel lights, high beam indicator, turn signal indicators, brake failure/parking brake warning indicator, temperature gauge, and combination fuel gauge and constant voltage regulator (CVR). Other gauges include tachometer, voltmeter and oil pressure gauge.

CHEROKEE, TRUCK & WAGONEER MODELS

Instrument cluster is composed of speedometer housing, panel lights, high beam indicator, turn signal indicators, ammeter, oil pressure gauge, temperature and fuel gauges, constant voltage regulator (CVR), brake failure warning bulb, lock-out warning bulbs (Quadra-Trac), emergency drive indicator, heater control lights, wiper/washer control lights, and blower motor fan switch.

OPERATION

AMMETER

Used to indicate current flow into and out of battery, depending on vehicle electrical load. It is regular equipment on all but "CJ" and Scrambler models.

FUEL LEVEL GAUGE

System consists of a fuel gauge, sending unit in fuel tank, appropriate wiring and constant voltage regulator (CVR). Gauge is grounded through variable resistor of sending unit. A float attached to a slide rheostat follows fuel level and varying resistance increases or decreases indicator reading.

TEMPERATURE GAUGE

System consists of gauge and sending unit, appropriate wiring and constant voltage regulator (CVR). Gauge is grounded through variable resistor of sending unit. Changes in coolant temperature vary resistance in sending unit, increasing or decreasing indication on gauge.

VOLTMETER

Used on "CJ" and Scrambler models only, system consists of a voltmeter and related wiring. Voltmeter indicates regulated voltage to provide an indication of the charging system's ability to maintain battery charge.

OIL PRESSURE GAUGE

Consists of magnetic type gauge, a variable resistance sending unit and wiring on all "CJ" and Scrambler models. There are 2 coils in gauge, one directly grounded, the other connected to sending unit. Resistance is controlled in sending unit by oil pressure. Magnetic fields are created around both coils in gauge. Needle is attracted to coil having greater current flow.

On all other models, oil pressure gauge system consists of CVR-powered gauge, variable resistance sending unit, and CVR. Gauge needle, attached to

bi-metal strip, responds to temperature changes. It moves as current flows from CVR through heating coil around bi-metal strip, and to ground at sending unit on engine.

CONSTANT VOLTAGE REGULATOR

On "CJ" and Scrambler models, CVR is built into fuel gauge. On all other models it is built into temperature gauge. CVR provides equal regulated voltage to each gauge.

The CVR's function is to regulate variable input voltage available from vehicle battery or charging system to provide a constant 5 volt output to gauges. The CVR does not produce a steady DC voltage output, but rather a pulsating voltage averaging 5 volts. Output voltage averaging lower or higher than 5 volts will result in proportionately higher or lower gauge readings.

TESTING

OIL PRESSURE GAUGE

1) To test accuracy of oil pressure gauge, use a variable resistance tester (J-24538 or equivalent).

2) Disconnect wire from sending unit on engine. Turn ignition "ON". Connect one lead of tester to ground and other lead to sending unit wire. Compare results with specifications shown in table.

OIL PRESSURE GAUGE TEST READINGS

Application	psi	Ohms
"CJ" & Scrambler	0	234-246
	40	100-106
	80	32-35
Cherokee, Truck & Wagoneer	0	69-77
	10	35-38
	60	13-15
	80	9-11

FUEL & TEMPERATURE GAUGES

1) Test with a variable resistance tester (J-24538 or equivalent) or extra fuel tank sending unit. If using fuel tank sender unit, attach one ohmmeter lead to sending unit and other lead to sending unit ground wire. Move float arm and mark arm location at each of the appropriate resistance values.

2) Disconnect sending wire from sending unit. Connect one lead of tester or extra sending unit to sending wire and other to ground. Turn ignition to "ON" position. Adjust tester or sender to known ohm values and observe gauge indication at each ohm setting.

TEMPERATURE SENDING UNIT RESISTANCES

Gauge Needle Position	Ohms
"C"	73
Beginning of Band	36
End of Band	13
"H"	9

JEEP (Cont.)

FUEL GAUGE SENDING UNIT RESISTANCES

Gauge Needle Position	Ohms
Empty	[1] 61
1/2 Full	23
Full	10

[1] — "CJ" and Scrambler models 73 ohms.

Fig. 1: Testing Temperature Gauge

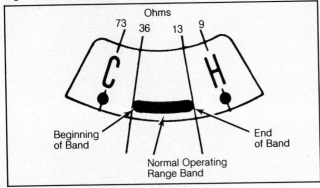

When known resistance is sent to gauge, needle should move to listed position.

VOLTMETER

Connect voltmeter of known accuracy across battery terminals. Turn ignition switch "ON" and compare indication of test voltmeter with indication of vehicle voltmeter. Replace if readings vary.

REMOVAL & INSTALLATION

SPEEDOMETER & GAUGES

Instrument panel must be removed to gain access to speedometer and gauges for repair or replacement.

INSTRUMENT CLUSTER

"CJ" & Scrambler Models

1) Disconnect battery ground cable. Separate speedometer cable from speedometer head. If equipped

Fig. 2: Jeep Instrument Cluster

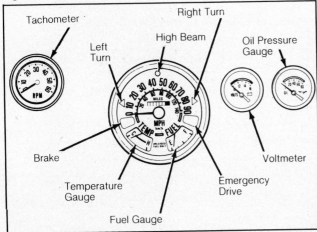

"CJ" and Scrambler models.

with air conditioning, remove screws attaching evaporator to instrument panel and lower evaporator.

2) Remove attaching screws and remove cluster. Note position of all lamps and electrical wires. Remove cluster electrical connectors. To install, reverse removal procedures.

Cherokee, Truck & Wagoneer Models

1) Disconnect battery ground cable. Disconnect speedometer cable. Cover steering column. Remove cluster retaining screws. Tilt top of cluster toward interior of vehicle. Mark electrical connectors and hoses and disconnect heater vacuum hoses and electrical connections. Disconnect blend air door control cable.

NOTE: **Tag hoses to ensure proper connections when installing the cluster.**

2) Remove instrument cluster assembly. To install, reverse removal procedure.

Fig. 3: Jeep Instrument Cluster

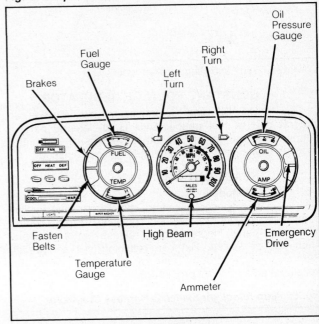

Cherokee, Truck and Wagoneer models.

PRINTED CIRCUITS

NOTE: **Only Cherokee, Truck and Wagoneer use printed circuit board. "CJ" and Scrambler models use direct wiring for all gauges and cluster lamps.**

Cherokee, Truck & Wagoneer

1) Remove instrument cluster, radio noise suppressor, and all lamps from cluster (twist counterclockwise to remove). Remove circuit board and gauge assembly. Remove retaining nuts from ammeter and oil pressure gauges. Lift ammeter, oil pressure gauge and plate out of cluster as an assembly.

2) Remove retaining nuts from fuel and temperature gauges. Remove large ground screw from circuit board above speedometer. Remove speedometer, fuel gauge and temperature gauge as an assembly. To install, reverse removal procedure, checking gauge lenses for fingerprints.

Fig. 4: Rear View of Jeep Instrument Cluster

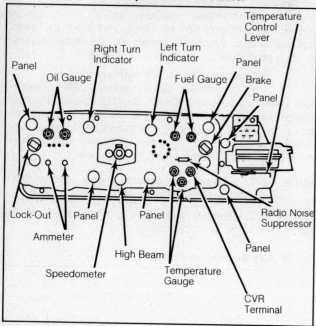

Cherokee, Truck and Wagoneer models.

CONSTANT VOLTAGE REGULATOR

On "CJ" and Scrambler models, CVR is an integral part of fuel gauge. CVR is an integral part of temperature gauge on all other models. If regulator requires replacement, entire gauge must be replaced.

HEADLIGHT SWITCH

All Models

Disconnect connector plug from switch. Pull control knob out to second position. From behind instrument panel, depress knob release button and pull knob out of switch. Remove retaining nut and bezel. Remove switch through rear of instrument panel. To install, reverse removal procedures.

Fig. 5: Jeep Headlight Switch & Harness Connector

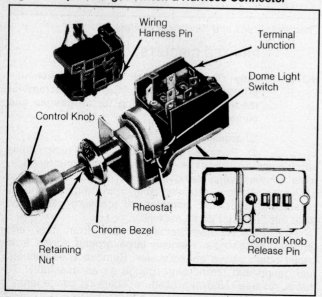

Remove switch through rear of instrument panel.

ALL MANUFACTURERS

DESCRIPTION

Turn signal and hazard flasher circuits are integral systems using a common switch assembly mounted within upper steering column housing. Signal lever is on left side of column and hazard switch knob is on right side.

Two different flasher units are used. The hazard flasher is a variable load type and will operate regardless of the number of lights burned out. If one signal light is burned out, signal circuit will not function on same side due to insufficient current draw to operate flasher. *For wiring diagrams of individual models, refer to chassis wiring diagrams in WIRING DIAGRAM Section.*

Fig. 1: Wiring Diagram of Typical Turn Signal and Hazard Flasher System

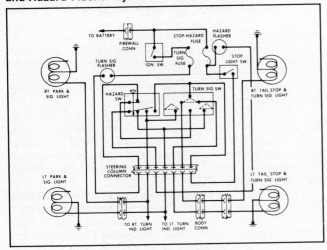

OPERATION

TURN SIGNALS

Signal systems operate only when ignition switch is turned on. Normal frequency of signal lights is about 60-120 flashes per minute. Switch has 2 detent positions for each signal direction.

With signal lever in first detent, lights will blink, but will go off if switch lever is released. Second switch detent will hold signal on, until steering wheel canceling fingers automatically turn signal off.

HAZARD FLASHER

With knob activated, all park and stop lights flash simultaneously regardless of ignition switch position. Depressing brake pedal will override flasher operation until pedal is released.

During hazard switch operation on Chrysler Corp. vehicles, the turn signal should be off to avoid creating electric feed back through accessory circuits. This could cause intermittent operation of circuits left turned on.

FLASHER LOCATION

CHRYSLER CORP.

Hazard

Located to the right of the fuse block on all models.

Turn Signal

Located to the right of the fuse block on all models.

FORD MOTOR CO.

Hazard

On "F" and Bronco models, under instrument panel to the left of steering column, on back side of fuse panel. On "E" models, in wiring harness near left side cowl.

Turn Signal

Located on fuse block on "F" and Bronco models, or on wiring harness near left side cowl on "E" models.

GENERAL MOTORS

Hazard

Mounted on the fuse panel.

Turn Signal

Located near fuse block at left of steering column on all models.

JEEP

Hazard

Mounted on the fuse panel.

Turn Signal

Mounted on the fuse panel.

TESTING & TROUBLE SHOOTING

TURN SIGNAL & HAZARD SYSTEM

Hazard Flasher Inoperative

1) Switch turn signals on. If signals operate, check hazard circuit fuse. Check power to hazard circuit fuse and test fuse. If fuse is blown, check for shorts and/or replace fuse. If fuse is satisfactory, check power to hazard flasher. Replace with a good flasher.

2) If system still fails, check power to hazard switch in steering column. Repair circuit between hazard flasher element and switch if necessary. To determine if switch is at fault, connect a known good switch in column to chassis connector and operate switch by hand. If hazard system now operates, repair or replace switch.

Turn Signals Inoperative

1) Turn on hazard system. If all lights operate, inspect for blown turn signal fuse or defective flasher. If fuse is blown, check for shorts between fuse and lamps. If turn signal fuse and flasher are satisfactory, check wire terminals in harness connector for continuity and power feed to and from switch.

2) To determine if switch is bad, connect a known good switch in column to chassis connector and operate switch by hand. If signals now operate, replace switch.

Turn Signals Inoperative (One Side)

1) Turn on hazard system. If one or more lights are inoperative, replace lights as necessary. Test light sockets for power or poor ground connection.

2) If all lights operate with hazard system on, inspect for improper lamp or inoperative turn signal switch. If turn signal flasher can be heard, but lights do not operate, check for a short circuit.

Wiper/Washer Systems

CHRYSLER CORP.

All Models

DESCRIPTION

Standard 2-speed and intermittent wiper motors have permanent magnetic fields and are controlled by feeding power to different brushes for low and high speed. Motor speed is selected by rotating switch knob.

A 6-ampere circuit breaker is integral with wiper switch in protecting wiper system. Washer system is electrically operated and consists of an electric pump, sealed motor, reservoir, rubber hoses and nozzles.

NOTE: **Wiper motors are basically the same. The intermittent wiper system does employ the following additions: Delay mode of 2-15 seconds, high speed is higher than standard, with a extra wipe after wash.**

TROUBLE SHOOTING

WIPER SYSTEM

Wiper Inoperative

Binding linkage. Faulty wiper switch. Open or grounded wiring. Faulty motor.

Motor Runs But Output Crank Does Not Turn

Stripped intermediate gear or output gear. Output gear slips on output shaft. Crank arm not fastened properly to output gear shaft.

Motor Does Not Shut Off

Defective park switch.

Blades Will Not Park

Motor park switch open. Faulty instrument panel switch. Arm set at incorrect position. Open park wiring circuit.

Motor Will Not Run, Circuit Breaker Does Not Cycle

Open circuit in wiring. Loose bulkhead connector. Motor not grounded. Faulty circuit breaker, instrument panel switch or motor.

Motor Will Not Run, Circuit Breaker Cycles

Grounded wiring. Binding linkage. Faulty motor or instrument panel switch circuit breaker.

Motor Stops In Any Position When Switch is Turned Off

Motor park switch open. Open park wiring circuit. Faulty instrument panel switch.

Motor Will Not Stop When Switch Turned Off

Defective park switch.

WASHER SYSTEM

Pump Runs But No Fluid Comes Out

No fluid in reservoir. Nozzle jet plugged or under intake grille. Broken hose or faulty pump.

System Operates Intermittently

Loose or faulty wiring connections. Faulty switch or motor.

System Output Low

Low aimed nozzles. Leaking hoses. Poor electrical connections. Defective motor.

Pump Motor Does Not Run

Broken wires. Faulty motor or switch. Poor ground. Loose wiring terminals.

TESTING

MOTOR WILL NOT RUN

1) Position panel switch in low-speed position. If motor can be heard running, check motor output shaft. If shaft is not turning, gearbox assembly requires replacement.

2) If the shaft is turning, check drive link to output shaft for worn parts or disconnected components. If motor cannot be heard running, connect a voltmeter or test lamp between motor terminal "L" and ground.

3) If voltage is present and panel switch circuit breaker is not cycling, check for open ground circuit. Ground strap must make good contact.

4) If motor runs, panel switch is not grounded, switch is faulty or there is an open in wiring. Common brush may not be making good contact with commutator and may require freeing-up or repositioning of spring. Armature may have an open circuit.

5) If voltage is present only part of the time, the circuit breaker is cycling. Problem may be a faulty circuit breaker or a short in the wiring, motor, or switch panel. Remove wiper arms and blades, disconnect harness at the motor and connect an ammeter between battery and terminal "L".

6) If motor runs with average ammeter reading below 6 amperes, motor is good and trouble is in switch panel or wiring. If motor does not run and draw is more than 6 amperes, check wiper linkage for binding. Disconnect drive link from motor. If motor runs and draws less than 3 amperes, repair linkage.

7) If motor fails to run or draws more than 3 amperes, check motor and gearbox for internal jamming. If no internal jamming exists, check motor for brush leads shorting to housing or armature for burned or blackened windings which could indicate an internal short.

MOTOR RUNS AT LOW SPEED ONLY

Position switch in high position and connect test lamp between terminal "H" and ground. If lamp does not light, an open exists in wiring or switch. If lamp lights, brush is not making contact with armature.

Fig. 1: Two Speed Intermittent Wiper Motor Terminals

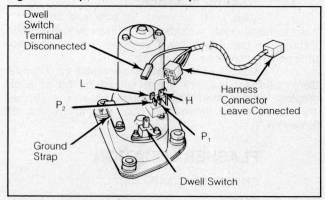

Standard terminal similar.

CHRYSLER CORP. (Cont.)

MOTOR RUNS AT HIGH SPEED ONLY

Position switch in low position and connect test lamp between terminal "L" and ground. If lamp does not light, an open exists in wiring or switch. If lamp lights at terminal "L", brush is not making contact with armature.

MOTOR CONTINUES TO RUN WITH SWITCH IN OFF OR PARK POSITION

Remove wiring harness and connect a jumper wire from terminal "P2" to terminal "L", then connect a jumper from "P1" to battery. If motor now runs to park position and stops, panel switch is defective. If motor continues to run and does not park, gearbox assembly requires replacement.

MOTOR WILL NOT STOP IN PARK POSITION WHEN SWITCH IS IN OFF POSITION

1) Remove wiring connector and clean terminals. If problem continues, place switch in park position and connect a voltmeter or test lamp between terminal "P₁" and "L". If 12 volts are present or test lamp lights, check for voltage at "P₂".

2) If voltage is zero or test lamp does not light, motor park switch is defective and must be replaced. If 12 volts are present or lamp lights, an open exists in panel switch or wiring.

2-SPEED WIPER SWITCH

1) Disconnect wiring from switch and remove switch from instrument panel. Use a continuity tester or ohmmeter to check for continuity between contact terminals of switch as shown in table.

2) For test purposes, first position is "OFF", "LOW" is first detent from "OFF" position and "HIGH" is second detent from "OFF" position. Ground is the case of wiper switch.

SWITCH CONTINUITY

Off	Low	High
B to B/U	B to B/U	B to B/U
B to P1	B to P1	B to P1
A to P2	B to A	B to H
H-Open	P2-Open	P2-Open
	H-Open	A-Open

Fig. 3: Chrysler 2-Speed Wiper Wiring Diagram

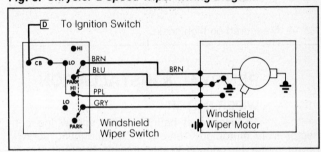

INTERMITTENT WIPER SWITCH

1) Disconnect wiring from switch and remove switch from instrument panel. Use a continuity tester or ohmmeter to check for continuity between contact terminals of switch as shown in table. For test purposes, first position is "OFF", next is position for "DELAY WIPE", "LOW" is first detent and "HIGH" is second detent.

2) Case of wiper switch is grounded. Resistance at maximum delay position should be between 270,000 ohms and 330,000 ohms. Resistance at minimum delay position should be zero with ohmmeter set on the high ohm scale. Positive lead of ohmmeter connected to "P₂" and negative lead connected to "G" should show low resistance.

Fig. 2: Chrysler Intermittent Wiper Wiring Diagram

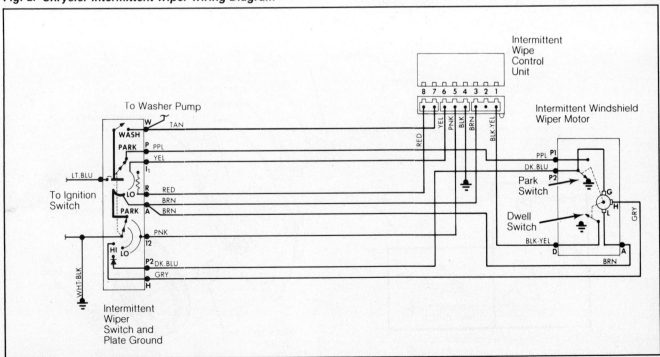

3) Negative lead of ohmmeter connected to "P$_2$" and positive connected to "G" should show an open circuit or very high resistance. If there is the same resistance in both minimum and maximum delay positions, switch is defective.

INTERMITTENT SWITCH CONTINUITY

Off	Delay	Low/High
B-P$_1$	B-I$_1$	B-A
A-G	R-I$_1$	P$_2$-G
....	P$_2$-G	[1] H-G

[1] — Measured on high scale.

REMOVAL & INSTALLATION

WIPER MOTOR
1) Disconnect battery cable, and wiring connector from motor and remove motor mounting screws. Lower motor far enough to gain access to crank arm-to-drive link retainer bushing.

2) Remove crank arm by prying retainer bushing from crank arm pin. Remove motor and nut attaching crank arm to motor drive shaft. Remove crank arm from motor. To install, reverse removal procedure.

WASHER PUMP
1) Drain fluid from reservoir. Remove reservoir mounting screws, reservoir and pump assembly. Disconnect electrical lead and rubber hose from bottom of pump.

2) Using an extension and deep socket, remove pump mounting nut and plastic washer by reaching through reservoir neck. Remove pump and rubber grommet from reservoir. To install, reverse removal procedures.

OVERHAUL

WIPER MOTOR
Disassembly
Hold wiper motor in a vise and remove housing through bolts. Remove housing and armature assembly. Remove flat washers and spring washer.

Reassembly
1) Hold gear box in vise with brush holder up. Pull brushes back in brush slots and push brush lead into holding notch. Clean commutator with ink eraser. Install flat washer, spring washer and flat washer on armature shaft.

2) Place armature shaft in brush holder assembly. Release brush leads from brush holder notches, (ensuring that brushes are spring loaded against commutator). Align the window in the motor housing with the brush holder. Install housing quickly over armature so magnets do not pull armature out of brush holder.

3) Make sure motor housing is flush with gear housing and over the 4 detents. Install through bolts. Install part number tag and retaining screw. Bench test motor by connecting 12 volt power source. Connect positive lead in series with ammeter to terminal "L".

4) On 2-speed motor, ground the ground strap with a jumper wire. On intermittent wipe motors, connect a jumper wire from terminal "P2" to ground. On all models, tap the assembly gently with mallet to align bearings. Stop tapping when meter reads less than 2.5 amps. Install bulkhead seal.

Fig. 4: Chrysler Corp. Wiper Motor Exploded View

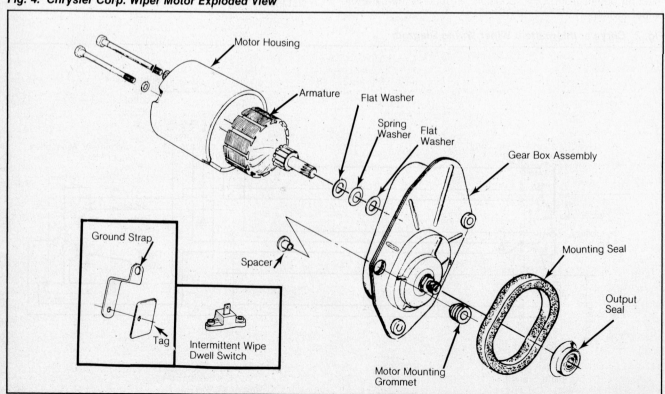

FORD — BRONCO II & RANGER

DESCRIPTION

Windshield wipers are actuated by a permanent magnet, rotary type electric motor. The 2 wiper arms and blades are mounted on pivot shafts at each side of windshield.

The pivot shafts are connected to the motor by linkage arms and attaching clips. Both standard and interval wiper/washer systems feature a lever type wiper/washer switch mounted on the steering column.

OPERATION

STANDARD SYSTEM

Switch has 3 positions: "OFF", "LOW" and "HI", with "OFF" being the lowest position and "HI" being the highest position from floor. To operate washer, pull the switch toward the driver. Switch must be in "LOW" or "HI" to operate washer.

INTERMITTENT SYSTEM

"LOW" and "HI" speed operation is the same as the standard wiper system. When the wiper switch is in the "INTERVAL" position, wipers make single swipes separated by a pause. The control knob on the end of the wiper control switch sets the length of the pause from 1 to 12 seconds.

To operate the washer, pull the control lever out. If the lever is in "LOW" or "HI" position, washers operate with no change in wiper operation. If the wiper control switch is in "OFF" or "INT" position, wipers will run as long as lever is pulled. When the lever is released, washers will stop immediately but wipers will operate for 1 to 4 cycles and then return to "OFF" or "INT" operation.

TESTING

WIPER MOTOR CURRENT DRAW

1) Disconnect battery ground. Disconnect the linkage from the motor and disconnect the electrical plug

Fig. 1: Motor Current Draw Test

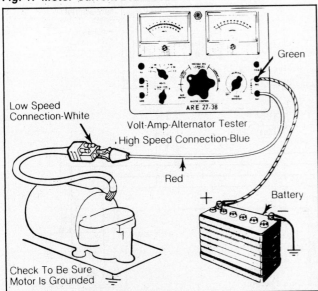

Current draw should not exceed 3 amps.

to test the motor on the vehicle. Connect the negative lead from ammeter to the battery positive post.

2) Connect the positive lead first to the low speed connection and then to the high speed connection at the connector plug as shown in *Fig. 1*. In either case, current draw should not exceed 3 amps.

CIRCUIT BREAKER

1) Before connecting the circuit breaker to the volt-amp tester, short the leads together and adjust the current draw until it equals circuit breaker rating. Connect the breaker to the ammeter. Leave the breaker connected to the tester for 10 minutes. Hold the current reading on the ammeter at the rated current. If the circuit breaker opens during the 10 minutes, replace the circuit breaker.

2) Short the tester leads together and adjust the current draw until it is twice the rated current. Connect the breaker. Hold the current reading on the ammeter at twice the rated current. The circuit breaker should open and the current drop to zero within 30 seconds.

SWITCH CONTINUITY

1) Check the continuity between switch terminals. *See Fig. 2.* Either a self-powered test light or an ohmmeter can be used with standard system. An ohmmeter must be used with interval system.

2) To detect marginal operation of the switch, move the switch lever while each reading is taken. If the switch does not exibit continuity or exibits poor continuity in any switch position, replace the switch.

WIPER SWITCH CONTINUITY

Switch Position	Standard Switch	Interval Switch
"OFF"	P-L	....
"LOW"	B-L	B-L
"HIGH"	B-H	B-H-L
"WASH"	B-W	B-W
"INTERVAL"	....	B-I

Fig. 2: Wiper Switch Connectors

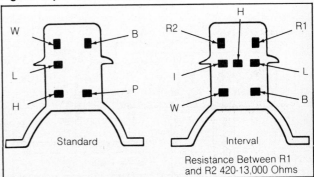

Standard   Interval

Resistance Between R1 and R2 420-13,000 Ohms

PARKING TEST

1) Stop wiper blades with ignition switch so that wiper blades are not in park position. Connect jumper wires as shown in *Fig. 3*. Wiper should run not more than one full cycle and then park. If the motor will not park or will not run to park position, replace motor.

2) If the motor stops, check the windshield wiper manual control switch and wiring for continuity. If switch and wiring check out okay and wiper does not stop in "OFF" or interval setting, replace interval governor.

Wiper/Washer Systems

FORD — BRONCO II & RANGER (Cont.)

Fig. 3: Motor Park Test

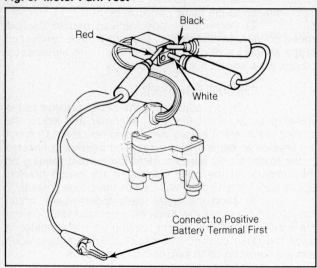

Red
Black
White

Connect to Positive
Battery Terminal First

Wipers should run not more than one full cycle and park.

REMOVAL & INSTALLATION

WIPER MOTOR

Removal

1) Turn the wiper switch on. Turn the ignition switch on until the blades are straight up and then turn ignition off to keep blades positioned up. Remove the right wiper arm and blade. Disconnect battery ground. Remove right pivot nut and allow the linkage to drop into cowl.

2) Remove linkage access cover. Reach through the access cover opening and unsnap the wiper motor clip. Push the clip away from the linkage until it clears the nib on the crank pin. Push the clip off the linkage. Remove the wiper motor wiring connector. Remove wiper motor attaching screws and remove the motor.

Installation

To install, reverse removal procedure. Install the clip first to the linkage. Do NOT try to install the linkage to the motor crank pin and then try to install the clip. The clip is properly installed if the nib is protruding through the center of the clip.

WIPER CONTROL SWITCH

Removal & Installation

Disconnect battery ground. Remove the trim shrouds. Disconnect the quick connect electrical connector. Peel back the foam sight shield and remove the wiper/washer switch. To install, reverse removal procedure.

INTERVAL GOVERNOR

Removal & Installation

Disconnect battery ground. Remove steering coulmn shroud. Unplug governor connector from wiper control switch. Unplug instrument panel wiring harness connector from governor. Remove mounting screws and remove governor. To install, reverse removal procedure.

WIPER ARMS

Removal

Raise the blade up from the windshield and move the slide latch away from the pivot shaft. This unlocks the wiper arm from the pivot shaft and holds the blade off of the glass. Pull off the wiper arm.

Installation

1) To install, push the main arm head over the pivot shaft. Make sure the pivot shaft is in the park position. Hold the main arm head onto the pivot shaft while raising the blade end of wiper arm and push slide latch into the lock under the pivot shaft head.

2) Lower blade to windshield. If blade does not touch the windshield, slide latch is not completely in place.

Fig. 4: Bronco II and Ranger Wiper System Wiring Diagram

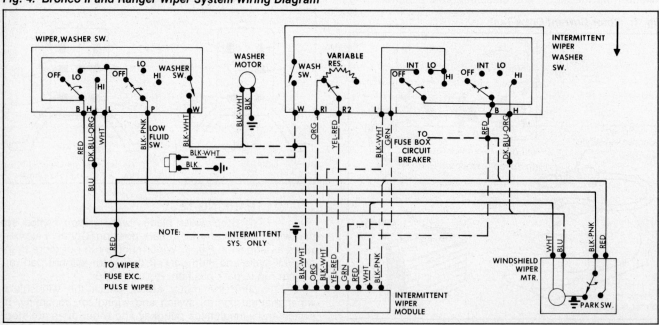

PIVOT SHAFT AND LINKAGE

1) Perform wiper motor removal procedure up to and including the removal of wiper linkage from motor crank pin. Slide the right pivot shaft and linkage assembly out through the right access opening.

2) Remove left wiper arm and blade. Remove left linkage access cover. Remove left pivot nut, lower the linkage and slide out through the left access opening.

Installation

Install the clip completely on the right linkage. Make sure the clip is completely on. Do NOT put the linkage on and then try to install the clip. Slide the left pivot shaft and linkage through the access opening and position the pivot shaft in place. Reinstall the left wiper pivot shaft nut and linkage cover.

WASHER PUMP AND RESERVOIR

Removal

Disconnect lock tab wire connector and hose. Remove retaining screws and lift the assembly from fender. Disconnect washer and radiator overflow hoses.

Installation

To install, reverse removal procedure.

Wiper/Washer Systems

FORD — EXCEPT BRONCO II & RANGER

All Models

DESCRIPTION

Two speed permanent magnet windshield wiper motor is used. The 2-speed motor uses a 3 brush plate and switch assembly. Motor is operated at low speed (control selector is in low position) by grounded brush and Blue wire on "E" models, and by grounded brush and White wire brush on all other models.

To operate motor at high speed, (control selector in high position), grounded brush and White wire brush are used to operate motor at high speed on "E" models and grounded brush and Blue wire brush on all other models. When control selector is moved to park position, motor will continue at low speed until park switch lower contacts open, stopping motor in park position.

Optional interval wipers are available on all models. Intermittent operation is controlled by a variable resistor in the windshield wiper control switch, which combined with the electronic governor allows a variable pause between wiping cycles.

For normal operation on "F" models, turn wiper control knob to right for low or high speed. For intermittent operation, rotate wiper control knob to left. The more the knob is rotated to left, the greater the time interval between wiper blade sweeps.

On "E" models the wiper switch knob slides toward the right with the first position being intermittent, the second is low and the third is high. As the control is moved to the left of intermittent position, the interval between blade sweeps is at a maximum. As the control moves to the right of intermittent detent, the blade sweep interval is reduced.

The electric windshield washer system consists of an instrument panel control switch integral with the wiper control switch, a reservoir and motor assembly, nozzles and connecting hoses.

TESTING

WIPER MOTOR CURRENT DRAW

"E" Models

1) Disconnect linkage from motor and use suitable connector sleeves (kit no. C4AZ-14294-B or equivalent) between motor terminals and a volt-amp meter. Connect positive (Red) lead from meter to center terminal on motor end plate and Green lead from meter to battery positive post.

2) Connect a jumper wire from negative post of battery to low speed terminal on motor end plate and check current draw. Move jumper wire from low speed to high speed terminal and check current draw.

3) Current draw should not exceed 3.5 amperes. If current draw is excessive, check output arm and windlatch mechanism for binding or damage before replacing motor. See Fig. 1.

Bronco and "F" Models.

1) Disconnect linkage from motor and disconnect electrical plug from motor. Connect Green lead from a volt-amp meter to battery positive post and positive (Red) lead from meter to low speed connection at plug. Check current draw.

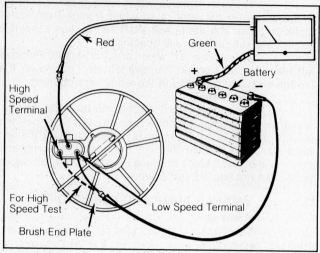

Fig. 1: Testing Motor Current Draw

"E" Models.

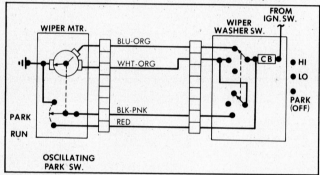

Fig. 2: Wiring Diagram 2-Speed Non-Interval Wipers

Bronco and "F" models.

2) Move positive (Red) lead from the meter to high speed connection at plug and check current draw. Current draw should not exceed 3.0 amperes at either connection. See Fig. 3.

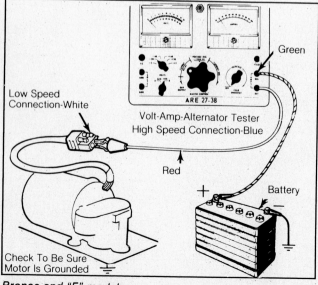

Fig. 3: Motor Current Draw Test

Bronco and "F" models.

FORD — EXCEPT BRONCO II & RANGER (Cont.)

Fig. 4: Wiring Diagram 2-Speed Non-Interval Wipers

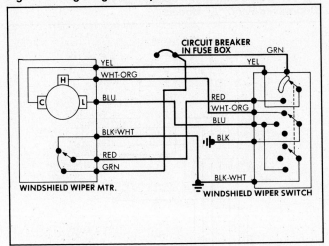

"E" Models.

CIRCUIT BREAKER

Circuit breaker is located in wiper control switch on all rotary switches and in fuse panel for slide wiper control switches. On models with the circuit breaker located in the fuse panel, the rating is 7.5 amps. The circuit breaker integral with the switch is rated at 7 amps. The following test does not apply to vehicles with the circuit breaker located in the fuse panel. See Fig. 5.

Fig. 5: Circuit Breaker Test

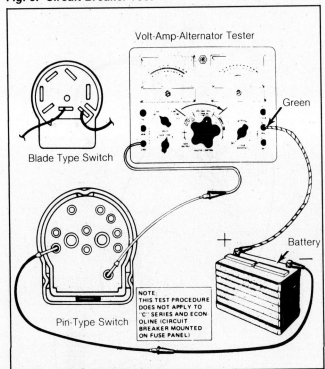

Does not apply to fuse-panel mounted circuit breaker.

1) Before connecting tester leads as shown in Fig. 5, short tester leads together and adjust current draw until it equals circuit breaker rating. Connect switch to tester and leave switch connected for 10 minutes.

2) Current reading should remain at rated current. If circuit breaker opens during the ten minutes, replace wiper switch assembly. Short tester leads together and adjust current draw until it is twice rated current.

3) Connect switch to tester and current reading on ammeter should drop to zero within 20 seconds. If it takes longer than 20 seconds for breaker to open, replace wiper switch assembly.

WIPER SWITCH CONTINUITY TEST

1) Check continuity between switch terminals as shown in illustrations. Either a self powered test light or an ohmmeter can be used to test a standard 2-speed switch. An ohmmeter must be used to test a switch with the intermittent system.

2) To detect marginal operation of switch, rotate knob or slide switch while each reading is being taken. If switch does not exhibit continuity as shown or poor continuity exists, replace switch.

Fig. 6: Blade Type Switch Connector

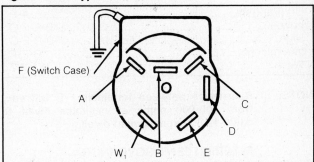

BLADE TYPE SWITCH CONTINUITY

Switch Position	Terminals
Off (Park)	C-D, A-B
Low	A-B-C
High	A-B-E
Wash	A-B-W1

Intermittent Switch Position	Intermittent Terminals
Off (Park)	A-B, D-E
Low	1A-B, D-E-F
High	1D-E-F, A-B-C
Intermittent	[1] E-F, A-B
Wash	A-B-W1

[1] — Variable resistance between terminals D-E should be minimum 200-1000 ohms and maximum 5600-8400 ohms.

Fig. 7: Blade Type (Slide Switch) Connector

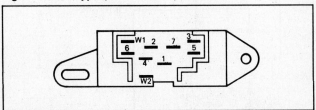

Non-Interval.

Wiper/Washer Systems

FORD — EXCEPT BRONCO II & RANGER (Cont.)

SLIDING TYPE (NON-INTERVAL) SWITCH CONTINUITY

Switch Position (Non-Interval)	Terminals
Off (Park)	1-5, 3-7
Low	1-4, 2-7
High	1-4, 2-6
Wash	W1-W2

Fig. 8: Blade Type (Slide Switch) Connector Interval Type

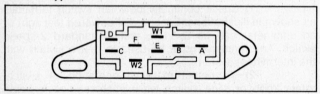

SLIDING TYPE (INTERVAL) SWITCH CONTINUITY

Switch Position (Interval)	Terminals
Off (Park)	A-E
Low	B-E-F-C
High	D-B-F-C
Intermittent	B-E-F
Wash	W1-W2

NOTE: Resistance between terminals F-C will vary from 100-900 ohms at minimum dwell to 8,000-12,000 at maximum dwell.

INTERMITTENT GOVERNOR

If intermittent operation is unsatisfactory, check motor current draw, then check control switch and all connecting wires for continuity. If motor, switch and connecting wires are satisfactory, replace electronic governor assembly.

Fig. 9: Wiring Diagram 2-Speed Interval Bronco and "F" Models

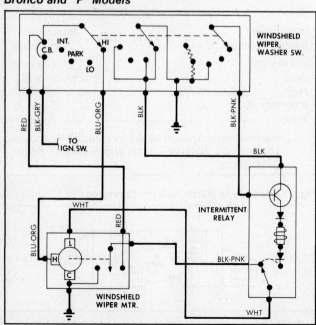

Fig. 10: Wiring Diagram 2-Speed Interval (Depressed Park) "E" Models

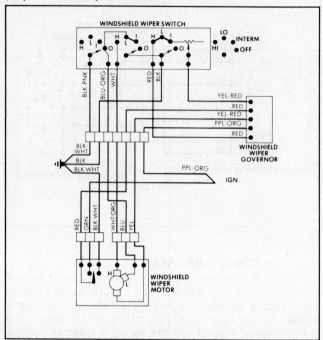

Fig. 11: Motor Park Test

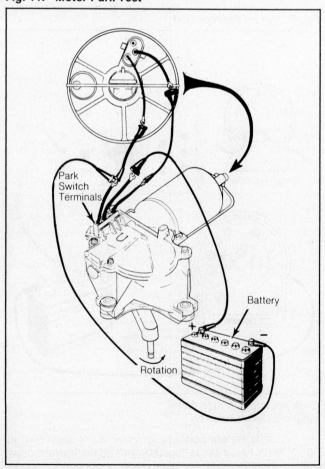

"E" Models.

FORD — EXCEPT BRONCO II & RANGER (Cont.)

WASHER PUMP CURRENT DRAW

Connect test leads of ammeter as shown in Fig. 12. The current draw should not exceed 4 amps, or be less than 1.7 amps, while the washer pump is pumping fluid.

Fig. 12: Washer Pump Current Draw Test

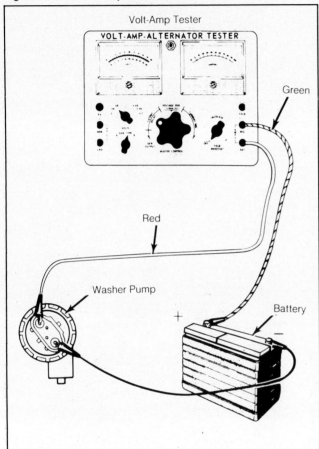

REMOVAL & INSTALLATION

WIPER MOTOR

"E" Models

1) Disconnect battery ground cable, remove fuse panel and bracket assembly. Disconnect wires at motor brush cap and gear box cover. Remove wiper arm blade assemblies from pivot shaft, outer air inlet cowl and clip retaining motor drive arm to linkage mounting arm and pivot shaft assembly.

2) Remove motor attaching bolts and remove motor from vehicle. To install, reverse removal procedures while noting the following: If a new motor is installed, motor must be in park position.

Bronco & "F" Models

1) Disconnect negative battery cable. Remove wiper arms and blade assemblies. Remove cowl grille attaching screws and raise cowl. Disconnect washer nozzle hose and remove cowl grille.

2) Remove wiper linkage clips from motor output arm. Disconnect motor wiring connector. Remove motor attaching screws and remove motor. To install, reverse removal procedure.

WIPER CONTROL SWITCH

"E" Models

1) Disconnect battery ground cable and remove windshield wiper switch knob. Remove ignition switch bezel. Depress button on top of headlight switch and pull knob and shaft from switch.

2) Remove screws at bottom of finish panel and pry 2 upper retainers away from instrument panel assembly. Disconnect connector from wiper switch, remove switch attaching bolts and remove switch from vehicle. To install, reverse removal procedures.

Bronco and "F" Models

Disconnect battery ground cable and remove wiper switch knob, bezel nut and bezel. Pull switch out from under instrument panel and disconnect plug connector from switch. Remove switch from vehicle. To install, reverse removal procedure.

INTERMITTENT GOVERNOR

"E" and "F" Models

Governor is mounted on lower flange of instrument panel. Disconnect wire connectors from governor, remove attaching screws and remove governor. To install, reverse removal procedure.

Fig. 13: Motor Brush End Plate Assembly

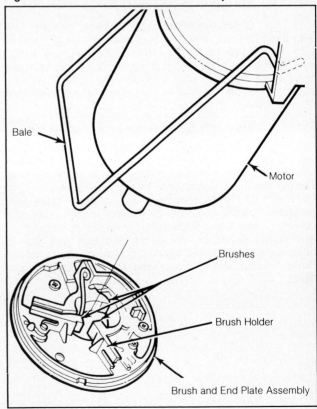

"E" Models

WASHER PUMP & RESERVOIR

1) Disconnect lock tab wire connector using a small screwdriver. Remove hose and drain reservoir. Remove retaining screws and lift motor from vehicle.

2) With reservoir drained, remove reservoir attaching screw and remove reservoir. To install, reverse removal procedure, noting that reservoir must be filled before connecting electrical connections or operating pump.

OVERHAUL

WIPER MOTOR

NOTE: **The wiper motor for "F" and Bronco models is not serviceable. It must be replaced as a complete assembly. Wiper motor for "E" models is serviceable only in kits of major sub-assemblies. The kits available are for the cover and switch assembly and the brush end plate.**

COVER & SWITCH ASSEMBLY

Remove 4 cover retaining screws and remove assembly. Replace with appropriate kit. Be sure that ground strap is under the cover screw. Tighten screws to 15-25 INCH lbs. (1.7-2.8 N.m).

NOTE: **"E" model switch assembly is identified by the letter "U" stamped on the outside surface.**

BRUSH END PLATE

Observe position of bale retainer and pry it off with a screwdriver. Remove end plate and plug. Replace with appropriate kit. When installing new kit, use a fine wire probe through the hub opening to position the brushes on the commutator. Rotate end plate to position key in notch and assemble plug. Do not overbend bale retainer when reinstalling.

WASHER MOTOR, SEAL & IMPELLOR

1) With reservoir assembly removed from vehicle, pry out retaining ring with small blade screwdriver. Using pliers, grip one wall around the electrical terminal and pull out the motor, seal and impellor assembly.

2) Before installing new assembly, make sure reservoir chamber is free of foreign matter. Lubricate outside of seal with powdered graphite before installation. Align small projection on motor end cap with slot in reservoir so seal seats against bottom of motor cavity. Reverse disassembly procedures for remaining components.

GENERAL MOTORS — INTEGRAL WIPER/WASHER MOTOR

All Exc. "P" & "S" Models

DESCRIPTION

Two speed motor, permanent magnet type, consists of partsfield magnets, armature and drive gear within upper and lower housings. The washer pump is assembled on the outside surface of the upper half of the housing and is an integral part of the wiper motor assembly. Wiper motor is protected by an automatic reset circuit breaker. Vehicle wiring is protected by fuse in fuse block.

OPERATION

The basic washer pump is a spring loaded piston enclosed in a plastic cylinder housing with an actuator plate extending from the cylinder housing. A valve assembly, consisting of two exhaust and one intake check valve, is attached to the end of the cylinder housing.

A tang on the piston actuator plate holds the plate in a lock-out position, (no pumping action). To start the pump, push washer button which will energize the relay. This pulls the relay armature toward the coil allowing the ratchet gear pawl to engage the ratchet gear and begin rotation. This sequence starts pumping action.

Fig. 1: Washer Actuator Plate and Valve Assembly

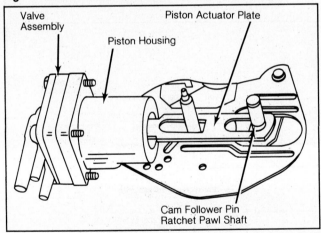

Valve Assembly — Piston Actuator Plate — Piston Housing — Cam Follower Pin Ratchet Pawl Shaft

Tang holds plate in lock-out position.

TROUBLE SHOOTING

ALL MODELS

Wiper Inoperative

Check fuse, wiring harness, wiper ground and dash connections.

Wiper Will Operate One Speed Only

Check for open wiring between terminals 2 or 3 and the dash switch. Check dash switch and if not operable, check "Low" and "High" brush leads.

Wiper Blades Will Not Return To Park

Check for open wire from terminal 5 to dash switch. If not open, dash switch or wiper park switch needs replacing.

Wiper Will Not Shut Off

Disconnect wiring from terminals 4 and 5. Replace park switch assembly if motor stops. If motor still

runs, remove wires from terminals 1, 2 and 3. Connect a 12 volt lead to terminal 1 only and if motor does not run it indicates a ground in wires from wiper motor to terminal 2 or 3 at dash switch. If it runs, check for internal ground in high or low brushes.

Washer Pump Will Not Run

Turn ignition switch to "ON" position. Ensure washer solution is adequate, then push wash button and listen for relay to energize. With ignition still "ON" and wiring connected to wiper terminals, connect test lamp lead to ground and probe terminals 6 and 7.

- Light "OFF" at both terminals; check for open in circuit to the pump.
- Light "ON" at one terminal, replace coil-park switch assembly.
- Light "ON" at both terminals, but one light is dim; ground the dim light terminals. If pump runs, check for open in wire between pump and dash switch or for a defective dash switch.

NOTE: **Delay wiper system is available as optional equipment. A separate control assembly is utilized which provides a variable delay of 1 to 20 seconds.**

REMOVAL & INSTALLATION

WIPER MOTOR

Removal (Exc. "G" Models)

1) Ensure wiper motor is in park position, then disconnect ground cable from battery, electrical harness at motor and hoses at washer pump. Reach through access hole in cowl grille and loosen wiper drive rod attaching screws.

2) Remove drive rod from wiper motor crank arm. Remove wiper motor-to-dash panel attaching screws and remove motor assembly.

Installation

To install, reverse removal procedure. Lubricate crank arm pivot prior to reinstallation.

Removal ("G" Models)

1) Ensure wiper motor is in park position, then disconnect battery ground cable and remove wiper arms. Remove cowl panel cover. Loosen nuts holding linkage to crank arm and lift linkage off arm. Disconnect wiring to motor. Remove left dash defroster outlet from flex hose and position hose to one side.

2) Remove screw securing left hand heater duct to engine cover shroud and slip heater duct down and out. Remove washer hoses, then remove screws securing wiper motor to cowl and lift wiper motor from under dash.

Installation

To install, reverse removal procedure. Ensure wiper motor is in park position before installing. Lubricate wiper motor crank arm pivot prior to installation.

OVERHAUL

Repairs to motor/gear box section of the wiper assembly are limited to the switch, armature, cap and brush holder assembly plus the external parts, crankarm, spacer/seal (plastic) and output shaft seal.

Wiper Washer Systems

GENERAL MOTORS — INTEGRAL WIPER/WASHER MOTOR (Cont.)

Fig. 2: Wiper/Washer Motor Terminal Check Diagram

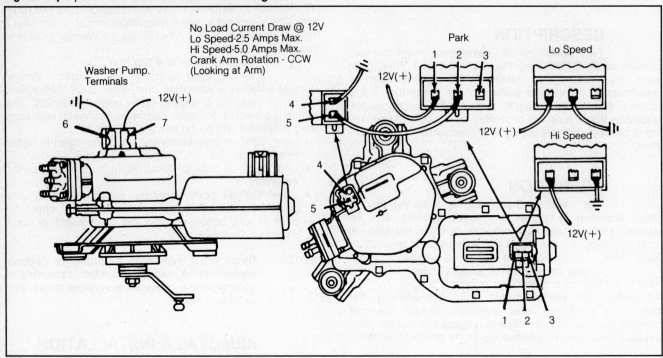

Fig. 3: Wiper/Washer System Wiring Diagram

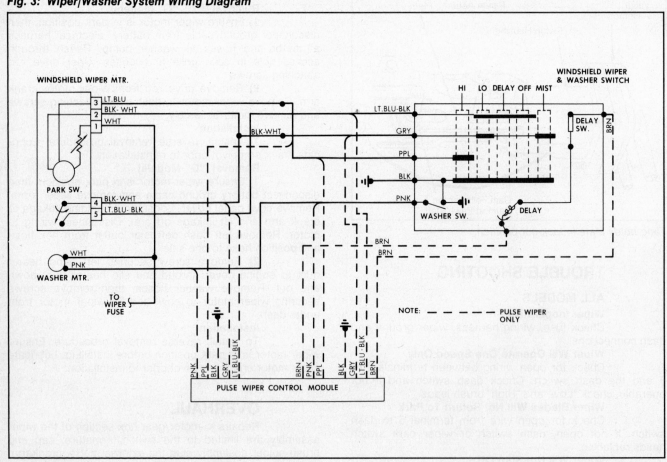

Blazer, Pickup and Suburban models shown.

GENERAL MOTORS — INTEGRAL WIPER/WASHER MOTOR (Cont.)

Fig. 4: Wiper/Washer System Wiring Diagram

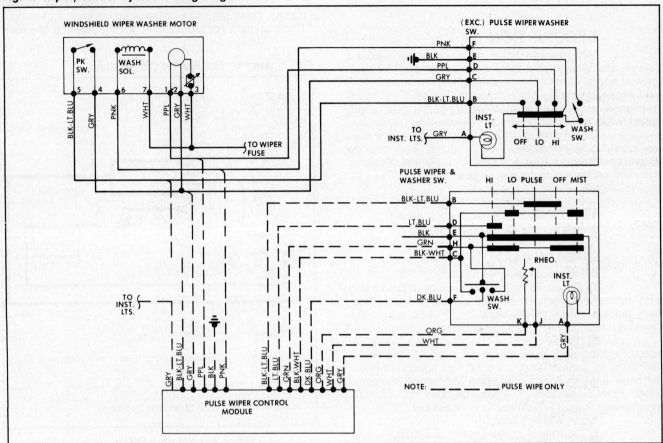

Van models shown.

Wiper/Washer Systems

GENERAL MOTORS — SQUARE MOTOR

"P" Models

DESCRIPTION

Two speed motor is a compound wound (series and shunt) type. Gear train consists of a helical gear at end of armature shaft, driving an intermediate gear and pinion assembly. Pinion drives output gear and shaft. The crank arm, which is attached to output gear shaft, drives wiper transmissions through connecting link arms.

Circuit protection for wipers is through a fuse on fuse block. Windshield washer pump is a positive displacement type using a piston arrangement. Pump is mounted on shaft of wiper output gear.

TESTING & TROUBLE SHOOTING

WIPER ON CAR

Wiper Inoperative

1) Check wiring harness, wiper ground strap and dash switch connections and mounting. Check fuse. With ignition switch "ON", check for 12 volts at harness terminal which connects to No. 2 terminal.

2) To by-pass switch, disconnect wiring at motor and connect jumper wire from No. 1 and No. 3 terminals to ground. Connect a 12 volt source to No. 2 terminal. If wiper does not operate, disconnect transmissions from crank arm. If wiper still does not operate, remove motor from vehicle and test. *See Wiper Off Car.*

Wiper Will Not Shut Off

1) Determine whether wiper has both speeds, low speed only or high speed only. Operate wiper by by-passing switch as previously outlined. *See Wiper Inoperative.* If wiper operates correctly and has both speeds, lead to switch from No. 1 terminal is grounded or switch is faulty.

2) If wiper has low or high speed only, lead to switch from No. 3 terminal is open or switch is faulty. If wiper still does not operate, remove motor from vehicle and test. *See Wiper Off Car.*

Operates Low Speed Only & Shuts Off With Dash Switch In High Position

Reverse harness leads connected to No. 1 and 3 terminals.

Does Not Return To Park With Wiper Off

Check ground strap connection. Park switch contacts may be dirty, bent or broken.

Speed Normal In Low, But Too Fast In High

Terminal board resistor may be open. Remove from vehicle to test terminal board.

Wiper Operates Intermittently

Loose ground strap or dash switch mounting.

WIPER OFF CAR

NOTE: Use ammeter with reading of 30 amps (minimum) in feed wire circuit.

Wiper Inoperative

1) Connect an ammeter and battery to No. 2 terminal and a jumper wire from No. 1 and 3 terminals to ground. Wiper should operate at low speed. If ammeter reading is 0, check for loose splice joints or loose solder connection at No. 2 terminal.

2) If reading is 1.0-1.5 amps, check for sticking brushes, open armature or loose splice joint. If reading is 11 amps, check for broken gear or other stalling condition.

Fig. 1: Jumper Wire Testing Connections

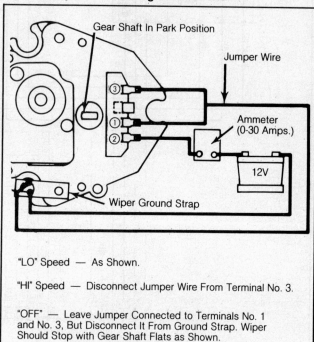

"LO" Speed — As Shown.

"HI" Speed — Disconnect Jumper Wire From Terminal No. 3.

"OFF" — Leave Jumper Connected to Terminals No. 1 and No. 3, But Disconnect It From Ground Strap. Wiper Should Stop with Gear Shaft Flats as Shown.

Wiper Will Not Shut Off

1) If wiper has both speeds, park switch contacts may not be opening or internal motor lead to No. 1 terminal is grounded. If wiper has low speed only, shunt field coil may be grounded or internal wiper lead to No. 3 terminal is grounded.

2) If wiper has high speed only, shunt field is open or internal lead to No. 3 terminal is open.

Wipers Operate Intermittently

Check for sticking brushes, loose splice joints or other loose connections.

Fig. 2: General Motors Square Motor Wiper System Wiring Diagram

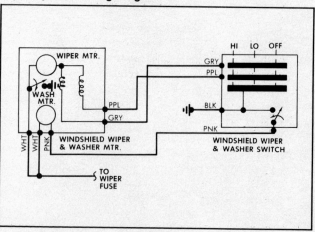

GENERAL MOTORS — SQUARE MOTOR (Cont.)

Fig. 3: Exploded View of Wiper Motor and Drive Assembly

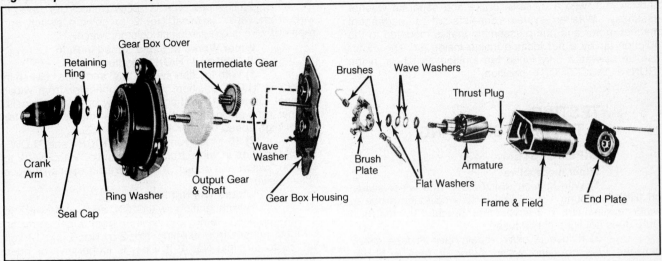

OVERHAUL

GEAR BOX

Disassembly

1) Remove washer pump. Remove pump drive cam by wedging shaft with 2 screwdrivers. Clamp crank arm in vise and remove retaining nut. Arm must be secure in vise to avoid stripping wiper gears.

2) Remove crank arm, seal cap, retaining ring and end play washers. Drill out gear box cover rivets and remove cover.

3) Remove output gear and shaft assembly. Slide intermediate gear and pinion off shaft. Remove terminal board and park switch by unsoldering motor leads and drilling out rivets holding terminal board and park switch ground strap to plate.

Reassembly

1) Lubricate gear teeth with suitable cam lubricant. Position cover over locating dowel pins. Reconnect ground strap.

2) Place wiper in park position. Install crank arm on output shaft so identification marks line up with marks in cover. Clamp crank in vise and tighten retaining nut. To complete reassembly, reverse disassembly procedure.

WIPER MOTOR

Disassembly

Disassemble gear box, remove through bolts, tap motor frame lightly and remove motor from mounting plate. Release brush spring tension and slide armature and end plate from motor frame. Pull end plate from armature. Remove end play adjusting washers and note arrangement for proper reassembly.

NOTE: A thrust plug is located between armature shaft and end plate.

Reassembly

Lubricate armature shaft bushings with light machine oil. Install washers with concave side of washers toward each other. End play is automatically controlled by proper installation of washers. To complete reassembly, reverse disassembly procedure.

WASHER PUMP

Disassembly

1) Squeeze solenoid cover and remove. Remove ratchet dog retaining screw. Hold solenoid plunger in position and lift solenoid assembly and ratchet dog from pump frame. Separate ratchet dog from solenoid mounting plate.

2) Disconnect ratchet pawl spring, remove pawl retaining ring and slide ratchet pawl off cam follower shaft. Remove ratchet dog from pump frame, move ratchet wheel spring out of shaft groove and slide ratchet wheel off its shaft.

3) Separate pump and pump actuator plate from frame by pulling pump housing until grooves in housing clear the frame. Remove actuator plate from ratchet wheel and cam follower shafts. Remove screws attaching valve assembly to pump housing and remove valve.

Reassembly

Position gasket between housing and valve plate in the housing and valve plate grooves. Install triple "O" ring between valve body and pipe assembly. To complete reassembly, reverse disassembly procedure.

MOTOR SPECIFICATIONS

Application	Specification
Operating Voltage	12 Volts
Current Draw (No Load Max.)	
"LO" Speed	4 Amps
"HI" Speed	3.5 Amps
Current Draw (Stall, Cold)	12 Amps
Crank Arm Speed (Minimum)	
"LO" Speed	31 RPM
"HI" Speed	55 RPM

Wiper/Washer Systems

GENERAL MOTORS — S10

DESCRIPTION

Wiper system is a permanent magnet positive park system with a dynamic brake and separate washer assembly. Washer system consists of a permanent magnet motor and pump assembly that is mounted to the solution jar by a nut located inside inside jar. The motor can be operated only when the ignition switch is in the "RUN" or "ACCESSORY" position.

TESTING & TROUBLE SHOOTING

WIPER SYSTEM

Wiper Inoperative

1) With ignition switch "ON" and wiper switch on "HIGH", ground 12 volt test lamp amd touch probe to wiper terminal No. 1. If lamp lights, proceed to step 3). If lamp does not light, check fuse.

2) If fuse is okay, repair open in feed circuit between fuse box and wiper motor. If fuse is blown, replace fuse. If fuse blows, check for short in wiring or high amperage draw in motor.

3) If lamp lit in step 1), place switch in "LOW". Connect jumper wire to ground. If wiper runs, repair open in ground strap. If wiper does not run, problem is in motor. Repair or replace motor as necessary.

Wiper Has Low Speed Only

1) With ignition switch "ON" and wiper switch in "HIGH" position, remove connector from wiper terminal. Connect 12 volt source to high speed terminal No. 1. If wiper is inoperative, repair wiper motor.

2) With wiper in "HIGH", check for open wire from wiper terminal No. 1 to column switch and repair. If wire is okay, replace column switch.

Wiper Has High Speed Only

1) With ignition switch "ON" and wiper switch in "LOW" position, remove connector from wiper terminal.

Connect 12 volt source to terminal No. 2. If wiper does not run, repair wiper motor.

2) If wiper runs in "LOW", check for open in wire from wiper terminal No. 2 to column switch and repair. If wire is okay, replace column switch.

Wiper Works at Same Speed in Both "LOW" and "HIGH" Positions

1) With ignition switch "ON" and wiper switch in "LOW" or "HIGH" position, remove connector from wiper terminal. Connect 12 volt source to low or high terminals. If wiper runs at one speed, repair wiper motor. Check for low or high speed brushes shorting.

2) If wiper runs in both "HIGH" and "LOW", check for open in wires from terminals No. 1 and No. 2 to column switch and repair. If there are no opens, replace column switch.

Wipers Will Not Park

1) With ignition switch "ON" and wiper switch in "PARK" position, remove connector from wiper terminal. Connect jumper from terminal No. 2 to No. 3 and 12 volt source to terminal No. 4. If wiper is inoperative or does not park, repair wiper motor.

2) Check park switch actuator and brush holder. If wiper runs and parks in step 1), turn column switch "OFF". Check current flow between terminals No. 2 and No. 3 on harness. If lamp lights, check for open in wire from terminal No. 4 to fuse block and repair.

3) If there is no current flow in step 2), check for open in wires from terminal No. 3 to column switch and repair. If there are no opens, replace column switch.

Wiper Will Not Shut Off

1) With ignition "ON" and wiper switch "OFF", remove connector from wiper terminal. Connect jumper from terminals No. 2 and No. 3 and 12 volts to terminal No. 4.

2) If wiper still runs, repair wiper motor (check park switch actuator and brush holder assembly). If wiper parks, replace column switch.

Fig. 1: Wiper Motor and Switch Wiring Diagram

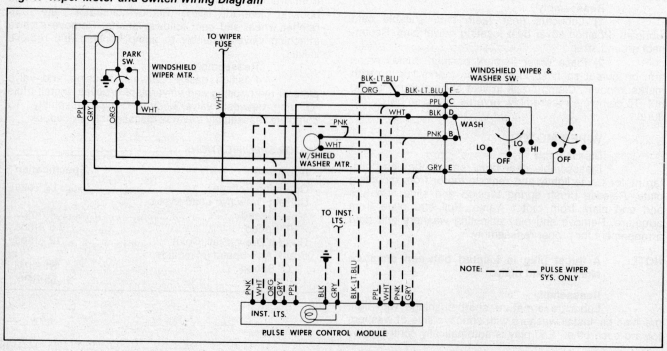

Wiper/Washer Systems

GENERAL MOTORS — S10 (Cont.)

Intermittent Wiper Condition

1) Remove wiper fuse from fuse block and connect an ammeter accross fuse block terminals. Operate wipers in "HIGH" with windshield dry. Current draw will fluctuate. If current draw is below 5.0 amps, a weak circuit breaker is indicated. Replace brush holder assembly.

2) If current draw exceeds 5.0 amps, remove wiper arms and blades and repeat test. If current still exceeds 5 amps, go to step **3)**. If current draw is okay, replace wiper blade elements and repeat test. If current draw is okay, problem is corrected.

3) If current draw exceeded 5.0 amps in step **2)**, disconnect wiper linkage from motor crank arm and repeat test. If current draw is okay, wiper transmission linkage is binding. Repair or replace as needed.

4) If current draw exceeds 5.0 amps with linkage disconnected, repair wiper motor. Check for shorted or grounded armature.

Wiper Motor Runs But Blades Do Not Move

1) Check wiper linkage connection to crank arm. If linkage disconnected, connect linkage and check system.

2) If linkage is connected, wiper gear is stripped. Repair motor.

Wiper Motor Parks But Above Normal Position

1) With ignition switch "ON" and wiper switch in "PARK" position, remove connector from wiper terminal. Check for open between terminal No. 3 and ground. If there is an open, repair open in motor or replace holder assembly.

2) If there is no open, check arm and blade location and/or transmission linkage.

REMOVAL & INSTALLATION

WIPER MOTOR

Removal

1) Disconnect negative battery cable. Remove wiper arms. Remove cowl vent and grille. Loosen but do not remove transmission drive link to motor crank arm attaching nuts.

2) Detach drive link from motor crank arm. Disconnect motor electrical leads. Remove motor attaching screws. Rotate motor upward and outward to remove.

Installation

Install motor by reversing removal procedure. Check operation of system.

WIPER MOTOR COVER

Removal

Remove wiper motor. From housing side, drill the ends off 7 rivets holding cover to housing with an 11/64" drill bit. Remove cover.

Installation

To install, attach the cover to housing with self-tapping screws.

WIPER HOUSING

Removal

1) Remove wiper motor. Remove wiper motor cover. Remove crank gear lock nut, crank arm, shaft seal, thrust collar and washer. Push end of gear shaft through housing and remove gear assembly and washer.

2) File burr from retaining ring groove and where crank arm seats on shaft. Remove intermediate gear and washers. Drill ends off the 4 rivets holding bearings and bearing straps in place with an 11/64" drill bit. Be careful not to get metal chips into motor.

Fig. 2: Windshield Wiper Motor Components

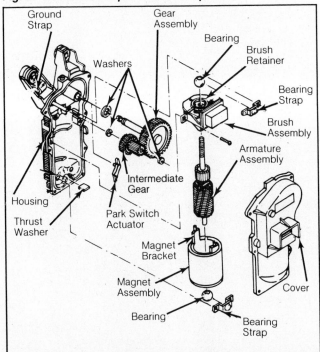

Replace rivets with self-tapping screws when reassembling.

Fig. 3: Wiper Motor Brush Retainer Assembly

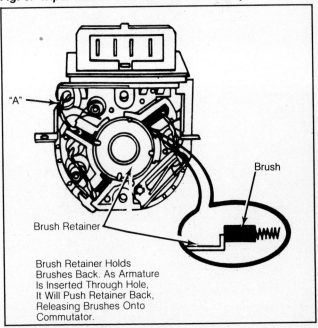

Brush Retainer Holds Brushes Back. As Armature Is Inserted Through Hole, It Will Push Retainer Back, Releasing Brushes Onto Commutator.

Braided contact wire "A" must be behind brush retaining spring.

3) Remove the 6-lobed socket screws holding brush assembly in place. Remove armature, brush and magnet assembly together to avoid realignment of brushes. Proper alignment is shown in illustration. *See Fig. 3.*

Installation

To install, reverse removal procedure, using new housing, new retaining ring and self-tapping screws. Place thrust pin casing with insert about 1/32" above rear of pin as shown in *Fig. 4.*

Fig. 4: Wiper Thrust Pin Adjustments

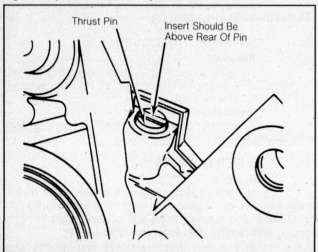

Thrust Pin

Insert Should Be
Above Rear Of Pin

JEEP

All Models

DESCRIPTION

Jeep vehicles use a 2-speed electric motor, which is a compound wound (series and shunt) type. A crank arm, attached externally to the gear shaft, operates linkage which activates the wiper blades.

All models except "CJ" and Scrambler have an optional intermittent feature. All models use an electric washer system, consisting of a motor, reservoir, and necessary hoses and nozzles.

The pump assembly is mounted in the bottom of the reservoir. The motor case is grounded to the vehicle body and is energized by a feed wire from the control switch.

TROUBLESHOOTING

CHEROKEE, TRUCK & WAGONEER ONLY
Wiper Inoperative or Operates at One Speed Only

Foreign objects interfering with linkage. Open circuit in ignition switch, wiper switch, harness or terminals. Loose or misaligned connection between wiring harness plug and motor plug. Faulty ground strap connection.

Wipers Do Not Park

1) Disconnect motor and connect Black lead to White lead. Feed 12 volts to Red lead. Replace motor if it fails to park. If it parks, turn ignition switch "ON" and wiper switch to "PARK".

2) Connect test light leads to Pink wire with tracer (at motor plug) and to ground. Also check continuity between Yellow wire with tracer and Blue wire with tracer. Check harness connections between motor and instrument panel switch. If okay, replace panel switch.

Wiper Motor Quits While Wiping

1) With engine idling, blower motor on high, operate wipers at high setting for 5 cycles (3 seconds of water and 57 seconds of drying).

2) If motor struggles to a complete stop, clean glass, replace blades, and test circuit breaker in panel switch. As a last resort, replace motor. If motor stopped suddenly in original test, check circuit breaker first.

No Intermittent Wiper (Other Functions Okay)

1) If blades stop and start erratically, test circuit breaker, wiper switch continuity, and continuity of wiring between switch, governor, wiper motor and ground.

2) If operation is intermittent on low speed only, check for loose connections at governor.

Windshield Washer Does Not Operate

Check fluid level, condition of hoses, and for restrictions (particularly ice or dirt in jet opening). Check fuse in panel. Check for good connection at plug terminal.

TESTING

"CJ" & SCRAMBLER

NOTE: The wiper motor must be grounded for proper operation and also during all of the following test procedures.

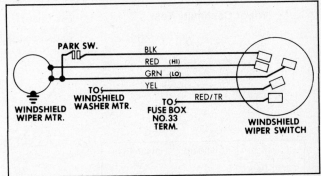

Fig. 1: Jeep 2-Speed Wiper System Wiring Diagram

"CJ" and Scrambler models shown.

1) Place ignition switch in "ON" position. Use a test lamp to check for 12 volts at switch terminal B. *See Fig. 2.* If test lamp lights but motor does not operate, ensure ground is good by connecting a jumper wire from motor ground strap to a good body ground.

2) If motor still will not operate, disconnect jumper wire. Disconnect wiring from switch. Connect a jumper wire between terminals number 2 and B, which should give low speed operation of motor.

3) If motor does not operate on low speed, possible causes are an open condition in Green wire leading from switch, a loose internal connection in motor, or a stuck low speed brush.

4) Connect a jumper wire between terminals number 3 and B, which should give high speed operation of motor. If motor does not operate on high speed, possible causes are an open condition in Red wire leading from switch, a loose internal connection in motor, or a stuck high speed brush.

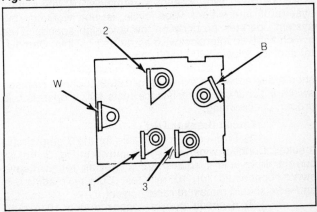

Fig. 2: Identification of Test Connections

"CJ" & Scrambler models shown.

5) Position wiper blades in a position other than park, and connect a jumper wire between terminals number 1 and B. Motor should run at low speed and stop with blades in park position.

6) If in step 5), motor does not run with jumper connected, possible causes are an open in Black wire from switch, a loose internal connection in motor, a bad connection between park point set to low speed brush, or a misaligned or damaged set of contact points.

7) If in step 5), motor runs but does not position wipers in park position, cam on drive gear is not breaking contact points sufficiently.

Wiper/Washer Systems
JEEP (Cont.)

Fig. 3: Testing Wiper/Washer System

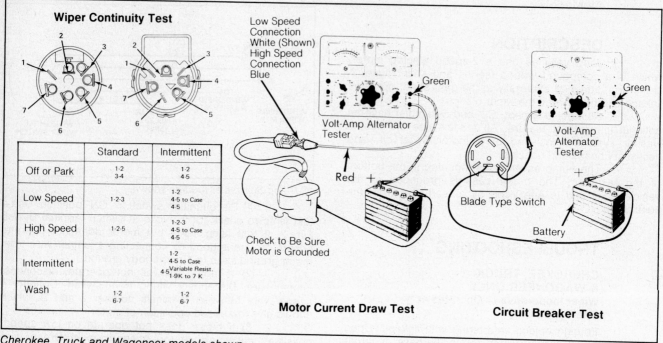

Cherokee, Truck and Wagoneer models shown.

CHEROKEE, TRUCK & WAGONEER

Wiper Switch Test

1) Check wiper switch continuity, using a continuity light (J-21008 or equivalent) or an ohmmeter. Continuity should exist at switch positions indicated in *Fig. 3*.

2) Using an ohmmeter, check variable resistance between No. 4 and 5 terminals of intermittent system if intermittent wipe cycle is not working, but system operates properly on low and high speeds. Turn switch knob counterclockwise as far as possible. Ohmmeter should indicate 5600-8400 ohms.

3) As knob is turned clockwise, resistance should decrease to a minimum of 100-900 ohms. Replace switch if continuity or resistance tests fail. If operation is proper, check wiring.

Circuit Breaker Test

1) Two tests are available for the 7 amp circuit breaker. Connect wiper switch as shown in *Fig. 3*. Adjust current draw until it equals circuit breaker rating. Leave switch connected for 10 minutes. Current reading on ammeter should remain at rated current.

2) If circuit breaker opens during 10 minute period, replace switch assembly. Adjust current draw until it is twice the circuit breaker rating (14 amps). Current reading on ammeter should drop to zero within 15 seconds. If it takes longer, replace switch assembly.

Intermittent Governor Test

1) Special electronic testing equipment is required to check governor. However, check all other components in event of unsatisfactory intermittent wiper cycle. If all components function properly, install new governor.

2) The 6" governor lead plugs into wiper control switch. The shorter 4" lead plugs into instrument panel switch.

Current Draw Test

1) Remove wiper arms and blades, and disconnect motor lead. Connect negative lead of ammeter to positive battery post. *See Fig. 3*. Connect other ammeter test lead to Blue wire with tracer (low speed) of motor harness.

2) Current draw should be approximately 1 amp, but not more than 3 amps. Connect ammeter lead to Blue wire terminal (high speed). Current draw should remain about the same, but never over 3 amps.

Park Test

1) Disconnect motor from harness connection. Temporarily, contact a battery feed to either the Blue wire or Blue wire with tracer. This will move wiper arms and blades away from normal park position. Insert jumper wire from White to Black wire terminals.

Fig. 4: Jeep 2-Speed Wiper System Wiring Diagram

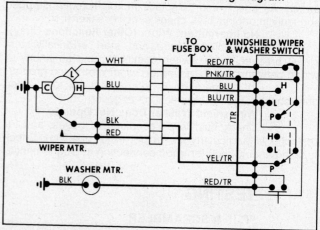

Standard system for Cherokee, Truck and Wagoneer models.

JEEP (Cont.)

Fig. 5: Jeep 2-Speed Wiper System Wiring Diagram

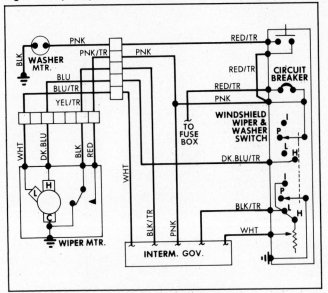

*Cherokee, Truck and Wagoneer models
with intermittent governor.*

2) Contact a battery feed to Red wire terminal of motor harness. Motor should operate until wipers have reached normal park position. If not, replace wiper motor.

REMOVAL & INSTALLATION

WIPER MOTOR

"CJ" & Scrambler Models

1) Remove necessary components from windshield frame. Remove windshield hold-down knobs, and fold windshield down. Remove left access hole cover, and disconnect drive link from left wiper pivot.

2) Disconnect wiper motor wiring harness from switch. Remove attaching screws and wiper motor. To install, reverse removal procedures.

Cherokee, Truck & Wagoneer Models

Remove motor adapter plate-to-dash panel screws. Disconnect wiper wiring harness at motor. Pull motor and linkage out of opening so that drive link-to-crank stud retaining clip can be removed with screwdriver. Remove motor assembly. To install, reverse removal procedure.

OVERHAUL

WIPER MOTOR

Disassembly (Cherokee, Truck & Wagoneer Only)

1) Using care not to damage ceramic magnets, mark position of drive crank with respect to output shaft. Remove drive crank, mounting bracket, and ground strap.

2) Remove gear housing cover and gasket, idler gear, pinion, motor through bolts, and motor housing. Remove end play spring, output gear and shaft, switch lever, washer, and seal from gear housing.

3) Disassemble brushes, harness and springs from end head (terminal board). Remove end head assembly, parking lever pin, and old lubricant. Inspect

gear housing and all components, replacing parts as necessary. Lubricate all bearing surfaces and gears.

Reassembly (Cherokee, Truck & Wagoneer Only)

1) Install switch washer and lever in gear housing, with cam rider pointing toward output shaft hole. Install seal and output gear and shaft in gear housing. Be sure switch lever is clear of cam and gear assembly. Place idler gear and pinion on shaft, and insert shaft through switch lever and washer into gear housing.

2) Maintain .001-.007" (.03-.18 mm) clearance between push nut and gear. Install end spring, parking lever pin, and attach brush terminals and switch terminals to end head. Attach end head to gear housing. Install springs and brushes in end head. Lightly lubricate armature end shaft and ball. Install armature in gear housing.

3) Plastic thrust button in end play spring should bear against end of armature shaft. Install motor housing over armature. Align motor housing and gear housing marks, and install through bolts. Lubricate gear housing cavity generously, and install gasket and cover on gear housing. Attach ground strap and mounting bracket.

4) Install grommets in mounting bracket, and secure motor assembly to bracket. Install plain washer and spring washer on output shaft, and position drive crank on output shaft in previously marked position. Tighten nut to 10 ft. lbs. (14 N.m).

Fig. 6: Exploded View of Wiper Motor Assembly

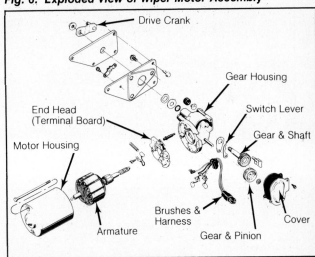

Cherokee, Truck and Wagoneer models shown.

SECTION 7

ENGINES

CONTENTS

NOTE: ALSO SEE GENERAL INDEX.

IMPORTANT: Because of the many model names used by vehicle manufacturers, accurate identification of models is important. See Model Identification at the front of this publication.

Engine Trouble Shooting

GASOLINE ENGINE TROUBLE SHOOTING

CONDITION	POSSIBLE CAUSE	CORRECTION
Engine Lopes At Idle	Intake manifold-to-head leaks	Replace manifold gasket, see ENGINES
	Blown head gasket	Replace head gasket, see ENGINES
	Worn timing gears, chain or sprocket	Replace gears, chain or sprocket
	Worn camshaft lobes	Replace camshaft, see ENGINES
	Overheated engine	Check cooling system, see COOLING
	Blocked crankcase vent valve	Remove restriction
	Leaking EGR valve	Repair leak and/or replace valve
	Faulty fuel pump	Replace fuel pump
Engine Has Low Power	Leaking fuel pump	Repair leak and/or replace fuel pump
	Excessive piston-to-bore clearance	Install larger pistons, see ENGINES
	Sticking valves or weak valve springs	Check valve train components, see ENGINES
	Incorrect valve timing	Reset valve timing, see ENGINES
	Worn camshaft lobes	Replace camshaft, see ENGINES
	Blown head gasket	Replace head gasket, see ENGINES
	Clutch slipping	Adjust pedal and/or replace components, see CLUTCHES
	Engine overheating	Check cooling system, see COOLING
	Auto. trans. pressure regulator valve faulty	Replace pressure regulator valve
	Auto. trans. fluid level too low	Add fluid as necessary, see TRANSMISSIONS
	Improper vacuum diverter valve operation	Replace vacuum diverter valve
	Vacuum leaks	Inspect vacuum system and repair as required
	Leaking piston rings	Replace piston rings, see ENGINES
Faulty High Speed Operation	Low fuel pump volume	Replace fuel pump
	Leaking valves or worn valve springs	Replace valves and/or springs, see ENGINES
	Incorrect valve timing	Reset valve timing, see ENGINES
	Intake manifold restricted	Remove restriction
	Worn distributor shaft	Replace distributor
Faulty Acceleration	Improper fuel pump stroke	Remove pump and reset pump stroke
	Incorrect ignition timing	Reset ignition timing, see TUNE-UP
	Leaking valves	Replace valves, see ENGINES
	Worn fuel pump diaphragm or piston	Replace diaphragm or piston
Intake Backfire	Improper ignition timing	Reset ignition timing, see TUNE-UP
	Faulty accelerator pump discharge	Replace accelerator pump
	Improper choke operation	Check choke and adjust as required
	Defective EGR valve	Replace EGR valve
	Fuel mixture too lean	Reset air/fuel mixture, see TUNE-UP
	Choke valve initial clearance too large	Reset choke valve initial clearance
Exhaust Backfire	Vacuum leak	Inspect and repair vacuum system
	Faulty vacuum diverter valve	Replace vacuum diverter valve
	Faulty choke operation	Check choke and adjust as required
	Exhaust system leak	Repair exhaust system leak
Engine Detonation	Ignition timing too far advanced	Reset ignition timing, see TUNE-UP
	Faulty ignition system	Check ignition system, see ELECTRICAL
	Spark plugs loose or faulty	Retighten or replace plugs
	Fuel delivery system clogged	Inspect lines, pump and filter for clog
	EGR valve inoperative	Replace EGR valve
	PCV system inoperative	Inspect and/or replace hoses or valve
	Vacuum leaks	Check vacuum system and repair leaks
	Excessive combustion chamber deposits	Remove built-up deposits
	Leaking, sticking or broken valves	Inspect and/or replace valves
External Oil Leakage	Fuel pump improperly seated or worn gasket	Remove pump, replace gasket and seat properly
	Valve cover gasket broken	Replace valve cover gasket
	Oil filter gasket broken	Replace oil filter and gasket
	Oil pan gasket broken or pan bent	Straighten pan and replace gasket
	Timing chain cover gasket broken	Replace timing chain cover gasket

GASOLINE ENGINE TROUBLE SHOOTING (Cont.)

CONDITION	POSSIBLE CAUSE	CORRECTION
External Oil Leakage (Cont.)	Rear main oil seal worn	Replace rear main oil seal
	Oil pan drain plug not seated properly	Remove and reinstall drain plug
	Camshaft bearing drain hole blocked	Remove restriction
	Oil pressure sending switch leaking	Remove and reinstall sending switch
Excessive Oil Consumption	Worn valve stems or guides	Replace stems or guides, see ENGINES
	Valve "O" ring seals damaged	Replace "O" ring seals, see ENGINES
	Plugged oil drain back holes	Remove restrictions
	Improper PCV valve operation	Replace PCV valve
	Engine oil level too high	Remove excess oil
	Engine oil too thin	Replace with thicker oil
	Valve stem oil deflectors damaged	Replace oil deflectors
	Incorrect piston rings	Replace piston rings, see ENGINES
	Piston ring gaps not staggered	Reinstall piston rings, see ENGINES
	Insufficient piston ring tension	Replace rings, see ENGINES
	Piston ring grooves or oil return slots clogged	Replace piston rings, see ENGINES
	Piston rings sticking in grooves	Replace piston rings, see ENGINES
	Piston ring grooves excessively worn	Replace piston and rings, see ENGINES
	Compression rings installed upside down	Replace compression rings correctly, see ENGINES
	Worn or scored cylinder walls	Rebore cylinders or replace block
	Mismatched oil ring expander and rail	Replace oil ring expander and rail, see ENGINES
	Intake gasket dowels too long	Replace intake gasket dowels
	Excessive main or connecting rod bearing clearance	Replace main or connecting rod bearings, see ENGINES
No Oil Pressure	Low oil level	Add oil to proper level
	Oil pressure sender or gauge broken	Replace sender or gauge
	Oil pump malfunction	Remove and overhaul oil pump, see ENGINES
	Oil pressure relief valve sticking	Remove and reinstall valve
	Oil pump passages blocked	Overhaul oil pump, see ENGINES
	Oil pickup screen or tube blocked	Remove restriction
	Loose oil inlet tube	Tighten oil inlet tube
	Loose camshaft bearings	Replace camshaft bearings, see ENGINES
	Internal leakage at oil passages	Replace block or cylinder head
Low Oil Pressure	Low engine oil level	Add oil to proper level
	Engine oil too thin	Remove and replace with thicker oil
	Excessive oil pump clearance	Reduce oil pump clearance, see ENGINES
	Oil pickup tube or screen blocked	Remove restrictions
	Oil pressure relief spring weak or stuck	Eliminate binding or replace spring
	Main, rod or cam bearing clearance excessive	Replace bearing to reduce clearance, see ENGINES
High Oil Pressure	Improper grade of oil	Replace with proper oil
	Oil pressure relief valve stuck closed	Eliminate binding
	Oil pressure sender or gauge faulty	Replace sender or gauge
Noisy Main Bearings	Inadequate oil supply	Check oil delivery to main bearings
	Excessive main bearing clearance	Replace main bearings, see ENGINES
	Excessive crankshaft end play	Replace crankshaft, see ENGINES
	Loose flywheel or torque converter	Tighten attaching bolts
	Loose or damaged vibration damper	Tighten or replace vibration damper
	Crankshaft journals out-of-round	Re-grind crankshaft journals
	Excessive belt tension	Loosen belt tension
Noisy Connecting Rods	Excessive bearing clearance or missing bearing	Replace bearing, see ENGINES
	Crankshaft rod journal out-of-round	Re-grind crankshaft journal
	Misaligned connecting rod or cap	Remove rod or cap and re-align
	Incorrectly tighten rod bolts	Remove and re-tighten rod bolts

Engine Trouble Shooting

GASOLINE ENGINE TROUBLE SHOOTING (Cont.)

CONDITION	POSSIBLE CAUSE	CORRECTION
Noisy Pistons and Rings	Excessive piston-to-bore clearance	Install larger pistons, see ENGINES
	Bore tapered or out-of-round	Rebore block
	Piston ring broken	Replace piston rings, see ENGINES
	Piston pin loose or seized	Replace piston pin, see ENGINES
	Connecting rods misaligned	Re-align connecting rods
	Ring side clearance too loose or tight	Replace with larger or smaller rings
	Carbon build-up on piston	Remove carbon
Noisy Valve Train	Worn or bent push rods	Replace push rods, see ENGINES
	Worn rocker arms or bridged pivots	Replace rocker arms or pivots, see ENGINES
	Dirt or chips in valve lifters	Remove lifters and remove dirt/chips
	Excessive valve lifter leak-down	Replace valve lifters, see ENGINES
	Valve lifter face worn	Replace valve lifters, see ENGINES
	Broken or cocked valve springs	Replace or reposition springs
	Too much valve stem-to-guide clearance	Replace valve guides, see ENGINES
	Valve bent	Replace valve, see ENGINES
	Loose rocker arms	Retighten rocker arms, see ENGINES
	Excessive valve seat run-out	Re-face valve seats, see ENGINES
	Missing valve lock	Install new valve lock
	Push rod contacting cylinder head	Replace with shorter push rod
	Excessively worn camshaft lobes	Replace camshaft, see ENGINES
	Plugged valve lifter oil holes	Eliminate restriction or replace lifter
	Faulty valve lifter check ball	Replace lifter check ball, see ENGINES
	Rocker arm nut installed upside down	Remove and reinstall correctly
	Valve lifter incorrect for engine	Remove and replace valve lifters
	Faulty push rod seat or lifter plunger	Replace plunger or push rod
Noisy Valves	Improper valve lash	Re-adjust valve lash, see ENGINES
	Worn or dirty valve lifters	Clean and/or replace lifters
	Worn valve guides	Replace valve guides, see ENGINES
	Excessive valve seat or face run-out	Re-face seats or valve face
	Worn camshaft lobes	Replace camshaft, see ENGINES
	Loose rocker arm studs	Re-tighten rocker arm studs, see ENGINES
	Bent push rods	Replace push rods, see ENGINES
	Broken valve springs	Replace valve springs, see ENGINES
Burned, Sticking or Broken Valves	Weak valve springs or warped valves	Replace valves and/or springs, see ENGINES
	Improper lifter clearance	Re-adjust clearance or replace lifters
	Worn guides or improper guide clearance	Replace valve guides, see ENGINES
	Out-of-round valve seats or improper seat width	Re-grind valve seats
	Gum deposits on valve stems, seats or guides	Remove deposits
	Improper spark timing	Re-adjust spark timing
Broken Pistons/Rings	Undersize pistons	Replace with larger pistons, see ENGINES
	Wrong piston rings	Replace with correct rings, see ENGINES
	Out-of-round cylinder bore	Re-bore cylinder bore
	Improper connecting rod alignment	Remove and re-align connecting rods
	Excessively worn ring grooves	Replace pistons, see ENGINES
	Improperly assembled piston pins	Re-assemble pin-to-piston, see ENGINES
	Insufficient ring gap clearance	Install new rings, see ENGINES
	Engine overheating	Check cooling system
	Incorrect ignition timing	Re-adjust ignition timing, see TUNE-UP
Excessive Exhaust Noise	Leaks at manifold to head, or to pipe	Replace manifold or pipe gasket
	Exhaust manifold cracked or broken	Replace exhaust manifold, see ENGINES

Engine Trouble Shooting

DIESEL ENGINE TROUBLE SHOOTING

NOTE: Diesel engine mechanical diagnosis is the same as gasoline engines for items such as noisy valves, bearings, pistons, etc. The following trouble shooting covers only items pertaining to diesel engines

CONDITION	POSSIBLE CAUSE	CORRECTION
Engine Won't Crank	Bad battery connections or dead batteries	Check connections and/or replace batteries
	Bad starter connections or bad starter	Check connections and/or replace starter
Engine Cranks Slowly, Won't Start	Bad battery connections or dead batteries	Check connections and/or replace batteries
	Engine oil too heavy	Replace engine oil
Engine Cranks Normally, But Will Not Start	Glow plugs not functioning	Check glow plug system, see FUEL
	Glow plug control not functioning	Check glow plug controller, see FUEL
	Fuel not injected into cylinders	Check fuel injectors, see FUEL
	No fuel to injection pump	Check fuel delivery system
	Fuel filter blocked	Replace fuel filter
	Fuel tank filter blocked	Replace fuel tank filter
	Fuel pump not operating	Check pump operation and/or replace pump
	Fuel return system blocked	Inspect system and remove restriction
	No voltage to fuel solenoid	Check solenoid and connections
	Incorrect or contaminated fuel	Replace fuel
	Incorrect injection pump timing	Re-adjust pump timing, see FUEL
	Low compression	Check valves, pistons, rings, see ENGINES
	Injection pump malfunction	Inspect and/or replace injection pump
Engine Starts, Won't Idle	Incorrect slow idle adjustment	Reset idle adjustment, see TUNE-UP
	Fast idle solenoid malfunctioning	Check solenoid and connections
	Fuel return system blocked	Check system and remove restrictions
	Glow plugs go off too soon	See glow plug diagnosis in FUEL
	Injection pump timing incorrect	Reset pump timing, see FUEL
	No fuel to injection pump	Check fuel delivery system
	Incorrect or contaminated fuel	Replace fuel
	Low compression	Check valves, piston, rings, see ENGINES
	Injection pump malfunction	Replace injection pump, see FUEL
	Fuel solenoid closes in RUN position	Check solenoid and connections
Engine Starts/Idles Rough Without Smoke or Noise	Incorrect slow idle adjustment	Reset slow idle, see TUNE-UP
	Injection line fuel leaks	Check lines and connections
	Fuel return system blocked	Check lines and connections
	Air in fuel system	Bleed air from system
	Incorrect or contaminated fuel	Replace fuel
	Injector nozzle malfunction	Test and/or replace nozzles, see FUEL
Engine Starts and Idles Rough Without Smoke or Noise, But Clears After Warm-Up	Injection pump timing incorrect	Reset pump timing, see FUEL
	Engine not fully broken in	Put more miles on engine
	Air in system	Bleed air from system
	Injector nozzle malfunction	Check nozzles, see FUEL
Engine Idles Correctly, Misfires Above Idle	Blocked fuel filter	Replace fuel filter
	Injection pump timing incorrect	Reset pump timing, see FUEL
	Incorrect or contaminated fuel	Replace fuel
Engine Won't Return to Idle	Fast idle adjustment incorrect	Reset fast idle, see TUNE-UP
	Internal injection pump malfunction	Replace injection pump, see FUEL
	External linkage binding	Check linkage and remove binding
Fuel Leaks on Ground	Loose or broken fuel line	Check lines and connections
	Internal injection pump seal leak	Replace injection pump, see FUEL
Loss of Engine Power	Restricted air intake	Remove restriction
	EGR valve malfunction	Replace EGR valve
	Blocked or damaged exhaust system	Remove restriction and/or replace components
	Blocked fuel tank filter	Replace filter
	Restricted fuel filter	Remove restriction and/or replace filter

Engine Trouble Shooting

DIESEL ENGINE TROUBLE SHOOTING (Cont.)

CONDITION	POSSIBLE CAUSE	CORRECTION
Loss of Engine Power (Cont.)	Blocked vent in gas cap	Remove restriction and/or replace cap
	Tank-to-injection pump fuel supply blocked	Check fuel lines and connections
	Blocked fuel return system	Remove restriction
	Incorrect or contaminated fuel	Replace fuel
	Blocked injector nozzles	Remove nozzle and remove blockage, see FUEL
	Low compression	Check valves, rings, pistons, see ENGINES
Cylinder Knocking Noise	Injector nozzles sticking open	Test injectors and/or replace, see FUEL
	Very low nozzle opening pressure	Test injectors and/or replace
Loud Engine Noise With Black Smoke	Basic timing incorrect	Reset timing, see FUEL
	EGR valve malfunction	Replace EGR valve
	Internal injection pump malfunction	Replace injection pump, see FUEL
	Incorrect injector pump housing pressure	Check pressure and adjust, see FUEL
Engine Overheating	Cooling system leaks	Check cooling system and repair leaks
	Belt slipping or damaged	Check tension and/or replace belt
	Thermostat stuck closed	Remove and replace thermostat, see COOLING
	Head gasket leaking	Replace head gasket
Oil Light on at Idle	Low oil pump pressure	Check oil pump operation, see ENGINES
	Oil cooler or line restricted	Remove restriction and/or replace cooler
Engine Won't Shut Off	Injector pump fuel solenoid does not return fuel valve to OFF position	Remove and check solenoid and replace if needed
VACUUM PUMP DIAGNOSIS		
Excessive Noise	Loose pump-to-drive assembly screws	Tighten screws
	Loose tube on pump assembly	Tighten tube
	Valves not functioning properly	Replace valves
Oil Leakage	Loose end plug	Tighten end plug
	Bad seal crimp	Remove and re-crimp seal

Chrysler Corp. 6 Engines

3.7 LITER 6-CYLINDER

ENGINE CODING

ENGINE IDENTIFICATION

Engine identification number is stamped on block, below No. 6 spark plug. First position indicates model year. Next 3 digits designate engine cubic inch displacement.

ENGINE IDENTIFICATION CODE

Engine	Code
3.7L 1-Bbl.	225

ENGINE REMOVAL

See Engine Removal at end of ENGINE Section.

SPECIAL ENGINE MARKS

Information identifying undersize and oversize components will be found at various locations on engine. Coding and location is as follows:

- "M" or "R" followed by number indicates which main or rod journals are .001" (.03 mm) undersize. Found on center crankshaft counterweight.
- "M-10" or "R-10" indicates all main or rod journals are .010" (.25 mm) undersize. Found on center crankshaft counterweight.
- "A" Indicates all cylinder bores .020" (.51 mm) oversize. Found on top of front pad on right side of block.
- "★" Indicates .008" (.20 mm) oversize valve lifters. Found on top of front pad on right side of block.
- "O/S" Indicates .005" (.13 mm) oversize valve stems and is stamped on the thermostat boss at front of cylinder head.

MANIFOLDS & CYLINDER HEAD

MANIFOLD ASSEMBLY

Removal

1) Label and disconnect all lines, hoses and linkages from carburetor and air cleaner. Remove air cleaner and carburetor. Remove carburetor air heater. Disconnect exhaust pipe at manifold.

2) Remove air injection tube (if equipped). Remove manifolds as an assembly. Remove nut and bolts securing manifolds together, to separate manifolds.

Installation

1) Clean all gasket mating surfaces. Install new gasket between intake and exhaust manifolds. Snug bolts and stud nut securing manifolds together, but DO NOT tighten at this time.

2) Coat new manifolds gasket on both sides with gasket sealer and install on cylinder head. Position manifold assembly on cylinder head.

3) Install steel conical washer on center stud with cup side facing nut. Install brass washers at each end of exhaust manifold with flat sides facing manifold. Install triangular washers on remaining studs. Install nuts with cone side facing washers. Snug all bolts and nuts to approximately 10 INCH Lbs. (1 N.m).

4) Tighten nut first, then 2 bolts securing manifolds together. Starting at center of manifold assembly and working outward, tighten manifold nuts.

5) Install carburetor air heater, air injection tube (with new gasket), carburetor, linkages, lines, hoses and air cleaner. Connect exhaust pipe to manifold.

CYLINDER HEAD

Removal

1) Drain cooling system and remove air cleaner. Label and disconnect all wiring, hoses, lines and linkages from carburetor, distributor, manifolds and cylinder head.

2) Disconnect exhaust pipe at manifold. Remove rocker cover and rocker arm shaft assembly. Label push rods to insure installation in original location, then remove. Remove cylinder head and manifolds as an assembly. Remove manifolds from cylinder head.

CAUTION: **Do not use sealer of any type or aluminum paint on head gasket.**

Installation

Clean all gasket mating surfaces. Install gasket and cylinder head on block with manifolds removed. Install cylinder head bolts, and tighten in 2 steps. To complete installation, reverse removal procedure. *See Fig. 1.*

Fig. 1: Cylinder Head Bolt Tightening Sequence

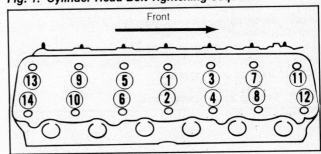

Tighten cylinder head bolts in 2 steps.

VALVES

VALVE ARRANGEMENT

E-I-E-I-E-I-I-E-I-E (Front-to-rear)

ROCKER ARM SHAFT ASSEMBLY

1) Stamped steel rocker arms are arranged on single rocker arm shaft. Hardened steel spacers are used between pairs of rocker arms. Shaft is supported and attached to seven mounts on cylinder head. *See Fig. 2.*

Fig. 2: Rocker Arm Shaft Assembly

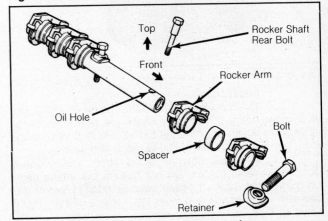

Install long retainer in center position.

3.7 LITER 6-CYLINDER (Cont.)

2) Note the following for installation:

- The oil hole must be installed upward and toward front of engine.
- Install long retainer at center position and special bolt at rear of engine.
- Shaft retainers must seat on rocker shaft and not on extended bushing of rocker arm.

VALVE SPRINGS

CAUTION: When removing valves from cylinder head, always remove burrs from valve stem lock grooves to prevent damage to valve guides.

Removal

With cylinder head removed, compress valve springs using valve spring compressor. Remove valve retainer locks, spring retainers, springs and oil seals. Ensure removed valves are installed in original locations.

Inspection

1) Valve springs should be tested whenever they are removed from cylinder head. Using valve spring tester, check spring tension. *See Fig. 3.* Replace springs that do not meet specifications.

2) Inspect each spring for squareness, using a steel square and flat surface. Replace spring if more than 1/16" (1.6 mm) out of square.

Fig. 3: Testing Valve Spring Tension

Use torque wrench and spring tester.

Installation

1) Coat valve stems with engine oil and insert in cylinder head. If valves or seats are reground, check valve stem height using gauge tool (C-3746). If valve is too long, grind valve tip down until length is within limits.

2) Install new oil seals firmly and squarely down over valve guides. Do not bottom out intake seals on guide tops. Intake oil seals require 1/16" (1.5 mm) gap between top of guide and inner top surface of seal. Install valve springs, retainers and locks.

VALVE SPRING INSTALLED HEIGHT

1) If valves or seats are reground, measure installed height of spring. Measure from bottom surface of spring seat in cylinder head (or top of spacer) to bottom surface of spring retainer.

2) If height is not within limits, install a 1/16" spacer between valve spring and cylinder head to correct spring height.

VALVE SPRING INSTALLED HEIGHT SPECIFICATIONS

Application	Measurement In. (mm)
All	1 5/8 - 1 11/16 (41.3-42.9)

VALVE STEM OIL SEALS

Cup type oil seal is used on all valves. Long seal is used on intake valve and short seal is used on exhaust valve. If seals are removed for any reason, replace with new seals. *See Fig. 4.*

Fig. 4: Intake and Exhaust Valve Assemblies

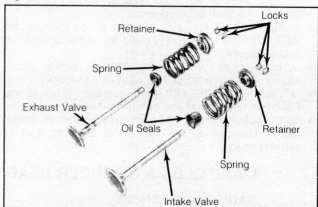

Short seal is used on exhaust valves.

VALVE GUIDE SERVICING

1) With valve spring assembly removed and valve guide cleaned, install sleeve tool (C-3973) over valve stem. Install valve in cylinder head.

2) Attach dial indicator to cylinder head, and position at right angle to valve stem being measured. *See Fig. 5.* Total sideplay should not exceed .017" (.43 mm).

Fig. 5: Measuring Valve Stem-to-Guide Clearance

Total sideplay should not exceed .017" (.43 mm).

3.7 LITER 6-CYLINDER (Cont.)

3) If valve guides require reaming, do not attempt to ream from standard to .030" (.76 mm) in one step. Use step procedure to obtain .030" (.76 mm) oversize.

4) Replacement valves with oversize stems are available in .005" (.13 mm), .015" (.38 mm), and .030" (.76 mm) oversize.

HYDRAULIC VALVE LIFTERS

1) Prior to testing, disassemble lifter and clean all parts to remove varnish and carbon. Reassemble lifter.

2) To test, remove cap from plunger and plunger from lifter body. Fill lifter body with clean kerosene and install plunger. Unseat check valve to permit complete installation of plunger, then replace cap. See Fig. 6.

Fig. 6: Hydraulic Lifter Assembly

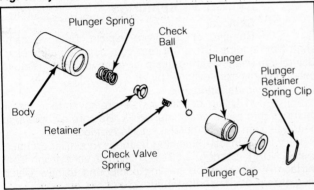

Do not lose check balls.

3) Place lifter upright in lifter testing tool (C-4343). Test leakdown by compressing tool. If plunger collapses immediately, disassemble, clean and retest. If rapid leakdown still occurs, replace lifter.

4) Check all lifters for "dished" wear condition and replace as necessary. If lifter or lifter bore in cylinder block is scuffed, scored, or shows signs of sticking, ream bore to next oversize and replace with oversize lifter.

CAMSHAFT

ENGINE FRONT COVER

Removal

1) Drain cooling system and remove radiator. Remove drive belts, fan and pulley from water pump. Remove power steering crankshaft pulley. Remove vibration damper using puller.

2) Loosen oil pan bolts to provide clearance between pan and front cover. Remove front cover bolts and cover.

Installation

1) Clean all gasket mating surfaces and remove any burrs. Apply 1/8" bead of silicone sealer at junction of rubber pan seals and cork oil pan gaskets. Using new gasket, install and tighten cover. Tighten oil pan bolts.

2) Lubricate front cover seal lip with Lubriplate. Position hub slot key in crankshaft. Install vibration damper onto crankshaft using puller (C-3732A) with installing adapter. Reverse removal procedure to complete installation. See Fig. 7.

Fig. 7: Removing and Installing Vibration Damper

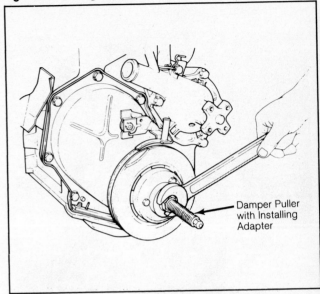

Press vibration damper onto crankshaft, using puller and installing adapter.

FRONT COVER OIL SEAL

Removal

Drain cooling system and remove radiator and fan. Remove crankshaft pulley and vibration damper. See Fig. 7. Pry seal out from behind lip, using care not to damage crankshaft seal surface of front cover.

Installation

1) Install new seal by installing the threaded shaft part of seal installer (C-4251) into threads of crankshaft. Place seal into opening with seal spring facing the engine.

2) Place installing adapter (C-4251-2) with the thrust bearing and nut on the shaft. Tighten nut until tool is flush with the timing chain cover. Reverse removal procedure to complete installation.

TIMING CHAIN

Checking For Stretch

1) Remove front cover. Place torque wrench and socket on camshaft sprocket bolt. Using 30 ft. lbs. (41 N.m) torque (with head installed), or 15 ft. lbs. (20 N.m) torque (with head removed), turn camshaft sprocket in normal direction of rotation to remove chain slack. DO NOT allow crankshaft to move.

2) Place a steel ruler next to timing chain to measure amount of chain movement. Apply same torque in reverse direction, and measure amount of chain movement. See Fig. 8. If movement exceeds 1/8" (3 mm), replace timing chain.

Removal

Remove front cover. Remove camshaft sprocket attaching bolt, then remove timing chain and camshaft sprocket.

Installation

Turn crankshaft to line up timing mark of crankshaft sprocket with centerline of camshaft. Install camshaft sprocket and timing chain with timing marks aligned. See Fig. 9. Tighten camshaft sprocket bolt. Reverse removal procedures to complete installation.

Chrysler Corp. 6 Engines

3.7 LITER 6-CYLINDER (Cont.)

Fig. 8: Measuring Timing Chain Stretch

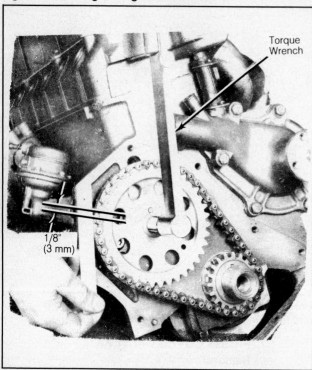

Do not permit crankshaft to move.

Fig. 9: Aligning Timing Chain Sprockets

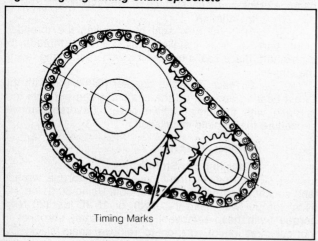

Timing marks on sprockets must align as shown.

VALVE TIMING

1) Rotate crankshaft until No. 6 exhaust valve is closing and No. 6 intake valve is opening.

2) Insert a 1/4" spacer between rocker arm and valve stem tip of No. 1 intake valve. Insertion of spacer should bleed down lifter, bottoming lifter plunger.

3) Install dial indicator on No. 1 intake valve, so indicator point is in contact with the valve spring retainer. Dial indicator stem must be parallel with valve stem. Zero dial indicator.

4) Rotate crankshaft clockwise until dial indicator shows .010" (.25 mm) of lift. If valve timing is correct, the timing of the crankshaft pulley should read from 12° BTDC to TDC.

CAMSHAFT

Removal

1) Remove air cleaner, rocker cover and rocker shaft assembly. Identify push rods for reinstallation in original locations, then remove. Remove lifters, using valve lifter removing tool (C-4129). Keep lifters in order for reinstallation in original locations.

2) Remove timing chain and sprockets, distributor, oil pump and fuel pump. Install a long bolt in end of camshaft to aid in removal. Remove camshaft, using care not to damage camshaft bearings.

Installation

If camshaft is being replaced, check lifters for "dished" wear, and replace as necessary. Lubricate camshaft lobes and bearing journals. Carefully install camshaft in cylinder block. Reverse removal procedure to complete installation.

CAMSHAFT BEARINGS

Removal

Remove engine from vehicle. Remove camshaft from engine. Drive out rear cam bearing welch plug. Using camshaft bearing installer/remover tool, remove bearing shells from cylinder block.

Installation

1) Using bearing installer/remover tool, install bearings into place in cylinder block. Be sure oil hole(s) in bearings align with oil hole(s) in cylinder block.

2) Insert remaining bearings in similar manner. Install No. 1 bearing 3/32" (2.4 mm) inward from front surface of block. Apply sealing compound to new welch plug at rear of camshaft. Be sure plug does not leak.

PISTONS, PINS & RINGS

OIL PAN

See Oil Pan Removal at end of ENGINE Section.

PISTON & ROD ASSEMBLY

Removal

1) With cylinder head and oil pan removed, use ridge cutter to remove any ridge or deposits on upper end of cylinder bore. Piston must be at bottom of stroke and covered with cloth to collect cuttings.

2) Ensure connecting rods and caps are marked for cylinder identification. Rotate crankshaft so connecting rod is centered in cylinder bore. Remove rod cap.

3) Cover rod cap bolts with rubber hose to protect crankshaft. Push piston and rod assembly out through top of cylinder block. Use care not to nick crankshaft journal or cylinder wall. Install rod caps on mating rods.

Installation

1) Compression ring gaps must be located on piston, so they will be on left side of engine and staggered about 60° apart.

NOTE: Neither gap should line up with oil ring gaps, and "ID" mark on each compression ring must face top of piston.

2) Rotate oil ring expander so gaps are on right side of engine. Rotate steel rails so gaps are opposite and positioned above piston pin holes.

3.7 LITER 6-CYLINDER (Cont.)

3) Immerse pistons and rings in clean engine oil. Slide ring compressor over piston and tighten. Do not allow position of rings to change. Lightly oil cylinder bores.

4) Position piston and rod assembly into bore. Notch on top of piston and oil squirt hole in connecting rod must point toward front of engine. Rotate crankshaft so connecting rod journal is in center of cylinder bore.

5) Install piston and rod assembly into bore and carefully guide connecting rod onto crankshaft journal to prevent damage. Tap piston head lightly with hammer handle to seat connecting rod and bearing against crankshaft. Install and tighten rod cap and bearing.

FITTING PISTONS

1) With piston and cylinder bores dry and clean, measure for piston-to-cylinder wall clearance. Measurements should be taken at 70°F (21°C).

2) Measure piston skirt diameter 90° to piston pin axis. Measure cylinder bore halfway down cylinder and 90° to crankshaft centerline.

3) Check cylinder bore for taper or out-of-round condition using a micrometer or cylinder bore gauge.

4) Cylinder bore must not be more than .005" (.13 mm) out-of-round. Taper must not exceed .010" (.25 mm). If not within limits, bore and hone cylinders. Pistons are available in standard and .020" (.51 mm) oversize.

5) After boring and honing operations, always wash cylinders thoroughly with scrub brush and soapy water, then rinse well. Oil the bores after cleaning to prevent rust.

FITTING RINGS

1) Using a feeler gauge, check ring end gap in cylinder bore. Ring must be square in bore and about 2" from bottom of cylinder bore.

2) Using a feeler gauge, check side clearance of ring in ring groove of piston. *See Fig. 10.* Steel oil ring rails should not bind in ring groove and side clearance must not be excessive.

3) Install rings on piston, starting at bottom with oil ring expander and rails, then working upward until top compression ring is installed. "ID" mark on each compression ring must face upward.

Fig. 10: Measuring Ring Side Clearance

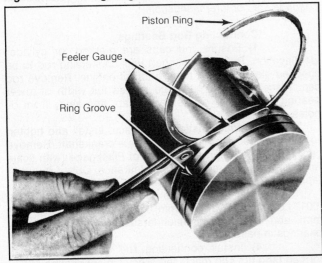

Ensure ring grooves are clean.

PISTON PIN REPLACEMENT
Removal

Arrange piston pin removal tool (C-3724 or equivalent) as shown in *Fig. 11*. Spring must be removed from anvil. Install nut loosely on main screw. When pin falls from connecting rod, stop press to prevent damage to bottom of anvil.

Fig. 11: Removing Piston Pin

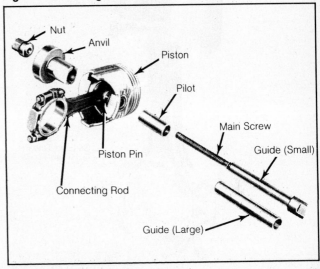

Notice arrangement of removal tool.

Installation

1) Measure piston pin fit in the piston. If pin is not a sliding fit in piston at 70°F (21°C), piston and pin must be replaced as an assembly. Lubricate piston pin bore and connecting rod bore. Arrange pin removal tool (C-3724) for installation of piston pin. See Fig. 12.

Fig. 12: Installing Piston Pin

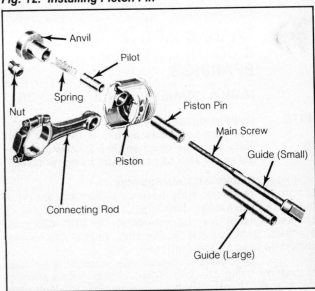

Ensure pin fit in piston is a sliding fit at 70°F (21°C).

2) Install spring inside pilot, and install spring and pilot in the anvil. Position notch on piston and oil hole in connecting rod on same side (front of engine). *See Fig. 13.* Press pin into position until pin bottoms against pilot on tool.

Fig. 13: Correct Rod-to-Piston Relationship

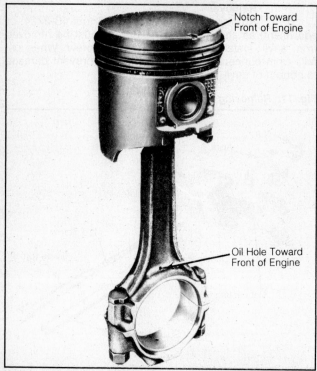

Notch Toward Front of Engine

Oil Hole Toward Front of Engine

When removing and installing pistons, cover rod cap bolts with rubber hose to protect crankshaft and cylinders.

Checking Pin Fit

Arrange piston pin tool parts as for removal of pin. Place assembly in vise, securing main screw butt end between vise jaws. Attach torque wrench to nut, and test torque up to 15 ft. lbs. (20 N.m). If connecting rod moves downward on piston pin, replace connecting rod.

CRANKSHAFT, MAIN & CONNECTING ROD BEARINGS

MAIN & CONNECTING ROD BEARINGS

NOTE: Use Plastigage method for checking bearing clearances. Be sure oil film is removed from surfaces to be checked. The following procedures are with oil pan and oil pump removed.

Crankshaft Main Bearings

1) Check main bearing clearances one at a time. To accurately determine clearance, weight of crankshaft must first be eliminated. A .010" (.25 mm) minimum thickness cardboard shim (matchbook cover) should be used for this purpose.

2) Remove crankshaft main caps on either side of bearing being checked. When checking clearance of No. 1 or No. 4 main bearings, remove only adjacent main cap. Place a cardboard shim between the bearing shell(s) and cap(s) which were removed. Install "shimmed" bearing cap(s) and tighten to 10-15 ft. lbs. (14-20 N.m).

3) Remove main cap of bearing to be checked. Use Plastigage method as explained in Connecting Rod Bearings, tightening main cap to specification.

4) When installing new bearings, always install in pairs. New bearings are available in standard, .001" (.03 mm), .002" (.05 mm), .003" (.08 mm), .010" (.25 mm), and .012" (.31 mm) undersize.

5) Lower main bearings 1, 2 and 4 are interchangeable. Upper main bearings 1, 2 and 4 are interchangeable. However, upper (grooved face) main bearings are not interchangeable with lower (plain face) main bearings. Thrust bearings are not interchangeable with any other bearing. *See Fig. 14.*

6) Replace main bearings one at a time. To extract upper main bearing from cylinder block, insert pin tool (C-3059) into oil hole of crankshaft journal. Rotate crankshaft clockwise, allowing pin tool to push upper bearing out of cylinder block.

7) When installing a new upper main bearing, slightly chamfer sharp edges from plain side of new bearing, then start bearing in place. Using pin tool, install upper bearing in reverse order of removal procedures.

8) Check crankshaft end play. If not within specifications, replace thrust bearing (No. 3 main bearing).

Fig. 14: Main Bearing Identification

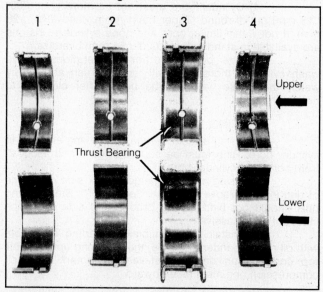

1   2   3   4

Upper

Thrust Bearing

Lower

Upper (grooved) main bearings and lower (plain) main bearings are not interchangeable.

Connecting Rod Bearings

1) Ensure rod caps are marked for cylinder identification. Rotate crankshaft until connecting rod to be checked starts moving toward top of engine. Remove rod cap. Place strip of Plastigage across full width of lower bearing, about 1/4" off center of cap, and away from oil holes.

2) With Plastigage in place, install and tighten rod cap to specification. Do not rotate crankshaft. Remove cap. Measure compressed width of Plastigage (with scale furnished) to determine bearing clearance. Out-of-round or taper on any journal must not exceed .001" (.03 mm).

3) New bearings are available in standard, .001" (.03 mm), .002" (.05 mm), .003" (.08 mm), .010" (.25 mm), and .012" (.31 mm) undersize. Always install new bearings in pairs.

4) Install connecting rod bearings so small formed tang fits into machined groove in connecting rod.

Chrysler Corp. 6 Engines

3.7 LITER 6-CYLINDER (Cont.)

REAR MAIN BEARING OIL SEAL

Removal

1) Remove oil pan. Remove rear seal retainer and rear main bearing cap. Remove lower seal from seal retainer.

2) Remove upper seal by pressing on seal end with a small screwdriver, then pull seal from cylinder block. Use care not to damage crankshaft.

Installation

1) Lightly oil upper seal lip with engine oil. With paint stripe on seal positioned to rear of engine, hold seal tightly against crankshaft.

2) Rotate crankshaft while sliding seal into groove. Use care not to damage seal lip, or allow back of seal to become nicked or shaved by groove in block.

3) Install rear main bearing cap. Clean the seal retainer and wipe clean. Apply 1/8" bead of silicone sealer in bottom of retainer groove, starting and finishing 1/2" from ends of the groove. Install lower seal half into retainer with paint stripe to rear.

4) Install 2 side seals into grooves in seal retainer. Lightly grease side seals. Install seal retainer and tighten before silicone sealer cures (10-15 minutes). DO NOT use sealer or cement on seal ends or seal lip.

ENGINE OILING

Crankcase Capacity

5 quarts (4.75L). Add 1 quart (.95L) when replacing oil filter.

Oil Filter

Replace oil filter at first oil change and every other oil change thereafter.

Normal Oil Pressure

30-70 psi (2.1-4.9 kg/cm²) at 2000 RPM.

Pressure Regulator Valve

Located in oil pump body, not adjustable.

Fig. 15: Engine Oiling System

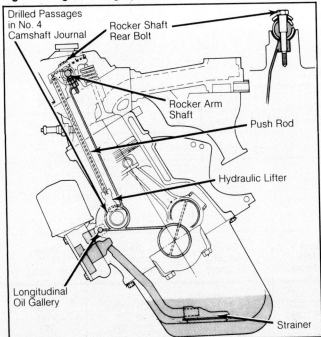

ENGINE OILING SYSTEM

Rotor-type oil pump is mounted externally on right side of crankcase. Pickup tube and strainer is screwed into crankcase wall at pump mounting pad. Main gallery extends along right side of crankcase.

From oil pump, oil is force fed directly to camshaft and to crankshaft to lubricate these components and their respective bearings.

From No. 4 camshaft journal, oil is continually supplied to lubricate rocker arm shaft and rocker arms. Valve rocker arms route a full flow of oil through push rods to lifters. A reduced metered flow from rocker arms lubricates tips of valve stems. See Fig. 15.

OIL PUMP

Removal

Carefully remove oil pump cover, using care not to allow outer rotor to drop out. Remove outer rotor. Remove oil pump.

Disassembly

While supporting gear to eliminate load on aluminum body of pump, press off pump drive gear. Pump may now be completely disassembled. See Fig. 16.

Fig. 16: Oil Pump Assembly

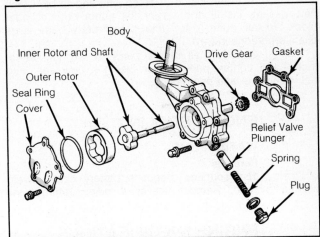

Inspection

1) Clean all parts thoroughly. Replace pump assembly if mating surface is scratched or grooved. Check wear of cover with a straightedge and feeler gauge. Replace pump assembly if wear is excessive.

2) Replace shaft and both rotors if inner rotor thickness or outer rotor thickness is not within limits, or if outer rotor diameter is not within limits.

3) Measure outer rotor-to-pump body clearance with a feeler gauge. If not within specifications, replace pump assembly.

4) Install inner rotor in pump body. Place a straightedge over pump body, between bolt holes. Using a feeler gauge, measure clearance over inner rotor. Replace pump assembly if clearance is excessive.

5) Install both rotors in pump body. Using a feeler gauge, check clearance between tips of inner and outer rotors. Excessive clearance requires replacement of shaft and both rotors.

6) Make following inspection of relief valve assembly: Check relief valve plunger for wear and binding in bore. Check spring for free length of 2 1/4" (57.2 mm).

Chrysler Corp. 6 Engines

3.7 LITER 6-CYLINDER (Cont.)

Spring tension should test between 22.3-23.3 lbs. (1.56-1.63 kg/cm²) when compressed to a length of 1 19/32" (40.5 mm).

OIL PUMP SPECIFICATIONS

Application	Specifications In. (mm)
Pump Cover Wear	.0014 (.036) Max.
Inner Rotor Thickness	.826 (20.98) Min.
Outer Rotor Thickness	.826 (20.98) Min.
Outer Rotor Diameter	2.47 (62.74) Min.
Outer Rotor-to-Pump Body	.013 (.33) Max.
Clearance Over Inner Rotor	.003 (.076) Max.
Rotor Tip Clearance	.009 (.23) Max.

Reassembly

1) Reassemble pump in reverse order of disassembly, using new parts as required. When pressing drive gear onto shaft, note the following:

2) Install inner rotor and shaft assembly into pump body. Insert a 1/32" thick washer in the inner rotor shaft hole. Using the washer to support the shaft, press drive gear onto the shaft. Remove the washer.

Installation

1) Prime inside of pump with engine oil. Using new gasket, install and tighten oil pump onto cylinder block. Install outer rotor into pump body with large chamfered edge inward.

2) Ensure all internal parts are well lubricated. Install and tighten pump cover, using a new seal ring between cover and pump body.

ENGINE COOLING

WATER PUMP

Removal

1) Disconnect negative battery cable. Drain cooling system. Remove all drive belts. Remove all coolant hoses connected to water pump. Remove fan, spacer (or fluid unit), pulley and bolts as an assembly.

CAUTION: After removing fluid unit, do not place drive unit so shaft points downward. Silicone fluid from fluid unit could drain into fan drive bearing, causing lubricant failure.

2) Position by-pass hose lower clamp in center of hose, and disconnect hose. Remove water pump.

Installation

To install water pump, reverse removal procedures, using new gasket.

NOTE: For information on cooling system capacities and other cooling system components, see appropriate article in "Engine Cooling Systems," at end of ENGINE Section.

TIGHTENING SPECIFICATIONS

Application	Ft. Lbs. (N.m)
Camshaft Sprocket Bolt	50 (68)
Connecting Rod Caps	45 (61)
Cylinder Head Bolts	
Step 1	35 (47)
Step 2	70 (95)
Flex Plate or Flywheel Bolts	55 (75)
Intake-to-Exhaust Manifold	
Bolts	20 (27)
Stud Nut	30 (41)
Main Bearing Caps	85 (115)
Manifolds Assembly-to-Cylinder Head	10 (14)
Oil Pump	
Cover-to-Body	17 (23)
Pump-to-Cylinder Block	17 (23)
Rear Main Bearing Seal Retainer	30 (41)
Rocker Arm Shaft Bolts	25 (34)

ENGINE SPECIFICATIONS

GENERAL SPECIFICATIONS

Year	DISPLACEMENT		Fuel System	HP@RPM	Torque Ft. Lbs.@RPM	Compr. Ratio	BORE		STROKE	
	Cu. In.	Liters					In.	mm	In.	mm
1983	225	3.7	1-Bbl.	.....	.....	8.4:1	3.40	86.4	4.125	104.8

VALVES

Engine Size & Valve	Head Diam. In. (mm)	Face Angle	Seat Angle	Seat Width In. (mm)	Stem Diameter In. (mm)	Stem Clearance In. (mm)	Valve Lift In. (mm)
3.7L Intake	1.615-1.625 (41.02-41.28)	44½-45°	45-45½°	.070-.090 (1.78-2.29)	.372-.373 (9.45-9.47)	.001-.003 (.03-.08)	.378 (9.60)
Exhaust	1.355-1.365 (34.42-34.67)	42½-43°	45-45½°	.040-.060 (1.02-1.52)	.371-.372 (9.42-9.45)	.002-.004 (.05-.10)	.378 (9.60)

Chrysler Corp. 6 Engines

3.7 LITER 6-CYLINDER (Cont.)

ENGINE SPECIFICATIONS (Cont.)

PISTONS, PINS, RINGS

| Engine | PISTONS | PINS | | RINGS | | |
	Clearance In. (mm)	Piston Fit In. (mm)	Rod Fit In. (mm)	Ring No.	End Gap In. (mm)	Side Clearance In. (mm)
3.7L	.0005-.0015 (.013-.038)	.00035-.00085 (.0009-.0216)	.0007-.0017 (.018-.043)	1 & 2 3	.010-.020 (.25-.51) .015-.055 (.38-1.40)	.0015-.0030 (.038-.080) .0002-.0050 (.005-.130)

CRANKSHAFT MAIN & CONNECTING ROD BEARINGS

| Engine | MAIN BEARINGS | | | | CONNECTING ROD BEARINGS | | |
	Journal Diam. In. (mm)	Clearance In. (mm)	Thrust Bearing	Crankshaft End Play In. (mm)	Journal Diam. In. (mm)	Clearance In. (mm)	Side Play In. (mm)
3.7L	2.7495-2.7505 (69.837-69.863)	.0010-.0025 (.025-.064)	No. 3	.0035-.0095 (.089-.241)	2.1865-2.1875 (55.537-55.563)	.0010-.0022 (.025-.056)	.007-.013 (.18-.33)

VALVE SPRINGS

| Engine | Free Length In. (mm) | PRESSURE Lbs. @ In. (Kg @ mm) | |
		Valve Closed	Valve Open
3.7L	1.92 (48.8)	49-57@1.69 (22-26@42.86)	137-150@1.31 (62-68@33.34)

CAMSHAFT

Engine	Journal Diam. In. (mm)	Clearance In. (mm)	Lobe Lift In. (mm)
3.7L No. 1	1.998-1.999 (50.75-50.77)	.001-.003 (.03-.08)	.....
No. 2	1.982-1.983 (50.34-50.37)		
No. 3	1.967-1.968 (49.96-49.99)		
No. 4	1.951-1.952 (49.56-49.58)		

Chrysler Corp. V8 Engines

5.2 & 5.9 LITER V8

ENGINE CODING

ENGINE IDENTIFICATION

Engine identification number is stamped on engine, just rear of right engine mount. First 2 positions indicate year and manufacturing plant code. Next 3 digits are cubic inch displacement. Next 4 digits are build date, and last four digits are engine sequence numbers.

ENGINE IDENTIFICATION CODES

Engine	Code
5.2L 2 Bbl. & 4-Bbl.	318
5.9L 2 Bbl. & 4-Bbl.	360

ENGINE REMOVAL

See "Engine Removal" at end of ENGINE Section.

SPECIAL ENGINE MARKS

Information identifying undersize and oversize components will be found at various engine locations. It is decoded as follows:

- "M" or "R" followed by number, indicates which main or rod bearing journal is .001" (.03 mm) undersize. This mark will be stamped on No. 8 crankshaft counterweight on 5.2L engines and on No. 3 crankshaft counterweight on 5.9L engines.
- "MX" or "RX" indicates all main or rod bearing journals are .010" (.25 mm) undersize. Marked on No. 8 crankshaft counterweight (5.2L), or No. 3 crankshaft counterweight (5.9L).
- "A" indicates .020" (.51 mm) oversize cylinder bores. Follows engine identification number.
- "◆" indicates .008" (.20 mm) oversize lifters. Located on top pad, front of engine, and stamped on flat ground on outside surface of each oversize lifter bore.
- "X" indicates .005" (.13 mm) oversize valve stems. Found on milled pad near two 3/8" tapped holes on each end of cylinder head.

MANIFOLDS & CYLINDER HEAD

INTAKE MANIFOLD

Removal

1) Drain cooling system and disconnect battery ground cable. Remove alternator, air cleaner, fuel line and PCV system.

2) Disconnect accelerator linkage, coil wires and temperature indicator sending wire. Disconnect bypass hose and heater hoses.

3) Remove distributor cap and wires. Remove vacuum hose between carburetor and distributor. Remove evaporation control system and rocker covers. Remove intake manifold, coil and carburetor as an assembly.

Installation

1) Clean all gasket mating surfaces. On 5.2L 2-Bbl. only, lightly coat intake manifold side gaskets with gasket sealer. On 5.2L 4-Bbl. and 5.9L engines, DO NOT use any sealer on side composition gaskets.

2) Install manifold side gaskets. Coat front and rear intake manifold end gaskets and cylinder block with a quick-dry cement.

3) Install end gaskets, ensuring end holes in gaskets are locked into tangs of head gasket. Place a 1/4" bead of silicone sealer at each of the 4 intake manifold-to-cylinder head gasket corners.

4) Position intake manifold on engine. Inspect gaskets for correct positioning, then install attaching bolts finger tight. Tighten in 3 steps. See Fig. 1.

Fig. 1: Intake Manifold Tightening Sequence.

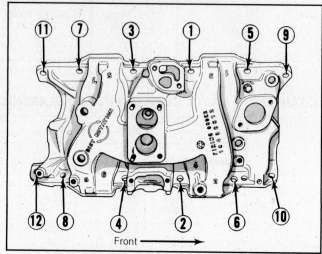

Tighten all bolts in 2 steps, then tighten bolts 5 through 12 to final specification.

EXHAUST MANIFOLDS

Removal

Disconnect exhaust pipe from exhaust manifold. Remove exhaust manifold from cylinder head.

Installation

1) If end studs came out when removing end nuts from manifolds, replace with new studs and nuts. Coat coarse threads of new end studs with sealer, then install into head.

2) Position manifold over end studs on cylinder head. Install conical washers and nuts on end studs.

3) Install 2 remaining conical washers and 2 bolts to inboard ends of outer manifold arms. Install 2 bolts (without washers) to center arm of manifold.

4) Starting at center arm of exhaust manifold and working outward, tighten exhaust manifold. Connect and tighten exhaust pipe.

CYLINDER HEAD

Removal

1) Drain cooling system and disconnect battery ground cable. Remove intake and exhaust manifolds. Remove rocker arm shaft assemblies.

2) Identify push rods for installation in their original locations, then remove. Remove cylinder heads from engine.

Installation

1) Clean all gasket surfaces of cylinder block and head. Coat new head gaskets with head gasket sealer and install on cylinder block.

2) Install cylinder heads. Apply sealer to cylinder head bolts. Install and tighten head bolts in 2 steps. See Fig. 2. Reverse removal procedure to complete installation.

5.2 & 5.9 LITER V8 (Cont.)

Fig. 2: Cylinder Head Tightening Sequence

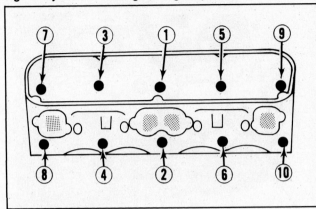

Tighten all bolts to 50 ft. lbs. (68 N.m), then final tighten bolts to 95 ft. lbs. (129 N.m).

VALVES

VALVE ARRANGEMENT

E-I-I-E-E-I-I-E (Both banks, front-to-rear)

ROCKER ARM SHAFT ASSEMBLY

Rocker arms are stamped steel type. They are mounted on a shaft, which is attached to cylinder head at 5 support pedestals. Pedestals are cast into cylinder head. Exhaust rocker arms are designed to allow clearance for rotators. Rocker arms have right and left positions. See Fig. 3.

Fig. 3: Identifying Rocker Arms

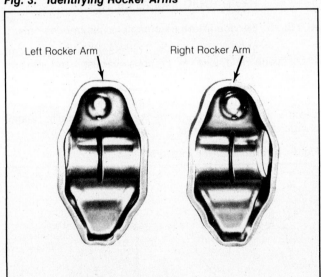

Left Rocker Arm   Right Rocker Arm

Right and left rocker arms differ.

1) If rocker arm assemblies are disassembled, reassemble rocker arms on shaft as shown in Fig. 4.

2) Notch on end of rocker arm shaft must point to centerline of engine and toward front of engine on left bank, and to rear of engine on right bank.

3) Install long retainers one position inward from ends of rocker arm shaft.

Fig. 4: Location of Rocker Arms.

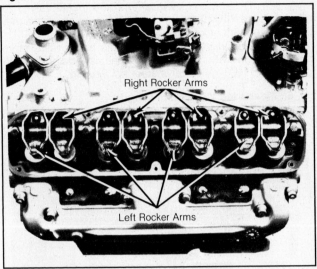

Right Rocker Arms

Left Rocker Arms

Install long retainers one position inward from ends of shaft.

VALVE SPRINGS

CAUTION: Installing incorrect exhaust valve springs on engines with positive rotators can cause severe engine damage.

Removal

1) With cylinder head removed, compress valve springs using valve spring compressor. Remove retainer locks, valve spring retainers (or rotators), valve springs and valve stem cup seals.

2) Before removing valves, remove any burrs from valve stem lock grooves to prevent damage to valve guides. Identify valves to ensure installation in original locations.

3) Note that all intake valve springs are Blue; 5.2L exhaust valve springs with rotators are White, and 5.9L exhaust valve springs with rotators are Yellow. See Fig. 5.

Fig. 5: Exploded View of Valve Assembly

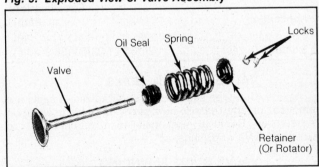

Oil Seal   Spring   Locks

Valve

Retainer
(Or Rotator)

Use proper, color-coded valve springs.

Inspection

1) Whenever valve springs are removed, use a spring tester to test springs for proper tension.

2) Check each spring for squareness, using a steel square and flat surface. If spring is more than 5/64" (2 mm) out-of-square, replace it.

Chrysler Corp. V8 Engines
5.2 & 5.9 LITER V8 (Cont.)

Installation

1) Lubricate valve stems and install valves in cylinder head. If valves or seats have been reground, check valve stem height using gauge tool (C-3968).

2) If valve is too long, grind tip of valve stem until length is within limits. If engine is equipped with rotators, DO NOT grind valve stem tip. *See Fig. 6.*

Fig. 6: Measuring Valve Stem Length

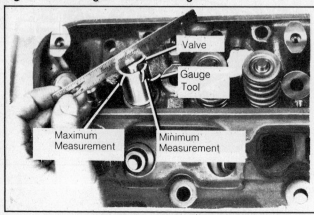

Do not grind tips of valves that use valve rotators.

3) Install new oil seals. Install exhaust valve oil seals down against top of valve guides. Position intake oil seals firmly and squarely over valve guides, but do not bottom seal against top of guide.

4) Using spring compressor, install valve springs, retainers (or rotators) and locks.

VALVE SPRING INSTALLED HEIGHT

1) If valves and/or seats are reground, measure installed height of springs. Measure from bottom of spring seat (or top of spacer) to bottom of spring retainer (or rotator).

2) If installed height is incorrect, install a 1/16" (1.7 mm) spacer in head counterbore to correct spring height. Never shim to a height less than specifications.

VALVE SPRING INSTALLED HEIGHT SPECIFICATIONS

Application	Specification In. (mm)
Intake Valves	1 5/8 - 1 11/16 (41.27-42.86)
Exhaust Valves	1 29/64 - 1 33/64 (36.9-38.5)

VALVE STEM OIL SEALS

Cup-type seal is used on all valves. If seals are removed for any reason, new seals must be used upon reassembly. Removal and installation procedures are explained in Valve Springs.

VALVE GUIDE SERVICING
Wear Check

1) With valve spring components removed and valve guide cleaned, install sleeve tool (C-3937) over valve stem (to place valve at proper height), then install valve in cylinder head.

2) Attach a dial indicator to cylinder head and position indicator at right angle to valve stem being measured. Total side play should not exceed .017" (.43 mm). *See Fig. 7.*

Fig. 7: Measuring Valve Stem-to-Guide Clearance.

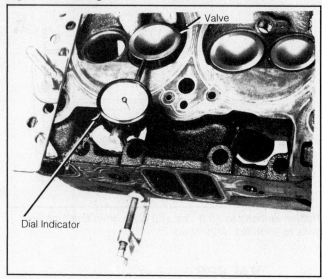

Total side play should not exceed .017" (.43 mm).

CAUTION: Never ream guides from standard to .030" (.76 mm) oversize in one step. Always ream guides in progressive steps when reaming to .030" (.76 mm) oversize.

Servicing

Ream guides to correct oversize if valve-to-guide clearance is excessive, or if valve stems are scored or scuffed. Oversize valves are available in .005" (.13 mm), .015" (.38 mm) and .030" (.76 mm).

HYDRAULIC VALVE LIFTERS

NOTE: Service lifters as complete assemblies only.

1) Prior to testing, disassemble lifter. Clean lifter inside and out to remove varnish and carbon deposits.

2) To test, remove cap from plunger and plunger from lifter body. *See Fig. 8.* Fill lifter body with clean kerosene. Unseat check valve (or ball). Install plunger and cap.

Fig. 8: Hydraulic Lifter Assembly

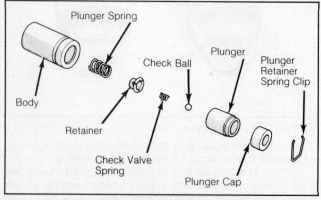

Parts are not interchangeable between lifters.

3) Place lifter upright in lifter tester (C-4343) and check leakdown by compressing tool. If lifter collapses immediately, disassemble, clean and retest.

5.2 & 5.9 LITER V8 (Cont.)

4) If upon retesting, rapid leakdown still occurs, replace lifter. Worn lifters that show a "dished" wear condition must also be replaced.

5) If lifter or lifter bore in cylinder block is scuffed, scored, or shows signs of sticking, ream bore to next oversize and replace with oversize lifter.

CAMSHAFT

ENGINE FRONT COVER

Removal

1) Disconnect battery. Drain cooling system and remove radiator and water pump assembly. Remove power steering pump (if equipped). Remove crankshaft pulley and vibration damper.

2) Remove fuel lines and fuel pump. Loosen oil pan bolts and remove front bolts at each side. Remove front cover and gasket, using care not to damage oil pan gasket.

Installation

1) Check that mating surfaces of cover and cylinder block are clean and free from burrs. Apply a 1/8" bead of silicone sealer to oil pan gasket.

2) Apply Lubriplate to front cover oil seal lip. Install front cover and attaching bolts, but DO NOT tighten bolts at this time.

3) Install vibration damper onto crankshaft to align oil seal, then tighten damper center bolt. Tighten front cover bolts, then oil pan bolts. Reverse removal procedure to complete installation.

FRONT COVER OIL SEAL

Removal

1) Disconnect battery. Remove belts from crankshaft pulley and remove fan and shroud from engine. Remove crankshaft pulley and vibration damper.

2) Pry seal outward from behind lip, being careful not to damage crankshaft or seal recess in front cover.

Installation

1) Install new seal by using seal installing tool (C-4251 or equivalent). Install threaded shaft of tool into threads of crankshaft. Place seal into opening, with spring toward inside of engine.

Fig. 9: Installing Front Cover Seal

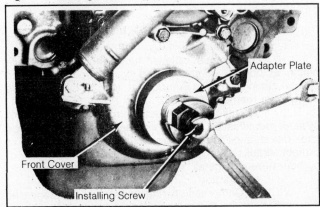

Tighten nut until tool is flush with cover.

2) Place adapter with thrust bearing and nut on shaft. Tighten nut until tool is flush with front cover.

3) Reinstall crankshaft pulley, vibration damper, fan, shroud, and belts. Reconnect battery. *See Fig. 9.*

TIMING CHAIN

Checking for Stretch

1) Position scale next to timing chain to measure any movement of chain. *See Fig. 10.* Place torque wrench with socket over camshaft sprocket lock bolt. When applying specified torque, DO NOT allow crankshaft to turn.

2) Apply torque in direction of crankshaft rotation to remove chain slack. Torque should be 30 ft. lbs. (41 N.m) with cylinder heads installed, or 15 ft. lbs. (21 N.m) with cylinder heads removed.

Fig. 10: Measuring Timing Chain Stretch

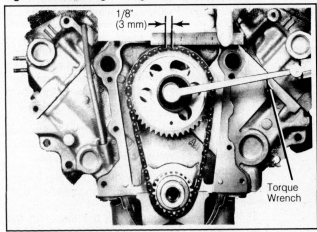

Torque is 30 ft. lbs. (41 N.m) with heads installed; 15 ft. lbs. (20 N.m) with heads removed.

3) Apply same torque in reverse direction, and measure amount of chain movement. If movement exceeds 1/8" (3 mm), install new timing chain.

Removal

With front cover removed, remove camshaft sprocket attaching bolt, washer and fuel pump eccentric. Remove timing chain with crankshaft and camshaft sprockets.

Fig. 11: Aligning Timing Chain Sprocket Marks

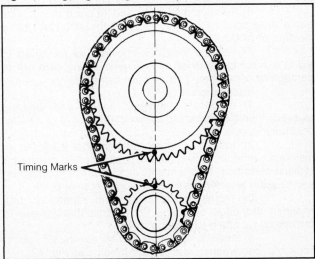

Align chain and sprockets on bench prior to installation.

Installation

1) Place camshaft and crankshaft sprockets on bench with timing marks on an imaginary centerline through bore of both sprockets. *See Fig. 11.*

2) Place timing chain around both sprockets. Turn crankshaft and camshaft to line up with keyway locations in sprockets.

3) With chain placed on sprockets, slide both sprockets evenly over their respective shafts. Use a straightedge to measure alignment of timing marks.

4) Install fuel pump eccentric, cup washer and camshaft bolt. Tighten bolt and check camshaft end thrust.

VALVE TIMING

1) Rotate crankshaft until No. 6 exhaust valve is closing and No. 6 intake valve is opening.

2) Insert a 1/4" spacer between rocker arm and valve stem tip of No. 1 intake valve. Insertion of spacer should bleed down lifter, bottoming lifter plunger.

3) Install dial indicator on No. 1 intake valve, so indicator point is in contact with the valve spring retainer. Dial indicator stem must be parallel with valve stem. Zero dial indicator.

CAUTION: Do not turn crankshaft any further clockwise than specified, as valve spring might bottom and result in serious valve train damage.

4) Rotate crankshaft clockwise until dial indicator shows .010" (.25 mm) of lift for 5.2L engines, or .034" (.86 mm) lift for 5.9L engines.

5) If valve timing is correct, the timing of the crankshaft pulley should read from 10° BTDC to 2° ATDC.

CAMSHAFT

NOTE: Whenever a new camshaft is installed, install new valve lifters.

Removal

1) With engine removed from vehicle, remove intake manifold, front cover and timing chain. Remove rocker arm and shaft assemblies.

2) Identify push rods and valve lifters for reinstallation in original locations, then remove. Replace any lifter that exhibits a "dished" wear condition.

3) Remove distributor and lift out distributor/oil pump drive shaft. Remove camshaft thrust plate, noting location of oil tab.

4) Install a long bolt into front of camshaft to aid in extracting camshaft from engine. Using care not to damage camshaft bearings, remove camshaft.

Installation

1) Lubricate camshaft lobes and bearing journals. Insert camshaft to within 2" (50.8 mm) of its final position in block.

2) Install camshaft holding tool (C-3509) in distributor drive hole, and hold in position using distributor retainer plate bolt. This prevents camshaft from contacting and possibly knocking out welch plug in rear of block.

3) Install thrust plate and chain oil tab, ensuring top edge of tab is flat against thrust plate to provide oil for chain lubrication.

4) Install timing chain and sprockets, fuel pump eccentric, cup washer, and camshaft bolt. *See Fig. 12.*

5) Remove camshaft holding tool. Install camshaft to final position. To complete installation, reverse removal procedures.

Fig. 12: Exploded View of Camshaft Assembly

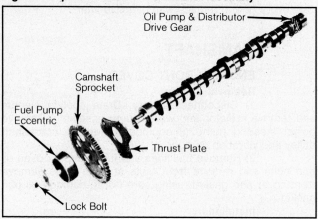

Ensure top edge of chain oil tab is flat against thrust plate.

CAMSHAFT END THRUST

End thrust is taken by thrust plate behind camshaft sprocket. End play should be .002-.010" (.05-.25 mm). If not within specifications, replace thrust plate.

CAMSHAFT BEARINGS

Removal

With engine completely disassembled, drive out rear cam bearing welch plug. Using camshaft bearing remover/installer tool, drive out bearings.

Installation

1) Using camshaft bearing remover/installer tool, install new bearings into place. Ensure oil holes align.

2) Note that No. 2 bearing must index with oil passage to left cylinder head, and No. 4 bearing must index with oil passage to right cylinder head. Replace camshaft welch plug at rear of engine.

PISTONS, PINS & RINGS

OIL PAN

See "Oil Pan Removal" at end of ENGINE Section.

PISTON & ROD ASSEMBLY

Removal

1) Remove cylinder head and oil pan. Place piston at bottom of stroke and cover top of piston to collect cuttings. Remove ridge at top of cylinder bore using ridge reamer.

2) Inspect connecting rods and caps for cylinder identification and mark as necessary. Remove rod cap. Cover exposed rod cap bolts with rubber hose to protect crankshaft. Carefully push piston out top of cylinder bore and install rod caps on mating rods.

Installation

1) Compression ring gaps must be staggered so neither is in line with oil ring rail gaps. Ensure identification marks on compression rings are facing upward.

5.2 & 5.9 LITER V8 (Cont.)

2) Oil ring expander ends should be butted under notch (front) of piston. Oil ring rail gaps should be facing middle of engine (when installed), and spread 3" apart. *See Fig. 13.*

Fig. 13: Positioning Oil Rings for Installation.

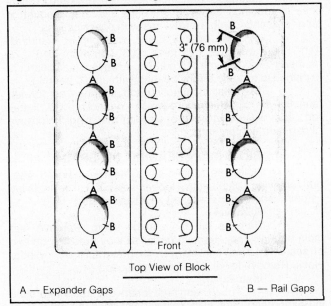

A — Expander Gaps   B — Rail Gaps

Do not allow ring gaps to change during installation.

3) Immerse piston head and rings in clean engine oil and slide ring compressor over piston, and tighten. Do not allow position of rings to change.

4) Be sure connecting rod bolts are covered, to protect cylinder bore and crankshaft journal surfaces from being damaged during piston installation.

5) Rotate crankshaft so connecting rod journal is in center of cylinder bore. Position piston in cylinder bore. Notch on piston head must face front of engine, and larger connecting rod chamfer must face crankshaft fillet.

6) Tap piston into cylinder bore using hammer handle. Guide connecting rod into place on crankshaft journal. Install rod cap, and tighten.

FITTING PISTONS

NOTE: **Make all measurements at room temperature (70°F, 21°C).**

1) Check cylinder bore for taper or out-of-round, using a micrometer. Maximum allowable cylinder bore taper is .010" (.25 mm), and out-of-round must not exceed .005" (.13 mm).

2) If cylinder walls show excessive taper or out-of-round, or are badly worn, they will require reboring and honing for installation of new pistons and rings.

3) If cylinders are honed, wash thoroughly with scrub brush and soapy water, then rinse well. Oil bores after cleaning to prevent rust. Piston assemblies are available in standard and .020" (.51 mm) oversize.

4) With piston and cylinder bores dry and clean, measure piston diameter at top of skirt, 90° to piston pin axis. Measure cylinder bore halfway down cylinder and 90° to crankshaft centerline. Difference between measurements is piston-to-cylinder wall clearance.

FITTING RINGS

1) Measure ring end gap in cylinder bore with feeler gauge. Ring must be square in bore, about 2" (50.8 mm) from bottom of bore.

2) With ring lands clean, measure ring side clearance between ring and ring land with feeler gauge. Oil ring rails should be free in groove.

3) When installing oil rings, ensure ring expander ends are butted under notch (front) of piston. Oil ring rail gaps should be facing middle of engine upon installation, and spread 3" apart. *See Fig. 13.*

4) When installing compression rings, ensure end gaps are staggered, so neither is in line with oil ring rail gaps. Ensure identification marks on compression rings are facing upward. *See Fig. 13.*

PISTON PIN REPLACEMENT
Removal

1) Use piston pin removal tool (C-4158 or equivalent) for pin removal, using proper pilots and anvils. Install pilot on main screw, and install screw through piston pin.

2) Install anvil (with spring removed) over threaded end of main screw, with small end of anvil against piston boss. Install nut loosely on main screw, and press piston pin out. *See Fig. 14.*

Fig. 14: Tools for Piston Pin Removal & Installation

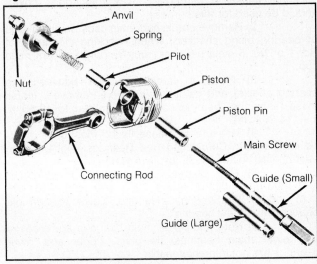

Spring is used during installation only.

Installation

1) Test piston pin fit in piston. Pin should be a sliding fit in piston at room temperature (70°F, 21°C). Piston pins are available in standard, .003" (.08 mm) and .008" (.20 mm) oversize.

2) Arrange piston pin tool for installation of piston pin. Install spring inside pilot, and install spring and pilot in anvil. Lubricate piston pin bores and connecting rod pin bore. Install piston pin over main screw.

3) Place piston (with notch up) and connecting rod over pilot, so pilot extends through piston pin bores. Assemble rods to pistons of the right cylinder bank (2, 4, 6 and 8) with indent on piston head opposite to larger chamfer on large bore end of connecting rod.

4) Assemble rods to pistons of the left cylinder bank (1, 3, 5 and 7) with indent on piston head on the same side as the large chamfer on large bore end of connecting rod.

5) Install main screw and piston pin in piston, and install nut on main screw to hold assembly together. Press piston pin in, until piston pin bottoms on the pilot.

Checking Pin Fit

Assemble piston pin tool as for piston pin removal. Secure butt end of main screw in vise. Attach a torque wrench to nut, and test torque to 15 ft. lbs. (20 N.m.). If connecting rod moves downward on piston pin, replace connecting rod and retest.

CRANKSHAFT, MAIN & CONNECTING ROD BEARINGS

MAIN & CONNECTING ROD BEARINGS

NOTE: Use Plastigage method for checking bearing clearances. The following procedures are with oil pan and oil pump removed. Remove oil film from surfaces to be checked.

Main Bearings

1) Check main bearing clearances one at a time. To accurately determine clearance, weight of crankshaft must first be eliminated. A .010" (.25 mm) minimum thickness cardboard shim (matchbook cover) should be used for this purpose.

2) Remove crankshaft main caps on either side of bearing being checked. When checking clearance of No. 1 or No. 5 main bearings, remove only adjacent main cap.

3) Place a cardboard shim between the bearing shell(s) and cap(s) which were removed. Install these "shimmed" bearing cap(s) and tighten to 10-15 ft. lbs. (14-20 N.m).

4) Measure clearance, using Plastigage method explained in Connecting Rod Bearings. Tighten main bearing cap bolts to 85 ft. lbs. (115 N.m).

5) New bearings are available in standard, .001" (.03 mm), .002" (.05 mm), .003" (.08 mm), .010" (.25 mm) and .012" (.31 mm) undersize. Never use an old bearing with a new bearing.

6) Note that upper main bearings are grooved and lower main bearings are plain. Upper and lower bearings are not interchangeable.

7) Replace main bearings one at a time. To extract upper main bearing from cylinder block, insert pin tool (C-3059 or equivalent) into oil hole of crankshaft journal. Rotate crankshaft clockwise, allowing pin tool to push upper bearing out of cylinder block.

8) When installing a new upper main bearing, slightly chamfer sharp edges from plain side of new bearing, then start bearing in place. Using pin tool, install upper bearing in reverse order of removal procedures.

9) Check crankshaft end play. If not within specifications, replace thrust bearing (No. 3 main bearing).

Connecting Rod Bearings

1) After ensuring rod caps are marked for cylinder identification, remove rod caps. Turn crankshaft until connecting rod to be checked starts moving toward the top of the engine.

2) Place Plastigage across width of bearing shell in cap, approximately 1/4" (6 mm) off center and away from oil holes. Tighten bearing cap to specification. Do not rotate crankshaft.

3) Remove bearing cap, and compare width of flattened Plastigage with inch scale on package. Difference in readings between the ends indicates amount of taper present. Compare readings with specifications.

4) New bearings are available in standard, .001" (.03 mm), .002" (.05 mm), .003" (.08 mm), .010" (.25 mm) and .012" (.31 mm) undersize. Always install bearings in pairs. Do not use a new bearing with an old bearing.

5) Install connecting rod bearings so formed tang fits into machined groove in connecting rod. Install rod caps, with "V" groove of bearing matching "V" groove of cap, and tighten nuts.

REAR MAIN BEARING OIL SEAL

Split-type rubber seals may be installed without removing crankshaft. Rubber seals must be installed as pairs, and cannot be used with rope seals.

Removal

Remove oil pan and oil pump. Remove rear main bearing cap. Remove upper seal by pressing on end of seal with small screwdriver, then extract from cylinder block. Remove lower seal from main cap.

Installation

1) On 5.2L engines, insert cap seals into slots in bearing cap. Seal with Yellow paint goes in right side of cap (cap in installed position). Make sure seals are installed with narrow sealing edges up.

2) Also make sure that edges of cap seals line up exactly with shoulder in bearing cap, to prevent oil leakage. Install seal edge toward inside of shoulder, and pull outward on small end of seal until edge lines up with shoulder.

3) On all models, lightly oil seal lips. With crankshaft surface clean and lightly oiled, rotate upper seal half into block with paint stripe to rear. Use care not to cut or shave seal outer surface.

4) Place lower seal in bearing cap with paint stripe to rear. On 5.9L engines, apply sealer on cap surface next to rear main seal ends. Install cap immediately and tighten.

ENGINE OILING

Crankcase Capacity

Capacity of all engines is 5 quarts (4.7L). Add 1 quart (.95L) when replacing oil filter.

Oil Filter

Replace at first oil change, and every other oil change thereafter.

Normal Oil Pressure

30-80 psi (2.1-5.6 kg/cm²) at 2000 RPM.

Oil Pressure Regulator Valve

Located in oil pump, not adjustable.

ENGINE OILING SYSTEM

System has a rotor type oil pump and full-flow type oil filter. Oil is forced by pump through a series of oil passages in engine to provide lubrication to engine components.

5.2 & 5.9 LITER V8 (Cont.)

Oil is supplied to hollow rocker arm shaft (left side) from No. 2 camshaft bearing and to hollow rocker arm shaft (right side) from No. 4 camshaft bearing, through indexed holes in camshaft.

Oil flows to only one support pedestal on each head, to lubricate rocker shaft and upper valve train components. Pedestal is second from rear on right head, and second from front on left head. *See Fig. 15.*

Fig. 15: Engine Oiling System

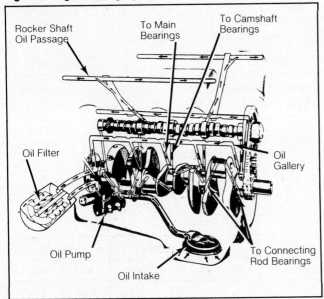

OIL PUMP

Removal

Remove oil pan. Remove attaching bolts and oil pump from rear main bearing cap. Ensure oil pump and rear main bearing cap machined surfaces are clean and free from burrs.

Disassembly

Remove pump cover and seal ring. Remove inner rotor and shaft. Lift out outer rotor. Remove cotter pin, oil pressure relief valve plug, spring and plunger. *See Fig. 16.*

Fig. 16: Oil Pump Assembly

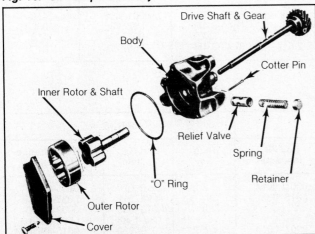

Install outer rotor into pump body with large chamfered edge inward.

Inspection

1) Clean all parts thoroughly. Replace oil pump if mating surface of pump cover is scratched or grooved. Measure clearances indicated in Oil Pump Specifications table and replace parts as follows:

2) Using a feeler gauge and straightedge, measure pump cover wear and flatness. If not within limits, replace oil pump. Replace inner rotor and shaft if thickness measures too thin.

3) Replace outer rotor if diameter and thickness measure below limits. Using a feeler gauge, measure clearance between outer rotor and pump body. If not correct, replace pump.

4) With inner and outer rotor in pump body, measure clearance between rotor tips. Replace shaft and both rotors if clearance is excessive.

5) Place a straightedge across the oil pump body (away from cover bolt holes). Using a feeler gauge, measure clearance between rotors and straightedge. If clearance over rotors is excessive, replace oil pump.

6) Test relief valve spring for free length of 2 1/32 - 2 3/64" (51.6 to 52.0 mm). Spring should test between 16.2-17.2 lbs. (7.35-7.80 kg) when compressed to 1 11/32" (34.1 mm). Replace spring which fails specifications.

OIL PUMP SPECIFICATIONS

Application	Specifications In. (mm)
Pump Cover Wear	.0014 (.035) Max.
Inner & Outer Rotor Thickness	
5.2L Engine	.826 (20.98) Min.
5.9L Engine	.944 (23.98) Min.
Outer Rotor Diameter	2.47 (62.74) Min.
Outer Rotor-to-Pump Body	.013 (.33) Max.
Rotor Tip Clearance	.009 (.23) Max.
Clearance Over Rotors	.003 (.076) Max.

Reassembly

Assemble pump in reverse order of disassembly, using new seal ring and new parts as required. Note that outer rotor must be installed into pump body with large chamfered edge inward. Prime oil pump with engine oil before installing.

Installation

Install oil pump to rear main bearing cap. Ensure that drive shaft is positioned properly in pump, and that it does not bind. Oil pump and rear main bearing cap surfaces must mate properly to prevent oil leakage.

ENGINE COOLING

WATER PUMP

Removal

1) Drain cooling system. If equipped with A/C, remove radiator. Remove all drive belts. Remove fan, spacer (or fluid unit), pulley and bolts as an assembly.

CAUTION: After removing fluid unit, do not place drive unit with shaft pointing downward. Silicone fluid from fluid unit may drain into fan drive bearing, causing lubricant failure.

2) If not equipped with A/C, remove alternator bracket attaching bolts, and position alternator out of way.

Chrysler Corp. V8 Engines
5.2 & 5.9 LITER V8 (Cont.)

On A/C models, remove alternator and adjusting bracket and power steering pump. Position components aside.

3) Remove heater and by-pass hoses. Remove A/C compressor pulley, field coil assembly, and front bracket. Remove water pump.

Installation

Clean all gasket mating surfaces. Install water pump using new gasket. Reverse removal procedure to complete installation.

NOTE: For information on cooling system capacities and other cooling system components, see appropriate article in "Engine Cooling Systems," at end of ENGINE Section.

TIGHTENING SPECIFICATIONS

Application	Ft. Lbs. (N.m)
Camshaft Sprocket Bolt	50 (68)
Camshaft Thrust Plate	18 (24)
Connecting Rod Nuts	45 (61)
Cylinder Head Bolts	
Step 1	50 (68)
Step 2	95 (129)
Exhaust Manifold	
Bolts	20 (27)
Nuts	15 (20)
Flywheel-to-Crankshaft Bolts	55 (75)
Intake Manifold Bolts	
Step 1	25 (34)
Step 2 (4 inner bolts)	40 (54)
Step 3 (Remaining bolts)	45 (61)
Main Bearing Cap Bolts	85 (115)
Oil Pump Attaching Bolt	30 (41)
Rocker Arm Shaft Mounting Bolts	17 (23)
Vibration Damper Bolt	100 (136)

ENGINE SPECIFICATIONS

GENERAL SPECIFICATIONS

| Year | DISPLACEMENT | | Fuel System | HP@RPM | Torque Ft. Lbs.@RPM | Compr. Ratio | BORE | | STROKE | |
	Cu. In.	Liters					In.	mm	In.	mm
1983	318	5.2	2-Bbl. & 4-Bbl.	.....	.....	8.6:1	3.91	99.3	3.31	84.1
	360	5.9	2-Bbl. & 4-Bbl.	.....	.....	8.5:1	4.00	101.6	3.58	90.9

VALVES

Engine Size & Valve	Head Diam. In. (mm)	Face Angle	Seat Angle	Seat Width In. (mm)	Stem Diameter In. (mm)	Stem Clearance In. (mm)	Valve Lift In. (mm)
5.2L							
Intake	1.780 (45.21)	44½-45°	45-45½°	.065-.085 (1.65-2.16)	.372-.373 (9.45-9.47)	.001-.003 (.02-.08)	.373 (9.47)
Exhaust	1.517 (38.53)	44½-45°	45-45½°	.080-.100 (2.03-2.54)	.371-.372 (9.42-9.45)	.002-.004 (.05-.10)	.400 (10.16)
5.9L							
Intake	1.880 (47.75)	44½-45°	45-45½°	.065-.085 (1.65-2.16)	.372-.373 (9.45-9.47)	.001-.003 (.02-.08)	.410 (10.41)
Exhaust	1.617 (41.07)	44½-45°	45-45½°	.080-.100 (2.03-2.54)	.371-.372 (9.42-9.45)	.002-.004 (.05-.10)	.410 (10.41)

PISTONS, PINS, RINGS

| Engine | PISTONS | PINS | | RINGS | | |
	Clearance In. (mm)	Piston Fit In. (mm)	Rod Fit In. (mm)	Ring No.	End Gap In. (mm)	Side Clearance In. (mm)
5.2L	.0005-.0015 (.013-.038)	.000-.0005 (.000-.038)	.0007-.0014 (.018-.035)	1 & 2	.010-.020 (.25-.51)	.0015-.0030 (.038-.076)
				3	.015-.055 (.38-1.40)	.0002-.0050 (.005-.127)
5.9L	.0005-.0015 (.013-.038)	.00025-.00075 (.0064-.0190)	.0007-.0014 (.018-.035)	1 & 2	.010-.020 (.25-.51)	.0015-.0030 (.038-.076)
				3	.015-.055 (.38-1.40)	.0002-.0050 (.005-.127)

Chrysler Corp. V8 Engines

5.2 & 5.9 LITER V8 (Cont.)

ENGINE SPECIFICATIONS (Cont.)

CRANKSHAFT MAIN & CONNECTING ROD BEARINGS

Engine	MAIN BEARINGS				CONNECTING ROD BEARINGS		
	Journal Diam. In. (mm)	Clearance In. (mm)	Thrust Bearing	Crankshaft End Play In. (mm)	Journal Diam. In. (mm)	Clearance In. (mm)	Side Play In. (mm)
5.2L	2.4495-2.5005 (63.487-63.513)	.0005-.0020 [1] (.013-.051)	3	.002-.007 (.05-.18)	2.124-2.125 (53.95-53.98)	.0005-.0022 (.013-.056)	.006-.014 (.15-.36)
5.9L	2.8095-2.8105 (71.361-71.387)	.0005-.0020 [1] (.013-.051)	3	.002-.009 (.05-.23)	2.124-2.125 (53.95-53.98)	.0005-.0022 (.013-.056)	.006-.014 (.15-.36)

[1] — Desired clearance for No. 1 main bearing is .0005-.0015" (.018-.038 mm).

VALVE SPRINGS

Engine	Free Length In. (mm)	PRESSURE Lbs. @ In. (Kg @ mm)	
		Valve Closed	Valve Open
5.2L			
Intake	2.00 (50.8)	78-88@1.69 (35-40@42.85)	170-184@1.31 (77-83@33.35)
Exhaust	1.81 (46.0)	80-90@1.48 (36-41@37.69)	180-194@1.06 (81-87@27.00)
5.9L			
Intake	2.00 (50.8)	78-88@1.69 (35-40@42.85)	170-184@1.31 (77-83@33.35)
Exhaust	1.81 (46.0)	80-90@1.48 (36-41@37.69)	181-197@1.06 (81-89@27.00)

CAMSHAFT

Engine	Journal Diam. In. (mm)	Clearance In. (mm)	Lobe Lift In. (mm)
5.2L & 5.9L [1]			
No.1	1.998-1.999 (50.75-50.77)	.001-.003 (.025-.076)	.....
No. 2	1.982-1.983 (50.34-50.37)		
No. 3	1.967-1.968 (49.96-49.99)		
No. 4	1.951-1.952 (49.56-49.58)		
No. 5	1.5605-1.5615 (39.64-39.66)		

[1] — End play is .002-.010" (.05-.15 mm).

Ford 4 Engines

2.0 & 2.3 LITER 4-CYLINDER

ENGINE CODING

ENGINE IDENTIFICATION

Engine is identified by the letter code in the eighth position of the Vehicle Identification Number (VIN). The VIN is stamped on a metal tab, attached to the upper left side of the instrument panel and is visible through the windshield. The VIN can also be found on the Safety Standard Certification Label located on the door lock edge of the left door.

ENGINE IDENTIFICATION CODES

Engine	Code
2.0L 1-Bbl.	C
2.3L 1-Bbl.	A

ENGINE REMOVAL

See Engine Removal at end of ENGINE Section.

MANIFOLDS & CYLINDER HEAD

INTAKE MANIFOLD

Removal

1) Drain cooling system. Remove air cleaner. Disconnect accelerator cable. Disconnect all vacuum hoses that may interfere with intake manifold removal.

2) Remove hot water hose from manifold cover nipple fitting. Remove engine oil dipstick. Disconnect heat tube at EGR valve. Disconnect fuel line at carburetor fuel filter.

3) Remove engine oil dipstick tube retaining bolt from intake manifold. Disconnect and remove PCV valve from intake manifold and engine block.

4) Remove distributor cap from distributor with wires connected. Remove plastic spark plug wire connector from valve cover.

Fig. 1: Intake Manifold Bolt Tightening Sequence

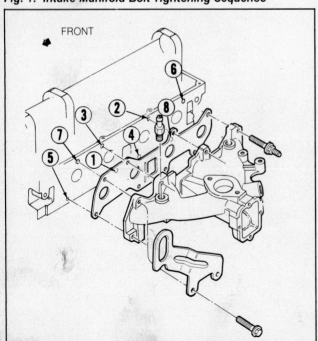

5) Remove intake manifold retaining bolts. Remove intake manifold.

Installation

1) Clean all intake manifold gasket mating surfaces. Reinstall intake manifold on engine with new intake manifold gasket. Tighten all bolts in proper tightening sequence. *See Fig. 1.*

2) Reverse removal procedures to install remaining components.

EXHAUST MANIFOLD

Removal

1) Remove air cleaner and duct assembly. Remove EGR line at exhaust manifold and loosen at EGR tube.

2) Remove check valve at exhaust manifold. Remove hose from rear of by-pass valve. Remove screw retaining heater hoses to valve cover.

3) Remove exhaust manifold-to-cylinder head attaching bolts. Remove exhaust pipe-to-exhaust manifold attaching bolts. Remove exhaust manifold.

Installation

Install exhaust manifold and tighten manifold-to-cylinder head attaching bolts in proper tightening sequence. *See Fig. 2.* Reverse removal procedure to install remaining components.

Fig. 2: Exhaust Manifold Bolt Tightening Sequence

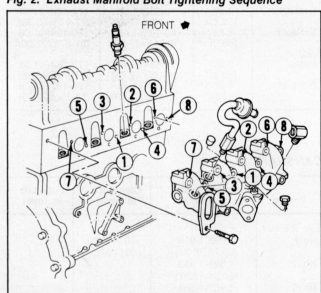

CYLINDER HEAD

Removal

1) Drain cooling system. Remove air cleaner assembly. Remove heater hose retaining screw from valve cover.

2) Disconnect spark plug wires from spark plugs. Remove distributor cap. Remove distributor and remove distributor cap and wires as an assembly. Remove sparks plugs.

3) Disconnect all vacuum hoses that may interfere with cylinder head removal. Remove valve cover retaining bolts and remove valve cover. Remove intake manifold retaining bolts.

4) Remove alternator belt. Remove belts attaching alternator bracket to cylinder head. Remove

2.0 & 2.3 LITER 4-CYLINDER (Cont)

upper radiator hose. Remove timing belt cover retaining bolts. Remove power steering pump bracket, if equipped.

5) Loosen timing belt idler pulley retaining bolts. Position idler pulley in unloaded position and tighten retaining bolts. Remove timing belt from cam pulley and idler pulley.

6) Remove heat stove from exhaust manifold. Remove exhaust manifold-to-cylinder head attaching bolts. Remove timing belt idler pulley. Remove timing belt idler pulley spring from cylinder head.

7) Disconnect oil pressure sending unit wire. Remove cylinder head retaining bolts. Remove cylinder head.

Installation

Clean all gasket mating surfaces. Position new cylinder head gasket on block. Reinstall cylinder head and tighten retaining bolts in proper tightening sequence. *See Fig. 3.* Reverse removal procedure to install remaining components.

Fig. 3: Cylinder Head Bolt Tightening Sequence

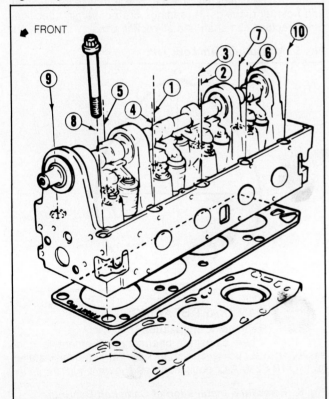

CAMSHAFT

ENGINE FRONT COVER

Removal

1) Loosen thermactor pump bolts and remove drive belt. Remove fan blade and water pump pulley attaching bolts. Remove fan and pulley.

2) Loosen alternator retaining bolts and remove drive belt. Drain cooling system and remove upper radiator hose.

3) Remove crankshaft pulley bolt and pulley. Remove thermostat housing and gasket.

4) Remove bolts attaching power steering pump to engine and position pump aside. Remove front cover attaching bolts and remove front cover.

Installation

Reverse removal procedure to install engine front cover and all other remaining components.

TIMING BELT

Removal

Align timing pointer with TDC mark on crankshaft pulley. Remove engine front cover. Release tension from timing belt by loosen timing belt tensioner bolts. Remove timing belt from gears.

Installation

Reverse removal procedures and align timing belt and gears as described under Valve Timing.

VALVE TIMING

Checking Timing

1) Remove access plug from engine front cover. Set crankshaft to top dead center (TDC) by aligning timing mark on crankshaft pulley with "TC" mark on engine front cover.

CAUTION: Always turn engine in direction of normal rotation. Backward rotation may cause timing belt to jump time.

2) Look through access hole in engine front cover to be sure that timing mark on camshaft gear is lined up with pointer on inner timing belt cover. *See Fig. 4.*

3) Remove distributor cap and check that rotor is pointing at number 1 spark plug wire terminal in distributor cap. Reinstall distributor cap and access plug.

Fig. 4: Timing Belt Alignment Mark Locations

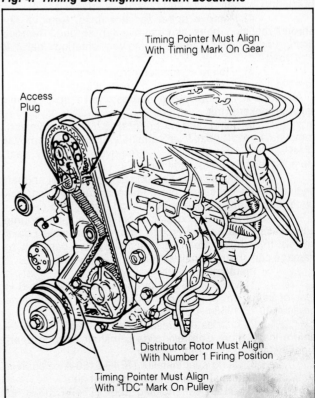

Ford 4 Engines

2.0 & 2.3 LITER 4-CYLINDER (Cont)

Adjusting Timing

1) Remove engine front cover. Loosen timing belt tensioner adjustment screw. Retract tensioner and tighten adjusting screw to hold tensioner in retracted position.

2) Remove crankshaft pulley and timing belt guide. Remove timing belt and inspect for wear or damage. Replace belt if damaged or excessively worn.

3) Align crankshaft gear and camshaft gear as described under Checking Timing procedure. Remove distributor cap and set rotor so that it points to number 1 firing position by turning auxiliary shaft.

4) Install timing belt over crankshaft gear, auxiliary gear and camshaft gear, in that order. Loosen tensioner adjustment bolt to allow tensioner to move against timing belt.

5) Remove spark plugs. Rotate crankshaft 2 complete turns in normal rotation to remove slack from timing belt. Tighten tensioner pivot and adjustment bolts. Make sure that timing marks are still properly aligned.

6) Install crankshaft pulley and timing belt guide. Install engine front cover and spark plugs. Start engine and check ignition timing. Adjust ignition timing if necessary.

CAMSHAFT

Removal

1) Drain cooling system. Remove air cleaner assembly. Disconnect spark plug wires from spark plugs and valve cover and position aside.

2) Disconnect all vacuum hoses that may interfere with camshaft removal. Remove valve cover bolts and valve cover.

3) Remove alternator retaining bolts and remove drive belt. Remove bolts that attach alternator bracket to cylinder head and position alternator aside.

4) Remove upper radiator hose. Remove fan shroud retaining bolts and remove fan shroud. Remove timing belt cover. Remove power steering belt, if equipped.

5) Release tension from timing belt and remove timing belt. Using valve spring compressor lever (T74P-6565-A or equivalent) depress valve springs and remove rocker arms.

6) Using gear puller (T74P-6256 or equivalent), remove camshaft gear from camshaft. Using seal remover (T74P-6700-A or equivalent), remove camshaft seal. Remove rear camshaft retainer.

7) Raise vehicle on hoist. Remove right and left engine mount bolts and nuts. Place a transmission jack under engine and raise engine as high as possible.

8) Place wood blocks between engine mounts and chassis brackets. Remove transmission jack. Lower vehicle from hoist. Remove camshaft, using care not to damage camshaft journals or lobes.

Installation

1) Make sure that threaded plug is installed in rear of camshaft. Coat camshaft lobes with polyethylene grease (D0AZ-19584-A or equivalent).

2) Lubricate camshaft journals with heavy oil before installation. Carefully slide camshaft through bearings. Install camshaft rear retainer.

3) Using seal installer (T74P-6150-A or equivalent), install camshaft seal. Install camshaft gear.

4) Use gear holding tool (T74P-6256-B or equivalent) to hold camshaft gear while tightening bolt.

Reverse removal procedures to complete camshaft installation.

CAMSHAFT END THRUST

1) Remove engine front cover. Push camshaft toward rear of engine. Install a dial indicator so that indicator plunger is on camshaft gear attaching bolt.

2) Zero dial indicator. Using a large screwdriver between camshaft gear and cylinder head, pull camshaft forward and release it. Read dial indicator.

3) If dial indicator reading is greater than .009" (.29 mm), replace thrust plate at rear of cylinder head. Remove dial indicator from engine. Reinstall engine front cover.

CAM LOBE LIFT

1) Remove air cleaner. Remove valve cover. Using a vernier caliper, measure both distance "A" and "B" of each cam lobe. See Fig. 5. Measurement "A" minus measurement "B" is cam lobe lift.

2) Check lift of each lobe in consecutive order and note all readings. If readings are not within specifications, replace camshaft and all rocker arms.

Fig. 5: Measuring Cam Lobe Lift

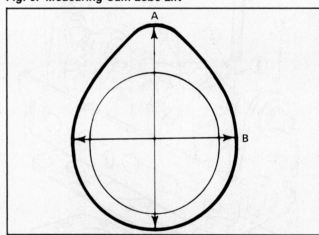

CAMSHAFT BEARINGS

Removal & Installation

When camshaft bearing replacement is necessary, do so using camshaft bearing remover/installer tool (T71P-6250-A or equivalent) as shown in Fig. 6.

Fig. 6: Removal & Installation of Camshaft Bearings

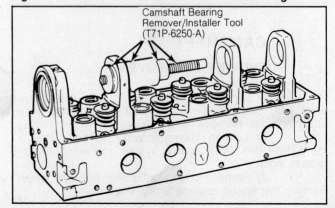

2.0 & 2.3 LITER 4-CYLINDER (Cont)

AUXILIARY SHAFT

Removal

1) Remove engine front cover. Release tension from timing belt. Remove fuel pump. Remove distributor assembly.

2) Using auxiliary shaft/camshaft gear puller (T74P-6256-B or equivalent), remove gear from front of auxiliary shaft. Remove 2 bolts from auxiliary shaft retaining plate. Remove retaining plate.

3) Carefully slide auxiliary shaft from engine. Do not allow distributor drive gear or fuel pump lobe to contact bearing surfaces.

Installation

Reverse removal procedures to install all components.

VALVES

VALVE ARRANGEMENT

I-E-I-E-I-E-I-E (front-to-rear)

VALVE SPRINGS AND/OR VALVE STEM OIL SEALS

Removal

1) Remove air cleaner. Remove screw retaining heater hose to valve cover. Disconnect vacuum hoses as necessary. Disconnect spark plug wires from spark plugs and position aside.

2) Remove valve cover from engine. Using valve spring compressor lever (T74P-6565-A or equivalent), compress valve spring and remove rocker arm.

3) Remove spark plug and place air line adapter (6513-ABA or equivalent) into spark plug hole. Apply 140 psi to cylinder.

4) Again compress valve spring and remove retainer locks and spring retainer. Release pressure from valve spring and remove spring. Remove and discard valve stem oil seal.

Installation

1) Install new valve stem oil seal using seal installer tool (T73P-6571-A or equivalent). Install and compress valve spring. With valve spring compressed, install spring retainer and retainer locks.

2) Apply polyethylene grease (D0AZ-19584-A or equivalent) to all contact surfaces of rocker arm. Compress valve spring and install rocker arm.

3) Remove air pressure and air line adapter from spark plug hole and reinstall spark plug. Install all remaining components in reverse order of removal.

VALVE SPRING INSTALLED HEIGHT

1) Valve spring installed height should be measured with rocker arms removed. Measurement should be made from cylinder head spring pad to top of valve spring retainer.

2) If height is not within specifications, install .030" (.76 mm) spacers between cylinder head spring pad and valve spring. Do not install more spacers than are necessary to obtain specified height.

VALVE SPRING INSTALLED HEIGHT SPECIFICATIONS

Application	Measurement In. (mm)
2.0L	1.49-1.55 (37.8-39.4)
2.3L	1.53-1.59 (38.9-40.4)

VALVE GUIDE SERVICING

Always use reamers in proper sequence (smallest first). Reface valve seat after valve guide has been reamed. After reaming, use a scraper to break sharp corner at top inside diameter of valve guide bore. Valves with oversized stems are available with stems that are .003" (.08 mm), .015" (.38 mm) and .030" (.76 mm) oversized.

HYDRAULIC VALVE LIFTER

1) Service lifters only as complete assemblies. Disassemble lifters and thoroughly clean. DO NOT interchange parts between lifters.

2) Reassemble lifters and test with hydraulic lifter test fluid and lifter leak-down tester tool.

3) Leak-down rate on hydraulic lifters is 2-8 seconds at 1/8" (3.2 mm) travel.

Fig. 7: Exploded View of Hydraulic Lifter Assembly

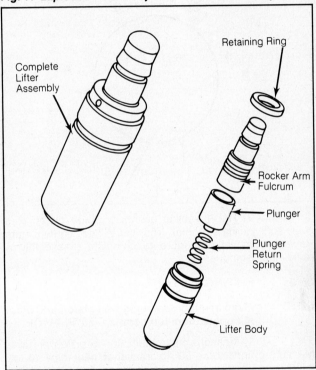

HYDRAULIC VALVE LIFTER ADJUSTMENT

Valve lifters are set at zero lash. No adjustment is possible.

PISTONS, RINGS & PINS

OIL PAN

See Oil Pan Removal at end of ENGINE Section.

PISTON & ROD ASSEMBLY

Removal

1) Remove cylinder head. Raise vehicle on hoist. Remove engine mount to chassis bracket nuts. Remove starter lead wires and remove starter.

2) Place a block of wood on a transmission jack and position jack under engine. Raise engine as high as it will go.

Ford 4 Engines

2.0 & 2.3 LITER 4-CYLINDER (Cont)

3) Place wood blocks between engine mounts and chassis brackets to support engine. Remove jack. Remove rear engine support to crossmember nuts.

4) Remove oil pan retaining bolts and remove oil pan. Remove oil pump pick-up tube. Remove connecting rod cap and bearing.

5) Push pistons up into cylinder bores. Lower vehicle from hoist. Remove pistons from cylinder bores.

Installation

1) Install bearings in rods and rod caps. Ensure that ring gaps are properly spaced on piston. See Fig. 8. Install ring compressor on piston and install pistons into block.

Fig. 8: Correctly Spacing Piston Ring Gaps

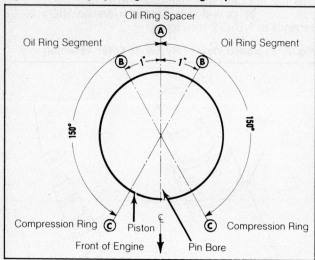

2) Raise vehicle on hoist. Guide piston rods over rod journals. Install rod caps and tighten nuts. Reverse removal procedure to complete reassembly of remaining components.

FITTING PISTONS

NOTE: **Make all measurements with piston and block at normal room temperature (70°F, 21°C).**

1) Measure piston skirt 90° to piston pin axis. Measure cylinder bore 90° to crankshaft centerline, at top, middle, and bottom of bore. Use these measurements to determine piston-to-cylinder bore clearance.

PISTON SIZE CHART

Cylinder Measurement	Piston Color Code & Size
2.0L	
3.5165-3.5177"	Red: 3.5150-3.5156"
(89.319-89.349 mm)	(89.281-89.296 mm)
3.5178-3.5189"	Blue: 3.5162-3.5168"
(89.352-89.380 mm)	(89.311-89.327 mm)
3.5190-3.5201"	Yellow: 3.5174-3.5180"
(89.383-89.411 mm)	(89.342-89.357 mm)
2.3L	
3.7795-3.7806"	Red: 3.7780-3.7786"
(95.999-96.027 mm)	(95.961-95.976 mm)
3.7807-3.7818"	Blue: 3.7792-3.7798"
(96.029-96.058 mm)	(95.992-96.007 mm)
3.7819-3.7831"	Yellow: 3.7804-3.7810"
(96.060-96.091 mm)	(96.022-96.037 mm)

2) Measure cylinder bore 90° to crankshaft centerline at top of bore (below ring travel) and at bottom of bore (above ring travel). These measurements determine cylinder taper. Taper (difference between the 2 measurements) must not exceed .010" (.25 mm).

3) Measure cylinder bore at center of piston travel, 90° to crankshaft centerline. Measure bore at center of piston travel in line with crankshaft centerline. Out-of-round is the difference between the 2 measurements, and must not exceed .005" (.13 mm).

4) If taper or out-of-round are beyond limits, or cylinder walls are deeply scored, hone or bore cylinders for installation of new pistons. After cylinders have been honed or bored, measure cylinder diameter. Compare cylinder diameter measurements with those in Piston Size Chart to obtain correct size piston.

FITTING RINGS

1) Select proper ring set for size of cylinder bore. Position ring in cylinder bore in which it is going to be used.

2) Push ring down into bore to area where normal ring wear is not encountered. Use a piston to position ring so that it is square with cylinder wall.

3) Measure gap between ends of ring using feeler gauge. If ring gap is less than or greater than specified, a smaller or larger ring will have to be used.

4) Check side clearance of compression rings with feeler gauge, of specified thickness, inserted between ring and its lower land on piston. Feeler gauge should slide freely around entire circumference of piston without binding.

5) If feeler gauge binds because of high spots on lower land of piston, piston should be replaced.

PISTON PIN REPLACEMENT

Removal

Using an arbor press and piston pin removing/installing tool (T68P-6135-A or equivalent), press piston pin from piston and connecting rod.

Installation

1) Apply a light coat of oil to all parts that are to be assembled. Position piston and connection rod as shown in Fig. 9.

2) Using arbor press and piston pin removing/installing tool, press piston pin through piston and connecting rod until centered in connecting rod.

Fig. 9: Correct Positioning of Piston and Connecting Rod for Installation of Piston Pin

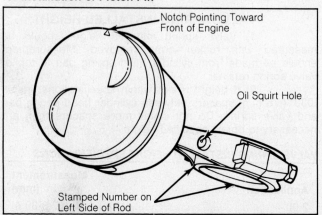

2.0 & 2.3 LITER 4-CYLINDER (Cont)

CRANKSHAFT, MAIN & CONNECTING ROD BEARINGS

MAIN & CONNECTING ROD BEARINGS

1) Fit main and rod bearings one at a time, while leaving all other bearings securely fastened. To determine bearing clearance, remove bearing cap.

2) Place a strip of Plastigage on bearing surface across full width of bearing cap, about 1/4" off center away from oil holes.

3) Install bearing cap and tighten bolts to specifications. Do not allow crankshaft to turn.

4) Remove cap and measure compressed width of Plastigage with scale furnished with Plastigage kit.

5) Standard size bearings may be used in combination with a .001" or .002" undersize bearing.

6) If .002" undersize bearings are used in more than one journal, they must be installed in cylinder block or piston rod side of crankshaft journal.

7) After bearings are installed, lightly oil crankshaft journal and bearing surfaces and install bearing cap.

CRANKSHAFT END PLAY

NOTE: Engine must be removed from vehicle to check crankshaft end play.

1) Force crankshaft toward rear of engine. attach dial indicator to rear of engine so that indicator contact rests against crankshaft flange.

2) Zero dial indicator. Push crankshaft forward and note dial indicator reading.

3) If end play exceeds specification, replace thrust bearing. If end play is less than specified, check for damaged or improperly aligned thrust bearing.

REAR MAIN BEARING OIL SEAL

NOTE: Engine or transmission will have to be removed from vehicle to replace rear main bearing oil seal.

Removal

Install 2 metal screws into seal. Pull on screws until seal is removed from engine.

Fig. 10: Rear Main Bearing Oil Seal Installation

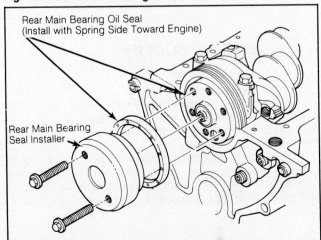

Rear Main Bearing Oil Seal
(Install with Spring Side Toward Engine)

Rear Main Bearing
Seal Installer

Installation

1) Position seal on seal installer tool (T82L-6701-A or equivalent). *See Fig. 10*. Place tool and seal assembly on engine.

2) Install 2 bolts through seal installer into crankshaft. Alternately tighten bolts until seal is completely installed. Remove seal installer tool.

ENGINE OILING

Crankcase Capacity

Capacity is 4 quarts (3.8 liters) for 2.0L engine and 5 quarts (4.7 liters) for 2.3L engines. Add 1 quart (.9 liters) when oil filter is replaced.

Oil Filter

Oil Filter should be replaced every 7500 miles.

Normal Oil Pressure

With engine hot and running at 2000 RPM, oil pressure should be 40-60 psi (2.8-4.2 kg/cm²).

Oil Pressure Regulator Valve

Valve is located in oil pump body and is not adjustable.

ENGINE OILING SYSTEM

System is pressure fed from a rotor-type oil pump. Oil flows through oil filter before entering main oil gallery. *See Fig. 11*.

Fig. 11: Engine Oiling System

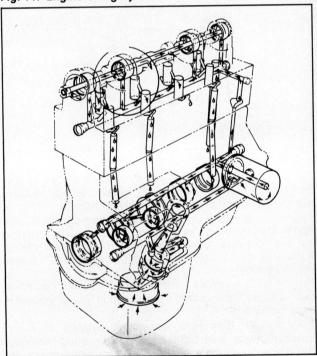

OIL PUMP

Removal

Remove oil pan. Remove nut securing pick-up tube bracket to main bearing cap stud. Remove 2 bolts that attach oil pump to engine block. Remove oil pump assembly. Be careful not to drop oil pump drive shaft.

Ford 4 Engines

2.0 & 2.3 LITER 4-CYLINDER (Cont)

Disassembly

1) Remove 2 bolts attaching oil pick-up tube to oil pump. Remove pick-up tube and gasket. Remove pump cover attaching screw and remove cover.

2) Remove inner rotor and shaft assembly. Remove outer race. Drill a small hole in pressure relief valve chamber cap. *See Fig. 12.*

3) Insert a small screw into cap and remove from pump housing. Remove pressure relief valve spring and plunger from pump housing.

Fig. 12: Exploded View of Oil Pump Assembly

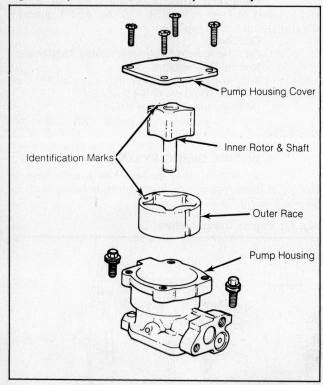

Pump Housing Cover

Inner Rotor & Shaft

Identification Marks

Outer Race

Pump Housing

Inspection

1) Clean all parts in solvent and dry thoroughly with compressed air. Be sure that all dirt or metal particles are removed from pressure relief valve chamber.

2) Check inside of pump housing, outer race and rotor for excessive wear or damage. Check mating surface of pump cover for wear. If pump cover mating surface is excessively worn, scored or grooved, replace pump assembly.

3) Measure rotor tip clearance. *See Fig. 13.* If rotor tip clearance exceeds specification, pump assembly must be replaced.

4) With rotor assembly installed in pump housing, place a straight edge across pump housing. Using a feeler gauge, measure clearance between straight edge and both inner and outer rotors.

5) Maximum rotor end play should not exceed .005" (.13 mm). If clearance limit is exceeded, pump must be replaced.

6) Check oil pump driveshaft to housing clearance by measuring outside diameter of shaft and inside diameter of housing bearing. Clearance should be .0015-.0030" (.038-.076 mm). If not, replace pump assembly.

Fig. 13: Checking Inner Rotor Tip Clearance

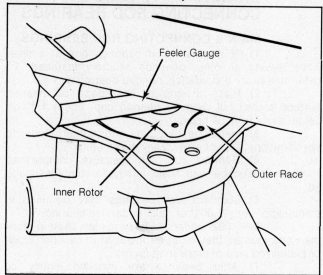

Feeler Gauge

Outer Race

Inner Rotor

7) Check pressure relief valve to bore clearance. Check tension of pressure relief valve spring. Spring tension should be 15.2-17.2 lbs. (6.9-7.8 kg) when spring is extended to 1.2" (30.4 mm). If spring tension is not correct, replace pump assembly.

Reassembly

Reverse disassembly procedure and note the following: Thoroughly oil all parts before assembly. Be sure that dimple on outer race in facing outward and on same side as identification mark on rotor. Install a new pressure relief valve cap.

Installation

Prime oil pump before installation. Reverse removal procedure to install all components.

OIL PUMP SPECIFICATIONS

Application	Specification In. (mm)
Rotor Tip Clearance	.012 (.30)
Rotor End Play	.005 (.13)
Drive Shaft-to-Housing Bearing Clearance	.0015-.0030 (.038-.076)
Relief Valve-to-Bore Clearance	.0015-.0030 (.038-.076)

ENGINE COOLING

WATER PUMP

Removal

1) Drain cooling system. Remove fan shroud attaching bolts and place shroud over fan. Remove bolts that attach fan to water pump. Remove fan and shroud from vehicle.

2) If equipped, loosen air conditioning compressor adjusting idler pulley and remove drive belt. Loosen power steering pump bolts and remove alternator and power steering pump belts.

2.0 & 2.3 LITER 4-CYLINDER (Cont)

3) Remove water pump pulley. Remove heater hose from water pump. Remove timing belt cover. Remove lower radiator hose from water pump. Remove water pump attaching bolts and remove water pump from engine.

Installation

Reverse removal procedure and note the following: Make sure that gasket surfaces are clean. Apply sealer (D8AZ-19554-A or equivalent) to water pump bolts prior to installation.

NOTE: For information on cooling system capacities and other cooling system components, see appropriate article in "Engine Cooling Systems," at end of ENGINE Section.

TIGHTENING SPECIFICATIONS

Application	Ft. Lbs. (N.m)
Auxiliary Shaft Gear Bolt	28-40 (38-54)
Auxiliary Shaft Thrust Plate	6-9 (8-12)
Belt Tensioner	
Adjusting Bolt	14-21 (19-28)
Pivot Bolt	28-40 (38-54)
Camshaft Gear Bolt	50-71 (68-96)
Camshaft Thrust Plate	6-9 (8-12)
Connecting Rod Cap	
1st Step	25-30 (34-41)
2nd Step	30-36 (41-49)
Cylinder Head	
1st Step	50-60 (68-81)
2nd Step	80-90 (108-122)
Exhaust Manifold	16-23 (22-31)
Flywheel-to-Crankshaft	56-64 (76-87)
Intake Manifold	14-21 (19-28)
Main Bearing Cap	
1st Step	50-60 (68-81)
2nd Step	80-90 (108-122)
Oil Pump-to-Block	14-21 (19-28)
Water Pump	14-21 (19-28)
Valve Cover	6-8 (8-11)

ENGINE SPECIFICATIONS

GENERAL SPECIFICATIONS

| Year | DISPLACEMENT | | Fuel System | HP@RPM | Torque Ft. Lbs.@RPM | Compr. Ratio | BORE | | STROKE | |
	Cu. In.	Liters					In.	mm	In.	mm
1983	122	2.0	1-Bbl.	.....	.....	.....	3.518	89.4	3.126	79.4
	140	2.3	1-Bbl.	.....	.....	.....	3.780	96.0	3.126	79.4

VALVES

Engine Size & Valve	Head Diam. In. (mm)	Face Angle	Seat Angle	Seat Width In. (mm)	Stem Diameter In. (mm)	Stem Clearance In. (mm)	Valve Lift In. (mm)
2.0L							
Intake	1.598-1.622 (40.59-41.19)	44°	45°	.060-.080 (1.52-2.03)	.3416-.3423 (8.677-8.694)	.0010-.0027 (.025-.069)	.....
Exhaust	1.370-1.390 (34.79-35.31)	44°	45°	.070-.090 (1.79-2.29)	.3411-.3418 (8.664-8.682)	.0015-.0032 (.038-.081)	.....
2.3L							
Intake	1.723-1.747 (43.76-44.37)	44°	45°	.060-.080 (1.52-2.03)	.3416-.3423 (8.677-8.694)	.0010-.0027 (.025-.069)	.....
Exhaust	1.490-1.510 (37.85-38.35)	44°	45°	.070-.090 (1.77-2.29)	.3411-.3418 (8.664-8.682)	.0015-.0032 (.038-.081)	.....

PISTONS, PINS, RINGS

| Engine | PISTONS | PINS | | RINGS | | |
	Clearance In. (mm)	Piston Fit In. (mm)	Rod Fit In. (mm)	Ring No.	End Gap In. (mm)	Side Clearance In. (mm)
2.0L & 2.3L	.0014-.0022 (.036-.056)	.0002-.0004 (.005-.010)	Interference Fit	1 & 2	.010-.020 (.25-.51)	.002-.004 (.05-.10) Snug Fit
				3	.015-.055 (.38-1.39)	

Ford 4 Engines

2.0 & 2.3 LITER 4-CYLINDER (Cont)

ENGINE SPECIFICATIONS (Cont.)

CRANKSHAFT MAIN & CONNECTING ROD BEARINGS

Engine	MAIN BEARINGS				CONNECTING ROD BEARINGS		
	Journal Diam. In. (mm)	Clearance In. (mm)	Thrust Bearing	Crankshaft End Play In. (mm)	Journal Diam. In. (mm)	Clearance In. (mm)	Side Play In. (mm)
2.0L & 2.3L	2.3982-2.3990 (60.914-60.935)	.0008-.0015 (.020-.038)	No. 3	.004-.008 (.10-.20)	2.0462-2.0472 (51.973-51.999)	.0008-.0015 (.020-.038)	.0035-.0105 (.089-.267)

VALVE SPRINGS

Engine	Free Length In. (mm)	PRESSURE Lbs. @ In. (Kg @ mm)	
		Valve Closed	Valve Open
2.0L Intake	1.922 (48.82)	71-79@1.52 (32-36@38.6)	.....
Exhaust	1.992 (48.82)	142-156@1.12 (64-71@28.4)	.....
2.3L Intake	1.890 (48.00)	71-79@1.56 (32-36@39.6)	.....
Exhaust	1.890 (48.00)	159-175@1.16 (72-79@29.5)	.....

CAMSHAFT

Engine	Journal Diam. In. (mm)	Clearance In. (mm)	Lobe Lift In. (mm)
2.0L & 2.3L	1.7713-1.7720 (44.991-45.009)	.001-.003 (.025-.076)	.2381 (6.047)

Ford 4 Engines

2.2L 4-CYLINDER DIESEL

ENGINE CODING

ENGINE IDENTIFICATION

Engine can be identified by the eighth digit of the Vehicle Identification Number (VIN). The VIN is stamped on a metal plate located on top instrument panel. The VIN plate is visible through lower left of windshield.

ENGINE IDENTIFICATION CODE

Engine	Code
2.2L Diesel	P

MANIFOLDS & CYLINDER HEAD

INTAKE MANIFOLD

Removal

1) Disconnect negative battery cables from both batteries. Disconnect air inlet hose from air cleaner and intake manifold.

2) Disconnect and remove fuel injection lines from nozzles and injection pump. Remove nut attaching lower fuel return line bracket to intake manifold.

3) Disconnect and remove lower fuel return line from injection pump and upper fuel return line. Remove air conditioning compressor drive belt.

4) Remove air conditioning compressor and position aside with hoses attached. Remove power steering pump and rear bracket and position aside with hoses connected.

5) Remove air inlet adapter and dropping resistor. Disconnect fuel filter inlet line and remove fuel filter mounting braket and position aside.

6) Remove nuts attaching fuel line heater to cylinder head and position aside. Remove nuts attaching intake manifold to cylinder head. Remove intake manifold.

Installation

Install all components in reverse order of removal procedure.

EXHAUST MANIFOLD

Removal

1) Disconnect negative battery cables from both batteries. Remove nuts attaching exhaust inlet pipe to exhaust manifold.

2) Remove heater hose bracket from exhaust manifold and valve cover. Remove vacuum pump support brace from exhaust manifold and vacuum pump bracket.

3) Remove bolt attaching engine oil dipstick tube to exhaust manifold. Remove nuts attaching exhaust manifold to cylinder head. Remove exhaust manifold.

Installation

Reverse removal procedure to install all components.

CYLINDER HEAD

Removal

1) Remove intake and exhaust manifolds. Loosen number 3 intake port nut and Banjo bolt on injection pump.

2) Disconnect lower fuel return line from intake manifold stud and upper fuel return line. Remove bolt attaching power steering pump rear support to cylinder head.

3) Remove upper radiator hose from thermostat housing. Remove by-pass hose from thermostat housing and water pump. Remove bolts attaching air conditioning compressor to bracket and position compressor aside.

4) Remove valve cover. Remove rocker arm shaft assembly. Remove remaining head bolts. Remove cylinder head from engine.

Installation

1) Position new cylinder head gasket on engine block. Place cylinder head on block. Install rocker arm shaft assembly, but do not tighten bolts.

2) Install head bolts. Tighten cylinder head bolts and rocker arm shaft assembly bolts in specified sequence. See Fig. 1. Reverse removal procedure to install remaining components.

Fig. 1: Cylinder Head Bolt Tightening Sequence

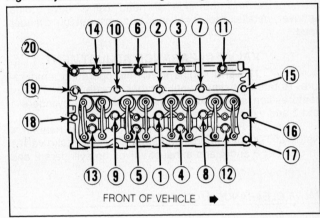

FRONT OF VEHICLE ➡

VALVES

VALVE ARRANGEMENT

I-E-I-E-I-E (front-to-rear)

ROCKER ARM SHAFT ASSEMBLY

Removal

Remove valve cover. Remove bolts attaching rocker arm shaft assembly to cylinder head. Remove rocker arm shaft assembly. Remove push rods if necessary.

Installation

1) Install rocker shaft on cylinder head. Tighten attaching bolts, 2 or 3 turns at a time, until shaft supports are seated on cylinder head.

2) Tighten cylinder head bolts and rocker arm shaft bolts evenly. Adjust valve clearance. Reinstall valve cover.

VALVE SPRINGS AND/OR VALVE STEM OIL SEALS

Removal

1) Remove valve cover and remove rocker arm shaft assembly. Rotate crankshaft until piston in affected cylinder is at TDC.

2) Using spring compressor tool (T83T-6513-B and T74P-6565-A or equivalent), compress spring and remove retainer locks, spring retainer and valve spring. Remove valve stem oil seal.

Ford 4 Engines

2.2L 4-CYLINDER DIESEL (Cont.)

Installation

Reverse removal procedure to install all components.

VALVE GUIDE SERVICING

Inspection

1) Using a dial indicator and valve stem clearance checking tool (T65T-6505-H or equivalent), check valve stem-to-guide clearance.

2) Rock valve stem back and forth and measure movement. If clearance exceeds specified limits, valve guide replacement is required.

Removal

Using a valve guide remover/installer tool (Rotunda 14-0315 or equivalent), drive out old valve guide toward combustion chamber side of cylinder head.

Installation

Coat outer surface of guide with engine oil. Drive guide into top side of head using valve guide remover/installer tool, until tool bottoms out on cylinder head.

VALVE CLEARANCE ADJUSTMENT

1) Warm engine to normal operating temperature. Rotate crankshaft until number 1 piston is at TDC of compression stroke. Adjust intake valves on cylinders 1 and 2 and exhaust valves on cylinders 1 and 3.

2) Rotate crankshaft 360° to place number 4 piston at TDC of compression stroke. Adjust intake valves on cylinder 3 and 4 and exhaust valves on cylinders 2 and 4.

VALVE CLEARANCE ADJUSTMENT

Application	Clearance In. (mm)
2.2L	.012 (.30)

Fig. 2: Valve Clearance Adjustment Sequence

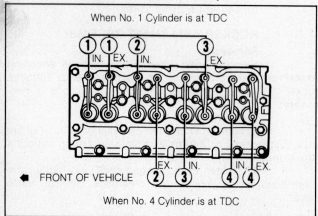

CAMSHAFT

ENGINE FRONT COVER

Removal

1) Disconnect negative battery cables from both batteries. Remove cooling fan and fan shroud. Drain cooling system and crankcase.

2) Loosen idler pulley and remove air conditioning compressor and/or power steering pump belt. Remove power steering pump bracket and position pump and bracket aside.

3) Remove alternator belt. Remove water pump. Remove crankshaft pulley. Remove nuts attaching engine front cover to engine block. Remove engine front cover.

Installation

Reverse removal procedure to install all components. When installing front cover on engine block, use front cover aligning tool (T61K-6019-A or equivalent).

FRONT COVER OIL SEAL

Removal

1) Disconnect negative battery cables from both batteries. Remove air conditioning compressor and/or power steering pump belt.

2) Remove alternator/water pump belt. Install damper removal spanner (T83T-6316-D) and remove crankshaft lock bolt.

3) Using a puller, remove crankshaft pulley. Remove front cover oil seal from engine front cover using front seal remover tool (T72J-6700 or equivalent).

Installation

Coat seal lip with engine oil. Using seal driver (T83T-6019-A or equivalent) and front cover alignment tool (T83T-6313-C or equivalent), install seal. Reverse removal procedure to install remaining components.

TIMING GEARS

Removal

1) Remove engine front cover. Remove oil pan. Rotate crankshaft to align timing marks. Remove camshaft gear attaching bolt.

2) Remove washer and friction gear from camshaft gear. Remove injection pump attaching bolt and remove washer and friction gear.

3) Install hub and gear remover (T83T-6306-A or equivalent) on camshaft drive gear. Remove gear.

4) Repeat step **3)** for removal of injection pump gear. Remove nuts attaching idler gear thrust plates and spindles to engine block. Remove idler gear assemblies.

Fig. 3: Timing Gear Alignment Mark Locations

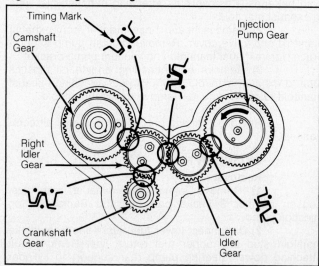

2.2L 4-CYLINDER DIESEL (Cont.)

Installation
Reverse removal procedure to install all components using *Fig. 3* to align timing marks on all gears.

CAMSHAFT

Removal

1) Remove engine from vehicle. Remove valve cover, rocker arm shaft assembly and push rods. Remove engine front cover.

2) Remove camshaft gear. Remove oil pan and oil pump. Remove camshaft thrust plate. Carefully remove camshaft

Installation

Reverse removal procedure to install all components. Make sure that camshaft gear is properly aligned with other timing gears.

CAMSHAFT END THRUST

1) Remove camshaft from engine. Install thrust plate on camshaft. Install camshaft gear and friction gear on camshaft. Install and tighten lock bolt.

2) Measure end thrust by inserting a feeler gauge between thrust plate and camshaft gear. If camshaft end thrust is not .0008-.0071" (.02-.18 mm), replace thrust plate.

INJECTION PUMP TIMING

For injection pump gear timing, refer to Timing Gear removal and installation procedures.

PISTONS, RINGS & PINS

OIL PAN
See Oil Pan Removal at end of ENGINE Section.

PISTON & ROD ASSEMBLY

Removal

1) Disconnect negative battery cables at both batteries. Drain cooling system. Remove cylinder head. Drain crankcase and remove oil pan.

Fig. 4: Correctly Spacing Piston Ring Gaps

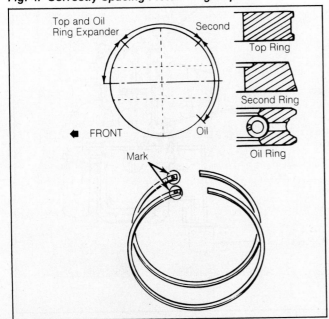

2) Remove ridge from top of cylinder wall. Remove rod cap. Push piston and rod assembly out top of cylinder block. Mark rod and rod cap so that piston assembly can be installed in its original location.

Installation

1) Lightly oil rings, piston and cylinder wall. Ensure ring gaps are properly spaced around piston. *See Fig. 4.* Make sure bearing halves are properly seated in connecting rod and cap.

2) Install a ring compressor and compress rings. Install piston in cylinder. Ensure piston and connecting rod assembly are installed in proper direction. *See Fig. 5.* Install and tighten rod cap. Reverse removal procedure to complete installation.

Fig. 5: Correct Positioning of Piston and Rod Assembly for Installation into Engine Block

FITTING PISTONS

NOTE: Make all measurements with piston and block at normal room temperature (70°F, 21°C).

1) Measure piston 90° to piston pin axis .63" (16 mm) from bottom of piston. Measure cylinder bore 90° to crankshaft centerline, at top, middle, and bottom of bore. Use these measurements to determine piston-to-cylinder bore clearance.

2) Measure cylinder bore 90° to crankshaft centerline at top of bore (below ring travel) and at bottom of bore (above ring travel). These measurements determine cylinder taper. Taper (difference between the 2 measurements) must not exceed .010" (.25 mm).

3) Measure cylinder bore at center of piston travel, 90° to crankshaft centerline. Measure bore at center of piston travel in line with crankshaft centerline. Out-of-round is the difference between the 2 measurements, and must not exceed .005" (.13 mm).

4) If taper or out-of-round are beyond limits, installation of new pistons is required.

FITTING RINGS

1) Position rings into cylinder bore at a point where bore diameter is smallest. Ring must be square in bore. Measure ring end gap with a feeler gauge. Maximum allowable end gap is .059" (1.5 mm).

2) Using a feeler gauge, check ring side clearance. Maximum allowable side clearance is .012" (.3 mm). Ensure rings turn freely in their ring grooves.

3) When installing rings on piston, ensure gaps are correct. *See Fig. 4.* The stamped mark on piston rings must be upward.

Ford 4 Engines

2.2L 4-CYLINDER DIESEL (Cont.)

CYLINDER LINERS

Removal

1) Disconnect negative battery cables from both batteries. Drain cooling system and crankcase. Remove cylinder head. Remove oil pan.

2) Remove piston and rod assemblies. Install cylinder liner remover (Rotunda 14-0316 or equivalent) into cylinder. Rotate pilot screw clockwise to remove cylinder liner.

Installation

1) Apply engine oil on the cylinder block bore and outside diameter of new liner. Position cylinder liner on cylinder block.

2) Install cylinder liner installer (Rotunda 14-0317 or equivalent). Rotate pilot screw to draw sleeve into block.

3) After cylinder liner is fully seated in block, check height of cylinder liner protrusion above top of block. Liner protrusion above block should be .026-.031" (.66-.79 mm).

4) Reverse removal procedure to install all remaining components.

PISTON PIN REPLACEMENT

Removal & Installation

Using arbor press and adapter, press piston pin from piston and rod. To install piston pin, make sure that rod and piston are properly positioned. *See Fig. 5.*

CRANKSHAFT, MAIN & CONNECTING ROD BEARINGS

MAIN & CONNECTING ROD BEARINGS

1) Fit main and rod bearings one at a time, while leaving all other bearings securely fastened. To determine bearing clearance, remove bearing cap.

2) Place a strip of Plastigage on bearing surface across full width of bearing cap, about 1/4" off center away from oil holes.

3) Install bearing cap and tighten bolts to specifications. Do not allow crankshaft to turn.

4) Remove cap and measure compressed width of Plastigage with scale furnished with Plastigage.

5) Standard size bearings may be used in combination with a .001" or .002" undersize bearing.

6) If .002" undersize bearings are used in more than one journal, they must be installed in cylinder block or piston rod side of crankshaft journal.

7) After bearings are installed, lightly oil crankshaft journal and bearing surfaces and install bearing cap.

CRANKSHAFT END THRUST

NOTE: **Engine must be removed from vehicle to check crankshaft end play.**

1) Force crankshaft toward rear of engine. Attach dial indicator to rear of engine so that indicator contact rests against crankshaft flange.

2) Zero dial indicator. Push crankshaft forward and note dial indicator reading.

3) If end play exceeds specification, replace thrust washer with an appropriate undersized thrust washer.

REAR MAIN BEARING OIL SEAL

Removal

Disconnect negative battery cables from both batteries. Remove transmission and flywheel. Remove crankshaft rear cover. Using a screwdriver, carefully pry rear main bearing oil seal out of crankshaft rear cover.

Installation

Coat seal lip with engine oil. Using rear main bearing oil seal installer (T80T-4000-W or equivalent),

Fig. 6: Engine Oiling System

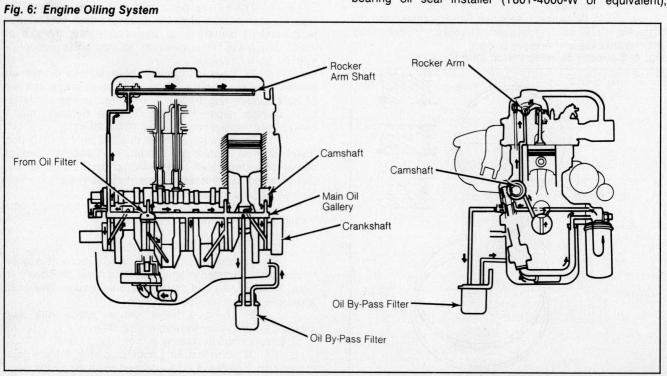

Rocker Arm Shaft

Rocker Arm

From Oil Filter

Camshaft

Camshaft

Main Oil Gallery

Crankshaft

Oil By-Pass Filter

Oil By-Pass Filter

Ford 4 Engines

2.2L 4-CYLINDER DIESEL (Cont.)

install new seal into rear cover. Reverse removal procedure to install remaining components.

ENGINE OILING

Crankcase Capacity
Capacity is 7 qts. (6.6L).
Normal Oil Pressure
Normal oil pressure is 57 psi (4 kg/cm²) at 3600 RPM.

ENGINE OILING SYSTEM

System is pressure fed from a rotor-type oil pump. Oil flows through one oil filter before entering main oil gallery and through another oil filter as it leaves oil pump. *See Fig. 6.*

OIL PUMP

Removal
1) Disconnect negative battery cables from both batteries. Remove oil pan. Disconnect oil pump outlet tube from engine block.
2) Remove oil pump set screw, located on side of engine block. Remove oil pump from engine.

Inspection
1) Clean all parts in solvent and dry thoroughly with compressed air. Be sure that all dirt or metal particles are removed from pump.
2) Check inside of pump housing, outer race and rotor for excessive wear or damage. Check mating surface of pump cover for wear. If pump cover mating surface is excessively worn, scored or grooved, replace pump assembly.
3) Measure rotor tip clearance. *See Fig. 7.* If rotor tip clearance exceeds specification, pump assembly must be replaced.

Fig. 7: Checking Inner Rotor Tip Clearance

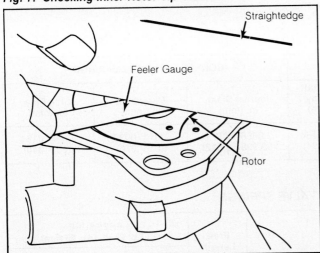

4) With rotor assembly installed in pump housing, place a straight edge across pump housing. Using a feeler gauge, measure clearance between straightedge and both inner and outer rotors.
5) Maximum rotor end play should not exceed specifications. If clearance limit is exceeded, pump must be replaced.

6) Check oil pump driveshaft to housing clearance by measuring outside diameter of shaft and inside diameter of housing bearing. If clearance is not to specification, replace pump assembly.

OIL PUMP SPECIFICATIONS

Application	Specification In. (mm)
Rotor Tip Clearance	.012 (.30)
Rotor End Play	.005 (.13)
Drive Shaft-to-Housing Bearing Clearance	.0039 (.099)

Installation
Reverse removal procedure to install all components.

ENGINE COOLING

WATER PUMP

Removal
1) Disconnect negative battery cables from both batteries. Remove fan and fan shroud. Loosen alternator and vacuum pump mounting brackets and remove drive belt.
2) Loosen air conditioning compressor and/or power steering pump idler gear and remove drive belt. Drain cooling system.
3) Disconnect heater hose and by-pass hose from thermostat housing. Remove bolts and nuts attaching water pump to engine block. Remove water pump.

Installation
Clean gasket mating surfaces. Using new gasket, install water pump by reversing removal procedure.

NOTE: For information on cooling system capacities and other cooling system components, see appropriate article in "Engine Cooling Systems," at end of ENGINE Section.

TIGHTENING SPECIFICATIONS

Application	Ft. Lbs. (N.m)
Camshaft Gear	45-51 (61-69)
Camshaft Thrust Plate	12-18 (16-24)
Connecting Rod Cap	50-54 (68-73)
Crankshaft Pulley	253-289 (343-392)
Cylinder Head	80-85 (108-115)
Exhaust Manifold	17-20 (23-27)
Idler Gears	12-17 (16-23)
Injection Pump Drive Gear	29-51 (39-69)
Intake Manifold	12-17 (16-23)
Main Bearing Cap	80-85 (108-115)
Rocker Arm Shaft Bolts	
Through Cylinder Head	80-85 (108-115)
Into Cylinder Head	12-17 (16-23)

Ford 4 Engines
2.2L 4-CYLINDER DIESEL (Cont.)

ENGINE SPECIFICATIONS

GENERAL SPECIFICATIONS

| Year | DISPLACEMENT | | Fuel System | HP@RPM | Torque Ft. Lbs.@RPM | Compr. Ratio | BORE | | STROKE | |
	Cu. In.	Liters					In.	mm	In.	mm
1983	134	2.2	Fuel Inj.	59@4000	90@2500	22.0:1	3.50	88.9	3.50	88.9

VALVES

Engine Size & Valve	Head Diam. In. (mm)	Face Angle	Seat Angle	Seat Width In. (mm)	Stem Diameter In. (mm)	Stem Clearance In. (mm)	Valve Lift In. (mm)
2.2L Intake	1.591-1.599 (40.41-40.61)	45°	45°	.079 (2.01)	.3130-.3150 (7.950-8.001)	.0015-.0046 (.038-.117)	.....
Exhaust	1.412-1.422 (35.86-36.12)	30°	30°	.079 (2.01)	.3150-.3197 (8.001-8.120)	.0020-.0051 (.051-.129)	.....

PISTONS, PINS, RINGS

| Engine | PISTONS | PINS | | RINGS | | |
	Clearance In. (mm)	Piston Fit In. (mm)	Rod Fit In. (mm)	Ring No.	End Gap In. (mm)	Side Clearance In. (mm)
2.2L	.0021-.0031 (.053-.079)	.0006 (.015)	.0006-.0016 (.015-.041)	No. 1	.0157-.0217 (.399-.551)	.0020-.0035 (.051-.089)
				No. 2	.0118-.0157 (.299-.399)	.0016-.0031 (.041-.079)
				Oil	.0138-.0217 (.351-.551)	.0012-.0028 (.030-.071)

CRANKSHAFT MAIN & CONNECTING ROD BEARINGS

| Engine | MAIN BEARINGS | | | | CONNECTING ROD BEARINGS | | |
	Journal Diam. In. (mm)	Clearance In. (mm)	Thrust Bearing	Crankshaft End Play In. (mm)	Journal Diam. In. (mm)	Clearance In. (mm)	Side Play In. (mm)
2.2L	2.5586-2.5591 (64.988-65.001)	.0016-.0036 (.041-.091)	No. 3	.0055-.0154 (.140-.391)	2.0866-2.0871 (52.999-53.012)	.0014-.0030 (.036-.076)	.0094-.0134 (.239-.340)

CAMSHAFT

Engine	Journal Diam. In. (mm)	Clearance In. (mm)	Lobe Lift In. (mm)
2.2L No. 1	2.0438-2.0473 (51.913-52.001)	.0024-.0047 (.061-.119)	.....
No. 2	2.0339-2.0374 (51.661-51.750)	.0024-.0047 (.061-.119)	.....
No. 3	2.0142-2.0177 (51.161-51.250)	.0024-.0047 (.061-.119)	.....

VALVE SPRINGS

| Engine | Free Length In. (mm) | PRESSURE Lbs. @ In. (Kg @ mm) | |
		Valve Closed	Valve Open
2.2L Inner	1.736 (44.1)	.....	.....
Outer	1.807 (45.9)	.....	.....

Ford V6 Engines

2.8 LITER V6

ENGINE CODING

ENGINE IDENTIFICATION

Engine can be identified by the eighth digit of vehicle identification number (VIN). The VIN is stamped on a metal plate and is attached to the upper left corner of the instrument panel. The VIN plate is visible through windshield on left side of vehicle.

ENGINE IDENTIFICATION CODES

Engine	Code
2.8L 2-Bbl.	S

ENGINE REMOVAL

See Engine Removal at end of ENGINE Section.

MANIFOLDS & CYLINDER HEAD

INTAKE MANIFOLD

Removal

1) Disconnect negative battery cable. Remove air cleaner assembly. Disconnect throttle cable from engine. Drain cooling system.

2) Remove water hose from water outlet to radiator. Remove water hose from intake manifold to thermostat housing rear cover.

3) Remove distributor cap and spark plug wires as an assembly. Disconnect vacuum hose and wiring harness from distributor.

4) Observe and mark position of rotor and distributor housing for reassembly reference. Remove distributor hold down bolt and distributor.

5) Remove valve covers. Remove fuel line and fuel filter. Remove intake manifold attaching bolts and nut.

6) Lightly tap intake manifold with a plastic mallet to break gasket seal. Lift intake manifold from engine.

Installation

1) Clean all gasket mating surfaces. Apply sealing compound to sealing surfaces. Place intake manifold gasket in position.

2) Make sure that tab on right bank cylinder head gasket fits into cutout on manifold gasket.

3) Apply sealing compound to attaching bolt bosses on intake manifold. Install attaching bolts and tighten in specified sequence. *See Fig. 1.*

4) Reverse removal procedure to complete installation of all remaining components.

Fig. 1: Intake Manifold Bolt Tightening Sequence

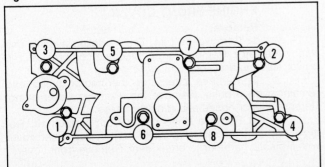

EXHAUST MANIFOLD

Removal

1) Remove air cleaner assembly. Remove nuts attaching shroud to exhaust manifold. Remove nuts attaching exhaust inlet pipe to exhaust manifold.

2) Remove thermactor components as necessary for exhaust manifold removal. Disconnect choke heat tubes at carburetor.

3) Remove exhaust manifold attaching bolts. Remove exhaust manifold from cylinder head.

Installation

Install new exhaust pipe-to-manifold gasket. Reverse removal procedures to complete installation of all components.

CYLINDER HEAD

Removal

1) Remove intake manifold. Remove rocker arm shaft assembly. Remove push rods and keep them in order so that they can be installed in their original positions.

2) Remove exhaust manifolds. Remove cylinder head attaching bolts. Remove cylinder head from engine and discard gaskets.

Installation

NOTE: **Cylinder head gaskets are marked with word "front" and "top" for correct installation positioning. Left and right gaskets are not interchangeable.**

1) Position head gasket on engine block. Install cylinder head alignment studs into upper left and upper right cylinder head bolt holes in engine block.

2) Position cylinder heads over alignment studs and onto engine block. Install cylinder head attaching bolts and remove alignment studs. Tighten all bolts in specified sequence. *See Fig. 2.*

3) Reverse removal procedure to complete installation of remaining components.

Fig. 2: Cylinder Head Bolt Tightening Sequence

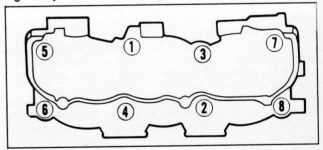

VALVES

VALVE ARRANGEMENT

Right Side — I-E-I-E-E-I
Left Side — I-E-E-I-E-I

ROCKER ARM SHAFT ASSEMBLY

Removal

1) Remove air cleaner assembly. Remove spark plug wires. Remove PCV valve and hose. Remove carburetor choke air deflector plate.

2) Remove valve cover attaching bolts and washer. Make sure that washers are installed in their original positions.

3) Disconnect transmission fluid dipstick tube from valve cover. Disconnect kickdown linkage from carburetor.

4) Position thermactor air hose and wiring harness away from right valve cover. Remove engine oil fill cap.

5) Disconnect vacuum line at canister purge solenoid. Disconnect hose from canister to purge solenoid. If equipped with power brakes, disconnect brake booster hose.

6) Lightly tap valve cover with a plastic hammer to break seal. Remove valve covers. Loosen rocker arm shaft attaching bolts 2 turns at a time until all bolts are removed. Lift rocker arm shaft assembly from cylinder head.

Disassembly
Remove spring washer and roll pin from each end of rocker arm shaft. Slide rocker arms, springs and rocker arm shaft supports off of shaft. Be sure to mark all parts so that they can be assembled in same order.

Fig. 3: Exploded View of Rocker Arm Shaft Assembly

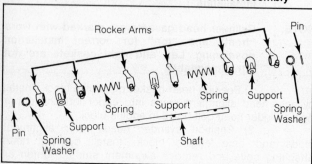

Reassembly
When rocker arm shaft is reassembled, oil holes in shaft must point downward. This position of the shaft can be noted by a notch on front face of shaft. Coat all parts with heavy engine oil and reassemble in reverse order of disassembly.

Installation
1) Loosen valve lash adjusting screws a few turns. Apply heavy engine oil to entire rocker arm shaft assembly. Install oil baffle. Install rocker arm shaft assembly on cylinder head.

2) Install all rocker arm shaft attaching bolts. Tighten bolts evenly, 2 turns at a time. Reverse removal procedure to complete installation of all remaining components.

VALVE SPRINGS AND/OR VALVE STEM OIL SEALS
Removal
1) Remove air cleaner. Remove valve covers and rocker arm shaft. Remove spark plug wire and spark plug from cylinder in which valve spring will be removed.

2) Remove both push rods from cylinder to be serviced. Install air line adapter in spark plug hole. Apply air pressure to cylinder.

3) Using valve spring compressor tool (T74P-6565-A and B or equivalent), compress valve spring and remove spring retainer locks, spring retainer and spring. Remove valve stem oil seal.

Installation
Install new valve stem oil seal. Position spring over valve. Compress spring and install retainer and locks. Reverse removal procedure to complete installation of remaining components.

VALVE SPRING INSTALLED HEIGHT
1) Valve spring installed height should be measured with rocker arms removed. Measurement should be made from cylinder head spring pad to bottom side of valve spring retainer.

2) If height is not within specifications, install spacers between cylinder head spring pad and valve spring to obtain specified height. Do not install more spacers than are necessary to obtain specified height.

VALVE SPRING INSTALLED HEIGHT SPECIFICATIONS

Application	Measurement In. (mm)
2.8L	1 37/64 - 1 39/64 (40.08-40.88)

VALVE GUIDE SERVICING
Always use reamers in propers sequence (smallest first). Reface valve seat after valve guide has been reamed. After reaming, use a scraper to break sharp corner at top inside diameter of valve guide bore. Valves with oversized stems are available with stems that are .003" (.08 mm), .015" (.38 mm) and .030" (.76 mm) oversized.

VALVE CLEARANCE ADJUSTMENT
1) Engine must be cold when valve clearance adjustment procedure is performed. Remove valve covers.

2) Turn engine until both valves, of cylinder being adjusted, are fully closed. Insert feeler gauge between rocker arm and top of valve.

3) If valve clearance is not to specification, loosen adjuster lock nut and turn adjusting screw to obtain specified clearance. After tightening lock nut, recheck clearance.

VALVE CLEARANCE ADJUSTMENT

Application	In. (mm)
2.8L	
Intake	.014 (.36)
Exhaust	.016 (.41)

CAMSHAFT
ENGINE FRONT COVER
Removal
1) Remove oil pan. Drain cooling system and remove radiator. Remove air conditioning compressor and power steering bracket.

2) Remove alternator thermactor pump and remaining drive belts. Remove fan. Remove water pump. Remove heater hoses and radiator hoses.

3) Remove drive pulley from crankshaft. Remove front cover retaining bolts. Lightly tap front cover with a plastic hammer to break seal. Remove front cover.

2.8 LITER V6 (Cont.)

Installation

1) Apply sealing compound to engine block and back side of front engine cover. Install front engine cover retaining bolts but do not tighten.

2) Install front cover alignment tool (T74P-6019-A or equivalent) into front cover seal. Tighten engine front cover attaching bolts. Reverse removal procedure to install remaining components.

FRONT COVER OIL SEAL

Removal

Drain cooling system. Remove radiator, crankshaft pulley and water pump drive belt. Using seal remover tool (1175-AC or equivalent) and an impact slide hammer, remove front cover oil seal from engine front cover.

Installation

1) Coat new front cover oil seal with Lubriplate. Slide oil seal and seal installer tool (T74P-6700-A or equivalent) onto crankshaft.

2) Drive oil seal in until installer tool contacts front cover. Reverse removal procedure to complete installation.

TIMING GEARS

Removal

1) Drain cooling system and crankcase. Remove oil pan. Remove radiator. Remove water pump and engine front cover. Remove camshaft gear retaining bolt.

2) Remove camshaft gear. Using a gear puller and a shaft protector (T71P-7137-H or equivalent), remove crankshaft gear.

Installation

1) Align keyway on camshaft gear with key on camshaft. Slide gear onto camshaft and install camshaft gear retaining bolt.

Fig. 4: Aligning Timing Marks on Timing Gears

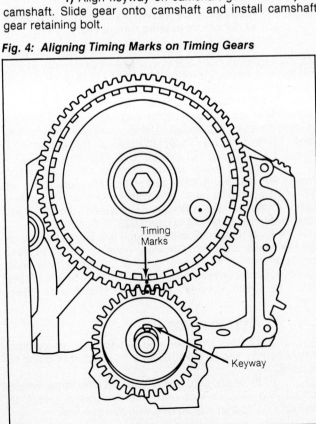

Timing Marks

Keyway

2) Align keyway in crankshaft gear with key in crankshaft and timing marks on both gears. See Fig. 4. Slide gear onto crankshaft.

3) Reverse removal procedure to complete installation of remaining components.

CAMSHAFT

Removal

1) Disconnect negative battery cable from battery. Drain crankcase. Remove radiator. Remove fan, spacer, drive belt and pulley.

2) Remove spark plug wires from spark plugs. Remove distributor cap and wires as an assembly. Disconnect distributor wiring harness and vacuum hose. Remove distributor.

3) Remove alternator and thermactor pump. Remove fuel lines, fuel filter and carburetor. Remove intake manifold. Remove valve covers. Remove rocker arm shaft assemblies.

4) Remove push rods and keep them in order so that they can be installed in their original locations. Remove tappets from their bores. Remove oil pan. Remove crankshaft damper.

5) Remove water pump and engine front cover as an assembly. Remove camshaft gear attaching bolt and washer. Slide gear off of camshaft. Remove camshaft thrust plate. Carefully slide camshaft out of engine.

Installation

1) Coat camshaft journals with heavy engine oil. Apply Lubriplate to camshaft lobes. Carefully install camshaft into engine block.

2) Install camshaft thrust plate and tighten screws. Check camshaft end thrust. Reverse removal procedure to install remaining components.

CAMSHAFT END THRUST

CAUTION: Prying against aluminum/nylon gear, with valve train load on camshaft, can break or damage the gear. When checking camshaft end thrust, back off valve lash adjusters or loosen rocker arm shaft to remove load from camshaft.

1) Remove engine front cover. Push camshaft toward rear of engine. Install a dial indicator so that indicator plunger is on camshaft gear attaching bolt.

2) Zero dial indicator. Using a large screwdriver between camshaft gear and engine block, pull camshaft forward and release it. Read dial indicator.

3) If dial indicator reading is greater than .009" (.29 mm), replace thrust plate at rear of engine block. Remove dial indicator from engine. Reinstall engine front cover.

CAM LOBE LIFT

1) Remove air cleaner. Remove valve cover. Using a vernier caliper, measure both distance "A" and "B" of each cam lobe. See Fig. 5. Distance "A" minus distance "B" is cam lobe lift.

2) Check lift of each lobe in consecutive order and note all readings. If readings are not within specifications, replace camshaft and all rocker arms.

Ford V6 Engines

2.8 LITER V6 (Cont.)

Fig. 5: Measuring Cam Lobe Lift

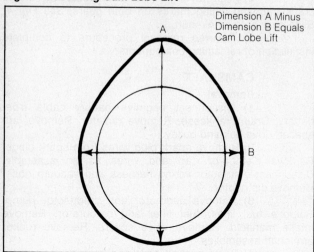

Dimension A Minus
Dimension B Equals
Cam Lobe Lift

CAMSHAFT BEARINGS

Removal

1) Remove engine from vehicle and place on engine stand. Remove flywheel. Remove camshaft. Remove rear bearing bore plug.

2) Using camshaft bearing remover/installer (T71P-6250-A or equivalent), remove camshaft bearings from engine block. Use special adapter tube tool (T72C-6250 or equivalent), when removing front and rear bearings.

Installation

1) Install camshaft bearings in engine block using camshaft bearing remover/installer tool. When installing bearing, make sure that oil hole in bearing is aligned with oil hole in engine block.

2) Oil hole alignment of number 2 and 3 bearings can be checked by inserting a piece of welding rod through engine block and camshaft bearing.

3) Reverse removal procedure to complete installation of remaining components.

PISTONS, RINGS & PINS

OIL PAN

See Oil Pan Removal at end of ENGINE Section.

PISTON & ROD ASSEMBLY

Removal

1) Drain cooling system and crankcase. Remove intake manifold, cylinder heads, oil pan and oil pump.

2) Rotate crankshaft until piston to be removed is at bottom of its stroke. Place a cloth on top of piston to collect cuttings. Remove any ridges or deposits from upper end of cylinder bore.

3) Make sure that all connecting rod caps are marked so that they can be installed in their original locations. Remove connecting rod nuts and cap.

4) Push piston out through top of engine block using handle of a hammer. Remove bearing inserts from connecting rod and cap.

Installation

1) Apply light engine oil to piston rings, piston and cylinder walls. Make sure that ring gaps are properly spaced around piston. *See Fig. 6.*

Fig. 6: Correctly Spacing Piston Ring Gaps

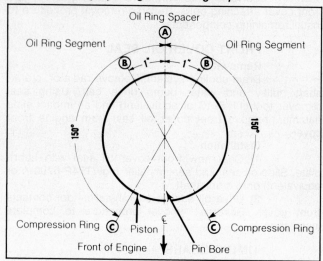

2) Install piston ring compressor on piston. Using a hammer handle, push piston into cylinder block until top of piston is just below top of cylinder block.

3) Carefully guide connecting rod onto crankshaft journal. Apply a light coat of engine oil to journals and bearings. Install connecting rod cap and tighten nuts.

FITTING PISTONS

NOTE: **Make all measurements with piston and block at normal room temperature (70°F, 21°C).**

1) Measure piston skirt 90° to piston pin axis. Measure cylinder bore 90° to crankshaft centerline, at top, middle, and bottom of bore. Use these measurements to determine piston-to-cylinder bore clearance.

2) Measure cylinder bore 90° to crankshaft centerline at top of bore (below ring travel) and at bottom of bore (above ring travel). These measurements determine cylinder taper. Taper (difference between the 2 measurements) must not exceed .010" (.25 mm).

3) Measure cylinder bore at center of piston travel, 90° to crankshaft centerline. Measure bore at center of piston travel in line with crankshaft centerline. Out-of-round is the difference between the 2 measurements, and must not exceed .005" (.13 mm).

4) If taper or out-of-round are beyond limits, or cylinder walls are deeply scored, hone or bore cylinders for installation of new pistons. After cylinders have been honed or bored, measure cylinder diameter. Select proper piston to obtain specified piston to cylinder bore clearance.

FITTING RINGS

1) Select proper ring set for size of cylinder bore. Position ring in cylinder bore in which it is going to be used.

2) Push ring down into bore to area where normal ring wear is not encountered. Use a piston to position ring so that it is square with cylinder wall.

2.8 LITER V6 (Cont.)

3) Measure gap between ends of ring using feeler gauge. If ring gap is less than or greater than specified, a smaller or larger ring will have to be used.

4) Check side clearance of compression rings with feeler gauge, of specified thickness, inserted between ring and its lower land on piston. Feeler gauge should slide freely around entire circumference of piston without binding.

5) If feeler gauge binds because of high spots on lower land of piston, piston should be replaced.

PISTON PIN REPLACEMENT

Removal

Using an arbor press and piston pin removing/installing tool (T68P-6135-A and T72C-6135 or equivalent), press piston pin from piston and connecting rod.

Installation

1) Apply a light coat of oil to all parts that are to be assembled. Position piston and connection rod as shown in *Fig. 7.*

2) Using arbor press and piston pin removing/installing tool, press piston pin through piston and connecting rod until centered in connecting rod.

Fig. 7: Correct Positioning of Piston and Connecting Rod for Installation of Piston Pin

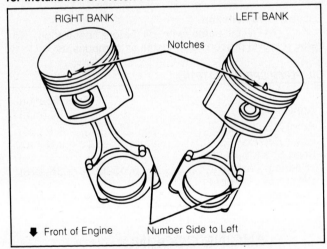

CRANKSHAFT, MAIN & CONNECTING ROD BEARINGS

MAIN & CONNECTING ROD BEARINGS

1) Remove engine from vehicle. Place engine on engine stand. Drain crankcase. Invert engine and remove oil pan and oil pump.

2) Remove main bearing cap for which new bearings are to be installed. Insert upper bearing remover/installer tool (6331-E or equivalent) in crankshaft journal oil hole. *See Fig. 8.*

3) Slowly rotate crankshaft in normal direction of engine rotation to force upper bearing out of engine block.

4) When installing main bearings, clean crankshaft journal. Coat upper main bearing with heavy engine oil. Place bearing over crankshaft on locking tab side of engine block.

Fig. 8: Installation of Upper Main Bearing Remover/Installer Tool

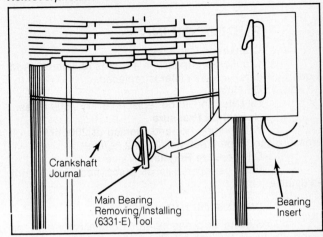

5) Partially install bearing so that bearing remover/installer tool can be inserted into journal oil hole. Slowly rotate crankshaft in opposite direction of normal engine rotation until bearing tang is seated.

6) Fit main and rod bearings one at a time, while leaving all other bearings securely fastened. To determine bearing clearance, remove bearing cap.

7) Place a strip of Plastigage on bearing surface across full width of bearing cap, about 1/4" off center away from oil holes.

8) Install bearing cap and tighten bolts to specifications. Do not allow crankshaft to turn.

9) Remove cap and measure compressed width of Plastigage with scale furnished in Plastigage kit.

10) Standard size bearings may be used in combination with a .001" or .002" undersize bearing.

11) If .002" undersize bearings are used in more than one journal, they must be installed in cylinder block or piston rod side of crankshaft journal.

12) After bearings are installed, lightly oil crankshaft journal and bearing surfaces and install bearing cap.

THRUST BEARING ALIGNMENT

Loosen bolts on number 3 main bearing cap. Pry crankshaft toward front of engine. With prying pressure on crankshaft, tighten main bearing cap bolts.

REAR MAIN BEARING OIL SEAL

Removal

1) Remove transmission from vehicle. Remove pressure plate and clutch disc, if equipped. Remove flywheel, flywheel housing and rear plate.

2) Punch 2 holes in rear main bearing oil seal. Punch holes directly opposite of each other. Install a sheet metal screw in each hole.

3) Using 2 large screwdrivers, pry on both screws at the same time until seal is removed from engine block.

Installation

1) Coat outside diameter of oil seal with engine oil. Coat inside diameter of oil seal with lubriplate.

2) Using seal installer tool (T72C-6165 or equivalent), drive oil seal into engine block until seal is

Ford V6 Engines

2.8 LITER V6 (Cont.)

firmly seated. Reverse removal procedure to complete installation of remaining components.

ENGINE OILING

Crankcase Capacity

Crankcase capacity is 4 quarts (3.8 liters). Add 1 quart (.9 liters) when oil filter is replaced.

Oil Filter

Oil Filter should be replaced every 7500 miles.

Normal Oil Pressure

With engine hot and running at 2000 RPM, oil pressure should be 40-60 psi (2.8-4.2 kg/cm²).

Oil Pressure Regulator Valve

Valve is located in oil pump body and is not adjustable.

ENGINE OILING SYSTEM

System is pressure fed from a rotor-type oil pump. Oil flows through oil filter before entering main oil gallery. See Fig. 9.

Fig. 9: Engine Oiling System

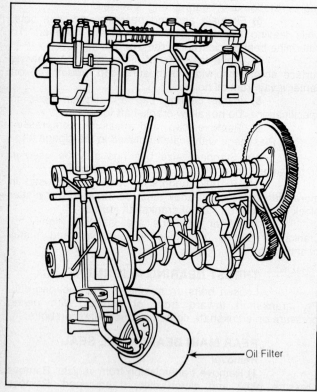

Oil Filter

OIL PUMP

Removal

Remove oil pan. Remove bolt attaching oil pick-up screen support arm to main bearing cap. Remove oil pump attaching bolts. Lift oil pump off of engine. Remove oil pump drive shaft from engine.

Inspection

1) Clean all parts in solvent and dry thoroughly with compressed air. Be sure that all dirt or metal particles are removed from pressure relief valve chamber.

2) Check inside of pump housing, outer race and rotor for excessive wear or damage. Check mating surface of pump cover for wear. If pump cover mating surface is excessively worn, scored or grooved, replace pump assembly.

3) Measure rotor tip clearance. See Fig. 10. If rotor tip clearance exceeds specification, pump assembly must be replaced.

Fig. 10: Checking Inner Rotor Tip Clearance

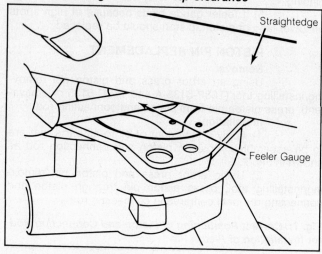

Straightedge

Feeler Gauge

Installation

Fill oil pump with oil before installation. Reverse removal procedure to install all components.

OIL PUMP SPECIFICATIONS

Application	Specification In. (mm)
Rotor Tip Clearance	.012 (.30)
Rotor End Play	.004 (.10)
Drive Shaft-to-Housing Bearing Clearance	.0015-.0030 (.038-.076)
Relief Valve-to-Bore Clearance	.0015-.0030 (.038-.076)

ENGINE COOLING

WATER PUMP

Removal

1) Drain cooling system. Disconnect lower radiator hose and heater return hose from water inlet housing.

2) Remove fan and fan clutch assembly using fan clutch removing tools (T83T-6312-A and B or equivalent) as shown in Fig. 11.

3) Loosen alternator mounting bolts and remove drive belt. On models with air conditioning, remove alternator and bracket.

4) On all models, remove water pump pulley. Remove water pump attaching bolts. Remove water pump assembly, water inlet housing and thermostat from front of engine.

Installation

Reverse removal procedure to install all components.

Ford V6 Engines

2.8 LITER V6 (Cont.)

NOTE: For information on cooling system capacities and other cooling system components, see appropriate article in "Engine Cooling Systems," at end of ENGINE Section.

Fig. 11: Removing Fan & Fan Clutch Assembly

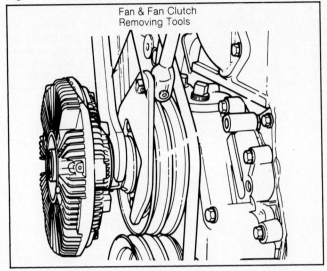

Fan & Fan Clutch Removing Tools

TIGHTENING SPECIFICATIONS

Application	Ft. Lbs. (N.m)
Camshaft Gear Bolt	30-36 (41-49)
Camshaft Thrust Plate	13-16 (18-22)
Connecting Rod Nut	19-24 (26-33)
Crankshaft Pulley-to-Crankshaft	85-96 (115-130)
Cylinder Head Bolt	
1st Step	29-40 (39-54)
2nd Step	40-51 (54-69)
3rd Step	70-85 (95-115)
Exhaust Manifold	20-30 (27-41)
Flywheel-to-Crankshaft	47-52 (64-71)
Front Cover-to-Engine Block	13-16 (18-22)
Main Bearing Cap Bolt	65-75 (88-102)
Rocker Arm Shaft Bolt	43-50 (58-68)

	INCH Lbs. (N.m)
Intake Manifold	
1st Step	36-72 (4-8)
2nd Step	72-132 (8-15)
3rd Step	132-180 (15-20)
4th Step	180-216 (20-24)
Oil Pump-to-Engine Block	72-120 (8-14)
Valve Cover	36-60 (4-7)
Water Pump	84-108 (9-12)

ENGINE SPECIFICATIONS

GENERAL SPECIFICATIONS

Year	DISPLACEMENT		Fuel System	HP@RPM	Torque Ft. Lbs.@RPM	Compr. Ratio	BORE		STROKE	
	Cu. In.	Liters					In.	mm	In.	mm
1983	170	2.8	2-Bbl.	......	......	......	3.65	92.7	2.70	68.6

VALVES

Engine Size & Valve	Head Diam. In. (mm)	Face Angle	Seat Angle	Seat Width In. (mm)	Stem Diameter In. (mm)	Stem Clearance In. (mm)	Valve Lift In. (mm)
2.8L Intake	1.562-1.577 (39.67-40.06)	44°	45°	.060-.079 (1.52-2.01)	.3159-.3167 (8.023-8.044)	.0008-.0025 (.020-.064)	......
Exhaust	1.261-1.276 (32.02-32.41)	44°	45°	.060-.079 (1.52-2.01)	.3149-.3156 (7.998-8.016)	.0018-.0035 (.045-.089)	......

PISTONS, PINS, RINGS

Engine	PISTONS Clearance In. (mm)	PINS Piston Fit In. (mm)	PINS Rod Fit In. (mm)	RINGS Ring No.	RINGS End Gap In. (mm)	RINGS Side Clearance In. (mm)
2.8L	.0011-.0019 (.028-.048)	.0003-.0006 (.008-.015)	Interference Fit	1 & 2	.015-.023 (.38-.58)	.0020-.0033 (.051-.084) Snug Fit
				3	.015-.055 (.38-1.39)	

Ford V6 Engines

2.8 LITER V6 (Cont.)

ENGINE SPECIFICATIONS (Cont.)

CRANKSHAFT MAIN & CONNECTING ROD BEARINGS

Engine	MAIN BEARINGS				CONNECTING ROD BEARINGS		
	Journal Diam. In. (mm)	Clearance In. (mm)	Thrust Bearing	Crankshaft End Play In. (mm)	Journal Diam. In. (mm)	Clearance In. (mm)	Side Play In. (mm)
2.8L	2.2433-2.3441 (56.979-59.540)	.0008-.0015 (.020-.038)	No. 3	.004-.008 (.10-.20)	2.1252-2.1260 (53.980-54.000)	.0006-.0016 (.015-.040)	.004-.011 (.10-.28)

VALVE SPRINGS

Engine	Free Length In. (mm)	PRESSURE Lbs. @ In. (Kg @ mm)	
		Valve Closed	Valve Open
2.8L	1.91 (48.5)	60-68@1.59 (27-31@40.4)	138-149@1.22 (63-68@31.0)

CAMSHAFT

Engine	Journal Diam. In. (mm)	Clearance In. (mm)	Lobe Lift In. (mm)
2.8L		.0010-.0026 (.025-.066)	.2555 (6.49)
No. 1	1.7285-1.7293 (43.904-43.924)		
No. 2	1.7135-1.7143 (43.523-43.543)		
No. 3	1.6985-1.6992 (43.141-43.160)		
No. 4	1.6835-1.6842 (42.761-42.779)		

Ford V6 Engines

3.8 LITER V6

ENGINE CODING

ENGINE IDENTIFICATION

Engine size is identified by eighth digit of Vehicle Identification Number (VIN). The VIN is stamped on a metal tab attached to left upper side of instrument panel, near windshield. The VIN is also located on the Safety Compliance Certification Label, located on left door lock pillar.

ENGINE IDENTIFICATION CODE

Engine	Code
3.8L 2-Bbl.	3

ENGINE REMOVAL

See Engine Removal at end of ENGINE Section.

MANIFOLDS & CYLINDER HEAD

INTAKE MANIFOLD

Removal

1) Drain cooling system. Remove air cleaner assembly and heat tube. Disconnect accelerator cable and transmission linkage at carburetor and position aside.

2) Remove accelerator mounting bracket. Disconnect cruise control unit (if equipped) and position aside. Disconnect carburetor bowl vent hose and fuel line at carburetor.

3) Disconnect air pump hose from check valve (at rear of intake manifold). Disconnect all coolant hoses attached to intake manifold.

4) Disconnect heater tube at manifold and remove tube support bracket. Label and disconnect vacuum hoses and electrical wiring at carburetor and intake manifold.

5) If A/C equipped, remove air compressor support bracket. Remove carburetor and studs from manifold. Loosen EGR tube from EGR valve adapter.

6) Remove EGR spacer adapter bolts. Work spacer loose from manifold. Disconnect EGR tube from adapter. Remove EGR spacer, adapter and valve as an assembly.

7) Remove intake manifold. If necessary to pry on manifold to break seal, use care not to damage machined surfaces.

Installation

1) Clean all gasket surfaces. If intake manifold was disassembled, apply pipe thread sealer to temperature sending unit, all threaded vacuum fittings, spark knock sensor/adapter assembly and electric PVS.

2) Apply 1/16" bead silicone sealer to thermostat housing. Apply small amount of contact adhesive to cylinder head-to-manifold mating surface. *See Fig. 1.*

3) Assemble new intake manifold side gaskets into place, using locating pins to aid in assembly.

4) Apply 1/8" bead silicone sealer at 4 corners of cylinder head-to-block junction, and along front and rear manifold-to-block mating surfaces. *See Fig. 1.* Assemble components before sealer sets up.

5) Carefully lower intake manifold into position using locating pins as a guide. Coat manifold bolt threads and bottom of bolt heads with pipe thread sealer.

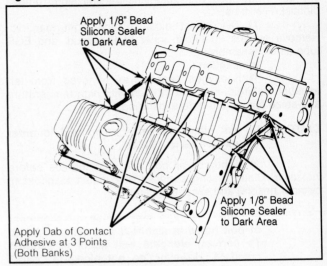

Fig. 1: Sealer Application Points

Apply 1/8" Bead Silicone Sealer to Dark Area

Apply 1/8" Bead Silicone Sealer to Dark Area

Apply Dab of Contact Adhesive at 3 Points (Both Banks)

Assemble components within 15 minutes of silicone sealer application.

6) Install and tighten manifold bolts in 3 steps. *See Fig. 2.* Reverse removal procedures to complete installation.

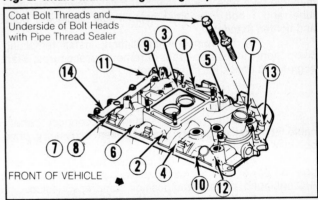

Fig. 2: Intake Manifold Tightening Sequence

Coat Bolt Threads and Underside of Bolt Heads with Pipe Thread Sealer

FRONT OF VEHICLE

Tighten first to 5 ft. lbs. (7 N.m); then to 10 ft. lbs. (14 N.m); and finally to 18 ft. lbs. (25 N.m).

EXHAUST MANIFOLD

Removal

1) To remove left side exhaust manifold, proceed as follows. Remove dipstick tube bracket.

2) If equipped with speed control, reposition air cleaner assembly and disconnect servo chain at carburetor. Detach speed control servo bracket and position servo/bracket assembly aside.

3) Disconnect wiring from oxygen sensor (If equipped). Disconnect spark plug wires. Disconnect exhaust pipe from manifold. Remove exhaust manifold.

4) To remove right side exhaust manifold, proceed as follows. Remove air cleaner assembly and heat tube. Disconnect air hose from downstream air tube check valve.

5) Remove downstream air tube bracket attaching bolt at rear of right cylinder head. Disconnect secondary ignition wiring from coil and spark plugs.

6) Remove spark plugs. Remove outer heat shroud. If equipped with automatic transmission, remove dipstick/filler tube.

7) Disconnect exhaust pipe from manifold. Remove exhaust manifold, inner heat shroud, and EGR tube as an assembly.

Installation

1) If oxygen sensor was removed from left exhaust manifold, coat the threads with high temperature anti-seize compound before installing.

CAUTION: Do not allow anti-seize compound to enter the oxygen sensor flutes.

2) Lightly oil all bolt and stud threads before installing. Clean mating surfaces of exhaust manifold(s), cylinder head(s) and exhaust pipe(s).

CAUTION: Manifold warpage may cause misalignment of bolt holes in manifold and cylinder head. To correct, elongate bolt holes in exhaust manifold. However, do not elongate "pilot" bolt holes in manifold, as explained below.

3) Position left exhaust manifold and gasket on cylinder head and install a bolt in manifold pilot hole (lower front bolt hole of center manifold tube). Install remaining manifold bolts and tighten manifold.

4) Position right exhaust manifold, gasket, and inner half of heat shroud on cylinder head. Start 1 bolt in manifold pilot hole (lower rear bolt hole of center manifold tube) and 1 bolt in another hole. Install remaining bolts and tighten manifold.

5) To complete installation, install remaining components in reverse order of removal procedures. Start engine and check for exhaust leaks.

CYLINDER HEAD

Removal

1) Drain cooling system. Disconnect battery cable at negative battery post. Loosen accessory drive belt idler and remove drive belt.

2) To remove left cylinder head, remove and position power steering pump aside. Remove oil fill cap. If A/C equipped, remove and position compressor aside.

3) To remove right cylinder head, remove diverter valve and hose assembly at by-pass valve and downstream air tube. Remove accessory drive idler. Remove air pump pulley and pump.

4) Remove alternator and bracket. Remove intake manifold. Remove rocker arm cover attaching bolts.

5) Carefully break silicone seal between cover and head, by inserting a putty knife under cover flange and working cover loose. Remove rocker arm covers.

6) Remove exhaust manifolds. Loosen rocker arm bolts and position rockers to one side.

7) Identify push rods for reinstallation in original locations, and remove. Remove cylinder heads and discard bolts.

CAUTION: Use new head bolts to preclude compression leaks or coolant loss at cylinder head mating surface. Torque retention can vary with used head bolts, causing leaks.

Installation

1) Clean all gasket surfaces. Using dowel pins as guides, place head gaskets and cylinder heads on cylinder block.

2) Apply a thin coat of pipe thread sealer to threads of short head bolts. Coat head bolt flat washers with oil and install bolts and washers.

3) Tighten cylinder head bolts in 4 steps. Back off head bolts 2 to 3 turns, then retighten head bolts using 4-step procedure. *See Fig. 3.*

4) Coat all push rods with heavy engine oil and install in their original locations.

5) Make sure lifter is on low base circle of camshaft lobe prior to installing and tightening rocker arms. Install and tighten rocker arm assemblies one at a time.

CAUTION: Fulcrums must be fully seated in cylinder head and push rods seated in rocker arm sockets, prior to final tightening of rocker arm assemblies.

6) Install exhaust manifolds. Apply 1/8 - 3/16" bead of sealer to rocker arm cover flange. Make sure sealer fills the channel in cover flange.

7) Install and tighten rocker arm covers within 15 minutes of sealer application. Reverse removal procedure to complete installation.

NOTE: After using 4-step method of tightening head bolts twice, it is not necessary to retighten head bolts after extended engine operation.

Fig. 3: Cylinder Head Tightening Sequence

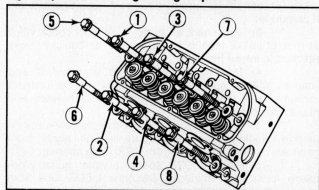

Use 4-step method to tighten head bolts twice.

VALVES

VALVE ARRANGEMENT

E-I-E-I-E-I (Left bank, front to rear)
I-E-I-E-I-E (Right bank, front to rear)

ROCKER ARM ASSEMBLY

1) Inspect all rocker arm components for excessive wear or damage, and replace as necessary.

2) Before installing rocker arm assembly, lubricate end of each push rod with heavy engine oil.

3) Make sure lifter rests on base circle of camshaft lobe (lifter at lowest travel) when installing rocker arm assemblies.

4) Ensure fulcrums are seated in cylinder head, and push rods are seated in rocker arm sockets prior to final tightening of rocker arms.

5) After installing rocker arms, lubricate top of valve stem, fulcrum seat and socket area of rocker arm with heavy engine oil.

Ford V6 Engines

3.8 LITER V6 (Cont.)

VALVE SPRINGS

Removal

1) Remove cylinder head. Identify all valve parts for reinstallation in original locations. Remove rocker arm assemblies, spark plugs and exhaust manifolds.

2) Using valve spring compressor, compress valve spring and remove retainer locks. Release spring compressor and remove spring retainer, spring and seal.

Inspection

1) Inspect valve stem for wear and out-of-round condition. Check valve for binding in valve guide.

2) Using valve spring tester, check springs for proper pressure. Replace springs that fail specifications.

3) Inspect each spring for squareness, using a steel square and flat surface. Measure gap between top of spring coil and square, while slowly rotating spring.

4) If valve spring is more than 5/64" (1.98 mm) out-of-square, replace it.

Installation

1) Lubricate valve stem with heavy engine oil and install valve stem oil seal. Install spring seat (if removed), spring and retainer.

2) Compress spring and install retainer locks. Apply polyethelene grease (or equivalent) to valve stem tips and install remaining components.

VALVE SPRING INSTALLED HEIGHT

CAUTION: Install spacers only if necessary. Excess use of spacers will overstress the valve train and cause unnecessary damage.

1) Measure spring height from top of spring seat to underside of spring retainer, using dividers and a ruler. See Fig. 4.

2) If height is greater than specified, install .030" (.076 mm) spacer(s) between cylinder head spring pad and spring, to bring height within limits.

Fig. 4: Checking Valve Spring Installed Height

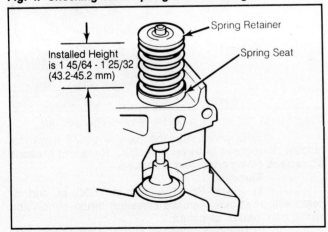

Installed Height is 1 45/64 - 1 25/32 (43.2-45.2 mm)

Spring Retainer

Spring Seat

Measure from top of spring seat to underside of spring retainer.

VALVE SPRING INSTALLED HEIGHT SPECIFICATIONS

Application	Specification In. (mm)
All	1 45/64 - 1 25/32 (43.2-45.2)

VALVE STEM OIL SEALS

Cup-type oil seals are used on all valves. Lubricate valve stem with heavy engine oil and install new valve stem seal with cup side down. Use a 5/8" deep-well socket and light mallet to seat oil seal on valve stem.

VALVE GUIDE SERVICING

1) When reaming valve guides, always use reamers in proper sequence. Reface valves and seats after reaming operation.

2) Use a scraper to break sharp corner at top (ID) of valve guide bore, after reaming. Replacement valves are available with standard, .015" (.38 mm) and .030" (.76 mm) oversize stems.

HYDRAULIC VALVE LIFTERS

1) Service lifters as complete assemblies only. Do not interchange parts. Disassemble and clean lifters. See Fig. 5. Reassemble lifters and test with hydraulic lifter test fluid and a lifter leak-down tester.

Fig. 5: Hydraulic Lifter Assembly

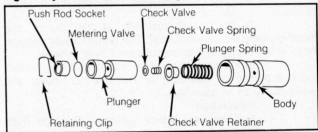

Push Rod Socket — Metering Valve — Check Valve — Check Valve Spring — Plunger Spring — Plunger — Body — Retaining Clip — Check Valve Retainer

Parts are not interchangeable between lifters.

2) Leak-down rate on hydraulic lifters is 20-200 seconds for plunger to leak down 1/8" (3.18 mm), under a 50 lb. (23 kg) load.

VALVE CLEARANCE ADJUSTMENT

1) Turn crankshaft to place No. 1 piston on TDC at end of compression stroke. Check clearances of valves listed in Valve Clearance Adjustment table, using the following procedure:

2) Using lifter bleed-down tool, slowly apply pressure to push rod end of rocker arm to bleed down lifter, until lifter plunger is completely bottomed.

3) While holding lifter in this position, use a feeler gauge to measure clearance between rocker arm tip of valve stem.

4) Desired collapsed lifter clearance is .088-.189" (2.24-4.80 mm). If clearance is too small, install a shorter push rod; if clearance is excessive, install a longer push rod.

5) To check clearance of remaining valves, rotate crankshaft 360° to place No. 5 piston on TDC at end of compression stroke. With crankshaft in this position, check clearance of valves listed in table.

VALVE CLEARANCE ADJUSTMENT

Piston On TDC	Check Int. Nos.	Check Ex. Nos.
No. 1	1-3-6	1-3-4
No. 5	2-4-5	3-5-6

Ford V6 Engines

3.8 LITER V6 (Cont.)

CAMSHAFT

ENGINE FRONT COVER

Removal

1) Drain cooling system and disconnect negative battery cable. Remove air cleaner assembly and intake duct.

2) Remove fan shroud and fan clutch assembly attaching bolts and remove components. Loosen accessory drive belt idler and remove drive belt and water pump pulley.

3) If equipped, remove power steering pump and position to one side (leaving hoses connected). If A/C equipped, remove air compressor front support bracket.

4) Disconnect by-pass and heater hoses at water pump. Disconnect upper radiator hose at thermostat housing.

5) Disconnect coil wire from distributor cap and remove cap with secondary wires attached. Remove distributor.

6) If equipped with tripminder, remove fuel flow meter support bracket. Raise vehicle. Remove crankshaft pulley and vibration damper. Remove fuel pump crash shield.

7) Disconnect fuel line at fuel pump, and remove pump. Remove oil filter. Disconnect lower radiator hose at water pump. Remove oil pan. Lower vehicle.

8) Remove front cover attaching bolts, including bolt behind oil filter adapter. Remove front cover and water pump as an assembly.

Installation

1) Clean all gasket surfaces. Replace front cover oil seal and lubricate with engine oil. Apply gasket sealer to front cover gasket and position on cylinder block.

2) Install and tighten front cover and water pump assembly. Coat threads of bolt No. 10 with pipe thread sealer. *See Fig. 6.* Reverse removal procedure to complete installation.

Fig. 6: Front Cover Attaching Bolt Locations

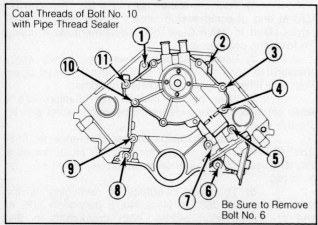

Coat Threads of Bolt No. 10 with Pipe Thread Sealer

Be Sure to Remove Bolt No. 6

Tighten front cover bolts to 15-22 ft. lbs. (20-30 N.m)

FRONT COVER OIL SEAL

NOTE: If seal installing tool (T82L-6316-A) and adapter (T70P-6B070-A) are available, new oil seal may be installed without removing front cover. If tools not available, front cover will have to be removed.

Removal

Remove front cover from engine. Using screwdriver, carefully pry oil seal from front cover.

Installation

Lubricate new oil seal with engine oil. Using a seal installer, drive oil seal into front cover recess. Reverse removal procedure to complete installation.

TIMING CHAIN & SPROCKET

NOTE: The following procedures are performed with engine front cover removed.

Checking Timing Chain Deflection

1) Turn crankshaft clockwise (as viewed from front of engine) until No. 1 piston on TDC at end of compression stroke.

2) Remove right rocker arm cover. Loosen No. 3 exhaust rocker arm and rotate to one side.

3) Install dial indicator, with indicator point on end of push rod, and in same plane as push rod movement. *See Fig. 7.*

4) Zero the dial indicator. Slowly turn crankshaft counterclockwise, until slightest movement is seen on dial indicator needle, then stop.

Fig. 7: Dial Indicator Installation For Checking Timing Chain Deflection & Cam Lobe Lift

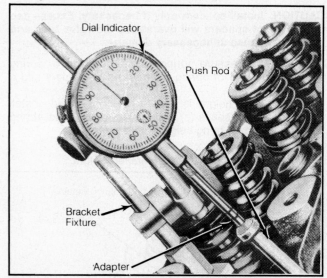

Dial Indicator

Push Rod

Bracket Fixture

Adapter

Ensure push rod end is in center of valve lifter socket.

5) Observe vibration damper timing mark, for number of degrees of travel from TDC. If reading exceeds 6°, replace timing chain and sprockets.

Removal

1) Place No. 1 piston on TDC at end of compression stroke. Remove camshaft thrust button and spring from end of camshaft.

2) Remove camshaft sprocket attaching bolts. Remove camshaft sprocket, crankshaft sprocket and timing chain.

Installation

1) Lubricate timing chain with engine oil and position chain on sprockets. Align timing marks and slide both sprockets and timing chain onto engine. *See Fig. 8.*

2) Install and tighten camshaft sprocket attaching bolts. Lubricate thrust button with polyethelene grease (or equivalent). Install button and spring into camshaft.

Ford V6 Engines

3.8 LITER V6 (Cont.)

3) Ensure the thrust button and spring are bottomed out in the camshaft recess. They must not be allowed to fall out during front cover installation.

Fig. 8: Aligning Sprocket Timing Marks

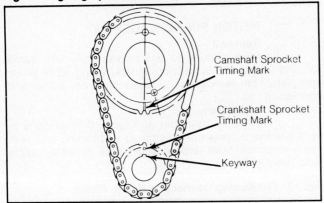

Tighten camshaft sprocket attaching bolts to 15-22 ft. lbs. (20-30 N.m).

CAMSHAFT
Removal
1) Drain cooling system and crankcase. Remove radiator. If A/C equipped, remove condenser. Remove grille. Remove intake manifold.

2) Identify rocker arm assemblies, push rods and valve lifters for reinstallation in original locations, then remove these components.

3) Remove front cover and water pump as an assembly. Remove camshaft thrust button, spring and timing chain and sprocket.

4) Remove oil pan. Remove camshaft through front of engine, using care not to damage camshaft lobes or bearings. *See Fig. 9.*

Fig. 9: Camshaft Assembly

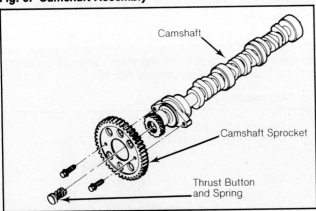

Camshaft bearings are not interchangeable between bores.

Installation
Lubricate cam lobes and bearings with heavy engine oil. Carefully install camshaft into position. Reverse removal procedure to complete installation.

CAMSHAFT END THRUST
The 3.8L V6 engine does not use a thrust plate, thereby eliminating camshaft end play. Camshaft is restrained by a spring-loaded thrust button.

CAM LOBE LIFT
1) Remove rocker arm cover, fulcrum bolt, fulcrum seat, rocker arm and fulcrum guide. Make sure push rod end is in valve lifter socket.

2) Use a dial indicator to check lobe lift in consecutive order. Position dial indicator point (or cup-shaped adapter) on end of push rod (in same plane as push rod movement). *See Fig. 7.*

3) Turn crankshaft until lifter and push rod are at lowest position. Zero dial indicator.

4) Rotate crankshaft slowly until push rod is in fully raised position. Record dial indicator reading and compare with specifications.

5) Maximum allowable lift loss is .005" (.13 mm). If lift on any lobe is below specifications, replace camshaft and valve lifter operating on worn lobe(s).

CAMSHAFT BEARINGS
Removal
1) Remove engine from vehicle. Remove flywheel and rear cover plate. Remove camshaft and rear bearing bore plug.

2) Remove crankshaft and push pistons to top of cylinder bores. Using camshaft bearing remover/installer tool, remove camshaft bearings.

Installation
1) Camshaft bearings are available in standard and .015 (.38 mm) undersize. The bearings are not interchangeable between bores.

2) Using camshaft bearing remover/installer tool, press bearings into place. Ensure that oil holes in bearings are aligned with oil holes in cylinder block.

3) Install front bearing .136-.146" (3.455-3.705 mm) below front face of cylinder block. Reverse removal procedure to complete installation.

PISTONS, RINGS & PINS

OIL PAN
See Oil Pan Removal at end of ENGINE Section.

PISTON & ROD ASSEMBLY
Removal
1) Remove intake manifold, cylinder heads and oil pan. Turn crankshaft until piston to be removed is at bottom of stroke.

2) Cover piston with cloth to collect metal cuttings. Using ridge reamer, remove ridge at top of cylinder bore.

CAUTION: Never cut more than 1/32" (.79 mm) into ring travel area when removing ridge.

3) Ensure connecting rods and caps are marked for cylinder identification. Place piston to be removed at bottom of its stroke.

4) Remove rod cap and cover rod studs with rubber hose to avoid damage to crankshaft and cylinder walls.

5) Push piston and rod assembly out top of cylinder block. Install rod cap on mating rod.

Installation
1) Coat piston, rings and cylinder wall with heavy engine oil. Ensure that ring gaps are properly spaced on piston. *See Fig. 10.*

3.8 LITER V6 (Cont.)

2) Install ring compressor, ensuring position of rings does not change. Position piston in cylinder with notch on piston head toward front of engine.

3) Tap piston into cylinder bore using a wooden hammer handle. Guide connecting rod onto crankshaft journal Install and tighten rod cap. Check rod side clearance.

Fig. 10: Correctly Spaced Piston Ring Gaps

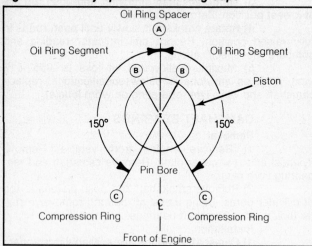

Ensure ring gaps do not change when installing ring compressor.

FITTING PISTONS

NOTE: Take measurements at normal room temperature (70°F, 21°C).

1) Measure piston skirt 90° to piston pin axis. Measure cylinder bore 90° to crankshaft centerline, at top, middle and bottom of bore. Use measurements to determine piston-to-cylinder bore clearance.

2) Measure bore 90° to crankshaft centerline at top (below ring travel) and at bottom (above ring travel). Taper is the difference between the 2 measurements, and must not exceed .010" (.25 mm).

3) Measure cylinder bore at center of piston travel as follows: Take one measurement 90° to crankshaft centerline, and another in line with crankshaft centerline. Difference between the 2 measurements is out-of-round, and must not exceed .005" (.13 mm).

4) If taper or out-of-round are not within limits, or cylinder walls are deeply scored, hone or bore cylinders for installation of new pistons. Check Piston Size Code Chart.

PISTON SIZE CODE CHART

Size Code	Size In. (mm)
Red	3.8095-3.8101 (96.761-96.777)
Blue	3.8107-3.8113 (96.792-96.807)
.004" Oversize	3.8119-3.8125 (96.822-96.838)

FITTING RINGS

1) Position ring squarely in cylinder bore at a point where normal ring wear is not present. Use care not to damage ring or cylinder bore. Check ring end gap with a feeler gauge.

2) Using a feeler gauge, check side clearance of compression rings. Measure clearance between ring and its lower land.

3) If feeler gauge does not slide freely around entire circumference of piston, or if lower lands have high steps, replace piston.

PISTON PIN REPLACEMENT
Removal
Mark pistons to ensure assembly with same rod and installation in same cylinders. Using arbor press and piston pin remover tool, press pin from piston and connecting rod.

Installation
1) Apply light coat of engine oil to all parts to be assembled. Assemble piston to connecting rod with notch in piston head and oil squirt hole in rod on same side. *See Fig. 11.*

Fig. 11: Positioning Connecting Rod to Piston

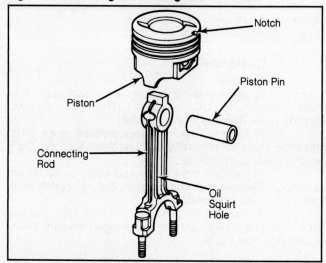

Assemble with oil squirt hole in rod and notch in piston head on same side.

2) Light tap with mallet may be needed to start pin into piston and rod assembly. Using arbor press and pin installing tool, press pin into piston and rod assembly until pin is centered in piston. *See Fig. 12.*

Fig. 12: Installing Piston Pin

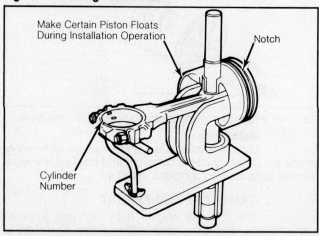

Lightly oil parts prior to assembly.

3.8 LITER V6 (Cont.)

CRANKSHAFT, MAIN & CONNECTING ROD BEARINGS

MAIN & CONNECTING ROD BEARINGS

NOTE: Use Plastigage method for checking bearing clearances. Following procedures are performed with oil pan and oil pump removed, and oil film removed from surfaces to be checked.

Crankshaft Main Bearings

1) Fit main bearings one at a time, while leaving other bearings securely fastened. Make sure main bearing caps are marked for identification.

2) Remove main bearing cap. Support crankshaft weight by placing a jack beneath the counterweight adjacent to the bearing being checked.

3) Use Plastigage method (as explained in Connecting Rod Bearings) to measure main bearing clearance, tightening main cap to specification.

4) Standard size bearings may be used in combination with a .001" (.025 mm) or .002" (.051 mm) undersize bearing.

5) If .002" (.051 mm) undersize main bearings are used on more than one journal, bearings must be installed in cylinder block side of crankshaft.

6) Replace main bearing sets one at a time, while leaving other bearings securely fastened. Remove bearing cap to which new bearings are to be installed.

7) Insert upper bearing remover/installer tool (6331 or equivalent) into crankshaft journal oil hole.

8) With tool in place, turn crankshaft in normal direction of rotation to push upper bearing out of block.

9) Lightly oil new bearing and crankshaft journal. Partially install plain end of upper bearing in place. Insert tool (6331 or equivalent) into journal oil hole.

10) Slowly turn crankshaft in opposite direction of normal rotation, until bearing seats in cylinder block. Remove tool. Install and tighten main bearing cap.

11) To install rear main bearing cap, clean bearing cap-to-block mating surfaces. Apply 1/8" bead silicone sealer to bearing cap-to-cylinder block parting line. See Fig. 14.

12) Install and tighten rear main bearing cap within 15 minutes of sealer application.

Connecting Rod Bearings

1) Ensure rod caps are marked for cylinder identification. Place crankshaft journal of cylinder to be checked at bottom of stroke. Remove rod cap.

2) Place strip of Plastigage on bearing surface over full width of cap about 1/4" (6 mm) off center, and away from oil holes. Install cap and tighten to specification. Do not allow crankshaft to turn.

3) Remove cap and measure compressed width of Plastigage. A standard bearing may be used with a .001" (.025 mm) or .002" (.051 mm) undersize bearing to obtain proper bearing clearance.

THRUST BEARING ALIGNMENT

1) Install thrust bearing cap after all other main bearing caps have been tightened. Install thrust bearing cap bolts finger tight.

2) Pry crankshaft forward against thrust surface of upper half of bearing. Hold crankshaft forward, and pry thrust bearing cap to rear. Tighten cap bolts, while retaining forward pressure on crankshaft.

REAR MAIN BEARING OIL SEAL

NOTE: Starting with engine build date January 1, 1983, a new one-piece rear main bearing oil seal has replaced the split-lip type seal.

Removal (Split-Lip Seal)

1) Remove oil pan. Loosen main bearing cap attaching bolts to allow crankshaft to drop slightly, but not more than 1/32" (.79 mm). Remove main bearing cap and remove seal from cap.

2) Use a seal remover tool to remove upper seal. If tool not available, install a small sheet metal screw in one end of seal and pull on screw to remove seal.

CAUTION: Avoid shaving any rubber from outside diameter of seal when installing seal in block.

Installation

1) Install seals with undercut side toward front of engine, and locating tabs facing rear of engine. After installing seals, be sure to remove tabs.

2) Carefully clean oil seal grooves in bearing cap and block. Dip split-lip seal halves in engine oil.

3) Rotate upper seal on crankshaft journal until approximately 3/8" (9.5 mm) of seal protrudes below parting surface. See Fig. 13.

Fig. 13: Installing Rear Main Bearing Oil Seal

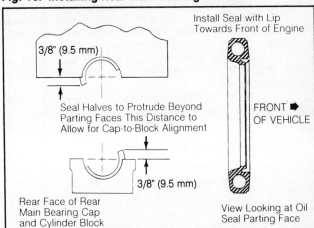

Install seals with locating tabs facing rear of engine, then remove tabs.

4) Tighten all other bearing cap bolts. Install lower seal in main bearing cap. See Fig. 13. Allow seal to protrude approximately 3/8" (9.5 mm) above parting surface.

5) Apply 1/16" bead of silicone sealer to both sides of cylinder block-to-cap mating surface, and to both sides of bearing cap. See Fig. 14.

6) Install and tighten rear main bearing cap before sealer sets up (approximately 15 minutes). Install oil pan.

Removal (One-Piece Seal)

1) Remove transmission. If equipped, remove clutch cover and clutch disc. Remove flywheel.

2) Using a sharp awl, punch a hole in the seal metal surface between the lip and cylinder block.

Ford V6 Engines

3.8 LITER V6 (Cont.)

Fig. 14: Silicone Sealer Application Points

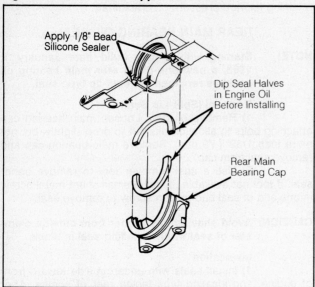

Apply 1/8" Bead Silicone Sealer

Dip Seal Halves in Engine Oil Before Installing

Rear Main Bearing Cap

Do not allow sealer to contact lip of seal.

3) Screw the threaded end of slide hammer tool (T77L-9533-B or equivalent) into hole and extract seal. Use care not to damage crankshaft.

Installation

1) Lubricate seal lip and crankshaft with engine oil. Position seal on seal installing tool (T82L-6701-A or equivalent) with spring side of seal toward engine.

2) Position seal and installing tool in place. Start the 2 bolts of seal installing tool into crankshaft. Alternately tighten each bolt to properly seat the seal.

3) Note that rear face of the seal must be within .005" (.13 mm) of the rear face of the cylinder block after installation.

4) To complete installation, install remaining components in reverse order of removal procedures.

ENGINE OILING

Crankcase Capacity

Capacity is 5 quarts (4.75L). Add 1 quart (.95L) when replacing oil filter.

Oil Filter

Full-flow filter has an integral by-pass valve. Replace filter at first oil change, then every second oil change thereafter.

Normal Oil Pressure

54-59 psi (3.8-4.1 kg/cm²) at 2500 RPM.

Oil Pressure Regulator Valve

Valve located in pump body, not adjustable.

ENGINE OILING SYSTEM

Engine lubrication system is a force-feed type. A rotary gear type pump supplies oil under full pressure to crankshaft, connecting rods, valve lifters and camshaft.

From lifters, a controlled flow of oil is supplied to rocker arms through hollow push rods. All other moving parts are lubricated by gravity flow or splash method. Oil pump shaft is driven by distributor shaft, through an intermediate shaft.

OIL PUMP

Removal & Disassembly

1) Remove engine front cover. With oil filter removed, remove pump cover. Lift pump gears out of front cover pocket. *See Fig. 15.*

Fig. 15: Oil Pump Assembly

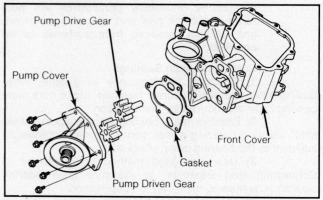

Pump Drive Gear

Pump Cover

Pump Driven Gear

Gasket

Front Cover

Prior to installing pump cover, pack pump gears and gear pocket with petroleum jelly.

2) Drill small hole in relief valve plug. Insert self-threading screw into plug, to aid in prying plug from chamber. Remove spring and valve from valve body.

Fig. 16: Relief Valve Location

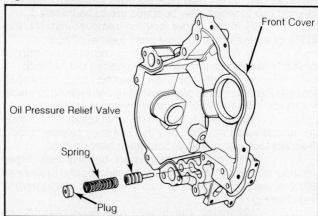

Front Cover

Oil Pressure Relief Valve

Spring

Plug

Install new relief valve plug flush with machined surface of front cover.

Inspection

1) Clean gasket material from pump cover and front cover mating surface. Remove burrs or nicks from front cover mating surface.

2) Install gears in front cover. Place straightedge across gears and gasket surface of front cover. Insert feeler gauge between straightedge and front cover gasket surface to determine gear end clearance.

3) If end clearance is below specifications, measure gear thickness with micrometer. If gear thickness is below limits, replace gear and recheck end clearance.

4) If gear thickness is within limits, measure gear pocket depth in front cover. If depth is more than specification, replace front cover.

5) Measure oil pump gear side clearance by inserting feeler gauge between a gear tooth and side wall of gear pocket. If not within limits, measure gear diameter.

3.8 LITER V6 (Cont.)

6) If gear diameter measures less than specifications, replace gear and recheck side clearance. If diameter is within limits, measure gear pocket width. If less than specifications, replace front cover.

7) Check pump cover flatness, using a feeler gauge and straightedge. If clearance exceeds specifications, replace cover.

8) Clean relief valve and bore. Inspect valve and bore for scoring or wear. Replace valve and/or cover if unserviceable.

9) Check relief valve-to-bore clearance. No side play or binding should be apparent. Check spring for fatigued or collapsed condition.

10) Test tension of relief valve spring. Relief valve spring should test to 15.2-17.1 lbs. (6.9-7.8 kg) at 1.20" (30.5 mm).

OIL PUMP SPECIFICATIONS

Application	Specification In. (mm)
Gear End Clearance	.002-.005 (.05-.13)
Gear Thickness	.872-.873 (22.15-22.17)
Gear Pocket Depth	.868-.870 (22.05-22.10)
Gear Side Clearance	.002-.005 (.05-.13)
Gear Diameter	1.664-1.666 (42.27-42.32)
Gear Pocket Width	1.671-1.674 (42.44-42.52)
Pump Cover Flatness	.004 (.10) Max.
Relief Valve-to-Bore Clearance	.0017-.0029 (.043-.074)

CAUTION: Failure to properly pack oil pump gears with petroleum jelly may result in pump failure.

Reassembly & Installation

1) Lubricate relief valve with engine oil and install in bore. Position spring in bore and install new plug.

2) Pack gear pocket in front cover with petroleum jelly. DO NOT use chassis lubricant.

3) Install gears in cover pocket, making sure petroleum jelly fills all air pockets between gears and gear pocket.

4) Position cover gasket and install and tighten pump cover. Install remaining components in reverse order of removal.

ENGINE COOLING

WATER PUMP

Removal

1) Drain cooling system. Remove air cleaner and intake duct. Remove fan shroud and fan clutch assembly.

2) Loosen accessory drive belt idler, and remove drive belt and water pump pulley. If equipped with power steering, remove pump mounting bracket bolts and position pump aside.

3) If equipped with A/C, remove compressor front support bracket and leave compressor in place. If equippped with tripminder, remove fuel flow meter support bracket.

4) Disconnect by-pass hose and heater hose at water pump. Remove water pump and discard gasket.

Installation

1) Clean all gasket surfaces. Apply gasket sealer to new gasket, and position gasket on water pump.

2) Position water pump on front cover and install attaching bolts. Coat threads of No. 10 bolt with pipe thread sealer. *See Fig. 6.*

3) To complete installation, install remaining components in reverse order of removal procedures.

NOTE: For information on cooling system capacities and other cooling system components, see appropriate article in "Engine Cooling Systems," at end of ENGINE Section.

TIGHTENING SPECIFICATIONS

Application	Ft. Lbs. (N.m)
Camshaft Sprocket	15-22 (20-30)
Connecting Rod Cap	31-36 (42-49)
Cylinder Head	
Step 1	47 (64)
Step 2	55 (75)
Step 3	63 (86)
Step 4	74 (101)
Step 5	Back off 2-3 turns
Step 6	Repeat steps 1-4
Engine Front Cover	15-22 (20-30)
Exhaust Manifold	15-22 (20-30)
Flywheel-to-Crankshaft	54-64 (73-87)
Intake Manifold	
Step 1	5 (7)
Step 2	10 (14)
Step 3	18 (24)
Main Bearing Cap	65-81 (88-110)
Oil Pump Cover	18-22 (24-30)
Rocker Arm Fulcrum	
Step 1	5-11 (7-15)
Step 2	18-26 (24-35)
Vibration Damper	93-121 (126-165)

ENGINE SPECIFICATIONS

GENERAL SPECIFICATIONS

Year	Displacement		Fuel System	HP@RPM	Torque Ft. Lbs.@RPM	Compr. Ratio	Bore		Stroke	
	Cu. In.	Liters					In.	mm	In.	mm
1983	232	3.8	2-Bbl.	.....	.....	.....	3.81	96.8	3.39	86.1

Ford V6 Engines

3.8 LITER V6 (Cont.)

ENGINE SPECIFICATIONS (Cont.)

PISTONS, PINS, RINGS

| Engine | PISTONS | PINS | | RINGS | | |
	Clearance In. (mm)	Piston Fit In. (mm)	Rod Fit In. (mm)	Ring No.	End Gap In. (mm)	Side Clearance In. (mm)
3.8L	.0014-.0022 (.035-.055)	.0002-.0005 (.005-.012)	Press Fit	1 & 2	.010-.020 (.25-.50)	.0016-.0037 (.040-.094)
				3	.015-.058 (.38-1.48)	.....

CRANKSHAFT MAIN & CONNECTING ROD BEARINGS

| Engine | MAIN BEARINGS | | | | CONNECTING ROD BEARINGS | | |
	Journal Diam. In. (mm)	Clearance In. (mm)	Thrust Bearing	Crankshaft End Play In. (mm)	Journal Diam. In. (mm)	Clearance In. (mm)	Side Play In. (mm)
3.8L	2.5190-2.5198 (63.983-64.003)	.0010-.0014 (.025-.036)	No. 3	.004-.008 (.10-.20)	2.3103-2.3111 (58.682-58.702)	.0010-.0014 (.025-.036)	.0047-.0114 (.119-.290)

VALVES

Engine Size & Valve	Head Diam. In. (mm)	Face Angle	Seat Angle	Seat Width In. (mm)	Stem Diameter In. (mm)	Stem Clearance In. (mm)	Valve Lift In. (mm)
3.8L Int.	1.79 (45.5)	44°	45°	.06-.08 (1.5-2.0)	.3416-.3423 (8.677-8.694)	.0010-.0027 (.025-.069)	.415 (10.54)
Exh.	1.47 (37.3)	44°	45°	.06-.08 (1.5-2.0)	.3411-.3418 (8.664-8.682)	.0015-.0032 (.038-.081)	.417 (10.59)

CAMSHAFT

Engine	Journal In. (mm)	Clearance In. (mm)	Lobe Lift In. (mm)
3.8L	2.0505-2.0515 (52.082-52.108)	.001-.003 (.03-.08)	.240 [1] (6.10) .241 [2] (6.12)

[1] — Intake lobes.
[2] — Exhaust lobes.

VALVE SPRINGS

| Engine | Free Length In. (mm) | PRESSURE Lbs. @ In. (Kg @ mm) | |
		Valve Closed	Valve Open
3.8L	.....	75@1.70 (34@35.5)	215@1.40 (98@35.5)

4.9 LITER 6-CYLINDER

ENGINE CODING

ENGINE IDENTIFICATION

Engine is identified by a letter code in eighth position of Vehicle Identification Number (VIN). The VIN is visible through windshield on left upper side of instrument panel. The VIN is also located on the Safety Compliance Certification Label, attached to left door lock pillar.

ENGINE IDENTIFICATION CODE

Engine	Code
4.9L 1-Bbl.	Y

ENGINE REMOVAL

See Engine Removal at end of ENGINE Section.

MANIFOLDS & CYLINDER HEAD

MANIFOLD ASSEMBLY

Removal

1) Remove air cleaner. Disconnect accelerator cable or rod at carburetor. Remove accelerator retracting spring.

2) Remove kickdown rod retracting spring (vehicles with automatic transmission). Remove accelerator rod bellcrank assembly.

3) Label and disconnect all vacuum lines at carburetor. Disconnect fuel inlet line at carburetor. Disconnect muffler inlet pipe from exhaust manifold.

4) Disconnect power brake vacuum line (if equipped). Remove crankcase vent hose from intake manifold.

5) Remove manifolds from cylinder head. Separate manifolds by removing nuts securing manifolds together. Discard all gaskets.

Installation

1) Clean mating surfaces of cylinder head and manifolds. If one of the manifolds is to be replaced, transfer tube fittings and install new studs.

2) Lightly coat intake and exhaust manifold mating surfaces with graphite grease. Using new gasket, position exhaust manifold over studs of intake manifold.

3) Install lock washers, and tighten nuts finger tight. Coat manifold assembly and cylinder head mating surfaces lightly with graphite grease.

4) Using new gasket, install and tighten intake manifold. Ensure gaskets have not become dislodged. Tighten nuts securing manifolds together. *See Fig. 1.*

5) Using new gaskets as required, install remaining components in reverse order of removal. Make necessary linkage and carburetor adjustments.

CYLINDER HEAD

CAUTION: Do not pry between cylinder head and block when detaching head assembly, as gasket surface may be damaged.

Removal

1) Drain cooling system and remove air cleaner. Remove PCV valve and carburetor fuel inlet line. Disconnect vent hose at intake manifold. Label and remove all vacuum lines at carburetor.

2) Remove accelerator cable retracting spring and disconnect accelerator cable from carburetor. On vehicles with automatic transmission, disconnect kickdown rod at carburetor.

3) Disconnect upper radiator hose and heater hose at coolant outlet elbow. Remove coil bracket retaining bolt, and position coil to one side.

4) Disconnect muffler inlet pipe from exhaust manifold. Remove rocker arm cover. Loosen rocker arm stud nuts, and rotate rocker arms to one side.

5) Identify push rods for reinstallation in original locations, and remove. Disconnect spark plug wires at spark plugs.

6) Remove cylinder head bolts and attach lifting eyes to cylinder head. Using an engine hoist and lifting sling, raise cylinder head and manifold assembly from engine.

Installation

1) Clean all gasket mating surfaces. Check flatness of block and head gasket surfaces. Position new gasket over dowel pins on cylinder block.

2) Install lifting eyes on cylinder head (in previous locations used to detach head assembly). Using lifting device, position cylinder head over block.

3) Carefully lower head assembly onto block, ensuring dowel pins properly engage in head. Remove hoist and lifting eyes.

4) Coat threads of head bolts with engine oil, and install. Tighten head bolts in 3 steps. *See Fig. 2.*

5) Lubricate push rod ends, rocker arm fulcrum seats and sockets with polyethylene grease or equivalent, then install. Reverse removal procedure to install remaining components.

Fig. 1: Intake & Exhaust Manifold Tightening Sequence

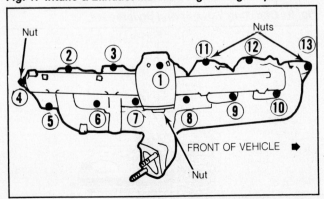

Tighten to 22-32 ft. lbs. (30-43 N.m).

Fig. 2: Cylinder Head Tightening Sequence

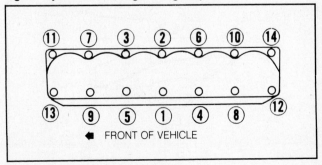

Tighten to specification in 3 steps.

Ford 6 Engines

4.9 LITER 6-CYLINDER (Cont.)

VALVES

VALVE ARRANGEMENT

E-I-E-I-E-I-E-I-E-I (Front-to-rear)

ROCKER ARM STUDS

Removal

1) Use stud removing tool (T79T-6527-A or equivalent) to remove defective studs. Follow tool manufacturer's instructions. *See Fig. 3.*

2) Use screw extractor to remove a stud that is broken off flush with stud boss. *See Fig. 3.*

Fig. 3: Removing Rocker Arm Stud

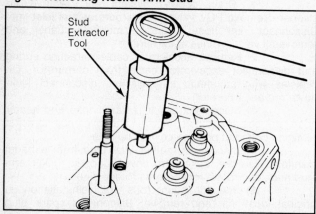

Follow tool manufacturer's instructions.

CAUTION: **Make sure metal particles from reaming process do not enter valve area.**

Installation

1) Replacement studs may be pressed into head, using stud replacement tool (T79T-6527-B or equivalent). Apply polyethylene grease or equivalent to end of stud.

2) Align stud and replacement tool over stud bore. Tap sliding driver until it bottoms. When driver contacts stud boss, stud is installed at proper height.

3) Correct rocker arm stud bore diameter is .3685-.3695" (9.360-9.385 mm). If not within limits, ream stud bore to correct oversize.

4) Studs are available in oversizes of .006" (.152 mm), .010" (.254 mm), and .015" (.381 mm).

Fig. 4: Rocker Arm Assembly

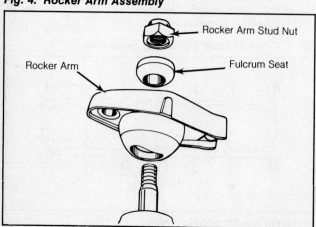

VALVE SPRINGS

Removal

1) Remove air cleaner. Remove accelerator cable retracting spring and disconnect accelerator cable at carburetor. Remove PCV valve from rocker arm cover, and remove rocker arm cover.

2) Remove spark plug from cylinder to be serviced. Crank engine to position piston at TDC after compression stroke.

3) Install an air hose and adapter to spark plug hole and apply air pressure. DO NOT remove air pressure until all valve components are reinstalled.

4) Remove rocker arm stud nut, fulcrum seat, rocker arm, and push rod. Reinstall stud nut. Using spring compressor tool, compress spring and remove retainer locks. Remove spring retainer, spring and oil seal.

Fig. 5: Valve Assembly for 4.9L Engine

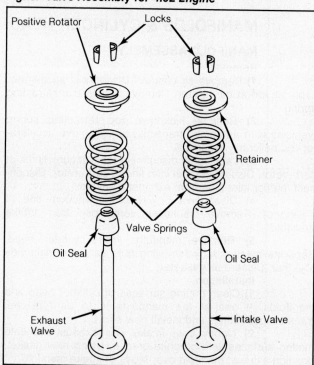

Install springs with closed coil end downward.

Inspection

1) Inspect valve stem for wear and binding in valve guide. Using a valve spring tester, check valve

Fig. 6: Checking Valve Spring Squareness

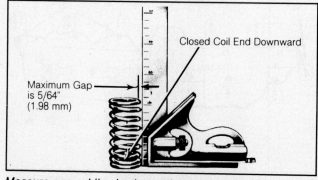

Measure gap, while slowly rotating spring.

4.9 LITER 6-CYLINDER (Cont.)

spring tension. Replace springs that fail to meet specifications.

2) Using a steel square and flat surface, measure gap between top of coil of spring and square, while slowly rotating spring. Replace spring if more than 5/64" (1.98 mm) out-of-square. *See Fig. 6.*

Installation

1) Lubricate valve stem with heavy engine oil. Install new valve stem oil seal. Install spring with closed coil end downward. Install spring retainer, and compress spring to install retainer locks.

2) Apply polyethylene grease or equivalent to both ends of push rod, top of valve stem, and fulcrum seat and socket.

3) Install push rod, rocker arm, fulcrum seat and stud nut. Adjust valve clearance as explained in Valve Clearance Adjustment.

4) Remove air hose and adapter. Install spark plug. Reverse removal procedure to install remaining components.

VALVE SPRING INSTALLED HEIGHT

CAUTION: Do not install spacers, unless necessary to meet specifications. Excessive use of spacers will overstress the valve train, causing unnecessary damage.

1) Using dividers and a scale, measure assembled height of valve spring from surface of cylinder head spring pad to underside of spring retainer. *See Fig. 7.*

Fig. 7: Checking Valve Spring Installed Height

Underside of Spring Retainer

Surface of Spring Pad

Do not install spacers unless necessary.

2) If spring height is excessive, install necessary .030" (.76 mm) spacer(s) between cylinder head spring pad and valve spring to correct the height.

VALVE SPRING INSTALLED HEIGHT SPECIFICATIONS

Application	Specification In. (mm)
Intake Valve	1 11/16 - 1 23/32 (42.85-43.66 mm)
Exhaust Valve	1 9/16 - 1 19/32 (39.70-40.49 mm)

VALVE STEM OIL SEALS

Cup-type Teflon oil seals are used on valves. Install cupped side down over valve stem. Use procedures set forth in Valve Springs, to replace seals.

VALVE GUIDE SERVICING

1) When reaming valve guides, always use reamers in proper size sequence. Reface valve seats after reaming operation. Use a scraper to break sharp corner at top of valve guide bore, after reaming.

2) Replacement valves are available in .003" (.08 mm), .015" (.38 mm) and .030" (.76 mm) oversize. *See Fig. 8.*

Fig. 8: Reaming Valve Guides

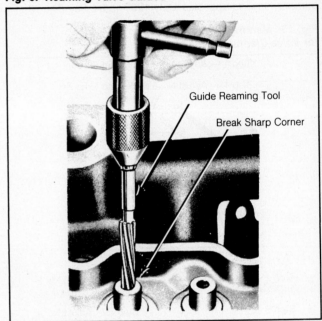

Guide Reaming Tool

Break Sharp Corner

Always use reamers in proper size sequence.

HYDRAULIC VALVE LIFTERS

1) Lifters should be serviced as complete assemblies only. Lifters must be disassembled and cleaned prior to testing, and must be tested using hydraulic lifter test fluid. Parts are not interchangeable. *See Fig. 9.*

Fig. 9: Hydraulic Lifter Assembly

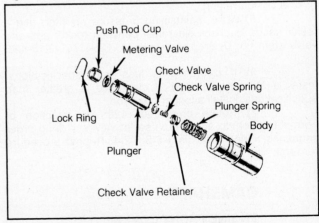

Push Rod Cup

Metering Valve

Check Valve

Check Valve Spring

Plunger Spring

Body

Lock Ring

Plunger

Check Valve Retainer

Parts are not interchangeable between lifters.

2) Leak down rate on all lifters is 10-50 seconds at 1/16" (1.6 mm) plunger travel, using lifter leak down testing device. Replace lifter assembly if any sign of malfunction is apparent.

Ford 6 Engines

4.9 LITER 6-CYLINDER (Cont.)

VALVE CLEARANCE ADJUSTMENT

A positive stop rocker arm stud eliminates the necessity of adjusting valve clearance. To obtain correct valve clearance, a .060" (1.524 mm) undersize or .060" (1.524 mm) oversize push rod is used.

1) With ignition switch "OFF," use a remote starter switch to turn crankshaft. Rotate crankshaft until No. 1 piston is at TDC at end of compression stroke.

2) Mark timing mark on vibration damper with chalk, then make 2 additional chalk marks on vibration damper, spaced approximately 120° apart. See Fig. 10.

Fig. 10: Marking Vibration Damper for Valve Clearance Adjustment.

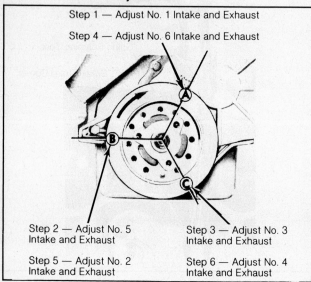

Step 1 — Adjust No. 1 Intake and Exhaust

Step 4 — Adjust No. 6 Intake and Exhaust

Step 2 — Adjust No. 5 Intake and Exhaust

Step 3 — Adjust No. 3 Intake and Exhaust

Step 5 — Adjust No. 2 Intake and Exhaust

Step 6 — Adjust No. 4 Intake and Exhaust

Space chalk marks approximately 120° apart.

3) Prior to checking adjustment, all valve components must be in good repair and installed and tightened properly. Inspect each stud nut and stud for worn condition prior to adjustment procedure, and replace as necessary.

4) Place No. 1 piston on TDC at end of compression stroke. Slowly collapse lifter plunger until completely bottomed, using lifter compressor tool (T70P-6513-A or equivalent).

5) While maintaining pressure on lifter, use a feeler gauge to check clearance between rocker arm and valve stem tip. Desired clearance is .125-.175" (3.18-4.45 mm).

6) If clearance is less than specifications, install a shorter push rod. If clearance is greater than specifications, install a longer push rod.

7) Rotate crankshaft 120° (in direction of normal rotation) to adjust next set of valves in firing order sequence. Firing order is 1-5-3-6-2-4. Repeat procedure for remaining valves.

CAMSHAFT

ENGINE FRONT COVER

Removal

1) Drain crankcase and cooling system. Remove radiator and shroud. Remove alternator adjusting arm bolt, and swing arm to side.

2) Remove fan, drive belts, spacer and pulleys. Remove vibration damper. Remove oil pan front bolts and front cover attaching bolts. Remove front cover and gasket.

Installation

1) Cut front oil pan seal flush with cylinder block/pan junction. Remove seal. Clean all gasket mating surfaces. Cut and fit new pan seal. Seal must fit flush with cylinder block/pan junction.

2) Coat cylinder block and front cover gasket surfaces with oil resistant sealer. Install front cover gasket. Apply silicone sealer to junction of block and pan. Lubricate front cover oil seal.

3) Position front cover in place. Start front cover and pan attaching bolts. Slide front cover alignment tool (T68P-6019-A or equivalent) over crankshaft and into seal bore.

4) Install alternator adjusting arm. Tighten oil pan bolts first, then tighten front cover bolts. Remove alignment tool. Reverse removal procedure to install remaining components.

FRONT COVER OIL SEAL

Removal

With front cover removed from engine, drive oil seal out of cover using pin punch. Clean out seal recess in front cover.

Installation

1) Lubricate new seal. Drive in seal with installing tool (T68P-6700-A or equivalent), until seal is fully seated in front cover recess.

2) Check seal after installation to ensure spring is properly positioned in seal. Install front cover. See Fig. 11.

Fig. 11: Installing Front Cover Oil Seal

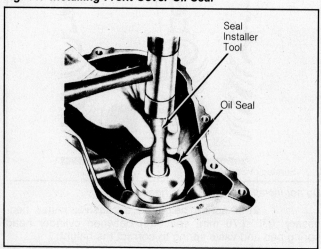

Seal Installer Tool

Oil Seal

Fully seat seal in front cover recess.

TIMING GEARS

CAUTION: To avoid possible damage to camshaft lobes, never rotate camshaft or crankshaft unless timing gears are installed.

Checking Gear Backlash

1) Remove engine front cover. Make 6 chalk marks on the camshaft gear, about 60° apart. Attach a dial indicator to front of cylinder block. See Fig. 12.

4.9 LITER 6-CYLINDER (Cont.)

Fig. 12: Checking Timing Gear Backlash

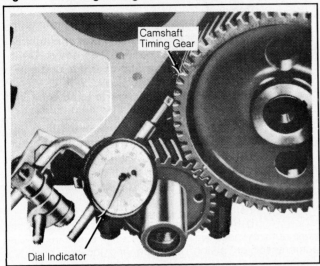

Backlash should be .004-.010 (.10-.25 mm).

2) Using the dial indicator to measure amount of gear backlash, take measurements at each of the 6 chalk marks on the camshaft gear.

Fig. 13: Aligning Timing Marks

Use gear puller to remove gears.

3) To obtain an accurate reading, hold the gear firmly against the block. Backlash should be .004-.010" (.10-.25 mm). If any reading is not within limits, replace timing gears as a set.

Removal

Drain cooling system and crankcase. Remove engine front cover and oil slinger. Align camshaft and crankshaft gear timing marks. *See Fig. 13.* Use gear puller to remove camshaft and crankshaft gears.

Installation

1) Ensure camshaft key spacer and thrust plate are correctly installed. Align both gear keyways with respective keys, and press on gears using gear installing tool (T65L-6306-A or equivalent).

2) Check that timing marks on camshaft and crankshaft gears are still aligned. Install front cover and related components.

CAMSHAFT

Removal

1) Drain cooling system and crankcase. Remove radiator and shroud. Identify lifters for reassembly in original locations, then remove lifters. Remove front cover.

2) Disconnect fuel lines at fuel pump and remove pump. Disconnect vacuum hose and wires to distributor, and remove distributor.

3) Turn crankshaft to align gear timing marks. Remove camshaft thrust plate bolts, gear, key, thrust plate and spacer. Remove camshaft, taking care not to damage camshaft lobes or bearings.

Installation

1) Coat camshaft lobes with polyethylene grease (or equivalent) and coat journals with engine oil. Assemble key, spacer and thrust plate to camshaft. Align gear keyway with key and install gear.

2) Install camshaft, gear and thrust plate as an assembly. With timing marks aligned, tighten thrust plate attaching bolts.

3) Replace front cover oil seal. Reverse removal procedures to install remaining components, using new gaskets.

CAMSHAFT END THRUST

1) Remove engine front cover. Push camshaft rearward into engine. Install dial indicator with point positioned on camshaft gear retaining bolt. Zero dial indicator.

2) Place large screwdriver between camshaft gear and block. Pull camshaft forward and then release.

Fig. 14: Camshaft Assembly

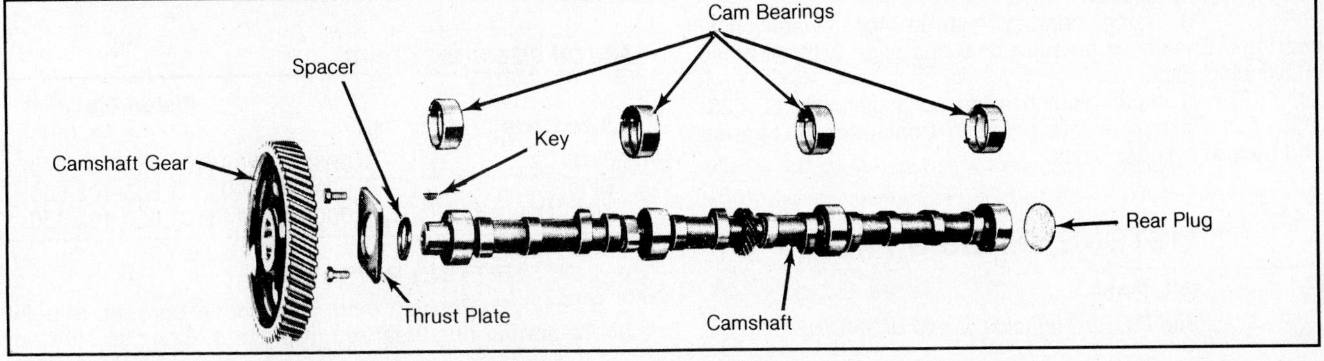

Install camshaft, gear and thrust plate as an assembly.

Ford 6 Engines

4.9 LITER 6-CYLINDER (Cont.)

Replace thrust plate if dial indicator reading is not within limits.

CAM LOBE LIFT

1) Remove rocker arm cover, stud nut, fulcrum seat and rocker arm. Make sure push rod end is in valve lifter socket. Install a remote starter switch. Use a dial indicator to check lobe lift in consecutive order.

2) Position dial indicator and cup-shaped adapter on end of push rod (in same plane as push rod movement). *See Fig. 15.*

Fig. 15: Checking Camshaft Lobe Lift

Make sure push rod is in valve lifter socket.

3) Rotate crankshaft until lifter and push rod are at lowest position. Zero dial indicator. Rotate crankshaft slowly until push rod is in fully raised position. Record dial indicator reading and compare with specifications.

4) Maximum allowable lift loss is .005" (.127 mm). If lift on any lobe is below specifications, replace camshaft and valve lifter operating on worn lobe(s).

CAMSHAFT BEARINGS

Removal

1) Remove engine from vehicle and remove flywheel. Remove camshaft and rear cam bearing plug. Remove crankshaft.

2) Push pistons to top of cylinders. Using a camshaft bearing installer/remover tool, drive out camshaft bearings.

Installation

1) Using bearing installer tool, install new bearings. Ensure oil holes in bearings align with oil holes in cylinder block.

2) Install front bearing so a distance of .020-.035" (.51-.64 mm) exists between front edge of bearing and face of cylinder block.

PISTONS, RINGS & PINS

OIL PAN

See Oil Pan Removal at end of ENGINE Section.

PISTON & ROD ASSEMBLY
Removal

1) Remove cylinder head, oil pan and oil pump. Turn crankshaft until piston to be removed is at bottom of stroke. Place cloth over piston to collect metal cuttings.

2) Using ridge cutter, remove ridge and deposits from upper end of cylinder bore. Never cut into ring travel area in excess of 1/32" (.8 mm) when removing ridge.

3) Make sure all connecting rod caps are marked for cylinder identification. Remove connecting rod cap.

4) Using wooden hammer handle, push connecting rod and piston out top of cylinder. Avoid damage to crankshaft journal or cylinder wall, when removing piston and rod.

Installation

1) Properly install piston rings. Oil piston and rings and cylinder wall with light engine oil. Install ring compressor on piston, ensuring ring location does not change.

2) Place rod journal at bottom of its stroke. Place piston into cylinder bore, with notch on top of piston towards front of engine. Tap piston into cylinder bore, using wooden hammer handle.

3) Carefully guide rod over crankshaft journal, until it seats on journal. Install and tighten rod cap. Check rod side play.

FITTING PISTONS

NOTE: **Take measurements at normal room temperature (70°F, 21°C).**

1) Measure piston at centerline of piston pin, 90° to piston pin axis. Measure cylinder bore 90° to crankshaft centerline, at top, middle and bottom of bore. Use measurements to determine piston-to-cylinder bore clearance.

2) Measure cylinder bore 90° to crankshaft centerline at top of bore (below ring travel) and at bottom of bore (above ring travel). Taper is the difference between the 2 measurements, and must not exceed .010" (.254 mm).

3) Measure cylinder bore at center of piston travel, 90° to crankshaft centerline. Measure bore at center of piston travel, in line with crankshaft centerline. Out-of-round is the difference between the 2 measurements, and must not exceed .005" (.127 mm).

4) If taper or out-of-round are not within limits, or cylinder walls are deeply scored, hone or bore cylinders for installation of new pistons. Check Piston Size Code Chart.

PISTON SIZE CODE CHART

Size Code	Piston Diameter In. (mm)
Red	3.9982-3.9988 (101.554-101.570)
Blue	3.9994-4.0000 (101.585-101.600)
.003" Oversize	4.0008-4.0014 (101.620-101.636)

FITTING RINGS

1) Position ring in cylinder bore at a point where normal ring wear is not present. Exercise care not

4.9 LITER 6-CYLINDER (Cont.)

to damage ring or cylinder bore. Ring must be square in bore. Check ring end gap with a feeler gauge.

2) Check side clearance of compression rings, with feeler gauge inserted between ring and its lower land. Feeler gauge should slide freely around entire circumference of piston without binding.

3) Properly install rings on piston. Space oil ring segments 1" (25.4 mm) from oil ring spacer. *See Fig. 16.*

Fig. 16: Correctly Spaced Piston Rings

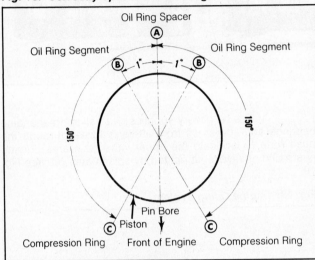

Space oil ring segments 1" (25.4 mm) from oil ring spacer.

PISTON PIN REPLACEMENT

Removal

Using arbor press and pin removal tool, press piston pin from piston and connecting rod.

Installation

1) Lightly coat parts to be assembled with engine oil. Position piston and connecting rod as shown. *See Fig. 17.*

Fig. 17: Positioning Piston to Connecting Rod

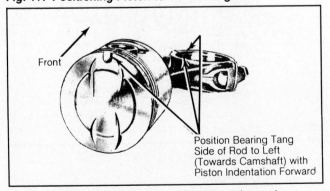

Front

Position Bearing Tang Side of Rod to Left (Towards Camshaft) with Piston Indentation Forward

Press in piston pin until centered in connecting rod.

2) When properly assembled, notch on piston head will face toward front of engine, and bearing tang side of connecting rod will be positioned toward camshaft side of engine.

3) Start piston pin in piston and connecting rod. Using arbor press and pin installing tool, press piston pin through piston until pin is centered in the connecting rod.

CRANKSHAFT, MAIN & CONNECTING ROD BEARINGS

MAIN & CONNECTING ROD BEARINGS

NOTE: **Use Plastigage method for checking bearing clearances. Perform following procedures with oil pan and oil pump removed. Remove oil film from surfaces to be checked.**

Crankshaft Main Bearings

1) Fit main bearings one a time, while leaving other bearings securely fastened. Make sure main bearing caps are marked for identification.

2) Remove main bearing cap. Support crankshaft weight by placing a jack under the counterweight adjacent to the bearing being checked.

3) Use Plastigage method as explained in Connecting Rod Bearings to measure bearing clearance, tightening main cap to specification.

4) Standard size bearings may be used in combination with a .001" (.025 mm) or .002" (.051 mm) undersize bearing.

5) If .002" (.051 mm) undersize main bearings are used on more than one journal, install them on cylinder block side of crankshaft.

NOTE: **To replace the rear main bearing, the engine must be removed from vehicle.**

6) Replace one main bearing set at a time. Loosen all main bearing caps until they are finger tight. Remove bearing cap to which new bearings are to be installed.

7) Insert upper bearing remover/installer tool (6331-E or equivalent) into crankshaft journal oil hole. Turn crankshaft in direction of normal rotation to push upper bearing out of block.

NOTE: **Upper and lower bearing halves are not interchangeable. Upper half is drilled and grooved to provide entry of oil.**

8) Lightly oil bearing and journal surfaces. Partially install plain end of upper bearing in place. Insert tool (6331-E or equivalent) into journal oil hole.

9) Turn crankshaft slowly in opposite direction of normal rotation until bearing is seated. Remove tool. Install and tighten main bearing cap.

Connecting Rod Bearings

1) Ensure rod caps are marked for cylinder identification. Place crankshaft journal of cylinder to be checked at bottom of its stroke. Remove rod cap.

2) Place strip of Plastigage on bearing surface over full width of cap about 1/4" (6 mm) off center, and away from oil holes. Install and tighten cap to specification. Do not allow crankshaft to turn.

3) Remove cap and measure width of compressed Plastigage. A standard bearing may be used in combination with a .001" (.025 mm) or .002" (.051 mm) undersize bearing to obtain proper bearing clearance.

THRUST BEARING ALIGNMENT

1) Install thrust bearing cap after all other main caps have been tightened. Install thrust bearing cap bolts finger tight.

Fig. 18: Aligning Thrust Bearing

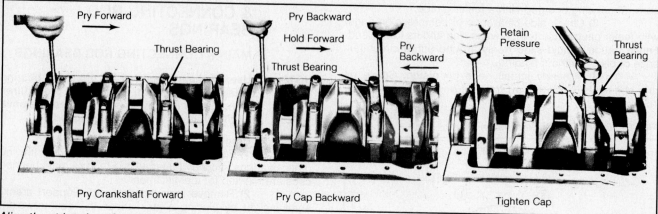

Pry Forward — Thrust Bearing — Pry Crankshaft Forward — Hold Forward — Pry Backward — Thrust Bearing — Pry Cap Backward — Retain Pressure — Pry Backward — Thrust Bearing — Tighten Cap

Align thrust bearing after all other main bearing caps have been tightened.

2) Pry crankshaft forward against thrust surface of upper half of bearing. Hold crankshaft forward, and pry thrust bearing cap to rear. Tighten cap bolts, while retaining forward pressure on crankshaft. *See Fig. 18.*

REAR MAIN BEARING OIL SEAL

NOTE: **The seal may be replaced without removing crankshaft from engine.**

Removal
1) Remove starter and transmission. Remove pressure plate and clutch disc (if equipped). Remove flywheel and engine rear cover plate.

2) Using an awl, punch 2 holes in oil seal on opposite sides of crankshaft, just above bearing cap-to-cylinder block split line.

3) Install sheet metal screws in holes. Using small wood blocks as a fulcrum for pry bars, pry against both screws at same time to remove seal. Use care not to damage crankshaft oil seal surface.

Installation
1) Inspect and clean crankshaft surface. Lightly coat crankshaft and new oil seal with engine oil. Start seal in place. Use seal installing tool to drive in seal.

2) Seal is properly installed when installing tool contacts cylinder block. Reverse removal procedure to complete installation.

ENGINE OILING

Crankcase Capacity
Capacity is 5 quarts (4.75L). Add 1 quart (.95L) when replacing oil filter.

Oil Filter
Full-flow filter has an integral by-pass valve. An anti-drain back feature prevents reverse flow of oil when the engine is shut down. Replace filter at first oil change, then every second oil change thereafter.

Normal Oil Pressure
40-60 psi (2.8-4.2 kg/cm²) at 2000 RPM.

Oil Pressure Regulator Valve
Valve located in pump body, not adjustable.

ENGINE OILING SYSTEM
Oil supply from pan is forced through lubrication system by a rotor-type oil pump. Oil flows through the full-flow oil filter, which routes oil into the main oil gallery.

The oil gallery supplies oil to all internal engine bearings and lifters. Oil from lifters is forced through the push rods to lubricate the upper valve train area. Timing gears and chain are lubricated by splash method. *See Fig. 19.*

Fig. 19: Engine Oiling System

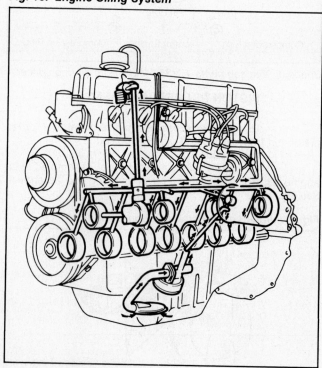

OIL PUMP

NOTE: **If any part of the oil pump requires replacement, the complete pump assembly must be replaced.**

Removal
Remove oil pan. Remove nut securing oil pump inlet tube bracket to engine, and remove oil pump attaching bolts. Remove oil pump assembly.

Ford 6 Engines

4.9 LITER 6-CYLINDER (Cont.)

Disassembly

1) Remove oil inlet tube. Remove cover attaching bolts and cover. Remove inner rotor and shaft and outer rotor.

2) Drill small hole into oil pressure relief valve cap. Insert self-threading sheet metal screw into cap, and pull cap from chamber. Remove spring and plunger. *See Fig. 20.*

Fig. 20: Oil Pump Assembly

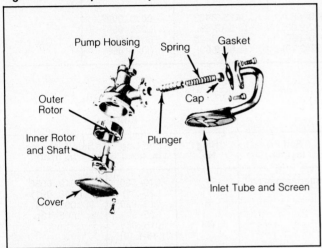

Oil pump cannot be repaired.

Inspection

1) Wash all parts thoroughly, and dry with compressed air. Check inside of pump housing, outer rotor and inner rotor and shaft for damage, scoring or excessive wear. Check mating surface of pump cover for wear, scoring or grooved condition.

2) Remove rotor assembly from pump housing. Using feeler gauge, measure inner to outer rotor tip clearance. Install rotor assembly in pump housing. Lay a straightedge over rotor assembly and housing. Insert feeler gauge between straightedge and housing to measure rotor end play.

3) Measure outer rotor-to-housing clearance using feeler gauge. Measure the shaft outside diameter and the housing bearing inside diameter. Difference between readings is the shaft-to-housing bearing clearance.

4) Relief valve spring should test to 20.6-22.6 lbs. (9-10 kg) at 2.49" (63.2 mm). Inspect relief valve spring for worn or collapsed condition.

5) Check relief valve plunger for scores and free operation in bore. Check clearance between relief valve plunger and bore.

OIL PUMP SPECIFICATIONS

Application	Specification In. (mm)
Rotor Tip Clearance	.012 (.30)
Rotor End Play	.004 (.10) Max.
Outer Rotor-to-Housing Clearance	.001-.013 (.03-.33)
Shaft-to-Housing Clearance	.0015-.0030 (.038-.076)
Relief Valve-to-Bore Clearance	.0015-.0030 (.038-.076)

Reassembly

Clean and oil all parts thoroughly. Install relief valve plunger, spring and new cap. Stake cap into position. Reassemble remaining components in reverse order of disassembly, using new gasket for oil inlet tube.

Installation

Prime oil pump by filling inlet opening with oil and rotating pump shaft until oil emerges from outlet opening. Install and tighten oil pump to cylinder block.

ENGINE COOLING

WATER PUMP

Removal

1) Drain cooling system. Remove alternator drive belt. On A/C equipped vehicles, remove air compressor drive belt.

2) Remove fan, spacer and pulley. Disconnect heater hose, lower radiator hose, and radiator supply line at water pump. Remove water pump.

Installation

1) Clean all gasket mating surfaces. Transfer fittings to new pump. Coat new gasket on both sides with gasket sealer, and position on water pump.

2) Install water pump and tighten attaching bolts. Reverse removal procedure to install remaining components.

NOTE: For information on cooling system capacities and other cooling system components, see appropriate article in "Engine Cooling Systems," at end of ENGINE Section.

ENGINE SPECIFICATIONS

GENERAL SPECIFICATIONS

Year	Displacement		Fuel System	HP@RPM	Torque Ft. Lbs.@RPM	Compr. Ratio	Bore		Stroke	
	Cu. In.	Liters					In.	mm	In.	mm
1983	300	4.9	1-Bbl.	.....	.....	.....	4.00	101.6	3.98	101.1

Ford 6 Engines

4.9 LITER 6-CYLINDER (Cont.)

ENGINE SPECIFICATIONS (Cont.)

VALVES

Engine Size & Valve	Head Diam. In. (mm)	Face Angle	Seat Angle	Seat Width In. (mm)	Stem Diameter In. (mm)	Stem Clearance In. (mm)	Valve Lift In. (mm)
4.9L Intake	1.769-1.793 (44.93-45.54)	44°	45°	.060-.080 (1.52-2.03)	.3416-.3423 (8.68-8.69)	.0010-.0027 (.025-.069)	.....
Exhaust	1.551-1.569 (39.40-39.85)	44°	45°	.070-.090 (1.78-2.29)	.3416-.3423 (8.68-8.69)	.0010-.0027 (.025-.069)	.....

PISTONS, PINS, RINGS

Engine	PISTONS Clearance In. (mm)	PINS Piston Fit In. (mm)	PINS Rod Fit In. (mm)	RINGS Ring No.	RINGS End Gap In. (mm)	RINGS Side Clearance In. (mm)
4.9L	.0014-.0022 (.036-.056)	.0002-.0004 (.005-.010)	Interference Fit	1	.010-.020 (.25-.51)	.0019-.0036 (.048-.091)
				2	.010-.020 (.25-.51)	.002-.004 (.05-.10)
				Oil	.015-.055 (.38-1.40)	Snug

CRANKSHAFT MAIN & CONNECTING ROD BEARINGS

Engine	MAIN BEARINGS Journal Diam. In. (mm)	MAIN BEARINGS Clearance In. (mm)	MAIN BEARINGS Thrust Bearing	MAIN BEARINGS Crankshaft End Play In. (mm)	CONNECTING ROD BEARINGS Journal Diam. In. (mm)	CONNECTING ROD BEARINGS Clearance In. (mm)	CONNECTING ROD BEARINGS Side Play In. (mm)
4.9L	2.3982-2.3990 (60.914-60.934)	.0008-.0015 (.020-.038)	No. 5	.004-.008 (.10-.20)	2.1228-2.1236 (53.919-53.939)	.0008-.0015 (.020-.038)	.006-.013 (.15-.33)

VALVE SPRINGS

Engine	Free Length In. (mm)	PRESSURE Lbs. @ In. (Kg @ mm) Valve Closed	PRESSURE Lbs. @ In. (Kg @ mm) Valve Open
4.9L Intake	1.99 (50.5)	76-84@1.70 (34-38@43.2)	187-207@1.30 (85-94@33.0)
Exhaust	1.87 (47.5)	77-85@1.58 (35-39@40.1)	182-202@1.18 (83-92@30.0)

CAMSHAFT

Engine	Journal In. (mm)	Clearance In. (mm)	Lobe Lift In. (mm)
4.9L [1]	2.017-2.018 (51.23-51.26)	.001-.003 (.03-.08)	.249 (6.32) .247 [2] (6.27)

TIGHTENING SPECIFICATIONS

Application	Ft. Lbs. (N.m)
Camshaft Thrust Plate	9-12 (12-16)
Connecting Rod Cap	40-45 (54-61)
Cylinder Head	
Step 1	55 (75)
Step 2	65 (88)
Step 3	85 (115)
Flywheel-to-Crankshaft	75-85 (102-115)
Intake-to-Exhaust Manifold	28-33 (38-45)
Main Bearing Cap	60-70 (81-95)
Manifolds-to-Cylinder Head	22-32 (30-45)
Oil Filter Adapter	40-50 (54-68)
Oil Pump Attaching Bolt	10-15 (14-20)
Rocker Arm Nut	17-23 (23-31)
Vibration Damper Bolt	130-150 (176-203)

[1] — End play is .001-.007" (.03-.18 mm).
[2] — Lobe lift specification for F-100 & F-150 4 x 2 with 2.47:1 or 2.75:1 axle ratio and manual transmission (except Calif.).

Ford V8 Engines

5.0 & 5.8 LITER V8

ENGINE CODING

ENGINE IDENTIFICATION

Engine is identified by a letter code in the eighth position of Vehicle Identification Number (VIN). The VIN is stamped on a metal tab, attached to left upper side of instrument panel, near windshield. The VIN is also found on the Safety Compliance Certification Label, located on left door lock pillar.

ENGINE IDENTIFICATION CODES

Engine	Code
5.0L 2-Bbl.	F
5.8L 2-Bbl.	G

ENGINE REMOVAL

See Engine Removal at end of ENGINE Section.

MANIFOLDS & CYLINDER HEAD

INTAKE MANIFOLD

Removal

1) Drain cooling system. Remove air cleaner, intake duct assembly, and crankcase ventilation hose.

2) Disconnect accelerator cable, speed control linkage, and transmission kickdown rod from carburetor. Remove accelerator cable bracket.

3) Disconnect electric choke and carburetor solenoid wires. Disconnect primary and secondary wires from coil. Disconnect spark plug wires from plugs.

4) Remove distributor cap and wires as an assembly. Remove fuel line at carburetor. Disconnect fuel evaporation hoses.

5) Disconnect vacuum hoses at distributor and remove distributor. Disconnect upper radiator hose, by-pass hose and heater hose from intake manifold.

6) Disconnect temperature sending unit wire. Remove intake manifold and carburetor as an assembly. Remove and discard gaskets and seals. Discard attaching bolt sealing washers.

NOTE: Manifold installation must be completed promptly after applying RTV sealer, as sealer sets up in 15 minutes.

Fig. 1: Intake Manifold Tightening Sequence

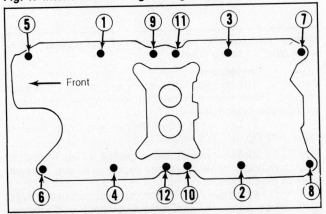

Retighten manifold after engine has reached normal operating temperature.

Installation

1) Clean all gasket mating surfaces. Apply 1/8" bead of RTV sealer at 4 corners of cylinder block seal mounting surface-to-cylinder head junction.

2) Apply 1/16" bead of RTV sealer to top of seal ends, across full width of seal. Position manifold gaskets and seals on engine.

3) Install and tighten manifold, taking care not to misalign seals and gaskets. *See Fig. 1.*

4) Reverse removal procedure to install remaining components. Retighten manifold bolts after engine has reached normal operating temperature.

EXHAUST MANIFOLD

Removal

1) Remove air cleaner and intake duct assembly (F-100, F-250 and Bronco). Remove crankcase ventilation hose.

2) Remove bolts attaching air cleaner inlet duct. Disconnect exhaust pipe(s). If equipped, remove exhaust manifold heat shield.

3) If removing left side exhaust manifold, remove dipstick tube, speed control bracket and exhaust heat control valve. Remove exhaust manifold(s).

Installation

Clean mating surfaces of exhaust manifold(s) and cylinder head. Using new gaskets where required, install exhaust manifold(s) in reverse order of removal.

CYLINDER HEAD

Removal

1) Remove intake manifold and carburetor as an assembly. Remove rocker arm covers. Loosen alternator and air pump adjusting arm bolt.

2) Remove alternator and air pump mounting bracket bolt and spacer, then swing alternator out of way. On "E" series models, remove ignition coil.

3) Remove air cleaner inlet duct. Remove bolts from A/C bracket at front of cylinder head on all "F" series and Bronco models. Remove oil dipstick and tube.

4) Remove speed control bracket (if equipped). Disconnect muffler inlet pipe from exhaust manifolds.

5) Loosen rocker arm fulcrum bolts, and rotate rocker arms to one side. Remove push rods in sequence, for later installation in original locations.

6) On "E" series models, remove thermactor air supply manifold, supply hose, and pump valve as an assembly.

7) On "F" series and Bronco models, disconnect thermactor air supply hoses at check valves. On all models, remove cylinder head.

NOTE: A specially treated composition head gasket is used. DO NOT apply sealer to gasket.

Installation

1) Clean all gasket mating surfaces. Check cylinder head and block for flatness. Position new cylinder head gasket over dowel pins on block surface.

2) Position cylinder heads on block and install head bolts. Tighten 5.8L head bolts in 3 steps. Tighten 5.0L head bolts in 2 steps. *See Fig. 2.*

3) Prior to their installation, lubricate push rod ends, valve stem tips, rocker arms and fulcrum seats with polyethelene grease (or equivalent).

4) Reverse removal procedure to install remaining components, using new gaskets as necessary.

Ford V8 Engines

5.0 & 5.8 LITER V8 (Cont.)

Fig. 2: Cylinder Head Tightening Sequence

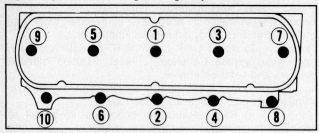

Tighten 5.0L in 2 steps, and 5.8L in 3 steps.

VALVES

VALVE ARRANGEMENT

E-I-E-I-E-I-E-I (Left bank, front to rear)
I-E-I-E-I-E-I-E (Right bank, front to rear)

ROCKER ARM ASSEMBLY

Inspect fulcrum bolts, fulcrums, rocker arms and fulcrum guides for abnormal or excessive wear. Coat rocker arm parts with polyethelene grease (or equivalent) prior to installation. *See Fig. 3.*

Fig. 3: Rocker Arm Assembly

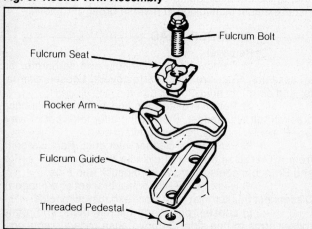

Worn parts must be replaced.

VALVE SPRINGS

Removal

1) Remove air cleaner and rocker arm covers. Remove spark plug from cylinder to be serviced. Rotate crankshaft to bring applicable piston to TDC after compression stroke.

2) Remove rocker arm fulcrum bolt, fulcrum, rocker arm and push rod. On exhaust valves, remove stem cap.

3) Install an air hose and adapter into the spark plug hole and apply air pressure to cylinder. Install fulcrum bolt for use with valve spring compressor.

4) Using valve spring compressor, compress valve spring and remove locks, retainer, sleeve, and valve spring. Remove and discard oil seal. *See Fig. 4.*

NOTE: Wrap a rubber band or tape around end of valve stem. This will keep valve from falling into cylinder, in the event air pressure forces piston downward.

Fig. 4: Compressing Valve Spring for Removal

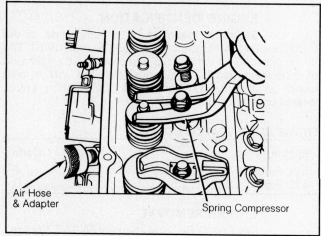

Do not remove air pressure from cylinder until valve components are reassembled.

Inspection

1) Inspect valve stem for wear and out-of-round condition. Check valve for binding in valve guide.

2) Using valve spring tester, check springs for proper tension. Replace springs that fail specifications.

3) Inspect each spring for squareness, using a steel square and flat surface. Replace spring if more than 5/64" (1.98 mm) out-of-square. *See Fig. 5.*

Fig. 5: Checking Valve Spring Squareness

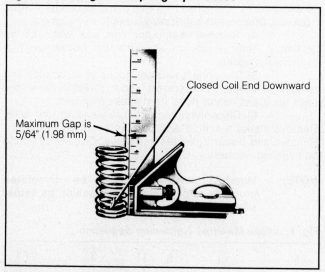

Measure gap between top of spring coil and square, while slowly rotating spring.

Installation

1) Lubricate valve stem and install valve stem oil seal. Place spring in position over valve, and install spring retainer and sleeve.

2) Compress valve spring, and install retainer locks. *See Fig. 6.* Remove tool and fulcrum bolt.

3) Apply polyethelene grease (or equivalent) to push rod ends, valve stem tip, rocker arm and fulcrum, prior to their installation.

4) Install valve stem caps on exhaust valves. Turn off air pressure, and remove air hose and adapter. Install components in reverse order of removal procedure.

Ford V8 Engines

5.0 & 5.8 LITER V8 (Cont.)

Fig. 6: Exploded View of Valve Assemblies

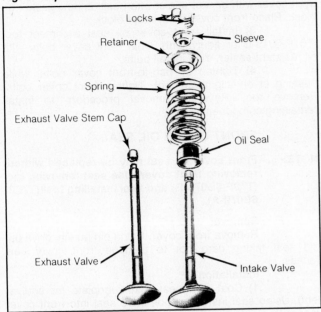

Lubricate valve components prior to assembly.

VALVE SPRING INSTALLED HEIGHT

CAUTION: Install spacers only if necessary. Excessive use of spacers will overstress the valve train and cause unnecessary damage.

1) Using dividers and a ruler, measure spring height from surface of cylinder head pad, to underside of spring retainer. *See Fig. 7.*

2) If height is greater than specifications, install .030" (.76 mm) spacer(s) between head and spring to bring height within limits.

Fig. 7: Checking Installed Height of Valve Spring

Install .030" (.76 mm) spacer(s) to correct spring height.

VALVE SPRING INSTALLED HEIGHT SPECIFICATIONS

Application	Measurement In. (mm)
5.0L	
Intake	1 43/64 - 1 45/64 (42.47-43.26)
Exhaust	1 37/64 - 1 39/64 (40.04-40.88)
5.8L	
Intake	1 49/64 - 1 51/64 (44.85-45.64)
Exhaust	1 37/64 - 1 39/64 (40.08-40.88)

VALVE STEM OIL SEALS

Cup-type oil seals are used on all valves. Lubricate valve stem with engine oil, and install new valve stem seal with cup side down over valve guide. Use a 5/8" deep-well socket and mallet to drive the oil seal onto valve stem.

VALVE GUIDE SERVICING

Always use reamers in proper sequence. Reface valve seat after valve guide is reamed. After reaming, use a scraper to break sharp corner at top inside diameter of valve guide bore. Oversize valves are available in .015" (.38 mm) and .030" (.76 mm).

HYDRAULIC VALVE LIFTERS

1) Service lifters as complete assemblies only. DO NOT interchange parts. Disassemble lifters and thoroughly clean.

2) Reassemble lifters and test with hydraulic lifter test fluid and a lifter leak-down tester tool.

3) Leak-down rate on hydraulic lifters is 10-50 seconds at 1/16" (1.60 mm) plunger travel. *See Fig. 8.*

Fig. 8: Hydraulic Lifter Assembly

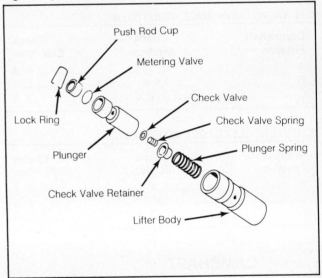

Parts are not interchangeable between lifters.

VALVE CLEARANCE ADJUSTMENT

1) Prior to proceeding, ensure that all valve components are in a serviceable condition, properly installed, and tightened.

2) Check clearance by slowly bleeding down the lifter plunger (until bottomed) of the valve being checked, using lifter compressor tool.

3) With the lifter plunger bottomed, use a feeler gauge to measure clearance between the rocker arm and valve stem tip.

4) If clearance is too small, install a .060" (1.52 mm) undersize push rod. If clearance is excessive, install a .060" (1.52 mm) oversize push rod. Desired clearance is .125-.175" (3.18-4.45 mm).

5) With ignition switch "OFF," use a remote starter to rotate crankshaft. Rotate crankshaft until No. 1 piston is at TDC at end of compression stroke.

6) Using TDC timing mark on vibration damper as a reference, make 2 chalk marks on vibration damper, spaced approximately 90° apart. *See Fig. 9.*

Ford V8 Engines

5.0 & 5.8 LITER V8 (Cont.)

Fig. 9: Marking Vibration Damper for Valve Clearance Adjustment.

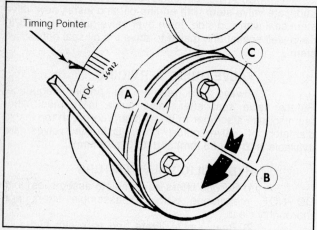

Space marks approximately 90° apart.

7) With crankshaft in positions designated in the following tables, check valve clearance between rocker arm and valve stem tip.

5.0L VALVE CLEARANCE ADJUSTMENT

Crankshaft Position	Check Int. Nos.	Check Exh. Nos.
A	1, 7, 8	1, 5, 4
B	5, 4	2, 6
C	2, 3, 6	7, 3, 8

5.8L VALVE CLEARANCE ADJUSTMENT

Crankshaft Position	Check Int. Nos.	Check Exh. Nos.
A	1, 4, 8	1, 3, 7
B	3, 7	2, 6
C	2, 5, 6	4, 5, 8

CAMSHAFT

ENGINE FRONT COVER

Removal

1) Remove air cleaner and duct assembly. Drain cooling system and crankcase. Remove fan shroud and position over fan.

2) Remove A/C idler pulley and bracket (if equipped). Remove all hoses and brackets attached to water pump.

3) On "E" series models, remove radiator. Remove all drive belts, fan, spacer, pulley and shroud.

4) On EEC vehicles, remove coil and bracket from water pump. Remove crankshaft pulley and vibration damper. Remove fuel pump.

5) Remove oil pan-to-front cover bolts and cut oil pan gasket flush with cylinder block. Remove front cover and water pump as an assembly.

Installation

1) Clean all gasket surfaces. Install new front cover oil seal. Cut and fit new oil pan gasket. Apply sealer to oil pan gasket surface and install new gasket.

2) Install oil pan front seal. Coat block and front cover with gasket sealer and position new gasket on block. Place front cover on cylinder block.

3) Install front cover oil seal alignment tool (T61P-6019-B or equivalent). Coat front cover bolts with oil resistant sealer, then install bolts.

4) Tighten oil pan-to-front cover bolts, while pushing in on alignment tool. Tighten front cover bolts. Remove tool. Reverse removal procedure to install remaining components.

FRONT COVER OIL SEAL

NOTE: Front cover oil seal may be replaced without removing front cover. Use seal removing tool (T70P-6B070-B) and seal installing tool (T70P-6B070-A).

Removal

Remove front cover. Using pin punch, drive out old seal taking care not to damage front cover seal recess.

Installation

1) Coat new seal with Lubriplate (or equivalent). Using seal installing tool, drive seal into front cover recess.

2) Check that seal is fully seated and spring is properly positioned in seal. Reassemble in reverse order of removal.

TIMING CHAIN & SPROCKET

NOTE: The following procedures are performed with engine front cover removed.

Checking Timing Chain Deflection

1) Turn crankshaft opposite normal direction of rotation to take up slack on left side of timing chain.

2) Establish a reference point on the block, and measure from this point to left side of chain. See Fig. 10.

Fig. 10: Measuring Timing Chain Deflection

Maximum deflection is 1/2" (12.7 mm).

Ford V8 Engines

5.0 & 5.8 LITER V8 (Cont.)

3) Rotate crankshaft in normal direction of rotation to take up slack on right side of chain.

4) Force left side of chain outward and measure distance between reference point and chain.

5) Deflection is the difference between the 2 measurements. If deflection exceeds 1/2" (12.7 mm), replace timing chain and sprockets.

Removal

Crank engine until timing marks are aligned. *See Fig. 11.* Remove camshaft sprocket bolt, washers and fuel pump eccentric. Remove both sprockets and timing chain as an assembly.

Fig. 11: Aligning Timing Marks

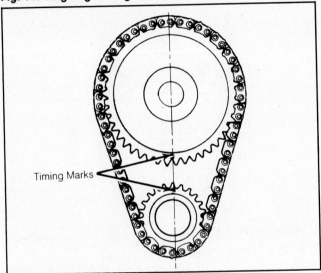

Remove and install chain and sprockets as an assembly.

Installation

1) Position timing chain and sprockets with timing marks aligned, and slide onto crankshaft and camshaft as an assembly.

2) Install fuel pump eccentric, washers and camshaft sprocket bolt, and tighten bolt. Lubricate fuel pump eccentric and timing chain and sprockets with heavy engine oil. Install front cover.

CAMSHAFT

Removal

1) Remove grille on "E" series models. Drain cooling system and crankcase. Remove radiator, front cover, timing chain and sprockets.

2) Remove intake manifold and carburetor as an assembly. Remove valve covers. Loosen rocker arm fulcrum bolts, and rotate rocker arms to one side.

3) Remove push rods and valve lifters in sequence so as to return to original locations.

4) Remove camshaft thrust plate, and carefully pull camshaft out through front of engine. Use care to avoid damage to camshaft bearings and journals. *See Fig. 12.*

Installation

1) Oil camshaft journals, and apply polyethelene grease (or equivalent) to lobes. Carefully slide camshaft into position.

2) Coat camshaft thrust plate with engine oil, and install with the groove toward cylinder block. Lubricate lifters with heavy engine oil, and install.

Fig. 12: Camshaft Assembly

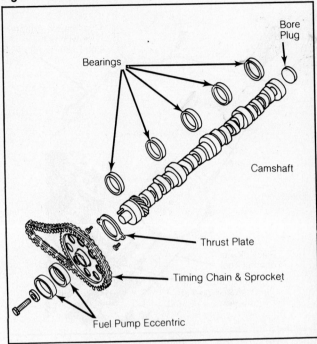

Install thrust plate with groove toward cylinder block.

3) Lubricate rocker arms, fulcrum seats, valve stem tips and push rod ends with polyethelene grease (or equivalent) prior to installing.

4) Reassemble engine in reverse order of removal procedures, using new gaskets. Check valve clearance.

CAMSHAFT END THRUST

CAUTION: Do not pry against camshaft sprocket, without first relieving the valve train load on the camshaft.

1) Loosen rocker arm fulcrum bolts to relieve load on camshaft. Push camshaft toward rear of engine, and install dial indicator. Position indicator point on camshaft sprocket attaching bolt. Zero dial indicator.

2) Place a large screwdriver between camshaft sprocket and cylinder block. Pull camshaft forward and release. Camshaft end play should be .001-.007" (.03-.18 mm). If beyond limits, replace thrust plate.

CAM LOBE LIFT

1) Remove rocker arm cover, fulcrum bolt, fulcrum seat, rocker arm and fulcrum guide. Make sure push rod end is in valve lifter socket. Install a remote starter switch to rotate crankshaft.

2) Use a dial indicator to check lobe lift in consecutive order. Position dial indicator point (or cup-shaped adapter) on end of push rod (in same plane as push rod movement). *See Fig. 13.*

3) Rotate crankshaft until lifter and push rod are at lowest position. Zero dial indicator. Rotate crankshaft slowly until push rod is fully raised. Record dial indicator reading and compare with specifications.

4) Maximum allowable lift loss is .005" (.13 mm). If lift on any lobe is below specifications, replace camshaft and valve lifter operating on worn lobe(s).

Ford V8 Engines

5.0 & 5.8 LITER V8 (Cont.)

Fig. 13: Checking Camshaft Lobe Lift

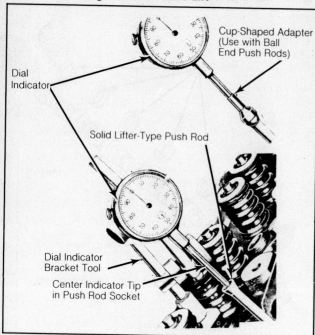

Make sure push rod is in valve lifter socket.

CAMSHAFT BEARINGS

NOTE: **Camshaft bearings are not interchangeable from one bore to another.**

Removal

1) Camshaft bearings are replaced with engine removed from vehicle. Remove camshaft, flywheel, crankshaft, and rear bearing bore plug.

2) Push pistons to top of cylinders. Using camshaft bearing installer/remover tool, remove camshaft bearings.

Installation

1) Using camshaft bearing installer/remover tool, install bearings into place. Make sure oil holes are properly aligned in each bore.

2) Install front bearing .005-.020" (.13-.51 mm) rearward of front face of cylinder block. Install new rear bearing bore plug.

PISTONS, RINGS & PINS

OIL PAN

See Oil Pan Removal at end of ENGINE Section.

PISTON & ROD ASSEMBLY

CAUTION: **Never cut more than 1/32" (.79 mm) into ring travel area.**

Removal

1) Remove cylinder head, oil pan and oil pump. Place piston at bottom of stroke, and cover with a cloth to collect cuttings.

2) Use ridge reamer to remove any ridge or deposit on upper end of cylinder bore. Ensure connecting rods and caps are marked for cylinder identification.

3) Remove rod cap. Push piston and rod out top of cylinder bore. Use care not to damage crankshaft journal or cylinder wall. Install rod cap on mating rod.

Installation

1) Coat cylinder bore, piston and rings with engine oil. Ensure that ring gaps are properly spaced. *See Fig. 14.* Install a ring compressor on piston.

NOTE: **Large chamfered side of rod's bearing end must be positioned towards crank pin thrust face of crankshaft.**

Fig. 14: Correctly Spaced Piston Rings

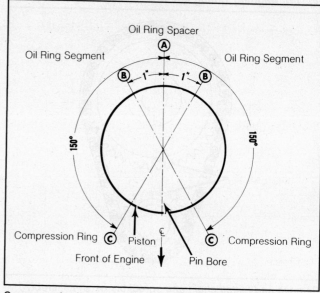

Space each oil ring segment 1" (25.4 mm) from oil ring spacer.

2) Install each piston and rod assembly in its respective bore, with arrow (or notch) on piston head facing front of engine.

3) Guide connecting rod onto crankshaft journal until connecting rod bearing seats on crankshaft. Install and tighten rod caps.

FITTING PISTONS

NOTE: **Take measurements at normal room temperature (70°F, 21°C).**

1) Measure piston skirt 90° to piston pin axis. Measure cylinder bore 90° to crankshaft centerline, at top, middle, and bottom of bore. Use measurements to determine piston-to-cylinder bore clearance.

2) Measure cylinder bore 90° to crankshaft centerline at top of bore (below ring travel) and at bottom of bore (above ring travel). Taper (difference between the 2 measurements) must not exceed .010" (.25 mm).

3) Measure cylinder bore at center of piston travel, 90° to crankshaft centerline. Measure bore at center of piston travel in line with crankshaft centerline. Out-of-round is the difference between the 2 measurements, and must not exceed .005" (.13 mm).

4) If taper or out-of-round are beyond limits, or cylinder walls are deeply scored, hone or bore cylinders for installation of new pistons. See Piston Size Code Chart.

5.0 & 5.8 LITER V8 (Cont.)

PISTON SIZE CODE CHART

Size Code	Size In. (mm)
5.0L	
Red	3.9984-3.9990 (101.559-101.575)
Blue	3.9996-4.0002 (101.590-101.605)
.003" Oversize	4.0008-4.0014 (101.620-101.636)
Yellow	4.0020-4.0026 (101.651-101.666)
5.8L	
Red	3.9978-3.9984 (101.544-101.559)
Blue	3.9990-3.9996 (101.575-101.590)
.003" Oversize	4.0002-4.0008 (101.605-101.620)
Yellow	4.0014-4.0020 (101.636-101.651)

FITTING RINGS

1) Carefully position ring in cylinder bore at a point where normal ring wear is not present. Ring must be square in bore. Check ring end gap with a feeler gauge.

2) Using a feeler gauge, check side clearance of compression rings. Feeler gauge should slide freely around entire circumference of piston without binding. If lower lands have high steps, replace the piston.

PISTON PIN REPLACEMENT

Removal

Using arbor press and piston pin removal tool, press piston pin from piston and connecting rod.

Installation

1) Lightly coat all parts to be assembled with engine oil. Position piston to connecting rod as shown. See Fig. 15.

2) Start piston pin in piston and connecting rod. Using arbor press and pin installing tool, press pin through piston and connecting rod until it is centered in connecting rod.

Fig. 15: Correct Positioning of Piston to Connecting Rod

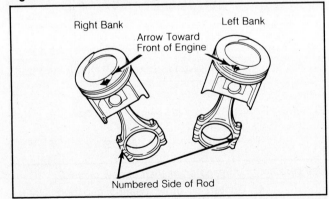

Position large chamfered side of rod's bearing end towards crank pin thrust face of crankshaft.

CRANKSHAFT, MAIN & CONNECTING ROD BEARINGS

MAIN & CONNECTING ROD BEARINGS

NOTE: Use Plastigage method for checking bearing clearances. Following procedures are performed with oil pan and oil pump removed. Oil film should be removed from surfaces to be checked.

Crankshaft Main Bearings

1) Fit main bearings one at a time, while leaving other bearings securely fastened. Make sure main bearing caps are marked for identification.

2) Remove main bearing cap. Support crankshaft weight by placing a jack under the counterweight adjacent to the bearing being checked.

3) Use Plastigage method (as explained in Connecting Rod Bearings) to measure main bearing clearance, tightening caps to specifications.

4) Standard size bearings may be used in combination with a .001" (.025 mm) or .002" (.051 mm) undersize bearing.

5) If .002" (.051 mm) undersize main bearings are used on more than one journal, they must be installed in cylinder block side of crankshaft journal.

6) Replace main bearing sets one at a time, while leaving other bearings securely fastened. Remove bearing cap to which new bearings are to be installed.

7) Insert upper bearing remover/installer tool (6331 or equivalent) into crankshaft journal oil hole.

8) Turn crankshaft in normal direction of rotation, allowing tool to push upper bearing out of cylinder block.

9) Lightly oil bearing and journal surfaces. Partially install plain end of upper bearing in place. Insert tool (6331 or equivalent) into journal oil hole.

10) Turn crankshaft slowly in opposite direction of engine rotation, until bearing is seated. Remove tool. Install and tighten main bearing cap.

Connecting Rod Bearings

1) Ensure rod caps are marked for cylinder identification. Place crankshaft journal of cylinder to be checked at bottom of stroke and remove rod cap.

2) Place strip of Plastigage on bearing surface over full width of cap, about 1/4" (6 mm) off center, and away from oil holes.

3) Install cap and tighten to specifications. Do not allow crankshaft to turn. Remove cap and measure compressed width of Plastigage with scale furnished.

Fig. 16: Measuring Connecting Rod Side Clearance.

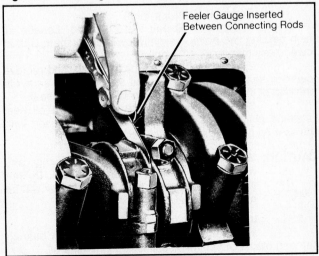

Side clearance is .010-.020" (.25-.51 mm).

Ford V8 Engines

5.0 & 5.8 LITER V8 (Cont.)

Fig. 17: Aligning Thrust Bearing

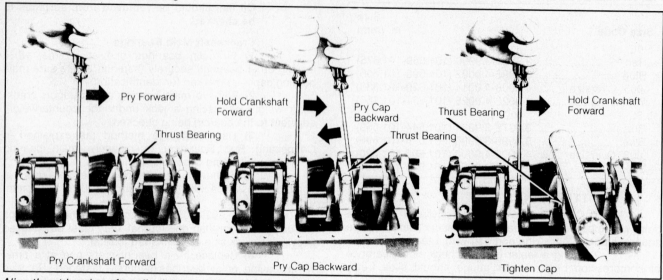

Pry Forward

Hold Crankshaft Forward

Thrust Bearing

Pry Cap Backward

Thrust Bearing

Thrust Bearing

Hold Crankshaft Forward

Pry Crankshaft Forward

Pry Cap Backward

Tighten Cap

Align thrust bearing after all other bearings have been tightened.

4) To obtain proper bearing clearance, a standard bearing may be used in combination with a .001" (.025 mm) or .002" (.051 mm) undersize bearing.

5) Measure connecting rod side clearance after bearings and caps have been installed. *See Fig. 16.*

THRUST BEARING ALIGNMENT

1) Install thrust bearing cap after all other main bearing caps have been tightened. Install thrust bearing cap bolts finger tight.

2) Pry crankshaft forward against thrust surface of upper half of bearing. Hold crankshaft forward, and pry thrust bearing cap to rear. Tighten cap bolts, while retaining forward pressure on crankshaft. *See Fig. 17.*

REAR MAIN BEARING OIL SEAL

NOTE: **Starting with engine build date December 1, 1982, a new one-piece rear main bearing oil seal has replaced the split-lip type seal on 5.0L engines.**

Removal (Split-Lip Seal)

1) Remove oil pan and oil pump. Loosen all main bearing cap bolts to slightly lower crankshaft. Do not lower more than 1/32" (.79 mm).

2) Remove rear main bearing cap, and remove lower oil seal half. Carefully install a small metal screw in one end of the seal, and pull on screw to remove seal.

3) If equipped, remove and discard oil seal retaining pin from bearing cap. The pin is not used with the split-lip type replacement oil seal.

CAUTION: **When installing seal, avoid shaving any rubber from outside surface of seal. Do not allow oil to get onto area where sealer will be applied.**

Installation

1) Carefully clean oil seal grooves in bearing cap and block. Dip split-lip seal halves in engine oil.

2) Carefully install upper seal into groove in cylinder block, with undercut side of seal toward front of engine.

3) Rotate seal on crankshaft journal until approximately 3/8" of seal protrudes below parting surface. *See Fig. 18.*

Fig. 18: Installing Split-Lip Type Oil Seal

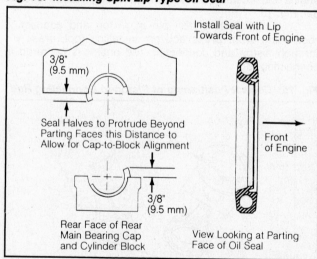

Install Seal with Lip Towards Front of Engine

3/8" (9.5 mm)

Seal Halves to Protrude Beyond Parting Faces this Distance to Allow for Cap-to-Block Alignment

Front of Engine

3/8" (9.5 mm)

Rear Face of Rear Main Bearing Cap and Cylinder Block

View Looking at Parting Face of Oil Seal

Use care not to damage crankshaft or new oil seal.

4) Tighten all other bearing cap bolts. Install lower seal in rear main bearing cap, with undercut side of seal toward front of engine.

5) Allow seal to protrude approximately 3/8" above parting surface, to mate with upper seal when cap is installed.

6) Apply 1/16" bead of silicone sealer to both sides of cylinder block-to-cap mating surface, and to both sides of bearing cap. *See Fig. 19.*

7) Install and tighten rear main bearing cap before sealer sets up (approximately 15 minutes). Install oil pump and pan.

5.0 & 5.8 LITER V8 (Cont.)

Fig. 19: Split-Lip Type Oil Seal Sealer Application Points

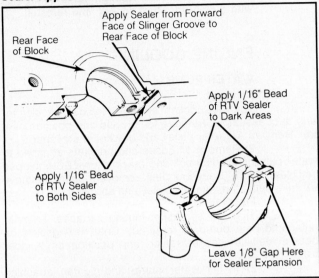

Do not allow sealer to contact lip of seal.

Removal (One-Piece Seal)

1) Remove transmission. If equipped, remove clutch cover and clutch disc. Remove flywheel.

2) Using a sharp awl, punch a hole in the seal metal surface between the lip and cylinder block.

3) Screw the threaded end of slide hammer tool (T77L-9533-B or equivalent) into hole and extract seal. Use care not to damage crankshaft.

Installation

1) Lubricate seal lip and crankshaft with engine oil. Position seal on seal installing tool (T82L-6701-A or equivalent) with spring side of seal toward engine.

2) Position seal and installing tool in place. Start the 2 bolts of seal installing tool into crankshaft. Alternately tighten each bolt to properly seat the seal.

3) Note that rear face of the seal must be within .005" (.13 mm) of the rear face of the cylinder block after installation.

4) To complete installation, install remaining components in reverse order of removal procedures.

ENGINE OILING

Crankcase Capacity

Capacity is 5 quarts (4.75L). Add 1 quart (.95L) when replacing oil filter.

Oil Filter

Full-flow filter has an integral by-pass valve. An anti-drainback feature prevents reverse flow of oil when the engine is shut down. Replace filter at first oil change, then every second oil change thereafter.

Normal Oil Pressure

40-60 psi (2.8-4.2 kg/cm²) at 2000 RPM.

Oil Pressure Regulator Valve

Valve located in pump body, not adjustable.

ENGINE OILING SYSTEM

System is pressure fed from rotor-type oil pump. Oil flows through full-flow oil filter before entering main oil gallery.

Oil from main gallery enters main bearings and camshaft bearings. Drilled oil holes in crankshaft provides lubrication to rod bearings.

Oil moves through secondary drilled passages to lifters. From there it is routed through hollow push rods up to top of head assembly to lubricate rocker arms. Oil is returned to oil pan through drain holes in cylinder heads. *See Fig. 20.*

Fig. 20: Engine Oiling System

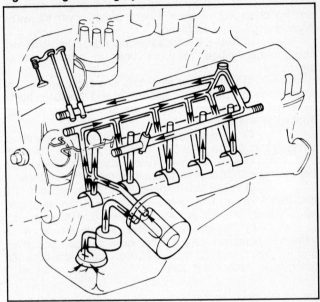

OIL PUMP

Removal

Remove oil pan. Remove nut securing oil pump inlet tube and screen to engine. Remove oil pump attaching bolts and intermediate drive shaft. Remove oil pump assembly.

Disassembly

1) Remove oil pump inlet tube. Remove cover attaching bolts and cover. Remove inner rotor and shaft and outer rotor. *See Fig. 21.*

Fig. 21: Oil Pump Assembly

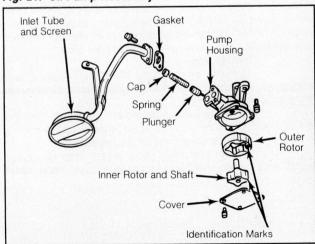

Dimple on outer rotor must face same side as identification mark on inner rotor.

Ford V8 Engines

5.0 & 5.8 LITER V8 (Cont.)

2) Drill small hole into oil pressure relief valve cap. Insert self-threading sheet metal screw into cap, and pull cap from chamber. Remove spring and plunger.

NOTE: If any part of the oil pump requires replacement, the complete pump assembly must be replaced.

Inspection

1) Wash all parts thoroughly, and dry with compressed air. Check internal parts of pump for damage, scoring or excessive wear. Check pump cover for wear, scoring or grooved condition.

2) Remove rotor assembly from pump housing. Using feeler gauge, measure inner to outer rotor tip clearance.

3) Install rotor assembly in pump housing. Lay a straightedge over rotor assembly and housing. Insert feeler gauge between straightedge and housing to measure rotor end play.

4) Measure outer rotor-to-housing clearance, using feeler gauge. Measure the shaft outside diameter and the housing bearing inside diameter. Difference between readings is shaft-to-housing bearing clearance.

5) Relief valve spring should test to 10.6-12.2 lbs. (5-5.5 kg) at 1.74" (44.2 mm) for 5.0L engines; and 18.2-20.2 lbs. (8-9 kg) at 2.49" (63.3 mm) for 5.8L engines.

6) Inspect relief valve spring for worn or collapsed condition. Check relief valve plunger for scores and for free operation in bore. Check clearance between relief valve plunger and bore.

OIL PUMP SPECIFICATIONS

Application	Specification In. (mm)
Rotor Tip Clearance	.012 (.30) Max.
Rotor End Play	.004 (.10) Max.
Outer Rotor-to-Housing Clearance	.001-.013 (.03-.33)
Shaft-to-Housing Clearance	.0015-.0030 (.038-.076)
Relief Valve-to-Bore Clearance	.0015-.0030 (.038-.076)

Reassembly

Clean and oil all parts thoroughly. Install relief valve plunger, spring and new cap. Stake cap into position. Install remaining components in reverse order of disassembly, using new gasket for oil inlet tube.

Installation

1) Prime oil pump by filling inlet opening with engine oil, then rotate pump shaft until engine oil emerges from outlet opening.

2) Firmly seat intermediate shaft into distributor socket. The stop on the shaft should touch roof of crankcase. Position stop on shaft as necessary.

3) Remove shaft and insert into oil pump. Install and tighten shaft and pump as an assembly. Install oil pan.

CAUTION: If pump and shaft do not readily seat, do not force into position. Realign drive shaft hex with distributor shaft socket, and reinstall.

ENGINE COOLING

WATER PUMP

Removal

1) Drain cooling system. Remove air cleaner and duct assembly. Remove fan shroud and position over fan. Remove A/C idler pulley and bracket (if equipped).

2) Remove all hoses and brackets attached to water pump (including coil and bracket, on EEC-equipped vehicles). On "E" Series models, remove radiator. Remove all drive belts, fan, spacer, pulley and shroud.

Installation

1) Clean all gasket mating surfaces. Transfer fittings to new pump (if required). Coat new gasket on both sides with gasket sealer, and position on cylinder front cover.

2) Install water pump and tighten attaching bolts. Reverse removal procedure to install remaining components.

NOTE: For information on cooling system capacities and other cooling system components, see appropriate article in "Engine Cooling Systems," at end of ENGINE Section.

TIGHTENING SPECIFICATIONS

Application	Ft. Lbs. (N.m)
Camshaft Thrust Plate	9-12 (12-16)
Camshaft Sprocket Bolt	40-45 (54-61)
Connecting Rod Cap	
5.0L	19-24 (26-33)
5.8L	40-45 (54-61)
Cylinder Head	
5.0L	
Step 1	55-65 (75-88)
Step 2	65-72 (88-98)
5.8L	
Step 1	85 (115)
Step 2	95 (129)
Step 3	105-112 (142-152)
Exhaust Manifold	18-24 (24-33)
Flywheel-to-Crankshaft	75-85 (102-115)
Intake Manifold	23-25 (31-34)
Main Bearing Cap	
5.0L	60-70 (81-95)
5.8L	95-105 (129-142)
Oil Filter Adapter	20-30 (27-40)
Oil Pump-to-Cylinder Block	22-32 (30-43)
Rocker Arm Fulcrum Bolt	18-25 (24-34)
Vibration Damper	70-90 (95-122)

Ford V8 Engines

5.0 & 5.8 LITER V8 (Cont.)

ENGINE SPECIFICATIONS

GENERAL SPECIFICATIONS

| Year | DISPLACEMENT | | Fuel System | HP@RPM | Torque Ft. Lbs.@RPM | Compr. Ratio | BORE | | STROKE | |
	Cu. In.	Liters					In.	mm	In.	mm
1983	302	5.0	2-Bbl.	.....	.....	.....	4.00	101.6	3.00	76.2
	351	5.8	2-Bbl.	.....	.....	.....	4.00	101.6	3.50	88.9

VALVES

Engine Size & Valve	Head Diam. In. (mm)	Face Angle	Seat Angle	Seat Width In. (mm)	Stem Diameter In. (mm)	Stem Clearance In. (mm)	Valve Lift In. (mm)
5.0L Intake	1.690-1.694 (42.93-43.03)	44°	45°	.060-.080 (1.52-2.03)	.3416-.3423 (8.677-8.694)	.0010-.0027 (.025-.069)	.....
Exhaust	1.439-1.463 (36.55-37.16)	44°	45°	.060-.080 (1.52-2.03)	.3411-.3418 (8.664-8.682)	.0015-.0032 (.038-.081)	.....
5.8L Intake	1.770-1.794 (44.96-45.57)	44°	45°	.060-.080 (1.52-2.03)	.3416-.3423 (8.677-8.694)	.0010-.0027 (.025-.069)	.....
Exhaust	1.453-1.468 (36.91-37.29)	44°	45°	.060-.080 (1.52-2.03)	.3411-.3418 (8.664-8.682)	.0015-.0032 (.038-.081)	.....

PISTONS, PINS, RINGS

Engine	PISTONS Clearance In. (mm)	PINS Piston Fit In. (mm)	PINS Rod Fit In. (mm)	RINGS Ring No.	RINGS End Gap In. (mm)	RINGS Side Clearance In. (mm)
5.0L	.0018-.0026 (.046-.066)	.0002-.0004 (.005-.010)	Interference Fit	1 & 2	.010-.020 (.25-.51)	.002-.004 (.05-.10)
				3	.010-.035 (.25-.89)	Snug Fit
5.8L	.0018-.0026 (.046-.066)	.0003-.0005 (.008-.013)	Interference Fit	1 & 2	.010-.020 (.25-.51)	.002-.004 (.05-.10)
				3	.010-.035 (.25-.89)	Snug Fit

CRANKSHAFT MAIN & CONNECTING ROD BEARINGS

Engine	MAIN BEARINGS Journal Diam. In. (mm)	MAIN BEARINGS Clearance In. (mm)	MAIN BEARINGS Thrust Bearing	MAIN BEARINGS Crankshaft End Play In. (mm)	CONNECTING ROD BEARINGS Journal Diam. In. (mm)	CONNECTING ROD BEARINGS Clearance In. (mm)	CONNECTING ROD BEARINGS Side Play In. (mm)
5.0L	2.2482-2.2490 (57.104-57.125)	.0008-.0015 (.013-.038)	No. 3	.004-.008 (.10-.20)	2.1228-2.1236 (53.919-53.939)	.0008-.0015 (.020-.038)	.010-.020 (.25-.51)
5.8L	2.9994-3.0002 (76.185-76.205)	.0008-.0015 (.020-.038)	No. 3	.004-.008 (.10-.20)	2.3103-2.3111 (58.682-58.702)	.0008-.0015 (.020-.038)	.010-.020 (.25-.51)

Ford V8 Engines

5.0 & 5.8 LITER V8 (Cont.)

ENGINE SPECIFICATIONS (Cont.)

VALVE SPRINGS

Engine	Free Length In. (mm)	PRESSURE Lbs. @ In. (Kg @ mm)	
		Valve Closed	Valve Open
5.0L			
Intake	2.04 (51.8)	74-82@1.78 (34-37@45.2)	196-212@1.36 (89-96@34.5)
Exhaust	1.85 (47.0)	76-84@1.60 (35-38@40.6)	190-210@1.20 (86-95@30.5)
5.8L			
Intake	2.04 (51.8)	74-82@1.78 (34-37@45.2)	190-210@1.36 (86-95@30.5)
Exhaust	1.85 (47.0)	76-84@1.60 (35-38@40.6)	190-210@1.20 (86-95@30.5)

CAMSHAFT

Engine	Journal Diam. In. (mm)	Clearance In. (mm)	Lobe Lift In. (mm)
5.0L & 5.8L [1]			
No. 1	2.0805-2.0815 (52.845-52.870)	.001-.003 (.03-.08)	[2]
No. 2	2.0655-2.0665 (52.464-52.489)		[3]
No. 3	2.0505-2.0515 (52.083-52.108)		
No. 4	2.0355-2.0365 (51.702-51.727)		
No. 5	2.0205-2.0215 (51.321-51.346)		

[1] — End play is .001-.007" (.03-.18mm).
[2] — 5.0L Int. is .2375" (6.033 mm); Exh. is .2474" (6.284 mm).
[3] — 5.8L Int. & Exh. is .2600" (6.604 mm).

6.9 LITER V8 DIESEL

ENGINE CODING

ENGINE IDENTIFICATION

Engine is identified by a letter code in the eighth position of Vehicle Identification Number (VIN). The VIN is stamped on a metal tab, attached to left upper side of instrument panel, near windshield. The VIN is also found on the Safety Compliance Certification Label, located on left door lock pillar.

ENGINE IDENTIFICATION CODE

Application	Code
6.9L Diesel	1

ENGINE REMOVAL

See Engine Removal at end of ENGINE Section.

MANIFOLDS & CYLINDER HEADS

INTAKE MANIFOLD

Removal

1) Disconnect batteries. Remove air cleaner. Install intake manifold cover (T83T-9424-A). Remove engine oil filler neck. Remove bolts attaching injection pump-to-drive gear.

2) Disconnect electrical connectors to injection pump. Disconnect accelerator cable and speed control cable from throttle lever, if equipped.

3) Remove accelerator cable bracket, with cables attached from intake manifold and position aside. Cap all fuel lines and fittings. Remove fuel filter-to-injection pump fuel line and cap fittings.

4) Remove and cap injection pump inlet elbow and fitting adapter. Remove fuel return line on injection pump, rotate out of the way and cap all fittings. Remove fuel injection lines from nozzles and cap lines and nozzles.

5) Using injection pump mounting wrench (T83T-9000-B), remove 3 nuts attaching injection pump-to-injection pump adapter. Lift injection pump, with nozzle lines attached, up and out of engine compartment.

6) Remove fuel return hose from No. 7 and 8 rear nozzles and from fuel tank. Remove engine wiring harness from engine and engine harness ground cable from back of left cylinder head. Remove intake manifold bolts and manifold from cylinder head.

Installation

1) Install and tighten new intake manifold. Install engine wiring harness on engine. Connect and tighten engine wiring harness ground wire to rear of left cylinder head.

2) Install new "O" ring on drive gear end of injection pump. Move injection pump down and into position. Position alignment dowel on injection pump into alignment hole on drive gear.

3) Install and tighten bolts attaching injection pump-to-drive gear. Install nuts attaching injection pump-to-adapter. Align scribe lines on injection pump flange and injection pump adapter and tighten nuts.

4) Remove caps from nozzles and fuel lines. Using fuel line nut wrench (T83T-9396-A), install and tighten fuel line nuts on nozzles. Connect fuel return line to injection pump and tighten nuts.

5) Using solvent, clean old sealant from injection pump elbow threads and dry thoroughly. Apply a light coating of pipe sealant on elbow threads.

6) Install elbow in injection pump adapter and tighten to 72 INCH lbs. (8 N.m). If necessary, tighten further to align elbow with injection pump fuel inlet line, but do not exceed 360° rotation or 120 INCH lbs. (14 N.m).

7) To complete installation, reverse removal procedure making sure to apply 1/8" bead of RTV sealant to injection pump adapter housing. Start engine and check for leaks.

Fig. 1: Intake Manifold Tightening Sequence

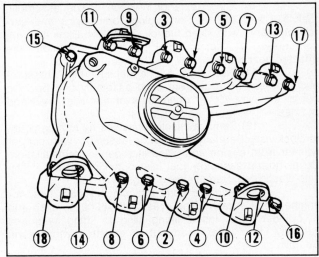

Tighten bolts gradually to 24 ft. lbs. (33 N.m)

EXHAUST MANIFOLDS

Removal

1) Disconnect batteries. Raise vehicle. Disconnect exhaust pipes from manifolds. Bend tabs back on left exhaust manifold. Remove bolts and manifold.

2) Lower vehicle. Bend tabs back on right exhaust manifold. Remove bolts and manifold.

Installation

To install, reverse removal procedure.

CYLINDER HEADS

Removal

1) Disconnect batteries. Drain cooling system. Remove overflow reservoir tube from the radiator neck and upper and lower radiator hoses from the radiator.

2) Remove screws holding 2 halves of the fan shroud together and screws attaching 2 halves to the radiator and remove shroud.

3) Using fan clutch pulley holder and nut wrench (T83T-6312-A and B), remove radiator fan and clutch assembly by turning nut clockwise (left hand thread).

4) Disconnect alternator and fuel supply line heater wiring from alternator. Remove alternator adjusting bolt and pivot bolt and remove vacuum pump.

5) Remove fuel filter inlet, outlet and return lines and cap lines and fittings with protective cap set (T83T-6395-A). Remove alternator and vacuum pump mounting bracket and fuel filter bracket with filter attached.

Ford V8 Engines

6.9 LITER V8 DIESEL (Cont.)

6) Remove heater hose from cylinder head. Remove intake manifold. Remove crankcase depression regulator tube and grommet from valley pan.

7) Remove bolts attaching valley pan strap to front of engine block and remove strap. Remove valley pan drain plug and valley pan.

8) Raise vehicle. Disconnect muffler inlet pipe from exhaust manifolds. Remove right side clamp holding engine oil dipstick tube in position and bolt attaching transmission oil dipstick tube-to-cylinder head.

9) Lower vehicle. Remove right side engine oil dipstick and dipstick tube. Remove valve cover attaching screws and remove covers. Remove valve rocker arm post mounting bolts. Remove valve rocker arms, posts and pushrods in order and mark for reinstallation.

10) Clean exterior of each nozzle assembly, fuel inlet and fuel leak-off piping connections and surrounding area with clean fuel oil or solvent. Blow dry with compressed air. Remove fuel line retaining clamps from effected nozzle lines.

11) Disconnect nozzle fuel inlet (high pressure) and fuel leak-off tees from each assembly and position out of the way. Cover open ends of fuel inlet lines and nozzles.

12) Remove injection nozzles by turning counterclockwise. Carefully pull nozzle assembly with copper washer from engine and place in order for reinstallation. Cover nozzle assembly fuel inlet opening and nozzle tip with plastic cap. Remove glow plugs.

13) Remove bolts attaching cylinder head-to-engine block. Attach lifting eyes (T70P-6000) to each end of cylinder head. Install lifting sling to lifting eyes and carefully lift cylinder head out of engine compartment. Remove gasket.

Fig. 2: Cylinder Head Tightening Sequence

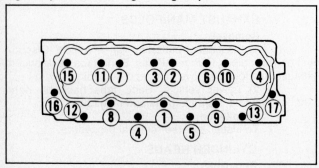

Tighten bolts in 3 steps to 40 ft. lbs. (54 N.m), 60 ft. lbs. (82 N.m) and 75 ft. lbs. (102 N.m).

Installation

Reverse removal procedure to install cylinder heads and note the following: Ensure that gasket surfaces on head and cylinder block are clean and that cylinder head bolt threads and threads in block are clean. Gasket requires no sealer. Apply 1/8" bead of RTV sealant to each end of cylinder block before installing valley cover.

VALVES

VALVE ARRANGEMENT

I-E-I-E-I-E-I-E (Left bank, front to rear)
E-I-E-I-E-I-E-I (Right bank, front to rear)

ROCKER ARM SHAFT ASSEMBLY

Removal & Installation

Remove valve cover attaching screws and remove covers. Remove valve rocker arm post mounting bolts. Remove valve rocker arms, posts and pushrods in order and mark for reinstallation. To install, reverse removal procedure.

VALVE SPRINGS

Removal

With cylinder head removed, compress valve spring and remove valve keepers. *See Fig. 3.* Release spring compressor and remove retainer, spring, damper, seal and exhaust valve rotators.

Installation

To install valve springs, reverse removal procedure. Lubricate and install valve stem oil seal on valve stem before installing remaining components.

Fig. 3: Valve Spring Removal

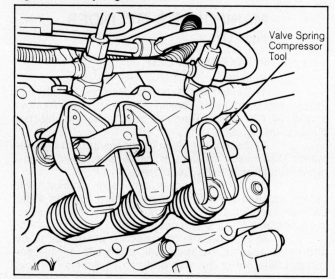

VALVE STEM OIL SEALS

An "O" ring type oil seal is installed on valve stem before valve spring is installed. See Valve Springs.

VALVE GUIDE SERVICING

If valve stem-to-guide clearance is excessive, insert sleeves are available. To install, drill out valve guide and ream drilled guide bore for insert sleeve. Chill repair insert in dry ice. Using arbor press, carefully press insert in cylinder. Replace valve guide.

HYDRAULIC VALVE LIFTERS

NOTE: **Hydraulic lifters used on the diesel engine are of the roller type. Lifters are serviced as complete assemblies only and parts are not interchangeable between lifters.**

Removal

Provide some means of keeping the lifters and push rods in order so that they can be installed in their original locations. Remove valve covers, rocker arm shafts and push rods. Remove lifter guide retainer. Remove lifters.

6.9 LITER V8 DIESEL (Cont.)

Disassembly

Using small screwdriver, remove plunger retainer. Remove pushrod seat and metering valve. Remove plunger and plunger spring.

Inspection

Clean all parts in clean solvent or diesel fuel. Check for nicks, burrs or scoring on parts. Make sure lifter roller operates smoothly and without excessive play.

Reassembly

Coat all parts with clean engine oil, then reverse disassembly procedure.

Installation

Lubricate lifters and bores with clean engine oil. Install lifters into their original position in block. Install lifter guides and guide retainer. Reverse removal procedure to complete assembly.

Fig. 4: Exploded View of Hydraulic Valve Lifter

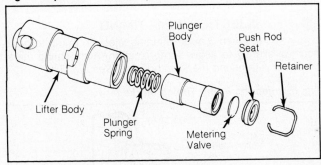

CAMSHAFT

ENGINE FRONT COVER

Removal

1) Disconnect batteries. Drain cooling system. Remove overflow reservoir tube from the radiator neck and upper and lower radiator hoses from the radiator.

2) Remove screws holding 2 halves of the fan shroud together and screws attaching 2 halves to the radiator and remove shroud.

3) Using fan clutch pulley holder and nut wrench (T83T-6312-A and B), remove radiator fan and clutch assembly by turning nut clockwise (left hand thread). Remove engine oil filler neck.

4) Remove bolts attaching injection pump-to-drive gear. Disconnect electrical connectors-to-injection pump. Disconnect accelerator cable and speed control cable from throttle lever, if equipped.

5) Remove accelerator cable bracket, with cables attached from intake manifold and position aside. Cap all fuel lines and fittings. Remove fuel filter-to-injection pump fuel line and cap fittings.

6) Remove and cap injection pump inlet elbow and fitting adapter. Remove fuel return line on injection pump, rotate out of the way and cap all fittings. Remove fuel injection lines from nozzles and cap lines and nozzles.

7) Using injection pump mounting wrench (T83T-9000-B), remove 3 nuts attaching injection pump-to-injection pump adapter. Lift injection pump, with nozzle lines attached, up and out of engine compartment.

8) Loosen power steering pump and A/C compressor and remove drive belts. Loosen vacuum pump and alternator and remove drive belts. Remove water pump pulley.

9) Disconnect heater hose from water pump. Remove heater hose fitting from water pump. Remove alternator adjusting arm and adjusting arm bracket.

10) Remove A/C compressor and position out of the way. Remove A/C compressor brackets. Remove power steering pump and bracket and position out of the way. Remove water pump attaching bolts and pump.

11) Raise vehicle. Remove crankshaft pulley. Remove bolt attaching damper to crankshaft. Install crankshaft vibration damper remover (T83T-6316-A) and remove crankshaft vibration damper.

12) Remove ground cables at front of engine. Remove 5 bolts attaching front cover-to-engine block and oil pan. Lower vehicle. Remove bolts attaching engine front cover-to-engine block and remove cover.

Installation

Clean all sealing surfaces. Apply gasket sealer to engine block sealing surfaces. Install engine block gaskets. Apply 1/8" bead of RTV sealant on front of engine block and 1/4" bead on front of oil pan. Reverse removal procedure to complete installation.

FRONT COVER OIL SEAL

Removal

Remove and support front cover. Using an arbor press, drive handle tool (T80T-4000-W) and a 3 1/4" diameter spacer, drive crankshaft seal out of front cover.

Installation

Coat new front seal with Polyethylene grease. Using seal replacer (T83T-6700-A), a spacer and arbor press, install new seal.

TIMING GEAR

Removal

Remove engine front cover. Remove camshaft allen screw. Install gear puller (T83T-6316-A) and remove gear.

Installation

To install, reverse removal procedure and adjust engine timing.

CAMSHAFT

Removal

1) Remove engine from vehicle and support on engine stand. Remove injection pump and adapter, intake manifold, hydraulic valve lifters and engine front cover.

2) Using flare nut wrench, loosen fuel supply pump threaded connections and retighten snugly. Do not remove lines at this time.

3) Loosen fuel supply pump mounting bolts 1-2 turns. Apply force with hand to loosen fuel pump if gasket is stuck. Rotate engine, by nudging starter, until fuel cam lobe is at low position.

4) Disconnect fuel supply pump inlet, outlet and fuel return line. Remove fuel pump attaching bolts and remove pump and discard gasket.

5) Remove camshaft allen screw. Install gear puller (T83T-6316-A) and remove timing gear. Install gear puller (T77E-4220-B) and shaft protector and remove fuel pump cam and spacer.

6) Remove thrust plate attaching bolts and thrust plate. Using camshaft bearing tool (T65L-6250-A) and camshaft adapter (Rotunda 14-0314), carefully remove camshaft by pulling toward front of engine.

Ford V8 Engines

6.9 LITER V8 DIESEL (Cont.)

Installation

Lubricate camshaft journals and lobes with motor oil. Coat camshaft lobes with Polyethylene grease. Position camshaft to align timing marks on gears. Install remaining components in reverse order of removal.

CAMSHAFT END THRUST

1) Push camshaft toward rear of engine. Install dial indicator so that indicator point is on camshaft sprocket attaching screw. Zero dial indicator.

2) Place a large screwdriver between camshaft sprocket and cylinder block. Pull camshaft forward and release. Camshaft end play should be .001-.009" (.03-.23 mm). If beyond limits, replace thrust plate.

CAM LOBE LIFT

1) Remove fresh air inlet tube and air cleaner and cover opening. Remove rocker arm covers, fulcrum bolts, fulcrum seats, and rocker arms. Make sure push rod end is in valve lifter socket.

2) Use a dial indicator to check lobe lift in consecutive order. Position dial indicator point (or cup-shaped adapter) on end of push rod (in same plane as push rod movement. See Fig. 5.

Fig. 5: Checking Camshaft Lobe Lift

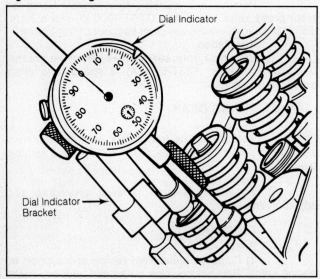

Make sure push rod is in valve lifter socket.

3) Disconnect Brown lead (I terminal) and Red/Blue lead (S terminal) at starter relay. Install a remote starter switch between battery and S terminal of starter relay.

CAUTION: **Starter relay is located on right inner fender near hood/fender parting line. Do not hook starting switch to glow plug relay, located on top of inner fender below starter relay.**

4) Rotate crankshaft until lifter and push rod are at lowest position. Zero dial indicator. Rotate crankshaft slowly until push rod is fully raised. Record dial indicator reading and compare with specifications.

5) Maximum allowable lift loss is .005" (.13 mm). If lift on any lobe is below specification, replace camshaft and valve lifter operating on worn lobes(s).

CAMSHAFT BEARINGS

NOTE: **Camshaft bearings are not interchangeable from one bore to another.**

Removal

1) Camshaft bearings are replaced with engine removed from vehicle. Remove camshaft, flywheel, crankshaft, and rear bearing bore plug.

2) Push pistons to top of cylinders. Using camshaft bearing installer/remover tool, remove camshaft bearings.

Installation

1) Using camshaft bearing installer/remover tool, install bearings into place. Make sure oil holes are properly aligned in each bore.

2) Install front bearing .040-.060" (1.0-1.5 mm) rearward of front face of cylinder block. Install new rear bearing bore plug.

INJECTION PUMP TIMING

Loosen 3 nuts retaining injection pump to gear housing slightly to allow pump rotation. Align timing mark on pump with timing mark on housing. See Fig. 6.

Fig. 6: Injection Pump Timing Marks

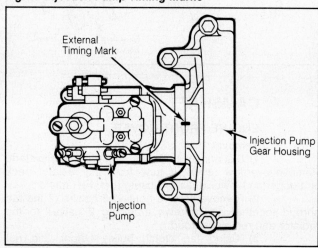

PISTONS, RINGS & PINS

OIL PAN

See Oil Pan Removal at end of ENGINE Section.

PISTON & ROD ASSEMBLY

CAUTION: **Never cut more than 1/32" (.79 mm) into ring travel area.**

Removal

1) Remove cylinder head, oil pan and oil pump. Place piston at bottom of stroke, and cover with a cloth to collect cuttings.

2) Use ridge reamer to remove any ridge or deposit on upper end of cylinder bore. Ensure connecting rods and caps are marked for cylinder identification.

3) Remove rod cap. Push piston and rod out top of cylinder bore. Use care not to damage crankshaft journal or cylinder wall. Install rod cap on mating rod.

6.9 LITER V8 DIESEL (Cont.)

Installation

1) Coat cylinder bore, piston and rings with engine oil. Ensure that ring gaps are properly spaced. *See Fig. 7.* Install a ring compressor on piston.

NOTE: **Large chamfer on connecting rod faces toward front of engine on right bank rods and toward rear of engine on left bank rods.**

Fig. 7: Correctly Spaced Piston Rings

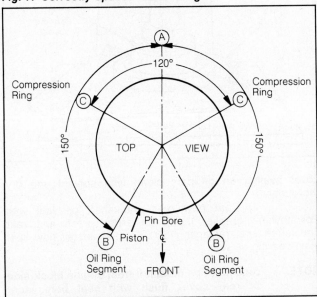

2) Install each piston and rod assembly in its respective bore, with arrow (or notch) on piston head facing toward camshaft.

3) Guide connecting rod onto crankshaft journal until connecting rod bearing seats on crankshaft. Install and tighten rod caps. Reverse removal procedure to complete installation.

FITTING PISTONS

NOTE: **Make all measurements with piston and block at normal room temperature (70°F, 21°C).**

1) Measure piston skirt 90° to piston pin axis. Measure cylinder bore 90° to crankshaft centerline, at top, middle, and bottom of bore. Use these measurements to determine piston-to-cylinder bore clearance.

2) Measure cylinder bore 90° to crankshaft centerline at top of bore (below ring travel) and at bottom of bore (above ring travel). These measurements determine cylinder taper. Taper (difference between the 2 measurements) must not exceed .010" (.25 mm).

3) Measure cylinder bore at center of piston travel, 90° to crankshaft centerline. Measure bore at center of piston travel in line with crankshaft centerline. Out-of-round is the difference between the 2 measurements, and must not exceed .005" (.13 mm).

4) If taper or out-of-round are beyond limits, or cylinder walls are deeply scored, hone or bore cylinders for installation of new pistons. After cylinders have been honed or bored, measure cylinder diameter. Oversize pistons are available in sizes of .010" (.25 mm), .020" (.50 mm) and .030" (.76 mm).

FITTING RINGS

1) Carefully position ring in cylinder bore at a point where normal ring wear is not present. Ring must be square in bore. Check ring end gap with a feeler gauge.

2) Using a feeler gauge, check side clearance of compression rings. Feeler gauge should slide freely around entire circumference of piston without binding. If lower lands have high steps, replace the piston.

PISTON PIN REPLACEMENT

Removal

Using arbor press and piston pin removal tool, press piston pin from piston and connecting rod.

Installation

1) Lightly coat all parts to be assembled with engine oil. Position piston to connecting rod as shown.

2) Start piston pin in piston and connecting rod. Using arbor press and pin installing tool, press pin through piston and connecting rod until it is centered in connecting rod.

CRANKSHAFT, MAIN & CONNECTING ROD BEARINGS

MAIN & CONNECTING ROD BEARINGS

NOTE: **Use Plastigage method for checking bearing clearances. Following procedures are performed with oil pan and oil pump removed. Oil film should be removed from surfaces to be checked.**

Crankshaft Main Bearings

1) Fit main bearings one at a time, while leaving other bearings securely fastened. Make sure main bearing caps are marked for identification.

2) Remove main bearing cap. Wipe oil from all contact surfaces such as crankshaft journal, bearing insert, bearing caps, etc.

3) Use Plastigage method (as explained in Connecting Rod Bearings) to measure main bearing clearance, tightening caps to specifications.

4) Standard size bearings may be used in combination with a .010" (.25 mm), .020" (.50 mm) or .030" (.76 mm) undersize bearing. If undersize main bearings are used, crankshaft must be reground.

Connecting Rod Bearings

1) Ensure rod caps are marked for cylinder identification. Place crankshaft journal of cylinder to be checked at bottom of stroke and remove rod cap.

2) Place strip of Plastigage on bearing surface over full width of cap, about 1/4" (6 mm) off center, and away from oil holes.

3) Install cap and tighten to specifications. Do not allow crankshaft to turn. Remove cap and measure compressed width of Plastigage with scale furnished.

4) To obtain proper bearing clearance, a standard bearing may be used in combination with a .010" (.25 mm), .020" (.50 mm) or .030" (.76 mm) undersize bearing. If undersize connecting rod bearings are used, crankshaft must be reground.

5) Measure connecting rod side clearance after bearings and caps have been installed. *See Fig. 8.*

Ford V8 Engines

6.9 LITER V8 DIESEL (Cont.)

Fig. 8: Measuring Connecting Rod Side Clearance

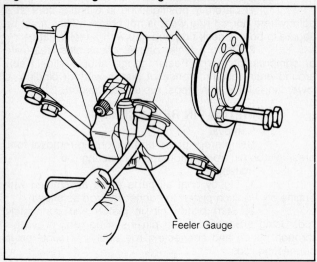

Side clearance is .008-.020" (.20-.51 mm).

THRUST BEARING ALIGNMENT

1) Install thrust bearing cap after all other main bearing caps have been tightened. Install thrust bearing cap bolts finger tight.

2) Pry crankshaft forward against thrust surface of upper half of bearing. Hold crankshaft forward, and pry thrust bearing cap to rear. Tighten cap bolts, while retaining forward pressure on crankshaft. *See Fig. 9.*

REAR MAIN BEARING OIL SEAL
Removal

Remove transmission. If equipped, remove clutch cover and clutch disc. Remove flywheel. Remove and support rear cover. Using an arbor press and 4 1/8" diameter spacer, remove rear oil seal. *See Fig. 10.*

Installation

1) Clean rear cover and engine block gasket surfaces. Remove old RTV sealant from oil pan-to-rear

Fig. 10: Rear Main Bearing Oil Seal Removal

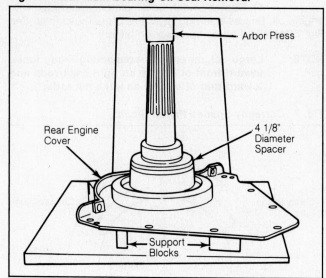

cover sealing on oil pan, clean with solvent and dry thoroughly.

2) Coat new rear crankshaft oil seal with Polyethylene grease. Using an arbor press and rear crankshaft seal replacer (T83T-6701-A), install new rear main bearing oil seal.

NOTE: **Seal must be installed from engine block side of rear cover flush with seal bore inner surface.**

3) Install seal pilot (T83T-6701-B) on crankshaft. Apply gasket sealant to engine block gasket surfaces. Install rear cover gasket to engine block.

4) Immediately prior to rear cover installation, apply a 1/4" bead of RTV sealant on oil sealing surface. Push rear cover into position on engine block, install bolts and tighten. Reverse removal procedure to complete installation.

Fig. 9: Aligning Thrust Bearing

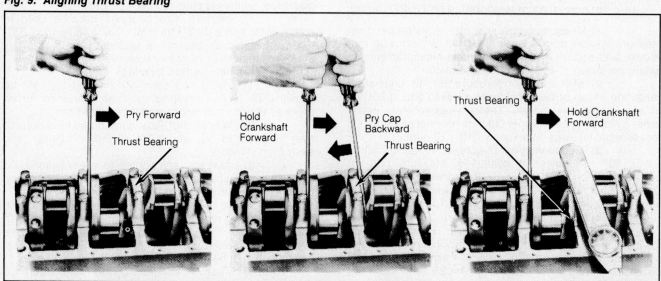

Align thrust bearing after all other bearings have been tightened.

6.9 LITER V8 DIESEL (Cont.)

FRONT OIL SEAL

Removal

1) Disconnect batteries. Remove screws holding 2 halves of the fan shroud together and screws attaching 2 halves to the radiator and remove shroud.

2) Using fan clutch pulley holder and nut wrench (T83T-6312-A and B), remove radiator fan and clutch assembly by turning nut clockwise (left hand thread).

3) Loosen and remove A/C compressor, power steering pump, alternator and vacuum pump drive belts. Raise vehicle. Remove crankshaft pulley. Remove bolt attaching damper to crankshaft.

4) Install crankshaft vibration damper remover (T83T-6316-A) and remove crankshaft vibration damper. To prevent crankshaft rotation, install breaker bar into removal tool. Using a screwdriver, pry out front oil seal from the front cover.

Installation

1) Coat new oil seal with Polyethylene grease. If necessary, rotate crankshaft to align damper key with seal installing tool.

2) On engines with 3 weldnuts on front cover, place seal into front seal replacer (T83T-6700), install over end of crankshaft and attach bridge to weldnuts. Draw seal into front cover by rotating center screw clockwise. Seal is automatically installed at proper depth when tool bottoms on front cover.

3) On engines without 3 weldnuts on front cover, place seal into front seal replacer (T83T-6700), install over end of crankshaft and tighten nut against washer and tool to carefully force seal into front cover plate.

4) On all engines, lubricate damper seal nose with engine oil and install crankshaft vibration damper using damper replacer (T83T-6316-B). Add RTV sealant to engine side of washer to prevent oil leakage past keyway.

5) Install and tighten bolt attaching vibration damper to crankshaft. Install and tighten crankshaft pulley. Lower vehicle. Reverse removal procedure to complete installation.

ENGINE OILING

Crankcase Capacity

9 quarts (8.5L) including filter change.

Oil Filter

Replace every 5,000 miles or 12 months, whichever comes first.

Normal Oil Pressure

40-60 psi (2.81-4.22 kg/cm²) at 2000 RPM.

Oil Pressure Regulator Valve

In oil pump body, non-adjustable.

ENGINE OILING SYSTEM

Full pressure lubrication through a full flow oil filter and oil cooler is supplied by a gear-type oil pump. Main oil gallery feeds oil through drilled passages to camshaft and crankshaft to lubricate bearings. Valve lifter gallery feeds the valve lifters, which feed the rocker arms through hollow push rods.

OIL PUMP

Removal

Remove oil pan, oil pump and pick-up tube.

Fig. 11: Engine Oiling System

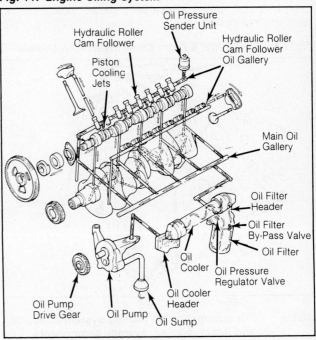

Disassembly & Reassembly

NOTE: Oil pump is serviced as a complete assembly only.

Installation

Remove old gasket material and clean mating surfaces of oil pan, oil pick-up tube, engine block and front and rear covers with solvent and dry thoroughly. Prime oil pump with engine oil. Rotate pump drive gear to distribute oil within pump body. Reverse removal procedure to install.

ENGINE COOLING

WATER PUMP

Removal

1) Disconnect batteries. Drain cooling system. Remove overflow reservoir tube from the radiator neck and upper and lower radiator hoses from the radiator.

2) Remove screws holding 2 halves of the fan shroud together and screws attaching 2 halves to the radiator and remove shroud.

3) Using fan clutch pulley holder and nut wrench (T83T-6312-A and B), remove radiator fan and clutch assembly by turning nut clockwise (left hand thread).

4) Loosen power steering pump, A/C compressor, vacuum pump and alternator and remove drive belts. Remove water pump pulley. Disconnect heater hose from water pump and remove fitting.

5) Remove alternator adjusting nut and bracket. Remove A/C compressor and move out of the way. Remove A/C compressor brackets. Remove power steering pump and bracket and move out of the way. Remove water pump bolts and pump.

Installation

Clean all gasket mating surfaces. Install fabricated dowel pins for water pump alignment. *See Fig. 12.*

Ford V8 Engines

6.9 LITER V8 DIESEL (Cont.)

Coat 2 top and bottom bolts with RTV sealer. Using new gasket, install pump. Reverse removal procedure to complete installation.

Fig. 12: Water Pump & Front Cover Installation Dowels

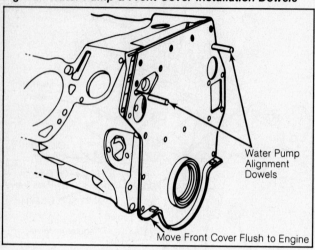

Water Pump
Alignment
Dowels

Move Front Cover Flush to Engine

NOTE: For information on cooling system capacities and other cooling system components, see appropriate article in "Engine Cooling Systems," at end of ENGINE Section.

TIGHTENING SPECIFICATIONS

Application	Ft. Lbs. (N.m)
Camshaft Gear Screw	12-18 (17-24)
Connecting Rod Cap Bolts	[1]
Cylinder Head Bolts	[2]
Exhaust Manifold Bolts	30 (41)
Flywheel-to-Crankshaft	38 (52)
Injection Nozzle	33 (45)
Injection Pump Adapter	14 (19)
Injection Pump Outlet Fitting Nut	22 (30)
Intake Manifold Bolts	24 (33)
Main Bearing Cap Bolts	[3]
Vibration Damper-to-Crankshaft	90 (122)
Water Pump Cover Bolts	14 (19)

[1] — Tighten to 38 ft. lbs. (52 N.m), then to 46-51 ft. lbs. (62-68 N.m)

[2] — Tighten to 40 ft. lbs (54 N.m), then to 60 ft. lbs. (82 N.m) and finally to 75 ft. lbs. (102 N.m).

[3] — Tighten to 75 ft. lbs. (102 N.m), then to 95 ft. lbs. (129 N.m).

ENGINE SPECIFICATIONS

GENERAL SPECIFICATIONS

Year	DISPLACEMENT		Fuel System	HP@RPM	Torque Ft. Lbs.@RPM	Compr. Ratio	BORE		STROKE	
	Cu. In.	Liters					In.	mm	In.	mm
1983	420	6.9	Diesel	.....	.....	20.7:1	4.00	101.6	4.18	106.2

VALVES

Engine Size & Valve	Head Diam. In. (mm)	Face Angle	Seat Angle	Seat Width In. (mm)	Stem Diameter In. (mm)	Stem Clearance In. (mm)	Valve Lift In. (mm)
6.9L Intake	.....	30°	30°	.065-.095 (1.65-2.41)	.3716-.3723 (9.439-9.456)	.0012-.0029 (.030-.073)	.....
Exhaust	.....	37.5°	37.5°	.065-.095 (1.65-2.41)	.3716-.3723 (9.439-9.456)	.0012-.0029 (.030-.073)	.....

PISTONS, PINS, RINGS

Engine	PISTONS	PINS		RINGS		
	Clearance In. (mm)	Piston Fit In. (mm)	Rod Fit In. (mm)	Ring No.	End Gap In. (mm)	Side Clearance In. (mm)
6.9L	.0055-.0075 (.140-.190)	.0003-.0007 (.008-.018)	.0004-.0009 (.010-.023)	1	.014-.024 (.36-.61)	.002-.004 (.05-.10)
				2	.010-.024 (.25-.61)	.002-.004 (.05-.10)
				3	.060-.070 (1.52-1.78)	.001-.003 (.03-.08)

Ford V8 Engines

6.9 LITER V8 DIESEL (Cont.)

ENGINE SPECIFICATIONS (Cont.)

CRANKSHAFT MAIN & CONNECTING ROD BEARINGS

Engine	MAIN BEARINGS				CONNECTING ROD BEARINGS		
	Journal Diam. In. (mm)	Clearance In. (mm)	Thrust Bearing	Crankshaft End Play In. (mm)	Journal Diam. In. (mm)	Clearance In. (mm)	Side Play In. (mm)
6.9L	3.1228-3.1236 (79.319-79.339)	.0018-.0046 (.046-.117)	No.3	.001-.012 (.03-.30)	2.4980-2.4990 (63.449-63.475)	.0011-.0036 (.028-.091)	.008-.020 (.20-.51)

VALVE SPRINGS

Engine	Free Length In. (mm)	PRESSURE Lbs. @ In. (Kg @ mm)	
		Valve Closed	Valve Open
6.9L Intake	2.04 (51.8)	60@1.80 (27@45.7)	.....
Exhaust	2.04 (51.8)	60@1.80 (27@45.7)	.....

CAMSHAFT

Engine	Journal Diam. In. (mm)	Clearance In. (mm)	Lobe Lift In. (mm)
6.9L	2.0990-2.1000 (53.315-53.340)	.001-.005 (.03-.13)	.....

ENGINE CODING

ENGINE IDENTIFICATION

Engine is identified by a letter code in eighth position of Vehicle Identification Number (VIN). VIN is located near windshield on left upper side of instrument panel. The VIN number is also located on the Safety Compliance Certification Label, attached to left door lock pillar.

ENGINE IDENTIFICATION CODE

Engine	Code
7.5L 4-Bbl.	L

ENGINE REMOVAL

See Engine Removal at end of ENGINE Section.

MANIFOLDS & CYLINDER HEAD

INTAKE MANIFOLD
Removal
1) Drain cooling system. Remove air cleaner and ducting. Disconnect coolant hoses at intake manifold and water pump, and position aside.

2) Remove PCV valve and hose. Label and disconnect all vacuum hoses at carburetor, vacuum control valve and intake manifold.

3) Disconnect spark plug wires at spark plugs and remove wires from brackets on rocker arm covers. Disconnect high-tension lead at coil. Remove distributor cap and spark plug wires as an assembly.

4) Remove distributor with vacuum hoses attached. Disconnect accelerator linkage. If equipped, disconnect transmission kickdown linkage and speed control linkage bracket at carburetor.

5) Remove accelerator linkage attaching bolts. Position all linkages out of way. Disconnect fuel line at carburetor.

6) Label and disconnect all electrical wiring from intake manifold. Remove coil and bracket assembly. Remove intake manifold and carburetor as an assembly.

Installation
1) Clean all gasket surfaces. Apply 1/8" bead silicone sealer to 4 corners of cylinder block seal mounting surface. *See Fig. 1.*

Fig. 1: Intake Manifold Sealer Application Points

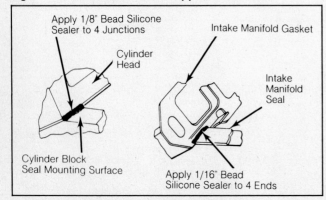

Apply 1/8" Bead Silicone Sealer to 4 Junctions

Intake Manifold Gasket

Cylinder Head

Intake Manifold Seal

Cylinder Block Seal Mounting Surface

Apply 1/16" Bead Silicone Sealer to 4 Ends

Install intake manifold within 15 minutes after sealer application.

2) Install manifold gasket and front and rear seals. Apply 1/16" bead silicone sealer along full width of front and rear seal ends. *See Fig. 1.*

3) Position intake manifold over 4 studs in cylinder heads. Check for proper alignment of gaskets and seals before tightening. Tighten intake manifold, then repeat tightening sequence. *See Fig. 2.*

Fig. 2: Intake Manifold Tightening Sequence

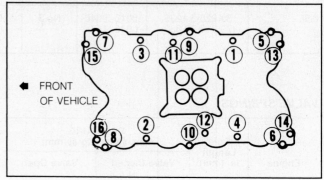

FRONT OF VEHICLE

Tighten to 22-32 ft. lbs. (30-43 N.m), then repeat tightening sequence.

4) To install remaining components, reverse removal procedure. Retighten intake manifold after engine has reached normal operating temperature.

EXHAUST MANIFOLD
Removal
1) If removing right exhaust manifold, remove air cleaner, ducting and heat shroud. Remove spark plug wires from spark plugs.

2) Disconnect exhaust pipe from exhaust manifold. Remove attaching bolts, then remove manifold, lifting bracket and spark plug heat shields.

Installation
1) Clean mating surfaces of cylinder head and manifold. Clean mounting flange of manifold and exhaust pipe.

2) Apply light film of graphite grease to manifold machined surface. Position spark plug wire heat shields and exhaust manifold on cylinder head.

3) Install attaching bolts and washers, starting at 4th bolt hole from front of each manifold. Position lifting bracket under bolts at 3rd exhaust port from front of engine.

4) On right exhaust manifold, install shoulder stud for air intake heat shroud at 1st and 6th bolt holes from front of manifold.

5) Install shoulder stud for dipstick tube in 1st hole of left exhaust manifold. Tighten exhaust manifold. Using new gaskets, install and tighten exhaust pipes.

CYLINDER HEAD
Removal
1) Drain cooling system. Remove intake manifold. Disconnect exhaust pipes at manifolds. Loosen alternator attaching bolts and remove bolt attaching alternator bracket to right cylinder head.

2) If A/C equipped, loosen drive belt. Shut off compressor at service valves and remove valves and hoses from compressor.

3) Remove A/C compressor support bracket attaching nuts from water pump. Remove and position

Ford V8 Engines

7.5 LITER V8 (Cont.)

compressor aside. Remove compressor upper mounting bracket from cylinder head.

4) If equipped, remove bolts attaching power steering reservoir bracket to left cylinder head. Position reservoir and bracket out of way.

5) Remove rocker arm covers. Remove rocker arm assemblies and push rods in sequence, so they can be installed in their original positions.

6) Remove cylinder heads and exhaust manifolds as assemblies. Discard cylinder head gaskets.

Installation

1) Clean gasket mating surfaces. Check flatness of cylinder head and block mating surfaces. If exhaust manifolds were removed, install on cylinder head.

2) Place 2 long head bolts in 2 rear lower bolt holes of left cylinder head. Place 1 long head bolt in rear lower bolt hole of right cylinder head. Keep bolts in position until heads are installed.

3) Position head gaskets on block. DO NOT apply sealer to head gasket surfaces. Install and tighten cylinder heads in 3 steps. *See Fig. 3.*

Fig. 3: Cylinder Head Tightening Sequence

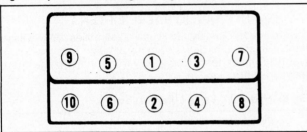

Tighten first to 80 ft. lbs. (108 N.m); then to 110 ft. lbs. (149 N.m); and finally to 130-140 ft. lbs. (176-190 N.m).

4) To install remaining components, reverse removal procedure. Adjust valve clearance as explained in Valve Clearance Adjustment.

Fig. 4: Rocker Arm Assembly

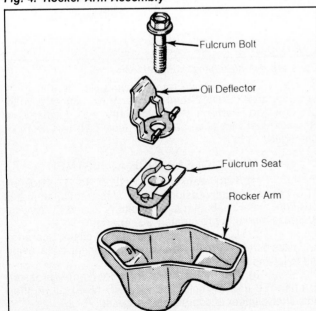

- Fulcrum Bolt
- Oil Deflector
- Fulcrum Seat
- Rocker Arm

Tighten rocker arm fulcrum bolt to 18-25 ft. lbs. (24-34 N.m).

VALVES

VALVE ARRANGEMENT

E-I-E-I-E-I-E-I (Left bank, front to rear)
I-E-I-E-I-E-I-E (Right bank, front to rear)

ROCKER ARM ASSEMBLY

1) Inspect all rocker arm components for excessive wear or damage, and replace as necessary.

2) Before installing rocker arm assembly, lubricate top of valve stem, fulcrum seat and socket area of rocker arm with polyethylene grease (or equivalent).

3) Ensure fulcrum seat base is inserted in its slot on cylinder head, before tightening fulcrum bolt. *See Fig. 4.*

VALVE SPRINGS

Removal

1) Remove air cleaner and duct assembly. Remove rocker arm cover and spark plug from cylinder to be serviced.

2) Crank engine until piston is at TDC at end of compression stroke. Remove rocker arms and push rods from valves to be serviced.

3) Install an air hose with adapter into spark plug hole and turn on air supply. DO NOT shut off air pressure until told to do so.

4) Install rocker arm fulcrum bolt. Use spring compressor tool to compress valve spring and remove retainer locks. Remove retainer, spring and oil seal. *See Fig. 5.*

Fig. 5: Removing and Installing Valve Spring

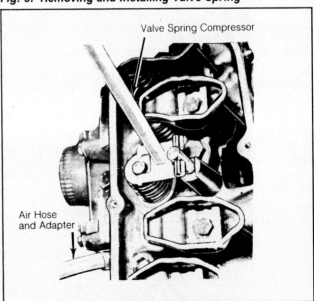

Valve Spring Compressor

Air Hose and Adapter

If air pressure fails to hold valve closed, remove cylinder head and inspect for possible valve damage.

Inspection

1) Wrap a rubber band or tape around end of valve stem. This will keep valve from falling into cylinder, if air pressure forces piston downward. Turn off air supply.

2) Inspect valve stem for wear and out-of-round condition. Move valve up and down in guide and check for binding.

3) Using valve spring tester, test springs for proper tension. Replace springs that fail to meet specifications.

4) Inspect each spring for squareness, using a steel square and flat surface. Measure gap between top spring coil and square, while slowly rotating spring. Replace spring if more than 5/64" out-of-square. *See Fig. 6.*

Fig. 6: Checking Valve Spring Squareness

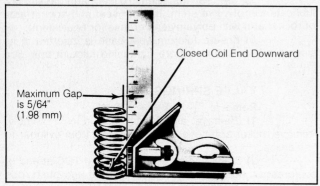

Measure gap, while slowly rotating spring.

Installation

1) If valve proves satisfactory, hold valve in closed position and turn air pressure on again. Install valve stem oil seals.

2) Place spring in position over valve and position spring retainer in place. Compress valve spring and install retainer locks. *See Fig. 5.*

3) Apply polyethylene grease (or equivalent) to push rod ends, valve stem tip, fulcrum seats and sockets.

4) Install push rods and rocker arms. Turn off air pressure. Remove air hose and adapter. To install remaining components, reverse removal procedure.

VALVE SPRING INSTALLED HEIGHT

CAUTION: Install spacers only if necessary. Excess use of spacers will overstress the valve train, causing unnecessary damage.

1) Using dividers and a scale, measure installed height of valve spring. Measure from surface of cylinder head spring pad to underside of spring retainer (or rotator). *See Fig. 7.*

Fig. 7: Checking Installed Height of Valve Spring

Do not install spacer(s) unless necessary.

2) If height is greater than specified, install .030" (.76 mm) spacer(s) between cylinder head spring pad and valve spring, to correct spring height.

VALVE SPRING INSTALLED HEIGHT SPECIFICATIONS

Application	Measurement In. (mm)
All	1 51/64 - 1 53/64 (45.64-46.43)

VALVE STEM OIL SEALS

Umbrella-type oil seals are used on all valves. Lubricate valve stem with engine oil and install new seal with cup-side down over valve guide. Use a 5/8" deep-well socket and light mallet to seat seal on valve stem.

VALVE GUIDE SERVICING

When reaming guides, always use reamers in proper sequence. Always reface valve seats and valves after valve guides are reamed. Replacement valves are available with standard, .015" (.38 mm), and .030 (.76 mm) oversize stems.

HYDRAULIC VALVE LIFTERS

1) Service lifters as assemblies only. Disassemble lifters and clean, prior to testing. Test lifters with hydraulic lifter test fluid. DO NOT interchange parts between lifters. *See Fig. 8.*

Fig. 8: Hydraulic Valve Lifter Assembly

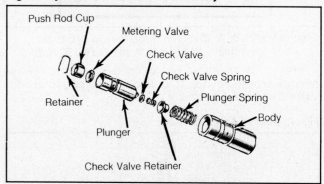

Parts are not interchangeable between lifters.

2) Leak-down rate on hydraulic lifters is 10-50 seconds at 1/16" (1.59 mm) plunger travel, under a 50 lb. (23 kg) load. Perform test using lifter leak-down tester. Replace lifter if it fails leak-down test, or if it is worn or damaged.

VALVE CLEARANCE ADJUSTMENT

1) Turn crankshaft to place No. 1 piston on TDC at end of compression stroke. With crankshaft in this position, make chalk marks at points A, B and C. *See Fig. 9.* Space marks approximately 90° apart.

2) Using *Fig. 9* as a reference, check clearance of valves listed in Valve Clearance Adjustment table, using the following procedure:

3) Using lifter bleed-down tool, apply pressure to push rod end of rocker arm. Slowly bleed down lifter, until lifter plunger is completely bottomed.

4) While holding lifter in this position, check clearance between rocker arm and valve stem tip with a feeler gauge.

7.5 LITER V8 (Cont.)

Fig. 9: Crankshaft Positions for Checking Valve Clearance

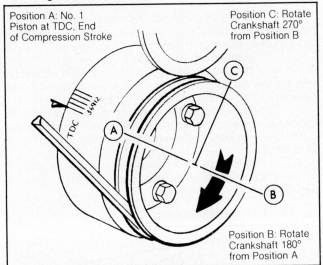

Position A: No. 1 Piston at TDC, End of Compression Stroke

Position C: Rotate Crankshaft 270° from Position B

Position B: Rotate Crankshaft 180° from Position A

Space chalk marks approximately 90° apart.

5) Desired collapsed lifter gap clearance is .075-.175" (1.91-4.45 mm); allowable clearance is .100-.150" (2.54-3.81 mm).

6) If clearance is less than specified, install a .060" (1.52 mm) shorter push rod; if clearance is greater, install a .060" (1.52 mm) longer push rod.

VALVE CLEARANCE ADJUSTMENT

Crankshaft Position	Check Int. Nos.	Check Ex. Nos.
A	1, 7, 8	1, 5, 4
B	4, 5	2, 6
C	2, 3, 6	3, 7, 8

CAMSHAFT

ENGINE FRONT COVER

Removal

1) Drain cooling system and crankcase. Remove fan and radiator shroud. Disconnect radiator hoses at engine and oil cooler lines at radiator and remove radiator.

2) Remove all drive belts and water pump pulley. Remove air pump. If equipped, remove A/C compressor support bracket from water pump. Disconnect heater hose from water pump and loosen by-pass hose clamp at pump.

3) Remove crankshaft pulley, vibration damper and Woodruff key from crankshaft. Disconnect and plug fuel line inlet at fuel pump and remove fuel pump. Remove bolts attaching front cover to cylinder block.

4) Using a thin blade knife, cut oil pan seal flush with cylinder block face. Remove front cover and water pump as an assembly. Discard front cover gasket and pan seal.

Installation

1) Coat gasket surface of oil pan with gasket sealer. Cut and position required section of a new seal on oil pan. Apply silicone sealer at block-to-pan junction.

Apply gasket sealer to front cover and cylinder block gasket surfaces.

2) Position front cover on cylinder block. Install front cover seal alignment tool (T68P-6019-A or equivalent) on crankshaft. *See Fig. 10.* Coat threads of cover bolts with oil-resistant sealer and install bolts.

Fig. 10: Aligning Front Cover

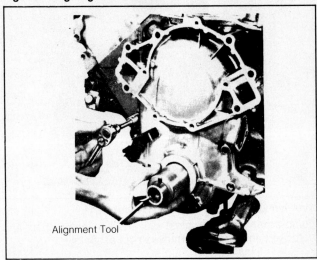

Alignment Tool

To install alignment tool, it may be necessary to force cover downward against pan seal.

3) While pushing in on alignment tool, tighten oil pan-to-cover bolts. Remove tool and tighten cover-to-cylinder block bolts. To install remaining components, reverse removal procedure.

FRONT COVER OIL SEAL

Removal

With engine front cover removed, drive out old oil seal with pin punch. Clean seal recess in front cover.

Installation

Coat new seal with polyethylene grease (or equivalent), and install seal using seal installing tool. Ensure seal spring remains in proper position.

TIMING CHAIN & SPROCKET

NOTE: The following procedures are performed with engine front cover removed.

Checking Timing Chain Deflection

1) Rotate crankshaft counterclockwise (as viewed from front of engine), to take up slack on left side of timing chain.

2) Establish a reference point on the block, and measure from this point to left side of chain. *See Fig. 11.*

3) Rotate crankshaft clockwise to take up slack on right side of chain. Force left side of chain outward and measure distance between reference point and chain.

4) Deflection is the difference between the 2 measurements. If deflection exceeds 1/2" (12.7 mm), replace timing chain and sprockets.

Removal

Turn crankshaft until timing marks are aligned. Remove camshaft sprocket bolt and washer, 2-piece fuel

Ford V8 Engines

7.5 LITER V8 (Cont.)

Fig. 11: Measuring Timing Chain Deflection

Maximum deflection is 1/2" (12.7 mm).

pump eccentric and front oil slinger. Slide timing chain and sprockets forward and remove as an assembly.

Installation

1) Assemble timing chain and sprockets so sprocket timing marks are aligned. *See Fig. 12.* Install chain and sprockets as an assembly.

2) Lubricate timing chain with engine oil. To install remaining components, reverse removal procedure.

Fig. 12: Aligning Timing Marks

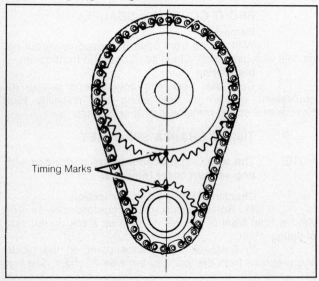

Remove and install chain and sprockets as an assembly.

CAMSHAFT

Removal

1) Remove radiator, front cover, timing chain and sprockets. Remove intake manifold and carburetor as an assembly. Remove rocker arm covers.

2) Loosen all rocker arm bolts. Rotate rocker arms to one side. Remove push rods and valve lifters, keeping them in order for later installation in their original locations.

3) If equipped, remove A/C condenser from chassis, and carefully secure condenser to left fender well.

4) Remove grille. Remove camshaft thrust plate attaching bolts and remove camshaft, taking care not to damage camshaft bearings or journals.

Installation

1) Oil camshaft journals and apply polyethylene grease (or equivalent) to cam lobes. Carefully slide camshaft into position. Install and tighten thrust plate.

2) Lubricate lifters with engine oil and install. Lubricate rocker arms, fulcrum seats, valve stem tips and push rods with polyethylene grease (or equivalent) prior to installing.

3) Reassemble components in reverse order of removal procedures, using new gaskets where required. *See Fig. 13.*

Fig. 13: Camshaft Assembly

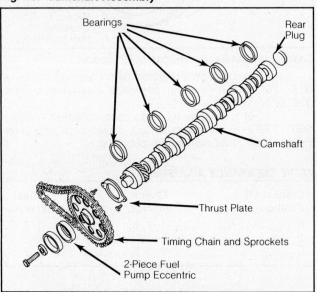

Tighten camshaft sprocket bolt to 40-45 ft. lbs. (54-61 N.m).

CAMSHAFT END THRUST

CAUTION: Do not pry against camshaft sprocket, without first relieving the valve train load on the camshaft.

1) Loosen rocker arm fulcrum bolts to relieve load on camshaft. Push camshaft towards rear of engine.

2) Install dial indicator so that indicator point is on camshaft sprocket attaching bolt. Zero dial indicator.

3) Pull camshaft forward and release. Check dial indicator reading to obtain end play. If end play is excessive, replace camshaft thrust plate.

CAM LOBE LIFT

1) Remove rocker arm cover. Remove fulcrum bolt, fulcrum seat and rocker arm. Make sure push rod end is in valve lifter socket. Use a remote starter switch to turn crankshaft.

2) Use a dial indicator to check lobe lift in consecutive order. Position dial indicator point (or cup-shaped adapter) on end of push rod (in same plane as push rod movement).

7.5 LITER V8 (Cont.)

3) Turn crankshaft until lifter and push rod are at lowest position. Zero dial indicator. Turn crankshaft slowly until push rod is fully raised. Compare dial indicator reading with specifications.

4) Maximum allowable lift loss is .005" (.13 mm). If lift on any lobe is below specifications, replace camshaft and valve lifter(s) operating on worn lobe(s).

CAMSHAFT BEARINGS

Removal

1) Remove engine from vehicle. Remove camshaft, flywheel and crankshaft. Push pistons to top of cylinders.

2) Remove camshaft rear bearing bore plug. Using camshaft bearing installer/remover tool, remove cam bearings.

Installation

1) Using camshaft bearing installer/remover tool, install bearings into place. Oil holes in bearings and cylinder block must be aligned.

2) Install front bearing .040-.060" (1.02-1.52 mm) rearward of front face of cylinder block. Coat new rear bore plug with sealer and install. See *Fig. 14*.

Fig. 14: Installing Camshaft Bearings

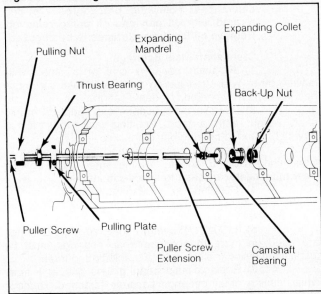

Install front cam bearing .040-.060" (1.02-1.52 mm) rearward from front face of block.

PISTON, RINGS & PINS

OIL PAN

See Oil Pan Removal at end of ENGINE Section.

PISTON & ROD ASSEMBLY

Removal

1) Remove cylinder heads, oil pan and oil pump. Place piston at bottom of its stroke and cover with a cloth to collect metal cuttings. Use ridge reamer to remove ridge or deposits from upper end of cylinder bore.

NOTE: Never cut into ring travel area in excess of 1/32" (.79 mm), when removing ridge.

2) Ensure that all connecting rods and caps are marked for cylinder identification. Remove rod cap. Push piston and rod out top of cylinder. Use care not to damage crankshaft journal or cylinder wall. Install rod cap on mating rod.

Installation

1) Coat cylinder bore, piston and rings with engine oil. Space ring gaps as shown in *Fig. 15*. Install ring compressor. Do not allow ring gaps to change.

Fig. 15: Correctly Spaced Ring Gaps

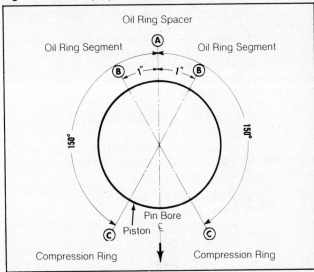

Space oil ring segments 1" (25.4 mm) from oil ring spacer.

2) Position crankshaft journal at bottom of stroke. Place piston into bore, with notch in piston head towards front of engine.

3) Carefully push piston into cylinder bore until it is slightly below top of cylinder, then push it downward until rod bearing seats on crankshaft journal.

4) Install and tighten connecting rod cap. Check side clearance between connecting rods on each crankshaft journal. Install cylinder heads, oil pump and oil pan.

FITTING PISTONS

NOTE: Take measurements at normal room temperature (70°F, 21°C).

1) Measure piston at centerline of piston pin, 90° to piston pin axis. Measure cylinder bore 90° to crankshaft centerline, at top, middle, and bottom of bore. Use measurements to determine piston-to-bore clearance.

2) Measure cylinder bore 90° to crankshaft centerline at top of bore (below ring travel) and at bottom of bore (above ring travel).

3) Taper is the difference between the 2 measurements. Taper must not exceed .010" (.25 mm).

4) Measure cylinder bore at center of piston travel, 90° to crankshaft centerline. Measure bore at center of piston travel, in line with crankshaft centerline.

5) Out-of-round is the difference between the 2 measurements, and must not exceed .005" (.13 mm).

6) If taper or out-of-round are not within limits, or cylinder walls are deeply scored, bore and hone cylinders for installation of new pistons. Check Piston Size Code Chart.

Ford V8 Engines

7.5 LITER V8 (Cont.)

PISTON SIZE CODE CHART

Code	Piston Size In. (mm)
Red	4.3585-4.3591 (110.706-110.721)
Blue	4.3597-4.3603 (110.736-110.752)
.003" Oversize	4.3609-4.3615 (110.767-110.782)

FITTING RINGS

1) Position ring squarely in cylinder bore at a point where normal ring wear is not present. Use care not to damage ring or cylinder bore. Check ring end gap with a feeler gauge.

2) Check side clearance of compression rings, by inserting feeler gauge between ring and its lower land.

3) Feeler gauge should slide freely around entire circumference of piston without binding. If lower lands have high steps, replace piston.

PISTON PIN REPLACEMENT

Removal

Using an arbor press and piston pin remover/installer tool, press piston pin from piston and connecting rod. See Fig. 16.

Fig. 16: Tool Arrangement for Removing and Installing Piston Pin

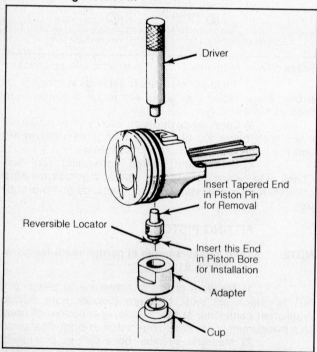

Install pin until end of pin is 1/16-1/8" (1.59-3.18 mm) below chamfer of pin bore.

Installation

1) Apply light coat of engine oil to all parts to be assembled. Assemble piston to connecting rod with numbered side of rod toward outboard side of engine, and notch in piston head positioned forward. See Fig. 17.

2) Start piston pin in piston and connecting rod. Using arbor press and pin remover/installer tool, press pin into piston and connecting rod until end of pin is 1/16-1/8" (1.59-3.18 mm) below chamfer of piston pin bore.

Fig. 17: Proper Piston to Connecting Rod Position

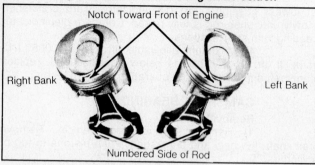

Position numbered side of connecting rod toward outboard side of engine.

CRANKSHAFT, MAIN & CONNECTING ROD BEARINGS

MAIN & CONNECTING ROD BEARINGS

NOTE: Use Plastigage method for checking bearing clearances. Following procedures are performed with oil pan and oil pump removed. Remove oil film from surfaces to be checked.

Crankshaft Main Bearings

1) Fit main bearings one at a time, while leaving other bearings securely fastened. Make sure main bearing caps are marked for identification.

2) Remove main bearing cap. Support crankshaft weight with a jack. Position jack under counterweight, next to bearing being checked.

3) Use Plastigage method (as explained in Connecting Rod Bearings) to measure main bearing clearance, tightening caps to specifications.

4) Standard size bearings may be used in combination with a .001" (.025 mm) or .002" (.051 mm) undersize bearings.

5) If .002" (.051 mm) undersize main bearings are used on more than one journal, bearings must be installed in cylinder block side of crankshaft journal.

6) Replace main bearing sets one at a time, while leaving other bearings securely fastened. Remove bearing cap to which new bearings are to be installed.

7) Insert upper bearing remover/installer tool (6331 or equivalent) into crankshaft journal oil hole. Turn crankshaft in direction of engine rotation, forcing upper bearing out of block.

8) Lightly oil bearing and journal surfaces. Partially install plain end of upper bearing in place. Insert tool (6331 or equivalent) into journal oil hole.

9) Turn crankshaft slowly in opposite direction of engine rotation until bearing is seated, then remove tool. Install and tighten main bearing cap.

Connecting Rod Bearings

1) Ensure rod caps are marked for cylinder identification. Place crankshaft journal of cylinder to be checked at bottom of stroke and remove rod cap.

2) Place strip of Plastigage on bearing surface over full width of cap about 1/4" off center, and away from oil holes. Install cap and tighten to specifications. Do not allow crankshaft to turn.

Fig. 18: Aligning Thrust Bearing

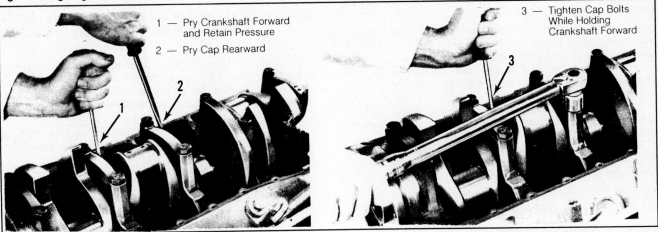

1 — Pry Crankshaft Forward
and Retain Pressure
2 — Pry Cap Rearward

3 — Tighten Cap Bolts
While Holding
Crankshaft Forward

Align thrust bearing after all other bearings have been tightened.

3) Remove cap and measure compressed width of Plastigage. A standard bearing may be used with a .001" (.025 mm) or .002" (.051 mm) undersize bearing to obtain proper bearing clearance.

4) With rod cap and bearing installed, check connecting rod side clearance between rod and crankshaft thrust face.

THRUST BEARING ALIGNMENT

1) Install thrust bearing cap after all other main bearing caps have been tightened. Install thrust bearing cap bolts finger tight.

2) Pry crankshaft forward against thrust surface of upper half of bearing. Hold crankshaft forward, and pry thrust bearing cap to rear.

3) Tighten thrust bearing cap bolts, while retaining forward pressure on crankshaft. *See Fig. 18.*

REAR MAIN BEARING OIL SEAL

Removal

1) Remove oil pan and oil pump (if required). Loosen all main bearing cap bolts to slightly lower crankshaft. Do not lower more than 1/32" (.79 mm).

2) Remove rear main bearing cap and remove lower oil seal half. Use seal removing tool to remove upper seal.

3) If seal removing tool not available, install a small metal screw in one end of the seal. Pull on screw to remove seal. Use care not to damage crankshaft seal surface.

4) If equipped, remove oil seal retaining pin from bearing cap. The pin is not used with the split-lip type seal.

Installation

1) Carefully clean oil seal grooves in bearing cap and block. Dip split-lip seal halves in engine oil.

2) Carefully install upper seal into groove in cylinder block, with undercut side of seal towards front of engine.

CAUTION: Avoid damage to outside diameter of seal when installing in groove. Do not allow oil to get onto area where sealer will be applied.

Fig. 20: Silicone Sealer Application Points

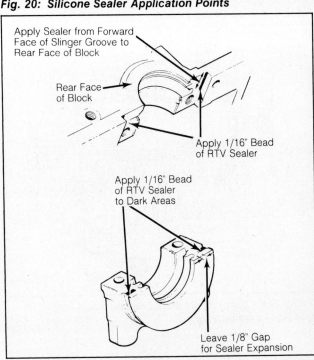

Apply Sealer from Forward
Face of Slinger Groove to
Rear Face of Block

Rear Face
of Block

Apply 1/16" Bead
of RTV Sealer

Apply 1/16" Bead
of RTV Sealer
to Dark Areas

Leave 1/8" Gap
for Sealer Expansion

Do not allow sealer to contact lip of seal.

Fig. 19: Installing Rear Main Bearing Oil Seal

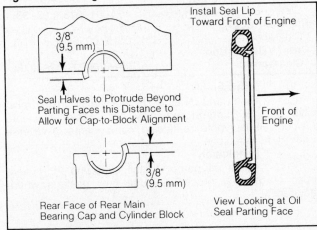

Install Seal Lip
Toward Front of Engine

3/8"
(9.5 mm)

Seal Halves to Protrude Beyond
Parting Faces this Distance to
Allow for Cap-to-Block Alignment

Front of
Engine

3/8"
(9.5 mm)

Rear Face of Rear Main
Bearing Cap and Cylinder Block

View Looking at Oil
Seal Parting Face

Use care not to damage crankshaft or new oil seal.

3) Rotate seal on crankshaft journal until approximately 3/8" of seal protrudes below parting surface. *See Fig. 19.*

4) Tighten all main bearing cap bolts, except rear main. Install lower seal in rear main bearing cap with undercut side of seal towards front of engine.

5) Allow seal to protrude approximately 3/8" above parting surface, to mate with upper seal when cap is installed.

6) Apply 1/16" bead of silicone sealer to both sides of cylinder block-to-cap mating surface, and to both sides of bearing cap. *See Fig. 20.*

7) Install and tighten rear main bearing cap before sealer sets up (approximately 15 minutes). Install remaining components in reverse order of removal.

ENGINE OILING

Crankcase Capacity
Capacity is 5 quarts (4.75L). Add 1 quart (.95L) when replacing oil filter.

Oil Filter
Change filter at first oil change, and at every other oil change thereafter.

Normal Oil Pressure
At normal operating temperature, oil pressure should be 40-65 psi (2.8-4.6 kg/cm²) at 2,000 RPM.

Oil Pressure Regulator Valve
Located in pump body, not adjustable.

ENGINE OILING SYSTEM

Distributor driven oil pump provides full pressure lubrication to all camshaft and crankshaft bearings.

Engine feeds oil through hydraulic valve lifters and hollow push rods to rocker arms and upper valve train area.

Timing chain and sprockets are lubricated by drainage from No. 1 camshaft bearing. *See Fig. 21.*

Fig. 21: Engine Oiling System

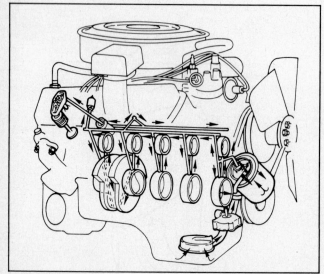

Timing chain components are lubricated by oil flow from No. 1 cam bearing.

OIL PUMP

NOTE: **If any part of the oil pump requires replacement, replace the entire pump.**

Removal
1) Raise engine a minimum of 4" from engine mounts. Loosen oil pan attaching bolts and lower pan.

2) Remove oil pump and oil inlet tube and lay assembly in pan. Remove pan with pump assembly.

Disassembly
1) Remove oil inlet tube from pump. Remove pump cover. Remove inner rotor and shaft and outer rotor from oil pump.

2) Drill small hole in oil pressure relief valve cap. Insert self-threading sheet metal screw into cap, and pull cap from chamber. Remove spring and plunger.

Inspection
1) Wash all parts thoroughly and dry with compressed air. Check pump housing, outer rotor, inner rotor and shaft, and pump cover for damage, scoring or excessive wear.

2) Remove rotor assembly from pump housing. Using feeler gauge, measure inner-to-outer rotor tip clearance.

3) Install rotor assembly in pump housing. Lay a straightedge over rotor assembly and housing. Insert feeler gauge between straightedge and housing to measure rotor end play.

4) Using a feeler gauge, measure clearance between outer rotor and pump housing. Measurement is outer rotor-to-housing clearance.

5) Measure the shaft outside diameter and the housing bearing inside diameter. Difference between readings is the shaft-to-housing bearing clearance.

6) Relief valve spring should test to 20.6-22.6 lbs. (9-10 kg) at 2.49" (63.5 mm). Inspect relief valve spring for worn or collapsed condition.

7) Check relief valve plunger for scores and free operation in bore. Check clearance between relief valve plunger and bore.

OIL PUMP SPECIFICATIONS

Application	Specifications In. (mm)
Rotor Tip Clearance	.012 (.30)
Rotor End Play	.004 (.10) Max.
Outer Rotor-to-Housing Clearance	.001-.013 (.03-.33)
Shaft-to-Housing Clearance	.0015-.0030 (.038-.076)
Relief Valve-to-Bore Clearance	.0015-.0030 (.038-.076)

Reassembly
Clean and oil all parts thoroughly. Install relief valve plunger, spring and new cap. Stake cap into position. Reassemble remaining components in reverse order of disassembly.

Installation
Prime oil pump. Install oil pump in reverse order of removal procedure. Use new gaskets where required.

7.5 LITER V8 (Cont.)

ENGINE COOLING

WATER PUMP

Removal

1) Drain cooling system. Remove fan shroud and fan. Loosen power steering pump attaching bolts. If A/C equipped, remove compressor top bracket. Remove A/C idler pulley and bracket assembly.

2) Remove all drive belts. Remove air pump, alternator and bracket, and power steering pump. Disconnect all hoses from water pump, and loosen by-pass hose clamp at pump.

3) Remove remaining attaching bolts and remove water pump. Remove separator plate from water pump and discard gaskets.

Installation

To install, reverse removal procedures. Use new gaskets coated on both sides with water resistant sealer.

NOTE: For information on cooling system capacities and other cooling system components, see appropriate article in "Engine Cooling Systems," at end of ENGINE Section.

TIGHTENING SPECIFICATIONS

Application	Ft. Lbs. (N.m)
Camshaft Sprocket	40-45 (54-61)
Camshaft Thrust Plate	9-12 (12-16)
Connecting Rod Cap	45-50 (61-68)
Cylinder Head	
Step 1	80 (108)
Step 2	110 (149)
Step 3	130-140 (176-190)
Exhaust Manifold	28-33 (38-45)
Flywheel-to-Crankshaft	75-85 (102-115)
Intake Manifold	22-32 (30-43)
Main Bearing Cap	95-105 (129-142)
Oil Filter	
Adapter-to-Cylinder Block	40-50 (54-68)
Insert-to-Cylinder Block/Adapter	45-55 (61-75)
Oil Pump Attaching Bolts	22-32 (30-43)
Rocker Arm Fulcrum Bolt	18-25 (24-34)
Vibration Damper-to-Crankshaft	70-90 (95-122)

ENGINE SPECIFICATIONS

GENERAL SPECIFICATIONS

Year	DISPLACEMENT		Fuel System	HP@RPM	Torque Ft. Lbs.@RPM	Compr. Ratio	BORE		STROKE	
	Cu. In.	Liters					In.	mm	In.	mm
1983	460	7.5	4-Bbl.	.....	.....	.....	4.36	110.7	3.85	97.8

VALVES

Engine Size & Valve	Head Diam. In. (mm)	Face Angle	Seat Angle	Seat Width In. (mm)	Stem Diameter In. (mm)	Stem Clearance In. (mm)	Valve Lift In. (mm)
7.5L Intake	2.075-2.090 (52.70-53.09)	44°	45°	.060-.080 (1.52-2.03)	.3416-.3423 (8.677-8.694)	.0010-.0027 (.025-.069)	.....
Exhaust	1.646-1.661 (41.81-42.19)	44°	45°	.060-.080 (1.52-2.03)	.3416-.3423 (8.677-8.694)	.0010-.0027 (.025-.069)	.....

CAMSHAFT

Engine	Journal Diam. In. (mm)	Clearance In. (mm)	Lobe Lift In. (mm)
7.5L [1]	2.1238-2.1248 (53.945-53.970)	.001-.003 (.03-.08)	.252 [2] (6.40) .278 [3] (7.06)

VALVE SPRINGS

Engine	Free Length In. (mm)	PRESSURE Lbs. @ In. (Kg @ mm)	
		Valve Closed	Valve Open
7.5L Int. & Exh.	2.06 (52.3)	76-84@1.81 (34-38@46.0)	218-240@1.33 (99-109@33.8)

[1] — End play is .001-.006" (.05-.15 mm).
[2] — Intake.
[3] — Exhaust.

Ford V8 Engines

7.5 LITER V8 (Cont.)

ENGINE SPECIFICATIONS (Cont.)

PISTONS, PINS, RINGS

	PISTONS	PINS		RINGS		
Engine	Clearance In. (mm)	Piston Fit In. (mm)	Rod Fit In. (mm)	Ring No.	End Gap In. (mm)	Side Clearance In. (mm)
7.5L	.0022-.0030 (.056-.076)	.0002-.0004 (.005-.010)	Interference Fit	1 & 2 3	.010-.020 (.25-.51) .010-.035 (.25-.89)	.0025-.0045 (.064-.114) Snug

CRANKSHAFT MAIN & CONNECTING ROD BEARINGS

	MAIN BEARINGS				CONNECTING ROD BEARINGS		
Engine	Journal Diam. In. (mm)	Clearance In. (mm)	Thrust Bearing	Crankshaft End Play In. (mm)	Journal Diam. In. (mm)	Clearance In. (mm)	Side Play In. (mm)
7.5L	2.9994-3.0002 (76.185-76.205)	.0008-.0015 (.020-.038)	No. 3	.004-.008 (.10-.20)	2.4992-2.5000 (63.480-63.500)	.0008-.0015 (.020-.038)	.010-.020 (.25-.51)

1.9 LITER 4-CYLINDER

ENGINE CODING

ENGINE IDENTIFICATION

Engine identification number is stamped on a machined pad on left rear side of cylinder block. Pad is located just above oil pan near engine rear cover. Engine type is identified by a letter code (A), in eighth position of Vehicle Identification Number.

ENGINE IDENTIFICATION CODES

Engine	Code
1.9L 2-Bbl.	UMB, UMC, UMD, UMF UMH, UMJ, UMK, UMM

ENGINE REMOVAL

See Engine Removal at end of ENGINE Section.

MANIFOLDS & CYLINDER HEAD

INTAKE MANIFOLD

Removal

1) Drain entire engine cooling system, including cylinder block. Remove air cleaner assembly. Disconnect upper radiator hose and heater hoses from intake manifold, and position out of way.

2) Label and disconnect all vacuum hoses, ventilation hoses and electrical connectors at intake manifold, carburetor and distributor. Disconnect fuel inlet and return hoses from carburetor. Disconnect accelerator cable.

3) Remove bolt and detach oil dipstick tube bracket from intake manifold. Disconnect EGR pipe from EGR valve adapter. Remove intake manifold and carburetor as an assembly.

Installation

Clean all gasket surfaces. Using new gasket, install intake manifold and nuts. Starting at middle of intake manifold and working outward, tighten manifold nuts. Reverse removal procedures to complete installation.

CYLINDER HEAD

Removal

1) Remove cam cover. Remove bolt and detach EGR pipe clamp from rear of cylinder head. Raise vehicle and disconnect exhaust pipe at manifold. Lower vehicle and drain cooling system. Disconnect heater hoses from intake manifold and cylinder head.

2) If equipped, remove A/C compressor and power steering pump and position aside. Disconnect accelerator linkage and fuel hoses at carburetor. Disconnect all necessary electrical connections, vacuum hoses and ventilation hoses, at cylinder head, intake manifold, carburetor and distributor.

3) Rotate distributor until No. 4 piston is on TDC at end of compression stroke. Remove distributor cap and mark rotor to housing relationship. Disconnect spark plug wires at spark plugs, and remove distributor cap with spark plug wires attached. Remove distributor.

4) Remove fuel pump. Lock automatic timing chain adjuster shoe in fully retracted position, by depressing adjuster lock lever with a screwdriver and rotating clockwise (as viewed from top of engine), while pushing in

on shoe. *See Fig. 1.* After locking automatic adjuster, check that chain tension is released.

Fig. 1: Releasing Timing Chain Tension

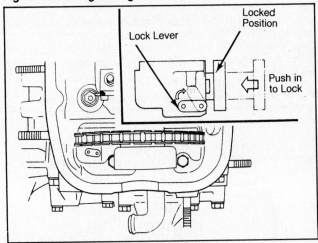

Depress automatic adjuster lock lever and rotate in direction indicated.

5) Remove timing sprocket attaching bolt, and slide camshaft sprocket and fuel pump eccentric from camshaft. Keep the sprocket on the chain damper and tensioner, without removing chain from the sprocket.

6) Disconnect air pump hose and check valve at air injection manifold. Remove cylinder head, intake and exhaust manifold as an assembly.

Installation

Clean all gasket surfaces. Clean head bolt threads and threads in block. Install new head gasket with words "TOP" facing upward. Install cylinder head and head bolts. Tighten head bolts in progressive steps. *See Fig. 2.* Install remaining components. Adjust valves.

Fig. 2: Cylinder Head Tightening Sequence

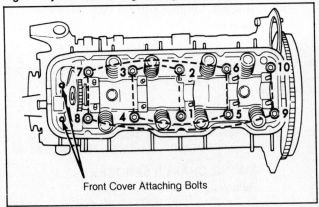

Tighten in progressive steps to 60 ft. lbs. (81 N.m), then tighten to 72 ft. lbs. (98 N.m).

CAMSHAFT

ENGINE FRONT COVER

Removal

1) Remove cylinder head. Remove oil pan and pick up tube from oil pump. Remove all drive belts from crankshaft pulley, then remove vibration damper.

General Motors 4 Engines

1.9 LITER 4-CYLINDER (Cont.)

2) If equipped with A/C and/or power steering pump, remove these components with their respective brackets. Remove distributor. Remove front cover and discard gasket.

Installation

1) Clean all gasket mating surfaces. Install new gasket onto cylinder block. Align punch mark on oil pump gear with oil filter side of cover. Center of dowel pin on pump drive gear must align with pump cover alignment mark. *See Fig. 3.*

Fig. 3: Aligning Oil Pump for Front Cover Installation

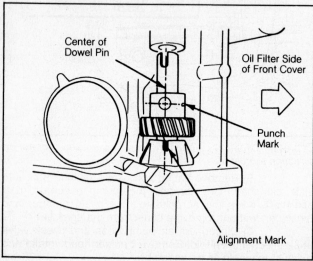

Oil pump gear must engage with pinion gear on crankshaft.

2) Rotate crankshaft to position No. 1 piston at TDC. Install front cover by engaging pinion gear with oil pump gear on crankshaft. Ensure slotted end of oil pump shaft is parallel with front of cylinder block, and that offset is forward. Install and tighten front cover bolts. Reverse removal procedures to install remaining components.

FRONT COVER OIL SEAL

Removal

Disconnect negative battery cable. Drain cooling system and remove radiator. Remove engine fan. Remove all drive belts from crankshaft pulley. Remove vibration damper. Carefully pry out front cover oil seal with screwdriver.

Installation

Install new seal using seal installing tool (J-26587 or equivalent). Lubricate seal lips with engine oil. Install remaining components in reverse order of removal.

TIMING CHAIN & SPROCKETS

Removal

1) Remove front cover. Lock automatic timing chain adjuster shoe in fully retracted position, by depressing adjuster lock lever and rotating clockwise (as viewed from top of engine), while pushing in on shoe. *See Fig. 1.* After locking automatic adjuster, check that chain tension is released.

2) Remove timing chain and sprockets. Use a gear puller to remove crankshaft sprocket and pinion gear, if removal is necessary.

Installation

1) Check timing sprockets for wear or damage and replace as necessary. If removed, install crankshaft

sprocket and pinion gear onto crankshaft with grooved side toward front cover. Turn crankshaft to place Woodruff key upward.

2) The timing chain has 2 link plates that are marked for sprocket alignment purposes. The positioning of the marked plates on the chain are such, that there are more plain links on one side of chain than on the other side. The side of the chain with more plain links between the marked plates, is installed on chain guide side (left side) of engine.

3) Install timing chain on crankshaft, aligning marked link on chain with mark on crankshaft timing sprocket. *See Fig. 4.*

Fig. 4: Aligning Timing Chain and Sprockets

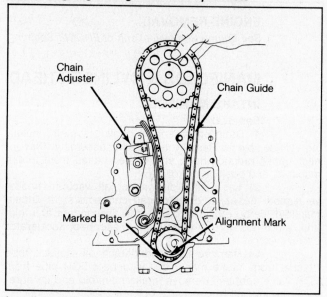

Install timing chain with most links between marked plates, towards chain guide side (left side) of engine.

4) Install chain over camshaft sprocket with triangular timing mark aligned with marked plate on chain. Install and tighten camshaft sprocket on camshaft. If removed, install automatic chain adjuster, and release lock. Reverse removal procedures to install remaining components.

CAMSHAFT

Removal

1) Remove cam cover. Rotate crankshaft to position No. 4 piston on TDC at end of compression stroke. Remove distributor cap and mark rotor-to-housing position. Remove distributor. Remove fuel pump.

2) Lock automatic timing chain adjuster shoe in fully retracted position, by depressing adjuster lock lever and rotating clockwise (as viewed from top of engine), while pushing in on shoe. *See Fig. 1.* After locking automatic adjuster, check that chain tension is released.

3) Remove camshaft sprocket attaching bolt and fuel pump eccentric, being careful not to allow chain to come off of camshaft sprocket. Keep timing sprocket on chain damper and tensioner without removing chain from sprocket. Remove rocker arm shaft and bracket assembly. Remove camshaft.

Installation

1) Heavily coat camshaft journals and mating bearing surface in cylinder head with engine oil. Position camshaft on cylinder head, and install rocker arm shaft and bracket assembly. Ensure that mark on No. 1 rocker arm shaft bracket is aligned with mark on camshaft thrust flange, and that TDC mark on front cover is aligned with crankshaft pulley groove.

2) Using care not to allow chain to separate from camshaft sprocket, assemble sprocket to camshaft. Install fuel pump eccentric and sprocket attaching bolt and washer.

3) Remove half-moon seal from front of cylinder head to tighten camshaft sprocket bolt. Replace half-moon seal in cylinder head. Depress shoe on automatic adjuster to release lock. Reverse removal procedures to install remaining components.

CAMSHAFT END THRUST

Position camshaft on cylinder head. Attach dial indicator to front end of head. *See Fig. 5* Push camshaft rearward and zero dial indicator. Push camshaft forward to record maximum movement. If end play exceeds .008" (.20 mm), check for cylinder head and camshaft wear. Replace worn components.

Fig. 5: Measuring Camshaft End Thrust

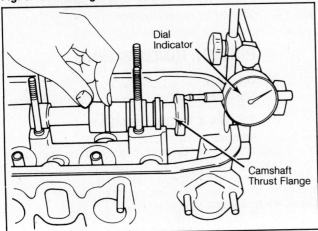

Maximum camshaft end play is .008" (.20 mm).

VALVES

VALVE ARRANGEMENT

Intake valves (Right side)
Exhaust valves (Left side)

ROCKER ARM SHAFT ASSEMBLY

Removal

1) Remove cam cover. Starting with outer rocker arm shaft brackets and working inward, loosen nuts a little at a time. Remove nuts and metal springs.

2) Remove rocker arm shaft assembly and brackets. If disassembly is necessary, keep components in order for reassembly in original positions.

Installation

1) If rocker arm shaft was disassembled, reassemble with cylinder number on face of brackets pointing toward front of engine. Position punch marks on shafts upward. Ensure longer shaft is installed on exhaust valve side of engine.

2) Position mark on camshaft thrust flange upward, to align with mark on No. 1 bracket. See Fig. 6.

Heavily lubricate rocker arm shaft, rocker arms and valve stems with engine oil. Position rocker arm shaft assembly onto cylinder head.

Fig. 6: Correct Rocker Arm Shaft Assembly Installation

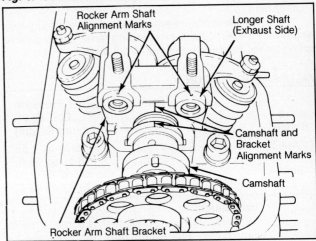

Tighten rocker arm shaft brackets to 16 ft. lbs. (22 N.m).

3) Install metal springs and stud nuts. Hold outer edges of metal springs between jaws of an adjustable wrench while tightening nuts, to prevent spring damage. Starting with center bracket and working outward in a circular pattern, tighten stud nuts in steps. Install remaining components and adjust valves.

VALVE SPRINGS

NOTE: Do not remove air pressure from cylinder until valve spring components are reassembled.

Removal

1) Disconnect negative battery cable. Remove air cleaner assembly and cam cover. Remove rocker arm shaft and bracket assembly. See Rocker Arm Shaft Assembly. Disconnect spark plug wire from cylinder to be serviced and remove spark plug.

2) Install an air hose and adapter to spark plug hole, and apply air pressure. Using valve spring compressor tool (J-26513 or equivalent), compress valve spring. *See Fig. 7.* Remove retainer locks, spring cap and inner and outer springs. Remove oil seal and lower spring seat.

Fig. 7: Compressing Valve Spring

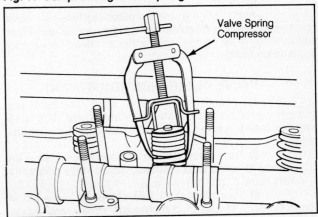

Do not remove air pressure until components are reassembled.

General Motors 4 Engines
1.9 LITER 4-CYLINDER (Cont.)

Inspection

1) Using a flat surface and steel square, measure valve springs for out-of-round condition. Take measurement between top of spring and square, while slowly rotating spring. Out-of-round must not exceed 5/64" (2 mm).

2) Measure inner and outer valve spring free length with a ruler. Check valve spring tension with a valve spring tester. Replace springs that fail tests.

VALVE SPRING TENSION

Valve Spring	Pressure Lbs. @ In. (kg @ mm)
Inner	18-21 @ 1.52 (8-10 @ 38.6)
Outer	32-37 @ 1.60 (15-17 @ 41.0)

Installation

1) Install lower spring seat. Lubricate valve stem and lower spring seat with engine oil. Install new oil seal over valve stem and onto valve guide. Ensure that lip on inside of oil seal fits into valve guide groove. Install inner and outer springs and spring cap.

2) Using spring compressor tool, compress springs and install retainer locks. Ensure retainer locks are fully seated in valve stem groove. Remove air pressure. Heavily lubricate rocker arm shaft assembly and valve stems with engine oil, prior to installing. Install remaining components in reverse order of removal.

VALVE STEM OIL SEALS

Lubricate oil seals with engine oil and install over valve stem and onto valve guide. Ensure that lip on inside of oil seal fits into valve guide groove.

VALVE GUIDE SERVICING

Valve guides and valves should be replaced as a unit. Replace valve and guide when valve stem diameter is less than .310" (7.88 mm) on intake valves, and less than .309" (7.85 mm) on exhaust valves.

Removal

Disassemble head. Insert valve guide remover/installer tool (J-26512 or equivalent) into valve guide, from combustion chamber side of cylinder head. Drive valve guide out top of cylinder head.

Installation

Apply engine oil to outer surface of valve guide, and position in guide bore. Using tool (J-26512 or equivalent), drive guide into cylinder head until tool bottoms on head.

VALVE CLEARANCE ADJUSTMENT

1) Ensure rocker arm shaft brackets are properly tightened. Cold valve clearances are .006" (.15 mm) for intake valves, and .010" (.25 mm) for exhaust valves.

2) Turn crankshaft to position No. 1 piston on TDC at end of compression stroke. Adjust valve clearance of valves listed in table. See Fig. 8.

3) Turn crankshaft 1 revolution to place No. 4 piston on TDC at end of compression stroke, and adjust remaining valves.

VALVE CLEARANCE ADJUSTMENT

Piston On TDC	Adjust Int. Nos.	Adjust Exh. Nos.
1	1, 2	1, 3
4	3, 4	2, 4

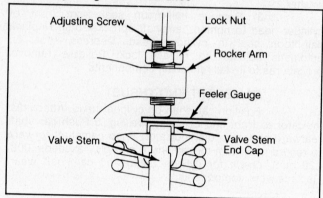

Fig. 8: Adjusting Valve Clearance

Cold valve clearances are .006" (.15 mm) for intake valves and .010" (.25 mm) for exhaust valves.

PISTON, RINGS & PINS

OIL PAN

See Oil Pan Removal at end of ENGINE Section.

PISTON & ROD ASSEMBLY

Removal

1) Remove cylinder head and oil pan. With piston placed at bottom of stroke, remove ridge from top of cylinder bore using ridge reamer. Mark connecting rods and caps for cylinder identification. Mark side of rod and cap which faces right side of engine.

2) Position piston to be removed at bottom of stroke. Remove rod cap and upper bearing from connecting rod. Using wooden hammer handle (or equivalent),

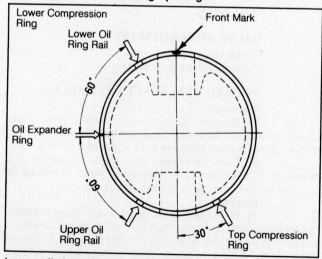

Fig. 9: Desired Piston Ring Spacing

Lower oil ring rail and lower compression ring share same gap position on piston.

1.9 LITER 4-CYLINDER (Cont.)

push piston out top of cylinder bore. Install rod cap on mating rod.

Installation

1) Properly position rings on piston and install upper bearing in rod. *See Fig. 9.* Coat rod bearing surfaces, cylinder bore and piston and rings with engine oil. Install ring compressor over piston and rings, ensuring position of rings does not change.

2) Position crankshaft journal to uppermost position. With mark on piston head positioned toward front of engine, install piston and rod assembly into cylinder bore while guiding rod onto crankshaft journal. Install and tighten rod cap. Ensure crankshaft turns without binding.

FITTING PISTONS

NOTE: **Take measurements at normal room temperature (70°F, 21°C).**

1) Measure diameter of piston (skirt) 90° to piston pin bore, at a point 1 9/16" below piston head. Measure cylinder bore diameter at bottom of bore (above ring travel), at a point where least wear can be measured. Difference between the two measurements is piston-to-cylinder bore clearance.

2) Using cylinder bore gauge, measure cylinder bore diameter 90° to crankshaft. Also measure diameter in line with crankshaft. Take measurements from 1/32" to 2 5/64" below upper face of cylinder block. Reboring is necessary if wear exceeds .008" (.2 mm). If measurement exceeds .016" (.4 mm), replace cylinder block.

3) Cylinder bore diameter is designated by a letter code, stamped on cylinder block upper face. Corresponding letter code denotes size of piston used.

FITTING RINGS

1) Position ring into cylinder bore at a point where bore diameter is smallest. Ring must be square in bore. Measure ring end gap with a feeler gauge.

2) Using feeler gauge, measure side clearance between piston rings and ring lands. Take measurements

Fig. 10: *Piston-to-Connecting Rod Positioning.*

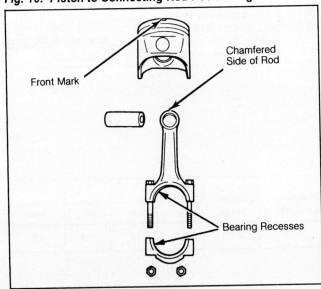

Note position of bearing recesses.

at several points around circumference of piston. Replace piston and rings if measurement exceeds specification, or if abnormal wear is noticeable on piston rings or ring lands.

PISTON PIN REPLACEMENT

Removal

Using arbor press and piston pin remover tool, press pin from piston and connecting rod.

Installation

Apply coat of engine oil to piston pin bores in piston and connecting rod. Assemble connecting rod to piston with chamfered side on rod's pin bore end on same side as mark (front) on piston head. *See Fig. 10.* Using arbor press and pin installer tool, press piston pin into piston and rod assembly.

CRANKSHAFT, MAIN & CONNECTING ROD BEARINGS

MAIN & CONNECTING ROD BEARINGS

NOTE: **Use Plastigage method for checking bearing clearances. Following procedures are performed with oil pan removed, and oil film removed from surfaces to be checked.**

Crankshaft Main Bearings

1) Check main bearing clearances one at a time. Make sure main bearing caps are marked for identification. Use Plastigage method (as explained in Connecting Rod Bearings) to measure main bearing clearance, tightening caps to specification.

2) Install upper main bearings in cylinder block and position crankshaft in place. Install thrust washers on both sides of No. 3 journal, with oil grooves towards crankshaft counterweight. Force crankshaft endwise and check end clearance with feeler gauge inserted between crankshaft and thrust washer.

3) Install main bearings and caps. Arrows on bearing caps must be positioned toward front of engine. Tighten bearing caps in progressive steps, in the following sequence: No. 3, No. 4, No. 2, No. 5 and No. 1.

4) Replacement bearings are available in standard, .010" (.25 mm) undersize and .020" (.50 mm) undersize.

Connecting Rod Bearings

1) Mark connecting rod and rod caps for cylinder identification. Place crankshaft journal of cylinder to be checked towards bottom of stroke and remove rod cap.

2) Place strip of Plastigage across journal surface, in line with crankshaft centerline, about 1/4" off center, and away from oil holes. Install cap and tighten to specification. Do not allow crankshaft to turn.

3) Remove cap and measure width of compressed Plastigage with scale furnished. Replacement bearings are available in standard, .010" (.25 mm) undersize and .020" (.50 mm) undersize.

THRUST BEARING ALIGNMENT

1) Install bearings on cylinder block. Position crankshaft over bearings. Install thrust bearing in position on both sides of No. 3 journal.

General Motors 4 Engines

1.9 LITER 4-CYLINDER (Cont.)

2) Move crankshaft fully endwise. Using a feeler gauge, check clearance between crankshaft and thrust bearing. If clearance exceeds .012" (.30 mm), replace thrust bearings.

REAR MAIN BEARING OIL SEAL

Removal

Remove starter and position aside. Remove transmission. Remove clutch cover and pressure plate assembly. Remove flywheel and cover. Pry old seal out of retainer and discard seal.

Installation

Position new seal in retainer. Fill gap between lips of seal with grease, and coat seal lips with engine oil. Place retainer on a flat surface and drive seal into place using seal installer tool (J-22928-A). Reverse removal procedure to complete installation.

ENGINE OILING

Crankcase Capacity

Capacity is 4 quarts (3.8L), with or without oil filter replacement.

Oil Filter

Replace at every other oil change, or more often under severe or dusty operating conditions.

Normal Oil Pressure

With engine at normal operating temperature, oil pressure should be 30-40 psi (2.1-2.8 kg/cm²) at speeds of 35-40 MPH.

Oil Pressure Regulator Valve

Located in oil pump body, not adjustable.

ENGINE OILING SYSTEM

Engine lubrication system is pressure circulation type with full-flow oil filter. Pump delivers oil to main gallery, where it is routed to crankshaft journals. Through oil passages in crankshaft, oil is fed to connecting rod journals, connecting rods, and then to piston pins.

A branched oil passage from No. 3 crankshaft journal, routes oil to cylinder head. This oil flows through rocker arm shafts to lubricate rocker arms. An oil well, located on upper face of cylinder head, provides lubrication to camshaft.

Timing chain and sprockets are lubricated with oil feed from No. 1 crankshaft journal oil passage, and sprayed by oil jet on chain guide. A by-pass valve is incorporated into the lubrication system.

OIL PUMP

Removal

Remove oil pan. Remove bolt attaching oil inlet pipe to engine. Remove oil pump from front cover.

Installation

Prime oil pump. Assemble pump and inlet tube to engine. Install and tighten attaching bolts.

ENGINE COOLING

WATER PUMP

Removal

1) Disconnect negative battery cable. Remove lower fan shroud and drain radiator. If not A/C equipped, remove fan.

2) On A/C models, remove air pump and alternator mounting bolts and pivot pump and generator in towards engine. Remove drive belts from water pump pulley. Remove fan and pulley and air pump drive pulley. Remove fan set plate and pulley. Remove water pump.

Installation

Reverse removal procedures to install water pump. Adjust belt tensions. Start engine and check for coolant leaks.

NOTE: For information on cooling system capacities and other cooling system components, see appropriate article in "Engine Cooling Systems," at end of ENGINE Section.

TIGHTENING SPECIFICATIONS

Application	Ft. Lbs. (N.m)
Camshaft Sprocket Bolt	58 (79)
Connecting Rod Cap Nuts	43 (58)
Cylinder Head Bolts	¹ 72 (98)
Engine Front Cover Bolts	18 (24)
Engine Rear Plate Bolts	36 (49)
Exhaust Manifold Nuts	16 (22)
Flywheel-to-Crankshaft Bolts	76 (103)
Intake Manifold Nuts	16 (22)
Main Bearing Cap Bolts	72 (98)
Rocker Shaft Bracket Bolts	16 (22)
Vibration Damper Bolt	87 (118)

¹ — Tighten in progressive steps to 60 ft. lbs. (81 N.m), then tighten to 72 ft. lbs. (98 N.m)

ENGINE SPECIFICATIONS

GENERAL SPECIFICATIONS

Year	DISPLACEMENT		Fuel System	HP@RPM	Torque Ft. Lbs.@RPM	Compr. Ratio	BORE		STROKE	
	Cu. In.	Liters					In.	mm	In.	mm
1983	119	1.9	2-Bbl.	.....	.....	8.4:1	3.4	87	3.2	82

General Motors 4 Engines

1.9 LITER 4-CYLINDER (Cont.)

ENGINE SPECIFICATIONS (Cont.)

VALVES

Engine Size & Valve	Head Diam. In. (mm)	Face Angle	Seat Angle	Seat Width In. (mm)	Stem Diameter In. (mm)	Stem Clearance In. (mm)	Valve Lift In. (mm)
1.9L Int.	1.59 (4.04)	45°	45°	.....	.310 Min. (7.88 Min.)	.0009-.0022 (.023-.056)	.....
Exh.	1.34 (34.0)	45°	45°	.....	.309 Min. (7.85 Min.)	.0015-.0031 (.038-.078)	.....

PISTONS, PINS, RINGS

Engine	PISTONS Clearance In. (mm)	PINS Piston Fit In. (mm)	PINS Rod Fit In. (mm)	RINGS Ring No.	RINGS End Gap In. (mm)	RINGS Side Clearance In. (mm)
1.9L	.0018-.0026 (.045-.065)	[1]	Press Fit	1	.012-.020 (.30-.50)	.006 Max. (.15 Max.)
				2	.008-.016 (.20-.40)	.006 Max. (.15 Max.)
				3	.008-.035 (.20-.90)	.006 Max. (.15 Max.)

[1] — Pin should press into piston with finger pressure.

CRANKSHAFT MAIN & CONNECTING ROD BEARINGS

Engine	MAIN BEARINGS Journal Diam. In. (mm)	MAIN BEARINGS Clearance In. (mm)	MAIN BEARINGS Thrust Bearing	MAIN BEARINGS Crankshaft End Play In. (mm)	CONNECTING ROD BEARINGS Journal Diam. In. (mm)	CONNECTING ROD BEARINGS Clearance In. (mm)	CONNECTING ROD BEARINGS Side Play In. (mm)
1.9L	2.2016-2.2022 (55.920-55.935)	.0008-.0025 (.021-.064)	No. 3	.012 Max. (.30 Max.)	1.9262-1.9268 (48.925-48.940)	.0007-.0025 (.018-.064)	.014 Max. (.35 Max.)

VALVE SPRINGS

Engine	Free Length In. (mm)	PRESSURE Lbs. @ In. (Kg @ mm) Valve Closed	PRESSURE Lbs. @ In. (Kg @ mm) Valve Open
1.9L Inner	1.78 (45.3)	.....	.....
Outer	1.85 (46.9)		

CAMSHAFT

Engine	Journal Diam. In. (mm)	Clearance In. (mm)	Lobe Lift In. (mm)
1.9L [1]	1.336-1.337 (33.94-33.96)	.0016-.0035 (.040-.090)	.....

[1] — End play is .002-.006" (.05-.15 mm).

General Motors 4 Engines

2.0 LITER 4-CYLINDER

ENGINE CODING

ENGINE IDENTIFICATION

Engine may be identified from the Vehicle Identification Number stamped on a metal tab located on top of instrument panel at lower left of windshield. VIN number code also appears on pad at right front of cylinder block below cylinder head.

Engine unit and code number label is found on timing cover. Engine code is found of a pad at left front of cylinder block below cylinder head. The VIN number contains 17 digits. The 8th digit identifies engine type (Y).

ENGINE IDENTIFICATION CODES

Engine	Code
2.0L 2-Bbl.	UKA, UKB, UKC, UKD, UKF, UKK
	UKM, UKU, UKX, UKX, UKY
	UKZ, UWA, UWB, UWC, UWM

ENGINE REMOVAL

See Engine Removal at end of ENGINE Section.

MANIFOLDS & CYLINDER HEAD

INTAKE MANIFOLD

Removal

1) Disconnect negative battery cable. Remove air cleaner and distributor cap. Raise vehicle. Remove middle right side bellhousing-to-block bolt and move wiring harness. Remove distributor hold-down nut.

2) Disconnect necessary vacuum lines and electrical wires. Remove fuel pump bolts and let pump hang. Lower vehicle. Disconnect accelerator cable and fuel inlet line. Remove carburetor. Drain cooling system.

3) Disconnect fuel vapor pipes at head. Remove vacuum pipe-to-head bolt at rear of head and disconnect vacuum hoses. Disconnect necessary hoses at intake. Remove intake nuts and bolts. Remove intake manifold and gasket.

Installation

1) Clean mating surface of intake manifold and cylinder head. Position new intake manifold gasket on cylinder head.

2) Install intake manifold and attaching bolts and nuts. Tighten manifold attaching nuts and bolts. Reverse removal procedure to complete installation.

EXHAUST MANIFOLD

Removal

Disconnect negative battery cable. Remove air cleaner. Raise vehicle. Remove exhaust pipe from manifold. Remove A.I.R. hose pipe bracket bolt and dipstick tube bracket. Remove fuel vapor canister harness pipes, exhaust manifold bolts and manifold.

NOTE: **If exhaust manifold is to be replaced, disconnect air pump plumbing from manifold.**

Installation

Clean all mating surfaces on exhaust manifold and cylinder head. Position manifold against head and install manifold attaching bolts and tighten. Reverse removal procedure to complete installation.

CYLINDER HEAD

Removal

1) Disconnect negative battery cable and remove air cleaner. Drain cooling system. Raise vehicle. Disconnect exhaust pipe from manifold. Lower vehicle.

2) Disconnect necessary wires, vacuum lines and linkage. Remove fuel vapor canister harness pipes and distributor cap and mark distributor. Remove distributor.

3) Remove rocker cover, rocker arm and push rods. Remove radiator and heater hoses, upper fan shroud and fan. Remove air management valve, air pump, upper A.I.R. bracket and fuel line from fuel pump. Remove head bolts and head.

Installation

1) Clean gasket surfaces on cylinder head and block. Ensure that all gasket surfaces are free of nicks, heavy scratches and foreign materials. Coat both sides of gasket with sealing compound.

2) Position cylinder head gasket on block using dowel pins as a guide. Carefully lower head into place seating head on dowel pins. Coat head bolt heads and threads with sealing compound. Install head bolts and tighten in proper sequence shown in *Fig. 1*.

Fig. 1: Cylinder Head Tightening Sequence

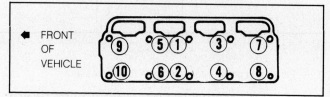

Tighten cylinder head bolts in 3 steps.

VALVES

VALVE ARRANGEMENT

E-I-I-E-E-I-I-E (Front-to-Rear)

VALVE STEM OIL SEALS/SPRINGS

Removal

1) Remove rocker arm cover. Remove spark plug, rocker arm and push rod on cylinder to be serviced. Install air adaptor tool (J-23590) to spark plug hole.

Fig. 2: Compressing Valve Spring

2.0 LITER 4-CYLINDER (Cont.)

2) Apply compressed air to hold valve in place. Using valve spring compressor tool, compress spring. Remove valve locks, cap, spring, valve stem oil seal and shim. *See Fig. 2.*

Installation

Reverse removal procedure to complete installation. Make sure locks seat in upper groove. Adjust valves.

VALVE SPRING INSTALLED HEIGHT

Using a thin narrow scale, measure from top of spring seat to bottom of cap. If measurement exceeds specified height, install a shim .028" (.7 mm) thick to correct spring height. *See Fig. 3.*

CAUTION: At no time should a spring be shimmed to give a spring height under minimum specifications.

Fig. 3: Measuring Valve Spring Installed Height

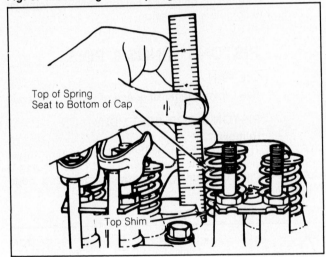

Top of Spring
Seat to Bottom of Cap

Top Shim

VALVE SPRING INSTALLED HEIGHT

Application	Installed Height In. (mm)
2.0L	¹ 1.6 (40.6)

¹ — Plus Shim.

VALVE GUIDE SERVICING

Valves with oversize stems are available in .003" (.089 mm), .015" (.394 mm) and .030" (.775 mm) diameters. To ream valve guide bores for oversize valves, use valve reamer tool (J-5330-1, 2 or 3 respectively).

HYDRAULIC VALVE LIFTER ASSEMBLY

Lifters are serviced as assemblies only and parts are not interchangeable. It is important to place lifters in order for proper installation in original position. Clean and inspect lifter assemblies and fill with SAE 10W oil to reassemble. Before installing lifters, coat bottom of lifter with Molykote (or equivalent).

VALVE CLEARANCE ADJUSTMENT

NOTE: Valves must be adjusted when lifter is on base circle of camshaft lobe.

1) Using starter, rotate engine until No. 1 cylinder is at TDC on compression stroke. The following valves may be adjusted: No. 1 and 2 intake; No. 1 and 3 exhaust.

2) To adjust, back off adjusting nut until lash is felt at push rod. Tighten adjusting nut until all lash at push rod is removed. Turn adjusting nut an additional 1 1/2 turns to center lifter plunger.

3) Rotate crankshaft 360°. Adjust the following valves: No. 3 and 4 intake; No. 2 and 4 exhaust. Install rocker arm cover. Check timing and idle speed.

CAMSHAFT

ENGINE FRONT COVER

Removal

1) Disconnect negative battery cable. Drain cooling system. Remove upper fan shroud, accessory drive belts, fan and pulley.

2) Remove radiator and heater hoses. Remove water pump and crank pulley. Remove accessory drive pulley retaining bolts.

3) Install hub puller (J-24420) on hub. Turn puller screw and remove hub. Remove front cover retaining bolts and remove front cover.

Installation

1) Clean mating surfaces on block and front cover. Apply a bead of anaerobic sealer to cover. Apply a bead of RTV sealer to oil pan sealing surface.

2) Install front cover to block attaching screws. Apply a bead of anaerobic sealer to water pump. Reverse removal procedure to complete installation.

FRONT COVER OIL SEAL

Removal

With cover removed, carefully pry seal out of cover, taking care not to damage surface of crankshaft.

Installation

Install new seal with open end toward inside of cover. Using seal driver tool (J-23042), drive seal into cover. Reverse removal procedure to complete installation.

TIMING CHAIN

Removal

1) With front cover removed, align marks on camshaft sprocket with marks on crankshaft sprocket as shown in *Fig. 4.*

2) Remove timing chain tensioner. Remove camshaft sprocket and timing chain. Crankshaft sprocket can be removed using puller tool (J-2288-8-20 or puller legs J-22888-11).

Installation

1) If crankshaft sprocket was removed, install sprocket using sprocket tool (J-5590). Lubricate thrust surface of camshaft with Molykote (or equivalent).

2) Position chain over camshaft and crankshaft sprockets, making sure marks on camshaft sprocket align with mark on crankshaft sprocket.

3) Position camshaft sprocket on camshaft making sure hole in camshaft sprocket aligns with dowel pin on camshaft.

4) Draw camshaft sprocket onto camshaft using camshaft retaining bolts and tighten. Lubricate

Fig. 4: Timing Chain Sprocket Alignment

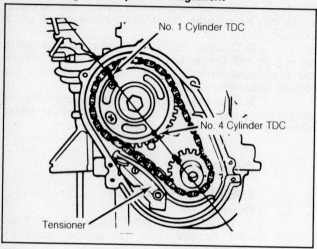

Align timing marks before removing old chain.

timing chain with oil. Reverse removal procedure to complete installation.

CAMSHAFT
Removal
1) Remove rocker cover, timing chain and sprocket. Drain cooling system. Remove radiator. Mark position of rotor. Raise vehicle.

NOTE: **Use extreme care when removing camshaft, as all journals are same size and damage to bearing may result.**

2) Remove fuel pump. Remove distributor hold-down nut and clamp. Lower vehicle. Remove distributor. Remove rocker arm studs and push rod guides. Remove lifters and camshaft.

Installation
1) Measure camshaft journals for an out-of-round condition. If journals are out of round in excess of .0009" (.023 mm), camshaft should be replaced.

2) Lubricate camshaft journals with engine oil and install camshaft. Reverse removal procedure to complete installation.

CAM LOBE LIFT
1) With valve cover removed, remove rocker arm assemblies. Position dial indicator with ball socket adapter (J-8520) on push rod. Slowly rotate engine in direction of rotation until lifter is on base circle of cam lobe.

2) Zero dial indicator. Rotate engine until push rod is fully raised. Record lobe lift reading and compare with specifications. If not within limits, replace camshaft and lifters.

CAMSHAFT BEARINGS
Removal
1) With camshaft and crankshaft removed, remove camshaft rear cover. Using bearing removal tool (J-6098) fasten nut and thrust washer to end of threads.

2) Insert tool pilot in camshaft front bearing and install puller screw through pilot. Install tool with shoulder toward bearing with sufficient amount of threads engaged.

3) Using an additional wrench to hold puller screw stationary, turn nut until bearing is pulled from block. Remove remaining bearings (except front and rear).

4) Insert pilot in camshaft rear bearing to remove rear intermediate bearing. Assemble tool on driver handle and remove front and rear bearings by driving toward center of cylinder block.

Installation
1) Using bearing removal tool, fasten nut and thrust washer to end of threads. Insert pilot in camshaft bearing and install puller screw through pilot.

2) Insert bearing in bore with oil hole aligned between 2:00 and 3:00 o'clock position on rear and intermediate bearing. Front bearing has oil holes at 11:00 o'clock and between 2:00 and 3:00 o'clock position.

3) Using additional wrench to hold puller screw stationary, turn nut until bearing is pulled into bore. Install remaining bearings in same manner.

4) Apply RTV sealer to groove in engine block and camshaft rear cover. Position camshaft cover on block, install retaining bolts and tighten. Reverse removal procedure to complete installation.

PISTONS, RINGS & PINS

OIL PAN
See Oil Pan Removal at end of ENGINE Section.

PISTON & ROD ASSEMBLY
Removal
1) Inspect cylinder bores above ring travel area. With piston at bottom of stroke and covered with a cloth to collect the cuttings, remove ridge using ridge reamer tool.

Fig. 5: Piston Ring Gap Spacing

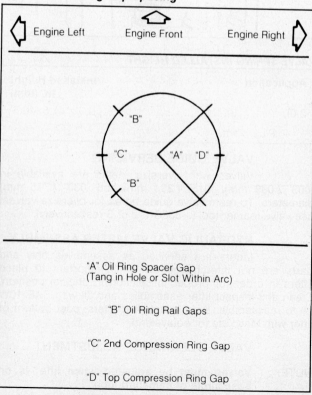

"A" Oil Ring Spacer Gap
(Tang in Hole or Slot Within Arc)

"B" Oil Ring Rail Gaps

"C" 2nd Compression Ring Gap

"D" Top Compression Ring Gap

2.0 LITER 4-CYLINDER (Cont.)

NOTE: Mark all pistons, connecting rods and caps for identification to ensure correct installation.

2) Remove rod bearing cap and install guide hose over threads of rod bolts to protect bearing journal. Push piston and rod assembly out top of cylinder bore.

Installation

1) Lubricate connecting rod bearings with clean engine oil. Install bearings in rod and rod caps. Coat pistons, rings and cylinder walls lightly with oil.

2) Install guide hose over connecting rod bolts. Make sure ring gaps are spaced as shown in *Fig. 5*. Install ring compressor tool on piston.

NOTE: Be sure to install new pistons in same cylinder for which they were fitted and used pistons from cylinder in which they were removed.

3) Install piston and rod assembly with connecting rod tang slot on opposite side of crankshaft. Remove guide hose from connecting rod bolts.

4) Using a hammer handle, tap lightly on piston and guide rod onto crankshaft journal. Install bearings and caps and tighten.

FITTING PISTONS

NOTE: When fitting new pistons a feeler gauge of .0020" (.050 mm) in thickness is used. A feeler gauge of .0024" (.060 mm) thickness is used for fitting used pistons. The feeler gauge must be at least 6" (150 mm) long and not over 1/2" (13 mm) wide.

1) Select a piston without rings which will slide through cylinder bore freely. Insert piston and feeler gauge into cylinder bore until bottom of piston skirt is 1/2-1" (12-25 mm) from top of cylinder bore.

2) Ensure that feeler gauge is at 90° angle to piston pin. If piston hangs on feeler gauge and does not fall free, piston is correctly fitted to that cylinder bore.

FITTING RINGS

1) Position ring into cylinder bore at a point about 1/4" (6 mm) above ring travel. Ring must be square in bore. Measure ring end gap with a feeler gauge.

2) Before installing compression rings on pistons, check side clearance. Insert outer edge of ring in its respective groove, and slide ring around entire circumference of groove. The ring should slide freely in groove.

3) Check side clearance of compression rings, with feeler gauge inserted between ring and ring groove. Install rings with gaps properly positioned. Note that anti-rotation tang of oil ring spacer is inserted into oil hole (or slot) of piston.

PISTON PIN REPLACEMENT

Removal

Install piston and connecting rod assembly on fixture and support tool (J-24086-20) and place in an arbor press. Press pin out of connecting rod.

Installation

Lubricate piston pin holes in piston and connecting rod lightly with oil. Position connecting rod in piston and hold in place with piston pin guide and piston pin. Using support tool and arbor press, press pin into piston and connecting rod.

CAUTION: After arbor press hub bottoms on support assembly, do not exceed 5000 lbs. pressure or tool will be damaged.

CRANKSHAFT, MAIN & CONNECTING ROD BEARINGS

MAIN & CONNECTING ROD BEARINGS

Crankshaft Main Bearings

1) Main bearings are precision insert type and do not utilize shims for adjustment. If clearances are excessive, both upper and lower halves are to be replaced.

2) Wipe oil from crankshaft journal, bearing and cap. If engine is out of vehicle and upside down, crankshaft will rest on upper bearings and total clearance can be measured between lower bearing and journal.

3) If engine is to remain in vehicle, support crankshaft at front and rear to remove clearance from upper bearings. When checking No. 1 bearing, loosen accessory drive belts to prevent tapered reading on Plastigage.

NOTE: Bearing cap bolts must be evenly tightened to specification in order to assure proper reading.

4) Always replace upper and lower inserts as a unit. A standard, .0006" (.016 mm) and .0009" (.022 mm) undersize bearing should produce proper clearance. If not, it will be necessary to regrind crankshaft journal for use with next undersize bearing.

NOTE: Install main bearing cap with arrows pointing toward front of engine.

Connecting Rod Bearings

1) Connecting rod bearings are precision insert type and do not utilize shims for adjustment. After ensuring that rod caps are marked for identification, remove rod caps. Use Plastigage method to check for proper bearing clearances.

NOTE: Place piece of Plastigage the full width of crankpin, as contacted by bearing and parallel to crankshaft.

2) If clearances are found to be excessive, a new bearing will be required. Service bearings are available in standard size and .005" (.13 mm) and .010" (.25 mm) undersize for use with new and used standard size crankshafts.

CAUTION: If bearing is fitted to an out-of-round crankpin, be sure to fit to maximum diameter of crankpin. If bearing is fitted to minimum diameter and crankpin is out-of-round .0009" (.023 mm), interference between bearing and crankpin will result causing rapid bearing failure. Do not file rods or rod caps.

THRUST BEARING ALIGNMENT

Install all main bearing caps except thrust bearing and tighten. Install thrust bearing cap and bolts finger tight. Using soft-faced hammer, tap end of crankshaft rearward, then forward. Retighten all main bearing caps and measure crankshaft end play. See Fig. 6.

Fig. 6: Measuring Crankshaft End Play

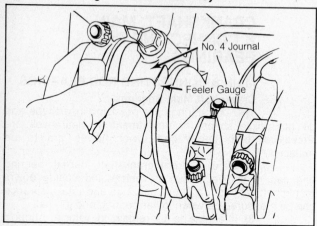

Main bearing caps must be tight when checking end play.

REAR MAIN BEARING OIL SEAL

NOTE: The following procedures are performed with the oil pan and oil pump removed.

Removal & Installation

1) Remove rear main bearing cap. Remove upper and lower seal and clean seal channel of any oil.

NOTE: Loosening numbers 2, 3 and 4 main bearing bolts may be necessary for installing the new upper seal.

2) Apply a thin coat of oil over complete seal surface of rubber seal. Roll seal into position in cylinder case. Turning crankshaft will help seal roll into position. Position sealing lip inboard.

3) Apply oil in manner described above to other half of new seal and install in main bearing cap.

4) Place a piece of Plastigage on rear main journal and install bearing cap and tighten. Remove bearing cap and check Plastigage for proper bearing clearance.

5) Clean Plastigage from journal and bearing. Apply a thin film of anaerobic sealant to bearing cap as shown in Fig. 7. Apply a light coat of oil on crankshaft surface that will contact seal. Install main bearing cap and tighten. Reverse removal procedure to complete installation.

Fig. 7: Sealer Application to Bearing Cap

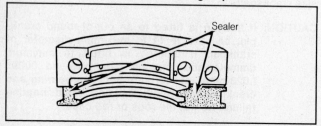

ENGINE OILING

Crankcase Capacity

Four quarts (3.7L) with or without filter change.

Oil Filter

Replace at every other oil change, or more often under severe conditions.

ENGINE OILING SYSTEM

A gear type oil pump provides full pressure lubrication through a full flow oil filter. Oil is drawn up through screen and tube and passed through pump to oil filter. From the filter, oil is routed to main oil gallery, and through drilled holes above camshaft to left of camshaft centerline and on to lifters. Lifter pumps oil through push rods to rocker arms. Oil draining back from rocker arms is directed by cast dams (which are a part of crankcase casting) to supply camshaft lobes with oil. Passages supplying oil to camshaft bearings also supply crankshaft bearings through passages drilled in crankshaft.

OIL PUMP

Removal

With oil pan removed, remove pump to rear main bearing cap bolt. Remove pump and extension shaft.

Disassembly

1) Remove pump cover attaching bolts and remove cover. Mark gears for reassembly in same position.

2) Remove idler gear, drive gear and shaft from pump body. Remove pressure regulator valve retaining pin and remove pressure regulator spring and valve.

3) If pick-up screen and pipe assembly are to be replaced, place pump in a soft-jawed vise. Extract pipe from pump cover.

Fig. 8: Oil Pump Component Identification

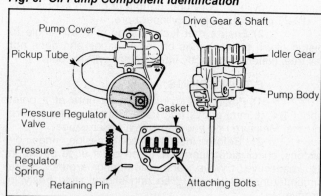

NOTE: Pick-up screen is not removable from pipe and must be replaced as an assembly.

Inspection

1) Wash all parts in solvent and dry with compressed air. Inspect pump body and cover for cracks or excessive wear.

2) Inspect gears for damage or excessive wear. Check for looseness of drive gear shaft in body.

NOTE: The pump gears and pump body cannot be serviced separately. If either gears or pump body is worn or damaged, replace entire oil pump assembly.

2.0 LITER 4-CYLINDER (Cont.)

3) Inspect pump cover for wear that would allow oil to leak past ends of gears.

4) Inspect pick-up screen and pipe assembly for damage. Check pressure regulator for fit in pump body.

Reassembly

1) If pick-up screen and pipe assembly was removed, it should be replaced. Loss of press fit could cause an air leak resulting in loss of oil pressure.

NOTE: **Be careful of twisting, shearing or collapsing pipe when installing it in pump body.**

2) Position pump in a soft-jawed vise. Apply sealer to end of pipe. Using pipe installer tool (J-8369) and soft-faced hammer, tap the pipe into place.

3) Reverse disassembly procedure to complete reassembly.

Installation

1) Assemble pump and extension shaft with retainer to rear main bearing cap.

2) Align end of shaft with lower end of distributor drive gear. Align pump with 2 dowel pins at bottom of cap.

3) Install pump to rear bearing cap retaining bolt and tighten. Reverse removal procedure to complete installation.

ENGINE COOLING

WATER PUMP

Removal

1) Disconnect negative battery terminal. Remove accessory drive belts. Remove upper fan shroud. Drain cooling system.

2) Remove radiator and heater hose. Remove water pump retaining bolts and remove water pump.

Installation

1) Clean all gasket surfaces. Apply sealer to pump gasket and position gasket on pump.

2) Position pump on engine, install retaining bolts and tighten. Reverse removal procedure to complete installation.

NOTE: **For information on cooling system capacities and other cooling system components, see appropriate article in ENGINE COOLING SYSTEMS Section.**

TIGHTENING SPECIFICATIONS

Application	Ft. Lbs. (N.m)
Camshaft Sprocket	66-88 (90-120)
Connecting Rod Caps	34-42 (46-58)
Crankshaft Pulley Hub	66-88 (90-120)
Crankshaft Pulley	29-44 (40-60)
Cylinder Head Bolts	65-75 (88-102)
Exhaust Manifold	19-29 (26-40)
Flywheel-to-Crankshaft	45-59 (61-80)
Intake Manifold	22-29 (30-40)
Main Bearing Caps	63-77 (85-105)
Oil Pump	26-38 (35-52)
Rocker Arm Stud	43-49 (58-66)
Water Pump	14-22 (20-30)

	INCH Lbs. (N.m)
Cam Thrust Plate	48-156 (6-18)
Front Cover	72-108 (8-12)
Oil Pump Cover	72-108 (8-12)

ENGINE SPECIFICATIONS

GENERAL SPECIFICATIONS

Year	DISPLACEMENT		Fuel System	HP@RPM	Torque Ft. Lbs.@RPM	Compr. Ratio	BORE		STROKE	
	Cu. In.	Liters					In.	mm	In.	mm
1983	122	2.0	2-Bbl.	.....	.....	9.3:1	3.50	89	3.15	80

VALVES

Engine Size & Valve	Head Diam. In. (mm)	Face Angle	Seat Angle	Seat Width In. (mm)	Stem Diameter In. (mm)	Stem Clearance In. (mm)	Valve Lift In. (mm)
2.0L Intake	1.595-1.605 (40.51-40.77)	45°	46°	.049-.059 (1.25-1.50)	.3139-.3144 (7.973-7.986)	.0011-.0026 (.028-.066)	.393 (9.98)
Exhaust	1.373-1.383 (34.87-35.13)	45°	46°	.063-.075 (1.60-1.90)	.3129-.3136 (7.948-7.965)	.0014-.0031 (.035-.078)	.393 (9.98)

General Motors 4 Engines

2.0 LITER 4-CYLINDER (Cont.)

ENGINE SPECIFICATIONS (Cont.)

PISTONS, PINS, RINGS

| Engine | PISTONS | PINS | | RINGS | | |
	Clearance In. (mm)	Piston Fit In. (mm)	Rod Fit In. (mm)	Ring No.	End Gap In. (mm)	Side Clearance In. (mm)
2.0L	.0007-.0017 (.017-.043)	.00026-.00036 (.0065-.0091)	.0007-.0020 (.019-.052)	1	.010-.020 (.25-.50)	.0012-.0027 (.030-.068)
				2	.010-.020 (.25-.50)	.0012-.0027 (.030-.068)
				3	....	.0008 (.199)

CRANKSHAFT MAIN & CONNECTING ROD BEARINGS

| Engine | MAIN BEARINGS | | | | CONNECTING ROD BEARINGS | | |
	Journal Diam. In. (mm)	Clearance In. (mm)	Thrust Bearing	Crankshaft End Play In. (mm)	Journal Diam. In. (mm)	Clearance In. (mm)	Side Play In. (mm)
2.0L	2.4945-2.4954 [1] (63.360-63.384)	.0010-.0022 [2] (.026-.058)	No. 4	.002-.007 (.05-.21)	1.9983-1.9994 (50.758-50.784)	.0010-.0031 (.025-.079)	.004-.015 (.10-.38)

[1] — No. 5 Journal is 2.4937-2.4946" (63.340-63.364 mm).
[2] — No. 5 bearing clearance is .0018-.0030" (.046-.078 mm).

VALVE SPRINGS

| Engine | Free Length In. (mm) | PRESSURE Lbs. @ In. (Kg @ mm) | |
		Valve Closed	Valve Open
2.0L	....	77@1.6 (342@40.6)	182@1.3 (810@33.9)

CAMSHAFT

Engine	Journal Diam. In. (mm)	Clearance In. (mm)	Lobe Lift In. (mm)
2.0L	1.868-1.870 (47.44-47.49)	.0010-.0040 (.026-.101)	.263 (6.67)

2.8 LITER V6

ENGINE CODING

ENGINE IDENTIFICATION

Engine identification number is stamped on a machined pad on front of cylinder block, just rearward of engine front cover. Engine type is identified by a letter code (B), in eighth position of Vehicle Identification Number.

ENGINE IDENTIFICATION CODES

Engine	Code
2.8L 2-Bbl.	UNA, UNC, UNR, UNS, UNW
	UNZ, UXC, UXD, UXJ, UXK
	UXY, UXZ, UYB, UYC, UYD
	UYF, UYX, UYY, UZB, UZF
	UZK, UZM, UZU, UZW

ENGINE REMOVAL

See Engine Removal at end of ENGINE Section.

MANIFOLDS & CYLINDER HEADS

INTAKE MANIFOLD

Removal

1) Disconnect negative battery cable. Drain radiator. Remove air cleaner. Label and disconnect all electrical connectors, vacuum hoses and emissions hoses, at distributor, carburetor and intake manifold. Disconnect fuel line at carburetor.

2) Disconnect spark plug wires at spark plugs. Remove distributor cap and mark position of rotor. Remove distributor.

3) Remove all brackets attached to rocker arm covers, and remove covers. Remove upper radiator hose and heater hose from engine. Remove A/C drive belt and rotate compressor aside. Remove intake manifold and discard gaskets.

Installation

1) Clean all gasket mating surfaces. Apply 3/16" bead silicone sealer to front and rear sealing ridges of cylinder block. Install new intake manifold side gaskets onto cylinder heads. Gaskets are stamped "Left Side" and "Right Side."

2) Hold gaskets in place by extending silicone sealer bead 1/4" onto ends of side gaskets. New side

Fig. 1: Intake Manifold Gasket Modification

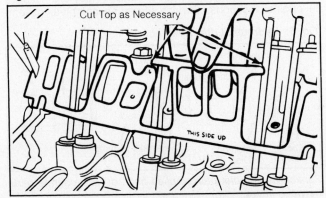

Gaskets are stamped "Left Side" and "Right Side."

gaskets will have to be cut, to install behind push rods. *See Fig. 1.*

3) Install intake manifold. Make sure sealing areas between cylinder ridges and ends of manifold are completely sealed. Install and tighten manifold attaching bolts and nuts. *See Fig. 2.* To complete installation, reverse removal procedure.

Fig. 2: Intake Manifold Tightening Sequence

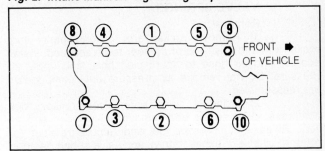

Tighten attaching bolts and nuts to 13-25 ft. lbs. (18-34 N.m).

EXHAUST MANIFOLD

1) Disconnect battery. Raise vehicle. Disconnect exhaust pipes. On left side, remove 4 rear manifold bolts and 1 nut. Lower vehicle.

2) Disconnect air management valve, hoses and wires. Remove power steering bracket. Remove exhaust manifold bolts and manifolds.

CYLINDER HEADS

Removal

1) Remove intake manifold. Raise vehicle and disconnect exhaust pipes at manifolds. Drain coolant from block. Remove oil dipstick tube attachment. Lower vehicle. Loosen rocker arm nuts and rotate rockers to side.

2) Remove push rods in sequence, for reinstallation in original locations. Remove alternator, power steering pump, A/C compressor, and respective mounting brackets for these components. Position assemblies aside. Remove cylinder heads.

Installation

1) Clean all gasket mating surfaces. Clean head bolt threads and threads in cylinder block.

2) Head gaskets are marked "This Side Up." Properly install gaskets in place on cylinder block. Install cylinder heads. Apply sealing compound to head bolt threads and install bolts. Tighten bolts in sequence. *See Fig. 3.*

Fig. 3: Cylinder Head Tightening Sequence

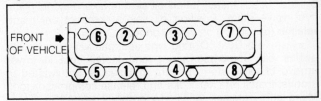

Tighten head bolts to 55-77 ft. lbs. (74-108 N.m).

3) Coat rocker arm balls and mating surface of rocker arms with Molykote (or equivalent), prior to installing. Install remaining components in reverse order of removal. Adjust valves.

General Motors V6 Engines

2.8 LITER V6 (Cont.)

VALVES

ROCKER ARM STUDS

Cylinder heads use threaded rocker arm studs. Replace damaged rocker arm studs with new studs. If threads in head are damaged, the head can be retapped, and a helical type insert installed. If a helical insert is not available, replace cylinder head.

VALVE SPRINGS
Removal

1) Remove rocker arm cover, spark plug, rocker arm and push rod of cylinder to be serviced. Install adapter and air hose to spark plug hole, and apply air pressure. Do not remove air pressure until components are reassembled.

2) Using a valve spring compressor tool, compress valve spring and remove valve locks and oil seal. Release compressor tool and remove retainer (or rotator), oil shield (exhaust only), and valve spring damper. On intake valves, remove teflon oil seal. See Fig. 4.

Fig. 4: Intake and Exhaust Valve Assemblies

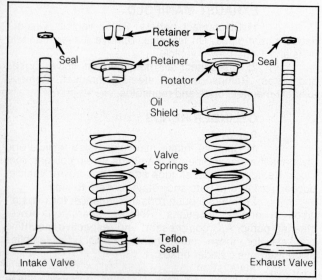

Teflon oil seal is used in combination with "O" ring seal, on intake valves only.

Inspection

Using valve spring tester, check valve spring tension. Springs should test to within 10 lbs. of specification (without dampers.) Replace spring if not within limits.

Installation

1) Position valve spring and damper on cylinder head. Install teflon oil seal (intake only) in place over valve stem. Position oil shield (exhaust only) and retainer (or rotator) on valve spring.

2) Coat "O" ring type seal and valve stem with engine oil. Compress spring and install seal in lower groove of valve stem. Ensure that seal is not twisted in groove. Install retainer locks and release compressor tool. Make sure retainer locks are properly seated in upper groove of valve stem.

VALVE SPRING INSTALLED HEIGHT

CAUTION: Never shim valve springs to a height less than specifications.

1) Installed height of valve springs should be 1.58" (40 mm). For intake valves, measure from top of spring damper tabs to bottom of retainer. For exhaust valves, measure from top of spring damper tabs, to point where top of valve spring contacts inside bottom of oil shield.

2) If measurement exceeds specified height, install a .030" (.76 mm) shim at spring seat. See Fig. 5.

Fig. 5: Checking Valve Spring Installed Height

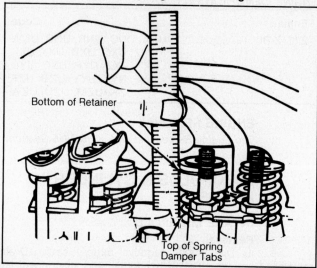

Installed height is 1.58" (40 mm). Never shim to a height less than specification.

VALVE STEM OIL SEALS

All valves use an "O" ring type oil seal, installed in lower groove of valve stem. Intake valves also use a teflon type seal, in combination with the "O" ring type seal.

The teflon type seal is installed over the valve guides of the intake valves. Lightly coat valve stem with engine oil, to help prevent twisting of the "O" ring type seal during installation.

VALVE GUIDE SERVICING

If valve stem-to-guide clearance exceeds specifications, ream valve guide to proper oversize. Valves are available with .0035" (.089 mm), .0155" (.394 mm) and .0305" (.775 mm) oversize stems. Always use reamers in proper size sequence.

HYDRAULIC VALVE LIFTERS

If lifters are removed, ensure they are installed in original locations. Service lifters as complete assem-

Fig. 6: Hydraulic Lifter Assembly

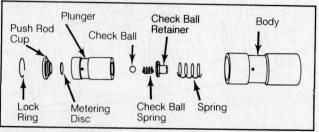

Service as complete assemblies only; do interchange parts between lifters.

blies only. If lifter is damaged or worn, replace lifter. If lifters are disassembled for cleaning and inspection, they should be reassembled and tested in a lifter leakdown rate tester. See Fig. 6.

Some engines will have both standard and .010" (.25 mm) oversize valve lifters. The lifter boss of engines with oversize lifters will be marked with a dab of White paint, and "0.25 O.S." stamped on lifter boss. See Fig. 7.

Fig. 7: Identifying Oversize Lifters

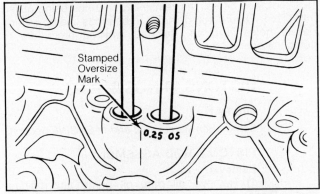

Lifter bosses are also marked with a dab of White paint.

VALVE CLEARANCE ADJUSTMENT

1) Adjust valves by backing off adjusting nut until lash (play) is felt at push rod. Now tighten nut until all lash is removed. Tighten adjusting nut an additional 1 1/2 turns. See Fig. 8.

2) Rotate crankshaft to bring No. 1 piston on TDC at end of compression stroke. Adjust valves indicated in Valve Clearance Adjustment table.

3) Rotate crankshaft 360° to bring No. 4 piston on TDC at end of compression stroke. Adjust remaining valves. When adjustment is complete, install rocker arm covers. Start engine and check timing and idle speed.

VALVE CLEARANCE ADJUSTMENT

Piston On TDC	Adjust Int. Nos.	Adjust Exh. Nos.
No. 1	1, 5, 6	1, 2, 3
No. 4	2, 3, 4	4, 5, 6

Fig. 8: Valve Lash Adjustment

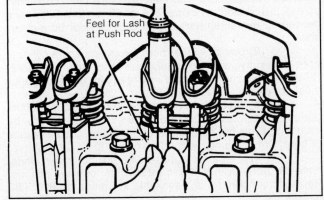

Tighten adjusting nut 1 1/2 turns after push rod lash is eliminated.

CAMSHAFT

FRONT ENGINE COVER

Removal

Disconnect negative battery cable. Remove all drive belts. Drain cooling system. Remove water pump. If equipped, remove A/C compressor and mounting bracket. Remove vibration damper. Disconnect lower radiator hose at front cover and heater hose at water pump. Remove front cover.

NOTE: Install and tighten front cover and water pump before sealer sets up.

Installation

1) Clean sealing surfaces thoroughly. Apply 3/32" bead of anaerobic sealant to front cover-to-block sealing surface. Apply 1/8" bead silicone sealer to bottom of front cover sealing surface. See Fig. 9.

2) Place front cover on engine and install stud bolt and 2 lower bolts. Coat water pump bolts with pipe thread sealer. Apply 3/32" bead anaerobic sealer to water pump sealing surface, and install water pump and attaching bolts. Tighten all bolts. Reverse removal procedure to complete installation.

Fig. 9: Front Cover Sealer Application

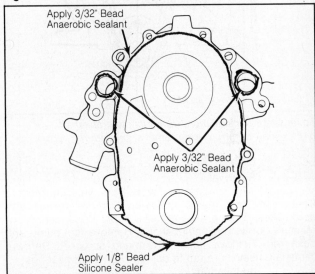

Install and tighten front cover and water pump before sealer sets up.

FRONT COVER OIL SEAL

Removal

The oil seal may be replaced with front cover installed. Remove vibration damper. Using large screwdriver, pry seal out of cover. Use care not to damage crankshaft.

Installation

Install new seal with open side of seal toward inside of front cover. Use seal installing tool to drive seal into position. Install vibration damper and related parts.

TIMING CHAIN

Removal

1) Remove front cover. Rotate crankshaft to position No. 4 piston on TDC at end of compression stroke. Timing marks on sprockets should be aligned.

General Motors V6 Engines

2.8 LITER V6 (Cont.)

With crankshaft in this position, No. 1 piston will be on TDC at end of exhaust stroke. *See Fig. 10.*

2) Remove camshaft sprocket bolts, then remove sprocket and chain. To facilitate reinstallation, do not allow camshaft or crankshaft to turn.

Installation

Install timing chain and camshaft sprocket. Timing marks must be aligned. *See Fig. 10.* Use attaching bolts to draw sprocket onto camshaft and tighten bolts. Lubricate chain with engine oil. Install remaining components in reverse order of removal.

Fig. 10: Timing Sprockets Alignment

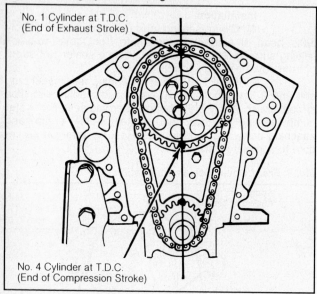

No. 1 Cylinder at T.D.C.
(End of Exhaust Stroke)

No. 4 Cylinder at T.D.C.
(End of Compression Stroke)

To facilitate reinstallation, do not allow crankshaft or camshaft to turn, during removal procedure.

CAMSHAFT

Removal

With engine removed from vehicle, remove front cover and intake manifold. Remove rocker arm assemblies, push rods and valve lifters in sequence, for reinstallation in original locations. Remove fuel pump and push rod. Remove timing chain and sprocket. Remove camshaft, using care not to damage camshaft bearings.

Installation

Lubricate journals with engine oil and apply Molykote (or equivalent) to camshaft lobes. Carefully install camshaft. Prior to installing rocker arm assemblies, coat rocker arm ball and mating rocker arm surface with Molykote (or equivalent). Reverse removal procedure to complete installation.

CAM LOBE LIFT

1) With valve cover removed, remove rocker arm assemblies. Mount dial indicator on rocker arm stud. Position dial indicator and ball socket adapter on push rod.

2) Slowly rotate engine in direction of rotation until lifter is on base circle of camshaft. Zero dial indicator. Rotate engine until push rod is fully raised. Record lobe lift reading and compare with specifications. If not within limits, replace camshaft and lifters.

CAMSHAFT BEARINGS

Removal

Remove engine from vehicle. Remove camshaft. Ensure rod and main bearing caps are marked, and remove all caps. Push pistons to top of bores. Remove crankshaft. Remove camshaft rear cover from cylinder block. Using a camshaft bearing remover/installer tool, remove camshaft bearings.

Installation

Using bearing remover/installer tool, install front and rear bearings first. These act as guides for the tool pilot, and center the remaining bearings being pulled into place. Ensure that oil holes in bearings line up with oil gallery holes in block. Reverse removal procedure to complete operation.

PISTONS, RINGS & PINS

OIL PAN

See Oil Pan Removal at end of ENGINE Section.

PISTON & ROD ASSEMBLY

Removal

1) Remove oil pan, oil pump and cylinder heads. Place piston at bottom of stroke and cover piston with a cloth to collect cuttings. Use a ridge reamer to remove any ridge or deposits from upper portion of the cylinder bore.

2) If necessary, mark connecting rod and cap for reinstallation in original location. Remove connecting rod cap and install rubber hose over rod bolts. Push piston and rod out top of bore. Install cap to its respective connecting rod.

Installation

1) Install rings on piston, and properly space ring gaps. *See Fig. 11.* Apply a light coat of engine oil to piston, rings and cylinder bore. Using ring compressor, compress piston rings. Ensure ring gaps do not change during compressor installation.

2) Cover rod bolts with protective rubber hose. Install piston with notch (or machined hole) in piston head, toward front of engine. Rod bearing tang slot must be positioned away from camshaft. Remove rubber hose from rod bolts. With rod bearings installed, install and tighten rod caps.

FITTING PISTONS

1) Using telescope gauge and micrometer, measure cylinder bore diameter. Measure piston diameter across piston skirt, at center line of piston pin. Difference between 2 measurements is piston-to-cylinder bore clearance.

2) Using cylinder bore gauge, measure cylinder bore taper by working gauge up and down in bore. Difference between high and low readings is taper. Taper must not exceed .001" (.02 mm).

3) Measure cylinder bore out-of-round. Take out-of-round measurements at different points in bore, by rotating gauge horizontally, around entire circumference of bore. Out-of-round must not exceed .001" (.02 mm).

4) If taper or out-of-round are not within limits, hone or bore cylinders for installation of new pistons. Replacement pistons are available in standard, .020" (.50

2.8 LITER V6 (Cont.)

mm) oversize and .040" (1.0 mm) oversize. When reboring cylinders, all main bearing caps must be installed and tightened to specification.

FITTING RINGS

1) Position ring at bottom of cylinder bore, about 1/4" above ring travel. Ring must be square in bore. Measure ring end gap with a feeler gauge.

2) Before installing compression rings on pistons, check side clearance. Insert outer edge of ring in its respective groove, and slide ring around entire circumference of groove. The ring should slide freely in groove. If ring grooves have high steps on lower lands, piston must be replaced.

3) Check side clearance of compression rings, with feeler gauge inserted between ring and ring groove. Install and properly space rings on piston. Ensure oil ring spacer ends are butted, and not overlapped. Note that anti-rotation tang of oil ring spacer is inserted into oil hole (or slot) of piston. See Fig. 11.

Fig. 11: Desired Ring Gap Locations

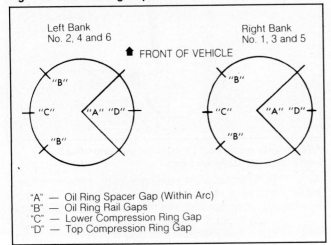

Insert tang of oil ring spacer in oil hole (or slot) of piston. Hole is located within arc of oil ring spacer gap "A".

PISTON PIN REPLACEMENT

Removal

Using an arbor press and piston pin remover/installer tool, press piston pin from piston and connecting rod.

Installation

Check clearance of piston pin in piston. Replace piston and pin assembly if not within limits. Lubricate piston and connecting rod pin bores. Assemble connecting rod to piston. Using piston pin remover/installer tool and an arbor press, press piston into place. Check piston for freedom of movement on piston pin.

CRANKSHAFT, MAIN & CONNECTING ROD BEARINGS

MAIN & CONNECTING ROD BEARINGS

NOTE: Precision bearings are used in this engine, and shimming is not acceptable for adjust-

ment. Never file or grind connecting rods or caps when fitting bearings.

Crankshaft Main Bearings

1) If bearings are being checked with engine in vehicle, crankshaft must be supported at both front and rear. Ensure that all bearing caps, other than the one being checked, are tightened to specifications. When checking No. 1 main bearing, remove all drive belts from crankshaft pulley.

2) Start with rear main bearing cap and work forward. Remove main cap and place Plastigage across full width of bearing, about 1/4" off center and away from oil holes. Install and tighten main cap to specification.

3) Remove main cap and determine clearance, by measuring width of compressed Plastigage at widest point. Bearings must be replaced if clearance is not within specifications.

4) New bearings are available in standard, .0006" (.016 mm) and .0012" (.032 mm) undersize, for use with standard size crankshaft. These undersize bearing halves may be used in combination to obtain correct clearance. Always replace both upper and lower bearings as a unit.

5) Main bearings are removed from cylinder block using main bearing remover/installer tool. Insert tool in crankshaft oil hole and rotate crankshaft clockwise. If tool unavailable, a cotter pin may be bent, as necessary, to do the job.

6) Lubricate journal and bearing. Insert plain end of new bearing between crankshaft and notched side of block. Insert bearing remover/installer tool into crankshaft oil hole. Rotate crankshaft counterclockwise to install bearing into place.

7) Install lower bearing half into cap, then lubricate with engine oil. Install and tighten main bearing cap with arrow pointing toward front of engine.

8) Check crankshaft end play after aligning thrust bearing. Check end play by prying crankshaft forward, and inserting feeler gauge between crankshaft counterweight and forward face of No. 3 main bearing cap.

Connecting Rod Bearings

1) Remove rod cap and use Plastigage method to check bearing clearance. With crank pin and bearing clean, place Plastigage across full width of bearing, about 1/4" off center, and away from oil holes. Install and tighten rod cap to specification. Do not allow crankshaft to turn.

2) Remove rod cap and determine clearance, by measuring width of compressed Plastigage at widest point. If clearance exceeds specifications, select a new undersize bearing and remeasure clearance.

3) Clean crankshaft journal and bearing seat in rod and cap. Insert bearings in rod and cap, then coat bearings with engine oil. Pull piston and rod assembly down onto crankshaft. Install and tighten rod cap. After all rods are installed, check side play between rod cap and crank pin thrust face.

4) Replacement bearings are available in standard, .0005" (.013 mm) and .0010" (.026 mm) undersize, for use with standard size crankshaft.

THRUST BEARING ALIGNMENT

1) Make sure all main bearing caps, except No. 3, are installed and tightened. Tighten No. 3 thrust bearing cap bolts to 11 ft. lbs. (15 N.m).

2) Tap end of crankshaft rearward, then forward, to line up main bearing and crankshaft thrust surfaces. Tighten thrust bearing cap. Retighten all main bearing cap bolts, including thrust bearing. Rotate crankshaft to ensure there is no excessive drag.

REAR MAIN BEARING OIL SEAL

NOTE: Following procedure is for repair of upper rear main bearing oil seal, rather than replacement.

1) Remove oil pan, oil pump and rear main bearing cap. Remove lower seal from cap, but do not discard. Using upper seal packing tool (J-29114-2 or equivalent), gently drive upper oil seal into groove in cylinder block, approximately 1/4" on both sides. See Fig. 12.

Fig. 12: Driving Oil Seal into Cylinder Block

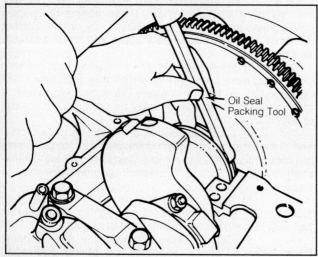

Drive upper seal into cylinder block groove approximately 1/4".

2) Measure the distance upper seal was driven into groove on one side. Add 1/16" to this measurement. Cut a length of the combined measurement from old oil seal removed from cap. Repeat this procedure for the other side.

Fig. 13: Installing Replacement Oil Seal Ends into Block

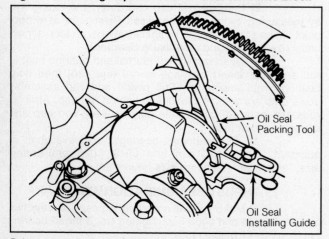

Drive cut seal ends into block, until tool bottoms on built-in stop.

3) Coat short pieces of rope seal with engine oil. Using packing tool (J-29114-2 or equivalent) and oil seal guide tool (J-20114-1 or equivalent), work piece of replacement seal into guide tool, then drive seal into cylinder block until packing tool bottoms. See Fig. 13. A built-in stop is designed into the guide tool and packing tool combination. Repeat procedure for opposite side.

4) Using seal installing tool (J-25950 or equivalent), install new oil seal into rear main bearing cap. Cut ends of lower seal flush with machined surface of main cap. See Fig. 14.

Fig. 14: Installing Rear Seal Lower Half

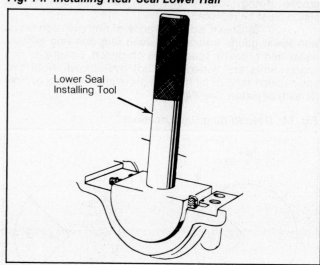

After installing seal, cut protruding seal ends flush with machined surface of cap.

5) Install main bearing in cap. Using Plastigage method to check clearance, install and tighten rear main bearing cap. Remove cap and measure bearing clearance.

6) If out of specification, check seal for frayed ends or loose seal material, that may be preventing proper seating of cap. If seal is known to be properly installed, check bearing-to-crankshaft journal clearance.

7) Clean crankshaft and bearing surfaces. Apply anaerobic sealant to bearing cap at both sides of seal groove. Do not allow sealer to contact rope seal or main bearing. Install and tighten cap. Install oil pump and oil pan.

ENGINE OILING

Crankcase Capacity
Capacity is 4.5 quarts (4.2L), with oil filter replacement.

Oil Filter
Replace at every other oil change, or more often under severe or dusty operating conditions.

Normal Oil Pressure
With engine at normal operating temperature, oil pressure should be 30-40 psi (2.1-2.8 kg/cm²) at speeds of 35-40 MPH.

Oil Pressure Regulator Valve
Located in oil pump body, not adjustable.

ENGINE OILING SYSTEM

Oil is supplied under full pressure by a gear-type pump. The left main oil gallery (along upper left side of camshaft) supplies oil to left bank hydraulic lifters.

2.8 LITER V6 (Cont.)

Oil from the left gallery is directed to the camshaft bearings, crankshaft and right oil gallery, through intersecting drilled passages.

The right oil gallery supplies oil to the right side hydraulic lifters. From valve lifters, oil is supplied to upper valve train through hollow push rods. All other components are lubricated by splash or nozzle method.

OIL PUMP

Removal

With engine removed from vehicle, remove oil pan. Remove bolt attaching oil pump to rear main bearing cap, then remove oil pump with extension shaft.

Disassembly

1) Remove pump cover. Mark gears at a meshing point, so they may be reassembled with same gear teeth indexing. Remove idler gear and drive gear and shaft from pump body.

2) Remove pressure regulator valve retaining pin, valve and spring. If necessary to replace, remove oil inlet tube from body. Do not disturb screen on oil inlet tube.

NOTE: **If pump gears or body are damaged or worn, the entire pump assembly must be replaced.**

Inspection

1) Wash all parts and dry with compressed air. Inspect pump body, pump cover and pump gears for damage or excessive wear.

2) Check drive gear shaft for looseness in pump body. Inspect oil inlet tube and screen for damage. Check pressure regulator valve for fit in bore.

Reassembly

1) If removed, install oil inlet tube and screen. Apply sealer to end of tube, and tap tube into place, using plastic hammer. Install pressure regulator valve, spring and retaining pin.

2) Install idler gear and drive gear and shaft into pump body. Make sure gear teeth previously marked, are indexing. Install pump cover.

Installation

Prime oil pump. Assemble pump and extension shaft (with retainer), to rear main bearing cap. Ensure top

end of hexagon extension shaft engages with hexagon socket of distributor drive gear. Install and tighten oil pump attaching bolt.

ENGINE COOLING

WATER PUMP

Removal

Disconnect negative battery cable. Drain cooling system. Remove heater hose from water pump. Remove water pump.

Installation

Apply 3/32" bead of anaerobic sealer to water pump sealing surface. Coat bolt threads with pipe thread sealer. Install and tighten water pump. Install remaining components in reverse order of removal.

NOTE: **For information on cooling system capacities and other cooling system components, see appropriate article in "Engine Cooling Systems," at end of ENGINE Section.**

TIGHTENING SPECIFICATIONS

Application	Ft. Lbs. (N.m)
Camshaft Rear Cover Bolts	6-9 (8-12)
Camshaft Sprocket Bolts	15-20 (20-27)
Connecting Rod Cap Nuts	34-44 (46-60)
Crankshaft Pulley Bolts	20-30 (27-41)
Cylinder Head Bolts	55-77 (74-108)
Exhaust Manifold Bolts	20-30 (27-41)
Exhaust Manifold Studs	24-35 (32-48)
Flywheel-to-Crankshaft Bolts	45-59 (61-80)
Front Cover Bolts	20-30 (27-41)
Front Cover Studs	24-35 (32-48)
Intake Manifold Bolts	13-25 (18-34)
Main Bearing Cap Bolts	63-83 (85-112)
Oil Pump Attaching Bolt	26-35 (35-47)
Rocker Arm Studs	43-53 (58-72)
Water Pump	
6 mm Bolts	6-9 (8-12)
8 mm Bolts	13-18 (18-24)

ENGINE SPECIFICATIONS

GENERAL SPECIFICATIONS

Year	DISPLACEMENT		Fuel System	HP@RPM	Torque Ft. Lbs. @RPM	Compr. Ratio	BORE		STROKE	
	Cu. In.	Liters					In.	mm	In.	mm
1983	173	2.8	4-Bbl.	......	......	8.5:1	3.50	89.0	2.99	76.0

VALVES

Engine Size & Valve	Head Diam. In. (mm)	Face Angle	Seat Angle	Seat Width In. (mm)	Stem Diameter In. (mm)	Stem Clearance In. (mm)	Valve Lift In. (mm)
2.8L Intake	......	45°	46°	.049-.059 (1.25-1.50)	......	.0010-.0027 (.026-.068)	......
Exhaust	......	45°	46°	.063-.075 (1.60-1.90)	......	.0010-.0027 (.026-.068)	......

General Motors V6 Engines

2.8 LITER V6 (Cont.)

ENGINE SPECIFICATIONS (Cont.)

PISTONS, PINS, RINGS

| Engine | PISTONS | PINS | | RINGS | | |
	Clearance In. (mm)	Piston Fit In. (mm)	Rod Fit In. (mm)	Ring No.	End Gap In. (mm)	Side Clearance In. (mm)
2.8L	.0007-.0017 (.017-.043)	.00025-.00035 (.0065-.0091)	[1] .0007-.0020 (.0187-.0515)	1	.010-.020 (.25-.50)	.0012-.0027 (.030-.070)
				2	.010-.020 (.25-.50)	.0016-.0037 (.040-.095)
				3	.020-.055 (.51-1.40)	[2] .0078 (.199)

[1] — Interference fit.
[2] — Maximum clearance permitted.

CRANKSHAFT MAIN & CONNECTING ROD BEARINGS

| Engine | MAIN BEARINGS | | | | CONNECTING ROD BEARINGS | | |
	Journal Diam. In. (mm)	Clearance In. (mm)	Thrust Bearing	Crankshaft End Play In. (mm)	Journal Diam. In. (mm)	Clearance In. (mm)	Side Play In. (mm)
2.8L	2.4937-2.4946 (63.340-63.364)	.0016-.0031 (.041-.081)	No. 3	.002-.008 (.06-.21)	1.9983-1.9993 (50.758-50.784)	.0014-.0037 (.035-.095)	.006-.017 (.16-.44)

VALVE SPRINGS

| Engine | Free Length In. (mm) | PRESSURE Lbs. @ In. (Kg @ mm) | |
		Valve Closed	Valve Open
2.8L	1.91 (48.50)	88@1.57 (39.91@40)	195@1.18 (88.45@30)

CAMSHAFT

Engine	Journal Diam. In. (mm)	Clearance In. (mm)	Lobe Lift In. (mm)
2.8L	1.867-1.870 (47.44-47.49)	.0010-.0040 (.026-.101)	[1] .231 (5.87) [2] .263 (6.67)

[1] — Intake.
[2] — Exhaust.

4.1 & 4.8 LITER 6-CYLINDER

ENGINE CODING

ENGINE IDENTIFICATION

Engine may be identified by a letter code in eighth position of Vehicle Identification Number (VIN). The VIN is stamped on a metal tab, attached to left side of dash, near windshield. Engine identification number is also stamped on a machined pad, at right hand side of cylinder block, rearward of distributor bore.

ENGINE IDENTIFICATION CODES

Engine	Code
4.1L 2-Bbl.	UAB, UAD, UAK, UAM, UAN
	UAR, UAS, UAT, UAU, UAW
	UAX, UAY, UAZ, UUN, UUR
	UUS, UUT, UUU, UUW
4.8L 1-Bbl.	UTA, UTB, UTC, UTD

ENGINE REMOVAL

See Engine Removal at end of ENGINE Section.

MANIFOLDS & CYLINDER HEAD

EXHAUST MANIFOLD

NOTE: **Intake manifold is integral with cylinder head on 4.1L Engine.**

Removal (4.1L Engine)

1) Disconnect negative battery cable at battery. Remove air cleaner. If equipped, remove power steering pump and air pump drive belts. Remove both pumps and mounting brackets. Remove air injection manifold from exhaust manifold.

2) Raise vehicle. Disconnect exhaust pipe from exhaust manifold, and catalytic converter bracket at transmission mount. Lower vehicle. Remove exhaust manifold.

Installation

Ensure gasket surfaces are clean. Place manifold in position with new gasket. Install and tighten exhaust manifold bolts. Reverse removal procedure to complete installation. *See Fig. 1.*

Fig. 1: 4.1L Exhaust Manifold Tightening Sequence

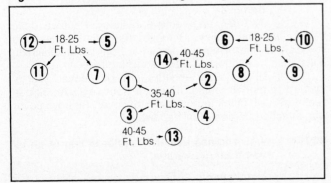

Note that bolt tightening specifications vary.

INTAKE & EXHAUST MANIFOLD

Removal (4.8L Engine)

1) Disconnect negative battery cable at battery. Remove air cleaner. Disconnect both throttle controls at bellcrank, and remove throttle return spring. Disconnect fuel line and vacuum lines at carburetor.

2) Disconnect crankcase vent hose at rocker arm cover and vapor hose at canister. Disconnect exhaust pipe at flange. Remove manifold assembly attaching bolts and clamps. Remove intake and exhaust manifold assembly.

Installation

Ensure gasket surfaces are clean. Place manifold in position with new gasket. Install and tighten clamps and bolts. Reverse removal procedure to complete installation.

CYLINDER HEAD

Removal

1) Drain cooling system and disconnect upper radiator hose at engine. Remove exhaust manifold (4.1L) or intake and exhaust manifold assembly (4.8L). Remove rocker arm covers. Remove rocker arm assemblies and push rods in sequence, for reinstallation in original locations.

2) Disconnect and label all wires and vacuum hoses that may interfere with head removal. If equipped, disconnect air injection hose at check valve. Remove cylinder head.

CAUTION: **Do not apply gasket sealer to composition steel asbestos gaskets.**

Installation

1) Ensure that gasket surfaces of cylinder head and block are clean, and all head bolt threads and threads in block are clean. Coat threads of head bolts with sealer.

2) To install cylinder head and remaining components, reverse removal procedure. Tighten head bolts in sequence. *See Fig. 2.* Lubricate rocker arm parts with Molykote (or equivalent). Adjust valves.

Fig. 2: Cylinder Head Tightening Sequence

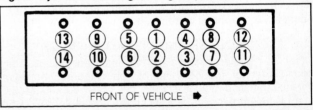

Tighten front left-hand head bolt to 85 ft. lbs. (115 N.m), and all others to 95 ft. lbs. (129 N.m).

VALVES

VALVE ARRANGEMENT

E-I-I-E-E-I-I-E-E-I-I-E (Front to rear)

ROCKER ARM STUDS

Rocker arm studs that are loose in head or have damaged threads, can be replaced with oversize studs. Use reamer (J-5715) for .003" (.08 mm) oversize replacement studs, and reamer (J-6036) for .013" (.33 mm) oversize replacement studs.

Removal

Remove damaged stud using stud remover (J-5802-A). Install tool over stud. Tighten nut on tool to extract stud from cylinder head.

General Motors 6 Engines

4.1 & 4.8 LITER 6-CYLINDER (Cont.)

Installation

Ream hole for oversize studs. Coat press-fit area of stud with hypoid axle grease. Drive rocker stud into place with stud driver (J-6880). When driver bottoms on head, stud is at correct height.

VALVE SPRINGS

Removal

1) Remove valve cover. Remove spark plug, rocker arm assembly and push rod of cylinder to be serviced. Install air hose and adapter in spark plug hole, and apply air pressure. Do not remove air pressure until all components are reinstalled.

2) Use valve spring compressor to compress valve spring, and remove retainer locks. Release spring compressor and remove spring retainer (or rotator), shield, spring, damper (if equipped), and oil seal. See Fig. 3.

Fig. 3: Exploded View of Valve Spring Assembly

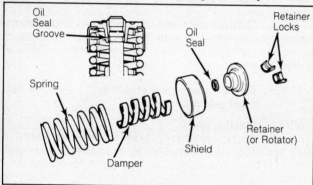

Damper is not used on 4.1L engines.

Installation

Install damper, spring, shield and retainer. Use compressor tool to compress valve spring, and install new oil seal and retainer locks. Remove compressor tool. Remove air hose and adapter. Install remaining components in reverse order of removal.

VALVE SPRING INSTALLED HEIGHT

Measure valve spring installed height from spring seat (or top of shim), to top of spring (or valve shield). Installed height should be 1.63-1.69" (41.4-43.0 mm). If height exceeds specifications, install a 1/16" (1.58 mm) thick shim under spring.

VALVE STEM OIL SEALS

"O" ring-type seals are used. Lightly coat seal with engine oil and install in lower groove of valve stem. Make sure seal is not twisted in groove.

VALVE GUIDE SERVICING

Valve guides are integral with cylinder head. If guide is worn, it must be reamed for installation of valves with oversize stems. Valves are available with .003" (.08 mm), .015" (.38 mm) and .030" (.76 mm) oversize stems. Use reamers in sequence when reaming valve guides.

HYDRAULIC VALVE LIFTERS

Disassemble lifters and thoroughly clean. Inspect all components for wear and damage. If any components are worn or damaged, complete lifter assem-

bly must be replaced. If push rod seat or lifter body wear is noted, inspect mating engine components for wear. See Fig. 4.

Fig. 4: Cutaway View of Valve Lifter Assembly

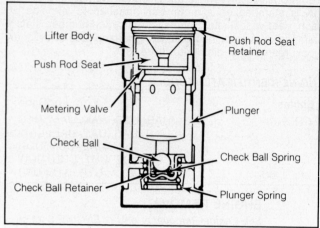

Replace lifters as complete assemblies; do not interchange parts between lifters.

VALVE CLEARANCE ADJUSTMENT

1) Remove distributor cap. Mark distributor housing at No. 1 and No. 6 rotor firing positions.

2) With distributor rotor in the positions designated in *Valve Adjustment* table, adjust valves as follows: Loosen rocker arm adjusting nut until push rod lash (play) is felt. Tighten adjusting nut until all lash is removed. When lash has been removed, tighten adjusting nut 1 full turn to complete procedure.

VALVE CLEARANCE ADJUSTMENT

Rotor Position	Adjust Int. Nos.	Adjust Exh. Nos.
No. 1	1, 2, 4	1, 3, 5
No. 6	3, 5, 6	2, 4, 6

CAMSHAFT

ENGINE FRONT COVER

Removal

1) Drain and remove radiator. Remove drive belt(s), fan and pulley. Remove crankshaft pulley and vibration damper. Remove oil pan-to-front cover attaching bolts, then front cover-to-block attaching bolts.

2) On 4.8L engine only, pull cover slightly forward to permit cutting of oil pan front seal. Cut oil pan seal flush with block at both sides of cover. Remove cover with attached portion of oil pan seal.

NOTE: 4.1L engines use RTV sealer in lieu of an oil pan front rubber seal.

Installation

1) Clean all gasket mating surfaces. On 4.8L engines, cut tabs from new oil pan front seal. See Fig. 5.. Install seal to front cover, pressing locating tips into holes in cover. On 4.1L engines, place a 3/16" bead of RTV sealer on cover-to-pan sealing surface.

4.1 & 4.8 LITER 6-CYLINDER (Cont.)

Fig. 5: Oil Pan Front Seal Modification

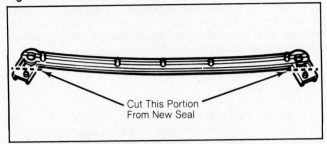

Use a sharp instrument to ensure a clean cut.

2) Coat front cover gasket with sealer, and position on cover. Apply 1/8" bead of RTV sealer to joint formed by oil pan and cylinder block. Install oil seal centering tool (J-23042 or equivalent) in front cover seal and install cover to cylinder block.

3) Install and partially tighten oil pan-to-cover bolts. Install front cover-to-cylinder block bolts. Remove centering tool and tighten bolts. To install remaining components, reverse removal procedure.

FRONT COVER OIL SEAL

Removal (Front Cover Installed)
Remove vibration damper. Pry seal out of cover with screwdriver, using care not to damage cover seal surface.

Installation
Install new seal with open end toward inside of cover. Drive seal into place using seal driver (J-23042).

Removal (Cover Removed)
Pry seal out of cover with screwdriver, using care not to damage cover seal surface.

Installation
Install new seal with open end of seal toward inside of cover. Support cover at seal recess area. Using a seal installing tool, drive seal into position.

TIMING GEARS

Inspection
With engine front cover removed, check backlash between timing gear teeth. Backlash should be .004-.006" (.10-.15 mm) for new gears, and .004-.008" (.10-.20 mm) for used gears. Check both gears for runout with a dial indicator. Maximum camshaft gear runout is .004" (.10 mm). Maximum crankshaft gear runout is .003" (.08 mm).

Removal
1) Remove camshaft from engine. Position camshaft and gear on arbor press, and properly support hub of gear. Make sure thrust plate is positioned so Woodruff key in shaft will not be damaged when camshaft is pressed out of gear. Press camshaft from gear. *See Fig. 6.*

2) Remove crankshaft gear from crankshaft, using gear puller (J-8105 or equivalent).

Installation
1) With crankshaft properly supported, use hollow driver (J-5590 or equivalent), to drive gear onto crankshaft.

2) To install camshaft gear, position camshaft in a press with camshaft supported at back of front journal. Place gear spacer ring and thrust plate over camshaft and install Woodruff key in keyway. Press gear onto camshaft until it bottoms on gear spacer ring.

Fig. 6: Removing Camshaft from Gear

Properly support hub of camshaft gear, to avoid gear damage.

CAMSHAFT

Removal
1) Remove engine from vehicle. Remove valve cover and loosen all rocker arm nuts. Rotate rocker arms to side and withdraw push rods in sequence, for reinstallation in original locations.

2) Remove valve lifter side cover and remove lifters. Remove front engine cover and fuel pump. Align crankshaft and camshaft timing gear marks. Remove

Fig. 7: Timing Gear Mark Alignment

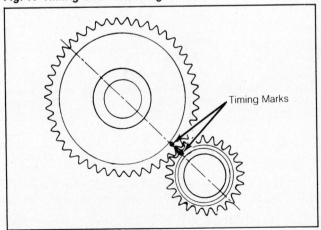

Remove camshaft thrust plate bolts through access holes in camshaft gear.

General Motors 6 Engines

4.1 & 4.8 LITER 6-CYLINDER (Cont.)

camshaft thrust plate bolts through access holes in camshaft gear. Carefully remove camshaft.

Installation

Coat camshaft lobes with Lubriplate (or equivalent). Reverse removal procedure to install camshaft, ensuring timing marks on gears are aligned. Take care to avoid damage to camshaft lobes or bearings. Install new valve lifters. Reassemble and install engine in vehicle. Change oil and oil filter. *See Fig. 7.*

CAMSHAFT END THRUST

Check camshaft end play with feeler gauge. End play should be .001-.005" (.03-.13 mm). *See Fig. 8.*

Fig. 8: Checking Camshaft End Play

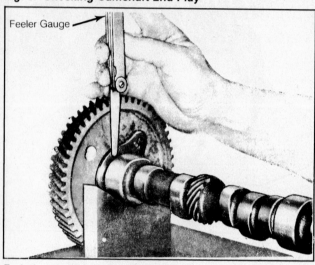

End play is .001-.005" (.03-.13 mm).

CAM LOBE LIFT

1) With valve cover removed, remove rocker arm assemblies. Mount dial indicator on rocker arm stud. Position dial indicator and ball socket adapter on push rod. *See Fig. 9.*

Fig. 9: Checking Camshaft Lobe Lift

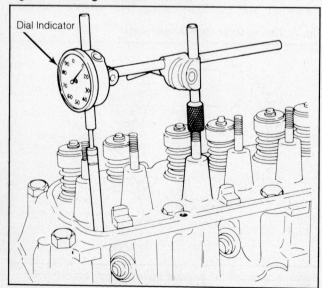

If readings are not within specifications, replace camshaft and lifters.

2) Slowly rotate engine in direction of rotation until lifter is on base circle of camshaft. Zero dial indicator. Rotate engine until push rod is fully raised. Record lobe lift reading and compare with specifications. If not within limits, replace camshaft and lifters.

CAMSHAFT BEARINGS

Removal

With engine removed from vehicle, remove camshaft, oil pan and oil pump. Drive camshaft rear plug from block. Drive camshaft bearings from engine. Remove front and rear bearings after center bearings have been removed.

Installation

Install front and rear bearings first, to act as guide for pilot of tool, and to center remaining bearings being pulled into place. Oil holes in cam bearings must align with oil holes in block. Install new camshaft rear plug.

PISTONS, RINGS & PINS

OIL PAN

See Oil Pan Removal at end of ENGINE Section.

PISTON & ROD ASSEMBLY

Removal

1) Remove oil pan, oil pump and cylinder head. Position piston at bottom of stroke, and cover with cloth to collect metal cuttings. Remove ridge at top of cylinder bore with a ridge reamer.

2) If necessary, mark connecting rod for cylinder identification. Remove connecting rod cap nuts and cap, and cover rod bolts with rubber hose. Push piston and rod assembly out top of cylinder block.

Installation

1) Before installing piston and rod assembly, ensure ring gaps are properly spaced. *See Fig. 10.* Lightly coat pistons, rings and cylinder walls with engine oil. Install rod bearings in rod and cap, and lubricate with engine oil.

2) Compress piston rings with ring compressor. Do not allow position of rings to change. Cover connecting rod bolts with rubber hose. Install piston and rod assembly, with notch on top of piston facing front of engine. Install and tighten connecting rod cap.

FITTING PISTONS

1) Using telescope gauge and micrometer, measure cylinder bore diameter at a point 2 1/2" (64 mm) from top of bore. Measure piston diameter across piston skirt, at center line of piston pin. Difference between the two measurements is piston-to-cylinder bore clearance.

2) Using cylinder bore gauge, measure cylinder bore taper by working gauge up and down in bore. Measure cylinder bore out-of-round. Take measurements at different points in bore, by rotating gauge horizontally, around entire circumference of bore. Out-of-round must not exceed .002" (.05 mm). Taper must not exceed .005" .13 mm).

3) If taper or out-of-round are not within limits, hone or bore cylinders for installation of new pistons.

4.1 & 4.8 LITER 6-CYLINDER (Cont.)

FITTING RINGS

1) Position ring into cylinder bore at a point about 1/4" above ring travel. Ring must be square in bore. Measure ring end gap with a feeler gauge.

2) Before installing compression rings on pistons, check side clearance. Insert outer edge of ring in its respective groove, and slide ring around entire circumference of groove. The ring should slide freely in groove.

3) Check side clearance of compression rings, with feeler gauge inserted between ring and ring groove. Install rings with gaps properly positioned. Note that anti-rotation tang of oil ring spacer is inserted into oil hole (or slot) of piston. See Fig. 10.

Fig. 10: Desired Ring Gap Locations

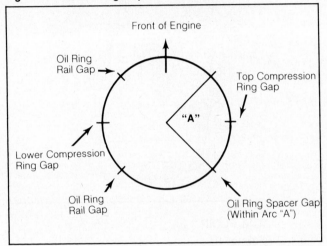

Insert tang of oil ring spacer in oil hole (or slot) of piston. Hole is located within arc of oil ring spacer gap "A".

PISTON PIN REPLACEMENT

Removal

Using an arbor press and piston pin remover/installer tool, press piston pin from piston and connecting rod.

Installation

Check clearance of piston pin in piston, and replace piston and pin assembly if not within limits. Lubricate piston pin holes in piston and connecting rod. Position connecting rod on piston and press in piston pin, using pin remover/installer tool and an arbor press. Check piston for freedom of movement on piston pin.

CRANKSHAFT, MAIN & CONNECTING ROD BEARINGS

MAIN & CONNECTING ROD BEARINGS

NOTE: Following procedures are performed with oil pan and oil pump removed. Remove oil film from surfaces to be checked.

Crankshaft Main Bearings

Some production crankshafts are ground to .009" (.23 mm) undersize at the assembly plant. They are identified as follows:

- Crankshaft counterweight of undersize journal, will be stamped on one side with the number "9," along with a large spot of light green paint.
- Main bearing cap will be painted light green on each side.

1) Mark or identify main bearing cap before removing. Support crankshaft weight, using a jack placed under counterweight next to the bearing being checked. Loosen drive belts from crankshaft pulley, prior to checking No. 1 bearing.

2) Remove main bearing cap and place a piece of Plastigage across full width of bearing, about 1/4" off center, and away from oil holes. Install cap and tighten to specifications. Do not allow crankshaft to turn.

3) Remove cap and measure width of Plastigage with scale furnished. Standard, .001" (.03 mm) or .002" (.05 mm) undersize bearing halves may be used in combination to obtain correct clearance. Always replace both upper and lower bearing halves.

4) With the exception of rear main bearing, main bearings are removed from cylinder block using remover/installer tool (J-8080 or equivalent). Insert tool in crankshaft oil hole and rotate crankshaft clockwise. If tool not available, a cotter pin may be bent, as necessary, to do the job.

5) To remove rear main bearing from block, partially drive out bearing with a drift. Use a pair of pliers (with jaws taped) to hold bearing thrust surface to the oil slinger, and rotate crankshaft to remove bearing.

6) Lubricate journal and bearings. Insert plain end of new bearing between crankshaft and notched side of block. Insert bearing remover/installer tool into crankshaft oil hole, and rotate bearing into place. To install rear main bearing, use pliers (as used in removal), to aid in installation.

7) Install lower bearing half into cap. Install and tighten main bearing caps with arrows pointing toward front of engine. Align thrust bearing, then check crankshaft end play. Check end play by prying crankshaft forward, and inserting feeler gauge between crankshaft counterweight and forward face of rear main bearing cap.

Connecting Rod Bearings

1) Ensure rod caps are marked for cylinder identifcation. Remove rod cap and bearings. Inspect bearings for wear or damage and replace as necessary.

2) Check crankshaft rod bearing journal for out-of-round or taper. Maximum crankshaft out-of-round or taper must not exceed .001" (.03 mm).

3) Check rod bearing clearance using the Plastigage method (as explained in Main Bearings). If clearance exceeds specifications, standard, .001" (.03 mm), or .002" (.05 mm) undersize bearings may be used in combination to produce correct clearance. If clearance is still excessive, crankshaft must be reconditioned.

4) Clean crankshaft journal and bearing surface in rod. Insert bearings in rod and cap, then lubricate bearing surfaces with oil. Pull piston and rod assembly down onto crankshaft. Install and tighten rod cap.

THRUST BEARING ALIGNMENT

Ensure all other main bearing caps have been properly tightened. Tighten rear main bearing cap to 10-12 ft. lbs. (14-16 N.m). Tap crankshaft rearward, then forward, using a lead hammer. Tighten rear main bearing cap. Retighten all main bearing caps.

General Motors 6 Engines

4.1 & 4.8 LITER 6-CYLINDER (Cont.)

REAR MAIN BEARING OIL SEAL
Removal
Remove rear main bearing cap and pry out old seal. Remove upper half of seal by tapping end with brass punch until seal protrudes enough to be removed with pliers.

Installation
1) Fabricate an oil seal installation tool, if one is not supplied with replacement oil seal. *See Fig. 11.* Coat seal lips with engine oil. Keep oil off of seal ends. Position tool between crankshaft and seal groove in cylinder block. Position seal between tip of tool and crankshaft.

Fig. 11: Rear Main Oil Seal Installation Tool

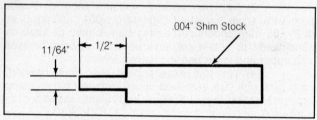

This tool is sometimes supplied with replacement oil seal.

2) Roll seal around crankshaft, using tool as a "shoehorn" to protect seal from sharp corner of seal groove in cylinder block. Tool must remain in position until seal is positioned with both ends flush with block.

3) Install lower seal into bearing cap, using tool as a "shoehorn". Feed seal into cap using light pressure with thumb and finger. Apply sealer to cap-to-block mating surface of cylinder block, being careful to keep sealer off the seal split line. Install and tighten bearing cap.

ENGINE OILING
Crankcase Capacity
Capacity is 4 quarts (3.8L) for 4.1L, and 5 quarts (4.75L) for 4.8L. Add 1 quart (.95L) when replacing oil filter.

Oil Filter
Replace at every other oil change, or more often under severe conditions.
Normal Oil Pressure
With engine at normal operating temperature, oil pressure should be 30-40 psi (2.1-2.8 kg/cm²) at 2000 RPM.

Oil Pressure Regulator Valve
In pump body, not adjustable.

ENGINE OILING SYSTEM
Gear-type pump provides full pressure lubrication. Oil drawn through pick-up screen, is pressurized through pump and routed to oil filter. A bypass valve allows oil flow to main gallery in the event back pressure is encountered at filter.

Main gallery supplies oil to camshaft bearings, lifters and main bearings. Connecting rod bearings are supplied oil from crankshaft main bearings, through cross-drilled passages.

Oil passing through hollow push rods lubricates valve train. Oil drains back to crankcase through drain holes. Timing gears are lubricated through nozzle, which is fed from front camshaft bearing. *See Fig. 12.*

Fig. 12: Engine Oiling System

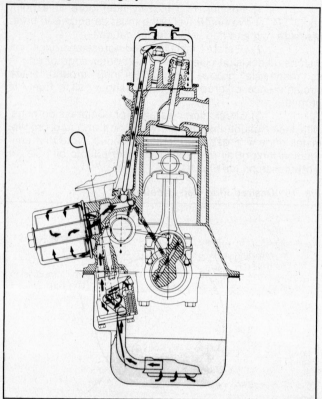

OIL PUMP
Removal
Remove oil pan. Remove oil inlet tube attaching bolt and oil pump attaching bolts. Remove oil pump and tube assembly.
Disassembly
Remove oil inlet tube assembly. Remove pump cover. Mark idler gear and drive gear at a meshing point, for later reassembly of gears in same meshing position. Remove idler gear and drive gear with shaft, from pump body. Remove pressure regulator valve retaining pin, then remove spring and valve.

NOTE: **If any part of oil pump requires replacement, the entire pump assembly must be replaced.**

Inspection
1) Clean all parts. Inspect pump body and cover for cracks and excessive wear. Inspect pump gears for damage or excessive wear. Check drive gear shaft for looseness in pump body.
2) Inspect oil inlet tube assembly for damage. Check pressure regulator valve for fit in bore.
Reassembly
Install oil inlet tube assembly. Apply sealer to end of tube, and tap tube into place, using plastic hammer. Install idler gear into pump body with smooth side of gear toward cover opening. Reassemble remaining components in reverse order of disassembly.
Installation
Prime oil pump with engine oil prior to installation. Install oil pump and pick-up tube in reverse order of removal.

4.1 & 4.8 LITER 6-CYLINDER (Cont.)

Fig. 13: Oil Pump Assembly

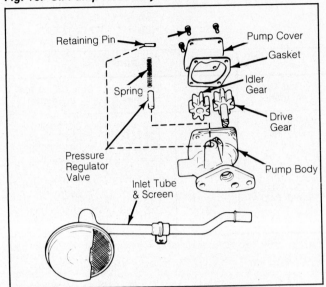

Be sure to mark gears at a meshing point, prior to disassembly.

ENGINE COOLING

WATER PUMP

Removal

Disconnect negative battery cable at battery. Drain cooling system. Remove all drive belts, then remove fan and pulley from water pump. Remove lower radiator hose and heater hose from water pump. If necessary, remove alternator adjusting bracket from water pump. Remove water pump.

Installation

Clean all gasket mating surfaces. Install components in reverse order of removal procedure, using new gasket.

NOTE: **For information on cooling system capacities and other cooling system components, see appropriate article in "Engine Cooling Systems," at end of ENGINE Section.**

TIGHTENING SPECIFICATIONS

Application	Ft. Lbs. (N.m)
Camshaft Thrust Plate Bolts	7 (9)
Connecting Rod Cap Nuts	
4.1L	35 (47)
4.8L	40 (54)
Cylinder Head Bolts	[1] 195 (129)
Engine Front Cover Bolts	7 (9)
Exhaust Manifold Bolts (4.8L)	[2] 30 (41)
Flywheel-to-Crankshaft Bolts	
4.1L	60 (81)
4.8L	110 (149)
Intake Manifold Bolts (4.8L)	40 (54)
Main Bearing Cap Bolts	65 (88)
Oil Pump Attaching Bolts	10 (13)
Vibration Damper Bolt (4.8L)	60 (81)
Water Pump Bolts	15 (20)

[1] — Tighten left-hand front bolt to 85 ft. lbs. (115 N.m)

[2] — For 4.1L, *see Fig. 1* in this article.

ENGINE SPECIFICATIONS

GENERAL SPECIFICATIONS

Year	DISPLACEMENT		Fuel System	HP@RPM	Torque Ft. Lbs.@RPM	Compr. Ratio	BORE		STROKE	
	Cu. In.	Liters					In.	mm	In.	mm
1983	250	4.1	2-Bbl.	.....	.....	8.25:1	3.88	98.5	3.53	89.7
	292	4.8	1-Bbl.	.....	.....	8.00:1	3.88	98.5	4.12	104.7

VALVES

Engine Size & Valve	Head Diam. In. (mm)	Face Angle	Seat Angle	Seat Width In. (mm)	Stem Diameter In. (mm)	Stem Clearance In. (mm)	Valve Lift In. (mm)
4.1L & 4.8L Int.	.....	[1] 45°	46°	.035-.060 (.89-1.52)	.....	.0010-.0027 (.025-.069)	.....
Exh.	.....	[1] 45°	46°	.062-.093 (1.58-2.36)	.....	.0015-.0032 (.038-.081)	.....

[1] — 4.8L face angle is 46°.

General Motors 6 Engines

4.1 & 4.8 LITER 6-CYLINDER (Cont.)

ENGINE SPECIFICATIONS (Cont.)

PISTONS, PINS, RINGS

	PISTONS	PINS		RINGS		
Engine	Clearance In. (mm)	Piston Fit In. (mm)	Rod Fit In. (mm)	Ring No.	End Gap In. (mm)	Side Clearance In. (mm)
4.1L	.0010-.0020 (.025-.051)	.0008-.0016 (.020-.041)	.0008-.0016 (.020-.041)	1	.010-.020 (.25-.51)	.0012-.0027 (.030-.069)
				2	.010-.020 (.25-.51)	.0012-.0032 (.030-.081)
				3	.015-.055 (.38-1.40)	.005 Max. (.13 Max.)
4.8L	.0026-.0036 (.066-.091)	.0008-.0016 (.020-.041)	.008-.0016 (.020-.041)	1 & 2	.010-.020 (.25-.51)	.002-.004 (.05-.10)
				3	.015-.055 (.38-1.40)	.0050-.0055 (.127-.140)

CRANKSHAFT MAIN & CONNECTING ROD BEARINGS

	MAIN BEARINGS				CONNECTING ROD BEARINGS		
Engine	Journal Diam. In. (mm)	Clearance In. (mm)	Thrust Bearing	Crankshaft End Play In. (mm)	Journal Diam. In. (mm)	Clearance In. (mm)	Side Play In. (mm)
4.1L	2.2979-2.2994 (58.366-58.405)	[1] .0010-.0024 (.025-.061)	No. 7	.002-.006 (.05-.15)	1.999-2.000 (50.77-50.80)	.0010-.0026 (.025-.066)	.006-.017 (.15-.43)
4.8L	2.2979-2.2994 (38.366-58.405)	[1] .0010-.0024 (.025-.061)	No. 7	.002-.006 (.05-.15)	2.099-2.100 (53.31-53.34)	.0010-.0026 (.025-.066)	.006-.017 (.15-.43)

[1] — Rear main bearing (No. 7) clearance is .0016-.0035" (.041-.89 mm).

VALVE SPRINGS

Engine	Free Length In. (mm)	PRESSURE Lbs. @ In. (Kg @ mm)	
		Valve Closed	Valve Open
4.1L & 4.8L	2.08 (52.8)	78-86@1.66 (35-39@42.2)	170-180@1.26 (77-81@32.0)

CAMSHAFT

Engine	Journal Diam. In. (mm)	Clearance In. (mm)	Lobe Lift In. (mm)
4.1L [1]	1.8677-1.8697 (47.440-47.490)	.....	[2] .2217 (5.631)
4.8L [1]	1.8677-1.8697 (47.440-47.490)	.....	.2315 (5.880)

[1] — End play is .003-.008" (.08-.20 mm).
[2] — Calif. vehicles exhaust lobe lift is .2315 (5.88 mm).

5.0 & 5.7 LITER V8

ENGINE CODING

ENGINE IDENTIFICATION

Engine identification number is stamped on a machined pad on front of cylinder block, immediately forward of right cylinder head. Engine types are identified by a letter code (VIN code), in eighth position of Vehicle Identification Number.

ENGINE IDENTIFICATION CODES

Engine	Code
5.0L 4-Bbl.	
VIN Code F	UDA, UDB
VIN Code H	UCA, UCB, UCC, UCD, UCF, UCH
	UCJ, UCK, UCM, UCN, UCR, UCT
	UCU, UDC, UDD, UDF, UDG, UDH,
	UDJ, UDK, UDM, UDN, UDR, UDS,
	UDT, UDU
5.7L 4-Bbl.	
VIN Code L	URA, URB, URC, URD, URF, URH
	URJ, URK, URM, URN, UUA, UUB
	UUC, UUD, UUF, UUH, UUJ
VIN Code M	USA, USB, USC, USD, USF, USH
	USJ, USK, USM, USN, USR, USS
	UST, USU, USW, USX, USY, USZ

ENGINE REMOVAL

See Engine Removal at end of ENGINE Section.

MANIFOLDS & CYLINDER HEAD

INTAKE MANIFOLD

Removal

1) Disconnect negative battery cable. Remove air cleaner. Drain cooling system. On Van models, remove engine cover. On all models, remove A.I.R. crossover hose.

Fig. 1: Silicone Sealer Application Points

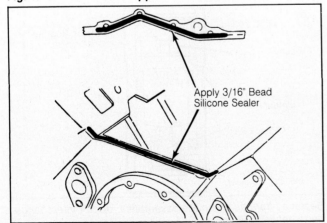

Apply 3/16" Bead
Silicone Sealer

Install intake manifold before sealer sets up (10-15 minutes).

2) Remove heater and radiator hoses. Remove alternator upper bracket. Label and disconnect necessary wires and hoses. Disconnect fuel line at carburetor. Disconnect carburetor linkage.

3) Remove spark plug wires (one side). Remove distributor cap and mark position of rotor with chalk. Remove distributor. If equipped, remove air compressor and bracket.

4) Remove brake vacuum pipe. On 4-Bbl. models, remove carburetor. Remove manifold bolts and intake manifold.

Installation

1) Clean all gasket mating surfaces. Apply 3/16" bead silicone sealer at front and rear intake manifold mounting surface of cylinder block. Extend bead of sealer 1/2" up each cylinder head. *See Fig. 1.*

2) Install intake manifold gaskets on cylinder heads. Install manifold and tighten attaching bolts. *See Fig. 2.* Install distributor with rotor pointing to chalk mark. To complete installation, reverse removal procedure.

Fig. 2: Intake Manifold Tightening Sequence

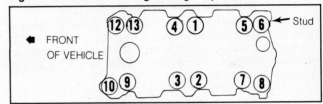

FRONT OF VEHICLE

Stud

Torque all bolts to 30 ft. lbs. (41 N.m).

EXHAUST MANIFOLD

Removal

Remove heat stove tube. Remove spark plug heat shields. Disconnect exhaust pipe from manifold and wire aside. Remove end bolts, then remove center bolts and remove manifold.

Installation

NOTE: **If installing a new right side manifold, the carburetor heat stove must be transferred from the old unit.**

Clean all gasket mating surfaces. Install manifold and tighten attaching bolts. To complete installation, reverse removal procedure. Start engine and check for leaks.

CYLINDER HEAD

Removal

1) Remove intake and exhaust manifolds. Remove A/C compressor and bracket (if equipped). Remove alternator. Remove valve covers.

2) Loosen rocker arm nuts and rotate rocker arms to side. Remove push rods in sequence for reinstallation in original locations. Drain coolant from cylinder block. Remove cylinder heads.

Installation

1) Clean all gasket surfaces. Use gasket sealer on steel head gaskets. Do not use sealer on asbestos head gaskets. Position gaskets on cylinder block and install heads.

2) Coat threads of head bolts with thread sealer. Install and tighten head bolts. *See Fig. 3.* To complete installation, reverse removal procedure. Lubricate rocker arm parts with Molykote (or equivalent) prior to installation. Adjust valves.

Fig. 3: Cylinder Head Tightening Sequence

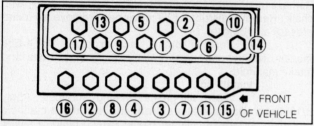

Tighten cylinder head bolts to 65 ft. lbs. (88 N.m).

VALVES

VALVE ARRANGEMENT

E-I-I-E-E-I-I-E (Both banks, front to rear)

ROCKER ARM STUDS

Rocker arm studs that are loose in head or have damaged threads can be replaced with oversize studs. Use reamer (J-5715) for .003" (.08 mm) oversize replacement studs, and reamer (J-6036) for .013" (.33 mm) oversize replacement studs.

Removal

Remove stud using stud remover (J-5802-1). Install tool over stud. Tighten nut on tool to extract stud from cylinder head.

Installation

Ream hole for oversize stud. Coat press-fit area of stud with hypoid axle grease. Drive stud into place with stud driver (J-6880). When driver bottoms out on head, stud is at correct height.

VALVE SPRINGS

Removal

1) With rocker arm cover removed, remove spark plug, rocker arm and push rod of cylinder to be serviced. Install air hose with adapter in spark plug hole, and turn on air supply. Do not remove air supply until all components are reinstalled.

2) Using valve spring compressor, compress valve spring and remove retainer locks. Release spring compressor and remove retainer, shield, spring, damper, and oil seal. See Fig. 4.

Fig. 4: Valve Spring Assembly

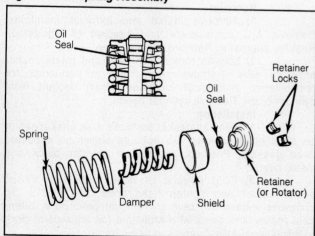

Rotators are used on exhaust valves.

Installation

Install damper, spring, shield and retainer. Using compressor tool, compress valve spring, and install new oil seal and retainer locks. Remove compressor tool. Remove air hose and adapter. Install remaining components in reverse order of removal.

VALVE SPRING INSTALLED HEIGHT

1) Measure installed height from spring seat (or top of shim), to top of spring shield. Installed height should be 1 11/16-1 3/4" (42.85-44.45 mm) for intake valves, and 1 9/16-1 5/8" (39.70-41.28 mm) for exhaust valves.

2) If installed height exceeds specifications, install a 1/16" (1.59 mm) thick shim between spring seat and spring. Installed height should never be more than specified height.

VALVE STEM OIL SEALS

"O" ring type seal is used. Coat seal with engine oil and install in second groove of valve stem. Make sure seal is not twisted on valve stem.

VALVE GUIDE SERVICING

If valve stem to guide clearance is excessive, valves with oversize stems are available. Replacement valves are available with .003" (.08 mm), .015" (.38 mm) and .030" (.76 mm) oversize stems. Always use reamers in proper size sequence.

HYDRAULIC VALVE LIFTERS

1) Disassemble lifters and thoroughly clean. Inspect all components for wear and damage. If any components are worn or damaged, complete lifter assembly must be replaced.

2) If push rod seat or lifter body wear is noted, inspect mating engine components for wear. Prior to installing, lubricate bases of lifters with Molykote (or equivalent). See Fig. 5.

Fig. 5: Cutaway View of Valve Lifter Assembly

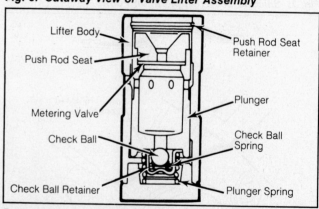

Replace lifters as complete assemblies; do not interchange parts between lifters.

VALVE CLEARANCE ADJUSTMENT

1) Rotate engine until No. 1 piston is on TDC at end of compression stroke. With piston in this position, adjust valves listed in Valve Clearance Adjustment table, using the following procedure:

2) Loosen rocker arm adjusting nut until play is felt in push rod. Tighten adjusting nut until play in push

5.0 & 5.7 LITER V8 (Cont.)

rod is removed. When play has been removed, tighten adjusting nut 1 full turn.

3) Rotate crankshaft 360° to bring No. 6 piston on TDC at end of compression stroke. Adjust remaining valves listed in table.

VALVE CLEARANCE ADJUSTMENT

Piston on TDC	Adjust Int. Nos.	Adjust Exh. Nos.
1	1, 2, 5, 7	1, 3, 4, 8
6	3, 4, 6, 8	2, 5, 6, 7

CAMSHAFT

ENGINE FRONT COVER

Removal

1) Disconnect negative battery cable at battery. Drain cooling system. If necessary, remove radiator shroud and position rearward, towards engine. Remove all accessory drive belts, fan and pulley.

2) Remove vibration damper. Remove all mounting brackets and coolant hoses attached to water pump. Remove water pump. Remove front cover and gasket.

Installation

1) Clean all gasket mating surfaces. Remove any excess oil pan gasket material extending beyond cylinder block. Apply a 1/8" bead silicone sealer to joint formed at oil pan and cylinder block.

2) Coat front cover gasket with gasket sealer and position on cover. Install cover-to-pan seal. Position cover on cylinder block. Loosely install cover-to-block upper attaching bolts. Tighten bolts alternately and evenly while pressing downward on cover, to allow dowels in block to enter holes in cover.

3) Install remaining cover bolts. Tighten all front cover bolts. Reverse removal procedure to install remaining components.

FRONT COVER OIL SEAL

Removal (Front Cover Installed)

Remove vibration damper. Pry seal out of cover with screwdriver, using care not to damage cover seal surface.

Installation

Install new seal with open end toward inside of cover. Drive seal into place using seal driver (J-23042).

Removal (Front Cover Removed)

Pry seal out of cover with screwdriver, using care not to damage cover seal surface.

Installation

Install new seal with open end of seal toward inside of cover. Support cover at seal recess area. Using a seal installing tool, drive seal into position.

TIMING CHAIN

Removal

Remove engine front cover. Crank engine over until timing marks on camshaft and crankshaft sprockets are aligned. Remove camshaft sprocket and timing chain. If crankshaft sprocket replacement is necessary, use a gear puller to remove sprocket.

Installation

Use a hammer and hollow driver to install crankshaft sprocket onto crankshaft. Install camshaft sprocket and timing chain. Ensure timing marks on sprockets are aligned. Install and tighten sprocket bolts. *See Fig. 6.*

Fig. 6: Aligning Timing Sprocket Marks

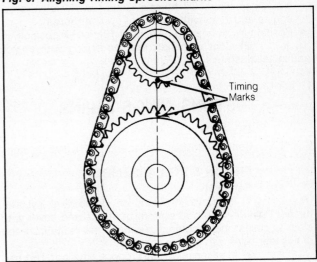

Tighten camshaft sprocket bolts to 20 ft. lbs. (27 N.m).

CAMSHAFT

Removal

Remove intake manifold, engine front cover and timing chain. Remove valve covers. Loosen all rocker arms nuts and rotate rockers to one side. Remove push rods and lifters in sequence, for reinstallation in original locations. Remove radiator and grille. Remove fuel pump and push rod. Remove camshaft.

Installation

1) Coat camshaft lobes with Molykote (or equivalent), and coat journals with engine oil. Install camshaft. Temporarily place camshaft sprocket on camshaft and align timing marks. Install camshaft sprocket and chain. Tighten camshaft sprocket attaching bolts.

2) Lubricate timing chain with engine oil. When a new camshaft is installed, always install new lifters, and change oil and replace filter. Install remaining components. Adjust valves.

CAM LOBE LIFT

1) With valve cover removed, remove rocker arm assemblies. Mount dial indicator on rocker arm stud. Position dial indicator and ball socket adapter on push rod.

2) Slowly rotate engine in direction of rotation until lifter is on base circle of camshaft. Zero dial indicator. Rotate engine until push rod is fully raised. Record lobe lift reading and compare with specifications. If not within limits, replace camshaft and lifters.

CAMSHAFT BEARINGS

Removal

Remove engine from vehicle. Remove oil pan, oil pump, crankshaft and camshaft. Push pistons to top of cylinder bores. Remove rear bore plug. Using camshaft bearing remover/installer tool, remove camshaft bearings.

General Motors V8 Engines

5.0 & 5.7 LITER V8 (Cont.)

Installation

1) Bearings are installed using bearing remover/installer tool. Install front and rear camshaft bearings first, to act as guides for remover/installer tool pilot. Note the following prior to installing camshaft bearings:

- Position No. 1 bearing so that oil holes are equal distance from 6 o'clock position.
- Position oil holes of No. 2, 3 and 4 bearings at 5 o'clock position. Oil holes will be toward left side of engine and even with bottom of cylinder bores.
- Position No. 5 bearing oil hole at 12 o'clock position.

2) Coat camshaft rear bore plug with sealer, and install flush to 1/32" (.79 mm) deep.

PISTONS, RINGS & PINS

OIL PAN

See Oil Pan Removal at end of ENGINE Section.

PISTON & ROD ASSEMBLY

Removal

1) Remove oil pan, oil pump and cylinder heads. Position piston at bottom of stroke and cover with cloth to collect metal cuttings. Remove any ridge from top of cylinder bore with a ridge reamer.

2) If necessary, mark connecting rod and cap for cylinder identification. Remove connecting rod cap, and cover rod bolts with rubber hose. Push piston and rod assembly out top of cylinder bore.

Installation

1) Before installing piston and rod assembly, ensure ring gaps are properly spaced. See Fig. 7. Lightly coat pistons, rings and cylinder walls with engine oil. Install rod bearings in rod and cap, and lubricate with engine oil.

Fig. 7: Desired Ring Gap Spacing

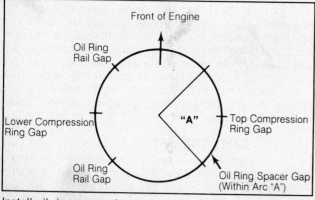

Install oil ring spacer in groove, and insert anti-rotation tang in drilled hole.

2) Compress piston rings with ring compressor. Do not allow position of rings to change. Cover rod bolts with rubber hose. Install piston and rod assembly into cylinder bore, with bearing tang slots facing away from camshaft. Install and tighten rod cap.

FITTING PISTONS

1) Using telescope gauge and micrometer, measure cylinder bore diameter at a point 2 1/2" from top of bore. Measure piston diameter across piston skirt, at

centerline of piston pin. Difference between two measurements is piston-to-cylinder bore clearance.

2) Using cylinder bore gauge, measure cylinder bore taper by working gauge up and down in bore. Taper must not exceed .001" (.03 mm) To determine out-of-round, take measurements at different points in bore, by rotating bore gauge horizontally, around entire circumference of bore. Out-of-round must not exceed .002" (.05 mm).

3) If taper or out-of-round are not within limits, hone or bore cylinders for installation of new pistons.

FITTING RINGS

1) Position ring in cylinder bore at a point about 1/4" above ring travel. Ring must be square in bore. Measure ring end gap with a feeler gauge.

2) Check side clearance of compression rings prior to installing. Also, check ring for binding in ring groove. To check for binding, insert outer edge of ring in its respective groove, and slide ring around entire curcumference of piston groove. If binding occurs, check piston groove for high steps, or check ring for distortion.

PISTON PIN REPLACEMENT

Removal

Using an arbor press and piston pin remover/installer tool, press piston pin from piston and connecting rod.

Installation

Check clearance of piston pin in piston. Replace piston and pin if not within limits. Lubricate piston pin holes in piston and connecting rod with engine oil. Using pin remover/installer tool and arbor press, press piston pin into piston and connecting rod. Check piston for freedom of movement on piston pin.

CRANKSHAFT, MAIN & CONNECTING ROD BEARINGS

MAIN & CONNECTING ROD BEARINGS

NOTE: Following procedures are performed with oil pan and oil pump removed. Remove oil film from surfaces to be checked.

Crankshaft Main Bearings

Some production crankshafts are ground to .009" (.23 mm) undersize at the assembly plant. They are identified as follows:

- Crankshaft counterweight of undersize journal, will be stamped on one side with the number "9", along with a large spot of Light Green paint.
- Main bearing cap will be painted Light Green on each side.

1) Measure main bearing clearances one at a time, while all other main caps are properly tightened. Mark or identify main bearing cap before removing. Support crankshaft weight, using a jack placed under counterweight next to the bearing being checked.

2) Start with rear main bearing (No. 7) and work forward. Also, remove drive belts from crankshaft pulley, prior to checking front (No. 1) bearing.

3) Remove main bearing cap and place a piece of Plastigage across full width of bearing, about 1/4" off

5.0 & 5.7 LITER V8 (Cont.)

center, and away from oil holes. Install cap and tighten to specifications. Do not allow crankshaft to turn.

4) Remove cap and measure width of Plastigage with scale furnished. Standard, .001" (.03 mm) or .002" (.05 mm) undersize bearing halves may be used in combination to obtain correct clearance. Always replace both upper and lower bearing halves.

5) Main bearings are removed from cylinder block using remover/installer tool (J-8080 or equivalent). Insert tool in crankshaft oil hole and rotate crankshaft clockwise. If tool not available, a cotter pin may be bent, as necessary, to do the job.

6) Lubricate journal and bearings. Insert plain end of new bearing between crankshaft and notched side of block. Insert bearing remover/installer tool into crankshaft oil hole, and rotate bearing into place.

7) Install lower bearing half into cap. Install and tighten main bearing caps with arrows pointing toward front of engine. Check crankshaft end play after aligning thrust bearing. Check end play by prying crankshaft forward, and inserting feeler gauge between crankshaft counterweight and forward face of rear main bearing cap.

Connecting Rod Bearings

1) Ensure rod caps are marked for cylinder identification. Remove rod cap and bearings. Inspect bearings for wear or damage and replace as necessary.

2) Check crankshaft rod bearing journal for out-of-round or taper. Maximum crankshaft out-of-round or taper must not exceed .001" (.03 mm).

3) Check rod bearing clearance using the Plastigage method (as explained in Main Bearings). If clearance exceeds specifications, standard, .001" (.03 mm), or .002" (.05 mm) undersize bearings may be used in combination to produce correct clearance. If clearance is still excessive, crankshaft must be reconditioned.

4) Clean crankshaft journal and bearing surface in rod. Insert bearings in rod and cap, then lubricate bearing surfaces with oil. Pull piston and rod assembly down onto crankshaft. Install and tighten rod cap.

THRUST BEARING ALIGNMENT

Ensure all other main bearing caps have been properly tightened. Tighten rear main bearing cap to 10-12 ft. lbs. (14-16 N.m). Tap crankshaft rearward, then forward, using a lead hammer. Tighten rear main bearing cap. Retighten all main bearing caps.

REAR MAIN BEARING OIL SEAL

Removal

Remove rear main bearing cap and pry out old seal. Remove upper half of seal by tapping end with brass punch until seal protrudes enough to be removed with pliers.

Installation

1) Fabricate an oil seal installation tool. *See Fig. 8.* Coat seal lips with engine oil. Keep oil off of seal ends.

Fig. 8: Rear Main Oil Seal Installation Tool

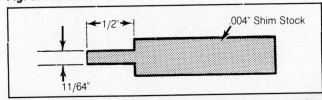

This tool is sometimes supplied with replacement oil seal.

2) Position tool between crankshaft and seal groove in cylinder block. Position seal between tip of tool and crankshaft, with oil seal lip toward front of engine. *See Fig. 9.*

Fig. 9: Rear Main Bearing Oil Seal Identification

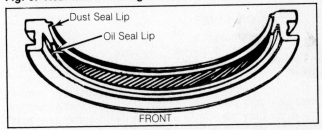

Install oil seal with lip towards front of engine.

3) Roll seal around crankshaft, using tool as a "shoehorn" to protect seal from sharp corner of seal groove in cylinder block. Leave tool in position, until both ends of seal are flush with block.

4) Install lower seal into bearing cap, using tool as a "shoehorn". Feed seal into cap using light pressure with thumb and finger. Apply sealer to cap-to-block mating surface of cylinder block, being careful to keep sealer off the seal split line. Install and tighten rear main bearing cap.

ENGINE OILING

Crankcase Capacity

Capacity is 4 quarts (3.8L). Add 1 quart (.95L) when replacing oil filter.

Oil Filter

Replace oil filter at every other oil change, or more often under dusty or severe conditions.

Normal Oil Pressure

With engine at normal operating temperature, oil pressure should be 30-40 psi (2.1-2.8 kg/cm²) at speeds of 35-40 MPH.

Oil Pressure Regulator Valve

In pump body, not adjustable.

ENGINE OILING SYSTEM

Gear-type oil pump delivers full pressure lubrication to main oil gallery, through full-flow oil filter.

Fig. 10: Engine Oiling System

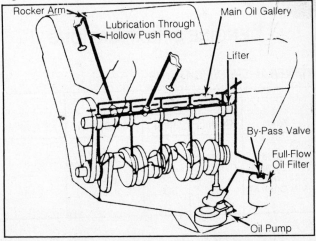

Timing chain and sprockets are lubricated by oil drainage from No. 1 camshaft bearing.

General Motors V8 Engines
5.0 & 5.7 LITER V8 (Cont.)

Through drilled passages in block, main oil gallery feeds oil to all crankshaft and camshaft bearings.

Valve lifter oil gallery feeds lifters. From lifters, oil is routed through hollow push rods to upper valve train components. Timing chain and sprockets are lubricated by oil drainage from No. 1 camshaft bearing. See Fig. 10.

OIL PUMP
Removal

Remove oil pan. Remove pump-to-rear main bearing cap bolt, and remove pump and extension shaft.

Disassembly

Remove pump cover. If necessary, remove inlet tube and screen assembly. Mark gears at a meshing point, so they may be reassembled with same gear teeth indexing. Remove gears. See Fig. 11.

Fig. 11: Oil Pump Assembly

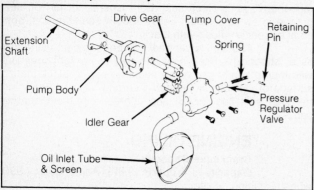

Be sure to mark gears at a meshing point, prior to disassembly of pump.

Inspection

1) Wash all parts and dry with compressed air. Inspect pump body and cover for cracks or excessive wear. Inspect pump gears for damage or excessive wear. If pump gears or body are damaged or worn, replace entire pump assembly.

2) Check drive gear shaft for looseness in pump body. Inspect oil inlet tube and screen assembly for damage. Check pressure regulator valve for fit in bore.

Reassembly

If removed, install oil inlet tube and screen assembly. Apply sealer to end of tube, and tap tube into place, using plastic hammer. Install pump gears into pump body, with marked gear teeth indexing. Idler gear must be installed with smooth side of gear toward cover opening. Reassemble remaining components in reverse order of disassembly.

Installation

Prime oil pump with engine oil. Assemble pump and extension shaft to engine. Ensure slot on top of extension shaft engages with drive tang on end of distributor shaft. Install and tighten attaching bolt. Install oil pan.

ENGINE COOLING

WATER PUMP
Removal

Disconnect negative battery cable at battery. Drain cooling system. Remove all drive belts, coolant hoses and mounting brackets attached to water pump. If necessary, remove fan shroud and position rearward toward engine. Remove fan and pulley. Remove water pump and gaskets.

Installation

Clean all gasket surfaces. Apply 1/8" bead silicone sealer to water pump gasket surfaces. Using new gaskets, install and tighten water pump. Install remaining components in reverse order of removal.

NOTE: For information on cooling system capacities and other cooling system components, see appropriate article in "Engine Cooling Systems," at end of ENGINE Section.

TIGHTENING SPECIFICATIONS

Application	Ft. Lbs. (N.m)
Camshaft Sprocket Bolts	20 (27)
Connecting Rod Nuts	45 (61)
Cylinder Head Bolts	65 (88)
Exhaust Manifold Bolts	20 (27)
Flywheel-to-Crankshaft Bolts	60 (81)
Intake Manifold Bolts	30 (41)
Main Bearing Cap Bolts	70 (108)
Oil Pump Bolt	65 (88)
Vibration Damper Bolt	60 (81)
Water Pump Bolts	30 (41)

ENGINE SPECIFICATIONS

GENERAL SPECIFICATIONS

Year	DISPLACEMENT		Fuel System	HP@RPM	Torque Ft. Lbs.@RPM	Compr. Ratio	BORE		STROKE	
	Cu. In.	Liters					In.	mm	In.	mm
1983										
VIN Code F	305	5.0	4-Bbl.	......	......	8.6:1	3.74	95.0	3.48	88.4
VIN Code H	305	5.0	4-Bbl.	......	......	9.2:1	3.74	95.0	3.48	88.4
VIN Code L	350	5.7	4-Bbl.	......	......	8.2:1	4.00	101.6	3.48	88.4
VIN Code M	350	5.7	4-Bbl.	......	......	8.3:1	4.00	101.6	3.48	88.4

5.0 & 5.7 LITER V8 (Cont.)

ENGINE SPECIFICATIONS (Cont.)

VALVES

Engine Size & Valve	Head Diam. In. (mm)	Face Angle	Seat Angle	Seat Width In. (mm)	Stem Diameter In. (mm)	Stem Clearance In. (mm)	Valve Lift In. (mm)
5.0L & 5.7L Int.	.....	45°	46°	.031-.063 (.79-1.58)	.....	.0010-.0027 (.025-.069)	.....
Exh.	.....	45°	46°	.063-.094 (1.58-2.38)	.....	.0010-.0027 (.025-.069)	.....

PISTONS, PINS, RINGS

Engine	PISTONS Clearance In. (mm)	PINS Piston Fit In. (mm)	PINS Rod Fit In. (mm)	RINGS Ring No.	RINGS End Gap In. (mm)	RINGS Side Clearance In. (mm)
5.0L & 5.7L	.0007-.0017 (.018-.043)	.00025-.00035 (.0064-.0089)	.0008-.0016 (.020-.041)	1	.010-.020 (.25-.51)	.0012-.0032 (.031-.081)
				2	.010-.025 (.25-.64)	.0012-.0032 (.031-.081)
				3	.015-.055 (.38-1.40)	.002-.007 (.05-.18)

CRANKSHAFT MAIN & CONNECTING ROD BEARINGS

Engine	MAIN BEARINGS Journal Diam. In. (mm)	MAIN BEARINGS Clearance In. (mm)	MAIN BEARINGS Thrust Bearing	MAIN BEARINGS Crankshaft End Play In. (mm)	CONNECTING ROD BEARINGS Journal Diam. In. (mm)	CONNECTING ROD BEARINGS Clearance In. (mm)	CONNECTING ROD BEARINGS Side Play In. (mm)
5.0L & 5.7L No. 1	2.4484-2.4493 (62.189-62.212)	.002-.008 (.05-.20)	No. 5	.002-.006 (.05-.15)	2.0988-2.0998 (53.310-53.335)	.0013-.0035 (.033-.089)	.008-.014 (.20-.36)
Nos. 2,3,4	2.4481-2.4490 (62.182-62.205)	.001-.002 (.03-.05)					
No. 5	2.4479-2.4488 (62.177-62.200)	.002-.003 (.05-.08)					

CAMSHAFT

Engine	Journal Diam. In. (mm)	Clearance In. (mm)	Lobe Lift In. (mm)
5.0L [1]	1.8682-1.8692 (47.452-47.478)	.....	[2] .2484 (6.309) [3] .2667 (6.774)
5.7L [1]	1.8682-1.8692 (47.452-47.478)	.....	[2] .2600 (6.604) [3] .2733 (6.942)

VALVE SPRINGS

Engine	Free Length In. (mm)	PRESSURE Lbs. @ In. (Kg @ mm) Valve Closed	PRESSURE Lbs. @ In. (Kg @ mm) Valve Open
5.0L & 5.7L Int.	2.03 (51.56)	76-84@1.70 (34-38@43.2)	194-206@1.25 (88-93@31.8)
Exh.	2.03 (51.56)	76-84@1.70 (34-38@43.2)	194-206@1.25 (88-93@31.8)

[1] — End play is .004-.012 (.10-.31 mm).
[2] — Intake.
[3] — Exhaust.

General Motors V8 Engines

6.2 LITER V8 DIESEL

ENGINE CODING

ENGINE IDENTIFICATION

Engine code letter is suffix of Engine Identification Number. Number is on a label on rear of left valve cover.

ENGINE IDENTIFICATION CODES

Application	
	Code
6.2L Diesel	
VIN Code C	UHA, UHB, UHC, UHD, UHF
	UHH, UHJ, UHN, UHR, UHS
	UHT, UHU, UHW
VIN Code J	AHA, AHB, UJA, UJB, UJK
	UJM, UJN, UJR, UJU, UJY
	UJZ, UTT, UTW

ENGINE REMOVAL

See Engine Removal at end of ENGINE Section.

MANIFOLDS & CYLINDER HEADS

INTAKE MANIFOLD

Removal (Pickup)

1) Disconnect batteries. Remove air cleaner. Disconnect PCV hoses and secondary fuel filter lines. Remove secondary fuel filter and adapter.

2) Loosen vacuum pump hold down clamp and rotate pump to gain acess to intake manifold bolt. Remove EPR/EGR valve bracket and A/C bracket, if equipped. Remove intake manifold bolts and injection pipe clips. Remove intake manifold from engine.

Installation

1) Clean all gasket surfaces. Install new manifold gasket making sure to open EGR passage in gasket if vehicle is equipped with EGR. Install intake manifold and tighten bolts in proper sequence.

2) Fill secondary fuel filter with clean fuel prior to installing filter. Reconnect fuel filter lines. Reverse remainder of removal procedure to complete installation.

Removal (Van)

1) Disconnect batteries. Remove engine cover and air cleaner. Disconnect necessary wires and hoses and remove EGR/EPR switches. Remove crankcase depression regulator valve and disconnect hoses to valve.

2) Remove crankcase depression regulator valve hoses from intake manifold. Remove rear A/C compressor bracket, if equipped. Remove fuel filter-to-intake manifold bracket.

3) Remove vacuum pump. Place a rag or cover over hole to prevent foreign material from entering engine. Remove intake bolts and fuel line clips. Remove intake manifold.

Installation

1) Clean all gasket surfaces. Install new manifold gasket making sure to open EGR passage in gasket if vehicle is equipped with EGR. Install intake manifold and tighten bolts in proper sequence.

2) Reconnect fuel filter lines. Reverse remainder of removal procedure to complete installation.

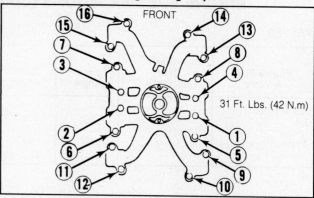

Fig. 1: Intake Manifold Tightening Sequence

Tighten bolts gradually to 31 ft. lbs. (42 N.m).

EXHAUST MANIFOLD

Removal (Pickup - Right Side)

Disconnect batteries. Raise vehicle. Disconnect exhaust pipe from manifold flange. Lower vehicle. Disconnect glow plug wires. Remove air cleaner duct bracket. Remove glow plugs. Remove manifold bolts. Remove manifold.

Removal (Pickup - Left Side)

Disconnect batteries. Remove dipstick tube nut and tube. Disconnect glow plug wires and remove glow plugs. Remove manifold bolts. Raise vehicle. Disconnect exhaust pipe from manifold flange. Remove manifold from bottom.

Removal (Van - Right Side)

Disconnect batteries. Raise vehicle. Disconnect exhaust pipe from manifold flange. Lower vehicle. Disconnect glow plug wires. Remove manifold bolts. Remove manifold.

Removal (Van - Left Side)

Disconnect upper battery. Raise vehicle. Disconnect glow plug wires. Lower vehicle. Disconnect exhaust from manifold flange. Remove manifold bolts. Remove manifold.

Installation (All Models)

To install, reverse removal procedures.

CYLINDER HEADS

Removal (Pickup)

1) Remove intake manifold. Remove injection line clips from brackets. Disconnect injection lines from injector nozzles and cover nozzles. Remove injection lines at pump and mark for reassembly reference.

2) Remove fuel supply line from injection pump. Remove wiring harness and bracket from engine. Remove valve cover. Drain coolant. Remove dipstick tube. Disconnect ground wire from cowl at right side of engine.

3) Raise vehicle. Disconnect exhaust pipe from manifold. Lower vehicle. If equipped, remove A/C compressor from engine without disconnecting refrigerant lines and lay it on left side of engine compartment.

4) Remove alternator from engine and lay it on right side of engine compartment. Disconnect glow plug wires. Remove rocker arm assemblies and push rods making sure to note their positions to allow installation in the same location.

5) Disconnect radiator, heater and by-pass hoses. Disconnect ground strap. Remove thermostat

6.2 LITER V8 DIESEL (Cont.)

crossover housing from cylinder head. Remove cylinder head bolts and cylinder head.

Installation

1) Reverse removal procedure to install cylinder heads and note the following: Left rear cylinder head bolt must be installed in cylinder head prior to placing cylinder head on engine.

2) Ensure that gasket surfaces on head and cylinder block are clean and that cylinder head bolt threads and threads in block are clean. Gasket requires no sealer. Coat cylinder head bolt threads with sealer. Tighten cylinder head bolts gradually in sequence. Push rods must be installed with the painted end up.

Fig. 2: Cylinder Head Tightening Sequence

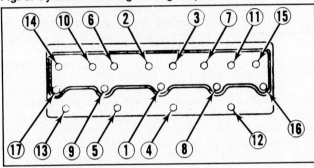

Tighten bolts gradually to 95 ft. lbs. (129 N.m).

Removal (Van)

1) Remove intake manifold. Install protective covers. Remove injection line clips from brackets. Raise vehicle. Disconnect injection lines from injector nozzles and cover nozzles.

2) Lower vehicle. Remove injection lines at pump and tag lines for reinstallation. If equipped with cruise control, remove transducer. If A/C equipped, remove upper fan shroud and A/C belt.

3) Raise vehicle. Disconnect exhaust pipes from manifolds. Remove left exhaust manifold. Remove power steering lower adjusting bolts.

4) Disconnect glow plug wires and temperature switch. If A/C equipped, remove rear A/C brace from exhaust manifold. Disconnect glow plug wires.

5) Lower vehicle. If A/C equipped, discharge A/C system, disconnect A/C lines at compressor and remove compressor from brackets and remove compressor. Remove upper power steering attachment and move aside.

6) Loosen dipstick tube front bracket and remove from stud. Remove oil fill tube upper bracket. Disconnect T.V. cable. Remove glow plug controller and bracket. Remove glow plug relay.

7) Disconnect oil pressure switch and loom. Remove loom bracket and vacuum line clip bolt at head. Remove rocker cover bolts. Disconnect fuel return line bracket. Remove rocker cover.

8) Remove rocker arm assemblies and push rods making sure to note their positions to allow installation in the same location. Drain cooling system.

9) Remove air cleaner resonator and bracket. Remove transmission fill tube nut and position aside. Disconnect heater, radiator and by-pass hoses at crossover.

10) Remove alternator upper bracket, coolant crossover and cylinder head bolts. Disconnect transmis-

sion dipstick at rear of right head and remove tube. Remove cylinder head.

Installation

1) Reverse removal procedure to install cylinder heads and note the following: Left rear cylinder head bolt must be installed in cylinder head prior to placing cylinder head on engine.

2) Ensure that gasket surfaces on head and cylinder block are clean and that cylinder head bolt threads and threads in block are clean. Gasket requires no sealer. Coat cylinder head bolt threads with sealer. Tighten cylinder head bolts gradually in sequence. Push rods must be installed with the painted end up.

VALVES

VALVE ARRANGEMENT

I-E-I-E-I-E-I-E (Left bank, front to rear)
E-I-E-I-E-I-E-I (Right bank, front to rear)

ROCKER ARM SHAFT ASSEMBLY

Removal & Installation

Remove valve covers. Loosen rocker arm shaft bolts gradually and evenly to release valve spring pressure. Remove bolts and rocker arm shafts. To install, reverse removal procedure.

Fig. 3: Rocker Arm Shaft Mounting

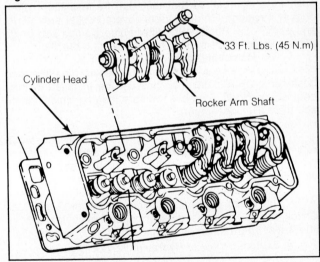

Loosen bolts gradually and evenly.

VALVE SPRINGS

Removal

With cylinder head removed, compress valve spring and remove valve keepers. Release spring compressor and remove retainer, spring, damper, seal and exhaust valve rotators.

Installation

To install valve springs, reverse removal procedure. Lubricate and install valve stem oil seal on valve stem before installing remaining components.

VALVE SPRING INSTALLED HEIGHT

Valve spring installed height is measured from top of shim at bottom of spring, or spring seat to top of valve spring. If distance exceeds specified height, install a

1/16" (1.5875 mm) thick shim. Installed height should never be more than 1/16" (1.5875 mm) less than specified height.

VALVE SPRING INSTALLED HEIGHT

Application	Height In. (mm)
All	1.811 (46)

VALVE STEM OIL SEALS

An "O" ring type oil seal is installed on valve stem before valve spring is installed. See Valve Springs.

VALVE GUIDE SERVICING

If valve stem-to-guide clearance is excessive, guides are removable and can be replaced, or valves with oversize stems are available. Use a reamer (J-7049) to ream guides to correct size for oversize valve stems.

HYDRAULIC VALVE LIFTERS

NOTE: **Hydraulic lifters used on the diesel engine are of the roller type. Lifters are serviced as complete assemblies only and parts are not interchangeable between lifters.**

Removal (Pickup)
Provide some means of keeping the lifters and push rods in order so that they can be installed in their original locations. Remove valve covers, rocker arm shafts and push rods. Remove the lifter guide clamps and guide plates. Remove lifters using removal tool (J-29834).

Removal (Van)
Provide some means of keeping the lifters and push rods in order so that they can be installed in their original locations. Remove cylinder heads, guide clamp and plate. Remove lifters.

Disassembly
With valve lifter removed from engine, remove retainer ring. Remove push rod seat and oil metering valve. Remove plunger and plunger spring. Remove check valve retainer from plunger and remove valve spring.

Inspection
Clean all parts in clean solvent or diesel fuel. Check for nicks, burrs or scoring on parts. Make sure lifter roller operates smoothly and without excessive play.

Fig. 4: Exploded View of Hydraulic Valve Lifter

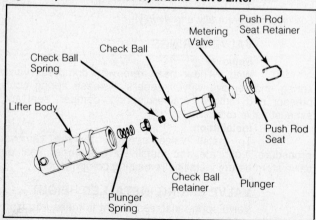

Always prime lifters with oil before installing.

Reassembly
Coat all parts with clean engine oil, then reverse disassembly procedure.

Installation
Prime lifters by working plunger while lifter is submerged in clean kerosene or diesel fuel. Coat roller and bearings with assembly lube. Install lifters into their original position in block. Install lifter guide plate and clamp. Rotate crankshaft 2 full turns while checking to see that lifters are not binding against guide plates.

CAMSHAFT

ENGINE FRONT COVER
Removal
1) Drain coolant from engine. Disconnect battery ground cable. Remove fan belt, fan, fan shroud and pulley. Remove A/C hose bracket nuts. Remove oil fill tube. Remove alternator pivot bolt and drive belt. Remove alternator lower bracket.

2) Remove power steering belt and pump. Remove A/C compressor. Do not disconnect hoses or lines from either device. Support pump and compressor out of the way. Remove air conditioning compressor belt. Disconnect by-pass and lower radiator hose. Remove water pump bolts. Remove water pump plate and water pump.

3) Rotate engine and align marks on injection pump gear and camshaft gear. Scribe an alignment mark on injection pump flange and on front cover. Remove crankshaft pulley. Remove harmonic balancer using a puller.

4) Remove front cover-to-oil pan bolts. Remove fuel return line clips. Remove injection pump driven gear. Remove injection pump retaining nuts from front cover. Remove baffle and remaining front cover bolts. Remove front cover.

Installation
1) Clean sealing surfaces and apply a 3/32" bead of sealer to surface of cover that mates with engine and oil pan. Install front cover and baffle.

2) Install injection pump, noting alignment marks made during removal. Install injection pump drive gear, making sure to align timing marks on pump gear and cam gear. To complete installation, reverse remainder of removal procedure.

FRONT COVER OIL SEAL
With Cover Removed
Pry seal out of cover with a screwdriver. Install new seal with open end of seal toward inside of cover and drive into position. Support cover at seal area before driving in seal.

With Cover Installed
With harmonic balancer removed, pry seal out of front cover. Install seal with open end of seal toward engine and drive into place with a driver (J-22102) and a hammer.

TIMING CHAIN & SPROCKETS
Removal
Remove front engine cover as previously outlined. Remove bolts securing camshaft gear. Remove injection pump drive gear. Remove cam sprocket, crank sprocket and timing chain.

6.2 LITER V8 DIESEL (Cont.)

Installation
Install camshaft sprocket, crankshaft sprocket and timing chain, making sure timing marks on sprockets are aligned. Install and tighten sprocket bolts. Rotate crankshaft 360°. Install front cover as previously outlined, making sure to align marks on injection pump gear and injection pump drive gear. Whenever the timing chain, sprockets or gears are replaced, it is necessary to retime the engine.

CAMSHAFT
Removal (Pickup)
1) Remove intake manifold, engine front cover and timing chain. Remove valve covers, rocker arms and push rods, keeping parts in order to enable installation in the same location. Disconnect exhaust pipe from manifolds.

2) Remove cylinder heads with exhaust manifolds attached. Remove grille, A/C condenser and radiator if necessary. Remove vacuum pump. Remove lifters, guide plates and clamps, keeping parts in order to enable installation in same location. Remove fuel pump. Remove camshaft retainer plate and camshaft.

Installation
Lubricate camshaft journals and lobes with motor oil. If a new camshaft is being installed, coat camshaft lobes with Molykote. Position camshaft to align timing marks on sprockets. Install remaining components in reverse order of removal.

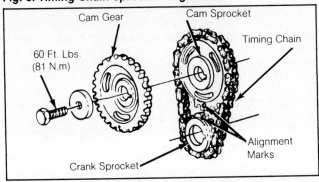

Fig. 5: Timing Chain Sprocket Alignment

Removal (Van)
1) Disconnect batteries. Remove headlight bezels, grille, and bumper. Remove lower valence panel, hood latch, coolant recovery bottle and upper tie bar. If A/C equipped, disconnect lines and remove condenser.

2) Disconnect low coolant wire and engine oil cooler lines at radiator. Disconnect automatic transmission cooler lines, if equipped. Disconnect upper and lower radiator hoses. Remove radiator and fan assembly.

3) Remove cylinder heads. Remove alternator lower bracket, water pump and crank pulleys. Using damper remover (J-23523) and pilot (J-29788), remove torsional damper.

4) Remove timing cover plate and water pump. Rotate crankshaft and align timing marks. Remove injection pump driven gear and inner baffle.

5) Align injection pump and front cover by scribing a line across pump flange and front cover. Remove front cover, fuel pump and lifters.

6) Remove injection pump drive gear, timing chain and crankshaft gear. Remove camshaft retainer plate and camshaft.

Installation
Lubricate camshaft journals and lobes with motor oil. If a new camshaft is being installed, coat camshaft lobes with Molykote. Position camshaft to align timing marks on sprockets. Install remaining components in reverse order of removal.

CAM LOBE LIFT
With valve cover removed, remove rocker arm. Mount dial indicator on cylinder head. Position indicator stem on push rod with an adapter (J-8520). Rotate engine slowly until lifter is on heel of camshaft and set dial indicator to "O". Rotate engine slowly until push rod is at fully raised position. Dial indicator will give total camshaft lobe lift. Lift should be within specifications.

CAMSHAFT BEARINGS
Use camshaft bearing installation and removal tool (J-6098) to remove bearings. Install front and rear bearings first by driving toward center of cylinder block. Align oil holes in front 4 bearings with oil holes in bearing bore in block. Position rear camshaft bearing oil hole at or near the 6 o'clock position. Install new rear cam bore plug flush with block, using sealer

PISTONS, RINGS & PINS

OIL PAN
See Oil Pan Removal at end of ENGINE Section.

PISTON & ROD ASSEMBLY
Removal
1) With oil pan, oil pump and cylinder heads removed, remove any ridge in top of cylinder bore with a ridge reamer. Check connecting rod and cap for identification marks or numbers and identify if necessary.

NOTE: **Each piston is fitted to its individual cylinder and should be marked for that cylinder.**

2) Remove connecting rod cap nuts and rod cap. Cover rod bolts with hose to protect crankshaft journals. Push piston and rod assembly up and out of cylinder block. It will be necessary to rotate crankshaft to various positions to facilitate removing piston and rod assemblies.

NOTE: **When cleaning pistons, DO NOT wire brush any part of piston assembly.**

Installation
1) Before installing piston and rod assembly, position ring gaps in positions shown in illustration. *See Fig. 6.* Place connecting rod in bore with bearing tang slots facing away from camshaft.

2) Lubricate rod bearings, cylinder bore and crankshaft journal. Compress piston rings and push piston and rod assembly into position. Install rod cap and tighten rod cap nuts to specifications.

Fig. 6: Piston Ring Gap Positioning

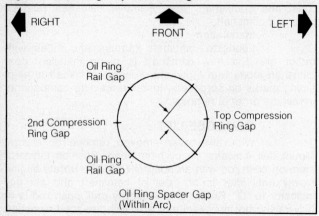

Stagger ring gaps to minimize compression loss.

FITTING PISTONS

NOTE: **A cylinder requiring only minor clean-up (less than .005", .172 mm, taper or wear), that cannot be fitted to the original piston after honing, may be able to use a high-limit standard size piston instead of boring the cylinder to the next oversize.**

1) With piston and rod assemblies removed, wipe cylinder bores clean and measure diameter of cylinder with a dial indicator. If cylinder is worn or is tapered more than .005" (.127 mm), cylinder must be bored for oversize pistons.

2) If bore is worn or tapered less than .005" (.127 mm), cylinder can be cleaned and honed. If cylinders are bored, various oversize pistons are available.

3) To check fit of rings in cylinder bore, insert ring in cylinder bore and push ring into bore 1/4" with head of piston and measure ring end gap with a feeler gauge.

4) Before installing rings on pistons, ensure ring grooves are clean of carbon and inspect grooves for nicks or burrs. Install rings with gaps staggered. *See Fig. 6.*

PISTON PIN REPLACEMENT

Removal

With piston and rod assembly removed from engine, remove piston pin retaining rings. Slide pin out of piston and connecting rod.

Installation

Check clearance of pin in piston. If clearance exceeds specifications, piston and pin must be replaced. Lubricate piston pin and install into piston and rod. Secure pin with retaining rings. Rotate retaining rings in their grooves to ensure that they are completely seated. Check piston for freedom of movement on piston pin.

CRANKSHAFT, MAIN & CONNECTING ROD BEARINGS

MAIN & CONNECTING ROD BEARINGS

NOTE: **Following procedures are performed with oil pan and oil pump removed.**

Crankshaft Main Bearings

1) Main bearings are selective fit by manufacturer during production. A standard size bearing may be used in combination with a .001" (.0254 mm) undersize bearing to obtain correct clearance. This combination will decrease clearance .0005" (.0127 mm).

2) Main bearings may be removed and replaced with crankshaft still installed in engine. Mark or identify main bearing caps to cylinder block before removing caps. Bearings are removed from cylinder block using a bearing removal tool. Install tool in oil hole in crankshaft and rotate crankshaft clockwise.

3) Crankshaft clearance, taper or out-of-round conditions can be checked using the Plastigage method. If clearance exceeds specifications, a .001" (.0254 mm) or .002" (.0508 mm) undersize bearing may be installed to obtain correct clearance. Both bearings must be replaced on any journal not within specifications.

4) If correct clearance cannot be obtained or if journal is tapered or is out-of-round more than .0002" (.005 mm), crankshaft must be removed and ground for undersize bearings.

5) To install bearings, ensure crankshaft journal and bearing surface in cap and block are clean. Lubricate journal and install bearing cap. If bearings were removed with crankshaft still installed, use bearing removal and installation tool inserted in crankshaft oil hole to install upper bearing. Install main cap noting identification marks and tighten main bearing bolts evenly and to specifications.

Connecting Rod Bearings

1) Mark or identify rod cap to rod before removing rod cap nuts. With rod nuts removed, remove rod cap and bearing. Cover rod bolts with hose to protect crankshaft. Push up on piston and rod assembly and remove bearing from rod. Inspect bearings for wear or damage and replace as necessary.

2) Check crankshaft rod bearing journal for out-of-round or taper conditions. If crankshaft is out-of-round or is tapered more than .001" (.0254 mm), crankshaft must be removed and ground for undersize bearings.

3) Check crankshaft clearance using the Plastigage method. If clearance exceeds specifications, a .001" (.0254 mm) or .002" (.0508 mm) undersize bearing may be installed to obtain correct clearance. If clearance is still excessive, crankshaft must be removed and ground for undersize bearings. Connecting rod bearings are available in .010" (.254 mm) and .020" (.508 mm) undersize.

4) To install bearings, clean crankshaft journal and bearing surface in rod. Insert bearing in rod and cap. Lubricate journal an pull piston and rod assembly down, aligning bearing on journal. Install rod cap noting identification marks and tighten rod nuts evenly and to specifications.

THRUST BEARING ALIGNMENT

Pry crankshaft forward as far as possible and check crankshaft end play with a feeler gauge inserted between front of rear main bearing and crankshaft. Replace center main bearing if end play is not to specification.

6.2 LITER V8 DIESEL (Cont.)

Fig. 7: Checking Crankshaft End Play

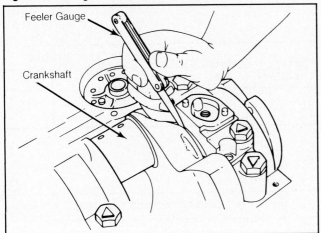

Feeler Gauge

Crankshaft

*Use a feeler gauge to check for maximum of .002-.007"
(.05-.18 mm) end play.*

REAR MAIN BEARING OIL SEAL

To perform in-vehicle repair on rear main seal, General Motors recommends packing 1 piece of old main seal (lower half) into each side of block seal groove (using tools J-29114-2, J-33154-2 and J-33154-1) along with old upper half of the seal.

After packing extra seal material into block, the excess is trimmed and then bottom half of seal is replaced with new material. However, if replacement of complete seal is desired, it can be done using a tool kit (K-D Tools #492 or S&G Tools #31700) and the following procedure:

Removal & Installation

1) With oil pan removed, remove rear main bearing cap. Loosen all main cap bolts slightly. Thread the screw threads of removal tool into upper half of rear main seal. Withdraw upper half of seal from block.

2) Feed the steel mesh cable through upper rear main seal groove until it comes out on the opposite side of crankshaft. Install a guide funnel over cable end. Lubricate new upper rear main seal and insert it in the gripping end of mesh cable.

3) Pull on opposite end of mesh cable and guide new seal into groove. Remove tool from end of seal. Apply sealer (Loctite 496) to rear main cap seal groove and install seal. Seat seal in groove and trim end of seal flush with bearing cap.

4) Place a piece of Plastigage on rear main journal. Install rear main cap and tighten all main bearing caps to specifications. Remove rear main cap and check Plastigage for bearing clearance.

5) If out of specification, check ends of seal for frayed ends or excess material that may be preventing main cap from seating properly. Clean Plastigage from journal and bearing.

6) Apply a thin film of anaerobic sealant to surface of cap that mates with block. Keep sealant off bearing and seal. Apply a light coat of engine oil to surface of crankshaft that rides on seal. Install rear main bearing cap and tighten to specifications.

ENGINE OILING

Crankcase Capacity
7 quarts (6.6L) including filter change.

Oil Filter
Replace every 5,000 miles or 12 months, whichever comes first.

Normal Oil Pressure
40 psi at 2000-3000 RPM.
(2.81 kg/cm² at 2000-3000 RPM.)

Oil Pressure Regulator Valve
In oil pump body, non-adjustable.

ENGINE OILING SYSTEM

Full pressure lubrication through a full flow oil filter and oil cooler is supplied by a gear-type oil pump. Main oil gallery feeds oil through drilled passages to camshaft and crankshaft to lubricate bearings. Valve lifter gallery feeds the valve lifters, which feed the rocker arms through hollow push rods.

OIL PUMP

Removal
Remove oil pan. Remove pump-to-rear main bearing cap bolt. Remove oil pump and extension shaft.

Disassembly
1) Remove pump cover attaching screws and pump cover. Mark gears so they may be reassembled with same tooth indexing. Remove idler gear, drive gear and shaft from pump housing.

2) Remove pressure regulator valve retaining pin from pump cover. Remove regulator valve from pump cover. Do not disassemble pickup screen and pipe. Screen and pipe are only serviced as an assembly with the pump.

NOTE: If pump gears or body are damaged or worn, replacement of entire pump assembly is necessary.

Reassembly & Installation
Clean and check all parts for fit and wear. Reverse removal and disassembly procedure to assemble and install. Smooth side of idler gear faces cover. Check operation of pump before installing.

NOTE: Bottom of screen must be parallel with bottom of pan.

ENGINE COOLING

WATER PUMP

Removal
1) Disconnect batteries. Remove fan and fan shroud. Drain radiator. If A/C equipped, remove A/C hose bracket nuts. Remove oil fill tube.

2) Remove alternator pivot bolt, belt and lower bracket. Remove power steering belt. Remove power steering pump and position aside.

3) Remove A/C belt, if equipped. Disconnect by-pass hose and lower radiator hose. Remove water pump bolts, plate and pump.

Installation
Apply anarobic seal to sealing surface of plate so that sealer is wet to touch when bolts are tightened. Reverse removal procedure to complete installation.

NOTE: For information on cooling system capacities and other cooling system components, see appropriate article in "Engine Cooling Systems," at end of ENGINE Section.

General Motors V8 Engines

6.2 LITER V8 DIESEL (Cont.)

ENGINE SPECIFICATIONS

GENERAL SPECIFICATIONS

| Year | DISPLACEMENT | | Fuel System | HP@RPM | Torque Ft. Lbs.@RPM | Compr. Ratio | BORE | | STROKE | |
	Cu. In.	Liters					In.	mm	In.	mm
1983	378	6.2	Diesel	.....	.....	21.5:1	3.97	101	3.82	97

CRANKSHAFT MAIN & CONNECTING ROD BEARINGS

| Engine | MAIN BEARINGS | | | | CONNECTING ROD BEARINGS | | |
	Journal Diam. In. (mm)	Clearance In. (mm)	Thrust Bearing	Crankshaft End Play In. (mm)	Journal Diam. In. (mm)	Clearance In. (mm)	Side Play In. (mm)
6.2L	[1] 2.9494-2.9504 (74.917-74.941) [2] 2.9492-2.9502 (74.912-74.936)	[1] .0018-.033 (.045-.083) [2] .0022-.0037 (.055-.093)	No. 3	.0039-.0098 (.10-.25)	2.398-2.399 (60.913-60.939)	.0018-.0039 (.046-.099)	.0248-.0067 (.63-.17)

[1] — Journals 1, 2, 3, 4.
[2] — Journal 5.

PISTONS, PINS, RINGS

| Engine | PISTONS | PINS | | RINGS | | |
	Clearance In. (mm)	Piston Fit In. (mm)	Rod Fit In. (mm)	Ring No.	End Gap In. (mm)	Side Clearance In. (mm)
6.2L	.004-.005 (.102-.138)	.0004-.0006 (.0101-.0153)	.0003-.0012 (.0081-.0309)	1	.012-.022 (.30-.55)	.003-.007 (.080-.178)
				2	.030-.039 (.75-1.0)	.002-.003 (.040-.080)
				3	.010-.020 (.25-.51)	.002-.004 (.040-.096)

VALVES

Engine Size & Valve	Head Diam. In. (mm)	Face Angle	Seat Angle	Seat Width In. (mm)	Stem Diameter In. (mm)	Stem Clearance In. (mm)	Valve Lift In. (mm)
6.2L Int.	.....	45°	46°	.035-.060 (.89-1.53)	.....	.001-.003 (.026-.069)	.421 (10.7)
Exh.	.....	45°	46°	.062-.093 (1.57-2.36)	.....	.001-.003 (.026-.069)	.421 (10.7)

VALVE SPRINGS

Engine	Free Length In. (mm)	PRESSURE Lbs. @ In. (Kg @ mm)	
		Valve Closed	Valve Open
6.2L	.....	80@1.81 (36@46)	230@1.39 (105@35)

CAMSHAFT

Engine	Journal Diam. In. (mm)	Clearance In. (mm)	Lobe Lift In. (mm)
6.2L	¹ 2.166-2.164 (55.025-54.975) ² 2.008-2.006 (51.025-50.975)	.001-.004 (.026-.010)	.2808 (7.133)

¹ — Journals 1, 2, 3, 4.
² — Journal 5.

TIGHTENING SPECIFICATIONS

Application	Ft. Lbs. (N.m)
Camshaft Sprocket Bolt	60 (81)
Connecting Rod Nuts	48 (65)
Crankshaft Balancer Bolt	151 (205)
Cylinder Head Bolts	95 (129)
Exhaust Manifold Bolts	22 (30)
Front Cover Bolts	31 (42)
Injection Nozzle	52 (71)
Injection Pump Attaching Bolts	31 (42)
Injection Pump Driven Gear Bolt	16 (22)
Intake Manifold Bolts	31 (42)
Main Bearing Cap Bolts	
Inner	111 (150)
Outer	100 (136)
Oil Pump Attaching Bolts	67 (91)
Rocker Arm Shaft Bolts	42 (55)
Thermostat Housing Bolts	31 (42)
Water Pump Attaching Bolts	31 (42)
Water Pump Cover Bolts	17 (23)
Vacuum Pump Retaining Bolts	31 (42)

General Motors V8 Engines

7.4 LITER V8

ENGINE CODING

ENGINE IDENTIFICATION

Engine code number is suffix of engine identification number. Number is located on pad of front top center of engine block immediately forward of intake manifold.

ENGINE IDENTIFICATION CODES

Application	Code
7.4L 4-Bbl. (VIN W) ...... TKA, TKB,TKC,TKD,TKF,TKH	

ENGINE REMOVAL

See Engine Removal at end of ENGINE section.

MANIFOLDS & CYLINDER HEAD

INTAKE MANIFOLD

Removal

1) Drain cooling system and remove air cleaner. Disconnect battery ground cable. Disconnect upper radiator hose and heater hose at manifold. Disconnect water pump by-pass at water pump. Disconnect PCV hose at valve cover.

2) Disconnect accelerator linkage and fuel inlet line at carburetor. Disconnect vacuum line at distributor. Remove distributor cap and mark rotor position. Remove distributor. Remove air cleaner bracket, accelerator return spring bracket and accelerator bellcrank.

3) If equipped with air conditioning, remove compressor and bracket without disconnecting lines and lay lines aside.

4) Remove upper alternator mounting bracket. Remove intake manifold bolts and pry manifold loose. Remove manifold with carburetor attached and discard all gaskets.

Installation

1) Clean all gasket surfaces and install gaskets on cylinder heads. Install new end seals on cylinder block. Install manifold and tighten bolts in sequence. *See Fig. 1.*

2) Install distributor, noting marked position of rotor. To complete installation, reverse removal procedures.

Fig. 1: Intake Manifold Tightening Sequence

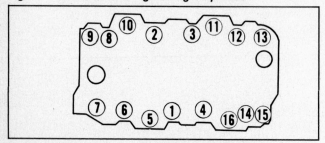

Tighten bolts gradually to 30 ft. lbs. (41 N.m).

EXHAUST MANIFOLD

Removal

Remove air cleaner and spark plugs. Disconnect exhaust pipe from manifold and wire exhaust pipe aside. Remove end bolts and remove center bolts. Remove manifold.

Installation

Clean surfaces. Install manifold and tighten bolts. Connect exhaust pipe to manifold. Install spark plugs and tighten. Install air cleaner.

CYLINDER HEAD

Removal

1) Remove intake manifold. Remove alternator lower mounting bolt and position alternator aside. Remove carburetor at air heater from exhaust manifold, if equipped.

2) Remove spark plugs. Disconnect exhaust pipes at manifolds and remove manifolds.

3) Disconnect PCV hose frome valve covers. Remove valve covers. Loosen rocker arm nuts and pivot rocker arms aside. Remove push rods. Identify push rods to ensure that they are installed in original positions.

4) Drain coolant from cylinder block. Remove all cylinder head bolts. Pry cylinder head loose from cylinder block and remove cylinder head.

Installation

1) Reverse removal procedures to install cylinder heads. Ensure that gasket surfaces on head and cylinder block are clean and that cylinder head bolt threads and threads in block are clean.

2) If cylinder head gasket is steel type, coat both sides with sealer. Asbestos gasket requires no sealer. Coat cylinder head bolt threads with sealer. Tighten cylinder head bolts in sequence. *See Fig. 2.*

Fig. 2: Cylinder Head Tightening Sequence

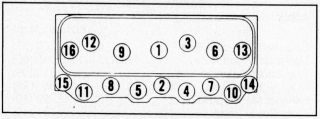

Tighten bolts gradually to 80 ft. lbs. (108 N.m).

VALVES

VALVE ARRANGEMENT

E-I-E-I-E-I-E-I (Left bank, front to rear).
I-E-I-E-I-E-I-E (Right bank, front to rear).

ROCKER ARM STUDS

Push rod guides are attached to cylinder head by rocker arm studs. Replace as necessary and tighten studs. Coad threads on cylinder head end of new stud with sealer.

VALVE SPRINGS

Removal

With cylinder head removed, compress valve spring and remove valve keepers. Release spring compressor and remove retainer, spring, damper, seal and valve rotators, if equipped on exhaust.

Installation

To install valve springs, reverse removal procedures. Lubricate and install valve stem oil seal on valve stem before installing remaining components.

7.4 LITER V8 (Cont.)

VALVE SPRING INSTALLED HEIGHT

Valve spring installed height is measured from top of shim or spring seat to top of valve spring or valve spring shield. If distance exceeds specified height, install a 1/16" (1.6 mm) thick shim. Installed height should never be more than 1/16" (1.6 mm) less than specified height.

VALVE SPRING INSTALLED HEIGHT SPECIFICATIONS

Application	In. (mm)
7.4L	1.797 (45.6)

Fig. 3: Exploded View of Valve Spring Assembly

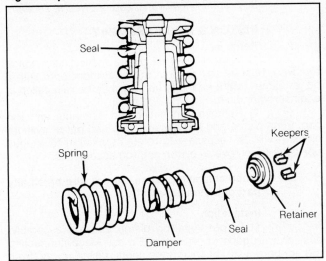

Some engines have a rotator on each exhaust valve.

VALVE STEM OIL SEALS

A valve stem oil seal coated with oil is installed on valve stem before valve spring is installed. See Valve Springs.

VALVE GUIDE SERVICING

If valve stem-to-guide clearance is excessive, guides may be removed. Replacement valves with oversize stems are available. Use a reamer (J-7049) to ream guides to correct size for oversize valve stems.

HYDRAULIC VALVE LIFTERS

Disassembly

Hold plunger in lifter using a push rod. Pry out retainer with small blade screwdriver. Remove push rod seat and metering valve. Remove ball check valve and spring by prying ball retainer loose with screwdriver.

Reassembly

1) Clean and inspect components. If any parts are worn or damaged, complete lifter must be replaced.

2) Position check ball on small hole in bottom of plunger. Insert check ball spring on seat in ball retainer and position retainer on ball so that spring seats on ball. Using a screwdriver, press plunger into position.

3) Slide lifter body over spring and plunger. Line up oil feed holes. Fill assembly with SAE 10 oil and depress plunger. With plunger depressed, insert 1/16" (1.6 mm) drift punch into feed holes.

4) Release plunger and refill with SAE 10 oil. Install metering valve, push rod seat and retainer. Depress push rod seat and remove drift punch.

Fig. 4: Cutaway View of Hydraulic Valve Lifter

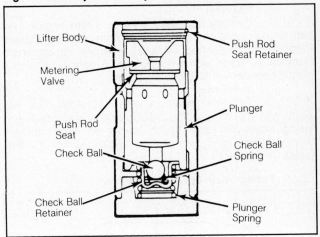

If any parts are worn, complete lifter must be replaced.

VALVE CLEARANCE ADJUSTMENT

1) Rotate engine until timing marks are aligned and No. 1 cylinder is in firing position. Back off rocker arm adjusting nut on No. 1 intake and exhaust rocker arm until play in push rod is detected.

2) Tighten rocker arm nut until play in push rod is just eliminated, then tighten adjusting nut one additional turn. With engine at No. 1 firing position, adjust intake valves 1, 2, 5 and 7 and exhaust valves 1, 3, 4 and 8.

3) Rotate engine to No. 6 firing position and follow same procedure for adjusting valves. With engine at No. 6, firing position, adjust intake valves 3, 4, 6 and 8 and exhaust valves, 2, 5, 6 and 7.

CAMSHAFT

ENGINE FRONT COVER

Removal

1) Remove fan belt, fan and pulley. Remove radiator shroud and water pump. Remove accessory drive pulley and harmonic balancer retaining bolt. Remove harmonic balancer with a puller.

2) Remove cover retaining screws and pull cover forward slightly. Using a sharp knife, cut oil pan front seal flush with cylinder block. Remove cover and gasket.

Installation

1) Clean cover, oil pan and cylinder block gasket surfaces. Cut tabs off new oil pan front seal. Install seal in front cover, pressing seal tips in holes provided in cover.

2) Apply a bead of RTV sealer to joint formed at oil pan and cylinder block. Install new cover gasket and coat with sealer.

3) Position front cover over crankshaft, press downward against oil pan and push over dowel pins. Slightly tighten 2 bolts in oil pan. Install and tighten remaining bolts.

4) Tighten 2 oil pan bolts. Lubricate seal contact surface on harmonic balancer and pull into position using a puller. Install and tighten harmonic balancer bolt.

5) Reverse removal procedure to install remaining components.

TIMING CHAIN & SPROCKET
Removal
Remove front engine cover. Crank engine over until timing marks on camshaft and crankshaft are aligned. Remove bolts securing camshaft sprocket to camshaft. Remove sprocket with timing chain. A light blow with a plastic hammer will dislodge sprocket.

Installation
To install new crankshaft sprocket, pull into place with mounting bolts. Install camshaft sprocket and timing chain. Be sure timing marks on sprockets are aligned. *See Fig. 5.* Install and tighten sprocket bolts. Install front cover.

Fig. 5: Timing Chain Sprocket Alignment

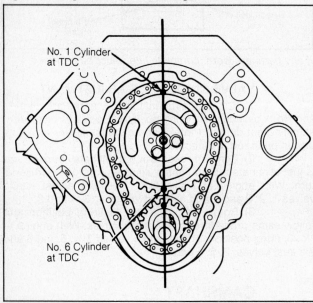

Crank engine until timing marks on camshaft and crankshaft are aligned.

CAMSHAFT
Removal
1) Remove intake manifold engine front cover and timing chain. Remove valve covers. Loosen rocker arms until push rods and valve lifters can be removed.

2) Remove grille and radiator. Remove fuel pump and push rod. Screw 2 bolts into camshaft and withdraw camshaft.

Installation
1) Lubricate camshaft journals and lobes with motor oil. If new camshaft is installed, coat camshaft lobes with Molykote.

2) Position camshaft to align timing marks on sprockets. Install remaining components. Adjust hydraulic valve lifters.

CAM LOBE LIFT
1) With valve cover removed, remove rocker arm. Mount dial indicator on cylinder head. Position indicator stem on push rod with an adapter (J-8520).

2) Rotate engine slowly until lifter is on heel of camshaft and set dial indicator to zero. Rotate engine slowly until push rod is at fully raised position. Dial indicator will give total camshaft lobe lift.

CAMSHAFT BEARINGS
1) Use camshaft bearing installation and removal tool (J-6098) to remove bearings. Install front and rear bearings first by driving toward center of cylinder block.

2) Align oil holes in first 4 bearings with oil holes in bearing bore in block. Position rear camshaft bearing oil hole at or near 6 o'clock position.

PISTONS, RINGS & PINS

OIL PAN
See Oil Pan Removal at end of ENGINE section.

PISTON & ROD ASSEMBLY
Removal
1) With oil pan, oil pump and cylinder heads removed, remove any ridge in top of cylinder bore with a ridge reamer. Mark bearings so they may be reinstalled in original rod and cap.

2) Remove connecting rod cap nuts and rod cap. Push piston and rod assembly up and out of cylinder block. It will be necessary to rotate crankshaft to various positions to remove all piston and rod assemblies.

NOTE: When cleaning pistons, do not wire brush any part of piston assembly.

Installation
1) Before installing piston and rod assembly, position ring gaps as shown in *Fig. 6.* Place connecting rod in bore with bearing tang slots facing away from camshaft.

Fig. 6: Piston Ring Gap Positioning

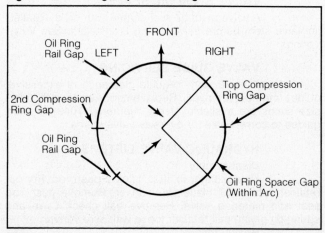

Stagger ring gaps to minimize compression loss.

2) Lubricate rod bearings, cylinder bore and crankshaft journal. Compress piston rings and push piston and rod assembly into position. Install rod cap and tighten rod cap nuts.

FITTING PISTONS
1) With piston and rod assemblies removed, wipe cylinder bores clean. Measure diameter of cylinder with a dial indicator. If cylinder is worn or tapered more than .005" (.127 mm), cylinder must be bored for oversize piston.

7.4 LITER V8 (Cont.)

2) If bore is worn or tapered less than .005" (.127 mm), cylinder can be cleaned and honed and .001" (.025 mm) oversize piston may be installed. If cylinders are bored, various oversize pistons are available.

FITTING RINGS

1) To check fit of rings in cylinder bore, insert ring in bore and push ring into bore 2" with head of piston. Measure ring end gap with feeler gauge.

2) Before installing rings on pistons, ensure ring grooves are clean of carbon and inspect grooves for nicks or burrs. Install rings with gaps staggered.

PISTON PIN REPLACEMENT

Removal

With piston and rod assembly removed, remove piston pin using removal and installation tool (J-24086 or equivalent) and an arbor press. Separate piston from connecting rod.

Installation

1) Check clearance of pin in piston. If clearance exceeds specification by .001" (.0254 mm), piston and pin must be replaced. Position piston and rod so that valve notch in top of piston faces opposite side of bearing tang slots in connecting rod.

2) Lubricate piston pin and press in place using removal and installation tool and arbor press. Check piston for freedom of movement on piston pin.

Fig. 7: Piston Pin Removal and Installation

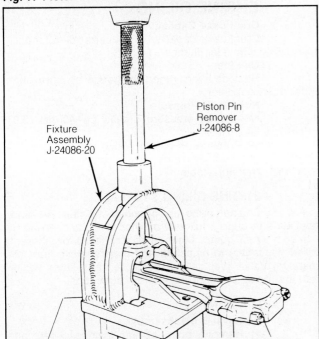

Piston pin fit should be .00025-.00035" (.0064-.0089 mm).

CRANKSHAFT, MAIN & CONNECTING ROD BEARINGS

MAIN & CONNECTING ROD BEARINGS

NOTE: Following procedures are performed with oil pan and oil pump removed.

Crankshaft Main Bearings

1) Main bearings are precision insert type and do not use shims for adjustment. A standard size bearing may be used in combination with a .001" (.0254 mm) undersize bearing to obtain correct clearance. This combination will decrease clearance .0005" (.0127 mm).

2) If correct clearance could not be obtained during production, a crankshaft with .009" (.229 mm) undersize main bearing journals is fitted. A .009" (.229 mm) or .010" (.254 mm) bearing may be used to obtain correct clearance.

3) If engine is fitted with a crankshaft with .009" (.229 mm) undersize main bearing journals, it will be identified by a "9" stamped in crankshaft counterweight along with large spot of light green paint. The bearing cap will also be painted.

4) Main bearings may be removed and replaced with crankshaft still installed in engine. Mark or identify main bearing caps to cylinder block before removing caps.

5) Bearings are removed from cylinder block using a bearing removal tool. Install tool in oil hole in crankshaft and rotate crankshaft clockwise.

6) Crankshaft clearance taper or out-of-round conditions can be checked using the Plastigage method. If clearance is excessive, a .001" (.025 mm) or .002" (.051 mm) undersize bearing may be installed to obtain correct clearance. Both bearings must be replaced on any journal with inaccurate clearance.

7) If correct clearance cannot be obtained or journal tapers or is out-of-round more than .001" (.025 mm), crankshaft must be removed and ground for undersize bearings. Bearings are available in standard, .001", .002" .009", .010 and .020" (.025, .051, .229, .254 and .508 mm) undersize.

8) To install bearings, ensure crankshaft journal and bearing surface in cap and block are clean. Lubricate journal and install bearing cap.

9) If bearings were removed with crankshaft still installed, use bearing removal and installation tool inserted in crankshaft oil hole to install upper bearing. Install main cap noting identification marks. Tighten main bearing bolts.

Connecting Rod Bearings

1) Mark each rod cap and rod set before removing rod cap nuts. With rod nuts removed, remove rod cap and bearing. Push up on piston and rod assembly and remove bearing from rod. Inspect bearings for wear or damage and replace as necessary.

2) Check crankshaft rod bearing journal for out-of-round or excessive taper. If crankshaft is out-of-round or tapers more than .001" (.025 mm), crankshaft must be removed and ground for undersize bearings.

3) Check crankshaft clearance using the Plastigage method. If clearance is excessive, a .001" (.025 mm) or .002" (.051 mm) undersize bearing may be installed to correct clearance.

4) If clearance is still excessive, crankshaft must be removed and ground for undersize bearings. Connecting rod bearings are available .010" (.264 mm) and .020" (.508 mm) undersize.

5) To install bearings, clean crankshaft journal and bearing surface in rod. Insert bearing in rod and cap. Lubricate journal and pull piston and rod assembly down, aligning bearing on journal. Install rod cap, noting identification marks and tighten rod nuts evenly.

General Motors V8 Engines

7.4 LITER V8 (Cont.)

Fig. 8: Checking Crankshaft End Play

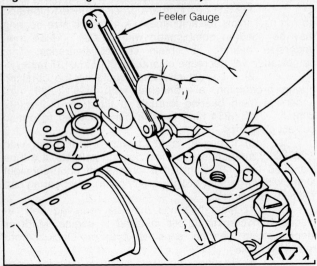

Using a feeler gauge, end play should not exceed .006-.010" (.152-.254 mm).

THRUST BEARING ALIGNMENT

Pry crankshaft forward as far as possible and check end play with a feeler gauge inserted between front of rear main bearing and crankshaft. Replace rear main bearing if end play is excessive.

REAR MAIN BEARING OIL SEAL

Removal

Remove rear main bearing cap and pry out old seal. Remove upper half of seal by tapping end with brass punch until end of seal protrudes enough to be removed with pliers.

Installation

1) Fabricate an installation tool. *See Fig. 9.* Coat seal lips and seal bead of upper seal with motor oil.

2) Keep ends of seal dry of oil and position tool between crankshaft and seal seat in cylinder block. Position seal between tip of tool and crankshaft.

3) Installation tool must remain in position until seal is positioned with both ends flush with block.

Fig. 9: Rear Main Seal Installation Tool

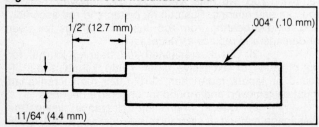

Use seal installer tool like a shoehorn to help install and protect seal.

4) Roll seal around crankshaft, using tool as a "shoehorn" to protect seal from sharp corner of seat surface in cylinder case. Make sure oil seal lip is positioned towards front of engine.

5) Remove tool, taking care not to remove seal. Install lower half of seal in bearing cap, using tool as a shoehorn again. Feed seal into cap using light pressure with thumb and finger.

6) Install bearing cap with sealant applied to face, taking care to keep sealant off split line.

Fig. 10: Rear Main Oil Seal

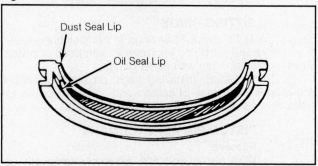

Oil seal lip faces inside of engine.

FRONT COVER OIL SEAL

With Cover Removed

Pry seal out of cover with a screwdriver. Install new seal with open end of seal facing toward inside of cover. Support cover at seal area before driving in seal.

With Cover Installed

With harmonic balancer removed, pry seal out of front cover. Insert seal with open end of seal facing toward engine. Install using driver (J-22102) and hammer.

ENGINE OILING

Crankcase Capacity

Crankcase capacity is 6 quarts (5.7L). Add 1 quart (.95L) with filter change.

Oil Filter

Replace every other oil change or more often under dusty conditions.

Normal Oil Pressure

Normal oil pressure should be 40 psi (2.81 kg/cm²) @ 2000 RPM.

Oil Pressure Regulator Valve

Pressure regulator valve is located in oil pump body and is nonadjustable.

ENGINE OILING SYSTEM

Engine oiling is provided by full pressure lubrication through a full flow oil filter which is supplied by a gear type oil pump. Main oil gallery feeds oil, through drilled passages, to camshaft and crankshaft to lubricate bearings. Valve lifter gallery feeds the valve lifters, which feed the rocker arms through hollow push rods.

OIL PUMP

Removal & Disassembly

1) Remove pump-to-rear main cap bolt and remove pump and extension shaft. Remove pump cover attaching screws and pump cover.

2) Remove pressure regulator from pump cover. Mark gears so they may be reassembled with same tooth indexing. Remove idler gear, drive gear and shaft from pump body.

3) Do not disassemble pickup screen and pipe. Screen and pipe are serviced as an assembly with pump.

Reassembly & Installation

Check operation of oil pump. Check all parts for fit and wear. If pump gears or body are damaged or

7.4 LITER V8 (Cont.)

worn, replacement of entire pump assembly is necessary. Reverse removal and disassembly procedure to assemble and install.

ENGINE COOLING

WATER PUMP

Removal

1) Disconnect negative battery ground cable. Drain cooling system and remove accessory drive belts. Remove fan hub attaching bolts. Remove fan and pulley.

2) Remove bolts attaching lower alternator brace to water pump and swing brace aside. Remove lower radiator hose, heater hose and bypass hose from water pump. Remove water pump attaching bolts and water pump.

Installation

Transfer heater and bypass hose fittings to new water pump. Clean all gasket mating surfaces. Apply silicone to gasket surfaces. Reverse removal procedures to complete installation.

ENGINE SPECIFICATIONS

GENERAL SPECIFICATIONS

TIGHTENING SPECIFICATIONS

Application	Ft. Lbs. (N.m)
Camshaft Sprocket Bolt	20 (27)
Connecting Rod Cap Nuts	50 (68)
Cylinder Head Bolts	80 (108)
Exhaust Manifold Bolts	20 (27)
Flywheel Bolts	65 (88)
Harmonic Balancer Bolt	85 (115)
Intake Manifold Bolts	30 (41)
Main Bearing Cap Bolts	110 (149)
Oil Pump Bolts	65 (88)
Rocker Arm Stud	50 (68)
Water Pump Bolts	30 (41)

NOTE: For information on cooling system capacities and other cooling system components, see appropriate article in "Engine Cooling Systems," at end of ENGINE Section.

Year	DISPLACEMENT		Fuel System	HP@RPM	Torque Ft. Lbs.@RPM	Compr. Ratio	BORE		STROKE	
	Cu. In.	Liters					In.	mm	In.	mm
1983	454	7.4	4-Bbl.	.....	.....	8.5:1	4.250	107.95	4.000	101.6

VALVES

Engine Size & Valve	Head Diam. In. (mm)	Face Angle	Seat Angle	Seat Width In. (mm)	Stem Diameter In. (mm)	Stem Clearance In. (mm)	Valve Lift In. (mm)
7.4L Intake	2.065 (52.45)	45°	46°	.031-.063 (.787-1.60)	[1] .3715-.3722 (9.44-9.45)	.0010-.0027 (.025-.069)	.398 (10.11)
Exhaust	1.720 (43.69)	45°	46°	.063-.094 (1.60-2.39)	[1] .3713-.3720 (9.43-9.45)	.0012-.0029 (.030-.074)	.430 (10.92)

[1] — Standard size valve specifications only. Always check stem clearance to determine valve guide and stem wear.

PISTONS, PINS, RINGS

Engine	PISTONS	PINS		RINGS		
	Clearance In. (mm)	Piston Fit In. (mm)	Rod Fit In. (mm)	Ring No.	End Gap In. (mm)	Side Clearance In. (mm)
7.4L	.003-.004 (.076-.102)	.0025-.0035 (.0064-.0089)	[1] .0013-.0021 (.033-.053)	1	.010-.020 (.254-.508)	.0017-.0032 (.043-.081)
				2	.010-.020 (.254-.508)	.0017-.0032 (.043-.081)
				3	.015-.055 (.381-1.397)	.005-.0065 (.127-.165)

[1] — Interference fit.

General Motors V8 Engines

7.4 LITER V8 (Cont.)

ENGINE SPECIFICATIONS (Cont.)

CRANKSHAFT MAIN & CONNECTING ROD BEARINGS

Engine	MAIN BEARINGS				CONNECTING ROD BEARINGS		
	Journal Diam. In. (mm)	Clearance In. (mm)	Thrust Bearing	Crankshaft End Play In. (mm)	Journal Diam. In. (mm)	Clearance In. (mm)	Side Play In. (mm)
7.4L	[1] 2.7481-2.7490 (69.80-69.82) [2] 2.7476-2.7486 (69.79-69.81)	[1] .0013-.0025 (.033-.064) [2] .0024-.0040 (.061-.102)	No. 5	.006-.010 (.152-.254)	2.1990-2.200 (55.85-55.88)	.0009-.0025 (.023-.064)	.013-.023 (.330-.584)

[1] — Journal No. 1, 2, 3 & 4.
[2] — Journal No. 5.

VALVE SPRINGS

Engine	Free Length In. (mm)	PRESSURE Lbs. @ In. (Kg @ mm)	
		Valve Closed	Valve Open
7.4L	2.12 (53.85)	84-96@1.80 (38-44@45.72)	210-230@1.40 (95-104@35.56)

CAMSHAFT

Engine	Journal Diam. In. (mm)	Clearance In. (mm)	Lobe Lift In. (mm)
7.4L Intake	1.9482-1.9492 (49.48-49.50)	.....	2343 (5.95)
Exhaust	1.9482-1.9492 (49.48-49.50)	.....	.2530 (6.43)

Jeep 4 Engines

2.5 LITER 4-CYLINDER

ENGINE CODING

ENGINE IDENTIFICATION

The three character engine identification code is stamped into the front, top left-hand corner of engine block. In addition, engines built for sale in Georgia and Tennessee have a non-repeating number stamped into the left rear block flange.

ENGINE IDENTIFICATION CODES

Application	Code
2.5L	
Federal Man. Trans.	KK
Calif. Man. Trans.	KY

ENGINE REMOVAL

See Engine Removal at end of ENGINE Section.

SPECIAL ENGINE MARKS

Some engines are produced at factory with oversize or undersize components. These engines are identified by a letter code stamped on a boss between ignition coil and distributor. Letters are decoded as follows:
- "B" indicates all cylinder bores .010 (.25 mm) oversize.
- "C" indicates all camshaft bearing bores .010 (.25 mm) oversize.
- "M" indicates all main bearing journals .010 (.25 mm) undersize.
- "P" indicates all connecting rod journals .010 (.25 mm) undersize.

MANIFOLDS & CYLINDER HEAD

INTAKE MANIFOLD

Removal

1) Disconnect negative battery cable. Remove air cleaner and PCV valve. Drain cooling system. Disconnect throttle linkages, vacuum lines, fuel lines, and electrical connections to carburetor.

2) Remove carburetor and carburetor spacer. Remove bellcrank and throttle linkage brackets and move to one side.

3) Remove heater hose at intake manifold. Remove air pump and bracket, if equipped, noting position

Fig. 1: Intake Manifold Tightening Sequence

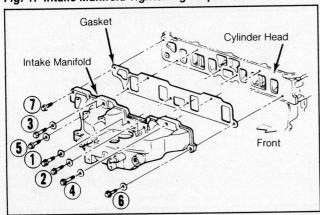

Tighten bolts to 37 ft. lbs. (50 N.m).

of spacers for installation. Remove manifold-to-cylinder head bolts, and remove manifold.

Installation

1) Install manifold and gasket on cylinder head. Start all bolts and finger tighten only.

2) Tighten manifold-to-cylinder head bolts using sequence shown in *Fig. 1*. Reverse removal procedure to complete installation.

EXHAUST MANIFOLD

Removal

1) Remove air cleaner and carburetor preheat tube. If equipped, remove oxygen sensor. Remove oil dipstick tube attaching bolt.

2) Disconnect exhaust pipe from manifold. Remove exhaust manifold bolts, and remove manifold with gasket.

Installation

1) Install manifold and gasket on cylinder head. Start all bolts and finger tighten only.

2) Tighten manifold-to-cylinder head bolts using sequence shown in *Fig. 2*. Reverse removal procedure to complete installation.

Fig. 2: Exhaust Manifold Tightening Sequence

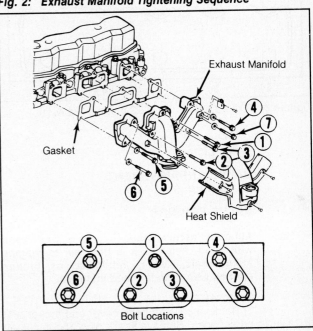

Tighten bolts to 39 ft. lbs. (52 N.m).

CYLINDER HEAD

Removal

1) Disconnect negative battery cable. Remove air cleaner, PCV valve, spark plugs and wires, and rocker arm cover.

2) Drain cooling system and remove upper radiator hose and rear heater hose. Disconnect exhaust pipe from exhaust manifold. Tag and disconnect vacuum hoses.

3) If equipped, remove air pump and bracket, noting number and position of spacers. Disconnect fuel line from carburetor and move aside to allow clearance for cylinder head removal.

4) Remove power steering pump and bracket and place to one side without disconnecting hoses.

Jeep 4 Engines

2.5 LITER 4-CYLINDER (Cont.)

Remove dipstick. Remove rocker arm assemblies and push rods. Note and mark their positions for installation in their original positions.

5) Remove cylinder head bolts and dislodge cylinder head by inserting a bar into alternator bracket and prying upward. Place cylinder head on 2 blocks of wood to prevent damage to valves.

Installation

1) Make sure gasket surfaces are clean of foreign matter and free of nicks. Install new gasket in position over dowel pins on cylinder block. Carefully install cylinder head over dowel pins and gasket.

NOTE: **Make sure all cylinder head bolt threads are clean and oiled. If threads are dirty, correct torque cannot be achieved.**

2) Coat threads and underside of cylinder head bolts with sealer and install in cylinder head finger tight. Gradually tighten bolts in steps following sequence in *Fig. 3*. Reverse removal procedures to complete installation.

Fig. 3: Cylinder Head Tightening Sequence

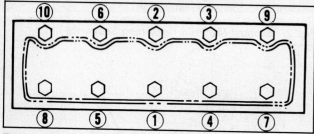

Tighten bolts to a final torque of 92 ft. lbs. (125 N.m)

VALVES

VALVE ARRANGEMENT

I-E-I-E-E-I-E-I

VALVE SPRINGS

NOTE: **Although normal maintenance is performed with head removed, it is possible to replace stem seals, locks, retainers, or broken springs with cylinder head installed.**

Removal

1) Remove cylinder head cover and rocker arm of valve to be serviced. Remove spark plug and install air hose adaptor (J-22794 or equivalent) in spark plug hole. Apply a minimum constant air pressure of 90 psi (6.3 kg/cm²).

NOTE: **Do not remove air pressure until all components have been reinstalled.**

2) Using a spring compressor (J-5892-1 or equivalent), compress valve spring and remove locks. Remove tool, cap, shield, spring, and oil seal.

Installation

To install, reverse removal procedure using a new valve stem oil seal.

VALVE SPRING INSTALLED HEIGHT

Installed height of valve spring must not exceed specifications. Measure spring height from top of spring seat to top of valve spring or oil shield. If installed height exceeds specifications, install 1/16" (1.6 mm) valve spring seat shim.

CAUTION: **Never shim a spring excessively. Installed height should never be less than specified.**

VALVE SPRING INSTALLED HEIGHT SPECIFICATIONS

Application	In. (mm)
Intake & Exhaust	1.66 (42.2)

VALVE STEM OIL SEALS

Oil seals are used on all valve stems, and should be replaced when valve service is performed. To install, set valve shield, spring, and cap in place. Compress valve spring with compressor tool. Install oil seal in lower groove of stem ensuring it is flat and not twisted. Install locks and release compressor tool.

VALVE GUIDE SERVICING

1) With cylinder head and rocker assemblies removed, use valve spring compressor to compress valve springs and remove locks. Release tool and remove spring cap, spring shield, spring, and oil seal. Remove valves from cylinder head and place in rack in proper sequence to ensure they are installed in original positions.

2) After cleaning, measure valve stem diameters at top, middle, and at bottom. Exhaust valves are tapered, and are approximately .001" (.025 mm) larger at the top than at head end. Using a telescoping gauge, measure valve-to-valve guide clearance.

3) If clearance is not within specifications, use next oversize valve stem size, and ream valve guide to fit using a suitable reamer. Valves are available with standard, .003" (.08 mm) and .005" (.13 mm) oversize stem diameters.

HYDRAULIC VALVE LIFTERS

1) Valve lifters are serviced as complete assemblies, and parts are not interchangable between lifters. Inspect for signs of scuffing on barrel and face of lifter body. Inspect lifter face and cam lobe for concave wear or pitting, and if present, replace camshaft or lifters as necessary.

2) If lifters are disassembled for cleaning or inspection, they should be tested using a suitable leak-

Fig. 4: Hydraulic Valve Lifter Assembly

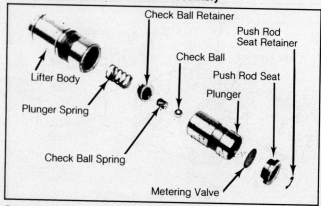

Parts are not interchangeable between lifters.

2.5 LITER 4-CYLINDER (Cont.)

down tester according to manufacturers instructions. Leak-down should take between 12 and 90 seconds. Replace any lifter not within specification.

CAMSHAFT

ENGINE FRONT COVER

Removal

1) Remove drive belts. Remove crankshaft vibration pulley center bolt and slide damper and damper hub from shaft.

2) Remove fan and fan shroud. Remove oil pan-to-front cover bolts. Pull cover slightly forward, only enough to permit cutting of oil pan front seal.

3) Using a sharp knife or other suitable cutting device, cut oil pan front seal flush with engine block at both sides of cover. Remove front cover and gasket.

Installation

1) Clean mating surfaces of block and front cover. Cut tabs from replacement oil pan front seal. *See Fig. 5.* Install seal on front cover, pressing tips of seal into holes in cover.

Fig. 5: Oil Pan Seal Modification for Front Cover Installation

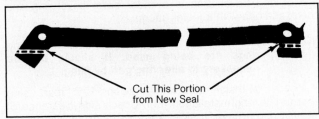

Cut This Portion from New Seal

This is necessary for replacing cover with oil pan installed.

2) Coat gasket with sealer and place in position on cover. Apply a 1/8" bead of RTV sealant to joint formed at cylinder block and oil pan.

3) Install alignment tool (J-23042 or equivalent) in front cover seal, and position front cover to block. Install and partially tighten 2 oil pan-to-front cover bolts.

NOTE: **Use of an alignment tool is necessary so seal damage does not result from vibration damper installation, and to ensure correct seal position around hub.**

4) Install and tighten all front cover-to-block attaching bolts, and remove alignment tool. Reverse removal procedure to complete installation.

FRONT COVER OIL SEAL

Removal & Installation

1) With vibration damper removed, pry oil seal from front cover using care not to damage cover.

2) Position new seal with lip toward rear of engine. Drive into cover using seal installer (J-23042 or equivalent).

3) Lightly coat oil seal contact area of balancer with engine oil. Position balancer on crankshaft and push it onto the crankshaft until it contacts crankshaft gear. Install balancer center bolt and tighten. Reverse removal procedure to complete installation.

NOTE: **Apply a locking agent to damper-to-hub bolts before installation.**

CAMSHAFT & TIMING GEAR

Removal

1) Remove air cleaner and drain cooling system. Remove front cover. Disconnect radiator hoses, and remove radiator.

2) Remove valve cover, rocker arms, push rods, and hydraulic lifters, making sure to place them in proper order for installation. Remove distributor, fuel pump, and oil pump drive. *See Fig. 6.*

Fig. 6: Oil Pump Drive Shaft Removal

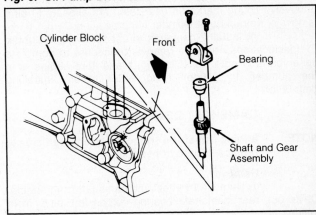

Cylinder Block   Front   Bearing   Shaft and Gear Assembly

3) Remove 2 camshaft thrust plate bolts through holes in camshaft gear. *See Fig. 7.* Remove camshaft and gear assembly by pulling out through front of block. Support camshaft carefully when removing to prevent damage to camshaft bearings.

Fig. 7: Removing Thrust Plate Attaching Bolts

Camshaft Gear

Align holes in gear with bolt heads.

4) If gear must be removed from camshaft, use press plate and appropriate adaptor with arbor press. Press shaft out of gear. Thrust plate must be properly aligned to ensure Woodruff key in camshaft does not damage thrust plate when the shaft is pressed out of gear.

Installation

1) Firmly support camshaft at back of front journal in arbor press using press plate and adapter.

Jeep 4 Engines

2.5 LITER 4-CYLINDER (Cont.)

Install gear spacer ring and thrust plate over end of camshaft, and install Woodruff key to shaft keyway.

2) Install camshaft gear and press onto camshaft until it bottoms against spacer ring. Measure end clearance of thrust plate. If less than .0015" (.04 mm), spacer ring should be replaced. If more than .005" (.13 mm), thrust plate should be replaced.

3) Coat camshaft journals with high quality engine oil supplement (EOS). Install camshaft in engine block being careful not to damage camshaft bearings. Align timing marks by rotating camshaft and crankshaft until valve timing marks on gear teeth are aligned. Engine is now in the number 4 cylinder firing position.

4) Install 2 camshaft thrust screws and tighten to specifications. Reverse removal procedure to complete assembly and note the following: Make sure engine is in the number 1 cylinder firing order before installing distributor.

CAMSHAFT BEARINGS

NOTE: **Engine must be removed from vehicle to replace camshaft bearings.**

Removal
1) Remove flywheel and camshaft from engine. Drive out rear camshaft bearing expansion plug from inside out.

2) Using camshaft bearing removal tool (J-21473-1 or equivalent), drive front bearing toward rear and rear bearing toward front. Install extension (J-21054-1) on removal tool and drive center bearing out toward rear.

Installation
1) Install bearings by reversing removal procedure and noting the following: Make sure oil holes in bearings and engine block are aligned.

2) Install front camshaft bearing approximately 1/8" (3.2 mm) behind front of engine block to expose oil hole for timing gear oil nozzle.

PISTONS, RINGS & PINS

OIL PAN

See Oil Pan Removal at end of ENGINE Section.

PISTON & ROD ASSEMBLY

NOTE: **New pistons must be installed in same cylinders for which they were fitted. Install used pistons in same cylinders from which they were removed.**

Removal
1) With cylinder head and oil pan removed, use a ridge reamer to remove any ridge or deposits from upper end of cylinder bore. Piston must be at bottom of stroke and covered with cloth to collect cuttings.

2) Check connecting rod and piston for proper identification and mark if necessary. Remove bearing cap. Remove piston and rod assembly through top of cylinder block, taking care not to damage cylinder wall or crankshaft journal.

Installation
1) Lightly coat cylinder bores and pistons with oil. Ensure ring gaps are evenly spaced. Install ring compressor on piston, ensuring ring gap spacing does not change.

2) Insert piston and rod assembly into cylinder bore with notches on top of piston facing front of engine. Using hammer handle, gently tap piston assembly into cylinder bore, taking care not to damage cylinder bore.

3) Install bearing caps and tighten nuts. Reverse removal procedures to complete installation.

FITTING PISTONS

1) Using an inside micrometer, measure bore of each cylinder crosswise to block to determine smallest diameter. Measure piston skirt diameter perpendicular to piston boss approximately 2" from crown. If clearance is excessive, reboring and oversize pistons are necessary.

NOTE: **Measure block and pistons at room temperature, or improper fitting will result.**

2) Pistons and rings are available in standard, .005" (.13 mm), .010" (.25 mm) and .030" (.76 mm) oversize. When selecting rings, make sure they correspond to the piston size.

FITTING RINGS

1) Check end gap by placing a ring in lower end of ring travel area in cylinder bore. Level ring and check end gap with a feeler gauge.

NOTE: **An incorrect ring gap indicates the wrong rings are being used. It should not be necessary to alter ring gap by filing.**

2) Install rings with end gaps 120° apart using appropriate ring installation tool. Check side clearance of rings in ring groove. If side clearance is excessive, piston must be replaced.

PISTON PIN REPLACEMENT

NOTE: **Piston pins are a press fit in rods. When determining fit, piston and pin must be at room temperature, and pin must gravity fall from piston.**

Removal
Using an arbor press and piston pin removal and installation tool (J-24086 or equivalent), press pin from piston and rod.

Installation
1) Lightly lubricate piston pin holes in piston and rod with graphite lubricant. Position rod in its original piston so that raised notch at bearing end is 180° opposite notches in top of piston when installed. *See Fig. 8.*

Fig. 8: Correct Positioning of Connecting Rod to Piston

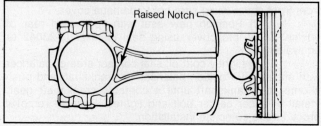

Raised notch on rod to rear of engine.

2.5 LITER 4-CYLINDER (Cont.)

2) Position piston and rod in arbor press and insert pilot of pin installation tool through piston and rod. Note position of notches on piston.

3) Start pin into piston and rod. Press on installation tool until guide bushing bottoms, indicating pin is fully installed. Remove piston from press and check piston pin for freedom of movement in piston bore.

CRANKSHAFT, MAIN & CONNECTING ROD BEARINGS

NOTE: **Bearings may be replaced with either the crankshaft installed or removed from engine. Always replace bearings in pairs. Do not shim or use a new bearing with an old one.**

MAIN & CONNECTING ROD BEARINGS
Main Bearings (Crankshaft Removed)

NOTE: **Main bearings are available in standard, .001" (.025 mm), .002" (.050 mm) and .010" (.25 mm) undersize. Standard size bearing may be used in combination with a .001" (.025 mm) undersize main bearing. This will decrease clearance .0005" (.013 mm) from that of two standard bearing inserts.**

1) Remove main bearing inserts from engine block and bearing caps. Measure main bearing journals with a micrometer and check for excessive wear or damage. Using Plastigage method, measure bearing clearance and replace bearings as necessary.

2) Coat bearings with oil and position in engine block and main bearing caps. Install crankshaft and caps with arrows pointing towards rear of engine. Tighten cap bolts.

Main Bearings (Crankshaft Installed)

NOTE: **Main bearings are available in standard, .001" (.025 mm), .002" (.050 mm) and .010" (.25 mm) undersize. Standard size bearing may be used in combination with a .001" (.025 mm) undersize main bearing. This will decrease clearance .0005" (.013 mm) from that of two standard bearing inserts.**

1) With oil pan, oil pump and spark plugs removed, remove cap from main bering requiring replacement and remove lower bearing insert from cap.

2) Insert upper main bearing removal and installation tool in oil hole in crankshaft journal. If tool is

Fig. 9: Fabricated Upper Main Bearing Removal & Installation Tool

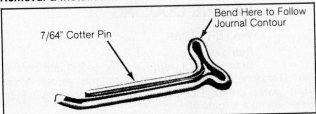

not available, tool may be fabricated from a 7/64" cotter pin. *See Fig. 9.*

3) Rotate crankshaft clockwise as viewed from front of engine. This will roll upper bearing insert out of block.

4) Apply oil to replacement bearing insert and position plain (unnotched) end between crankshaft and notched side of block. Rotate crankshaft to pull bearing into place. Remove tool from oil hole in crankshaft journal.

5) Apply oil to lower bearing insert and place in bearing cap. Install main bearing cap with arrows pointing toward rear of engine. Install and tighten main bearing cap bolts. Complete installation in reverse of removal procedure.

Connecting Rod Bearings

1) Before removal of rod caps, stamp side of connecting rod and cap with corresponding cylinder number to assure matched reassembly. With oil pan and oil pump removed, turn crankshaft and rod to be serviced to bottom of stroke.

2) Remove connecting rod cap and bearing and push piston assembly up far enough to remove upper bearing shell. Wipe bearings and journal clean of oil.

3) Measure crankshaft journal for out-of-round and taper. If not within specifications, replace or recondition crankshaft.

4) Using Plastigage method, measure bearing clearance and replace bearings as necessary. Bearings are available in standard, .001" (.025 mm), .002" (.050 mm) and .010" (.25 mm) undersize.

NOTE: **Standard size bearings may be used in combination with a .001" (.025 mm) undersize bearing.**

5) Coat bearing surfaces with oil, and install inserts in rod and bearing cap. Tighten cap nuts. When all rod bearings have been installed, tap each rod lightly (parallel to journal) to ensure they have proper clearance. Measure all rod side clearances between rod caps. Reverse removal procedure to complete installation.

THRUST BEARING ALIGNMENT

Measure crankshaft end play by forcing the crankshaft to the extreme front position. Measure at front end of thrust bearing with a feeler gauge, if not within specifications thrust bearing must be replaced.

REAR MAIN BEARING OIL SEAL

NOTE: **Rear main bearing oil seal is a one piece unit and can be replaced without removing oil pan or crankshaft.**

Removal
Remove transmission, clutch housing and flywheel. Remove rear main bearing oil seal by prying it out with a screwdriver, taking care not to scratch crankshaft.

Installation
Center new oil seal over crankshaft with lip of seal toward front of engine. Tap around perimeter of seal with a soft-faced hammer until seal seats in groove. Use care to prevent seal from binding on crankshaft and not seating fully. Install flywheel, clutch housing and transmission.

Jeep 4 Engines

2.5 LITER 4-CYLINDER (Cont.)

ENGINE OILING

Crankcase Capacity

Capacity is 3 quarts (2.8L), including 1/2 quart (.47L) for filter change.

Oil Filter

A disposable, full-flow oil filter is mounted on the lower right side of engine block. Change every 5,000 miles or 5 months, whichever comes first.

Normal Oil Pressure

36-41 psi (2.5-2.9 kg/cm²) at 2000 RPM.

Oil Pressure Regulator Valve

Non-adjustable; located in oil pump body.

ENGINE OILING SYSTEM

Engine lubrication is accomplished through a gear type pump which picks up oil from the oil pan sump, pumps it through the full flow oil filter and into oil passage which runs along the right side of the block and intersects the hydraulic lifter bores.

Oil is then routed to the camshaft and crankshaft bearings through smaller drilled passages. Oil is supplied to the rocker arms through the hydraulic lifters which feed oil up the push rod tubes to the rocker arms. By-pass valves are located in the oil filter mounting boss and oil pump to allow for any clogged or restricted conditions.

Many internal parts have no direct oil feed and rely on gravity or splash oiling from other direct feed components. Oil returns to the sump through oil return holes in cylinder head and block. *See Fig. 10.*

Fig. 10: Engine Oiling System

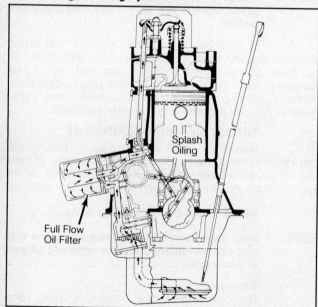

Arrows show oil flow route.

OIL PUMP

Removal

Oil pump is located in oil sump, oil pan must be removed for access. *See Oil Pan Removal at end of ENGINE Section.* Remove 2 flange bolts and nut from main bearing cap bolt. Remove oil pump and screen as an assembly.

Disassembly

Remove pump cover attaching screws, cover, idler gear, and drive gear and shaft. Remove pressure regulator valve and spring from pump bore.

NOTE: **Do not disturb oil pickup tube on strainer or oil pump. This pipe is attached at factory and cannot be removed.**

Inspection

Inspect pump cover, body and gears for cracks, excessive wear and damage. Check drive gear shaft for a tight fit in pump body. Check oil strainer and relief grommet for damage. If any of these conditions are found, complete oil pump assembly must be replaced.

Reassembly

Reverse disassembly procedure noting the following: Install idler gear in pump body so that smooth side of gear is toward cover.

Installation

Position oil pump gear shaft tang to align with oil pump drive shaft slot. Install oil pump-to-block positioning flange over pump drive shaft lower bushing. Do not use gasket. Tighten pump attaching bolts. Install oil pan using a new gasket.

OIL PUMP SPECIFICATIONS

Application	Clearance
Gear-to-Body	.004" (.10 mm) Maximum
Gear End Clearance	.002-.005" (.05-.13 mm)

Fig. 11: Exploded View of Oil Pump Assembly

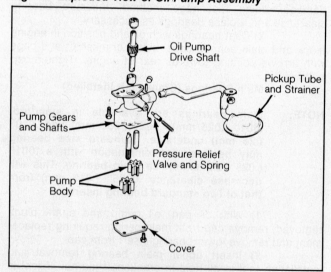

Install idler gear with smooth side toward cover.

ENGINE COOLING

WATER PUMP

Removal

Drain coolant, remove drive belt(s) and cooling fan. Disconnect lower radiator hose and heater hoses from water pump. Remove attaching bolts and lift off water pump and gasket.

Jeep 4 Engines

2.5 LITER 4-CYLINDER (Cont.)

Installation

Scrape and clean gasket mating surfaces. Install new gasket. Position water pump on block, then install and tighten attaching bolts. To complete installation, reverse removal procedure.

NOTE: **For information on cooling system capacities and other cooling system components, see appropriate article in "Engine Cooling Systems," at end of ENGINE Section.**

TIGHTENING SPECIFICATIONS

Application	Ft. Lbs. (N.m)
Camshaft Thrust Plate Bolts	7 (9)
Connecting Rod Cap Nuts	30 (40)
Cylinder Head Bolts	92 (125)
Damper Pulley Hub Bolt	162 (220)
Exhaust Manifold Bolts	37 (50)
Flywheel-to-Crankshaft Bolts	68 (93)
Front Cover Bolts	7 (9)
Intake Manifold Bolts	26 (34)
Main Bearing Cap Bolts	65 (88)
Oil Pump-to-Block Bolts	18 (25)
Pulley-to-Crankshaft Hub Bolts	25 (34)
Rocker Arm Bolts	20 (27)
Water Pump Bolts	17 (23)

ENGINE SPECIFICATIONS

GENERAL SPECIFICATIONS

Year	DISPLACEMENT		Fuel System	HP@RPM	Torque Ft. Lbs.@RPM	Compr. Ratio	BORE		STROKE	
	Cu. In.	Liters					In.	mm	In.	mm
1983	151	2.5	2-Bbl.	......	......	8.24:1	4.00	101.6	3.00	76.2

VALVES

Engine Size & Valve	Head Diam. In. (mm)	Face Angle	Seat Angle	Seat Width In. (mm)	Stem Diameter In. (mm)	Stem Clearance In. (mm)	Valve Lift In. (mm)
2.5L Int.	1.72 (43.69)	45°	46°	.035-.075 (.90-1.90)	.3418-.3425 (8.68-8.70)	.001-.003 (.025-.076)	.398 (10.1)
Exh.	1.50 (38.4)	45°	46°	.058-.097 (1.47-2.47)	.3418-.3451 (8.68-8.77)	.002-.003 (.050-.076)	.398 (10.1)

PISTONS, PINS, RINGS

Engine	PISTONS	PINS		RINGS		
	Clearance In. (mm)	Piston Fit In. (mm)	Rod Fit In. (mm)	Ring No.	End Gap In. (mm)	Side Clearance In. (mm)
2.5L	¹ .0025-.0033 (.064-.084)	.0003-.0005 (.003-.013)	Press Fit	1	.010-.022 (.25-.56)	.003 (.076)
				2	.010-.028 (.25-.71)	.003 (.076)
				3	.015-.055 (.38-1.4)	.003 (.076)

¹ — Top clearance. Bottom clearance is .0017-.0041" (.043-.104 mm).

CRANKSHAFT MAIN & CONNECTING ROD BEARINGS

Engine	MAIN BEARINGS				CONNECTING ROD BEARINGS		
	Journal Diam. In. (mm)	Clearance In. (mm)	Thrust Bearing	Crankshaft End Play In. (mm)	Journal Diam. In. (mm)	Clearance In. (mm)	Side Play In. (mm)
2.5L	2.2988 (58.39)	.0005-.0022 (.013-.056)	No. 5	.0035-.0085 (.089-.216)	2.00 (50.8)	.0005-.0026 (.013-.066)	.017 (.436)

Jeep 4 Engines

2.5 LITER 4-CYLINDER (Cont.)

ENGINE SPECIFICATIONS (Cont.)

VALVE SPRINGS

Engine	Free Length In. (mm)	PRESSURE Lbs. @ In. (Kg @ mm)	
		Valve Closed	Valve Open
2.5L	.....	78-86@1.66 (35-39@42.2)	172-180@1.25 (78-82@31.8)

CAMSHAFT

Engine	Journal Diam. In. (mm)	Clearance In. (mm)	Lobe Lift In. (mm)
2.5L	1.869 (47.47)	.0007-.0027 (.018-.069)	.230 (5.8)

Jeep 6 Engines

4.2 LITER 6-CYLINDER

ENGINE CODING

ENGINE IDENTIFICATION

Engine identification code is stamped on a machined surface on right side of cylinder block, between No. 2 and No. 3 cylinders. The letter portion of the code identifies engine displacement, carburetor type, and compression ratio.

ENGINE IDENTIFICATION CODE

Engine	Code
4.2L 2-Bbl.	C

ENGINE REMOVAL

See Engine Removal at end of ENGINE Section.

SPECIAL ENGINE MARKS

Some engines are produced at factory with oversize or undersize components. These engines are identified by a letter code stamped on a boss between ignition coil and distributor. Letters are decoded as follows:
- "B" indicates all cylinder bores .010 (.25 mm) oversize.
- "C" indicates all camshaft bearing bores .010 (.25 mm) oversize.
- "M" indicates all main bearing journals .010 (.25 mm) undersize.
- "P" indicates all connecting rod journals .010 (.25 mm) undersize.

MANIFOLDS & CYLINDER HEAD

INTAKE & EXHAUST MANIFOLDS

Removal

1) Remove air cleaner. Disconnect fuel line at carburetor. Label and disconnect all vacuum hoses, ventilation hoses and electrical connectors at carburetor.

2) Disconnect throttle cable from throttle bellcrank. If equipped, disconnect throttle valve rod. Disconnect PCV vacuum hose and heater wire from manifold. Drain radiator and disconnect coolant hoses from intake manifold.

3) Disconnect vacuum hoses from ported vacuum switch (CTO valve) and EGR valve. Disconnect EGR tube fittings from intake and exhaust manifolds.

4) Disconnect vacuum hose at diverter valve. Disconnect air injection hoses at air pump and air injection manifold check valve, and remove with diverter valve attached.

5) Remove air pump. If equipped, remove power steering pump (with hoses attached) and position aside. If A/C equipped, remove drive belt idler pulley.

6) Disconnect exhaust pipe from manifold. Remove oxygen sensor if equipped. Remove intake and exhaust manifolds.

Installation

1) Clean mating surfaces of manifolds and cylinder head. Position exhaust manifold-to-cylinder head and install alignment sleeves over end studs.

2) Exhaust manifold does not use a manifold-to-cylinder head gasket. Tighten bolts 1 and 2, then remove alignment sleeves.

3) Loosely connect EGR tube to intake manifold. Install intake manifold gasket and intake manifold. Loosely connect EGR tube to exhaust manifold.

4) Tighten intake manifold bolts 3 and 4. Install remaining nuts and bolts. Tighten manifolds in sequence. See Fig. 1.

Fig. 1: Intake & Exhaust Manifolds Tightening Sequence

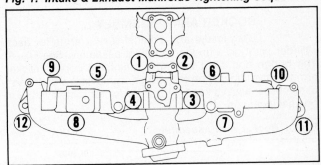

Tighten manifolds to 23 ft. lbs. (31 N.m).

5) Install remaining components in reverse order of removal. Start engine and inspect for coolant and vacuum leaks.

CYLINDER HEAD

NOTE: **Rocker arm cover is made of molded plastic. Use care when removing and installing to prevent damage to cover.**

Removal

1) Drain cooling system and disconnect radiator hose at thermostat housing. Remove air cleaner and rocker arm cover. Remove bridge and pivot assembly, rocker arms and push rods in order, for reinstallation in original locations.

2) Alternately loosen rocker arm bolts 1 turn at a time when removing rocker arm assemblies to avoid damage to bridge. Disconnect power steering pump (if equipped), air pump and brackets, and position aside.

3) Remove intake and exhaust manifold assembly from cylinder head. If A/C equipped, remove drive belt idler bracket from cylinder head. Remove alternator bracket-to-head mounting bolt. Remove A/C compressor from mounting bracket and position aside.

4) Remove spark plugs and disconnect temperature sending unit wire. Disconnect negative battery cable. Remove ignition coil and bracket. Remove cylinder head and discard gasket.

Installation

Clean all gasket mating surfaces. Apply an even coat of sealing compound to both sides of cylinder head gasket, and position on block with word "TOP" facing

Fig. 2: Cylinder Head Tightening Sequence

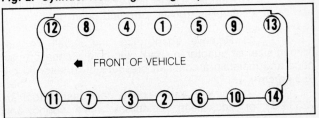

Tighten head bolts to 85 ft. lbs. (115 N.m).

up. Install and tighten cylinder head. *See Fig. 2.* Reverse removal procedures to complete installation.

VALVES

VALVE ARRANGEMENT

E-I-I-E-I-E-E-I-E-I-I-E (Front-to-rear)

ROCKER ARM ASSEMBLY

Both intake and exhaust rocker arms for each cylinder pivot on a bridge and pivot assembly. *See Fig. 3.* The bridge and pivot assembly maintains correct rocker arm-to-valve tip alignment. When removing rocker arm assemblies, always keep parts in order for reinstallation in original locations.

Fig. 3: Rocker Arm Assembly

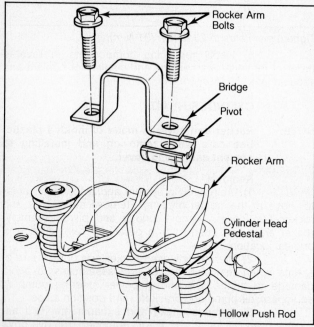

Tighten rocker arm bolts to 19 ft. lbs. (26 N.m).

VALVE SPRINGS

Although normal service is performed with cylinder head removed, it is possible to replace seals, locks, retainers, or broken springs with cylinder head installed.

NOTE: **On A/C equipped vehicles, a flexible air hose adapter must be used when servicing No. 1 cylinder.**

Removal

1) Remove rocker arm cover. Remove bridge and pivot assemblies, rocker arm, and push rod of valve to be serviced.

2) Remove spark plug and install 14 mm (thread size) air adaptor in spark plug hole. Connect an air hose and maintain a constant pressure of at least 90 psi (6.3 kg/cm²).

3) Using a valve spring compressor tool (J-22534-01 or equivalent), compress valve spring and remove locks. Remove valve spring retainer, valve spring, and oil seal.

Inspection

Using valve spring tester, check valve springs for proper tension. Measure free length of valve springs. Replace springs that are not within specification.

Installation

1) Use a 7/16" deep-well socket and light hammer to gently tap valve stem seal into place on valve stem. Ensure sharp edges of valve lock groove do not damage oil seal during installation. Install valve spring and retainer. Compress spring with valve spring compressor tool, and install locks.

2) Tap each valve spring from side to side to ensure spring is seated properly. Turn off air supply and remove air hose and adapter. Install remaining components in reverse order of removal.

VALVE STEM OIL SEALS

A nylon valve stem oil seal is used on all valves to keep engine oil from entering combustion chambers through valve guides. Replace oil seals if deteriorated, or when valve service is performed. Replacement seals are available for valves with oversize stems

VALVE GUIDE SERVICING

Valve guides are integral with cylinder head and are not replaceable. Replacement valves are available in .003" (.08 mm), .015" (.13 mm), and .030" (.76 mm) oversize stems.

1) To check stem-to-guide clearance, clean valve guide bore with solvent and a rifle brush. Use a ball gauge and micrometer to measure guide wear.

2) Take measurements of guide crosswise and lengthwise to head, inserting ball gauge 3/8" into guide bore from top of head.

3) If either measurement exceeds .003 (.08 mm), ream valve guide for installation of valve with oversize stem. Always ream valve guides in progressive steps, using reamers in sequence to obtain desired size.

HYDRAULIC VALVE LIFTERS

1) Service lifters as complete assemblies only. Parts are not interchangeable between lifters. Inspect lifter body for signs of scuffing. Inspect base of lifter for concave wear. If concave wear is present, replacement of camshaft and lifters is necessary.

Fig. 4: Hydraulic Lifter Assembly

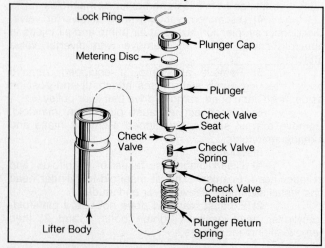

Do not interchange parts between lifters.

4.2 LITER 6-CYLINDER (Cont.)

2) Disassemble and clean lifters, then reassemble. *See Fig. 4.* Using lifter leak-down rate tester and lifter test fluid, test lifter leak down rate.

3) Compress lifter plunger and record time required for tester needle to align with .125" mark on scale. Leak-down rate should be 20-110 seconds.

4) Replace lifters that fail test. Do not attempt to prime lifters with engine oil prior to installation. Lifters will fill with oil within 3-8 minutes of engine operation.

CAMSHAFT

ENGINE FRONT COVER

Removal

1) Remove drive belt(s), fan and spacer from water pump. Remove crankshaft pulley and vibration damper. Remove oil pan-to-cover bolts and front cover-to-cylinder block bolts. Remove front cover and gasket.

2) Cut oil pan gasket end tabs flush with front face of cylinder block and remove tabs. Clean all gasket mating surfaces.

Installation

1) Apply gasket sealer to both sides of new front cover gasket and fit gasket to block. Cut end tabs from new oil pan gasket and fit onto oil pan. Cement these pieces to oil pan.

2) Install oil pan seal on lower end of front cover. Heavily coat end tabs of oil pan seal with non-hardening sealing compound.

3) Position front cover to engine. Place front cover alignment and seal installing tool (J-22248 or equivalent) into front cover. Install cover attaching bolts. Tighten all bolts and remove alignment tool. Reverse removal procedures to complete installation.

FRONT COVER OIL SEAL

Removal

Remove drive belt(s). Remove crankshaft pulley and vibration damper. Use seal remover tool (J-9256) to remove oil seal.

Installation

1) Position new oil seal onto front cover alignment and seal installing tool (J-22248 or equivalent), with seal lip facing outward. Apply light coat of sealer to outside diameter of seal case.

2) Install draw screw from tool (J-9163) into seal installing tool. Tighten nut on tool assembly to press seal into cover until it bottoms. Apply light film of engine oil to seal lip and install remaining components in reverse order of removal.

TIMING CHAIN & SPROCKETS

Removal

Remove engine front cover. Rotate crankshaft to align timing marks on camshaft and crankshaft sprockets. Remove camshaft and crankshaft sprockets and timing chain as an assembly.

Installation

Assemble timing chain, crankshaft sprocket and camshaft sprocket with timing marks aligned. *See Fig. 5.* Install chain and sprockets onto crankshaft and camshaft as an assembly. Install and tighten camshaft sprocket retaining bolt and washer. Install front cover.

Fig. 5: Timing Chain Sprocket Alignment

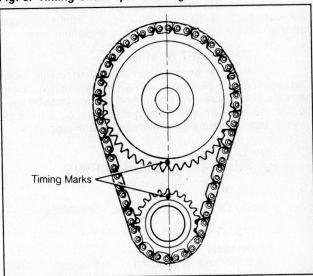

Timing Marks

Remove and install timing chain and sprockets as an assembly.

VALVE TIMING

1) Remove spark plugs and rocker arm cover. Remove rocker arms and bridge and pivot from No. 1 cylinder. Rotate crankshaft until No. 6 piston is on TDC at end of compression stroke. Rotate crankshaft counterclockwise 90° (as viewed from front of engine).

2) Install dial indicator on end of No. 1 intake valve push rod. Zero dial indicator. Rotate crankshaft clockwise until dial indicator shows .016" (.41 mm) lift. Timing mark on vibration damper should align with TDC mark on timing scale. If timing mark is more than 1/2" off TDC in either direction, valve timing is incorrect.

CAMSHAFT

Removal

1) Drain cooling system and remove radiator. If A/C equipped, remove condensor and receiver assembly as a charged unit. Remove fuel pump, ignition wires and distributor.

2) Remove cylinder head and hydraulic lifters. Remove engine front cover and timing chain and sprockets. Remove front bumper and grille as required. Carefully remove camshaft.

Installation

Lubricate camshaft with engine oil supplement. Carefully install camshaft into place to prevent damage to camshaft bearings. Reverse removal procedure to complete installation.

CAM LOBE LIFT

1) Remove rocker arm cover, rocker arms and bridge and pivot assembly. Remove spark plugs.

2) Using mounting fixture, attach dial indicator to cylinder head so indicator point rests on top of push rod. Dial indicator point must be in same plane as push rod vertical movement.

3) Rotate crankshaft slowly until valve lifter is on base circle of cam lobe. In this position, push rod will be at its lowest point. Zero dial indicator.

Jeep 6 Engines

4.2 LITER 6-CYLINDER (Cont.)

4) Rotate engine until push rod is in fully raised position and record reading. Compare recorded lobe lift with specifications. If less than specifications, replace camshaft. Check remaining cam lobes in same manner.

CAMSHAFT BEARINGS

Remove engine from vehicle to install camshaft bearings. To provide steady pressure when installing bearings, use a screw-type camshaft bearing installer tool. Do not use a driver-type bearing installer tool. Ensure oil holes in bearings are aligned with oil holes in block.

PISTONS, RINGS & PINS

OIL PAN

See Oil Pan Removal at end of ENGINE Section.

PISTON & ROD ASSEMBLY

Removal

1) Remove cylinder head and oil pan. Position piston at bottom of stroke and cover with a cloth to collect metal cuttings. Using a ridge reamer, remove any ridge or deposits on upper end of cylinder bore.

2) If necessary, mark connecting rods and caps for cylinder identification. Remove connecting rod bearing cap and bearings.

3) Install pieces of rubber hose over connecting rod bolts to protect cylinder walls and crankshaft. Push piston and rod assembly out top of cylinder block and install rod cap on mating rod.

Installation

1) Lightly coat pistons, rings, and cylinder walls with engine oil. Properly position rings on piston. *See Fig. 6.* Using ring compressor, compress rings on piston. Ensure position of rings does not change.

2) Install upper bearing into rod, and cover rod studs with protective rubber hose. Position piston in bore with arrow on piston head pointing toward front of engine.

3) Install piston and rod assembly into its respective bore, while guiding connecting rod onto crankshaft journal. Install and tighten rod cap.

FITTING PISTONS

1) Measure each cylinder bore with an inside micrometer, approximately 2 5/16" below top of cylinder bore. Using a micrometer, measure piston 90° to piston pin at centerline of pin. Difference between 2 measurements is piston-to-cylinder bore clearance.

2) Using bore gauge or inside micrometer, measure cylinder bore 90° to crankshaft at top of bore, and also at bottom of bore. Taper is the difference between the 2 measurements.

3) Turn measuring tool 120° and measure at top and bottom of bore. Turn tool another 120° and repeat measurement. Difference between the 2 measurements is out-of-round.

4) If out-of-round or taper exceed .001" (.025 mm), bore and hone cylinder for installation of oversize piston.

FITTING RINGS

1) Measure ring side clearance with feeler gauge fitted between ring land and ring. Rotate ring in groove around entire circumference of piston. Ring must not bind in groove.

2) Push ring down into bore, near bottom of ring travel. Ring must be square in bore. Measure ring end gap with feeler gauge.

3) Install rings on piston. *See Fig. 6.* Install upper and lower rings with gaps positioned 180° apart. Ensure ring markings (indicating top of ring) point up.

Fig. 6: Ring Gap Positions & Markings

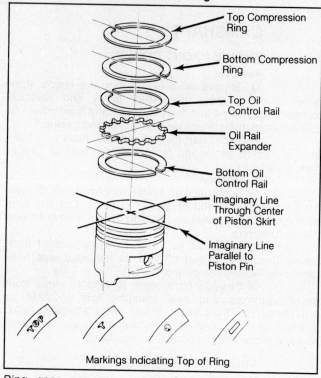

Top Compression Ring

Bottom Compression Ring

Top Oil Control Rail

Oil Rail Expander

Bottom Oil Control Rail

Imaginary Line Through Center of Piston Skirt

Imaginary Line Parallel to Piston Pin

Markings Indicating Top of Ring

Ring gaps can vary as much as 20° from positions illustrated.

PISTON PIN REPLACEMENT

Removal

Using piston pin remover/installer tool and an arbor press, press piston pin out of piston and rod assembly. Discard piston pin.

Inspection

To check replacement piston pin for fit, position piston so pin bore is in a vertical position. At room temperature, replacement pin should slide completely through pin bore without using force. If pin jams in bore, replace piston.

Installation

1) Assemble connecting rod to piston. When properly assembled, arrow on piston head will point toward front of engine, and oil hole in connecting rod will face camshaft side of engine. Use piston pin remover/installer tool and arbor press to press pin through connecting rod and piston.

2) Pin should be centered in connecting rod. The piston pin requires a 2000 lb. (907 kg.) press fit. If little effort is required to install pin in connecting rod, or if rod moves on pin, replace connecting rod.

Jeep 6 Engines

4.2 LITER 6-CYLINDER (Cont.)

CRANKSHAFT, MAIN & CONNECTING ROD BEARINGS

MAIN & CONNECTING ROD BEARINGS

Crankshaft Main Bearings

1) Check main bearing clearances one at a time. Use Plastigage method (as explained in Connecting Rod Bearings) to check main bearing clearances, tightening caps to specification.

2) When required, undersize bearings of different sizes may be used in combination to obtain correct bearing clearance. Using this method, ensure that all odd-sized bearings are installed on same side of crankshaft.

3) Never use a pair of bearings which differ more than .001" (.03 mm) in size. Bearings are available in standard, .001" (.03 mm), .002" (.05 mm), .010" (.25 mm), and .012" (.30 mm) undersize.

4) Main bearing caps are numbered 1 to 7 (front-to-rear). Main bearing journal size (except rear main) is identified in production by a color-coded paint mark on adjacent counterweight toward rear end of crankshaft. Rear main journal has a paint mark on the crankshaft rear flange.

5) To replace main bearings, remove main cap and bearing. Remove bearing from cap. Loosen all other bearing caps. Fabricate a bearing remover/installer tool, using a 7/64" cotter pin. See Fig. 7.

Fig. 7: Rear Main Bearing Remover/Installer Tool

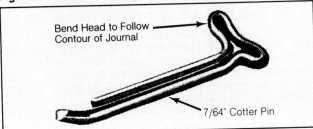

Bend Head to Follow Contour of Journal

7/64" Cotter Pin

Tool is inserted into crankshaft oil hole to aid in removal and installation.

6) Install cotter pin into crankshaft oil hole. Rotate crankshaft clockwise to force bearing out of block. Because there is no oil hole in No. 4 main journal, use a wooden tongue depressor or similar soft-faced tool to remove and install bearing.

7) Apply a light film of oil to replacement upper bearing. Start plain end of bearing into bearing tang side of block. Use cotter pin tool to push upper main bearing into place, by rotating crankshaft in opposite direction of removal. Fit lower bearing into cap. Install and tighten main cap with arrow pointing towards front of engine.

Connecting Rod Bearings

Undersize bearings of different sizes may be used in combination to achieve desired clearance. Never use a pair of bearings on same journal that differ more than .001" (.03 mm) in size. Rod journal size is identified by a color-coded paint mark on adjacent counterweight, toward rear end of crankshaft.

1) Rotate crankshaft to position connecting rod at bottom of stroke. Ensure rod cap is marked for cylinder identification. Remove connecting rod cap. Place strip of Plastigage across full width of lower bearing half, at center of bearing.

2) Install and tighten bearing cap to specification. Do not rotate crankshaft. Remove rod cap and measure width of compressed Plastigage with scale furnished.

3) Install new bearings if clearance is excessive. Lubricate crankshaft and bearing with engine oil. Install and tighten bearing cap.

THRUST BEARING ALIGNMENT

Before final tightening of No. 3 thrust bearing cap, pry crankshaft forward then rearward to align thrust faces of bearings.

REAR MAIN BEARING OIL SEAL

Removal

Remove oil pan and rear main bearing cap. Loosen remaining main bearing cap bolts. Using a brass drift, tap upper seal around crankshaft until seal protrudes enough to permit removal with pliers. Remove lower seal from bearing cap.

Installation

1) Clean crankshaft seal surface. Lightly coat lips of new seal halves with engine oil and their outer surfaces with liquid soap. See Fig. 8. Install upper seal into block with lip facing toward front of engine.

2) Install lower seal into bearing cap with lip facing front. Make sure seal is firmly seated in bearing cap recess. Apply silicone sealer to chamfered edges of bearing cap and to both sides of seal ends. See Fig. 8. Install rear main bearing cap. Tighten all main bearing cap bolts.

Fig. 8: Rear Main Bearing Oil Seal Installation

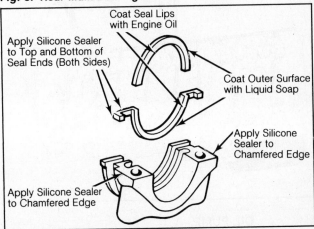

Coat Seal Lips with Engine Oil

Apply Silicone Sealer to Top and Bottom of Seal Ends (Both Sides)

Coat Outer Surface with Liquid Soap

Apply Silicone Sealer to Chamfered Edge

Apply Silicone Sealer to Chamfered Edge

Do not apply sealer to cylinder block mating surface.

ENGINE OILING

CAUTION: Always use short (4.25") oil filter on 6-cylinder CJ vehicles. Longer (5.44") oil filter may contact engine mount or frame rail and puncture, causing possible engine damage.

Crankcase Capacity

Capacity is 5 quarts (4.8L). Add 1 quart (.95L) when replacing oil filter.

Oil Filter

Replace every 7500 miles or 7 1/2 months, whichever comes first. Filter is full-flow type mounted on right side of crankcase.

Jeep 6 Engines

4.2 LITER 6-CYLINDER (Cont.)

Normal Oil Pressure

37-75 psi (2.6-5.3 kg/cm²) maximum at +1600 RPM. Minimum oil pressure should be 13 psi (.9kg/cm²) at 600 RPM.

Oil Pressure Regulator Valve

Located in pump body. Not adjustable.

ENGINE OILING SYSTEM

Oil under pressure is forced from gear-type oil pump to a full-flow oil filter. A by-pass valve is located in oil filter mounting base.

Oil flows from filter to main oil gallery. Branched passages from main oil gallery direct oil to upper main bearings. Internally drilled passages in crankshaft route oil to connecting rod journals.

Oil flows through each connecting rod, which disperses oil flow through a squirt hole in the rod. This dispersed oil lubricates camshaft lobes, distributor drive gear, cylinder walls and piston pins.

Lifters receive oil directly from main gallery, which is directed through hollow push rods to lubricate upper valve train area. Passages from main gallery lubricate camshaft bearings. Front camshaft bearing directs oil through camshaft sprocket, which slings oil to lubricate timing chain. See Fig. 9.

Fig. 9: Engine Oiling System

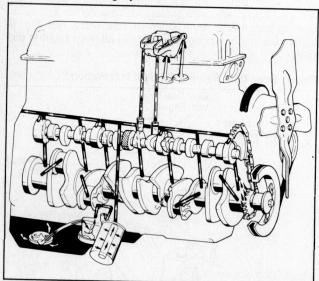

OIL PUMP

Removal & Disassembly

Drain crankcase and remove oil pan. Remove oil pump. Do not disturb position of oil inlet tube in pump body. If tube position is moved within pump body, a new tube and screen assembly must be installed to ensure an air-tight seal. Remove pump cover.

Inspection

1) Place straightedge across gears in pump body. Using feeler gauge, measure gear end clearance between pump body and straightedge. If gear end clearance is excessive, replace oil pump assembly.

2) Using feeler gauge, measure gear-to-body clearance by inserting feeler gauge between a gear tooth and pump body wall. Take measurement directly opposite the point of gear mesh. Rotate gears and measure each tooth in this manner. Replace both gears and idler shaft if not within limits.

3) If oil pressure relief valve inspection is necessary, oil inlet tube and screen assembly must be removed and replaced with a new unit. Remove cotter pin, spring retainer, spring and relief valve from pump body. Check valve and bore for sticking condition and wear, and replace as necessary.

Reassembly & Installation

1) If removed, install oil pressure relief valve, spring, retainer and cotter pin. See Fig. 10. Apply light film of non-hardening sealing compound around end of tube and drive tube into pump body. Ensure tube support bracket is aligned with bolt hole in pump body.

Fig. 10: Oil Pump Assembly

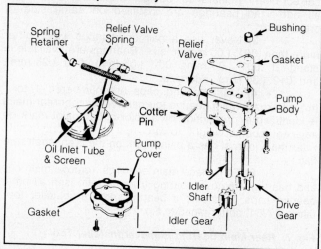

Tighten pump cover bolts to 70 INCH lbs. (8 N.m).

2) Install idler shaft, idler gear and drive gear into pump body. Prime pump by filling pump cavity with petroleum jelly. Do not use grease. Apply sealer around perimeter of pump cover. Install and tighten pump cover. Using new gasket, install and tighten oil pump. Install oil pan and refill crankcase.

OIL PUMP SPECIFICATIONS

Application	Specification In. (mm)
Gear-to-Body Clearance	.0005-.0025 (.013-.063)
Gear End Clearance	.004-.008 (.10-.20)

ENGINE COOLING

WATER PUMP

Removal

Drain cooling system. Disconnect radiator and heater hoses from pump. Remove drive belts from pump pulley. If equipped, remove fan shroud from radiator. If necessary, rotate fan shroud to facilitate water pump removal. Remove water pump and discard gasket.

Installation

Clean all gasket mating surfaces. Using new gasket, install and tighten water pump. Reverse removal procedure to complete installation.

NOTE: For information on cooling system capacities and other cooling system components, see appropriate article in "Engine Cooling Systems," at end of ENGINE Section.

Jeep 6 Engines

4.2 LITER 6-CYLINDER (Cont.)

ENGINE SPECIFICATIONS

GENERAL SPECIFICATIONS

| Year | DISPLACEMENT | | Fuel System | HP@RPM | Torque Ft. Lbs.@RPM | Compr. Ratio | BORE | | STROKE | |
	Cu. In.	Liters					In.	mm	In.	mm
1983	258	4.2	2-Bbl.	.....	.....	9.2:1	3.75	95.3	3.90	98.9

VALVES

Engine Size & Valve	Head Diam. In. (mm)	Face Angle	Seat Angle	Seat Width In. (mm)	Stem Diameter In. (mm)	Stem Clearance In. (mm)	Valve Lift In. (mm)
4.2L Int.	1.782-1.792 (45.26-45.52)	29°	30°	.040-.060 (1.02-1.52)	.3715-.3725 (9.436-9.462)	.001-.003 (.03-.08)	.405 (10.29)
Exh.	1.401-1.411 (35.59-35.84)	44°	44.5°	.040-.060 (1.02-1.52)	.3715-.3725 (9.436-9.462)	.001-.003 (.03-.08)	.405 (10.29)

PISTONS, PINS, RINGS

Engine	PISTONS Clearance In. (mm)	PINS Piston Fit In. (mm)	PINS Rod Fit In. (mm)	RINGS Ring No.	RINGS End Gap In. (mm)	RINGS Side Clearance In. (mm)
4.2L	.0009-.0017 (.023-.043)	.0003-.0005 (.008-.013)	Press Fit	1 & 2 3	.010-.020 (.25-.51) .010-.025 (.25-.64)	.0017-.0032 (.043-.081) .001-.008 (.03-.20)

CRANKSHAFT MAIN & CONNECTING ROD BEARINGS

Engine	MAIN BEARINGS Journal Diam. In. (mm)	MAIN BEARINGS Clearance In. (mm)	MAIN BEARINGS Thrust Bearing	MAIN BEARINGS Crankshaft End Play In. (mm)	CONNECTING ROD BEARINGS Journal Diam. In. (mm)	CONNECTING ROD BEARINGS Clearance In. (mm)	CONNECTING ROD BEARINGS Side Play In. (mm)
4.2L	2.4996-2.5001 (63.489-63.502)	.0010-.0025 (.025-.064)	No. 3	.0015-.0065 (.038-.165)	2.0934-2.0955 (53.172-53.226)	.0010-.0025 (.025-.064)	.010-.019 (.25-.48)

Jeep 6 Engines

4.2 LITER 6-CYLINDER (Cont.)

ENGINE SPECIFICATIONS (Cont.)

MAIN BEARING JOURNALS 1-6 COLOR CODE CHART

Journal Code & Size In. (mm)	Upper Bearing Code & Size	Lower Bearing Code & Size
Yellow [1] 2.4996-2.5001 (63.490-63.503)	Yellow Std.	Yellow Std.
Orange [2] 2.4991-2.4996 (63.477-63.490)	Yellow Std.	Black [3] .001"
Black [2] 2.4896-2.4991 (63.464-63.477)	Black [3] .001"	Black [3] .001"
Green 2.4981-2.4986 (63.452-63.464)	Black [3] .001"	Green [3] .002"
Red 2.4896-2.4901 (63.236-63.249)	Red [3] .010"	Red [3] .010"

[1] — May be fitted with Yellow (standard) and Black (.001" undersize) bearings.
[2] — May be fitted with Black (.001" undersize) and Green (.002" undersize) bearings.
[3] — Undersize.

ROD BEARING JOURNALS COLOR CODE CHART

Journal Code & Size In. (mm)	Upper Bearing Code & Size	Lower Bearing Code & Size
Yellow 2.0948-2.0955 (53.208-53.226)	Yellow Std.	Yellow Std.
Orange 2.0941-2.0948 (53.190-53.208)	Yellow Std.	Black [1] .001"
Black 2.0934-2.0941 (53.172-53.190)	Black [1] .001"	Black [1] .001"
Red 2.0848-2.0855 (52.954-52.972)	Red [1] .010"	Red [1] .010"

[1] — Undersize.

VALVE SPRINGS

Engine	Free Length In. (mm)	PRESSURE Lbs. @ In. (Kg @ mm)	
		Valve Closed	Valve Open
4.2L	1.99 (50.5)	64-72@1.79 (29-33@45.5)	188-202@1.41 (85-92@35.8)

MAIN BEARING JOURNAL 7 COLOR CODE CHART

Journal Code & Size In. (mm)	Upper Bearing Code & Size	Lower Bearing Code & Size
Yellow 2.4990-2.4995 (63.475-63.487)	Yellow Std.	Yellow Std.
Orange 2.4985-2.4990 (63.462-63.475)	Yellow Std.	Black [1] .001"
Black 2.4980-2.4985 (63.449-63.462)	Black [1] .001"	Black [1] .001"
Green 2.4975-2.4980 (63.437-63.449)	Black [1] .001"	Green [1] .002"
Red 2.4890-2.4895 (63.220-63.233)	Red [1] .010"	Red [1] .010"

[1] — Undersize.

CAMSHAFT

Engine	Journal Diam. In. (mm)	Clearance In. (mm)	Lobe Lift In. (mm)
4.2L			
No. 1	2.029-2.030 (51.54-51.56)	.001-.003 (.03-.08)	.253 (6.43)
No. 2	2.019-2.020 (51.28-51.31)	.001-.003 (.03-.08)	.253 (6.43)
No. 3	2.009-2.010 (51.03-51.05)	.001-.003 (.03-.08)	.253 (6.43)
No. 4	1.999-2.000 (50.77-50.80)	.001-.003 (.03-.08)	.253 (6.43)

TIGHTENING SPECIFICATIONS

Application	Ft. Lbs. (N.m)
Camshaft Sprocket Bolts	50 (68)
Connecting Rod Cap Nuts	33 (45)
Cylinder Head Bolts	85 (115)
Engine Front Cover Bolts	16 (22)
Exhuast Manifold Bolts & Nuts	23 (31)
Flywheel-to-Crankshaft Bolts	105 (142)
Intake Manifold Bolts	23 (32)
Main Bearing Cap Bolts	80 (108)
Oil Pump Cover Bolts	6 (8)
Oil Pump Attaching Bolts	
Short	10 (14)
Long	17 (23)
Rocker Arm Bolts	19 (26)
Vibration Damper Bolt	80 (108)
Water Pump Bolts	13 (18)

Jeep V8 Engines

6.0 LITER V8

ENGINE CODING

ENGINE IDENTIFICATION

Engine code number located on a plate attached to front of right rocker cover. Letter portion of code identifies engine displacement, carburetor type, and compression ratio.

ENGINE IDENTIFICATION CODE

Engine	Code
6.0L 2-Bbl.	N

SPECIAL ENGINE MARKINGS

Some engines are produced at factory with oversize or undersize components. These engines are identified by a letter code stamped adjacent to engine code number on right valve cover. Letters are decoded as follows:

- "B" indicates all cylinder bores .010 (.25 mm) oversize.
- "C" indicates all camshaft bearing bores .010 (.25 mm) oversize.
- "F" indicates all connecting rod bearings .010" (.25 mm) undersize.
- "M" indicates all main bearing journals .010 (.25 mm) undersize.
- "PM" indicates all connecting rod and main bearings .010 (.25 mm) undersize.

ENGINE REMOVAL

See Engine Removal at end of ENGINE Section.

MANIFOLDS & CYLINDER HEAD

INTAKE MANIFOLD

Removal

1) Drain coolant from radiator and cylinder block. Remove air cleaner. Disconnect spark plug wires from spark plugs and position wires and plastic separators away from intake manifold area.

2) Disconnect upper radiator hose, by-pass and heater hoses from intake manifold. Disconnect primary and secondary ignition wires from coil. Remove coil and bracket.

3) Label and disconnect all electrical connectors, ventilation hoses and vacuum hoses from intake manifold, carburetor and distributor. Disconnect fuel line from carburetor. Disconnect throttle linkages from carburetor and intake manifold, and position aside.

4) Disconnect air pump hoses from air pump and injection manifolds. Position hoses and diverter valve aside. Remove carburetor. Remove intake manifold. Discard gasket and seals.

Installation

1) Clean all gasket mating surfaces. Coat both sides of new gaskets with non-hardening sealer. Position gaskets onto cylinder heads. Install new end seals. Apply non-hardening sealer to seal ends.

2) Install and tighten intake manifold. Install remaining components in reverse order of removal.

EXHAUST MANIFOLD

Removal

1) Disconnect ignition wires. Disconnect air hose at injection manifold. Disconnect exhaust pipe at exhaust manifold.

2) Remove exhaust manifold retaining screws. Separate exhaust manifold from cylinder head. Remove air injection manifold, fittings and washers.

Installation

1) Clean all gasket mating surfaces. Install air injection manifold on exhaust manifold.

2) Install and tighten exhaust manifold. Install and tighten remaining components in reverse order of removal.

CYLINDER HEAD

Removal

1) Disconnect negative battery cable. Drain cooling system and cylinder block. Remove air cleaner and rocker arm covers. Alternately loosen rocker arm bolts 1 turn at a time to avoid damage to bridges, and remove rocker arm assemblies and push rods. Keep rocker arm assemblies and push rods in order for reinstallation in original locations.

2) Remove spark plugs. Remove intake and exhaust manifolds. Loosen all drive belts. If A/C equipped, remove compressor mounting bracket. Disconnect alternator support brace from cylinder head.

3) Remove air pump and power steering pumps and their respective mounting brackets, and position aside. Remove cylinder heads and discard gaskets.

Installation

1) Clean threads of head bolts and threads in cylinder block. Clean all gasket mating surfaces. Apply an even coat of sealer to both sides of head gaskets. Position gasket on block with stamped word "TOP" facing upward.

2) Install and tighten cylinder head. *See Fig. 1.* To complete installation, reverse removal procedure. It is not necessary to retighten head bolts after engine has been operated.

Fig. 1: Cylinder Head Tightening Sequence

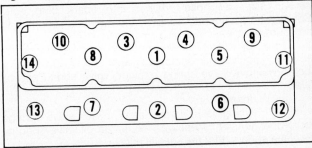

Tighten head bolts to 110 ft. lbs. (149 N.m)

VALVES

VALVE ARRANGEMENT

E-I-I-E-E-I-I-E (Both banks, front to rear)

ROCKER ARM ASSEMBLY

Both intake and exhaust rocker arms for each cylinder pivot on a bridge and pivot assembly. *See Fig. 2.* The bridge and pivot assembly maintains correct rocker arm-to-valve tip alignment. When removing rocker arm assemblies, always keep parts in order for reinstallation in original locations.

Jeep V8 Engines

6.0 LITER V8 (Cont.)

Fig. 2: Rocker Arm Assembly

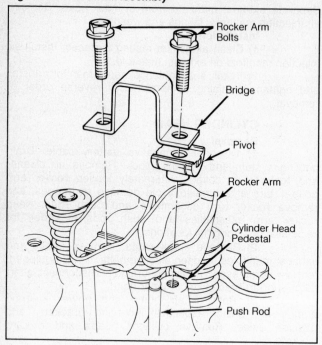

Tighten rocker arm bolts to 19 ft. lbs. (25 N.m).

VALVE SPRINGS

Although normal service is performed with cylinder head removed, it is possible to replace seals, locks, retainers, or borken springs with cylinder head installed.

Removal

1) Remove air cleaner. Remove rocker arm cover. Remove bridge and pivot assemblies, rocker arm, and push rod of valve to be serviced.

2) Remove spark plug and install 14 mm (thread size) air hose adapter into spark plug hole. Connect an air hose to adapter and maintain constant air pressure of at least 90 psi (6.3 kg/cm²).

3) Using valve spring compressor tool (J-22534 or equivalent), compress valve spring and remove locks. Remove valve spring retainer, valve spring and oil seal.

Inspection

Using valve spring tester, check valve springs for proper tension. Measure free length of valve springs. Replace springs that fail specification.

Installation

1) Use a 7/16" deep-well socket and light hammer to gently tap valve stem seal into place on valve stem. Ensure sharp edges of valve lock groove do not damage oil seal during installation. Install valve spring with closed-coil end down, then install retainer.

2) Compress spring with valve spring compressor tool, and install locks. Tap each valve spring from side to side to ensure spring is seated properly. Turn off air supply and remove air hose and adapter. Install remaining components in reverse order of removal.

VALVE STEM OIL SEALS

Nylon valve stem seals are used on all valves. Replace seals whenever they become deteriorated, or valve service is performed. Use a 7/16" deep-well socket and light mallet to seat valve seals onto stems. Ensure sharp edges of valve lock groove do not damage seal during installation.

VALVE GUIDE SERVICING

Valve guides are integral with cylinder head and are not replaceable. Replacement valves are available with .003" (.08 mm), .015" (.38 mm), and .030" (.76 mm) oversize stems.

1) Clean valve guide bore with solvent and a rifle brush. Use a ball gauge and micrometer to measure guide wear. Take measurements of guide crosswise and lengthwise to head, inserting ball gauge 3/8" into guide bore from top of head.

2) Difference between the two measurements is guide bore out-of-round. Ream valve guides if out-of-round measurement exceeds .0025" (.06 mm).

3) If guide measures more than .003" (.08 mm) larger than guide bore diameter listed in specifications, ream valve guide for installation of valve with oversize stem.

4) Always ream valve guides in progressive steps, using reamers in sequence to obtain desired size.

HYDRAULIC VALVE LIFTERS

1) Service lifters as complete assemblies only. Parts are not interchangeable between lifters. Inspect lifter body for signs of scuffing. Inspect base of lifter for concave wear. If concave wear is present, replacement of camshaft and lifters is necessary.

2) Disassemble and clean lifters, then reassemble. *See Fig. 3.* Using lifter leak-down rate tester and lifter test fluid, test lifter leak-down. Compress lifter plunger and record time required for tester needle to align with .125" mark on scale. Leak-down rate should be 20-110 seconds.

3) Replace lifters that fail test. Do not attempt to prime lifters with engine oil prior to installation. Lifters will fill with oil within 3-8 minutes of engine operation. Discard tappets not within specifications.

Fig. 3: Hydraulic Valve Lifter Assembly

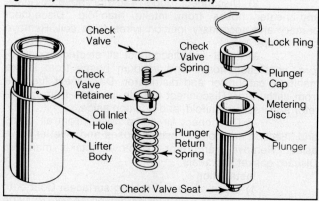

Do not interchange parts between lifters.

CAMSHAFT

ENGINE FRONT COVER

Removal

1) Drain radiator and cylinder block. Disconnect radiator hoses, heater hose and by-pass hose from

6.0 LITER V8 (Cont.)

manifold and water pump. Remove all drive belts. Remove fan and hub assembly. If A/C equipped, remove compressor and bracket from engine and position aside. Do not disconnect A/C hoses.

2) Remove alternator and mounting bracket. Remove idler pulley. If equipped, remove power steering pump and bracket assembly. Remove air pump and mounting bracket as an assembly, with hoses attached. Remove fuel pump and distributor. Remove crankshaft damper pulley and vibration damper.

3) Remove front oil pan bolts. Remove bolts attaching front cover-to-cylinder block, noting their lengths and locations for reinstallation in same positions. Remove front cover. Remove front cover lower locating dowel pin from cylinder block.

Installation

1) Use sharp tool to cut both sides of oil pan gasket flush with engine block. Using cut pieces as a template, cut and fit replacement gasket pieces from new gasket. Clean all gasket mating surfaces. Install new front oil pan seal to bottom of front cover.

2) Align tabs of replacement oil pan gasket pieces with oil pan seal on front cover and cement into place on bottom of front cover. Apply non-hardening sealer to both sides of front cover gasket and install on front cover. Apply non-hardening sealer to oil pan-to-cylinder block junctions.

3) Place front cover in position on cylinder block and install front oil pan bolts. Tighten bolts slowly and evenly until cover aligns with upper locating dowel pin. Insert lower locating dowel pin through appropriate hole in front cover, and drive pin into cylinder block.

4) Install and tighten remaining front cover bolts. Install remaining components in reverse order of removal. Fill cooling system. Start engine and inspect for oil and coolant leaks.

FRONT COVER OIL SEAL

Removal

Loosen all drive belts. Remove crankshaft pulley and vibration damper. Use oil seal remover tool (J-9256) to remove oil seal.

Installation

Clean seal contact surface of vibration damper, then lubricate with engine oil. Apply non-hardening sealer to outer metal case of new seal. Position seal into recess in front cover. Using seal installer tool (J-26562), install front seal. Install remaining components.

TIMING CHAIN & SPROCKETS

Removal

Remove front cover and oil slinger. Rotate crankshaft until timing marks on sprockets are aligned. Remove camshaft sprocket bolt, washer, distributor drive gear and fuel pump eccentric. Remove timing chain and both sprockets as an assembly.

Installation

1) Assemble timing chain over camshaft and crankshaft sprockets with timing marks on sprockets aligned. See Fig. 4. Install chain and sprockets as an assembly. Ensure timing marks on sprockets are aligned.

2) Install remaining components while noting the following: Fuel pump eccentric must be installed with stamped word "REAR" facing camshaft. Camshaft washer fits into recess in distributor drive gear.

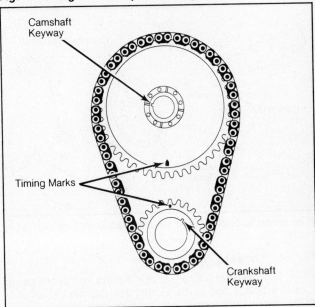

Fig. 4: Timing Chain & Sprocket Alignment

Camshaft Keyway

Timing Marks

Crankshaft Keyway

Tighten camshaft sprocket bolt to 30 ft. lbs. (41 N.m).

VALVE TIMING

1) Remove spark plugs. Remove left rocker arm cover. Remove bridge and pivot assemblies and rocker arms from No. 1 cylinder.

2) Rotate crankshaft until No. 6 piston is on TDC at end of compression stroke. Rotate crankshaft counterclockwise 90° (as viewed from front of engine).

3) Install dial indicator on No. 1 intake valve push rod end. Use rubber hose to secure indicator point to end of push rod. Dial indicator point must be in same plane as push rod vertical movement. Zero dial indicator.

4) Slowly rotate crankshaft in direction of normal rotation until dial indicator shows .020" lift. Timing mark on vibration damper should align with TDC mark on timing scale. If timing mark is off more than 1/2" in either direction, valve timing is incorrect.

CAMSHAFT

Removal

1) Drain radiator and cylinder block. Remove radiator. If A/C equipped, remove condenser and receiver assembly as a charged unit. Remove rocker arm covers. Remove bridge and pivot assemblies, rocker arms and push rods in order, for reinstallation in original locations.

2) Remove intake manifold. Remove valve lifters in order for reinstallation in original locations. Remove front cover. Rotate crankshaft to align timing marks on camshaft and crankshaft sprockets.

3) Remove timing chain and sprockets as an assembly. Remove hood latch support bracket. Remove front bumper or grille (as required). Remove camshaft.

Installation

To install camshaft, reverse removal procedures while noting the following: Heavily coat camshaft and lifters with an engine oil supplement prior to installation. Fuel pump eccentric must be installed with stamped word "REAR" facing camshaft sprocket. Camshaft washer fits into recess in distributor drive gear. See Fig. 5.

Jeep V8 Engines
6.0 LITER V8 (Cont.)

Fig. 5: Camshaft Assembly

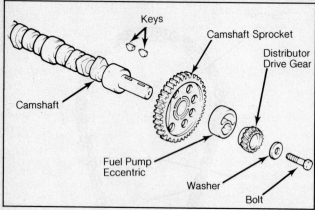

Fuel pump eccentric must be installed with stamped word "REAR" facing camshaft sprocket.

CAM LOBE LIFT

1) Remove rocker arm covers and spark plugs. Remove bridge and pivot assemblies and rocker arms in order, for reinstallation in original locations.

2) Using mounting fixture, attach dial indicator to cylinder head so indicator point rests on top of push rod. Use a piece of rubber hose to secure indicator point to end of push rod. Dial indicator point must be in same plane as push rod vertical movement. *See Fig. 6.*

3) Rotate crankshaft slowly until valve lifter is on base circle of cam lobe. In this position, push rod will be at its lowest travel. Zero dial indicator.

4) Rotate engine until push rod is in fully raised position and record reading. Correct lobe lift is .260-.270" (6.60-6.86 mm). If less than specifications, replace camshaft and lifters. Check remaining cam lobes in same manner.

Fig. 6: Dial Indicator Installation for Checking Cam Lobe Lift & Valve Timing

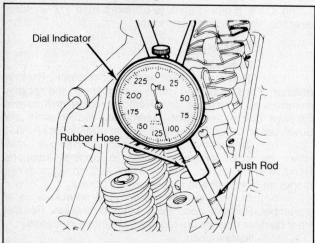

Correct cam lobe lift is .260-.270" (6.60-6.86 mm).

CAMSHAFT BEARINGS

Remove engine from vehicle to install camshaft bearings. Use screw-type camshaft bearing remover/installer tool (J-21054-1) and proper adapters, to replace camshaft bearings. Do not use a driver-type

bearing remover/installer tool. Ensure oil holes in bearings are aligned with oil holes in block.

PISTONS, RINGS & PINS

OIL PAN
See Oil Pan Removal at end of ENGINE Section.

PISTON & ROD ASSEMBLY
Removal
1) Remove cylinder heads and oil pan. Position piston at bottom of stroke and cover with a cloth to collect metal cuttings. Using a ridge reamer, remove any ridge or deposits on upper end of cylinder bore.

2) If necessary, mark connecting rods and caps for cylinder identification. Remove connecting rod bearing cap and bearings.

3) Install pieces of rubber hose over connecting rod bolts to protect cylinder walls and crankshaft. Push piston and rod assembly out top of cylinder block and install rod cap on mating rod.

Installation
1) Lightly coat piston, rings, and cylinder wall with engine oil. Properly position rings on piston. *See Fig. 7.* Using ring compressor, compress rings on piston. Ensure position of rings does not change.

2) Install upper bearing into rod, and cover rod studs with protective rubber hose. Position piston in bore with notches on piston head pointing toward front of engine.

3) Install piston and rod assembly into its respective bore, while guiding connecting rod onto crankshaft journal. Install and tighten rod cap.

FITTING PISTONS
1) Measure each cylinder bore approximately 2 5/16" below top of cylinder bore. Measure each piston 90° to piston pin at centerline of pin. Difference between the two measurements is piston-to-cylinder bore clearance.

2) Using bore gauge or inside micrometer, measure cylinder bore 90° to crankshaft at top of bore, and also at bottom of bore. Taper is the difference between the two measurements.

3) Turn measuring tool 120° and measure at top and bottom of bore. Turn tool another 120° and repeat measurement. Difference between the two measurements is out-of-round.

4) If out-of-round exceeds .003" (.08 mm), or taper exceeds .005" (.13 mm), bore and hone cylinder for installation of oversize piston.

FITTING RINGS
1) Measure ring side clearance with feeler gauge fitted between ring land and ring. Measure clearance while rotating ring in groove. Ring must not bind in groove.

2) Measure end gap of each compression ring in cylinder bore. Push a ring down into bore, near bottom of ring travel. Ring must be square in bore. Measure ring end gap with feeler gauge.

3) Install rings on piston. *See Fig. 7.* Install upper and lower rings with gaps positioned 180° apart. Ensure ring markings (indicating top of ring), point upward.

Fig. 7: Ring Gap Positions & Markings

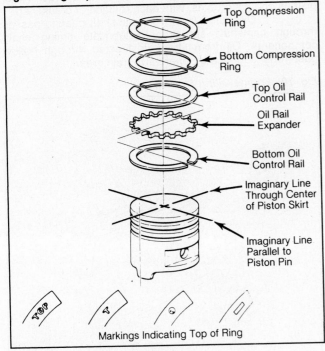

Markings Indicating Top of Ring

Ring gaps can vary as much as 20° from positions illustrated.

PISTON PIN REPLACEMENT
Removal
Using piston pin remover/installer tool and an arbor press, press piston pin out of piston and rod assembly. Discard piston pin.

Inspection
To check replacement piston pin for fit, position piston so pin bore is in a vertical position. At room temperature, replacement pin should slide completely through pin bore without using force. If pin jams in bore, replace piston.

Installation
1) Assemble connecting rod to piston so that notches on piston head will face forward and connecting rod squirt hole will face inward, when assembly is installed in engine. Use piston pin remover/installer tool and arbor press to press pin through connecting rod and piston.

2) Pin should be centered in connecting rod. The piston pin requires a 2000 lb. (907 kg.) press fit. If little effort is required to install pin in connecting rod, or if rod moves on pin, replace connecting rod.

CRANKSHAFT, MAIN & CONNECTING ROD BEARINGS

MAIN & CONNECTING ROD BEARINGS

NOTE: Plastigage method is used for checking bearing clearances. The following procedures are with oil pan removed and oil film removed from surfaces to be checked.

Crankshaft Main Bearings
1) Check main bearing clearances one at a time. Use Plastigage method (as explained in Connecting Rod Bearings) to check main bearing clearances, tightening caps to specification.

2) When required, undersize bearings of different sizes may be used in combination to obtain correct bearing clearance. Using this method, ensure that all odd-sized bearings are installed on same side of crankshaft. Never use a pair of bearings that differ more than .001" (.03 mm) in size.

3) Main bearing caps are numbered 1 to 5 (front to rear). Main journal size (except rear main) is identified in production by a color-coded paint mark on adjacent counterweight toward rear end of crankshaft. Rear main journal has a paint mark on the crankshaft rear flange.

4) To replace main bearings, remove main cap and bearing. Remove bearing from cap. Loosen all other bearing caps. Fabricate a bearing remover/installer tool, using a 7/64" cotter pin. See Fig. 8.

Fig. 8: Rear Main Bearing Remover/Installer Tool

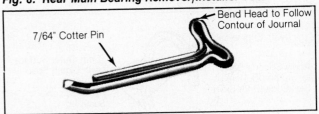

7/64" Cotter Pin

Bend Head to Follow Contour of Journal

Tool is inserted 1/2" into crankshaft oil hole to aid in bearing removal and installation.

5) Install cotter pin into crankshaft oil hole. Rotate crankshaft in direction of bearing tang slot in block to force bearing out of block.

6) Apply a light film of oil to new upper bearing. Start plain end of bearing into bearing tang side of block. Use cotter pin tool to push upper main bearing into place, by rotating crankshaft in opposite direction of removal.

7) Install remaining bearings using same procedure. Install lower bearings into caps. Install and tighten main caps with arrows pointing toward front of engine.

Connecting Rod Bearings
1) Undersize bearings of different sizes may be used in combination to achieve desired clearance. Never use a pair of bearings on same journal that differ more than .001" (.03 mm) in size. Rod journal size is identified by a color-coded paint mark on adjacent counterweight, toward rear end of crankshaft.

2) Rotate crankshaft to position connecting rod at bottom of stroke. Ensure rod cap is marked for cylinder identification. Remove connecting rod cap. Place strip of Plastigage across full width of lower bearing half, at center of bearing.

3) Install and tighten bearing cap to specification. Do not rotate crankshaft. Remove rod cap and measure width of compressed Plastigage with scale furnished. Install new bearings if clearance is excessive. Lubricate crankshaft and bearing with engine oil prior to installation.

THRUST BEARING ALIGNMENT
Before final tightening of No. 3 thrust bearing cap, pry crankshaft forward then rearward to align thrust faces of bearings.

REAR MAIN BEARING OIL SEAL
Removal
Remove oil pan and rear main bearing cap. Loosen remaining main bearing cap bolts. Using a brass drift, tap upper seal around crankshaft until seal protrudes enough to permit removal with pliers. Remove lower seal from bearing cap.

Installation
1) Clean crankshaft seal surface. Lightly coat lips of new seal halves with engine oil and outer surface of seal case with liquid soap. *See Fig. 9.* Install upper seal into block with lip facing toward front of engine.

2) Install lower seal into bearing cap with lip facing front. Make sure seal is firmly seated in bearing cap recess. Apply silicone sealer to chamfered edges of bearing cap and to both sides of seal ends. *See Fig. 9.* Install rear main bearing cap. Tighten all main bearing cap bolts.

Fig. 9: Rear Main Bearing Oil Seal Installation

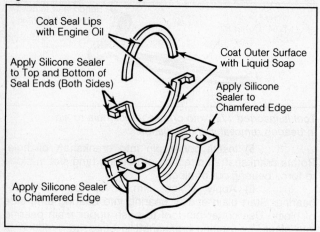

Coat Seal Lips with Engine Oil

Apply Silicone Sealer to Top and Bottom of Seal Ends (Both Sides)

Coat Outer Surface with Liquid Soap

Apply Silicone Sealer to Chamfered Edge

Apply Silicone Sealer to Chamfered Edge

Do not apply sealer to cylinder block mating surface.

ENGINE OILING

Crankcase Capacity
Capacity is 4 quarts (3.8L). Add 1 quart (.95L) when replacing oil filter.

Oil Filter
Replace filter every 7500 miles or 7 1/2 months, whichever comes first. Filter is full-flow type, mounted on engine front cover.

Normal Oil Pressure
37-75 psi (2.6-5.3 kg/cm²) maximum at +1600 RPM. Minimum oil pressure should be 13 psi (.9 kg/cm²) at 600 RPM.

Oil Pressure Regulator Valve
Located in pump body, not adjustable.

ENGINE OILING SYSTEM
Oil is forced from a gear-type oil pump to a full-flow oil filter. Oil is directed to right main oil gallery through a passage that extends internally up left front side of cylinder block. A passage that intersects with right main oil gallery directs oil to left main oil gallery.

Right and left main oil galleries directly lubricate lifters. Passages extend down from right oil gallery to lubricate camshaft and crankshaft bearings.

Crankshaft is internally drilled to provide oil to connecting rod bearings and journals. A squirt hole in each connecting rod cap disperses oil to cylinder walls, pistons and piston pins, with each rotation of crankshaft.

Oil routed from front camshaft bearing passes through camshaft sprocket to lubricate timing chain components. Oil from lifters is directed through hollow push rods to lubricate upper valve train area.

Fig. 10: Engine Oiling System

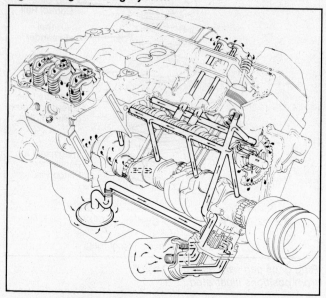

OIL PUMP
Removal & Disassembly
Remove retaining bolts and separate oil pump cover, gasket and oil filter as an assembly from pump body (engine front cover). Slide drive gear, idler gear and idler shaft out of pump body. Unscrew oil pressure relief valve cap and remove spring and plunger from pump cover. Thoroughly clean all parts.

Inspection
1) The Plastigage method (preferred) or the feeler gauge method (alternate) can be used to measure gear end clearance. Using either method, ensure the pump gears are up into pump body as far as possible, to accurately determine clearance.

2) Using Plastigage method, place strip of Plastigage across full width of each gear. Install pump cover and gasket and tighten to specification. Remove pump cover and measure width of compressed Plastigage with scale furnished.

3) Using feeler gauge method, place straight-edge across gears and pump body. Insert feeler gauge between straightedge and pump body to measure clearance.

4) With gears installed in pump body, insert feeler gauge between gear tooth and inner wall of pump body, directly opposite point of gear mesh. Rotate gears and measure clearance between each gear tooth and pump body in same manner.

5) Check relief valve plunger for wear or binding in pump cover. If wear is apparent or binding occurs, replace pump cover and relief valve plunger.

Reassembly & Installation
Install oil pressure relief valve, spring and retaining cap into pump cover. Install idler shaft, idler gear and drive gear into pump body. Fill gear cavity with petroleum jelly to properly prime pump. Do not use grease

Jeep V8 Engines

6.0 LITER V8 (Cont.)

of any type. Using new gasket, install and tighten pump cover.

OIL PUMP SPECIFICATIONS

Application	Specification In. (mm)
Gear End Clearance	
Plastigage Method	.002-.008 (.05-.20)
Feeler Gauge Method	.004-.008 (.10-.20)
Gear-to-Body Clearance	.0005-.0025 (.013-.064)

ENGINE COOLING

WATER PUMP

Removal

1) Disconnect negative battery cable. Drain radiator and remove upper radiator hose. Loosen all drive belts. If equipped with fan shroud, separate shroud from radiator, then install one radiator/shroud bolt to retain radiator in place.

2) Remove fan and hub from water pump. Remove fan and shroud from engine compartment. If A/C equipped, remove mounting stud from water pump that compressor bracket is secured to. Remove alternator and bracket and position aside.

3) If power steering equipped, remove front half of power steering bracket from water pump mounting stud. Disconnect all coolant hoses from water pump. Remove water pump and discard gasket.

Installation

Clean all gasket mating surfaces. Check front cover cavity for corrosion. Using new gasket, install and tighten water pump. To complete installation, reverse removal procedures.

NOTE: **For information on cooling system capacities and other cooling system components, see appropriate article in "Engine Cooling Systems," at end of ENGINE Section.**

TIGHTENING SPECIFICATIONS

Application	Ft. Lbs. (N.m)
Camshaft Sprocket Bolt	30 (41)
Connecting Rod Cap Nuts	33 (45)
Cylinder Head Bolts	110 (149)
Engine Front Cover Bolts	25 (34)
Exhaust Manifold	
2 Center Bolts	25 (34)
4 Outer Bolts	15 (20)
Flywheel-to-Crankshaft Bolts	105 (142)
Intake Manifold Bolts	43 (58)
Main Bearing Cap Bolts	100 (136)
Oil Pump Cover Bolts	5 (7)
Rocker Arm Bolts	19 (26)
Vibration Damper Bolt	[1] 90 (122)
Water Pump Bolts	4 (5)

[1] — Bolt threads clean and lubricated.

ENGINE SPECIFICATIONS

GENERAL SPECIFICATIONS

Year	DISPLACEMENT Cu. In.	DISPLACEMENT Liters	Fuel System	HP@RPM	Torque Ft. Lbs.@RPM	Compr. Ratio	BORE In.	BORE mm	STROKE In.	STROKE mm
1983	360	6.0	2-Bbl.	.....	.....	8.25:1	4.08	103.6	3.44	87.4

VALVES

Engine Size & Valve	Head Diam. In. (mm)	Face Angle	Seat Angle	Seat Width In. (mm)	Stem Diameter In. (mm)	Stem Clearance In. (mm)	Valve Lift In. (mm)
6.0L Int.	2.020-2.030 (51.31-51.56)	29°	30°	.040-.060 (1.02-1.52)	.3715-.3725 (9.44-9.46)	.001-.003 (.03-.08)	.426 (10.82)
Exh.	1.675-1.685 (42.55-42.90)	44°	44.5°	.040-.060 (1.02-1.52)	.3715-.3725 (9.44-9.46)	.001-.003 (.03-.08)	.426 (10.82)

Jeep V8 Engines

6.0 LITER V8 (Cont.)

ENGINE SPECIFICATIONS (Cont.)

PISTONS, PINS, RINGS

	PISTONS	PINS		RINGS		
Engine	Clearance In. (mm)	Piston Fit In. (mm)	Rod Fit In. (mm)	Ring No.	End Gap In. (mm)	Side Clearance In. (mm)
6.0L	.0012-.0020 (.030-.051)	.0003-.0005 (.008-.013)	Press Fit	1	.010-.020 (.25-.51)	.0015-.0030 (.038-.076)
				2	.010-.020 (.25-.51)	.0015-.0035 (.038-.089)
				3	.015-.045 (.38-1.14)	.000-.007 (.00-.18)

CAMSHAFT

Engine	Journal Diam. In. (mm)	Clearance In. (mm)	Lobe Lift In. (mm)
6.0L			
No. 1	2.1195-2.1205 (53.835-53.861)	.001-.003 (.03-.08)	.266 (6.76)
No. 2	2.0895-2.0905 (53.073-53.099)	.001-.003 (.03-.08)	.266 (6.76)
No. 3	2.0595-2.0605 (52.311-52.337)	.001-.003 (.03-.08)	.266 (6.76)
No. 4	2.0295-2.0305 (51.549-51.575)	.001-.003 (.03-.08)	.266 (6.76)
No. 5	1.9995-2.0005 (50.787-50.815)	.001-.003 (.03-.08)	.266 (6.76)

VALVE SPRINGS

Engine	Free Length In. (mm)	PRESSURE Lbs. @ In. (Kg @ mm)	
		Valve Closed	Valve Open
6.0L	1.99 (50.5)	64-72@1.79 (29-33@45.5)	202-220@1.36 (92-100@34.5)

CHRYSLER CORP.

6-CYLINDER ENGINE

3.7L

1) Disconnect battery ground cable. Remove engine oil dipstick. Raise vehicle and support with safety stands. Drain engine oil.

2) Remove engine-to-transmission strut. Remove torque converter inspection cover plate (if equipped with automatic transmission). Remove oil pan retaining bolts and oil pan.

3) When installing, apply a drop of sealer on 4 corners of rubber seal and cork gasket. California engines require a high temperature left side oil pan gasket.

V8 ENGINES

5.2L & 5.9L

1) Disconnect battery ground cable. Remove engine oil dipstick. Raise vehicle and support with safety stands. Drain engine oil.

2) Remove exhaust crossover pipe. Remove left engine-to-transmission support strut. Remove torque converter inspection cover plate (if equipped with automatic transmission). Remove oil pan retaining bolts and oil pan.

3) When installing, apply a drop of sealer to corners of rubber seal and cork gasket. On 5.9L engines, ensure notches on side gaskets align with corresponding notches on engine block.

FORD

4-CYLINDER ENGINES

2.0L & 2.3L

1) Remove air cleaner assembly. Remove engine oil dipstick. Remove engine mount retaining nuts. Disconnect oil cooler lines at radiator.

2) Remove fan shroud. If equipped with automatic transmission, remove radiator attaching bolts and raise and support radiator.

3) On all vehicles, raise vehicle on hoist. Drain crankcase. Remove starter. Disconnect exhaust manifold tube at thermactor check valve.

4) Remove transmission mount nuts. On vehicles with automatic transmission, remove bellcrank from converter housing. Disconnect oil cooler line retainer from engine block. Remove front crossmember.

5) On vehicles with manual transmissions, disconnect right front lower shock absorber mount.

6) On all vehicles, position a jack under engine and raise engine. Place a 2 1/2" block of wood under engine to support it. Remove jack.

7) On vehicles with automatic transmissions, place a jack under transmission and raise slightly.

8) On all vehicles, remove oil pan retaining bolts and lower pan to chassis. Remove oil pump drive and pickup tube assembly. Remove oil pan from vehicle.

2.2L DIESEL

1) Disconnect battery cables from both batteries. Remove engine oil dipstick. Disconnect air intake hose from air cleaner and intake manifold.

2) Drain cooling system. Remove cooling fan and fan shroud. Disconnect radiator hoses from radiator. Remove radiator.

3) Disconnect and plug fuel inlet and outlet lines at fuel pump. Remove fuel filter from mounting bracket. Remove fuel filter bracket from cylinder head.

4) Remove engine mount nuts. Raise vehicle on hoist. Loosen transmission mount bolts. Drain crankcase. Remove primary oil filter from left side of engine.

5) Remove by-pass filter mounting bracket and hoses. Lower vehicle from hoist. Attach a lifting device to engine.

6) Raise engine until engine mount studs clear mounts. Slide engine forward and lift engine about 3". Install wood blocks between mounts and engine.

7) Lower engine onto blocks. Remove engine lifting device and raise vehicle on hoist.

8) Remove oil pan attaching bolts and lower oil pan onto crossmember. Disconnect oil pump pickup tube and lay it in oil pan. Remove oil pan from vehicle.

6-CYLINDER ENGINE

4.9L

Bronco & Pickup Models

1) Drain crankcase and cooling system. Remove radiator. On California vehicles, disconnect hoses to air by-pass/air control valve and remove valve.

2) On all vehicles, raise vehicle on hoist. Remove starter. Remove front engine mount nuts. Raise front of engine with transmission jack.

3) Place 1" blocks of wood under engine mounts. Lower engine onto blocks and remove transmission jack.

4) Remove oil pan bolts and lower pan to crossmember. Remove oil pump inlet tube bolts and lay tube in bottom of pan. Remove oil pan.

Van Models

1) Remove engine cover, air cleaner and carburetor. If equipped with air conditioning, discharge refrigerant and remove compressor.

2) Remove EGR valve. On E350 models, remove thermactor check valve. On all models, remove upper radiator hose. Remove fan shroud.

3) If equipped with automatic transmission, remove transmission fill tube. On all models, remove exhaust pipe-to-manifold bolts.

4) Raise vehicle on hoist. Disconnect and plug fuel pump inlet line. Remove alternator heat shield and front engine mount nuts.

5) Disconnect lower radiator hose and transmission cooler lines. Remove power steering return line clip located in front of crossmember.

6) Remove starter and engine oil dipstick tube. Raise engine and place 3" blocks under engine mounts. Lower engine and remove jack.

7) Remove oil pan bolts. Remove oil pump pickup tube and screen from oil pump. Remove oil pan.

Oil Pan Removal
FORD (Cont.)

V6 ENGINES

2.8L

1) Disconnect negative battery cable at battery. Remove air cleaner assembly. Remove fan shroud and position over fan.

2) Remove distributor cap and position away from firewall. Remove distributor from engine. Remove front engine mount attaching nuts.

3) Remove engine oil dipstick tube. Raise vehicle on hoist. Remove transmission fill tube from transmission oil pan and plug hole (auto. trans.).

4) Remove oil filter. Disconnect exhaust pipes from exhaust manifolds. Disconnect oil cooler bracket and lower cooler assembly. Remove starter motor.

5) Disconnect front stabilizer bar and position forward. Place a jack under engine and raise engine as far as possible.

6) Place wood blocks between engine mounts and frame. Lower engine and remove jack. Remove oil pan attaching bolts and lower oil pan.

7) Remove oil pump pickup tube and lower into oil pan. Remove oil pan from vehicle.

3.8L

1) Disconnect negative battery cable. Remove air cleaner, fan shroud and engine oil dipstick. Raise vehicle on a hoist.

2) Drain engine oil and remove oil filter. Disconnect exhaust pipes from exhaust manifolds. Disconnect transmission shift linkage at transmission.

3) Disconnect transmission oil cooler lines at radiator. Remove engine support nuts. Using a jack, raise engine as high as possible.

4) Place wood blocks between engine supports and brackets. Lower engine and remove jack. Remove oil pan attaching bolts and lower oil pan.

5) Remove oil pump pickup tube and lay tube in bottom of pan. Remove oil pan from vehicle.

V8 ENGINES

5.0L & 5.8L

Bronco & Pickup Models

1) Remove engine oil dipstick (on pan entry models only). Remove fan shroud and position over fan. Disconnect engine mounts.

2) On automatic transmission models, disconnect oil cooler line at left side of radiator. Raise engine and place wood blocks under engine supports.

3) Drain engine oil. Remove oil pan attaching bolts and lower oil pan onto crossmember. Remove 2 bolts holding oil pump pickup tube to oil pump.

4) Remove nut attaching oil pickup tube to No. 3 main bearing cap stud. Lower pickup tube and screen assembly into oil pan. Remove oil pan.

Van Models

1) Disconnect negative and positive battery cables from battery. Remove engine cover. Remove air cleaner and drain cooling system.

2) If equipped with air conditioning or power steering, remove compressor or power steering pump and position out of way.

3) Disconnect upper radiator hose from radiator. Remove fan shroud bolts. Remove oil filler tube. Remove engine oil dipstick-to-exhaust manifold bolt.

4) Raise vehicle on hoist. Remove splash shield located under alternator. Disconnect lower radiator hose from radiator.

5) If equipped, disconnect transmission cooler lines from radiator. Remove engine mount nuts. Disconnect fuel line at fuel pump.

6) Drain crankcase and remove dipstick tube from oil pan. Disconnect exhaust pipes from exhaust manifolds.

7) If equipped, remove automatic transmission dipstick and tube. Disconnect shift linkage rods from transmission.

8) Remove center drive shaft support and remove drive shaft from transmission. Place transmission jack under oil pan and raise engine. Insert wood blocks between engine and mounts to support engine.

NOTE: **Engine and transmission assembly will pivot around rear engine mount. Engine must remain centered in engine compartment to obtain the required lift.**

9) Remove oil pan attaching bolts and lower oil pan. Remove oil pump and pickup tube bolts. Remove nut attaching pickup tube to No. 3 bearing cap stud and lay tube in oil pan. Remove oil pan.

6.9L DIESEL

1) Disconnect negative battery cables from both batteries. Remove engine oil dipstick. Remove transmission oil dipstick. Remove air cleaner.

2) Remove fan and fan clutch assembly. Drain cooling system. Disconnect lower radiator hose from radiator.

3) Disconnect power steering return hose from pump. Disconnect all wiring from alternator. Raise vehicle on hoist.

4) Disconnect transmission cooler lines from radiator. Disconnect and plug fuel inlet line at fuel pump. Drain crankcase and remove oil filter.

5) Remove transmission dipstick tube from vehicle. Disconnect exhaust pipes from both exhaust manifolds.

6) Remove upper exhaust pipe stud from right exhaust manifold. Remove engine mount nuts. Lower vehicle from hoist.

7) Raise engine until transmission housing contacts body. Place wood blocks between engine mounts and frame.

8) Lower engine onto blocks. Raise vehicle on hoist. Remove flywheel inspection plate. Remove fuel pump inlet line from crossmember.

9) Remove oil pan attaching bolts and allow oil pan to drop. Remove oil pump and oil pump pickup tube from engine and lay it in oil pan. Remove oil pan from vehicle.

7.5L

Van Models

1) Remove engine cover. Remove air intake tube and air cleaner assembly. Disconnect battery cables from battery. Drain cooling system.

FORD (Cont.)

2) Disconnect throttle and transmission linkage from carburetor. Disconnect power brake vacuum line from engine.

3) Disconnect fuel line, choke lines, and air cleaner adapter from carburetor. Disconnect radiator hoses from radiator.

4) Disconnect transmission and engine oil cooler lines from radiator. Remove fan, fan shroud and radiator.

5) Remove power steering pump and position aside with hoses connected. Remove engine oil dipstick tube and engine mount attaching bolts.

6) Remove oil filler tube and bracket. If equipped, remove air conditioning lines or rotate them downward at rear of compressor to clear dashboard.

7) Raise vehicle on a hoist. Drain crankcase and remove oil filter. Remove exhaust crossover pipe from exhaust manifolds.

8) Disconnect manual and kickdown linkages from transmission. Remove drive shaft and coupling shaft assembly.

9) Remove transmission dipstick tube assembly. Remove engine oil dipstick and tube from oil pan.

10) Position a jack under oil pan and raise engine about 4" or until transmission touches floor board. Insert wood blocks between engine and mounts to support engine.

NOTE: **Engine and transmission will pivot around rear engine mount. Engine must remain centered in engine compartment to achieve required lift.**

11) Remove oil pan attaching bolts and lower oil pan onto crossmember. Remove oil pump and pickup tube assembly and lay it in oil pan. Remove oil pan.

GENERAL MOTORS

4-CYLINDER ENGINES

1.9L & 2.0L
2WD Models

1) Remove engine. Remove oil pan attaching hardware. Remove oil level gauge guide tube from intake manifold and oil pan. Remove oil pan.

2) When installing, apply a thin coat of sealer to each end of gasket and at seams of rear main and front cover. Align holes of gasket on block and install oil pan.

4WD Models

1) Disconnect negative battery cable. Remove starter front brace bolt and motor mount through bolts. Raise vehicle.

2) Remove front splash shield, brake and fuel line clip retaining bolts and crossmember bolts. Remove crossmember while rotating around lines.

3) Drain crankcase. Remove starter bolts. Disconnect steering damper at frame. Scribe pitman arm location. Disconnect pitman arm, steering gear and front axle at frame.

4) Disconnect front propellar shaft at front differential. Slide differential forward and remove oil pan bolts. Raise engine only enough to remove pan.

CAUTION: Raising engine too far could cause damage to EGR system.

5) When installing, apply a thin coat of sealer to each end of gasket and at seams of rear main and front cover. Align holes of gasket on block and install oil pan.

V6 ENGINE

2.8L
2WD Models

1) Remove engine. Remove oil pan attaching hardware. Remove oil pan.

2) When installing, apply a 1/8" (3 mm) bead of sealer on entire oil pan sealing flange. Align holes of gasket on block and install oil pan.

4WD Models

1) Disconnect battery. Remove dipstick. Raise vehicle. Remove drive belt splash, front axle and transfer case shields.

2) Disconnect fuel lines. Remove #2 crossmember. On Auto. Trans. models, remove converter hanger bolts, disconnect exhaust pipes at manifold and slide exhaust rearward.

3) On all models, disconnect front propeller shaft at drive pinion. Disconnect engine braces at flywheel cover and loosen braces at block.

4) Remove flywheel cover. Remove starter bolts and lay starter aside. Disconnect steering shock absorber at frame bracket. Remove steering gear bolts.

5) Mark position of idler arm location for reinstallation, then remove attaching bolts. Pull steering gear and linkage forward. Remove differential housing mounting bolts and move housing forward.

6) Remove motor mount bolts. Drain oil pan. Remove oil pan bolts. Raise engine. Remove oil pan.

7) When installing, apply a 1/8" (3 mm) bead of sealer on entire oil pan sealing flange. Align holes of gasket on block and install oil pan.

6-CYLINDER ENGINES

4.1 & 4.8L
Van Models

1) Disconnect negative battery cable and remove engine cover. Remove air cleaner and studs. Remove fan guard. Remove radiator upper supports. Raise vehicle.

2) On Man. Trans. models, disconnect clutch cross shaft from left front mount bracket. Remove transmission-to-bellhousing upper bolt. Remove transmission rear mount bolts and install two 7/16" x 3" bolts. Raise transmission using jack and install 2" block between mount and crossmember.

3) On all models, remove starter and drain engine oil. Remove engine mount bolts. Raise engine

Oil Pan Removal

GENERAL MOTORS (Cont.)

sufficiently to insert wooden blocks between engine mounts and crossmember brackets.

4) Remove flywheel splash shield or torque converter cover as applicable. Remove oil pan attaching bolts and remove oil pan.

Except Van Models

1) Disconnect negative battery cable. Raise vehicle and drain engine oil. Remove starter and flywheel splash shield or torque converter housing underpan as applicable.

2) Remove bolts from front engine mount. Raise front of engine, reinstall mount bolts, and lower engine. Remove oil pan bolts and oil pan.

V8 ENGINES

5.0 & 5.7L

1) Raise vehicle on hoist and drain engine oil. Remove exhaust crossover pipe. On models with automatic transmission, remove converter housing underpan.

2) On 4WD pickup models with automatic transmission, remove strut rods at engine mounts. On all models, remove oil pan mounting bolts and oil pan.

6.2L (DIESEL)

Van Models

1) Disconnect negative battery cable. Remove engine cover, engine oil and transmission oil dipsticks. Disconnect engine oil dipstick tube at left rocker cover.

2) Disconnect transmission oil dipstick at bellhousing and pull from transmission. Disconnect T.V. cable at injection pump rod and at transmission dipstick tube.

3) Remove upper bellhousing bolt and vacuum pump. Raise vehicle. Remove propellar shaft. Disconnect speedometer cable at transmission.

4) Disconnect torque converter clutch connector, shift linkage and oil cooler lines at transmission.

Remove flexplate inspection cover and flexplate-to-torque converter bolts.

5) Support transmission. Remove transmission mount-to-crossmember nut and remove crossmember. Remove bellhousing-to-cylinder case bolts.

6) Remove transmission and flexplate. Remove dipstick tube from engine oil pan. Drain crankcase. Disconnect engine oil cooler lines at cylinder case. Remove starter.

7) Disconnect battery and cooler line clips. Remove oil pan bolts. Lower pan from block. Remove oil pump to main cap bolt, disconnect drive shaft and let assembly fall in pan. Remove oil pan.

NOTE: It may be necessary to rotate crankshaft so that forward throw and No. 1 and 2 journals are up, giving front of pan clearance.

Except Van Models

1) Disconnect negative battery cables. Raise vehicle and drain engine oil. Remove transmission dust cover.

2) Remove oil pan bolts. Remove left engine mount bolt. Raise engine and remove oil pan.

3) When installing, apply a 1/32" bead of sealer on entire oil pan sealing flange. Sealer must be wet to the touch when bolts are tightened.

7.4L

1) Disconnect negative battery cable. Loosen fan shroud. Remove air cleaner and distributor cap. Raise vehicle and drain oil. On Man. Trans. models, remove starter.

2) On all models, remove flywheel splash shield or converter cover as applicable. Remove oil filter. On gauge equipped models, remove oil pressure line from block.

3) On all models, remove front engine mount through bolts. Raise engine and remove oil pan bolts and oil pan.

JEEP

4-CYLINDER ENGINE

1) Disconnect negative battery cable. Raise vehicle and drain oil. Remove starter. Remove oil pan bolts and oil pan.

2) When installing, apply small amount of sealer in depression where oil pan gasket contacts block.

6-CYLINDER ENGINE

1) Disconnect negative battery cable. Raise vehicle and drain oil. Remove starter.

2) On "CJ" models, position a jack under transmission housing, disconnect right support cushion bracket from block and raise engine enough to gain clearance for oil pan removal.

3) On all models, remove oil pan attaching bolts, oil pan, seals, and side gaskets.

4) When installing, apply sealer to side gaskets and oil pan gasket ends.

V8 ENGINE

1) Disconnect negative battery cable and drain engine oil. If equipped with manual transmission, bend tabs down on dust shield to aid engine removal. Remove oil pan attaching bolts and oil pan.

2) When installing, apply sealer to oil pan gaskets and ends.

Engine Removal

CHRYSLER CORP.

6-CYLINDER ENGINE

VAN MODELS

1) Disconnect battery and remove oil dipstick. Raise vehicle and remove air pump tube from exhaust pipe. Remove exhaust pipe. Remove inspection cover from transmission and drain crankcase. Remove engine-to-transmission strut.

2) Remove oil pan (it may be necessary to turn crankshaft to clear front of oil pan). Turn oil pickup tube upward to protect it from damage. Remove flex plate-to-torque converter bolts and transmission housing bolts. Remove right motor mount nut.

3) Lower vehicle and drain cooling system. Remove engine cover, carburetor air cleaner and carburetor. If equipped with A/C, discharge system and disconnect and cap condenser lines. Remove fan shroud, windshield washer and overflow reservoirs. Remove front bumper, grille and support brace. Disconnect radiator hoses. Remove radiator and support as an assembly.

4) Remove steering pump bracket bolts and set pump aside with hoses attached. Remove air pump. Disconnect throttle linkage, all hoses, electrical connections and lines to coil, alternator and other engine accessories. Remove alternator with brackets, fan blade, pulley and drive belts. Disconnect and cap flexible fuel pump line.

5) Remove starter and set aside. Remove distributor cap, spark plug wires and left engine mount nut. Attach lifting fixture to engine and place jack under transmission. Remove remaining transmission housing bolts and remove engine from front of vehicle.

ALL OTHER MODELS

1) Scribe hood hinges for reinstallation and remove hood. Drain cooling system and remove battery. Remove radiator, heater hoses and radiator. Set fan shroud aside and discharge air conditioning system (if equipped). Remove air cleaner, vacuum lines, distributor cap and wiring.

2) Remove carburetor, linkage, starter wiring and oil pressure wire. Remove starter, alternator, charcoal canister and horns. Remove A/C and power steering hoses (if equipped). Remove exhaust pipe at manifold. Remove transmission housing and inspection plate bolts. Attach "C" clamp to front of housing to prevent torque converter from coming out.

3) Remove torque converter drive plate bolts. Mark converter and drive plate to aid in reassembly. Support transmission with stand (C-3201-A) and disconnect engine from torque converter drive plate. Install engine lifting fixture and attach chain. Remove engine front mount bolts and remove engine from vehicle.

V8 ENGINES

VAN MODELS

1) Disconnect battery and remove oil dipstick. Raise vehicle and remove exhaust crossover pipe. Remove inspection cover from transmission. Drain engine oil and remove engine-to-transmission strut. Remove oil pan (it may be necessary to rotate engine to clear front of pan). Remove oil pump and pickup tube.

2) Remove flex plate-to-torque converter bolts. Remove starter and set aside. Remove lower transmission housing bolts and engine mount nuts. Lower vehicle and drain cooling system. Remove engine cover and discharge air conditioning system. Disconnect and plug condenser lines. Remove front bumper, grille and support brace.

3) Remove air cleaner and carburetor. Disconnect radiator hoses and remove condenser, radiator and support as an assembly. Remove A/C compressor bracket bolts and set compressor aside. Remove air pump. Remove power steering pump and set aside with hoses attached. Disconnect throttle linkage, heater and vacuum hoses and all electrical connections to coil, alternator and other engine accessories.

4) Remove alternator, fan blade (or fluid fan unit), pulley and all drive belts. Disconnect and cap flexible line at fuel pump. Remove left exhaust manifold heat shield, spark plug wires and distributor cap. Attach lifting fixture to intake manifold. Place floor jack under transmission and remove upper transmission housing bolts. Use lifting device to remove engine from front of vehicle.

ALL OTHER MODELS

1) Scribe hood hinges for reassembly and remove hood. Drain cooling system and remove battery and air cleaner. Remove coolant hoses and radiator. Discharge A/C system (if equipped) and remove vacuum lines, distributor cap and wiring. Remove carburetor, linkage, starter wires and oil pressure wire.

2) Remove A/C hoses and power steering hoses (if equipped). Remove starter, alternator, charcoal canister and horns. Remove exhaust crossover pipe at manifold. Remove transmission housing bolts and inspection plate. Attach "C" clamp to front of transmission torque converter housing to prevent converter from falling out.

3) Remove drive plate bolts and mark converter and drive plate to aid in reassembly. Support transmission with stand (C-3201-A) and disconnect engine from torque converter drive plate. Install engine lifting fixture and remove engine front mounts. Remove engine from engine compartment.

TIGHTENING SPECIFICATIONS

Application	Ft. Lbs. (N.m)
Front Mount-to-Engine	
6-Cylinder	50 (68)
V8	65 (88)
Flex Plate-to-Converter	23 (31)
Flex Plate-to-Crankshaft	55 (75)
Flywheel-to-Crankshaft	55 (75)

Engine Removal
FORD

4-CYLINDER ENGINES

2.0L & 2.3L

1) Drain cooling system. Remove air cleaner and duct assembly. Disconnect negative battery cable at engine. Disconnect positive battery cable at battery.

2) Mark location of hood hinges and remove hood. Disconnect upper and lower radiator hoses from engine. Remove radiator shroud attaching screws.

3) Remove upper radiator supports. Remove cooling fan and fan shroud. Remove radiator. Remove oil fill cap. Disconnect primary wire from distributor.

4) Disconnect wires from oil pressure sending unit and water temperature sending unit. Disconnect wires from alternator and starter.

5) Disconnect accelerator cable and kickdown rod from carburetor. Remove air conditioning compressor from bracket and position aside with hoses attached.

6) Disconnect power brake vacuum hose. Disconnect chassis fuel line from fuel pump. Disconnect heater hoses from engine. Remove engine mount nuts.

7) Raise vehicle on hoist. Drain crankcase. Remove starter motor. Disconnect exhaust pipe from exhaust manifold. Remove dust cover from transmission.

8) On vehicles with manual transmissions, remove flywheel housing lower attaching bolts and clutch slave cylinder.

9) On vehicles with automatic transmissions, remove converter-to-flywheel bolts, then remove converter housing lower attaching bolts.

10) On all vehicles, lower vehicle from hoist. Support transmission with jack. Remove flywheel housing-to-converter housing attaching bolts.

11) Attach an engine lifting device to engine. Lift engine out of vehicle.

2.2L DIESEL

1) Mark location of hood hinges and remove hood. Disconnect negative battery cables from both batteries.

2) Disconnect negative battery cables from engine and remove cables from vehicle. Drain cooling system.

3) Disconnect air intake hose from air cleaner and remove air cleaner assembly. Disconnect upper and lower radiator hoses from engine.

4) Remove cooling fan. Remove radiator shroud attaching screws. Remove upper radiator supports. Remove radiator and shroud assembly.

5) Disconnect radio ground strap. Remove number 2 glow plug relay from firewall, with harness attached, and place on engine.

6) Disconnect engine wiring harness at main connector located on left fender apron. Disconnect wiring from starter.

7) Disconnect accelerator cable from injection pump. Remove cold start cable from injection pump. Discharge air conditioning system.

8) Remove air conditioning compressor lines from compressor. Remove pressure and return hoses from power steering pump.

9) Disconnect vacuum fitting from vacuum pump. Disconnect and plug fuel inlet line at fuel line heater and injection pump.

10) Disconnect heater hoses from engine. Loosen engine mount nuts. Raise vehicle on hoist. Drain crankcase and remove oil pan and primary oil filter.

11) Disconnect oil pressure sending unit hose from oil filter mounting adapter. Disconnect exhaust pipe from exhaust manifold.

12) Remove engine mount nuts. Remove transmission-to-engine bolts. Lower vehicle from hoist. Attach a lifting device to engine. Carefully remove engine from vehicle.

6-CYLINDER ENGINE

4.9L

Bronco & Pickup Models

1) Drain cooling system and crankcase. Mark hood hinge position and remove hood. Remove air cleaner assembly.

2) Remove air conditioning compressor and condensor, if equipped. Disconnect negative battery cable. Disconnect heater hoses from engine.

3) Disconnect flexible fuel line at fuel pump. Remove radiator. Remove cooling fan, spacer and water pump pulley.

4) Disconnect accelerator cable at carburetor and remove retracting spring. If equipped with power brakes, disconnect power brake vacuum hose from engine.

5) Disconnect kickdown rod at bellcrank assembly (auto. trans.). Disconnect exhaust pipe from exhaust manifold.

6) Disconnect body ground strap and battery ground cable from engine. Disconnect engine wiring harness from distributor and all sending units.

7) Remove alternator mounting bolts and position alternator aside with wires attached. If equipped with power steering, remove pump from mounting brackets and position aside with lines attached.

8) If equipped with air conditioning, bleed system and disconnect lines from compressor. Raise vehicle on hoist.

9) Remove starter, automatic transmission fluid filler tube bracket (if equipped) and engine rear plate upper right bolt.

10) On vehicles with manual transmission, remove flywheel housing lower retaining bolts and disconnect clutch retracting spring.

11) On vehicles with automatic transmission, remove converter housing access cover and flywheel-to-converter nuts. Secure converter assembly in housing.

12) Remove transmission oil cooler lines from clip at engine. Remove converter housing-to-engine lower retaining bolts.

13) On all vehicles, remove insulator-to-intermediate support bracket nut from each front engine support. Lower vehicle and support transmission with a floor jack.

14) Remove remaining flywheel or converter housing-to-engine bolts. Attach lifting device-to-engine. Raise engine slightly and carefully pull from transmission. Remove engine from vehicle.

Van Models

1) Remove engine cover. Drain cooling system. Remove air cleaner assembly. Disconnect battery. Remove front bumper.

2) Remove grill and lower gravel deflector as an assembly. Disconnect radiator hoses from engine. Disconnect transmission oil cooler lines at radiator.

Engine Removal

FORD (Cont.)

3) Remove radiator and shroud. Disconnect heater hoses from engine. Disconnect alternator and position aside. Remove power steering pump drive belt.

4) Remove power steering pump and bracket from engine. Disconnect and plug fuel line at fuel pump. Disconnect distributor and sending unit wires from engine.

5) Disconnect brake booster hose from engine. Disconnect accelerator cable and remove bracket from engine.

6) Disconnect automatic transmission kickdown at bellcrank. Remove exhaust manifold heat deflector and inlet pipe-to-manifold nuts.

7) Disconnect both ends of transmission vacuum line at intake manifold and junction. Remove upper transmission-to-engine bolts.

8) Remove automatic transmission dipstick tube support at intake manifold. Raise vehicle on hoist. Drain crankcase and remove oil filter.

9) Disconnect wires from starter and remove starter. Remove flywheel inspection cover. Remove converter-to-flywheel nuts.

10) Remove front engine mount nuts. Remove remaining transmission-to-engine bolts. Lower vehicle from hoist.

11) Attach a lifting device to engine. Remove engine from vehicle.

V6 ENGINES

2.8L

1) Disconnect or remove all thermactor components that may interfere with engine removal. Disconnect negative battery cable from battery.

2) Drain cooling system. Remove hood. Remove air cleaner and intake duct assembly. Disconnect upper and lower radiator hoses from radiator.

3) Remove fan shroud attaching bolts and position shroud over fan. Remove radiator and shroud. Remove alternator from engine and position aside.

4) Disconnect alternator ground wire from engine block. If equipped, remove air conditioning compressor and power steering pump and position aside.

5) Disconnect heater hoses from engine. Remove ground wires from engine block. Disconnect and plug fuel tank line at fuel pump.

6) Disconnect throttle cable linkage at carburetor and intake manifold. Disconnect primary wires from distributor.

7) If equipped, remove power brake vacuum hose from engine. Disconnect wiring from oil pressure and engine temperature sending units.

8) Raise vehicle on hoist. Disconnect exhaust pipes from exhaust manifolds. Remove starter. Remove front engine mount nuts and through bolts.

9) On vehicles with automatic transmissions, remove the converter inspection cover and disconnect flywheel from converter.

10) Remove kickdown rod. Remove converter housing-to-engine bolts. Remove adapter plate-to-converter housing bolt.

11) On vehicles with manual transmissions, remove clutch linkage. On all vehicles, lower vehicle from hoist. Attach a lifting device to engine. Remove engine from vehicle.

3.8L

1) Drain cooling system. Disconnect negative battery cable from battery. Disconnect under hood wiring connector, if equipped.

2) Mark position of hood hinges and remove hood. Remove air cleaner assembly with intake duct and heat tube attached. Remove fan shroud and cooling fan.

3) Disconnect upper and lower radiator hoses from radiator. Loosen drive belt idler pulley and remove water pump pulley.

4) Disconnect thermactor hose from downstream air tube check valve. Remove downstream air tube bracket attaching bolt at rear of right cylinder head.

5) Remove ignition coil secondary wire from coil. If equipped with power steering, remove pump mounting bracket bolts.

6) Without disconnecting hoses, set pump and bracket assembly aside. If equipped with A/C, remove compressor mounting bracket bolts.

7) Without disconnecting hoses, position compressor assembly aside. Remove alternator and position aside. Disconnect heater hoses from heater.

8) If equipped with speed control, disconnect servo chain at carburetor, remove servo bracket attaching screws and remove servo.

9) Disconnect vacuum hoses and wiring as required. Remove engine ground strap. Disconnect transmission linkage at carburetor.

10) Disconnect accelerator cable and remove cable bracket. Disconnect fuel supply line and PCV hose at carburetor. Remove carburetor.

11) With EGR spacer and gasket in position, attach engine lifting plate (T75T-6000-A) over carburetor studs and tighten nuts.

12) Use all studs to mount lifting plate to prevent damage to aluminum intake manifold. When using lifting plate, do not remove engine with transmission attached.

13) Raise vehicle and drain crankcase. Disconnect and plug flexible fuel line at fuel pump. Remove transmission converter housing dust shield.

14) Remove flywheel-to-torque converter nuts. Remove starter and transmission oil cooler line clips. Remove exhaust pipes from exhaust manifolds.

15) Remove transmission-to-engine lower attaching bolts. Remove engine mount-to-crossmember nuts. Lower vehicle from hoist.

16) Position a jack under transmission to support transmission assembly. Remove upper transmission-to-engine bolts. Protect radiator with plywood.

17) Raise engine and carefully pull out of engine compartment. While lifting engine from vehicle, avoid bending or damaging rear cover plate.

V8 ENGINES

5.0L, 5.8L & 7.5L
Bronco & Pickup Models

1) Drain cooling system and crankcase. Mark hood hinges and remove hood. Disconnect battery and ground cables from cylinder block.

2) Remove air cleaner and intake duct assembly with crankcase ventilation and carbon canister hoses attached. Disconnect radiator hoses from radiator.

Engine Removal

FORD (Cont.)

3) Disconnect transmission oil cooler lines (if equipped). If equipped with air conditioning, discharge system, remove condenser, and disconnect hoses.

4) Remove fan shroud, radiator, fan, spacer and pulley. Remove alternator attaching bolts and position aside. Disconnect oil pressure sending unit wire.

5) Disconnect flexible fuel line at fuel tank line. Disconnect vacuum lines, carbon canister hose, heater hoses and electrical wiring from engine.

6) Disconnect accelerator cable, transmission shift rod and speed control linkages and retracting spring from carburetor (if equipped).

7) Disconnect power brake booster vacuum hose, if equipped. Remove flywheel housing-to-engine upper bolts. Raise front of vehicle. Remove starter.

8) Disconnect exhaust pipes from exhaust manifolds. Disconnect engine mounts from brackets on frame.

9) If equipped with automatic transmission, remove converter inspection plate and converter-to-flywheel attaching bolts.

10) Remove remaining flywheel housing-to-engine bolts. Lower vehicle and support transmission with a floor jack.

11) Attach lifting device to engine. Carefully raise engine and pull it from transmission. Lift engine from vehicle taking care not to damage rear cover plate.

Van Models

1) Remove engine cover. Disconnect battery. Drain cooling system. Remove grille assembly with gravel deflector. Remove upper grill support bracket.

2) Remove hood lock support and condenser upper mounting brackets (if equipped). Discharge air conditioning system.

3) Remove condenser and disconnect lines at compressor. Remove accelerator cable bracket. Disconnect radiator hoses from radiator.

4) Disconnect heater hoses from engine. If equipped with automatic transmission, disconnect oil cooler lines at radiator.

5) Remove fan shroud and fan assembly. Remove radiator. Disconnect wires from alternator. Remove air cleaner assembly.

6) Remove air duct and exhaust manifold shroud. Remove flex tube from exhaust manifold. Disconnect throttle cable from carburetor.

7) If equipped with automatic transmission, remove transmission shift rod. Disconnect fuel lines. Remove carburetor and spacer plate.

8) Disconnect all vacuum hoses from engine. Raise vehicle on hoist. Drain crankcase and remove oil filter. Disconnect exhaust pipes from exhaust manifolds.

9) Disconnect transmission filler tube from right cylinder head. Remove engine mount attaching bolts and nuts. Remove starter.

10) On vehicles equipped with a manual transmission, remove housing-to-engine bolts. On vehicles equipped with a automatic transmission, remove converter inspection cover bolts.

11) Remove nuts attaching converter to the flywheel. Remove bolts attaching adapter plate to converter housing. Remove converter housing-to-engine bolts.

12) On all vehicles, remove ground strap from engine block. Lower vehicle from hoist. Support transmission with floor jack.

13) If equipped, remove power steering pump drive belt and front bracket. Disconnect engine wire loom and position aside.

14) Install lifting bracket (T75T-6000-A or equivalent) to intake manifold. Remove upper housing-to-engine bolts.

15) Attach a lifting device to engine. Carefully move engine foward and remove from vehicle.

6.9L DIESEL

1) Disconnect negative battery cables from both batteries. Mark hood hinges and remove hood. Drain cooling system.

2) Remove air cleaner and intake duct assembly. Remove fan shroud halves. Remove fan and fan clutch assembly.

3) Disconnect upper and lower radiator hoses from radiator. Disconnect automatic transmission cooler lines from radiator. Remove radiator.

4) If equipped, remove air conditioning compressor drive belt. Remove air conditioning compressor and position aside with lines attached.

5) Remove power steering pump drive belt. Remove power steering pump and position aside with hoses attached.

6) Disconnect fuel supply line heater and alternator wires. Disconnect all sending unit wires from engine. Disconnect accelerator cable from injection pump.

7) Remove accelerator bracket from engine and position aside with accelerator cable. Remove transmission kickdown rod from injection pump.

8) Disconnect main wiring harness connector from right side of engine. Disconnect engine ground strap from rear of engine.

9) Disconnect fuel return lines from engine. Remove upper transmission-to-engine bolts. Disconnect heater hoses from engine. Raise vehicle on hoist.

10) Disconnect both battery ground cables from front of engine. Disconnect and plug fuel supply line at fuel pump. Remove starter.

11) Disconnect exhaust pipes from exhaust manifolds. Remove engine mount-to-engine nuts. Remove flywheel inspection plate.

12) Remove flywheel to converter attaching bolts. Lower vehicle from hoist. Support transmission with floor jack.

13) Remove lower transmission-to-engine bolts. Attach a lifting device to engine. Carefully remove engine from vehicle.

TIGHTENING SPECIFICATIONS

Application [1]	Ft. Lbs. (N.m)
Bronco II & Ranger	
Converter-to-Flywheel	27-49 (37-66)
Converter Housing-to-Engine	28-38 (38-52)
Flywheel Housing-to-Engine	28-38 (38-52)
Lower Mount-to-Frame	71-94 (96-127)
Lower Mount-to-Upper Mount	65-85 (88-115)
Upper Mount-to-Engine	45-60 (61-81)
Bronco, Pickup & Van	
Converter-to-Flywheel	20-34 (27-46)
Converter Housing-to-Engine	
C5 Trans.	
3.8L	28-38 (38-52)
C6 Trans.	
Diesel Engine	50-65 (68-88)
Gas Engine	40-50 (54-68)
AOT Trans.	40-50 (54-68)
Flywheel Housing-to-Engine	40-50 (54-68)
Engine Mount-to-Engine	
3.8L	60-80 (81-108)
5.0L & 5.8L	50-70 (68-95)
Engine Mount-to-Frame Bracket	
3.8L, 5.0L & 5.8L	50-70 (68-95)
Lower Mount-to-Frame	
7.5L Only	50-70 (68-95)
Lower Mount-to-Upper Mount	
7.5L Only	40-58 (54-79)
Upper Mount-to-Engine	
7.5L Only	50-70 (68-95)

[1] — Tightening specifications not available for 6.9L diesel engine.

Engine Removal
GENERAL MOTORS

4-CYLINDER ENGINES

1.9L

1) Open hood, mark position of hood hinges and remove hood. Disconnect negative battery cable and raise vehicle. Remove rear transmission mount nuts. Support transmission and remove crossmember at frame and top transmission bolts. Reinstall crossmember and remove transmission support.

2) Remove engine-to-transmission bolts. Remove torque converter cover. Remove exhaust manifold. Disconnect starter leads and remove motor mount bolts. Disconnect fuel lines and transmission cooler lines (automatic transmission). Lower vehicle and drain coolant.

3) Disconnect necessary wires and hoses from alternator, carburetor and other accessories. If equipped, remove power steering pump and air conditioning compressor and lay aside.

4) Loosen alternator and disconnect front heater hose. Remove upper fan shroud, radiator and heater hoses, fan assembly and transmission oil cooler lines. Remove radiator assembly.

5) Disconnect accelerator cable and spring, and detent cable from carburetor. Using a floor jack, support transmission. Install lifting device and remove engine from vehicle.

2.0L

1) Disconnect battery cables. Drain cooling system. Remove hood. Disconnect radiator hose at radiator. Remove upper radiator hose at radiator. Remove upper fan shroud. Remove radiator and fan.

2) Disconnect heater hoses at engine and wiring harness at bulkhead. Remove air cleaner. Disconnect accelerator cable at carburetor and fuel hose at frame. Remove negative battery cable at block.

3) Disconnect ground strap at bulkhead. Raise vehicle. Remove clutch bell crank. Disconnect exhaust pipe at manifold. Remove motor mount through bolt and left side body mount bolts. Remove left air dam bolts.

4) Raise body to gain access to upper bellhousing bolts and remove bolts. Lower body. Remove flywheel dust shield. Lower vehicle. Support transmission. Disconnect power steering pump and remove A/C compressor, if equipped. Remove engine.

6-CYLINDER ENGINES

4.1L & 4.8L
Van Models

1) Disconnect negative battery cable and drain cooling system. Remove engine cover and air cleaner. If equipped, discharge A/C system and remove compressor.

2) Disconnect accelerator linkage from carburetor and remove carburetor. Remove grille and cross brace. Remove windshield washer jar and, if equipped, A/C vacuum reservoir.

3) Disconnect radiator hoses, oil cooler lines (if equipped), A/C condensor bracket (if equipped) and radiator support brackets. Swing A/C condensor out of the way (if equipped) and remove radiator.

4) Remove all hoses, wiring, linkage and lines from engine. Raise vehicle and remove fuel line from fuel pump. Drain crankcase and remove propeller shaft. Remove exhaust pipe at manifold and linkage from transmission.

5) Remove speedometer cable and transmission mount bolts. If equipped with manual transmission, disconnect clutch linkage and remove clutch cross shaft. Remove engine mount bolts.

6) Lower vehicle and attach lifting device. Raise engine slightly to remove right hand motor mount. Remove engine with transmission.

Except Van Models

1) Disconnect battery. Remove air cleaner and drain cooling system. Disconnect accelerator cable and detent cable (automatic transmission) from throttle lever. Disconnect wiring from engine.

2) Remove radiator hoses from radiator and heater hoses from engine. Remove radiator, fan and water pump pulley. Disconnect fuel line from fuel pump. Remove hood. Raise vehicle.

3) Remove starter, flywheel or converter splash shield and exhaust pipe from manifold. If equipped with automatic transmission, remove converter-to-flex plate bolts. Remove engine mount bolts. On 4WD models, remove strut rods at motor mounts.

4) On all models, remove clutch/torque converter housing retaining bolts and support transmission with chain. Lower vehicle and attach lifting device. Remove engine.

V6 ENGINE

2.8L
2WD Models

1) Disconnect battery. Raise vehicle. Remove propeller shaft. Disconnect speedometer cable. On Auto. Trans. models, disconnect torque converter clutch connector. On all models, disconnect shift linkage.

2) Remove crossmember-to-transmission mount nuts and frame bolts. Disconnect exhaust bolts at manifold. Remove bolts at rear of catalytic converter. Remove transmission mount-to-transmission bolts and mount.

3) Support engine and transmission and remove crossmember. Remove exhaust manifold flange-to-converter, including support. On Auto. Trans. models, remove strut bolts at dust cover and dust cover-to-cylinder case bolts.

4) On all models, remove starter. Lower vehicle. Remove hood and air cleaner. Drain cooling system. Disconnect radiator hoses at engine. Remove A/C compressor and position aside, if equipped. Remove upper half of fan shroud.

5) Disconnect heater hoses at engine and cooler lines at radiator. Remove fan. Disconnect coolant bottle hose. Remove radiator. Disconnect power steering pump and position aside. Disconnect all necessary hoses and wires.

6) Install lift device. Remove motor mount through bolts. Disconnect additional wiring and TV cable while pulling engine. If equipped with A/C, remove compressor bracket and install lift hook. Raise and remove engine and transmission as an assembly.

4WD Models

1) Disconnect battery. Disconnect underhood light, if equipped. Remove hood. Raise vehicle. On Blazer models, remove body mounts. On Pickup models, loosen front and remove 2 body mounts. On all models, remove front air dam end bolts.

GENERAL MOTORS (Cont.)

2) Raise body from frame enough to gain access to top transmission bolts. Remove top transmission-to-engine mounting bolts. Lower body. Remove remaining transmission-to-engine bolts. Remove 2nd crossmember bolts and remove crossmember.

3) Disconnect exhaust pipe at manifold. Disconnect catalytic converter hanger. Remove torque converter cover bolts. Disconnect front propeller shaft at front differential. Remove torque converter cover. Disconnect transmission cooler lines at engine clips.

4) Remove motor mount bolts. Remove flexplate-to-torque converter bolts. Remove front splash shield and lower fan shroud bolts. Lower vehicle. Drain cooling system. Remove upper fan shroud. Disconnect radiator hoses and transmission cooler lines at radiator.

5) Remove radiator, fan and air cleaner. If equipped, remove A/C compressor and power steering pump and position aside. Disconnect fuel lines at fuel pump. Disconnect necessary wires, vacuum lines and emission hoses.

6) Disconnect accelerator, TV cables and cruise control cables, if equipped. Disconnect engine wiring harness at bulkhead connector. Disconnect heater hoses at engine. Support transmission and install engine lift device. Remove engine.

V8 ENGINES

5.0 & 5.7L

Van Models

1) Disconnect battery cables and drain cooling system. Remove coolant reservoir, grille, upper radiator support and lower grille valance. Disconnect transmission oil cooler lines (if equipped) and radiator hoses. If equipped with A/C, discharge system and remove condenser and vacuum reservoir.

2) Remove washer jar with bracket, radiator brackets, radiator and shroud. Remove air cleaner, air stove pipe and accelerator cable from carburetor. If equipped with power steering, remove pump and lay aside.

3) Disconnect wiring from firewall connection and remove carburetor. Remove thermostat housing, oil fill pipe and disconnect heater hoses. If equipped with cruise control, remove servo, transducer and bracket.

4) Raise vehicle. Disconnect exhaust pipe at manifold. Remove propeller shaft and shift linkage. Disconnect fuel line from pump. Disconnect speedometer cable. Remove transmission mount bolts and engine mount bracket-to-frame bolts.

5) Drain crankcase. Remove engine mount through bolts. Raise engine slightly and remove engine mounts. Block up engine with wooden block between oil pan and crossmember. Lower vehicle and install lifting device. Remove engine/transmission assembly.

Except Van Models

1) Disconnect battery cables and drain cooling system. Remove hood, air cleaner, accessory drive belts, fan and water pump pulley. Disconnect all hoses, lines, linkage and wiring from engine. If equipped with A/C, remove compressor and lay aside.

2) Disconnect transmission oil cooler lines (if equipped) and remove radiator with shroud. If equipped with power steering, remove pump and lay aside. Disconnect fuel line from fuel pump.

3) Raise vehicle and drain crankcase. On 4WD models with automatic transmission, remove strut rods at motor mounts. On all models, disconnect crossover pipe from exhaust manifold.

4) Remove flywheel or converter splash shield. Remove starter and wiring along right pan rail. Remove gas gauge wiring. If equipped with automatic transmission, remove converter-to-flex plate attaching bolts.

5) Support transmission and remove clutch-/torque converter housing-to-engine bolts. Remove lower engine mount bracket-to-frame bolts. Lower vehicle and attach lifting device. Remove engine.

6.2L (DIESEL)

Van Models

1) Disconnect batteries. Remove headlight bezels, grille, bumper and lower grill valance. Remove washer jar, upper fan shroud and tie bar, and engine cover. If equipped with A/C, discharge system, disconnect condenser lines and remove condenser.

2) Disconnect low coolant wire. Drain cooling system. Disconnect engine and transmission oil cooler lines, and upper and lower radiator hoses at radiator. Remove radiator and fan assembly. Scribe or paint a mark on front cover and injection pump flange and remove fuel injection pump.

3) Raise vehicle. Disconnect exhaust pipe at manifold. Remove inspection cover, flex plate-to-torque converter bolts, and motor mount through bolts. Disconnect block heater at element and ground wire-to-block. Remove clutch/torque converter housing-to-engine bolts. Remove starter.

4) Lower vehicle. If equipped with cruise control, remove transducer. If equipped with A/C, remove rear brace, disconnect lines at compressor, and remove brackets and compressor. If equipped with power steering, remove pump and position aside. Remove oil fill tube upper bracket and glow plug relay.

5) Disconnect oil pressure sender and loom. Remove air cleaner resonator and bracket. Remove transmission fill tube nut. Disconnect heater, radiator and by-pass hoses at crossover. Remove alternator upper bracket and coolant crossover. Disconnect fuel lines at fuel pump. Install lifting device. Remove engine.

Except Van Models

1) Disconnect batteries. Raise vehicle. Remove transmission dust cover. Disconnect torque converter and exhaust pipe. Remove starter bolts, disconnect wires and remove starter. Remove clutch/torque converter housing bolts and left and right motor mount bolts.

2) Disconnect block heaters. Remove wire harness, transmission cooler lines and front battery cable clamp at oil pan. Disconnect fuel return and oil cooler lines at engine. Remove lower fan shroud bolts. Lower vehicle. Remove hood and drain cooling system.

3) Remove air cleaner with resonator and primary filter from cowl. Disconnect ground cable at alternator bracket, alternator wires and clips. Disconnect TPS, EGR-EPR and fuel cutoff at injection pump. Remove harness from clips at rocker covers and disconnect glow plugs.

4) Disconnect EGR-EPR solenoids, glow plug controller, temperature sender and move harness aside. Disconnect left side ground strap. Remove fan, upper radiator hoses at engine, and fan shroud. Remove power steering pump and belt. Remove power steering reservoir and position aside.

Engine Removal

GENERAL MOTORS (Cont.)

5) Disconnect vacuum at cruise servo and accelerator cable at injection pump. Disconnect heater hose and lower radiator hose at engine. Disconnect oil cooler lines, heater hose and overflow at radiator.

6) Disconnect automatic transmission cooler lines. Remove upper radiator cover, radiator and detent cable. Support transmission and remove engine.

7.4L

1) Remove hood. Disconnect battery. Remove air cleaner. Drain radiator and block. Disconnect radiator and heater hoses. Remove radiator and fan shroud. Disconnect all hoses, lines, linkage and wiring from engine.

2) Remove power steering pump and A/C compressor, if equipped. Raise vehicle. Drain crankcase. Disconnect exhaust pipe at manifold and torque converter bracket (automatic transmission) at transmission rear mount. Remove starter.

3) Remove flywheel splash shield or converter housing cover. Remove converter-to-flywheel attaching bolts (automatic transmission). Remove mount through bolts and clutch/torque converter housing-to-engine bolts.

4) Lower vehicle. Using floor jack, raise transmission. Attach lifting device and raise engine. Remove motor mount-to-engine brackets. Remove engine.

TIGHTENING SPECIFICATIONS

Application	Ft. Lbs. (N.m)
Flywheel Housing-to-Engine	30 (41)
Converter-to-Flywheel Bolts	35 (47)
Rear Mount-to-Transmission	40 (54)
Rear Mount-to-Crossmember Bolt	40 (54)
Crossmember Mounting Bolt	25 (34)

JEEP

NOTE: **Procedures are for engine removal without transmission attached.**

4-CYLINDER ENGINE

1) Disconnect negative battery cable and drain cooling system. Remove air cleaner. Raise and support vehicle on safety stands. Remove exhaust pipe from exhaust manifold. Remove starter and engine mount nuts.

2) Remove hydraulic clutch slave cylinder and flywheel inspection plate. Remove clutch/converter housing-to-engine bolts. Disconnect wiring, lines, linkage and hoses from engine. Lower vehicle and support transmission with floor jack.

3) Disconnect throttle cable, choke wire and solenoid wire from carburetor. Remove radiator hoses, heater hoses, radiator and shroud. Remove power steering hoses, if equipped. Attach engine sling and remove engine.

6-CYLINDER ENGINE

1) On CJ models, disconnect negative battery cable and drain cooling system. On all other models, open hood and mark hinge location for installation reference. Drain cooling system and remove hood and battery. On all models, remove air cleaner. Disconnect and plug fuel line at pump and fuel return line at frame.

2) Disconnect heater hoses. Disconnect throttle cable and rod (if equipped) at carburetor. Disconnect all wiring, lines, linkage and hoses from engine. Remove radiator, fan and shroud (if equipped). Remove starter and motor mount nuts. Disconnect exhaust pipe at manifold.

3) If equipped with manual transmission, remove clutch housing bolts, clutch linkage and shield. If equipped with automatic transmission, remove transmission cover and mark position of converter on drive plate. Remove converter bolts. Remove bolts securing transmission converter housing to engine. Disconnect oil cooler lines from transmission oil pan.

4) On all models, support transmission with a floor jack. If equipped with power steering, disconnect hoses at steering gear and tie up out of way to prevent leakage. If equipped with A/C, disconnect lines at compressor after seating service valves and bleeding lines. Attach a sling to engine and remove engine from vehicle.

V8 ENGINE

1) On CJ models, disconnect negative battery cable and drain cooling system. On all other models, open hood and mark hinge location for installation reference. Drain cooling system and remove hood and battery. On all models, remove air cleaner, radiator hoses, heater hoses and oil cooler lines (if equipped).

2) Drain fluid from power steering pump reservoir and disconnect hoses. If equipped with air conditioning, turn both service valves clockwise to front seated position and bleed refrigerant charge by slowly loosening service valve fittings. Remove service valves from compressor. Remove Cruise Command vacuum servo bellows and mounting bracket as an assembly, if equipped.

3) Disconnect all wires, lines, linkage and hoses from engine. On automatic transmissions, disconnect filler tube bracket from right cylinder head. Do not remove tube from transmission case.

4) On all models, use lifting device to support engine and remove front support-to-frame bolts. Remove upper drive plate housing screws (automatic transmission) or upper flywheel screws (manual transmission). Disconnect exhaust pipe at manifold and support bracket. Remove starter. Support transmission using a floor jack.

5) On models equipped with automatic transmission, remove adapter plate inspection covers and mark assembled position of converter and drive plate. Remove lower throttle valve and inner manual linkage support. Disconnect throttle valve at lower end of bellcrank. Remove converter-to-drive plate bolts and remaining bolts securing transmission.

6) On models equipped with manual transmission, remove clutch housing lower cover and remaining bolts securing clutch housing to engine. On all models, raise engine and pull forward to remove from vehicle.

TIGHTENING SPECIFICATIONS

Application	Ft. Lbs. (N.m)
4-Cylinder	
Clutch Housing-to-Block	54 (73)
Flywheel-to-Crankshaft	68 (92)
Front Support Bracket-to-Block	35 (47)
Front Support Cushion-to-Crossmember	37 (50)
Rear Support Bracket-to-Transmission	33 (45)
6-Cylinder	
Automatic Transmission-to-Block	35 (47)
Clutch Housing-to-Block	
Top	27 (37)
Bottom	43 (58)
Drive Plate-to-Converter	22 (30)
Drive Plate/Flywheel-to-Crankshaft	105 (142)
Front Support Bracket-to-Block	35 (47)
Front Support Cushion-to-Crossmember	37 (50)
Rear Support Bracket-to-Transmission	33 (45)
V8	
Automatic Transmission-to-Block	35 (47)
Clutch Housing-to-Block	30 (41)
Drive Plate-to-Converter	22 (30)
Drive Plate/Flywheel-to-Crankshaft	105 (142)
Front Support Bracket-to-Block	35 (47)
Front Support Bracket-to-Crossmember	37 (50)
Rear Support Bracket-to-Transmission	33 (45)

Engine Cooling Systems

GENERAL COOLING SYSTEM SERVICING

DESCRIPTION

The basic liquid cooling system consists of a radiator, water pump, thermostat, cooling fan, pressure cap, heater, if equipped, and various connecting hoses and cooling passages in the block and cylinder head. In addition, many cars use a fan clutch, which may incorporate a thermostatic control, or a flexible blade fan, or both, to reduce noise and power requirements at high engine speeds. Some models, with exhaust emission control, use a thermostatic vacuum switch to advance ignition timing in the event of overheating. As most new models require the use of a permanent, year round (ethylene glycol) type antifreeze, coolant recovery systems are being used more commonly to prevent coolant loss.

MAINTENANCE

DRAINING

Remove radiator cap, open heater control valve to maximum heat position, if equipped, open drain cocks or remove plugs in bottom of radiator and in engine block. In-line engines usually have one plug or cock, while V-engines will have 2, one in each bank of cylinders.

CLEANING

A good cleaning compound will remove most rust and scale. Follow manufacturer's instructions in the use of the cleaner. If considerable rust and scale will have to be removed, flushing will be necessary. Clean radiator air passages by blowing out with compressed air from back to front of radiator.

FLUSHING

1) Back flushing is a very effective means of removing rust and scale from a cooling system. For best results the radiator, engine and heater core should be flushed separately.

2) To flush radiator, connect flushing gun to water outlet of radiator and disconnect water inlet hose. Use a leadaway hose, connected to radiator inlet, to prevent flooding the engine. Use air in short bursts only, as a clogged radiator could be easily damaged. Continue flushing until water runs clear.

3) To flush engine, first remove thermostat and replace housing. Connect flushing gun to water outlet of engine. Disconnect heater hoses from engine. Flush using short air bursts until water runs clean. Flush heater core as described for radiator. Make sure heater valve is set to maximum heat position before flushing heater.

REFILLING

Engine should be running while refilling cooling system to prevent air from being trapped in engine block. After system is full, continue running engine until thermostat is open, then recheck fill level. Do not overfill system. *Refer to Cooling System Capacity tables, in this section, for correct fill level.*

TESTING

THERMOSTAT

Visually inspect thermostat for corrosion and proper sealing. If this is satisfactory, suspend thermostat and a thermometer in a container of water. Do not allow either thermostat or thermometer to touch bottom of container as this concentration of heat could cause an incorrect reading. Heat water until thermostat just begins to open. If thermostat does not open, replace.

Fig. 1: Testing Thermostat

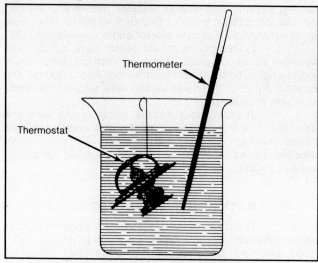

Thermostat should open as water is heated.

PRESSURE TESTING

A pressure testing tool is used to test both radiator cap and complete cooling system. Test as follows, or follow tool manufacturer's instructions.

Radiator Cap

Visually inspect radiator cap, dip in water and connect to tester. Pump tester to bring pressure to upper limit of cap specification. *Pressure cap specifications are given in appropriate manufacturer's article in this section.* If cap fails to hold pressure within given specification, replace cap.

Fig. 2: Testing Radiator Pressure Cap

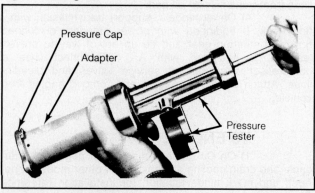

Attach cap to tester and apply pressure.

Cooling System

1) With engine stopped, wipe radiator filler neck seat clean. Fill radiator to correct level. Attach cooling system tester to radiator and pump until pressure is at upper level of radiator rating. If pressure drops, inspect for internal leaks.

2) If no leaks are apparent, detach tester and run engine until normal operating temperature is reached. Reattach tester and pump until pressure reaches approxi-

GENERAL COOLING SYSTEM SERVICING (Cont.)

mately 7 psi (.5 kg/cm²). Race engine. If needle on tester fluctuates, it indicates a combustion leak.

NOTE: **Pressure may build up quickly. Release any pressure above the limit of pressure cap specifications or cooling system damage may result.**

3) If needle does not fluctuate, race engine a few more times and check for water at tailpipe. Excessive water would indicate a faulty head gasket, cracked block or cylinder head near exhaust ports. Remove oil dipstick and if water globules appear in the oil, a serious internal leak is indicated.

ANTI-FREEZE CONCENTRATION

Test anti-freeze concentration. The tester should have a temperature compensating feature. Failure to take temperature into consideration could cause an error as large as 30°F in freeze or overheating protection. Follow manufacturer's instructions for correct use of tester.

Fig. 3: Pressure Testing Cooling System

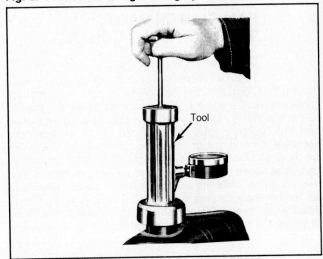

Be sure tester has a temperature compensating feature.

COOLANT RECOVERY SYSTEMS

DESCRIPTION

A coolant recovery system differs from a normal cooling system in that an overflow bottle is connected to the radiator overflow hose. The overflow bottle is transparent or translucent to permit checking of coolant level without removing radiator cap. No adjustment or test is required beyond keeping vent hole or hose clean and checking pressure relief of radiator cap.

OPERATION

As coolant temperature rises and pressure in system exceeds pressure relief valve of radiator cap, excess coolant flows into overflow bottle. As engine cools and coolant contracts, vacuum is formed in system, drawing coolant, stored in overflow bottle, back into radiator. In a properly maintained cooling system, the only coolant losses will be through evaporation.

Fig. 1: Coolant Recovery System

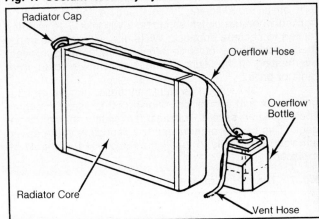

System should eliminate loss of coolant.

RADIATOR CAPS

DESCRIPTION

The radiator cap consists of a pressure valve and a vacuum valve. The cap has several different functions: It prevents coolant loss when vehicle is in motion; prevents impurities from entering cooling system minimizing corrosion; allows atmospheric pressure to eliminate the vacuum that occurs in system during cooldown; and raises coolant boiling point approximately 2°F per psi of pressure by maintaining a constant cooling system pressure. *For radiator cap testing specifications, see appropriate manufacturer's article in this section.*

Fig. 1: Radiator Cap Operation

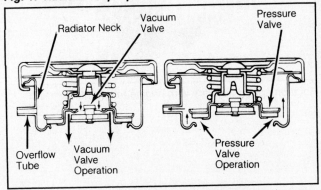

Cap should maintain constant cooling pressure in system.

Engine Cooling Systems

VARIABLE SPEED COOLING FANS

FAN CLUTCH WITH THERMOSTATIC CONTROL

DESCRIPTION

This unit consists of a thermostatically controlled fluid fan and torque control clutch. The thermal control drive is a silicone filled coupling connecting the fan to the fan pulley. The drive is operated by a control valve and the control valve is operated by a temperature sensitive bimetal coil or strip. The control valve maintains the flow of silicone through the clutch. During periods of operation when radiator discharge air temperature is low, the fan clutch limits the fan speed. High radiator discharge air temperature causes bimetal to allow a greater flow of silicone to enter the clutch. This increases the drag between the driven member and driving member, resulting in a higher fan speed and increased cooling.

TESTING

In cases of engine overheating or insufficient air conditioning, proceed as follows:

1) Start with a cool engine to ensure complete fan clutch disengagement. Cover radiator grille sufficiently to induce high engine temperature.

2) Start engine and operate at 2000 RPM and turn on air conditioning, if equipped. A fan roar will be noticed when fan clutch engages. It will take 5-10 minutes for fan to become engaged. While operating engine under these conditions, observe temperature light to prevent overheating. If hot light comes on, remove cover from radiator grille.

3) As soon as clutch engages, remove radiator grille cover and turn air conditioning off to assist in engine cooling. After several minutes fan clutch should disengage. This can be determined by a reduction in fan speed and roar. If fan fails to function as described, it should be replaced.

Fig. 1: Thermal Control Fan Drive Unit

Rotation speed will vary with engine temperature.

FAN CLUTCH WITHOUT THERMOSTATIC CONTROL

DESCRIPTION

This unit is basically the same as the thermostatically controlled fan clutch except it is not controlled by a temperature sensitive coil. The fan clutch allows the fan to be driven in a normal manner at low speeds while a higher engine speed limits the rotational speed of the fan to a predetermined rate. The silicone in the clutch housing provides a more positive drive at lower speeds and allows greater slippage between the driven member and driving member at higher engine speeds.

TESTING

In case of engine overheating during low speed or idle operation, increase engine speed to approximately 1000 RPM in neutral gear. If condition is not corrected by increasing engine speed, replace fan drive unit with a unit that is known to be operating properly and test by operating vehicle under same conditions. Replace unit assembly if trouble is corrected with test unit. All units are non-adjustable. Replace, if unit is damaged or operating improperly.

FLEX-BLADE FAN

DESCRIPTION

This unit is a fixed blade assembly designed to flex the blades as the engine RPM increases. As RPM increases, blade pitch decreases, saving power and decreasing noise level. No adjustment or test is required beyond keeping fan belt adjusted to proper tension and ensuring that unit is not damaged.

Fig. 2: Flex-Blade Fan

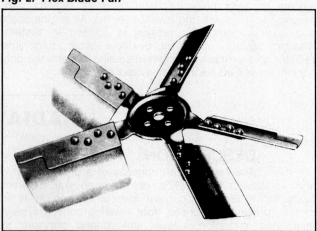

Blades should flex as engine RPM increases.

ENGINE COOLANT SPECIFICATIONS

CHRYSLER CORP.

THERMOSTAT

Thermostat, located in water outlet elbow, is a pellet type with an opening temperature of 195°F (90°C). Thermostat should be fully open at 219°F (104°C) on all engines.

PRESSURE CAP

All models use a 16 psi (1.1 kg/cm²) pressure cap which should be tested at 14-17 psi (1.0-1.2 kg/cm²). Center of cap is equipped with a vent valve which allows a small flow through cap when temperature is below boiling point. Valve closes when boiling point is reached. Valve also opens when coolant is cooling and contracting, permitting liquid to return to radiator from coolant reserve tank.

WATER PUMP

Pump is serviced only as an assembly. When replacing water pump, be sure correct pump is used. Pump impeller must be compatible with pulley system drive ratio. It is possible to replace pump without discharging air conditioning system. When replacing water pump because of bearing or shaft failure, carefully inspect fan for cracks, loose blades or rivets caused by excessive vibration. If necessary, replace fan.

MAINTENANCE

Inspect cooling system every 12 months or 15,000 miles. Drain and flush cooling system at 36 months or 52,000 miles, and every 24 months or 30,000 miles thereafter. Maintain a coolant level of 50% ethylene glycol anti-freeze and 50% water year-round.

COOLANT CAPACITY

Application	Quarts (L)
3.7L	[1] 12.0 (11.4)
5.2L	[2] 16.0 (15.1)
5.9L	[2] 14.5 (13.7)

[1] — Add 2 quarts (1.9) for A/C or extra cool.
[2] — Add 1 quart (.9) for A/C, extra cool or aux. heat.

FORD

THERMOSTAT

Thermostat, located in water outlet elbow, has an opening temperature of 192°F (89°C) on 4-cylinder and V8 engines, 197°F (92°C) on 6-cylinder engines and 180°F (82°C) on V8 Diesel engines.

PRESSURE CAP

All models use a 13 psi (.9 kg/cm²) pressure cap which should be tested at 10-14 psi (.7-1.0 kg/cm²).

WATER PUMP

If wear or damage exists, water pump replacement is recommended. No attempt to overhaul or repair pump should be made.

MAINTENANCE

Vehicle maintenance schedule "B" or (B) is on glovebox and engine emission control information decal.

Check coolant condition annually. Drain, clean, flush and refill system if dirt or rust impairs cooling ability. Hoses and clamps should be inspected every 3 years or 50,000 miles, whichever occurs first.

COOLANT CAPACITY

Application	Quarts (L)
2.0L & 2.3L Engines	
With A/C	7.2 (6.8)
Without A/C	6.5 (6.2)
2.2L Engines (Diesel)	
With A/C	10.7 (10.1)
Without A/C	10.0 (9.5)
2.8L Engines	
With A/C	7.8 (7.4)
Without A/C	7.2 (6.8)
3.8L Engines	
Standard or Extra Cooling	11.0 (10.4)
Super Cooling or A/C	12.0 (11.4)
4.9L Engines	
Bronco & Pickup	
Standard or Extra Cooling	13.0 (12.3)
Super Cooling or A/C	14.0 (13.2)
Van [1]	
With Heater	15.0 (14.2)
With Heater & A/C	20.0 (18.9)
5.0L Engines	
Bronco & Pickup	
Standard or Extra Cooling	13.0 (12.2)
Super Cooling or A/C	14.0 (13.2)
Van	
Standard Cooling	15.0 (14.2)
Extra Cooling	17.5 (16.6)
Super Cooling or A/C	18.5 (17.5)
5.8L Engines	
Bronco & Pickup	
Standard or Extra Cooling	15.0 (14.2)
Super Cooling or A/C	16.0 (15.1)
Van [1]	
Standard or Extra Cooling	20.0 (18.9)
Super Cooling or A/C	21.0 (20.0)
6.9L Engines (Diesel)	31.0 (29.3)
7.5L Engines	
Pickup	
Man. Trans. & Extra Cooling	16.5 (15.6)
All Other Options	17.5 (16.6)
Van [1]	28.0 (26.5)

[1] — Add .80 (.76) for auxiliary heater.

GENERAL MOTORS

THERMOSTAT

All models use a thermostat that starts to open at 195°F (91°C), and is fully open at 222°F (106°C).

PRESSURE CAP

All models use a 15 psi (1.0 kg/cm²) pressure cap which should be tested at 14-17 psi (.9-1.2 kg/cm²).

WATER PUMP

Water pump is serviced only as an assembly.

Engine Cooling Systems

ENGINE COOLANT SPECIFICATIONS (Cont.)

MAINTENANCE

Inspect cooling system every 12 months or 15,000 miles. Drain and flush cooling system every 24 months or 30,000 miles. Maintain coolant level with a 50% mixture of ethylene glycol based anti-freeze and low mineral content water year-around.

COOLANT CAPACITY

Application	Quarts (L)
All Models	
1.9L Engines	9.4 (8.9)
2.0L Engines	9.6 (9.2)
2.8L Engines	12.0 (11.5)
4.1L Engines	
Van Models	17.0 (16.1)
All Other Models	15.5 (14.7)
4.8L Engines	
"P" Models	13.8 (13.1)
All Other Models	15.5 (14.7)
5.0L & 5.7L Engines	
"P" Models	
With A/C	19.2 (18.0)
Without A/C	15.6 (14.8)
Van Models	
With A/C	20.0 (19.0)
Without A/C	19.0 (18.0)
All Other Models	
With A/C	18.0 (17.1)
Without A/C	17.5 (16.6)
6.2L Engines (Diesel)	
With A/C	24.5 (23.3)
Without A/C	23.0 (21.7)
7.4L Engines	
With A/C	24.5 (23.3)
Without A/C	23.0 (21.7)

JEEP

THERMOSTAT

Thermostat, located in water outlet elbow, is a pellet type with an opening temperature of 195°F (90°C). Thermostat should be fully open at 218°F (103°C) on all engines.

PRESSURE CAP

All models use a 14 psi (1.0kg/cm²) pressure cap. Test cap at 12-15 psi (.8-1.0 kg/cm²) for 30 seconds or more.

WATER PUMP

Water pump impeller is pressed on the rear of pump shaft and bearing assembly. Pump is serviced as an assembly only.

MAINTENANCE

At 12,500 miles or 12 months, change engine coolant. Thereafter, change engine coolant at the start of winter. Maintain coolant level with a 50% mixture of ethylene glycol based anti-freeze and low mineral content water year-around.

COOLANT CAPACITY

Application	Quarts (L)
All Models	
2.5L Engines	8 (7)
4.2L Engines	11 (10)
6.0L Engines	14 (13)

SECTION 8

CLUTCHES

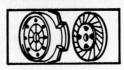

CONTENTS

NOTE: **ALSO SEE GENERAL INDEX.**

IMPORTANT: **Because of the many model names used by vehicle manufacturers, accurate identification of models is important. See Model Identification at the front of this publication.**

Clutches

CLUTCH TROUBLE SHOOTING

CONDITION	POSSIBLE CAUSE	CORRECTION
Chattering or Grabbing	Incorrect lever adjustment	See adjustment in CLUTCHES
	Oil, grease or glaze on facings	Disassemble and clean or replace
	Loose "U" joint flange	See DRIVE AXLES
	Worn input shaft spline	See CLUTCHES
	Binding pressure plate	See CLUTCHES
	Binding release lever	See CLUTCHES
	Binding disc hub	See Removal in CLUTCHES
	Unequal pressure plate contact	Replace worn/misaligned components
	Loose/bent clutch disc	See Removal & Installation in CLUTCHES
	Incorrect transmission alignment	See Removal in MANUAL TRANSMISSION
	Worn pressure plate, disc or flywheel	See Removal & Installation in CLUTCHES
	Broken or weak pressure springs	Replace pressure plate
	Sticking clutch pedal	See General Servicing in CLUTCHES
	Incorrect disc facing	Replace and match components
	Engine loose in chassis	Tighten all mounting bolts
Spinning	Dry or worn bushings	Lubricate and replace worn parts
	Misaligned clutch housing	See Removal in MANUAL TRANSMISSION
	Bent or distorted clutch disc	Replace and match components
	Excessive pedal free play	See Adjustment in CLUTCHES
Dragging	Oil or grease on facings	Clean and replace if necessary
	Incorrect lever or pedal adjustment	See Adjustment in CLUTCHES
	Dust or dirt on clutch	See General Servicing in CLUTHCES
	Worn or broken facings	Replace worn/damaged components
	Bent clutch disc or pressure plate	Replace and match components
	Clutch disc hub binding on shaft	See General Servicing in CLUTCHES
	Binding pilot bushing	See Gereral Servicing in CLUTCHES
	Sticking release bearing sleeve	See CLUTCHES
Rattling	Weak or broken release lever spring	Replace spring and check alignment
	Damaged pressure plate	Replace and match components
	Broken clutch return spring	Replace spring
	Worn splines on disc or input shaft	Replace disc and/or input shaft
	Worn clutch release bearing	Replace spring and check alignment
	Dry or worn pilot bushing	Lubricate or replace bushing
	Unequal release lever contact	Align or replace lever
	Incorrect pedal free play	See Adjustment in CLUTCHES
	Warped clutch disc	Replace and match components
Slipping	Pressure springs worn or broken	Replace damaged components
	Oily, greasy or worn clutch facings,	Clean or replace components
	Incorrect clutch alignment	See CLUTCHES
	Warped clutch disc or pressure plate	Replace and match damaged components
	Binding release levers or clutch pedal	See General Servicing in CLUTCHES
Squeaking	Worn or damaged release bearing	Replace worn/damaged parts
	Dry or worn pilot/release bearing	Lubricate or replace if necessary
	Pilot bearing turning in crankshaft	See Removal in CLUTCHES
	Worn input shaft bearing	Replace bearing and seal
	Incorrect transmission alignment	See Removal in MANUAL TRANSMISSION
	Dry clutch fork between pivot	See General Servicing in CLUTCHES
Heavy and/or Stiff Pedal	Sticking release bearing sleeve	See General Servicing in CLUTCHES
	Dry or binding pedal hub	Lubricate and align components
	Floor mat interference with pedal	Lay mat flat in proper area
	Dry or binding ball/fork pivots	Lubricate and align components
Grinding	Dry release bearing	See General Servicing in CLUTCHES
	Dry or worn pilot bearing	Lubricate or replace bearing
	Worn input shaft bearing	Replace bearing
Whirring	Incorrect pedal free play	See Adjustment in CLUTCHES
	Incorrect transmission alignment	See Removal in MANUAL TRANSMISSION

Clutches

CHRYSLER CORP.

Dodge, Plymouth

DESCRIPTION

Clutches used on all Chrysler Corp. vehicles are single, dry disc design. Adjustment for wear is not provided in clutch itself. Clutch pedal linkage is adjustable to maintain pedal free play. Clutch linkage on all models is mechanical type.

Fig. 1: Exploded View of Clutch Assembly

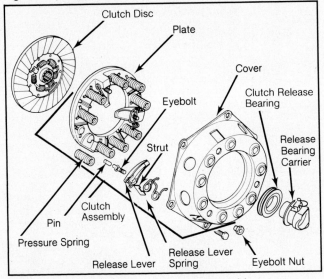

Mark clutch cover position before disassembly.

REMOVAL & INSTALLATION

TRANSMISSION

Removal (NP 435 Trans.)

1) Disconnect negative battery cable from battery. Remove retaining screws from floor pan boot and slide up and off shift lever.

2) Remove shift lever retainer by pressing down, rotating retainer counterclockwise and releasing retainer. Remove 4 bolts attaching skid plate to underside of frame.

3) Remove 5 bolts attaching front of skid plate-to-transmission crossmember. Remove skid plate. Disconnect speedometer cable.

4) Disconnect front and rear propeller shafts and secure out of the way. Disconnect shift rods at transfer case. Support transfer case with jack.

5) Remove extension-to-transfer case bolts. Move transfer case rearward and disengage front input spline. Lower transfer case from vehicle. Disconnect back-up light switch.

6) Install engine support over frame rails. Be sure support ends are against underside of oil pan flange. Support transmission and remove center crossmember.

7) Remove transmission to clutch housing bolts. Slide transmission rearward until drive pinion shaft clears clutch disc. Remove transmission.

Installation

Grease transmission pilot bushing located in end of crankshaft using multi-purpose grease. Do not lubricate end of pinion shaft, clutch disc splines or clutch release levers. Reverse removal procedures to install transmission.

Removal (Overdrive-4 Trans.)

1) Disconnect negative cable from battery. Remove retaining screws from floor pan boot and slide up and off shift lever. Remove shift lever.

2) Remove retaining clips, washers and control rods from shift unit levers. Remove 2 bolts and washers securing shift unit to mounting plate on extension housing and remove unit.

3) Drain transmission fluid. Mark propeller shaft position for reinstallation and disconnect at rear universal joint. Pull shaft yoke out of transmission extension housing.

4) Disconnect speedometer cable and back-up light switch. Install engine support. Be sure support ends are against underside of oil pan flange. Raise engine and disconnect extension housing from center crossmember.

5) Support transmission and remove center crossmember. Remove transmission-to-clutch housing bolts. Slide transmission rearward until drive pinion shaft clears clutch disc. Lower transmission.

Installation

Grease transmission pilot bushing located in end of crankshaft using multi-purpose grease. Use multi-purpose lubricant around inner end of pinion shaft pilot bushing in flywheel and on pinion bearing retainer release bearing sleeve. Do not lubricate end of pinion shaft, clutch disc splines or clutch release levers. Reverse removal procedures to install transmission.

CLUTCH

Removal

1) With transmission and transfer case (if equipped) removed, remove clutch housing pan. Disconnect clutch fork return spring. Remove fork rod spring washer from pin and remove fork rod, adjusting nut, washer and insulator.

2) Remove clutch fork and release bearing (if not removed with transmission).

3) Mark position of clutch cover on flywheel for reassembly. Remove clutch cover bolts by loosening 1 or 2 turns at a time until all bolts are removed. Remove clutch cover and disc from flywheel.

Installation

1) Ensure flywheel surface is clean. Install clutch cover and disc with aligning tool. Ensure cover is in original position on flywheel.

2) Tighten cover bolts a few turns at a time, alternately and evenly. Lubricate bearing sleeve cavity with grease.

3) Apply thin grease coat to release fork pads, clutch fork fingers and pivot contact area. Reverse removal procedure and install transmission.

PILOT BEARING (BUSHING)

Removal

Thread a tapered pilot into bushing, and install puller screw into pilot. Turn puller screw until bushing is removed from crankshaft.

Installation

Soak new bushing in oil before installing. Using driver (SP-3549 or C4171 on head SP-3551), tap new bushing into crankshaft flush to end. Place grease in crankshaft cavity forward of bushing, and coat inner surface of bushing.

CHRYSLER CORP. (Cont.)

CLUTCH HOUSING ALIGNMENT

NOTE: If clutch housing is removed while making adjustments or repairs, it will be necessary to check and/or align housing.

1) Remove 1 flywheel-to-crankshaft bolt and replace with bolt approximately 3" long. Mount dial indicator (C-3339 or equivalent) on bolt using "C" clamp. Position stem of dial indicator on face of clutch housing.

2) Pry crankshaft forward until bottomed against crankshaft thrust bearing. Zero dial indicator. Rotate flywheel using turning tool (C-771 or equivalent) and watch indicator reading. Runout should not exceed .006" (.15 mm).

3) If runout is excessive, loosen housing bolts and insert shim between clutch housing and block at point of maximum runout. Reposition stem of dial indicator to inside of pilot bore of clutch housing.

4) Zero dial indicator. Rotate flywheel using turning tool (C-771 or equivalent) and watch indicator reading. Runout should not exceed .008" (.20 mm). If runout is greater, install offset dowels in same size pairs. Select dowels from sizes listed.

OFFSET DOWEL SELECTION CHART

Runout In. (mm)	Offset Dowel In. (mm)
.009-.020 (.23-.51)	.007 (.18)
.022-.034 (.56-.86)	.014 (.36)
.036-.050 (.91-1.27)	.021 (.53)

5) Remove clutch housing and original dowels from rear face of engine block. Install offset dowels with slots parallel to point of maximum runout and seated in block up to shoulder of offset.

6) Install clutch housing and tighten bolts. Remount dial indicator and check runout. Minor adjustment can be made by turning dowel with a screwdriver until runout is correct.

ADJUSTMENT

CLUTCH LINKAGE

Adjust clutch fork push rod to obtain 3/32" (2.4 mm) free play at clutch fork push rod pivot pin. Free play will provide correct pedal free play of approximately 1".

TIGHTENING SPECIFICATIONS

Application	Ft. Lbs. (N.m)
Clutch Cover-to-Flywheel Bolts	
5/16"	17 (23)
3/8"	30 (41)
Clutch Fork Pivot Bolts	17 (23)
Housing-to-Engine Block Bolts	
7/16"	50 (68)
3/8"	30 (41)
Transmission-to-Clutch Housing	50 (68)
Transmission-to-Flywheel Bolts	55 (75)

FORD — HYDRAULIC

Bronco II & Ranger
Pickup (6.9L Diesel & 7.5L)

DESCRIPTION

Hydraulic clutch consists of a clutch disc and pressure plate. Pilot bearings, roller or bushing type, are mounted in flywheel and require no lubrication unless clutch assembly is serviced. No adjustment of clutch linkage or pedal position is required.

REMOVAL & INSTALLATION

TRANSMISSION

Removal (Bronco II & Ranger)

1) With gearshift in "Neutral", remove boot retainer screws. Remove retainer cover-to-gearshift lever retainer bolts. Disconnect clutch master cylinder push rod from clutch pedal.

2) Remove gearshift lever assembly by pulling shim and bushing straight up and away from gearshift lever retainer. Cover shift tower opening in extension housing.

3) Disconnect clutch hydraulic system master cylinder push rod from clutch pedal. Disconnect negative battery cable. Raise and support vehicle. Disconnect driveshaft at rear axle drive flange.

4) Pull driveshaft rearward and disconnect from transmission. Install plug in extension housing. Remove clutch housing dust shield and slave cylinder and secure aside.

5) Remove speedometer cable from extension housing. Disconnect starter motor and back-up light switch. Place jack under engine and wood block under oil pan. On 4WD vehicles, remove transfer case. Remove starter motor. Place transmission jack under transmission.

6) Remove bolts, lockwashers and flat washers attaching transmission-to-engine rear plate. Remove transmission mount and damper-to-crossmember bolts.

7) Remove crossmember-to-frame side rail nuts and remove crossmember. Lower engine jack.

8) Remove clutch housing from the locating dowels. Slide transmission rearward until input shaft spline clears clutch disc. Remove transmission from vehicle.

Installation

To install transmission, reverse removal procedures. Be sure to align splines on input shaft with splines in clutch disc.

Removal (2WD Pickup)

1) Remove floor mat and body floor pan cover. Remove gearshift lever shift ball and boot as an assembly. Remove weather pad.

2) Raise and support vehicle. Position transmission jack under transmission and disconnect speedometer cable. Disconnect back-up light switch at rear of gear shift housing cover.

3) Disconnect propeller shaft and clutch linkage from transmission and wire aside. Remove transmission attaching bolts. Move transmission rearward until input shaft clears clutch housing. Lower transmission.

Installation

To install transmission, reverse removal procedures. Install guide studs in clutch housing and raise

transmission until input shaft splines are aligned with clutch disc splines. Clutch release bearing and hub must be properly positioned in release lever fork.

Removal (4WD Pickup)

1) From inside vehicle, remove floor mat. Remove screws holding access cover to floor pan. Place shift lever in "Reverse" and remove shift lever cover. Remove insulator and dust cover.

2) From transfer case and transmission, remove shift lever, shift ball and boot as assemblies. Raise and support vehicle. Drain transmission. Disconnect front and rear propeller shafts from transfer case and wire aside.

3) Remove retainer ring holding shift link in place and remove shift link from transfer case. Remove speedometer cable.

4) Place jack under transfer case. Remove transfer case-to-transmission bolts and remove transfer case. Remove rear support bracket-to-transmission. Place jack under transmission and remove rear support bracket and brace.

5) Remove transmission-to-bell housing bolts. Remove transmission.

Installation

To install transmission, reverse removal procedures. Install 2 guide studs in bell housing top holes to guide transmission into position.

CLUTCH

NOTE: **On all models, new slave cylinder is equipped with a strap that positions push rod and provides a bearing insert. Following slave cylinder installation, clutch pedal depression will break strap allowing proper system operation.**

Removal (Bronco II & Ranger)

1) With transmission removed, remove lock pin and disconnect master cylinder push rod from clutch pedal. On 2.0L & 2.3L engines, remove bolt attaching dust shield to clutch housing and remove dust shield.

2) Push slave cylinder rearward then outward to remove. Retain plastic bearing inserts for reassembly.

3) On 2.2L Diesel and 2.8L engines, remove bolts attaching slave cylinder to clutch housing and remove slave cylinder. Remove push rod from release lever.

4) On all models, remove 2 bolts attaching fluid reservoir to cowl access cover. Remove master cylinder from opening in firewall and remove hydraulic assembly.

Installation

1) Position hydraulic system in engine compartment. Slave to master cylinder tube routing is above brake tubes and below steering column shaft. On 2.8L vehicles, tube must lay on top of clutch housing.

2) Insert master cylinder push rod through opening in firewall. Attach master cylinder to firewall. Position fluid reservoir on cowl opening cover and install attaching nuts.

3) Install slave cylinder, engage push rod and insert plastic bearings. Attach cylinder to clutch housing. On 2.0L and 2.3L engines, snap dust shield in place and tighten bolts.

4) On 2.2L Diesel and 2.8L vehicles, install bolts attaching slave cylinder to clutch housing.

FORD — HYDRAULIC (Cont.)

5) On all models, apply SAE 30 oil or equivalent to master cylinder push rod bushing. Install bushing and push rod on clutch pedal. Install lock pin. Depress clutch pedal repeatedly to verify proper operation.

Fig. 1: 2.2L Bronco II Hydraulic Clutch System

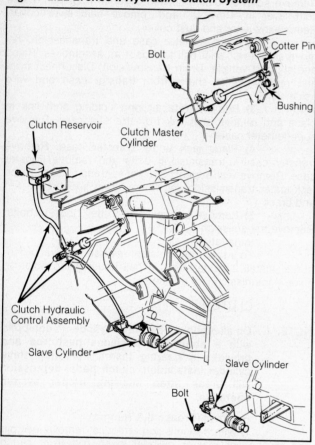

Fig. 2: Pickup Hydraulic Clutch System

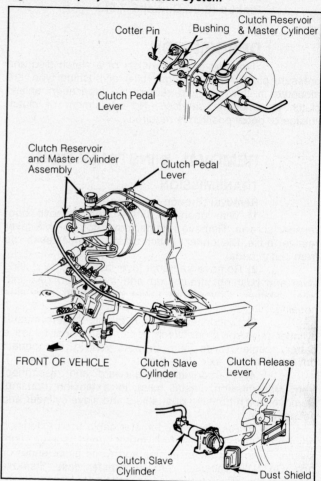

Removal (Pickup)

1) Once transmission has been removed, from inside vehicle, remove cotter pin holding master cylinder push rod to clutch pedal lever. Disconnect push rod and remove bushing.

2) Remove 2 nuts holding clutch reservoir and master cylinder assembly to firewall. At engine compartment, remove clutch reservoir and master cylinder assembly from firewall. Note routing of clutch tubing to slave cylinder.

3) Push slave cylinder rearward then outward to disengage 2 release cylinder retaining tabs from retainer bracket. Disengage push rod from release lever while removing slave cylinder.

Installation

1) Position clutch fluid reservoir and master cylinder on firewall and from inside vehicle tighten 2 nuts. Route clutch tubing and slave cylinder to bell housing.

2) Install slave cylinder push rod onto cylinder. Engage push rod into release lever and slide slave cylinder into bell housing lugs. Apply SAE 30 engine oil or equivalent to master cylinder push rod bushing.

3) From inside vehicle, install bushing on clutch lever pedal. Connect clutch master cylinder push rod to clutch pedal lever and install cotter pin.

4) Depress clutch pedal repeatedly to verify proper operation.

TESTING

CLUTCH PEDAL TRAVEL

1) Measure travel of clutch slave cylinder push rod. With clutch pedal pushed fully to floor, slave cylinder push rod should extend at least .53" (13.5 mm) against clutch lever head. If push rod travel meets or exceeds limit, system is functioning properly.

2) If slave cylinder does not have acceptable travel, check reservoir fluid level with slave cylinder in place. If reservoir requires fluid, check hydraulic system for leakage.

3) Remove rubber boots from cylinder and check for leakage past cylinders. Slight moisture is acceptable, if leakage is excessive, replace system.

TIGHTENING SPECIFICATIONS

Application	Ft. Lbs. (N.m)
Dust Cover-to-Bell Housing	
2.0 & 2.3L Engine	5-10 (7-13)
Flywheel Housing-to-Engine	40-50 (55-67)
Master Cylinder-to-Firewall	15-20 (21-27)
Slave Cylinder-to-Clutch Housing	
2.2L & 2.8L Engine	15-20 (21-27)
Transmission-to-Flywheel	37-42 (51-56)

Clutches

FORD — MECHANICAL

**Bronco, Pickup, Van
(Exc. Pickup 6.9L Diesel & 7.5L)**

DESCRIPTION

Two types of clutches are used in Ford vehicles. Each type has a single-disc dry plate. One plate is non-centrifugal and the other is semi-centrifugal. Clutch release is accomplished through mechanical linkage. The pedal pressure is transmitted through a series of rods and an equalizer shaft.

REMOVAL & INSTALLATION

TRANSMISSION

NOTE: **Do not depress clutch pedal while transmission is removed.**

Removal ("E" Models With 3-Speed Trans.)

1) Raise and support vehicle. Drain transmission fluid. Disconnect propeller shaft from flange at transmission. Secure propeller shaft out of the way.

2) Disconnect speedometer cable from extension housing. Disconnect gear shift rods from transmission shift levers. Position jack under transmission.

3) Raise transmission. Remove 4 transmission extension housing-to-insulator and retainer bolts. Remove 4 transmission-to-flywheel housing bolts. Install engine support bar on frame. Remove transmission.

Installation

To install transmission, reverse removal procedures. Splines on input shaft and splines in clutch disc must be aligned. Move transmission forward on guide pins until input shaft pilot enters bearing or bushing in crankshaft. If front bearing retainer binds, work release bearing lever until hub slides onto front bearing retainer.

Removal ("F" Models With 3-Speed Trans.)

1) Raise and support vehicle. Support engine with a jack and wood block under oil pan. Drain transmission fluid. Position transmission jack under transmission and secure transmission to jack.

2) Disconnect gear shift linkage at transmission. Disconnect speedometer cable. Disconnect back-up light switch. Disconnect propeller shaft from transmission.

3) Remove rear support, insulator and retainer assembly. Remove transmission-to-flywheel housing bolts. Move transmission rearward until input shaft clears clutch housing. Remove transmission.

Installation

Before installing transmission, apply multi-purpose lubricant to release bearing inner hub surfaces, release lever fulcrum and fork and transmission front bearing retainer. To complete installation, reverse removal procedures.

Removal (2WD "F" Models With Warner T-18 or T-19B 4-Speed Trans.)

1) Remove floor mat and body floor pan cover. Remove gearshift lever shift ball and boot as an assembly. Remove weather pad.

2) Raise and support vehicle. Position transmission jack under transmission and disconnect speedometer cable. Disconnect back-up light switch at rear of gear shift housing cover.

3) Disconnect propeller shaft and clutch linkage from transmission and wire aside. Remove transmission attaching bolts. Move transmission rearward until input shaft clears clutch housing. Lower transmission.

Installation

To install transmission, reverse removal procedures. Install guide studs in clutch housing and raise transmission until input shaft splines are aligned with clutch disc splines. Clutch release bearing and hub must be properly positioned in release lever fork.

Removal (4WD Bronco & "F" Models With Warner T-18 or T-18B 4-Speed Trans.)

1) From inside vehicle, remove floor mat. Remove screws holding access cover to floor pan. Place shift lever in "Reverse" and remove shift lever cover. Remove insulator and dust cover.

2) From transfer case and transmission, remove shift lever, shift ball and boot as assemblies. Raise and support vehicle. Drain transmission. Disconnect front and rear propeller shafts from transfer case and wire aside.

3) Remove retainer ring holding shift link in place and remove shift link from transfer case. Remove speedometer cable.

4) Place jack under transfer case. Remove transfer case-to-transmission bolts and remove transfer case. Remove rear support bracket-to-transmission. Place jack under transmission and remove rear support bracket and brace.

5) Remove transmission-to-bell housing bolts. Remove transmission.

Installation

To install transmission, reverse removal procedures. Install 2 guide studs in bell housing top holes to guide transmission into position.

Removal (Bronco & "F" Models With NP 435 4-Speed Trans.)

1) Remove floor mat. Remove shift lever, boot and ball as an assembly. On 4WD models, remove transfer case shift lever, rubber boot and ball as an assembly.

2) Remove floor pan transmission cover. Remove weather pad on F150 and F350 models.

3) On all models, remove gearshift lever and knob by removing inner cap, spring seat and spring. Remove gearshift lever from housing.

4) Disconnect back-up light switch, located on left-hand side of gearshift housing cover. Raise and support vehicle. Disconnect speedometer cable. Remove rear propeller shaft and wire aside.

5) On 4WD models, drain transfer case. Remove front propeller shaft from transfer case and wire aside. Remove cotter key holding shift link and remove shift link. Remove speedometer cable from transfer case.

6) Remove support bracket-to-transfer case bolts. Place jack under transfer case. Remove transfer case-to-transmission bolts. Remove transfer case.

7) On all models, place transmission jack under transmission. Remove transmission attaching bolts at clutch housing. Remove transmission.

Installation

To install transmission, reverse removal procedures. Be sure input shaft splines are aligned with clutch disc splines. Clutch release bearing and hub must be properly positioned in release lever fork.

Clutches

FORD — MECHANICAL (Cont.)

Removal (2WD F100 & F250 Models With S.R.O.D Trans.)

1) Raise and support vehicle. Mark propeller shaft position for reinstallation. Disconnect propeller shaft from rear universal joint flange.

2) Remove propeller shaft from output shaft. Insert extension housing seal installer into extension housing. Disconnect speedometer cable. Remove back-up light switch.

3) Remove shift lever to turret assembly screws. Remove shift lever. Support engine with transmission jack. Remove extension housing-to-engine rear support bolts.

4) Raise engine enough to remove weight from crossmember. Remove crossmember bolts and remove crossmember. Support transmission on jack and remove transmission-to-flywheel housing bolts.

5) Move transmission rearward until input shaft clears flywheel housing. Remove transmission.

Installation

To install transmission, reverse removal procedures. Install guide pins in flywheel housing lower mounting bolt holes. Move transmission on guide pins until input shaft splines enter clutch hub splines and case is against flywheel housing.

Removal (4WD Bronco & F150 Models With S.R.O.D Trans.)

1) Raise and support vehicle. Drain transmission and/or transfer case. Disconnect 4WD indicator switch at transfer case. Disconnect back-up light switch wire at transmission.

2) Mark position of front and rear propeller shaft. Disconnect rear propeller shaft from transfer case and wire aside. Remove speedometer cable from transfer case. Remove retaining clips and shift rod from transfer case control lever and shift lever.

3) Disconnect vent hose from transfer case. Remove shift lever-to-transmission turret screws. Remove shift lever from turret. Support transmission with jack and remove transmission housing-to-engine rear bracket.

4) Raise transmission to remove weight from crossmember. Disconnect gusset-to-support and remove gusset on left side. Remove transmission support plate bolts.

5) Remove support plate-to-crossmember bolts. Remove support plate and remove right gusset. Remove crossmember. Remove transfer case heat shield.

6) Support transfer case. Remove transfer case-to-transmission adapter bolts. Slide transfer case off output shaft and lower transfer case from vehicle. Remove gasket between transfer case and adapter.

7) Support transmission with a jack. Remove transmission-to-flywheel housing bolts. Move transmission rearward until input shaft clears flywheel housing. Remove transmission.

Installation

To install transmission, reverse removal procedures. Install guide pins in flywheel housing lower mounting bolt holes. Move transmission on guide pins until input shaft splines enter clutch hub splines and case is against flywheel housing.

Removal ("E" Models With 4-Speed Overdrive)

1) Place wood block under clutch pedal to prevent clutch depression. Raise and support vehicle. Mark propeller shaft position for reinstallation. Disconnect propeller shaft from rear universal joint flange.

2) Slide propeller shaft off transmission output shaft. Insert extension housing seal installer into extension housing. Disconnect speedometer cable from extension housing.

3) Remove retaining clips, flat washers and spring washers. Secure shift rods to shift levers. Remove shift control-to-transmission extension housing bolts. Remove shift control-to-transmission case nuts.

4) Remove rear transmission support bolts connecting crossmember support to transmission extension housing. Support transmission using a jack. Raise transmission to remove weight from No. 3 crossmember.

5) Remove No. 3 crossmember bolts and remove crossmember. Raise engine enough to remove weight from crossmember. Remove retaining bolts and remove crossmember.

6) Remove transmission-to-flywheel housing bolts. Move transmission rearward until input shaft clears flywheel housing. Remove transmission.

Installation

To install transmission, reverse removal procedures. Install guide pins in flywheel housing lower mounting bolt holes. Move transmission on guide pins until input shaft splines enter clutch hub splines and case is against flywheel housing.

CLUTCH

Removal

With transmission removed, remove starter and clutch housing. Mark flywheel and clutch cover for reassembly. Loosen clutch cover bolts evenly until spring tension is released. Remove clutch assembly from vehicle.

Installation

To install, clean flywheel surface and reverse removal procedures. Apply grease to release lever fingers and lever pivot ball. Do not grease release lever pivot assembly on Vans. Tighten cover bolts evenly and alternately. Reinstall transmission.

PILOT BEARING

NOTE: **Needle roller bearing and adaptor is used as clutch pilot bearing on all models. Bearing and adaptor are a single unit and cannot be serviced separately.**

Removal

With transmission removed, remove clutch pressure plate and disc. Using impact slide hammer and puller (T59L-100B and T58L-101-A), remove pilot bearing.

Installation

Using pilot bearing replacer and clutch aligner (T74P-7137-A and T71P-7137-H), install pilot bearing with seal facing transmission. Reinstall clutch pressure plate, disc and transmission.

CLUTCH HOUSING ALIGNMENT

1) Remove transmission and flywheel housing. Reinstall flywheel housing and rear engine plate without transmission. Tighten mounting bolts.

2) Mount dial indicator on bolt using "C" clamp. Position stem of dial indicator on face of clutch housing. Push crankshaft rearward to remove any end play.

3) Set dial indicator to zero. Rotate flywheel and watch indicator reading. Face runout should not exceed .010" (.254 mm). Bore runout should not exceed .015" (.381 mm).

FORD — MECHANICAL (Cont.)

4) If runout is excessive, remove clutch housing and original dowels from rear face of engine block. Install offset dowels in same size pairs. Install clutch housing and shim between flywheel housing and engine if face alignment is necessary.

5) Remount dial indicator and check alignment. If bore alignment is excessive and face alignment is accurate, shim flywheel housing to limit of face misalignment. Check bore alignment, if not within limit, replace housing.

Fig. 1: Mounting Clutch and Linkage

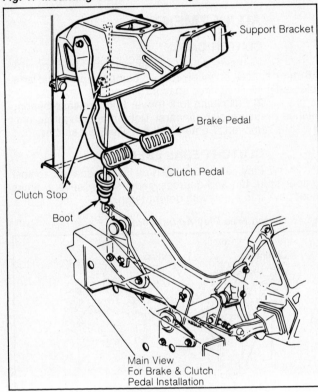

Mark flywheel and clutch cover for reassembly.

ADJUSTMENT

CLUTCH PEDAL FREE TRAVEL

1) The amount of pedal movement from full stop to point where release bearing contacts clutch fingers is pedal free travel. Specified travel is 3/4-1 1/2" (19-38 mm). If incorrect, adjust linkage.

2) Remove retracting spring. Loosen both lock nuts on rod. Position bullet end of rod tight against clutch release lever. Push rod tight against arm to eliminate all free play.

3) Insert a .135" (3.4 mm) spacer or gauge between lock nut and bullet. Tighten nut against spacer with all free play eliminated.

4) Tighten second lock nut against first, finger tight. Remove spacer and tighten lock nuts together. This will give specified pedal free play.

5) If not to specification, repeat adjustment until correct free play is obtained.

Fig. 2: Clutch Pedal Free Travel Adjustment

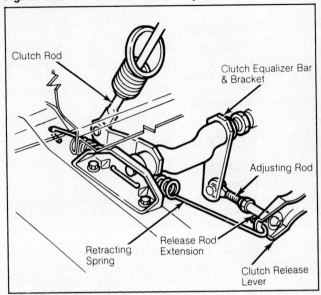

Turn clutch rod bullet to adjust free play.

TIGHTENING SPECIFICATIONS

Application	Ft. Lbs. (N.m)
Adjusting Nut Lock Nuts	18 (25)
Clutch Cover-to-Flywheel	25 (34)
Clutch Housing-to-Engine Block	45 (61)
Crossmember Bolts	50-70 (67-94)
Flywheel Housing-to-Engine	40-50 (55-67)
Transmission-to-Clutch Housing	45 (61)
Transmission-to-Flywheel Housing	42-50 (57-67)

Clutches

GENERAL MOTORS — S10

Chevrolet, GMC

DESCRIPTION

Diaphragm spring clutch utilizes a single, slotted diaphragm type spring to provide both pressure plate action and tension. The clutch is operated by a constant length cable. Adjustment mechanism is located in the pedal pivot assembly.

REMOVAL & INSTALLATION

TRANSMISSION

Removal

1) Disconnect negative battery cable. Remove upper starter motor retaining nut. Remove shift lever boot screws and slide boot off shift lever. Remove shift lever bolts at transmission.

2) On 77MM 4-speed transmission, shift transmission into "Neutral" and remove shift lever.

3) On all models, disconnect electrical connection and clip at transmission shift tower. Raise and support vehicle. Remove propeller shaft. Disconnect exhaust pipe at manifold.

4) Disconnect speedometer cable and electrical connector at transmission. Support transmission. Remove transmission mounting bolts. Disconnect clutch cable at transmission.

5) Remove catalytic converter hanger. Remove crossmember. Remove lower dust cover bolts. Remove lower starter motor bolts. Remove transmission-to-engine bolts and remove transmission.

Installation

To install the transmission, reverse all of the removal procedures.

CLUTCH

Removal

1) With transmission removed, remove flywheel housing. Slide clutch fork from ball stud. Remove fork from dust boot.

2) Install support (J-33169 or J-33034) in clutch disc during removal. Letter "X" should be painted in white or etched on clutch cover and flywheel. If letter is not evident, mark flywheel and clutch cover for reassembly.

3) Loosen clutch-to-flywheel bolts 1 or 2 turns at a time until clutch plate spring tension is released. Remove support tool, clutch cover and disc.

Installation

Lubricate ball stud and fork fingers with grease. Lubricate outside groove and completely pack recess of release bearing. Reverse removal procedure, making sure clutch hub and pilot bearing are aligned.

CLUTCH CABLE

Removal

1) Hold pedal up against bumper stop and release pawl from detent. Disconnect clutch cable from clutch release lever.

2) Remove hush panel and disconnect neutral start switch. Remove clutch pedal stop-to-clutch pedal mounting bracket. Remove pivot bolts and pedal assembly from bracket.

3) Disconnect clutch cable. Lift locking pawl and slide cable forward between detent and locking pawl.

4) In engine compartment, remove bolts holding cable to firewall. Remove cable. Replace cable if kinked or frayed or if boot is damaged.

Installation

1) Route cable and install cowl bolts. Fit cable under pawl and into detent cable groove. Install pedal assembly and pivot bolt. Install pedal bumper, neutral start switch and hush panel.

2) Hold pedal against bumper and connect other end of cable to clutch fork. Lift and depress pedal several times, then check adjustment.

ADJUSTMENT

CLUTCH CABLE

1) Insert detent pin in adjuster. Position .18" (4.6 mm) spacer between rubber bumper and pedal arm. Hold pedal firmly against spacer.

2) Pull clutch fork forward until release bearing touches pressure plate fingers. Tighten adjusting nut until all lash is removed. Tighten lock nut. Remove spacer.

CLUTCH PEDAL FREE PLAY

Play can be adjusted by lifting pedal up against bumper stop. Lift and depress pedal slowly several times to set pawl into mesh with detent teeth.

Fig. 1: Clutch Free Play Adjustment

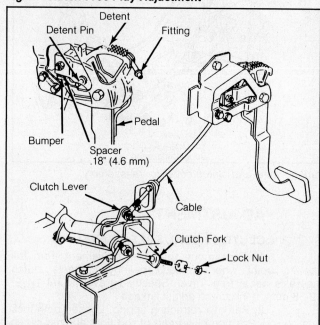

Lift and depress pedal slowly several times to adjust free play.

TIGHTENING SPECIFICATIONS

Application	Ft. Lbs. (N.m)
Crossmember-to-Frame	25 (34)
Flywheel-to-Engine Bolts	
4-Cyl.	70 (95)
V6	50 (68)
Flywheel Housing-to-Engine Bolts	55 (75)
Clutch Cover-to Flywheel	20 (25)

GENERAL MOTORS — EXC. S10

Chevrolet, GMC

DESCRIPTION

Chevrolet and GMC vehicles use 2 types of clutches, a coil spring design and a diaphragm spring design. Coil spring single plate clutch is a dry disc type with no wear adjustment provided in clutch itself. Coil spring clutch uses 3 release levers for pressure plate actuation and coil springs for pressure plate tension.

Diaphragm spring clutch uses a single, slotted diaphragm type spring for both pressure plate action and tension. All models use mechanical linkage to actuate clutch. Removal and installation procedures and adjustments are the same for Chevrolet and GMC.

REMOVAL & INSTALLATION

TRANSMISSION

Removal (3-Speed 76MM & 4-Speed 89MM Trans.)

1) Raise and support vehicle. Drain the transmission and the transfer case, if equipped. Disconnect speedometer cable.

2) On all models except "K" series, disconnect parking brake lever and controls. Disconnect back-up light switch. On all models, disconnect propeller shaft.

3) On "K" models, disconnect transfer case shift lever at transfer case. Support transfer case and remove transfer case-to-adapter bolts. Remove transfer case.

4) On all models, remove shift controls from transmission. Support transmission with a jack and remove crossmember.

5) Remove transmission-to-clutch housing bolts. Move transmission rearward to free from engine. Remove transmission.

Installation

Apply light coat of grease to main drive gear bearing retainer and splined part of transmission main drive gear shaft. Align main drive gear shaft with clutch disc hub by rotating transmission companion flange or output yoke. To complete installation, reverse removal procedures.

Removal (4-Speed 117MM Trans.)

1) Remove transmission shift lever boot retainer screws. Slide boot and retainer off lever. Remove shift lever by pushing down and turning collar counterclockwise.

2) Raise and support vehicle. Drain transmission and disconnect speedometer cable. Disconnect front propeller shaft universal joint at yoke and secure aside.

3) If equipped, support transfer case and remove transfer case-to-adapter bolts. Remove transfer case.

4) Disconnect exhaust pipes at exhaust manifold. Remove transmission mount-to-crossmember bolts. Support transmission. Remove frame-to-crossmember bolts and remove crossmember.

5) Remove upper transmission-to-clutch housing bolts and install guide pins. Remove remaining transmission-to-clutch housing bolts. Slide transmission rearward until drive gear clears clutch assembly. Remove transmission.

Installation

Apply grease to main drive gear bearing retainer and splined part of transmission main drive gear shaft. To complete transmission installation, reverse removal procedures.

CLUTCH

Removal

1) With transmission removed, disconnect rod and return spring at clutch fork. Remove clutch and flywheel housing. Snap fork off of ball pivot. Remove release bearing from clutch fork. Mark position of clutch cover on flywheel for reassembly.

2) Install a used clutch drive gear to support clutch assembly during removal. Loosen clutch cover bolts 1 or 2 turns at a time until clutch plate spring tension is released. Remove used clutch drive gear and remove clutch cover and disc.

Installation

Lubricate clutch fork ball seat and recess in release bearing. Reverse removal procedure, making sure clutch hub and pilot bearing are aligned.

ADJUSTMENT

CLUTCH PEDAL FREE PLAY

Pickup

1) Disconnect return spring at clutch fork. Rotate linkage until clutch pedal is seated against pedal stop.

2) Force clutch fork push rod rearward until throw-out bearing just contacts clutch release levers. Loosen clutch swivel lock nut.

3) Adjust swivel until swivel can be easily inserted in gauge hole. Remove swivel from gauge hole and install in equalizer shaft lower hole.

4) Tighten lock nut and check pedal. Free play should be 1 3/8-1 5/8" on "C" and "K" models and 1 1/4-1 1/2" on "P" models.

Fig. 1: Pickup Free Play Adjustment

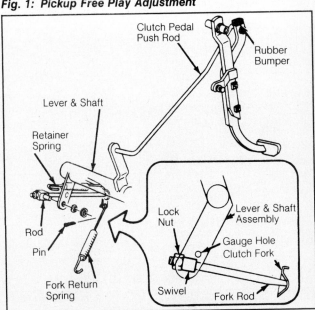

Insert swivel in gauge hole to check free play.

Clutches

GENERAL MOTORS — EXC. S10 (Cont.)

Van

1) Disconnect return spring at clutch fork. Loosen clutch fork swivel nut "A" about 1/2".

2) Force push rod toward rear until clutch release bearing just contacts clutch fingers. Rotate push rod adjusting nut until 1/4" clearance between nut and swivel is obtained.

3) Tighten clutch fork swivel lock nut. Check that pedal free travel is about 1 1/4-1 1/2".

Fig. 2: Van Free Play Adjustment

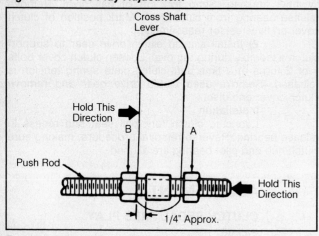

Turn adjusting nut "A" to change clearance.

TIGHTENING SPECIFICATIONS

Application	Ft. Lbs. (N.m)
Clutch Cover-to-Flywheel Bolts	30 (41)
Clutch Housing-to-Engine Bolts	30 (41)
Transmission-to-Clutch Housing Bolts	75 (102)

JEEP — HYDRAULIC

4-Cyl. "CJ" & Scrambler

DESCRIPTION

Clutch assembly consists of a single dry-disc driven plate and a one-piece diaphragm spring type clutch cover. Clutch cover is 9" in diameter and driven plate is 8 1/2" in diameter. No internal adjustment for driven plate is provided. Clutch is actuated through a hydraulic clutch cylinder and slave cylinder.

REMOVAL & INSTALLATION

TRANSMISSION

Removal (T4 & T5 Transmission)

1) Remove screws attaching shift lever boot to floorpan. Slide boot over lever. Remove shift lever and lever housing from transmission. Raise vehicle and support with safety stands.

2) Disconnect rear propeller shaft from transfer case and secure out of the way. Place a jack under clutch housing to support engine. Remove rear crossmember from frame.

3) Disconnect speedometer cable, back-up light switch and 4WD indicator switch. Disconnect transfer case vent hose. Disconnect front propeller shaft and secure aside.

4) Remove transfer case shift lever by removing shifter shaft retaining nut. Remove cotter pins retaining shift control link pins in shift rods and remove pins. Remove shifter shaft and disengage shift lever from shift control links. Move lever out of the way.

NOTE: On some models, shifter shaft must be unthreaded from shift lever for removal. On other models, shaft can be removed by sliding it out of lever.

5) Support transmission and transfer case with jack. Remove bolts securing transmission to clutch housing and remove transmission and transfer case. Remove transfer case from transmission.

CLUTCH

Removal

1) With transmission, transfer case and throw-out bearing removed, remove clutch housing. Mark position of clutch cover on flywheel for reassembly.

2) Loosen clutch cover bolts 1 or 2 turns at a time until clutch cover spring tension is released. Remove cover bolts and remove clutch cover and disc.

Installation

1) Check all components for wear or damage and replace as necessary. Using clutch alignment tool, align clutch disc and loosely install clutch cover. Be sure marks made during removal are aligned.

2) To avoid clutch cover warpage, tighten each cover bolt a few turns at a time. Reverse removal procedures to complete installation.

CLUTCH MASTER CYLINDER

Removal

1) Disconnect hydraulic line at clutch master cylinder. Plug line and cylinder opening to prevent dirt from entering. Remove cotter pin and washer holding cylinder push rod on clutch pedal.

2) Slide push rod off pedal pivot. Remove nuts attaching clutch master cylinder to mounting studs on dash panel and remove cylinder.

Fig. 1: Exploded View of 4-Cylinder "CJ" & Scrambler Hydraulic Clutch Assembly

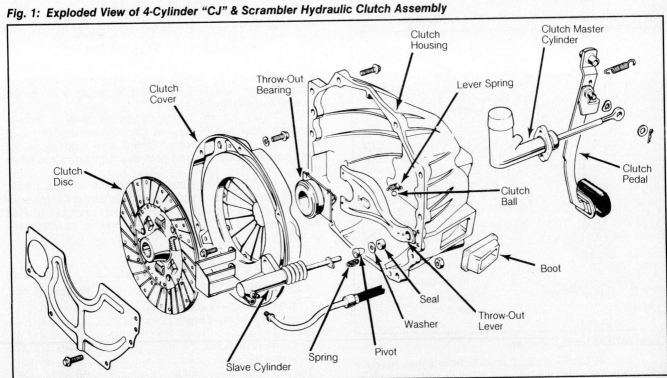

JEEP — HYDRAULIC (Cont.)

Installation
Lubricate cylinder bore, spring and plunger assembly, ball-end of push rod, seal and lip of dust cover. Reverse removal procedure and bleed hydraulic system.

CLUTCH SLAVE CYLINDER
Removal
1) Disconnect hydraulic line at clutch slave cylinder. Cap line to prevent fluid loss. Remove clutch fork lever-to-cylinder push rod retaining spring.

2) Remove bolts attaching slave cylinder to clutch housing and remove slave cylinder, heat shield, clutch fork pivot, washer and seal.

Installation
Reverse removal procedures and bleed the hydraulic system.

OVERHAUL

CLUTCH MASTER CYLINDER
Disassembly
1) Remove reservoir cap and rubber cover. Remove push rod dust cover and discard dust cover. Remove snap ring holding push rod in cylinder bore and discard snap ring.

2) Remove push rod, retaining washer and seal as an assembly. Discard push rod seal. Remove plunger, valve spring and valve stem assembly from cylinder bore by tapping cylinder body on wood block.

3) Compress valve spring slightly. Pry tab of valve stem retainer upward to release retainer, spring and stem assembly from plunger. Remove seal from plunger and discard. Remove spring retainer and valve stem from valve spring.

NOTE: Retainer tab is located in rectangular slot in side of stem retainer.

Fig. 2: Exploded View of Clutch Master Cylinder

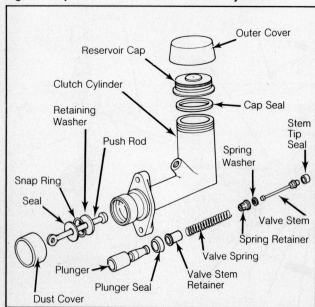

Clean parts in brake fluid only.

4) Remove valve stem from retainer. Remove spring washer and stem tip seal from end of valve stem.

Discard stem tip seal and spring washer. Clean parts with brake fluid or brake cleaning solvent. Inspect cylinder bore for wear, nicks or scores. Replace if necessary.

Reassembly
1) Lubricate cylinder bore with brake fluid. Make sure lip of plunger seal faces stem end of plunger. Install stem tip seal so seal shoulder fits in undercut at end of valve stem.

2) End of valve stem should pass through stem retainer and seat in small bore in end of plunger. Bend retainer tab downward to lock stem and retainer on plunger. Reverse disassembly procedures to complete assembly.

CLUTCH SLAVE CYLINDER
Disassembly
1) Clean cylinder exterior. Remove dust boot from cylinder. Remove cylinder push rod, plunger and spring as an assembly. Remove spring seal from plunger.

2) Remove snap ring holding push rod in plunger. Remove push rod and boot. Remove boot from push rod. Clean parts with brake fluid or brake cleaning solvent. Inspect cylinder bore for wear, nicks or scores. Replace if necessary.

Reassembly
Reverse disassembly procedures. Lubricate cylinder bore and seal with brake fluid before reassembly.

Fig. 3: Exploded View of Clutch Slave Cylinder

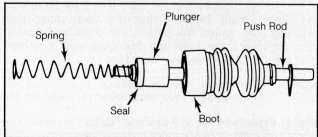

HYDRAULIC SYSTEM BLEEDING
1) Make sure clutch master cylinder is full of brake fluid (SAE J-1703, DOT 3 or equivalent). Compress slave cylinder plunger by pushing throw-out lever as far forward as possible.

2) Attach rubber hose to bleeder screw. Immerse other end of hose in glass container 1/2 full of brake fluid. Loosen bleeder screw and hold throw-out lever forward. Depress and hold clutch pedal to end of its travel.

3) Tighten bleeder screw and release pedal. Repeat bleeding operation until fluid entering container is free of bubbles. Do not allow reservoir to run out of fluid during bleeding. Refill clutch master cylinder to level mark on reservoir.

TIGHTENING SPECIFICATIONS

Application	Ft. Lbs. (N.m)
Clutch Cover-to-Flywheel Bolts	23 (31)
Clutch Housing-to-Engine Bolts	54 (73)
Clutch Housing-to-Transmission Bolts	54 (73)
Crossmember Bolts	34-40 (46-54)
Flywheel-to-Engine Bolts	65 (73)
Transmission Cover Bolts	55-65 (75-88)

JEEP — MECHANICAL LINKAGE

All Models
(Exc. 4-Cylinder "CJ" & Scrambler)

DESCRIPTION

Clutch assembly includes a dry-disc driven plate and 1 of 2 types of clutch covers; a 10 1/2" diameter direct spring type or a 11" semi-centrifugal type. No internal adjustment for clutch disc wear is provided. Release lever height should be checked and adjusted. Clutch is actuated through mechanical type linkage.

REMOVAL & INSTALLATION

TRANSMISSION

Removal (T4, T5, T18A & T176 Transmission)

1) Remove screws attaching shift lever boot to floorpan. Slide boot over lever. On models with T4 or T5 transmission, remove shift lever and lever housing from transmission.

2) On T18A transmission, unthread shift lever cap and remove cap, gasket, spring seat, spring and shift lever as an assembly. Remove shift lever locating pins from housing.

3) On T176 transmission, press and turn shift lever retainer counterclockwise to release lever. Remove lever, boot, spring and seat as an assembly.

4) On all models, raise vehicle and support with safety stands. Disconnect rear propeller shaft from transfer case and secure out of the way.

5) On Cherokee, Truck and Wagoneer models, disconnect parking brake cable at equalizer. Remove rear cable clip from crossmember. On all models, place a jack under clutch housing to support engine. Remove rear crossmember from frame.

6) Disconnect speedometer cable, back-up light switch and 4WD indicator switch. Disconnect transfer case vent hose. Disconnect front propeller shaft and secure aside.

7) On "CJ" and Scrambler models, remove transfer case shift lever by removing shifter shaft retaining nut. Remove cotter pins holding shift control link pins in shift rods and remove pins. Remove shifter shaft and disengage shift lever from shift control links. Move lever out of the way.

NOTE: On some models, shifter shaft must be unthreaded from shift lever for removal. On other models, shaft can be removed by sliding it out of lever.

8) On Cherokee, Truck and Wagoneer models, remove cotter pin and washers connecting link to shift lever. Disconnect link from shift lever. On all models, support transmission and transfer case with jack.

9) Remove bolts securing transmission to clutch housing and remove transmission and transfer case. Remove transfer case from transmission.

CLUTCH

Removal

1) With transmission removed, remove starter motor, throw-out bearing and clutch housing. Mark position of clutch cover on flywheel for reassembly.

2) Loosen each clutch cover bolt 1 or 2 turns at a time to relieve spring tension on cover. Remove clutch cover and driven plate from flywheel.

Installation

1) Check clutch cover release lever height. Correct as necessary. Sparingly lubricate release lever pivots.

2) Using clutch alignment tool, mount assembled plate on flywheel. Be sure marks made during removal are aligned. Install cover attaching bolts and tighten alternately and evenly.

3) Reverse the removal procedures to complete clutch installation.

Fig. 1: Exploded View of Cherokee and Truck Clutch Linkage Assembly

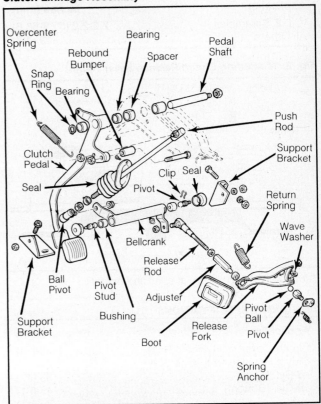

ADJUSTMENT

CLUTCH PEDAL FREE PLAY

1) Lift clutch pedal upward and against pedal stop. Raise vehicle.

2) Adjust lower ball pivot assembly on pedal-to-bellcrank rod until inner bellcrank lever is parallel with front face of clutch housing.

3) Loosen release rod adjuster jamnut. Turn release rod adjuster to obtain specified pedal free play.

CLUTCH PEDAL FREE PLAY

Application	Inches (mm)
"CJ" & Scrambler	1.00-1.25 (25.4-31.7)
All Others	.38-.63 (9.6-16.0)

Clutches

JEEP — MECHANICAL LINKAGE (Cont.)

CLUTCH RELEASE LEVER

1) Position gauge plate (J-1048) on flywheel. Position clutch cover over gauge plate with release fingers aligned with machined lands on plate. Gauge plate hub should be centered between release levers. Attach cover to flywheel.

2) Tighten cover screws in rotation, 1 or 2 turns at a time. Set each release lever by depressing 2 or 3 times. Measure height of each lever in relation to gauge hub using a height gauge tool (J-23330).

3) Turn adjusting lever nuts until all 3 levers are at specified height. Work levers up and down and recheck measurements.

CLUTCH LEVER RELEASE HEIGHT

Application	Inches (mm)
"CJ" & Scrambler	2.0-2.2 (51.8-68.6)
All Others	.19 (4.7)

Fig. 2: Measuring Clutch Release Lever Height

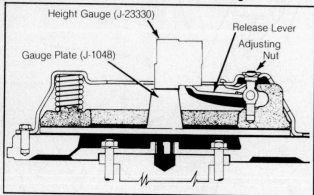

Turn nuts until levers are at specified height.

TIGHTENING SPECIFICATIONS

Application	Ft. Lbs. (N.m)
Clutch Cover-to-Flywheel Bolts	40 (54)
Clutch Housing-to-Engine Bolt	
6-Cyl. (Top)	35 (47)
6-Cyl. (Bottom)	45 (61)
V8	30 (41)
Crossmember Bolts	34-70 (47-54)
Transmission-to-Clutch Housing Bolts	54 (73)

SECTION 9

DRIVE AXLES

CONTENTS

NOTE: ALSO SEE GENERAL INDEX.

IMPORTANT: Because of the many model names used by vehicle manufacturers, accurate identification of models is important. See Model Identification at the front of this publication.

Drive Axles
TROUBLE SHOOTING

CONDITION	POSSIBLE CAUSE	CORRECTION
General Knocking or Clunking	Excessive differential side gear clearance	See Overhaul in DRIVE AXLES
	Worn rear axle pinion shaft	See Overhaul in DRIVE AXLES
	Worn case or differential cross shaft in case	See Overhaul in DRIVE AXLES
	Excessive end play of axle shafts-to-differential cross shaft	See Overhaul in DRIVE AXLES
	Gear teeth mutilitated	See Overhaul in DRIVE AXLES
	Improper axle shaft spline fit	See Overhaul in DRIVE AXLES
	Total axle backlash too great	See Overhaul in DRIVE AXLES
	Incorrect driveline angle	See Adjustment in PROPELLER SHAFT ALIGNMENT
Clunking During Initial Engagement	Excessive differential side gear clearance	See Overhaul in DRIVE AXLES
	Excessive ring and pinion backlash	See Overhaul in DRIVE AXLES
	Worn or loose pinion shaft	See Overhaul in DRIVE AXLES
	Worn or damaged inboard joint	See Overhaul in DRIVE AXLES
Gear Howl or Whine	Improper pinion depth	See Overhaul in DRIVE AXLES
	Improper ring gear backlash adjustment	See Overhaul in DRIVE AXLES
	Improper ring gear runout	See Overhaul in DRIVE AXLES
	Impropr bearing preload	See Overhaul in DRIVE AXLES
	Excessive pinion bearing wear	See Overhaul in DRIVE AXLES
Clicking or Chatter on Turns	Wrong lubricant in differential	Drain and refill differential
	Clutch plates worn	See Overhaul in POSITIVE TRACTION DIFFERENTIALS
	Worn or damaged outboard joints	See Overhaul in DRIVE AXLES
	Differential side gears or pinion worn	See Overhaul in DRIVE AXLES
Knock or Click Approximately Every Second Revolution	Flat spot on rear wheel bearing	See Overhaul in DRIVE AXLES
Grunt Noise on Stops	Lack of lubricant in propeller shaft slip yoke	See UNIVERSAL JOINTS
Groan in Forward or Reverse	Wrong lubricant in differential	Replace lubricant
Knock in Drive Line in High Gear at 10 MPH	Worn or damaged universal joints	See UNIVERSAL JOINTS
	Side gear hub counterbore in differential worn oversize	See Overhaul in DRIVE AXLES
Ping, Snap or Click in Drive Line	Loose upper or lower control arm bushing bolts	See Replacement in FRONT SUSPENSION
	Loose companion flange	See Overhaul in DRIVE AXLES
Scraping Noise	Slinger, companion flange or end yoke rubbing on rear axle carrier	See Overhaul in DRIVE AXLES
Car Will Not Move	Broken axle shaft	See Overhaul in DRIVE AXLES
	Broken pinion stem	See Overhaul in DRIVE AXLES
	Broken welds	See Overhaul in DRIVE AXLES
	Axle lock up	See Overhaul in DRIVE AXLES
	Broken gear teeth	See Overhaul in DRIVE AXLES
	Broken wheel bearing	See Overhaul in DRIVE AXLES
Axle Backlash	Excessive ring and pinion clearance	See Overhaul in DRIVE AXLES
	Loose fitting differential pinion shaft	See Overhaul in DRIVE AXLES
	Excessive side gear-to-case clearance	See Overhaul in DRIVE AXLES
Leakage at Differential or Driveshaft	Rough outside surface on splined yoke	See Overhaul in DRIVE AXLES
	Drive pinion seal or nut	See Overhaul in DRIVE AXLES
	Axle cover gasket, or axle shaft seal	See Overhaul in DRIVE AXLES
	Bad welds or improper axle vent hose	See Overhaul in DRIVE AXLES
	Case porosity	Apply heat resistant silicone sealer to case

Drive Axles

TROUBLE SHOOTING (Cont.)

CONDITION	POSSIBLE CAUSE	CORRECTION
Roughness, Shudder or Vibration Upon Heavy Acceleration	Double cardan joint ball seats worn, and ball set spring may be broken	See UNIVERSAL JOINTS
	Excessive joint angle	See Propeller Shaft Alignment in DRIVE AXLES
	Sticking inboard joint assembly	See UNIVERSAL JOINTS
	Worn or damaged inboard or outboard joints	See UNIVERSAL JOINTS
Roughness, Vibration or Body Boom Experienced at Any Speed	Rough rear wheel bearings	See Overhaul in DRIVE AXLES
	Unbalanced or damaged propeller shaft	Check and/or balance propeller shaft
	Unbalanced or damaged tires	Check and/or balance tires
	Worn or damaged universal joints	See UNIVERSAL JOINTS
	Bent of damaged drive shaft, or undercoating on drive shaft	Check drive shaft balance
	Tight universal joints	Lubricate or replace as necessary
	Burrs or gouges on companion flange	Resurface or replace flange
	Drive shaft or companion shaft runout too great	Repair or replace as necessary
	Excessive looseness at slip yoke spline	See Overhaul in DRIVE AXLES

Drive Axles

GEAR TOOTH CONTACT PATTERNS

INSPECTION

PRELIMINARY INSPECTION

Wipe lubricant from internal parts. Rotate gears, and inspect for wear or damage. Mount a dial indicator to housing, and check backlash at several points around ring gear. Backlash must be within specifications at all points. If no defects are found, check gear tooth contact pattern.

GEAR TOOTH CONTACT PATTERN

NOTE: **Drive pattern should be well centered on ring gear teeth. Coast pattern should be centered, but may be slightly toward toe of ring gear teeth.**

1) Paint ring gear teeth with marking compound. Wrap a cloth or rope around drive pinion flange to act as a brake. Rotate ring gear until a clear tooth contact pattern is obtained.

2) Contact pattern will indicate whether correct pinion bearing mounting shim has been installed and if drive gear backlash has been set properly. Backlash between drive gear and pinion must be maintained within specified limits, until correct tooth pattern is obtained.

ADJUSTMENTS

GEAR BACKLASH & PINION SHIM CHANGES

NOTE: **Backlash is adjusted by shifting shims from 1 side of differential case to the other, or by turning adjusting nuts on which differential side bearings ride. Changing the pinion shims changes the distance from top of pinion to centerline of ring gear.**

1) With no change in backlash, moving pinion further from ring gear moves drive pattern toward heel and top of tooth, and moves coast pattern toward toe and top of tooth.

2) With no change in backlash, moving pinion closer to ring gear moves drive pattern toward toe and bottom of tooth, and moves coast pattern toward heel and bottom of tooth.

3) With no change in pinion shim thickness, an increase in backlash moves ring gear further from pinion. Drive pattern moves toward heel and top of tooth, and coast pattern moves toward heel and top of tooth.

4) With no change in pinion shim thickness, a decrease in backlash moves ring gear closer to pinion gear. Drive pattern moves toward toe and bottom of tooth, and coast pattern moves toward toe and bottom of tooth.

Fig. 1: Drive Axle Gear Tooth Pattern

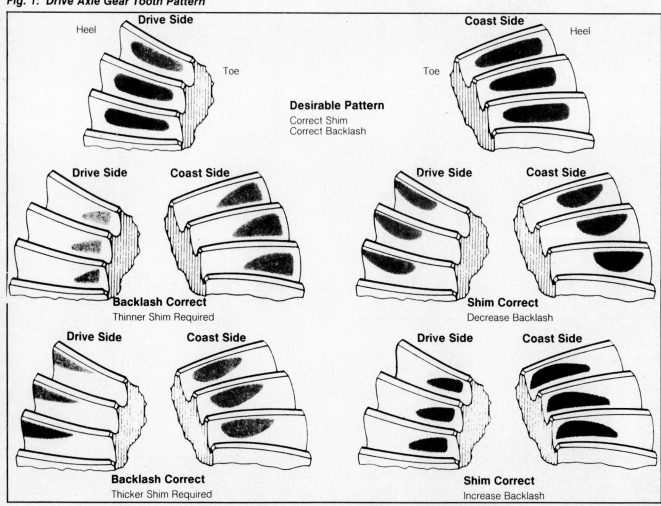

AXLE RATIO IDENTIFICATION

CHRYSLER CORP.

A metal tag is attached to one of the rear axle housing cover bolts. Tag gives number of teeth for ring gear and pinion gear. To obtain gear ratio, divide larger number by smaller number.

FORD

The axle ratio code is stamped on the Vehicle Certification Plate located on the rear face of left door on all models. The first 2 digits of the code identify the ratio and capacity of the rear axle.

The third digit of the code identifies the ratio and capacity of the front axle. Rear axles have a tag bolted to drive axle that contains drive axle ratio. Code designations are as follows:

FORD AXLE RATIO IDENTIFICATION

Code	Ratio
Conventional Rear Differentials	
17	2.47:1
14, 21	3.00:1
31	3.07:1
18, 72	3.08:1
15	3.25:1
74, 84	3.45:1
16	3.50:1
23, 33, 43	3.54:1
19, 26	3.55:1
24, 34, 86	3.73:1
22, 32, 52, 62	4.10:1
53, 65	4.56:1
Locking Rear Differentials	
H5	2.73:1
B1	3.00:1
H8	3.08:1
F4	3.45:1
C3, B3, D3, E3	3.54:1
H9	3.55:1
C4, E4, F6	3.73:1
C2, D2	4.10:1
Conventional Front Differentials	
CE, CF, CH, AB, AC, AG, FA, FB, FC, FF, FG, GA, GC, GD, YA, YD	3.00:1
SA, TA	3.07:1
AE	3.08:1
EA, EB, EC, EE, EF, EH, EG, HA, HC, AAB, AAE	3.50:1
JE, JF, JG, NE, NF, ACB, ACC, NA, RB, RF, SA, SB, SF, TA, TE, UA, UD, EA, GA, KE, LE	3.45:1
HA, LA, XA, VA, ABA, E0TA-ACA	3.54:1
ACB, AEB	3.73:1
E2TA-ACA	4.09:1
ABD, ABE, ABF, LA, LB, LF, DA, E1TA-ABA	4:10:1
Locking Front Differentials	
CA, CB	3.00:1
VE, VF, VH, KA, KB, KC, KF, KG	3.50:1
ZE, ZF, ZG, MA, MF, VA	3.54:1
ADB	3.73:1

GENERAL MOTORS

Identification code for rear axles is stamped on rear surface of right rear axle tube. Identification code for front axles is stamped on top rear of left axle tube. On Dana built front axles, axle ratio code is on tape stripe around right front axle tube.

GENERAL MOTORS AXLE RATIO IDENTIFICATION

Code	Ratio
Conventional Rear Differentials	
KYA, KYB	2.56:1
TUF, TUM, TAB, TUH, CAB, CAH, CAN, TUR, KCX	2.73:1
CAJ, CAL, TWA, KXT, TWB, KXS, KCF, KXX, KXU	3.08:1
TKB, TKU, RMB, RMR	3.21:1
CYD, CYA, CZN, CYW	3.23:1
KZA, KZB, KHB, CAD, CAK, CYB, CYX, CZA, KZT	3.42:1
KBA, CSF, CSH, KBU, KBA, KBH, CSH, CYH, CYC, RJZ, KKA,KKC, CZB, CYY, KKX, KKW, CST, CAY, CZR, CYC, CYH	3.73:1
RRM	3.75:1
CZM, CYA, RHA, KJB, KMC, CZC, KVN, KMT, CZS, CMH, CYS, KMH, KVB	4.10:1
CYK, KFA, KSF, KSN, KSZ, KRC, CZT, KST, KRU, KSY, KWA	4.56:1
KTA	5.13:1
Locking Rear Differentials	
KYC, KYD	2.56:1
TUJ, TUK, TUN, KCY, TAD, TUZ, CAU	2.73:1
KXW, TWD, KCH, KXY, CAW, CAR, TWC	3.08:1
CZU	3.23:1
KZC, KHA, KZU, CYN, CZH, CDZ, CAS, CYF, CYM, CAX, KHC	3.42:1
CNA, SJ, CNB, CSK, CYS, CYN, TJA, RJB, KKD, KKF, KBF, TKD, CZJ, CZF, KKU, KKY, CSW, CSR, CZW, CYN, CYJ	3.73:1
CYT, CTA, RHB, KJC, KUD, KUF, KMD, CZK, KUR, KMU, CZX, KMN	4.10:1
CYU, KFB, KSH, KSR, KWB, KRD, CZY, ZSU, KRW	4.56:1
Front Differentials	
TJA, WA	2.73:1
WB, THC, TMA	3.08:1
TFA, WC	3.23:1
THA, THD, WF, WH	3.42:1
TBA, TBB, TBD, TBF, TBJ, WM	3.73:1
TCA, TCB, TCC, MFA	4.10:1
TDA, TDB	4.56:1

JEEP

On "CJ" and Scrambler models, the front axle code number is cast into bottom surface of housing. On all other models the front axle code number is cast into upper surface of reinforcing rib at left side of axle housing. A gear ratio tag is attached to left side of axle housing cover on front axles.

On all models except "J20" truck models, rear axle ratio code letter is located on axle housing tube boss,

Drive Axles

AXLE RATIO IDENTIFICATION (Cont.)

adjacent to dowel hole. On "J20" truck models, rear axle model number is cast into boss on lower right side of axle housing, adjacent to housing cover.

JEEP AXLE RATIO IDENTIFICATION

Code	Ratio
Conventional Differentials	
D	2.73:1
B	3.31:1
A	3.54:1
H	3.73:1
C	4.10:1
Locking Differentials	
DD	2.73:1
CC	3.31:1
AA	3.54:1
HH	3.73:1
CC	[1] 4.10:1

[1] — "J20" Truck models only.

Drive Axles

CHRYSLER CORP. 8⅜" & 9¼" RING GEAR

Dodge, Plymouth
All 150 Models, Rear Axle

DESCRIPTION

The axle assembly is hypoid gear type with an integral carrier housing. It is used on light duty vehicles with semi-floating axles. Pinion bearing preload adjustment is made with a collapsible spacer. Differential bearing preload adjustment is made with the adjusting nuts on which bearing cups seat.

A removable housing cover permits inspection and minor servicing of differential without removal from vehicle. Service procedures are the same for both size assemblies, except for some tightening specifications and special tool numbers.

AXLE RATIO & IDENTIFICATION

A small metal tag attached to rear axle housing cover bolt, identifies axle ratio. Chrysler Corp. also uses Spicer (Dana) axles for some applications. To distinguish these models from Chrysler Corp. models, refer to *Spicer (Dana) axle articles in this Section.*

REMOVAL & INSTALLATION

AXLE SHAFTS & BEARINGS

Removal

1) Raise vehicle and remove wheel, tire and brake drum. Loosen housing cover attaching bolts to drain lubricant. Remove housing cover. Remove pinion shaft lock screw and differential pinion shaft.

2) Force axle shaft toward center of vehicle. Remove "C" washer lock from groove in axle shaft. Pull axle shaft out of housing, using care not to damage roller bearing. Remove oil seal from housing bore.

3) To remove axle shaft bearing from axle housing, use bearing puller (C-4167). Attach a slide hammer to puller and remove axle shaft bearing and inspect. Discard if axle or bearing shows any signs of brinnelling, spalling or pitting.

4) Dents caused by axle shaft splines should be polished smooth, or rubber on outside diameter of seal will be torn and seal leakage will result. Inspect both axle and bearing. If either show signs of excessive wear, discard bearing.

NOTE: Always install new axle shaft oil seal.

Installation

1) Clean all parts thoroughly. Install axle shaft bearing squarely into housing bore. Making sure bearing is bottomed against shoulder in bore. Oil and install oil seal in housing bore.

2) Slide axle shaft into place being careful not to damage oil seal. Install "C" washer lock into groove in axle shaft. Pull outward on axle shaft so that "C" washer lock seats in counterbore of differential side gear.

3) Install differential pinion shaft through case and pinions. Aligning hole in shaft with lock screw hole in case. Install pinion shaft lock screw and tighten securely. Install housing cover and identification tag.

Fig. 1: Exploded View of Chrysler Corp. 8⅜" Drive Axle Assembly — 9¼" Similar.

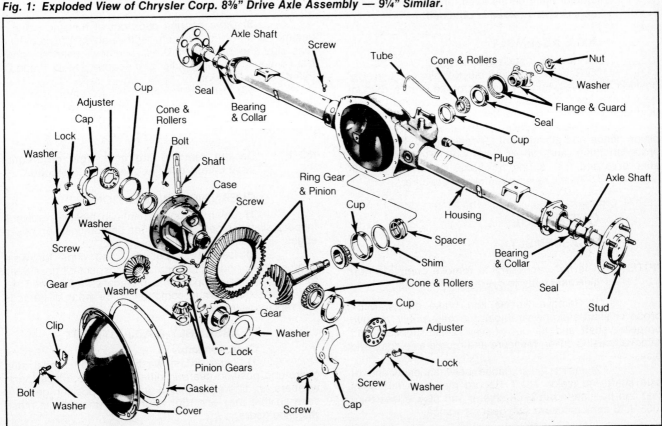

CHRYSLER CORP. 8⅜" & 9¼" RING GEAR (Cont.)

PINION FLANGE & SEAL

Removal

1) Raise vehicle, mark propeller shaft universal joint, drive pinion flange and pinion stem for reassembly. Disconnect propeller shaft and tie out of way. Remove rear wheels and brake drums to prevent false preload reading.

2) Using an INCH lb. torque wrench, measure and record pinion bearing preload. Remove drive pinion nut and pull off flange using puller. Pry out oil seal, taking care not to damage machined surface.

Installation

1) Install new pinion oil seal squarely into bore in housing until seal flange seats against housing flange face. Position pinion flange on pinion stem, making sure marks are aligned. Install pinion washer (convex side out) and nut. Tighten nut to specifications and rotate pinion through several revolutions to be sure bearing rollers are properly seated.

NOTE: **Outside diameter of seal is precoated with a special sealer, so no sealing compound is required.**

2) Measure pinion bearing preload. Continue tightening pinion nut until preload is same as that noted before disassembly. Under no circumstances should preload be more than 10 INCH lbs. (1.1 N.m) over original setting.

CAUTION: **Under no circumstances should pinion nut be backed off to lessen preload. If desired preload is exceeded, a new collapsible spacer must be installed, and nut retightened until proper preload is obtained.**

AXLE ASSEMBLY

Removal & Installation

1) Raise vehicle and block brake pedal in "Up" position. Remove wheels, tires and brake drums. Disconnect brake lines at wheel cylinders and cap to prevent fluid loss. Disconnect parking brake cables.

2) Mark propeller shaft universal joint, drive pinion flange and pinion stem for reassembly. Disconnect propeller shaft and tie out of way. Remove shock absorbers and rear spring "U" bolts. Remove rear axle assembly. To install, reverse removal procedure.

OVERHAUL

DISASSEMBLY

NOTE: **It is not necessary to remove complete rear axle assembly to overhaul differential.**

1) Remove wheels and brake drums. Mark propeller shaft and universal joint for reassembly, remove propeller shaft and tie out of way. Drain lubricant and remove housing cover. Measure and record axle shaft end play.

2) Insert feeler gauge between each end of axle shaft and pinion shaft. Record maximum thickness that can be inserted in each side. If end play is less than .005" (.13 mm), measure side gear clearance.

3) Using 2 feeler gauges of equal thickness, insert 1 gauge above and 1 gauge below side gear hub next to thrust surface. If clearance is more than .012" (.30 mm), replace side gear. Remove axle shafts as previously described.

4) Measure and record differential side play, ring gear runout and pinion bearing preload. Mark differential gear and case at point of maximum runout. There should be no side play and ring gear runout should not exceed .005" (.13 mm).

5) If ring gear runout exceeded .005" (.13 mm), differential case flange runout must be checked. Using Hex Adjuster tool (C-4164 or equivalent), tighten adjusters until all case side play is eliminated.

6) Mount dial indicator to housing and place indicator stem on ring gear flange of differential case. Rotate case several times, checking reading on dial indicator. If reading varies more than .005" (.13 mm), replace differential case.

7) Remove drive pinion flange and seal as previously described. Mark side bearing caps and axle housing for reassembly. Remove adjuster locks, loosen but do not remove bearing caps. Insert Hex Adjuster tool (C-4164 or equivalent) through axle tube and loosen hex adjuster on each side.

8) Remove bearing caps, adjusters and differential case assembly. Be sure to keep all bearing cups and adjusters with their respective bearing cones. Using soft drift punch and hammer, drive pinion shaft out of housing.

NOTE: **Bearing cones, cups, collapsible spacer and shim(s) must be replaced after driving out pinion.**

9) Drive bearing cups out of housing using a hammer and soft drift punch, remove shim(s) from behind rear cup and record thickness. Remove bearing cones from pinion shaft using puller and adapter (C-293-P and C-293-42 or equivalent).

10) Mount differential case assembly in a soft-jawed vise. Remove and discard ring gear bolts (left-hand thread). Using a soft-faced hammer, drive ring gear off differential case.

NOTE: **Do not remove ring gear from differential case unless case or gear set is replaced.**

CLEANING & INSPECTION

1) Clean all components in cleaning solvent. Inspect all machined surfaces for smoothness or raised edges, and polish or flatten as required.

2) Inspect all bearings and cups for wear and/or pitting and replace as a set. Inspect all gear teeth for wear and/or chipping and replace as a matched set only. Inspect all splined components for wear or damage and replace as required.

REASSEMBLY & ADJUSTMENT

Case Assembly

1) Install thrust washers on differential side gears and position gears in differential case. Place thrust washers on differential pinion gears and position gears in case so that they are 180° apart when they are in mesh with side gears.

Drive Axles

CHRYSLER CORP. 8³⁄₈" & 9¼" RING GEAR (Cont.)

2) Rotate side gears until holes in pinion gears are in alignment with pinion shaft holes in case. Install differential pinion shaft, making sure hole in shaft is aligned with lock screw hole in case.

Fig. 2: 8³⁄₈" & 9¼" Ring Gear — Relieving Chamfer Edge.

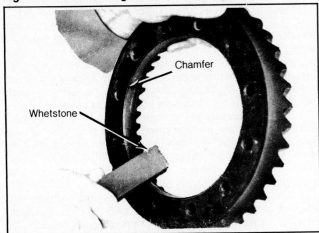

Surfaces of ring gear & case flange must be smooth.

3) Make sure contact surface of ring gear and case flange is clean and free of all nicks and burrs. Using a fine whetstone, relieve any sharp edge of the chamfer on inside diameter of ring gear. Relieving chamfer insures that no burrs will become imbedded between case flange and ring gear causing ring gear distortion. *See Fig. 2..*

Fig. 3: Installing Ring Gear on Differential Case

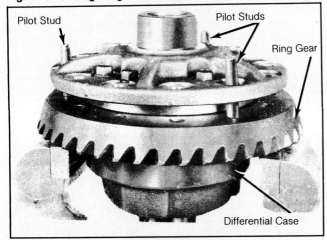

Warm ring gear to install on differential case.

4) Heat ring gear using heat lamp, hot oil or water; not to exceed 300°F (149° C). Do not use torch to heat ring gear. Install 3 equally spaced pilot studs on ring gear. Place heated ring gear on jaws of vise and install case using new left-hand threaded bolts. *See Fig. 3.*

5) Tighten ring gear-to-case bolts alternately and evenly to specifications. Install side bearings on case using Bearing Installer and Driver (C-4340 & C-4171 on 8³⁄₈" ring gear. C-4213 & C-4171 on 9¼" ring gear). Lubricate assembly with hypoid gear lubricant.

Drive Pinion Depth

1) Install both drive pinion bearing cups into axle housing bores. Assemble pinion locating spacer (SP-60-30) over body of main stem (SP-5385) followed by rear pinion bearing cone. Insert assembly into axle carrier from rear.

NOTE: Tool numbers used apply to 8³⁄₈" ring gear axles. For equivalent tool numbers for 9¼" ring gear axles, *see Equivalent Tool Number Chart.*

2) On 8³⁄₈" assembly, hold spacer and main stem assembly in position and install front pinion bearing over spacer (SP-5382) and position over main stem of tool. On 9¼" assembly, position spacer and main stem assembly in housing. Install front pinion bearing cone and washer (SP-6022).

3) Procedure from this point is same for both assemblies except for tool numbers (see note in preceding step). Position Compression Sleeve (Sp-3194B), centralizing washer (SP-534), and main screw nut (SP-3193) on main stem. Hold compression sleeve with Companion Flange Wrench (C-3281) and tighten nut. Allow tool to rotate while nut is being tightened to prevent damaging bearings and cups. *See Fig. 4.*

Fig. 4: Seating Pinion Bearing Cups on 8³⁄₈" & 9¼" Differentials.

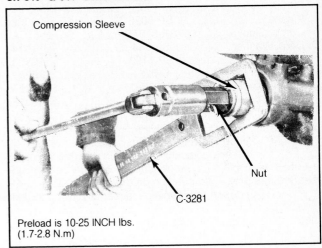

Preload is 10-25 INCH lbs.
(1.7-2.8 N.m)

Rotate while tightening pinion nut.

3) Loosen tool nut, then retighten to obtain pinion bearing preload of 10-25 INCH lbs. (1.7-2.8 N.m). Rotate tool after tightening to properly seat pinion bearings. Install gauge block (SP-5383) on main tool and tighten screw.

4) Position cross bore arbor (SP-6029) in housing side bearing seats and center arbor in bore. Position bearing caps on carrier pedestals and insert .002" (.051 mm) spacer between arbor and each cap. Install cap bolts and tighten to 10 ft. lbs. (14 N.m).

5) Use feeler gauge to determine proper thickness of shims that will fit snugly between arbor and gauge block. This fit must be snug but not excessively tight.

6) To select correct shim pack, read markings on end of pinion head. When marking is minus, add that amount of thickness to feeler gauge thickness to obtain thickness of correct shim pack. When marking is plus, subtract that amount of thickness. Remove all tools and rear pinion bearing cup from housing. *See Fig. 5.*

Drive Axles

CHRYSLER CORP. 8⅜" & 9¼" RING GEAR (Cont.)

Fig. 5: Measuring Shim Pack Thickness

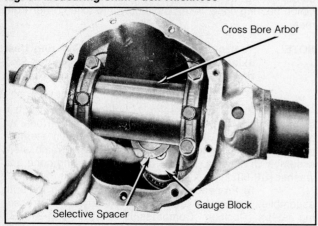

Using selective spacer, determine correct shim thickness.

EQUIVALENT TOOL NUMBER CHART

Application	8⅜"	9¼"
Spacer	SP-6030	SP-6017
Main Stem	SP-5385	SP-526
Spacer	SP-5382	SP-1730
Washer	SP-6022	SP-6022
Comp. Sleeve	SP-3194B	SP-535A
Cent. Washer	SP-534	SP-534
Nut	SP-3193	SP-533
Holding Tool	C-3281	C-3281
Gauge Block	SP-5383	SP-6020
Cross Bore Arbor	SP-6029	SP-6018
Bearing Installer	DD-955	DD-955

Pinion Bearing Preload

1) Place selected shim in pinion shaft bore and reinstall rear pinion bearing cup. Lubricate rear pinion bearing and press into position on drive pinion stem.

2) Insert drive pinion assembly through axle housing. Install collapsible spacer and front pinion bearing onto stem of gear. Install pinion flange and tighten nut until front bearing is seated.

NOTE: Use care not to collapse spacer. If spacer is collapsed, new spacer must be installed.

3) With front bearing fully seated, remove pinion flange. Install new pinion oil seal into housing so flange of seal is fully seated against housing flange face.

4) Install pinion flange, Belleville washer (convex side out) and nut on pinion stem. While rotating pinion assembly (to insure proper bearing seating), tighten pinion flange nut until all end play is removed.

5) Tighten pinion nut to specified torque and measure pinion bearing preload by rotating pinion through several revolutions with an INCH lb. torque wrench. Continue tightening pinion flange nut in small increments until correct bearing preload is obtained. Do not back off nut to lessen bearing preload. If desired preload is exceeded, a new collapsible spacer must be installed and nut retightened until proper preload is obtained.

Backlash & Side Bearing Preload

1) Two precautions must be observed when checking and adjusting ring gear backlash and differential bearing preload.

- Index gears so same teeth are meshed during all backlash measurements. Permissible backlash variation is .003" (.08 mm). For example, if backlash at minimum point is .006" (.15 mm) and backlash at maximum point is .009" (.23 mm), variation is correct.
- It is also important to maintain specified adjuster torque to obtain accurate differential bearing preload.

2) Using Hex Adjuster tool (C-4164) turn each adjuster until bearing free play is eliminated with approximately .010" (.25 mm) backlash. Seat differential roller bearings. Differential bearings do not always move with adjusters. To ensure accurate adjustment, bearings must be seated by oscillating drive pinion ½ turn in each direction 5-10 times each time adjusters are moved.

3) Install dial indicator on cover flange. Position indicator stem against drive side of ring gear. Check backlash every 90° to find point of minimum backlash. Mark each position so backlash readings will be taken with same teeth meshed. Rotate ring gear to point of minimum backlash.

4) Loosen right adjuster and tighten left adjuster until backlash is .003-.004" (.08-.10 mm) with each adjuster tightened to 10 ft. lbs. (14 N.m). Seat bearings as previously described. Tighten bearing cap bolts to 100 ft. lbs. (136 N.m). Using Hex Adjuster tool (C-4164), tighten right adjuster to 70 ft. lbs. (95 N.m). Seat bearings and continue to tighten right adjuster until torque remains constant at 70 ft. lbs. (95 N.m).

5) Check backlash again with indicator. If backlash is not between .006-.008" (.15-.20 mm), increase torque on right adjuster and seat bearings. Continue this operation until backlash is .006-.008" (.15-.20 mm). Tighten left adjuster to 70 ft. lbs. (95 N.m) and seat bearings. With adjustments completed, install adjuster locks. Make sure lock teeth are engaged in adjuster threads. Tighten lock screws to 90 INCH lbs. (8 N.m).

Final Inspection & Assembly

With pinion bearing preload and ring gear backlash properly adjusted, make a tooth pattern contact check. When pattern is satisfactory, install axle shafts, brake drums, wheels and tires, axle housing cover and refill with hypoid gear lubricant.

AXLE ASSEMBLY SPECIFICATIONS

Application	Specifications
Ring Gear Backlash	.006-.008" (.15-.20 mm)
Pinion Bearing Preload	
New Bearings	20-35 INCH Lbs. (2.3-4.0 N.m)
Used Rear, New Front Bearing	10 INCH Lbs. (1.1 N.m)
Maximum Ring Gear Runout	.005" (.13 mm)

TIGHTENING SPECIFICATIONS

Application	Ft. Lbs. (N.m)
Ring Gear-to-Diff. Case Bolts [1]	
8⅜" Ring Gear	55 (75)
9¼" Ring Gear	70 (95)
Drive Pinion Nut (Minimum)	210 (286)
Side Bearing Cap Bolts	
8⅜" Ring Gear	55 (75)
9¼" Ring Gear	100 (136)
Bearing Adjuster Lock Bolts	90 INCH lbs.(8 N.m)

[1] — Left-hand threaded bolts.

FORD SEPARATE HOUSING

**Bronco, E100/150, F100/150
Rear Axle**

DESCRIPTION

The axle is a banjo-type housing with a removable carrier. Drive pinion is straddle-mounted, and pinion depth is adjusted by shims. Ring gear and differential case are mounted on the removable carrier.

Preload on side bearings is set by adjusting nuts on which bearing cups rest. Its removable carrier and its lack of a rear cover plate help distinguish this unit from Dana (Spicer) units. It is used with semi-floating axles in all applications. Ring gear diameter is 9.0" (228.6 mm).

AXLE RATIO & IDENTIFICATION

Axle ratio and model identification numbers may be found on the metal tag, attached to axle by 1 carrier bolt. Other information on tag includes date code, ring gear diameter and assembly plant code. The information on this tag must be used to order replacement parts.

Fig. 1: Ford Drive Axle Identification Tag

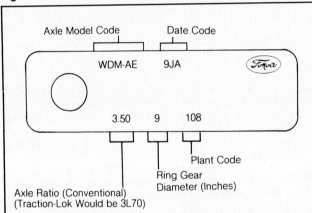

Use information on tag to order replacement parts.

REMOVAL & INSTALLATION

AXLE SHAFTS

Models With Ball Type Bearing

1) Remove wheels and brake drums. Working through hole in axle flange, remove 4 wheel bearing retainer nuts. Using a slide hammer connected to axle, pull out axle and bearing. Remove backing plate, and suspend from frame with wire. Replace oil seal, using seal remover (1175-AC) and slide hammer.

2) To install, reverse procedure. Use new bearing retainer gasket. Make sure bearing is firmly seated in axle housing.

Models With Tapered Roller Bearing

Follow same procedure as outlined for ball bearing removal. Use a slide hammer to remove bearing cup from axle housing. To install, reverse removal procedure. Place bearing cup over tapered bearing, before sliding axle into housing.

NOTE: If axle is removed for service or overhaul, a new oil seal must be installed.

AXLE BEARINGS & SEALS

Models With Ball Type Bearing

1) With axle removed, drill a ¼-½" (6-12 mm) hole in bearing retainer ring. Drill hole to a depth of ¾ the thickness of retainer ring. Do not drill through ring into axle shaft.

2) Place a chisel across drilled hole. Strike with a hammer until ring separates. Remove ring, and press bearing from axle shaft using a press and axle bearing plate (T75L-1165-B). Press a new bearing and retainer onto axle shaft. Drive new seal into axle housing. Do not attempt to press new bearing and retaining ring onto axle at the same time.

Models With Tapered Roller Bearing

1) With axle removed, drill a ¼-½" (6-12 mm) hole in bearing retainer ring. Drill hole to a depth of ¾ the thickness of retainer ring. Do not drill through ring into axle shaft.

2) Place a chisel across drilled hole. Strike with a hammer until ring separates and can be removed. Remove bearing cup from housing and place over bearing.

3) Place removal collet (T75L-1165A, B or C, or equivalent) over bearing. Place axle shaft in press, position over a support plate and press off bearing.

NOTE: If removal collet is not used, bearing must be discarded.

4) Install retainer plate on axle shaft (if removed). Lubricate new seal and bearing. Place seal and bearing on axle, making sure cup rib ring is facing axle flange.

5) Press bearing onto axle, making sure that it is fully seated. Do not attempt to press bearing retainer on at the same time. Press on a new bearing retainer.

PINION FLANGE & SEAL

Removal

1) Mark propeller shaft end yoke and pinion flange for reassembly reference. Disconnect propeller shaft, and tie out of way. Scribe marks on pinion shaft and pinion flange for reassembly reference.

2) Measure and record pinion bearing preload. Remove pinion nut, washer and flange. Remove oil seal with slide hammer and seal remover.

Installation

1) Press new oil seal into bore in bearing retainer, and seal outer edge with oil resistant sealer. Install pinion flange, washer and new nut. Tighten pinion shaft nut slowly, while rotating pinion flange to insure proper seating of pinion bearings.

2) Continue tightening nut, taking frequent preload readings. If recorded preload reading was less than specifications, tighten to specifications. If recorded reading was more than specification, tighten to original reading.

3) Install drive shaft. Do not back off pinion nut to lessen preload. If backed off, a new spacer must be installed.

DIFFERENTIAL CARRIER

Remove both axle shafts. Mark propeller shaft end yoke and pinion flange for reassembly reference. Remove propeller shaft. Drain rear axle lubricant. Remove

Drive Axles

FORD SEPARATE HOUSING (Cont.)

Fig. 2: *Exploded View of Ford Separate Housing Drive Axle*

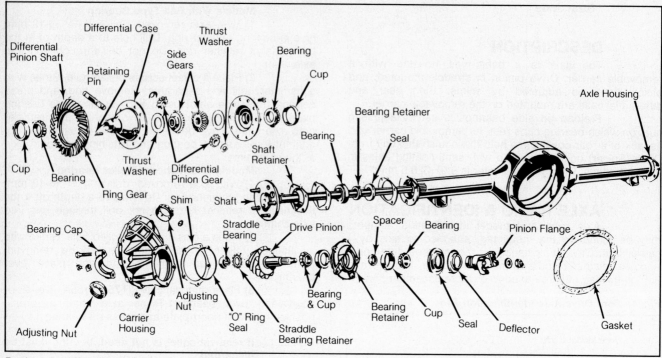

Banjo-type differential is used on these drive axles.

carrier attaching bolts and differential carrier. To install, reverse removal procedure.

OVERHAUL

DISASSEMBLY

1) Mark differential bearing caps for reassembly reference. Remove adjusting nuts, and remove differential case from carrier. Remove differential side bearings from case. Remove ring gear attaching bolts and discard. Tap ring gear from case, using a soft faced hammer.

2) Drive out differential pinion shaft retaining pin. Mark case halves for reassembly reference, and separate case. Using brass drift, drive out pinion shaft. Remove differential side gears, pinion gears, and thrust washers from case.

3) Remove pinion shaft nut, washer, pinion flange, and seal from carrier. Remove pinion shaft and bearing retainer, noting number and thickness of shims between retainer and carrier. Remove straddle bearing and retainer from carrier, using driver. Press pinion bearings from pinion shaft. Press bearing cups from bearing retainer.

REASSEMBLY & ADJUSTMENT

NOTE: **Lubricate all parts with hypoid gear lubricant during assembly.**

Differential Case Assembly

1) Place differential side gear and thrust washer into differential case bore. From outside of case, drive differential pinion shaft into case, just far enough to retain pinion thrust washer and pinion gear. Place second pinion thrust washer and gear into position in case.

2) Drive pinion shaft into place, making sure shaft retainer holes are in alignment with holes in case. Install second side gear and thrust washer. Assemble case halves, and install retainer pin. Install differential side bearings and ring gear, and tighten ring gear bolts to specifications.

NOTE: **Ring and pinion gears should not be used if numbers do not match.**

Drive Pinion Depth

1) Press new pinion bearing cups into pinion retainer housing until fully seated, making sure a .0015" (.038 mm) feeler gauge cannot be inserted between bearing cup and bottom of bore.

2) Install new straddle bearing and retainer (with concave side up) in carrier. Fully seat bearing and retainer. Press rear pinion bearing onto pinion shaft.

3) Determine pinion shim thickness by performing the following steps:
- If same ring and pinion gears are being reused, install original shim pack.
- If new ring and pinion gears are being installed, use "nominal" thickness shim, and make tooth contact pattern to see if additional shims are required.

4) Adjust pinion depth using rear axle pinion depth gauge (T79P-4020-A or equivalent) as follows:
- Assemble aligning adapter and gauge disc over threaded shaft.
- Install gauge block on threaded shaft, and tighten securely.
- Insert gauge assembly and new rear pinion bearing into pinion bearing retainer assembly.
- Install front pinion bearing. Install handle on tool assembly with tapered end in front pinion bearing.

Drive Axles

FORD SEPARATE HOUSING (Cont.)

5) Install pinion bearing retainer and gauge assembly into carrier (without a pinion shim). Tighten retainer assembly mounting bolts to 30-45 ft. lbs. (41-61 N.m). Rotate gauge block so it rests against pilot boss. Install gauge tube in differential bearing bore. Install and tighten bearing cap and bolts. *See Fig. 3.*

6) Using a feeler gauge, select the thickest blade that will enter between gauge block and gauge tube. *See Fig. 3.* Insert feeler blade directly along top of gauge block to insure a correct reading. The fit should provide a slight drag.

7) Select correct shim to be inserted, by comparing feeler gauge thickness with shim requirement in Shim Chart. Remove assembly and install drive pinion and ring gear.

Fig. 3: Measuring Ford Pinion Depth With Gauge (T79P-4020-A)

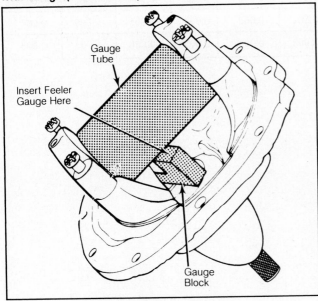

Using feeler gauge, measure pinion depth.

Pinion Bearing Preload
(With Collapsible Preload Spacer)

1) Place new preload spacer on drive pinion shaft. Install front pinion bearing and bearing retainer. Press bearing into position, being careful not to crush spacer. Install "O" ring in groove in bearing retainer, and place selected pinion depth shim on carrier housing. Install pinion assembly and tighten bolts.

2) Install pinion flange, washer and nut. Tighten pinion flange nut to 175 ft. lbs. (238 N.m). Check pinion bearing preload.

3) Continue to tighten pinion flange nut until proper preload is obtained. Do not exceed 175 ft. lbs. (238 N.m) at this time. Do not back off nut to obtain preload. If torque on pinion shaft is less than 175 ft lbs. (238 N.m) after preload is set, a new collapsible spacer must be installed.

Backlash & Side Bearing Preload

1) Place cups on differential side bearings, and set differential case in carrier. Slide assembly along bores until a slight amount of backlash is felt between gear teeth. Set adjusting nuts in bores so nuts just contact bearing cups. Each nut should be engaging approximately the same number of threads.

2) Carefully position bearing caps on carrier, install bearing cap bolts, and tighten to specifications. Make sure adjusting nuts turn freely as bolts are tightened. If not, remove caps and inspect for damaged threads. Loosen cap bolts and retorque to 25 ft. lbs. (34 N.m).

3) Loosen right adjusting nut until it is away from cup. Tighten left nut until ring gear is just forced into pinion with no backlash. Make sure right nut is still loose. Install dial indicator. *See Fig. 4.*

Fig. 4: Adjusting Side Bearing Preload

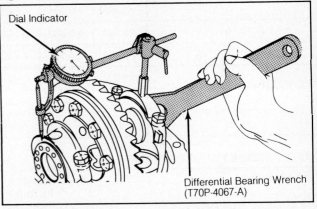

Loosen right adjusting nut, and tighten left side.

4) Tighten right nut until it first contacts bearing cup. Continue tightening until side bearing preload (case spread) is to specifications. Turn pinion gear several times in each direction to seat bearings and make sure no binding is evident.

5) Tighten bearing cap bolts to specifications. Install a dial indicator on carrier, so that contact tip of indicator bears against face of gear tooth on outer diameter of ring gear.

6) Measure backlash at several locations on ring gear. If backlash measurements vary more than .004" (.10 mm), there is excessive runout in gear or mounting.

7) If backlash is not correct, loosen 1 adjusting nut and tighten opposite nut an equal amount. This will move ring gear into adjustment. After this procedure, always check case spread specifications.

8) When side bearing preload and ring gear backlash are correctly set, perform gear tooth pattern check, and install carrier into axle housing.

NOTE: When moving adjusting nuts, final movement should always be made in a tightening direction. If nut must be loosened 1 notch, loosen 2 notches and then tighten 1 notch.

TIGHTENING SPECIFICATIONS

Application	Ft. Lbs. (N.m)
Side Bearing Cap Bolts	70-85 (95-115)
Ring Gear Bolts	70-85 (95-115)
Pinion Flange Nut	
Collapsible Spacer (Min.)	175 (238)
Pinion Bearing	
Retainer-to-Carrier	30-45 (41-60)
Carrier-to-Housing	25-40 (34-54)
Adjusting Nut Lock Bolts	12-25 (17-33)
Bearing Retainer Plate Bolt	20-40 (28-54)

Drive Axles

FORD SEPARATE HOUSING (Cont.)

PINION DEPTH SHIM ADJUSTMENT CHART (INCHES)

Old Pinion Marking	New Pinion Marking								
	-4	-3	-2	-1	0	+1	+2	+3	+4
+4	+0.008	+0.007	+0.006	+0.005	+0.004	+0.003	+0.002	+0.001	0
+3	+0.007	+0.006	+0.005	+0.004	+0.003	+0.002	+0.001	0	-0.001
+2	+0.006	+0.005	+0.004	+0.003	+0.002	+0.001	0	-0.001	-0.002
+1	+0.005	+0.004	+0.003	+0.002	+0.001	0	-0.001	-0.002	-0.003
0	+0.004	+0.003	+0.002	+0.001	0	-0.001	-0.002	-0.003	-0.004
-1	+0.003	+0.002	+0.001	0	-0.001	-0.002	-0.003	-0.004	-0.005
-2	+0.002	+0.001	0	-0.001	-0.002	-0.003	-0.004	-0.005	-0.006
-3	+0.001	0	-0.001	-0.002	-0.003	-0.004	-0.005	-0.006	-0.007
-4	0	-0.001	-0.002	-0.003	-0.004	-0.005	-0.006	-0.007	-0.008

AXLE ASSEMBLY SPECIFICATIONS

Application	Specifications In. (mm)
Ring Gear Backlash	.008-.015 (.20-.38)
Ring Gear Runout (Max.)	.004 (.10)
Backlash Variation (Max.)	.004 (.10)
Side Bearing Preload (Case Spread)	
New Bearings	.008-.012 (.20-.30)
Used Bearings	.005-.008 (.13-.20)
Side Gear Thrust	
Washer Thickness	.030-.032 (.76-.81)
Pinion Gear Thrust	
Washer Thickness	.030-.033 (.76-84)
Nominal Pinion Shim Thickness	.015 (.38)
	INCH Lbs. (N.m)
Pinion Bearing Preload (Rotating Torque)	
Collapsible Spacer	
New Bearings	8-14 (1.0-1.5)
Used Bearings	16-29 (1.8-3.3)

FORD 6 3/4" RING GEAR

Bronco II, Ranger

DESCRIPTION

The rear axle is a hypoid design ring and pinion gear encased in an integral cast housing. A one piece differential case contains a conventional 2 pinion differential assembly.

AXLE RATIO & IDENTIFICATION

A metal tag stamped with axle model, date of manufacture, ratio, ring gear diameter, and assembly plant is attached to rear cover.

Fig. 1: Rear Axle Identification Tag

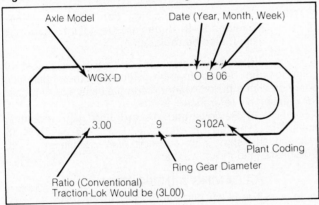

Use information on tag to order replacement parts.

REMOVAL & INSTALLATION

AXLE SHAFTS

Removal

1) Raise vehicle and support with safety stands. Remove wheel assemblies and brake drums. Working through hole in flange, remove nuts retaining wheel bearing retainer plate.

2) Using a slide hammer on axle shaft flange pull axle shaft from housing. Remove backing plate, and suspend from frame with wire. Remove oil seal, using seal remover and slide hammer.

NOTE: **If axle is removed for service or overhaul, a new oil seal and backing plate gasket must be used.**

Installation

1) Install a new gasket on the housing flange and install the brake backing plate. Coat the wheel bearing bore with lubricant prior to assembly.

2) Carefully slide the axle shaft into the housing do not damage oil seal. Start axle splines into side gear, and push shaft in until bearing bottoms in housing.

3) Install bearing retainer plate on mounting bolts at axle housing, and install attaching nuts. Install brake drum and drum retaining nuts. Install wheel assemblies and lower vehicle.

Fig. 2: Bronco II & Ranger 6 3/4" Integral Housing Axle Assembly

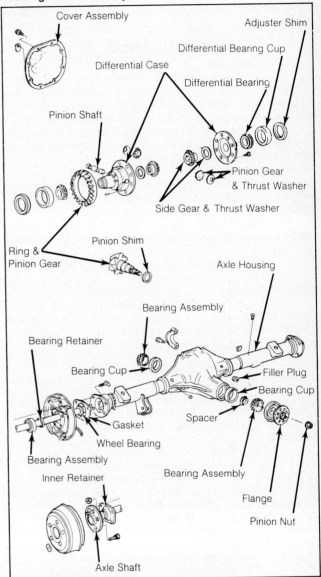

AXLE BEARINGS & SEALS

Disassembly

1) Remove axle shaft as previously described. Loosen the inner retainer ring by nicking it deeply with a cold chisel in several places. It will then slide off easily.

2) Remove the bearing from the axle shaft with Pinion Bearing Cone remover (T71P-4621-B). Do not apply heat to bearing when removing it from axle.

Reassembly

1) Place the retainer plate and a new bearing on the axle shaft, and press new wheel bearing on shaft with Pinion Bearing Cone Replacer (T62F-4621-A).

2) Bearing should seat firmly against shaft shoulder. Do not attempt to press on both bearing and inner retainer ring at the same time.

Drive Axles

FORD 6 3/4" RING GEAR (Cont.)

3) Using the bearing installation tool, press bearing inner retainer ring on shaft until retainer seats firmly against bearing. Do not heat bearing to install on axle.

PINION FLANGE & SEAL
Removal
1) Mark propeller shaft end yoke and pinion companion flange for reassembly reference. Disconnect propeller shaft, and tie out of the way. Scribe marks on pinion shaft and pinion flange for reassembly reference.

2) Measure and record pinion bearing preload. Remove pinion nut, washer and flange. Remove oil seal with slide hammer and seal remover.

Installation
1) Press new oil seal into bore in bearing retainer, and seal outer edge with oil resistant sealer. Install pinion flange, washer and new nut.

2) Tighten pinion shaft nut slowly, while rotating pinion flange to ensure proper seating of pinion bearings.

3) Continue tightening nut, taking frequent preload readings. If recorded preload reading was less than specifications, tighten to specifications.

4) If recorded reading was more than specification, tighten to original readings. Install drive shaft. Do not back off pinion nut to lessen preload. If backed off, a new spacer must be installed.

REAR AXLE ASSEMBLY
Removal
1) Raise vehicle and support with safety stands, under rear crossmember. Remove housing cover and drain lubricant. Remove axle shafts as previously described.

2) Remove brake backing plates and wire plates to frame. Mark and disconnect propeller shaft at companion flange. Disconnect axle vent from housing.

3) Disconnect brake line from housing clips. Disconnect upper arms and shock absorbers from housing. Lower housing on jack until coil springs can be removed. Disconnect lower arms from housing and remove axle housing.

Installation
To install, reverse removal procedures. Apply Loctite to threads holding axle vent and brake block (if used) to axle housing.

OVERHAUL

DISASSEMBLY

NOTE: **Differential case and drive pinion may be serviced with axle housing installed in vehicled.**

1) Raise vehicle and support with safety stands, under rear frame crossmember. Lower hoist until axle drops down far enough for working ease.

2) Remove housing cover and drain lubricant. Mount a dial indicator and measure and record ring gear backlash and runout. Remove rear wheels and brake drums.

3) Remove axle shafts as previously discribed. Place alignment marks on propeller shaft, yoke and companion flange for reassembly reference. Remove propeller shaft.

4) Mark 1 differential bearing cap for reassembly reference and note arrow position. Loosen bearing cap bolts and bearing caps. Pry differential case, bearing cups, and shims out until loose in bearing caps.

NOTE: **Bearing cups and caps must be installed in original positions.**

5) Remove bearing caps and differential. Remove pinion nut and companion flange. Drive pinion out of front bearing with soft-faced hammer.

6) Remove pinion from rear of housing. Remove seal with slide hammer type puller. Remove front bearing. Mount bearing puller on pinion shaft and press shaft out of bearing.

NOTE: **Do not remove pinion bearing cups unless damaged. If cups are replaced, bearings must also be replaced.**

7) Remove, measure, and record thickness of shim located behind bearing. Remove differential side bearings with a puller. Mark differential case and ring gear for reassembly reference.

8) Remove and discard ring gear mounting bolts. Press or tap off ring gear. Drive out pinion shaft lock pin and shaft with a punch. Remove pinion gears, side gears, and thrust washers.

CLEANING & INSPECTION
Clean all parts throughly in cleaning solvent. When replacing ring gear and pinion, note original factory shim thickness to adjust for variations in both carrier casting and original gear set dimension. Variations are marked on pinion gear head and ring gear.

NOTE: **Ring and pinion gear set must be replaced in matched sets.**

REASSEMBLY
1) Lubricate all parts with rear axle lubricant. Place side gears and thrust washers into case. Place pinion gears and thrust washers exactly opposite each other in case openings and in mesh with side gears.

2) Install ring gear with new mounting bolts. If bolts are covered with Green coating over 1/2" of threaded area, install and tighten bolts. If new bolts do not have Green coating, apply a small amount of Loctite to bolt threads and tighten bolts.

NOTE: **Ring gear bolts should not be reused.**

ADJUSTMENT
1) If new components have been installed, proper gear set assembly must be checked using a Rear Axle Pinion Depth Guage (T79P-4020) to determine correct pinion shim.

2) If bearing cups have been replaced, new cone and roller assemblies should be installed. Cups must be seated in bores so that a .0015" (.04 mm) feeler gauge will not fit between cup and bottom of bore.

FORD 6 3/4" RING GEAR (Cont.)

3) Rear pinion bearing must be must be pressed on so that it is firmly seated against spacer shim and pinion gear.

Pinion Depth

1) Assemble depth gauge and install aligning adapter. Use disc gauge that is .25" (6.5 mm) thick, and gauge block screw. Place rear pinion bearing over aligning disc and into bearing cup of carrier housing.

2) Install front pinion bearing into front bearing cup. Place tool handle onto screw and hand tighten. See Fig. 3. Make sure pinion depth measuring tool is properly installed and tightened.

Fig. 3: Installation of Pinion Depth Gauge

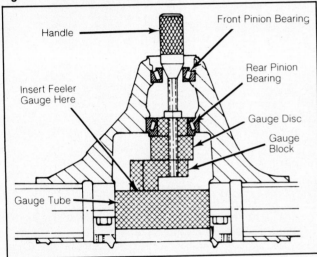

3) Apply a light film of oil to pinion bearings. Rotate gauge block several times to seat bearings. Rotational torque on gauge block assembly should be 20 INCH lbs. (2.25 N.m) with new bearings.

4) Final position of gauge block should be 45° above axle shaft centerline. Clean differential bearing bores throughly and install gauge tube. Tighten bearing cap bolts.

5) Using flat pinion shims as a gauge for shim selection, hold gauge block in proper position and measure clearance between gauge block and tube.

6) Correct shim selection is accomplished when a slight drag is felt as shim is drawn between gauge block and tube.

Pinion Bearing Preload

1) Place preselected shim on pinion shaft. Press bearing onto shaft until bearing and shim are firmly seated against shoulder of shaft.

2) Lubricate bearings with axle lubricant. Install front pinion bearing in housing. Install new pinion oil seal. Insert companion flange into seal and hold firmly in place.

3) From rear of carrier housing, insert pinion shaft into flange. Start a new pinion nut on pinion shaft and gradually tighten pinion nut (hold flange), checking bearing preload often.

4) As soon as preload is measured, turn pinion shaft in both directions several times to seat bearings. Tighten pinion nut and continue to measure pinion bearing preload until specified pinion torque is obtained.

5) If bearing preload is exceeded before torque specification is reached, replace collapsible spacer, install new pinion nut, and repeat procedures. Do not loosen pinion nut to reduce pinion bearing preload.

Differential Bearing Preload & Ring Gear Backlash

1) With pinion depth set and pinion installed, place differential case, and gear assembly with bearings and cups into carrier. Install a .265" (6.7 mm) shim on left (ring gear side) side of differential. Install left bearing cap finger tight.

2) Choose largest shim that will fit with a slight drag and install it on right (pinion gear side) side of differential. Install right bearing cap and tighten all cap bolts to specifications. Rotate gear assembly to ensure free operation.

3) Check ring and pinion backlash. If backlash is less than specified, add .020" (.50 mm) to shim size on left side. If backlash is still not within specifications, increase or decrease shim size where necessary to correct reading. See Fig. 4.

Fig. 4: Backlash Adjustment

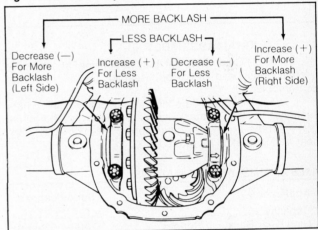

4) Retighten bearing cap bolts and rotate gear assembly several times. Recheck backlash and correct as necessary.

5) Increase both left and right shim sizes .006" (.15 mm), and reinstall for correct preload. Make sure shims are seated and gear assembly turns freely. Using marking compound, check gear tooth contact pattern.

BACKLASH-TO-SHIM THICKNESS CONVERSION

Required Change In Backlash In. (mm)	Change In Shim Thickness In. (mm)
.001 (.025)	.002 (.051)
.002 (.051)	.002 (.051)
.003 (.076)	.004 (.10)
.004 (.10)	.006 (.15)
.005 (.13)	.006 (.15)
.006 (.15)	.008 (.20)
.007 (.18)	.010 (.25)
.008 (.20)	.010 (.25)
.009 (.23)	.012 (.30)
.010 (.25)	.014 (.35)
.011 (.28)	.014 (.35)
.012 (.30)	.016 (.41)
.013 (.33)	.018 (.46)
.014 (.35)	.018 (.46)
.015 (.38)	.020 (.51)

FORD 6 3/4" RING GEAR (Cont.)

Fig. 5: Measuring Ring Gear Backlash

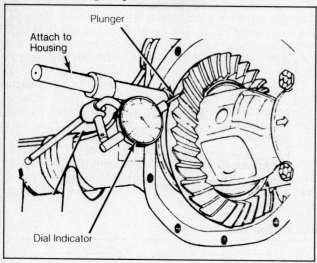

FINAL ASSEMBLY

1) Clean differential case housing lip and apply a continuous bead of silicone sealant. Install cover and tighten bolts.

2) Install axle shafts and tighten retaining nuts securing backing plates. Install propeller shaft. Install brake drums and wheel assemblies. Fill axle with lubricant. Adjust brakes if required.

AXLE ASSEMBLY SPECIFICATIONS

Application	Specifications
Capacity	3.5 pts. (1.7L)
Ring Gear Backlash Runout	.003" (.08 mm)
Side Gear Thrust Washer	.030-.032" (.76-.81 mm)
Pinion Gear Thrust Washer	.030-.032" (.76-.81 mm)
Norminal Pinion Shim	.030" (.76 mm)
Ring Gear Backlash	.008-.015" (.20-.38 mm)
Maximum Backlash Variation	
Between Teeth	.004" (.10 mm)
Pinion Bearing Preload	
Original Bearings	
(With Oil Seal)	8-14 INCH lbs. (.9-1.6 N.m)
New Bearings	16-29 INCH lbs. (1.8-3.2 N.m)

TIGHTENING SPECIFICATIONS

Application	Ft. Lbs. (N.m)
Bearing Cap Bolts	70-85 (95-115)
Pinion Shaft Lock Bolt	15-30 (20-40)
Ring Gear Attaching Bolts	70-85 (95-115)
Rear Cover Bolts	25-35 (34-47)
Pinion Nut	170 (230)

FORD 7 1/2" RING GEAR

Bronco II, Ranger

DESCRIPTION

The rear axle is a hypoid design ring and pinion gear encased in an integral cast iron housing. A one piece differential case contains a conventional 2 pinion differential assembly. Semi-floating axle shafts are retained by "C" washer locks at splined end of shafts.

AXLE RATIO & IDENTIFICATION

A metal tag stamped with axle model, date of manufacture, ratio, ring gear diameter, and assembly plant is attached to rear cover.

Fig. 1: Rear Axle Identification Tag

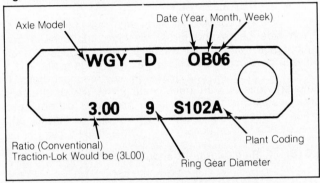

Use information on tag to order replacement parts.

REMOVAL & INSTALLATION

AXLE SHAFTS & BEARINGS
Removal
1) Raise vehicle and support with safety stands. Remove wheel assemblies and brake drums. Remove housing cover and drain lubricant.
2) Remove differential pinion shaft lock bolt and pinion shaft. Push axle toward center and remove "C" locks.
3) Remove axles being careful not to cut axle seal. Using a slide hammer and puller, remove bearing and seal as a unit.

Installation
1) Lubricate bearing with rear axle lubricant and install with a driver. Install seal. If seal becomes cocked during installation, remove it and replace it with a new one.
2) Insert axle in housing with care to avoid damage to oil seal. Install "C" locks and push shafts outboard to seat locks in counterbore of differential side gears.
3) Replace pinion gears and washers (if removed) and install pinion shaft and lock bolt. Apply silicone sealant in a 1/8" to 3/16" bead on face of carrier housing and install housing cover.

NOTE: No gasket other than the silicone seal is used. Cover assembly must be installed within 15 minutes of application of sealant.

Fig. 2: Ford 7 1/2" Integral Housing Axle Assembly

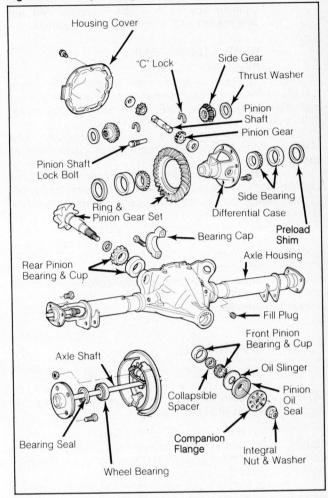

PINION FLANGE & OIL SEAL

NOTE: Pinion flange and oil seal replacement affects bearing preload. Preload must be carefully reset during reassembly.

Removal
1) Raise vehicle and support with safety stands. Remove wheel assemblies and brake drums. Scribe alignment marks on companion flange and propeller shaft for installation reference. Remove propeller shaft.
2) Using an INCH lb. torque wrench, measure and record torque required to rotate pinion through several revolutions.
3) Mark companion flange in relation to pinion shaft. Hold companion flange and remove pinion nut. Remove companion flange and seal with puller.

Installation
1) Install seal. Align marks on flange and pinion. Install flange and new integral nut and washer. Hold companion flange and gradually tighten nut.
2) Rotate pinion occasionally and check pinion bearing preload often, until original preload is obtained.

Drive Axles

FORD 7 1/2" RING GEAR (Cont.)

NOTE: If desired preload is exceeded, a new collapsible spacer must be installed and nut retightened until proper preload is obtained.

REAR AXLE ASSEMBLY

Removal

1) Raise vehicle and support with safety stands, under rear crossmember. Remove housing cover and drain lubricant. Remove axle shafts as previously described.

2) Remove brake backing plates and wire plates to frame. Mark and disconnect propeller shaft at companion flange.

3) Disconnect axle vent from housing (at brake junction block on some models). Disconnect brake line from housing clips. Disconnect upper arms and shock absorbers from housing.

4) Lower housing on jack until coil springs can be removed. Disconnect lower arms from housing and remove axle housing.

Installation

To install, reverse removal procedures. Apply Loctite to threads holding axle vent and brake block (if used) to axle housing.

OVERHAUL

DISASSEMBLY

NOTE: Differential case and drive pinion may be serviced in vehicle.

1) Raise vehicle and support with safety stands, under rear frame crossmember. Lower hoist until axle drops down far enough for working ease. Remove housing cover and drain lubricant.

2) Mount a dial indicator, measure, and record ring gear backlash and runout. Remove rear wheel assemblies and brake drums. Remove "C" locks and axle shafts as previously described.

3) Place alignment marks on propeller shaft, yoke and companion flange for reassembly reference. Remove propeller shaft. Mark 1 differential bearing cap for reassembly reference and note arrow position.

4) Loosen bearing cap bolts and bearing caps. Pry differential case, bearing cups, and shims out until loose in bearing caps. Remove bearing caps and differential.

NOTE: Bearing cups and caps must be installed in original positions.

5) Remove pinion nut and companion flange. Drive pinion out of front bearing with soft-faced hammer. Remove pinion from rear of housing. Remove seal with slide hammer type puller.

6) Remove front bearing. Mount bearing puller on pinion shaft and press shaft out of bearing. Remove, measure, and record thickness of shim located behind bearing.

NOTE: Do not remove pinion bearing cups unless damaged. If cups are replaced, bearings must also be replaced.

7) Remove differential side bearings with a puller. Mark differential case and ring gear for reassembly reference. Remove and discard ring gear mounting bolts.

8) Press or tap off ring gear. Drive out pinion shaft lock pin and shaft with a punch. Remove pinion gears, side gears and thrust washers.

CLEANING & INSPECTION

Clean all parts thoroughly in cleaning solvent. When replacing ring gear and pinion, note original factory shim thickness to adjust for variations in both carrier casting and original gear set dimension. Variations are marked on pinion gear head and ring gear.

NOTE: Ring and pinion gear set must be replaced in matched sets.

REASSEMBLY

1) Lubricate all parts with rear axle lubricant. Place side gears and thrust washers into case. Place pinion gears and thrust washers exactly opposite each other in case openings, and in mesh with side gears.

2) Install ring gear with new mounting bolts. If bolts are covered with green coating over 1/2" of threaded area, install and tighten bolts. If new bolts do not have green coating, apply small amount of Loctite to bolt threads and tighten bolts.

NOTE: Ring gear bolts should not be reused.

ADJUSTMENT

1) If new components have been installed, proper gear set assembly must be checked using a Rear Axle Pinion Depth Gauge (T79P-4020) to determine correct pinion shim.

2) If bearing cups have been replaced, new cone and roller assemblies should be installed. Cups must be seated in bores so that a .0015" (.04 mm) feeler gauge will not fit between cup and bottom of bore.

3) Rear pinion bearing must be pressed on so that it is firmly seated against spacer shim and pinion gear.

Pinion Depth

1) Assemble depth gauge and install aligning adapter, gauge disc (.89" (23 mm), and gauge block screw. Place rear pinion bearing over aligning disc and into bearing cup of carrier housing.

2) Install front pinion bearing into front bearing cup. Place tool handle onto screw and hand tighten. See Fig. 3. Make sure pinion depth measuring tool is properly installed and tightened.

3) Apply a light film of oil to pinion bearings. Rotate gauge block several times to seat bearings. Rotational torque on gauge block assembly should be 20 INCH lbs. (2.25 N.m) with new bearings.

4) Final position of gauge block should be 45° above axle shaft centerline. Clean differential bearing bores thoroughly and install gauge tube. Tighten bearing cap bolts.

5) Using flat pinion shims as a gauge for shim selection, hold gauge block in proper position and measure clearance between gauge block and tube.

FORD 7 1/2" RING GEAR (Cont.)

Fig. 3: Installation of Pinion Depth Measuring Tools

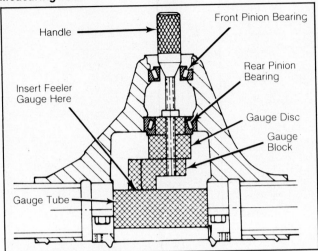

Check tool for proper installation.

6) Correct shim selection is accomplished when a slight drag is felt as shim is drawn between gauge block and tube.

Pinion Bearing Preload

1) Place preselected shim on pinion shaft. Press bearing onto shaft until bearing and shim are firmly seated against shoulder of shaft. Install new collapsible spacer on pinion shaft.

2) Lubricate bearings with axle lubricant. Install front pinion bearing in housing. Install new pinion oil seal. Insert companion flange into seal and hold firmly in place.

3) From rear of carrier housing, insert pinion shaft into flange. Start a new pinion nut on pinion shaft and gradually tighten pinion nut (hold flange).

4) Check bearing preload often. As soon as preload is measured, turn pinion shaft in both directions several times to seat bearings.

5) Tighten pinion nut and continue to measure pinion bearing preload until specified pinion torque is obtained. If bearing preload is exceeded before torque specification is reached, replace collapsible spacer.

6) Install new pinion nut and repeat procedures. Do not loosen pinion nut to reduce pinion bearing preload.

Differential Bearing Preload & Ring Gear Backlash

1) With pinion depth set and pinion installed, place differential case and gear assembly with bearings and cups into carrier.

2) Install a .265" (6.7 mm) shim on left (ring gear side) side of differential. Install left bearing cap finger tight.

3) Choose largest shim that will fit with a slight drag and install it on right (pinion gear side) side of differential. Install right bearing cap and tighten all cap bolts to specification.

4) Rotate gear assembly to ensure free operation. Check ring and pinion backlash. If backlash is less than specified, add .020" (.50 mm) to shim size on right side and subtract .020" (.50 mm) from shim size on left side.

5) If backlash is still not within specifications, increase or decrease shim size where necessary to correct reading. *See Fig. 4.*

Fig. 4: Backlash Adjustment

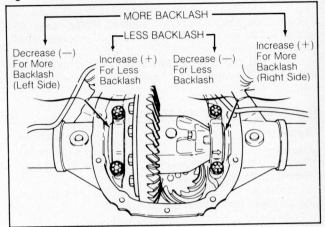

6) Retighten bearing cap bolts and rotate gear assembly several times. Recheck backlash and correct as necessary. Increase both left and right shim sizes .006" (.15 mm) and reinstall for correct preload.

7) Make sure shims are seated and gear assembly turns freely. Using marking compound, check gear tooth contact pattern.

BACKLASH-TO-SHIM THICKNESS CONVERSION

Required Change In Backlash In. (mm)	Change In Shim Thickness In. (mm)
.001 (.025)	.002 (.051)
.002 (.051)	.002 (.051)
.003 (.076)	.004 (.10)
.004 (.10)	.006 (.15)
.005 (.13)	.006 (.15)
.006 (.15)	.008 (.20)
.007 (.18)	.010 (.25)
.008 (.20)	.010 (.25)
.009 (.23)	.012 (.30)
.010 (.25)	.014 (.35)
.011 (.28)	.014 (.35)
.012 (.30)	.016 (.41)
.013 (.33)	.018 (.46)
.014 (.35)	.018 (.46)
.015 (.38)	.020 (.51)

Fig. 5: Measuring Ring Gear Backlash

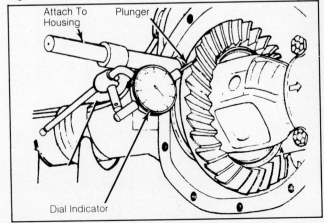

Drive Axles

FORD 7 1/2" RING GEAR (Cont.)

FINAL ASSEMBLY

1) Clean differential case housing lip and apply a continuous bead of silicone sealant. Install cover and tighten bolts. Install backing plates and propeller shaft, and tighten bolts.

2) Install wheel bearings, seals, brake drums, and wheel assemblies. Fill axle with lubricant. Adjust brakes if required.

AXLE ASSEMBLY SPECIFICATIONS

Application	Specifications
Capacity	3.5 pts. (1.7L)
Ring Gear Backface Runout	.003" (.08 mm)
Side Gear Thrust Washer	
Thickness	.030-.032" (.76-.81 mm)
Pinion Gear Thrust Washer	
Thickness	.030-.032" (76-81 mm)
Nominal Pinion Shim Thickness	.030" (.76 mm)
Ring Gear Backlash	.008-.015" (.20-38 mm)
Maximum Backlash Variation	
Between Teeth	.004" (10 mm)
Pinion Bearing Preload	
Original Bearings	
(With Oil Seal)	8-14 INCH lbs. (.9-1.6 N.m)
New Bearings	16-29 INCH lbs. (1.8-3.2 N.m)

TIGHTENING SPECIFICATIONS

Application	Ft. Lbs. (N.m)
Bearing Cap Bolts	70-85 (95-115)
Pinion Shaft Lock Bolt	15-30 (20-40)
Ring Gear Bolts	70-85 (95-115)
Rear Cover Bolts	25-35 (34-47)
Pinion Nut	170 (230)

Drive Axles

GENERAL MOTORS 7½", 8½", 8⅞", & 9½" RING GEAR

Chevrolet & GMC
Rear Axle C, K, G, S & P10 Models
Rear Axle G20 Models
Front Axle K10/20 Models

NOTE: The General Motors 8½" ring gear drive axle is used as the front drive axle on K10/20 models. For removal and installation instructions, see articles on Locking Hubs and 4-Wheel Drive Steering Knuckles. These models may also be equipped with a Spicer front drive axle. See appropriate article in this section.

DESCRIPTION

Axle assembly is hypoid gear type with integral carrier housing. It is used on Light Duty emission vehicles with semi-floating axles. Pinion bearing preload is made with a collapsible spacer. Differential side bearing preload adjustment and drive pinion depth adjustment are made by shims.

A removable 10-bolt housing cover permits inspection and minor servicing of differential, without removal from vehicle. Service procedures are the same for all 4 assemblies, except for tightening specifications and special tool numbers.

AXLE RATIO & IDENTIFICATION

General Motors uses several types of axles. The 7½", 8½", 8⅞" and 9½" axles can be distinguished from others by the configuration of their housing covers and by the number of attaching bolts. *To determine drive axle ratio, see article on Drive Axle Ratio Identification in this section.*

Fig. 1: General Motors 7½", 8½", 8⅞" & 9½"
Ring Gear Cover Gasket

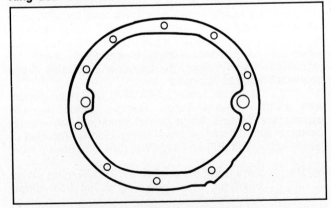

Illustration is for axle identification purposes.

REMOVAL & INSTALLATION

AXLE SHAFTS & BEARINGS

NOTE: For front axle shaft and bearing removal, see articles on Spicer (Dana) Full-Floating Axles or 4-Wheel Drive Steering Knuckles in this section.

Removal

1) Raise vehicle. Remove wheel and brake drums. Drain lubricant from drive axle. Remove housing cover. Remove pinion shaft lock screw.

NOTE: On vehicles equipped with 8⅞" ring gear and Eaton positive traction differential, proceed to step 3). On all remaining models, proceed to next step.

2) Remove pinion shaft. Push flanged end of axle shaft toward center of vehicle. Remove "C" lock from splined end of axle shaft, and remove axle shaft.

3) On vehicles with 8⅞" ring gear and Eaton positive traction differential, remove pinion shaft lock screw. Partly withdraw pinion shaft.

4) Rotate differential case until pinion shaft touches edge of housing. *See Fig. 2.*

Fig. 2: Positioning General Motors Case for Axle Removal.

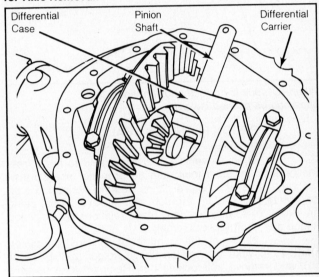

Rotate case until pinion shaft touches edge of housing.

5) Reach into case with screwdriver, and rotate "C" lock until open end points directly inward. When "C" lock is correctly positioned, axle shaft can be pushed inward, allowing "C" lock to be removed. Remove axle shaft. *See Fig. 3.*

CAUTION: Do not hammer on axle shaft. It should slide easily when "C" lock is correctly positioned. When removing axle shaft on the 9½" ring gear axle, be sure thrust washer in differential case does not slip out.

6) With axle shaft removed, insert bearing removal tool (J-23689 or equivalent) into axle housing behind bearing. Attach slide hammer to tool and remove bearing and seal.

Installation

1) Reverse removal procedure, noting the following. Install axle shaft housing bearing, until it bottoms against housing. Install axle shaft housing seal, until flush with outer edge of axle tube.

2) After installing axle shaft and "C" lock, pull axle shaft outward so "C" lock seats in side gear counterbore. On models equipped with Eaton positive

GENERAL MOTORS 7½", 8½", 8⅞", & 9½" RING GEAR (Cont.)

traction differential, make sure "C" lock is correctly positioned in thrust block. *See Fig. 3.*

Fig. 3: Correct Positioning of "C" Lock for Removal

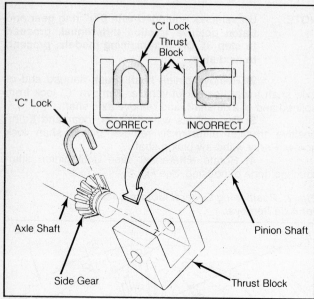

When "C" lock is correctly positioned, axle shaft can be pushed inward.

PINION FLANGE & SEAL
Removal

1) Raise vehicle, and allow axle to hang free. Disconnect universal joint, and tie propeller shaft out of the way. Note and record pinion bearing preload. To do so, rotate pinion shaft through several revolutions, using an INCH lb. torque wrench. Mark relationship of pinion flange and shaft for reassembly.

2) Count the number of threads on pinion shaft. Hold yoke with pinion flange holder (J-8614-10 or 11), and remove self-locking nut. Remove yoke using a puller. Pry old seal from housing.

Installation

1) Pack seal lip cavity with lithium-base extreme pressure lubricant. Place seal in bore. Using gauge plate (J-22804-1) and seal driver (J-21057 or J-23911), drive seal into place. Make sure seal is square in carrier. Pack cavity between end of pinion splines and pinion flange with a non-hardening sealer.

2) Using pinion flange holder (J-8614-10 or 11), install flange on pinion shaft. Install washer and nut in original position, taking note of scribe marks and number of exposed threads. Measure pinion preload. Tighten nut in small increments, until preload exceeds original figure by 1-5 INCH lbs. (.1-.6 N.m). Install propeller shaft, and lower vehicle.

CAUTION: Do not attempt to hammer flange onto pinion shaft, as it will damage ring gear and pinion.

AXLE ASSEMBLY
Removal

1) Raise vehicle. Raise axle until tension is released from springs and shock absorbers. Disconnect propeller shaft from flange. Tie propeller shaft out of way.

2) Disconnect shock absorbers at lower mounts. Disconnect vent hose from vent connector. Disconnect and plug brake hose at connector on axle housing.

3) Remove rear brake drums. Disconnect parking brake cable at actuating levers and at flange plate. Remove "U" bolt nuts, washers, spacers and clamp plates. Lower axle assembly and remove from vehicle.

Installation

To install axle assembly, reverse removal procedure. Bleed brake system.

OVERHAUL

DISASSEMBLY

NOTE: **Check and record ring gear backlash and pinion bearing preload before disassembly.**

1) Remove lock screws retaining pinion shaft, and remove pinion shaft. Remove axle shafts, and roll out differential pinions and thrust washers. Mark pinions and thrust washers for reassembly. Remove side gears and thrust washers. Mark side gears and thrust washers for reassembly.

2) Mark differential bearing caps and housing for reassembly. Loosen bearing cap bolts, and tap surface of bearing caps to loosen. Using pry bar inserted in differential carrier, pry against housing to remove carrier.

NOTE: **Be careful, as carrier bearings are preloaded. Carrier will fall free after being pried past a certain point.**

3) After removing carrier, place bearing cups with appropriate shims. Install bearing caps onto housing in their original position prior to removal. Using puller (J-22888 & J-8107-2 for 7½" ring gear, J-8107-4 for 8½" & 8⅞" ring gears or J-8107-3 for 9½" ring gear), remove differential side bearings.

4) Remove ring gear bolts, and tap ring gear off carrier using a soft drift and hammer. Using an INCH lb. torque wrench, check torque required to rotate drive pinion. If no preload reading is obtained, check for looseness of pinion assembly. Looseness indicates pinion bearings should be replaced.

5) Install holder (J-8614-10 or 11) on flange, with notches toward flange. Remove pinion nut and washer, and remove flange. Install pinion nut half way on pinion. Install differential cover using 2 bolts. Tap end of pinion, using soft drift and large hammer to remove pinion.

NOTE: **Care must be used to avoid damaging pinion bearings, when removing pinion from differential housing.**

6) Remove differential cover, and remove pinion assembly. Remove pinion oil seal and front bearing from housing. Inspect bearings and bearing cups, and replace as required. Discard oil seal, pinion nut and collapsible spacer.

CLEANING & INSPECTION

1) Clean all parts in cleaning solvent. Inspect all bearings, bearing cups, races and rollers for scoring,

GENERAL MOTORS 7½", 8½", 8⅞", & 9½" RING GEAR (Cont.)

chipping or excessive wear. Inspect axle shaft and side gear splines for excessive wear.

2) Inspect ring gear and pinion for scoring, cracking or chipping. Inspect differential case, pinion side gears, thrust washers and pinion shaft for cracks, scoring, galling or excessive wear.

REASSEMBLY & ADJUSTMENT

Case Assembly

Using guide pins if necessary, install ring gear squarely onto case. Tighten ring gear bolts evenly and alternately. Install side gears, differential pinions and thrust washers into case. Install differential pinion shaft and lock screw, and tighten lock screw finger tight.

Drive Pinion Depth & Bearing Preload

1) Drive pinion rear bearing shim thickness must be determined whenever a new axle housing, ring and pinion set, or pinion bearings are installed. Shim pack thickness is determined by using gauging tool set (J-21777).

2) If removed, install pinion bearing cups into housing. Place lubricated pinion bearings into cups. Position gauge plate (J-23597-11 for 7½"; J-21777-29 for 8½"; J-21777-36 for 8⅞"; or J-21777-85 for 9½" ring gear) and rear pinion bearing pilot on preloaded stud.

3) Install through rear pinion bearing, front pinion bearings and front pinion bearing disc (J-21777-42). Install hex nut until snug. Rotate bearings to insure proper seating. Hold preload stud stationary with a wrench on flats. Tighten hex nut until 20 INCH lbs. (2.2 N.m) are required to rotate bearings. *See Fig. 4.*

Fig. 4: Sectional View of Pinion Depth Tool Set (J-21777)

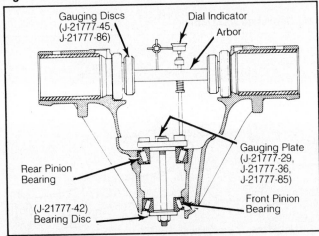

Gauging Discs
(J-21777-45,
J-21777-86)

Dial Indicator

Arbor

Rear Pinion
Bearing

Gauging Plate
(J-21777-29,
J-21777-36,
J-21777-85)

(J-21777-42)
Bearing Disc

Front Pinion
Bearing

Appropriate discs & plates must be used with each differential.

4) Mount side bearing gauging discs (J-21777-45) on ends of arbor. Place arbor into carrier making sure discs are properly seated. Install side bearing caps and bolts. Tighten bolts to avoid movement.

5) Position dial indicator on mounting post of arbor, with contact button resting on top surface of plunger. Preload dial indicator ½ revolution, then tighten in this position.

6) Place plunger onto gauging area of gauge plate. Rock plunger rod slowly back and forth across gauging area until dial indicator reads greatest deflection. Set indicator to zero. Repeat rocking action several times to verify setting.

7) Once zero reading is obtained, swing plunger until it is removed from gauging area. Dial indicator will now read required pinion shim thickness for a "nominal pinion". Record this reading.

8) Check drive pinion for painted or stamped markings on pinion stems, or for a stamped code number on small end of pinion gear. If marking is found to be plus or minus number (for example, +2 or -5) add or subtract that many thousandths of an inch from indicator reading. This will then be the required thickness of rear pinion bearing shim pack.

NOTE: **If no markings are found on pinion, use dial indicator reading as shim thickness.**

9) Remove bearing caps and gauging tool from housing. Place selected shim pack on pinion gear. Using a press, install lubricated pinion bearing onto pinion shaft.

10) Install a new collapsible spacer over pinion gear shaft. Position pinion assembly in housing. While holding pinion forward, carefully drive front pinion bearing onto pinion gear shaft until a few threads are exposed.

11) Install seal, pinion flange, washer and nut. Tighten until all end play is removed. Rotate pinion several times to seat bearings. Check preload using an INCH lb. torque wrench.

12) Continue tightening nut, and checking preload until specified preload is obtained. Do not back off nut to lessen preload. If preload is exceeded, a new collapsible spacer must be installed, and nut must be retightened until proper preload is obtained.

Side Bearing Preload

1) Lubricate bearings, and place differential assembly into position in housing. Hold in place by hand.

2) Install bearing strap (J-22779-6) on left bearing. Tighten bolts evenly to a snug fit. Install right bearing cap. Tighten bolts to a snug fit.

3) Position ring gear tight against pinion, so that backlash is .000-.001" (0-.025 mm). Insert gauging tool (J-22779) between left bearing cup and carrier housing.

4) While moving tool up and down, tighten adjusting nut until a slight drag is felt. Tighten lock bolt on side of tool.

5) Install .170" (4.32 mm) adjustment spacer and shim between right bearing and carrier. Insert a feeler gauge, thick enough to create a slight drag, between shim and carrier.

6) To determine correct side bearing shim thickness, measure thickness of adjusted gauging tool. Record measurement. Add together dimensions of shim, spacer and feeler gauge. Record measurement.

7) Subtract .010" (.25 mm) from ring gear (left) side measurement and add .010" (.25 mm) to opposite (right) side measurement. This allows for correct backlash adjustment.

8) To obtain correct preload, add .004" (10 mm) to both measurements. The total is the correct shim pack thickness for each side.

Example:

Ring Gear Side (Left) Shim Pack
  .250" (Gauging Tool Measurement)
 -.010" (Backlash Adjustment)
 +.004" (Bearing Preload)
 =.244" (Ring Gear Side Shim Pack)

Drive Axles

GENERAL MOTORS 7½", 8½", 8⅞", & 9½" RING GEAR (Cont.)

Opposite Ring Gear Side (Right) Shim Pack
.265" (Combined Measurement Total)
+.010" (Backlash Adjustment)
+.004" (Bearing Preload)
=.279" (Opposite Ring Gear Side Shim Pack)

9) Install ring gear side shim first. Wedge opposite side shim between bearing cup and spacer. Install shim so that chamfered side is against spacer.

NOTE: **If shim is not chamfered enough, and it scrapes spacer when it is installed, file or grind chamfer before installation.**

10) It may be necessary to partially remove differential, when right side shim is being installed. Tap shim into place with a soft-faced hammer. Tighten bearing cap bolts.

Backlash & Final Assembly
1) Check backlash at 4 locations around ring gear, using a dial indicator mounted to axle housing. Variation should not exceed .001" (.025 mm). If backlash is not within specifications, adjust side bearing shims as necessary.

CAUTION: Total shim pack thickness must not be changed. If a shim is removed from 1 side, the same thickness shim must be added to the other side.

2) After adjustment is completed, make a tooth contact pattern test, and make any necessary corrections. Install axle shafts and housing cover.

TIGHTENING SPECIFICATIONS

Application	Ft. Lbs. (N.m)
Ring Gear-to-Differential Case	
7½" Ring Gear	[1] 90 (120)
8½" Ring Gear	80 (109)
8⅞" Ring Gear	60 (82)
9½" Ring Gear	110 (150)
Side Bearing Cap	
7½", 8½" & 8⅞"	55 (75)
9½" Ring Gear	65 (88)
Pinion Shaft Lock Bolt	20 (27)

[1] — Use new bolts. Do not reuse old bolts.

AXLE ASSEMBLY SPECIFICATIONS

Application	In. (mm)
Ring Gear Backlash	.005-.008 (.13-.20)
Side Bearing Preload	.008 (.20)

Application	INCH Lbs. (N.m)
Pinion Bearing Preload	
7½" Ring Gear	
Used Bearings	8-12 (1.0-1.4)
New Bearings	24-32 (2.7-3.6)
8½" & 8⅞" Ring Gear	
Used Bearings	5-10 (.6-1.13)
New Bearings	15-30 (1.7-3.4)
9½" Ring Gear	
Used Bearings	5-15 (.6-1.7)
New Bearings	20-25 (2.3-2.8)

Fig. 5: Exploded View of General Motors 7½", 8½", 8⅞" & 9½" Ring Gear Axle Assembly

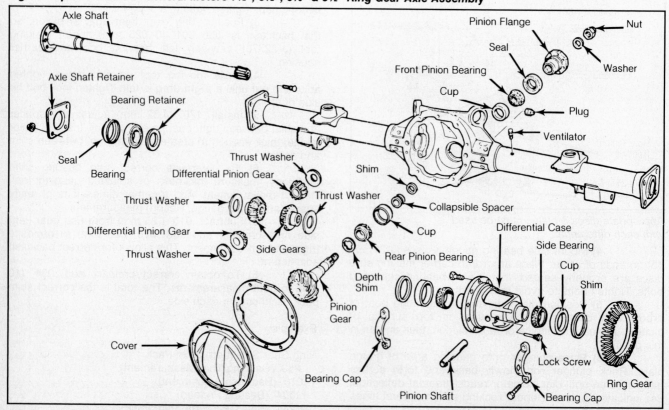

Drive Axles

GENERAL MOTORS 10½" RING GEAR

Chevrolet & GMC, Rear Axle
C20/30 Models, G30 Models, K20/30
Models, P20/30 Models

NOTE: The vehicle series numbers used in this article have been abbreviated for common reference to both Chevrolet and GMC models. Chevrolet models use numerical designations as listed; GMC models are identified as follows: 10 = 1500; 20 = 2500; 30 = 3500.

NOTE: The 10½" ring gear is not used on vehicles with dual rear wheels. Some models may use Spicer (Dana) axles. See appropriate articles in this section.

DESCRIPTION

The axle assembly is the hypoid gear type with integral carrier housing. It is used with full floating axles.

The drive pinion bearing preload adjustment is made with a collapsible spacer. The differential side bearing preload adjustment and the drive pinion depth adjustment are made by side bearing adjusting nuts.

A removable 14-bolt housing cover permits inspection and minor servicing of differential without removal from vehicle.

AXLE RATIO & IDENTIFICATION

General Motors uses several types of axles in its vehicles. The 10½" ring gear axle can be distinguished from the others by the configuration of its housing cover and by the number of attaching bolts. *See Fig. 1. To determine drive axle ratio, refer to Drive Axle Ratio Identification in this Section.*

Fig. 1: 10½" Ring Gear Housing Cover Gasket

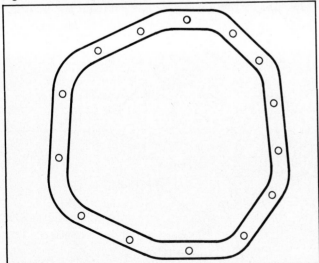

REMOVAL & INSTALLATION

AXLE SHAFTS

1) Remove axle shaft attaching bolts from wheel hub, and hit flange on axle shaft with a soft faced hammer to loosen shaft.

2) Grip rib on end of flange with pliers, and twist axle shaft to begin removal. When shaft is loose, remove it from housing. To install, reverse removal procedure, using new gaskets.

WHEEL HUB & SEAL

1) Remove axle shaft. Remove lock nut retainer, lock nut, adjusting nut retainer, adjusting nut and thrust washer from axle housing.

2) Pull hub and drum assembly straight off axle housing. Pry old oil seal from wheel hub, using care not to damage bore surface. Thoroughly clean seal conctact area.

3) Pack cavity between seal lips with high melting point wheel bearing lubricant. Position seal in hub bore. Using seal installer (J-24428), carefully press seal into hub, until seal is flush with edge of hub. Install hub onto axle housing and install axle shaft.

WHEEL BEARINGS

1) With wheel hub removed from vehicle, use a long drift or punch to drive inner bearing, cup, and oil seal from hub. Remove outer bearing retaining ring. Drive outer bearing out of hub, using outer bearing cup tool (J-24426).

CAUTION: Inner bearing cup and outer bearing retaining ring must be removed before attempting to remove outer bearing cup.

2) Place outer bearing assembly into hub. Using bearing cup installer (J-8608), drive bearing past retaining ring groove in hub.

NOTE: Be sure chamfer of bearing cup installer (J-8608) does not contact bearing cup.

3) Install outer bearing retaining ring, and drive outer bearing cup back against ring until seated. Place inner bearing cup into hub.

4) Using bearing cup driver (J-24427), drive cup into hub until seated against shoulder. Install new oil seal with oil seal installer (J-24428). Place hub assembly onto axle housing. Install adjusting nut, and adjust rear wheel bearing. *See Rear Wheel Bearing Adjustment in SUSPENSION Section.*

PINION FLANGE & SEAL

1) Disconnect propeller shaft, and tie out of the way. Scribe a line down pinion stem and pinion flange for reassembly reference.

2) Remove pinion nut and pull pinion flange from stem. Pry oil seal from bore, using care not to damage machined surfaces. Clean area thoroughly. Pack cavity between seal lips with high melting point bearing lubricant.

3) Place new seal into bore, and drive seal in until it bottoms against inner shoulder. Install pinion flange, pinion nut and propeller shaft.

AXLE ASSEMBLY

1) Raise vehicle and support weight at frame side rails. Remove rear wheels. Disconnect propeller shaft and tie out of the way. Remove wheel hub. Disconnect parking brake cable at lever and at flange plate.

2) Disconnect hydraulic brake hose at connector on axle housing. Disconnect shock absorbers at axle brackets. Raise axle assembly slightly to relieve tension

Drive Axles

GENERAL MOTORS 10½" RING GEAR (Cont.)

on springs. Remove spring "U" bolts, and lower axle assembly to floor. To install, reverse removal procedure.

OVERHAUL

DISASSEMBLY

1) Drain lubricant. Remove housing cover and axle shafts. Note and record ring gear backlash and pinion bearing preload for reassembly reference.

2) Remove adjusting nut lock retainers from bearing caps. Mark bearing caps for reassembly reference. Remove bearing caps. Loosen side bearing adjusting nuts and remove differential case assembly from axle housing.

3) Remove pinion bearing retainer bolts. Remove pinion and bearing retainer assembly. Note and record number and thickness of shims removed. Remove pinion flange and press pinion gear out of bearing retainer.

4) Press rear pinion bearing from gear. Drive front and rear pinion bearing cups and pinion oil seal from bearing retainer. Drive pinion straddle bearing from axle housing.

5) Mark differential case halves for reassembly reference. Remove ring gear bolts and ring gear. Split case halves. Remove side gears, differential spider, differential pinion gears, and thrust washers.

REASSEMBLY & ADJUSTMENT

Case Assembly

1) Lubricate differential pinion gears, side gears and thrust washers with hypoid gear oil. Place pinion gears and thrust washers on differential spider. Install side gears and spider assembly into left half of differential case.

2) Assemble both halves of case, making sure alignment marks on both halves are together. Install 2 guide pins in ring gear, directly opposite each other.

3) Start guide pins through holes in case flange, and tap ring gear lightly with soft face hammer until ring gear attaching bolts can be started. Tighten bolts evenly until ring gear is flush with case flange. Remove guide pins, and tighten all ring gear bolts alternately and evenly.

Pinion Depth & Bearing Preload

1) With pinion bearing retainer mounted in vise, install pinion gear and bearing assembly into retainer. Place pinion flange on gear stem. Install new pinion nut, and tighten nut in small increments until specified pinion bearing preload is obtained.

2) If original ring and pinion gears are to be reinstalled, use new pinion shims of same number and thickness as those removed.

3) If new gears are to be installed, compare pinion depth code number of new pinion gear with that of

Fig. 2: Exploded View of Chevrolet & GMC 10½" Ring Gear Axle Assembly

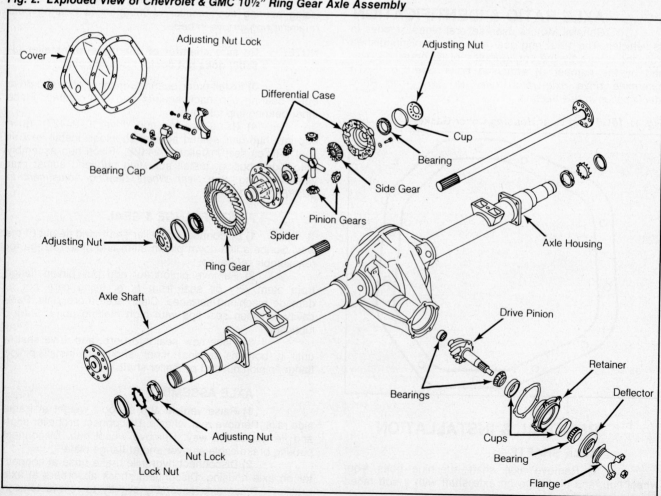

Drive Axles

GENERAL MOTORS 10½" RING GEAR (Cont.)

original pinion gear. From these 2 codes, determine correction factor by referring to Pinion Depth Code chart.

    4) Combine correction factor with thickness of new shim pack. Place new shim pack onto carrier housing, and install pinion bearing retainer assembly. Tighten retainer bolts in a crosswise sequence.

PINION DEPTH CODES

Original Code	Service Code	Correction In. (mm)
+2	+2	0 (0)
+2	+1	-.001 (-.025)
+2	0	-.002 (-.005)
+2	-1	-.003 (-.008)
+2	-2	-.004 (-.10)
+1	+2	+.001 (+.025)
+1	+1	0 (0)
+1	0	-.001 (-.025)
+1	-1	-.002 (-.005)
+1	-2	-.003 (-.008)
0	+2	+.002 (+.005)
0	+1	+.001 (+.025)
0	0	0 (0)
0	-1	-.001 (-.025)
0	-2	-.002 (-.005)
-1	+2	+.003 (+.008)
-1	+1	+.002 (+.005)
-1	0	+.001 (+.025)
-1	-1	0 (0)
-1	-2	-.001 (-.025)
-2	+2	+.004 (+.10)
-2	+1	+.003 (+.008)
-2	0	+.002 (+.005)
-2	-1	+.001 (+.025)
-2	-2	0 (0)

AXLE ASSEMBLY SPECIFICATIONS

Application	Measurement In. (mm)
Ring Gear Backlash	
Preferred	.005-.008 (.13-.20)
Acceptable	.003-.012 (.008-.30)
	INCH Lbs. (N.m)
Pinion Bearing Preload	
New Bearings	23-35 (2.6-4.0)
Used Bearings	5-15 (.6-1.7)

TIGHTENING SPECIFICATIONS

Application	Torque Ft. Lbs. (N.m)
Ring Gear	120 (163)
Side Bearing Cap	135 (184)
Drive Pinion Nut	[1]
Differential Bearing Adjusting Lock	20 (27)
Pinion Bearing Retainer	65 (84)

[1] - Torque as necessary to obtain correct preload. Tighten to approximately 350 Ft. Lbs. (476 N.m).

Backlash & Final Assembly

    1) Place lubricated bearing cups onto differential side bearings and place differential assembly into carrier. Install bearing caps in their original positions, and tighten cap bolts until just snug.

    2) Loosen right side bearing adjusting nut, and tighten left side adjusting nut until zero backlash is obtained. Back off left adjusting nut 2 slots to a locking position.

    3) Tighten right adjusting nut until case is in firm contact with left adjusting nut. Loosen right adjusting nut until it is free of bearing. Retighten nut until it just contacts bearing. Tighten right adjusting nut additional 2 slots (used bearings) or 3 slots (new bearings) to properly preload differential side bearings.

    4) Using a dial indicator, measure ring gear backlash in at least 4 locations around ring gear. Adjust to specifications by moving adjusting nuts in or out as necessary. If 1 adjusting nut is loosened, the other nut must be tightened an equal amount to maintain side bearing preload.

    5) With backlash adjustment complete, install adjusting nut lock fingers into slots in nuts, and attach fingers to bearing caps. Tighten bearing cap bolts, and perform gear tooth contact pattern check. Install axle housing cover.

Drive Axles

JEEP 8⅞" RING GEAR

Cherokee, CJ, J10,
Scrambler, Wagoneer; Rear Axle

DESCRIPTION

The Jeep 8⅞" ring gear axle assembly is a hypoid gear type with integral carrier housing. This semi-floating axle is used as the rear drive axle on CJ, Scrambler, Cherokee, J10 and Wagoneer models.

The axle is equipped with tapered axle shafts on CJ and Scrambler models, and with flanged axle shafts on Cherokee, J10 and Wagoneer models.

Pinion bearing preload is adjusted by varying shim thickness. A removable housing cover allows access to differential for inspection or minor servicing, without removing axle assembly.

AXLE RATIO & IDENTIFICATION

This Jeep axle assembly has a 10 bolt cover. Some Jeep models use a Spicer (Dana) axle. *Refer to Spicer (Dana) Semi-Floating or Full-Floating articles in this section, for correct identification. To determine drive axle ratio, refer to Drive Axle Ratio Identification article in this section.*

REMOVAL & INSTALLATION

AXLE HUB

Removal (CJ & Scrambler Models)

1) Remove dust cap, nut and washer. Raise vehicle and remove tire and wheel. Remove brake drum retaining screws, and remove drum. Using puller (J-25109-01), remove hub.

2) Inspect hub for loose or damaged wheel studs. Check keyway and tapered center bore for wear or cracks. Replace hub if necessary.

CAUTION: Do not use a knockout or slide hammer-type puller to remove hub. This type of puller may damage axle assembly.

**Installation of Original Hub
(CJ & Scrambler Models)**

1) Align axle key and hub keyway. Slide hub onto axle shaft as far as possible. Install nut and washer. Install drum retaining screws, wheel and tire.

2) Lower vehicle and tighten nut to 250 ft. lbs. (340 N.m). Tighten nut to align cotter key hole, do not back nut off.

NOTE: Installation procedures for a new hub and an old hub will differ. If axle shaft is replaced, hub must also be replaced, however, a new hub can be installed on an old axle shaft.

**Installation of New Hub
(CJ & Scrambler Models)**

1) Align axle key and hub keyway. Slide hub onto axle shaft as far as possible. Install 2 lubricated thrust washers and axle shaft nut. Install drum retaining screws, wheel and tire. Lower vehicle. *See Fig. I.*

2) Tighten axle shaft nut until distance from outer hub face to end of axle is 1⅝₁₆". Pressing hub on to

this dimension is necessary to form hub serrations correctly.

3) Remove axle shaft nut and 1 washer. Install nut, and tighten to 250 ft. lbs. (340 N.m). Tighten nut to align cotter key hole. Do not back off nut.

Fig. 1: Jeep Hub Installation Measurement

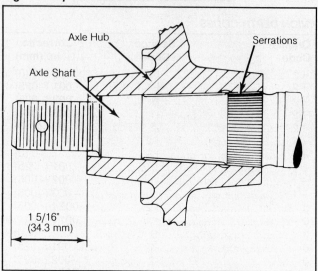

Tighten axle shaft nut until distance from outer hub face to end of axle is corrected.

AXLE SHAFTS & BEARINGS

Removal (CJ & Scrambler Models)

1) Remove axle hub as previously outlined. Disconnect parking brake cable at equalizer, and brake line at wheel cylinder. Remove backing plate, oil seal, and shims from axle shaft.

2) Using puller (J-2498), remove axle shaft. Remove and discard inner seal. Bearing cone is press fit on axle shaft, and must be removed using an arbor press and mandrel.

Installation (CJ & Scrambler Models)

1) Press new axle bearing onto shaft, with small diameter of cone towards outer end of shaft. Coat inner axle shaft seal with a light coat of oil. Coat outer surface of metal retainer with non-hardening sealer.

NOTE: Tapered axle shaft bearings have no provision for lubrication, and should be packed with a good wheel bearing lubricant before installation.

2) Install inner seal in axle housing using an installer (J-21788). Place axle shaft in housing, and align splined end with differential gears. Install outer bearing cup. Coat backing plate with sealer at mounting area.

3) Install original shims, oil seal assembly, and backing plate. Tighten backing plate bolts to 35 ft. lbs. (47 N.m). Oil seal and retainer are located on outside of backing plate.

4) If left axle was removed, end play must be adjusted. To adjust end play, remove left axle hub, if not previously removed. Strike ends of both axles with a lead hammer to seat bearings.

5) Attach axle shaft end play tool (J-2092) and a dial indicator to left axle. Move axles back and forth to

JEEP 8⅞" RING GEAR (Cont.)

measure end play. End play should be .004 -.008" (.10-.20 mm) with .006" (.15 mm) recommended.

    6) Add shims to increase end play; remove shims to decrease end play. Install hub and drum, as previously outlined. Adjust brakes, and bleed brake hydraulic system.

Fig. 2: Removing Bearing Retaining Ring from Cherokee, J-10 & Wagoneer Models

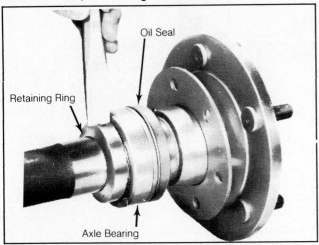

Drill retaining ring part way through, and cut with chisel.

Removal (All Other Models)

    1) Raise and support vehicle, and remove rear wheels. Remove brake drum. Remove nuts and lock washers attaching support plate and retainer to axle tube flange.

    2) Install slide hammer and adapter tool (J-2619-01 & J-21579) on axle flange, and remove axle shaft. Remove and discard oil seal from axle housing, and wipe seal bore in housing clean.

    3) Mount axle shaft in vise. Drill a ¼" hole in retaining ring approximately ¾ way through ring thickness, making sure not to let drill contact axle shaft. See Fig. 2.

    4) Position chisel over drilled hole in retaining ring and cut ring. Remove it from axle shaft. Cut through oil seal using hacksaw and remove seal and retainer plate, making sure not to damage seal contact surface.

    5) Remove axle shaft bearing using arbor press and mandrels.

CAUTION: Do not use a torch to remove axle shaft retaining ring or bearing.

Installation (All Other Models)

    1) Install retainer plate on axle shaft. Pack wheel bearing lubricant in oil seal cavity and between oil seal lips. Install seal on axle shaft with outer face of seal facing axle flange.

    2) Pack new axle bearing with wheel bearing lubricant. Install bearing on axle shaft, making sure bearing cup rib ring is facing axle flange.

    3) Install bearing retainer ring. Press axle shaft bearing and retaining ring on axle shaft simultaneously. Make sure both are seated properly against axle shaft shoulder.

    4) Install new oil seal in axle housing using an installer (J-21788). Install axle shaft through support plate.

Coat outside diameter of bearing cup with wheel bearing lubricant before installing in bearing bore.

    5) Tap flanged end of axle shaft lightly, using soft mallet to position axle shaft bearing in bearing bore of housing. Install axle shaft retainer and brake support plate to axle tube flange.

    6) Install attaching lock washers and nuts. Tighten to 35 ft. lbs. (47 N.m). Install brake drums and rear wheels. Lower vehicle.

PINION FLANGE & SEAL

Removal

    1) Raise and support vehicle. Remove both rear wheels and brake drums. Disconnect propeller shaft from flange. Mark propeller shaft position with flange. Connect an INCH Lb. torque wrench to flange nut. Rotate several times, and measure torque required to turn pinion.

    2) Record reading for assembly. Hold flange and remove nut. Mark position of flange on drive pinion. Discard pinion nut. Using a puller, remove flange. If surface is damaged or grooved, replace flange. Pry out old seal and discard.

Installation

    1) Coat seal lip with axle lubricant before installing. Install seal using installer (J-22661). Align drive pinion shaft and flange marks, and install flange on drive pinion.

    2) Tighten replacement nut only enough to remove end play. Check torque required to turn drive pinion. Refer to reading recorded during flange removal.

    3) Tighten nut enough to exceed recorded reading by 5 INCH Lbs. (.6 N.m). Repeat these steps until desired torque is obtained. Install propeller shaft aligning marks. Install brake drums and wheels.

CAUTION: Do not loosen and retighten nut. Do not over-tighten nut. If correct torque is exceeded, a new collapsible spacer must be installed, and drive pinion preload must be reset.

AXLE ASSEMBLY

Removal

    1) Raise and support vehicle forward of rear springs. Remove wheels with tires. Mark propeller shaft position with flange, and disconnect propeller shaft. Disconnect shock absorbers and brake line at "T" fitting.

    2) Plug open ends of lines to prevent dirt from entering system. Disconnect parking brake cable at equalizer. Support axle housing with a floor jack. Remove "U" bolts at spring.

    3) If vehicle has springs mounted below axles, disconnect shackle bolts and lower spring from axle. Slide axle housing out from under vehicle.

Installation

    To install axle assembly, reverse removal procedure. Bleed brake hydraulic system and check axle lubricant level.

OVERHAUL

DISASSEMBLY

NOTE: It is not necessary to remove complete axle assembly from vehicle for overhaul.

Drive Axles

JEEP 8⅞" RING GEAR (Cont.)

1) Remove axle shaft dust caps and retaining nuts. Raise and support vehicle. Remove axle housing cover, and drain lubricant. Remove axle hubs as previously outlined. Mark differential side bearing caps with a center punch for reassembly.

2) Loosen bearing cap bolts, until they are retained by just a few threads. This will prevent differential from falling out. Pry differential loose in housing. Remove bearing caps and differential.

3) Secure bearing shims to their respective bearing caps and cups. *See. Fig. 3.* Use puller (J-2497-01) to remove side bearings from differential. Make sure puller pulls against bearing cone and not bearing cage or rollers.

4) Remove ring gear retaining bolts, and tap ring gear off differential using a brass hammer. Drive out pinion shaft lock pin, using a ³⁄₁₆" drift punch. Drive out pinion shaft using a punch. With shaft removed, withdraw thrust block.

5) Roll pinion gears around on side gears until they can be removed. Remove side gears and thrust washers. *See Fig. 4.* With propeller shaft removed, hold flange and remove retaining nut. Remove flange using a puller.

6) Install housing cover with 2 bolts. Remove pinion seal. Strike end of drive pinion with a soft mallet. This will unseat front bearing cone from gear. Remove bearing cone. Remove and discard collapsible spacer. Remove housing cover, drive pinion, and rear bearing.

7) Remove front and rear bearing cups using a slide hammer and adapter. Pinion depth shims are behind rear bearing cone. Secure shims to cone for reassembly reference.

Fig. 4: *Removal of Jeep Pinion Shaft Lock Pin*

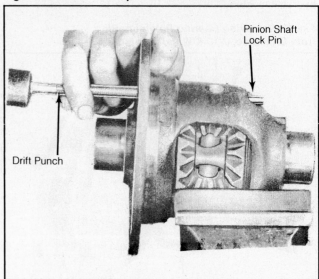

With shaft removed, withdraw thrust block.

Fig. 3: *Exploded View of CJ & Scrambler Drive Axle Assembly*

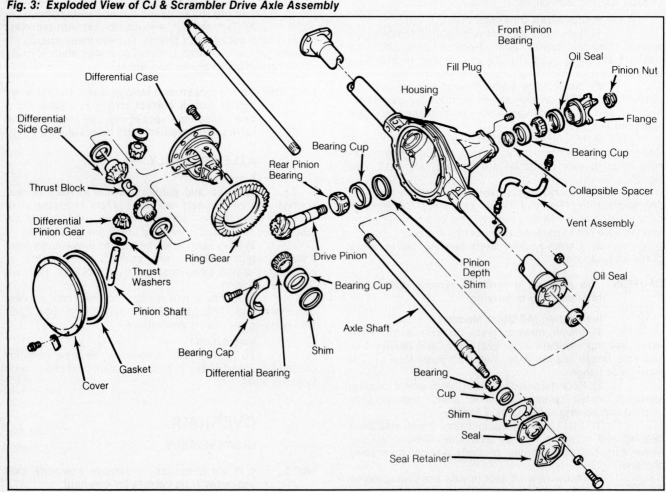

JEEP 8⅞" RING GEAR (Cont.)

CLEANING & INSPECTION

Clean all components in solvent. Allow bearings to air dry. Inspect all machined surfaces for smoothness or raised edges. Inspect all bearings and cups for wear or pitting and replace as necessary. Inspect all gear teeth for wear or chipping and replace as necessary.

REASSEMBLY & ADJUSTMENT

Drive Pinion Installation & Depth Adjustment

1) Pinion gear depth is distance from end face of pinion to the axle shaft centerline. This dimension is controlled by shims installed between pinion gear bearing and axle housing. *See Fig. 5.*

2) There are 2 numbers painted on pinion gear and 1 number painted on ring gear. The first number on pinion gear and number on ring gear identify both as a matched set.

NOTE: **Ring and pinion gears should not be used if numbers do not match, or if replacement gear sets are marked .009" or more.**

Fig. 5: Standard Setting Dimension & Pinion Depth Shim Location

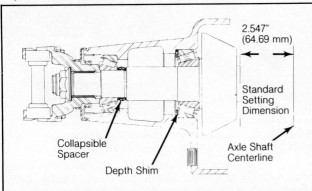

Pinion gear depth is the distance from end face of pinion to the axle shaft centerline.

3) Second number on pinion gear represents pinion depth variance. This indicates (in thousandths of an inch) the amount that the ring and pinion gear varied from standard setting to obtain the correct gear tooth contact pattern.

EXAMPLE:

- Standard pinion depth is 2.547" (64.69 mm). If pinion gear is marked "2", the set varied from the standard setting by .002" (.05 mm). This means that .002" (.05 mm) less shim will be required than for a gear set marked "0".

- Some factory-installed sets may have .010" (.25 mm) or .020" (.51 mm) machined off the pinion gear end face. Identifying numbers will appear differently.

Example:

- If gear is machined .010" (.25 mm), the identifying number will appear as +16. The "1" indicates that .010" (.25 mm) was removed from end face; and the "6" indicates that pinion depth variance is .006" (.15 mm). A gear machined .020" (.51 mm) would be identified in the same manner, only a "2" will be used rather than a "1". The marking would then be +26.

4) To determine a starting shim thickness to measure pinion depth and determine the correct shim thickness, measure thickness of shim removed during disassembly. Note pinion depth variance on old and new pinion gears.

5) Using Pinion Depth Variance Chart, determine amount to be added or subtracted from original shim thickness to determine starting shim thickness.

EXAMPLE:

- If the old pinion is marked -3 and the new pinion is marked +2, the chart indicates -.005". This means that .005" (.13 mm) would be reduced from original shim thickness to determine starting shim.

NOTE: **Do not use starting shim thickness as final shim thickness.**

6) Install rear bearing on pinion gear. Make sure large diameter of bearing cage faces gear end of pinion. Make sure bearing is fully pressed against rear face of gear.

7) Make sure pinion gear bearing bores in housings are clean. Install shim in rear bearing cup bore. If shim is chamfered, make sure chamfered side faces bottom of bore.

8) Install front and rear bearing cups, using mandrels and drivers. Install pinion gear in position in housing.

9) Install front bearing, rear universal joint yoke, and original pinion nut. Tighten pinion nut only enough to remove all end play.

NOTE: **Do not install new pinion nut or collapsible spacer at this time. These will be installed when pinion bearing preload is adjusted.**

10) Note pinion depth variance marked on pinion gear. Add or subtract this from standard pinion depth. This is correct pinion depth. Record this figure.

11) Assemble pinion depth measuring gauge arbor tool (J-5223-4) and centering discs (J-5223-23). With discs fully seated, install gauge assembly in differential bearing cup bores. Install bearing caps, and tighten bolts securely.

12) Position gauge block (J-5223-20) on end face of pinion. Make sure anvil end of gauge block is seated on gear, and that gauge block plunger is under arbor tool.

13) Attach gauge block clamp (J-5223-14) and bolt (J-5223-24) to housing cover bolt. Tighten clamp bolt down against gauge block to prevent block from moving. *See Fig. 6.*

14) Loosen gauge block thumb screws, and allow gauge block plunger to contact arbor tool. Now tighten thumb screw securing plunger in position. Remove clamp and then gauge block.

15) Using a 2 to 3-inch micrometer, measure distance from end of anvil on gauge block to end of plunger. This represents measured pinion depth. Record this measurement.

16) Remove bearing caps. Remove arbor and disc assembly. Remove pinion gear, bearing cup, and depth shim from axle.

17) Measure thickness of starting shim. Add this to measurement obtained in step **15)**. From this total,

Drive Axles

JEEP 8⅞" RING GEAR (Cont.)

subtract desired pinion depth measurement obtained in step 10). The result is the shim thickness required to obtain correct pinion depth.

EXAMPLE:

Standard Pinion Depth	2.547" (64.69 mm)
Pinion Depth Variance	+ .007" (.18 mm)
Desired Pinion Depth	=2.554" (64.87 mm)

Measured Pinion Depth	2.550" (64.77 mm)
Starting Shim Thickness	+ .098" (2.49 mm)
Total Measured Pinion Depth	=2.648" (67.26 mm)

Total Measured Pinion Depth	2.648" (67.26 mm)
Desired Pinion Depth	-2.554" (64.87 mm)
Correct Shim Thickness	=.094" (2.39 mm)

Fig. 6: Measuring Pinion Depth

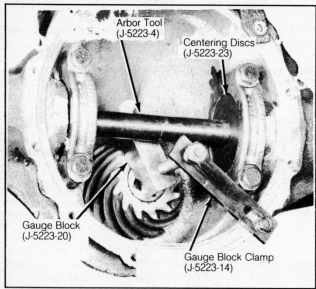

Tighten clamp down against gauge block to prevent block from moving.

Drive Pinion Bearing Preload

1) Install correct pinion gear depth shim(s) in housing bore. Install pinion gear and rear bearing.

2) Install new collapsible spacer and front bearing in housing. Install pinion oil seal using installer (J-22661). Install universal joint yoke and a new retaining nut. Tighten nut finger tight.

3) Now hold yoke and tighten nut. While tightening, rotate pinion to make sure bearings seat evenly.

4) Using an INCH Lb. torque wrench, measure torque required to turn pinion. If pinion bearing preload is not to specification, continue tightening yoke retaining nut until correct preload is obtained.

CAUTION: Do not exceed specified torque. If torque is exceeded, a new collapsible spacer must be installed, and preload must be reset. Do not loosen nut to reduce torque.

Assembling Differential Carrier

1) Install differential bearing onto case. Install thrust washers on differential gears (oil pocket side

toward gear). Install gears into bore in differential case. Install thrust washers behind differential pinion gears.

2) Mesh gears with differential gears, so holes are opposite and in line with each other. Roll gears around, until differential pinion gear holes are aligned with shaft holes in case. *See Fig. 7.*

Fig. 7: Installing Pinion Shaft and Thrust Block

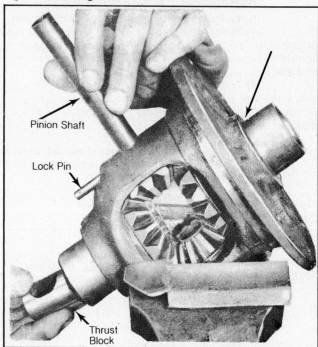

Install thrust washers behind differential pinion gears, mesh gears, and align gear and case holes

3) Install thrust block through a differential gear, aligning hole in block with pinion shaft holes. Install pinion shaft, with lock pin hole in shaft aligned with lock pin hole in case.

4) Measure any existing clearance between differential gears and case, using 2 feeler gauges on opposite sides of 1 gear. Clearance should be zero.

Adjusting Differential Bearings

1) Place bearing cup over each differential bearing. Install differential case assembly in axle housing. As a starting point, install an .080" (2.03 mm) shim on each side. Install bearing caps, and tighten bolts finger tight. Mount a dial indicator to housing so that plunger contacts ring gear mounting flange on differential.

2) Using 2 screwdrivers, pry between shims and housing. Pry assembly to one side, zero indicator. Pry assembly to opposite side and read indicator. Do not read or zero indicator while prying. The amount read on indicator is the amount of shim to be added to arrive at a no preload and no end play condition.

3) Shims are available in thicknesses ranging from .080" to .110" (2.03 to 2.79 mm) in .002" (.05 mm) increments. With all side play eliminated, check ring gear mounting flange for runout. Runout should not exceed .002" (.05 mm). Remove differential case from housing, and retain shims used to eliminate side play.

Ring Gear Installation

Place ring gear on differential housing case, and install retaining bolts. Two bolts installed in opposite

JEEP 8⅞" RING GEAR (Cont.)

holes may be used to pull ring gear into place. Tighten bolts to specifications.

Backlash Adjustment

1) Install differential assembly in housing, using shim selected to remove side play. Tighten bearing cap screws to 87 ft. lbs. (118 N.m). Attach a dial indicator to housing, so that indicator plunger contacts drive side of a tooth on ring gear and is at a right angle (90°) to it.

2) Rock ring gear, and note movement on dial indicator. Backlash should be .005-.009" (.13-.23 mm), with .008" (.20 mm) desired. To increase backlash, install a thinner shim on ring gear side. To decrease backlash, reverse procedure, however, do not change total thickness of shims.

Differential Bearing Preload

1) Differential bearings are preloaded by increasing each shim thickness by .004" (.10 mm). Install differential bearing shim in axle housing bearing bores. Assemble bearing cups on bearings (cups should completely cover rollers). Position differential so that bearings just start in axle housing bearing bores. Keep assembly square in housing and push in as far as possible.

2) Using a soft hammer, tap outer edge of bearing cups until seated in housing. Do not distort shim by hammering them into housing. Install bearing caps, aligning marks made at disassembly. Install and tighten bolts. Preloading differential bearings may change backlash setting, therefore recheck backlash and correct as necessary.

3) After all adjustments have been made, make a gear tooth pattern check to insure correct assembly. To complete reassembly, reverse disassembly procedures. Fill rear axle with lubricant.

AXLE ASSEMBLY SPECIFICATIONS

Application	In. (mm)
Axle Shaft	
End Play	.004-.008 (.10-.20)
Differential Bearing	
Preload (Shims)	.008 (.20)
Ring Gear Backlash	.005-.009 (.13-.23)
Pinion Gear	
Depth (Std. Setting)	2.547 (64.69)

	INCH Lbs. (N.m)
Pinion Bearing	
Preload	17-25 (1.9-2.8)

TIGHTENING SPECIFICATIONS

Application	Ft. Lbs. (N.m)
Differential Bearing	
Cap Bolts	87 (118)
Ring Gear Bolts	105 143)
Backing Plate Bolts	32 (44)
Rear Wheel	
Hub-to-Axle Nut	¹ 250 (340)
"U" Joint Bolt Clamp	16 (22)

¹ — CJ & Scrambler, 250 (340 N.m) Minimum.

PINION DEPTH SHIM ADJUSTMENT CHART (INCHES)

Old Pinion Marking	New Pinion Marking								
	-4	-3	-2	-1	0	+1	+2	+3	+4
+4	+0.008	+0.007	+0.006	+0.005	+0.004	+0.003	+0.002	+0.001	0
+3	+0.007	+0.006	+0.005	+0.004	+0.003	+0.002	+0.001	0	-0.001
+2	+0.006	+0.005	+0.004	+0.003	+0.002	+0.001	0	-0.001	-0.002
+1	+0.005	+0.004	+0.003	+0.002	+0.001	0	-0.001	-0.002	-0.003
0	+0.004	+0.003	+0.002	+0.001	0	-0.001	-0.002	-0.003	-0.004
-1	+0.003	+0.002	+0.001	0	-0.001	-0.002	-0.003	-0.004	-0.005
-2	+0.002	+0.001	0	-0.001	-0.002	-0.003	-0.004	-0.005	-0.006
-3	+0.001	0	-0.001	-0.002	-0.003	-0.004	-0.005	-0.006	-0.007
-4	0	-0.001	-0.002	-0.003	-0.004	-0.005	-0.006	-0.007	-0.008

Drive Axles

SPICER (DANA) IFS AXLE

Ford, Front Axle

NOTE: FRONT AXLE USAGE — The Spicer (Dana) model 28-IFS is used on Bronco II and 4WD Rangers. The 44-IFS, 44-IFS-HD & 50-IFS are used on all other 4WD models. The 44-IFS is used on vehicles with front coil springs. The 44-IFS-HD and 50-IFS axles are used on vehicles with leaf springs.

NOTE: For removal and installation instructions, see appropriate articles on LOCKING HUBS and 4-WHEEL DRIVE STEERING KNUCKLES in this Section.

DESCRIPTION

The Independent Front Suspension (IFS) front axle is of the integral carrier-housing, hypoid-gear type. The centerline of drive pinion is mounted above centerline of ring gear. The drive pinion bearing preload, and side bearing preload are all set or adjusted by shims.

AXLE RATIO & IDENTIFICATION

A metal tag, stamped with gear ratio and part number is secured to housing by 2 carrier bolts. If axle is equipped with limited slip differential, the axle I.D. tag will have the letters "LS" in the part number. If axle is equipped with Traction-Lok, the axle I.D. tag will have the letter "L" in the part number. The axle model can be determined by measuring the diameter of ring gear. See the Model Identification Table. To determine the drive axle ratio, refer to Drive Axle Ratio Identification in this Section.

AXLE MODEL IDENTIFICATION

Model	Ring Gear Diameter
28	7.50"
44	8.50"
50	9.25"

REMOVAL & INSTALLATION

AXLE SHAFTS & BEARINGS

Removal

1) Raise vehicle and support with safety stands. If equipped with locking hubs, see removal and installation instructions in *LOCKING HUBS and 4-WHEEL DRIVE STEERING KNUCKLES* articles in this Section.

2) Remove wheel and brake caliper assemblies. Remove hub dust cover and snap ring. Remove drive gear and pressure spring.

3) Remove wheel bearing lock nut, lock ring, and adjusting nut, using front wheel bearing spanner.

4) Remove hub and disc assembly. Remove spindle retaining nuts. Carefully remove spindle from knuckle studs and axle shaft.

5) It may be necessary to tap spindle with a soft mallet to break it loose. Remove spindle, splash shield, and axle shaft assembly.

6) Remove stub shaft and slip yoke assembly by removing 3 bolts attaching retainer plate to carrier housing.

7) Place axle shaft in vise, and drill a 1/4" hole in housing retainer ring to a depth 3/4 of the rings thickness.

8) With a chisel placed across hole, strike sharply with mallet to remove retaining ring. Replace bearing retaining ring upon assembly. Press bearing from axle shaft, using special axle bearing removal tools.

9) Remove seal and retainer plate from stub shaft. Discard and replace with new seal upon assembly. Do not strike axle shaft to free it. Do not use heat from any source to remove retaining ring.

10) If old bearing is to be reused and is still installed on axle shaft, lubricate it as follows: Push bearing retainer and seal toward flange end of shaft, being careful that seal does not come off machined part of shaft. Fill cavity between seal and bearing with grease.

11) Wrap masking tape around seal and bearing to retain grease. With masking tape in place, pull seal up toward bearing, forcing grease into bearing. If grease does not appear at small end of rollers, repeat procedure. *See Fig. 1.*

Fig. 1: Lubricating Bearing Installed on Axle Shaft

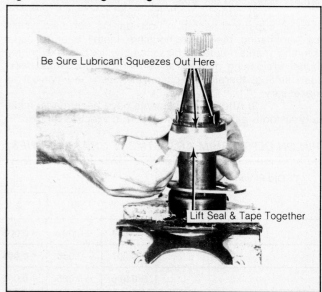

Grease must appear at small end of rollers.

Installation

1) Inspect retainer plate and stub shaft for nicks or burrs. Replace if necessary. Install retainer plate and new seal on shaft. Coat oil seal with grease. Place bearing on shaft.

2) Use axle bearing installer (T80T-4000-N) and pinion bearing cone remover (T71P-4621-B) to press bearing onto shaft. A .0015" (.04 mm) feeler gauge should not fit between bearing seat and bearing.

3) Install stub shaft in carrier, and install 3 retainer bolts. Tighten to specifications. Install right-hand axle shaft assembly into slip yoke. There is a blind spline on axle shaft assembly.

4) Install splash shield and spindle, using new nuts. Tighten to specifications. Install hub and disc assembly. Install caliper and wheel assembly.

PINION YOKE & SEAL

NOTE: Pinion seal can be serviced with axle assembly installed in vehicle.

SPICER (DANA) IFS AXLE (Cont.)

Removal

1) Disconnect drive shaft, and scribe a line down pinion shaft, yoke and nut. Remove nut and yoke. Do not hammer yoke off. Damage to pinion gear, ring gear and bearing could result.

2) Pry seal from bore, using care not to damage machined surfaces.

Installation

1) Lubricate cavity between seal lips with high melting point lubricant. Install seal into bore, making sure it bottoms against shoulder.

2) Place flange on shaft and draw it down with pinion nut. Tighten nut to specifications. Install drive shaft.

CAUTION: Failure to tighten pinion nut to full specifications will result in flange or pinion shaft failure.

AXLE ASSEMBLY

Removal

1) Raise vehicle on hoist, supporting axle assembly to take weight off springs. Disconnect drive shaft at pinion flange and tie out of the way.

2) Remove hub and disc assemblies. Disconnect vent tube (if equipped), and disconnect shock absorber at axle brackets. Disconnect springs and remove axle.

Installation

To install, reverse removal procedures.

OVERHAUL

DISASSEMBLY

1) Remove axle assembly from vehicle. Mark differential bearing caps for alignment reference. Loosen bearing cap bolts. Install axle housing spreader tool (D-113) with holding clamps.

CAUTION: Do not spread housing more than .010" (.25 mm). Permanent damage to housing could result.

2) Mount dial indicator on axle housing to measure amount of spread. Remove dial indicator after housing has been spread.

3) Remove bearing cap bolts. Note the matched numbers or letters stamped on the cap and carrier. These letters must be matched upon reassembly.

4) Carefully pry differential assembly out of housing. Remove spreader tool immediately so that housing does not take set. *See Fig. 2.*

5) On Bronco II & Ranger models, rotate the slip yoke and shaft assembly so the open side of snap ring is exposed. Remove snap ring from shaft. Remove slip yoke and shaft assembly from carrier. Remove differential case.

6) On all models, mount differential case in vise. Remove ring gear bolts. Using brass drift and hammer, remove ring gear. Remove pinion mate lockpin with small punch. Remove pinion mate shaft and thrust block.

7) Rotate pinion gears until gears are aligned with case opening. Remove gears and thrust washers. Remove pinion nut. With puller remove pinion yoke. Using soft-faced mallet, drive pinion shaft out of housing.

Fig. 2: Spreading Spicer (Dana) Carrier Housing

Do not spread housing more than .010" (.25 mm).

NOTE: Pinion bearing adjusting shims may remain on pinion shaft, stick to bearing, or fall loose. Collect them and save for reassembly.

8) From pinion shaft bore, remove oil seal and discard. Remove bearing cone. A baffle or oil slinger may also be present. Record the order in which they were removed so that they may be installed correctly.

9) Press pinion bearing off shaft. Using a puller, remove side bearings from differential case. During removal of side bearings, shims between bearings and case may be mutilated. If so, shims must be individually measured and their thicknesses recorded, so that new shim packs can be secured.

REASSEMBLY & ADJUSTMENT

Case Assembly

1) Place differential case in holding fixture or vise. Lubricate side gears, pinion gears, and all thrust washers. Install in case. Rotate side gears until holes in pinion gears and washers line up with holes in case.

2) Install spacer block (if equipped) and differential pinion shaft. If old thrust washers are used, check for preload of side gears. Clearance between side gears and case should be .000-.006" (.00-.15 mm). If not, shims can be installed (at least 1 on each side) or new thrust washers used.

3) On all models (except Bronco II and Ranger), install lock pin, and peen over hole to retain pin. On all models, inspect ring gear and case for burrs and nicks. Install ring gear and tighten bolt evenly. Install differential side bearings. Assemble case in housing without shims.

4) Install bearings caps, and tighten bolts just enough to seat bearing cups. Mount dial indicator to read at back of differential case flange.

5) Measure and record amount of side play by moving differential case back and forth with a screwdriver. The measurement will be used later to determine proper shim pack dimension. Remove case from housing. *See Fig. 4.*

SPICER (DANA) IFS AXLE (Cont.)

Fig. 3: *Exploded View of Spicer (Dana) Model 44-IFS Front Drive Axle*

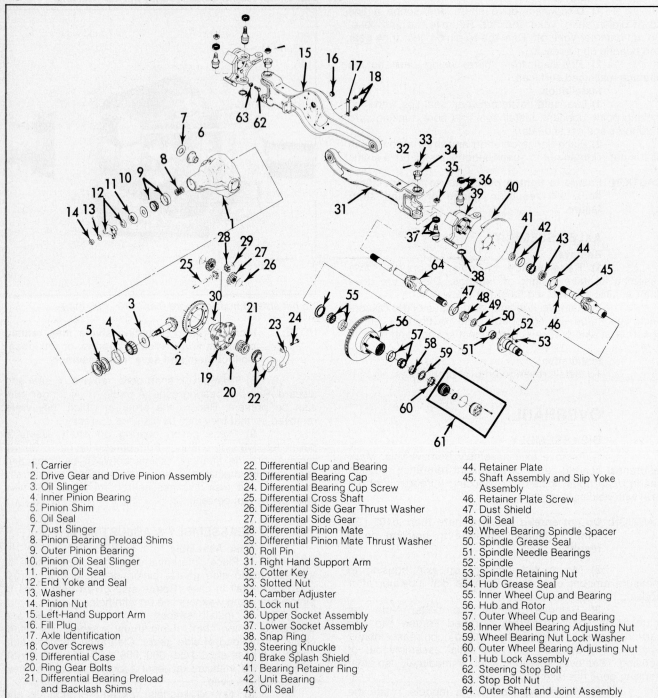

1. Carrier	22. Differential Cup and Bearing	44. Retainer Plate
2. Drive Gear and Drive Pinion Assembly	23. Differential Bearing Cap	45. Shaft Assembly and Slip Yoke Assembly
3. Oil Slinger	24. Differential Bearing Cup Screw	46. Retainer Plate Screw
4. Inner Pinion Bearing	25. Differential Cross Shaft	47. Dust Shield
5. Pinion Shim	26. Differential Side Gear Thrust Washer	48. Oil Seal
6. Oil Seal	27. Differential Side Gear	49. Wheel Bearing Spindle Spacer
7. Dust Slinger	28. Differential Pinion Mate	50. Spindle Grease Seal
8. Pinion Bearing Preload Shims	29. Differential Pinion Mate Thrust Washer	51. Spindle Needle Bearings
9. Outer Pinion Bearing	30. Roll Pin	52. Spindle
10. Pinion Oil Seal Slinger	31. Right Hand Support Arm	53. Spindle Retaining Nut
11. Pinion Oil Seal	32. Cotter Key	54. Hub Grease Seal
12. End Yoke and Seal	33. Slotted Nut	55. Inner Wheel Cup and Bearing
13. Washer	34. Camber Adjuster	56. Hub and Rotor
14. Pinion Nut	35. Lock nut	57. Outer Wheel Cup and Bearing
15. Left-Hand Support Arm	36. Upper Socket Assembly	58. Inner Wheel Bearing Adjusting Nut
16. Fill Plug	37. Lower Socket Assembly	59. Wheel Bearing Nut Lock Washer
17. Axle Identification	38. Snap Ring	60. Outer Wheel Bearing Adjusting Nut
18. Cover Screws	39. Steering Knuckle	61. Hub Lock Assembly
19. Differential Case	40. Brake Splash Shield	62. Steering Stop Bolt
20. Ring Gear Bolts	41. Bearing Retainer Ring	63. Stop Bolt Nut
21. Differential Bearing Preload and Backlash Shims	42. Unit Bearing	64. Outer Shaft and Joint Assembly
	43. Oil Seal	

All other models are similar.

Pinion Depth & Bearing Preload

1) Pinion is adjusted by shims placed between inner bearing cup and housing, and by shims placed between pinion shaft shoulder and outer bearing.

2) Shims behind inner bearing cup adjust position of pinion in relation to ring gear. Shims behind outer bearing adjust pinion inner and outer bearing preload.

3) If old pinion and ring gear assembly are used, proceed as follows: Install original shims and inner bearing cup. Install outer bearing cup. Press bearing cone onto pinion shaft and install shaft into housing.

4) Install outer bearing cone, companion flange, and nut. Do not install outer shims or seal at this time. Tighten nut to obtain bearing preload of 10-30 ft. lbs. (14-41 N.m).

5) Use a gauge to measure distance from ring gear center to machined button on end of pinion gear. Add or subtract shims from under inner bearing cup to obtain nominal dimension listed in specifications.

SPICER (DANA) IFS AXLE (Cont.)

Fig. 4: Measuring Differential End Play With Dial Indicator

Push back and forth and read dial indicator.

6) If new pinion and ring gear assembly are to be installed, proceed as follows: Determine pinion depth adjustment figure of old and new pinions and find shim adjustment figure from chart. Adjust original shim pack accordingly and proceed as in step **3)**.

NOTE: **An oil slinger between inner bearing cone and pinion, and a baffle, between inner bearing cup and carrier, have been added to front axle assemblies.**

7) Remove pinion gear, rear bearing cup, and starter shim. Install pinion depth shim of correct thickness in housing bearing cup bore. Reinstall rear bearing cup.

8) Install pinion bearing, oil slinger, yoke, washer, and old pinion nut. Tighten nut to specifications, while rotating pinion shaft. Position housing so that pinion shaft is in vertical position (pointing up).

9) With INCH lb. torque wrench, rotate shaft through several revolutions to measure rotating torque. Check measurement against pinion bearing preload in specifications. To decrease preload, add shims; to increase preload, subtract shims.

NOTE: **Ignore torque needed to start shaft rotating.**

10) After adjustment is made, install oil seal and recheck pinion depth. Check seals in front axle housing bores. If condition is questionable, replace using installer tool.

NOTE: **When installing front axle shafts be sure that seals are not dislodged.**

Fig. 5: Pinion Gear Markings Showing Depth Adjustment Figure

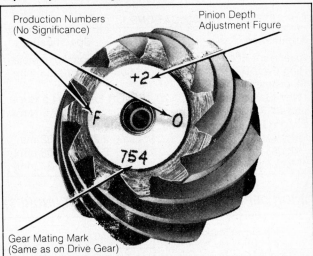

Ring gear and pinion numbers must match.

Side Bearing Preload

1) With pinion installed in housing and depth and preload adjustment properly made, install differential case into housing. Set dial indictor so that it reads at back of ring gear. Leave bearing cap bolts loose enough to allow movement of case.

2) Insert screwdriver between bearing cap and housing at opposite end from ring gear. Jam case toward ring gear side and, with force still applied to case, set dial indicator to zero.

3) Jam case the other way making sure that ring gear and pinion gears mesh, record reading, repeat several times until readings are the same. This reading is the amount of shims that will go between case and bearing on ring gear side.

4) Remove indicator and differential case from carrier. Remove master bearing from differential case. Install these shims. From the figure originally recorded under *Case Assembly*, subtract amount of shims just installed on case.

5) Add .015" (.38 mm) for bearing preload and install new shim pack on end of case opposite ring gear.

Example:

Original recorded side play	+.070"
Side play with pinion installed	-.032"
Amount left from original side play	=.038"
Additional amount for bearing preload	+.015"
Amount installed opposite of ring gear	=.053"

6) Install spreader to housing, spread housing and install differential case. Do not spread housing more than .010" (.25 mm). Remove spreader and install bearing caps. Make sure that caps are in original position. Tighten caps evenly to specifications.

Backlash & Final Assembly

1) Mount dial indicator to housing, and measure ring gear to pinion gear backlash in 3 places around ring gear. Variation between readings should not exceed .002" (.05 mm).

2) Adjust to specifications by moving shims from one side of differential case to the other, or by changing depth of pinion gear.

Drive Axles

SPICER (DANA) IFS AXLE (Cont.)

3) Check tooth contact pattern. See Tooth Pattern in this Section. Install cover and tighten bolts.

AXLE ASSEMBLY SPECIFICATIONS

Application	Specifications
Axle Shaft End Play	Non-Adjustable
Ring Gear Backlash	.005-.009" (.13-.23 mm)
Side Bearings Preload	
New Bearings	20-40 INCH lbs. (2.2-4.5 N.m)
Used Bearings	10-20 INCH lbs. (1.1-2.2 N.m)
Pinion Gear Depth (Nominal Dimension)	
Model 28 (7.50" R.G.)	2.228" (56.52 mm)
Model 44 (8.50" R.G.)	2.625" (66.68 mm)
Model 50 (9.25" R.G.)	2.810" (71.37 mm)

TIGHTENING SPECIFICATIONS

Application	Ft. Lbs. (N.m)
Pinion Shaft Flange Nut	
Bronco II & Ranger	175-225 (237-305)
All Others	210 (286)
Differential Side Bearing Cap Bolt	
Bronco II & Ranger	35-40 (48-54)
All Others	50 (68)
Ring Gear-to-Differential Case Bolt	55 (75)
Axle Shaft Retainer Bolt	30 (41)
Stub Shaft Retainer Bolts	40 (54)
Splash Sheild	60 (81)

PINION DEPTH SHIM ADJUSTMENT CHART (INCHES)

Old Pinion Marking	New Pinion Marking								
	-4	-3	-2	-1	0	+1	+2	+3	+4
+4	+0.008	+0.007	+0.006	+0.005	+0.004	+0.003	+0.002	+0.001	0
+3	+0.007	+0.006	+0.005	+0.004	+0.003	+0.002	+0.001	0	-0.001
+2	+0.006	+0.005	+0.004	+0.003	+0.002	+0.001	0	-0.001	-0.002
+1	+0.005	+0.004	+0.003	+0.002	+0.001	0	-0.001	-0.002	-0.003
0	+0.004	+0.003	+0.002	+0.001	0	-0.001	-0.002	-0.003	-0.004
-1	+0.003	+0.002	+0.001	0	-0.001	-0.002	-0.003	-0.004	-0.005
-2	+0.002	+0.001	0	-0.001	-0.002	-0.003	-0.004	-0.005	-0.006
-3	+0.001	0	-0.001	-0.002	-0.003	-0.004	-0.005	-0.006	-0.007
-4	0	-0.001	-0.002	-0.003	-0.004	-0.005	-0.006	-0.007	-0.008

Drive Axles

SPICER (DANA) SEMI-FLOATING AXLES

**Chrysler Corp.; Front & Rear Axles
Ford, General Motors, and Jeep; Rear
Axles**

NOTE: FRONT AXLE USAGE - The Spicer (Dana) models 44 & 60 are used as both front and rear drive axles, with semi-floating axles. The models 61 & 70 are used as rear drive axles, with semi-floating axles. Model 60 is also available with full-floating axles. See Spicer (Dana) Full-Floating Axles in this section.

NOTE: For removal and installation instructions, see appropriate articles on Locking Hubs and 4-Wheel Drive Steering Knuckles in this section.

DESCRIPTION

The axle assembly is of the hypoid gear type, with integral carrier housing and an over-hung mounted drive pinion. The drive pinion depth, pinion bearing preload and side bearing preload are all set or adjusted by shims.

Other than the components required for front wheel drive units, service and overhaul procedures for all axle models are the same, except for drive pinion depth and some torque specifications.

AXLE RATIO & IDENTIFICATION

Spicer (Dana) drive axles have a removable rear cover plate. The cover plate has a unique shape, that allows positive identification of Spicer (Dana) drive axles on any vehicle. *See Fig. 1.*

The axle model is often cast into the differential housing, or it can be determined by measuring the diameter of the ring gear. *To determine the drive axle ratio, refer to Drive Axle Ratio Identification in this section.*

Fig. 1: Spicer (Dana) Housing Cover Gasket.

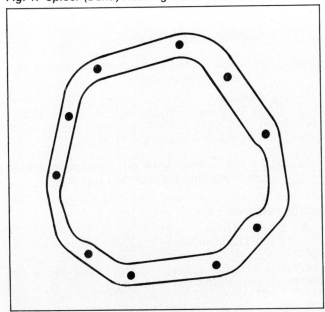

Gasket shape aids in identification.

MODEL I.D. BY RING GEAR DIAMETER

Model	Ring Gear Diameter
44	8.50"
60	9.75"
61	9.75"
70	10.50"

REMOVAL & INSTALLATION

NOTE: For front axle shaft and bearing removal, see Spicer (Dana) Full-Floating Axles or 4-Wheel Drive Steering Knuckles in this section.

AXLE SHAFTS & BEARINGS

NOTE: Spicer (Dana) semi-floating axles do not require an end play adjustment.

Removal (With Axle Bearing Installed)

1) Raise vehicle, and support with safety stands. Remove wheel, brake drum retaining clips, and brake drums.

NOTE: If it is necessary to back off brake shoes to remove drum, be sure that automatic adjuster lever is held away from starwheel before rotating starwheel.

2) Remove bearing retainer bolts, and pull axle shaft out of housing. If axle seems stuck, install wheel to flange, and use wheel for leverage. Do not strike axle shaft to free it.

3) Using a puller, remove bearing cup and oil seal from bore of axle housing. To remove bearing from axle, cut through bearing retaining ring with a chisel, using care not to nick axle shaft.

4) With retainer removed, press bearing off shaft. Remove outer oil seal and retainer plate from axle shaft.

CAUTION: Do not use heat from any source to remove retaining ring.

Fig. 2: Lubricating Bearing Installed on Axle Shaft

If grease does not appear at small end of rollers, repeat procedures.

Drive Axles

SPICER (DANA) SEMI-FLOATING AXLES (Cont.)

5) If old bearing is to be reused and is still installed on axle shaft, it can be lubricated as follows:

- Push bearing retainer and seal towards flange end of shaft. Be careful that seal does not come off machined part of shaft.
- Fill the cavity between seal and bearing with grease. Wrap masking tape around the seal and bearing to retain grease.
- With masking tape in place, pull seal up towards bearing, forcing grease into bearing.
- If grease does not appear at small end of rollers, repeat procedures.

NOTE: Be sure that no grease is on flange side of seal.

Fig. 3: Sectional View of Flanged Shaft End

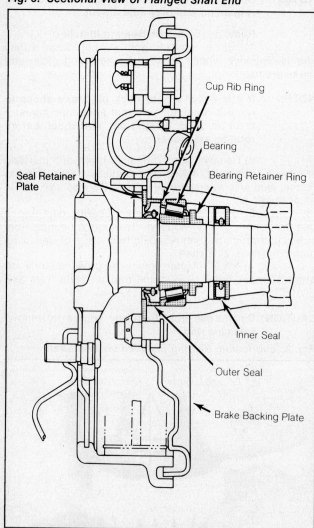

Cup Rib Ring

Bearing

Seal Retainer Plate

Bearing Retainer Ring

Inner Seal

Outer Seal

Brake Backing Plate

Note non-adjustable bearing is used.

Removal With Axle Bearing Installed

1) Raise vehicle, and support with safety stands. Remove wheel and tire assembly, and brake caliper.

2) Remove brake backing plate and bearing retaining plate nuts through access hole in axle shaft flange.

3) Bolt adapter (J-21579) to lug bolts on axle shaft flange. Attach a slide hammer to adapter, and remove axle shaft from housing.

4) Pry out axle shaft oil seal from axle housing. Mount axle shaft in a vise.

5) Drill a ¼" (6.35 mm) hole in bearing retainer ring. Drill hole to a depth ¾ of ring thickness. Do not allow drill to contact axle shaft.

6) Place a chisel over drilled hole in ring. Cut a deep groove in ring. This will enlarge ring and allow it to be removed from axle.

CAUTION: Do not heat retaining ring. Heat will transfer to bearing journal and weaken it.

7) Position support plate (J-23674) under bearing. Place bearing and support plate in a hydraulic press, and remove bearing from axle shaft.

8) Cut through oil seal, using a hacksaw. Remove seal and retainer plate. Inspect axle shaft seal surface for damage. Repair any scratches with crocus cloth.

Installation

1) Position retainer plate on axle shaft. Pack wheel bearing grease between oil seal lips.

2) Install oil seal on axle shaft. Make sure outer face of seal faces axle flange.

3) Position bearing on axle shaft. Make sure cup rib ring is facing axle flange. Install a new bearing retainer ring on axle shaft.

4) Using support plate used during bearing removal, press bearing and retainer ring on axle shaft at same time. Make sure bearing and ring are seated against axle shaft shoulder.

5) Install a new oil seal in axle housing tube. Slide axle shaft assembly into position in tube. Care must be taken not to damage seal lip.

6) Apply wheel bearing grease around outside of bearing before sliding into place. Tap flange with a soft mallet to drive axle into place.

7) Install brake backing plate and retainer plate nuts and lockwashers. Install brake drum. Install wheel and tire, and lower vehicle.

PINION YOKE & SEAL

NOTE: Pinion seal can be serviced with axle assembly installed in vehicle.

Removal

1) Disconnect drive shaft, and scribe a line down pinion shaft, yoke and nut. Remove nut using yoke holder (J-8614-01) and yoke remover (J-8614).

CAUTION: Do not hammer yoke off. Damage to pinion gear, ring gear and bearing could result.

2) Pry seal from bore, using care not to damage machined surfaces.

Installation

1) Lubricate cavity between seal lips with a high melting point lubricant. Install seal into bore, making sure that it bottoms against shoulder. Place flange on shaft and draw it down with pinion nut.

2) Tighten pinion nut to specifications. Failure to tighten pinion nut to full specifications will result in flange or pinion shaft failure. Install drive shaft.

SPICER (DANA) SEMI-FLOATING AXLES (Cont.)

AXLE ASSEMBLY

Removal

1) Raise vehicle on hoist. Support axle assembly to take weight off spring. Disconnect drive shaft at pinion flange, and tie out of the way. Remove hub and drum assembly.

2) Disconnect vent tube (if equipped). Disconnect parking brake cable(s) and service brake hydraulic lines. Disconnect shock absorbers at axle brackets. Disconnect springs and remove axle.

Installation

Reverse removal procedure. Do not fully tighten shock absorbers nut until assembly is completed. Bleed hydraulic lines, and adjust parking brake before moving vehicle.

OVERHAUL

DISASSEMBLY

NOTE: **Axle housing does not need to be removed to overhaul assembly. However, it is suggested that the entire axle unit be removed from the vehicle and held tight in a stand or rack.**

1) Remove housing cover, and mark differential bearing caps for alignment reference. Loosen bearing cap bolts and install axle housing spreader tool (D-113) with holding clamps. Mount dial indicator on axle housing to measure amount of spread.

CAUTION: **Do not spread housing more than .010" (.25 mm). Permanent damage to housing could result.**

2) Remove dial indicator after housing has been spread. Remove bearing cap bolts. Carefully pry differential assembly out of housing. Remove spreader tool immediately, so that housing does not take set.

Fig. 4: Correct Procedure to Spread Spicer (Dana) Carrier Housing

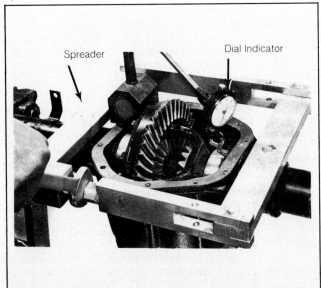

Do not leave spreader tension on housing or damage could result.

3) Mount differential in vise. Using brass drift and hammer, remove ring gear. Remove pinion mate lock pin with small punch. Remove pinion mate shaft thrust block. Rotate pinion gears until gears are aligned with case opening.

4) Remove gears and thrust washers. Remove pinion nut. Using puller, remove pinion yoke. Using soft-faced hammer, drive pinion shaft out of housing. From pinion shaft bore, remove oil seal and bearing cone.

NOTE: **Pinion bearing adjusting shims may remain on pinion shaft, stick to bearing, or fall loose. Collect them and save for reassembly.**

5) A baffle or oil slinger may also be present. Record the order in which they were removed, so they may be installed correctly. Discard seal. Remove inner bearing cone and press pinion bearing off shaft.

6) Using a puller, remove side bearings from differential case. Often during removal of side bearings, shim between bearings and differential case are mutilated. If so, shims must be individually measured and their thicknesses recorded, so that new shim packs can be secured.

REASSEMBLY & ADJUSTMENT

Case Assembly

1) Place differential case in holding fixture or vise. Lubricate side and pinion gears and all thrust washers. Install in case. Rotate side gears until holes in pinion gears and washers line up with holes in case.

2) Install spacer block (if equipped) and differential pinion shaft. If old thrust washers are used, check for preload of side gears. Clearance between side gears and case should be .000-.006" (0-.15 mm). If not, shims can be installed (at least 1 on each side) or new thrust washers used.

3) Install lock pin, and peen over hole to retain pin. Inspect ring gear and case for burrs and nicks. Install ring gear, and tighten bolts evenly. Install differential side bearings. Assemble case in housing without shims.

Fig. 5: Measuring Differential Case End Play With a Dial Indicator

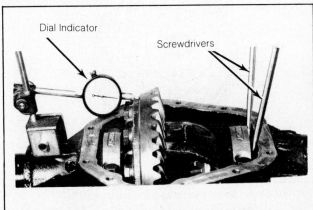

Check end play without shims installed in case.

4) Install bearing caps, and tighten bolts just enough to seat bearing cups. Mount dial indicator to read at back of differential flange. Measure and record amount of side play of differential case by moving it back and forth with a screwdriver. See Fig. 5.

Drive Axles

SPICER (DANA) SEMI-FLOATING AXLES (Cont.)

5) The measurement will be used later to determine proper shim pack dimension. Remove case from housing.

Pinion Depth & Bearing Preload

1) Pinion is adjusted by shims, placed between inner bearing cup and housing, or between pinion shaft shoulder and outer bearing. Shims behind inner bearing cup adjust position of pinion in relation to ring gear.

2) Shims behind outer bearing adjust pinion inner and outer bearing preload. If old pinion and ring gear assembly are used, proceed as follows:

- Install original shims and inner bearing cup. Install outer bearing cup.
- Press bearing cone onto pinion shaft and install shaft into housing.
- Install outer bearing cone, companion flange, and nut.
- Do not install outer shims or seal at this time.
- Tighten nut to obtain bearing preload of 10-30 ft. lbs. (14-41 N.m).
- Use a gauge to measure distance from ring gear center to machined button on end of pinion gear.
- Add or subtract shims from under inner bearing cup to obtain nominal dimension listed in specifications.

3) If new pinion and ring gear assembly are to be installed, proceed as follows:

- Determine pinion depth adjustment figure of old and new pinions. *See Fig. 6.* Find shim adjustment figure from chart.
- Adjust original shim pack accordingly and proceed as in step **2)**.

NOTE: The previous procedures also apply to pinion adjustment on the FRONT AXLE, which includes the oil slinger between the inner bearing cup and carrier.

Fig. 6: Location of Pinion Gear Markings Showing Depth Adjustment Figure

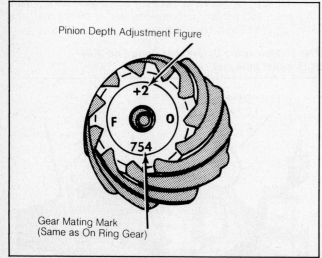

Number on pinion and on ring gear must match.

4) Remove pinion gear, rear bearing cup, and starting shim. Install pinion depth shim of correct thickness in housing bearing cup core, and reinstall rear bearing cup. Install pinion bearing preload shims.

5) Install pinion gear, front bearing, oil slinger (if equipped), yoke, washer, and old pinion nut. Tighten nut to specified torque, while rotating pinion shaft.

6) Position housing, so that pinion shaft is in vertical position, pointing upward. With INCH lb. torque wrench, rotate shaft through several revolutions to measure rotating torque. Ignore torque needed to start shaft rotating.

7) Check measurement against pinion bearing preload in specifications. To decrease preload, add shims; to increase preload, subtract shims. After adjustment is made, install oil seal and recheck pinion depth.

8) Front axles have axle shaft oil seals, which are pressed into the tube ends of the carrier. There are 2 different designs. Check seals in axle housing bores. If condition is questionable, replace seals using installer of proper size.

NOTE: When installing front axle shaft, be sure that these seals are not dislodged.

Side Bearing Preload

1) With pinion installed in housing, and depth and preload adjustments properly made, install differential case into housing. Set dial indicator so that it reads at back of ring gear.

2) Leave bearing cap bolts loose enough to allow movement of case. Insert screwdriver between bearing cap and housing at opposite end from ring gear. Jam case toward ring gear side and, with force still applied to case, set dial indicator to zero. See *Fig.5.*

3) Jam case the other way (making sure that ring and pinion gears mesh) and record reading. Repeat several times, until readings are the same. This reading is the amount of shims that will go between case and bearing on ring gear side.

4) Remove indicator and differential case from carrier. Remove master bearing from differential case. Install these shims. From the figure originally recorded under *Case Assembly,* subtract amount of shims just installed on case.

5) Add .015" (.38 mm) for bearing preload, and install new shim pack on end of case opposite ring gear.

Example:

+ .070" (1.78 mm) Original Recorded Side Play
- .032" (.81 mm) Side Play With Pinion Installed
= .038" (.97 mm) Amount Left From Original Side Play
+ .015" (.38 mm) Additional Amount for Bearing Preload
= .053" (1.35 mm) Amount Installed Opposite of Ring Gear

6) Install spreader to housing, spread housing, and install differential case. Do not spread housing more than .010" (.25 mm). Install differential assembly.

7) Remove spreader, and install bearing caps. Make sure that caps are in original position. Tighten caps evenly to specifications.

Backlash & Final Assembly

1) Mount dial indicator to housing, and measure ring gear to pinion gear backlash in 3 places around ring gear. Variation between readings should not exceed .002" (.051 mm).

2) Adjust to specifications by moving shims from one side of differential case to the other, or by changing depth of pinion gear. Check tooth contact pattern. *See Tooth Contact Pattern in this section.* Install cover and tighten bolts to specifications.

Drive Axles

SPICER (DANA) SEMI-FLOATING AXLES (Cont.)

Fig. 7: Exploded View of Spicer (Dana) Model 44 Semi-Floating Axle Assembly

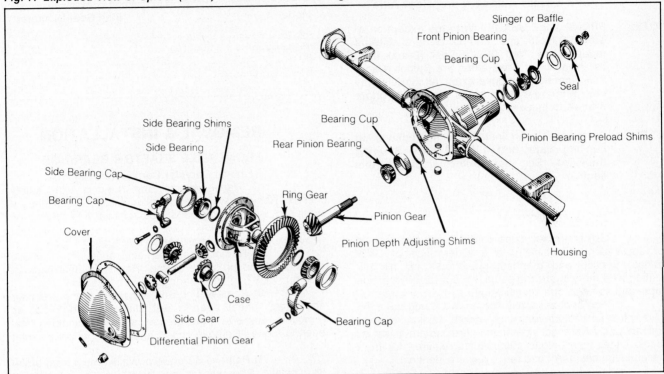

AXLE ASSEMBLY SPECIFICATIONS

Application	Specification In. (mm)
Axle Shaft End Play	Non-Adjustable
Ring Gear Backlash	.005-.009 (.12-.15)
Differential Bearing Preload	.015 (.38)

	INCH Lbs. (N.m)
Pinion Bearing Preload	
New Bearings	20-40 (2-5)
Used Bearings	10-20 (1-2)

TIGHTENING SPECIFICATIONS

Application	Ft. Lbs. (N.m)
Pinion Shaft Flange Nut	
44	210 (287)
60, 61 & 70	260 (354)
Differential Side Bearing Cap Bolt	
44	50 (68)
60, 61 & 70	80 (109)
Ring Gear-to-Differential Case Bolt	105 (143)

PINION DEPTH SHIM ADJUSTMENT CHART (INCHES)

Old Pinion Marking	New Pinion Marking								
	-4	-3	-2	-1	0	+1	+2	+3	+4
+4	+0.008	+0.007	+0.006	+0.005	+0.004	+0.003	+0.002	+0.001	0
+3	+0.007	+0.006	+0.005	+0.004	+0.003	+0.002	+0.001	0	-0.001
+2	+0.006	+0.005	+0.004	+0.003	+0.002	+0.001	0	-0.001	-0.002
+1	+0.005	+0.004	+0.003	+0.002	+0.001	0	-0.001	-0.002	-0.003
0	+0.004	+0.003	+0.002	+0.001	0	-0.001	-0.002	-0.003	-0.004
-1	+0.003	+0.002	+0.001	0	-0.001	-0.002	-0.003	-0.004	-0.005
-2	+0.002	+0.001	0	-0.001	-0.002	-0.003	-0.004	-0.005	-0.006
-3	+0.001	0	-0.001	-0.002	-0.003	-0.004	-0.005	-0.006	-0.007
-4	0	-0.001	-0.002	-0.003	-0.004	-0.005	-0.006	-0.007	-0.008

Drive Axles

SPICER (DANA) FULL-FLOATING AXLES

**Chrysler Corp., General Motors, Jeep;
Front & Rear Axles & Ford; Rear Axle**

NOTE: FRONT AXLE USAGE - With the exception of some C20/30 and K20/30 General Motors models and Ford (IFS) Spicer (Dana) front axles, all front drive axles are Spicer (Dana) Full-Floating front drive axles. All models may use other rear drive axles. See appropriate articles in this section.

NOTE: For removal and installation instructions on Locking Hubs and 4-Wheel drive Steering Knuckles. See appropriate article in this section.

DESCRIPTION

Spicer (Dana) axles come in different models for application in vehicle with a wide range of GVW ratings. Service and overhaul procedures for all full-floating axle models are the same, except for drive pinion depth and some torque specifications.

The axle assembly has an over-hung mounted drive pinion. The drive pinion depth, pinion bearing preload, and differential side bearing preload are all set by shims. Other than unique components required for front wheel drive units, front and rear axles are identical.

AXLE RATIO & IDENTIFICATION

Spicer (Dana) axles have a removable rear cover plate. The cover plate has a unique shape, that allows positive identification of Spicer (Dana) axles on any model vehicle. The axle model is often cast into the differential housing, or it can be determined by measuring the diameter of the ring gear. *See Model Identification Table.* To determine the drive axle ratio, *refer to Drive Axle Ratio Identification in this section.*

Fig. 1: Spicer (Dana) Housing Cover Gasket.

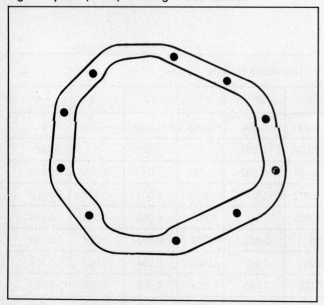

Illustration for identification purposes.

MODEL IDENTIFICATION BY RING GEAR SIZE

Model	Ring Gear Diameter
30	7.125"
44	8.50"
60	9.75"
61	9.75"
70	10.50"

REMOVAL & INSTALLATION

FRONT AXLE SHAFTS & BEARINGS
Removal Chrysler Corp., Model 44 Axle

1) Raise vehicle and support with safety stands. Remove wheel and brake caliper assemblies. If equipped with locking hubs, *see removal and installation instructions on Locking Hubs and 4-Wheel Drive Steering Knuckles in appropriate articles in this section.*

2) Remove dust cap and snap ring. Remove drive gear and pressure spring. Remove wheel bearing, lock nut, lock ring and bearing adjustment nut.

3) Remove hub and assembly. Spring retainer and outer wheel bearing will slide out when hub is removed. Remove hub grease seal and inner wheel bearing cone. Remove inner and outer wheel bearing cups.

4) Remove 6 torque prevailing nuts from brake disc shield. Remove retainer from steering knuckle. If necessary remove brake caliper adapter from steering knuckle. Position a pry bar behind inner axle shaft yoke.

5) Push bearing out of knuckle. Remove "O" ring from steering knuckle (if equipped). Carefully slide out axle shaft assembly. Remove axle seal and stone shield from shaft.

NOTE: Torque prevailing nuts should be discarded and replaced with new ones.

Installation

1) Apply RTV sealer to seal surface of axle shaft housing. Install lip seal on axle shaft stone shield. With lip toward axle spline.

2) Carefully insert axle shaft into housing so as not to damage differential seal at side gears. Install spindle and brake splash shield. Install 6 new nuts and tighten to specifications.

3) Install rotor, outer bearing nut, washer and lock nut onto spindle. Install brake adapter. Install inboard brake shoe on adapter. Slowly slide caliper over disc and into adapter.

4) Install anti-rattle springs and retaining clips and torque to specifications. Install wheel and hub dust cover. Test operation.

Removal Chrysler Corp. Model 60 Axle

1) Block brake pedal up. Raise vehicle and place on safety stand. Remove wheel and tire. If equipped with locking hubs, *see removal and installation instructions on Locking Hubs and 4-Wheel Drive Steering Knuckles in appropriate articles in this section.*

2) Remove brake caliper. Do not let caliper hang from brake line. Remove dust cap. Remove snap ring.

3) Remove flange nuts and lock washers. Remove drive flange and discard gasket. Straighten tang

SPICER (DANA) FULL-FLOATING AXLES (Cont.)

on lock ring. Remove outer lock nut, lock ring, inner lock nut and outer bearing.

4) Carefully slide hub and rotor off spline. Remove oil seal and inner bearing from hub. Remove bearing cups with a brass drift punch. Remove inner brake pad from adapter.

5) Remove rotor splash shield, brake adapter and spindle. Remove spindle from steering knuckle. Slide out inner and outer axle shaft with bronze spacer, seal and oil slinger.

Installation

1) Slide axle shaft into position. Place bronze spacer on axle shaft with chamfer side facing toward "U" joint. Install spindle, brake adapter and brake splash shield. Tighten nut to 50-70 ft.lbs. (68-95 N.m)

2) Drive in bearing cups using installer. Lubricate bearings. Install inner bearing in grease coated hub. Install new seal. Care must be taken not to damage seals.

3) Install hub and rotor assembly on spindle. Install outer wheel bearing and inner lock nut, tightening to 50 ft. lbs. (68 N.m). Back off, then retighten to 35 ft. lbs. (48 N.m).

4) Install outer lock nut and tighten to 65 ft. lb. (88 N.m). Install new gasket on hub. Install drive flange lock washers and nuts. Install snap ring and cap in hub. Install brake caliper, wheel and tire. Lower vehicle.

Removal General Motors

1) Raise vehicle and support on safety stands. Remove wheel and tire. Remove brake caliper. If equipped with locking hubs, *see removal and installation instructions on Locking Hubs and 4-Wheel Drive Steering Knuckles in appropriate articles in this section.*

2) Remove hub lock mechanism. Remove snap ring. Pry out driving hub and spring. Remove wheel bearing lock nut, lock ring and adjusting nut. Outer wheel bearing and retainer will come off with hub.

3) Remove inner bearing, cone and seal from hub using a brass drift punch. Remove inner and outer bearing cups (if necessary) using a brass punch. Remove spindle. Carefully pull axle shaft assembly through hole in steering knuckle.

Installation

1) Install axle shaft assembly in housing. Care must be taken not to damage seal. Install thrust washer with chamfered end toward slinger on axle. Install spindle using new nuts. Tighten bolts to 65 ft. lbs. (88 N.m).

2) Install inner and outer bearing cones in hub using drivers. Lubricate cones and bearings with wheel bearing lubricant. Install inner bearing in cone and install new seal. Install outer bearing and retainer in hub.

3) Position hub and rotor assembly on spindle. Install inner adjusting nut, tightening to 50 ft. lbs. (68 N.m), back off, then retighten to 35 ft. lbs. (47 N.m). Back off the inner adjusting nut again ⅜ turn maximum.

4) Assemble drag sleeve retainer washer over axle shaft against bearing adjusting nut. The tang on the inside diameter of this washer is assembled in the keyway of the spindle.

5) The pin on the inner nut must pass through 1 of the holes in the retainer washer. Assemble and tighten outer lock nut to 160-205 ft. lbs (218-279 N.m). Complete reassembly by reversing removal procedure.

Removal Jeep "CJ" & Scrambler

1) Raise vehicle and position on safety stands. Remove wheel and tire. If equipped with locking hubs, *see removal and installation instructions on Locking Hubs and 4-Wheel Drive Steering Knuckles in appropriate articles in this section.*

2) Remove disc brake caliper. Remove bolts attaching front hub to axle and remove hub body. Remove retaining ring from axle shaft. Straighten lip of lock washer. Remove outer lock nut, lock washer, inner lock nut, and tabbed washer.

3) Remove lock nut. Remove outer bearing and remove disc brake rotor. Remove axle spindle. Remove axle shaft and universal joint assembly.

Installation

1) Make sure all components are clean. Make sure drive flange bolt and bolt hole threads are clean. Install inner bearing and seal in hub.

2) Install axle shaft assembly taking care not to damage seal in axle housing. Install spindle and spindle bearing. Install disc brake caliper and splash shield.

3) Lubricate and install outer bearing in disc brake rotor. Install disc brake rotor on spindle. Install washer and adjusting nut and tighten to 50 ft. lbs. (68 N.m). Back off ⅙ turn. Install lock washer and outer lock nut to 50 ft. lbs. (68 N.m).

4) Bend lockwasher lip over lock nut. Install drive flange and gasket. Coat drive flange bolts with Adhesive-Sealant (Loctite 242 or equivalent). Install drive flange bolts.

5) Install drive flange snap ring in groove at outer end of axle shaft. Install disc brake caliper. Install hub grease cover. Install wheel assembly and lower vehicle.

REAR AXLE SHAFTS & BEARINGS

Removal

1) Remove flange nuts from hub studs. Using heavy hammer, rap sharply on center of axle flange to loosen tapered dowels. See Fig. 2. Remove dowels. Rap center of flange again to cause flange and axle assembly to spring away from hub.

2) Remove axle without using prying devices which might damage axle flange and hub mating surfaces. To service bearings, remove locking devices and bearing adjusting nut. Pull wheel straight off axle housing using care to avoid dropping bearing cones.

Fig. 2: Detailed View of Tapered Dowels

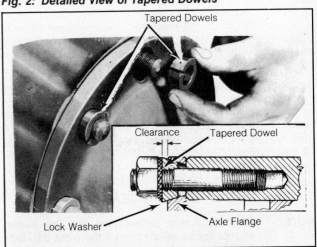

With flange nuts removed, rap center flange to loosen tapered dowels.

Drive Axles

SPICER (DANA) FULL-FLOATING AXLES (Cont.)

NOTE: Close inspection of hub and axle type is necessary to determine which procedure applies.

3) Remove and discard seal(s). Remove bearing cones from hub or axle housing. There are 2 methods used to position outer bearing cup in hub. Seating cup against a machined shoulder, and seating cup against a removable snap ring set into a machined groove:

- To remove machined shoulder type, drive each bearing cup out of hub using a long drift.
- To remove snap ring type, remove inner cup with a long drift.
- Remove snap ring with pliers.
- Drive outer bearing and cup out of hub.

Fig. 3: Cutaway View of Axle Shaft and Bearings

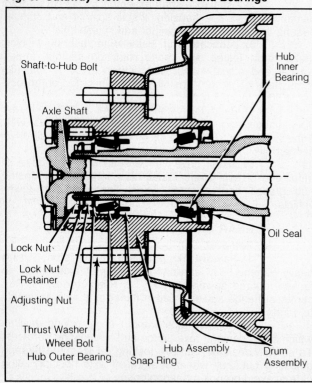

Showing snap ring bearing retainer.

Installation

1) To install machined shoulder type, drive or press inner and outer bearing cups into place. Make sure that cups are firmly seated against shoulders in hub.

2) To install snap ring type, insert outer bearing cone into hub. Insert bearing cup into hub and drive beyond snap ring groove. Install snap ring.

3) Drive cone and cup assembly back against snap ring making sure that it is fully seated. Install inner bearing cup and cone. Install seals. Adjust wheel bearing. *See Rear Wheel Bearing Adjustment in WHEEL ALIGNMENT section.*

PINION FLANGE & SEAL

NOTE: Front and rear differentials are the same, except for an oil slinger on the front differential pinion shaft. Pinion seal can be serviced with axle assembly installed in vehicle.

Removal

Disconnect drive shaft, and scribe a line down pinion shaft, flange and nut. Remove nut and flange. Pry seal from bore using care not to damage machined surfaces.

CAUTION: Do not hammer flange off. Damage to pinion gear and bearing could result.

Installation

Lubricate cavity between seal lips with a high melting point lubricant. Install seal into bore, making sure that it bottoms against shoulder. Place flange on shaft and draw it down with pinion nut. Tighten pinion nut to specifications. Install drive shaft.

CAUTION: Failure to tighten pinion nut to full specifications will result in flange or pinion shaft failure.

AXLE ASSEMBLY

Removal

1) Raise vehicle on hoist and support axle assembly to take weight off spring. Disconnect drive shaft at pinion flange and tie out of the way. Remove hub and brake assembly.

Fig. 4: Cutaway View of Axle Shaft and Bearings

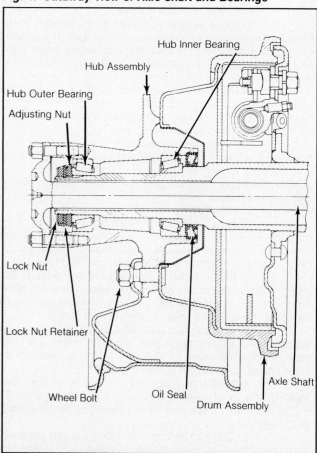

Showing machined shoulder bearing retainer.

2) Disconnect vent tube (if equipped), and disconnect parking brake cable(s) and service brake hydraulic lines. Disconnect shock absorbers at axle brackets. Disconnect springs and remove axle.

SPICER (DANA) FULL-FLOATING AXLES (Cont.)

Installation
Reverse removal procedure. Do not fully tighten shock absorber nut until assembly is completed. Bleed hydraulic lines and adjust parking brake before moving vehicle.

OVERHAUL

DISASSEMBLY

NOTE: **Remove axle housing assembly before beginning overhaul.**

1) Remove axles and housing cover. Be sure that side bearing caps are marked so that they can later be installed in their original positions. Remove bolt and side bearing caps. Use a housing spreader to spread differential housing .015-020" (.38-.51 mm).

2) Use a dial indicator to measure spread. Carefully pry differential case out of housing. Be careful not to damage machined surface of housing. Remove spreader immediately to prevent possibility of carrier taking set. *See Fig. 5.*

CAUTION: Do not spread housing more than .020" (.51 mm). Permanent damage to housing could result.

3) If differential case is 1 piece, proceed as follows:
- Remove bolts holding ring gear to differential case.
- Tap ring gear off with soft mallet.
- With a small punch, drive out lock pin.
- Remove differential shaft and thrust block.
- Remove differential pinion gears and thrust washers.

4) If differential case is 2 piece, proceed as follows:
- Remove bolts holding ring gear to differential case.
- Tap ring gear off with soft mallet.
- Mark differential case halves to aid reassembly.
- Remove bolts and separate case halves.
- Remove pinion gear spider, pinion gears, side gears, and all thrust washers.

Fig. 5: Correct Procedure for Spreading Housing

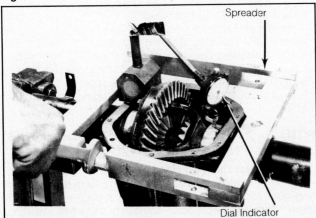

Do not leave differential spread or damage may result.

5) With puller remove pinion flange. Using a soft mallet, drive pinion shaft out of housing. Remove oil seal and bearing cone. If baffle or an oil slinger are also present, record the order in which they were removed.

NOTE: **Pinion bearing adjusting shims may remain on pinion shaft, stick to bearing, or fall loose. Collect and save them for reassembly.**

6) Discard seal. Remove inner bearing cone and press pinion bearing off pinion shaft. Using puller remove side bearings from differential case.

7) Often during removal of side bearings, shims between bearings and differential case are damaged. If so, shims must be individually measured and their thicknesses recorded, so that new shim packs can be obtained.

REASSEMBLY & ADJUSTMENT

Case Assembly
1) If differential case is 1 piece, proceed as follows:
- Place differential case in holding fixture or vise. Lubricate side and pinion gears and all thrust washers and install in case.
- Rotate side gears until holes in pinion gears and washers line up with holes in case. Install spacer block (if equipped) and differential pinion shaft.
- If old thrust washers are used, check for preload of side gears by measuring clearance between side gears and case. Clearance should be .000-.006" (.00-.15 mm); if not, shims can be installed in equal amounts on each side, or new thrust washers installed.
- Install lock pin and peen over hole to retain pin. Install ring gear and tighten bolts to specifications.

2) If differential case is 2 piece, proceed as follows:
- Lubricate all parts with differential lubricant. Install differential side gears and thrust washers, pinion gear spider, pinion gears, and thrust washers in case.
- Check for preload of side gears by measuring clearance between side gears and case. Clearance should be .000-.006" (.00-.15 mm); if not, shims can be installed in equal amounts on each side, or new thrust washers installed.
- Rejoin case halves using aligning marks made during disassembly. Tighten bolts to specifications.
- Install ring gear and tighten bolts to specifications.

3) Install differential side bearings. Assemble case in housing without shims. Install bearing caps and tighten bolts just enough to seat bearing cups. Mount dial indicator to read at back of differential flange.

4) Measure and record amount of side play of differential case by moving back and forth with a screwdriver. *See Fig. 6.* The measurement will be used

Fig. 6: Using Dial Indicator to Measure Differential End Play

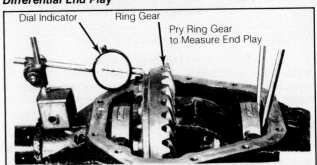

Differential case is installed without shims, for test only.

SPICER (DANA) FULL-FLOATING AXLES (Cont.)

later to determine proper shim pack dimension. Remove case from housing.

Pinion Depth & Bearing Preload

1) Pinion is adjusted by shims placed between inner bearing cup and housing, and by shims placed between pinion shaft shoulder and outer bearing. Shims behind inner bearing cup adjust position of pinion in relation to ring gear.

2) Shims behind outer bearing adjust pinion inner and outer bearing preload. If old pinion and ring gear assembly are used, proceed as follows:

- Install original shims and inner bearing cup. Install outer bearing cup. Press bearing cone onto pinion shaft and install shaft into housing.
- Install outer bearing cone, companion flange, and nut. Do not install outer shims or seal at this time. Tighten nut to obtain bearing preload of 10-30 ft. lb. (14-41 N.m).
- Use a gauge to measure distance from ring gear center to machined button on end of pinion gear.
- Add or subtract shims from under inner bearing cup to obtain nominal dimension listed in specifications.

3) If new pinion and ring gear assembly is to be installed, proceed as follows:

- Determine pinion depth adjustment figure of old and new pinions and find shim adjustment figure from, *Pinion Depth Chart. See Fig. 7.*
- Adjust original shim pack accordingly and proceed as in step **2)**.

4) Remove pinion flange and nut, and remove front pinion bearing cone. Install original preload shim pack. Lubricate and install bearing cone. Install pinion flange and nut. Tighten to specifications while rotating pinion shaft.

5) Place housing in position so that pinion shaft is vertical (pointing up). Using an INCH lb. torque wrench, rotate shaft through several revolutions to measure rotating torque.

Fig. 7: Pinion and Ring Gear Markings Showing Pinion Depth Adjustment Figure

Numbers on ring gear and pinion must match.

6) Check measurements against pinion bearing preload in specifications. To decrease preload, add shims; to increase preload, subtract shims. After adjustment is made, install oil seal and recheck pinion depth.

NOTE: Ignore torque needed to start shaft rotating.

7) Front axles only; check seals in axle housing bore. If condition is questionable, replace using installer. *See Fig. 8.*

NOTE: When installing front axle shaft, be sure that seals are not dislodged.

Fig. 8: Correct Procedure for Installing Inner Oil Seals

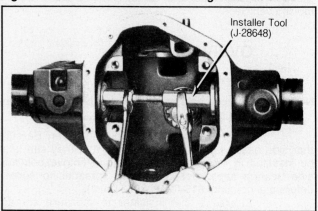

Installing oil seals in front axle housing using tool (J-28648).

Side Bearing Preload

1) With pinion installed in housing and depth and preload adjustments properly made. Install differential case into housing and set dial indicator so that it reads at back of ring gear. Leave bearing cap bolts loose enough to allow movement of case.

2) Insert screwdriver between bearing cap and housing at opposite end from ring gear. Jam case toward ring gear side and, with force still applied to case, set dial indicator to zero. Jam case the other way (making sure that ring and pinion gears mesh) and record reading.

3) Repeat several times until readings are the same. This reading is the amount of shims that will go between case and bearing on ring gear side. Install these shims. From the figure originally recorded under, *Case Assembly.*

4) Subtract amount of shims just installed on case. Add .015" (.38 mm) for bearing preload and install new shim pack on end of case opposite ring gear.

Example:
Original Recorded Side Play	+.070"
Side Play With Pinion Installed	-.032"
Amount Left From Original Side Play	=.038"
Additional Amount for Bearing Preload	+.015"
Amount Installed Opposite of Ring Gear	=.053"

5) Install spreader to housing, spread housing and install differential case. Remove spreader and install bearing caps. Make sure caps are in original position; then tighten caps evenly.

NOTE: Do not spread housing more than .020" (.51 mm). Permanent damage could result.

Backlash & Final Assembly

1) Mount dial indicator to housing and measure ring gear to pinion gear backlash in 3 places around ring gear. *See Specifications.* Variation between readings should not exceed .002" (.051 mm).

2) Adjust to specifications by moving shims from 1 side of differential case to the other, or by changing depth of pinion gear. Check tooth contact pattern. *See Tooth Contact Pattern in this section.* Install cover and tighten bolts to specifications.

Drive Axles

SPICER (DANA) FULL-FLOATING AXLES (Cont.)

AXLE ASSEMBLY SPECIFICATIONS

Application	Specifications In. (mm)
Ring Gear Backlash	.005-.009 (.13-.23)
Side Bearing Preload	.015 (.38)
Pinion Gear Depth (Nominal Dimension)	
Model 30	2.250 (57.15)
Model 44	2.625 (66.68)
Model 60 & 61	3.125 (79.38)
Model 70	3.500 (88.90)
	INCH lbs. (N.m)
Pinion Bearing Preload	
New Bearings	20-40 (2.3-4.5)
Used Bearings	10-20 (1.1-2.3)

TIGHTENING SPECIFICATIONS

Applications	Ft. Lbs. (N.m)
Pinion Shaft Flange Nut	
Models 30, 44 & 70	210 (285)
Models 60 & 61	270 (367)
Side Bearing Cap	
Model 30	45 (61)
Models 44, 60, 61 & 70	80 (109)
Ring Gear-to-Case	
Models 30 & 44	55 (75)
Models 60, 61 & 70	110 (150)
Axle Flange-to-Hub	
Models 30 & 44	35 (48)
Models 60 & 61	55 (75)
Model 70	85 (116)

PINION DEPTH SHIM ADJUSTMENT CHART (INCHES)

Old Pinion Marking	New Pinion Marking								
	-4	-3	-2	-1	0	+1	+2	+3	+4
+4	+0.008	+0.007	+0.006	+0.005	+0.004	+0.003	+0.002	+0.001	0
+3	+0.007	+0.006	+0.005	+0.004	+0.003	+0.002	+0.001	0	-0.001
+2	+0.006	+0.005	+0.004	+0.003	+0.002	+0.001	0	-0.001	-0.002
+1	+0.005	+0.004	+0.003	+0.002	+0.001	0	-0.001	-0.002	-0.003
0	+0.004	+0.003	+0.002	+0.001	0	-0.001	-0.002	-0.003	-0.004
-1	+0.003	+0.002	+0.001	0	-0.001	-0.002	-0.003	-0.004	-0.005
-2	+0.002	+0.001	0	-0.001	-0.002	-0.003	-0.004	-0.005	-0.006
-3	+0.001	0	-0.001	-0.002	-0.003	-0.004	-0.005	-0.006	-0.007
-4	0	-0.001	-0.002	-0.003	-0.004	-0.005	-0.006	-0.007	-0.008

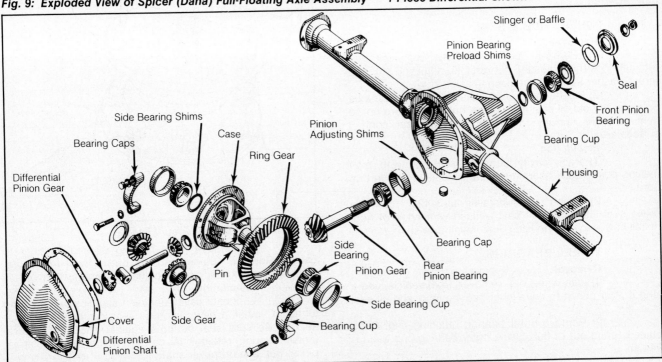

Fig. 9: Exploded View of Spicer (Dana) Full-Floating Axle Assembly — 1 Piece Differential Shown

Drive Axles

ROCKWELL 12" RING GEAR

Chevrolet & GMC Rear Axle

NOTE: DRIVE AXLE USAGE — The Rockwell 12" ring gear drive axle is used on some Chevrolet P30 and GMC P3500 models.

DESCRIPTION

The Rockwell drive axle uses a heavy duty hypoid drive pinion and ring gear. The differential and gear assembly is mounted on tapered roller bearings.

The straddle-mounted pinion has 2 tapered roller bearings in front of the pinion teeth.

The 3rd bearing is behind the pinion teeth. The preload on the differential side bearings is set by adjusting nuts on which bearing cups rest. The differential has a 2-piece case and 4 differential pinion gears.

AXLE RATIO & IDENTIFICATION

The 12" ring gear drive axle assembly is the only one used on General Motors vehicles that has a removable carrier. To determine axle ratio, *refer to Drive Axle Ratio Identification in this Section.*

REMOVAL & INSTALLATION

AXLE SHAFT

Removal

Remove dust cap, and install adapter (J-8117) in tapped hole on shaft flange. Install slide hammer, and remove axle shaft.

Installation

To install, reverse removal procedure, using new gaskets.

WHEEL HUB & SEAL

Removal

1) Remove axle shaft. Remove lock nut retainer, lock nut, adjusting nut retainer, adjusting nut, and thrust washer from axle housing.

2) Pull hub and drum assembly straight off axle housing. Pry old oil seal from wheel hub, using care not to damage bore surface. Thoroughly clean seal contact surface area.

Installation

1) Pack cavity between seal lips with high melting point wheel bearing lubricant. Position seal in hub bore.

2) Using seal installer (J-24428), carefully press seal into hub until seal is flush with edge of hub. Install hub onto axle housing, and install axle shaft.

WHEEL BEARINGS

Removal

1) With wheel hub removed from vehicle, use a long drift or punch to drive inner bearing, cup, and oil seal from hub.

2) Remove outer bearing retaining ring. Drive outer bearing out of hub, using outer bearing cup tool (J-24426).

CAUTION: Inner bearing cup and outer bearing retaining ring must be removed before attempting to remove outer bearing cup.

Installation

1) Place outer bearing assembly into hub. Using bearing cup installer (J-8608), drive bearing past retaining ring groove in hub. Be sure chamfer of bearing cup installer (J-8608) does not contact bearing cup.

2) Install outer bearing retaining ring, and drive cup into hub until seated. Place inner bearing cup into hub. Using bearing cup driver (J-24427), drive cup into hub until seated against shoulder.

3) Install new oil seal with oil seal installer (J-24428). Place hub assembly onto axle housing. Install adjusting nut, and adjust rear wheel bearing.

PINION FLANGE & SEAL

Removal

1) Disconnect propeller shaft and tie out of the way. Scribe a line down pinion nut, pinion stem and pinion flange for reassembly reference. Remove pinion nut and pull pinion flange from stem. *See Fig. 1.*

Fig. 1: Removing Pinion Flange from Rockwell 12" Axle.

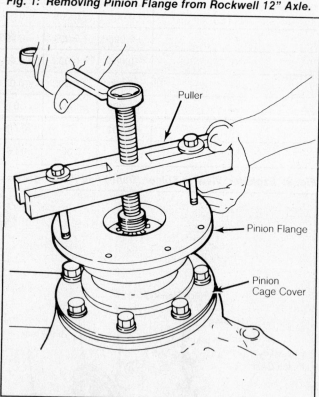

Do not use hammer to drive off flange.

2) Remove bolts holding oil seal retainer to carrier. Remove retainer and pry out oil seal from bore, using care not to damage machined surface.

Installation

Lubricate cavity between seal lips with bearing lubricant. Install a new pinion oil seal into bore, using (J-22281). Be sure seal bottoms against shoulder in bore. Install bearing retainer to carrier. Install pinion flange, pinion nut, and propeller shaft.

ROCKWELL 12" RING GEAR (Cont.)

Fig. 2: Exploded View of Rockwell 12" Axle Assembly

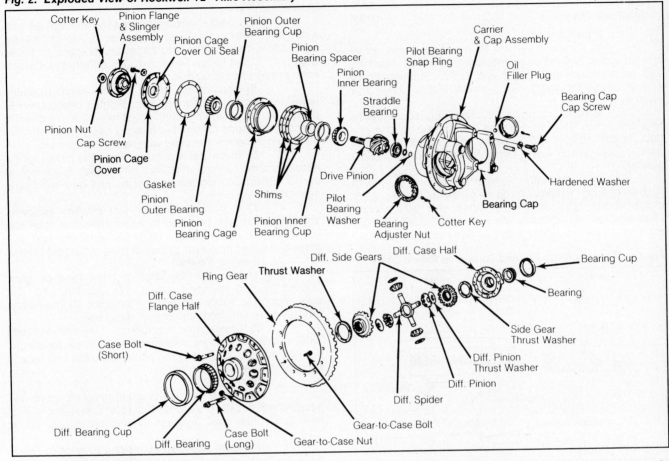

DIFFERENTIAL CARRIER

Removal

1) Drain differential. Remove axle shaft from drive unit and housing. Disconnect universal at pinion shaft. Remove carrier to housing stud nuts and washers. Loosen 2 top nuts and leave on studs to prevent carrier from falling out.

2) Break carrier loose from axle housing with soft mallet. Remove top nuts and washers, and work carrier free. Use a roller jack to safely remove carrier from housing.

Installation

To complete installation, reverse removal procedure.

OVERHAUL

DIASSEMBLY

NOTE: **Check and record ring gear backlash and pinion bearing preload before disassembly.**

Case & Gear Assembly

1) With carrier in holding fixture. Loosen jam nuts, and back off thrust adjusting screw. Center punch 1 differential carrier leg and bearing cap to identify for reassembly.

2) Remove differential adjusting nut locks and bearing cap bolts. Mark bearing caps and carrier for reassembly. Remove adjusting nuts and bearing caps. Remove differential and ring gear assembly from carrier.

3) Mark differential case halves for reassembly. Remove bolts, and separate case halves. Remove spider, pinions, side gears, and thrust washers. If necessary, remove rivets and separate gear and case.

Pinion & Cage Assembly

Hold flange and remove pinion nut and washer. Remove flange with puller. Remove pinion cage capscrews. Remove bearing cover and seal assembly. Remove drive pinion bearing cage. Wire shim pack together, and save for reassembly reference.

CLEANING & INSPECTION

1) Clean all parts in cleaning solvent. Inspect all bearings, bearing cups, races, and rollers for scoring, chipping, or excessive wear. Inspect axle shaft and side gear splines for excessive wear.

2) Inspect ring gear and pinion for scoring, cracking, or chipping. Inspect differential case, pinion side gears, thrust washers, and pinion shaft for cracks, scoring, galling, or excessive wear.

REASSEMBLY & ADJUSTMENT

Selecting Pinion Cage Shim Pack

To accurately install a new pinion and cage assembly into carrier, mathematically calculate the proper pinion cage shim pack thickness:

Example:

Original Pack Thickness	.030"
Original Variation Number (+2)	-.002"

ROCKWELL 12" RING GEAR (Cont.)

Standard Pack Thickness	.028"
New Variation Number (+5)	+.005"
New Pack Thickness	.033"

Pinion & Cage

1) If new cups are to be used, press firmly against pinion bearing cage shoulders. Lubricate bearings and cups. Press rear thrust and radial bearings firmly against pinion shoulders with a sleeve that will bear only on inner race.

2) Install radial bearing lock ring, and squeeze ring into pinion shaft groove with pliers. Insert pinion and bearing assembly in pinion cage, and position spacer(s) over pinion shaft. Press front bearing firmly against spacer.

3) Rotate cage several revolutions to ensure normal bearing contact. While in press under pressure, check bearing preload torque. Wrap soft wire around cage, and pull on horizonal line with pound scale. Record rotating torque, not starting torque. *See Fig,. 3.*

Fig. 3: Checking Cage Preload Torque on Pinion Shaft.

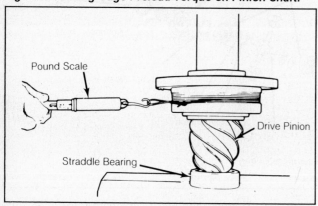

Pound Scale

Drive Pinion

Straddle Bearing

Preload torque is checked with a soft wire & pound scale.

4) Press flange or yoke against forward bearing and install washer and pinion shaft nut. Place pinion and cage assembly over carrier studs, hold flange and tighten pinion shaft nut to correct torque.

5) Recheck pinion bearing preload torque. Hold flange, and remove pinion shaft nut and flange. Lubricate pinion shaft oil seal, and cover outer edge of seal body with a non-hardening sealing compound. Press seal against cover shoulder with seal driver.

6) Install new gasket and bearing cover. Press flange against forward bearing, and install washer and pinion shaft nut. Tighten nut to correct specifications.

Differential & Ring Gear

Heat ring gear to 180°F (82°C) for 10 minutes before assembling to differential. Do not press or drive ring gear onto case. New differential case and ring gear bolts should be used in place of rivets (if required).

Differential Pinion & Side Gear

1) Position thrust washer and side gear in ring gear and case half assembly. Place spider with pinions and thrust washers in position. Install components, side gear, and thrust washer.

2) Align mating marks, position component case half, and draw assembly together with 4 bolts. Check assembly for free rotation of differential gears, and correct if necessary.

3) Install remaining bolts, and tighten to specifications. If bearings are to be replaced, press

squarely and firmly on differential case halves. Place differential in vise.

4) Insert checking tool (made from splined axle shaft end, with nut welded on the end) into differential nest. Allow splines of tool to engage with spline of 1 side gear only. Using torque wrench, rotate differential. Correct rolling resistance is 50 ft. lbs. (68 N.m).

5) Temporarily install bearing cups, threaded adjusting rings, and bearing caps. Tighten cap screws to proper torque. Bearing cups must be of a hand fit in bores. Once cups fit, remove bearing caps. Coat differential bearings cones and cups with rear axle lubricant.

6) Place bearing cups over assembled differential bearing cones. Position differential assembly in carrier. Insert bearing adjusting nuts, and turn hand tight against bearing cups.

7) If bearing caps do not position properly, adjusting nuts may be cross threaded. Remove caps and reposition adjusting nuts. Install flat washers and cap screws. Tighten stud nuts or cap screws to correct torque.

Bearing Preload

1) Use dial indicator at back face of gear. Loosen bearing adjusting nut on side opposite gear, but only enough to notice end play on indicator. Tighten same adjusting nut until zero end play is obtained.

2) Check gear for runout. If runout exceeds .008" (.20 mm), remove differential, and check for cause. Tighten adjusting nuts 1 notch each from zero end play to preload differential bearings.

Backlash

1) If drive gear is not going to be replaced, use established backlash recorded before disassembly. For new gears, the new backlash should be initially set at .010" (.25 mm).

2) Adjust backlash by moving gear only. This is done by backing off 1 adjusting ring, and advancing the opposite ring the same amount. Install cotter keys. Remove carrier from stand, and position with back face of hypoid (spiral bevel) gear upward.

3) Remove adjusting screw and lock nut. Install thrust screw and lock nut, and tighten thrust screw sufficiently to locate thrust block firmly against back face of hypoid gear.

4) To secure correct adjustment of .010-.015" (.25-.38 mm) clearance, loosen adjusting screw (thrust screw) ¼ turn and lock securely with nut. Recheck to ensure minimum clearance of .010" (.25 mm) during full rotation of bevel gear.

TIGHTENING SPECIFICATIONS

Application	Ft. Lbs. (N.m)
Pinion Bearing Cage Bolts	
Grade 5	25-35 (34-48)
Grade 7	30-40 (41-54)
Grade 8	35-50 (48-68)
Pinion Shaft Nut	300-400 (408-544)
Thrust Screw Jam Nut	150-190 (204-258)
Adjusting Ring Lock	20-30 (27-41)
Bearing Cap Bolts	115-140 (156-190)
Ring Gear-to-Case	85-115 (116-156)
Diff. Case Capscrews	60-75 (82-102)

Positive Traction Differentials

BORG WARNER LIMITED SLIP DIFFERENTIAL

**Chevrolet, GMC, C/K/G/10 Models;
Front & Rear Axles**

DESCRIPTION

The Borg Warner limited slip differential has 1 pinion shaft and 2 pinion gears. The side gears are clutch cone type, mounted in a split case asssembly. The assembly also houses a spring block containing 5 springs.

AXLE RATIO & IDENTIFICATION

See General Motors 8½", 8⅞", & 9¼" Ring Gear article and Drive Axle Ratio Identification in this section.

LUBRICATION

Check lubricant level every 7500 miles or 6 months. Drain and refill every 15,000 miles. Use Positraction lubricant.

Fig. 1: Exploded View of Brog Warner Limited Slip Differential

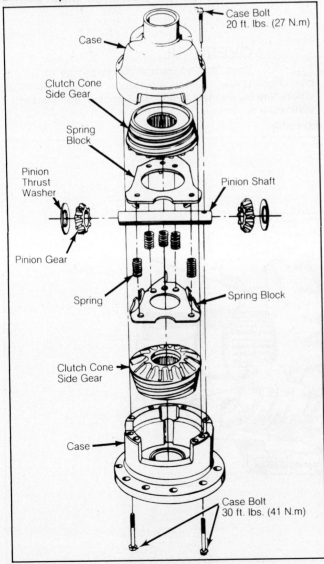

TESTING ON VEHICLE

1) Raise rear wheels off ground. Shut engine off. Place shift lever for automatic transmission in "P" (manual transmission in low and transfer case in "N", if equipped). Grip tread of tire, and attempt to rotate wheel.

2) If rotation is extremely difficult or impossible, differential is performing correctly. If either wheel turns relatively easily or continuously, differential is not performing correctly and should be replaced.

REMOVAL & INSTALLATION

The same procedure is used to remove and install Borg Warner differential as standard differential. *See Chevrolet and GMC 8½", 8⅞", & 9¼" Ring Gear article in this section.*

CAUTION: During removal and installation of axle shafts, do not rotate 1 axle shaft unless both are in position. Rotation of 1 axle shaft without the other in place may result in misalignment of 2 spline segments with which axle shaft splines engage. Difficult realignment procedures would then be necessary when axle shaft is reinstalled.

OVERHAUL

Borg Warner differential is serviced as an assembly only. Under no circumstances should differential be disassembled, reassembled, and installed in vehicle.

Positive Traction Differentials

CHRYSLER CORP. SURE-GRIP 9¼" RING GEAR

Dodge, Plymouth; Front & Rear Axles

DESCRIPTION

The cone clutch Sure-Grip is a limited slip type differential. It is similar in operation to conventional type differentials, except for helix-grooved clutch cones that clutch side gears to differential case. These grooves assure maximum lubrication of clutch surface during operation.

Clutch cones and side gears are spring preloaded by 2 thrust plates and 4 coil spring. During torque application to axle, initial spring preloading of the clutch cones is increased by the gear separating forces between side gears and differential pinions.

This progressively increases internal resistance (friction) in differential. This differential is not a positive or locking type unit, and will release before excessive driving force can be applied to 1 wheel.

AXLE RATIO & IDENTIFICATION

Sure-Grip differential is optional on Chrysler axles with 9¼" ring gear. *See Chrysler Corp. 8⅜" & 9¼" Ring Gear in this Section.*

LUBRICATION

Use only Mopar Hypoid Gear Lubricant or equivalent.

TESTING ON VEHICLE

1) Raise rear wheels off ground. Shut engine off. Place shift lever for automatic transmission in "P" (manual transmission in low and transfer case in "N", if equipped). Grip tread of tire, and attempt to rotate wheel.

2) If rotation is extremely difficult or impossible, differential is performing correctly. If either wheel turns relatively easily or continuously, differential is not performing correctly and should be replaced.

REMOVAL & INSTALLATION

The same procedure is used to remove and install Sure-Grip differential as standard differential. *See Chrysler Corp. 8⅜" & 9¼" Ring Gear article in this section.*

CAUTION: During removal and installation of axle shafts, do not rotate one axle shaft unless both are in position. Rotation of one axle shaft without the other in place may result in misalignment of 2 spline segments with which axle shaft splines engage. This would necessitate difficult realignment procedures when shaft is reinstalled.

OVERHAUL

Sure-Grip differential is serviced as an assembly only. Under no circumstances should Sure-Grip differential be disassembled, reassembled, and installed in vehicle.

Fig. 1: Sectional View of Chrysler Corp. Sure-Grip Differential Assembly

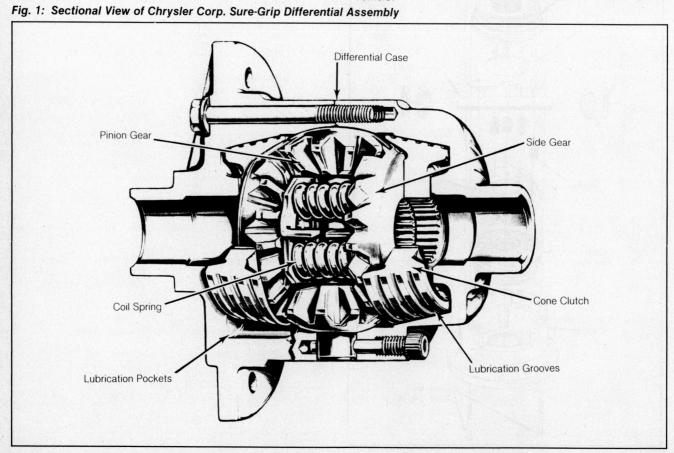

Positive Traction Differentials

EATON (ONE-PIECE CASE) LOCKING DIFFERENTIAL

Chevrolet, GMC C/K/G10/S
Front & Rear Axles

DESCRIPTION

The Eaton 1-piece case locking differential is a 2 pinion type, with a clutch disc pack behind each side gear.

The unit also utilizes a speed-sensitive device, which automatically locks both rear wheels if either wheel should spin excessively during slow vehicle operation.

AXLE RATIO & IDENTIFICATION

See *General Motors 7½", 8½", 8⅞", & 9½" Ring Gear article and Drive Axle Ratio Identification in this Section.*

LUBRICATION

Check lubricant level every 7500 miles or 6 months. Drain and refill every 15,000 miles. Use standard differential lubricant. Do not use Positraction lubricant.

TESTING ON VEHICLE

1) Raise vehicle so that both rear wheels can be rotated freely by hand. With 1 wheel held stationary, rotate other wheel approximately ½ turn every second.

2) Wheel should rotate freely. If both wheels turn, or try to turn, differential is defective. Raise vehicle as high as possible.

3) Have assistant in vehicle start the engine, and allow it to idle at 600-800 RPM. If equipped with automatic transmission, place transmission in drive, and apply brakes.

4) If equipped with manual transmission, depress clutch, and place transmission in first gear. Pull on 1 parking brake cable from under vehicle to lock 1 rear wheel.

5) With engine idling, slowly release brakes on automatic transmission models, or slowly release clutch on manual transmission models. Locked rear wheel should remain stationary, and free wheel should rotate slowly.

6) As free wheel speed increases, the differential should lock, causing both wheels to rotate or stop. If equipped with manual transmission, engine may stall.

Fig. 1: Exploded View of Eaton One-Piece Case Locking Differential

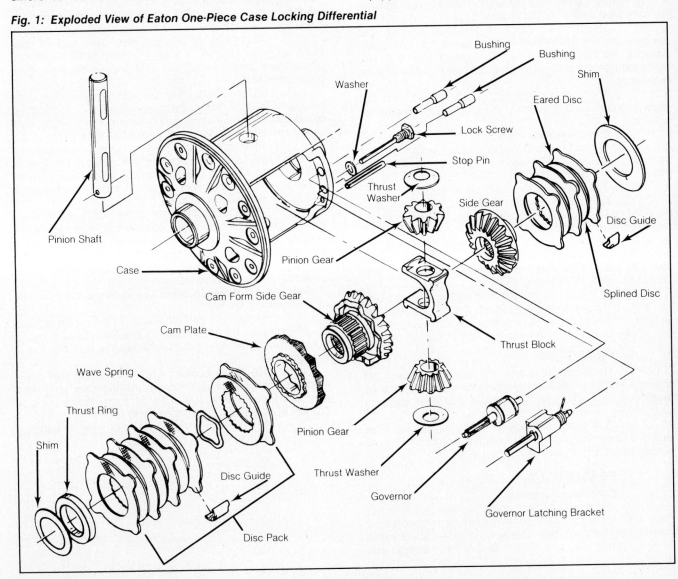

Positive Traction Differentials

EATON (ONE-PIECE CASE) LOCKING DIFFERENTIAL (Cont.)

7) It may be necessary to accelerate to 10 MPH to lock differential. If speed increases beyond 20 MPH without locking differential, unit is defective. Lock opposite wheel and repeat test.

REMOVAL & INSTALLATION

The same procedure is used to remove and install locking differential as conventional differential. *See General Motors 7½", 8½", 8⅞", & 9½" Ring Gear article in this Section.*

OVERHAUL

DISASSEMBLY

Differential

1) With differential removed from housing, remove ring gear and side bearings. Note or mark position of latching bracket and governor assembly for reassembly.

2) Using puller, remove latching bracket spring, while pulling out governor assembly bushing. Remove stop pin by driving through case with drift punch.

3) Remove pinion shaft lock screw, and remove pinion shaft. Roll pinion gears out of case. Remove reaction block and pinion thrust washers. Remove cam gears, disc packs, and disc pack guide clips on both sides.

4) If cam gear or clutch discs must be replaced, cam gear assembly must be disassembled as follows.

Cam Gear Assembly

1) Measure and record overall length of gear assembly. Measure from face of gear to backside of thrust ring, and include shim. This dimension will be required for reassembly if thrust ring is replaced.

2) If thrust ring is replaced, check thrust ring bore in case for wear. If bore is scored excessively, replace complete differential.

3) Position gear with hub end up. Compress disc pack, and place a bearing removal mandrel (J-22912), between thrust ring and top disc. Beveled side of tool should be toward thrust ring.

4) Position cam gear and tool in a press, with tool supported on both sides. Place a 1½ - 1¾" plug on gear hub. Press against plug with press to remove thrust ring. Make sure all components are kept in correct order.

INSPECTION

1) Clean all parts in solvent. Inspect all bearings and gear teeth for chipping or wear. Replace as necessary. Inspect clutch plates and discs for signs of wear or overheating.

2) If reaction block or flange shims must be replaced, measure thickness of original components, and replace with components of identical size.

REASSEMBLY

Cam Gear Assembly

1) Place cam gear on bench with hub end up. Place cam plate on gear so that cam form on plate is against cam form on gear. Position on cam plate 2 eared discs, 1 splined disc and 1 wave spring, alternately in that order.

2) Position on gear hub, 2 splined discs and 3 eared discs alternately, starting and ending with an eared disc. Place cam gear in a press with hub end up . Install thrust ring on gear hub with press.

3) Make sure thrust ring is square with hub. Press thrust ring on until it is flush with shoulder. When installing ring, press down on disc to make sure splined disc does not wedge between thrust ring and gear shoulder.

4) When unit is assembled, check for correct disc sequence. Make sure that the first splined disc (large spline) is correctly located on cam plate.

Differential

1) Install disc pack guide clips on disc ears of cam gear disc pack. Use grease to retain clips on ears. Install cam gear assembly, with original shim in flange end of case.

2) If a new thrust ring has been installed on cam gear, it may be necessary to reshim. Measure overall length of cam gear assembly, including shim. Compare this measurement with 1 previously recorded.

3) If measurement variation is more than .003" (.08 mm) either way, install a new shim that will obtain a reading within .003" (.08 mm) of original measurement. Place an axle shaft in vise in a vertical position.

4) Mount differential case over end of axle shaft, engaging spline of side gear with shaft. Grease 2 pinion gear thrust washers, and locate them in their proper positions.

5) Assemble on to bell end gear hub, 2 splined discs and 3 eared discs alternately. Begin and end with an eared disc. Install 4 small clutch pack guide clips on ears of bell end clutch pack, using grease for retention.

6) Install in case with original shims. Original shim must be used to maintain correct clearance specification. Install 1 pinion gear through small opening in case, while inserting other pinion gear and reaction block through larger opening in case.

7) Rotate both pinion gears and reaction block 90° so that open side of reaction block is toward small opening in case. Make sure both pinion gears and thrust washers remain in correct position.

8) Install pinion shaft and lock screw. Place governor assembly and latching bracket into case. Place straight end of latching bracket spring over and to outside of engagement shaft.

9) This will preload the latching bracket against governor assembly. The latching bracket bushing has a tapered hole, and the governor assembly bushing has a straight hole.

10) Press bushing and ¼" stop pin into case. Install governor bushing in case, making sure shaft end play is between .004-.020" (.10-.51 mm). Press latching bracket bushing into case so end play is removed.

11) Press stop pin flush with case, install ring gear and side bearings on differential.

Positive Traction Differentials

EATON (TWO-PIECE CASE) LOCKING DIFFERENTIAL

Chevrolet, GMC
C20/30, G/K/P30, Rear Axle

DESCRIPTION

The Eaton 2-piece locking differential is a 3 pinion type. With clutch disc packs behind both side gears. Unit also utilizes a speed-sensitive device which automatically locks both rear wheels if either wheel should spin excessively during slow vehicle operation.

AXLE RATIO & IDENTIFICATION

See General Motors 10½" Ring Gear article and Drive Axle Ratio identification in this Section.

LUBRICATION

Check lubricant level every 7500 miles or 6 months. Drain and refill every 15,000 miles. Use standard differential lubricant. Do not use Positraction lubricant.

Fig. 1: Exploded View of Eaton Two-Piece Case Locking Differential

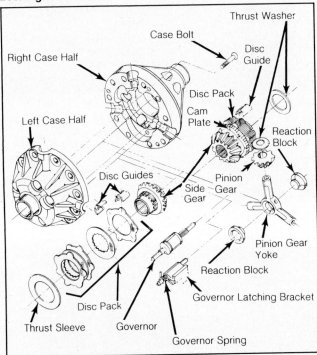

TESTING ON VEHICLE

1) Raise vehicle so that rear wheels can be rotated freely by hand. With 1 wheel held stationary, rotate the other wheel approximately ½ turn every second. Wheel should rotate freely.

2) If both wheels turn, or try to turn, differential is defective. Raise vehicle as high as possible. Leave 1 technician in vehicle. Start engine and allow to idle at 600-800 RPM.

3) If equipped with automatic transmission, place transmission in drive and apply brakes. If equipped

with manual transmission, depress clutch and place transmission in low gear.

4) Pull on 1 parking brake cable from under vehicle to lock 1 rear wheel. With engine idling, slowly release brakes on automatic transmission models and slowly release clutch on manual transmission models.

5) Locked rear wheel should remain stationary and free wheel should rotate slowly. As free wheel speed increases, differential should lock, causing both wheels to rotate or stop. If equipped with a manual transmission, engine may stall.

6) It may be necessary to accelerate to 10 MPH to lock differential. If speed increases beyond 20 MPH without locking differential, unit is defective. Lock opposite wheel and repeat test.

REMOVAL & INSTALLATION

The same procedure is used to remove and install locking differential as conventional differential. See General Motors 10¹/₂"Ring Gear articles in this Section.

OVERHAUL

DISASSEMBLY

Differential

1) With differential removed from housing, remove ring gear and side bearings. Remove 3 screws from front face of ring gear flange. Place differential on right side case half.

2) Using a screwdriver, gently pry case halves apart at yoke hole locations. Remove left side case half. Hold thumb against inside of gear hub when separating case halves. This will prevent side gear from falling out.

3) If governor and latching bracket are only components being replaced, proceed to step **8)** in Reassembly procedures. To further disassemble, pry under pinion gear yoke to remove from case half.

NOTE: If cam gear or clutch disc must be replaced, cam gear assembly must be disassembled as follows:

Cam Gear Assembly

1) Measure and record overall length of gear assembly. Measure from face of gear to back side of thrust ring and include shim. This dimension will be required for reassembly if thrust ring is replaced.

NOTE: Thrust ring should be replaced only if it is absolutely necessary.

2) If thurst ring is replaced, check thrust ring bore in case for wear. If bore is scored excessively, replace complete differential. Position gear with hub end up.

3) Compress disc pack and place bearing removal tool (J-22912) between thrust ring and tap disc. Beveled side of tool should be toward thrust ring. Position cam gear and tool in press with tool supported on both sides.

4) Place a 1½ - 1¾" plug on gear hub. Press against plug with a press to remove thrust ring. Make sure all components are in correct order.

EATON (TWO-PIECE CASE) LOCKING DIFFERENTIAL (Cont.)

INSPECTION

Clean all components in solvent. Inspect all bearings and gear teeth for chipping or wear. Replace as necessary. Inspect clutch plates and discs for signs of wear or overheating. If reaction blocks or flanges must be replaced, measure thickness of original components and replace with components of comparable size.

REASSEMBLY

NOTE: **If cam gear assembly was disassembled, reassemble as follows:**

Cam Gear Assembly

1) Place gear on bench with hub end up. Place cam plate on gear so that cam form on plate is against cam form on gear. Install 2 eared discs on cam plate, 1 splined disc and 1 wave spring alternately in that order.

2) Install on gear hub, 4 eared disc and 3 splined discs alternately, starting and ending with an eared disc. Place cam gear in a press with hub end up. Install thrust ring on gear hub with press.

3) Make sure thrust ring is square with hub. Press thrust ring on until it is flush with shoulder. When installing ring, press down on disc to make sure splined disc does not wedge between thrust ring and gear shoulder.

4) When unit is assembled, check for correct disc sequence. Make sure that the first splined disc (large spline) is correctly located on cam plate.

Differential

1) Install disc pack guide clips on disc ears of cam gear disc pack. Use grease to retain clips in ears. Install cam gear assembly and original shim in right case half.

2) If a new thrust ring was installed on cam gear, it may be necessary to reshim. Measure overall length of cam gear assembly, including shim. Compare this measurement with one previously recorded.

3) If measurement variation is more than .003" (.08 mm) either way, install a new shim that will obtain a reading within .003" (.08 mm) of original measurement.

4) Position right reaction block on gear face with buttonside of block facing up. Replace reaction block only if it is absolutely necessary. If a new block is being installed, measure face-to-face thickness of old block and obtain a new block of same thickness.

5) Install pinion gears and thrust washers on pinion yoke. Place yoke in correct position in housing. Make sure center of yoke is correctly positioned over reaction block button.

6) Tap on yoke lightly to correctly seat it in position. Position left reaction block on yoke with flange end up. Replace block only if it is absolutely necessary.

7) If a new block is being installed, measure face-to-face thickness of old block and obtain a new block of same thickness. The right and left reaction blocks are not necessarily the same thickness. If blocks are broken or it is impossible to measure thickness, complete differential must be replaced.

8) Install governor and latching bracket assemblies in correct position. Place straight end of latching bracket spring over and to outside of governor shaft. This will preload latching bracket against governor assembly.

9) Install original 3 eared discs and 2 splined discs on left side gear alternately, starting and ending with an eared disc.

10) Original disc must be used to maintain correct operating clearance in differential. Install 6 disc pack guide clips. Use grease to retain clips in place.

11) Install original shim in left case half. Remove disc pack from side gear and place in position in case half. Make sure guides are in correct position.

12) Install side gear in case, rotating gear to engage splines with splines on discs. Hold thumb on right case half. Make sure governor and latching bracket assembly holes are aligned in case halves. Install 3 screws.

13) Place 1 axle shaft in a vise in a vertical position. Install differential on axle shaft, making sure splines on axle are engaged in splines in side gear. Slowly rotate differential.

14) This can be easily done by inserting a short shaft or punch in a pinion yoke hole and pulling on shaft. Differential should turn smoothly without locking up or binding.

15) Differential will lock up if turned rapidly. Differential is now ready to be installed in housing.

Positive Traction Differentials

FORD TRACTION-LOK — BRONCO II & RANGER

DESCRIPTION

The limited slip differential has 1 pinion shaft and 2 pinion gears. The side gears are clutch cone type, mounted in a split case asssembly. The assembly also houses a spring block containing 5 springs.

AXLE RATIO & IDENTIFICATION

To determine the drive axle ratio, refer to *Drive Axle Ratio Identification* in this Section.

LUBRICATION

Check lubricant level every 5000 miles or 5 months. Manufacturer recommends no specific drain and refill interval. Use only Ford Hypoid Gear Lubricant.

TESTING ON VEHICLE

Raise 1 wheel, leaving opposite wheel firmly on ground. Install adapter and torque wrench to wheel mounting studs. With transmission in "N", note torque required to keep wheel rotating through several revolutions. Torque should be at least 30 ft. lbs. (41 N.m) while turning wheel.

REMOVAL & INSTALLATION

The same procedure is used to remove and install differential as standard differential. *See FORD 7 1/2" RING GEAR* article in this Section.

CAUTION: **During removal and installation of axle shafts, do not rotate 1 axle shaft unless both are in position. Rotation of 1 axle shaft without the other in place may result in misalignment of 2 spline segments with which axle shaft splines engage. Difficult realignment procedures would then be necessary when axle shaft is reinstalled.**

OVERHAUL

The Bronco II and Ranger Traction-Lok differential is serviced as an assembly only. Under no circumstances should differential be disassembled, reassembled, and installed in vehicle.

Fig. 1: Exploded View of Bronco II & Ranger Traction-Lok Differential

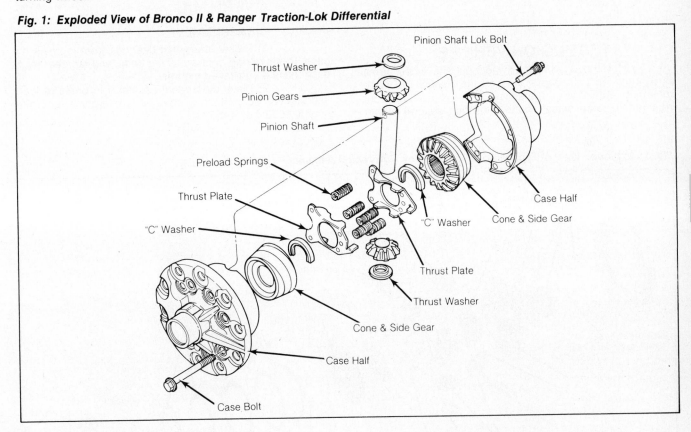

Positive Traction Differentials

FORD TRACTION-LOK — EXCEPT BRONCO II & RANGER

DESCRIPTION

Traction-Lok positive traction differential uses a multiple disc clutch to control differential action. Side gear mounting shims, friction discs, composite plate, clutch hub and guides are housed in differential cover.

Located in differential case, between side gears, is a 1-piece preload plate, block assembly, and 4 calibrated preload springs which apply an initial force to clutch pack.

Additional clutch capacity is derived from side gear thrust loads. Traction-Lok differential can have either 2 or 4 differential pinion gears.

AXLE RATIO & IDENTIFICATION

To determine the drive axle ratio, *refer to Drive Axle Ratio Identification in this Section.*

LUBRICATION

Check level of lubricant every 5,000 miles or 5 months. Manufacturer recommends no specific drain and refill interval. Use only Ford Hypoid Gear Lubricant.

TESTING ON VEHICLE

Raise 1 wheel, leaving opposite wheel firmly on ground. Install adapter and torque wrench to wheel mounting studs. With transmission in "N", note torque required to keep wheel rotating through several revolutions. Torque should be at least 40 ft. lbs. (54 N.m). Disregard initial starting torque.

REMOVAL & INSTALLATION

REMOVAL

1) Position safety stands under rear frame members, and support housing with either a floor jack or hoist. Disengage brake line from clips retaining it to housing.

2) Disconnect vent tube from housing. Remove brake backing plate assemblies from housing, and support with wire.

3) Do not disconnect brake line. Disconnect each rear shock absorber from mounting bracket stud on housing bracket. Lower axle sightly to reduce spring tension. At each rear spring, remove "U" bolt nuts, "U" bolts, and spring seat caps.

INSTALLATION

Reverse removal procedure, to complete installation.

OVERHAUL

DISASSEMBLY

1) Press differential bearings from journals on case. Remove ring gear attaching bolts, and tap gear from case using a soft-faced hammer.

2) Place differential assembly in press to load case halves so preload of springs is overcome, approximately 1000 lbs. (4455 N).

Fig. 1: Exploded View of Typical Ford Traction-Lok Differential Assembly

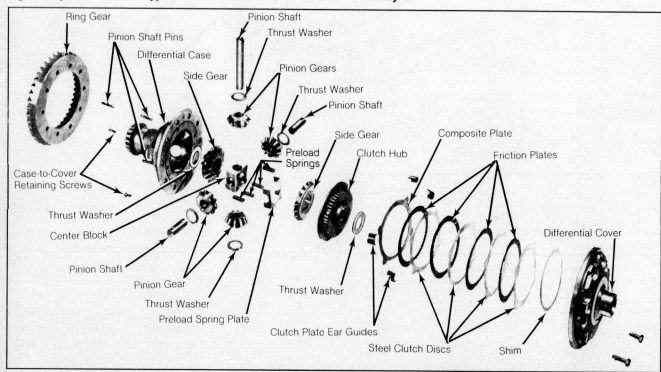

FORD TRACTION-LOK — EXCEPT BRONCO II & RANGER (Cont.)

3) If press is not available, two 7/16" bolts and nuts can be used in ring gear mounting holes (1 on each side) to compress case halves and overcome preload tension.

4) With case under pressure, loosen 2 case-to-cover retaining screws until 1 or 2 threads of each remain engaged. Release pressure, tap on cover to spring it loose. Remove 2 screws.

5) With cover facing down, lift off case. Remove preload spring plate and 4 preload springs. From cover, remove side gear, 4 clutch plate ear guides, clutch hub, friction plates, steel clutch discs and shims.

6) Using a drift, drive out pinion shaft lock pins from case. Drive long pinion shaft from case, working from end opposite lock pin hole. Remove 2 short pinion shafts, working from center outward.

7) Lift out thrust block, remove pinion gears, thrust washers, side gear and side gear thrust washer.

INSPECTION

1) Inspect clutch plates for unevenness or wear. Dog-eared plates must be free of burrs, nicks or scratches. Inspect internally splined clutch plates for condition of bond, bonding material, and wear.

2) Replace bonded plates if thickness is less than .085" (2.16 mm), or if plates are badly worn. Inspect all thrust surfaces and hubs for wear.

REASSEMBLY

1) Lubricate all parts with hypoid gear lubricant prior to assembly. Mount differential case in soft-jawed vise and place a side gear thrust washer and a side gear into counterbore in case.

2) Install pinion thrust washers, and place pinion gears on side gear, aligning holes in washers and ears with holes in case. Install center block so holes in block are aligned with holes in pinion gears and case.

3) Using a brass drift, drive pinion shafts into position from outside of case, making sure lock pin holes in shafts are aligned with corresponding holes in case.

4) Install shaft lock pins, making sure pinion and side gears move freely. Place 4 preload springs in holes provided in center block. Position preload plate over springs, making sure springs are properly seated.

Fig. 2: Sectional View of Center Block Installation

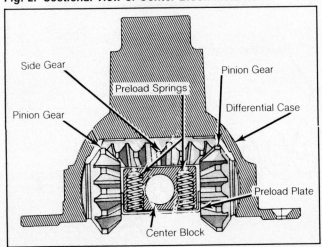

Center block has 2 machined and 2 rough surfaces.

5) Preload plate straddles center block over its narrower, or machined, width. Center block has 2 machined sides and 2 rough sides. Long shaft is driven through rough side, and short shaft is driven through machined side.

6) Mount differential cover in soft-jawed vise. Insert shim(s) of .050" (1.27 mm) total thickness in cover cavity. Install composite plate on back side of clutch hub, with friction material against hub.

7) Install friction plates and steel discs alternately onto hub, beginnning with friction plate and ending with steel disc. When new plates are used, soak in hypoid gear lubricant for 30 minutes before installation.

8) Place clutch hub with clutch plate into clutch gear cavities in differential cover, making sure splines on last friction plate are engaged on hub. Using a 5/8" x 2 1/2" bolt, compress clutch pack, and place shim template tool (T68P-4946-A) in clutch hub.

9) Some clearance should be observed between shim tool and cover-to-case mating surface. Using a feeler gauge, measure clearance. Refer to shim pack thickness chart to determine correct amount of shims to subtract from .050" (1.27 mm) shim pack originally installed.

Fig. 3: Sectional View of Clutch Pack Installation

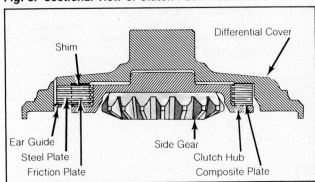

Shown with all clutch plates installed.

SHIM PACK THICKNESS

Gauge Reading	Correction	Total Shims
.001-.002"	None	.050"
.003-.007"	.005"	.045"
.008-.012"	.010"	.040"
.013-.017"	.015"	.035"
.018-.022"	.020"	.030"
.023-.027"	.025"	.025"
.028-.032"	.030"	.020"
.033-.037"	.035"	.015"
.038-.042"	.040"	.010"
.043-.047"	.045"	.005"
.048-.050"	.050"	None

10) Install selected shim in cover cavity, and install internal components as before. In order to correctly select proper shim, template tool must be used. Install 4 steel clutch ear guides and side gear.

11) Place both assemblies in press, force both halves together, and install cover-to-case screws. Install ring gear and ring gear attaching bolts. Tighten to 70-85 ft. lbs. (95-116 N.m)

Positive Traction Differentials

SPICER (DANA) POWER-LOK

Ford, General Motors
Front & Rear Axles

DESCRIPTION

The Power-Lok differential uses clutch packs, which are preloaded by Belleville spring plates to provide limited slip action.

The torque in the axle causes the pinion shafts to move up ramps on the differential case to increase preload on clutch packs. This varies the amount of torque directed to each wheel, and causes the wheel with the greatest traction to receive the greatest torque.

Power-Lok is used on Spicer (Dana) axles that have a 2-piece differential case and 4 differential pinion gears.

AXLE RATIO & IDENTIFICATION

To determine axle ratio, *refer to Drive Axle Ratio Identification in this Section.*

LUBRICATION

NOTE: **To insure proper operation of unit and to prevent differential chatter, manufacturers recommend that only special Positraction lubricants be used.**

TESTING ON VEHICLE

1) With engine not running and transmission in "N", raise 1 wheel off ground. Block both front and rear wheels of opposite side. Install adapter tool across 2 wheel studs, and attach torque wrench to center of tool.

2) Observe torque required to continuously turn wheel smoothly through several revolutions. Repeat test for opposite side. If differential is operating properly, torque should be 40-200 ft. lbs. (54-272 N.m). Disregard breakaway torque. Use rotating torque only.

REMOVAL & INSTALLATION

See Spicer (Dana) Semi-Floating or Full-Floating Axles in this Section.

OVERHAUL

DISASSEMBLY

1) During disassembly, note and record relationship of all parts to each other, especially clutch disc and plates.

2) Mark case halves, pinion mate shafts, and their corresponding ramps. Mark differential spiders for reassembly reference. *For front axle shaft and bearing removal, see articles on Spicer (Dana) Full-Floating Axles or 4-Wheel Drive Steering Knuckles in this Section.*

3) With axle assembly removed from vehicle, pull axle shafts out far enough to allow clearance for differential removal. Using a housing spreader, spread carrier.

4) Do not spread carrier over .020" (.51 mm). Remove bearing caps, and note letters stamped on caps and carrier. Remove differential. Mark bearing cups to indicate from which side of case they were removed.

5) If not previously done, scribe marks on both halves of differential case. Place case in vise. Remove case bolts and disassemble case. Keep stack of plates and discs exactly as they were removed.

INSPECTION

1) Inspect plates, discs, clutch rings, side gears, pinion mate gears, pinion mate shafts and spacer block for damage or wear.

2) Any part showing extreme wear or scoring should be replaced. The pinion mate shafts are unlike the shafts of a conventional differential, and therefore are not locked to differential case.

REASSEMBLY

NOTE: **During assembly, keep all parts clean, and lubricate with limited slip gear lubricant just prior to installation.**

Fig. 1: Exploded View of Spicer (Dana) Power-Lok Differential Assembly

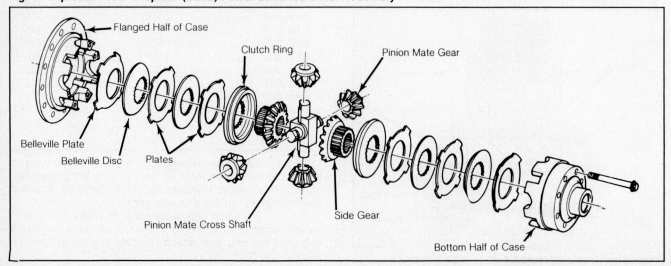

Flanged Half of Case
Clutch Ring
Pinion Mate Gear
Belleville Plate
Belleville Disc
Plates
Pinion Mate Cross Shaft
Side Gear
Bottom Half of Case

SPICER (DANA) POWER-LOK (Cont.)

NOTE: **All front axles have 3 friction surfaces; rear axles have 5 friction surfaces.**

1) Replace plates and disc in exactly the same order as they were removed. Apply proper lubricant on each part. With plates and disc now assembled to clutch ring, line up ears of plates so they will enter easily into ring gear case half.

2) Install side gear, plates and disc on other clutch ring, exactly as removed. Apply proper lubricant on each part. Line up ears of plate for case assembly. Assemble bottom half of case, making sure scribe marks are lined up.

3) Assemble case bolts finger tight only. Put axle in vise, splined end pointing up, and set differential on end of axle. Insert second axle making sure that splines of side gear and clutch ring are lined up.

4) Also make sure shafts are entered the full depth. Leave shafts in this position, and tighten case bolts evenly to 30-40 ft. lbs. (41-54 N.m). Remove shafts. Spread carrier housing to .020" (.51 mm) to receive differential assembly.

5) Assemble bearing cups to their correct sides, and install differential into housing. Install bearing caps exactly as removed, and torque to 70-90 ft. lbs. (95-122 N.m). After axle assembly is completed, refill axle housing with limited slip lubricant.

Fig. 2: Disc and Plate Arrangement for One Side of Power-Lok Differential

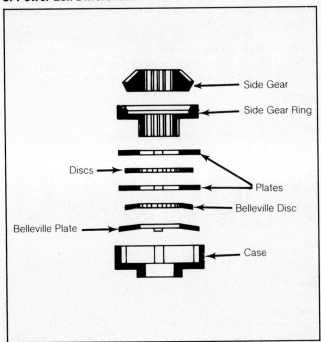

Apply lubricant on each part, and line up ears of plates for assembly.

Positive Traction Differentials

SPICER (DANA) TRAC-LOK

Jeep

DESCRIPTION

The Trac-Lok differential uses clutch packs which are preloaded by Belleville spring plates to provide limited slip action. Multiple disc clutches permit differential action when required for turning corners and transmit equal torque to both wheels when driving straight ahead.

When 1 wheel tries to spin because of reduced traction, clutch packs automatically provide more torque to wheel with greater traction. Trac-Lok is used on Spicer (Dana) axles with a 1-piece differential case and 2 differential pinion gears.

AXLE RATIO & IDENTIFICATION

To determine axle ratio, *refer to Drive Axle Ratio Identification in this Section.*

TESTING ON VEHICLE

1) With engine off and transmission in Neutral, raise 1 wheel off ground and block both front and rear wheels of opposite side. Install adapter tool across 2 wheel studs and attach torque wrench to center of tool.

2) Observe torque required to continuously turn wheel smoothly through several revolutions. Repeat test for opposite side. If differential is operating properly, torque should be 40-200 ft. lbs. (54-272 N.m).

NOTE: **Disregard breakaway torque. Use rotating torque only.**

REMOVAL & INSTALLATION

See Spicer (Dana) Semi-Floating or Full-Floating Axle article in this Section.

OVERHAUL

DISASSEMBLY

During disassembly, note and record relationship of all parts to each other (especially clutch disc and plates). Mark case halves, pinion mate shafts and their corresponding ramps and differential spiders for reassembly reference.

NOTE: **For front axle shaft and bearing removal, see articles on Spicer (Dana) Full-Floating Axles or 4-Wheel Drive Steering Knuckles, in this Section.**

1) With axle assembly removed from vehicle and axles pulled out from housing, remove cover plate screws and cover. Remove differential bearing caps.

2) Note letters stamped on bearing caps for reassembly in proper location. Mount speader and dial indicator to housing. Spread housing to .020" (.51 mm). DO NOT spread any wider. Remove differential using 2 pry bars. Mark differential bearing cups for reassembly. Place axle in a vise, with splined end pointing up 3" (76 mm) above vise. Assemble differential to axle shaft with ring gear screws facing up.

4) Remove ring gear and disassemble internal parts of case. Drive out lock pin using a long drift. With differential on axle shaft, remove cross pin and spacer block (if equipped). Use a hammer and drift.

Fig. 1: Exploded View of Spicer (Dana) Trac-Lok Differential Assembly

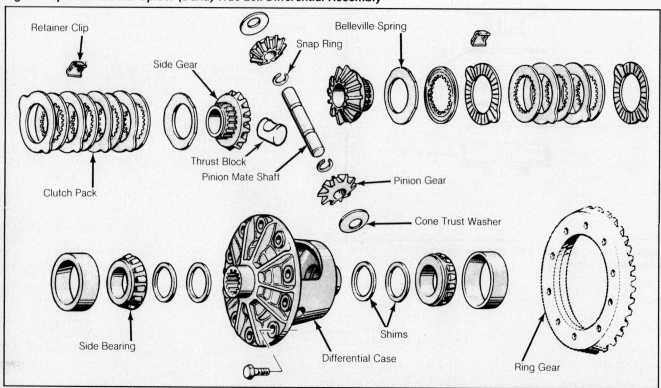

SPICER (DANA) TRAC-LOK (Cont.)

5) Place shop towels over vise jaws to protect gear teeth from becoming nicked after it is free from case. On model 60 Track-Lok, pinion mate shaft is retained by a single lock pin which should be driven from case at this time, using a ³/₁₂" drift.

6) Gear Rotating Tool (J-23781) is required to perform the following steps. The tool consists of 3 parts; gear rotating tool, forcing screw and stop plate. Install stop plate in lower differential side gear.

7) Position pawl end of gear rotating tool on step plate. Lubricate forcing screw and center hole in stop plate before using. Insert forcing screw through top of case and thread into gear rotating tool.

8) Thread forcing screw so that it becomes centered in stop plate. Tighten screw until differential side gears move away from pinion gears. This relieves load between gears allowing pinions some freedom of movement.

9) Use shim stock of .030" (.76 mm) thickness to remove spherical washers. Loosen forcing screw and retighten until a very slight movement of pinions is detected. Insert gear rotating pawl between 2 differential side gear teeth and roll pinion gears out of case.

NOTE: **When rotating differential gear, adjust forcing screw until required load is applied to allow differential gears to rotate freely.**

10) Retain top differential side gear and clutch pack in case by holding bottom of rotating tool while removing forcing screw. Remove rotating tool, stop plate, top differential gear and clutch pack from case.

11) Remove case from axle shaft. Invert case and remove remaining side gear and clutch pack. Remove retaining clips from both clutch packs and separate clutch plates and discs.

NOTE: **During disassembly, keep parts in same order as they were removed, so they can be installed in their original positions.**

Fig. 2: View Showing Typical Clutch Pack Arrangement

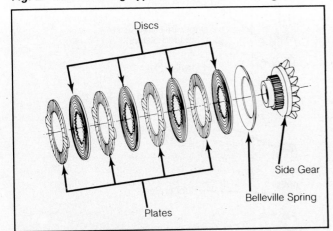

Not all combinations shown.

INSPECTION

Clean and dry all parts. Inspect plates, discs and clips for excessive wear or scoring. Inspect gears for extreme wear, cracks or chips. Inspect case for scoring, wear or metal pickup on machined surfaces.

NOTE: **If any 1 member of either clutch pack should be replaced, complete clutch pack for both sides should be replaced. If any 1 gear requires replacement, all differential gears and thrust washers should be replaced.**

REASSEMBLY

NOTE: **Lubricate all parts with positive traction lubricant prior to reassembly.**

1) Reassemble Belleville spring plate, disc and plates to differential side gears in same position as originally assembled. Install retaining clips to ears of plates, making sure clips are fully seated.

2) Install clutch packs and differential side gears into case. Mount case assembly onto axle shaft, held in vise. While holding gears in place by hand, assemble gear rotating tool the same way as during disassembly.

3) Position differential pinion gears in place so that holes in gears align with holes in case. Tighten forcing screws slightly.

NOTE: **On models with single lock pin through case, make sure hole in shaft is aligned with hole in case.**

4) Install pinion gear thrust washers using small screwdriver to guide washers into position. Remove forcing screw, rotating tool and stop plate. Position thrust block between side gears and install differential pinion mate shaft.

5) Be sure snap ring grooves of shaft are exposed enough to install snap rings. On model 60 Trac-Lok, align shaft, shaft retaining pin bore and case pin bore. Tap shaft into position and install retaining pin.

6) If case is mounted in a vise with machined side of ring gear flange facing upward, use a ⁵/₁₆" diameter punch to install retaining pin. Seat pin until punch bottoms in case bore.

7) If case is mounted in a vise, place machined side of ring gear flange downward. Wrap a length of tape around a ⁵/₁₆" diameter punch approximately 1¾" from end of punch. Install retaining pin until edge of tape is flush with pin bore.

8) Remove case from axle shaft. Install ring gear on case, using all new ring gear bolts. Align ring gear and case bolt holes. Install ring gear bolts finger tight only.

9) Remount case on axle shaft, and tighten bolts evenly to specified torque. Install Trac-Loc differential assembly in axle housing. To complete differential and axle assembly, follow service procedures previously outlined for conventional axles.

4-Wheel Drive Steering Knuckles

ALL MANUFACTURERS

DESCRIPTION

Open type steering knuckles are used on all models. Open type knuckles provide a sharper turning angle, which will decrease the vehicle turning radius.

All of the vehicle weight is carried by the axle housing and steering knuckle. The axle shafts are free floating. Depending upon vehicle model, the steering knuckles can be attached to the axle housing by either ball joints or roller bearings and pivot pins.

Other than the unique components required for front-wheel drive, all steering knuckles used on light duty trucks are mechanically similar.

OVERHAUL

BALL JOINT TYPE
Disassembly

1) Raise vehicle and support on safety stands. Remove wheels. Remove brake caliper and rotor. If equipped with locking hubs, remove hub lock mechanism. *See removal and installation instructions in appropriate Locking Hubs article in this Section.*

2) Disconnect tie rod end from steering knuckle. Remove spindle nuts and lightly tap spindle with a soft face hammer to free it from steering knuckle. Pull out axle shaft assembly. On Chevy "T" series, remove hub and bearing assembly.

3) Remove ball joint cotter keys and nuts. Break ball joints loose from steering knuckle. On Chrysler Corp. vehicles, lower ball joint does not need to be disconnected. Remove lower knuckle-to-knuckle arm nuts and separate components.

4) Clean all components with solvent and blow them dry with compressed air. Inspect all parts for burrs, chips, wear, flat spots or cracks. Replace all damaged parts and parts showing excessive wear.

Reassembly
To complete reassembly, reverse disassembly procedure. Torque all fittings to specifications.

NOTE: **When aligning upper ball joint nut to install cotter pin, always tighten nut to align. Never loosen nut to align holes.**

KING PIN TYPE
Disassembly (GMC K30)

1) Raise vehicle, and support on safety stands. Remove wheel and tire assembly. Remove brake caliper. If equipped with locking hubs, *see removal and installation instructions in appropriate Locking Hubs article in this Section.*

2) Remove hub lock mechanism. Remove snap ring. Pry out driving hub and spring. Remove wheel bearing lock nut. Outer wheel bearing and retainer will come off with hub.

3) Using a brass drift punch, remove inner bearing, cone, and seal from hub. Remove inner and outer bearing cups (if necessary) using a brass punch. Remove spindle. Carefully pull axle shaft assembly through hole in steering knuckle.

4) Disconnect steering linkage at knuckle. Remove nuts from upper king pin cap. Remove nuts alternately as spring will force cap up. Remove cap, compression spring, and gasket.

5) Remove nuts from lower cap. Remove cap and king pin. Remove upper king pin tapered bushing and knuckle from axle yoke. Remove upper king pin from yoke using puller.

6) Using a punch, drive out lower king pin bearing cup, cone, grease retainer, and seal. Drive out from top to bottom.

Fig. 1: Exploded View of Ball Joint Type Steering Knuckle Assembly

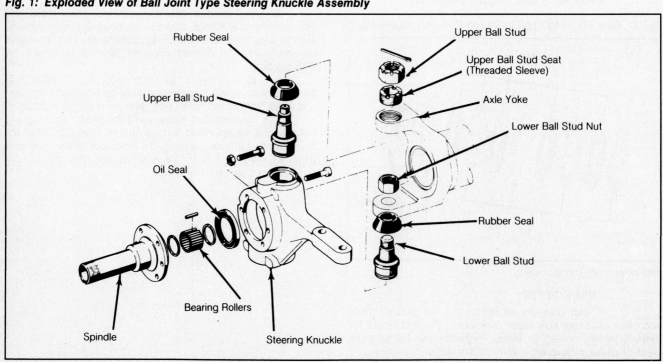

Fig. 2: Sectional View of Ball Joint Type Steering Knuckle Assembly

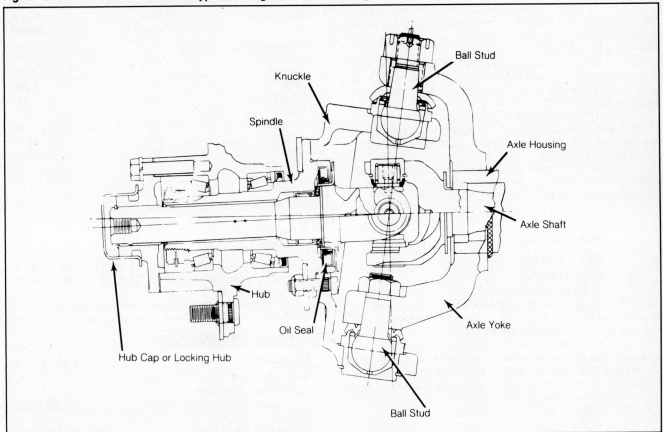

Fig. 3: Exploded View of Chevy "T10" Steering Knuckle

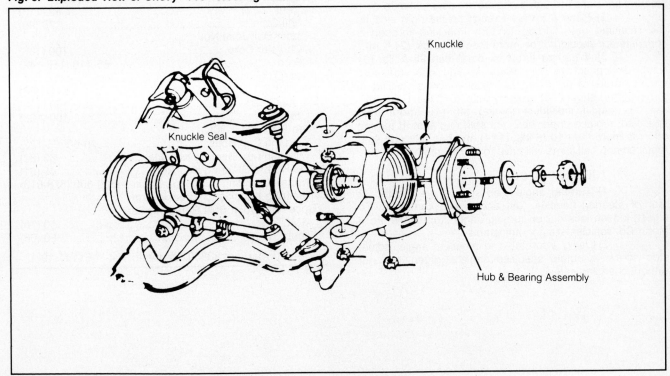

4-Wheel Drive Steering Knuckles

ALL MANUFACTURERS (Cont.)

Reassembly

1) Install a new grease retainer and bearing cup in bottom of yoke. Fill grease retainer with lubricant. Grease bearing cone, and install in cup. Install a new lower king pin oil seal.

2) Care must be taken not to distort seal as it is driven into place. It will protrude slightly from surface of yoke. Using socket, install upper king pin. Installation torque is 500-600 ft. lbs. (680-816 N.m).

3) Position felt seal on king pin. Install steering knuckle and tapered bushing on king pin. Install lower bearing cap and king pin. Tighten bolts alternately and evenly to specifications.

4) Install compression spring on upper king pin bushing. Install bearing cap using a new gasket. Tighten nuts alternately and evenly to specifications.

ADJUSTMENT

BALL JOINTS

GMC K10, K20

1) Raise vehicle, and position on safety stands. Disconnect tie-rod at steering knuckle. Connect a spring tension gauge to tie-rod hole in steering knuckle. Place steering knuckle in straight ahead position.

2) Measure force required to pull steering knuckle to the right after initial breakaway. The pull should not exceed 25 ft. lbs. (34 N.m). If pull required exceeds 25 ft. lbs. (34 N.m), remove upper ball joint stud nut, and loosen adjusting sleeve as required.

Jeep

1) Raise vehicle and remove front wheels. Disconnect steering damper and connecting rod. Remove cotter pin from right side tie rod retaining nut. Rotate steering knuckles through complete arc several times.

2) Place a torque wrench on the right side tie rod retaining nut. Torque to turn knuckles through a complete arc should not be more than 25 ft. lbs. (34 N.m).

3) If turning effort is more than 25 ft. lb. (34 N.m), disconnect tie rod ends at knuckles. Measure turning effort of right and left side knuckles. Individual turning effort should not be more than 10 ft. lbs. (14 N.m).

4) If individual turning effort is more than specified, replace upper ball joint split ring seat. If turning effort is more than 10 ft. lbs. (14 N.m) after split ring seat replacement, ball joints will have to be replaced.

TURNING ANGLE

1) Turning angle stop screws are located at rear of steering knuckle, just above axle centerline. To adjust, loosen lock nut on turning angle stop screw. Ford Motor Co. vehicles are non-adjustable.

2) Using a turntable to measure angle, adjust stop screw to obtain specified angle. Tighten lock nut without changing setting.

TURNING ANGLE ADJUSTMENT

Application	Left Wheel	Right Wheel
Chrysler Corp.		
D150/450	33°	33°
W150	37°	27°
W250	35°	[1] 29°
W350/450	34°	29°
Ford		
F150 & Bronco	36°	36°
F250	33.4°	33.4°
F350	30.3°	30.3°
Bronco II & Ranger	[2]	[2]
Jeep		
CJ-5	29°	29°"
CJ-7 & Scrambler	32°	32°
All Others	36-37°	36-37°

[1] — If equipped with 8.75 x 16.5 tires, turning angle is 26°. If equipped with 9.50 x 16.5 tires, turning angle is 24°.

[2] — Information not available from manufacturer.

TIGHTENING SPECIFICATIONS

Application	Ft. Lbs.(N.m)
Ball Joint Type	
Lower Ball Joint Nut	
Chrysler Corp.	80 (108)
Ford	
Bronco II & Ranger	104-146 (141-198)
Pickups & Vans	[1] 140-180 (190-244)
GMC	
T10	83 (113)
All Others	70 (95)
Upper Ball Joint Nut	
Chrysler Corp.	100 (136)
Ford	85-110 (116-149)
GMC	
T10	50 (68)
All Others	100 (136)
Jeep	100 (136)
King Pin Type (K30)	
King Pin Cap Bolts	70-90 (95-122)
Drag Link-to-Steering Knuckle	60 (82)
Tie Rod-to-Steering Knuckle	45 (61)
Upper King Pin	500-600 (678-813)
Steering Knuckle-to-Knuckle Arm	
Upper Ball Joint Split Retaining Seat	
GMC	50 (70)
Jeep	50 (68)

[1] — For part no. 33850, torque to 104-146 (141-197).

Locking Hubs

AUTOMATIC TYPE

Chevrolet, Chrysler Corp., Ford, GMC

DESCRIPTION

The automatic locking hub automatically engages to lock, and disengages to unlock the front axle shaft to (or from) the front hub. Shifting the transfer case into 4-wheel drive, immediately engages the automatic locking hubs.

The hubs remain engaged, even during coasting or downhill operation. The automatic locking hubs disengage, when the transfer case is shifted into 2-wheel drive, and when vehicle is slowly moved rearward several feet.

REMOVAL & INSTALLATION

REMOVAL

All Models

1) Remove 5 cap screws, and remove cover. Remove bearing race spring assembly. Remove sealing ring and seal bridge retainer. Remove bearing components.

2) Squeeze tangs of wire retaining ring together with needle nose pliers. Pull remaining components of automatic hub from wheel. *See Fig. 1.*

INSTALLATION

All Models

1) Make sure that drag sleeve retainer washer is in position, between wheel bearing adjusting nut and lock nut. Torque wheel bearing adjusting nut to specifications.

2) Make sure that spacer and retaining ring are in position on axle shaft. Install automatic locking hub into wheel hub. Align drag sleeve slots with tabs on drag sleeve retainer washer.

3) Align outer clutch housing splines with splines of wheel hub. Loosen cover screws 3 or 4 turns, and push in on cover to allow retaining ring to expand into rotor hub groove.

NOTE: Locking hubs should be replaced as a complete unit.

Fig. 1: Exploded View of Automatic Locking Hubs

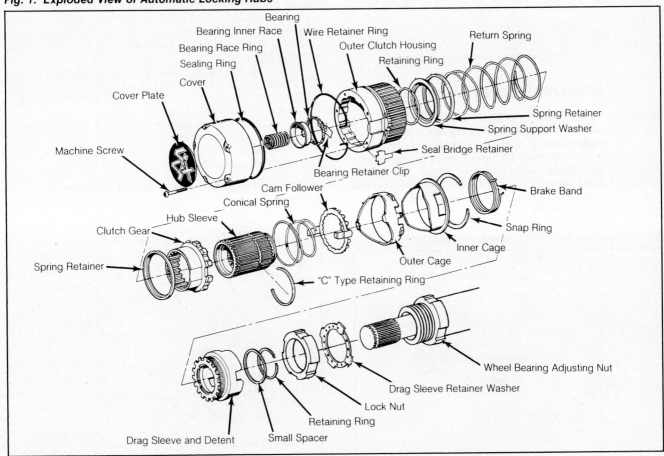

Locking Hubs
WARN SELECTIVE MANUAL TYPE

Jeep

DESCRIPTION

Locking hubs provide a means of engagement of front wheels on vehicles with front drive axle. When hub is engaged, full power is transmitted to both front wheels. When hubs are disengaged, front wheels are free to turn, but axle shafts and differential will remain idle.

Engagement is accomplished through action of gears within hub. With hub in engaged position, clutch body and hub body of hub assembly act as one piece to connect axle shaft to wheel hub. All Warn Selective Manual Hubs function similarly, regardless of differing external appearances.

IDENTIFICATION

All Warn Hubs employ brass control knobs to engage and disengage locking mechanism. Model number of hub is stamped into recess of control knob. *See table for model numbers of Warn Selective Manual Hubs.*

Warn Selective Manual Type Hubs

Application	Model No.
Jeep	
"CJ" & Scrambler	M243
All Other Models	M247

REMOVAL & INSTALLATION

NOTE: **Model M243 and M247 front drive hubs are serviced as either a complete assembly or subassembly, such as the hub body or clutch assembly only. Do not attempt to disassemble these units. If the entire hub or a subassembly has malfunctioned, replace the hub assembly or the defective subassembly as a unit only.**

Fig. 1: Exploded View of Warn Hub Model M243

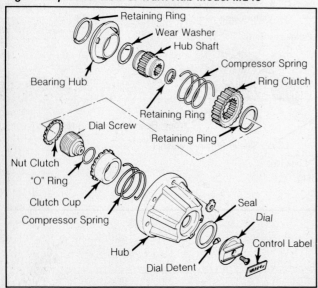

REMOVAL
Models M243 & M247

1) Remove bolts and tabbed lock washers (if equipped), attaching hub body to axle hub. Retain bolts and washers.

2) Remove retaining ring from axle shaft. Remove hub clutch and bearing assembly.

3) Clean hub components in solvent. Dry components, using compressed air or clean shop towel, or air dry.

4) Be sure old lubricant, dirt, water, or other foreign materials are flushed out.

CAUTION: **Do not turn hub control dial, until hub has been installed. The hub clutch nut and cup can be damaged severely, if dial is rotated while hub is off vehicle.**

INSTALLATION
Models M243 & M247

1) Lubricate hub components with all-purpose chassis lubricant. Apply light coat of lubricant only. Do not pack hub with lubricant.

2) On model M243, install hub clutch, bearing assembly, and retaining ring on axle shaft. Position new gasket on hub body, and install hub body and gasket.

3) On model M247, install hub clutch assembly and small retaining ring on axle shaft. Install large retaining ring in axle hub. Install new "O" ring if hub body is being replaced.

4) Align bolt holes in axle and hub body. Install bolts and tabbed lock washers (if equipped). Tighten bolts to 30 ft. lbs. (41 N.m), on model M243 and 30 INCH lbs. (3.4 N.m) on model M247.

5) Raise vehicle front end. Turn hub control dials to position "2" and rotate wheels. Wheels should rotate freely. If wheels drag, check hub installation. Also, be sure control dials fully engaged in 4x4 position.

Fig. 2: Exploded View of Warn Hub Model M247

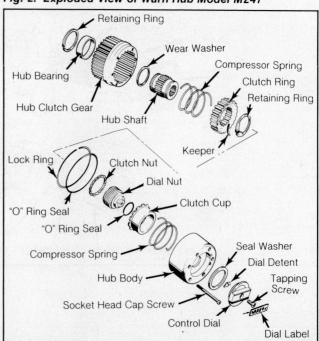

Locking Hubs

WARN SELECTIVE MANUAL TYPE (Cont.)

3) On model M247, install hub clutch assembly and small retaining ring on axle shaft. Install large retaining ring in axle hub. Install new "O" ring if hub body is being replaced.

4) Align bolt holes in axle and hub body. Install bolts and tabbed lock washers (if equipped). Tighten bolts to 30 ft. lbs. (41 N.m), on model M243 and 30 INCH lbs. (3.4 N.m) on model M247.

5) Raise vehicle front end. Turn hub control dials to position "2" and rotate wheels. Wheels should rotate freely. If wheels drag, check hub installation. Also, be sure control dials fully engaged in 4x4 position.

Fig. 3 Warn Hub Model M243 Clutch & Bearing Assembly

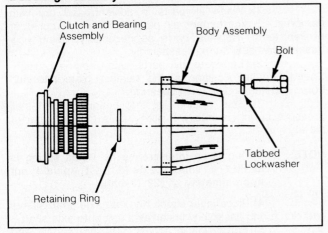

Fig. 4: Warn Hub Model 247 Clutch Assembly

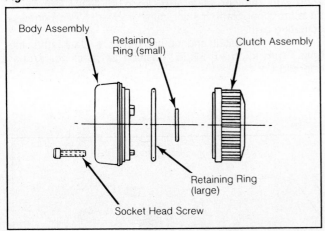

Locking Hubs

SPICER (DANA) INTERNAL LOCKING HUB

DESCRIPTION

Locking hubs provide a means of engagement and disengagement of wheels on front drive axles. When locking hubs are engaged, full power is transmitted to both front wheels.

When hubs are disengaged, front wheels are free to turn, and axle shafts and differential remain idle. Engagement is accomplished through the action of gears within hub.

With hub in engaged position, inner clutch ring and axle shaft sleeve act as 1 piece to connect axle shaft to wheel hub.

Fig. 1: Front View of Spicer (Dana) Locking Hub

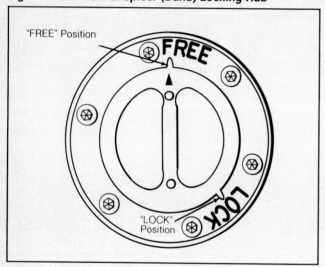

Notice "FREE" and "LOCK" positions.

IDENTIFICATION

Spicer (Dana) internal locking hubs are identified externally by a red plastic control knob, used to engage and disengage hub. They are identified internally by use of an actuating cam to engage and disengage hub.

REMOVAL & INSTALLATION

REMOVAL

1) With control knob set in "LOCK" position, remove retainer plate attaching bolts. Remove outer retainer plate assembly and separate knob from retainer.

2) Remove internal hub snap ring, and slide retainer ring and cam from hub. Relieve pressure on sleeve and ring assembly. Remove axle shaft snap ring.

3) Remove sleeve and ring assembly, inner clutch, pressure spring, and spring retainer plate.

INSTALLATION

1) Wash all parts in solvent, and dry with compressed air. Inspect all parts for wear, cracks, or broken teeth. Replace parts as necessary, using new gaskets and seal during reassembly.

2) Lubricate all parts with Moly X-L High-Speed Grease. Position spring retainer plate into hub bore, with flange side facing bearing.

3) Seat retainer against bearing cup. Install pressure spring in hub with large coils against retainer plate.

NOTE: **Spring is an interference fit. When spring is seated it should extend past spindle nut approximately $\frac{7}{8}$" (22.23 mm).**

4) Place inner clutch ring into axle shaft sleeve and clutch ring assembly. Install as a unit onto axle shaft.

5) Force unit in against pressure spring, and install axle shaft snap ring. Position actuating cam, with cams facing outward and retainer ring in hub bore.

6) Install internal hub snap ring. Install control knob into retainer plate with knob in "LOCK" position. Install retainer plate, making sure grooves in knob engage actuating cam.

7) Install and tighten retainer plate attaching bolts. Turn knob to "FREE" position to check for proper operation.

Fig. 2: Exploded View of Spicer (Dana) Internal Locking Hub

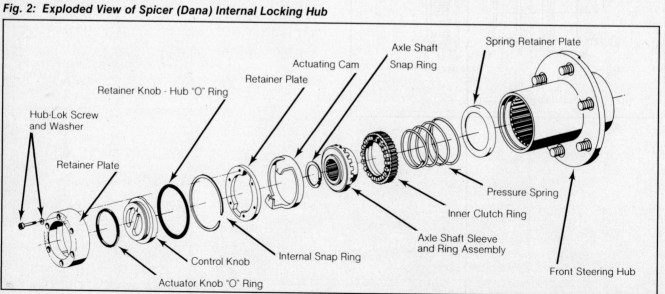

Locking Hubs

SPICER (DANA) EXTERNAL LOCKING HUB

DESCRIPTION

Locking hubs provide a means of engagement and disengagement of wheels on front drive axles. When locking hubs are engaged, full power is transmitted to both front wheels. When hubs are disengaged, front wheels are free to turn and axle shafts and differential remain idle.

Engagement is accomplished through the action of gears within the hub. With hub in engaged position, the inner clutch gear locks with the outer clutch and engages the axle shaft with wheel hub.

IDENTIFICATION

Spicer (Dana) external locking hubs are identified externally by a red plastic control knob used to engage and disengage hub. They are identified internally by use of an actuating cam to engage and disengage hub.

REMOVAL & INSTALLATION

REMOVAL

1) Remove hub screws and washers, noting how washers are installed on screws. Loosen gear hub housing, and slide away from hub and drum assembly.

2) Remove inner metal gasket, and discard. Remove gear hub housing. Remove outer gasket, and discard. Wipe clean all exposed components. Apply pressure on clutch gear, and remove snap ring.

3) Remove clutch gear and pressure spring from assembly, while knob is in "LOCK" position. Turn knob to "FREE" position. Usng a drift punch, drive cam lock pin out of assembly.

4) Remove actuating cam from knob. Remove knob from knob retainer. Using a cap screw, pull out on axle shaft. Remove snap ring, bushing, and inner clutch assembly. If wear is shown on either the inner or outer clutch gear, replace both as a set.

INSTALLATION

1) Before assembling hub, check splines on axle shaft. Make sure threaded screw holes in wheel hub

are clean. Apply Moly X-L hi-speed grease to thrust face of bushing and to splines of inner clutch gear.

2) Install inner clutch gear on bushing. Install bushing and inner clutch gear on axle shaft. Make sure splines on inner clutch gear are aligned with splines on axle.

3) Install a new snap ring. Make sure snap ring is fully seated. Apply Parker "O" Ring Lubricant to "O" ring area of control knob. Install "O" ring.

4) Place actuating knob into knob retainer with arrow pointing to "FREE" position. Install knob retainer snap ring. It may be necessary to use a small screwdriver to position snap ring in groove.

5) Place actuating cam on knob, making sure ears of cam are aligned with retainer slots. Install cam lock pin through cam groove and holes in actuator knob.

6) Make sure ends of pin are flush with outside diameter of cam. Turn actuator knob to "LOCK" position. Apply a small amount of Moly X-L hi-speed lubricant to cam grooves.

7) Install spring and outer clutch gear. Press down on clutch gear to compress spring. With spring compressed, install snap ring. Turn actuator knob to "FREE" position.

8) Install 2 retaining screws and washers into knob retainer to align hub components. Apply a small amount of lubricant to outer splines of outer clutch gear.

9) Remove excess lubricant from retainer gasket surface. Install a new outer retainer gasket. Assemble housing by aligning splines of housing with outer clutch gear splines.

10 Install a new inner metal gasket on hub housing. Install hub assembly to axle, using retainer screws as pilots to align gasket holes and wheel hub holes.

11) Tighten retainer screws to secure hub in place. Turn actuator knob to "LOCK" position. Install the 4 remaining screws. Tighten screws evenly to 30-35 ft. lbs. (41-48 N.m).

NOTE: It may be difficult to engage and disengage hub, until it has been used several times.

Fig. 1: Exploded View of Spicer (Dana) External Locking Hub

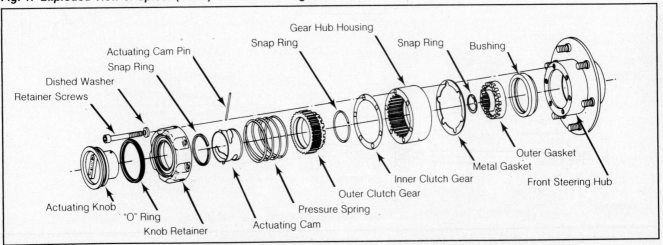

Propeller Shafts

PROPELLER SHAFT ALIGNMENT

All Models

DESCRIPTION

Propeller shafts are balanced, 1-piece, tubular shafts with universal joints at each end. The number used in a vehicle varies: 1 shaft, 2 shafts with center bearing, or 3 shafts in 4-wheel drive applications. Location of slip joints varies with model and manufacturer. *See Fig. 1.*

INSPECTION

Vibration can come from many sources. Before overhauling driveline, other sources of possible vibration should be checked first.

TIRES AND WHEELS

Check tire inflation and wheel balance. Check for foreign objects in tread, damaged tread, mismatched tread patterns or incorrect tire size.

CENTER BEARING

Tighten propeller shaft center bearing mounting bolts. If bearing insulator is deteriorated or oil-soaked, replace it.

ENGINE & TRANSMISSION MOUNTINGS

Tighten mounting bolts. If mountings are deteriorated, replace them.

PROPELLER SHAFT

Check propeller shaft for damage or dents that could effect balance. Check for undercoating adhering to shafts. If present, clean shafts thoroughly.

UNIVERSAL JOINTS

Check for foreign material stuck in joints. Check for loose bolts and worn bearings.

Fig. 1: Five Commonly Used Propeller Shaft Combinations

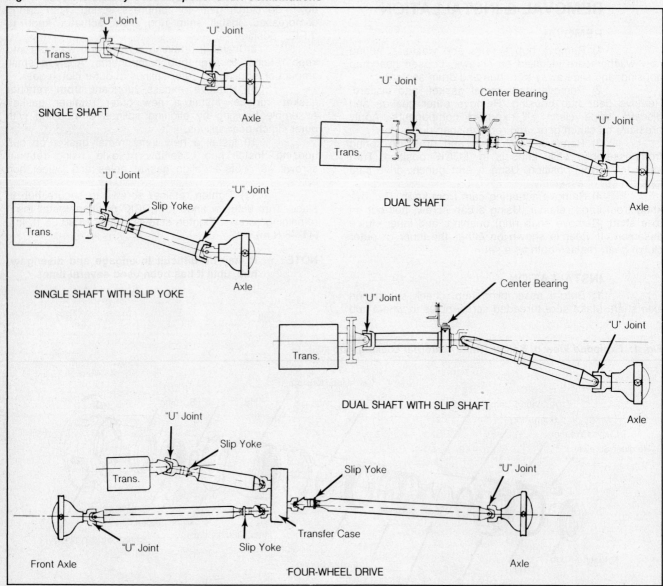

Four-wheel drive models use 3 propeller shafts.

Propeller Shafts

PROPELLER SHAFT ALIGNMENT (Cont.)

ADJUSTMENTS

PROPELLER SHAFT PHASING

Chevrolet & GMC

1) All models with 32 splines use an alignment key on spline, and can mate in correct position only. On "C" and "P" models with 2-piece shafts, proper phasing is accomplished with an alignment key on spline and can mate in correct position only.

2) On "G", "K", and "S" models with 2-piece shafts, rotate transmission yoke until trunnion is in vertical position. Install front propeller shaft with "U" joint trunnion in horizontal position. Install bearing support to crossmember. Align rear propeller shaft with "U" joint trunnion to horizontal position and install shaft.

All Other Models

Check that flanges on either end of propeller shaft are in same plane. Often there are arrows on slip joint and propeller shaft to aid in alignment. If flanges are not in same plane, disassemble universal joint and align.

PROPELLER SHAFT BALANCE

1) Often propeller shaft imbalance can be cured by disconnecting shaft, and rotating it 180° in relation to other components. Test by raising rear wheels off ground, and turning shaft with engine.

CAUTION: Do not run engine with transmission engaged for prolonged periods, as overheating of engine or transmission may occur.

2) On most models, balancing may be done by marking shaft in 4 positions, 90° apart. Place marks approximately 6" forward of weld, at rear end of shaft. Number marks 1 through 4.

3) Place a screw-type hose clamp in No. 1 position, and rotate shaft with engine. If there is little or no change, move clamp to No. 2 position, and repeat test.

4) Continue procedure until vibration is at lowest level. If no difference is noted with clamp moved to all 4 positions, vibrations may not be propeller shaft imbalance.

5) If vibration is lessened but not completely gone, place 2 clamps at that point, and run test again. The combined weight of clamps in 1 position may worsen vibration. If so, rotate clamps ½" apart, above and below best position, and repeat test.

6) Continue to rotate clamps as necessary, until vibration is at lowest point. When point is reached where vibration has been eliminated, bend end of clamp so it will not loosen. If vibration level is still unacceptable, repeat procedure at front end of propeller shaft.

Fig. 2: *View Showing Typical Slip Joint Alignment Arrows*

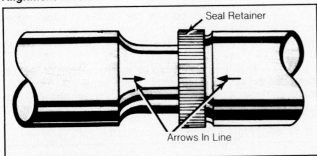

Align arrows to sides of seal retainer.

Fig. 3: *Propeller Shaft Phase Alignment for Chevrolet and GMC Models ("G", "K" & "S" 2-Piece Shaft)*

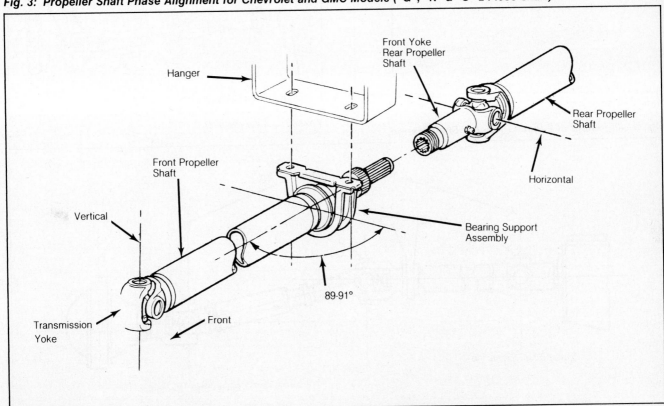

When aligning, set transmission and rear shaft trunnions vertically, others horizontally.

PROPELLER SHAFT ALIGNMENT (Cont.)

Fig. 4: Propeller Shaft Phase Alignment

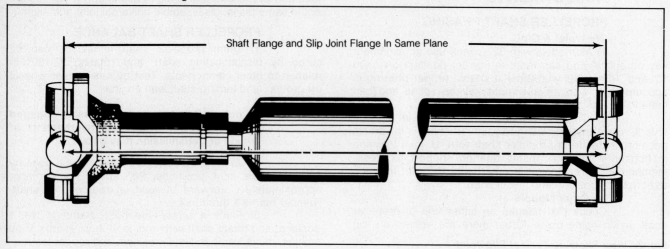

Shaft Flange and Slip Joint Flange In Same Plane

FLANGE ALIGNMENT & RUNOUT

1) All flanges must be perpendicular in both vertical and horizontal planes to engine crankshaft. The only exception is "broken back" type driveline, which has flanges that are not perpendicular in vertical plane. *See Fig. 5.*

Fig.5: Typical "Broken Back" Type Propeller Shaft Alignment

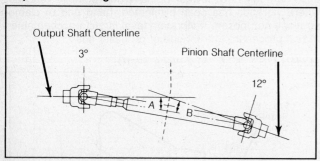

Angle "A" equals angle "B".

Fig. 6: Alignment of 2-Piece Propeller Shaft Flange

2) With nonparallel or "broken back" type installation, working angles of universal joints of a given propeller shaft are equal. *See Fig. 5.* Angle "A" = Angle "B".

3) This is calculated as follows: Angle of output shaft centerline is subtracted from angle of propeller shaft. Difference should equal angle of propeller shaft subtracted from pinion shaft angle.

Fig. 7: Aligning 1-Piece Propeller Shaft

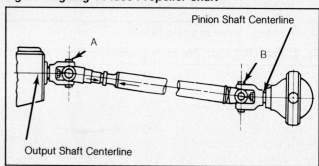

Yokes must be parallel.

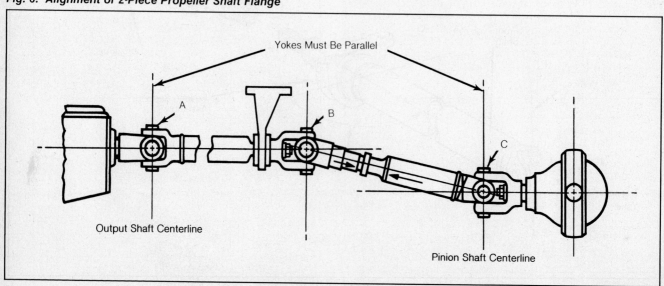

PROPELLER SHAFT ALIGNMENT (Cont.)

4) Parallel type joints maintain a constant velocity between output shaft and pinion shaft. Vibration is minimized and component life maximized when universal joints are parallel.

5) Using dial indicator, measure runout of transmission flange, center bearing flange, and pinion flange. If runout exceeds .003-.005" (.08-.13 mm), replace flange.

6) If dial indicator cannot be used, push rod with a slip fit through flange bearing bore. See if it aligns with opposite bore. If not, replace flange.

7) Rotate transmission flange until it is vertical, measuring from side. Check center bearing and pinion flanges. They cannot be more than 1° off vertical. *See Propeller Shaft Phasing in this article.*

8) Rotate transmission flange until it is vertical, measured from side. Then, measure angle from end, and record it. Check all other flanges for same angle. They must be within ½° of each other. Adjust as required.

9) If difficulty is encountered when making above adjustments, horizontal alignment should be checked. Even though vertical alignment is correct, horizontal alignment can be badly out of adjustment. This is especially true after major component replacement or serious accident. *See Fig. 9.*

10) To make horizontal alignment checks, set up straigtedges. *See Fig. 10.* With transmission flange horizontal, clamp a straightedge to it, so that straightedge is horizontal. Do the same with pinion flange.

11) Using a straightedge that is 12" longer than rear wheel track, clamp it to frame side rails. Use large framing squares to align. Measure distance "X" at each side. If 2 dimensions are not within ¹⁄₁₆" of each other, transmission flange is misaligned horizontally.

Fig. 8: *Vertical Alignment of Propeller Shaft*

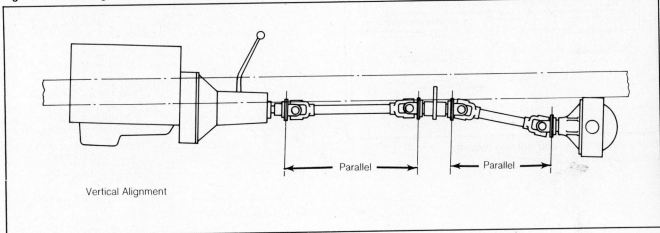

Pairs of flanges should be parallel.

Fig. 9: *Horizontal Alignment of Propeller Shaft*

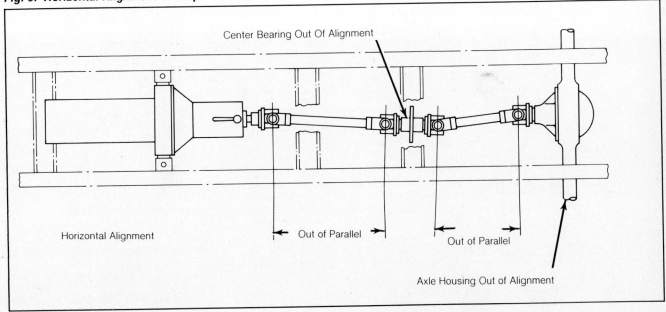

Plane of trunnions should be parallel.

Propeller Shafts

PROPELLER SHAFT ALIGNMENT (Cont.)

12) Measure distance "W" at each side. If 2 dimensions are not within $\frac{1}{16}$" (1.6 mm) of each other, pinion flange is misaligned horizontally.

13) Measure distance "Y" at each side, from edge of straightedge to center of axle shaft. If 2 dimensions are not within $\frac{1}{8}$" (3.2 mm) of each other, axle housing is misaligned.

Fig. 10: Checking Horizontal Alignment

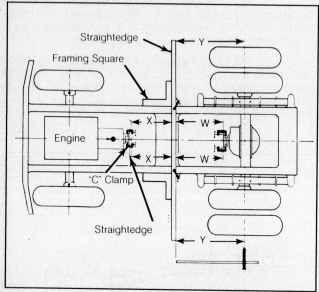

Using straightedge and framing square,
measure at 6 points shown.

Propeller Shafts

UNIVERSAL JOINTS

All Models

MAINTENANCE

If slip yoke has a tendency to stick in extension housing seal, remove propeller shaft from vehicle and clean yoke with solvent. Lubricate inside diameter of seal with synthetic oil seal lubricant, and outside diameter of seal with transmission fluid.

NOTE: **This procedure should also be followed, whenever shaft is removed from vehicle.**

OVERHAUL

ALL MODELS

NOTE: **Universal joints should not be disassembled or lubricated, unless external leakage or damage has occurred.**

Before disassembly, scribe alignment marks on yoke and shaft to allow reassembly in original position. If joints are rusted or corroded, apply penetrating oil before pressing out bearing cups or trunnion pin.

CROSS & ROLLER TYPE

Two different retaining methods are used for bearing cups, either snap rings or nylon retainers. Joints with snap rings may be taken apart and reassembled, using same cross and bearings. Joints with nylon retainers are disassembled by breaking nylon retainers. Retainers must be replaced after service.

Disassembly

1) Disconnect yoke attaching bolts or flange attaching bolts and remove propeller shaft from vehicle.

NOTE: **Do not use pry bar to hold propeller shaft while loosening bolts. Damage to bearing seals may result.**

2) Remove retaining strap (if equipped). Remove bushing retainers from yoke, and press out rollers and bearings. Remove last roller and bushing assembly by pressing on end of cross.

3) Remove cross assembly from yoke. Do not remove seal retainers from cross. Cross and retainers are serviced as an assembly.

Fig. 2: Exploded View of General Motors Universal Joint

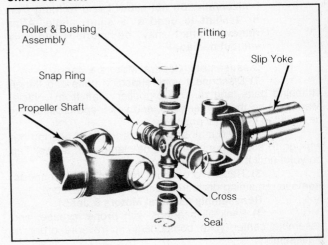

Reassembly

1) Coat roller and bearing assemblies with lubricant, and fill reservoirs in ends of cross. Place cross assembly in propeller shaft yoke, and place roller and bushing assemblies into position.

Fig. 1: Exploded View of General Motors and Jeep Constant Velocity Type Universal Joint

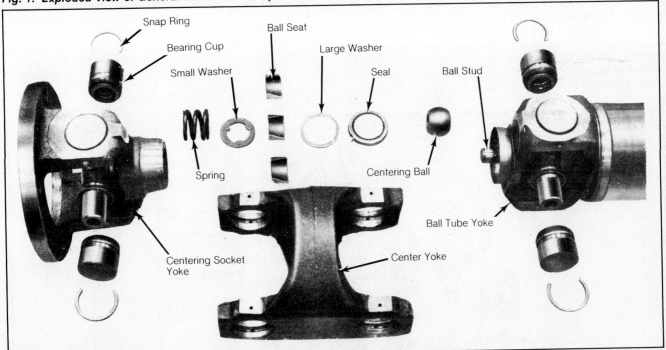

Propeller Shafts

UNIVERSAL JOINTS (Cont.)

2) Press both bushing assemblies into yoke until retainers can be installed, being careful to keep cross aligned in center of bushings.

3) Install retainers, then repeat procedure for remaining bushings. Install strap (if equipped). Install propeller shaft in vehicle, aligning scribe marks.

CONSTANT VELOCITY TYPE

NOTE: **To prevent damage to constant velocity joints, center ball when removing propeller shaft assembly. When handling shaft after removal, support shafts on both sides of constant velocity joint if shaft is being moved horizontally. Do not allow 1 end to hang free or 1 shaft to bend at a sharp angle. After removal, shaft may be carried vertically without damage.**

Disassembly (General Motors & Jeep)

1) Disconnect yoke attaching bolts and flange attaching bolts, and remove propeller shaft from vehicle. Mark joint so that center yoke, end yoke, and crosses will be installed in original positions.

2) Pry out all snap rings and press bearing out enough to allow bearing end to be clamped in a vise. Tap on yoke until it is free of bearing.

3) Repeat procedure for remaining bearings. Remove remaining parts from center yoke assembly.

Reassembly (General Motors & Jeep)

1) Pack all bearings with proper grease, and assemble center yoke components in reverse order of disassembly.

2) Using arbor press or vise, press 2 opposing bearings into position at same time until all bearings are installed. Be sure crosses and yokes remain aligned during this process.

3) Check for free movement of joint. If bind exists, seat bearings by sharply rapping yokes with a brass hammer. Never hammer on bearings.

4) Install propeller shaft in vehicle, making sure marks made during disassembly are aligned.

Disassembly (Ford)

1) With propeller shaft removed from vehicle, position assembly in a vise. Mark position of crosses, center yoke, and center socket in relationship with stud yoke welded to propeller shaft tube.

NOTE: **To obtain correct clearance, crosses must be installed on bosses in original positions.**

2) Remove snap rings in front of center yoke. Using a "C" clamp type tool (CJ91B or equivalent), tighten screw in tool until bearing protrudes ⅜" (10 mm).

3) Remove propeller shaft from vise. Tighten protruding part of bearing in vise. Rap against center yoke with hammer until bearing is free of yoke. Remove all bearings from cross in this manner.

4) Remove cross from center yoke. Remove centering socket from stud, and remove rubber seal from centering ball stud.

5) Remove snap rings from center and drive shaft yokes. Install "C" clamp tool, and tighten screws until bearing is pressing outward and center yoke contacts slinger ring. Do not press beyond this point or slinger will be damaged.

6) Clamp exposed end of bearing in vise, and hammer on center yoke until bearing is free. Press against cross with "C" clamp tool to remove remaining bearing.

7) Remove center yoke from cross, and remove cross from propeller shaft using same procedure.

Reassembly (Ford)

1) Clean all components in cleaning solvent. Place cross in propeller shaft yoke. Make sure cross bosses are installed in original position.

NOTE: **If a repair kit is being installed, bosses will be lubrication plugs.**

2) Press in bearings, and install snap rings. Fill socket relief and coat ball with proper grease. Position center yoke over cross. Press in bearings and install snap rings.

3) Install a new seal on centering ball stud. Place centering socket over stud. Place front cross in yoke. Make sure cross bosses (or lubrication plugs) are installed in original position.

4) Place cross loosely on center stop. Press first set of bearings into center yoke, then install second set. Install snap rings. Apply pressure to center yoke socket, and install remaining bearing cup. If replacement kit is used, remove plugs, and lubricate "U" joints. Reinstall plugs.

Fig. 3: Exploded View of Ford Constant Velocity Type Universal Joint

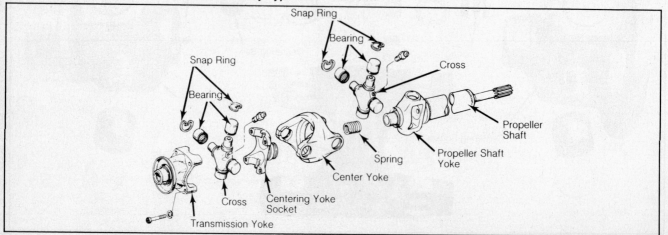

SECTION 10

BRAKES

CONTENTS

NOTE: ALSO SEE GENERAL INDEX.

IMPORTANT: Because of the many model names used by vehicle manufacturers, accurate identification of models is important. See Model Identification at the front of this publication.

Brakes

BRAKE SYSTEM TROUBLE SHOOTING

CONDITION	POSSIBLE CAUSE	CORRECTION
Brakes Pull Left or Right	Incorrect tire pressure	Inflate tires to proper pressure
	Front end out of alignment	See WHEEL ALIGNMENT
	Mismatched tires	Check tires sizes
	Restricted brake lines or hoses	Check hose routing
	Loose or malfunctioning caliper	See DISC BRAKES
	Bent shoe or oily linings	See DRUM BRAKES
	Malfunctioning rear brakes	See DRUM or DISC BRAKES
	Loose suspension parts	See SUSPENSION
Noises Without Brakes Applied	Front linings worn out	Replace linings
	Dust or oil on drums or rotors	See DRUM or DISC BRAKES
Noises with Brakes Applied	Insulator on outboard shoe damaged	See DISC BRAKES
	Incorrect pads or linings	Replace pads or linings
Brake Rough, Chatters or Pulsates	Excessive lateral runout	Check rotor runout
	Parallelism not to specifications	Reface or replace rotor
	Wheel bearings not adjusted	See SUSPENSION
	Rear drums out-of-round	Reface or replace drums
	Disc pad reversed, steel against rotor	Remove and reinstall pad
Excessive Pedal Effort	Malfunctioning power unit	See POWER BRAKES
	Partial system failure	Check fluid and pipes
	Worn disc pad or lining	Replace pad or lining
	Caliper piston stuck or sluggish	See DISC BRAKES
	Master cylinder piston stuck	See MASTER CYLINDERS
	Brake fade due to incorrect pads or linings	Replace pads or linings
	Linings or pads glazed	Replace pads or linings
	Worn drums	Reface or replace drums
Excessive Pedal Travel	Partial brake system failure	Check fluid and pipes
	Insufficient fluid in master cylinder	See MASTER CYLINDERS
	Air trapped in system	See BLEEDING
	Rear brakes not adjusted	See Adjustment in DRUM BRAKES
	Bent shoe or lining	See DRUM BRAKES
	Plugged master cylinder cap	See MASTER CYLINDER
	Improper brake fluid	Replace brake fluid
Pedal Travel Decreasing	Compensating port plugged	See MASTER CYLINDERS
	Swollen cup in master cylinder	See MASTER CYLINDERS
	Master cylinder piston not returning	See MASTER CYLINDERS
	Weak shoe retracting springs	See DRUM BRAKES
	Wheel cylinder piston sticking	See DRUM BRAKES
Dragging Brakes	Master cylinder pistons not returning	See MASTER CYLINDERS
	Restricted brake lines or hoses	Check line routing
	Incorrect parking brake adjustment	See DRUM BRAKES
	Parking brake cables frozen	See DRUM BRAKES
	Incorrect installation of inboard disc pad	Remove and replace correctly
	Power booster output rod too long	See POWER BRAKE UNITS
	Brake pedal not returning freely	See DISC or DRUM BRAKES
Brakes Grab or Uneven Braking Action	Malfunction of combination valve	See CONTROL VALVES
	Malfunction of power brake unit	See POWER BRAKE UNITS
	Binding brake pedal	See DISC or DRUM BRAKES
Pulsation or Roughness	Uneven pad wear caused by caliper	See DISC BRAKES
	Uneven rotor wear	See DISC BRAKES
	Drums out-of-round	Reface or replace drums

HYDRO-BOOST TROUBLE SHOOTING

CONDITION	POSSIBLE CAUSE	CORRECTION
No Boost — Hard Pedal	Loose/broken power steering belt	Replace belt
	No fluid in steering reservoir	Fill to proper level
	Leaks in booster/accumulator hoses	See POWER STEERING
	Leaks at tube fittings/connections	Replace or repair, as necessary
	External leakage at accumulator	Replace or repair, as necessary
	Faulty booster piston seal	Replace seal
	Leakage at flange vent	See POWER STEERING
	Faulty booster input rod seal	Check rod and replace seal
	Leakage at input rod end	See POWER STEERING
	Faulty cover seal	Replace seal
	Leakage between housing and cover	See POWER STEERING
	Faulty booster spool plug seal	Replace seal
	Internal leakage in booster	See POWER STEERING
	Contamination in fluid	See POWER STEERING
	Incorrect routing of hydraulic lines	See POWER STEERING
Pump Noisy on Brake Application	Insufficient fluid in reservoir	Fill to proper level
Brake Pedal Pulls Down on Engine Start	Restriction in gear/booster return lines	See POWER STEERING
Accumulator Leakdown	External leakage of accumulator	See POWER STEERING
	Internal leakage at accumulator	See POWER STEERING
	Internal leakage at accumulator valve	See POWER STEERING
Brake Grab on Application	Broken spool return spring	Replace spool spring
	Faulty spool action due to contamination	See POWER STEERING
Booster Chatter/Pedal Vibrates	Power steering pump belt slipping	Tighten belt
	Low fluid level in pump reservoir	Fill to proper level
	Air in system	Bleed system and add fluid
Slow Brake Pedal Return	Seal friction in booster	See POWER STEERING
	Faulty spool action	See POWER STEERING
	Broken piston return spring	Replace spring
	Restriction in return line from booster	See POWER STEERING
	Broken spool return spring	Replace spring
	Excessive pedal pivot friction	See POWER STEERING

Brake System Applications

CHRYSLER CORP.

BRAKE SYSTEM APPLICATIONS

Application	Type	Make & Design	Master Cylinder	Power Unit

150 Series (All)
  Front
  Rear
	Disc
	Drum
		Chrysler — Sliding Caliper
		Chrysler — Single Anchor
			Chrysler
			Dual Piston
				Bendix — Single Diaphragm

B250/350
  Front
  Rear
	Disc
	Drum
		Chrysler — Sliding Caliper
		[1] Chrysler — Single Anchor
			Chrysler
			Dual Piston
				[2] Bendix — Single Diaphragm

D250/350
  Front
  Rear
	Disc
	Drum
		Chrysler — Sliding Caliper
		Bendix — Single Anchor
			Chrysler
			Dual Piston
				Bendix — Dual Diaphragm

W250/350
  Front
  Rear
	Disc
	Drum
		[3] Bendix — Sliding Caliper
		Bendix — Single Anchor
			[4] Bendix
			Dual Piston
				Bendix — Dual Diaphragm

[1] — Bendix, Single Anchor used on B250.
[2] — Dual Diaphragm used on B350 w/4000 lb. front axle.
[3] — Chrysler, Sliding Caliper used on W250 w/Spicer 60 front axle.
[4] — Chrysler Dual Piston used on W250 w/Spicer 44 front axle.

FORD

BRAKE SYSTEM APPLICATIONS

Application	Type	Make & Design	Master Cylinder	Power Booster

Bronco, Bronco II,
  Ranger, F100/250, E100/150 [1]
  Front
  Rear
	Disc
	Drum
		Bendix — Sliding Caliper
		Bendix — Single Anchor
			Ford
			Dual Piston
				Bendix — Single Diaphragm

E250/350, F250/350 [2]
  Front
  Rear
	Disc
	Drum
		Dayton — Sliding Caliper
		Bendix — Single Anchor
			Ford
			Dual Piston
				[3] Bendix — Single Diaphragm

[1] — 2WD F250 under 6900 GVW.
[2] — 2WD F250 6900 GVW or higher.
[3] — E350 and F350 models use a Dual Diaphragm type power unit.

GENERAL MOTORS

BRAKE SYSTEM APPLICATIONS

[1] Application	Type	Make & Design	[2] Master Cylinder	Power Unit
C10 (Diesel) Front Rear	Disc Drum	Delco — Floating Caliper Delco — Single Anchor	Delco — Dual Piston	Bendix Hydroboost
C10 (Gas), K & G10, G20 Front Rear	Disc Drum	Delco — Floating Caliper Delco — Single Anchor	Delco — Dual Piston	[4] Bendix or Delco Single Diaphragm [4] Bendix or Delco Dual Diaphragm
C & K20 Front Rear	Disc Drum	Delco — Floating Caliper Delco — Single Anchor	Delco — Dual Piston	Bendix or Delco Dual Diaphragm
C30 Front Rear	Disc Drum	[3] Bendix — Floating Caliper Delco — Single Anchor	Delco — Dual Piston	Bendix or Delco Dual Diaphragm [4] Bendix Hydroboost
G30 Front Rear	Disc Drum	[3] Delco — Floating Caliper Delco — Single Anchor	Delco — Dual Piston [6] Bendix-Mini	Bendix or Delco Dual Diaphragm
K30 Front Rear	Disc Drum	Bendix — Sliding Caliper Delco — Single Anchor	Delco — Dual Piston	[4] Bendix Hydroboost
P30 Motor Home Chassis Front Rear	Disc [5] Drum	Bendix — Sliding Caliper Delco — Single Anchor	Delco — Dual Piston	Bendix Hydroboost
P30 Forward Control Front Rear	Disc [5] Drum	[3] Bendix — Floating Caliper Delco — Single Anchor	Delco — Dual Piston	Bendix or Delco Dual Piston [4] Bendix Hydroboost
S10/15 Front Rear	Disc Drum	Bendix — Sliding Caliper Delco — Single Anchor	Delco — Quick Take-Up	Bendix, Delco Single or Dual Diaphragm

[1] — Vehicle series numbers used in this chart are abbreviated for common reference to Chevrolet and GMC models.
[2] — All models with Low-Drag calipers use Delco Quick Take-Up master cylinder.
[3] — Models with Hydroboost use Bendix Sliding Caliper disc brakes.
[4] — Standard on some models, optional on others.
[5] — Bendix Sliding Caliper disc brakes used on models with 11,000 lb. rear axle.
[6] — Used on models with Hydroboost.

JEEP

BRAKE SYSTEM APPLICATIONS

Application	Type	Make & Design	Master Cylinder	Power Unit
"CJ" & Scrambler Front Rear	Disc Drum	Bendix — Sliding Caliper [1] Bendix — Single Anchor	Delco Dual Piston	Delco — Single Diaphragm
Cherokee, Wagoneer & J10 Pickup Front Rear	Disc Drum	Delco — Floating Caliper [2] Delco — Single Anchor	Delco Quick Take-Up	Delco — Single Diaphragm
J20 Pickup Front Rear	Disc Drum	Delco — Floating Caliper [2] Delco — Single Anchor	Delco Quick Take-Up	Delco — Tandem Diaphragm

[1] — Cable type adjuster.
[2] — Lever type adjuster.

Brake Servicing

HYDRAULIC BRAKE BLEEDING

DESCRIPTION

Hydraulic system bleeding is necessary any time air has been introduced into system. Bleed brakes at all 4 wheels if master cylinder lines have been disconnected or master cylinder has been run dry. Bleed brakes with pressure bleeding equipment or by manually pumping brake pedal while using bleeder tubes.

NOTE: **Hydro-Boost bleeding is a different procedure than hydraulic brake bleeding. See Hydro-Boost bleeding in Hydro-Boost article in this Section.**

HYDRAULIC CONTROL VALVES

On disc brake equipped vehicles, metering section of hydraulic control valve must be deactivated before bleeding to permit fluid to flow to front brakes. This is especially important when pressure bleeding.

Use pressure tool when applicable (C-4121, Chrysler Corp; J-23709, General Motors and Jeep with "D" type valve; J-26869, for Jeep with "W" type combination valve). If tool is not available, hold valve open by hand. DO NOT use "C" clamp or other non-yeilding device to hold valve open.

PRESSURE TANK BLEEDING

1) Clean master cylinder cap and surrounding area. Remove cap. With pressure tank at least 1/2 full, connect to master cylinder with adapters. Attach bleeder hose to first bleeder valve to be serviced. See Bleeding Sequence table.

2) Place other end of hose in clean glass jar partially filled with clean brake fluid so end of hose is submerged in fluid. Open release valve on pressure bleeder. Follow equipment manufacturers pressure instructions unless noted below.

3) Unscrew bleeder valve 3/4-1 turn noting fluid flow. When fluid flowing from cylinder to jar is free of bubbles, close bleeder valve securely. Bleed remaining cylinders in correct sequence and in the same manner. Remove tool from control valve.

PRESSURE BLEEDER SETTINGS

Application	psi (kg/cm²)
Chrysler Corp.	35 (2.5)
Ford	10-30 (.7-2.0)
General Motors	20-25 (1.5-1.8)
Jeep	...

MANUAL BLEEDING

NOTE: **When bleeding disc brakes, air may tend to cling to caliper walls. Lightly tap caliper, while bleeding, to aid in removal of air.**

1) Fill master cylinder. Install bleeder hose to first bleeder valve to be serviced. See Bleeding Sequence table. Submerge other end of hose in clean glass jar partially filled with clean brake fluid.

2) Open bleeder valve 3/4-1 turn. Depress brake pedal slowly through full travel. Close bleeder valve and release pedal. Repeat procedure until flow of fluid shows no signs of air bubbles.

Fig. 1: Wheel Cylinder Bleeding Procedure

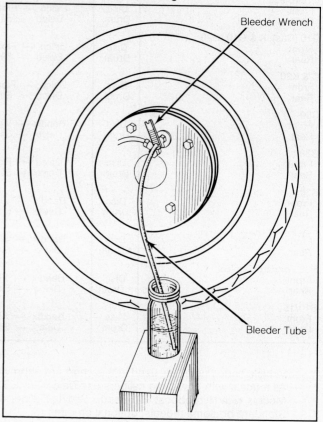

BLEEDING SEQUENCE

Before bleeding system, exhaust all vacuum from power unit by depressing brake pedal several times. Bleed master cylinder if equipped with bleeder screws. Bleed slave cylinder on vehicles equipped with remote mount power assist units. Bleed wheel cylinders and calipers in sequence. See Bleeding Sequence table.

BLEEDING SEQUENCE

Application	Sequence
Chrysler Corp.	RR, LR, RF, LF
Ford	RR, LR, RF, LF
General Motors	RR, LR, RF, LF
Jeep .... RR, LR, RF, LF, Master Cyl. Lines	

HYDRAULIC SYSTEM CONTROL VALVES

DESCRIPTION

All vehicles have some type of hydraulic system control valve or warning switch within the brake hydraulic system.

Unit is usually mounted on frame or firewall adjacent to master cylinder. The front and rear brake lines are routed through this valve to their respective caliper or wheel cylinder.

Vehicles with drum brakes on all wheels use a pressure differential brake warning switch only. Vehicles equipped with disc brakes use a combination pressure differential warning switch with a proportioning valve, or a metering valve, or both.

Fig. 1: Sectional View of Typical Hydraulic Control Valve

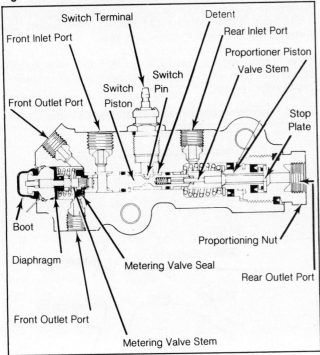

OPERATION

PRESSURE DIFFERENTIAL BRAKE WARNING SWITCH

This switch is used to warn vehicle operator that one of the hydraulic systems has failed. When hydraulic pressure is equal in both front and rear systems, switch piston remains centered and does not contact terminal in switch.

If pressure fails in system, hydraulic pressure moves piston toward failed side. Shoulder of piston then contacts switch terminal to provide gound for brake warning light.

PROPORTIONING VALVE

Valve operates by restricting, at a given ratio, hydraulic pressure to rear brakes when system hydraulic pressure reaches a certain point. This improves front-to-rear brake balance at high speed braking, when a percentage of rear weight is transferred to front wheels.

Valve reduces rear brake pressure, and delays rear wheel skid. On light brake application, valve allows full hydraulic pressure to rear brakes.

METERING VALVE

This valve holds off pressure to front disc brakes to allow rear drum brake shoes to overcome return spring pressure and make contact with rear drums. This prevents locking front brakes on slippery or icy surfaces under light braking conditions. Valve has no effect on front brake pressure during hard braking conditions.

TESTING

BRAKE WARNING LIGHT SYSTEM

Electrical Circuit

Disconnect wire from switch terminal and ground wire to chassis. Turn ignition switch "ON". Warning light should come on. If lamp does not light, bulb or wiring circuit is defective. Replace bulb or wiring as necessary. If lamp lights, turn off ignition and reconnect wire.

Warning Light Switch

1) Attach a bleeder hose to bleeder screw at either rear brake. Immerse other end of hose in container with brake fluid. Turn ignition "ON". Open bleeder screw while pressure is being applied to brake pedal. Warning lamp should light. Close bleeder screw before pressure is released from pedal.

2) Reapply pedal pressure (moderate to heavey). Light should go out. Repeat test on front brake system. System should function in same manner. Turn ignition "OFF". If lamp does not light during test on either system, but electrical system checked good, the warning light switch portion of valve is defective.

SERVICING

All hydraulic system switches and valves are non-adjustable and non-serviceable. If any part of valve is found to be defective, entire unit must be replaced.

RESETTING SWITCH

After failed side of system has been repaired, applying brake pedal with moderate force will hydraulically recenter piston and turn off brake warning light.

REMOVAL & INSTALLATION

Removal

Disconnect brake warning light connection at switch. Disconnect all brake hydraulic lines at valve. Cover open ends of line to prevent dirt from entering system. Remove valve mounting bolts. Remove valve from vehicle.

Installation

To install, reverse removal procedures. Bleed brake system. *See HYDRAULIC BRAKE BLEEDING in this Section.* Recenter brake warning light piston as previously outlined.

Master Cylinders
BENDIX/DELCO-MORAINE DUAL PISTON

Chevrolet, Dodge, GMC, Jeep, Plymouth

NOTE: Some models may use other units. See Brake System Applications.

DESCRIPTION

Bendix and Delco-Moraine tandem dual piston master cylinders are single casting type with front and rear pistons and a separate reservoir and outlet for each piston.

Rear piston is operated by push rod connected to brake pedal. Front piston is operated by rear piston. In a combination disc and drum system, reservoir which feeds disc brakes is larger to compensate for larger displacement of disc caliper cylinder.

Master cylinders for General Motors and some Jeep vehicles incorporate a quick take-up feature, that delivers a large volume of fluid at low pressure upon initial application of brakes. This fluid quickly displaces the retracted caliper, placing brake linings in contact with brake rotors and drums.

ADJUSTMENT

BRAKE PEDAL

NOTE: Adjustment for vehicles equipped with power boosters is accomplished at power booster. See Power Brake Units in this Section.

Vehicles without power assisted brakes incorporate a non-adjustable push rod. Brake pedal push rod length is preset by manufacturer.

REMOVAL & INSTALLATION

MASTER CYLINDER
Removal

1) Disconnect front and rear hydraulic brake lines at master cylinder, and cover ends to prevent entry of foreign matter.

2) On vehicles without power assist units, disconnect brake pedal push rod at brake pedal. Remove master cylinder retaining bolts, and remove cylinder assembly from vehicle.

Installation

1) Position master cylinder on vehicle and install cylinder retaining bolts. Connect front and rear hydraulic brake lines to cylinder.

2) Connect brake pedal push rod, if removed. Fill reservoir with clean brake fluid, and bleed hydraulic system. *See Hydraulic Brake Bleeding in this Section.*

OVERHAUL

MASTER CYLINDER
Disassembly

1) Clean outside of cylinder thoroughly and remove cover. Drain fluid, and turn cylinder over, pump piston to remove any remaining fluid.

2) On Jeep Cherokee, Truck, and Wagoneer models, remove reservoir with a pry bar. Remove reservoir grommets, retaining ring and quick-take-up valve.

3) On manual brake models, remove boot from cylinder to uncover push rod retainer. Pry up retainer tab to release retainer.

4) On all models, push piston down into cylinder bore. Remove secondary piston stop bolt from front fluid reservoir (if equipped). Remove snap ring from groove in cylinder bore.

5) Remove both piston assemblies. Remove any internal parts remaining in bore. On Jeep "CJ" and Scrambler models, remove push rod from primary piston. Remove and discard all rubber parts from piston assemblies.

6) On General Motors and Jeep "CJ" and Scrambler models, enlarge holes in tube seats using a 13/16" drill. Place a large flat washer over outlets and thread a 1/4" x 20 x 3/4" screw into seat.

7) Remove seat, screw and washer. On all other Jeep models, thread a 6 x 32 x 5/8" self tapping screw into tube seat, and push upward with 2 screwdrivers to remove seat.

Fig. 1: Removing Tube Seat from Master Cylinder

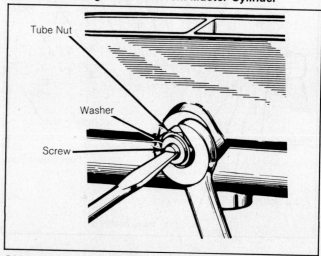

GM and Jeep "CJ" and Scrambler models only.

Inspection

Inspect cylinder bore for scoring or corrosion. Staining which has not pitted or roughened surface of cylinder can be removed with crocus cloth. If cylinder bore is scored, pitted or corroded, it should be replaced.

Reassembly

1) Install replacement tube seats by threading a spare brake line tube nut into hole. Turn nut in until tube seat bottoms. Do not cock tube seat in hole.

2) Remove nut and check for burrs which may have been loosened by nut. Install piston cups on secondary piston, with cup lips facing away from each other.

3) Install seal protector, piston seal, spring retainer and return spring on secondary piston. Install seal so lip faces interior of master cylinder when installed.

4) Lubricate cylinder bore with clean brake fluid and install secondary piston assembly. Luricate primary piston seals and install primary piston assembly in bore.

5) Hold primary piston down in bore and install snap ring in groove in bore. Install secondary piston stop

BENDIX/DELCO-MORAINE DUAL PISTON (Cont.)

bolt (if equipped). Install master cylinder reservoir, grommets and quick take-up valve (if removed).

6) Install master cylinder cover and new diaphragm. On vehicles with manual brakes, assemble

brake pedel push rod through retainer (if used), and push retainer over end of master cylinder. Install rubber boot over push rod.

Fig. 2: Exploded View of Typical Delco-Moraine Master Cylinder

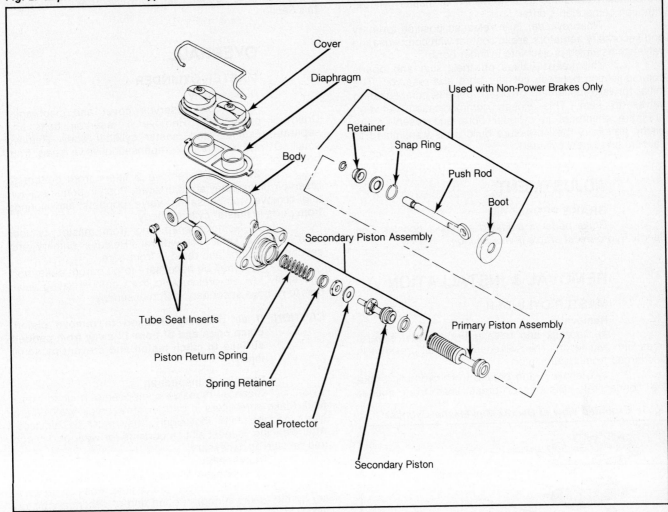

Bendix master cylinders are similar.

Master Cylinders

BENDIX MINI-MASTER

Chevrolet, GMC

DESCRIPTION

Functions of the Bendix Mini-Master cylinder are basically the same as a conventional master cylinder although components differ.

When cylinder is in released position, primary and secondary actuators are in contact with compensating valve stems which project into cylinder bore.

This keeps valves off their seat and opens communication between cylinder bore and reservoir. The initial forward movement of piston permits compensating valves to seat. This closes communication between pressure chambers in cylinder bore and reservoir. As piston travels further, pressure build up is transmitted to calipers and wheel cylinders.

ADJUSTMENT

BRAKE PEDAL

Brake pedal is adjusted at power booster. See *Bendix Hydro-Boost article in this Section.*

REMOVAL & INSTALLATION

MASTER CYLINDER

Removal

1) Depress and release brake pedal several times with engine off. This will ensure that all pressure is discharged from accumulator.

2) Clean dirt and grease from hydraulic brake line connections. Disconnect brake lines from master cylinder. Remove retaining nuts and washers from master cylinder to Hydro-Boost. Remove master cylinder. Cover open ends of brake lines.

Installation

To install, reverse removal procedures. Bleed brake hydraulic system. *See Hydraulic Brake Bleeding in this Section.*

OVERHAUL

MASTER CYLINDER

Disassembly

1) Remove reservoir cover and diaphragm. Drain all brake fluid. Remove 4 reservoir bolts and separate reservoir and master cylinder body. Remove small "O" ring and both compensating valve seals from bottom of reservoir.

2) DO NOT remove 2 filters from bottom of reservoir unless they are damaged. Push in primary piston and remove compensating valve poppets and springs from ports in master cylinder body.

3) Remove snap ring from master cylinder bore using a small screwdriver. Release primary and secondary pistons and remove from bore.

4) It may be necessary to plug front outlet port and apply low air pressure to front compensating valve port to remove secondary piston assembly.

CAUTION: If air pressure is used to remove piston, place open end of bore 1" away from padded surface to catch piston and prevent personal injury.

Cleaning & Inspection

Clean all reusable components in clean brake fluid. Make sure filters in bottom of reservoir are clean. If filters do not clean thoroughly, they must be replaced. After cleaning, inspect all components for wear or damage and replace as necessary.

Reassembly

1) Lubricate primary and secondary pistons, and cylinder bore with clean brake fluid. Position secondary spring (short spring) in open end of secondary piston actuator.

2) Position return spring (long spring) on projection at rear of secondary piston. Place secondary piston, actuator end first, in master cylinder bore and press assembly into bottom of bore. Insert primary piston, actuator end first into bore.

3) Using a smooth round end tool with snap ring placed over it, depress piston in bore. Install snap ring in groove. Place compensating valve seals and small "O" ring seal in recesses in bottom of reservoir. Make sure seals are fully seated.

4) Depress pistons and place compensating valve springs and poppets in valve ports. With piston still depressed, place reservoir in position. Install bolts and tighten to 12-15 ft. lbs. (16-20 N.m).

Fig. 1: Exploded View of Bendix Mini-Master Cylinder

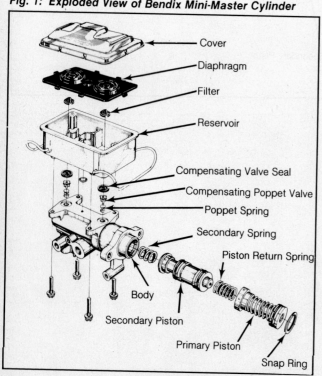

- Cover
- Diaphragm
- Filter
- Reservoir
- Compensating Valve Seal
- Compensating Poppet Valve
- Poppet Spring
- Secondary Spring
- Piston Return Spring
- Body
- Secondary Piston
- Primary Piston
- Snap Ring

CHRYSLER CORP. DUAL PISTON — ALUMINUM

Dodge, Plymouth

DESCRIPTION

The aluminum tandem dual piston master cylinder is of the venting type with nylon reservoir. The front and rear pistons have separate reservoirs and outlets.

The reservoir may be filled from 1 cap because reservoirs are connected at the top. Air entrapment is controlled by cup expanders in rear brake wheel cylinders. No residual pressure valves are installed on this master cylinder.

REMOVAL & INSTALLATION

POWER BRAKE MASTER CYLINDER
Removal

Disconnect primary and secondary brake lines from master cylinder and plug outlets. Remove nuts that retain cylinder to power brake unit. Slide master cylinder straight out and away from brake unit.

Installation

Position master cylinder over studs of power brake unit, aligning power cylinder brake push rod with cylinder piston. Install and tighten nuts. Connect both brake lines and bleed system. *See Hydraulic Brake Bleeding in this Section.*

MANUAL BRAKE MASTER CYLINDER
Removal

1) Disconnect primary and secondary brake lines from master cylinder and plug outlets. Disconnect stop light switch mounting bracket under instrument panel.

2) Grasp brake pedal and pull back to disengage push rod from master cylinder. This will destroy push rod retention grommet. Remove nuts retaining master cylinder to cowl panel. Slide master cylinder straight out and away from cowl.

Installation

1) Install new push rod retention grommet. Postion master cylinder to cowl panel, install, and tighten nuts. Connect brake lines and tighten.

2) From under instrument panel, moisten push rod grommet with water and align push rod with master cylinder piston. Using brake pedal, apply pressure to fully seat push rod into piston.

3) Install master cylinder boot and connect stop light switch mounting bracket. Bleed system. *See Hydraulic Brake Bleeding in this Section.*

CAUTION: Use extra care not to cross threads when installing brake lines to master cylinder. Torque to specifications only.

OVERHAUL

MASTER CYLINDER
Disassembly

1) Clean outside of reservoir and cylinder body. Remove reservoir caps and empty brake fluid. Position cylinder body in vise and rock reservoir from side to side, to remove from cylinder.

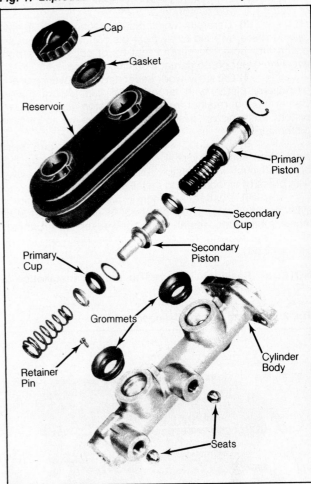

Fig. 1: Exploded View of Aluminum Master Cylinder

Cap

Gasket

Reservoir

Primary Piston

Secondary Cup

Primary Cup

Secondary Piston

Grommets

Retainer Pin

Cylinder Body

Seats

2) Remove grommets and use needle nose pliers to remove secondary piston retainer pin (if equipped), from inside master cylinder body. Remove snap ring and slide primary piston out of bore.

3) Tap open end of cylinder on bench to remove secondary piston. If piston sticks, use air pressure to force piston from cylinder. New cups must be installed if air pressure is used.

NOTE: If cup on primary piston is damaged or worn, a new primary piston must be installed.

4) If brass tube seats are damaged or worn, use screw extractor to remove seats.

Inspection

1) Wash master cylinder bore with brake fluid. Inspect bore for pitting, scratches or scoring.

NOTE: Do not hone aluminum master cylinder. If bore is found unserviceable, cylinder must be replaced.

2) Inspect piston for corrosion and scoring, replace as necessary. During overhaul, all rubber parts must be replaced.

Reassembly

1) Dip master cylinder and all components in clean brake fluid. Assembling seals dry could ruin seals.

2) Install check flow washer on secondary piston and carefully work primary cup on end with lip

CHRYSLER CORP. DUAL PISTON — ALUMINUM (Cont.)

facing away from piston. Slide cup retainer over front end of piston followed by spring.

3) Carefully work piston secondary cup into cylinder bore, with lip away from piston. Install secondary piston into bore. Be careful that lip of cups enters bore evenly in order not to damage sealing of cups.

4) Carefully work secondary cup over rear end of primary piston with larger lip of cup toward piston. Center spring retainer of primary piston on secondary piston. Push piston assemblies into bore up to primary piston cup.

5) Carefully work cup into bore and push piston into secondary seal. Work lip of primary cup into bore and push in on piston until seated. Depress piston with brass or wood rod and install snap ring.

6) Postion secondary piston retainer pin in cylinder housing and tap or press in until firmly seated. Install tube seats. Install housing-to-reservoir grommets and, using rocking motion, install reservoir on master cylinder body.

NOTE: Reservoir is keyed to prevent installation in wrong direction.

Fig. 2: Bleeding Master Cylinder

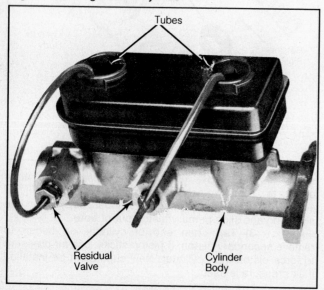

Bleeding Cylinder

1) Clamp master cylinder in vise and attach bleeder tubes (C-4029). Attach residual valves on outlet of each bleeder tube.

2) Fill reservoir with fluid. Using brass or wood rod, depress push rod slowly and allow pistons to return under spring pressure. Repeat until all air is expelled. Remove tubes, plug outlets and install caps.

TIGHTENING SPECIFICATIONS

Application	Ft. Lbs. (N.m)
Master Cylinder Retaining Nuts	17 (23)
Pedal Link Bolt	30 (41)
Brake Line Tube Nuts	12 (17)

CHRYSLER CORP. DUAL PISTON — CAST IRON

Dodge, Plymouth

DESCRIPTION

This tandem dual piston master cylinder is of the venting type, with reservoirs in a single casting and one outlet for each reservoir. Rear piston is operated by push rod connected to brake pedal. Front piston is operated by rear piston.

REMOVAL & INSTALLATION

MASTER CYLINDER

Removal

1) Disconnect front and rear hydraulic brake lines at master cylinder. Remove bolt retaining push rod to pedal linkage.

2) Remove master cylinder retaining bolts and lift master cylinder from vehicle.

Installation

1) Position master cylinder on vehicle and install cylinder retaining bolts. Tighten to 200 INCH lbs. (22.7 N.m). Connect front and rear hydraulic brake lines, and connect push rod to brake pedal linkage.

2) Fill reservoir with clean brake fluid and bleed entire brake system. *See Hydraulic Brake Bleeding in this Section.*

OVERHAUL

MASTER CYLINDER

Disassembly

1) Clean outside of cylinder and remove cover to drain brake fluid. Use screw extractor to remove tube seats. Remove snap ring from open end of cylinder and slide washer out.

2) Carefully remove primary piston assembly and slide secondary piston from cylinder. Clean all parts in solvent and blow dry with compressed air.

Inspection

1) Inspect cylinder bore for scoring or pitting. Light scratches or minor corrosion can usually be removed by using crocus cloth.

2) Deep scratches or scoring may be honed, provided bore diameter is not increase more that .002" (.05 mm). If this limit is exceeded, master cylinder must be replaced.

3) Check pistons for scoring, scratches and corrosion. Pistons must be replaced if any of these conditions exist. Replace all rubber parts when overhauling master cylinder.

Reassembly

1) Dip all components in brake fluid before reassembly. Carefully slide secondary piston assembly into cylinder bore. Slide primary piston into bore, hold washer in position and install snap ring. Install tube seats.

2) Clamp master cylinder in a vise, being careful not to damage housing. Attach bleed tubes (C-4029) to outlet ports of cylinder, with ends of tubes placed in master cylinder reservoirs.

3) Fill reservoirs with clean brake fluid and depress push rod slowly. Allow pistons to return to normal position under spring pressure.

4) Repeat procedure until all air bubbles are expelled. Remove bleeding tubes, and install cylinder cover and diaphragm. Remove cylinder from vise.

Fig. 1: Exploded View of Cast Iron Master Cylinder

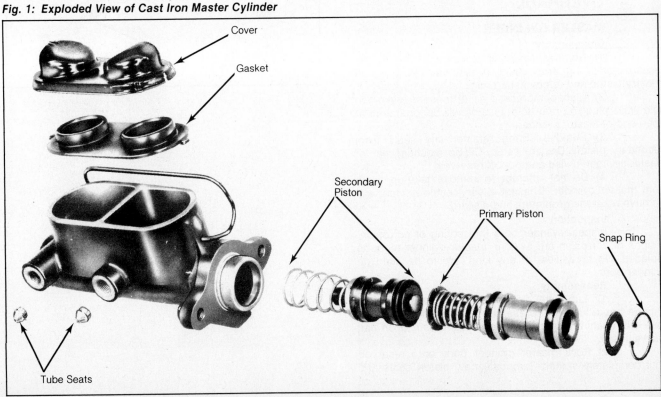

Master Cylinders

DELCO QUICK TAKE-UP

Chevrolet, GMC, Jeep

DESCRIPTION

The Delco Quick Take-Up master cylinder is a 2 piece unit with cast master cylinder body and plastic fluid reservoir. It is designed for use with systems utilizing low drag calipers.

This master cylinder includes a quick take-up valve. This valve delivers a large volume of fluid, at low pressure, upon initial application of brakes. The fluid quickly displaces retracted calipers, placing brake linings in contact with brake rotors and drums.

ADJUSTMENT

System is adjusted at power booster. *See Power Brake Units in this Section.*

REMOVAL & INSTALLATION

MASTER CYLINDER

Removal

1) Depress and release brake pedal several times, with engine off, to release any vacuum in power unit. Clean dirt and grease from brake line connections.

2) Disconnect brake lines from master cylinder. Plug open end of lines. Remove 2 master cylinder-to-power unit retaining nuts. Remove master cylinder.

Installation

To install, reverse removal procedures. Bleed hydraulic system. *See Hydraulic Brake Bleeding in this Section.*

OVERHAUL

MASTER CYLINDER

Disassembly

1) Remove reservoir cover and diaphragm. Discard remaining brake fluid in reservoir. Push in on primary piston and remove snap ring.

2) Apply compressed air at forward brake line hole while plugging rear hole. Pistons will be forced out at open end of master cylinder.

3) Remove spring retainer and seals from secondary piston. Discard seals. Clamp mounting ear of master cylinder in vise and pry off reservoir.

4) Do not attempt to remove take-up valve from master cylinder. It is not a serviceable component. Remove reservoir grommets and discard.

Inspection

Inspect cylinder bore for scoring or corrosion. If signs of corrosion are evident, master cylinder must be replaced. No abrasives, of any kind, are to be used on cylinder bore.

Reassembly

1) Lubricate new reservoir grommets with silicone brake lube and press into master cylinder. Make sure grommets are properly seated. Lay reservoir on flat, hard surface.

2) Rock master cylinder body onto reservoir until completely seated. Lubricate new piston seals and

install on secondary piston, with lip of seals towards ends of piston. Install spring retainer.

3) Install secondary piston spring and secondary piston assembly in master cylinder. Lubricate primary piston seals with clean brake fluid.

4) Install primary piston in master cylinder. Press in piston and install snap ring. Fit diaphragm in reservoir cover and install cover.

Fig. 1: Exploded View of Quick Take-Up Master Cylinder

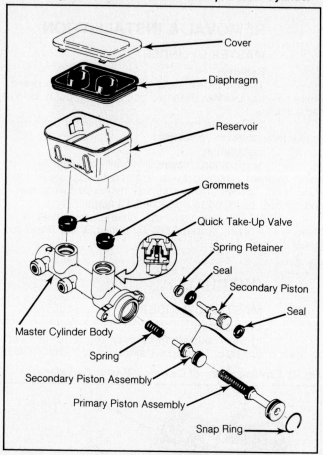

- Cover
- Diaphragm
- Reservoir
- Grommets
- Quick Take-Up Valve
- Spring Retainer
- Seal
- Secondary Piston
- Seal
- Master Cylinder Body
- Spring
- Secondary Piston Assembly
- Primary Piston Assembly
- Snap Ring

FORD DUAL PISTON MASTER CYLINDER

DESCRIPTION

Ford tandem dual piston master cylinder is a single casting with front and rear piston and a separate reservoir with an outlet for each piston.

Rear piston is operated by a push rod connected to brake pedal. Front, or floating, piston is operated by rear piston.

In a combination drum and disc system, reservoir which feeds disc brakes is larger, to correspond with large size of disc brake caliper cylinders. Master cylinder outlet which feeds drum brake has a residual valve under tube seat. Disc brake outlet has no valve, since disc brakes must not have any residual pressure.

Fig. 1: Exploded View of Master Cylinder Assembly

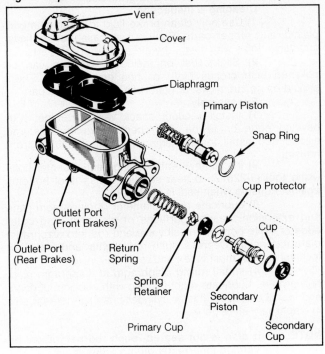

ADJUSTMENT

BRAKE PEDAL

On dual piston master cylinder or brake mounted vacuum booster equipped vehicles, brake systems are designed to permit full stroke of master cylinder, therefore no brake pedal clearance adjustment is required.

NOTE: Pedal free-travel will not be correct if power brake booster push rod clearance is not correct. See appropriate Power Brake Unit article in this Section.

REMOVAL & INSTALLATION

MASTER CYLINDER
Removal (Power Brakes)

1) Depress brake pedal to expel vacuum from brake booster. Disconnect all hydraulic lines at master cylinder.

2) Remove nuts retaining master cylinder to brake booster and remove master cylinder.

Removal (Manual Brakes)

1) Disconnect wires from stoplight switch. Remove retaining nut, shoulder bolt, spacers and bushing securing master cylinder push rod to brake pedal.

2) Remove stoplight switch from brake pedal. Disconnect fluid lines. Remove master cylinder to dash panel screws and remove master cylinder. Remove master cylinder push rod boot.

Installation

To install, reverse removal procedures, centralize pressure differential valve and bleed system. *See Hydraulic Brake Bleeding in this Section.*

OVERHAUL

MASTER CYLINDER
Disassembly

1) With master cylinder removed from vehicle, clean outside of cylinder, remove filler cap and diaphragm, and drain any remaining fluid in cylinder.

2) Remove dust boot (if equipped). Remove snap ring retaining piston assemblies. Remove push rod (if equipped), and primary piston assembly from cylinder bore.

3) Apply air pressure to forward outlet port of cylinder and carefully blow secondary piston assembly out of bore. DO NOT place fingers in front of piston.

4) Remove return spring, spring retainer, cup protector and cups from secondary piston.

Inspection

1) Clean all parts with denatured alcohol, and blow dry with compressed air. Inspect all parts for chipping, excessive wear, or damage.

2) Check all recesses, openings, and internal passages to be sure they are clean and open. Inspect master cylinder bore for signs of corrosion, pitting, etching, or scoring.

3) If any of these conditions exist, manufacturer recommends replacement of master cylinder assembly.

Reassembly

1) Lubricate all components including cylinder bore with clean brake fluid prior to assembly. Install 2 secondary cups, back-to-back, on secondary piston.

2) Assemble cup protector, primary cup, spring retainer and secondary piston return spring on opposite end of piston. Insert secondary piston assembly into bore in cylinder.

3) On vehicles equipped with standard brakes, position boot, snap ring and push rod retainer on push rod, and seat assembly in primary piston.

4) Install primary piston assembly into cylinder bore. On vehicles equipped with power brakes, position stop plate and snap ring on primary piston. Install primary piston and snap ring to cylinder bore.

Bleeding

1) Before installing master cylinder to vehicle, bleed unit. Support assembly in a vise and fill both reservoirs with fluid. Install plugs in brake outlet ports.

2) Loosen plug in rear outlet port and depress primary piston slowly to force air out of cylinder. Tighten plug while piston is depressed to prevent air from entering cylinder.

3) Repeat procedure until no air is evident. Proceed to the front outlet port when rear is bled, ensuring that rear plug is tight. Piston travel will be greatly restricted when all air is expelled. Remove plugs, install cover and diaphragm.

Power Brake Units

BENDIX SINGLE DIAPHRAGM

Chevrolet, Ford, GMC

DESCRIPTION

This unit uses engine manifold vacuum and atmospheric pressure to assist braking. Vacuum power unit contains power piston assembly, which houses control valve, reaction mechanism and return spring.

Control valve consists of air valve, floating control valve assembly, and push rod. Reaction mechanism includes reaction plate and levers. A vacuum check valve is mounted in front housing for connection to vacuum source.

REMOVAL & INSTALLATION

NOTE: **Power brake unit can be removed without removing master cylinder or disconnecting brake lines.**

Removal

1) Disconnect vacuum line from check valve or power unit. Remove nuts securing master cylinder to power unit.

2) Pull master cylinder forward away from unit. Disconnect brake pedal from push rod. Remove power unit-to-firewall bolts and remove unit.

Installation

To install, reverse removal procedures.

OVERHAUL

NOTE: **Only Chevrolet and GMC recommend overhaul of power brake unit.**

Disassembly

1) Scribe mark on housings for reassembly. Remove front housing seal and piston rod. Attach assembly to holding fixture (J-22805). Align tool so that check valve in front housing is not damaged.

2) Loosen lock nut and remove push rod clevis and lock nut (if equipped). Remove dust boot retainer, dust boot and silencer from diaphragm plate extension.

3) Partially straighten 4 deepest tabs on rear housing. Place spanner wrench (J-9504) over studs on rear housing and attach with nuts and washers. Press down on wrench and rotate rear housing clockwise to seperate. Remove wrench.

CAUTION: **Housings are under spring pressure.**

4) Remove air filter from diaphragm plate extension. Remove diaphragm from groove in diaphragm plate. Handle diaphragm carefully.

5) Hold diaphragm plate so that push rod is in horizontal position. Depress rod slightly and rotate piston until air valve lock falls from diaphragm plate hub. Remove reaction disc from diaphragm plate bore, using push rod to push disc from seat.

CAUTION: **Remove rear seal only if a new one is available. Do not reuse old seal.**

6) Remove rear shell bearing seal with punch. Remove vacuum check valve and grommet.

Cleaning & Inspection

1) Use only clean brake fluid to clean all metal, plastic, and rubber parts. Blow out all passages, orifices, and valve holes with clean, dry air, and air dry all parts.

2) Slight rust on inside of housing can be polished with crocus cloth or fine emery cloth. There should be no cut, nicks, or distortion of any rubber part.

Reassembly

1) Install vacuum check valve grommet with beveled edge on inside. Dip check valve in denatured alcohol and install. Install holding fixture (J-22805) on front housing.

2) Install new rear housing seal in center hole, using tool (J-22677) to seat seal in recess (tool bottoms against housing when seal is in place).

3) Lubricate outer diameter of diaphragm plate and extension, bearing surfaces of air valve, and outer edge of valve poppet. Install valve and rod into diaphragm plate extension. Depress push rod slightly and install air lock valve (lock must index and retain air valve).

4) Install rolling diaphragm in diaphragm plate hub groove. Lubricate reaction disc with silicone lubricant and install disc (use master cylinder push rod to seat disc in diaphragm plate bore).

NOTE: **If disc is not seated, push rod height will be gauged incorrectly during adjustment.**

5) Lubricate inside of bearing seal and diaphragm bead contact surface of rear shell. Install diaphragm plate assembly in rear housing. Place air filter element over push rod and into diaphragm plate extension.

6) Install filter retainer. With holding fixture in place, position spanner wrench (J-9504) over studs on

Fig. 1: Exploded View of Bendix Single Diaphragm Assembly

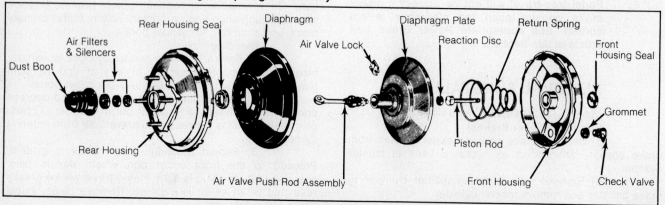

Rear Housing Seal — Diaphragm — Air Valve Lock — Diaphragm Plate — Return Spring — Reaction Disc — Front Housing Seal — Air Filters & Silencers — Dust Boot — Grommet — Rear Housing — Piston Rod — Air Valve Push Rod Assembly — Front Housing — Check Valve

BENDIX SINGLE DIAPHRAGM (Cont.)

rear housing and position front and rear housings together. Press down on wrench and rotate rear housing counterclockwise to lock housings.

7) Align scribe marks. Rebend tabs on rear housings. If tabs are cracked or broken, housing must be replaced. Remove wrench. Install air silencers over push rod end. Install push rod boot and boot retainer.

8) On clevis type push rods, install lock nut and push rod clevis. Lightly lubricate piston rod (except rounded end). Guide rod into center bore until fully seated against rection disc. Press front housing seal into housing until seal is bottomed in recess of housing.

ADJUSTMENT

PUSH ROD

Chevrolet & GMC

1) Place power unit in a vise with front housing up. Remove front seal to ensure all vacuum is released from unit. Place master cylinder rod, flat end first, in piston rod retainer. Press down on rod with 50 lbs. (23 kg) pressure to make sure rod is seated.

Fig. 2: Checking Push Rod Height

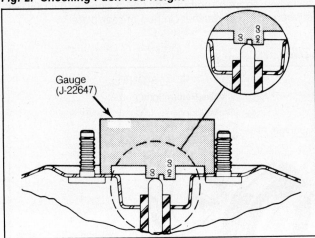

Chevrolet and GMC are checked with gauge (J-22647).

2) Place gauge (J-22647) over piston rod so it can be moved from left to right without contacting studs. The center section of gauge has 2 levels.

3) The piston rod should always contact the lower level and never contact the highest level. If the push rod does not contact gauge correctly, an adjustable push rod must be obtained.

4) Adjust locking screw on rod to obtain correct clearance with gauge. Apply silicone lubricant on the inside diameter of front housing seal and place seal in position in housing depression.

Ford

Check distance from outer end of push rod to front face of unit. Use a fabricated shop tool (gauge). *See Fig. 3.* Turn push rod screw in or out until length is .980-.995" (24.9-25.3 mm).

Fig. 3: Checking Push Rod Height

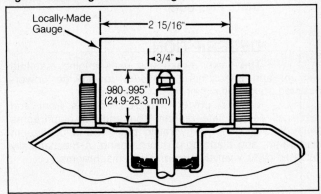

Ford models are checked with fabricated shop tool.

Power Brake Units

BENDIX TANDEM DIAPHRAGM

Chevrolet, Dodge, Ford,
GMC, Plymouth

DESCRIPTION

The power brake unit uses engine manifold vacuum and atmospheric pressure to provide power-assisted brake application.

Vacuum power chamber includes front and rear shell, center plate, tandem front and rear diaphragms (with plate assembly), hydraulic push rod and vacuum diaphragm, and diaphragm return spring. A mechanically actuated control valve is integral with diaphragms.

REMOVAL & INSTALLATION

NOTE: **Power brake unit can be removed without disconnecting brake lines at master cylinder.**

Removal

1) Disconnect vacuum line from check valve or power unit. Remove nuts securing master cylinder to power unit. Pull master cylinder forward away from unit.

2) On Dodge and Plymouth models, remove linkage bellcrank pivot bolt (if equipped). On all models, remove power brake unit from vehicle.

Installation

To install, reverse removal procedures. Before attaching master cylinder, check push rod for correct length.

OVERHAUL

NOTE: **Only Chevrolet and GMC recommend overhaul of power brake unit.**

Disassembly

1) Scribe a mark across front and rear housings for reassembly. Remove master cylinder push rod. Remove both seals from rod.

2) Remove vacuum check valve and grommet. Remove dust boot and silencer from operating valve rod.

3) Using an awl, remove dust guard retainer, dust guard and silencers from rear plate. Reinstall steel retainer on hub.

4) Squirt denatured alcohol down valve operating rod. This will lubricate rubber grommet in valve plunger.

5) Position 2 small blocks of wood on either side of air valve rod. Install end of air valve rod in a vise. Leave just enough room to position 2 open end wrenches between vise and retainer on hub of rear plate.

Fig. 1: Exploded View of Bendix Tandem Diaphragm Power Brake Unit

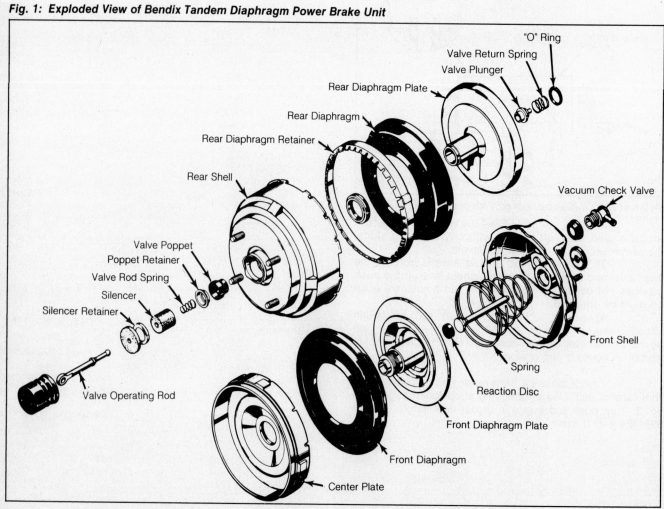

BENDIX TANDEM DIAPHRAGM (Cont.)

6) Using wrench closest to vise as a pry, force air valve off ball end of rod. Care must be taken not to damage plastic hub or allow vacuum cylinder to fall out.

7) Four of the 12 lances at the rear of the housing are deeper than the rest. These must be straightened so that they will clear cutouts in front housing.

NOTE: If the metal breaks while being straightened, the housing must be replaced.

8) Remove push rod and vacuum seal from front housing. Attach holding fixture (J-22805-01) to front housing studs. Ensure nuts and washers are tight.

9) Place unit and holding fixture in arbor press with rear of unit up. Place 1 1/2" wrench on holding fixture and allow wrench to contact rear of arbor press to prevent unit from turning. *See Fig. 2.*

Fig. 2: Using Arbor Press and Tools to Separate Bendix Tandem Diaphragm

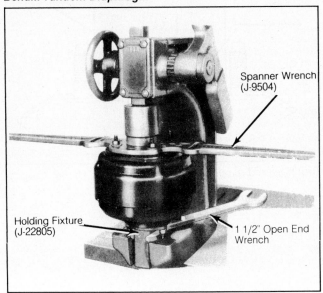

Spanner Wrench (J-9504)

Holding Fixture (J-22805)

1 1/2" Open End Wrench

10) Place spanner wrench (J-9504) over studs on rear of unit. Bolt wrench to studs. Place a piece of pipe (2" I.D., 3" long) over plastic diaphragm plate hub.

11) Place a piece of flat stock over pipe. Using arbor press, press down on pipe enough to relieve tension of diaphragm rubber lip and spring.

12) Rotate spanner wrench counterclockwise until lances in edge of rear housing are aligned with cutouts in front housing. Considerable effort may be required.

CAUTION: The return spring is compressed in power section and expands as housings are separated. If the housings will not separate, tap housings with a rubber hammer to break seal.

13) After housings are separated, slowly release press until spring tension has been released. Remove front housing and return spring.

14) Remove spanner wrench and holding fixture. Work edges of front diaphragm from under lances of rear housing. Remove vacuum assembly from rear housing. Care must be taken not to damage rear housing seal.

15) Wet rear diaphragm retainer with denatured alcohol. Remove retainer with fingers. Place a holding mandrel (J-22839) in a vise. Place the diaphragm and plate on tool. Seat tool in front plate hex opening.

16) Turn rear diaphragm plate counterclockwise. After both plates have been loosened, remove plates from tool. Place on a bench with front plate down. Unscrew and remove rear plate from front plate. Retain air valve plunger and valve return spring as plates are separated.

17) Remove square ring seal from shoulder of front diaphragm plate hub. Remove reaction disc from inside front diaphragm plate hub.

18) Carefully remove center plate from hub of front plate. Remove diaphragms from plate. Use a punch or a 1 1/4" socket to drive seal from rear housings.

Cleaning & Inspection

1) Clean all metal and rubber parts in alcohol. Remove rusted or corroded spots from metal areas with crocus or emery cloth. Dry all components with compressed air.

2) Just before reassembly, rewash all metal components in alcohol. Dry with compressed air. Use all parts included in kit and discard all old rubber parts.

Reassembly

1) Press new bearings and seal into rear housing. The flat rubber surface of the seal should be 5/16" below flat, inside surface of rear housing.

2) Place reaction disc in hub of front plate with small tip toward hole. Use a rounded rod to seat disc. Place holding mandrel (J-22839) in a vise.

3) Place front diaphragm on front plate with long fold of diaphragm down. Place seal protector (J-22733) over threads on front plate hub.

4) Apply silicone lubricant to front plate hub and to seal in center plate. Guide center plate, seal end first, onto front plate hub. Care must be taken not to damage center plate seal. Remove seal protector.

5) Apply silicone lubricant to bearing surfaces of air valve plunger. Care must be taken not to get lubricant on rubber grommet inside plunger.

6) Install square ring seal on shoulder of front plate hub. Install valve plunger return spring and plunger in base of front plate hub.

7) Set rear plate over front plate hub. By hand only, screw plate on hub. Make sure valve and spring are correctly aligned. Tighten plates to 12 ft. lbs. (16 N.m). Check plunger travel.

8) Assemble rear diaphragm to rear plate. Place lip of diaphragm in rear plate groove. Install diaphragm retainer over rear diaphragm and lip of center plate. Press retainer until it seats on shoulder of center plate.

9) Apply talcum powder to rear housing inside wall. Apply silicone lubricant to scalloped cutouts of front housing and seal in rear housing.

10) Install diaphragm and plate assembly into rear housing. Carefully guide rear plate hub through seal in rear housing.

11) Bosses on center plate must be aligned between lances in rear housing for reassembly. Work outer rim of front diaphragm into rear housing using a screwdriver. Make sure it is under lances in housing.

12) Attach holding fixture (J-22805-01) to front housing studs. Position front housing and holding fixture in arbor press.

Power Brake Units

BENDIX TANDEM DIAPHRAGM (Cont.)

13) Place spanner wrench (J-9504) over studs on rear housing. Bolt spanner wrench to studs. Place piece of pipe used during disassembly over plastic diaphragm plate hub. Place a piece of flat stock over pipe.

14) Install return spring so that small end of spring is against housing. Place rear housing over front housing and align scribe marks. Rotate spanner wrench clockwise until housings lock together.

15) Bend tabs in 4 deep lances back to original position. Remove spanner wrench and holding fixture.

16) Wet poppet valve with denatured alcohol. Install in rear plate hub, small end first. Wet poppet retainer with denatured alcohol and assemble with shoulder inside poppet.

17) Install retainer, filters and silencer over ridge on rod. Install return spring over ball end of operating valve rod. Wet grommet in valve plunger with denatured alcohol. Guide air valve rod into valve plunger.

18) Tap end of operating valve rod with plastic hammer to lock ball in grommet. Press filters and silencer into hub and install retainer on hub.

19) Install silencer in dust boot. Wet boot opening with denatured alcohol. Install over operating rod and rear housing flange. Install new check valve and grommet.

20) Apply silicone lubricant to piston end of push rod. Insert in front plate cavity. Twist rod to eliminate air bubbles at reaction disc. Assemble seal over push rod and press into recess front housing.

ADJUSTMENTS

PUSH ROD

Chevrolet & GMC

1) Place power unit in a vise with front housing up. Remove front seal to ensure all vacuum is released from unit. Place master cylinder rod, flat end first, in retainer. Press down on rod with 40-50 lbs. (18-22 kg) pressure to make sure rod is seated.

Fig. 3: Checking Push Rod Height Chevrolet and GMC

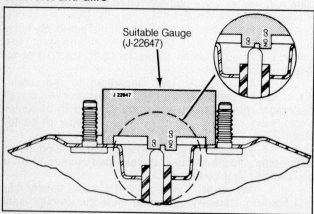

Suitable Gauge (J-22647)

J 22647

Push rod should clear GO side and should not touch NO-GO side.

2) Place measuring gauge (J-22647) over push rod so it can be moved from left to right without contacting studs. The center section of gauge has 2 levels. The push rod should always contact the lower level and never contact the highest level.

3) If the push rod does not contact gauge correctly, an adjustable push rod must be obtained. Adjust locking screw on rod to obtain correct clearance with gauge. Apply silicone lubricant on the inside diameter of front housing seal and place seal in position in housing depression.

Dodge & Plymouth

Push rod length is preset at factory and is non-adjustable.

Ford

Check distance from outer end of booster assembly push rod to front face of booster. Make a gauge to check that distance is .980-.995" (24.9-25.3 mm). *See Fig. 4.* Turn push rod screw in or out until specified length is obtained.

Fig. 4: Checking Push Rod Height on Ford Models

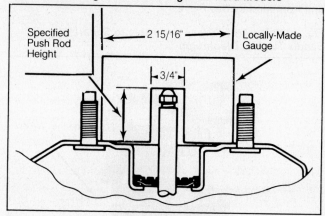

Specified Push Rod Height

2 15/16"

Locally-Made Gauge

3/4"

Turn push rod nut until it touches gauge.

Power Brake Units

BENDIX HYDRO-BOOST

Chevrolet, Dodge, GMC, Plymouth

NOTE: Bendix Hydro-Boost is standard on some models and optional on others. See Brake Application tables at the beginning of this Section.

DESCRIPTION

System utilizes power steering pump fluid pressure to operate booster. The assembly contains an open-center spool valve which controls pump pressure during braking. Also a lever mechanism is used to control the postion of the valve and a boost piston to operate master cylinder.

The unit also has a reserve system which stores sufficient fluid under pressure to provide at least 2 braking applications. Brakes can be applied manually if reserve system is depleted.

OPERATION

RELEASED POSITION (NO BRAKING)

With pedal released, spool valve return spring holds spool valve open. The spool valve allows fluid flow between power steering pump and power steering gear.

Fluid pressure is blocked from entering boost pressure chamber by lands on spool valve. Boost pressure chamber is vented through spool valve, to pump return port, and back to power steering pump.

BRAKING POSITION

As brake pedal is depressed, it moves pedal rod and spool valve. This closes fluid return to pump, and admits fluid into boost chamber from pressure port. Additional valve movement restricts flow between pump and steering gear.

As fluid pressure increases in boost chamber, it forces piston forward, actuating master cylinder piston and applying brakes. If fluid pressure is required for steering while braking, pump pressure will rise and spool valve will shift in an open direction allowing more fluid to flow to steering gear.

RESERVE SYSTEM

System consists of a charging valve, accumulator valve, and a spring loaded accumulator. Accumulator is integral with booster unit. System is open to pressure port of booster unit.

Charging valve has an orifice and ball check. Fluid from pump passes through orifice in valve, unseats ball check valve and enters accumulator. Ball check valve prevents reverse flow.

Accumulator valve is a poppet-type valve held closed by accumulator pressure. If no pump pressure is available, an actuator on spool valve sleeve opens accumulator valve. Fluid pressure can also enter accumulator from boost chamber through accumulator valve, when boost chamber pressure exceeds accumulator pressure.

A pressure relief valve vents accumulator to pump return port when pressure in accumulator exceeds approximately 1600 psi (112 kg/cm²).

ADJUSTMENT

BRAKE PEDAL
Chevrolet & GMC

1) Make adjustment in linkage until pedal travel is correct. Pedal travel is the distance pedal moves toward floor from a fully released position.

2) Pump pedal a minimum of 3 times with engine off before making measurement. Pedal travel should be 6" on all 4-wheel disc brake models, and 3 1/2" on all other models.

NOTE: Pedal adjustment procedure for Chrysler Corp. vehicles was not available.

TESTING

NOTE: Hydro-Boost cannot cause noisy brakes, fading brake pedal, or pulling brakes. If one of these conditions exists, other components of brake system are at fault.

PRELIMINARY CHECKS

Make the following checks, and repairs if necessary, before performing any test on the Hydro-Boost system.

1) Check fluid levels in master cylinder and power steering pump. Check power steering pump drive belt. Check power steering hoses for leaks or kinks.

2) Check for air in brake fluid or power steering fluid. Check engine idle speed. Check steering pump for proper pressure.

NOTE: If problem cannot be found in preliminary steps or tests, check areas of brake system that might cause condition. See Trouble Shooting at the beginning of this Section.

HYDRO-BOOST FUNCTIONAL TEST

1) Make all preliminary checks. Place transmission in Neutral and stop engine. Apply brake several times to deplete accumulator reserve.

2) Hold brake depressed with medium pressure. Start engine. Brake pedal should fall slightly, then push back against foot. If no action is felt, booster system is not operating properly.

ACCUMULATOR LEAKDOWN TEST

1) Start engine, and charge accumulator by either applying brake with heavy pedal force or turning steering wheel lock-to-lock.

2) Turn off engine and wait 1 hour. There should be 1 power-assisted brake application with engine off.

3) If reserve system will not retain a charge for 1 hour, but functions normally immediately following charging; or if accumulator can be heard charging and discharging but will not hold a charge, accumulator valves are at fault. Power piston/accumulator must be replaced.

NOTE: If Hydro-Boost is not functioning, ensure power steering system is operating before replacing Hydro-Boost unit.

Power Brake Units

BENDIX HYDRO-BOOST (Cont.)

Fig. 1: Hydro-Boost Fluid Flow Chart

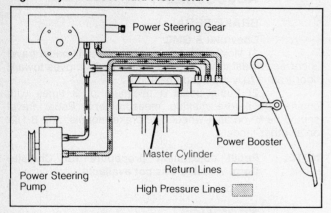

Power Steering Gear

Power Booster

Master Cylinder

Return Lines

High Pressure Lines

Power Steering Pump

REMOVAL & INSTALLATION

CHEVROLET & GMC

Removal

1) Depress and release brake pedal several times to ensure all pressure is discharged from accumulator. Disconnect hoses from booster.

2) Clean all dirt from hydraulic line connections at booster and master cylinder. Remove nuts that secure master cylinder to booster and support bracket. Support master cylinder, and cover exposed end with clean cloth.

NOTE: In most cases, it is not necessary to disconnect master cylinder brake lines to remove booster unit.

3) Remove booster pedal push rod cotter pin and disconnect push rod from brake pedal (Blazer and Pickups) or booster bracket pivot lever (Vans).

4) On Blazer and Pickup models, remove booster support bracket. On Vans, remove support braces. Remove booster bracket-to-firewall or support bracket nuts and remove booster assembly.

Installation

To install, reverse removal procedures. Lubricate pedal rod and linkage pivot bolts, pins, sleeves and bushings with lubricant (Delco Brake Lube). Bleed booster/power steering hydraulic system. Check brake pedal and stop lamp switch adjustment.

NOTE: Bleeding Hydro-Boost system is a separate procedure from bleeding the hydraulic systems. See Bleeding Hydro-Boost Systems in this article.

DODGE & PLYMOUTH

Removal

1) Depress brake pedal several times to be sure all pressure is released from accumulator. Remove nuts retaining master cylinder to booster. Lay master cylinder aside without kinking lines.

2) Disconnect and plug lines from booster fluid ports. Disconnect brake pedal return spring. Remove bolt from push rod to pedal. Remove mounting nuts and booster from vehicle.

Installation

To install, reverse removal procedures. Tighten all nuts and hose connections. Bleed booster/power

steering system. Check brake pedal and stop lamp switch adjustment.

NOTE: Bleeding Hydro-Boost system is a separate procedure form bleeding the hydraulic systems. See Bleeding Hydro-Boost Systems in this article.

BLEEDING

HYDRO-BOOST SYSTEMS

NOTE: If power steering fluid has foamed, due to low fluid level, it will be necessary to park vehicle for approximately 1 hour (reservoir cap loose) so that foam can dissipate.

Chevrolet & GMC

1) Fill reservoir with steering fluid and leave undisturbed for at least 2 minutes. Start engine and run momentarily. Add fluid if necessary. Repeat until fluid level remains constant after running engine.

2) Stop engine. Raise vehicle so front end is off the ground. Turn steering wheel right and left, lightly contacting stops. Add fluid if necessary.

3) Start engine and depress brake pedal several times while turning steering wheel from stop to stop. Turn engine off and depress brake pedal several times to deplete accumulator pressure. Add fluid if necessary.

4) If fluid is foamy, or has air in it, let vehicle stand several minutes, repeat procedures. The presence of air in the system will cause fluid level to rise with engine off. Continue to bleed system until all air is expelled.

Dodge & Plymouth

1) Check power steering pump reservoir and fill with power steering fluid (MOPAR Power Steering Fluid). Allow fluid to remain undistrubed for 2 minutes. Leave reservoir cap off during operation.

2) Start engine and run for 10 seconds. Check fluid level and add fluid, if necessary. Repeat procedure until fluid level remains constant.

3) Raise front of vehicle and allow tires to clear floor. Start engine and run at 1500 RPM. Apply and release brakes several times, at the same time turn wheels back and forth, lock-to-lock.

4) Turn stop engine and check fluid level. Add fluid, if necessary. Lower vehicle. Start engine and run at 1500 RPM.

5) Apply and release brake pedal several times, at the same time turn front wheels back and forth, lock-to-lock. Turn off engine and check fluid level. Add fluid, if necessary. If fluid level is low, repeat bleeding procedures.

BLEEDING BRAKE CYLINDERS

See Hydraulic Brake Bleeding in this Section.

OVERHAUL

Disassembly

1) Secure unit in vise (bracket end up) and use chisel to cut bracket nut that retains linkage bracket to power section. Cut nut at slot in threaded section to prevent damage to threads.

BENDIX HYDRO-BOOST (Cont.)

2) Remove linkage bracket from unit. Remove pedal rod boot (if equipped), and place rod retainer shearing tool over rod. See Tool Chart in this article for tool proper number.

3) Place a punch through pedal rod from lower side of tool and push punch on through to rest on higher side of tool. Lift up on punch to shear pedal rod retainer. Remove pedal rod.

4) Remove remnants of rubber grommet from groove near end of pedal rod and from groove inside input rod end. With small screwdriver, pry plastic guide out of output push rod retainer.

5) Disengage tabs of spring retainer from ledge inside opening near master cylinder mounting flange of booster. Remove retainer, piston return spring, and output rod from opening.

6) Place booster cover in a soft-jawed vise and remove 5 screws retaining booster housing to cover. Remove booster assembly from vise. Hold booster over a pan and separate cover from housing.

Fig. 2: Procedure for Removing Booster Pedal Rod

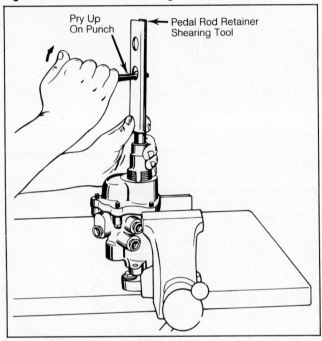

Fig. 4: Compressing Accumulator

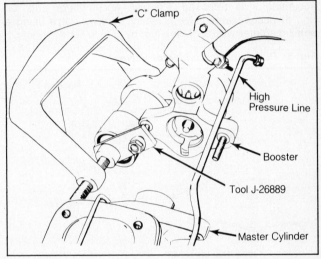

If deep scratches are evident replace input rod and piston.

Fig. 3: Exploded View of Bendix Hydro-Boost Assembly Components

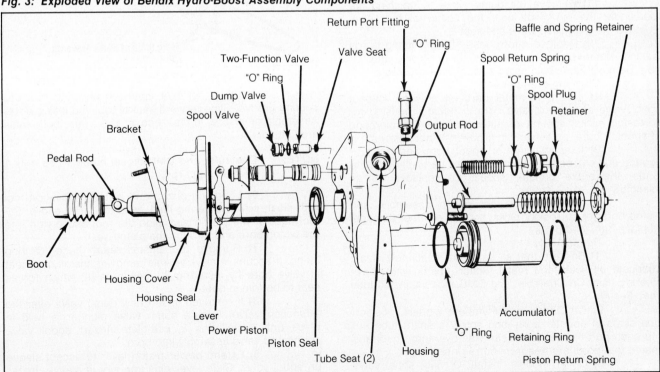

External accumulator unit shown.

Power Brake Units

BENDIX HYDRO-BOOST (Cont.)

7) Remove large seal ring from groove in cover and discard. Remove input rod and piston assembly, spool assembly and spool spring from booster housing. If spool valve is defective, complete assembly must be replaced.

8) Inspect power piston. If deep scratches are evident, input rod and piston must be replaced. Remove input rod seals and piston seal from piston bore. Place retaining cap tool over master cylinder stud and install nut. *See Fig. 4.*

9) Using a large "C" clamp, depress accumulator. Insert a punch into hole in housing and remove retaining ring with screwdriver.

10) Slowly back off clamp until tension on accumulator is released. Remove accumulator and "O" ring. If accumulator valve is faulty, remove valve using a small diameter wire tool. *See Fig. 5.*

Fig. 5: *Removing Accumulator Valves*

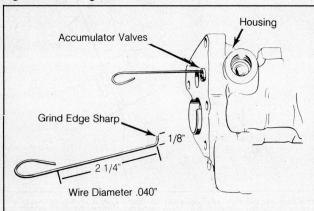

Use a short length of wire to fabricate removal tool.

11) Remove the dump valve by catching the tool under the pin guide near the center of the valve. Remove the 2-function valve and seat.

12) Remove return hose "O" ring fitting if it is leaking. Remove spool valve plug, retaining ring and "O" ring. Remove tube seats using a No. 4 screw extractor.

Cleaning & Inspection

1) Clean all metal parts in solvent. Inspect spool valve and spool valve bore in booster housing for corrosion, nicks, scoring or other damage. Discoloration of spool or bore, particularly in grooves, is not harmful.

2) If spool valve or spool bore has nicks or scoring that can be felt with a fingernail, particularly on the lands, the entire booster should be replaced as an assembly.

3) Inspect input rod, piston assembly, and piston bore for corrosion, nicks, scoring or other damage. Replace damaged parts.

Reassembly

1) Be sure that all parts are absolutely clean. Lubricate all seals and metal friction points with power steering fluid. On Chevrolet and GMC models, install tube seat. *See Fig. 6.*

2) On Dodge and Plymouth models, position tube seats in booster ports and screw a spare tube nut into each port to seat tube seat. Remove spare nuts and ensure that ports are free from burrs or shavings.

3) On all models, install "O" ring, spool valve plug and retaining ring. Coat piston seal and bore with clean power steering fluid and place seal in bore. Lip of

Fig. 6: *Installing General Motors Tube Seats*

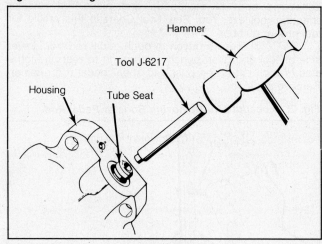

Lightly tap in tube seat with hammer.

seal must face away from master cylinder mounting flanges.

4) Lubricate input rod end, new input rod seals, and seal installer tool with clean power steering fluid. Slide seals on tool with lip of cups toward open end of tool. *See Fig. 7.*

Fig. 7: *Installing Input Rod Seals*

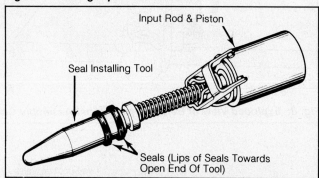

Lubricate all parts and tools with power steering fluid.

5) Slide tool over input rod end and down to second groove. Slide forward seal of tool and into groove. Assemble other seal in first groove. Make sure both seals are seated.

NOTE: **Chevrolet and GMC diesel models use only 1 seal on input rod.**

6) Lubricate piston and piston installation tool with clean power steering fluid. Hold the large end of the tool against the piston and slide the tool and piston into the piston bore and through the piston seal.

7) Remove tool. Install return hose "O" ring fitting. If accumulator valve was removed, install new seat in valve bore by installing 2-function valve, which forces seat to bottom in bore.

8) If removed, insert new dump valve over the 2-function valve. Ensure dump valve plunger is held in place until installation is complete. Insert spool valve spring and valve assembly into bore.

9) Extend power piston lever to accept sleeve on spool valve. Slide lever pins into slot in sleeve. Install new seal in groove in housing cover. Join booster housing and cover and secure with 5 screws.

BENDIX HYDRO-BOOST (Cont.)

10) Install output rod, spring and new spring retainer. Install new baffle and spring retainer by pushing in on it with a 7/8" socket. Lubricate accumulator seal with clean power steering fluid. Install seal and accumulator in housing.

11) Place retaining ring over accumulator. Place retaining cap tool over accumulator. Using a "C" clamp, compress accumulator straight in. Snap retaining ring into the housing groove, and remove "C" clamp and tool.

Fig. 8: Installing Input Rod Assembly into Booster

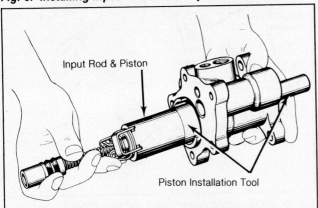

12) Position mounting on booster. Tab on inside diameter of large hole in bracket should fit into slot in threaded portion of booster hub.

13) Install new bracket nut with staking groove outward on the threaded hub of booster. Using deep socket and a torque wrench, tighten nut to 110 ft. lbs (150 N.m).

Fig. 9: Bendix Hydro-Boost Assembly

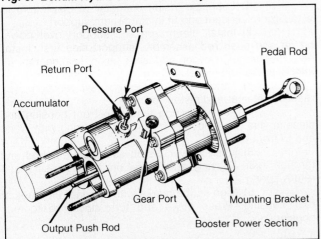

14) Using a hammer and punch, stake the nut in place. Asssemble boot (if used) on pedal rod. Assemble new grommet in groove near end of pedal rod. Moisten grommet with water and insert grommet end of the pedal rod into the input rod end of the booster housing.

15) Push on end of pedal rod to seat grommet. Slide the boot on the pedal rod and assemble the large end of the boot onto the hub of the power section.

TOOL NUMBER CHART

Application	GM No.	Chrysler No.
Retainer Shearer	J-24569	C-4396
Retaining Cap Tool	J-26889	
Input Rod Seal Tool		C-4394
Rear Drum Models		
Gasoline	J-24553	
Diesel	J-28485	
Rear Disc Models	J-28497	
Piston Installation Tool		
Diesel Models	J-25083	
All Others	J-24551	C-4393
Special Deep Socket	J-24554	C-4395
Tube Seat Installer	J-6217	

TIGHTENING SPECIFICATIONS

Application	Ft. Lbs. (N.m)
Booster Housing	20 (27)
Mounting Bracket Nut	110 (150)
Booster Brackets	25 (34)

Power Brake Units

DELCO-MORAINE SINGLE DIAPHRAGM

Chevrolet, GMC, Jeep

DESCRIPTION

A combined vacuum-hydraulic unit which uses a combination of intake manifold vacuum and atmospheric pressure to provide power assist. Reserve vacuum supply and vacuum check valve allow several brake applications, with vacuum assist, after engine has stopped.

Unit is composed of 2 main sections. The vacuum power cylinder and the dual master cylinder. Vacuum power cylinder contains power piston assembly, which houses control valve, reaction mechanism, and power piston return spring.

REMOVAL & INSTALLATION

POWER BRAKE UNIT

1) Disconnect push rod from brake pedal. Disconnect vacuum hose from vacuum check valve. Remove nuts retaining master cylinder to power unit and move master cylinder aside. Do not disconnect brake lines.

2) Remove nuts retaining power unit to dash panel. On Jeep "CJ" and Scrambler models, remove nuts retaining bell crank to dash panel . On all models, remove power unit from vehicle.

3) On Jeep "CJ" and Scrambler models, power unit and bellcrank are removed as an assembly. To install, reverse removal procedures.

OVERHAUL

POWER BRAKE UNIT

NOTE: **Jeep does not recommend overhaul of this unit. It is serviced as an assembly.**

Disassembly

1) Scribe marks on housings for reassembly reference and remove boot, front housing seal, vacuum check valve and grommet.

2) Attach power unit front housing to holding fixture base (J-22805-1) and clamp base in vise with power section up.

3) Place a spanner wrench (J-9504) on studs of rear housing. Press down and turn counterclockwise to unlock housings.

NOTE: **Do not put pressure on plastic power piston extension.**

4) Remove power piston bearing, return spring and power piston group. Remove piston rod and reaction retainer.

CAUTION: **Use care not to damage power piston assembly when removing reaction disc. Reaction disc must be replaced.**

5) Use awl, ice pick or similar tool to remove reaction disc. Remove reaction piston. Grasp assembly at outside edge of diaphragm support and diaphragm.

6) Hold pushrod down against a hard surface. Use a slight force or impact to dislodge diaphragm retainer.

Fig. 1: Exploded View of Typical Delco-Moraine Single Diaphragm Power Brake Unit

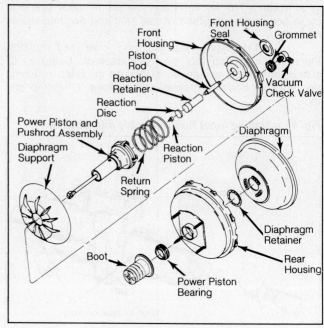

Do not disassemble power push rod assembly.

Cleaning & Inspection

1) Clean all metal, plastic, and rubber parts in denatured alcohol. Blow out all passages, orifices, and valve holes with clean, dry air. Air dry all parts.

2) Slight rust on inside of housings can be polished with crocus or emery cloth. There should not be any nicks or cuts on rubber part. Replace any damaged part.

Reassembly

1) Lubricate inside diameter of diaphragm lip with silicon lubricant and fit in diaphragm support.

2) Install diaphragm and support over power piston and push rod assembly, support side first. Install new diaphragm retainer and seat using seating tool (J-28458) and a soft mallet.

3) Install reaction piston, new reaction disc, reaction retainer and piston rod.

4) Attach holding fixture to front housing and place in vise. Install power piston return spring with White end to front housing.

5) Insert power piston assembly pushrod end through rear housing and place on front housing and return spring.

6) Align scribe marks with spanner on studs of rear housing. Press down and turn clockwise to lock housings.

NOTE: **Assembly can be aided by connecting a vacuum source to booster.**

7) Stake 2 housing tabs into sockets with screwdriver. Stake 2 tabs at 180° apart.

8) Lubricate inside and outside diameters of grommet and front housing seal and install seal, grommet, vacuum check valve and boot.

Power Brake Units

DELCO-MORAINE SINGLE DIAPHRAGM (Cont.)

ADJUSTMENT

PUSH ROD

NOTE: Chevrolet and GMC production push rod is not adjustable. If production rod is reused, gauging is to check proper assembly. If adjustable service push rod is used to replace production rod, gauging is to set to correct rod length.

Chevrolet & GMC
1) Place Go No Go gauge (J-22647) over push rod in a position which will allow gauge to be slipped to left or right without contacting studs. Center section of gauge has 2 levels.

Fig. 2: Checking Push Rod Height

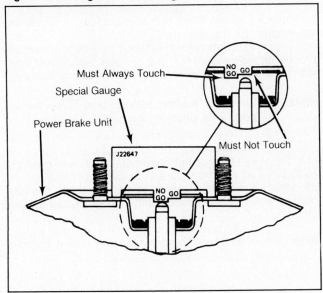

Non-adjustable production rod shown

2) Push rod should always contact longer section (lower level), and never contact shorter section (higher lever). Any variation beyond these 2 limits would require replacement of production rod or adjustment of service push rod.

Jeep
Push rod of replacement units is preset at factory and requires no field adjustment.

Power Brake Units

DELCO-MORAINE TANDEM DIAPHRAGM

Chevrolet, GMC, Jeep

DESCRIPTION

Unit is mounted on firewall and connected directly to brake pedal. A combination of vacuum and atmospheric pressure is used to provide power assist.

Power cylinder houses power piston assembly, which contains primary and secondary diaphragms, pistons, floating control valve, reaction piston, and disc.

REMOVAL & INSTALLATION

POWER BRAKE UNIT

Removal

1) Without disconnecting brake lines, remove master cylinder from power unit and position to one side. Disconnect vacuum hose from vacuum check valve.

2) Disconnect power brake push rod from brake pedal. Remove nuts mounting power unit to firewall and remove power unit.

CAUTION: Do not bend brake lines, and do not force push rod to the side when disconnecting.

Installation

To install, reverse removal procedures. On Jeep models, use a new bolt to retain push rod to brake pedal.

OVERHAUL

POWER BRAKE UNIT

Disassembly

1) Remove push rod boot, silencer, front housing seal, grommet, and vacuum check valve. Scribe a mark on front and rear housing for reassembly reference. Attach front housing to holding fixture (J-22805-01).

2) Place spanner wrench (J-9504) over rear housing studs, press down, and turn counterclockwise to unlock housings. Carefully separate housings. Remove power piston group, power piston return spring, and power piston bearing.

3) Remove push rod, reaction retainer and power head silencer. Grasp assembly at outside edge of divider and diaphragms. Hold with push rod down against a hard surface.

4) Use a slight force or impact to dislodge diaphragm retainer. Remove primary diaphragm, primary support plate and secondary power piston bearing. Remove housing divider, secondary support plate and diaphragm and power piston assembly.

Cleaning & Inspection

1) Clean all plastic, metal and rubber parts in denatured alcohol. Blow out all passages, orifices and valve holes. Air dry all parts.

2) Slight rust on housing may be cleaned with crocus or emery cloth. Do not reinstall any rubber parts with cuts, nicks or distortion. If in doubt, replace the part.

NOTE: Lubricate rubber, plastic, and metal friction parts with silicone lube before assembly.

Reassembly

1) Place power piston on bench with push rod end up. Install assembly cone (J-28458) over push rod end of piston. Lubricate inside diameter of secondary diaphragm with silicone lubricant and fit in secondary support plate.

2) Install secondary diaphragm and support plate over power piston and push down until it bottoms.

Fig. 1: Exploded View of Delco-Moraine Tandem Power Cylinder

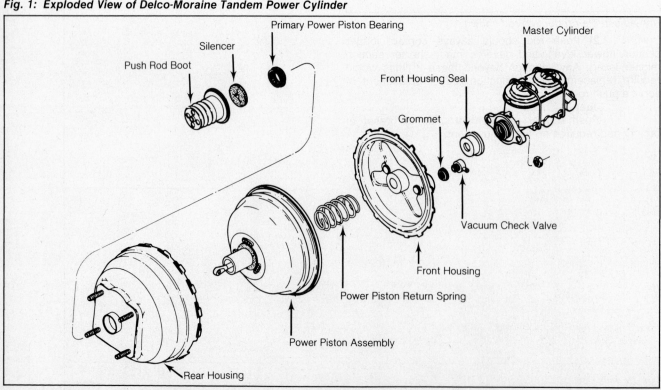

DELCO MORAINE TANDEM DIAPHRAGM (Cont.)

Fig.2: Exploded View of Delco-Moraine Tandem Power Piston Assembly

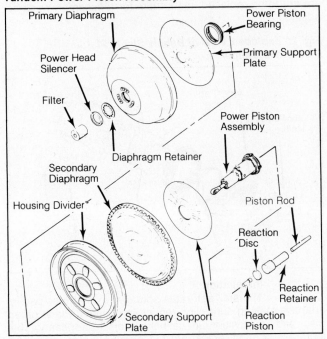

See Fig. 3. Lubricate inside diameter of secondary power piston bearing and install in housing divider with flat surface of bearing on the same side as 6 raised lugs on divider.

Fig. 3: Installing Secondary Diaphragm and Support Plate

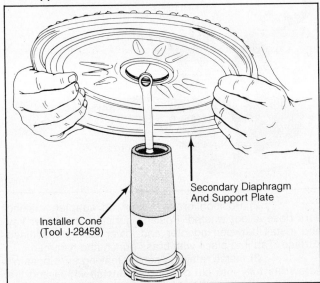

Use installer cone (J-28458).

3) Hold divider so that formed over flange faces up. Press divider down over assembly cone and onto power piston to rest against secondary diaphragm. Lubricate inside diameter of primary diaphragm and install in primary support plate.

4) Remove assembly cone from power piston. Place primary support plate and diaphragm assembly over power piston and push down until it bottoms. Place

diaphragm retainer over power piston and onto diaphragm.

5) Install assembly cone (J-28458) over power piston onto diaphragm retainer and strike with hammer until retainer is locked on neck of power piston. Remove assembly cone.

6) Install reaction retainer, piston rod, and power head silencer. Place primary power piston bearing in rear housing center hole. Lubricate with silicone lubricant on inner diameter.

7) Attach front housing to holding fixture and place fixture in vise. Install power piston assembly to rear housing. Install power piston return spring over reaction retainer and lower rear housing onto front housing.

8) Align scribe marks and press down on spanner wrench (J-9504), turning clockwise to lock housings. Stake 2 housing tabs into sockets at 2 locations 180° apart.

9) Lubricate inside and outside diameters of grommet and front housing seal. Install seal, grommet, vacuum check valve, silencer, and push rod boot.

PUSH ROD

NOTE: This adjustment applies to Chevrolet and GMC only. Jeep push rod is not adjustable.

1) Place power unit in padded vise with front housing up. Do not clamp tight. Insert master cylinder push rod, flat end first, into retainer. Ensure rod is properly seated.

2) Remove front housing seal to assure no vacuum is in unit. Place Go No Go gauge (J-22647) over push rod so it can be moved right or left without contacting studs. Push rod should contact longer section of gauge.

3) Rod is non-adjustable, and if out of limits, must be replaced with adjustable service rod. With service rod, adjust self-locking screw to meet gauging specifications.

Fig. 4: Adjusting Push Rod with Go No Go Gauge

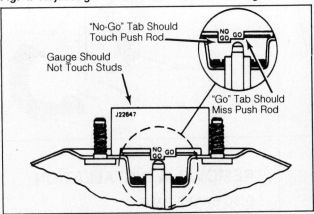

Chevrolet and GMC models only.

Brake Systems

CHRYSLER CORP. SLIDING CALIPER DISCS

Dodge, Plymouth

DESCRIPTION

Chrysler vehicles are equipped with single piston, sliding caliper disc brakes. Brake assembly consists of hub and disc assembly, caliper, disc pads, splash shield and adapter.

Cooling fins are cast integrally between machined braking surfaces. When the brake pedal is depressed, hydraulic pressure is applied against brake caliper piston. This force is transmitted to in-board brake pad and inner surface of rotor.

As force increases against inboard side, caliper slides inward on machined rotor plate ramps, providing vise-like clamping action on rotor.

ADJUSTMENT & SERVICING

DISC PAD ADJUSTMENT

Pad wear is automatically compensated for by piston moving outward in cylinder bore; therefore, no disc pad adjustment in service is required. However, it is a good idea to inspect condition of disc pads whenever wheels are removed. If any pad is excessively worn, ALL front pads must be replaced.

BLEEDING SYSTEM

See Hydraulic Brake Bleeding in this Section.

Fig. 1: Exploded View of Chrysler Single Piston Disc Brake Caliper

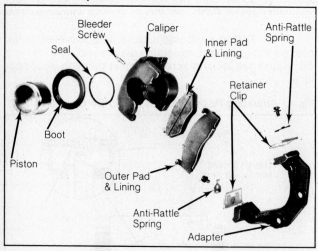

REMOVAL & INSTALLATION

DISC BRAKE PADS

Removal (W350/450 & W250 Extra)

1) Siphon fluid from master cylinder until cylinder is 1/3 full. Raise and support vehicle with safety stand. Remove wheel. Using a "C" clamp, bottom caliper piston in cylinder bore.

2) Remove clamp. Remove key retaining screws and drive out caliper support key with a brass punch. Remove caliper support spring and remove caliper from adapter and support out of the way.

3) Pry outer disc pad from caliper and remove inner disc pad and anti-rattle spring from adapter. If pads are not to be replaced, mark them for reassembly to same position.

Fig. 2: Exploded View of Bendix Single Piston Disc Brake Caliper

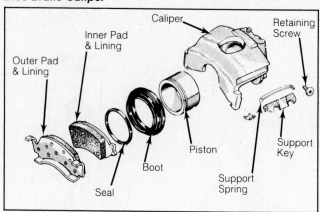

Installation

1) Install anti-rattle spring and inner disc pad in adapter, making sure clips remain in position. Place outer disc pad in position in caliper. If disc pad cannot be installed by hand, press into place using a block of wood and a "C" clamp.

Fig. 3: Installation of Outboard Pad and Liner

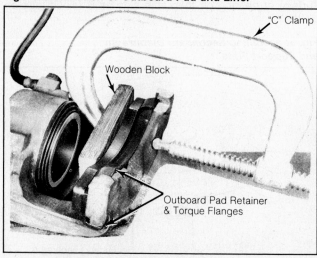

2) Position brake caliper on adapter, making sure hose is not twisted. Position spring over caliper key and install between adapter and lower caliper machined surface. Tap into place with brass punch and hammer.

3) Install retaining screw, making sure boss on screw fits fully into cut-out on key. Install wheel and tire and refill reservoir in master cylinder to within 1/4" of top. Pump brake pedal several times and recheck fluid level.

Removal (All Other Models)

1) Raise and support vehicle with safety stands. Remove wheel assembly. Remove caliper retainer and anti-rattle spring assemblies. Carefully lift caliper assembly out and away from rotor.

2) Pry between outer disc pad and fingers of housing to remove outer pad. Support caliper to prevent damage to brake line and remove inner disc pad.

CHRYSLER CORP. SLIDING CALIPER DISCS (Cont.)

Installation

1) Slowly push piston back into caliper. Care must be taken to ensure reservoir does not overflow while pushing in on piston. Slide outer disc pad into caliper.

2) There should be no free play between disc pad flange and caliper flange. If free play exists, bend disc pad flange until interference fit with caliper is obtained.

3) If necessary, install disc pad using a "C" clamp and wood block placed across disc pad. Place inner lining on adapter with disc pad flanges aligned with flange ways in adapter.

4) Slide caliper into position in adapter and over disc. Align caliper on adapter, taking care not to pull dust boot away from groove in piston.

5) Install anti-rattle springs and retaining clips and tighten retaining screws to 200 INCH lbs. (23 N.m). Pump brake pedal several times to obtain firm pedal. Recheck fluid level in master cylinder reservoir.

BRAKE CALIPER

Brake caliper removal and installation procedures are same as for disc brake pads, except it will be necessary to disconnect hydraulic brake hose at caliper.

DISC ROTOR

Removal (2WD Models)

1) Raise vehicle and support with safety stands. Remove brake caliper without disconnecting brake line.

2) Remove grease cover from end of hub. Remove cotter pin, nut lock, nut, thrust washer, and outer wheel bearing. Pull rotor and hub off wheel spindle.

Installation

Slide rotor and hub into position on spindle. Install outer wheel bearing, thrust washer and nut. Adjust wheel bearing. *See Wheel Bearing Adjustment in SUSPENSION Section.* To complete installation, reverse removal procedures.

Removal (4WD W/44FBJ Front Axle)

1) Raise vehicle and support with safety stands. Remove brake caliper without disconnecting brake line.

2) Using removal/installer tool (C-4170), remove wheel bearing adjusting lock nut. Remove locking ring and wheel bearing adjusting nut.

3) Remove rotor assembly. Outer wheel bearing and retainer spring plate will slide out as rotor is removed.

NOTE: Special tools and procedures are required to remove and install inner wheel bearings on four-wheel drive models with 44FBJ front axles. The following installation procedure is after inner bearings have been installed in rotor hub.

Installation

1) Mount rotor on spindle. Position inner wheel bearing in place and install inner lock nut using removal/installer tool (C-4170), and tighten to 50 ft. lbs. (68 N.m) to seat bearings.

2) Rotate wheel assembly and loosen inner lock nut. Retighten to 30-40 ft. lbs. (41-54 N.m) while rotating hub. Back off inner lock nut 135 to 150°.

3) Position locking washer by turning nut so that the pin pressed into the lock nut will enter the nearest hole in locking washer. Install and tighten outer lock nut to 50 ft. lbs. (68 N.m). Replace caliper assembly.

Removal (4WD W/Model 60 Front Axle)

1) Raise vehicle and support with safety stands. Remove brake caliper without disconnecting brake line as previously outlined.

2) Remove grease cover from end of hub. Remove snap ring from drive axle. Remove flange bolts and flange from hub.

3) Straighten lock tabs on outer wheel bearing lock ring. Using socket (DD-1241-JD), remove outer lock nut, lock ring, inner nut and outer wheel bearing. Remove rotor and hub assembly.

Installation

Install rotor and hub in position on spindle. Install outer bearing and inner lock nut and adjust wheel bearings. *See Wheel Bearing Adjustment in SUSPENSION Section.* To complete installation, reverse removal procedures.

OVERHAUL

BRAKE CALIPER

Disassembly

1) Raise vehicle and support with saftey stands. Remove wheel assembly. Remove retainer and anti-rattle spring assemblies. Carefully slide caliper out and away from rotor and support assembly on axle and steering linkage.

2) On vehicles equipped with single piston caliper, carefully depress brake pedal to hydraulically push piston out of bore in caliper. Pedal will fall away when piston has passed bore opening. Prop pedal in any position below first inch of travel to prevent fluid loss.

CAUTION: Under no conditions should air pressure be used to remove piston from bore.

3) Disconnect brake hose and remove caliper from vehicle. Remove dust boot. Work seal out of groove in piston bore with a wooden or plastic rod to prevent damage to cylinder.

Inspection

Clean all parts with alcohol and blow dry with compressed air. Inspect piston bore for scoring or pitting. Light scratches or corrosion can be removed by honing, providing bore diameter is not increased more than .002" (.05 mm). Discard used piston seal and boot.

Reassembly (W350/450 & W250 Extra)

1) Lubricate new piston seal with clean brake fluid and install into groove in cylinder bore, working around circumference with fingers until fully seated. Ensure seal is not twisted.

2) Lubricate new piston boot with brake fluid, and install into caliper by working into outer groove. Plug inlet and bleeder screw hole.

3) Lubricate piston and, with fingers spreading boot, press piston into boot until boot is forced into groove around piston. Remove plug. Carefully push piston down until bottomed in cylinder.

Reassembly (All Other Models)

1) Lubricate new piston seal with brake fluid and install to groove in bore, working around circumference with fingers until fully seated.

CHRYSLER CORP. SLIDING CALIPER DISCS (Cont.)

2) Ensure seal is not twisted. Coat new boot with brake fluid (leaving a generous amount inside boot) and install to piston.

3) Install piston into bore, pushing past piston seal until bottomed in bore. Position dust boot in counterbore. Use boot installer tools (C-4890 and C-4171) to drive boot into counterbore.

DISC ROTOR

1) Mount dial indicator on steering arm with contact tip of indicator against braking surface (about 1" from edge of rotor). Temporarily adjust wheel bearings to zero end play.

2) Measure lateral runout on both sides of rotor. Using micrometer, measure thickness at 12 equally spaced locations around rotor (about 1" from edge).

3) If rotor is scored, warped, or does not meet specifications, refinish or replace as needed. When refinishing rotor, always remove equal amounts of material from each face, to a maximum of .015" (.38 mm).

TIGHTENING SPECIFICATIONS

Application	Ft. Lbs. (N.m)
Caliper Adapter Bolts	
All with 1/2" Bolts	95-125 (129-170)
All with 5/8" Bolts	140-180 (190-245)

FORD SLIDING CALIPER DISCS

All Models With Front Disc Brakes

DESCRIPTION

All 250 Series (over 6900 GVW) and 350 Series use a dual piston type. All other models use a single piston type. On all models, caliper is secured to anchor plate by a retaining key and spring. Ventiliated rotor is cast with wheel hub. As brake pedal is depressed, fluid from master cylinder passes through the metering valve and into caliper cylinder.

ADJUSTMENT & SERVICING

DISC PADS

Pad wear is automatically compensated for by piston sliding outward in cylinder bore; therefore, no disc pad adjustment is required. When pad surface is worn to within .030" (.76 mm) of rivet, pad must be replaced.

BLEEDING SYSTEM

See Hydraulic Bleeding in *BRAKE Section.*

REMOVAL & INSTALLATION

DISC BRAKE PADS

NOTE: **Always replace both sets of brake pads together. Never service one wheel only.**

Removal (Single Piston Type)

1) To prevent master cylinder overflow when caliper is depressed, remove a small amount of brake fluid from master cylinder. Raise vehicle and support with safety stands. Remove front wheel.

2) Place a large "C" clamp on caliper, and tighten clamp to bottom piston in cylinder bore. Remove clamp. Remove key retaining screw. Using a brass rod and light hammer, drive out caliper support spring.

3) Remove caliper from spindle by pushing it downward against spindle and rotating upper end upward and out of spindle. Support caliper out of the way.

4) Remove outer disc pad from caliper. It may be necessary to tap pad to loosen pad flange from caliper. Remove inner disc pad from spindle assembly. Remove pad anti-rattle clip from spindle.

Installation

1) Install new anti-rattle clip in spindle. Place lower end of inner pad into spindle against anti-rattle clip and slide upper end of pad into position. Be sure clip is still in position.

2) With caliper piston fully bottomed in cylinder bore, position outer pad on caliper and press shoe tabs into place. If shoe cannot be pressed into place by hand, use a large "C" clamp. To complete installation, reverse removal procedures.

Removal (Dual Piston Type)

1) To prevent master cylinder overflow when caliper is depressed, remove a small amount of brake fluid from master cylinder. Raise vehicle and support with safety stands. Remove front wheel assembly. Remove key retaining screw.

2) Using a brass rod, and light hammer, drive out key and spring. Remove caliper by rotating key and spring end out away from rotor.

3) Slide opposite end of caliper clear of slice in the support and off the rotor. Do not allow caliper to hang from brake line. Remove caliper disc pad anti-rattle spring. Remove inner and outer disc pad.

Installation

1) Make sure caliper pistons are fully bottomed in caliper. Install disc pads and anti-rattle spring. Place caliper rail into the slide on support and rotate caliper onto rotor.

2) Place key and spring into position and start inserting between caliper and support. Use a screwdriver if necessary to hold caliper up against support.

NOTE: **Spring is between key and caliper. Spring tangs overlap ends of key.**

3) Drive key and spring into position aligning correct notch with existing hole in support. Install key retaining screw and tighten to 12-20 ft. lbs. (16-27 N.m). Check brake fluid level in master cylinder and fill as necessary.

BRAKE CALIPER

Removal & Installation

Caliper removal and installation procedures are same as for disc pad replacement, except it will be necessary to disconnect brake hose. After caliper installation, bleed brake system.

DISC ROTOR

Removal (2WD Models)

Raise vehicle and support with safety stands. Remove wheel and caliper assemblies. Remove dust cap, cotter pin, nut, washer, and outer bearing. Carefully remove hub and rotor assembly from spindle.

Installation

To install, reverse removal procedures. Adjust front wheel bearings. See Wheel Bearing Adjustment in *SUSPENSION Section.*

Removal (4WD Models)

1) Raise vehicle and support with safety stands. Remove wheel assembly. Remove locking hub assembly as outlined in Locking Hub article at end of this section.

2) Remove wheel bearing lock nut, and adjusting nut using a spanner (T59T-1197 for F100/250 and Bronco, T78T-1197-A for F350). Remove hub and disc assembly.

Installation

To install, reverse removal procedures. Ensure that both hub dials are in the same position. Adjust wheel bearings. See Wheel Bearing Adjustment in *SUSPENSION Section.*

OVERHAUL

BRAKE CALIPER

Disassembly (Single & Dual Piston)

1) Remove caliper as previously outlined. Remove plug from inlet port (if equipped) and drain fluid from cylinders.

2) Place a block of wood between caliper and cylinders. Apply low air pressure to brake hose inlet. Air pressure will force out piston(s).

FORD SLIDING CALIPER DISCS (Cont.)

Fig. 1: Using Compressed Air to Remove Caliper Piston

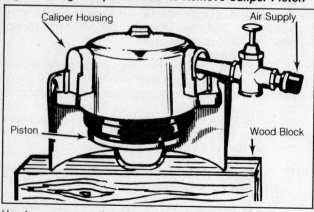

Use low pressure air to force out piston(s)

3) If a piston is jammed or cocked and will not easily come out, tap end of piston sharply with a brass hammer to straighten. Do not pry piston from bore.

4) Reapply low air pressure to remove cocked piston. Remove seal and boot from grooves. Discard seals and boots.

Fig. 2: Exploded View of Single Piston Caliper

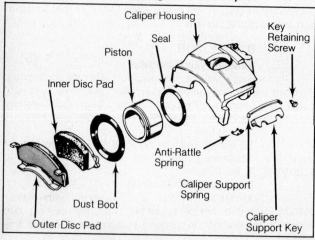

Cleaning & Inspection

1) Clean rust and corrosion form caliper machined surfaces with a wire brush, being careful not to get wire brush in cylinder bores. Clean all components with denatured alcohol and dry with compressed air.

2) Inspect cylinder bore, seal grooves, and boot grooves for wear or damage. Replace anti-rattle clip, caliper support spring and key.

Reassembly (Single Piston)

1) Lubricate piston seal with clean brake fluid and install in cylinder bore groove. Lubricate cylinder with clean brake fluid. Coat piston and outside beads of dust boot with clean brake fluid.

2) Push piston through boot until boot is around bottom (closed end) of piston. Position piston and boot directly over cylinder bore. Work bead of dust boot into groove near top of cylinder bore.

3) With bead seated in groove, press straight down on piston until it bottoms in cylinder bore. Care must be taken not to cock or jam piston in cylinder. If necessary use a "C" clamp and a block of wood to bottom piston in cylinder.

Fig. 3: Exploded View of Dual Piston Caliper

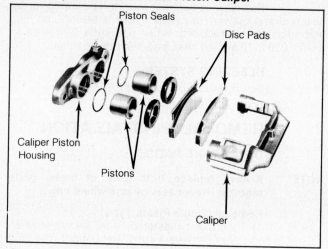

Reassembly (Dual Piston)

1) Lubricate new piston seals with clean brake fluid and install seals in grooves in cylinders. Lubricate cylinders with clean brake fluid.

2) Lubricate retaining lips of boots with clean brake fluid and install in grooves in cylinders. Coat pistons with clean brake fluid. Insert into cylinders by hand until they are beyond piston seals.

3) Position a wood block over one piston and press into cylinder, taking care not to cock piston. Install other piston in same manner.

DISC ROTOR SERVICING

Maximum of .020" (.51 mm) material may be taken off each side of braking surface. Cuts must be of equal depth on both sides of rotor.

DISC BRAKE ROTOR SPECIFICATIONS

Application	Disc Diameter In. (mm)	Lateral Runout In. (mm)	Parallelism In. (mm)	Original Thickness In. (mm)	Min. Refinish Thickness In. (mm)	Discard Thickness In. (mm)
E250/350, 4WD F250 & 2WD F250 over 6800 GVW	....	.010 (.25)	.001 (.03)	1.25 (31.8)	1.21 (30.7)	1.18 (29.9)
F100 4600 GVW w/Power Brakes	....	.010 (.25)	.001 (.03)	.98 (24.9)	.94 (23.9)	.81 (20.6)
Ranger	....	.010 (.25)	.001 (.03)	.93 (23.8)	.87 (22.1)	[2]
All Others	....	.010 (.25)	.001 (.03)	1.19 (30.2)	.15 (29.2)	1.12 (28.4)

[1] — Specifications given are for separte hub and rotor. With integral hub and rotor assembly: .003" (.08 mm).
[2] — Minimum safe thickness is stamped on each rotor.

GENERAL MOTORS FLOATING CALIPER DISCS

Chevrolet, GMC

NOTE: Delco floating caliper disc brakes are used on all gasoline engine models except those equipped with Bendix Hydro-Boost power brake units and/or 4-wheel disc brakes. All other models use Bendix sliding caliper disc brakes.

DESCRIPTION

Delco floating caliper disc brake assembly uses a single piston caliper. The caliper is mounted to an anchor plate which is bolted to the steering knuckle. The caliper assembly floats through 4 rubber bushings on 2 steel guide pins.

The pins are threaded into caliper anchor plate. When brakes are applied, hydraulic pressure is passed to caliper piston. This force pushes inner brake pad against inner rotor braking surface.

Pressure then moves caliper inward on guide pins, thus forcing outer disc pad against outer rotor braking surface. When brakes are released, pressure is removed from cylinder. Rotor runout moves piston back off of rotor to maintain sufficient rotor-to-pad clearance.

Fig. 1: Exploded View of Floating Caliper Assembly

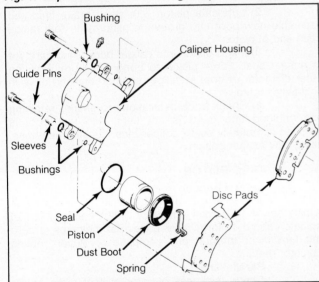

ADJUSTMENT & SERVICING

DISC BRAKE PADS

Pad wear is automatically compensated for by piston moving outward in cylinder bore. No disc pad adjustment in service is required.

Inspect condition of disc pads whenever wheels are removed. If any disc pad is worn to within 1/32" (.8 mm) of rivet heads, replace all disc pad sets on that axle.

BLEEDING SYSTEM

See Hydraulic Brake Bleeding in *BRAKE Section.*

REMOVAL & INSTALLATION

DISC BRAKE PADS
Removal

1) Remove 2/3 of brake fluid from front reservoir in master cylinder. Raise vehicle and support with safety stands. Remove wheel assembly. Place a large "C" clamp on caliper so that solid side of clamp rests against metal part of outer disc pad.

2) Tighten "C" clamp until caliper moves away from vehicle far enough to push piston to bottom of bore. Remove "C" clamp. Do not disconnect brake line to caliper. Remove 2 mounting bolts which retain caliper to support bracket.

3) Lift caliper off rotor and remove inner disc pad. Pry out outer disc pad. Place caliper on front suspension arm so that caliper weight is not supported by brake hose.

4) Remove shoe support spring from cavity in piston. Remove sleeves from inner ear in caliper. Remove rubber bushings from grooves in each of 4 caliper ears.

Installation

1) Install new rubber bushings in 4 caliper ears. Install sleeves in bushings with installer tool (J-22835). Position sleeves so that end toward disc pad is flush with machined surface of ear.

2) Install shoe support spring on inner disc pad. Place single tang end of spring over notch in center edge of pad. Now press 2 tangs at spring end of inner disc pad over bottom edge of pad.

3) Place inner disc pad in caliper (with spring attached) so that the ear end of disc pad is down and the bottom end is up. Install at an angle so that the spring rests on the inside diameter of piston.

4) Press down on both ends of disc pad until pad is in a flat position, resting on piston. Be sure to install inner brake pads on the correct side. Wear sensor will be toward the rear of the caliper when correctly installed.

5) Place outer disc pad in caliper with ears of pad over caliper ears. Tab at bottom of pad should be engaged in caliper cut-out. Note left and right disc pads. Place caliper over rotor, line up caliper ears with holes in the mounting bracket.

6) With caliper in place, make sure brake hose is not twisted. Start bolts through sleeves in inner caliper ears and mounting bracket. Make sure that bolts pass under retaining ears in inner disc pad.

7) Push bolts through holes in outer disc pads and caliper ears. Thread bolts into mounting bracket and tighten to 35 ft. lbs. (48 N.m). Fill master cylinder with new brake fluid.

8) Pump brake pedal several times to seat disc pads against rotor. Clinch upper ears of outer disc pad with channel lock pliers, placing 1 jaw on top of upper ear and other jaw on bottom of disc pad, in notch.

9) After clinching, ears should be flat against caliper housing with no radial clearance. If clearance exists, repeat procedure.

BRAKE CALIPER
Removal & Installation

Brake caliper removal and installation procedures are same as for disc brake pads, except that it will be necessary to disconnect brake hose.

Brake Systems

GENERAL MOTORS FLOATING CALIPER DISCS (Cont.)

DISC ROTOR

Removal (2WD Models)

1) Raise vehicle and support with safety stands. Remove brake caliper (do not disconnect brake line).

2) Remove grease cover from end of hub. Remove cotter pin nut, washer, and outer bearing. Remove rotor and hub assembly.

Installation

Install rotor and hub assembly on spindle. Install outer bearing, washer, and nut. Adjust wheel bearings. See Wheel Bearing Adjustment in *SUSPENSION Section*.

Removal & Installation (4WD Models)

1) Raise vehicle and support with safety stands. Remove wheel assembly. Remove locking hub assembly as outlined in Locking Hub article at end of this section.

2) Remove wheel bearing lock nut, lock ring and adjuster nut. Remove rotor and hub assembly.

3) To install, reverse removal procedures. Adjust wheel bearings, see Wheel Bearing Adjustment in *SUSPENSION Section*.

OVERHAUL

BRAKE CALIPER

Disassembly

1) Clean exterior of caliper with denatured alcohol and place on clean work surface. Remove brake hose, discarding copper gasket. Drain brake fluid from caliper.

2) Use clean shop towels to pad interior of caliper and apply compressed air at caliper inlet to remove piston. Use just enough pressure to ease piston out of bore.

3) Use screwdriver to pry boot out of caliper housing. Pry piston seal from its groove in caliper bore with a piece of wood or plastic. Do not use metal tool of any type to remove piston seal. Remove bleeder valve from housing.

Inspection

1) Boot, seal, rubber bushings, and sleeves are to be replaced each time caliper is overhauled. Clean all other parts in denatured alcohol. Dry parts with dry compressed air.

NOTE: **Using lubricated shop air will leave a film of mineral oil on metal parts. This may damage rubber parts upon contact during reassembly.**

2) Check guide pins for corrosion, breaks in plating or other damage. Do not attempt to clean pins; replace them. Check outside diameter of piston for scoring, nicks, corrosion, and worn or damaged plating. If surface defects exist, piston must be replaced.

3) Piston bore should be checked for similar defects. Bore is not plated, therefore, it may be polished with crocus cloth. Thoroughly clean after polishing. Replace caliper housing if bore corrosion cannot easily be cleaned out.

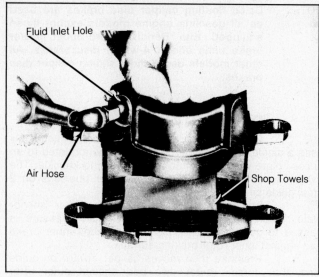

Fig. 2: Using Compressed Air to Remove Caliper Piston

Fluid Inlet Hole

Air Hose

Shop Towels

Compressed air must be filtered and dry.

Reassembly

1) Lubricate bore in caliper housing and new piston seal with clean brake fluid. Position seal in caliper bore groove.

2) Lubricate piston with clean brake fluid and assemble new boot into groove in piston with fold facing open end of piston.

3) Insert piston into caliper bore using care not to unseat seal. Force piston to bottom of bore. Position outer diameter of boot in caliper counterbore and drive in until fully seated.

4) Check boot installations to ensure retaining ring (molded into boot) is not bent, and that boot is installed completely below caliper face. Install brake hose, using new copper gasket.

DISC ROTOR

Lateral Runout

Adjust wheel bearings until all end play is eliminated. Attach dial indicator with contact tip of indicator about 1" from rotor edge. Set indicator to zero and turn rotor through one complete revolution, noting indicator reading.

Parallelism

Check thickness of rotor at 4 or more points around circumference of rotor. Make all measurements at same distance from edge of rotor. If thickness variation is excessive, refinish or replace rotor as necessary.

TIGHTENING SPECIFICATIONS

Application	Ft. Lbs. (N.m)
Brake Hose-to-Caliper	30 (41)
Caliper Mounting Bolts	35 (48)
Hydraulic Line-to-Brake Hose	13 (17)
Support Plate-to-Knuckle Bolts	12 (16)

Brake Systems

GENERAL MOTORS FLOATING CALIPER DISCS (Cont.)

DISC BRAKE ROTOR SPECIFICATIONS

Application	Disc Diameter In. (mm)	Lateral Runout In. (mm)	Parallelism In. (mm)	Original Thickness In. (mm)	Min. Refinish Thickness In. (mm)	Discard Thickness In. (mm)
10 Series & G20	11.86 (301.2)	.004 (.10)	.0005 (.013)	1.28 (32.5)	1.23 (31.2)	1.22 (30.9)
S/10	....	.004 (.10)	.0005 (.013)	....	.98 (24.84)	.96 (24.50)
All Other Models	[1] 12.5 (317.5)	.004 (.10)	.0005 (.013)	[2] 1.28 (32.5)	[3] 1.23 (31.2)	[3] 1.22 (30.9)

[1] — 14.25" (361.9 mm) rotor used on some P30 models.
[2] — 1.53" (38.9 mm) thick rotor used on some 30 series models.
[3] — On models with 1.53" (38.9 mm) rotor, refinish thickness is 1.48" (37.6 mm), discard at 1.47" (37.3 mm).

Brake Systems

GENERAL MOTORS SLIDING CALIPER DISCS

Chevrolet, GMC

NOTE: Bendix sliding caliper disc brakes are used on all models equipped with Bendix Hydro-Boost power units, 4-wheel disc brakes, and/or diesel engines. All other models use Delco floating caliper disc brakes. See appropriate article in this section.

DESCRIPTION

Bendix sliding caliper disc brakes use a single piston caliper. Front calipers are attached to a mount integral with the steering knuckle. Rear calipers are mounted to an adapter bolted to the drive axle.

When brakes are applied, hydraulic pressure is passed to caliper piston. This force is transmitted to inner brake pad against inner rotor braking surface. Pressure then moves caliper inward, forcing outer disc pads against outer braking surface.

When brake pedal is released, pressure is removed from caliper cylinder and rotor runout moves piston back into caliper cylinder to maintain sufficient rotor-to-pad clearance.

ADJUSTMENT & SERVICING

DISC PADS

Pad wear is automatically compensated for by piston moving outward in cylinder bore. No disc pad adjustment is required. Inspect condition of disc pads whenever wheels are removed. If any pad is worn to within 1/32" (.8 mm) of rivet heads, replace all pad sets on axle.

BLEEDING SYSTEM

See Brake Bleeding in *BRAKE Section.*

REMOVAL & INSTALLATION

DISC BRAKE PADS

Removal

1) To prevent master cylinder overflow when caliper is depressed, remove 2/3 of the brake fluid from master cylinder. Raise vehicle and support with safety stands.

2) Remove wheel assembly. Place a large "C" clamp on caliper and tighten clamp on bottom piston in cylinder bore. Remove clamp. Remove key retaining screw.

3) Drive out caliper support key and spring with brass rod and light hammer. Remove caliper by pushing down against mount and rotating up and away from mount.

4) Support caliper with wire. Do not let caliper hang with weight on brake hose. Remove inner disc pad and shoe clip from caliper.

5) Remove outer disc pad from caliper. It may be necessary to tap pad to loosen it in caliper housing.

Installation

1) Lubricate caliper and mount sliding surfaces with silicone lubricant. Install new anti-rattle clip in mount. Place lower end of inner pad into mount and against anti-rattle clip.

2) Slide upper end of pad into place. Be sure clip is still in correct position. With caliper piston fully bottomed in cylinder bore. Position outer pad on caliper and press tabs into place.

3) If pad cannot be properly positioned by hand, use a large "C" clamp, taking care not to mar lining. With disc pads installed, lift caliper and rest bottom edge of outer pad on outer edge of rotor.

4) Check that there is no clearance between bottom tab of outer pad and caliper abutment. Outer pad should be tight in caliper housing. Postion caliper on mounting surface.

5) Place spring over support key and tap into place until key retaining screw can be installed. Tighten screw. Fill master cylinder with new brake fluid. Reinstall wheel assembly and lower vehicle.

Fig. 1: Rear Sliding Caliper Disc Brake Components

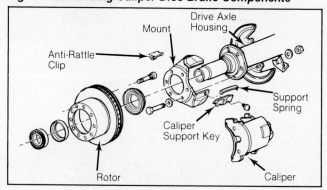

BRAKE CALIPER

Removal & Installation

Caliper removal and installation procedures are the same as those for disc pad replacement, except that it will be necessary to disconnect brake hose. Use new copper washers when reconnecting brake hose.

DISC ROTOR

Removal (2WD Models)

1) Raise vehicle and support with safety stands. Remove brake caliper without disconnecting brake line.

2) Remove grease cover from end of hub. Remove cotter pin, nut, washer, and outer bearing. Remove rotor and hub assembly.

Installation

Install rotor and hub assembly on spindle. Install outer bearing, washer, and nut. Adjust wheel bearings. See Wheel Bearing Adjustment in *SUSPENSION Section*

Removal (4WD Models)

Raise vehicle and support with safety stands. Remove wheel assembly. Remove locking hub assembly as outlined in Locking Hub article at end of this section. Remove wheel bearing lock nut, lock ring and adjuster nut. Remove rotor and hub assembly.

Installation

To install, reverse removal procedures. Adjust wheel bearings, see Wheel Bearing Adjustment in *SUSPENSION Section.*

Removal (Rear Wheel Disc Brakes)

1) Raise vehicle and support with safety stands. Remove brake caliper without disconnecting brake line. Support caliper out of the way.

GENERAL MOTORS SLIDING CALIPER DISCS (Cont.)

2) Remove axle shaft flange bolts. Remove drive axle. Bend lock tab on bearing lock nut and remove lock nut. Remove lock tab assembly. Remove inner bearing adjusting nut and washer. Remove rotor and hub assembly.

Installation

1) Install rotor and hub assembly into position on axle housing. Install outer bearing and washer. Make sure tang on washer is aligned with groove in axle housing.

2) Install inner bearing nut and adjust wheel bearings. See Wheel Bearing Adjustment in *SUSPENSION Section*.

3) Install drive axle shaft using a new flange gasket. Tighten bolts to 115 ft. lbs. (156 N.m). Install brake caliper as previously outlined.

OVERHAUL

BRAKE CALIPER

Disassembly

1) Wipe caliper clean around inlet port and remove plug. Drain fluid from caliper housing. Place caliper assembly on bench (piston side up).

2) Place several shop towels between piston and outer legs of caliper housing. Carefully apply low-pressure air at caliper inlet port until piston comes out of caliper housing.

3) If piston is seized, lightly tap around end of piston with soft-faced hammer. Do not attempt to catch piston by hand, since it may pop out of caliper with some force.

Fig. 2: Using Compressed Air to Remove Caliper Piston

Place shop towels under caliper to catch piston.

4) Remove boot from piston and seal from cylinder bore. Clean caliper housing and piston with denatured alcohol. Check cylinder bore, seal groove, and boot groove for damage or excessive wear. Replace piston if pitted.

Fig. 3: Exploded View of Sliding Caliper Assembly

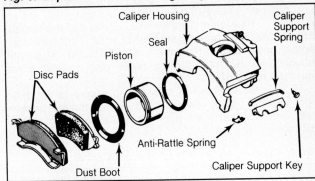

Reassembly

To assemble caliper, soak all parts in new brake fluid and reverse disassembly procedures. Use large "C" clamp to seat piston in cylinder bore.

DISC ROTOR

Lateral Runout

Adjust wheel bearings until all end play is eliminated. Attach dial indicator with contact tip of indicator on braking surface approximately 1" from rotor edge. Set indicator to zero and turn rotor through one complete revolution, noting indicator reading.

Parallelism

Check thickness of rotor at 4 or more points around circumference of rotor. Make all measurements at same distance from edge of rotor. If thickness variation is excessive, refinish or replace rotor as necessary.

TIGHTENING SPECIFICATIONS

Application	Ft. Lbs. (N.m)
Brake Line-to-Caliper	32 (44)
Support Key Retaining Screw	18 (24)
Caliper Mounting Bolts	35 (48)
Hydraulic Line-to-Brake Hose	13 (18)
Bleeder Valve Screws	5 (7)

DISC BRAKE ROTOR SPECIFICATIONS

Application	Disc Diameter In. (mm)	Lateral Runout In. (mm)	Parallelism In. (mm)	Original Thickness In. (mm)	Min. Refinish Thickness In. (mm)	Discard Thickness In. (mm)
S/10/15 & All w/Diesel Engine	11.86 (301.2)	.004 (.10)	.0005 (.013)	1.28 (32.5)	1.23 (31.2)	1.22 (30.9)
All Others						
Front (Drum Rear)	12.50 (317.5)	.004 (.10)	.0005 (.013)	1.53 (38.9)	1.48 (37.6)	1.47 (37.2)
Front (Disc Rear)	14.25 (361.9)	.004 (.10)	.0005 (.013)	1.53 (38.9)	1.48 (37.6)	1.47 (37.2)
Rear	13.75 (349.3)	.004 (.10)	.0005 (.013)	1.53 (38.9)	1.48 (37.6)	1.47 (37.2)

Brake Systems

JEEP FLOATING CALIPER DISCS

Cherokee, "J" Models, Wagoneer

DESCRIPTION

Floating caliper disc brake assembly uses a single piston caliper which "floats" on 2 bolts. As brake pedal is depressed, hydraulic pressure is passed through a proportioning valve to brake caliper piston.

This force is transmitted to inboard brake pad, forcing it against braking surface of rotor. Pressure then moves outer caliper housing and pad inward on caliper mounting bolts, thus forcing outer pad against outer braking surface of rotor.

When brake is released, pressure is removed from cylinders and inherent rotor runout moves pistons back into cylinders to maintain sufficient rotor-to-pad clearance.

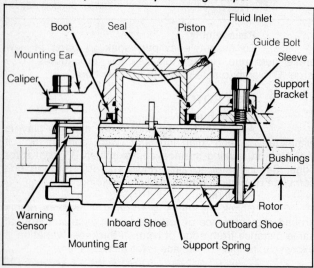

Fig. 1: Cutaway View of Jeep Floating Caliper

ADJUSTMENT & SERVICING

BRAKE PADS

Automatic adjustment is provided by outward relocation of piston as lining wears.

BLEEDING SYSTEM

See Hydraulic Brake Bleeding in this Section.

REMOVAL & INSTALLATION

BRAKE PADS

Removal

1) Drain 2/3 of the brake fluid from front reservoir using bleeder screw at front outlet port. Raise vehicle and support with safety stands. Remove front wheel assembly.

2) Place "C" clamp on caliper. Solid end of clamp should contact back of caliper. Screw end should contact metal part of outboard shoes.

3) Tighten "C" clamp until caliper moves far enough to force piston to bottom of bore. This will back shoes off rotor surface, easing lining removal and installation.

4) Remove both Allen head mounting bolts and lift caliper off rotor. Support caliper out of the way. Remove both brake pads.

5) Remove support spring from inboard shoe and note spring position for correct installation. Remove sleeves from inboard ears of caliper. Remove rubber bushings from all holes in caliper ears.

Installation

1) To install, reverse removal procedures. Lubricate new bushings, sleeves, bushing grooves and small ends of mounting bolts with silicone lubricant.

2) Install rubber bushings in all caliper mounting ears. Shoe ears should rest on upper surface of caliper mounting ears and lower shoe tabs should fit into cutout in caliper.

BRAKE CALIPER

Removal & Installation

Caliper removal and installation procedures are same as for disc pad replacement. To remove caliper from vehicle, disconnect brake line at caliper and cap hole to prevent contamination.

DISC ROTOR

Removal

1) Raise vehicle and support with safety stands. Remove wheel assembly and caliper. On models without free hubs, remove rotor hub cap, drive gear snap ring, drive gear, pressure spring and spring cup.

2) On models with front hubs, remove screws attaching hub body to hub clutch and remove body from clutch. Remove large and small retaining rings. Remove hub clutch from axle shaft.

3) On all models, straighten lip of outer lock nut retaining washer. Remove wheel bearing lock nuts and washers. Remove rotor and wheel bearings.

Installation

1) Lubricate bearings with EP-type water proof wheel bearing lubrication. Install bearing and new seal in rotor hub. Install rotor and inner lock nut and retaining washer.

NOTE: Bearing adjuster inner lock nut has locating peg on one side. When installed, peg must face away from bearing.

2) Install wheel but do not tighten nuts. While rotating wheel, tighten inner lock nut to 50 ft. lbs. (68 N.m), and then back of 60°. Install outer lock nut and retaining washer. Tighten outer lock nut to 50 ft. lbs. (68 N.m).

NOTE: Be sure locating peg is engaged in one of the retaining washer holes before installing outer lock nut.

3) On models without front hubs, install pressure spring cup, pressure spring, drive gear and snap ring. Coat rim of chrome hub cover with Permatex No. 3 (or equivalent) and install cap in rotor hub.

CAUTION: Spring cup must be installed so recessed side of cup faces outboard bearing and flat side of cup faces pressure spring.

4) On models with front hubs, install hubs. Install hub clutch on axle. Install large and small hub retaining rings. Install hub body on clutch and tighten to 30 INCH lbs. (7 N.m).

JEEP FLOATING CALIPER DISCS (Cont.)

OVERHAUL

Disassembly

1) Remove caliper from vehicle and remove pads. If pads are to be reused, mark location in caliper. Clean caliper exterior with clean brake fluid. Drain residual fluid from caliper and place caliper on a clean working surface.

2) Remove piston from caliper by applying compressed air to fluid port. Use just enough pressure to ease piston out of bore. Protect piston from damage with folded cloths. Do not try to catch piston by hand.

3) Pry dust boot out of bore with screwdriver. Do not scratch bore. Using a small plastic or wooden stick, pry piston seal from bore.

4) Remove bleeder screw, sleeves and rubber bushings. Clean all parts in clean brake fluid. Blow dry parts with dry, filtered air.

Fig. 2: Exploded View of Floating Caliper Assembly

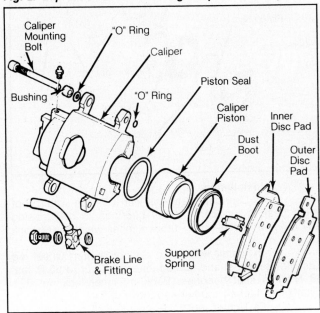

5) Examine parts for rust, corrosion, pitting, scratches, or cracks. Do not attempt to refinish piston in any way. Removal of nickel-chrome plating will lead to pitting, rusting, and eventual cocking in bore.

6) Minor stains on piston bore can be polished with crocus cloth only. Do not use emery cloth or any other abrasive. Wash bore thoroughly with brake fluid after using crocus cloth.

Reassembly

1) Lubricate bore and new seal with brake fluid and install seal in groove using fingers. Lubricate piston with brake fluid. Install new dust boot on piston.

2) Slide metal retainer portion of dust boot over open end of piston and push retainer towards end of piston until lip on fold seats in piston groove.

3) Push retainer portion of boot forward until boot is flush with rim at open end of piston and snaps into place. Insert piston in bore being careful not to unseat piston seal.

4) Push piston to bottom of bore using hammer handle (approximately 50 lbs. of force is required). Position dust boot retainer in counterbore at top of piston.

5) Seat dust boot retainer with installer tool (J-22904). Metal retainer portion of boot must be evenly seated in counterbore and must fit below face of caliper. Install bleeder screw.

6) Connect brake line to caliper using new copper gaskets. Install pads. Install caliper over rotor, bleed brakes, and install wheel assembly. Test system before moving vehicle.

ROTOR

Runout

1) Measure rotor lateral runout by mounting a dial indicator on support stand or steering spindle. Position indicator stylus so it contacts center of rotor lining.

2) Zero indicator and turn rotor 1 revolution. Note indicator reading. Runout must not exceed specifications. Refinish if necessary.

Parallelism

1) Measure rotor parallelism with a micrometer. Measure thickness at 4 or more equally spaced points around rotor circumference.

2) Make all measurements at same distance from edge of rotor. Variation must not exceed specification. Refinish if necessary.

NOTE: Thickness of machined rotor must not be below minimum thickness specification.

TIGHTENING SPECIFICATIONS

Application	Ft. Lbs. (N.m)
Caliper Mounting Bolts	30-40 (41-54)
Bleeder Screw	12 (16)
Brake Line-to-Caliper	13 (18)

DISC BRAKE ROTOR SPECIFICATIONS

Application	Disc Diameter In. (mm)	Lateral Runout In. (mm)	Parallelism In. (mm)	Original Thickness In. (mm)	Min. Refinish Thickness In. (mm)	Discard Thickness In. (mm)
Cherokee, Wagoneer & Pickup	12.00 (304.8)	.005 (.12)	.001 (.03)	....	1.215 (30.86)	1.215 (30.86)

Brake Systems

JEEP SLIDING CALIPER DISCS

"CJ", Scrambler

DESCRIPTION

Sliding caliper disc brake assemblies are of a single piston design. Calipers are mounted to an anchor mount connected to front drive axle.

As brake is depressed, hydraulic pressure is passed to brake caliper piston. This force is transmitted to inboard disc pad and against inner braking surface. As force increases against inner side, caliper slides inward, providing vise-like clamping action on rotor.

ADJUSTMENT & SERVICING

BRAKE PADS

Pad wear is automatically compensated for by piston moving outward in cylinder bore. No disc pad adjustment is necessary.

BLEEDING SYSTEM

See Brake Bleeding in this Section.

REMOVAL & INSTALLATION

BRAKE PADS

Removal

1) To prevent master cylinder overflow when caliper piston is depressed, remove 2/3 of the brake fluid from master cylinder reservoir.

2) Raise vehicle and support with safety stands. Remove wheel assembly. Using a screwdriver or "C" clamp, press caliper piston to bottom of bore. Remove support key retaining screw.

3) Drive out support key with a punch and hammer. Lift caliper assembly off anchor mount. Support caliper out of the way.

4) Remove inner disc pad from anchor mount. Remove anti-rattle spring from inner disc pad. Note position of spring for installation. Remove outer disc pad from caliper.

Installation

1) Install anti-rattle spring on rear flange of inner disc pad. Make sure looped section of spring faces away from rotor. Install inner disc pad in anchor mount.

2) Make sure anti-rattle spring stays in place. Install outer disc pad in caliper. Place caliper in position over rotor and onto anchor mount. Care must be taken not to tear or dislodge dust boot when installing caliper.

3) Align caliper with anchor mount. Install support key and support spring between abutment surfaces at trailing end of caliper and anchor mount.

4) Drive support key into place with a punch and hammer. Install support key screw and tighten.

5) Fill master cylinder with new brake fluid. Press on brake pedal several times to seat disc brake pads. Install wheel assembly and lower vehicle.

BRAKE CALIPER

Removal & Installation

Caliper removal and installation procedures are same as for disc pad replacement. It will be necessary to disconnect brake hose.

DISC ROTOR

Removal

1) Raise vehicle and support with safety stands. Remove caliper as previously outlined. Remove bolts attaching hub body to hub clutch. Remove hub body.

2) Remove axle shaft retaining ring. Remove hub clutch and bearing assembly. Straighten lip of outer lock nut retaining washer.

3) Remove outer lock nut, retaining washer, inner lock nut, and inner retainer ring. Remove hub clutch and bearing assembly.

Fig. 1: Exploded View of Jeep Sliding Caliper

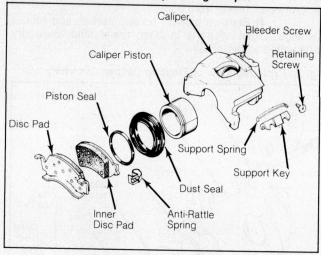

Installation

1) Lubricate bearings with EP-type waterproof wheel bearing lubricant. Install bearings in rotor, using new oil seal. Install rotor, tabbed inner washer and lock nut.

2) Install wheel but do not tighten wheel lug nuts. Rotate wheel and tighten inner lock nut to 50 ft. lbs. (68 N.m) to seat bearings. Back off inner lock nut 60°. Install outer tabbed washer and lock nut.

3) Tighten nut to a minimum of 50 ft. lbs. (68 N.m) and bend lip of tabbed washer over lock nut. Install hub clutch and bearing assembly on axle shaft.

4) Install retaining ring on axle shaft. Install hub body, gasket, and bearing assembly. Align bolt holes in hub body and rotor hub. Install bolts and lock washers. Install caliper and wheel assembly.

OVERHAUL

BRAKE CALIPER

Disassembly

1) Remove caliper and drain brake fluid. Place caliper assembly on bench, (piston side up). Place several shop towels between piston and outer legs of caliper housing.

2) Carefully apply air pressure to caliper inlet port until piston comes out of caliper housing. Use low air pressure to remove piston, as high pressure may cause piston to pop out with considerable force.

3) Remove dust seal from piston. Pry piston seal from piston bore with a plastic or wooden tool. Remove bleeder screw and plastic cap.

JEEP SLIDING CALIPER DISCS (Cont.)

Fig. 2: Using Compressed Air to Remove Caliper Piston

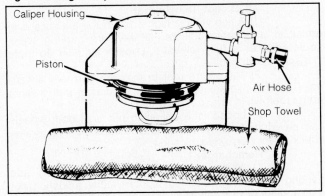

Do not catch piston with hands. Place shop towels under caliper assembly before removing piston.

4) Clean caliper housing and piston with denatured alcohol. Check cylinder bore, seal groove, and boot groove for damage and excessive wear. Replace piston if pitted.

Reassembly

1) Lubricate piston seal with clean brake fluid. Install seal in piston bore groove. Work seal into groove with finger. Install bleeder screw and plastic cap.

2) Place dust seal on piston bore. Do not lubricate seal. Reaching through top of seal, work large lip of seal into seal groove at top of piston bore. Make sure seal is completely seated in groove.

3) Lubricate caliper piston and small lip of dust seal with brake fluid and position piston over seal lip. Hold piston in place on dust seal. Apply reduced air pressure (air pressure should not exceed 15 psi) into caliper inlet port.

4) As air pressure expands dust seal, carefully work caliper piston into dust seal until small lip of seal seats in caliper piston groove. With seal seated in groove, release air pressure and push piston to bottom of bore with a hammer handle.

5) Install caliper. Install brake hose on caliper using a new washer. Tighten brake line bolt. Fill master cylinder and bleed system. Check brake application and refill master cylinder if necessary.

DISC ROTOR

Lateral Runout

1) Adjust wheel bearings until all end play is eliminated. Attach dial indicator with contact tip of indicator on braking surface 1" from rotor edge.

2) Set indicator to zero and turn rotor through 1 revolution noting indicator reading. If runout exceeds specifications, replace or refinish rotor.

Parallelism

Check thickness of rotor at 4 or more points around circumference of rotor. Make all measurements at same distance from edge of rotor. If thickness variation exceeds specifications, replace or refinish rotor.

TIGHTENING SPECIFICATIONS

Application	Ft. Lbs. (N.m)
Brake Hose-to-Caliper	13 (18)
Support Key Retaining Screw	15 (20)

DISC BRAKE ROTOR SPECIFICATIONS

Application	Disc Diameter In. (mm)	Lateral Runout In. (mm)	Parallelism In. (mm)	Original Thickness In. (mm)	Min. Refinish Thickness In. (mm)	Discard Thickness In. (mm)
"CJ" & Scrambler	11.70 (297.2)	.005 (.12)	.001 (.03)	....	.815 (20.70)	.815 (20.70)

Brake Systems

CHRYSLER CORP. SINGLE ANCHOR

Dodge, Plymouth

DESCRIPTION

Chrysler Corp. vehicles use both Chrysler and Bendix single anchor brake assemblies. All 10" brakes are Chrysler type. All 12" brakes are Bendix type.

Both types of brake assemblies consist of a support plate, 2 brake shoes, return springs, wheel cylinder, and a cable type adjuster assembly. The automatic adjuster assembly consists of a cable (with hook and anchor fitting), cable guide, adjuster lever, adjusting screw, pivot, socket, and spring.

ADJUSTMENT & SERVICING

BRAKE SHOES

1) With wheels raised off floor and parking brake lever fully released, remove adjusting hole cover. Use brake adjuster tool (C-3784) to expand brake shoes until slight drag is felt when wheel is rotated.

2) While holding automatic adjusting lever out of contact with adjusting screw, back off adjusting screw 10 or 12 notches. Check for free wheel rotation with no brake shoe drag.

3) Repeat adjustment for remaining wheels. Adjustment must be equal at all wheels. Replace adjusting hole covers and adjust parking brake.

BLEEDING SYSTEM

See Brake Bleeding in this Section.

PARKING BRAKE

All Except Ramcharger

1) Raise vehicle high enough to gain access to equalizer and cable adjuster. Make sure parking brake cable adjuster is fully released. Loosen adjuster so there is slack in both cables.

2) Make sure rear brakes are correctly adjusted. Tighten cable adjusting nut at the adjuster until a slight drag is felt while rotating the wheel.

3) Loosen the adjusting nut until both wheels can be rotated freely. Apply and release parking brake, checking for free wheel rotation.

Ramcharger

1) With service brakes fully adjusted and parking brake fully released, tighten cable adjusting nut until a slight drag is felt while rotating rear wheels.

2) Loosen cable adjusting nut until both rear wheels can be rotated freely. Back off adjusting nut an additional 2 turns. Apply and release parking brake several times, checking for free rotation at rear wheels.

REMOVAL & INSTALLATION

BRAKE SHOES

Chrysler 10" Brake Assembly

1) With drum removed, remove brake shoe return springs, noting that secondary spring overlaps primary spring. Slide automatic adjuster cable eye off anchor.

2) Disconnect cable from adjusting lever. Remove cable, overload spring, cable guide, and anchor

Fig. 1: Exploded View of Chrysler Type Brake Assembly

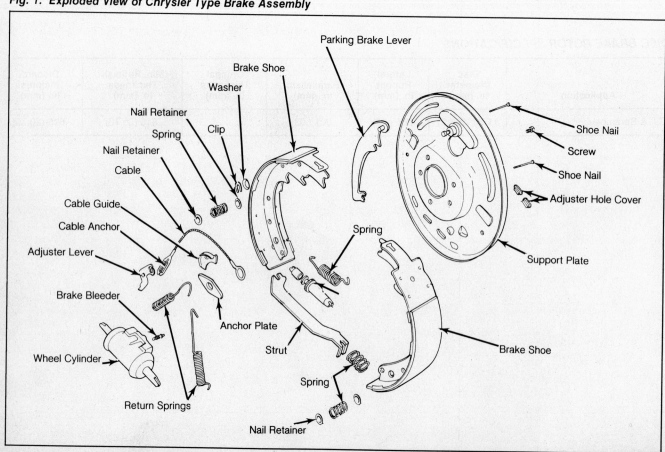

CHRYSLER CORP. SINGLE ANCHOR (Cont.)

Fig. 2: Exploded View of Bendix Type Brake Assembly

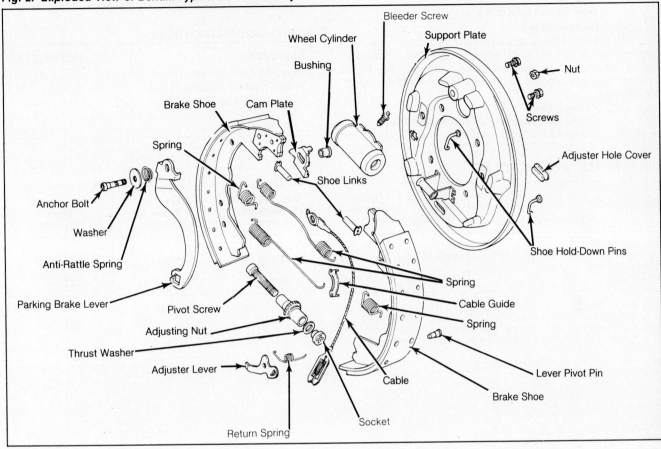

plate. Disconnect adjuster lever from spring and remove lever.

3) Remove automatic adjuster spring from brake shoes. Remove brake shoe retainers, springs, and shoe nails. Spread shoes apart and remove parking brake strut and spring.

4) Disconnect parking brake cable from lever and remove brake shoes. Reverse removal procedures to install brake shoes.

Bendix 12" Brake Assembly

1) With drum removed, disconnect adjusting lever return spring from lever. Remove lever and spring from pivot pin. Disconnect lever from cable.

2) Remove upper spring connecting both shoes. Disconnect and remove shoe hold-down springs.

3) Disconnect parking brake cable from parking brake lever. Remove spring connecting both shoes. Remove shoes and star wheel adjuster. Reverse removal procedures to install.

AXLE BEARING & SEAL

Removal

1) Remove wheel assembly and brake drum. On differential with bearing retaining plate on end of axle housing, remove retaining nuts through hole provided in axle flange. Using slide hammer, remove axle. Remove brake backing plate and attach it to frame with wire.

2) On differential without retaining plate on end of axle housing, it will be necessary to remove differential

cover and drain lubricant. Remove differential pinion shaft lock bolt and pinion shaft.

NOTE: **The pinion gears may be left in place. Once the axle shafts are removed, reinstall pinion shaft and lock bolt.**

3) Push flange end of axle shafts toward center of vehicle and remove "C" lock clips from button end of axle shaft. Remove axle from housing. Insert Rear Axle Remover and slide hammer into bore and position it behind bearing so tangs on tool engage bearing outer race. Remove bearing and seal as a unit.

Installation

To install, reverse removal procedures.

WHEEL CYLINDERS

1) Remove wheel, drum, and brake shoes. Remove cylinder connecting links and disconnect hydraulic brake line from cylinder.

NOTE: **On vehicles equipped with vacuum boosters, be sure there is no vacuum in system before disconnecting hydraulic lines.**

2) Remove brake cylinder retaining bolts and remove cylinder from backing plate. To install, reverse removal procedures.

CHRYSLER CORP. SINGLE ANCHOR (Cont.)

OVERHAUL

WHEEL CYLINDERS

Disassembly

With wheel cylinder removed from vehicle, remove rubber boots from ends of cylinders. Remove piston return spring, cylinder cups, and pistons from cylinder. Remove bleeder screw and inspect cylinder bore for damage.

Reassembly

If bore of cylinder is pitted or scratched, hone or replace as necessary. Soak all parts in clean brake fluid or assembly lubricant and reverse disassembly procedure. Clamp brake cylinder pistons against ends of cylinder.

TIGHTENING SPECIFICATIONS

Application	Ft. Lbs. (N.m)
Brake Hose-to-Wheel Cylinder	25 (34)
Wheel Cylinder Mounting Bolt	11-19 (15-26)
Hydraulic Brake Tube Nuts	
3/8" & 7/16"	13 (18)
1/2" & 9/16"	15 (20)

DRUM BRAKE SPECIFICATIONS

Application	Drum Diam. In. (mm)	Drum Width In. (mm)	Max. Drum Refinish Diam. In. (mm)	Brake Cyl. Diam. In. (mm)	Master Cyl. Diam. In. (mm)
AD, AW, B150/250, D150, W150	10.00 (254.0)	2.50 (63.5)	10.06 (255.5)	.94 (23.8)	1.13 (28.6)
B350, D250/350, W250/350	12.00 (304.8)	¹ 3.00 (76.2)	12.06 (306.3)	² 1.00 (25.4)	1.13 (28.6)

¹ — D250 w/Spicer 60 rear axle and W250: width is 2.50" (63.5 mm).
² — D250 w/Spicer 60, H.D. rear axle, D350 and W350: wheel cylinder specifications not available.
   B350 w/4000 ls. front axle: wheel cylinder diameter is 1.06" (26.9 mm).

FORD SINGLE ANCHOR

DESCRIPTION

The single anchor dual servo brake assembly is used on the rear of all 2WD trucks and on all 4 wheels of the 4WD vehicles (without disc brakes). This assembly consists of a support plate, 2 brake shoes, return springs, automatic adjuster components, and a wheel cylinder.

The automatic adjuster consists of a cable (with hood and anchor fitting), a cable guide, adjusting lever, adjusting screw, pivot nut, socket and spring.

The adjuster uses movement of the secondary shoe during reverse brake application to turn brake adjusting screw and maintain proper lining-to-drum clearance.

ADJUSTMENT & SERVICING

BRAKE SHOES

All Models

1) Adjustment is made with brake drums at room temperature and parking brakes correctly adjusted. Measure inside diameter of brake drum with measuring gauge (Rotunda 11-0001 for Bronco, Bronco II, Ranger, 100/150 Series; 11-0002 for 250/350 Series). See Fig. 1.

Fig. 1: Measuring Brake Drum Diameter

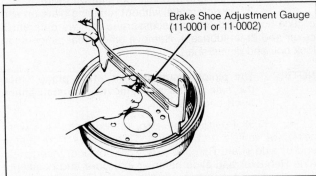

Check diameter with drum at room temperature.

2) Reverse tool and apply to brake shoes on a line parallel to the ground, through center of axle. Hold automatic adjuster lever away from adjusting screw and turn screw until outside diameter of shoes contacts gauge. See Fig. 2.

Fig. 2: Measuring Brake Shoe Diameter

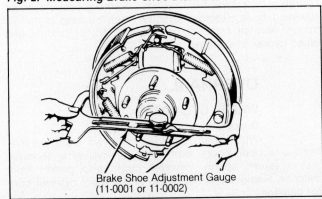

Shoes should just make contact with measuring gauge.

3) Apply a small amount of lubricant at shoe-to-backing plate contact points. Install brake drum and wheel assembly. Complete adjustment by applying brakes several times while driving vehicle in reverse. Check brake operation by making several stops while driving forward.

Fig. 3: Bronco, Bronco II, Ranger, E & F100/150 Rear Brake Assembly

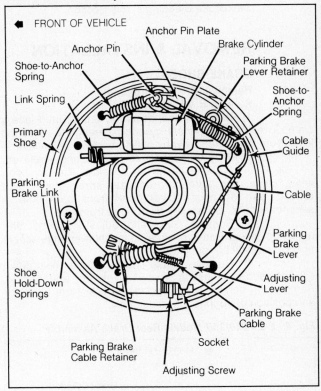

PARKING BRAKE

NOTE: If front brake cable tension limiting device is replaced, intial adjustment procedures must be performed before adjusting cable. If tensioner is not replaced, initial adjustment is not required.

Initial Adjustment

Depress the parking brake pedal. Grip the tension limiter bracket to prevent it from spinning. Tighten equalizer nut 2 1/2" up the rod. Check to make sure the cinch strap has slipped so that less the 1 3/8" remain exposed.

Regular Cable (E100/350)

1) Release parking brake pedal. Grip automatic adjuster to prevent it from spinning. Tighten equalizer nut 6 full turns past its original position.

2) Depress pedal and check tension. Release pedal and check rear wheel drag. If drag is noted on E250/350 models, remove drums and check for clearance between parking brake lever and cam plate. Clearance should be .015" (.38 mm) with brakes fully released. Adjust as necessary.

Regular Cable (Bronco, Bronco II, Ranger & F100/350)

1) Depress parking brake pedal 2 notches. Attach tension gauge (Rotunda 210018) behind equalizer assembly. Turn equalizer adjusting nut until tension gauge reads 250 ft. lbs. (340 N.m).

FORD SINGLE ANCHOR (Cont.)

2) Back off equalizer nut until tension gauge reads 50 ft. lbs. (68 N.m). Retighten adjusting nut until tension gauge reads 60-100 ft. lbs. (82-136 N.m). Check parking brake operation.

BLEEDING SYSTEM
See Brake Bleeding in this Section.

REMOVAL & INSTALLATION

BRAKE SHOES
Removal (Bronco, Bronco II, Ranger, E & F100/150)
1) Remove wheel assembly and drum. Place a clamp over ends of wheel cylinder. Disengage adjusting lever from adjusting screw by pulling backwards on lever.

2) Move outboard side of adjusting screw up, and back off pivot nut as far as possible. Pull adjusting lever, cable, and automatic adjuster spring down, and toward rear to unhook pivot hook from large hole in secondary shoe. Do not pry pivot hook from hole.

3) Remove automatic adjuster spring and adjusting lever. Remove shoe to anchor springs, cable anchor, and anchor pin plate.

4) Remove cable guide, shoe hold-down springs, shoes adjusting screw, pivot nut, and socket. Remove the parking brake spring and link. Note the color and position of springs for reassembly.

Fig. 4: E & F250/350 Models Rear Brake Assembly

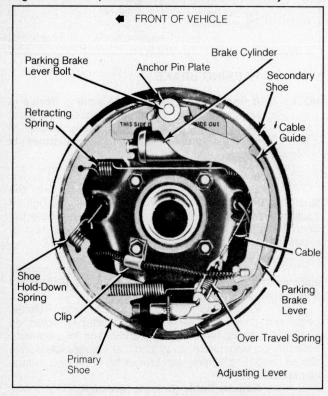

5) Disconnect parking brake cable from lever. Remove secondary shoe and disassemble parking brake lever from shoe by removing retaining clip and spring washer.

Installation
To install, reverse removal procedures. Make sure adjusting cable is in groove of cable guide. Check that cable does not bind on anchor pin, and adjusting screw is mounted on correct side. If adjuster screw is mounted on wrong side, adjuster will operate incorrectly.
Removal (E & F250/350)
1) Remove wheel assembly and brake drum. Remove parking brake assembly retaining nut from backing plate. Remove parking brake assembly. Remove adjusting cable assembly from anchor pin, cable guide, and adjusting lever.

2) Remove brake shoe return springs, hold down springs, and brake shoes. Remove and disassemble adjusting screw assembly.
Installation
Apply a light coat of high temperature grease to contact points of brake assembly and reverse removal procedures.

AXLE BEARING & SEAL
Removal
1) Remove wheel assembly and brake drum. On differential with bearing retaining plate on end of axle housing, remove retaining nuts through hole provided in axle flange. Using slide hammer, remove axle. Remove brake backing plate and attach it to frame with wire.

2) On differential without retaining plate on end of axle housing, it will be necessary to remove differential cover and drain lubricant. Remove differential pinion shaft lock bolt and pinion shaft.

NOTE: **The pinion gears may be left in place. Once the axle shafts are removed, reinstall pinion shaft and lock bolt.**

3) Push flange end of axle shafts toward center of vehicle and remove "C" lock clips from button end of axle shaft. Remove axle from housing. Insert Rear Axle Remover and slide hammer into bore and position it behind bearing so tangs on tool engage bearing outer race. Remove bearing and seal as a unit.
Installation
To install, reverse removal procedures.
WHEEL CYLINDER
Removal & Installation
Remove wheel assembly, drum, and brake shoes. Remove cylinder connecting links and disconnect hydraulic brake line from cylinder. Remove brake cylinder retaining bolts. Remove cylinder from backing plate. To install, reverse removal procedures. Adjust brakes and bleed hydraulic system.

OVERHAUL

WHEEL CYLINDERS
Disassembly
With wheel cylinder removed from vehicle, remove rubber boots from ends of cylinders. Remove piston return spring, cylinder cups, and piston from cylinder. Remove bleeder screw and inspect cylinder bore for damage.

FORD SINGLE ANCHOR (Cont.)

DRUM BRAKE SPECIFICATIONS

Application	Drum Diam. In. (mm)	Drum Width In. (mm)	Max. Drum Refinish Diam. In. (mm)	Brake Cyl. Diam. In. (mm)	Master Cyl. Diam. In. (mm)
Bronco, Bronco II, Ranger, E/F100 & 150	11.03 (280.2)	2.25 (57.2)	11.09 (281.7)	.94 (23.9)	1.00 (25.4)
E250, F250 (Exc. H.D.)	12.00 (304.8)	2.50 (63.5)	12.06 (306.3)	.94 (23.9)	1.00 (25.4)
F250 H.D. & E/F350	12.00 (304.8)	3.00 (76.2)	12.06 (306.3)	1.06 (27.0)	1.00 (25.4)

Reassembly

If bore of cylinder is lightly pitted or scratched, hone or replace as necessary. Soak all parts in brake fluid or assembly lube, and reverse disassembly procedures. Clamp brake cylinder pistons against ends of cylinder.

TIGHTENING SPECIFICATIONS

Application	Ft. Lbs. (N.m)
Front Backing Plate-to-Spindle	
7/16"	30-50 (41-68)
1/2"	55-70 (75-95)
1/2"	55-75 (75-102)
1 3/8"	30-40 (41-54)
Rear Backing Plate-to-Axle	
7/16"	35-45 (48-61)
1/2"	75-105 (102-143)
1/2"	50-70 68-95)
Hydraulic Tube Nuts	
3/8" & 7/16"	10-15 (14-20)
1/2" & 9/16"	10-17 (14-20)

Brake Systems

GENERAL MOTORS SINGLE ANCHOR

All Models (Rear Only)

DESCRIPTION

Delco single anchor, duo-servo type brake assemblies are used on the rear of all models. The assemblies consist of a support plate, 2 brake shoes, return springs, automatic adjuster components and a duo-servo wheel cylinder.

Automatic adjusters consist of a connecting link, override lever, override spring, return spring, actuating lever and an adjusting screw. Normal adjustment is accomplished through movement of actuating lever and secondary shoe during application of brakes when vehicle is operated in reverse.

ADJUSTMENT & SERVICING

BRAKE SHOES

1) Knock out lanced area in brake drum with a punch. If drum is installed, it must be removed and all metal removed from brake area.

2) Turn adjusting screw, through hole, until brake shoes expand and brake drums can just be turned by hand. The drag should be equal at all wheels.

3) Back off adjusting screw 30 notches at each wheel. If drum still drags, back off an additional 1 or 2 notches. Install hole cover in drum.

PARKING BRAKE

Rear Wheel Type (Foot Pedal Actuated)

1) With service brakes correctly adjusted, raise vehicle until both rear wheels are off ground. Loosen equalizer adjusting nut. Apply parking brake 4 notches from fully released position.

2) Tighten adjusting nut until a slight drag is felt when wheels are rotated forward. Tighten lock nut. Release parking brake and wheels should rotate forward freely. Lower vehicle.

Rear Wheel Type (Orscheln Lever Actuated)

1) With service brakes in proper adjustment, turn adjusting knob on lever counterclockwise to stop. Apply parking brake and raise vehicle until both rear wheels are off ground.

2) Loosen intermediate cable equalizer lock nut and adjust front nut until slight drag is felt when rear wheels are rotated forward. Tighten lock nut. Readjust lever adjusting knob to obtain definite snap-over-center feel. Release parking brake and check that no drag is present when wheels are rotated.

Transmission Mounted (Internal Shoe Type)

1) With at least 1 rear wheel raised off ground, block wheels and release parking brake. Remove cotter pin and clevis pin connecting pull rod and relay lever.

2) Rotate drum to bring one access hole into line with adjuster screw at bottom of brake shoes (manual transmission) or top of shoes (automatic transmission). Knock out plug in drum for access hole, if necessary.

3) Rotate adjusting screws with a screwdriver to expand shoes until tight against drum. Drum should not be able to be rotated by hand. Back off adjuster screw 10 notches. Place parking brake lever in full released position.

4) Pull on brake cable enough to take up slack in brake linkage. Adjust pull rod clevis to line up with hole in relay lever. Insert clevis pin and roller pin. Tighten clevis lock nut. Install a new plug in access hole in drum and lower vehicle.

BLEEDING SYSTEM

See Brake Bleeding in this Section.

REMOVAL & INSTALLATION

BRAKE SHOES

Removal

1) Raise vehicle and support with safety stands. Remove wheel assembly and brake drum. It may

Fig. 1: Exploded View of Single Anchor Brake Assembly

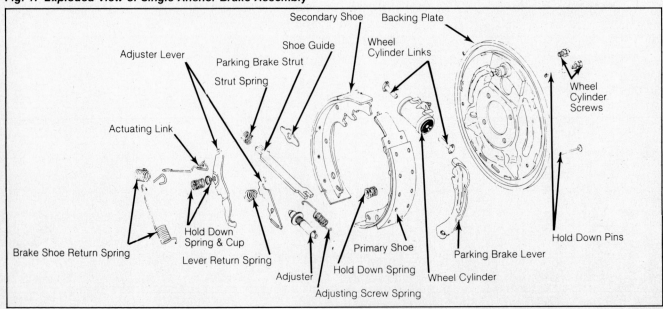

Secondary Shoe — Backing Plate — Shoe Guide — Wheel Cylinder Links — Adjuster Lever — Parking Brake Strut — Strut Spring — Actuating Link — Wheel Cylinder Screws — Hold Down Spring & Cup — Brake Shoe Return Spring — Lever Return Spring — Adjuster — Adjusting Screw Spring — Hold Down Spring — Primary Shoe — Wheel Cylinder — Parking Brake Lever — Hold Down Pins

GENERAL MOTORS SINGLE ANCHOR (Cont.)

be necessary to back off brake shoe adjustment before removing drum. Unlock primary and secondary shoe springs. Remove shoe hold down springs.

NOTE: On some vehicles, it may be necessary to remove axle shafts to remove hub and drum.

2) Lift up on actuator, unhook actuating link from anchor pin and remove link. Spread shoes enough to clear wheel cylinder links. Remove parking brake strut and spring. Disconnect cable from lever. Remove brake shoes.

Installation
1) Lubricate fulcrum end of parking brake lever with brake lubricant. Attach lever to secondary shoe. Make sure lever moves free. Connect brake shoes together with adjuster spring.

2) Place adjuster screw in postion. Make sure spring does not contact starwheel portion of adjusting screw. Right hand thread adjusting screw should be on left side.

3) Make sure starwheel lines up with hole in backing plate. Apply a thin coating of brake lubricant to contact surface on backing plate. Position brake shoes on backing plate.

4) Primary shoe (short lining) is to front. Connect cable to parking brake lever. Install strut between shoes. Install actuator, return spring and actuator link. Install shoe hold down springs.

5) Install both primary and secondary shoe springs. Measure inside diameter of brake drum with measuring gauge (J-21177). Expand brake shoes to dimension obtained on outside caliper portion of tool.

6) Install brake drum and wheel assembly. Bleed system if any portion of hydraulic system was opened. Check fluid level in master cylinder and add as necessary.

AXLE BEARING & SEAL
Removal
1) Remove wheel assembly and brake drum. On differential with bearing retaining plate on end of axle housing, remove retaining nuts through hole provided in axle flange. Using slide hammer, remove axle. Remove brake backing plate and attach it to frame with wire.

2) On differential without retaining plate on end of axle housing, it will be necessary to remove differential cover and drain lubricant. Remove differential pinion shaft lock bolt and pinion shaft.

NOTE: The pinion gears may be left in place. Once the axle shafts are removed, reinstall pinion shaft and lock bolt.

3) Push flange end of axle shafts toward center of vehicle and remove "C" lock clips from button end of axle shaft. Remove axle from housing. Insert Rear Axle Remover and slide hammer into bore and position it behind bearing so tangs on tool engage bearing outer race. Remove bearing and seal as a unit.

Installation
To install, reverse removal procedures.

WHEEL CYLINDER
Removal & Installation
Remove wheel assembly, drum, and brake shoes. Remove cylinder connecting links and disconnect hydraulic brake line from cylinder. Remove brake cylinder retaining bolts and remove cylinder from support plate. To install, reverse removal procedures.

OVERHAUL

WHEEL CYLINDER
Disassembly
Remove rubber boots from ends of cylinder. Remove piston return spring, cylinder cups, and pistons from cylinder. Remove bleeder screw and inspect bore for damage.

Reassembly
If bore of cylinder is pitted and/or scratched, hone or replace as needed. Soak rubber cylinder cups in brake fluid or assembly lube and reverse disassembly procedures.

TIGHTENING SPECIFICATIONS

Application	Ft. Lbs. (N.m)
Brake Hose Attaching Nut	13 (17)
Rear Brake Anchor Pin	140 (190)
Bleeder Valves	5 (7)
Brake Line Nut	13 (18)
Wheel Cylinder Attaching Bolts	4 (6)
Brake Line Clips	13 (18)

DRUM BRAKE SPECIFICATIONS

Application	Drum Diam. In. (mm)	Drum Width In. (mm)	Max. Drum Refinish Diam. In. (mm)	Brake Cyl. Diam. In. (mm)	Master Cyl. Diam. In. (mm)
C10 & G10					
to 4900 GVW	11.00 (279.4)	2.00 (50.8)	11.06 (280.9)	1.00 (25.4)	1.00 (25.4)
to 5600 GVW	11.00 (279.4)	2.00 (50.8)	11.06 (280.9)	1.00 (25.4)	1.12 (28.4)
C10 5200-6100 GVW	11.15 (283.2)	2.75 (69.9)	11.21 (284.7)	1.00 (25.4)	1.12 (28.5)
C, G, & K10; C, G, K, & P20					
to 6800 GVW	11.15 (283.2)	2.75 (69.9)	11.21 (284.7)	[1] .94 (23.8)	1.12 (28.5)
C, K, & P20; G & P30					
6800-8600 GVW	13.00 (330.2)	2.50 (63.5)	13.06 (331.7)	1.06 (26.9)	1.25 (31.8)
C, G, K, & P30	13.00 (330.2)	3.50 (88.9)	13.06 (331.7)	1.19 (30.2)	1.34 (34.0)
S10/15	9.45 (249.0)	....	9.56 (242.8)	.87 (22.1)	.95 (24.1)

[1] — 1" (25.4 mm) on some 20 series over 6400 GVW.

Brake Systems

JEEP SINGLE ANCHOR — CABLE ADJUSTER

"CJ", Scrambler

DESCRIPTION

Automatic adjuster brakes are 2 shoe, self-centering type with brake shoe anchor at upper end of shoes above wheel cylinder. Single cylinder is double acting. Automatic adjuster device is cable operated.

ADJUSTMENT & SERVICING

BRAKE SHOES

Brake shoes adjust automatically as brakes are applied when vehicle is operated in reverse. Brake shoes can be manually adjusted by rotating adjuster screw.

Remove access slot cover. Using a small blade screwdriver, push in on adjustment lever to separate from adjustment screw. Turn adjustment screw until brake drum is locked tight, then back screw off until wheel rotates freely. It may also be necessary to back shoes off a few notches to remove drum.

PARKING BRAKE

Rear Wheel Integral

Adjustment is not necessary in normal service; automatic service brake adjustments also adjust parking brake. In case of brake overhaul or to compensate for stretched cables, adjust as follows: Check first for binds, kinks or any frayed condition of cables.

Check that brake shoes are in proper adjustment before proceeding. Release parking brake. Loosen lock nuts at equalizer under vehicle. Tighten cables until wheels drag slightly when rotated by hand. Loosen cables until wheels rotate freely and no drag is felt. Tighten lock nut and check operation of parking brake.

BLEEDING SYSTEM

See Brake Bleeding in this Section.

REMOVAL & INSTALLATION

BRAKE SHOES

Removal

1) Raise vehicle and support with safety stands. Remove wheel assembly and drum. Grasp adjusting lever with pliers and remove tang from hole in secondary shoe.

2) Place clamping device over wheel cylinder to retain pistons during further disassembly. Remove secondary return spring, adjuster cable, primary return spring, cable guide, adjuster lever, and adjuster springs.

3) Remove hold-down springs and brake shoes. Disengage parking brake cable from parking brake lever.

Fig. 1: Exploded View of Jeep Brake Assembly With Cable Operated Adjuster

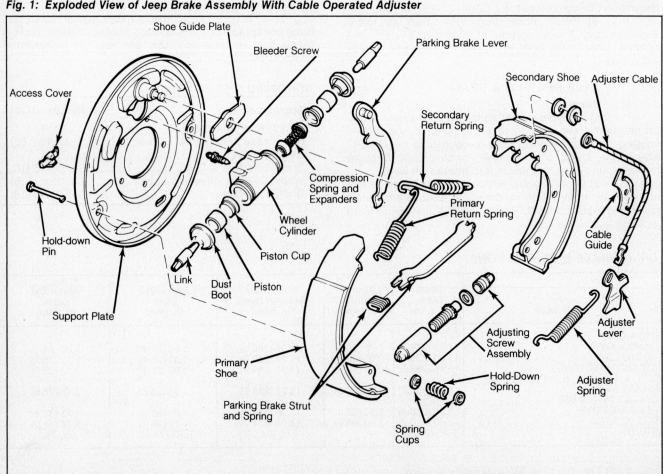

JEEP SINGLE ANCHOR — CABLE ADJUSTER (Cont.)

Installation

1) Lubricate support plate ledges, anchor pin, self-adjusting cable guide, adjuster screw threads, and pivot with molydisulphide grease or chassis lubricant.

2) Lubricate parking brake cable lever and install on secondary brake. Install washer and replacement lever retaining "U" clip. Crimp ends of clip to retain it on pivot.

3) Position brake shoe on brake support plate and install hold-down springs. Install parking brake cable in lever. Install parking brake strut and positioning spring.

4) Place adjuster cable eyelet on anchor pin and install primary return spring. Install cable guide to secondary brake shoe and install secondary return spring.

5) Install adjuster screw and spring on brake shoes and insert small hooked end of spring into large hole in primary brake shoe. Install large hooked end of spring in adjuster lever.

6) Position adjuster cable in cable guide groove. Insert hooked end of cable in adjuster lever. Grasp adjuster lever with pliers and hook adjuster lever tang in large hole in bottom of secondary shoe.

7) Initially adjust brakes using clearance gauge (J-21177) or manual adjustment procedure outlined in this story. See Brake Shoe Adjustment.

8) Install brake drums and, if brake lines were disconnected, bleed system. Install wheels and lower vehicle.

9) Apply and release brakes 10-15 times while driving forward and backward. This adjusts and balances brake system. Road test vehicle.

AXLE BEARING & SEAL

Removal

1) Remove wheel assembly and brake drum. On differential with bearing retaining plate on end of axle housing, remove retaining nuts through hole provided in axle flange. Using slide hammer, remove axle. Remove brake backing plate and attach it to frame with wire.

2) On differential without retaining plate on end of axle housing, it will be necessary to remove differential cover and drain lubricant. Remove differential pinion shaft lock bolt and pinion shaft.

NOTE: **The pinion gears may be left in place. Once the axle shafts are removed, reinstall pinion shaft and lock bolt.**

3) Push flange end of axle shafts toward center of vehicle and remove "C" lock clips from button end of axle shaft. Remove axle from housing. Insert Rear Axle Remover and slide hammer into bore and position it behind bearing so tangs on tool engage bearing outer race. Remove bearing and seal as a unit.

Installation

To install, reverse removal procedures.

WHEEL CYLINDER

Removal

1) Remove wheel assemblies, brake drums, and brake shoes. Disconnect brake line at each wheel cylinder. Do not bend line away from cylinder.

2) When cylinder is moved away from support plate, line will separate easily. Remove cylinder-to-support plate bolts and remove cylinder.

Installation

To install, reverse removal procedures. Start brake line fitting into cylinder before installing cylinder to support plate.

OVERHAUL

WHEEL CYLINDER

NOTE: **Vehicle manufacturer recommends that cylinders not be honed.**

Disassembly

1) Remove brake shoe links and dust boots. Push pistons, piston cups, and expander spring out of bore. Discard piston cups.

2) Clean all cylinder parts with clean brake fluid or brake solvent. Inspect cylinder bore and piston for pitting, wear or other damage and replace if necessary.

3) Light discoloration may be removed by polishing with crocus cloth only. Polish by rotating cylinder around crocus cloth supported on fingers. Do not polish in a lengthwise direction.

Reassembly

1) Lubricate cylinder bore and internal components with brake fluid. Do not lubricate dust boots. Position replacement piston cups on spring expanders and install assembled parts into cylinder bore.

2) Ensure expanders are seated in piston cups and that cups are installed with lips facing one another. Install pistons with flat sides facing interior of bore. Install dust boots and brake shoe links.

TIGHTENING SPECIFICATIONS

Application	Ft. Lbs. (N.m)
Support Plate	30-35 (41-48)
Brake Cylinder-to-Support Plate	18 (24)
Bleeder Screw 1/4"	4-5 (5-7)
Bleeder Screw 3/4"	4-12 (5-16)
Brake Line	10-17 (14-23)

DRUM BRAKE SPECIFICATIONS

Application	Drum Diam. In. (mm)	Drum Width In. (mm)	Max. Drum Refinish Diam. In. (mm)	Brake Cyl. Diam. In. (mm)	Master Cyl. Diam. In. (mm)
"CJ" & Scrambler	10.00 (254.0)	1.75 (44.5)	10.06 (255.5)	.88 (22.2)	1.00 (25.4)

JEEP SINGLE ANCHOR — LEVER ADJUSTER

Cherokee, J10/20, Wagoneer

DESCRIPTION

Single anchor brake assembly consists of a support plate, 2 brake shoes, brake shoe return springs, adjuster lever and single wheel cylinder.

ADJUSTMENT & SERVICING

BRAKE SHOES

Brake shoes adjust automatically when brakes are applied while vehicle is traveling in reverse. Manual adjustment is required if shoes have been removed and reinstalled. See Brake Shoe Installation in this Article.

During overhaul it is sometimes necessary to back off shoes to remove brake drums. This is done by turning star wheel adjuster which is accessible through a hole in brake backing plate. A thin blade screwdriver or similar tool must be used to disengage automatic adjuster lever while making manual adjustment.

Fig. 1: Exploded View of Drum Brake Assembly

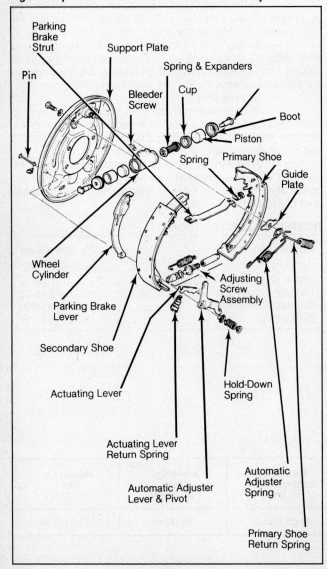

PARKING BRAKE

Adjustment is not necessary in normal service; automatic adjusters also adjust parking brake. In case of brake overhaul, or to compensate for stretched cables, parking brake is adjusted as follows:

1) Check for binds, kinks, or frayed condition of cables. Replace as necessary. Release parking brake. Loosen lock nuts at equalizer under vehicle.

2) Tighten cables until wheels drag slightly when rotated by hand. Loosen cables until wheels rotate freely and no drag is felt. Tighten lock nut and check operation of parking brake.

BLEEDING SYSTEM

See Brake Bleeding in this Section.

REMOVAL & INSTALLATION

BRAKE SHOES
Removal

1) Raise vehicle and support with safety stands. Remove necessary wheels. On models with full floating rear axle, remove 2 screws that locate drums on hubs.

2) On all models, remove primary return spring, automatic adjuster actuator spring and secondary shoe return spring. Remove hold-down springs and brake shoe assemblies.

3) Disengage parking brake cable from parking brake lever, (parking brake strut is removed with brake shoe assembly). Place wheel cylinder clamps over wheel cylinders to retain pistons.

4) Inspect lining wear. Replace riveted linings if worn to within 1/32" of rivet heads. Replace bonded linings if worn to thickness of 1/16".

5) Inspect lining wear pattern and replace lining if wear is uneven, check drums for distortion and runout.

6) Inspect lining for cracks, charred surface, broken rivets or contamination. Replace linings if necessary.

7) Inspect all springs, parking brake lever, automatic adjuster lever and pivot, and actuating lever.

8) Replace weak springs, bent levers, or parts that are worn or broken.
Installation

1) Apply a thin film of molydisulphide grease or chassis lubricant to support plate ledges, anchor pin, adjuster screw threads, and pivot.

2) Apply grease to adjuster lever-to-secondary brakeshoe contact surface, parking brake lever pivot, and portion of lever that contacts secondary brakeshoe.

3) Attach parking brake cable to parking brake lever on secondary shoe. Pinch "U" clip to retain lever on shoe. Install secondary brakeshoe, automatic adjuster lever, and lever pivot as an assembly.

4) Install brakeshoe hold-down spring. Install guide plate on anchor pin. Install parking brake strut and spring on brake shoes. Install adjusting screw and spring.

5) Short hooked end of spring goes on primary brake shoe. Long hooked end goes on secondary brake shoe. Install adjuster spring.

6) Install secondary brake shoe return spring on brake shoe and adjuster spring. Perform intial brake adjustment by measuring clearance with gauge and install drum.

JEEP SINGLE ANCHOR — LEVER ADJUSTER (Cont.)

7) If gauge is not available, install drum and adjust star wheel adjuster until drum just drags. Hold adjuster lever off of adjuster with thin bladed screwdriver and back off adjuster until drum turns freely.

8) Test brake operation before moving vehicle. For final adjustment, make 10 to 15 forward and reverse stops.

AXLE BEARING & SEAL

Removal

1) Remove wheel assembly and brake drum. On differential with bearing retaining plate on end of axle housing, remove retaining nuts through hole provided in axle flange. Using slide hammer, remove axle. Remove brake backing plate and attach it to frame with wire.

2) On differential without retaining plate on end of axle housing, it will be necessary to remove differential cover and drain lubricant. Remove differential pinion shaft lock bolt and pinion shaft.

NOTE: **The pinion gears may be left in place. Once the axle shafts are removed, reinstall pinion shaft and lock bolt.**

3) Push flange end of axle shafts toward center of vehicle and remove "C" lock clips from button end of axle shaft. Remove axle from housing. Insert Rear Axle Remover and slide hammer into bore and position it behind bearing so tangs on tool engage bearing outer race. Remove bearing and seal as a unit.

Installation

To install, reverse removal procedures.

WHEEL CYLINDER

Removal & Installation

1) Disconnect brake line but do not bend it away from cylinder. When cylinder is moved away from backing plate, line will separate easily.

2) Remove cylinder mounting bolts and remove cylinder. Reverse removal procedures, to complete installation.

OVERHAUL

WHEEL CYLINDER

NOTE: **Vehicle manufacturer recommends that wheel cylinders not be honed.**

Disassembly

1) Remove brake shoe links and dust boots. Push pistons, piston cups, and expander spring out of bore. Discard piston cups.

2) Clean all cylinder parts with clean brake fluid or brake solvent. Inspect cylinder bore and piston for pitting, wear, or other damage and replace if necessary.

3) Light discoloration may be removed by polishing with crocus cloth supported by finger. Do not polish in a lengthwise direction.

Reassembly

1) Lubricate cylinder bore and internal components with brake fluid. Do not lubricate dust boots. Position replacement piston cups on spring expanders. Install assembled parts into cylinder bore.

2) Ensure expanders are seated in piston cups and that cups are installed with lips facing each other. Install pistons with flat sides towards center. Install dust boots and brake shoe links.

TIGHTENING SPECIFICATIONS

Application	Ft. Lbs. (N.m)
Support Plate	
J20	45-55 (61-75)
All Others	35-55 (48-75)
Bleeder Screw	
1/4"	4-5 (5-7)
3/8"	7-12 (5-16)
Brake Line	10-17 (14-23)

DRUM BRAKE SPECIFICATIONS

Application	Drum Diam. In. (mm)	Drum Width In. (mm)	Max. Drum Refinish Diam. In. (mm)	Brake Cyl. Diam. In. (mm)	Master Cyl. Diam. In. (mm)
Cherokee, Wagoneer & J/10	11.00 (279.4)	2.00 (50.8)	11.06 (280.9)	.94 (23.8)	1.13 (28.6)
J/20	12.00 (304.8)	2.50 (63.5)	12.06 (306.3)	1.13 (28.6)	1.13 (28.6)

Locking Hubs

AUTOMATIC TYPE

Chevrolet, Chrysler Corp., Ford, GMC

DESCRIPTION

The automatic locking hub automatically engages to lock, and disengages to unlock the front axle shaft to (or from) the front hub. Shifting the transfer case into 4-wheel drive, immediately engages the automatic locking hubs.

The hubs remain engaged, even during coasting or downhill operation. The automatic locking hubs disengage, when the transfer case is shifted into 2-wheel drive, and when vehicle is slowly moved rearward several feet.

REMOVAL & INSTALLATION

REMOVAL

All Models

1) Remove 5 cap screws, and remove cover. Remove bearing race spring assembly. Remove sealing ring and seal bridge retainer. Remove bearing components.

2) Squeeze tangs of wire retaining ring together with needle nose pliers. Pull remaining components of automatic hub from wheel. *See Fig. 1.*

INSTALLATION

All Models

1) Make sure that drag sleeve retainer washer is in position, between wheel bearing adjusting nut and lock nut. Torque wheel bearing adjusting nut to specifications.

2) Make sure that spacer and retaining ring are in position on axle shaft. Install automatic locking hub into wheel hub. Align drag sleeve slots with tabs on drag sleeve retainer washer.

3) Align outer clutch housing splines with splines of wheel hub. Loosen cover screws 3 or 4 turns, and push in on cover to allow retaining ring to expand into rotor hub groove.

NOTE: Locking hubs should be replaced as a complete unit.

Fig. 1: Exploded View of Automatic Locking Hubs

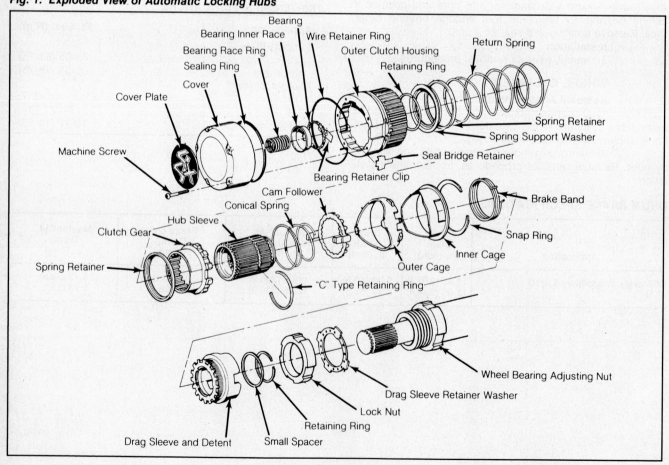

SPICER (DANA) EXTERNAL LOCKING HUB

DESCRIPTION

Locking hubs provide a means of engagement and disengagement of wheels on front drive axles. When locking hubs are engaged, full power is transmitted to both front wheels. When hubs are disengaged, front wheels are free to turn and axle shafts and differential remain idle.

Engagement is accomplished through the action of gears within the hub. With hub in engaged position, the inner clutch gear locks with the outer clutch and engages the axle shaft with wheel hub.

IDENTIFICATION

Spicer (Dana) external locking hubs are identified externally by a red plastic control knob used to engage and disengage hub. They are identified internally by use of an actuating cam to engage and disengage hub.

REMOVAL & INSTALLATION

REMOVAL

1) Remove hub screws and washers, noting how washers are installed on screws. Loosen gear hub housing, and slide away from hub and drum assembly.

2) Remove inner metal gasket, and discard. Remove gear hub housing. Remove outer gasket, and discard. Wipe clean all exposed components. Apply pressure on clutch gear, and remove snap ring.

3) Remove clutch gear and pressure spring from assembly, while knob is in "LOCK" position. Turn knob to "FREE" position. Usng a drift punch, drive cam lock pin out of assembly.

4) Remove actuating cam from knob. Remove knob from knob retainer. Using a cap screw, pull out on axle shaft. Remove snap ring, bushing, and inner clutch assembly. If wear is shown on either the inner or outer clutch gear, replace both as a set.

INSTALLATION

1) Before assembling hub, check splines on axle shaft. Make sure threaded screw holes in wheel hub are clean. Apply Moly X-L hi-speed grease to thrust face of bushing and to splines of inner clutch gear.

2) Install inner clutch gear on bushing. Install bushing and inner clutch gear on axle shaft. Make sure splines on inner clutch gear are aligned with splines on axle.

3) Install a new snap ring. Make sure snap ring is fully seated. Apply Parker "O" Ring Lubricant to "O" ring area of control knob. Install "O" ring.

4) Place actuating knob into knob retainer with arrow pointing to "FREE" position. Install knob retainer snap ring. It may be necessary to use a small screwdriver to position snap ring in groove.

5) Place actuating cam on knob, making sure ears of cam are aligned with retainer slots. Install cam lock pin through cam groove and holes in actuator knob.

6) Make sure ends of pin are flush with outside diameter of cam. Turn actuator knob to "LOCK" position. Apply a small amount of Moly X-L hi-speed lubricant to cam grooves.

7) Install spring and outer clutch gear. Press down on clutch gear to compress spring. With spring compressed, install snap ring. Turn actuator knob to "FREE" position.

8) Install 2 retaining screws and washers into knob retainer to align hub components. Apply a small amount of lubricant to outer splines of outer clutch gear.

9) Remove excess lubricant from retainer gasket surface. Install a new outer retainer gasket. Assemble housing by aligning splines of housing with outer clutch gear splines.

10 Install a new inner metal gasket on hub housing. Install hub assembly to axle, using retainer screws as pilots to align gasket holes and wheel hub holes.

11) Tighten retainer screws to secure hub in place. Turn actuator knob to "LOCK" position. Install the 4 remaining screws. Tighten screws evenly to 30-35 ft. lbs. (41-48 N.m).

NOTE: It may be difficult to engage and disengage hub, until it has been used several times.

Fig. 1: Exploded View of Spicer (Dana) External Locking Hub

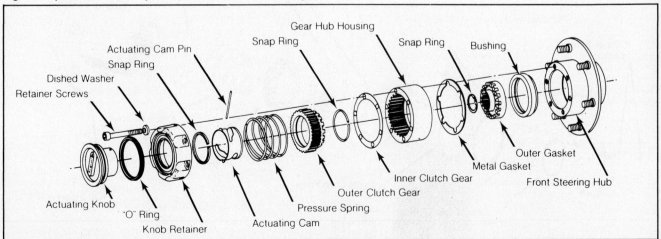

Locking Hubs

SPICER (DANA) INTERNAL LOCKING HUB

DESCRIPTION

Locking hubs provide a means of engagement and disengagement of wheels on front drive axles. When locking hubs are engaged, full power is transmitted to both front wheels.

When hubs are disengaged, front wheels are free to turn, and axle shafts and differential remain idle. Engagement is accomplished through the action of gears within hub.

With hub in engaged position, inner clutch ring and axle shaft sleeve act as 1 piece to connect axle shaft to wheel hub.

Fig. 1: Front View of Spicer (Dana) Locking Hub

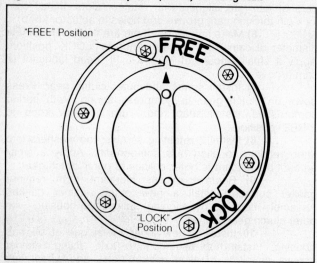

Notice "FREE" and "LOCK" positions.

IDENTIFICATION

Spicer (Dana) internal locking hubs are identified externally by a red plastic control knob, used to engage and disengage hub. They are identified internally by use of an actuating cam to engage and disengage hub.

REMOVAL & INSTALLATION

REMOVAL

1) With control knob set in "LOCK" position, remove retainer plate attaching bolts. Remove outer retainer plate assembly and separate knob from retainer.

2) Remove internal hub snap ring, and slide retainer ring and cam from hub. Relieve pressure on sleeve and ring assembly. Remove axle shaft snap ring.

3) Remove sleeve and ring assembly, inner clutch, pressure spring, and spring retainer plate.

INSTALLATION

1) Wash all parts in solvent, and dry with compressed air. Inspect all parts for wear, cracks, or broken teeth. Replace parts as necessary, using new gaskets and seal during reassembly.

2) Lubricate all parts with Moly X-L High-Speed Grease. Position spring retainer plate into hub bore, with flange side facing bearing.

3) Seat retainer against bearing cup. Install pressure spring in hub with large coils against retainer plate.

NOTE: Spring is an interference fit. When spring is seated it should extend past spindle nut approximately $\frac{7}{8}$" (22.23 mm).

4) Place inner clutch ring into axle shaft sleeve and clutch ring assembly. Install as a unit onto axle shaft.

5) Force unit in against pressure spring, and install axle shaft snap ring. Position actuating cam, with cams facing outward and retainer ring in hub bore.

6) Install internal hub snap ring. Install control knob into retainer plate with knob in "LOCK" position. Install retainer plate, making sure grooves in knob engage actuating cam.

7) Install and tighten retainer plate attaching bolts. Turn knob to "FREE" position to check for proper operation.

Fig. 2: Exploded View of Spicer (Dana) Internal Locking Hub

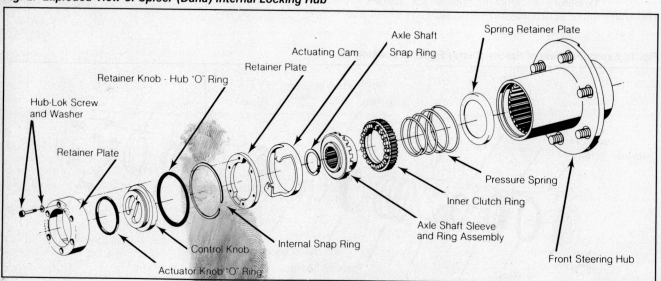

Locking Hubs

WARN SELECTIVE MANUAL TYPE

Jeep

DESCRIPTION

Locking hubs provide a means of engagement of front wheels on vehicles with front drive axle. When hub is engaged, full power is transmitted to both front wheels. When hubs are disengaged, front wheels are free to turn, but axle shafts and differential will remain idle.

Engagement is accomplished through action of gears within hub. With hub in engaged position, clutch body and hub body of hub assembly act as one piece to connect axle shaft to wheel hub. All Warn Selective Manual Hubs function similarly, regardless of differing external appearances.

IDENTIFICATION

All Warn Hubs employ brass control knobs to engage and disengage locking mechanism. Model number of hub is stamped into recess of control knob. *See table for model numbers of Warn Selective Manual Hubs.*

Warn Selective Manual Type Hubs

Application	Model No.
Jeep	
"CJ" & Scrambler	M243
All Other Models	M247

REMOVAL & INSTALLATION

NOTE: **Model M243 and M247 front drive hubs are serviced as either a complete assembly or subassembly, such as the hub body or clutch assembly only. Do not attempt to disassemble these units. If the entire hub or a subassembly has malfunctioned, replace the hub assembly or the defective subassembly as a unit only.**

REMOVAL

Models M243 & M247

1) Remove bolts and tabbed lock washers (if equipped), attaching hub body to axle hub. Retain bolts and washers.

2) Remove retaining ring from axle shaft. Remove hub clutch and bearing assembly.

3) Clean hub components in solvent. Dry components, using compressed air or clean shop towel, or air dry.

4) Be sure old lubricant, dirt, water, or other foreign materials are flushed out.

CAUTION: **Do not turn hub control dial, until hub has been installed. The hub clutch nut and cup can be damaged severely, if dial is rotated while hub is off vehicle.**

INSTALLATION

Models M243 & M247

1) Lubricate hub components with all-purpose chassis lubricant. Apply light coat of lubricant only. Do not pack hub with lubricant.

2) On model M243, install hub clutch, bearing assembly, and retaining ring on axle shaft. Position new gasket on hub body, and install hub body and gasket.

3) On model M247, install hub clutch assembly and small retaining ring on axle shaft. Install large retaining ring in axle hub. Install new "O" ring if hub body is being replaced.

4) Align bolt holes in axle and hub body. Install bolts and tabbed lock washers (if equipped). Tighten bolts to 30 ft. lbs. (41 N.m), on model M243 and 30 INCH lbs. (3.4 N.m) on model M247.

5) Raise vehicle front end. Turn hub control dials to position "2" and rotate wheels. Wheels should rotate freely. If wheels drag, check hub installation. Also, be sure control dials fully engaged in 4x4 position.

Fig. 2: Exploded View of Warn Hub Model M247

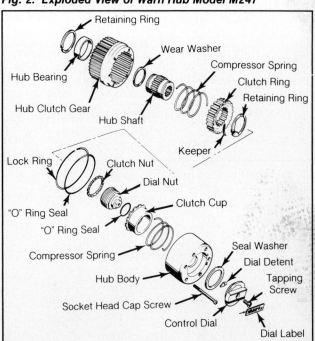

Fig. 1: Exploded View of Warn Hub Model M243

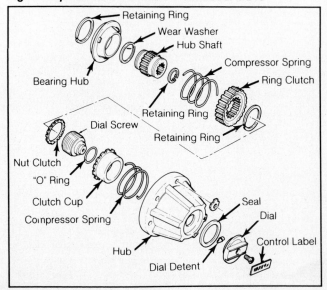

3) On model M247, install hub clutch assembly and small retaining ring on axle shaft. Install large retaining ring in axle hub. Install new "O" ring if hub body is being replaced.

4) Align bolt holes in axle and hub body. Install bolts and tabbed lock washers (if equipped). Tighten bolts to 30 ft. lbs. (41 N.m), on model M243 and 30 INCH lbs. (3.4 N.m) on model M247.

5) Raise vehicle front end. Turn hub control dials to position "2" and rotate wheels. Wheels should rotate freely. If wheels drag, check hub installation. Also, be sure control dials fully engaged in 4x4 position.

Fig. 3 Warn Hub Model M243 Clutch & Bearing Assembly

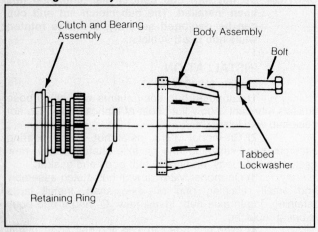

Fig. 4: Warn Hub Model 247 Clutch Assembly

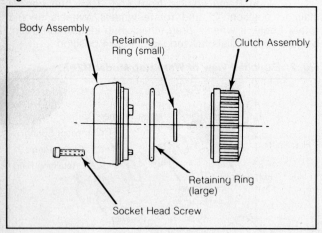

SECTION 11

WHEEL ALIGNMENT

CONTENTS

NOTE: **ALSO SEE GENERAL INDEX.**

IMPORTANT: Because of the many model names used by vehicle
manufacturers, accurate identification of models is important. See Model Identification at the front of this publication.

Wheel Alignment
TROUBLE SHOOTING

CONDITION	POSSIBLE CAUSE	CORRECTION
Premature Tire Wear	Improper tire inflation or balance	Check tire pressure and balance
	Front alignment out of tolerance	See Adjustments in WHEEL ALIGNMENT
	Steering or suspension worn	See SUSPENSION or STEERING
	Improper standing height	See RIDING HEIGHT SPECIFICATIONS
	Bent wheel	See WHEEL ALIGNMENT
	Improper torsion bar adjustment	See SUSPENSION
	Loose or worn wheel bearings	See Wheel Bearing Adj. in SUSPENSION
	Worn or defective shock absorbers	Replace shock absorbers
Pulls to One Side	Improper tire inflation/mismatched tires	Check tires and tire pressure
	Brakes dragging	See BRAKES
	Broken or sagging spring	See SUSPENSION
	Broken torsion bar	See SUSPENSION
	Power steering valve not centered	See STEERING
	Front alignment out of tolerance	See Adjustments in WHEEL ALIGNMENT
	Defective wheel bearing	See Wheel Bearings in SUSPENSION
	Uneven sway bar links	See SUSPENSION
	Frame bent	Check for frame damage
	Steering system bushing worn	See STEERING
	Idler arm bushing too tight	See STEERING LINKAGE
Hard Steering	Idler arm bushing too tight	See STEERING LINKAGE
	Ball joint tight or seized	See Ball Joint Checking in SUSPENSION
	Steering linkage too tight	See STEERING LINKAGE
	Power steering fluid low	Add proper amount of fluid
	Power steering drive belt loose	See STEERING
	Power steering pump defective	See STEERING
	Steering gear out of adjustment	See STEERING
	Incorrect wheel alignment	See WHEEL ALIGNMENT
	Damaged steering gear or suspension	See STEERING or SUSPENSION
	Bent steering knuckle or supports	See SUSPENSION
Vehicle "Wanders"	Strut rod or control arm bushing worn	See SUSPENSION
	Loose or worn wheel bearings	See Wheel Bearings in SUSPENSION
	Improper tire inflation	Check tire pressure
	Stabilizer bar missing or defective	See SUSPENSION
	Wheel alignment out of tolerance	See Adjustment in WHEEL ALIGNMENT
	Broken spring or bad shocks	See SUSPENSION
	Worn steering & suspension components	See SUSPENSION
Front End Shimmy	Tire out of balance/round	Check tire balance
	Excessive wheel runout	See WHEEL ALIGNMENT
	Insufficient or improper caster	See WHEEL ALIGNMENT
	Worn suspension or steering components	See SUSPENSION
	Wheel bearings worn or loose	See Wheel Bearing Adj. in SUSPENSION
	Power steering reaction bracket loose	See STEERING
	Steering gear box (rack) mounting loose	See STEERING
	Steering gear adjustment loose	See STEERING
	Worn spherical joints	See SUSPENSION
Toe-In Not Adjustable	Lower control arm bent	See SUSPENSION
	Frame bent	Check frame for damage
Camber Not Adjustable	Control arm bent	See SUSPENSION
	Frame bent	Check frame for damage
	Hub & bearing not seated properly	See SUSPENSION

Radial Tire Lead

Some alignment problems involving "lead" or pull to one side have been caused by off-center belts on radial tires. To diagnose this problem inflate tires to recommended pressure and drive vehicle both directions on an uncrowned road. Observe and note any "lead", then switch front tires and road test again. If lead is corrected without roughness, leave tires in position. If roughness results, replace tires. If lead reverses, install a known good tire on one side and repeat road test. If lead remains, install a known good tire in place of other front tire. If lead remains, recheck alignment. It may be necessary to adjust caster so that leading side is 1° more positive than other side.

WHEEL ALIGNMENT SPECIFICATIONS

CHRYSLER CORP.
WHEEL ALIGNMENT SPECIFICATIONS

Application	Axle Gap (Inches)	Caster (Degrees)	Camber (Degrees)	Toe-In (Inches)	Steering Axis Inclination (Degrees)
All "B" & "PB"	.....	+1 1/4 to +3 1/4	0 to +1	0 to 1/4	.....
AD 150 & All "D"	.....	-1/2 to +1 1/2	0 to +1	1/16 to 3/16	.....
All "W"	.....	+1/2 to +3 1/2	+1/2 to +1 1/2	1/8 to 3/8	.....

FORD
WHEEL ALIGNMENT SPECIFICATIONS

Application	Axle Gap (Inches)	Caster (Degrees)	Camber (Degrees)	Toe-In (Inches)	Steering Axis Inclination (Degrees)
E100/150	3 1/4 to 3 1/2	6 1/4 to 8	-1 3/4 to -1/4	1/32	7
	3 1/2 to 3 3/4	5 3/4 to 7 1/4	-1 1/2 to -1/4	1/32	7
	3 3/4 to 4	5 to 6 3/4	-1 to +3/4	1/32	7
	4 to 4 1/4	4 1/2 to 5 3/4	-1/2 to +1 1/4	1/32	7
	4 1/4 to 4 1/2	4 to 5 1/4	0 to +1 3/4	1/32	7
	4 1/2 to 4 3/4	3 1/4 to 4 1/2	+1/2 to +2 3/4	1/32	7
	4 3/4 to 5	2 1/2 to 4	+1 to +2 3/4	1/32	7
	5 to 5 1/4	2 to 3 1/4	+1 1/2 to +3 1/4	1/32	7
	5 1/4 to 5 1/2	1 1/2 to 2 3/4	+2 to +3 3/4	1/32	7
E250/350	3 1/4 to 3 1/2	9 to 10 1/2	-1 3/4 to -1/4	1/32	8
	3 1/2 to 3 3/4	8 1/2 to 9 3/4	-1 1/2 to +1/4	1/32	8
	3 3/4 to 4	7 1/8 to 9	-1 to +3/4	1/32	8
	4 to 4 1/4	7 1/8 to 8 1/2	-1/2 to +1 1/4	1/32	8
	4 1/4 to 4 1/2	6 1/2 to 7 3/4	0 to +1 3/4	1/32	8
	4 1/2 to 4 3/4	5 3/4 to 7	+1/2 to +2 1/4	1/32	8
	4 3/4 to 5	5 1/4 to 6 1/2	+1 to +2 3/4	1/32	8
	5 to 5 1/4	4 5/8 to 6	+1 1/2 to +3 1/4	1/32	8
	5 1/4 to 5 1/2	4 to 5 1/2	+2 to +3 3/4	1/32	8
F100/150 (2WD)	2 1/4 to 2 3/4	6 to 10	-3 to -1/2	1/32	8
	2 3/4 to 3 1/4	5 to 9	-2 to +1/2	1/32	8
	3 1/4 to 3 1/2	4 to 8	-1 1/4 to +1 1/4	1/32	8
	3 1/2 to 4	3 to 7	-1/4 to +2 1/4	1/32	8
	4 to 4 1/4	2 to 6	+1/2 to +3	1/32	8
	4 1/4 to 4 3/4	1 to 5	+1 1/2 to +4	1/32	8
F250/350 (2WD)	2 to 2 1/4	5 3/4 to 9	-2 1/2 to 0	1/32	8
	2 1/4 to 2 3/4	4 3/4 to 8	-1 1/2 to +1	1/32	8
	2 3/4 to 3 1/4	3 3/4 to 7	-3/4 to +1 3/4	1/32	8
	3 1/4 to 3 1/2	2 3/4 to 6	+1/4 to +2 3/4	1/32	8
	3 1/2 to 4	1 3/4 to 5	+1 to +3 1/2	1/32	8
	4 to 4 1/4	3/4 to 4	+2 to +4 1/2	1/32	8
F150 (4WD) & Bronco	2 3/4 to 3 1/4	6 to 9	-2 1/2 to -1/4	1/32	13
	3 1/4 to 3 1/2	5 to 8	-1 3/4 to +1/2	1/32	13
	3 1/2 to 4	4 to 7	-3/4 to +1 1/2	1/32	13
	4 to 4 1/4	3 to 6	+1 to +3 1/4	1/32	13
	4 1/4 to 4 3/4	2 to 5	+1 to +3 1/4	1/32	13
	4 3/4 to 5	1 to 4	+1 3/4 to +4	1/32	13
F250/350 (4WD)	4 3/4 to 5	3 to 5	-2 3/4 to -1/4	1/32	13
	5 to 5 1/2	3 1/8 to 5 1/8	-1 3/4 to +3/4	1/32	13
	5 1/2 to 6	3 1/8 to 5 1/8	-3/4 to +1 3/4	1/32	13
	6 to 6 1/4	3 1/4 to 5 1/4	+1/4 to +2 3/4	1/32	13
	6 1/4 to 6 3/4	3 3/8 to 5 3/8	+1 1/4 to +4	1/32	13
	6 3/4 to 7	3 1/2 to 5 1/2	+2 1/2 to +5	1/32	13

Wheel Alignment

WHEEL ALIGNMENT SPECIFICATIONS (Cont.)

FORD (Cont.)
WHEEL ALIGNMENT SPECIFICATIONS

Application	Axle Gap (Inches)	Caster (Degrees)	Camber (Degrees)	Toe-In (Inches)	Steering Axis Inclination (Degrees)
Ranger (2WD)	3 1/8	4 1/2 to 7 1/2	-1 1/4 to +1/4	1/32	13
	3 3/8	4 to 7	-3/4 to +3/4	1/32	13
	3 1/2	3 1/2 to 6 1/2	-1/4 to +1 1/4	1/32	13
	3 3/4	3 to 6	+1/4 to +1 3/4	1/32	13
	3 7/8	2 1/2 to 5 1/2	+3/4 to +2 1/4	1/32	13
	4 1/8	2 to 5	+1 1/4 to +2 3/4	1/32	13
	4 3/8	1 1/2 to 4 1/2	+1 3/4 to +3 1/4	1/32	13
Ranger (4WD) & Bronco II	3 1/8	4 to 7	-3/4 to +3/4	1/32	13
	3 3/8	3 1/2 to 6 1/2	-1/4 to +1 1/4	1/32	13
	3 1/2	3 to 6	+1/4 to +1 3/4	1/32	13
	3 3/4	2 1/2 to 5 1/2	+3/4 to +2 1/4	1/32	13
	3 7/8	2 to 5	+1 1/4 to +2 3/4	1/32	13
	4 1/8	1 1/2 to 4 1/2	+1 3/4 to +3 1/4	1/32	13
	4 3/8	1 to 4	+2 1/4 to +3 3/4	1/32	13

GENERAL MOTORS
WHEEL ALIGNMENT SPECIFICATIONS

Application	Axle Gap (Inches)	Caster (Degrees)	Camber (Degrees)	Toe-In (Inches)	Steering Axis Inclination (Degrees)
C10	2 1/2	3.6	0.7	3/16	......
	2 3/4	3.4	0.7	3/16	......
	3	3.1	0.7	3/16	......
	3 1/4	2.8	0.7	3/16	......
	3 1/2	2.6	0.7	3/16	......
	3 3/4	2.4	0.7	3/16	......
	4	2.0	0.7	3/16	......
	4 1/4	1.8	0.7	3/16	......
	4 1/2	1.5	0.7	3/16	......
	4 3/4	1.2	0.7	3/16	......
	5	1.0	0.7	3/16	......
C20/30	2 1/2	1.5	0.2	3/16	......
	2 3/4	1.2	0.2	3/16	......
	3	0.9	0.2	3/16	......
	3 1/4	0.6	0.2	3/16	......
	3 1/2	0.3	0.2	3/16	......
	3 3/4	0.1	0.2	3/16	......
	4	0	0.2	3/16	......
	4 1/4	-0.1	0.2	3/16	......
	4 1/2	-0.7	0.2	3/16	......
	4 3/4	-1.0	0.2	3/16	......
	5	-1.2	0.2	3/16	......
G10/20	1 1/2	3.5	0.5	3/16	......
	1 3/4	3.3	0.5	3/16	......
	2	3.1	0.5	3/16	......
	2 1/4	2.9	0.5	3/16	......
	2 1/2	2.7	0.5	3/16	......
	2 3/4		0.5	3/16	......
	3	2.4	0.5	3/16	......
	3 1/4	2.2	0.5	3/16	......
	3 1/2	2.1	0.5	3/16	......
	3 3/4	1.9	0.5	3/16	......
	4	1.8	0.5	3/16	......
	4 1/4	1.6	0.5	3/16	......

WHEEL ALIGNMENT SPECIFICATIONS (Cont.)

GENERAL MOTORS (Cont.)
WHEEL ALIGNMENT SPECIFICATIONS

Application	Axle Gap (Inches)	Caster (Degrees)	Camber (Degrees)	Toe-In (Inches)	Steering Axis Inclination (Degrees)
G30	1 1/2	2.8	0.2	3/16	.....
	1 3/4	2.5	0.2	3/16	.....
	2	2.2	0.2	3/16	.....
	2 1/4	1.9	0.2	3/16	.....
	2 1/2	1.6	0.2	3/16	.....
	2 3/4	[1]	0.2	3/16	.....
	3	1.0	0.2	3/16	.....
	3 1/4	0.7	0.2	3/16	.....
	3 1/2	0.5	0.2	3/16	.....
	3 3/4	0.2	0.2	3/16	.....
	4	0	0.2	3/16	.....
	4 1/4	-0.2	0.2	3/16	.....
K10/20/30	2 1/2 to 5	8 [2]	1.0 [2][3]	3/16	
P10	2 1/2	2.3	0.2	3/16	.....
	2 3/4	2.0	0.2	3/16	.....
	3	1.7	0.2	3/16	.....
	3 1/4	1.5	0.2	3/16	.....
	3 1/2	1.2	0.2	3/16	.....
	3 3/4	0.9	0.2	3/16	.....
	4	0.6	0.2	3/16	.....
	4 1/4	0.4	0.2	3/16	.....
	4 1/2	0.1	0.2	3/16	.....
	4 3/4	-0.1	0.2	3/16	.....
	5	-0.3	0.2	3/16	.....
P20/30	2	2.9 [4][5]	0.2	3/16	.....
	2 1/4	2.6 [4][5]	0.2	3/16	.....
	2 1/2	2.3 [4][5]	0.2	3/16	.....
	2 3/4	2.0 [4][5]	0.2	3/16	.....
	3	1.7 [4][5]	0.2	3/16	.....
	3 1/4	1.4 [4][5]	0.2	3/16	.....
	3 1/2	1.2 [4][5]	0.2	3/16	.....
	3 3/4	0.9 [4][5]	0.2	3/16	.....
	4	0.6 [4][5]	0.2	3/16	.....
	4 1/4	0.4 [4][5]	0.2	3/16	.....
	4 1/2	0.2 [4][5]	0.2	3/16	.....
	4 3/4	0.1 [4][5]	0.2	3/16	.....
S10/15 & T10/15	.....	+1 1/2 to +2 1/2	+0.3 to +1.3	[6]	.....

[1] — Information not available from manufacturer.
[2] — No adjustment provision.
[3] — K30 is 0.5°.
[4] — Add 0.3° on vehicles with hydroboost brake system.
[5] — Subtract 0.4° on vehicles with dual rear wheels.
[6] — .10°-.20° per wheel.

JEEP
WHEEL ALIGNMENT SPECIFICATIONS

Application	Axle Gap (Inches)	Caster (Degrees)	Camber (Degrees)	Toe-In (Inches)	Steering Axis Inclination (Degrees)
"CJ" & Scrambler	.....	+6 to +7	0 to +1/2	3/64 to 3/32	8 1/2
Cherokee, Wagoneer & Truck	.....	+4 to +5	0 to +1/2	3/64 to 3/32	8 1/2

Wheel Alignment

WHEEL ALIGNMENT PROCEDURES

PRE-ALIGNMENT

VEHICLE CHECKS

Before making wheel alignment adjustment, perform the following checks:

1) Tires should be equal in size and runout must not be excessive. Tires and wheels should be in balance, and inflated to manufacturer's specifications.

2) Wheel bearings must be properly adjusted.

3) Steering linkage and suspension must not have excessive looseness. Check for wear in tie rod ends and ball joints.

4) Steering gear box must not have excessive play. Check and adjust to manufacturer's specifications.

5) Vehicle must be at curb height with full fuel load and spare tire in vehicle. No extra load should be on vehicle.

6) Vehicle must be floor level with suspension settled. Jounce front and rear of vehicle several times and allow it to settle to normal riding height.

7) If steering wheel is not centered with front wheels in straight-ahead position, correct by shortening one tie rod adjusting sleeve and lengthening opposite sleeve equal amounts.

8) Ensure wheel lug nuts are tightened to torque specifications.

WHEEL LUG NUTS TIGHTENING SPECIFICATIONS

Application	Ft. Lbs. (N.m)
Chevrolet & GMC	
C, P, G10/20	75-100 (102-136)
All K Models	70-90 (95-122)
C, P/G30	
W/Single Rear Wheels	90-120 (122-163)
C, P/G30	
W/Dual Rear Wheels	110-140 (150-190)
W/Dual Rear Wheels 5/8" Studs	150 (204)
S10/20	90 (122)
Dodge & Plymouth	
All Models	
1/2"-20	105 (143)
5/8"-18	200 (272)
W/Flanged Type Nut	325 (442)
Ford	
All Models	
1/2"-20	90 (122)
9/16"-18 W/Single Rear Wheels	145 (197)
9/16"-18 W/Dual Rear Wheels	220 (299)
Jeep	
All Models (Exc. J20 Truck)	75 (102)
J20 Truck	130 (177)

DESCRIPTION

CAMBER

Camber is the tilting of the wheel, outward at either top or bottom, as viewed from front of vehicle. When wheels tilt outward at top from centerline of vehicle, camber is said to be positive. When wheels tilt inward at top, camber is said to be negative. Amount of tilt or camber angle, is measured in degrees from vertical.

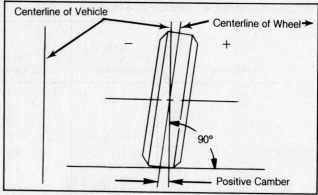

Fig. 1: Camber Angle

Camber is amount of tilt inward or outward from vertical.

CASTER

Caster is the tilting of front steering axis. This forward or backward tilt from vertical is viewed from side of vehicle. When axis is tilted backward from vertical, caster is said to be positive, creating a trailing action on front wheels. When axis is tilted forward, caster is negative, causing a leading action on front wheels.

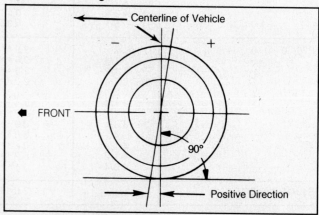

Fig. 2: Caster Angle

Caster is amount of tilt forward or backward from vertical.

TOE-IN

Toe-in is the turning in of the front wheels. Amount of toe-in is generally only a fraction of an inch. The toe specification ensures a parallel rolling of the front wheels.

ADJUSTMENT

TOE-IN

1) Measure toe-in with front wheels in straight-ahead position and steering wheel centered. Adjust toe-in by loosening clamps and adjusting sleeve or adjusting ends on right and left tie rods equally and in opposite directions to maintain steering wheel in centered position.

2) When tightening clamps, make sure that clamp bolts are positioned so there will be no interference with other parts throughout entire travel of steering linkage.

WHEEL ALIGNMENT PROCEDURES (Cont.)

NOTE: Face of tie rod end must be parallel with machined surface of steering rod end.

Fig. 3: Determining Corrected Caster Angle

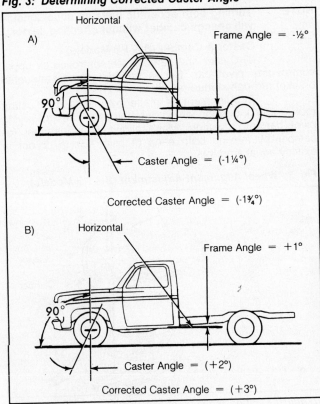

When caster is tilted backward from vertical, caster is positive; when tilted forward, caster is negative.

Fig. 4: Wheel Toe-In

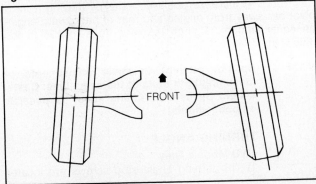

To adjust, turn sleeve on right and left tie rods an equal amount in opposite directions.

TOE-OUT ON TURNS

1) Toe-out check is a check for bent or damaged parts and not a service adjustment. With caster, camber and toe-in properly adjusted, check toe-out with weight of vehicle on wheels.

2) Use full-floating turn table under each wheel and repeat test with each wheel positioned for right and left turns.

3) Incorrect toe-out generally indicates a bent steering arm. Replace arm and recheck wheel alignment adjustments. Do not attempt to correct by straightening parts.

Fig. 5: Wheel Toe-Out on Turns

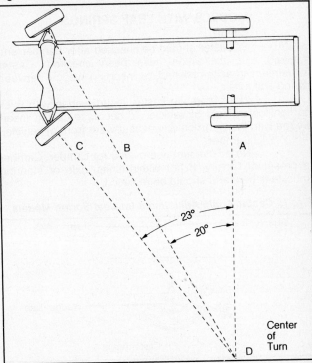

Test each wheel in right and left turn positions.

STEERING AXIS INCLINATION

1) This is a check for bent or damaged parts, and not a service adjustment. Vehicle must be level, both crosswise and lengthwise. Camber should be properly adjusted.

2) If camber cannot be brought within limits and steering axis inclination is correct, steering knuckle is bent. If camber and steering axis inclination are both incorrect by approximately the same amount, upper and lower control arms are bent.

3) Replace parts and recheck all wheel alignment adjustments. Do not attempt to correct by straightening parts.

Fig. 6: Steering Axis Inclination

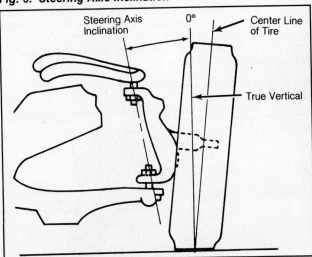

If axis and camber inclination are incorrect, check upper and lower control arms for bends.

Wheel Alignment
CHRYSLER CORP.

ADJUSTMENT

MODELS WITH LEAF SPRINGS

Caster

1) Caster should be checked after camber and steering axis inclination have been checked. Caster adjustment is accomplished by inserting wedge between spring and axle.

2) To increase caster, insert wedge with thick portion toward rear of vehicle. To decrease caster, insert wedge with thick portion of wedge toward front of vehicle.

Camber

No adjustment is provided for camber. Camber is preset at factory, if not within limits, axle or steering knuckle is bent and should be replaced.

Fig. 1: Caster Angle Adjustment for Leaf Spring Models

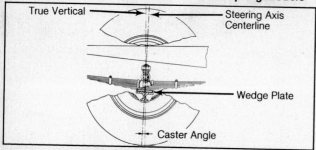

To adjust, insert wedge between spring and axle.

MODELS WITH COIL SPRINGS

Caster (AD, AW, D & W Models)

1) Caster is controlled by eccentric bolts which mount upper control arm-to-frame. To obtain positive caster, loosen forward eccentric bolt lock nut. Turn eccentric bolt to force front part of control arm outward, or loosen rear eccentric bolt lock nut, and turn eccentric to pull rear of control arm inward.

2) To obtain negative caster, loosen eccentric bolt lock nut, and turn forward eccentric bolt to pull front part of control arm inward, or loosen rear eccentric bolt lock nut, and turn eccentric bolt to force rear of control arm outward. Tighten eccentric bolt lock nuts to 70 ft. lbs. (95 N.m).

Camber (AD, AW, D & W Models)

1) Camber is controlled by eccentric bolts which mount upper control arm-to-frame. To increase camber, loosen eccentric bolt lock nuts. Turn both eccentric bolts an equal amount to force upper control arm outward.

Fig. 2: Wheel Alignment Adjustment (AD, AW, D & W Models)

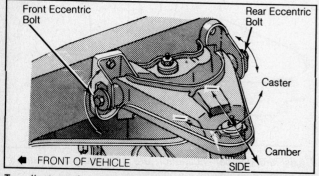

To adjust camber, turn eccentric bolts same amount.

2) To decrease camber, turn both eccentric bolts an equal amount to pull upper control arm inward. Tighten eccentric bolt lock nuts to 70 ft. lbs. (95 N.m).

NOTE: **Turning both eccentric bolts an equal amount will change camber without affecting caster.**

Caster & Camber (B & PB Models)

1) Caster and camber are controlled by upper control arm pivot bar. Bar is bolted to frame mounted bracket through slotted holes.

2) Alignment is made by installing adjusting tool (C-4581), and loosening one bolt at a time and prying pivot bar into position. Make alignment adjustment for camber by moving both ends of pivot bar in or out in exactly equal amounts.

Fig. 3: Wheel Alignment Adjustment (B & PB Models)

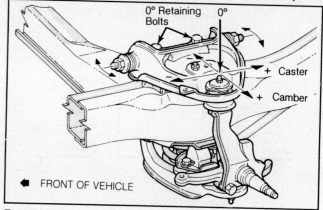

To adjust camber, move pivot bar ends equal amounts.

3) Adjustment for caster is made by moving each end of bar in exactly equal amounts in opposite directions.

4) Increase positive caster by moving front of pivot bar away from engine and rear of bar toward engine an equal amount. Tighten retaining bolts to 195 ft. lbs. (265 N.m).

NOTE: **Do not attempt to make adjustments by loosening both bolts at the same time. Caster should be held as nearly equal as possible on both wheels.**

TURNING ANGLE

4WD Models Only

1) The turning angle stop screws are located on back side of steering knuckle, just above axle shaft centerline. To adjust, loosen stop screw lock nut.

2) Using full-floating turn table under each wheel, adjust turning angle by adjusting stop screw IN to increase and OUT to decrease turning angle.

TURNING ANGLE ADJUSTMENT 4WD ONLY

Application	Left Wheel	Right Wheel
W150	37°	27°
W250	35°	[1] 29°
W350	45°	20°

[1] — If equipped with 8.7 x 16.5" tires, turning angle is 26°. If equipped with 9.5 x 16.5" tires, turning angle is 24°.

ADJUSTMENT

RIDING HEIGHT

NOTE: Before making wheel alignment adjustments, make sure front riding heights are within 1/8" of each other.

All Models

1) With vehicle on level surface, fuel tank full and no other load, jounce both front and rear until suspension settles. On E100/350 models, place 2 height blocks 3 1/2" high between top of axle and flange on lower part of jounce bracket on each axle.

2) Measure clearance at inside area of jounce bracket (toward wheel) between top of axle and spring seat lower surface on frame.

3) On Bronco, Bronco II, Ranger, and F100/350 models, place 2 height blocks 5" high between top of axle and outside lip of jounce bumper on each axle.

4) Measure clearance at inside of spring seat lower surface (toward center of vehicle) between top of axle and spring seat lower surface. If clearance is not correct, height must be corrected by installing proper springs or shims.

Fig. 1: Setting Riding Height

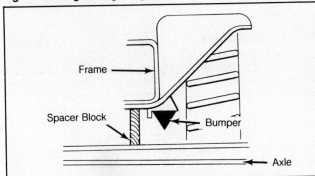

Front riding heights must be within 1/8" of each other before adjusting.

CASTER

Coil Springs

Caster is built-in at factory and no adjustment is provided. If not within limits, replace parts as required.

Leaf Springs

Caster angle is adjusted by inserting a shim between the spring and axle. Shims are available in 0°, 1° and 2° increments.

CAMBER

All Models (Exc. Bronco II & Ranger, Bronco & F150/350 4WD)

Camber is built-in at factory and no adjustment is provided. If not within limits, replace parts as necessary.

Bronco II & Ranger 2WD

1) Raise vehicle on hoist. Remove front wheel assemblies. Remove upper ball joint nut. Remove cotter pin on lower ball stud. Back nut down to end of stud.

2) Strike spindle near upper and lower ball joints to break spindle loose from ball joint studs. Use Camber Adjuster Removal Tool (D81T-3010-B) to wedge camber adjuster out of spindle.

3) Replace adjuster with desired camber adjuster. Camber adjusters are available in 0°, 1/2°, 1° and 1 1/2°.

4) To increase (positive) camber, align slot as follows: On drivers side, point slot to rear of vehicle. On passenger side, point slot rearward to front of vehicle.

5) To decrease (negative) camber, align slot as follows: on drivers side, point slot forward. On passenger side, point slot rearward.

6) Apply Loctite or equivalent to upper ball stud and hand start upper ball stud. Hand start lower ball nut. Partially tighten lower ball stud nut to 35 ft. lbs. (47 N.m). Tighten upper ball stud to 85-110 ft. lbs. (115-150 N.m).

7) Finish tightening lower ball stud to 104-146 ft. lbs. (141-198 N.m). Advance nut to the next castellation and install cotter pin. Install front wheel assemblies and lower vehicle.

Bronco II & Ranger 4WD

1) Raise vehicle on hoist and remove wheel assemblies. Remove upper ball joint cotter pin and nut. Loosen lower ball joint nut and back off nut to the end of the stud.

2) Strike inside of spindle near upper and lower ball joints to break loose from ball joint studs. Remove camber adjuster sleeve. If required, use Pitman Arm Puller (T64P-3590-F), to remove adjuster from spindle.

3) Install camber adjuster on top ball joint stud with arrow pointing outboard for positive camber and the arrow pointing inboard for negative camber, *See Fig. 2*. Zero camber bushings will not have an arrow and may be rotated in either direction as long as lugs on yoke engage slots in bushing.

Fig. 2: Camber Adjustment

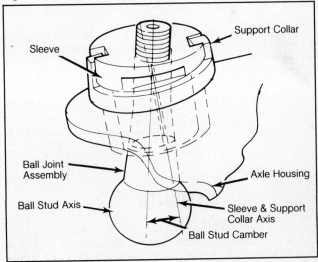

Adjust using upper ball joint mounting sleeves.

4) Remove lower ball joint stud nut and discard. Install a new nut on lower ball joint stud nut and tighten to 40 ft. lbs. (54 N.m). Install new nut on top ball joint stud and tighten to 85-100 ft. lbs (115-136 N.m).

5) Advance nut until castellation aligns with cotter pin hole and install cotter pin. Finish tightening lower nut to 95-110 ft. lbs (129-149 N.m). Reinstall wheel assemblies and lower vehicle. Check camber and adjust toe in.

Wheel Alignment

FORD (Cont.)

Bronco & F150/350 4WD

Under normal loading conditions, camber angle is built into axle and no adjustment is necessary. For unusual loading conditions, adjustments can be made.

Camber adjustment is provided by a series of interchangeable mounting sleeves for upper ball joint stud. Sleeves are available in 4 ranges of 1/2° increments from 1 1/2° negative to 1 1/2° positive. See procedures preivously described in Camber Bronco II & Ranger 4WD.

TURNING ANGLE

4WD Models (Except Bronco II & Ranger)

1) The turning angle stop screws are located on back side of steering knuckle, just above axle shaft centerline. To adjust, loosen stop screw lock nut.

2) Using full-floating turn table under each wheel, adjust turning angle by adjusting stop screw IN to increase and OUT to decrease turning angle.

TURNING ANGLE ADJUSTMENT 4WD ONLY

Application	Left Wheel	Right Wheel
Bronco & F150	36°	36°
F250	33.4°	33.4°
F350	30.3°	30.3°

GENERAL MOTORS

ADJUSTMENT

NOTE: **Difference in shim packs must not exceed .30" (7.62 mm). Front shim pack must be .10" (2.54 mm) minimum.**

CASTER

All Models (Exc. 4WD)

1) Measure frame angle directly behind cab using a bubble protractor or inclinometer. Determine existing caster. Determine difference between frame angle and caster angle. A down-in-rear, frame angle must be added to a positive caster angle.

2) An up-in-rear frame angle must be subtracted from a positive caster specification. A down-in-rear frame angle must be subtracted from a negative caster specification.

3) An up-in-rear frame angle must be added to a negative caster specification. Measure distance from top of jounce bumper bracket on lower control arm to bottom of frame crossmember.

4) To increase caster, add shims between forward upper control arm retaining bolt and frame, or subtract shims from rear retaining bolt. To decrease caster, subtract shims from forward bolt, or add shims to rear bolt.

4WD Models

Caster is built-in at the factory and no adjustment is provided. If not within limits, replace parts as necessary.

CAMBER

2WD Models

Camber is changed by adding or subtracting shims from between upper control arm shaft and frame bracket. Adding an equal number of shims at both front and rear of cross shaft will decrease positive camber.

4WD Models

Camber is built-in at the factory and no adjustment is provided. If not within limits, replace parts as necessary.

NOTE: **By adding or subtracting equal amounts of shims, camber may be corrected without affecting caster.**

JEEP

ADJUSTMENTS

CAMBER

Correct camber of 0° for all models is preset at time of manufacture and cannot be adjusted. If not within limits, replace parts as necessary.

CASTER

Correct caster is preset at factory to 6° for CJ and Scrambler models, and 4° for all other models. Adjustment is made by inserting shim between spring and axle.

To increase caster, insert thick portion of shim toward rear of vehicle. To decrease caster, insert thick portion of shim toward front of vehicle.

Fig. 1: Caster Adjustment

To adjust, insert shim between spring and axle.

JEEP (Cont.)

TURNING ANGLE

1) The turning angle stop screws are located on back side of steering knuckle, just above axle centerline. To adjust, loosen lock nut on stop screw.

2) Using full-floating turn table under each wheel, adjust stop screw IN to increase turning angle and OUT to decrease turning angle. Tighten lock nut.

TURNING ANGLE ADJUSTMENT

Application	Left Wheel	Right Wheel
CJ5	29°	29°
CJ7 & Scrambler	32°	32°
All Others	36-37°	36-37°

SECTION 12

SUSPENSION

CONTENTS

NOTE: **ALSO SEE GENERAL INDEX.**

IMPORTANT: Because of the many model names used by vehicle manufacturers, accurate identification of models is important. See Model Identification at the front of this publication.

Suspension
TROUBLE SHOOTING

CONDITION	POSSIBLE CAUSE	CORRECTION
Front End Noise	Loose or worn wheel bearings	See Wheel Bearing Adjustment in SUSPENSION
	Worn shocks or shock mountings	Replace shocks or mountings.
	Worn struts or strut mountings	Replace struts or strut mountings
	Loose or worn lower control arm	See Lower Control Arm Removal & Installation in SUSPENSION
	Loose steering gear-to-frame bolts	See Steering Gear Removal & Installation in STEERING
	Steering knuckle contacts lower control arm wheel stop	See Steering Knuckle in STEERING or Lower Control Arm in SUSPENSION
	Worn control arm bushings	See Control Arms in SUSPENSION
	Ball joints not lubricated	Lubricate ball joints & see Ball Joint Checking in SUSPENSION
Front Wheel Shake, Shimmy or Vibration	Tires or wheels out of balance	Check tire balance
	Incorrect wheel alignment	See Adjustment in WHEEL ALIGNMENT
	Propeller Shaft Unbalanced	See Propeller Shaft in DRIVE AXLES
	Loose or worn wheel bearings	See Wheel Bearing Adjustment in SUSPENSION
	Loose or worn tie rod ends	See Tie Rod Removal & Installation in SUSPENSION
	Worn upper ball joints	See Ball Joint Checking in SUSPENSION
	Worn shock absorbers	Replace shock absorbers
	Worn strut bushings	Replace strut bushings
Car Pulls to One Side	Mismatched or uneven tires	Check tire condition
	Broken or sagging springs	See Coil Spring Removal & Installation in SUSPENSION
	Loose or worn strut bushings	See Strut Removal & Installation in SUSPENSION
	Improper wheel alignment	See Adjustment in WHEEL ALIGNMENT
	Improper rear axle alignment	See DRIVE AXLES
	Power steering gear unbalanced	See STEERING
	Front brakes dragging	See BRAKES
Abnormal Tire Wear	Unbalanced tires	Check tire balance & rotation
	Sagging or broken springs	See Coil Spring in SUSPENSION
	Incorrect front end alignment	See Adjustment in WHEEL ALIGNMENT
	Faulty shock absorbers	Replace shock absorbers
Scuffed Tires	Toe-In incorrect	See Adjustment in WHEEL ALIGNMENT
	Suspension arm bent or twisted	See appropriate SUSPENSION article
Springs Bottom or Sag	Bent or broken springs	See Coil Spring in SUSPENSION
	Leaking or worn shock absorbers	Replace shock absorbers
"Dog" Tracking	Broken leaf spring	Replace leaf spring
	Bent rear axle housing	See DRIVE AXLES
	Frame misalignment	Check frame for damage
Spring Noises	Loose "U" Bolts	See SUSPENSION
	Loose or worn bushings	See SUSPENSION
	Worn or missing interliners	See SUSPENSION
Shock Absorber Noise	Loose shock mountings	Check & tighten mountings
	Worn bushings	Replace bushings
	Air in system	Bleed air from system
	Undercoating on shocks	Remove undercoating
Car Leans or Sways on Corners	Loose stabilizer bar	See SUSPENSION
	Faulty shocks or mountings	Replace shocks or mountings
	Broken or sagging springs	See Coil Spring in SUSPENSION
Shock Absorbers Leaking	Worn seals or reservoir tube crimped	See SUSPENSION
Broken Springs	Loose "U" bolts	See Coil Spring in SUSPENSION
	Inoperative shock absorbers	Replace shock absorbers

CHRYSLER CORP. COIL SPRING

Dodge, Plymouth

DESCRIPTION

Independent front suspension consists of upper and lower control arms, steering knuckles, coil springs, and hydraulic shock absorbers. Upper control arms are mounted to frame side rails, while lower control arms are mounted to crossmember.

Steering knuckles are mounted between upper and lower control arms by conventional ball joints. Coil springs are mounted between seat in frame and lower contol arm. Double-acting shock absorbers mount inside coil springs, and are fastened to lower control arms and frame.

ADJUSTMENT

WHEEL ALIGNMENT SPECIFICATIONS & PROCEDURES

See Wheel Alignment Specifications & Procedures in WHEEL ALIGNMENT Section.

WHEEL BEARING ADJUSTMENT

Van & 2WD Pickup Models

1) Tighten wheel bearing adjusting nut to 360-480 IN. Lbs. (40-53 N.m) while turning rotor. Back off adjusting nut to release all preload. Retighten nut finger tight.

2) End play should be .0001-.003" (.0025-.076 mm). Install nut lock and cotter pin. Coat grease cap lightly with grease and install.

4WD Pickup Models

1) Tighten inner lock nut to 50 ft. lbs. (68 N.m). Loosen lock nut and retighten to 30-40 ft. lbs. (41-54 N.m) while turning hub. Back off lock nut 135-150°. Install retaining washer (lock ring).

2) Install and tighten outer lock nut to 50 ft. lbs. (70 N.m) for 44FBJ axle or 65 ft. lbs. (88 N.m) for Model 60 front axle. End play should be within .001-.010" (.03-.25 mm).

BALL JOINT CHECKING

Ball joints are preloaded. If up and down movement exceeds .020" (.5 mm), replace ball joint.

REMOVAL & INSTALLATION

SHOCK ABSORBER

Removal

Raise and support vehicle. Turn wheels to allow best access to upper shock absorber mount. Remove upper mounting nut and retainer. Remove lower mounting bolts, and remove shock absorber from vehicle.

Installation

To install, fully extend shock absorber and reverse removal procedure.

COIL SPRING

Removal

1) Block brake pedal in up position. Raise vehicle and position safety stands under frame. Remove wheels, brake caliper retainer and anti-rattle spring. Remove caliper from disc by sliding out and away from disc.

2) Hang caliper out of the way, but do not hang from brake line. Remove inboard brake shoe. On Pickup models, remove grease cap, cotter key, lock nut, adjusting washer and outer bearing.

3) Carefully slide rotor from steering knuckle. Do not drag seal or inner bearing over steering knuckle threads. Remove splash shield.

4) Remove shock absorber and strut. Disconnect sway bar (if equipped). Install spring compressor (DD-1278), tighten finger tight, then back off 1/2 turn.

5) Remove cotter keys and ball joint nuts. Install ball joint breaker tool (C-3564-A or C-2564-A). Turn threaded portion of tool to lock against lower stud. Spread tool enough to place lower stud under pressure, then stike steering knuckle with hammer to loosen stud.

6) Remove tool. Slowly loosen spring compressor until all tension is relieved from coil spring. Remove compressor and coil spring.

Installation

To install, reverse removal procedure. Torque all nuts and bolts to specifications.

LOWER CONTROL ARM

Removal

Raise and support vehicle, and remove wheel. Remove coil spring as previously described. Remove lower control arm pivot, and remove lower control arm from vehicle.

Installation

To install, reverse removal procedures. Tighten all nuts and bolts with vehicle resting on ground.

UPPER CONTROL ARM

Removal

1) Raise and support vehicle and remove wheel and tire. On Van models, block brake pedal in up position and remove brake caliper retainer and anti-rattle spring. Remove caliper from disc and hang out of the way.

2) Do not hang from brake line. Remove inboard brake shoe. On all models, remove shock absorber and install spring compressor (DD-1278). Tighten finger tight and then back-off 1/2 turn.

3) Remove cotter keys and ball joint nuts. Position ball joint breaker tool (C-3564-A), with threaded portion of tool locking against upper stud.

4) Spread tool to place stud under pressure, then strike stud with hammer to loosen. Remove tool. Remove retaining bolts and control arm.

Installation

To install, reverse removal procedure. Do not tighten control arm pivot bolts until vehicle weight is supported by front suspension. Check wheel alignment.

LOWER BALL JOINT

Removal

With lower control arm removed, remove ball joint seal. Press out ball joint out of socket using remover tool (C-4212).

NOTE: **On some models it may be possible to remove ball joint with control arm still in vehicle, but disconnected from steering knuckle.**

Front Suspension

CHRYSLER CORP. COIL SPRING (Cont.)

Installation

Using removal tool, press ball joint into control arm. Install seal with driver (C-4034). Install control arm.

UPPER BALL JOINT

Removal

Raise and support vehicle under outer end of lower control arm. Remove wheel and tire. Remove upper ball joint nuts. Using ball joint breaker tool (C-3564-A), free upper ball joint. Using tool C-3561, unscrew ball joint from control arm.

Installation

To install, reverse removal procedure, and torque all nuts and bolts to specifications.

Fig. 1: Exploded View of Front Suspension Assembly

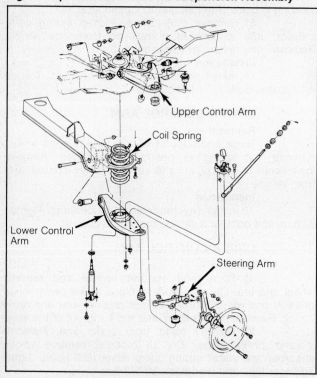

Upper Control Arm

Coil Spring

Lower Control Arm

Steering Arm

STEERING KNUCKLE

Removal

1) Block brake pedal in up position. Raise vehicle and remove wheel and tire assembly. Remove caliper retainer and anti-rattle spring assemblies. Remove caliper and hang out of way. Do not let caliper hang by hydraulic line.

2) Remove rotor and bearings. Place jack under outer end of lower control arm. Disconnect tie rod at steering knuckle. See *Steering Linkage in STEERING Section.*

3) Separate ball joint studs from steering knuckle as previously described. Remove steering knuckle from vehicle and separate components.

Installation

To install, reverse removal procedure, and torque all nuts and bolts to specifications.

TIGHTENING SPECIFICATIONS

Application	Ft. Lbs. (N.m)
Ball Joint Nuts	
11/16"-18	135 (183)
3/4"-16	175 (237)
Front Strut Mounting	
D150/350	50 (68)
All Other Models	100 (135)
Lower Control Arm-to-Crossmember	
Van	175 (237)
All Other Models	210 (285)
Lower Shock Absorber Mount	
2WD	17 (23)
4WD	55 (75)
Rear Strut Nut	
D150/350	85 (115)
All Other Models	52 (70)
Upper Ball Joint-to-Control Arm	125 (170)
Upper Control Arm (Eccentric) Bolt	70 (95)
Upper Shock Absorber Mount	[1] 25 (34)

[1] — On W150/250 with 44FBJ Axle and W250/350 with 60 Axle, torque to 55 ft. lbs. (75 N.m).

Front Suspension

FORD 2WD COIL SPRING — RANGER

Ranger

DESCRIPTION

Front suspension is coil spring, two "I-Beam" axles. Suspension is comprised of coil spring, I-beam axle arm, radius arm, upper and lower ball joint, steering knuckle, tie rod, shock absorber and optional stabilizer bar. One end of each axle is attached to a steering knuckle and radius arm assembly. Other end is attached to a frame pivot bracket. Knuckle is connected to axle by upper and lower ball joints. Ball joints never require lubrication. Steering knuckle movement is controlled by tie rods and steering linkage.

ADJUSTMENT & CHECKING

WHEEL ALIGNMENT SPECIFICATIONS & PROCEDURES

See Wheel Alignment Specifications & Procedures in WHEEL ALIGNMENT section.

WHEEL BEARING ADJUSTMENT

With wheel rotating, tighten adjusting nut to 17-25 ft. lbs. (23-34 N.m). Back-off adjusting nut 1/2 turn. Tighten adjusting nut to 10-15 INCH lbs. (1.1-1.7 N.m). Install lock and new cotter pin.

BALL JOINT CHECKING

Raise and support vehicle. Move lower edge of tire in and out while watching lower steering knuckle. If movement exceeds 1/32" (.8 mm), replace lower ball joint. To check upper ball joint, move upper edge of tire in and out. If movement between upper steering knuckle and upper axle exceeds 1/32" (.8 mm), replace upper ball joint.

REMOVAL & INSTALLATION

SHOCK ABSORBER

Removal

Remove nut and washer attaching shock absorber to spring seat. Remove nut and bolt retaining shock to radius arm and lower shock. Compress and remove shock absorber.

Installation

To install, extend shock absorber and reverse removal procedure.

STEERING KNUCKLE

Removal

1) Raise and support front of vehicle. Remove wheel and tire assembly. Remove caliper assembly from rotor and support aside.

2) Remove dust cap, cotter pin, nut, nut retainer, washer and outer bearing. Remove rotor from knuckle. Remove inner bearing cone and seal. Discard seal. Remove brake dust shield.

3) Disconnect steering linkage from steering knuckle by removing cotter pin and nut. Remove cotter pin from lower ball joint stud.

4) Remove nut from upper and lower ball joint stud. Strike lower side of steering knuckle to pop ball joints loose from knuckle. Remove steering knuckle.

Installation

1) Be sure upper and lower ball joint seals are in place. Place steering knuckle over ball joints. Apply thread locking compound (Loctite 242 or equivalent) to lower ball stud and tighten.

2) Install camber adjuster in upper steering knuckle over upper ball joint. If camber adjustment is necessary, special adapters must be installed.

3) Apply thread locking compound (Loctite 242 or equivalent) to upper ball joint stud and install nut. Hold camber adapter to avoid ball stud movement. Tighten nut.

4) Tighten lower ball stud nut and install cotter pin. Install dust shield. Pack bearings with bearing grease. Install inner seal cone and seal.

5) Install hub and rotor on steering knuckle. Install outer bearing cone, washer and nut. Adjust bearing end play and install cotter pin and dust cap. Install caliper. Connect steering linkage to steering knuckle. Tighten nut.

CAMBER ADAPTER

Removal

1) Remove nut from upper ball joint stud. Strike inside of steering knuckle to pop upper ball joint taper loose from knuckle.

2) If upper ball joint does not loosen, back lower ball joint nut 1/2 way down lower ball joint stud and strike side of lower steering knuckle. See Fig. 1.

3) Remove camber adjusting sleeve using camber adjuster remover (D81T-3010-B).

Fig. 1: Steering Knuckle Removal

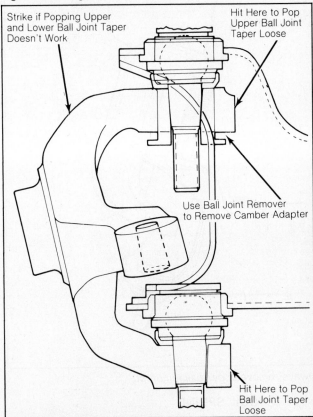

Strike if Popping Upper and Lower Ball Joint Taper Doesn't Work

Hit Here to Pop Upper Ball Joint Taper Loose

Use Ball Joint Remover to Remove Camber Adapter

Hit Here to Pop Ball Joint Taper Loose

Strike inside of steering knuckle to remove upper ball joint taper from knuckle.

Front Suspension

FORD 2WD COIL SPRING — RANGER (Cont.)

Installation

1) Install adapter in steering knuckle. On right knuckle, adapter slot must point forward in vehicle for camber change or rearward for negative camber change.

2) On left steering knuckle, adapter slot must point rearward for positive camber change and forward for negative camber change.

3) To complete installation, reverse removal procedures. Apply thread locking compound (Threadlock and Sealer E0AZ-19554-A or equivalent) to stud threads before installing nut.

UPPER AND LOWER BALL JOINT

Removal

1) Remove steering knuckle. Remove snap ring from ball joints. Assemble C-frame (T74P-4635-C) and receiving cup (D81T-3010-A). *See Fig. 2.*

2) Turn forcing screw clockwise until ball joint is removed from axle. Remove upper ball joint first. Assemble C-frame and receiving cup on lower ball joint. Turn forcing screw clockwise until ball joint is removed.

Installation

Lower ball joint must be installed first. To install, reverse removal procedures. Do not heat ball joint or axle to aid in installation.

Fig. 2: Upper Ball Joint Removal

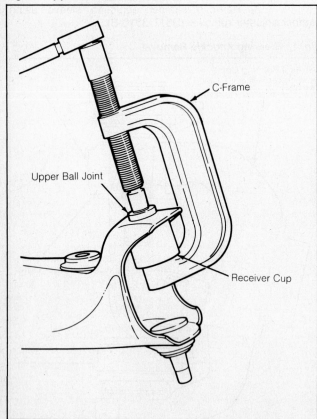

Always remove upper ball joint first.

COIL SPRING

Removal

1) Raise and support front of vehicle. Remove nut holding lower retainer to spring slot. Remove lower retainer.

2) Lower axle without stretching brake hose and tube assembly.

NOTE: **Axle must be supported by jack during removal and installation procedure. If brake hose length does not permit adequate clearance, caliper must be removed from steering knuckle.**

3) Remove coil spring using long pry bar. Insert pry bar between 2 axles. Force I-beam axle down far enough to lift spring over bolt that passes through lower spring seat. *See Fig. 3.*

4) Rotate spring so built-in retainer on upper spring seat is cleared. Remove spring.

Installation

To install, reverse removal procedures. Tighten all nuts and bolts.

Fig. 3: Coil Spring Assembly

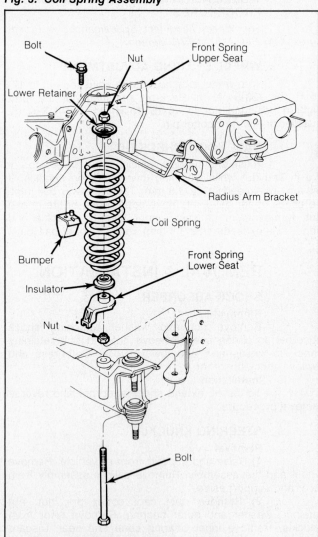

RADIUS ARM

Removal

1) Raise and support front of vehicle. Disconnect lower end of shock absorber from shock lower bracket. Remove front spring. Loosen axle pivot bolt.

FORD 2WD COIL SPRING — RANGER (Cont.)

NOTE: Axle must be supported by jack during removal and installation procedure. If brake hose length does not permit adequate clearance, caliper must be removed from steering knuckle.

2) Remove spring lower seat from radius arm and remove bolt and nut attaching radius arm to axle and front bracket.

3) Remove nut, rear washer and insulator from rear side of radius arm rear bracket. Remove radius arm and remove inner insulator and retainer from radius arm stud. *See Fig. 4.*

Installation

To install radius arm, reverse removal procedure and tighten all nuts and bolts.

Fig. 4: Radius Arm Removal and Installation

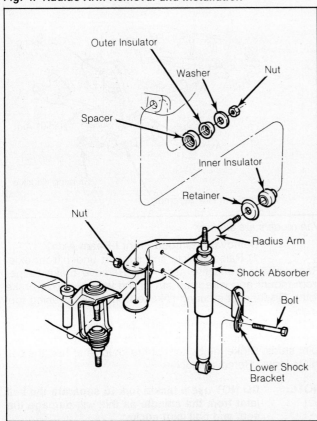

Remove radius arm and remove inner insulator and retainer from radius arm stud.

RADIUS ARM INSULATOR

Removal

1) Loosen axle pivot bolt. Loosen upper shock absorber pivot bolt and compress shock. Remove nut and washer attaching radius arm to radius arm bracket.

2) Remove outer insulator and spacer. Move radius arm and axle assembly forward, out of radius arm bracket. Remove inner insulator and retainer.

Installation

To install radius arm insulator, reverse removal procedures and tighten all nuts and bolts.

FRONT AXLE

Removal

1) Remove front wheel steering knuckle and front spring. Remove spring lower seat from radius arm.

2) Remove radius arm-to-front axle attaching bolt. Remove axle-to-frame pivot bracket bolt.

Installation

1) Position axle on frame pivot bracket and install bolt and nut finger tight. Position opposite end of axle to radius arm.

2) Install bolt from underneath bracket, radius arm and axle. Position axle against jounce bumper to place pivot bushing in proper position. Tighten axle-to-frame pivot bracket bolt.

3) Reverse removal procedures to complete installation.

STABILIZER BAR

Removal

Remove nuts and U-bolts retaining lower shock bracket/stabilizer bar bushing-to-radius arm. Remove retainers and remove stabilizer bar and bushing.

Installation

To install stabilizer bar, reverse removal procedure and tighten retainer bolts and U-bolt nuts.

TIGHTENING SPECIFICATIONS

Application	Ft. Lbs. (N.m)
Axle Arm-to-Bracket	120-150 (163-203)
Axle Arm Bracket-to-Frame Nut	70-92 (95-125)
Front Shock-to-Radius Arm Nut	48-68 (66-92)
Front Shock-to-Spring Seat Nut	25-35 (34-47)
Lower Ball Joint Stud Nut	104-146 (141-198)
Radius Arm Bracket-to-Frame Bolt ..	77-110 (104-152)
Radius Arm Bracket Connecting Bolts ..	35-50 (47-68)
Radius Arm-to-Frame	81-120 (109-163)
Stabilizer Bar-to-Bracket Bolt	35-50 (47-68)
Stabilizer Bar-to-Radius Arm Nut	48-64 (65-88)
Upper Ball Joint Stud Nut	85-110 (115-150)

Front Suspension

FORD 2WD COIL SPRING — EXCEPT RANGER

Pickup & Van

DESCRIPTION

Front suspension has two "I-Beam" axles. These are mounted to a frame pivot bracket at one end, and to the steering knuckle and a radius arm at the other. Forged axles are used on F250/350 and Van models. F100/150 models use a stamped front axle.

On forged axles, steering knuckle is mounted to the axle by a solid, constant diameter kingpin. Either Delrin or bronze bushings are pressed into steering knuckles to provide bearing surfaces for kingpin. On stamped axles, ball joints are used.

Radius arm runs rearward from axle to a bracket mounted on frame side rail. Coil spring is seated on top of radius arm and in a bracket mounted to frame. Hydraulic shock absorber is mounted between frame and radius arm to dampen road shock. A stabilizer bar is located in front of the axles.

ADJUSTMENT & CHECKING

WHEEL ALIGNMENT SPECIFICATIONS & PROCEDURES

See Wheel Alignment Specifications & Procedures in WHEEL ALIGNMENT Section.

WHEEL BEARING ADJUSTMENT

Tighten nut to 22-25 ft. lbs. (30-33 N.m) while turning rotor. Back off adjusting nut 1/8 turn. Install retainer and cotter pin without loosening nut any more. Bearing end play should be .001-.010" (.025-.254 mm).

BALL JOINT OR KINGPIN CHECKING

Raise vehicle. Adjust wheel bearings. Grab each wheel and shake in and out while watching front spindle assembly. Assembly must not move more than 1/32" (.8 mm) at the upper or lower arms relative to the axle. If worm beyond limits, replace ball joints or install new kingpins and bushings.

REMOVAL & INSTALLATION

STEERING KNUCKLE

Removal (Forged Front I-Beam Axle)

1) Raise vehicle and support under front axle. Remove wheel and tire assembly. Remove brake caliper from mount and wire it up out of the way. Remove brake rotor and brake dust shield. Disconnect tie rod end from knuckle using tool (3290-C).

2) Remove nut and lock washer from locking bolt. Tap out locking bolt. Remove upper and lower pin grease plugs. To protect grease plug threads during replacement, remove zerk fitting from one of the plugs.

3) Drill zerk fitting hole oversize, and install modified grease plug in upper spindle. Drive kingpin out from the top of the axle using pin punch and modified plug as a guide. Remove knuckle and thrust bearing. Knock out the kingpin seal.

Installation

1) Ensure king pin spindle is free of nicks, burrs and corrosion. Press kingpin seal into position with the metal backing facing up towards the bushing. Before installing steering knuckle, pack thrust bearing with chassis lubricant.

2) Position bearing with open end (lip side) down towards the lower bushing. Install kingpin in axle and steering knuckle, making sure notch in kingpin is aligned with lock pin hole in steering knuckle.

3) Install kingpin so letter "T", stamped on one end of pin, is facing up. Install a new lock pin with threads facing forward and the wedge groove facing the kingpin notch.

4) Install pin grease plugs. Lubricate kingpins with multipurpose grease. To complete installation, reverse removal procedure.

Fig. 1: F250/350 (2WD) Twin I-Beam Suspension

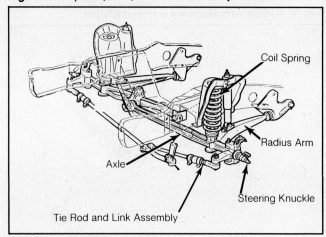

Van models are similar.

Removal (Stamped Front I-Beam Axle)

1) Raise vehicle and support under front axle. Remove wheel and tire assembly. Remove brake caliper from mount and wire it up out of the way. Remove brake rotor. Disconnect steering linkage from knuckle using tool (3290-C).

2) Remove the cotter pin from the upper ball joint stud. Remove the nut from the upper and lower ball joint studs. Strike the bottom of the knuckle to pop the ball joints loose. Remove knuckle.

NOTE: DO NOT use a pickle fork to separate the ball joint from the spindle as this will damage the seal and ball joint socket.

Installation

1) Before assembly, make sure the upper and lower ball joints seals are in place. Place the knuckle over the ball joints. Install the nut on the lower ball joint stud and partially tighten.

2) Install the camber adapter in the upper spindle over the ball joint stud. Install nut on upper ball joint stud. Hold the camber adapter with a wrench to keep the ball stud from turning.

3) Torque the nut to specifications and insert a new cotter pin. Torque lower ball joint nut and insert cotter pin. To complete installation, reverse removal procedure.

FORD 2WD COIL SPRING — EXCEPT RANGER (Cont.)

Fig. 2: Removing Steering Knuckle

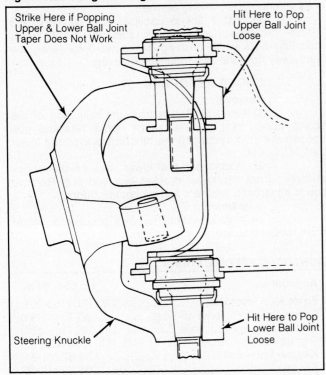

Strike Here if Popping Upper & Lower Ball Joint Taper Does Not Work

Hit Here to Pop Upper Ball Joint Loose

Steering Knuckle

Hit Here to Pop Lower Ball Joint Loose

Stamped front "I" beam axle is shown.

KINGPIN BUSHINGS

Removal (Forged Front I-Beam Axle)

1) Remove steering knuckle from vehicle as previously outlined. Drive bushing out of bore in steering knuckle, using a tool slightly smaller in diameter than bore.

2) If tool is not available, carefully drive a small center punch between the bushing and the spindle, at the split side of the bushing. Collapse the bushing and remove it from the spindle bore.

3) Clean bores in steering knuckle, and make sure lubrication grooves in knuckle are not plugged.

Installation

1) Position bushing in steering knuckle bore, with the open end of the grease groove of the bushing toward the axle. Using a driver which pilots in bushing, drive bushing into place in knuckle. Delrin bushings can be forced into place by hand.

2) Ream bronze bushings to .001-.003" (.025-.076 mm) larger than outside diameter of new kingpin. Clean all metal shavings from bushing after reaming. Lubricate bushing and kingpin, and install steering knuckle.

BALL JOINTS

Removal (Stamped Front I-Beam Axle)

Remove steering knuckle from vehicle. Remove snap ring from ball joints. Using "C" clamp tool (T74P-4635-C), press upper ball joint out of axle. Press out lower ball joint.

CAUTION: Do not use heat on ball joint or axle during removal and installation procedures.

Installation

Seat the lower ball joint squarely in the hole by hand. Using ball joint installation tool, press the ball joint in

until firmly seated. Use the same procedure for pressing in the upper ball joint. Install snap rings. To complete installation, reverse removal procedure.

COIL SPRING

Removal

1) Raise front of vehicle. Place safety stands under frame and a floor jack under axle. Disconnect lower shock absorber mount. Remove bolts securing upper spring retainer and remove retainer.

2) Remove nut securing lower spring retainer to spring seat and axle. Lower jack under axle and remove spring.

Installation

Place spring in position and raise front axle with jack. Place lower spring retainer over stud and lower seat, and tighten attaching nut. Place upper retainer over the spring and upper seat and tighten bolts. Connect lower shock absorber mount. Lower vehicle.

FRONT AXLE

Removal

1) Raise vehicle and position safety stands under frame. Remove disc brake caliper, rotor, steering knuckle and front coil spring. Remove stabilizer bar if equipped.

2) Remove lower spring seat from radius arm. Remove bolt connecting radius arm and bracket to front axle. Remove axle pivot bolt and remove axle.

Fig. 3: Stamped Front I-Beam Axle Assembly

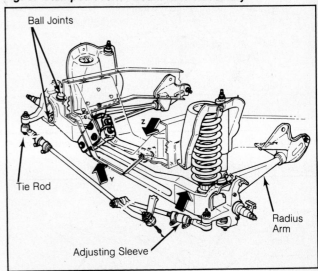

Ball Joints

Tie Rod

Adjusting Sleeve

Radius Arm

F100/150 models are shown.

Installation

1) Position axle. Install pivot bolt and nut finger tight. Connect radius arm and front bracket, then install and tighten bolt. Install lower spring seat, making sure it aligns over radius arm bolt.

2) Install coil spring. Tighten axle pivot bolt. Install steering knuckle, and stabilizer bar if equipped.

RADIUS ARM

Removal

1) Raise vehicle. Position safety stands under frame and a floor jack under axle. Disconnect lower shock absorber mount. Remove front spring. Remove lower spring seat.

FORD 2WD COIL SPRING — EXCEPT RANGER (Cont.)

2) Remove bolt holding radius arm to axle. Remove nut, rear washer and insulator from rear radius arm mount. Disconnect tie rod and remove radius arm.

Installation

To install the radius arm, reverse removal procedure. Torque all fittings to specifications.

STABILIZER BAR

Removal

1) Disconnect left and right ends of front stabilizer bar from the link assembly attached to beam bracket.

2) Disconnect the retainer bolts and remove the stabilizer bar. Disconnect the stabilizer link assembly by loosening left and right lock nuts from beam brackets.

Installation

1) Loosely assemble the entire assembly with both links outboard of the stabilizer bar. Pull stabilizer bar

rearward and install bar ends to the links and install link bolts with threads pointing outward.

2) Install link-to-stabilizer bar washers and tighten retaining nuts. Tighten stabilizer bar-to-frame mounting nuts while pushing bar forward to swing the links away from the axle mounting brackets.

SHOCK ABSORBER

Removal

1) Insert a wrench from the rear side of the spring upper seat to hold shock upper retaining nut. Loosen the stud by turning the hex on the exposed lower part of the stud.

2) Disconnect the lower end of the shock absorber from the lower bracket bolt and nut. Remove shock absorbers, washers and rubber insulators.

Installation

To install, reverse removal procedure. Install NEW rubber insulators.

TIGHTENING SPECIFICATIONS

Application	Ft. Lbs. (N.m)
Front Axle Pivot Bolt	120-150 (163-203)
Lower Spring Retainer-to-Seat	30-70 (41-95)
Radius Arm-to-Front Axle	240-320 (325-423)
Radius Arm-to-Bracket	80-120 (108-163)
Kingpin Lock Bolt	38-62 (51-84)
Kingpin Plug	35-50 (47-68)
Lower Ball Joint	140-180 (190-244)
Radius Arm-to-Axle	
F250/350 & Vans	240-320 (326-433)
F100/150	269-329 (365-446)
Radius Arm-to-Rear Bracket	80-120 (109-162)
Shock Bracket-to-Radius Arm	27-37 (37-50)
Stabilizer Bar-to-Frame	27-37 (37-50)
Upper Ball Joint	185-110 (115-150)
Upper Shock Absorber Mount	15-25 (20-27)
Upper Spring Retainer-to-Spring Seat	13-18 (18-24)

Fig. 4: Identification of Suspension Details

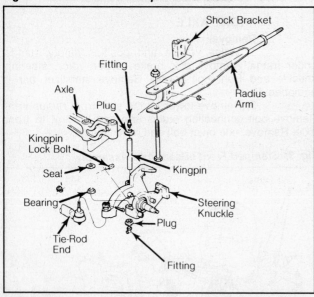

Van models (Exc. E250/E350 steering knuckle) are shown.

Fig. 5: Identification of Suspension Details

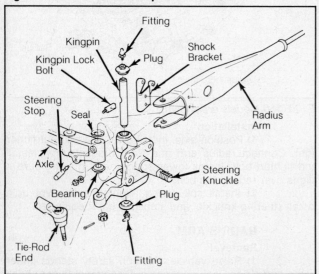

Van Models (E250/E350 Steering Knuckle) are shown.

FORD 4WD COIL SPRING — BRONCO II & RANGER

Bronco II, Ranger

DESCRIPTION

Independent front suspension consists of a 2-piece front driving axle assembly, 2 coil springs and 2 radius arms. Front driving axle consists of 2 independent axle arm assemblies. One end of each axle arm assembly is anchored to the frame. The other end of each axle arm assembly is supported by coil spring and radius arm. Hydraulic shock absorbers are direct, double acting type.

ADJUSTMENT & CHECKING

WHEEL ALIGNMENT SPECIFICATIONS & PROCEDURES

See Wheel Alignment Specifications & Procedures in WHEEL ALIGNMENT section.

WHEEL BEARING ADJUSTMENT

Manual Locking Hub

1) Raise and support vehicle. Remove lug nuts and remove wheel and tire. Remove retainer washers from lug nut studs and remove manual locking hub assembly from spindle.

2) Remove snap ring from end of spindle shaft. Remove axle shaft spacer, needle thrust bearing and bearing spacer.

3) Remove outer wheel bearing lock nut from knuckle using 4-prong nut spanner wrench (T83T-1197-A). Remove lock nut washer from spindle. Loosen inner wheel bearing lock nut using 4-prong wrench. Be sure slot in wrench is over pin on lock nut.

4) Tighten inner lock nut to 35 ft. lbs. (47 N.m) to seat bearing. Spin rotor and back off inner lock nut 1/4 turn. Install lock washer on spindle. If necessary, turn inner lock nut slightly so pin on lock nut aligns with closest hole in lock washer.

5) Install outer wheel bearing lock nut and tighten lock nut to 150 ft. lbs. (203 N.m).

6) Complete installation by reversing removal procedures. Check end play of wheel and tire assembly on spindle. End play should be .001-.003" (.02-.08 mm).

Automatic Locking Hub

1) Raise and support vehicle. Remove wheel lug nuts and remove wheel and tire. Remove retainer washers from lug nut studs. Remove automatic locking hub from spindle.

2) Remove snap ring from end of knuckle shaft. Remove axle shaft spacer, needle thrust bearing and bearing spacer. Carefully pull cam assembly off wheel bearing adjusting nut. Remove thrust washer needle thrust bearing from adjusting nut.

3) Loosen wheel bearing adjusting nut from spindle. Rotate hub and rotor. Tighten wheel bearing adjusting nut to 35 ft. lbs. (47 N.m) to seat bearings. Back off nut 1/4 turn. Retighten adjusting nut to 16 INCH lbs. (1.8 N.m).

4) Align closest hole in wheel bearing adjusting nut with center of spindle keyway slot. Advance nut to next hole, if necessary.

5) To complete installation, reverse removal procedures. Check end play of wheel and tire assembly on spindle. End play should be .001-.003" (.02-.08 mm).

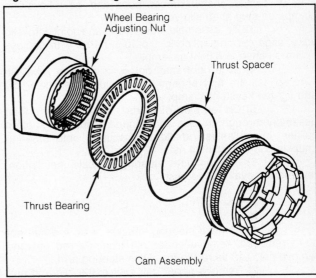

Fig. 1: *Wheel Bearing Adjusting Nut Assembly*

Tighten adjusting nut to 35 ft. lbs (47 N.m).

SHOCK ABSORBER

Removal

Remove nut and washer holding shock absorber to spring seat. Remove bolt and nut from lower bracket retaining shock absorber to radius arm. Slide shock out of lower bracket. Compress shock and remove.

Installation

Extend shock absorber through spring seat, install washer and nut and tighten. Reverse removal procedures to complete installation.

STEERING KNUCKLE

Removal

1) Raise and support vehicle. Remove wheel and tire. Remove caliper. Remove hub locks, wheel bearings and lock nuts. Remove hub and rotor. Remove outer wheel bearing cone.

2) Remove grease seal from rotor with seal remover (T50T-100-A). Discard seal. Remove inner wheel bearing. Remove inner and outer bearing cups from rotor.

3) Remove nuts holding spindle to steering knuckle. Tap spindle with plastic hammer to jar spindle from knuckle. Remove splash shield.

4) On vehicle right side, remove shaft and joint assembly by pulling assembly out of carrier. On right side of carrier, remove and discard keystone clamp from shaft and joint assembly and stub shaft.

5) Slide rubber boot onto stub shaft and pull shaft and joint assembly from splines of stub shaft. Wrap spindle in protective cloth and place 2nd step of spindle in vise.

6) Remove oil seal and needle bearing from spindle. If necessary, remove seal from shaft by driving off with a hammer.

Installation

1) Place bearing in bore with manufacturer identification facing outward. Drive bearing into bore. Install grease seal in bearing bore with lip side of seal facing upwards. Coat bearing seal lip with multi-purpose lubricant.

FORD 4WD COIL SPRING — BRONCO II & RANGER (Cont.)

2) If removed, install new shaft seal. On right side of carrier, install rubber boot and new keystone clamps on stub shaft slip yoke.

3) To assemble right shaft and joint into slip yoke, align missing spline in slip yoke barrel with gapless spline on shaft and joint assembly.

4) Slide right shaft and joint into slip yoke. Be sure splines are fully engaged. Slide boot over assembly and tighten keystone clamp.

5) On left side of carrier, slide shaft and joint assembly through knuckle and engage splines on shaft in carrier. Install splash shield and spindle onto steering knuckle. Tighten spindle nuts.

6) To complete steering knuckle installation, reverse removal procedures.

BALL JOINT
Removal

1) Remove steering knuckle. If tie rod has not been removed, remove cotter pin from tie rod nut and remove nut. Tap tie rod to free from steering arm.

2) Remove upper ball joint cotter pin and nut. Loosen lower ball joint nut. Tap inside of steering knuckle near upper and lower ball joints to break spindle loose from ball joint studs.

3) Remove camber adjuster sleeve. Place knuckle in vise and remove snap ring from bottom ball joint socket, if equipped.

4) Install C-frame (D79T-3010-AA) on lower ball joint. Turn forcing screw clockwise until lower ball joint is removed from steering knuckle.

5) Install C-frame on upper ball joint. Turn forcing screw clockwise until upper ball joint is removed from knuckle.

Installation

1) To install ball joint, reverse removal procedures. Always install lower ball joint first. Lower ball joint does not have a cotter pin hole in the stud.

2) Install camber adjuster on top ball joint stud with arrow pointing outward for positive camber and arrow pointing inward for negative camber.

3) Zero camber bushings will not have an arrow and may be rotated in either direction as long as lugs on yoke engage slots in bushing.

4) Camber adjuster will seat itself into steering knuckle at a predetermined position. Do not attempt to alter position of camber adjuster.

COIL SPRING
Removal

1) Raise and support vehicle. Position jack under spring located beneath axle. Remove bolt and nut holding shock absorber to radius arm. Slide shock out from bracket.

2) Remove nut holding spring to axle and radius arm. Remove retainer. Lower axle until spring tension is removed and clearance is adequate to remove spring.

3) Remove spring by rotating upper coil out of tabs in upper spring seat. Remove spacer and seat. Remove stud from axle if necessary.

Installation

Position upper end of spring so coil fits into spring stop in upper spring seat and top coil fits over upper spring retainer. To complete installation, reverse removal procedures.

Fig. 2: Coil Spring Installation

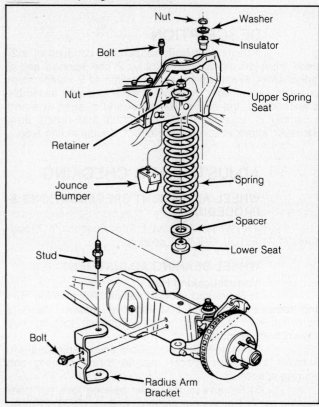

Position spring in upper spring seat and upper spring retainer.

RADIUS ARM
Removal

1) Raise and support front of vehicle. Place jack under axle. Disconnect lower end of shock absorber from shock lower bracket.

NOTE: **Axle must be supported by jack during removal and installation procedure. If brake hose length does not permit adequate spring removal clearance, caliper must be removed from steering knuckle.**

2) Remove front spring. Loosen axle pivot bolt. Remove spring lower seat and stud from radius arm. Remove bolts attaching radius arm-to-axle and front bracket.

3) Remove nut, rear washer and insulator from rear side of radius arm rear bracket. Remove radius arm from vehicle. Remove inner insulator and retainer from radius arm stud.

Installation

Position front end of radius arm front bracket to axle. Install bolts and stud in bracket. Install bolts and stud finger tight. To complete installation, reverse removal procedures.

RADIUS ARM INSULATOR
Removal

1) Loosen axle pivot bolt. Loosen upper shock absorber pivot bolt and compress shock.

FORD 4WD COIL SPRING — BRONCO II & RANGER (Cont.)

2) Remove nut and washer attaching radius arm to radius arm bracket. Remove outer insulator and spacer.

3) Move radius arm and axle assembly forward out of radius arm bracket. Remove inner insulator and retainer.

Installation

To install radius arm insulator, reverse removal procedure and tighten all nuts and bolts.

FRONT AXLE

Removal

1) Raise and support vehicle under radius arm brackets. Disconnect driveshaft from front axle yoke. Remove wheel and tire.

2) Remove disc brake calipers. Remove cotter pin and nut retaining steering linkage to spindle. Disconnect linkage from spindle.

3) Position jack under axle arm and compress coil spring. Remove nut retaining lower part of spring to axle arm. Lower jack and remove coil spring, spacer, seat and stud.

4) Remove bolt and nut and disconnect shock absorber from radius arm bracket. Remove stud and bolts connecting radius arm bracket and radius arm to axle arm. Remove bracket and radius arm.

5) Remove pivot bolt securing right hand axle arm assembly to crossmember. Remove keystone clamps securing axle shaft boot from axle shaft slip yoke and axle shaft. Slide over rubber boot.

6) Disconnect right driveshaft from slip yoke assembly. Lower jack and remove right axle arm assembly. Position another jack under differential housing.

7) Remove bolt connecting left axle arm to crossmember. Lower jacks and remove left axle arm assembly.

Installation

To complete front axle installation, reverse removal procedures.

STABILIZER BAR

Removal

Remove nuts and U-bolts retaining lower shock bracket/stabilizer bar bushing to radius arm. Remove retainers and remove stabilizer bar and bushing.

Installation

Place stabilizer bar on radius arm and bracket. To complete installation, reverse removal procedure.

TIGHTENING SPECIFICATIONS

Application	Ft. Lbs. (N.m)
Axle Pivot Bolt	120-150 (163-203)
Radius Arm-to-Rear Bracket Nut	80-120 (109-162)
Radius Arm Front Bracket	160-220 (217-298)
Radius Arm Bracket Front Bolts	27-37 (37-50)
Radius Arm Bracket Lower Bolts	160-220 (217-298)
Shock-to-Radius Arm Nut & Bolt	42-72 (57-97)
Shock-to-Upper Seat	25-35 (34-47)
Spring Retainer Nut	70-100 (95-135)
Stabilizer Bar Retainer Bolts	77-110 (104-150)
Stabilizer Bar U-Bolt Nuts	48-68 (66-92)

Front Suspension

FORD 4WD COIL SPRING — EXCEPT BRONCO II & RANGER

Bronco, F150 Pickup

DESCRIPTION

Front suspension consists of a two piece driving axle, two coil springs, two radius arms, a side strut bar and two hydraulic shock absorbers (some models may be equipped with four shock absorbers).

Radius arms attach to frame side rails and are clamped around axle housing. If vehicle is equipped with optional shock absorbers, the front clamp portion of the radius arm is also the lower shock mount.

Coil springs are mounted to radius arms directly over axle housing and to brackets attached to frame side rails. Standard equipment shock absorbers attach to frame side rails and radius arms behind coil spring. Optional shock absorbers mount in front of spring.

Fig. 1: Identification of Front Suspension Components

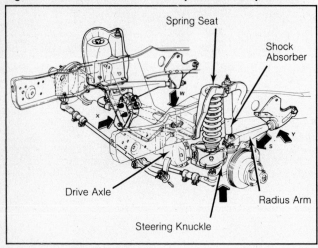

Bronco and F150 4WD models are shown.

Fig. 2: Exploded View of Wheel Bearing Assembly

ADJUSTMENT & CHECKING

WHEEL ALIGNMENT SPECIFICATIONS & PROCEDURES

See Wheel Alignment Specifications & Procedures in WHEEL ALIGNMENT section.

WHEEL BEARING ADJUSTMENT

1) Remove locking hubs. *See appropriate article in DRIVE AXLE section.* Using wrench (T59T-1197-B), tighten inner adjusting nut to 50 ft. lbs. (68 N.m) while turning rotor.

2) Back off nut 45°. Install lock washer. Install outer lock nut and tighten to 150 ft. lbs. (203 N.m). Final end play should be .001-.006" (.03-.15 mm).

BALL JOINT CHECKING

1) Adjust wheel bearings. Raise vehicle with weight off wheels. Grasp tire at top and bottom and shake wheel while watching movement of spindle.

2) If spindle moves more than 1/32" (.8 mm) at the upper or lower arms relative to the axle, ball joints should be replaced.

REMOVAL & INSTALLATION

WHEEL BEARINGS
Removal

1) Remove locking hubs. *See appropriate article in DRIVE AXLE section.* Remove wheel bearing lock nut, lock ring and adjusting nut. Remove hub/disc assembly. Outer wheel bearing will slide out.

2) Remove spindle nuts, then remove spindle from knuckle studs and axle shaft. Clean all parts, then remove spindle bore seal, V-block seal and thrust washer from outer axle shaft. Replace any worn parts.

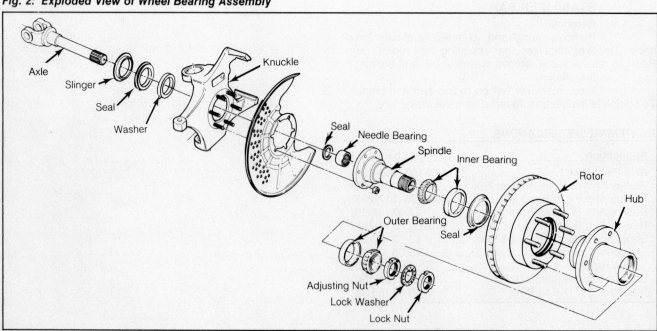

Clean all parts and use new grease for reassembly.

FORD 4WD COIL SPRING — EXCEPT BRONCO II & RANGER (Cont.)

3) Remove inner bearing cone and grease seal from hub with slide puller. Check bearing cups and drive out with punch if worn.

Installation

1) Lubricate needle bearing and spindle face. Assemble V-block seal next to needle bearing. Place spindle bore seal and thrust washer on axle shaft. Place spindle on knuckle studs and tighten nuts.

2) Place inner bearing cone and roller in cup, then install grease seal. Place hub/disc assembly on spindle. Install outer bearing cone and roller with adjusting nut. Adjust wheel bearings and install locking hubs.

COIL SPRING

Removal

1) Raise vehicle. Remove shock absorber-to-lower bracket bolt and nut. Remove lower spring retainer bolt. Remove upper spring attaching screw and upper retainer.

2) Place safety stands under frame rails and lower axle enough to relieve tension on spring. Remove spring and lower retainer from vehicle.

Installation

To install, reverse removal procedure.

RADIUS ARM

Removal

1) Raise vehicle and place safety stands under frame side rails. Remove shock absorber attaching bolts and remove shock absorber from radius arm. Remove lower spring attaching bolt. Loosen the axle pivot bolt.

2) Remove radius arm rear insulator. Lower axle and allow axle to move forward. Remove the two self-tapping screws attaching the front axle to radius arm bracket to axle tube.

3) Remove bolt and stud attaching radius arm to axle. Move axle forward and remove radius arm from axle. Pull radius arm from frame brackets.

Installation

1) Position washer and insulator on rear of radius arm and place radius arm into the frame bracket. Install attaching nut. Position radius arm to axle. Install new bolts and stud, using Locktite No. 242.

2) Attach radius arm to axle. Attach lower spring seat, insulator and retainer to spring and axle. Tighten rear radius rod attaching nut. Install shock absorber and tighten nuts.

STEERING KNUCKLE

Removal & Installation

See Steering Knuckles in DRIVE AXLE Section for removal and insulation.

QUAD SHOCK ABSORBERS

Removal

Remove self-locking nut, steel washer and rubber bushings from upper end of shock absorbers. Remove self-locking nut from lower end of shocks. Remove shock absorbers.

Installation

Replace rubber bushings when replacing shock absorbers. Place shock absorbers on mounting brackets with large diameter on top. Install bushings, steel washers and self-locking nuts and tighten.

STABILIZER BAR

Removal

1) Remove nuts, bolts and washers connecting stabilizer bar to links. Remove nuts and bolts of stabilizer bar retainer. Remove stabilizer bar insulator assembly.

2) Remove coil spring and lower spring seat. Remove stabilizer bar mounting bracket attaching stud and bracket. Remove stabilizer bar.

Installation

1) Locate brackets so locating tang is positioned in the radius arm notch (or quad shock bracket notch if vehicle has quad shocks).

2) Reposition the spring lower seat and reinstall the spring and retainer. To reinstall the stabilizer bar insulator assembly, loosely assemble all nuts, bolts and washers to the bar, brackets, retainers and links.

3) Position bar correctly. Torque retainer nuts with retainer around the insulator. Tighten all remaining nuts at the link assemblies.

TIGHTENING SPECIFICATIONS

Application	Ft. Lbs. (N.m)
Lower Spring Retainer	70-100 (90-134)
Radius Arm-to-Axle	
Lower Bolt	320-340 (434-461)
Upper Stud	240-260 (326-352)
Rear Radius Arm Nut	80-100 (109-134)
Shock Absorber Mounting Bolt	
Lower	40-60 (54-81)
Upper	25-35 (34-37)
Stabilizer Bar Link-to-Bracket	52-74 (71-100)
Stabilizer Bar Retaining Nuts	27-37 (37-50)
Upper Spring Retainer	13-18 (18-24)

Front Suspension

GENERAL MOTORS COIL SPRING — S10

Chevrolet, GMC

DESCRIPTION

Independent front suspension consists of upper and lower control arms with steering knuckle mounted by ball joints. The upper control arms are mounted with pivot shafts, through rubber bushings. The lower control arms have pressed in bushings and are mounted by bolts which thread through the frame. Coil springs are mounted between lower control arm and a formed seat in suspension crossmember. Hydraulic shock absorbers fit inside coil spring, between lower control arm and frame. A stabilizer bar is mounted to frame side rails and connected to lower control arms by link bolts.

Fig. 1: Exploded View of Front Suspension Assembly

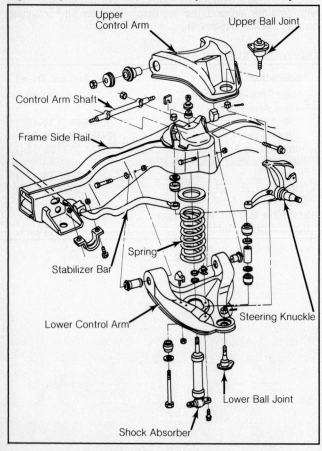

ADJUSTMENT & CHECKING

WHEEL ALIGNMENT SPECIFICATIONS & PROCEDURES

See Wheel Alignment Specifications & Procedures in WHEEL ALIGNMENT section.

WHEEL BEARING ADJUSTMENT

Tighten bearing nut to 12 ft. lbs. (16 N.m) while spinning wheel forward. Back off nut until it is just loose. Hand-tighten nut, then loosen slightly, (no more than 1/2 turn) until cotter pin can be inserted. End play should be .001-.005" (.03-.13 mm).

BALL JOINT CHECKING

Upper Ball Joint

1) Upper ball joint is spring-loaded. Raise vehicle and support with jack stands under the lower control arms. Stands should be as close as possible to each lower ball joint. Upper control arm bumper must not contact frame.

2) Place dial indicator against rim, then rock wheel in and out. Horizontal deflection should not exceed .125" (3.2 mm).

3) If dial indicator reading is excessive, or ball stud has been disconnected from knuckle and any looseness is detected or stud can be twisted with fingers, relpace ball joint.

Lower Ball Joint

1) Lower ball joint is a press fit. A wear indicator is built into the ball joint.

2) With vehicle weight on wheels, check to see that wear indicator protrudes .05" (1.3 mm) beyond surface of ball joint cover. If wear indicator is flush or recessed, replace ball joint.

REMOVAL & INSTALLATION

SHOCK ABSORBERS

Removal

Raise and support vehicle. Remove nuts at top of shock absorber. Remove 2 bolts retaining shock absorber pivot to lower control arm. Pull shock absorber down and remove from vehicle.

Installation

Position shock absorber into control arm with shaft extended. Hold shaft and tighten upper nut. Bolt pivot to control arm.

STABILIZER BAR

Removal

1) Raise and support vehicle. Remove nut from link bolt, pull bolt from linkage and remove retainers, grommets and spacer.

2) Remove bracket-to-frame bolts and remove stabilizer shaft, rubber bushings and brackets.

Installation

1) Position stabilizer bar on frame. Stabilizer bar identification markings should be on right side of vehicle. Loosely install frame bushings and brackets.

2) Slit in bushing should be toward front of vehicle. Install link units at lower control arms. Tighten all nuts and bolts.

COIL SPRINGS

Removal

1) Raise and support vehicle. Remove 2 shock absorber screws and push shock up through control arm into spring. Support under frame so that control arms hang free. Install support (J-23028) onto jack. Remove stabilizer bar-to-lower control arm attachment.

2) Raise jack to remove tension on lower control arm pivot bolts. Install a safety chain around spring and through lower control arm. Remove control arm bolts (rear bolt first).

3) Carefully lower jack until all tension is released from spring. Remove spring from vehicle.

GENERAL MOTORS COIL SPRING — S10 (Cont.)

Fig. 2: Lower Control Arm and Spring Removal

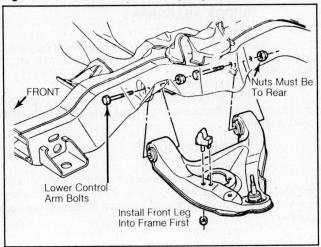

Install bolts with nuts toward rear of vehicle.

Installation
1) To install coil spring, reverse removal procedure. Spring must cover one drain hole in control arm, leaving the other open.

2) Install front control arm pivot bolt first. Bolts must be installed with the nuts toward rear of vehicle.

STEERING KNUCKLE
Removal
1) Raise and support vehicle at front lift points. Do not place stands under control arm, but position floor jack slightly below arm. Remove wheel, caliper, hub and disc rotor.

2) Remove 3 splash shield-to-knuckle attaching bolts. Remove tie rod from knuckle using puller.

3) Carefully remove seal if knuckle will be reused. Remove ball joint studs from knuckle. Raise jack until lower control arm is just supported.

4) Raise upper control arm to disengage ball joint stud. Raise knuckle from lower ball joint stud. Remove knuckle.

Installation
Clean all parts thoroughly, and inspect for damage. If out-of-round, deformation or damage is found, replace steering knuckle. To install, reverse removal procedure and tighten all nuts and bolts.

UPPER BALL JOINT
Removal
1) Raise and support vehicle under lower control arms, between spring seats and ball joints. Jacks must remain under lower control arm to retain position of spring and control arm.

2) Remove wheel. Loosen upper ball joint from steering knuckle. Remove cotter pin and upper ball stud nut.

3) Install ball joint remover (J-23742) between the ball studs. Loosen ball stud. Remove ball joint remover and support knuckle to protect brake line.

4) With control arm in raised position, drill out 4 rivets and remove ball joint assembly.

Installation
To install, reverse removal procedure. Use nuts and bolts in place of rivets to attach ball joint to control arm. Check and adjust front end alignment as necessary.

LOWER BALL JOINT
Removal
1) Raise and support vehicle with safety stands positioned under frame. Place jack under lower control arm spring seat. Remove tire and wheel. Remove lower stud cotter pin and stud nut.

2) Install ball joint remover (J-23742) between the ball studs. Loosen ball joint stud and remove ball joint remover. Guide lower control arm out of opening in splash shield by using putty knife or scraper.

3) Place a wooden block between upper control arm and frame to keep knuckle out of the way. Remove grease fitting from ball joint. Using "C" clamp type tool and drivers (J-9519-10), press ball joint out.

Installation
1) Using clamp and drivers (J9519-10), install new ball joint in control arm. Reverse removal procedure to complete installation.

2) Lubricate ball joint fitting until grease appears at seal. Check and adjust front alignment as necessary.

UPPER CONTROL ARM
Removal
1) Note location of alignment shims for re-installation. Remove nuts and shims. Raise and support front end of vehicle under lower control arms, between spring seats and ball joints.

2) Remove wheel and loosen upper ball joint from steering knuckle. Support hub to prevent weight from damaging brake hose. If necessary for clearance, remove upper control arm attaching bolts. Remove upper control arm.

Installation
1) To install, position upper control arm bolts in frame and install pivot shaft on bolts. Inner pivot bolts must be installed with bolts heads to front on front bushing and to rear on rear bushing.

2) Install shims in original position. Reverse removal procedure and adjust the wheel alignment as necessary.

LOWER CONTROL ARM
Removal
1) Raise vehicle and place safety stands under frame side rails. Remove coil spring and loosen ball joint stud.

2) Support control arm and guide arm out of splash shield. Remove control arm. Replace bushings if necessary.

Installation
To install, reverse removal procedure and tighten all nuts and bolts. Check wheel alignment and adjust as necessary.

TIGHTENING SPECIFICATIONS

Application	Ft. Lbs. (N.m)
Lower Control Arm-to-Frame	[1] 65 (90)
Upper Control Arm-to-Frame	45 (60)
Upper Control Arm Pivot Nuts	85 (115)
Upper Ball Joint Nut	65 (90)
Lower Ball Joint Nut	90 (120)
Stabilizer Bar Brackets	[1] 24 (33)
Shock Absorber-to-Control Arm Bolts	20 (27)

[1] — Tighten with weight on suspension.

Front Suspension

GENERAL MOTORS COIL SPRING — EXCEPT S10

DESCRIPTION

Independent front suspension consists of upper and lower control arms with steering knuckle mounted in between by ball joints. Upper and lower control arms are mounted to crossmember with pivot shafts, through either rubber or threaded steel bushings. Coil springs are mounted between lower control arm and a formed seat in suspension crossmember. Hydraulic shock absorbers fit between lower control arm and frame. A stabilizer bar is mounted to frame side rails and connected to lower control arms by links.

Fig. 1: Exploded View of Front Suspension Assembly

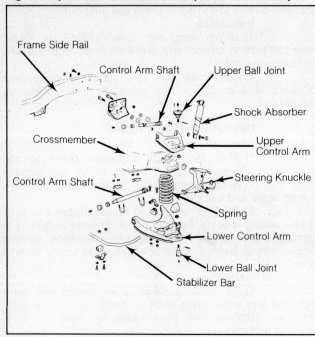

ADJUSTMENT & CHECKING

WHEEL ALIGNMENT SPECIFICATIONS & PROCEDURES

See Wheel Alignment Specifications & Procedures in WHEEL ALIGNMENT Section.

WHEEL BEARING ADJUSTMENT

Tighten bearing nut to 16 ft. lbs. (22 N.m) while spinning wheel forward. Back off nut until it is just loose. Hand-tighten nut, then loosen slightly (no more than 1/2 turn) until cotter pin can be inserted. End play should be .001-.005" (.03-.13 mm).

BALL JOINT CHECKING

1) Upper ball joint is spring-loaded. If upper stud has any lateral shake, or if it can be twisted with fingers, replace ball joint. Lower ball joint is a loose fit with no weight applied.

2) To check, lift vehicle. Support weight of control arms at wheel hub. Measure distance between ball joint stud and lower grease fitting.

3) Remove support from control arm and remeasure. If distance exceeds .095" (2.38 mm), replace ball joint.

REMOVAL & INSTALLATION

SHOCK ABSORBERS

Removal

Remove nuts and eye bolts securing upper and lower ends of shock absorber, and remove shock absorber from vehicle.

Installation

Position shock absorber over mounting bolts or into mounting brackets and install eye bolts. Tighten all bolts and nuts.

STABILIZER BAR

Removal

Raise vehicle. Remove nuts and bolts attaching stabilizer bar brackets to frame. Remove link bolts and bushings at lower control arm. Remove stabilizer bar from vehicle.

Installation

Position stabilizer bar on frame. Loosely install frame bushings and brackets. Install link units at lower control arms. Tighten all nuts and bolts. Lower vehicle.

COIL SPRINGS

Removal

1) Raise vehicle and support under frame so that control arms hang free. Disconnect shock absorber and stabilizer bar at lower control arm. Install a support tool (J-23028) onto jack. Position tool under lower control arm shaft so that shaft seats in grooves of tool.

2) Install a safety chain through lower control arm and spring. Raise jack to relieve tension on lower control arm shaft and remove control arm shaft bolts. Carefully lower jack until all tension is released from spring. Remove spring from vehicle.

Fig. 2: Coil Spring Removal

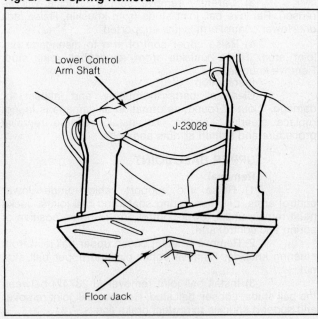

Use floor jack and support tool (J-23028).

Installation

To install coil spring, reverse removal procedure. On models with air cylinders in coil springs, check for leaks and damage before installation.

Front Suspension

GENERAL MOTORS COIL SPRING — EXCEPT S10 (Cont.)

STEERING KNUCKLE

NOTE: Front of vehicle should be supported with a twin-post hoist so the front coil spring remains compressed, yet the steering knuckle is accessible. If a frame hoist is used, support lower control arm with a jackstand to safely retain spring in its curb height position.

Removal
Raise and support vehicle as described. Remove wheel, hub, disc rotor and caliper. Remove disc splash shield. Remove upper and lower ball joint cotter pins and loosen nuts. Using ball joint remover (J-23742) to free steering knuckle from ball studs. Remove ball stud nuts and withdraw steering knuckle.

Installation
Clean all parts thoroughly, and inspect for damage. To install, reverse removal procedure and tighten all nuts and bolts.

CAUTION: When installing ball joint nuts, do not loosen nut to install cotter pin. If necessary, tighten one extra notch.

UPPER BALL JOINT

Removal
1) Raise vehicle. Support front end on safety stands positioned under lower control arms. Remove cotter pin from upper ball stud and loosen nut 2 turns. Remove brake caliper and suspend it from frame. Do not hang caliper by brake line.

2) Install ball joint remover (J-23742) between the ball studs. Loosen ball stud. Remove tool and stud nut. Drill out rivets and remove ball joint assembly.

Installation
To install, reverse removal procedure. Use nuts and bolts in place of rivets to attach ball joint to control arm.

Fig. 3: Removing Upper and Lower Ball Joints

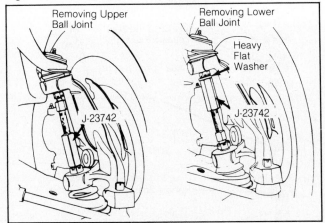

LOWER BALL JOINT

Removal
1) Raise vehicle. Support front end with safety stands positioned under lower control arms. Remove wheel and tire. Remove lower stud cotter pin and loosen stud nut 2 turns. Remove brake caliper and suspend out of way. Do not hang by brake line.

2) Install ball joint remover (J-23742) between the ball studs, and loosen ball stud. Remove tool and ball stud nut. Pull the brake disc and steering knuckle assembly up off the ball stud and support upper control arm with a block of wood. Press lower ball joint out of its seat and remove from vehicle.

Installation
Using "C" clamp and support (J-9519-10 and J-9519-16), install new ball joint in control arm. Reverse removal procedure to complete installation.

UPPER CONTROL ARM

Removal
1) Raise vehicle. Support front end with safety stands under lower control arms. Remove cotter pin from upper ball joint and loosen nut. Remove brake caliper and suspend out of way. Do not hang by brake line.

2) Using ball joint remover (J-23742), loosen ball joint in steering knuckle. Remove tool and ball joint nut, then raise control arm to clear steering knuckle. Remove nuts and bolts attaching control arm shaft to frame member, and remove control arm from vehicle.

Installation
To install, reverse removal procedure and check wheel alignment. *See WHEEL ALIGNMENT Section for procedures and specifications.*

LOWER CONTROL ARM

Removal
1) Raise vehicle and place safety stands under frame side rails. Remove coil springs. Support inboard end of control arm after springs are removed. Remove cotter pin from lower stud and loosen stud nut 1 turn. Remove brake caliper and suspend out of way. Do not hang from brake line.

2) Using ball joint remover (J-23742), position large cupped end of tool over upper ball stud nut and pilot threaded end of tool on the lower ball stud. Loosen ball stud, then remove tool and stud nut. Remove nuts attaching control arm to vehicle and remove control arm.

Installation
To install, reverse removal procedure, tighten all nuts and bolts, and check wheel alignment. *See WHEEL ALIGNMENT Section for procedures and specifications.*

TIGHTENING SPECIFICATIONS

Application	Ft. Lbs. (N.m)
Lower Control Arm-to-Frame	
G10,20	65 (88)
All Others	85 (115)
Upper Control Arm-to-Frame	
C & P10,G10,20	70 (95)
All Others	105 (142)
Upper Ball Joint Nut	
C & P10,G10,20	50 (68)
All Others	90 (122)
Lower Ball Joint Nut	90 (122)
Stabilizer Bar	25 (34)
Shock Absorber Upper Nut	
C & P Models	140 (190)
G Models	75 (102)
Shock Absorber Lower Nut	
C & P Models	60 (81)
G Models	75 (102)

4-Wheel Drive Steering Knuckles

ALL MANUFACTURERS

DESCRIPTION

Open type steering knuckles are used on all models. Open type knuckles provide a sharper turning angle, which will decrease the vehicle turning radius.

All of the vehicle weight is carried by the axle housing and steering knuckle. The axle shafts are free floating. Depending upon vehicle model, the steering knuckles can be attached to the axle housing by either ball joints or roller bearings and pivot pins.

Other than the unique components required for front-wheel drive, all steering knuckles used on light duty trucks are mechanically similar.

OVERHAUL

BALL JOINT TYPE

Disassembly

1) Raise vehicle and support on safety stands. Remove wheels. Remove brake caliper and rotor. If equipped with locking hubs, remove hub lock mechanism. See removal and installation instructions in appropriate Locking Hubs article in this Section.

2) Disconnect tie rod end from steering knuckle. Remove spindle nuts and lightly tap spindle with a soft face hammer to free it from steering knuckle. Pull out axle shaft assembly. On Chevy "T" series, remove hub and bearing assembly.

3) Remove ball joint cotter keys and nuts. Break ball joints loose from steering knuckle. On Chrysler Corp. vehicles, lower ball joint does not need to be disconnected. Remove lower knuckle-to-knuckle arm nuts and separate components.

4) Clean all components with solvent and blow them dry with compressed air. Inspect all parts for burrs, chips, wear, flat spots or cracks. Replace all damaged parts and parts showing excessive wear.

Reassembly

To complete reassembly, reverse disassembly procedure. Torque all fittings to specifications.

NOTE: **When aligning upper ball joint nut to install cotter pin, always tighten nut to align. Never loosen nut to align holes.**

KING PIN TYPE

Disassembly (GMC K30)

1) Raise vehicle, and support on safety stands. Remove wheel and tire assembly. Remove brake caliper. If equipped with locking hubs, see removal and installation instructions in appropriate Locking Hubs article in this Section.

2) Remove hub lock mechanism. Remove snap ring. Pry out driving hub and spring. Remove wheel bearing lock nut. Outer wheel bearing and retainer will come off with hub.

3) Using a brass drift punch, remove inner bearing, cone, and seal from hub. Remove inner and outer bearing cups (if necessary) using a brass punch. Remove spindle. Carefully pull axle shaft assembly through hole in steering knuckle.

4) Disconnect steering linkage at knuckle. Remove nuts from upper king pin cap. Remove nuts alternately as spring will force cap up. Remove cap, compression spring, and gasket.

5) Remove nuts from lower cap. Remove cap and king pin. Remove upper king pin tapered bushing and knuckle from axle yoke. Remove upper king pin from yoke using puller.

6) Using a punch, drive out lower king pin bearing cup, cone, grease retainer, and seal. Drive out from top to bottom.

Fig. 1: Exploded View of Ball Joint Type Steering Knuckle Assembly

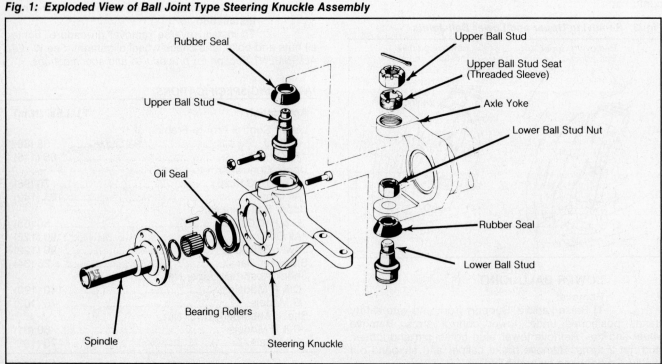

ALL MANUFACTURERS (Cont.)

Fig. 2: Sectional View of Ball Joint Type Steering Knuckle Assembly

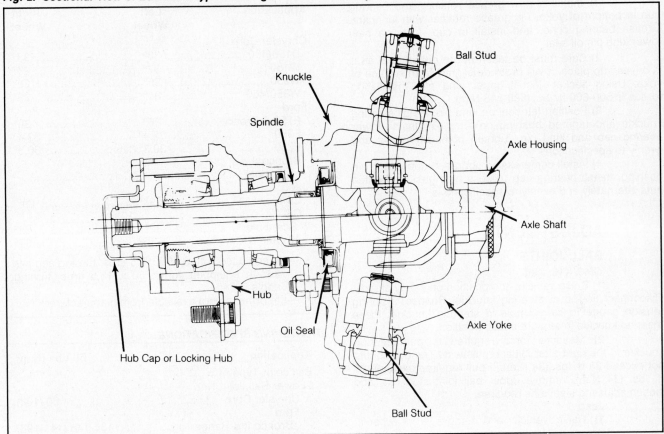

Fig. 3: Exploded View of Chevy "T10" Steering Knuckle

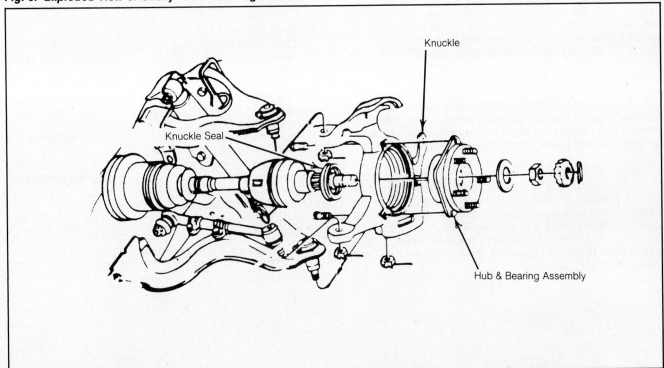

ALL MANUFACTURERS (Cont.)

Reassembly

1) Install a new grease retainer and bearing cup in bottom of yoke. Fill grease retainer with lubricant. Grease bearing cone, and install in cup. Install a new lower king pin oil seal.

2) Care must be taken not to distort seal as it is driven into place. It will protrude slightly from surface of yoke. Using socket, install upper king pin. Installation torque is 500-600 ft. lbs. (680-816 N.m).

3) Position felt seal on king pin. Install steering knuckle and tapered bushing on king pin. Install lower bearing cap and king pin. Tighten bolts alternately and evenly to specifications.

4) Install compression spring on upper king pin bushing. Install bearing cap using a new gasket. Tighten nuts alternately and evenly to specifications.

ADJUSTMENT

BALL JOINTS

GMC K10, K20

1) Raise vehicle, and position on safety stands. Disconnect tie-rod at steering knuckle. Connect a spring tension gauge to tie-rod hole in steering knuckle. Place steering knuckle in straight ahead position.

2) Measure force required to pull steering knuckle to the right after initial breakaway. The pull should not exceed 25 ft. lbs. (34 N.m). If pull required exceeds 25 ft. lbs. (34 N.m), remove upper ball joint stud nut, and loosen adjusting sleeve as required.

Jeep

1) Raise vehicle and remove front wheels. Disconnect steering damper and connecting rod. Remove cotter pin from right side tie rod retaining nut. Rotate steering knuckles through complete arc several times.

2) Place a torque wrench on the right side tie rod retaining nut. Torque to turn knuckles through a complete arc should not be more than 25 ft. lbs. (34 N.m).

3) If turning effort is more than 25 ft. lb. (34 N.m), disconnect tie rod ends at knuckles. Measure turning effort of right and left side knuckles. Individual turning effort should not be more than 10 ft. lbs. (14 N.m).

4) If individual turning effort is more than specified, replace upper ball joint split ring seat. If turning effort is more than 10 ft. lbs. (14 N.m) after split ring seat replacement, ball joints will have to be replaced.

TURNING ANGLE

1) Turning angle stop screws are located at rear of steering knuckle, just above axle centerline. To adjust, loosen lock nut on turning angle stop screw. Ford Motor Co. vehicles are non-adjustable.

2) Using a turntable to measure angle, adjust stop screw to obtain specified angle. Tighten lock nut without changing setting.

TURNING ANGLE ADJUSTMENT

Application	Left Wheel	Right Wheel
Chrysler Corp.		
D150/450	33°	33°
W150	37°	27°
W250	35°	[1] 29°
W350/450	34°	29°
Ford		
F150 & Bronco	36°	36°
F250	33.4°	33.4°
F350	30.3°	30.3°
Bronco II & Ranger	[2]	[2]
Jeep		
CJ-5	29°	29°"
CJ-7 & Scrambler	32°	32°
All Others	36-37°	36-37°

[1] — If equipped with 8.75 x 16.5 tires, turning angle is 26°. If equipped with 9.50 x 16.5 tires, turning angle is 24°.

[2] — Information not available from manufacturer.

TIGHTENING SPECIFICATIONS

Application	Ft. Lbs.(N.m)
Ball Joint Type	
Lower Ball Joint Nut	
Chrysler Corp.	80 (108)
Ford	
Bronco II & Ranger	104-146 (141-198)
Pickups & Vans	[1] 140-180 (190-244)
GMC	
T10	83 (113)
All Others	70 (95)
Upper Ball Joint Nut	
Chrysler Corp.	100 (136)
Ford	85-110 (116-149)
GMC	
T10	50 (68)
All Others	100 (136)
Jeep	100 (136)
King Pin Type (K30)	
King Pin Cap Bolts	70-90 (95-122)
Drag Link-to-Steering Knuckle	60 (82)
Tie Rod-to-Steering Knuckle	45 (61)
Upper King Pin	500-600 (678-813)
Steering Knuckle-to-Knuckle Arm	
Upper Ball Joint Split Retaining Seat	
GMC	50 (70)
Jeep	50 (68)

[1] — For part no. 33850, torque to 104-146 (141-197).

SECTION 13

STEERING

CONTENTS

NOTE: ALSO SEE GENERAL INDEX.

IMPORTANT: Because of the many model names used by vehicle manufacturers, accurate identification of models is important. See Model Identification at the front of this publication.

Steering

STANDARD STEERING COLUMN TROUBLE SHOOTING

CONDITION	POSSIBLE CAUSE	CORRECTION
Noise in Column	Coupling pulled apart	See STEERING COLUMNS
	Column not correctly aligned	See STEERING COLUMNS
	Broken lower joint	Replace joint
	Horn contact ring not lubricated	See Removal in STEERING WHEEL
	Bearings not lubricated	See STEERING COLUMNS
	Bearing worn or broken	Replace bearing and lubricate
	Shaft snap ring not properly seated	Reseat or replace snap ring
	Plastic spherical joint not lubricated	See STEERING COLUMNS
	Shroud or housing loose	Tighten holding screws
	Lock plate retaining ring not seated	See STEERING COLUMNS
	Loose sight shield	Tighten holding screws
High Steering Shaft Effort	Column assembly misaligned	See STEERING COLUMNS
	Improperly installed dust shield	Adjust or replace
	Damaged upper or lower bearing	Replace bearings
	Tight steering universal joint	See STEERING COLUMNS
High Shift Effort	Column is out of alignment	See STEERING COLUMNS
	Improperly installed dust shield	Adjust or replace
	Seals or bearings not lubricated	See STEERING COLUMNS
	Ignition switch screws too long	Replace with new shorter screws
	Neutral switch screws too long	Replace with new shorter screws
	Mounting bracket screws too long	Replace with new shorter screws
	Burrs on shift tube	Remove burrs or replace tube
	Lower bowl bearing assembled wrong	See STEERING COLUMNS
	Shift tube bent or broken	Replace as necessary
	Improper adjustment of shift levers	See STEERING COLUMNS
Improper Trans. Shifting	Sheared shift tube joint	Replace as necessary
	Sheared lower shaft lever weld joint	Replace as necessary
	Improper shift lever adjustment	See STEERING COLUMNS
	Improper gate plate adjustment	See STEERING COLUMNS
Excess Play in Column	Instrument panel bracket bolts loose	Tighten bolts and check bracket
	Broken weld nut on jacket	See STEERING COLUMNS
	Instrument bracket capsule sheared	See STEERING COLUMNS
	Column bracket/jacket bolts loose	Tighten bolts and check bracket
Steering Locks in Gear	Release lever mechanism damaged	See STEERING COLUMNS

TILT STEERING COLUMN TROUBLE SHOOTING

CONDITION	POSSIBLE CAUSE	CORRECTION
Steering Wheel Loose	Excess clearance in support	Check and replace if necessary
	Excess clearance in housing/pivot pin	Check and replace if necessary
	Damaged anti-lash spring in spheres	See TILT STEERING COLUMNS
	Upper bearing not seated properly	See TILT STEERING COLUMNS
	Upper bearing inner race seal missing	Replace if necessary
	Improperly adjusted tilt/telescopic lock	See adjustment in STEERING COLUMNS
	Loose support screws	Tighten and check bracket
	Bearing preload spring missing/broken	Replace spring
	Housing loose on jacket	Tighten and/or replace screws
Play in Column Mount	Loose support screws	Tighten and check bracket
	Loose shoes in housing	See TILT STEERING COLUMNS
	Loose tilt head pivot pins	See TILT STEERING COLUMNS
	Loose shoe lock pin in support	See TILT STEERING COLUMNS
Housing Scraping on Bowl	Bowl bent or out of round	See STEERING WHEEL removal
Wheel Will Not Lock	Shoe seized on its pivot pin	See TILT STEERING COLUMNS
	Shoe may have burrs/dirt in them	Clean or replace
	Shoe lock spring weak/broken	Replace if necessary

TILT STEERING COLUMN TROUBLE SHOOTING (Cont.)

CONDITION	POSSIBLE CAUSE	CORRECTION
Wheel Fails to Return	Pivot pins are bound up Wheel tilt spring is damaged Turn signal switch wires too tight	Clean or replace See TILT STEERING COLUMNS Loosen and check operation
Noise When Tilting	Upper tilt bumpers worn Tilt spring rubbing in housing	Replace if necessary Adjust and check operation
Hard Steering	Incorrect tire pressure Lack of lubricant in steering linkage Improper front end alignment Improper steering gear adjustment	Inflate to proper pressure Service Steering, Suspension and Linkage See WHEEL ALIGNMENT See STEERING

MANUAL STEERING GEAR TROUBLE SHOOTING

CONDITION	POSSIBLE CAUSE	CORRECTION
Rattle or Chucking Noise in Rack and Pinion	Rack and pinion mounting bracket loose Lack of/or incorrect lubricant Pitman arm loose on shaft Steering gear mounting bolts loose	Tighten all mounting bolts See RACK & PINION STEERING See STEERING Tighten all mounting bolts
Excessive Play	Front wheel bearing improperly adjusted Loose or worn steering linkage Loose or worn ball joints Loose or worn steering gear shaft Steering arm loose on gear shaft Incorrect front wheel alignment Steering gear housing bolts loose Steering gear adjustment too loose Steering arms loose on knuckles Rack and pinion mounting loose Rack and pinion out of adjustment Tie rod end loose Steering wheel loose Excessive Pitman shaft-to-ball nut lash	See FRONT SUSPENSION See STEERING LINKAGE See FRONT SUSPENSION See STEERING See STEERING See WHEEL ALIGNMENT Tighten all mounting bolts See adjustment in STEERING Tighten and check steering linkage Tighten all mounting bolts See adjustment in STEERING Tighten and check steering linkage See STEERING See STEERING
Poor Returnability	Lack of lubricant in ball joint or linkage Binding in linkage or ball joints Improper front end alignment Improper steering gear adjustment Improper tire pressure	Lubricate and service systems See STEERING LINKAGE and SUSPENSION See WHEEL ALIGNMENT See STEERING Inflate to proper pressure
Excessive Vertical Motion	Improper tire pressure Tires, wheels or rotors out of balance Worn or faulty shock absorbers Loose tie rod ends or steering Improper wheel alignment Loose or worn wheel bearings	Inflate to proper pressure Balance tires then check wheels and rotors Check and replace if necessary Tighten or replace if necessary See WHEEL ALIGNMENT See SUSPENSION
Steering Pulls to One Side	Improper tire pressure Mismatched front tires Wheel bearings not adjusted properly Bent or broken suspension components Improper wheel alignment Brakes dragging	Inflate to proper pressure Rotate or replace if necessary See FRONT SUSPENSION See FRONT SUSPENSION See WHEEL ALIGNMENT See BRAKES
Instability	Low or uneven tire pressure Loose or worn wheel bearings Loose or worn idler arm bushing Loose or worn strut bushings Incorrect front wheel alignment Steering gear not centered Springs or shock absorbers inoperative Improper cross shaft	Inflate to proper pressure See FRONT SUSPENSION See FRONT SUSPENSION See FRONT SUSPENSION See WHEEL ALIGNMENT See STEERING Check and replace if necessary See STEERING

Steering

POWER STEERING TROUBLE SHOOTING

CONDITION	POSSIBLE CAUSE	CORRECTION
Rattle or Chucking Noise in Steering	Pressure hoses touching engine parts	Adjust to proper clearance
	Loose Pitman shaft	Adjust or replace if necessary
	Tie rods ends or Pitman arm loose	Tighten and check system
	Rack and pinion mounts loose	Tighten all mounting bolts
	Free play in worm and piston assembly	See STEERING
	Loose sector shaft or thrust bearing adjustment	See STEERING
	Free play in pot coupling	See STEERING
	Worn shaft serrations	See STEERING
Growl in Steering Pump	Excessive pressure in hoses	Restriction in hoses see POWER STEERING
	Scored pressure plates	See POWER STEERING
	Scored thrust plates or rotor	See POWER STEERING
	Extreme wear of cam ring	See POWER STEERING
Rattle in Steering Pump	Vanes not installed properly	See POWER STEERING PUMPS
	Vanes sticking in rotor slots	See POWER STEERING PUMPS
Swish Noise in Pump	Defective flow control valve	See POWER STEERING PUMPS
Groan in Steering Pump	Air in fluid	See POWER STEERING PUMPS
	Poor pressure hose connection	Tighten and check, replace if necessary
Squawk When Turning	Damper "O" ring on valve spool cut	See POWER STEERING PUMPS
Moan or Whine in Pump	Pump shaft bearing scored	Replace bearing and fluid
	Air in fluid or fluid level low	See POWER STEERING PUMPS
	Hose or column grounded	Check and replace if necessary
	Cover "O" ring missing or damaged	See POWER STEERING PUMPS
	Valve cover baffle missing or damaged	See POWER STEERING PUMPS
	Interference of components in pump	See POWER STEERING PUMPS
	Loose or poor bracket alignment	Correct or replace if necessary
Hissing When Parking	Internal leakage in steering gear	Check valve assembly first
Chirp in Steering Pump	Loose or worn power steering belt	Adjust or replace if neceeary
Buzzing When Not Steering	Noisy pump	See POWER STEERING PUMPS
	Free play in steering shaft bearing	See STEERING
	Bearing loose on shaft serrations	See STEERING
Clicking Noise in Pump	Pump slippers too long	See POWER STEERING PUMPS
	Broken slipper springs	See POWER STEERING PUMPS
	Excessive wear or nicked rotors	See POWER STEERING PUMPS
	Damaged cam contour	See POWER STEERING PUMPS
Poor Return of Wheel	Wheel rubbing against turn signal	See STEERING WHEEL SWITCHES
	Flange rubbing steering gear adjuster	See STEERING
	Tight or frozen steering shaft bearing	See STEERING
	Steering Gear out of adjustment	See Adjustment in STEERING
	Sticking or plugged spool valve	See POWER STEERING PUMPS
	Improper front end alignment	See WHEEL ALIGNMENT
	Wheel bearings worn or loose	See FRONT SUSPENSION
	Ties rods or ball joints binding	Check and replace if necessary
	Intermediate shaft joints binding	See STEERING
	Kinked pressure hoses	Correct or replace if necessary
	Loose housing head spanner nut	See POWER STEERING
	Damaged valve lever	See POWER STEERING
	Sector shaft adjusted too tight	See adjustment in POWER STEERING
	Worm thrust bearing adjusted too tight	See adjustment in POWER STEERING
	Reaction ring sticking in cylinder	See POWER STEERING
	Reaction ring sticking in housing head	See POWER STEERING
	Steering pump internal leakage	See POWER STEERING PUMPS
	Steering gear-to-column misalignment	See STEERING COLUMNS
	Lack of lubrication in linkage	Service front suspension
	Lack of lubrication in ball joints	Service front suspension

POWER STEERING TROUBLE SHOOTING (Cont.)

CONDITION	POSSIBLE CAUSE	CORRECTION
Increased Effort When Turning Wheel Fast Foaming, Milky Power Steering Fluid, Low Fluid Level or Low Pressure	High internal pump leakage Power steering pump belt slipping Low fluid level Engine idle speed to low Air in pump fluid system Pump output low Steering gear malfunctioning	See POWER STEERING PUMPS Adjust or replace if necessary Check and fill to proper level Adjust to correct setting See POWER STEERING PUMPS See POWER STEERING PUMPS See STEERING
Wheel Surges or Jerks	Low fluid level Loose fan belt Insufficient pump pressure Sticky flow control valve Linkage hitting oil pan at full turn	Check and fill to proper level Adjust or replace if necessary See POWER STEERING PUMPS See POWER STEERING PUMPS See STEERING LINKAGE
Kick Back or Free Play	Air in pump fluid system Worn poppet valve in steering gear Excessive over center lash Thrust bearing out of adjustment Free play in pot coupling Steering gear coupling loose on shaft Steering disc mounting bolts loose Coupling loose on worm shaft Improper sector shaft adjustment Excessive worm piston side play Damaged valve lever Universal joint loose Defective rotary valve	See POWER STEERING PUMPS See POWER STEERING See POWER STEERING See POWER STEERING See POWER STEERING PUMPS See POWER STEERING PUMPS Tighten or replace if necessary Tighten or replace if necessary See POWER STEERING See POWER STEERING See POWER STEERING Tighten or replace if necessary See POWER STEERING
No Power When Parking	Sticking flow control valve Insufficient pump pressure output Excessive internal pump leakage Excessive internal gear leakage Flange rubs against gear adjust plug Loose pump belt Low fluid level Engine idle too low Steering gear-to-column misaligned	See POWER STEERING PUMPS See POWER STEERING PUMPS See POWER STEERING PUMPS See POWER STEERING PUMPS See STEERING COLUMN Adjust or replace if necessary Check and add proper amount of fluid Adjust to correct setting See STEERING
No Power Left Turns	Left turn reaction seal "O" ring worn Left turn reaction seal damaged/missing Cylinder head "O" ring damaged	See POWER STEERING See POWER STEERING See POWER STEERING PUMPS
No Power Right Turns	Column pot coupling bottomed Right turn reaction seal "O" ring worn Right turn reaction seal damaged Internal leakage through piston end plug Internal leakage through side plugs	See STEERING See POWER STEERING See POWER STEERING See STEERING See STEERING
Lack of Effort in Turning	Left and/or right reaction seal worn Left and/or right reaction oil passageway not drilled Left and/or right reaction seal sticking in cylinder head	Replace, see POWER STEERING Check housing and cylinder head See POWER STEERING
Wanders to One Side	Front end alignment incorrect Unbalanced steering gear valve	See WHEEL ALIGNMENT See STEERING
Low Pressure Due to Steering Pump	Flow control valve stuck or inoperative Pressure plate not flat against cam ring Extreme wear of cam ring Scored plate, thrust plate or rotor Vanes not installed properly Vanes sticking in rotor slots Cracked/broken thrust or pressure plate	See POWER STEERING See POWER STEERING PUMPS Replace and check adjustments See POWER STEERING PUMPS See POWER STEERING PUMPS See POWER STEERING PUMPS See POWER STEERING PUMPS

CHRYSLER CORP.

Dodge, Plymouth

REMOVAL & INSTALLATION

HORN BUTTON & STEERING WHEEL

All Models

Disconnect battery. If equipped with horn button, pull outward on button until it comes off. If equipped with horn pad, remove 2 retaining screws from behind steering wheel and lift pad off steering wheel.

Disconnect horn wire from switch terminal. Remove steering wheel retaining nut. Remove steering wheel using a puller (C-3428B). To install, reverse removal procedure.

CAUTION: Do not strike steering wheel to remove; severe damage could result.

DIRECTIONAL SIGNAL INDICATOR SWITCH

All Models

1) Disconnect fusible link under hood at battery. Remove horn switch pad and steering wheel. On tilt column steering systems, remove lock plate and cam assembly.

2) Remove turn signal lever screw and remove lever. On vehicles equipped with speed control, do not completely disconnect turn signal lever but allow to hang loose. Remove switch retainer screws, retainer, wire cover clips and cover.

3) Disconnect switch harness from main harness, lift switch from column, guiding wires and insulator through opening in upper clutch. Remove switch. To install, reverse removal procedures.

HAZARD FLASHER SWITCH

All Models

Hazard flasher switch is integral with the directional signal indicator switch. Combination is removed or installed as unit. See Directional Signal Indicator Switch in this article.

STEERING COLUMN LOCK & IGNITION SWITCH

All Models

1) Remove horn assembly, steering wheel and turn signal switch. Remove snap ring from upper end of steering shaft. Remove retaining screws and lock lever guide plate which exposes the lock cylinder release hole. Place ignition switch in "LOCK" position and remove key.

2) Insert a small screwdriver or similar tool into lock cylinder release hole and push in to release spring-loaded lock retainer. Pull ignition switch cylinder out of housing bore at same time retainer is depressed. Remove ignition switch assembly.

3) To install, reverse removal procedure noting the following: Ignition key cylinder is installed with cylinder in lock position and key removed. Insert cylinder into lock housing. Place cylinder into place until contact is made with pin on ignition switch cam.

4) Insert key into lock and rotate until slot in cylinder plate lines up with pin. Press key cylinder the remaining way into lock housing, making sure retainer bar snaps into its slot in lock housing.

Fig. 1: Depressing Tab for Lock Cylinder Removal

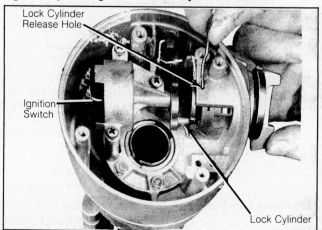

Illustration applies to all models.

FORD

Bronco, Bronco II, Pickup, Ranger & Van Models

REMOVAL & INSTALLATION

HORN PAD

All Models

Disconnect battery ground cable. Remove one screw from behind each steering wheel spoke. Remove horn pad switch assembly from steering wheel after disconnecting wire connector.

On vehicles with sport wheel option, pry button cover off with screwdriver. On vehicles with speed control, squeeze "J" clip ground wire terminal firmly and remove through hole in steering wheel. To install, reverse removal procedure.

STEERING WHEEL

All Models

1) Set wheels in straight ahead position and drive forward a short distance. Mark the relationship of steering wheel with steering column. Remove horn pad assembly as previously outlined.

2) Remove steering wheel retaining nut. Pull off steering wheel using a gear puller. To install, reverse removal procedure making sure mating marks made during disassembly are aligned.

DIRECTIONAL SIGNAL SWITCH & HAZARD FLASHER

Bronco, Pickup & Van Models

1) Disconnect battery ground cable. Remove horn pad switch and steering wheel as previously outlined.

Remove turn signal switch lever by unscrewing from steering column. Remove column shroud.

2) Disconnect turn signal switch wiring connector by lifting up on tabs and separating. Remove screws securing switch assembly to column. On fixed columns, remove switch assembly from vehicle by guiding switch and connector plug through opening in shaft socket.

3) On all tilt column models, disconnect connector plug from wiring connector by using a wire terminal removal tool. *See Fig. 1.* Record color code and location of each wire as it is removed.

4) Guide switch assembly out of column though shift socket hole. On "E" models with automatic transmission, disconnect lamp wire from turn signal switch harness before removing switch. To install, reverse removal procedure.

Fig. 1: Removing Wires from Connector

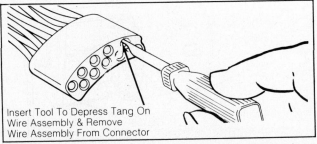

Insert Tool To Depress Tang On Wire Assembly & Remove Wire Assembly From Connector

Wiring must be removed from connector on all tilt column models.

Bronco II & Ranger Models

1) For tilt columns only, remove the upper extension shroud by squeezing it at the 6 and 12 o'clock positions and popping it free of the retaining plate. Remove the trim shroud.

2) On all models, remove the turn signal switch lever by pulling and twisting the lever straight out from the switch. Remove the foam sight shield from the switch. Disconnect the electrical connectors.

3) Remove the screws attaching the turn signal switch to the lock cylinder housing. Lift the switch away from the housing. To install turn signal switch, reverse removal procedures.

IGNITION LOCK CYLINDER
Bronco, Pickup & Van Models

1) Disconnect battery ground cable. On non-tilt column models, remove horn pad and steering wheel as previously outlined. Place automatic transmissions in "Park", or manual transmission in "Neutral".

2) Turn lock cylinder to "ON" positon. Insert a 1/8" (3.17 mm) diameter wire pin or punch in the access hole and depress the retaining pin. Pull out on the lock cylinder.

3) The access hole is located inside the column near base of lock cylinder housing on standard column models. On tilt column models, hole is located on the column housing adjacent to the hazard flasher button. To install, reverse removal procedures.

Bronco II & Ranger Models

1) Disconnect the battery cable. Remove the trim shroud. Remove the electrical from the key warning switch. Turn the lock cylinder to the "RUN" position.

2) Place 1/8" (3.18 mm) drill or small drift punch in the hole located at 4 o'clock and 1/4" from the outer edge of the lock cylinder housing. Depress the retaining pin and pull out the lock cylinder.

3) To install the lock cylinder, turn the cylinder to the "RUN" position. Depress the retaining pin and insert it into the lock cylinder housing. To complete installation, reverse removal procedure.

GENERAL MOTORS

Chevrolet, GMC

REMOVAL & INSTALLATION

STEERING WHEEL
Removal (All Models)

Disconnect battery. Remove horn button or pad, Remove snap ring and steering wheel nut. Mark steering wheel-to-shaft relationship. Use steering wheel puller to remove steering wheel.

Installation

To install steering wheel, reverse removal procedure while noting the following: Directional signal switch must be in neutral position while installing steering wheel to prevent damage to cancelling cam and switch assembly. Install snap ring after steering wheel retaining nut has been tightened.

DIRECTIONAL SIGNAL SWITCH
Removal ("C", "K", "S" & "T" Models")

1) Remove steering wheel. Remove column to instrument panel trim cover. Compress lock plate with compressor tool (J-23653). *See Fig. 2.*

Fig. 1: Removing Steering Wheel Using Puller

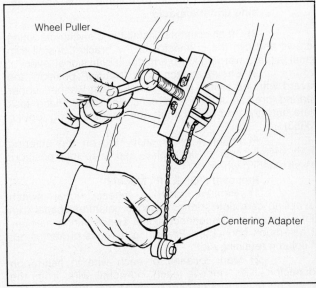

Wheel Puller

Centering Adapter

Do not hammer on puller while turning.

Fig. 2: Removing Lock Plate & Snap Ring

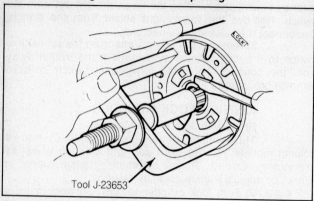

Tool J-23653

Do not reuse old snap ring.

2) Pry snap ring out of groove and discard. Lift off lock plate, directional signal cancelling cam, upper bearing preload spring and thrust washer from end of shaft.

3) Remove directional signal warning lever. Push in hazard waring knob and unscrew the knob. Remove the 3 switch mounting screws. On standard columns, pull the switch connector out of the bracket on the column.

4) Pull the switch straight up, guiding the wiring harness through the column housing and protector. Remove the wire protector by pulling downward out of column with pliers using tab provided.

5) On tilt columns, the steering must be in the "LOW" position to remove the directional signal switch. Removal procedure is the same as for standard column.

Installation
1) On standard columns, feed the connector and protector cover down through the housing and under the mounting bracket. On tilt columns, feed connector down through the housing and then install protector cover.

CAUTION: It is extemely important that only specified screws, bolts and nuts be used during reassembly. Use of overlength screws could prevent a portion of column from compressing under impact.

2) On all columns, install the 3 switch mounting screws and clip the connector to the bracket. Install trim panel, hazard warning knob and directional signal lever.

3) Ensure switch is in "Neutral" position and hazard warning switch is out. Install thrust washer, upper bearing preload spring and cancelling cam. Place lock plate onto the end of the shaft and depress using tool (J-23653).

4) Install a NEW snap ring on the steering shaft. Install cover on lock plate and snap into position. Install steering wheel.

Removal ("G" & "P" Models)
1) Remove steering wheel, signal switch cancelling cam and spring. Remove column-to-panel trim plate if present. Disconnect signal switch wiring harness at half-moon connector. Pry wiring harness protector out of column retaining slots.

2) Mark location of each wire in half-moon connector, then remove each individual wire from the connector using tool (J-22727). Insert tool into connector, then push in until tool bottoms.

3) Remove tool and pull wire from connector. Remove directional signal lever screw and remove lever. Push in on hazard warning knob and unscrew to remove knob.

4) On Tilt Columns only, remove automatic transmission selector dial screws (if equipped) and remove dial and indicator. Remove cap and dial illumination light from housing cover. Unscrew and remove tilt release lever.

5) Use puller tool (J-22708) to remove signal housing cover. On all columns, remove 3 signal switch mounting screws. Carefully remove switch assembly from column while guiding wire harness through opening in shift lever housing.

Fig. 3: Pulling Directional Signal Housing Cover

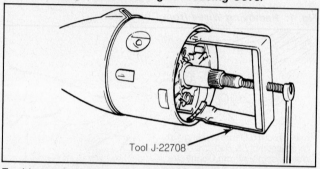

Tool J-22708

Tool is necessary on "G" & "P" tilt column models only.

Installation
1) To install switch, proceed as follows: Wrap ends of signal switch wires with tape and guide them through the opening at lower left side of bearing housing (Tilt Column) and out the lower end of shift lever housing and under dash seal.

2) Place directional signal switch in position and install screws. Torque screws to 25 INCH lbs. (2.8 N.m). With Tilt Columns, align openings in signal switch cover with proper lever positions and tap cover into place using plastic hammer.

3) Install tilt release lever. Install automatic transmission selector dial, pointer, dial illumination light and cap (if equipped). On all models, install signal switch lever and hazard warning knob.

4) Bend wire harness connector tabs out of each wire before installing in half moon connector. Install each wire in its marked position and reconnect signal switch harness.

5) Snap wire harness protector into column retaining slots and install signal canceling cam and spring. Install steering wheel and column-to-instrument panel trim plate (if equipped).

HAZARD FLASHER SWITCH
All Models
Hazard flasher switch is integral with directional signal indicator switch. Combination is removed or installed as an assembly. See Directional Signal Switch in this article.

STEERING COLUMN LOCK
All Models
1) Remove steering wheel and lock plate. Lift directional signal switch up far enough to slip over end of shaft. It is not necessary to remove switch entirely.

GENERAL MOTORS (Cont.)

2) Place key in lock cylinder and rotate to "RUN" position. Remove lock retaining screw being carefull not to drop screw down column. Rotate lock cylinder to align cylinder key with keyway in housing. Pull cylinder from housing.

Fig. 4: Removing Lock Cylinder Assembly

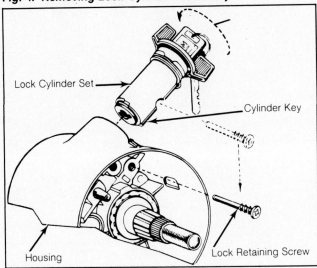

Align cylinder key with keyway in housing.

3) To install, hold lock cylinder and rotate key clockwise to stop. Align cylinder key and housing keyway and insert cylinder. Complete assembly by reversing removal procedure.

IGNITION SWITCH

1) To remove ignition switch, steering column must be lowered, but it is not necessary to remove steering wheel. *See Steering Column Removal in this Section.* If steering is not removed from vehicle, support column before proceeding.

2) Place ignition switch in "LOCK" postion. If lock cylinder has already been removed, pull up on actuating rod of switch until it stops, then push down one detent. This will position switch in "LOCK" position. Remove two screws, then remove ignition switch.

3) To install, switch and lock cylinder should be in "LOCK" position. With switch in correct position, install activating rod in switch. Install switch on column and tighten mounting screws. Install steering column and check system operation.

NOTE: Use only specified screws as overlength screws may prevent a portion of column from compressing under impact.

JEEP

All Models

REMOVAL & INSTALLATION

HORN BUTTON & STEERING WHEEL

CAUTION: Some steering wheel shaft nuts have metric threads. Metric threads have identifying groove cut perpendicular to steering wheel splines. Standard American threads do not have groove.

"CJ" & Scrambler Models

1) Disconnect battery cable, and place front wheels in straight ahead position. Remove horn button by pulling straight up. Remove steering wheel nut and washer.

2) Remove receiver and contact plate. Mark steering wheel and shaft for reassembly reference, and remove steering wheel using puller (J-21232). To install, reverse removal procedures.

Cherokee, Truck & Wagoneer

1) Disconnect battery cable and place front wheels in straight ahead position. On models with standard steering wheel, remove horn cover attaching screws from underside of wheel and remove cover.

2) On models with sport steering wheel, remove horn button by pulling button upward. On models with standard steering wheel, remove horn wire by disconnecting at steering wheel switch.

3) Unseat retainer that holds horn wire and spring in canceling cam yoke. Remove wire retainer and spring as an assembly. Remove steering wheel nut and washer.

4) On sport steering wheel models, remove receiver bushing attaching screws and remove bushing, horn button receiver and contact plate. Index mark steering wheel and shaft and remove steering wheel using puller (J-21232). To install, reverse removal procedure.

DIRECTIONAL SIGNAL SWITCH & HAZARD FLASHER

Removal (All Models)

1) Disconnect battery cable. On vehicles with tilt columns, place column in neutral position. Remove steering wheel and lock plate cover.

2) If shaft nut is metric threaded, use compressor tool J-23653-4 to compress lock plate and remove snap ring. On American threaded shaft nuts, use tool J-23653 to compress lock plate and unseat snap ring.

NOTE: The lock plate is under strong spring tension, do not attempt to remove snap ring without using compressor tool.

3) Discard snap ring. Remove lock plate, canceling cam, upper bearing preload spring and thrust washer. Place turn signal lever in right turn position and remove lever. Press hazard warning knob in and turn counterclockwise to remove.

4) Remove column wiring harness protectors, if equipped. Disconnect wiring harness connectors at base of column. Remove directional switch attaching screws and pull switch from column.

Installation

Install switch in housing, ensuring that actuating lever pivot is seated in the housing pivot boss. Complete assembly by reversing removal procedure.

LOCK CYLINDER

Removal (All Models)

1) Remove horn button, steering wheel and turn signal switch as previously outlined. Position lock cylinder in "LOCK" position on automatic transmission models, or in "ON" position on manual transmission models.

2) Then depress key cylinder retaining tab and remove lock cylinder from housing. The retaining tab is accessible through slot adjacent to turn signal switch mounting boss.

Installation

1) To install, insert key in lock cylinder. Hold cylinder sleeve and turn key clockwise until key stops. Align lock cylinder retaining tab with keyway in housing and insert cylinder into housing.

2) Push cylinder inward until it contacts lock sector. Rotate cylinder to engage it with lock sector. Push cylinder inward until cylinder retaining tab engages in housing groove.

3) Install turn signal switch and lock plate. Reverse removal procedures for remaining components.

IGNITION SWITCH

All Models

1) Insert key in lock cylinder and turn cylinder to Off-Unlock position. Disconnect battery and harness connectors at switch. Remove switch attaching screws. Disengage remote rod from switch slider and remove switch from column.

2) To install, move switch slider to Accessory position. Move switch slider back 2 clicks to Off-Unlock position. Engage remote rod in switch slider and position switch on column.

3) Do not move slider while positioning. Install attaching screws. Connect harness connectors and battery negative cable.

Steering Columns

CHRYSLER CORP.

Dodge, Plymouth

DESCRIPTION

All models use collapsible type steering columns. All columns have integral ignition switch and locking device. Tilt wheel features are available in all models. Transmission shift linkage is integral on all models with the exception of floor shift models.

REMOVAL & INSTALLATION

ALL MODELS

Removal

1) Disconnect battery negative cable. On vehicles equipped with column shift, disconnect link rod(s) by prying rod out of grommet in shift lever. Remove steering shaft lower coupling to worm shaft roll pin. *See Fig. 1.*

2) Disconnect wiring connectors at column jacket. Remove steering wheel center pad and horn switch (if equipped). Use gear puller to remove steering wheel.

NOTE: **Do not bump or hammer on steering shaft to remove steering wheel.**

3) Remove turn signal lever. Remove floor plate-to-floor pan attaching screws. Remove cluster bezel and panel lower reinforcement to expose steering column bracket. If equipped with automatic transmission, disconnect shift indicator pointer cable from shift housing.

4) Remove nuts attaching steering column bracket-to-instrument panel support. Carefully remove lower coupling from steering gear worm shaft.

5) Steering shaft may be equipped with either flexible coupling or a "Pot" coupling. Remove column assembly out through passenger compartment.

Installation

1) Install ground clip on left capsule slot. Plastic capsules should be preassembled in bracket slot.

Fig. 1: *Exploded View of Automatic Transmission Steering Column*

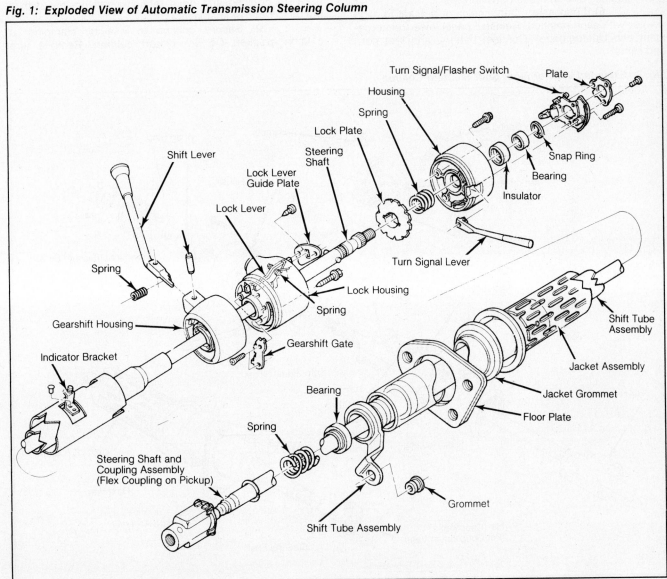

Van model is shown; Pickup models are similar.

Steering Columns

CHRYSLER CORP. (Cont.)

Insert column through floor pan opening. With front wheels straight ahead and splines on wormshaft and coupling aligned, engage coupling and install roll pin.

CAUTION: Do not apply end load to steering shaft.

2) Hold column assembly with bracket slots on mounting studs. Loosely install 2 upper bracket washers and nuts. Be sure both capsules are fully seated in slots in support bracket and tighten nuts to specification.

3) Position floor plate over floor pan opening, centering it around column, then install retaining bolts. Place steering wheel on shaft with splines aligned. Install nut and tighten to specifications. DO NOT drive wheel onto shaft, draw it down with retaining nut.

4) Install horn switch and connect wiring connector at column jacket. Before connecting link rod to column shift lever, a new grommet MUST be installed.

5) If equipped with automatic transmission, connect gear shift indicator pointer cable to indicator bracket. Slowly move shift lever from "1" (Low) to "P" (Park) pausing briefly at each position.

6) If necessary, bend indicator bracket to align pointer with each position. Reinstall panel lower reinforcement and cluster bezel. Connect battery, and test horn and lights.

FLOOR SHIFT MODELS

The steering column with a floor mounted gear shift is basically the same as previously described. Standard columns and service procedures are identical except as described below.
- Lower steering shaft bearing is mounted in an aluminum support.
- Shift housing has a spring attached between it and column jacket. This keeps housing rotated counterclockwise against rubber bumper. Spring and bumpers are easily removed by hand. *See Fig. 2.*

OVERHAUL

ALL EXCEPT TILT WHEEL MODELS
Disassembly

1) Pry out wiring trough retainers and lift off trough. New retainers may be required for reassembly. Use masking tape to protect paint and a deep socket to back up housing and drive retaining roll pin out with a punch to remove shift lever.

2) Secure column in vise by clamping at column bracket. Do not distort column. Remove turn

Fig. 2: Exploded View of Floor Shift Steering Column

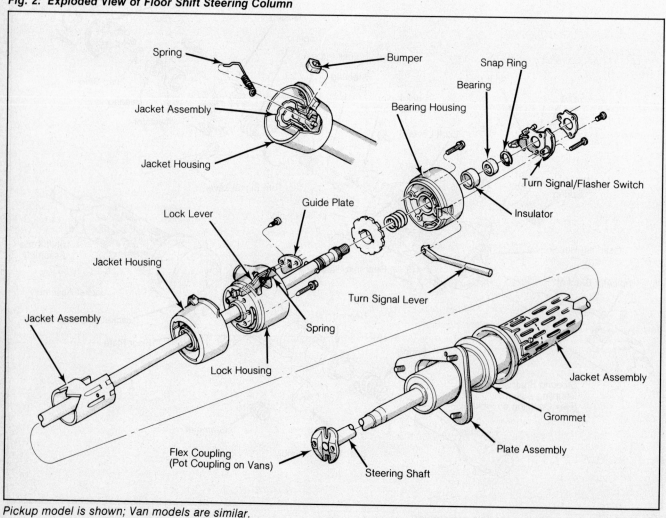

Pickup model is shown; Van models are similar.

CHRYSLER CORP. (Cont.)

signal switch and upper bearing retaining screws. Remove retainer and lift switch upward out of way.

3) Remove retaining screw and lift ignition key lamp assembly out of way. Remove snap ring from upper end of steering shaft. Remove 3 screws holding bearing housing-to-lock housing.

NOTE: **These screws must be removed before steering shaft removal.**

4) Remove bearing housing from shaft. Remove coil spring and lock plate from shaft. Remove shaft through lower end of column.

5) Remove 2 retaining screws and lock lever guide plate. This will expose lock cylinder release hole. Place cylinder in "LOCK" position and remove key.

6) Insert a small diameter screwdriver or similar tool into lock cylinder release hole. Push in to release spring-loaded lock retainer. At same time, pull lock cylinder out of housing bore. Remove 3 retaining screws and ignition switch assembly. *See Fig. 3.*

Fig. 3: Removing Lock Cylinder

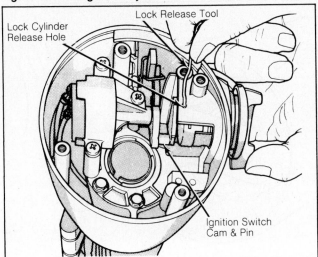

Cylinder must be in lock position.

7) Grasp lock lever and spring assembly and pull straight out of housing. Remove 4 lock housing-to-column jacket hex head retaining screws and remove housing from jacket.

8) Loosen shift tube set screw in shaft housing. Remove shift tube through lower end of jacket. Remove floor plate and grommet from jacket.

9) To disassemble flexible coupling, remove 4 bolts and 2 cross straps. Remove flexible coupling.

10) Pot coupling is removed by prying cover tangs out of coupling body and lifting seal and cover from body. Drive dowel pin down into coupling and discard. Pull body off shaft and shoe assembly.

Reassembly

1) During reassembly, coat all friction surfaces with multi-purpose grease NLG1 Grade 2, Part Number 2525035 (or equivalent). Clamp column in vise so that both ends of column are accessible.

2) Check column tube-to-mandrel rivets for tightness. If replacement is necessary, use 3/8" diameter by 3/4" long (3/8" grip) steel pop rivets. Do not use aluminum pop rivets.

3) Install floor plate and grommet on lower end of jacket. On automatic transmission models, position gearshift housing on column jacket. Install dust seal and shift tube support on shift tube. Slide shift tube into jacket.

4) Guide key upper end of tube into slot in gearshift housing. Position crossover load spring and shift lever in gearshift housing and tap rivet pin into place. Install shift lever gate on lock housing.

5) If equipped, feed gear selector dial lamp wire through hole behind transmission dial on lock housing and route wire through space between housing and jacket. Secure lamp assembly and install gear selector lens assembly.

6) Place shift lever in mid position, seal lock housing on top of jacket and indexing key in housing with slot in jacket. Install housing-to-jacket screws and tighten alternately. Install automatic transmission indicator bracket.

7) Grease and assemble the 2 lock levers, lock lever spring and pin. Install the assembly into the lock housing. Seat the pin firmly in the bottom of the slots. Make sure the lock lever spring leg is firmly in place in lock casting notch. *See Fig. 4.*

Fig. 4: Installing Lock Lever and Spring Assembly

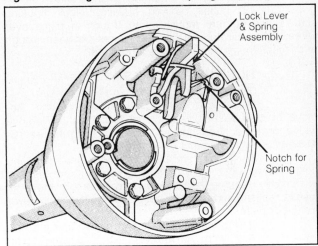

Lock lever spring must be fully seated in casting notch.

8) Install the lock lever guide plate and retaining screws. Position ignition switch to "OFF" position and hand lever in "PARK". Feed wires down through the space between housing and jacket. Position switch in housing and tighten mounting screws.

9) To install ignition lock, turn key to "LOCK" position and remove key. The cylinder will move inward and a spring loaded retainer will snap into place, locking the cylinder into the housing.

10) Fill coupling body 1/4" full with multi-purpose grease and place cover and seal on shaft. Press shoe pin into steering shaft so it protrudes an equal distance on each side of the shaft.

11) Place spring on side of shaft so it straddles the shoe pin. Place shoes on pin ends with flat side toward spring, engaging tangs. Squeeze shoes together and push assembly into coupling body.

12) Align master spline mark of coupling body with master spline on upper shaft. Drive in a new dowel pin flush to coupling body outer surface. Position seal and cover on body and crimp cover tangs on body.

Steering Columns

CHRYSLER CORP. (Cont.)

13) Move shaft in and out several times to distribute lubricant. Install bearing support (floor shift), bearing and spring on steering shaft and insert steering shaft into column assembly.

14) Install lock plate and new groove pin on steering shaft. Make sure pin is centered. Install steering column shaft lock plate sleeve over shaft lock plate pin and against lock plate.

15) Install bearing lower snap ring on steering shaft. Install coil spring. Install ignition key lamp assembly in housing. Place rubber insulator with grounding staple over column upper bearing and install assembly into bearing housing bore.

16) Use soap solution or rubber lubricant to ease installation. Install turn signal switch in bearing housing, feeding wires through opening in housing. Feed ignition key lamp wires through opening in housing.

17) Install retaining plate over switch and tighten screws. Install turn signal lever or turn signal/speed control lever on turn signal switch. If speed control, feed wires through opening provided in bearing housing.

18) Position housing assembly on steering shaft, feeding wires through space between housing and jacket. Install bearing and snap ring on shaft.

19) Install bearing housing-to-lock housing screws and tighten. Install wiring trough in place over wires, being careful not to pinch wires between trough and jacket. Install new retainers if required.

TILT WHEEL MODELS
Disassembly

1) Remove steering wheel and column. Remove bracket assembly-to-column jacket bolts. Remove wiring protector from jacket. Attach holding fixture (C-4132) to jacket and mount column in vise.

2) Remove tilt lever and turn signal or speed control lever. Push hazard warning knob in and unscrew to remove. Remove ignition key lamp assembly. Move tilt mechanism to full down tilt. Carefully remove plastic cover from lock plate.

3) Depress lock plate with finger and pry ring out of groove with screwdriver. Remove lock plate, cancelling cam and upper bearing spring. Remove three turn signal switch screws, place shift bowl in low (1) position.

4) Tie up wires and connectors to prevent snagging, remove switch and wiring. To remove lock cylinder, place in "LOCK" position. Insert a thin tool into slot next to switch mounting screw boss (right hand slot) and depress spring latch at bottom of slot to remove lock.

5) Remove housing cover screws and remove housing cover. Reinstall tilt lever and place column in full "UP" position. Remove tilt spring retainer with a phillips screwdriver.

6) Insert screwdriver in opening and press in 3/16". Turn about 1/8 turn counterclockwise until ears align with groove in housing and remove spring and guide.

7) Push upper steering shaft in sufficiently to remove steering shaft inner race seat and inner race. Put ignition switch in "ACC" position and remove ignition switch.

8) Place pivot pin remover (C-4016) over pivot pin, thread small portion of screw into pin. Hold screw in position, turn nut clockwise and remove pivot pin from

support. Remove opposite pivot pin. Use tilt release lever to disengage lock shoes.

9) Remove bearing housing by pulling upward to extend rack fully. Move housing to left to disengage rack from actuator. Remove actuator assembly. Remove roll pin and coupling assembly from lower end of steering shaft.

10) Remove shaft from upper end of column. Disassemble steering shaft by removing center spheres and anti-lash springs. Remove bolts securing support to lock plate and remove support from end of column jacket. If needed remove attaching screws and shift gate from support.

11) Using screwdriver remove shift tube retaining ring and thrust washer. With a small screwdriver disengage plastic shift tube support from lower end of jacket.

12) Remove shift tube from bowl using tool (C-4120). Insert bushing on end of tool in shift tube and force tube out of bowl. *See Fig. 5.*

Fig. 5: *Removing Shift Tube from Bowl on Tilt Wheel*

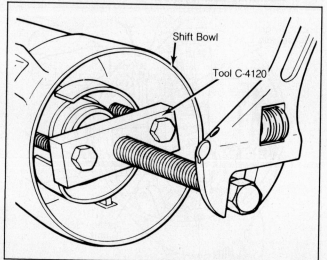

Do not hammer or pull on shift tube.

13) Remove shift tube from jacket at lower end. Remove lock plate by sliding out of jacket notches and tapping down toward hub at 12 o'clock position and under jacket opening.

14) Remove wave washer and bowl from jacket. Remove shift lever spring from bowl by winding spring up with pliers and pulling out. Remove tilt lever opening shield and turn signal lever opening shield from housing.

15) Remove lock bolt spring by removing spring retaining screw and moving spring clockwise. Remove snap ring from sector drive shaft. Use a small punch to tap drive shaft from sector. Remove drive shaft, sector and bolt.

16) Remove rack and spring, and also shim if one is used. Using a punch and hammer remove tilt release lever pin. Remove lever and release lever spring.

17) To relieve load on release lever, hold shoes inward and wedge block between top of shoes (over slots) and bearing housing. Remove lock shoe pin with punch and hammer, remove lock shoes and lock shoe springs.

CHRYSLER CORP. (Cont.)

NOTE: **Do not remove bearings from housing unless they are to be replaced. Never use old bearings.**

Reassembly

1) Install bearings in housing, if removed. Install lock shoe springs, lock shoes and shoe pin. Use a rod about .180" diameter to line up shoes. With tilt lever opening on left side, and shoes facing up, the 4 slot shoe is on the left.

2) Install spring, release lever and pin in bearing housing. Relieve load on release lever as outlined in step 17) of disassembly procedure. Install drive shaft and tap sector on shaft far enough to install snap ring. Install lock bolt and engage with sector cam surface.

3) Install rack and spring. Block tooth on rack must engage block tooth on sector. Install external tilt release lever, bolt spring and retainer. Install shift lever spring in bowl by winding up with pliers and pushing in.

4) Slide bowl into jacket, install wave washer and lock plate. Work lock plate into notches in jacket and carefully install shift tube in lower end of jacket.

5) Align key in tube with keyway in bowl and use tool (C-4119) to pull tube into bowl. *See Fig. 6.* Install thrust washer and retaining ring by pulling bowl up to

compress wave washer. Do not push hard or tap on end of tube.

Fig. 6: *Installing Shift Tube on Tilt Wheel Models*

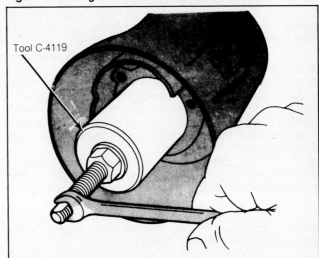

Align key in tube with keyway in bowl.

Fig. 7: *Exploded View of Tilt Wheel Column Upper Half*

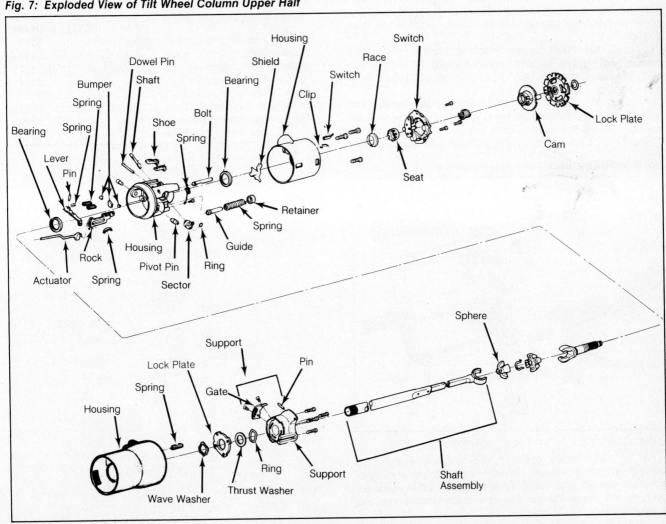

6) Install support by aligning "V" in support with notch in jacket and install retaining screws. Install lower bearing at end of shift tube. Locate about 3/16" inside tube (use lubricant to ease installation).

7) Install centering spheres and anti-lash spring in upper steering shaft and lower steering shaft from same side of spheres that spring ends protrude.

8) Check double coupling assembly that master serration of upper shaft will align with master serration of pot coupling. Place housing in full "UP" position, install guide, tilt spring and tilt spring retainer using screwdriver.

9) Turn retainer clockwise to engage. Install steering shaft in shift tube from upper end. Place ignition switch actuator rod through bowl from bottom and insert slot in support.

10) Extend rack downward from bearing housing, assemble housing over steering shaft, and engage rack over end of actuator rod. Install external tilt release lever.

11) While holding lock shoes in disengage position, assemble bearing housing over steering shaft until pivot pin holes line up. Install pivot pins.

12) With housing in full "UP" position, install guide. Ensure there is grease between guide and peg on support, tilt spring and spring retainer. Using a screwdriver in retainer slot, turn retainer clockwise to engage.

13) Install bearing inner race and tilt lever opening shield. Remove tilt release lever, install housing cover and tighten screws. Install signal switch wires and connector.

14) Push hazard warning plunger in, install switch and tighten screws. Install hazard warning knob and pull out. Install cancelling cam spring, cancelling cam and shift lock plate.

15) Using tool (C-4156), depress shift lock plate and install new retaining ring. *See Fig. 8.* Install tilt release lever and turn signal switch lever. To install ignition lock, turn key to "LOCK" position and remove key.

Fig. 8: Installing Lock Plate Retaining Ring

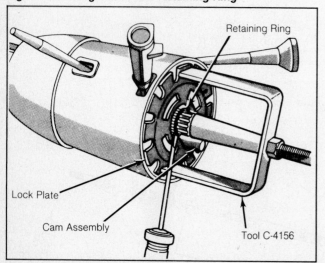

Depress lock plate for access to retaining ring groove.

16) Insert cylinder into housing enough to contact switch actuator. Press inward to move switch actuator rod up and down to align parts. When aligned, cylinder will move inward and spring loaded retainer will snap into place.

17) When replacing ignition switch, position key cylinder in "ACCESSORY" detent (full counterclockwise).

18) Place switch in "ACCESSORY" as follows: Spring loaded position at one end is "START". Move slider to extreme other end, this is "ACCESSORY". Fit actuator rod into slide hole and assemble loosely to column.

19) Push switch lightly down column to remove lash in actuator rod and tighten mounting screws. Do not move switch out of detent. Install wire protector over wires on column jacket.

20) Remove column from vise. Remove holding fixture. Position bracket assembly on steering column. Tighten bolts. Align master splines and install coupling assembly on steering shaft.

21) Drive in retaining roll pin. Install column on vehicle, replace steering wheel and road test vehicle.

TIGHTENING SPECIFICATIONS

Application	Ft. Lbs. (N.m)
Bracket-to-Column Bolt	10 (14)
Column Clamp Stud Nut	9 (12)
Flexible Coupling Bolts	17 (23)
Steering Wheel Retaining Nut	60 (82)
Support Plate Bolts	17 (23)
Upper Bracket Nuts	9 (12)

	INCH Lbs. (N.m)
Bearing Housing-to-Lock Housing Screws	35 (4)
Hazard Switch	24 (3)
Housing Cover Screws	100 (11)
Ignition Switch Screws	35 (4)
Lock Housing-to-Jacket	90 (10)
Shift Tube Support Screws	60 (7)
Tilt Release Spring Retaining Screw	35 (4)
Turn Signal Retaining Plate	26 (3)

FORD BRONCO II & RANGER

Bronco II & Ranger Models

DESCRIPTION

Steering columns are available in standard and tilt column models. The column has a modular construction. The wiper/washer, turn signal/hazard, horn/dimmer and ignition switch are mounted on the column. Switches can be serviced by removing the shroud.

The steering column is an energy absorbing type which collapses upon impact. A cylindrical impact bumper on the upper bracket is also included to absorb impact loads.

The key release button functions to prevent inadvertent locking of the steering wheel. The ignition switch is operated by a pin mounted on the lock actuator rack and is pinion driven by the key cylinder.

REMOVAL & INSTALLATION

STEERING COLUMNS

Removal

1) Disconnect the negative battery cable. Remove the upper-to-lower steering shaft bolt. Disengage the pot-joint from the column shaft by collapsing the intermediate shaft assembly.

2) Remove the steering wheel. *See appropriate Steering Wheel & Column Switches article.* Remove the steering column trim shrouds. On tilt columns, remove the upper extension shroud by squeezing it at the 6 & 12 o'clock positions.

3) Remove the steering column cover on the instrument panel. Disconnect all electrical connections to the steering column switches. Loosen the bolts retaining the steering column the brake pedal bracket.

4) Remove the 3 screws retaining the steering column toeplate to the dash. Remove the steering column-to-brake pedal bolts. Lower the steering column and pull it out from the vehicle.

Installation

Install the steering column by inserting the lower end of the steering column through the opening in the dash panel. Reverse removal procedure to complete assembly.

OVERHAUL

STANDARD COLUMNS

Disassembly

1) Remove steering wheel, column shrouds, turn signal and wiper/washer switches. Remove steering column from vehicle. Remove the upper bearing retainer plate and bearing snap ring.

2) Insert the blades of two screwdrivers under the bearing and pry it off the steering shaft. Using a screwdriver, pry out the lower bearing retainer and discard it.

3) Pull the lower end of the shaft assembly downward through the tube until the lower bearing/sleeve with lower shaft clears the lower end of the tube. Slide the lower bearing/sleeve off of the steering shaft.

4) Pull the steering shaft assembly out of the outer tube from the bottom of the tube. Scribe a mark on

the upper steering shaft where the upper and lower steering shaft sections form a joint line.

5) Also scribe marks on the upper and lower shafts to indicate shaft relationship. Separate upper and lower steering shaft sections. Remove and discard the insulator clips.

6) Remove the 2 bolts holding the lock cylinder housing to the outer tube flange bracket. Rotate the ignition key to "START" position. Pull the actuator interlock out of the clearance hole in the tube. Lift the casting off the steering shaft.

Reassembly

1) Turn the ignition switch to the "START" position to locate the actuator interlock through the clearance hole in the outer tube. Install and tigten the 2 cylinder housing-to-bracket bolts.

2) Install new steel insulator clips on the flats on the steering column upper shaft. Lubricate the lower 6 inches of the steering column upper shaft with chassis lube.

3) Assemble upper and lower shafts noting position of scribe marks for shaft-to-shaft relationship. Slide lower bearing, with sleeve, up into the outer tube as far as possible. Use a length of pipe to seat bearing retaining ring against the bearing.

4) Pin punch the steering column upper shaft serration diameter to ensure an interference fit between the bearing inner race and the steering column upper shaft. Slide the upper bearing and insulator as far as possible down the shaft.

5) Place a 3.25" (82.5 mm) length of 3/4" (19 mm) diameter pipe over the end of the shaft. Install the steering wheel nut and tighten until the bearing is fully seated. Remove the steering wheel nut and pipe and install the bearing snap ring.

6) Install the upper bearing retainer plate. Install column shrouds, turn signal and wiper/washer switches. Install steering column in vehicle.

TILT COLUMNS

Disassembly

1) Remove steering wheel, column shrouds, turn signal and wiper/washer switches. Remove steering column from vehicle. Remove the conical coil spring and upper bearing plate.

2) Remove the upper bearing C-clip. Move the tilt casting to the upper position to unload the tilt spring. Use tool (T67P-3D739-C) to remove the pivot pins. Lift off the tilt casting.

3) Tilt casting bearings may be removed with a drift punch. Using a screwdriver, pry out the lower bearing retainer and discard it.

3) Pull the lower end of the shaft assembly downward through the tube until the lower bearing/sleeve with lower shaft clears the lower end of the tube. Slide the lower bearing/sleeve off of the steering shaft.

4) Pull the steering shaft assembly out of the outer tube from the bottom of the tube. Scribe a mark on the upper steering shaft where the upper and lower steering shaft sections form a joint line.

5) Also scribe marks on the upper and lower shafts to indicate shaft relationship. Separate upper and lower steering shaft sections. Remove and discard the insulator clips.

Steering Columns
FORD BRONCO II & RANGER (Cont.)

Fig. 1: Exploded View of Bronco II & Ranger Standard Steering Column

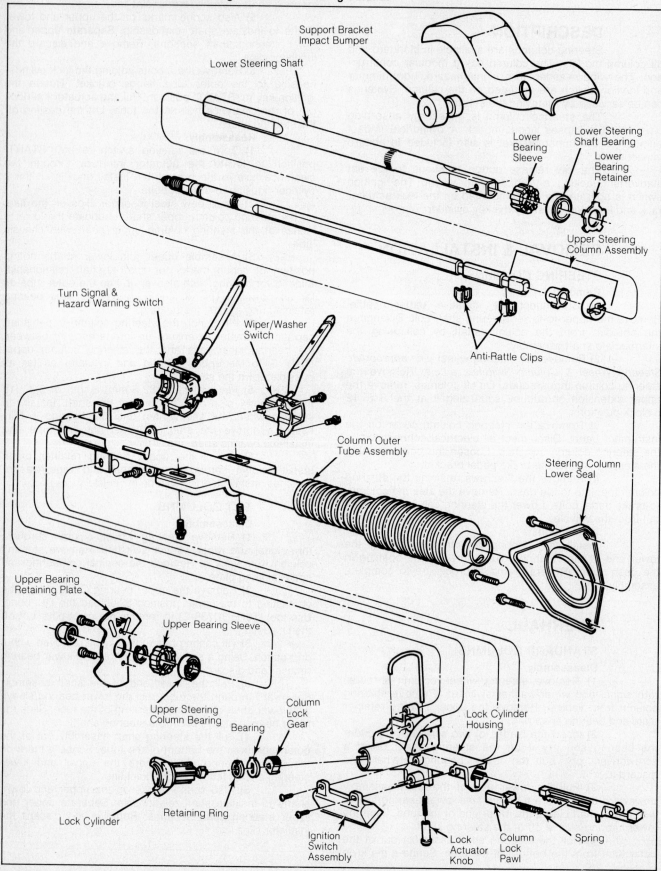

Support Bracket Impact Bumper

Lower Steering Shaft

Lower Bearing Sleeve

Lower Steering Shaft Bearing

Lower Bearing Retainer

Upper Steering Column Assembly

Turn Signal & Hazard Warning Switch

Wiper/Washer Switch

Anti-Rattle Clips

Column Outer Tube Assembly

Steering Column Lower Seal

Upper Bearing Retaining Plate

Upper Bearing Sleeve

Upper Steering Column Bearing

Bearing

Column Lock Gear

Lock Cylinder Housing

Lock Cylinder

Retaining Ring

Ignition Switch Assembly

Lock Actuator Knob

Column Lock Pawl

Spring

FORD BRONCO II & RANGER (Cont.)

Fig. 2: Exploded View of Bronco II & Ranger Tilt Steering Column

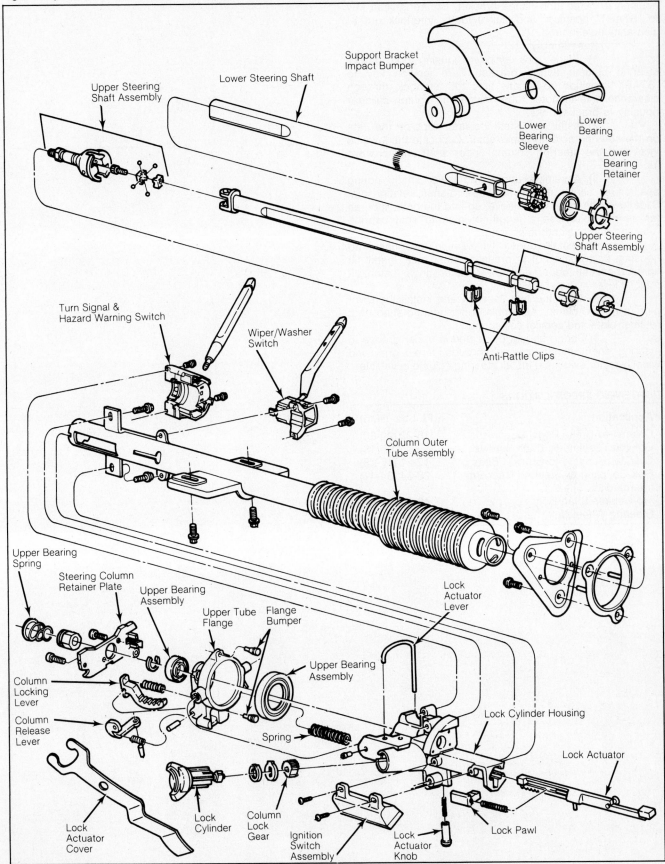

Steering Columns

FORD BRONCO II & RANGER (Cont.)

6) Remove 2 bolts connecting lock cylinder housing to outer tube flange bracket. Rotate ignition key to "START" position, and pull actuator interlock out of clearance hole in tube.

Reassembly

1) Place lock cylinder housing onto upper steering column flange bracket. Turn ignition key to "START" position to locate actuator interlock through clearance hole in outer tube. Install and tighten cylinder housing-to-bracket bolts.

2) Install new steel insulator clips on the flats on the steering column upper shaft. Lubricate the lower 6 inches of the steering column upper shaft with chassis lube.

3) Assemble upper and lower shafts noting position of scribe marks for shaft-to-shaft relationship. Slide lower bearing, with sleeve, up into the outer tube as far as possible. Use a length of pipe to seat bearing retaining ring against the bearing.

4) Install upper tilt casting bearings into housing, using care not to press on inner race. Install tilt spring between upper and lower tilt castings. Latch tilt release lever in upper position.

5) Align the two castings and install the pivot pins using a C-clamp. Assemble upper bearing snap ring, retainer plate and conical coil spring.

6) Spring should be seated in upper groove in steering shaft. Install column shrouds, turn signal and wiper/washer switches. Install steering column in vehicle.

TIGHTENING SPECIFICATIONS

Application	Ft. Lbs. (N.m)
Column-to-Brake Pedal Support	15-22 (20-30)
Column Toeplate-to-Dash Screws	12 (16)
Cylinder Housing-to-Bracket Bolts	12-21 (17-28)
Flex Coupling-to-Steering Gear Bolt	25-34 (34-47)
Intermediate Shaft-to-Column Shaft Bolt	40-50 (54-68)
Steering Wheel Nut	30-42 (41-57)

FORD EXC. BRONCO II & RANGER

Bronco, Pickup & Van

DESCRIPTION

All models use steering columns with shift control rod within column tube. Directional signal switch and lever, hazard warning control knob and ignition switch are mounted on columns.

Columns are equipped with anti-theft locking device and automatic transmission models have the transmission linkage in the column. Two types of columns are available, a standard column and a tilt column which features 5 positions.

REMOVAL & INSTALLATION

BRONCO & PICKUP
Removal

1) Set parking brake and disconnect negative battery cable. Remove steering wheel. See *Steering Wheels and Column Switches in this Section*. Remove bolt and nut attaching intermediate shaft to steering column. Disconnect shift linkage rods from column.

2) Remove steering floor opening cover plate screws. Place shift lever in first gear on manual transmissions, or "1" position on automatic transmissions. Spread shroud open and pull it up and away from instrument panel and column.

Fig. 1: Steering Column Installation

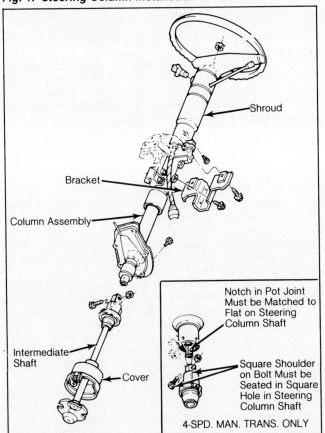

Bronco and Pickup models are shown.

3) Remove automatic transmission indicator actuation cable. Remove instrument panel column opening cover. Remove column support bracket-to-pedal support bracket bolts.

4) Disconnect turn signal and hazard flasher warning switch and ignition switch wiring harnesses. Remove column from vehicle. Remove support bracket from column.

Installation

Install column by reversing removal procedure. Adjust automatic transmission indicator cable.

VAN MODELS
Removal

1) Set parking brake and disconnect negative battery cable. Remove nuts attaching flexible coupling to steering shaft flange. Remove shift linkage rods from column. Remove steering wheel.

2) Place transmission in first gear and remove steering column floor opening cover plate. Remove shroud by pulling shroud tabs out of clip at bottom of column.

3) Remove instrument panel column opening cover. Remove bolts attaching column bracket to pedal support bracket. Disconnect turn signal, hazard warning and ignition switch wiring harnesses. Remove steering column.

Installation

Install steering column by reversing removal procedure. Align steering column and flexible coupling. See Adjustment section in this article.

OVERHAUL

STANDARD COLUMN
Disassembly (All Models)

1) Remove steering wheel and column. Remove turn signal lever. On 3-speed and automatic transmissions, drive out shift lever pivot pin and remove lever.

2) Remove turn signal and hazard switch retaining screws and partially withdraw switch from upper flange. Remove snap ring from upper steering shaft. Remove lower bearing retainer.

3) Using a light hammer, gently drive the steering shaft out the bottom of the steering column. Retain the ignition switch in the "LOCK" position and remove ignition switch and actuation rod.

4) On automatic transmissions, drill out shift tube retaining rivet from bottom of shift socket. On manual transmissions, withdraw shift tube assembly from bottom of column.

5) Remove the shift indicator and lens assembly from Van models only. Loosen upper flange retaining nuts. Pinch nuts toward each other and withdraw upper flange from outer tube.

6) Remove shift socket on 3-speed manual and automatic transmissions from outer tube. Remove flange extension on 4-speed transmissions from outer tube.

7) On all models, remove upper bearing and insulator cover from upper flange by gently tapping opposite side of flange with a light hammer.

Steering Columns

FORD EXC. BRONCO II & RANGER (Cont.)

Fig. 2: Steering Column Installation

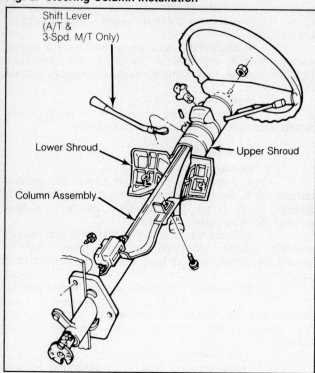

Shift Lever
(A/T &
3-Spd. M/T Only)

Lower Shroud

Upper Shroud

Column Assembly

Van model only is shown.

Reassembly

1) On 3-speed manual transmissions, place bushing in socket retainer in outer tube. Place bushing on upper hub and wave washer on lower hub of shift socket.

2) On automatic transmissions, install shift socket on outer tube and place wave washer in flange hub. On 4-speed manual transmissions, install flange extension on outer tube..

3) On all models, install flange onto outer tube by pinching nuts together and pressing flange in place. Retaining bolt "T" head will engage cutouts in outer tube as nuts are tightened.

4) Insert assembled shift tube assembly through lower column opening. Install shift tube retaining rivet through bottom of shift socket on automatic transmissions. Install steering shaft clip below knurl for upper bearing.

5) On Bronco and Pickup models only, check assembled shaft length. It should be 35.6" (.9 m). Adjust by gently tapping in the appropriate direction.

6) Load shaft up through bottom of column taking care not to collapse steering shaft. Place cover insulator onto upper bearing and press onto knurl on steering shaft until snap ring groove is visible above bearing.

7) Install snap ring. Install turn signal and hazard warning switch. Install lower bearing retainer. On Bronco and Pickup models, ensure that the centerline of the coupling shaft attachment hole extends .8" (20.3 mm) below the lower face of the retainer.

8) Minor adjustments can be made by gently tapping the shaft in the appropriate direction. On Van models, install the lower bearing retainer and ensure that lower steering shaft is fully seated against upper shaft.

9) Install ignition switch actuation rod. Mount ignition switch and hand start retaining nuts with the lock cylinder in lock position.

10) Tighten retaining nuts and remove clip. Install shift lever. Install turn signal switch lever.

TILT COLUMN

Disassembly (All Models)

1) Remove steering wheel. Remove column from vehicle. Remove turn signal lever. Drive out pivot pin and remove shift lever on automatic transmissions. Remove steering shaft lower flange and retaining clamp.

2) Remove lower bearing retainer. On automatic transmissions, remove shift tube retaining rivet from bottom of shift socket and withdraw shift tube from bottom of column.

3) On all models, remove lock drive gear. Remove turn signal switch screws, wiring harness to column clips and switch and wiring harness from column.

4) Remove cover casting screws. Remove casting from column. Unhook upper actuator from lower actuator and remove.

5) Remove and discard screws attaching lower flange to outer tube. Loosen ignition switch retaining screws and remove ignition rod from switch end.

6) Withdraw tilt mechanism, steering shaft and ignition actuation rod from steering column upper end. On automatic transmissions, remove shift socket. Remove key release lever mechanism to tilt mechanism on 4-speed manual transmission models.

Reassembly

1) Attach PRND21 ring to tilt mechanism on automatic transmissions. Attach flange extension and key release mechanism to tilt mechanism on manual 4-speed transmissions.

2) Install shift socket on automatic transmissions. Install tilt mechanism, feeding the steering shaft down the center of the column and the ignition switch actuation rod through the shift socket/flange extension along the top of the column outer tube.

NOTE: **Care must be taken not to change the length of the steering shaft on Bronco and Pickup models because of the telescoping feature.**

3) Install flange retainer assemblies using new hex screws. Install lower bearing retainer. Attach ignition switch loosely to the outer tube.

4) Connect upper and lower actuators. Install cover on column. Install turn signal switch and wiring harness in steering column. Attach wiring harness to steering column clips.

5) Install 2 screws attaching turn signal switch to the flange casting and one screw attaching warning buzzer terminal. Install turn signal lever. Install lock drive gear. Install lock cylinder with key in "ON" position.

6) Install the retaining pin flush with cylinder. With ignition switch mounting nuts loose, clip the switch through the opening in the side of the switch casting. Center the switch on the actuation rod.

7) Tighten retaining nuts and remove clip. Install shift lever and pivot pin. Install turn signal lever. Install steering column and steering wheel.

FORD EXC. BRONCO II & RANGER (Cont.)

Fig. 3: Exploded View of Tilt Column Assembly

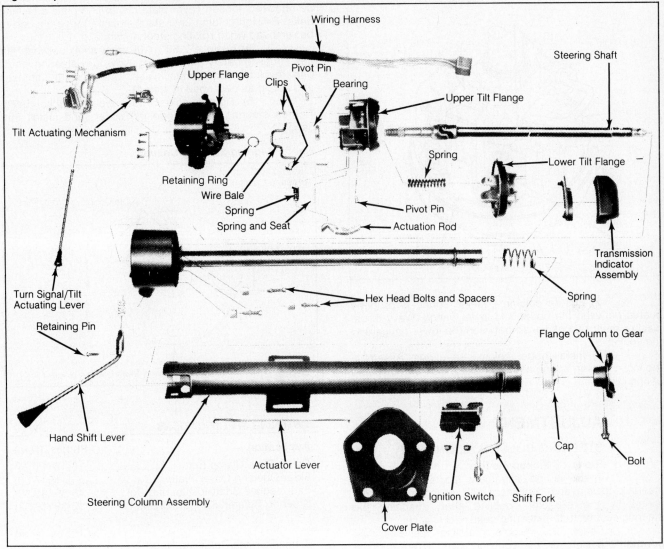

FLANGE & LOCKING MECHANISM

Disassembly (All Non-Tilt Models)

1) Remove flange retaining bolts. On manual transmissions, remove snap ring and spring from lock release lever assembly. On automatic transmissions, remove shift indicator insert from front of flange.

2) With lock cylinder in "ON" position, depress retaining pin and remove lock cylinder from flange. On all models, remove lock bearing snap ring and lock bearing.

3) Remove lock drive gear and actuator assembly. Remove lock actuator insert screw and lock actuator through opening in front of flange.

Reassembly

1) Install lock actuator insert in rear of flange and tighten screw. Insert lock actuator assembly through opening in front of flange until it bottoms against insert.

2) Install lock drive gear through lock cylinder opening such that last gear tooth aligns with last tooth in actuator assembly when actuator is fully rearward.

3) Install lock bearing and snap ring. With cylinder in "ON" position, and retaining pin depressed, insert lock cylinder into flange. On automatic transmissions, attach shift indicator insert to front of flange.

4) On manual transmissions, position spring on lock release lever assembly through hole in front of flange and install snap ring on lock release lever assembly. On all models, install retaining bolt through holes in flange and hand start nuts on rear side.

Disassembly (All Tilt Models)

1) Remove steering column from vehicle. Remove the spring cilps holding the wire bale. Lift off the wire bale. With a small drift, drive out the pin holding locking lever. See Fig. 4.

2) Remove lever and spring. Remove the column upper shaft snap ring. Separate upper and lower flange castings by removing the 2 pivot pins located in the side of the casting.

3) Pivot pins may be removed by using Remover Tool (T67P-3D739-C). Do not reuse pivot pins if the press fit is loose in the flange. Upper flange bearings may be replaced by tapping lightly on OUTER race.

Reassembly

1) Install the lower actuator with the ignition switch rod attached. Assemble the upper and lower flange and press in the pivot pins with a "C" clamp.

FORD EXC. BRONCO II & RANGER (Cont.)

Fig. 4: Tilt Mechanism Flange Sub-Assembly

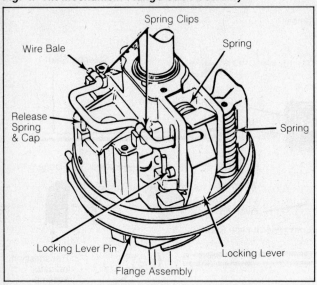

2) Ensure column position spring is properly seated between the upper and lower flange. Wavy thrust washer must be positioned between the lower flange and the socket.

3) Install upper column snap ring, Assemble the locking lever, spring and lever pin. Install wire bale and spring clips.

ADJUSTMENT

STEERING COLUMN ALIGNMENT
Bronco & Pickup Models
There is no alignment adjustment of the steering column and coupling shaft. Alignment is maintained by the slip-joint coupling shaft attaching the steering column to the steering gear.

Check the flexible coupling for clearance between the slots on the coupling shaft flange and the flexible coupling safety pins. The pin to flange clearance should be .010" (.25 mm).

NOTE: If it is determined that the coupling has been driven in a non-flat position for more than 12,000 miles, coupling should be replaced.

Van Models
1) Remove steering column trim panel. Loosen bolts securing steering column to brake and clutch pedal support. Loosen steering column trim panel. Loosen steering column opening cover plate to dash panel bolts. Loosen lower column clamp.

2) Make sure flexible coupling nuts are tight. With front wheels in straight ahead position, pull up on steering column until the flex coupling is in a flat to a 0.1" (2.5 mm) concaved position, pointing toward steering wheel.

3) Tighten steering column-to-support bracket bolts. Tighten steering column opening cover bolts. Insert a .160" (4.06 mm) shim between right flex coupling safety pin and slot. Now turn steering wheel one revolution clockwise.

4) Check to see if shim is tight. If shim cannot be removed, loosen cover plate clamp and plate attaching bolts. Realign column until shim remains loose enough to be removed when rotating steering wheel.

5) Insert a .160" (4.06 mm) shim between left flex coupling safety pin and slot. Now turn steering wheel one revolution counterclockwise. Check shim tightness and adjust as described in step **4)**.

6) Tighten column to support bracket bolts. Tighten steering column opening cover, and install trim panel.

Fig. 5: Aligning Steering Column

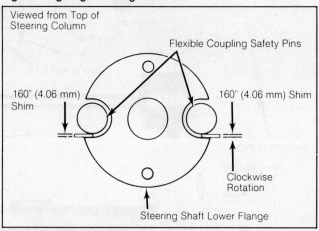

Van model only is shown.

TIGHTENING SPECIFICATIONS

Application	Ft. Lbs. (N.m)
Cover Plate Clamp Bolt	8-18 (11-24)
Floor Opening Cover Plate	5-15 (7-20)
Intermediate Shaft-to-Steering Col.	45-59 (61-80)
Steering Column Support Bracket	13-38 (18-52)

	INCH Lbs. (N.m)
Ignition Switch Retaining Nuts	40-65 (5-7)
Lower Bearing Retainer	12-20 (1-2)
Turn Signal/Hazard Warning Switch	15-25 (2-3)

GENERAL MOTORS

Chevrolet, GMC

DESCRIPTION

Collapsible steering columns with internal shift linkage and function locking features are used. Tilt steering wheel features are available on all models.

REMOVAL & INSTALLATION

CAUTION: **When working on a collapsible steering column, do not bump or hammer on column components. Correct column installation is important to prevent stress on components during mounting. Using improper screws, nuts and bolts could prevent assembly from compressing under impact.**

"C" & "K" MODELS

Removal

1) Loosen front of dash mounting plates. Disconnect battery ground cable. Remove steering wheel. Remove nuts and washers securing flanged end of steering shaft to the flexible coupling.

2) Disconnect transmission control linkage from column shift tube levers. Disconnect steering column harness and wiring. Remove floor pan trim cover screws and remove cover.

3) Remove screws securing 2 halves of floor pan cover, then remove screws securing halves and seal

Fig. 1: "C" & "K" Models Steering Column Installation

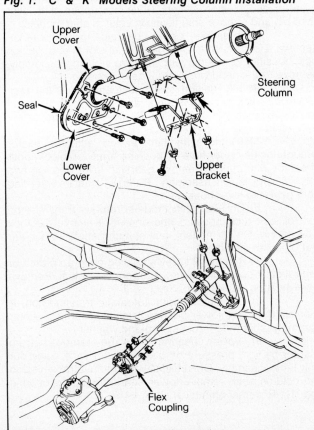

Upper Cover

Seal

Lower Cover

Upper Bracket

Steering Column

Flex Coupling

to floor pan and remove covers. Remove transmission indicator cable (if equipped).

4) Move front seat as far back as possible to provide maximum clearance. Remove 2 column bracket-to-instrument panel nuts and carefully remove column from vehicle, rotating column so that shift levers will clear hole in floor pan.

Installation

1) Assemble upper and lower dash covers to seal. Attach bracket to steering column. Tighten 4 retaining bolts.

NOTE: **If flexible joint coupling was removed from steering gear shaft, it must be installed before steering column is installed in car.**

2) Position steering column in vehicle. Assemble flange and flexible coupling. Install lock washers and nuts. Tighten nuts. Loosely install 2 bracket nuts to dash studs.

3) Install lower clamp (engine side of firewall) and tighten nuts. Install seal, upper and lower covers to cab side of firewall. Tighten 2 upper bracket nuts.

4) Remove plastic spacers from flexible coupling. Install automatic transmission indicator cable (if equipped).

5) Install instrument panel trim cover. Connect transmission control linkage. Install steering wheel. Connect battery ground cable.

"G" & P" MODELS

Removal

1) Disconnect battery ground cable. On column shift models, disconnect shifter rods at lower end of column. On "G" models, remove steering shaft flange-to-flexible coupling bolts.

2) On "P" models, remove intermediate steering shaft upper universal pinch bolt and mark coupling-to-shaft relationship. On all models, remove column clamp screws on engine side of firewall. Slide cover and seal down on column.

3) From inside vehicle, remove screws from floor pan cover and slide cover and seal up column. Remove steering wheel, then reinstall retaining nut and washer to prevent dislocation of steering shaft.

4) Disconnect wiring harness. On standard column with automatic transmission, disconnect tube for transmission indicator at instrument panel. On tilt column with automatic transmission, disconnect single wire at fuse block and unclip it from parking brake bracket.

5) On all models, remove cap screws from column support bracket at dash panel. Carefully withdraw column assembly, rotating it so that shift levers clear hole in floor pan.

Installation ("G" Models Only)

1) Adjust column lower bearing preload. See ADJUSTMENTS in this article. Install plastic spacers onto flexible coupling alignment pins.

2) From inside vehicle, carefully insert lower end of column through floor pan opening, guiding steering shaft flange onto flexible coupling. Install and tighten flange-to-coupling bolts.

3) Locate index slot in column jacket with protrusion on clutch band brake pedal support. Loosely install column-to-dash bracket and screws. Push column down until steering shaft flange bottoms on plastic spacers on flexible coupling and tighten bracket screws.

Steering Columns

GENERAL MOTORS (Cont.)

4) Remove plastic spacer from alignment pins. Check that the flexible coupling-to-steering shaft flange clearance is .250-.325" (6-8 mm). If not within specifications, bracket screws must be loosened and column raised or lowered as required. Retighten screws.

5) Push floor pan seal to floor pan. Install and tighten screws. Connect directional signal switch wiring harness. On vehicles with automatic transmissions, connect conductor tube for transmission indicator to instrument panel.

6) On all models, install steering wheel. Connect transmission linkage and battery ground cable.

Installation ("P" Models Only)

1) Adjust lower bearing preload to allow steering shaft end play. See ADJUSTMENTS in this article. Tighten shaft clamp on pot joint bolt.

2) Carefully insert lower end of column assembly into hole in floor pan. Guide steering shaft into universal yoke, lining up marks made at removal. Install yoke pinch bolt and tighten. Pinch bolt must pass through shaft undercut.

3) Position and attach lower clamp mounting bracket to firewall. Locate steering column protrusions against floor pan bracket.

4) At the same time, align protrusion on clutch and brake pedal support with index slot on column jacket. Install column-to-bracket clamp and tighten bolt.

NOTE: Do not allow toe pan bracket to override protrusions on steering column jacket.

5) Position steering column-to-dash panel bracket. Install and tighten bolts. Install seal at floor pan, then install bracket screws and tighten. Install dash panel trim plate, if equipped. Connect transmission shift linkage on column shift models.

6) On all models, connect wiring harness. On standard columns with automatic transmissions, connect conductor tube for transmission indicator to instrument panel. On all models, install steering wheel and connect battery ground cable.

"S" & "T" MODELS
Removal

1) Disconnect battery cable and remove steering wheel. In engine compartment, remove bolt and nut holding intermediate shaft to bottom of steering column. Remove clamp bolt at steering gear. Remove intermediate shaft.

2) Remove toe plate bolts. Unplug ignition switch connector and any other wiring. Remove bolt through upper edge of column (under instrument panel). Remove mounting nuts, lower column and remove from vehicle.

Installation

1) Place column in vehicle. Install column nuts loosely. Install and tighten toe plate bolts (starting with bolts toward center of vehicle). Tighten column nuts. Connect wiring. Position intermediate shaft on steering gear and tighten pinch bolt to 35-45 ft. lbs. (48-60 N.m).

2) Lock steering shaft and wheels in straight ahead position. Connect intermediate shaft joint to lower end of steering column. Install clamp bolt and tighten nut. Install steering wheel. Connect battery cable.

OVERHAUL

"C" & "K" MODELS
STANDARD COLUMN
Disassembly

1) Remove 4 dash panel bracket-to-column screws and place bracket in safe place to prevent damage to mounting capsules. Place column in a vise using both weld nuts of set "A" or "B". See Fig. 2.

CAUTION: Be sure to clamp correctly to avoid damaging column.

Fig. 2: Correct Installation of Steering Column in Vise

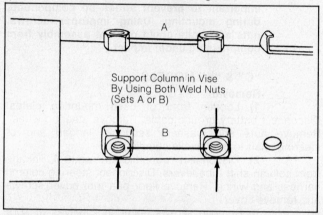

The vise jaws must clamp onto the sides of the weld nuts indicated by the arrows shown on set "B".

2) Remove directional signal switch, lock cylinder, and ignition switch. Drive out upper shift lever pivot pin and remove shift lever on column shift models.

3) Remove upper bearing thrust washer. Remove 4 screws attaching directional signal and ignition lock housing to column and remove housing assembly. Remove thrust cap from lower side of housing.

4) Lift ignition switch actuating rod and rack assembly, rack preload spring, and shaft lock bolt and spring assembly out of housing. Remove shift lever detent plate (shift gate).

5) Remove ignition switch actuator sector through lock cylinder hole by pushing firmly on block tooth of sector with punch. Remove gearshift lever housing and shroud from jacket assembly. Remove shift lever spring from gearshift lever housing

6) On floor shift models, remove transmission control lock tube housing and shroud. Remove the lock tube spring. On all models, pull steering shaft from lower end of jacket assembly.

7) Remove 2 screws holding back-up switch or neutral start switch to column and remove switch. Remove lower bearing retainer clip. See Fig. 3.

8) On vehicles with automatic transmission or floor shift, remove lower bearing retainer, bearing adapter assembly, shift tube thrust spring and washer.

9) Lower bearing may be removed from adapter by light pressure on bearing outer race. Slide out shift tube assembly. On vehicles with manual transmission and column shift, remove lower bearing adapter, bearing and "1st-Reverse" shift lever.

GENERAL MOTORS (Cont.)

Fig. 3: Removing Lower Bearing Retaining Clip

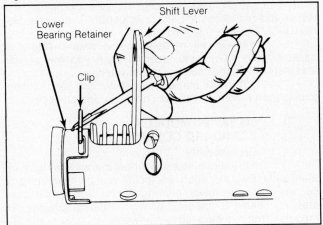

"C" & "K" model standard column is shown.

10) Lower bearing may be removed from adapter by light pressure on bearing outer race. Remove 3 screws from bearing at lower end and slide out shift tube assembly.

11) On all models with column shift, remove gearshift housing lower bearing from upper end of column.

Reassembly

1) Apply a thin coat of lithium grease to all friction surfaces. Install sector into directional signal and lock cylinder housing. Install sector in lock cylinder hole over sector shaft with tang end to outside of hole.

2) Press sector over shaft with blunt tool. Install shift lever detent plate onto housing. Insert rack preload spring into housing from bottom side. Long section should be toward handwheel and hook onto edge of housing.

3) Assemble locking bolt onto crossover arm on rack. Insert rack and lock bolt assembly into housing

Fig. 4: Exploded View of Steering Column Assembly

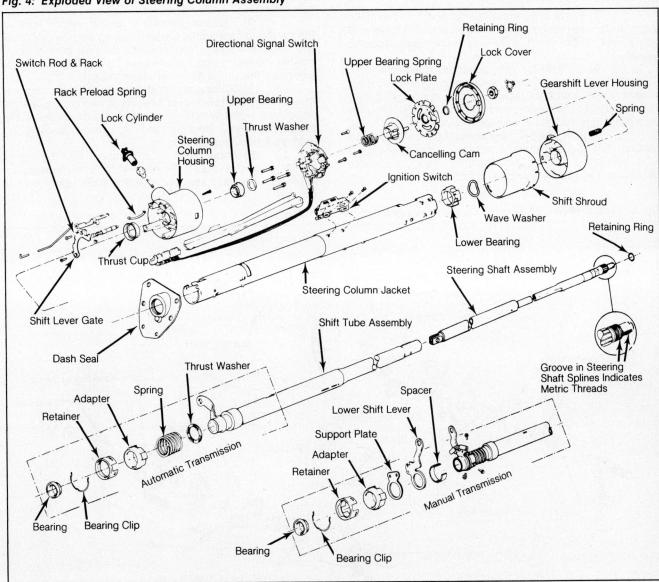

"C" & "K" models with column switch shown.

Steering Columns

GENERAL MOTORS (Cont.)

from bottom with teeth up (toward handwheel) and toward center line of column.

4) Align first tooth on sector with last tooth on rack; if aligned properly, block teeth will lineup when rack assembly is pushed all the way in.

5) Install thrust cup on bottom hub of housing. Install gearshift housing lower bearing from very end of jacket, while aligning indentations in bearing with projections on jacket.

CAUTION: If bearing is not properly installed, it will not rest on all the stops provided.

6) Install shift lever spring into gearshift lever (or lock tube) housing. Install housing and shroud assemblies onto upper end of mast jacket. Rotate housing to be sure it is seated in bearing.

7) With shift lever housing in place, install directional signal and lock cylinder housing onto jacket. Gearshift housing should be in "P" position and rack pulled downward. Be sure directional signal housing is seated on jacket. Install and tighten 4 screws.

8) Press lower bearing into adapter assembly. Insert shift tube assembly into lower end of jacket and rotate until upper shift tube key slides into housing keyway.

9) On vehicles with automatic transmission or floor shift, assemble spring, lower bearing and adapter assembly into bottom of jacket. Holding adapter in place, install lower bearing reinforcement and retainer clip. Be sure clip snaps into jacket and reinforcement slots.

10) On vehicles with manual transmission and column shift, loosely attach 3 screws in jacket and shift tube bearing. Assemble "1st-Reverse" lever and lower bearing and adapter assembly into bottom of jacket.

11) Holding adapter in place, install bearing reinforcement and retaining clip. Be sure clip snaps into jacket and reinforcement slots. Adjust lower bearing. See ADJUSTMENTS in this article.

12) On all models, install neutral-safety or backup switch. Slide the steering shaft into the column and install the upper bearing thrust washer.

13) Install the turn signal swithch, lock cylinder and ignition switch. Install the shift lever and pivot pin.

"G" & "P" MODELS
STANDARD COLUMN
Disassembly

1) Remove steering wheel nut and flat washer, then slide steering shaft assembly out of lower end of column. Remove lower bearing spring and clamp from steering shaft ("G" models) or from steering column ("P" models). Remove back-up lamp switch.

2) Drive out shift lever pin (except floor shift models) and remove shift lever. Remove directional switch cancelling cam and switch lever. Remove column wiring harness cover.

3) Remove directional signal switch screws. Rotate directional signal switch housing counterclockwise and remove housing from column. Remove plastic thrust washer assembly and then remove shift lever housing (or extension housing if floor shift) from column.

4) Housing and switch cannot be fully removed from column until shift lever housing is removed. Separate directional signal switch, switch control support assembly, directional signal housing and shift lever housing (or extension housing) assemblies.

5) Press steering shaft upper bearing out of switch contact support. Remove shift lever housing (or extension housing) seal and bushing from upper end of column.

Fig. 5: *Exploded View of Steering Column Assembly for "G" & "P" Models*

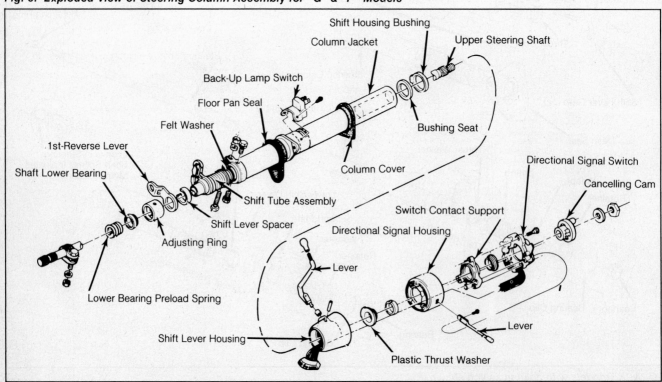

GENERAL MOTORS (Cont.)

6) Remove bolt and screws from adjusting ring clamp and remove clamp, adjusting ring, and lower bearing. Press lower bearing out of adjusting ring. On 3 speed columns, remove "1st-Reverse" shift lever and lever spacer.

7) On automatic transmission columns, remove selector plate clamping ring screws. On all models, place column upright on floor, supporting it with 2 pieces of wood.

8) Place a block of wood on upper end of shift tube. Press down on shift lever with foot while tapping on wood block to withdraw tube from column jacket. If removal is difficult, use a press.

9) Remove felt seal from shift tube. Remove firewall clamp, floor pan seal and dash seals from jacket. Inspect parts for excessive wear, rust or corrosion.

Reassembly

1) When lubrication is called for, use lithium soap grease. Install dash panel seal, floor pan and firewall clamps over end of column. Lubricate all bearing surfaces on shift tube. Place felt seal onto shift tube (next to spring) and place shift tube in jacket.

2) On 3 speed column shift models, temporarily install spacer, "1st-Reverse" shift lever and lower adjusting ring. Place a block of wood on top of adjusting ring and tap until shift tube bottoms. Remove adjusting ring, shift lever and spacer.

3) On automatic transmission columns, align 3 holes in selector plate with 3 holes in jacket. Shift tube spring retainer must be bottomed against jacket stops. Position clamping ring and install 3 screws.

4) On 3 speed columns, lubricate and install spacer and "1st-Reverse" (tang of lever towards top of column). On all columns, install lower bearing in adjusting ring, then install adjusting ring, clamp, and screws.

5) Install shift lever housing (or extension housing) seat and bushing to upper end of housing. Thread directional signal switch wiring harness through switch and shift lever (or extension) housings.

6) Lubricate inner diameter of shift (extension) housing and install onto upper end of column. Install switch housing plastic washer assembly. Press upper bearing into switch contact support.

7) Install directional signal switch housing, contact support, bearing, and switch. Torque screws to 25 INCH lbs. (2.8 N.m). Install column wiring harness cover and back-up lamp switch. Install directional signal and gearshift levers.

8) Loosely install lower bearing preload spring and clamp. Slide steering shaft assembly through column assembly. Install directional signal cancelling cam, steering shaft nut and lock washer.

"S" & "T" MODELS
STANDARD COLUMN

Disassemby

1) Remove column from vehicle and mount in vise or holding fixture (J-23074). Use screwdriver to pry out shaft lock cover. Depress lock plate with tool (J-23653). Remove retaining ring. Remove lock plate, cancelling cam and spring.

2) Remove screw and turn signal switch arm. Remove 3 screws and wire protector, then switch assembly. Insert key and turn lock to "RUN" position. Remove lock retaining screw from top, then pull cylinder out the side. Remove ignition and dimmer switches.

3) Remove thrust washer and 4 Allen screws. Remove sector from housing. Pull off housing. Remove wave washer, lever and spring from key release. Remove 3 screws and plate from bottom of housing.

4) Remove cap, switch pivot pin and switch. If equipped with bearing retainer, remove retainer, bushing, horn contact and bearing. If no retainer, housing must be replaced to replace bearing.

5) Remove spring and bolt assembly, spring thrust washer, rack actuator and rack spring. Remove shift lever bowl and shroud. Remove shift bowl lower bearing.

6) Remove back-up light switch. Remove retaining ring from top of shaft. Remove retainer clip at bottom of column. Remove retainer, bearing, spring, shift column (if equipped) and steering shaft.

Reassembly

1) Assemble steering shaft and shift tube. Install back-up light switch. Position gear shift bowl assembly. Assemble housing and tap sector into place with punch. On key release column, install lever, spring and wave washer.

2) Assemble rack so first rack tooth engages between first and second tooth of sector. On key release column, move ignition switch slider to "ACC". On all others, move to "ACC", then back 2 positions.

3) Place actuator rod in slider hole and install switch. Install dimmer switch and depress slightly to insert 3/32" drill. Force switch up and tighten screw and nut. Install ignition lock. Reverse disassembly procedures to complete reassembly.

"C" & "K" MODELS
TILT WHEEL

Disassembly

1) Remove 4 dash panel bracket-to-column screws. Set bracket aside to protect mounting capsules. Place column in a vise using both weld nuts of set "A" and "B" as shown in *Fig. 2*.

CAUTION: Do not place column in vise by clamping onto only one nut or by clamping onto sides of nut not indicated by arrows.

2) Remove directional signal switch, lock cylinder, and igniton switch. Remove tilt release lever,

Fig. 6: Removing Tilt Lever Spring Retainer

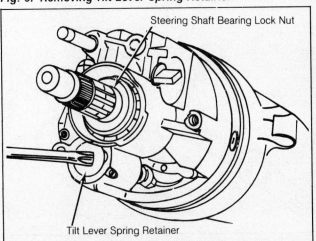

Steering Shaft Bearing Lock Nut

Tilt Lever Spring Retainer

Steering Columns

GENERAL MOTORS (Cont.)

then drive out shift lever pivot pin and remove shift lever and housing. Remove 3 directional signal housing screws and remove housing.

3) Install tilt release lever and place column in full up position. Remove tilt lever spring retainer.

4) Insert Phillips screwdriver into slot, press in approximately 3/16", then rotate 1/8" turn counterclockwise until retainer ears align with grooves in housing then remove retainer, spring, and guide. *See Fig. 6.*

5) Remove pot joint-to-steering shaft clamp bolt, then remove intermediate shaft and pot joint assembly. Push upper steering shaft in enough to remove steering shaft upper bearing inner race and seat.

6) Pry off lower bearing retainer clip, then remove bearing reinforcement, bearing and bearing adapter assembly from lower end of mast jacket. Remove upper bearing housing pivot pins using special tool (J-21854-1). *See Fig. 7.*

Fig. 7: Removing Bearing Housing Pivot Pins

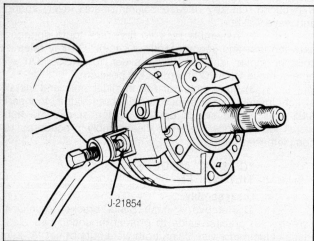

Tilt column models only are shown.

7) With tilt release lever installed, disengage lock shoes. Remove bearing housing by pulling upward to extend rack full down, then move housing to left to disengage ignition switch race from actuator rod.

8) Remove steering shaft assembly from upper end of column. Remove centering spheres and anti-lash

Fig. 8: Removing Shift Tube

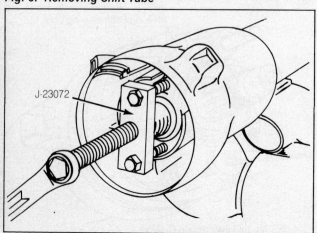

Tool screws must be fully engaged in lock plate.

spring to disassemble steering shaft. Remove transmission indicator wire, if equipped.

9) Remove steering shaft bearing housing support-to-gearshift housing screws, then remove bearing housing support. Remove ignition switch actuator rod. Use a screwdriver to remove shift tube retaining ring, then remove thrust washer.

10) Install a puller (J-23072) to lock plate, then turn center screws of tool clockwise to force shift tube from housing. *See Fig. 8.*

11) Remove shift tube (transmission control lock tube on floor shift models) from lower end of mast jacket. Remove tool from lock plate.

CAUTION: Guide lower end of shift tube through slotted opening in mast jacket. If tube is allowed to interfere with jacket, damage may result.

12) Remove housing support lock plate by sliding out of jacket notches, then tipping it down toward housing hub at 12 o'clock position and sliding it under jacket opening. Remove wave washer.

13) Remove shift lever housing from mast jacket (column shift models) or transmission control lock tube housing (floor shift models). Wind up shift lever spring with pliers and pull out. Remove spring plunger on floor shift models.

14) On all columns, disassemble bearing housing as follows: Remove tilt lever opening shield, then remove lock bolt spring retaining screw and move spring clockwise to remove it from bolt.

15) Remove sector drive shaft snap ring, then use a small punch to lightly tap drive shaft from sector. Remove drive shaft, sector and lock bolt. Remove rack and rack spring.

16) Use a punch to remove tilt release lever pin. Remove lever and release lever spring. Hold lock shoes inward and wedge a block between top of shoes (over slots) and bearing housing to relieve load on release lever.

17) Remove lock shoe retaining pin using a punch, then remove lock shoes and springs. Remove bearings from housing only if replacement is necessary.

Reassembly

1) Apply a thin coat of lithium grease or equivalent to all friction surfaces. If bearing was not disassembled, proceed to step **5)**. To reassemble bearing housing, press bearings into housing (if removed).

2) Install lock shoe springs, lock shoes, and shoe pin in housing. Use a .180" (4.6 mm) diameter rod to line up shoes for pin installation. Install shoe release lever, spring and pin.

3) If necessary to relieve load on release lever, hold shoes inward and wedge a block between top of shoes (over slots) and bearing housing. Install sector drive shaft into housing and lightly tap sector onto shaft far enough to allow installation of snap ring. Install snap ring.

4) Install lock bolt and engage it with sector cam surface. Install rack and spring while noting that the block tooth on rack should engage block tooth on sector. Install external tilt release lever. Install lock bolt spring and retaining screw and tighten.

5) Wind up shift lever spring with pliers and push into housing. Install plunger on floor shift models. Slide gearshift lever housing onto mast jacket. On all models, install bearing support lock plate wave washer.

6) Install lock plate and work it into notches by tipping plate toward hub at 12 o'clock position and sliding under jacket opening. Slide lock plate into notches in jacket.

7) Install shift tube into lower end of mast jacket, then align keyway of tube with key in shift lever housing. Install wobble plate end of special tool (J-23073) into upper end of shift tube (far enough to reach enlarged portion of tube).

8) Install adapter over end of tool and seat against lock plate. Install nut on end of tool and pull shift tube into housing.

CAUTION: Do not push or tap on end of shift tube and make sure shift tube lever is aligned with slotted opening at lower end of mast jacket or damage may result.

9) Pull shift lever housing up far enough to compress wave washer, then install bearing support thrust washer and retaining ring. Install bearing support while ensuring "V" in support is in line with "V" in jacket.

10) Install attaching screws through support and into lock plate, then tighten. Align lower bearing adapter with notches in jacket and push adapter into lower end of mast jacket. Install lower bearing, bearing reinforcement and retaining clip.

NOTE: Clip must be aligned with slots in reinforcement, jacket and adapter.

11) Install centering spheres and anti-lash spring into upper shaft. Install lower shaft from same side of spheres that spring ends protrude. Install steering shaft assembly into shift tube from upper end and carefully guide shaft through shift tube and bearing.

12) Install ignition switch actuator rod through shift lever housing and insert into slot in bearing support. Extend rack downward from bearing housing, then assemble bearing housing over steering shaft and engage rack over end of actuator rod.

13) Install tilt release lever, then hold lock shoes in disengaged position and position bearing housing over steering shaft until pivot pin holes line up. Install pivot pins.

14) Place bearing housing in full up position. Install tilt lever spring guide, spring and spring retainer. Using a Phillips screwdriver, push retainer in and turn clockwise to engage in housing. Install upper bearing inner race and seat, then install tilt lever opening shield.

15) Remove tilt release lever, then install directional signal housing and tighten screws. Install tilt release lever and shift lever, then drive shift lever pin in.

16) Install lock cylinder, directional signal switch, and ignition switch. Install intermediate shaft assembly to upper shaft after aligning groove across upper end of pot joint with flat on steering shaft.

17) Install and tighten clamp while noting that clamp bolt must pass through shaft undercut. Install neutral safety switch or back-up switch.

18) Install dash panel bracket-to-column attaching screws and tighten. The slotted openings in bracket must face upper end of steering column.

Fig. 9: Exploded View of Tilt Wheel Steering Column on "C" & "K" Models with Column Shift

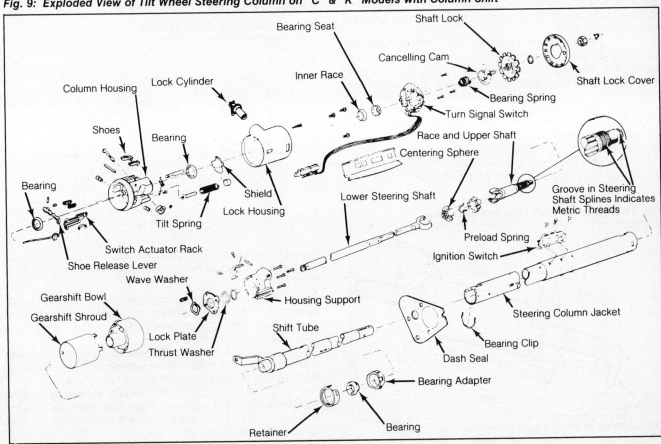

GENERAL MOTORS (Cont.)

"G" & "P" MODELS
TILT WHEEL
Disassembly

1) Place column in vise holding fixture (J-22573). Remove directional signal switch. Remove lower steering shaft and pot joint assembly. Remove lower bearing and adapter assembly from column, then press bearing out from adapter.

2) If column shift model, drive out the shift lever pivot pin and shift lever. Install tilt release lever and place column in full up position. Remove tilt lever spring and retainer using a screwdriver that just fits into slot opening.

3) Insert screwdriver into slot, push in approximately 3/16", then rotate clockwise approximately 1/8 turn until retainer ears align with grooves in housing and remove retainer and spring.

4) Remove steering shaft bearing lock nut using socket (J-22599). Remove upper bearing race seat and race. Remove two bearing housing pivot pins using tool (J-21854). *See Fig. 7.*

5) Pull up on tilt release lever (to disengage lock shoes) and remove bearing housing. If it is necessary to disassemble bearing housing, proceed as follows:

6) Press upper and lower bearings out of housing. Use a slide hammer to remove the bearing races from housing. Remove tilt release lever.

7) Drive out shoe release lever pivot pin using a punch. Remove lever spring and remove wedge. Drive out lock shoe retaining pin with a punch and remove shoes and shoe springs.

8) Remove steering shaft assembly through upper end of column. If it is necessary to disassemble shaft assembly, proceed as follows: Turn upper shaft 90° to lower shaft and slide upper shaft and centering spheres from lower shaft.

9) Rotate centering spheres 90° and remove centering spheres and preload spring from upper shaft. Remove 4 bearing housing support screws and remove support. If shift tube index plate (column shift only) must be removed, remove 2 retaining screws and remove plate.

10) Remove shift tube retaining ring with screwdriver. Remove thrust washer. Remove neutral start switch or back-up lamp switch retaining screws and remove switch.

11) Rework a shift tube removing tool (J-22551) by removing 1/2" from pilot end of tool. *See Fig. 10.*

12) Remove shift tube assembly using reworked tool as follows: Insert hooked end of tool into notch in shift tube just below shift lever housing key. Pilot the sleeve over threaded end of tool and into upper end of shift tube.

13) Force shift tube out of housing by turning nut onto the tool. If shift tube is not completely free when nut is bottomed on its threads, complete removal by hand.

14) On column shift models, guide lower shift lever though slotted opening in column to prevent damage to tube or column. On all models, remove lock plate by sliding out of column notches, tipping plate downward toward housing to compress wave washer and then removing wave washer and lock plate.

15) Remove shift lever housing. On column shift models, remove the shift lever spring by winding it up with pliers. On all models, remove dash panel seal mounting plate and instrument panel seal from column jacket.

Reassembly

1) Install dash panel seal, mounting plate and instrument panel seal on column. On column shift models, press a new shift lever spring into shift lever housing. Slide shift lever housing over upper end of column.

2) Place wave washer and lock plate in position. Work lock plate into notches by tipping plate toward housing (compressing wave washer) at open side of column. Lubricate lock plate and upper end of shift tube.

3) Carefully install shift tube into lower end of column (make sure foam seal is at lower end of shift tube). Align keyway in tube with key in shift lever housing and complete installation of shift tube using installer tool (J-22549). *See Fig. 11.*

Fig. 11: Installing Shift Pin Tube

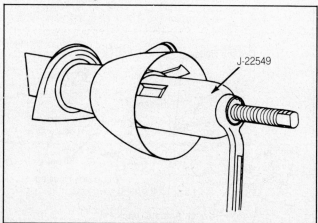

Keyway in tube must be aligned with the key in shift lever housing.

4) Shift lever housing key must bottom in shift tube slot to be fully installed. Lubricate and push foam seal in flush with column housing. Do not hammer or force tube when installing in column.

5) Pull up on shift lever housing (to compress wave washer) and install thrust washer and retaining ring. Be sure ring is seated in both slots of shift tube.

6) Lubricate inside diameter of bearing housing support and install support. Align bolt holes in support with bolt holes in lock plate. Install 4 support screws and torque to 45 INCH Lbs. (5.1 N.m)

Fig. 10: Reworked Shift Tube Removal Tube

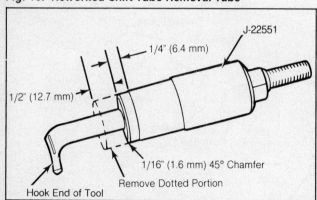

Do not hammer on shift tube during removal.

GENERAL MOTORS (Cont.)

7) Assemble steering shaft as follows: Lubricate and assemble centering spheres and preload spring. Install spheres into upper (short) shaft and rotate 90°. Install lower shaft 90° to upper shaft and over centering spheres.

8) Slowly straighten shafts while compressing preload spring. Install shaft assembly into housing from upper end. Install lower bearing and adapter, bearing reinforcement, wire clip, pot joint coupling and lower shaft.

9) Assemble bearing housing as follows: Press new upper and lower bearing races into bearing housing. Lubricate and install bearings into races. Place lock shoe springs in position in housing.

10) Install each shoe in place and compress spring until a straight punch can be used to hold shoes in position. Once shoes are in place, install retaining pin. Install shoe release lever and drive in pivot pin.

11) Install tilt release lever. Lubricate shoes and release lever. Install bearing housing assembly to support. Hold tilt release lever up until shoes have fully engaged support. Lubricate and install bearing housing pivot pins. Press pins in flush with housing.

12) Place housing in full "UP" position then install tilt spring and retainer (tapered end of spring first). Push into housing approximately 3/16" and rotate counterclockwise 1/8 turn.

13) Lubricate and install upper bearing upper race, race seat and lock nut. Tighten lock nut to remove lash and then further tighten 1/16 to 1/8 turn (column must be in straight-ahead position). Remove tilt release lever.

14) Install directional signal switch. Install shift lever and pivot pin if column shift model. Install neutral-start or back-up lamp switch.

"S" & "T" MODELS
TILT WHEEL
Disassembly

1) Remove steering wheel and remove column from vehicle. Clamp in holding device (J-23074). Pry out shaft lock plate cover with screwdriver. Depress lock plate with tool (J-23653). Remove retaining ring, shaft lock plate, cancelling cam and spring.

2) Remove screw, signal switch arm, 3 screws and wire protector. Remove signal switch. Insert key and turn lock to "RUN". Remove lock retaining screw and pull out lock cylinder. Remove 3 screws and tap out pivot pin with punch.

3) Remove spring, pivot/switch, lever, actuator and column cover. Reinstall lever and move column to full up position. Remove tilt spring retainer by pressing in on and turning retainer with screwdriver. See Fig. 6. Remove pivot pin with puller (J-21854).

4) Remove housing by pulling upward on tilt lever. Pull housing until it stops. Move housing to right to disengage rack from actuator. Remove tilt lever and all parts from top of column.

5) Remove steering column shaft from housing. Remove ignition, dimmer and backup light switches from column. Remove screws, support, retaining rings, thrust washer, lock plate and wave washer.

6) Remove gearshift bowl and shroud. At bottom of column, remove clip, retainer, bearing and spring. Remove shift tube assembly with puller (J-23072). See Fig. 8.

Reassembly

1) Reverse removal procedure to assemble column. When installing ignition switch, move slider to

Fig. 12: Exploded View of Standard Steering Column for "S" & "T" Models

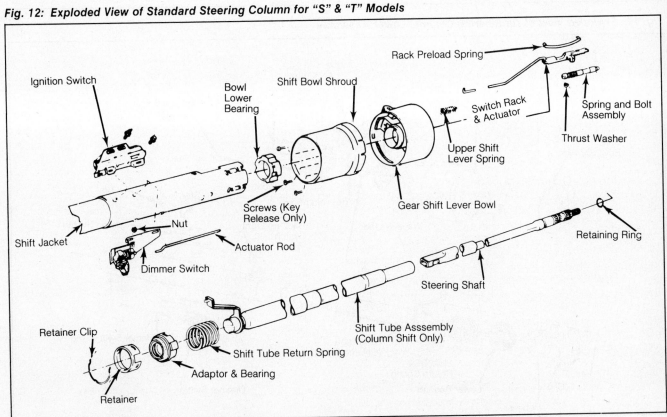

Steering Columns

GENERAL MOTORS (Cont.)

"ACC" position (non-key release) or to the "OFF LOCK" position (key release).

2) Position rod and install switch. Position dimmer switch and depress slightly to insert 3/32" (2.4 mm) drill. Force switch up and tighten screw and nut. Reassemble housing.

3) While holding up on lever to disengage lock shoes, install housing over column. Move rack downward and hold. Tip housing to left until rack engages pin on ignition switch actuator rod.

4) Push housing down until pivot pin holes are in alignment. Reverse the disassembly procedure to complete reassembly.

Fig. 13: Exploded View of Tilt Steering Column for "S" & "T" Models

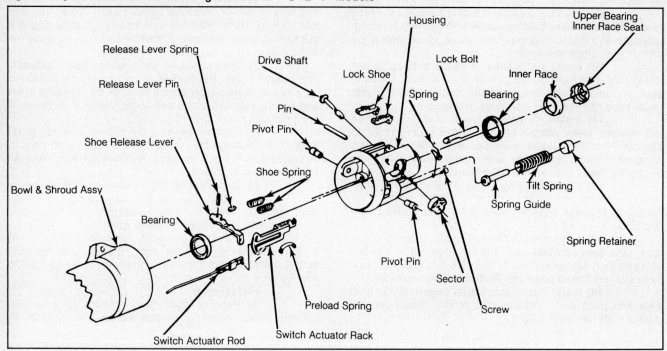

Fig. 14: Exploded View of Tilt Steering Column Lower Assembly

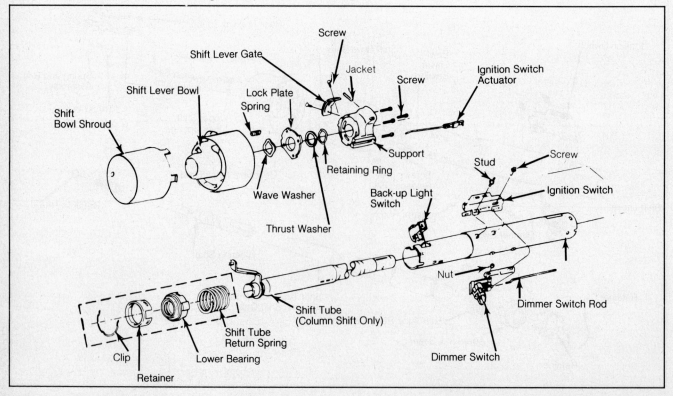

Steering Columns

GENERAL MOTORS (Cont.)

ADJUSTMENTS

LOWER BEARING ADJUSTMENT

"C" & "K" Models (Manual Transmissions)

1) Place the transmission in neutral and disconnect the linkage rods. Turn the shift lever (inside the truck) through the 2-3 shift arc. Drag measured at the shift knob must be no more than 2.0 Lbs. (.9 N).

2) If drag is more than 2.0 Lbs. (.9 N), readjust column. Loosen 3 clamping screws. Install a .005" (.127 mm) feeler gauge between the space and either of the shift levers. See Fig. 15.

Fig. 15: Adusting Lower Bearing

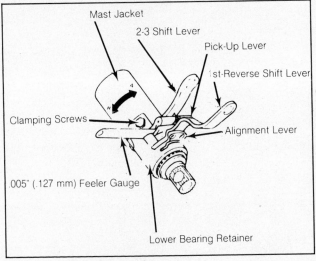

"C" & "K" models are shown.

3) Slide the clamping screws until the system is loose. Slide the screws in opposite direction until a definite drag is felt at the "1st-Reverse" shift lever. Tighten the clamping screws and remove the feeler gauge.

Fig. 16: Adjusting Steering Column Lower Bearing for "G" Models

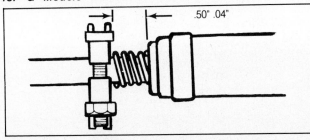

Apply 50 Lbs. (22.7 kg.) of force to steering wheel end of shaft while adjusting.

Fig. 17: Adjusting Steering Column Lower Bearing for "P" Models

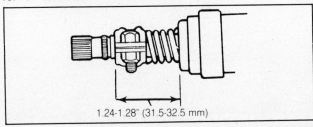

Apply 50 Lbs. (22.7 kg.) of force to steering wheel end of shaft while adjusting.

"G" & "P" Models (Manual Transmissions)

Loosen clamp on steering shaft. Apply 50 lbs. (22.7 kg.) force to steering wheel end of shaft. Adjust clamp to obtain clearance of .46"-.54" (11.7-13.7 mm) for "G" models and 1.24"-1.28" (31.5-32.5 mm) for "P" models. See Figs. 16 & 17. Tighten clamp bolts to specifications.

"S" & "T" Models

No adjustment information is available from the manufacturer.

SHIFTER TUBE ADJUSTMENT

"G" & "P" Models (Manual Transmissions)

Loosen adjusting ring attaching screws and clamp bolt. Rotate adjusting ring to give .005" (.127 mm) end play between adjusting ring and "1st-Reverse" shift lever. Tighten attaching screws and clamp bolt. See Fig. 18.

Fig. 18: Adjusting Shift Tube for Manual Transmission on "G" & "P" Models

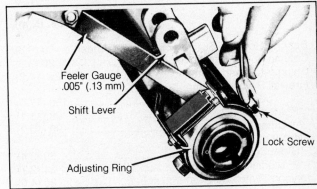

Rotate adjusting ring to give clearance.

"G" & "P" Models (Automatic Transmissions)

Place shift tube lever in "N" or "D". Loosen adjusting ring clamp screws and rotate adjusting ring to obtain .33-.36" (8.4-9.1 mm) end play between shift tube lever and adjusting ring. Tighten adjusting ring clamp screws. See Fig. 19.

Fig. 19: Adjusting Shift for Automatic Transmission on "G" & "P" Models

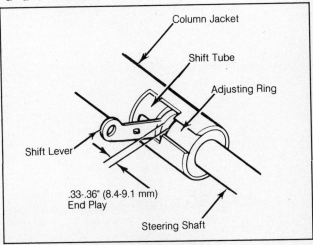

Rotate adjusting ring to give clearance.

"S" & "T" Models

No adjustment information is available from the manufacturer.

Steering Columns

GENERAL MOTORS (Cont.)

ADJUSTMENT SPECIFICATIONS

Application	INCHES (mm)
Lower Bearing Adjustment	
"G" Models	.46-.54 (12-13)
"P" Models	1.24-1.28 (31.5-32.5)
Shift Tube Adjustment	
Automatic Transmission	.33-.36 (8.4-9.1)
Manual Transmission	.005 (.13)

TIGHTENING SPECIFICATIONS

Application	Ft. Lbs. (N.m)
Flexible Coupling Bolt & Studs	
"P" Models	20 (27)
All Others	18 (24)
Lower Coupling-to-Worm Shaft Clamp	
"P" Models	75 (102)
All Others	30 (41)
Lower Jacket Bearing Clamp	30 (41)

	INCH Lbs. (N.m)
Bearing Housing Support Screw (Tilt Wheel) ..	60 (6.8)
Column Lock Plate Cover	20 (2.3)
Column-to-Dash Panel	125 (14.2)
Firewall Bracket Clamp	
"G" Models	150 (17.0)
"P" Models	98 (11.1)
All Other Models	90 (10.2)
Floor Pan Cover Plate	
"G" Models	30 (3.4)
"P" Models	24 (2.7)
Ignition Switch Screws	35 (4.0)
Lock Bolt Spring Screw (Tilt Wheel)	35 (4.0)
Lower Bearing Adjusting Ring Bolt	70 (7.9)
Turn Signal Housing	45 (5.1)

Steering Columns

JEEP

All Models

DESCRIPTION

All models use a collapsible column which is equipped with an anti-theft locking feature. All models are available with an optional Adjust-O-Tilt steering column. The Adjust-O-Tilt steering column is also equipped with the energy-absorbing and anti-theft features.

REMOVAL & INSTALLATION

CAUTION: When servicing the steering column, use ONLY specified attaching screws and bolts. Screws or bolts longer than specified could damage collapsible feature of the steering column. Attaching nuts and bolts for the column mounting bracket must be tightened to specifications to allow bracket to break away under impact.

ALL MODELS
Removal

1) Disconnect battery ground cable. If equipped with automatic transmission, disconnect transmission shift rod at steering column shift lever.

2) On Cherokee and Wagoneer with automatic transmission and power brakes, it will be necessary to shift transmission to "1" detent position to gain access to shift rod retaining clip at shift lever.

3) Remove upper steering shaft to intermediate shaft "U" joint pinch bolt. DO NOT attempt to separate upper steering shaft and intermediate shaft at this time.

4) On Cherokee and Wagoneer models with air conditioning, remove left duct extension. On all models, remove steering column to instrument panel bezel. On Cherokee, Wagoneer and truck models, bezel screws are located behind lower bezel half.

5) Remove bolts securing steering column mounting bracket to instrument panel. Remove bolts securing mounting bracket to steering column and remove bracket.

CAUTION: Store bracket in a safe place to prevent damage to breakaway capsules.

6) Remove upper and lower toe-plates. Disconnect wiring harness at ignition switch, removing black connector first.

7) If equipped with Cruise Command, disconnect electrical connector. Separate steering shaft from intermediate "U" joint and remove steering column assembly.

CAUTION: Handle steering column with care after removal. Blows on end of steering shaft or shift levers, leaning on column assembly, or dropping unit may cause damage to energy absorbing components.

Installation

1) Place steering column in vehicle. Connect upper steering shaft to intermediate shaft "U" joint. Install "U" joint pinch bolt and tighten to specification.

2) If equipped with Cruise Command, connect electrical connector. Connect ignition switch connectors, connecting White connector first. Install upper and lower toe plates. Install bolts but do not tighten.

3) Install mounting bracket on steering column. Align column with instrument panel. Install bracket to instrument panel bolts but do not tighten.

4) Pull up on column and tighten bolts to specifications. Make sure bolts are tightened while pulling up on column. Tighten toe plate bolts to specification.

5) Install both halves of instrument panel bezel. Install left air conditioning duct extension (if removed). Connect transmission shift rod to shift lever.

6) Connect battery ground cable. Check automatic transmission shift linkage operation and adjust as necessary. Check for correct operation of all electrical components.

OVERHAUL

STANDARD COLUMN (ALL MODELS)
Disassembly (Man. Trans.)

1) Remove steering column from vehicle as previously outlined. Remove mount bracket from column. Attach a holding fixture (J-23074) to mount bolt holes. Secure column in a vise by clamping on holding fixture.

2) Remove steering wheel and lock plate. See appropriate article in Steering Wheel & Column Switches.

Fig. 1: Removing Lock Plate Snap Ring

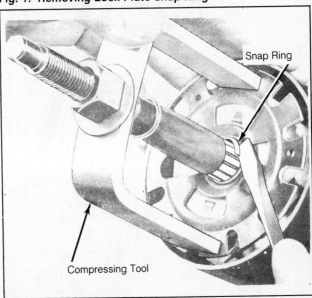

Discard old snap ring.

3) Remove compressor tool. Remove snap ring and discard. Remove lock plate, directional signal cancelling cam, upper bearing preload spring, and thrust washer from steering shaft.

CAUTION: After snap ring is removed from shaft, the steering shaft is free in column. Do not allow shaft to fall out end of column.

4) Remove hazard warning switch knob by pressing inward and unscrewing. On vehicles without Cruise Command, remove directional signal switch lever.

Steering Columns
JEEP (Cont.)

Fig. 2: Exploded View of Steering Column

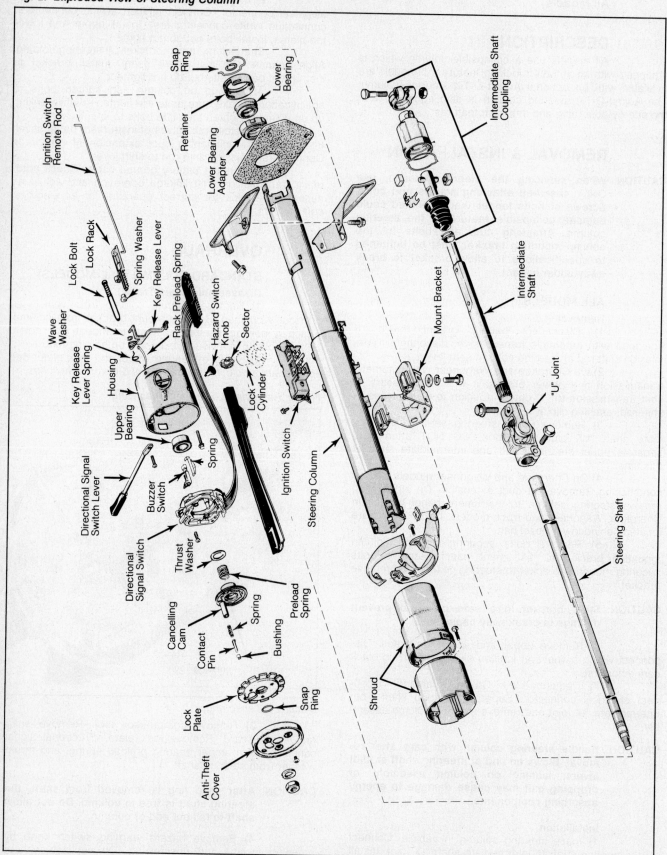

Manual transmission models with standard column is shown.

JEEP (Cont.)

5) On vehicles with Cruise Command, disconnect 2 of 4 wires at switch connector. Fold wires back along harness. Tape wires and a length of string to harness to aid removal.

6) Remove directional switch connector from bracket at lower end of column. Separate switch connector by lifting plastic lock tab on connector. Wrap tape around connector and harness to prevent snagging during removal. Remove directional signal switch screws.

7) Remove switch and harness by pulling straight up and out of column. On vehicles with Cruise Command, remove directional switch lever. Remove Cruise Command switch (in directional signal switch lever) and harness using string taped to harness.

8) Turn ignition switch 2 detent positions beyond "OFF" position. Using a thin bladed screwdriver, compress lock cylinder retaining tab and remove cylinder from column. The retaining tab is reached through slot next to directional switch mounting boss.

NOTE: **If retaining tab is not visible through slot, remove any casting flash that may be in slot.**

9) Remove ignition switch from lower end of column. Remove screws securing directional signal switch housing and shroud to column. Remove housing and shroud. Disconnect ignition swtich remote rod from lock rack.

10) Remove screws securing shroud to housing and remove shroud. Remove wave washer from key-release lever pivot. Remove key release lever and spring. Remove lock rack and bolt assembly. Remove rack preload spring. *See Fig. 3.*

Fig. 3: Removing Wave Washer

Manual transmission models with standard column is shown.

11) Using a punch, push on block tooth of sector and push sector through lock cylinder hole. Remove steering shaft. Remove lower bearing snap ring from retainer. Remove retainer, bearing and adapter.

Reassembly

1) Coat all friction surfaces with multi-purpose grease before reassembly. Position lock sector on sector shaft. Insert sector through lock cylinder hole. Use a blunt punch to push sector into place. Make sure sector turns freely after installation.

2) Install rack preload spring. Make sure bowed side of preload spring is against lock rack. Assemble lock rack and lock spring. *See Fig. 4.*

Fig. 4: Assembling Lock Bolt and Lock Rack

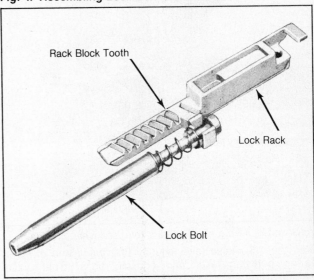

Lock bolt must be fully seated in rack.

3) Install assembled lock bolt and lock rack in housing. Make sure block tooth of lock rack is mated with block tooth of sector. *See Fig. 5.*

Fig. 5: Installing Lock Bolt and Lock Rack

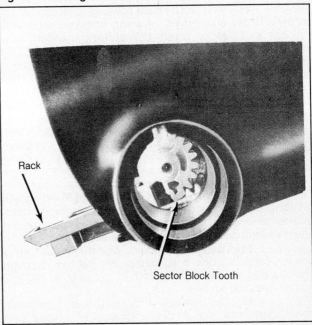

Block tooth of rack must mate with block tooth of sector.

4) Place key release lever return spring over post in housing. Place release lever finger in lock rack slot. Position hole in lever over threaded hole in housing post. Make sure inner end of spring contacts release lever. *See Fig. 6.*

Fig. 6: Installing Release Lever and Spring

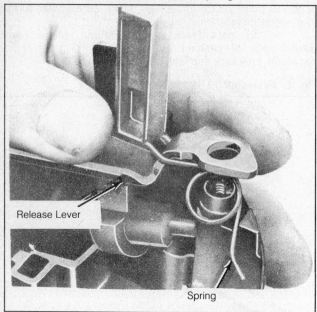

Inner end of spring must contact release lever.

5) Raise lever slightly and place end of lever spring between lever and housing boss. Coat wave washer with multi-purpose grease. Place wave washer on post over release lever.

6) Place shroud on directional signal switch housing. Install and tighten retaining screws. Make sure release lever wave washer is not dislodged when shroud is installed. Install remote rod on lock rack with short end of rod in rack.

7) Place assembled housing and shroud on column. Install and tighten retaining screws. Install lock cylinder to housing. Insert key in lock cylinder. Hold cylinder sleeve and rotate key clockwise until key stops.

8) Place lock cylinder in housing bore making sure cylinder tab is aligned with keyway in housing. Push cylinder inward until it bottoms. Rotate key counterclockwise until drive section of cylinder mates with sector. Push cylinder in fully until tab engages in housing groove.

9) Turn cylinder clockwise to stop, then counterclockwise to stop at "OFF-UNLOCK" position. Place ignition switch on jacket. Move switch to extreme left position ("ACC"). Move slider 2 positions to right ("OFF-UNLOCK"). Insert remote rod into switch slider hole.

10) Place switch on column. Install and tighten retaining screws. Install lower bearing, bearing adapter, retainer and snap ring in lower end of column. Insert steering shaft in column through lower end.

11) Bend directional signal switch wires against connector. Feed connector and harness through housing and shroud. Align switch in housing. Install and tighten retaining screws.

12) On vehicles without Cruise Command, install directional signal switch lever. On vechles with Cruise Command, install lever and switch assembly. Use string taped to harness during disassembly to help feed wires into housing.

13) Remove string and tape. Connect wires to switch terminal and install lever. Install thrust washer, upper bearing preload spring, and cancelling cam on steering shaft.

14) Position cancelling cam as shown in *Fig. 7*. Place directional signal switch in neutral position and install hazard warning switch knob.

Fig. 7: Installing Directional Signal Switch Cancelling Cam

Cancelling Cam

Cam must be positioned as shown for proper operation of turn signal switch.

15) Position lock plate on steering shaft. Place new snap ring on sleeve of compressor tool (J-23653 for American threads, J-23653-4 for metric threads). Thread tool sleeve onto end of steering shaft. Compress lock plate and install snap ring in steering shaft groove.

16) Install anti-theft cover. Remove support tool from steering column. Install mounting bracket and torque bolts to specification. Connect directional signal switch wire connector to column bracket Install steering wheel. Install column in vehicle.

Disassembly (Auto. Trans.)

1) Remove steering column from vehicle as previously outlined. Remove mounting bracket from column. Attach a holding fixture (J-23074) to mount bolt holes. Secure column in a vise by clamping holding fixture.

2) Remove steering wheel. Pry anti-theft cover off lock plate. Compress lock plate using compressor tool (J-23653 for American threaded steering shaft nut, J-23653-4 for metric nut). Remove snap ring from steering shaft.

3) Remove compressor tool. Remove snap ring and discard. Remove lock plate, directional signal cancelling cam, upper bearing preload spring, and thrust washer from steering shaft.

CAUTION: After snap ring is removed from steering shaft, shaft is free in column. Do not allow shaft to fall out end of column.

Steering Columns
JEEP (Cont.)

Fig. 8: *Exploded View of Steering Column*

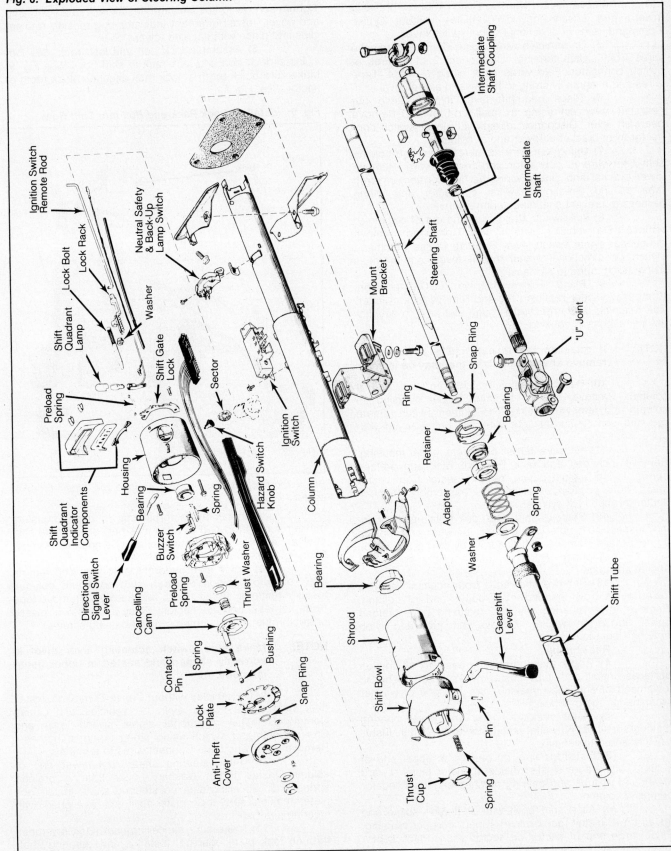

Automatic transmission models with standard column is shown.

JEEP (Cont.)

4) Remove steering shaft from lower end of column. Remove hazard warning switch knob by pressing inward and unscrewing. On vehicles without Cruise Command, remove directional signal switch lever.

5) On vehicles with Cruise Command remove wires from switch terminal. Disconnect 2 of 4 wires at switch connector. Fold wires back along harness. Tape wires and a length of string to harness to aid removal.

6) Place gearshift lever in "P". Drive out gearshift lever pin using a small drift punch. Remove gearshift lever. Disconnect directional signal switch connector from bracket at lower end of column.

7) Using stiff wire, compress lock tab holding shift light wire in connector and remove wire. Remove lower bracket and plastic wiring harness protector. Wrap tape around directional switch connector and wiring harness to prevent snagging during removal.

8) Pull switch straight up and out of column to remove. On vehicles with Cruise Command, remove directional signal switch lever. Remove Cruise Command switch (in directional signal switch lever) and harness using string taped to harness.

9) Place lock cylinder in "LOCK" position. Compess cylinder retaining tab and remove lock cylinder. The retaining tab is reached through slot next to directional signal boss in housing.

NOTE: If retaining tab is not visible through slot, remove any casting flash that may be in slot.

10) Remove ignition switch from lower end of column. Remove screws securing upper housing to column and remove housing. The ignition switch remote rod and shift quadrant light wire will be removed with upper housing.

11) Remove thrust cup from upper housing. Remove lock bolt and rack. Remove rack and preload spring. Using a blunt punch, remove sector from sector shaft. Note position of sector for reassembly. Remove sector through lock cylinder hole.

12) Remove shift gate lock from upper housing. Inspect shift gate lock detents for wear and replace as necessary. Remove shift quadrant by prying out 2 clips with a small punch. Remove quadrant light cover and socket assembly.

13) Remove shift bowl from column. Remove lower nylon bowl bearing from upper end of column. Remove lower bearing retainer, retaining ring, preload spring and nylon washer. Remove shift tube and nylon bearing from tube.

Reassembly

1) Apply multi-purpose grease to all friction surfaces. Install shift tube. Install nylon thrust washer in lower end of shift tube, making sure flat side of washer faces upper end of tube.

2) Install preload spring and lower bearing making sure bearing metal face is toward retainer. Install retainer and retainer clip.

3) Install lower nylon bearing in upper end of column. Make sure smaller inside diameter faces toward lower end of tube and bearing notches engage 3 locator crimps in column.

4) Align shift bowl with shift tube spline and install bowl. Install rack preload spring in upper housing. Place large end of sector on sector shaft. Place sector into place using a blunt punch.

5) Install shift gate lock and retaining screws. Tighten screws to specification. Install shift quadrant lamp and cover. Install quadrant indicator by pressing retainer clips into place with flat side toward bowl.

6) Assemble lock bolt and lock rack. *See Fig. 4.* Install lock bolt and lock rack in shift bowl. *See Fig. 9.* Make sure block tooth of lock rack engages block tooth of sector. *See Fig. 5.*

Fig. 9: Installing Lock Rack and Bolt into Shift Bowl

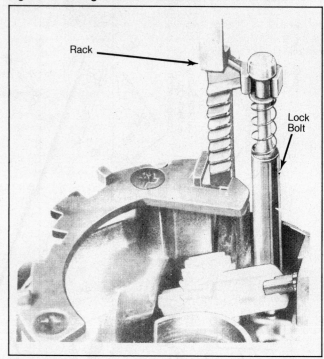

Rack

Lock Bolt

Block tooth of lock rack must engage the block tooth of sector.

7) Install nylon thrust cup in upper housing, making sure flared end of cup faces outward. Rotate shift bowl as far as possible counterclockwise and install upper housing. Tighten screws to specification.

8) Guide shift quadrant lamp wire and remote lock rod into position between shift bowl and column. Install directional signal switch and harness. Remove tape from harness and connector. Place harness in plastic protector. Install and tighten switch retaining screws.

NOTE: Make sure switch actuating lever pivot is correctly aligned and seated in upper housing boss.

9) On vehicles without Cruise Command, install directional signal switch lever. On vehicles with Cruise Command, install directional signal switch lever and Cruise Command switch using string taped to harness. Remove string and tape. Connect wires to terminals.

10) Intall steering shaft from lower end of column. Install thrust washer, upper bearing preload spring and cancelling cam on steering shaft. Install lock plate, making sure lock plate splines are aligned with steering shaft splines.

11) Make sure cancelling cam shaft protrudes through lock plate opening. Install a new steering shaft snap ring on lock plate compressor tool (J-23653 for

JEEP (Cont.)

American threaded steering shaft nut, J-23653-4 for metric threaded nut). Compress lock plate with tool.

12) Install snap ring in groove in steering shaft. Remove compressor tool. Install anti-theft cover. Install steering wheel. Install gearshift lever. Install lock cylinder in housing. Install ignition switch on column.

13) Place shift bowl in any position but "P". Rotate bowl until lock rack bottoms against lower surface of bowl. Move ignition switch slider to left toward "ACC" position.

14) Move slide two positions to right toward "OFF-UNLOCK" position. Insert remote rod into slider hole. Attach ignition switch to steering column. Move switch out of "OFF-UNLOCK" position. Install column in vehicle as previously outlined.

TILT WHEEL
(CHEROKEE, TRUCK & WAGONEER)
Disassembly

1) Remove steering column from vehicle as previously outlined. Remove mount bracket from column. Attach a holding fixture (J-23074) to mount bolt holes. Secure column in a vise by clamping on holding fixture.

2) Remove steering wheel. Remove lock plate. *See appropriate article in Steering Wheel & Column Switches.* Remove snap ring from groove in steering shaft and discard. *See Fig. 15.*

3) Remove directional signal cancelling cam, upper bearing prelaod spring thrust washer, spring seat and bearing race from steering shaft. Remove gearshift lever retaining pin and remove gearshift lever.

4) On vehicles without Cruise Command, remove directional signal switch lever. On vehicles with Cruise Command, remove wires from Cruise Command switch terminal. Fold 2 of 4 wires back and tape along harness. Tape a length of string to harness to aid removal.

5) Remove hazard warning switch knob by pressing in and turning counterclockwise. Disconnect directional signal switch connector at bracket on lower steering column. Remove wiring harness plastic connector from column jacket.

6) Wrap tape around directional signal switch connector to prevent snagging when removing. Remove directional signal switch retaining screws. Pull switch and harness straight up and out of column.

7) On vehicles with Cruise Command, remove directional switch lever. Remove Cruise Command switch (in directional signal switch lever) and harness using string taped to harness.

8) Insert igniton key in lock cylinder. Turn key to "LOCK" position. Compress cylinder retaining tab and remove lock cylinder. The retaining tab is reached through slot next to directional signal switch boss in housing.

NOTE: **If retaining tab is not visible through slot, remove any casting flash that may be in slot.**

9) Remove shift quadrant by prying 2 spring clips out of column. remove mounting bracket and light socket. Remove tilt release handle. Remove cover retaining screws and remove cover.

10) Remove lock sector tension spring screw. Unlock sector spring from sector shaft. Remove snap ring from sector shaft. Remove sector, shaft and retaining ring. Install tilt release handle. Place column in full upward tilt position.

11) Insert a screwdriver in tilt release spring retainer slot and compress retainer approximately 3/16". Rotate retainer 1/8 turn and remove retainer and spring.

CAUTION: **Tilt spring is under strong tension.**

12) Place housing in center position. Using puller (J-21854-1) remove tilt pivot pins. *See Fig. 10.* Lift tilt release lever to disengage lock shoes and remove housing. Remove both ball bearing assemblies from housing if bearings are to be replaced.

Fig. 10: Removing Tilt Pivot Pins

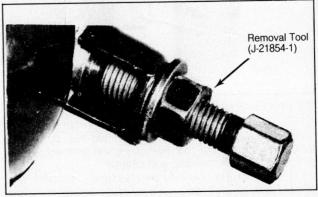

Removal Tool (J-21854-1)

Housing must be in the center (nontilt) position.

13) Remove tilt release lever. Using a punch, drive out release lever pin. Compress lock shoe spring to release spring tension on pin. *See Fig. 1.*

Fig. 11: Removing Release Lever Pin

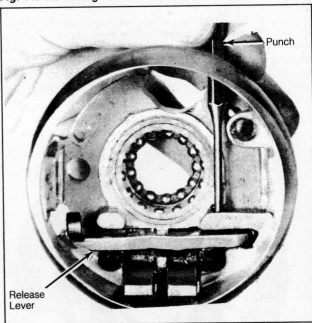

Punch

Release Lever

Compress lock shoe spring to release the spring tension on the pin.

14) Remove lock shoe pin from housing using pin punch. Remove lock shoes and lock shoe springs. Disconnect steering shaft at intermediate coupling. Remove shaft through upper end of column. *See Fig. 12.*

Fig. 12: Removing Lock Shoe Pin

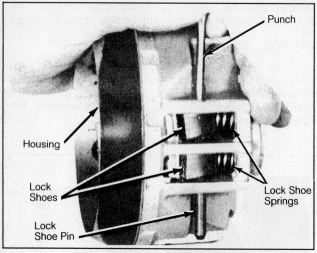

Compress lock springs to relieve tension on the pin.

15) Fold shaft at 90° and separate upper and lower halves at flex joint. Remove ignition switch. Remove lock rack and remote rod. Remove lower bearing retainer snap ring, retainer, bearing and adapter.

16) Remove screws securing support shift bowl. Remove shift gate screws and remove shift gate from support. Remove support and shift tube retaining ring and thrust washer. Using a puller (J-23072), pull shift tube from column.

17) Rotate shift bowl clockwise while sliding retainer plate out of jacket notches. Tip plate down toward shift bowl hub at 12 o'clock position and remove plate, bottom side first.

18) Remove wave washer and shift tube spring. Remove shift bowl from column jacket. Remove lower bearing retainer spring clip. Remove retainer, lower bearing and bearing adapter.

Reassembly

1) Coat all friction surfaces with multi-purpose grease before reassembly. Mount shift bowl on column.

Fig. 13: Positioning Shift Tube Installer Tools

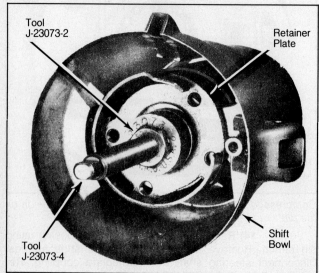

Spring loaded lower foot of tool must be engaged with shift tube inner shoulder.

Place shift tube spring, wave washer, and retainer plate in shift bowl.

2) Install shift tube through lower end of column. Make sure tube spline is aligned with shift bowl keyway. Place shift tube installer tools (J-23073-2 and J-23073-4) in shift tube.

3) Make sure spring loaded lower foot of tool is engaged with shift tube inner shoulder and tool guide is seated in shift tube. *See Fig. 13.*

4) Tighten tool spring tension nut until snug. Place installer tools (J-23073-3 and J-23073-4) over puller stud. Tighten tool nut (J-23073-2) and pull tube into place in shift bowl. Remove shift tube installer tools. *See. Fig. 14.*

Fig. 14: Pulling Shift Tube into Shift Bowl

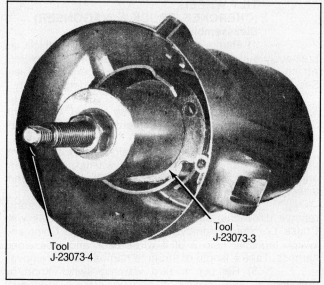

Shift tube retainer plate must be installed before pulling shift tube into bowl.

5) Install shift tube thrust washer and retainer plate snap ring. Install lower bearing adapter, making sure notched end of adapter faces lower end of column. Install lower bearing in column. Make sure metal face of bearing faces lower end of column.

6) Install lower bearing retainer and retainer spring clip. Install shift gate in support and install attaching screws. Install support in shift bowl. Make sure "V" notch in support is aligned with notch in column. Install support to shift bowl screws.

7) Assemble upper and lower steering shaft at flexible joint. Install steering shaft through upper end of column. Install ball bearings in housing if removed. Make sure there are 14 balls in each bearing.

8) Install tilt release handle. Insert ignition switch remote rod between shift bowl and column jacket, and into guide channel in left side of support. Engage lock rack in remote rod.

9) Guide housing over steering shaft and lock rack, making sure lock shoes align with teeth in support. Align housing and support pivot pin holes and drive in pivot pins using a soft faced mallet.

10) Install lock shoe spring, tilt bumpers and lock pin in housing. Install sector shaft in housing and lock sector in on shaft. Large block tooth of sector must engage large slot in rack.

JEEP (Cont.)

Fig. 15: *Exploded View of Tilt Wheel Steering Column (All EXcept "CJ" & Scrambler Models)*

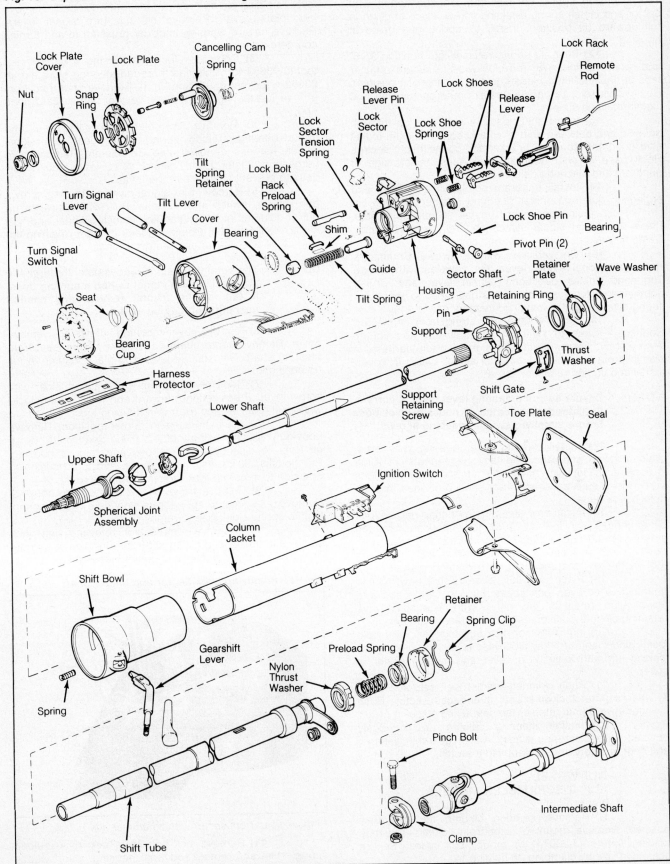

11) Install sector shaft snap ring. Hook lock sector tension spring on lock bolt. Engage spring with sector and install spring retaining screw. Place housing in full upward tilt position. Install tilt spring and guide in housing.

12) Push tilt spring retainer into housing 3/16" and rotate retainer 1/8 turn clockwise to secure retainer tabs in housing lugs. Place housing in center tilt position. Remove tilt release handle. Install cover on housing and install retaining screws.

13) Insert shift quadrant light wire up through housing and between shift bowl and column jacket. Install shift quadrant mounting bracket and connect light socket. Hook base of shift quadrant over tabs on left side of quadrant and place in position.

14) Install quadrant pointer in shift bowl and engage in quadrant. Install quadrant retainer clip with flat side of clip facing downward. Install tilt release handle. Place directional signal switch and harness in column. Guide harness between cover and column.

15) On vehicles without Cruise Command, install directional signal lever. On vehicles with Cruise Command, install directional signal lever and Cruise Command switch assembly. Use string taped to connector during disassembly to install connector.

16) Remove tape and string from connector. Connect 4 wires to switch terminal. Install and tighten lever screw. Place directional signal switch harness in plastic protector. Align directional signal switch in cover. Install and tighten retaining screws.

NOTE: **Ensure switch actuating lever pivot is correctly aligned and seated in housing pivot boss before installing switch attaching screws.**

17) Install bearing race, bearing race seat, preload spring, and cancelling cam on steering shaft. Align lock plate splines with steering shaft splines. Install lock plate. Make sure cancelling cam shaft protrudes through hole in lock plate.

18) Install new steering shaft snap ring on lock plate compressor tool (J-23653 for American threaded steering shaft nut, J-23653-4 for metric threaded nut). Position tool on steering shaft. Compress lock plate with tool. Install new snap ring in groove in steering shaft.

19) Place gearshift lever in shift bowl. Guide gearshift lever over lock sector tension spring and into bowl. Align retaining pin holes with a punch. Drive retaining pin into position using a soft faced hammer.

20) Insert ignition key into lock cylinder. Hold lock cylinder and turn key clockwise to stop. Align cylinder locking lug with keyway in cover and insert cylinder in cover.

21) Push cylinder against lock sector. Rotate cylinder counterclockwise until it engages sector. Push cylinder inward until retainer tab snaps into place.

22) Install steering column as previously outlined. Install steering wheel. Adjust gearshift linkage, and neutral safety and back-up lamp switch.

TILT WHEEL
"CJ" & SCRAMBLER MODELS
Disassembly
1) Remove steering column as previously outlined. Remove mount bracket from column. Attach a holding fixture (J-23074) to mount bolt holes. Secure column in vise by clamping on holding fixture.

2) Remove steering wheel. Remove gearshift lever retaining pin and remove lever (if equipped). Remove lock plate cover. Remove tilt and turn signal levers. Remove hazard warning knob by pressing in and turning counterclockwise.

3) Compress lock plate using a compressor tool (J-23653 for American threaded steering shaft nut, J-23653-4 for metric threaded nut). Remove snap ring from groove in steering shaft. Remove tool and discard snap ring.

4) Remove lock plate, cancelling cam and upper bearing preload spring. Disconnect turn signal switch harness at lower end of column. Remove wire harness protector from column. Wrap tape around harness to prevent snagging on removal.

5) Remove turn signal switch attaching screws and remove switch and harness. Pull switch straight up out of column. Insert ignition key in lock cylinder and turn key to "ON" position. Compress lock cylinder retaining tab with small screwdriver and remove cylinder.

NOTE: **The retaining tab is accessible through the slot next to turn signal switch mounting boss. If tab is not visible, remove any casting flashing that may be in slot.**

6) Remove cover retaining screws and remove cover. Remove upper bearing race and bearing seat from steering shaft. Reinstall tilt lever and place column in full up position.

7) Remove tilt spring, guide and retainer with screwdriver. Press retainer inward and turn counterclockwise until retainer tabs align with housing lugs.

8) Place housing in center position. Remove housing pivot pins using tool J-21854-1 See Fig. 10. Raise tilt lever to disengage lock shoes and remove housing. Pull housing up to disengage shoes, and turn housing to one side to separate lock rack from remote rod.

9) Remove tilt lever and shield from housing. Remove lock sector spring retaining screw and spring. Rotate spring clockwise to remove.

10) Remove lock sector retaining ring, lock sector and sector shaft. Tap shaft through sector and out of housing with a hammer and punch. See Fig. 16.

Fig. 16: Removing Lock Sector and Sector Shaft

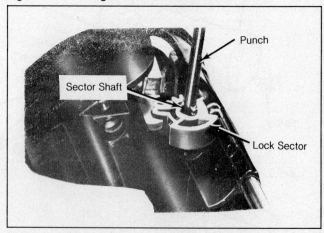

Remove shaft from sector with a hammer and punch.

11) Remove lock bolt, lock rack, rack preload spring, shim and remote rod from housing. Insert wedge

Steering Columns

JEEP (Cont.)

between lock shoes and housing to relieve spring tension on tilt and lock shoe pins.

12) Remove tilt lever pin from housing with pin punch. Remove lock shoe pin from housing with pin punch, and remove lock shoes, springs and wedge.

13) Remove upper and lower housing bearings and races, if damaged or worn. If removed, discard and replace with new races and bearings. Disconnect steering shaft at coupling.

14) Remove steering shaft though upper end of column. Remove support attaching bolt and remove support. Remove retainer plate. Tip upper end of plate rearward and turn plate counterclockwise to remove.

15) Remove shroud using twisting-pulling motion. Remove key release lever and lever spring from shroud. Tip lever forward and lift up to remove.

16) Disconnect ignition switch wire harness connector and remove switch. Remove snap ring, retainer and bearing assembly from lower end of column.

Reassembly

1) Coat all friction surfaces with multipurpose grease before reassembly. Install bearing assembly, bearing retainer and snap ring in lower end of column.

2) Install key release lever spring on lever and install assembled lever and spring in shroud. Align and install shroud on column jacket.

3) Install retainer plate by tipping plate to 12 o'clock position and sliding it under jacket opening. Align column jacket "V" notch with "V" on support and install support in column. Press key release lever down while pressing support into place.

4) Install support attaching screws finger tight then tighten alternately to specifications. Install remote rod in support by guiding rod through upper end of shroud and into rod slot in support.

5) Install steering shaft in column. Install bearings (if removed). Install lock shoe, springs and lock shoe pin in housing. Use .18" (4.6mm) diameter rod to align lock shoes and pin.

6) Install release lever, lever spring and lever pin in housing. Insert wedges between housing and lever to relieve spring tension. Install sector shaft in housing. Lightly tap shaft into housing using punch.

7) Install lock sector on shaft. Lightly tap sector onto shaft until shaft snap ring groove is exposed. Install sector snap ring. Install lock bolt in housing and engage bolt in lock sector cam surface.

8) Install lock rack, rack preload spring and shim in housing. Square block tooth of rack must engage square block tooth of sector. Install lock spring and retaining screw.

Fig. 17: Exploded View of Tilt Wheel Steering Column ("CJ" & Scrambler Models)

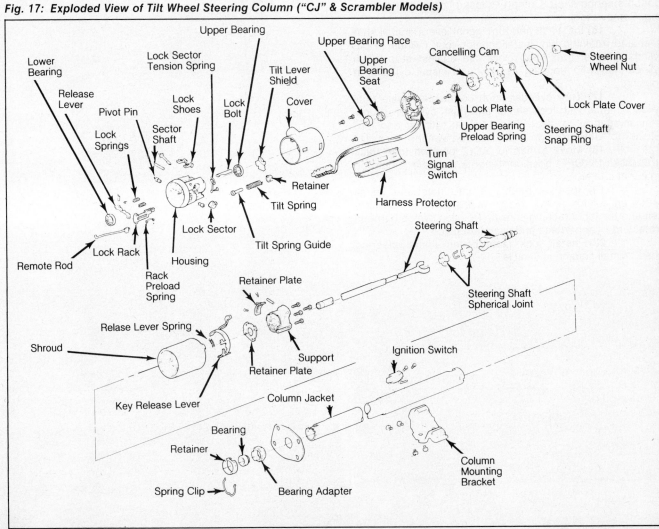

9) Align and install assembled housing on support. Hold lock shoes in disengaged position to ease housing installation. Align pivot pin holes in housing and support and install pivot pins.

10) When started in holes, seal pins fully using a hammer and punch. Press housing downward when first installing pins to avoid damage to pin holes.

11) Insert tilt lever in housing and place housing in full upward tilt position. Lubricate tilt guide and spring and install tilt spring on guide. Insert assembled tilt spring and guide in housing and install guide retainer on spring.

12) Install tilt lever shield. Remove tilt lever. Install cover on housing. Install turn signal switch. Guide switch harness and connector through column and into housing. Do not install switch attaching screws at this time.

13) Install hazard warning switch knob in turn signal switch and align and install switch attaching screws. Make sure turn signal switch is properly aligned before tightening screws. Pull out on hazard warning knob.

14) Install upper bearing race and seat in housing. Install upper bearing preload spring, cancelling cam and lock plate.

15) Install new steering shaft snap ring on compressor tool (J-23653 for American threaded steering shaft nut, J-23653-4 for metric threaded nut) and install tool on steering shaft. Compress lock plate and seat snap ring. Remove tool.

16) Install tilt and turn signal levers. Install shift lever and retaining pin. Install ignition lock cylinder. Hold cylinder sleeve, turn knob clockwise against stop, align cylinder tab with housing keyway and install cylinder in housing.

17) Turn cylinder knob counterclockwise until cylinder mates with lock sector and push cylinder in until retainer snaps into place. Insert key in cylinder and turn cylinder to "OFF" position. Install ignition switch.

18) Move switch to "ACC" position then back off 2 clicks to "OFF" position. Remote rod hole should be almost at center.

19) Insert remote rod into hole and install switch on column jacket. Move switch down to eliminate lash and tighten attaching screws. Position switch harness protectors over harness and snap into place.

20) Install lock plate cover. Install steering wheel. Install column in vehicle.

TIGHTENING SPECIFICATIONS

Application	Ft. Lbs. (N.m)
Column Mounting Bracket Bolt	20 (27)
Intermediate Shaft Pinch Bolt	45 (61)
Mounting Bracket-to-Instrument Panel Bolts	20 (27)
Steering Wheel Nut	30 (41)
Toe Plate Bolts	10 (14)

	INCH Lbs. (N.m)
Housing Screws	
Standard	60 (7)
Tilt	100 (11)
Ignition Switch Mounting Screws	35 (4)
Lock Sector Tension Spring Screw	35 (4)
Shroud Screws (Man. Trans.)	18 (2)
Support Screws (Tilt Column)	60 (7)
Tilt Lever Screw	35 (4)
Turn Signal Lever Screw	15 (2)
Turn Signal Switch Screws	35 (4)

CHRYSLER CORP.

SERVICE PROCECURES

2WD MODELS

Tie Rod Replacement

1) Raise vehicle on hoist and remove cotter key and nut from tie rod end. Install puller (C-3894-A) and remove tie rod end from center link. Loosen sleeve clamping bolt and unscrew tie rod end.

NOTE: **Removal of tie rod ends from steering arm or center link by methods other than using tie rod end puller (C-3894-A) will damage tie rod end seal.**

2) Screw new tie rod end onto sleeve. Connect rod end to knuckle arm or center link and torque to specifications. Install cotter key. Lower vehicle and adjust toe-in.

3) Position clamp on sleeve so that bolt is on the bottom. Clamp opening should be in line with slot in sleeve.

Fig. 1: Disassembled View of Steering Linkage

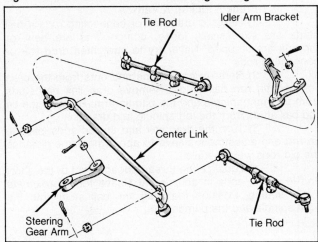

Pickup and Ramcharger models are shown.

Fig. 2: Disassembled View of Steering Linkage

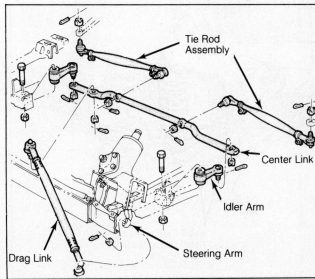

Vans and Wagon models are shown.

Ball Joints

Tension type lower ball joints are used on all models. Ball joints and tie rod ends are of the semi-lubricated type except on vehicles for off-highway use. Ball joints should be replaced if axial end play exceeds .020" (.5 mm).

4WD MODELS

Tie Rod Replacement

Tie rod replacement procedure on 4WD models is the same as 2WD models.

Drag Link

Drag link must be installed to steering knuckle arm with short half ("A") attaching to knuckle arm. *See Fig. 3.*

Fig. 3: Installing Drag Link on 4WD Models

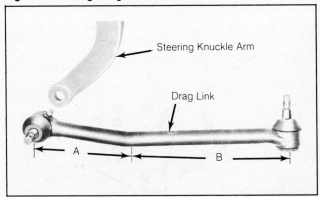

Distance "A" is measured from the bend in the drag link.

Ball Joints

Servicing ball joints used on steering knuckles requires dismantling of knuckles. *See Steering Knuckles in Suspension Section.* Any end play or looseness in ball joints on 4WD models requires replacement of ball joints.

TIGHTENING SPECIFICATIONS

Application	Ft. Lbs. (N.m)
Tie Rod Clamping Bolts	
Pickup & Van	[1] 13 (18)
Tie Rod End Nuts	
2WD Pickup	40 (54)
4WD Pickup	60 (82)
Van	
9/16" Nut	55 (75)
5/8" Nut	75 (102)

[1] - Heavy Duty models 26 Ft. Lb. (35 N.m) torque.

Steering Linkage
FORD

SERVICE PROCEDURES

DRAG LINK REPLACEMENT
Bronco II & Ranger

1) Raise and support vehicle with the wheels in a straight ahead position. Remove cotter pins and nuts from the ball stud at the Pitman arm and steering connecting rod.

2) Disconnect ball stud from linkage using puller (3290-C). Loosen tie rod adjusting sleeve bolts. Count the number of turns it takes to remove the drag link. To complete assembly, reverse removal procedure. Check and adjust toe-in.

Fig. 1: Disassembled View of Steering Linkage

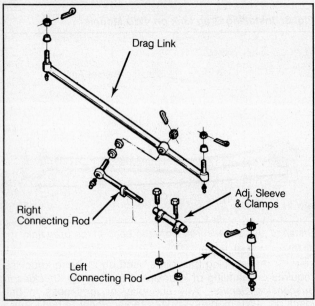

Van model is shown.

PITMAN ARM REPLACEMENT
Bronco, Pickup & Van

1) Replace pitman arm if arm is bent. Remove cotter pin and nut from drag link ball stud. Remove drag link ball stud from pitman arm. Remove pitman arm attaching nut and washer.

2) Remove pitman arm from steering gear sector shaft using tool (T64P-3590-F). Install new pitman arm on sector shaft with wheels in straight ahead position.

3) Install pitman arm nut and washer. Install drag link ball stud on pitman arm, and install cotter pin.

Bronco II & Ranger

1) Remove the cotter pin and nut fron the drag link ball stud at the Pitman arm. Remove the drag link ball stud from the Pitman arm using puller (3290-C). Remove the Pitman arm attaching nut and washer.

2) Remove the Pitman arm from the steering gear using puller (T64P-3590-F). Install new Pitman arm. Reverse removal procedure, ensuring Pitman arm and drag link nut are torqued to specifications.

TIE ROD & LINK REPLACEMENT
Bronco, Pickup & Van

1) Replace drag link or connecting rods if ball studs are excessively loose, components are bent or threads are stripped. Never try to straighten drag link or connecting rods.

2) Remove cotter pins and nuts from the drag link and tie rod ball studs. Remove drag link ball studs from the right spindle and the pitman arm. Remove the tie rod ball studs from the left spindle and drag link.

3) Turn the drag link and tie rod ends into the tie rod end adjustment sleeve to about the same distance the old rods were installed.

4) Equalize the thread engagement of the short and long rod ends in adjustment sleeve for approximate toe-in setting. Position the drag link ball studs into the right spindle and the pitman arm.

Fig. 2: Steering Linkage & Tie Rod Clamp Positioning

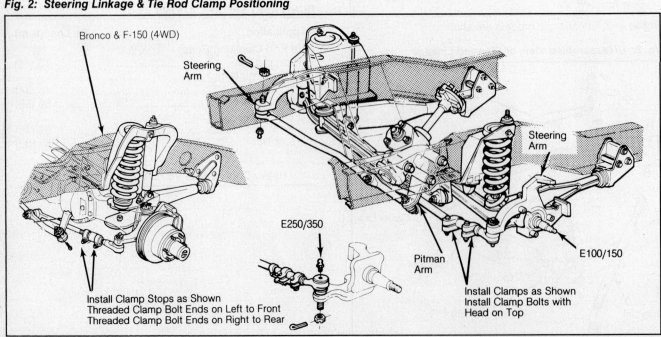

Bronce, F150 4-WD & Van models are shown, Pickup is similar.

FORD (Cont.)

5) Position the tie-rod ball studs into the left hand spindle and the drag link. Install all ball stud nuts and tighten. Install new cotter pins and check toe-in. Center adjustment sleeve clamps between locating nibs and tighten.

TIE ROD END REPLACEMENT
Bronco II & Ranger

1) Raise and support vehicle with the wheels in the straight ahead position. Remove the cotter key and nut from the tie rod ball stud. Loosen the bolts on the tie rod adjusting sleeve.

2) Remove the tie rod ball stud from the spindle using puller (3290-C). Count the number of turns it takes to remove the sleeve from the ball stud.

3) Install the new tie rod end in the adjusting sleeve the same number of turns. Reverse removal procedure to complete assembly. Adjusting sleeves must be in the correct position. *See Fig. 3.* Check and adjust toe-in.

TIGHTENING SPECIFICATIONS

Application	Ft. Lbs. (N.m)
Drag Link Ball Stud Nuts	50-75 (68-101)
Pitman Arm-to-Steering Gear Nut	170-230 (230-310)
Rod Clamps	30-42 (41-57)
Steering Gear-to-Frame	70 (95)
Tie Rod Adjusting Sleeve Nuts	29-41 (40-57)
Tie Rod Ball Stud Nuts	50-75 (68-101)
Steering Connecting Rod Nut	50-75 (68-101)

Fig. 3: Bronco II & Ranger Steering System

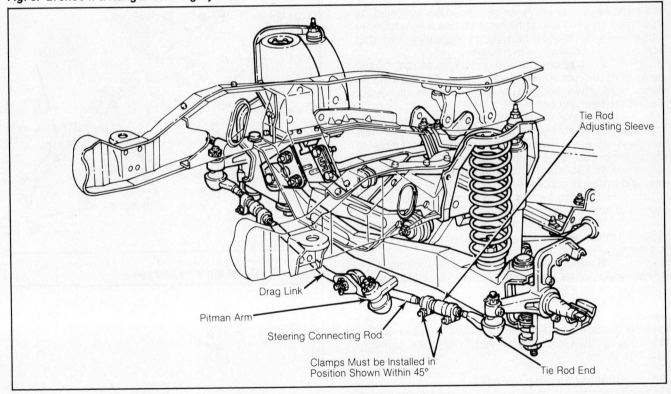

Tie Rod Adjusting Sleeve

Drag Link

Pitman Arm

Steering Connecting Rod

Clamps Must be Installed in Position Shown Within 45°

Tie Rod End

Steering Linkage

GENERAL MOTORS

STEERING SERVICE PRECAUTIONS

All steering component fasteners are made of special quality materials. Replacement fasteners must be of same part number or equivalent. Torque all fasteners to specification and install new cotter pins. When installing cotter pins, do not back off castellated nuts to align cotter pin hole, tighten nut to next slot that lines up with hole.

Do not hammer on ball studs or damage to threads may result. If threads are not clean and smooth, ball studs may turn in joint when nuts are tightened. Sleeve clamps must always be positioned as specified before tightening bolts.

SERVICE PROCEDURES

Tie Rod Replacement

1) Raise vehicle and remove tie rod fasteners. Use removal tool (J-6627), or remove outer ball stud by tapping on steering arm at tie rod end. Use a light hammer with a heavy hammer as backing. Remove inner ball stud from relay rod using same procedure.

2) To remove tie rod ends from tie rod, loosen clamp bolts and unscrew end assemblies. Tie rod adjuster clamp bolts often become rusted in service. If rusted, discard the nuts and bolts.

3) Apply penetrating oil between clamps and tube. Rotate clamps until they move freely. Use new fasteners of same part number during reassembly to assure proper clamping at specified torque.

4) Lubricate tie rod threads with EP chassis lube and install tie rod ends. Ensure both are threaded an equal distance from tie rod. Check that threads on ball studs and nuts are clean and smooth.

5) Check condition of ball stud seals and replace if necessary using tool (J-24434). Install ball studs in steering arms and relay rod.

6) Install ball stud nuts and new cotter pins. Adjust toe-in. See *Wheel Alignment Specifications & Procedures in WHEEL ALIGNMENT Section.*

7) Before tightening tie rod adjusting sleeve clamp bolt, note the following: Clamps must be between locating dimples at either end of sleeve. Adjuster sleeve slot must not be within open area of clamp jaw opening. *See Figs. 6 and 7.*

8) Rotate both inner and outer tie rod housing rearward to limit of ball joint travel before tightening clamps. After tightening clamps, return tie rod assembly to center of travel.

9) Check each tie rod for a rotation of at least 35° using a bubble protractor and a pair of vise grips. Lubricate inner and outer tie rod ends.

Fig. 2: "G" Model Steering Linkage

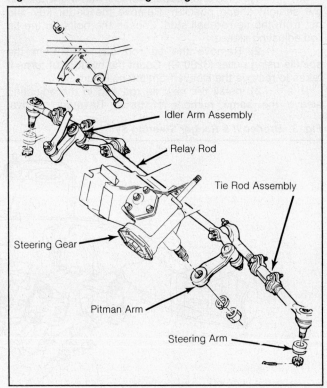

Fig. 3: "P" Model Steering Linkage

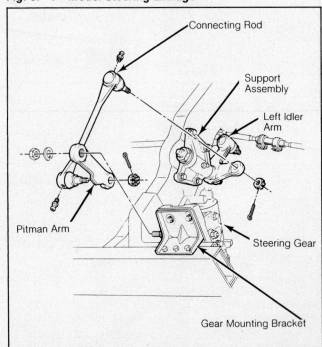

Fig. 1: "C" Model Steering Linkage

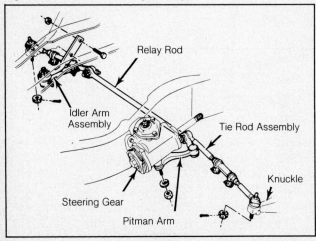

GENERAL MOTORS (Cont.)

Fig. 4: "K" Model Steering Linkage

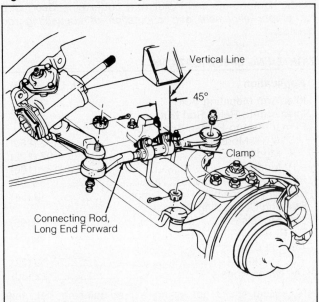

Vertical Line

45°

Clamp

Connecting Rod, Long End Forward

Fig. 5: "S" Model Steering Linkage

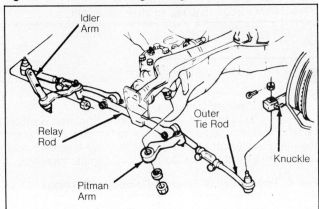

Idler Arm

Outer Tie Rod

Relay Rod

Knuckle

Pitman Arm

Relay Rod Replacement

1) Raise vehicle on hoist. Remove inner ends of tie rods from relay rod. Remove nuts from pitman arm and idler arm ball studs at relay rod. Remove relay rod from pitman and idler arms by tapping on relay rod ball stud bosses.

2) Use a light hammer with heavy hammer as a backing. Remove relay rod. To install, reverse removal procedure. Check ball studs and nuts for clean and smooth threads. Check stud seals and replace if necessary. Torque nuts and install new cotter pins.

Idler Arm Replacement

1) Place vehicle on hoist. Remove fasteners from ball stud and relay rod. Remove ball stud from relay rod by tapping on relay rod boss with a light hammer, while using a heavy hammer as a backing. Remove idler arm-to-frame bolts and remove idler arm assembly.

Fig. 7: Tie Rod Clamp Tightness

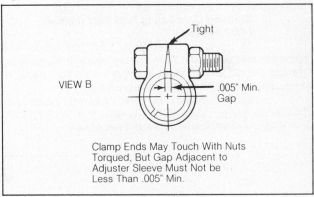

VIEW B

Tight

.005" Min. Gap

Clamp Ends May Touch With Nuts Torqued, But Gap Adjacent to Adjuster Sleeve Must Not be Less Than .005" Min.

NOTE: **Idler arm assembly should always be replaced if an up and down force of 25 lbs. (11 kg), applied at relay rod end of idler arm, produces a lash of more than 1/8" (3 mm) in straight ahead position.**

2) To install, reverse removal procedure while noting the following: Ensure that threads on studs and

Fig. 6: Tie Rod Clamp Position

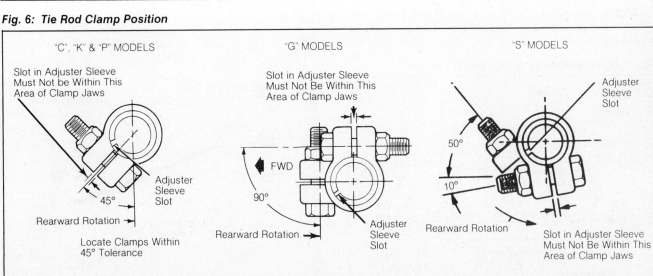

"C", "K" & "P" MODELS

Slot in Adjuster Sleeve Must Not be Within This Area of Clamp Jaws

Adjuster Sleeve Slot

45°

Rearward Rotation

Locate Clamps Within 45° Tolerance

"G" MODELS

Slot in Adjuster Sleeve Must Not Be Within This Area of Clamp Jaws

FWD

90°

Rearward Rotation

Adjuster Sleeve Slot

"S" MODELS

Adjuster Sleeve Slot

50°

10°

Rearward Rotation

Slot in Adjuster Sleeve Must Not Be Within This Area of Clamp Jaws

GENERAL MOTORS (Cont.)

nuts are clean and smooth. Check ball stud seals and replace if necessary.

3) Install connecting rod while making sure long end of rod is toward pitman arm. *See Figs. 6 & 7 for proper alignment and orientation of connecting rod clamps.*

Pitman Arm Replacement

1) Raise vehicle on hoist. Remove cotter pin from pitman arm ball stud and remove nut. Remove pitman arm or relay rod from ball stud by tapping on side of rod or arm (in which stud mounts) with a hammer while using heavier hammer as a backing.

2) Remove pitman arm nut from shaft or clamp bolt from pitman arm, and mark arm-to-shaft position. Remove pitman arm from shaft using suitable puller. To install, reverse removal procedure.

3) If a clamp type pitman arm is used, spread pitman arm with a wedge just enough to slip arm onto shaft by hand pressure. Do not hammer on or damage to steering gear may result. Be sure to reinstall the hardened steel washer before installing nut.

Steering Connecting Rod Replacement (4WD Models)

1) Remove cotter pins from ball studs and remove castellated nuts. Remove ball studs from steering arm and pitman arm boss by tapping with a light hammer while using a heavy hammer as a backing.

2) To install, reverse removal procedure. Ensure threads on studs and nuts are clean and smooth. Check ball stud seals and replace if necessary.

3) Install connecting rod on steering components, tighten nuts and install new cotter pins. *See Fig. 6 for proper alignment and orientation of connecting rod clamps.*

TIGHTENING SPECIFICATIONS

Application	Ft. Lbs. (N.m)
Idler Arm Mounting Bolt	30 (41)
Idler Arm-to-Relay Rod Nut	[1] 66 (90)
Pitman Arm-to-Pitman Shaft Nut	
"C" & "G" Models	192 (260)
"K" Models	92 (125)
"P" Models	132 (180)
Pitman Arm-to-Relay Rod Nut	[1] 66 (90)
Steering Connecting Rod Clamps	40 (54)
Steering Connecting Rod Nut	
"K" Models	[2] 70 (95)
Tie Rod Ball Stud Nuts	[3] 50 (68)
Tie Rod Clamps	
"S" Trucks	16 (22)
All Other Models	22 (30)

[1] — Seat the taper using a free-spinning nut, then install lock nut

[2] — Plus torque required to align cotter pin. Maximum torque of 100 ft. lbs. (136 N.m).

[3] — Plus torque required to align cotter pin.

JEEP

All Models

Tie Rod Replacement

1) Remove cotter pins and retaining nuts at both ends of tie rod and from end of connecting rod where it attaches to tie rod. Disconnect steering damper push rod at tie rod bracket. Remove tie rod ends from steering arms and connecting rod using a puller or expansion fork.

2) To install, attach tie rod ends to steering arms. Tighten nuts and install new cotter pins. Attach connecting rod, tighten nuts, and install new cotter pin. Attach steering damper. Check and adjust toe-in as necessary.

Steering Damper Replacement

1) With front wheels in straight-ahead position, remove lock nut securing damper to bracket on tie plate, then lift damper off stud. Remove lock nut securing push rod end to tie rod bracket and remove damper assembly.

Fig. 2: Positioning of Steering Dampener Bushings

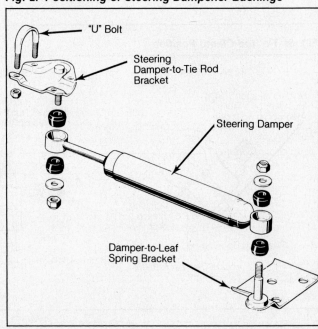

All models except "CJ" & Scrambler are shown.

Fig. 1: Disassembled View of Steering Linkage

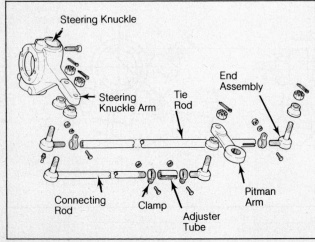

"CJ" & Scrambler models are shown.

JEEP (Cont.)

2) To install, install rubber bushings in damper eyelets, then secure eyelet at push rod end to stud on tie rod bracket with attaching hardware. Install rubber bushings in damper body eyelet.

3) Extend push rod by pulling back on damper body until eyelet can be located on, and secured to, stud on damper brakcet. Tighten all lock nuts.

Fig. 3: Disassembled View of Steering Linkage

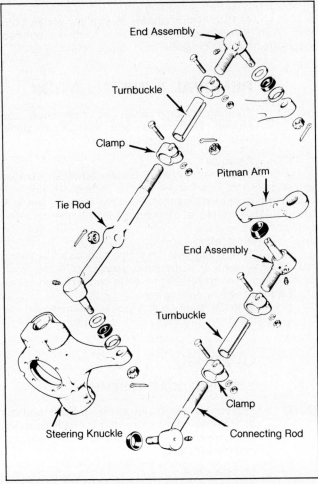

Cherokee, Wagoneer & Truck models are shown.

Fig. 4: Steering Damper Assembly

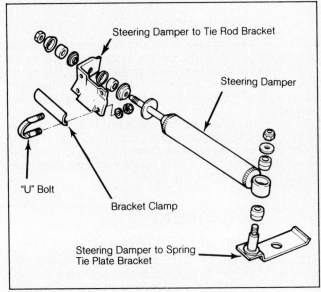

"CJ" & Scrambler models are shown.

Connecting Rod Replacement

1) Remove cotter pins and nuts from both ends of connecting rod, then remove rod. When installing be sure wheels are in straight ahead position and steering arm is parallel to centerline of vehicle.

2) Have steering gear steering arm properly indexed, with line marks on steering arm, and gear shaft in center of high point. With steering arm so positioned, install connecting rod.

TIGHTENING SPECIFICATIONS

Application	Ft. Lbs. (N.m)
Connecting Rod Clamp Bolt	
CJ & Scrambler Models	10-15 (14-20)
All Other Models	25-35 (34-48)
Connecting Rod 5/8"	
(To Castellated Nut Slot)	70 (95) Min.
Connecting Rod 9/16"	
(To Castellated Nut Slot)	60 (82) Min.
Pitman Arm-to-Shaft	160-210 (218-286)
Steering Damper Lock Nut	
CJ & Scrambler Models	16-28 (22-38)
All Other Models	24-36 (33-49)
Tie Rod Clamp Bolt	
CJ & Scrambler Models	10-15 (14-20)
All Other Models	25-35 (34-48)
Tie Rod Stud Nuts	
CJ & Scrambler	50 (68)
All Other Models	70 (95)

Manual Steering Gears
CHRYSLER RECIRCULATING BALL

Chrysler Corp. Vans

DESCRIPTION

Steering gear is a recirculating ball type. A ball nut travels up or down on the worm shaft, riding on recirculating balls acting as a screw thread. The worm shaft and ball nut assembly is supported in the gear housing by an adjustable ball thrust type upper and lower bearing.

The lower bearing cup is pressed into the gear housing, and the upper bearing cup is pressed into the worm shaft bearing adjuster. Sector shaft is integral with sector gear. The sector gear meshes with the rack teeth on the recirculating ball nut.

ADJUSTMENT

WORM BEARING PRELOAD

1) Disconnect steering gear arm from sector shaft with tool (C-4150). Remove horn pad from steering wheel. Loosen sector shaft adjusting screws lock nut and back out adjusting screw 2 turns.

2) Turn steering wheel 2 complete turns from straight ahead position. Place torque wrench on steering shaft nut. Rotate steering shaft at least 1 turn toward straight ahead position, while testing rotating torque with torque wrench.

3) If reading is not within specifications, adjust as follows: Loosen adjuster lock nut. Use spanner wrench (C-3884) to turn adjuster clockwise to increase preload, or counterclockwise to decrease preload. Hold adjuster from turning and tighten lock nut. Retest worm bearing preload.

BALL NUT RACK & SECTOR MESH

1) With worm bearing prelaod properly adjusted, turn steering wheel gently from one stop to the other,

Fig. 1: Steering Gear Adjustment Locations

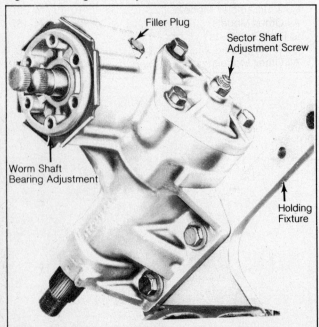

Filler Plug

Sector Shaft Adjustment Screw

Worm Shaft Bearing Adjustment

Holding Fixture

Worm bearing preload must be adjusted before sector shaft adjustment.

counting the number of turns. Turn steering back half-way to center position.

2) Turn sector shaft adjusting screw clockwise to remove all lash between ball nut rack and sector gear teeth, then torque adjusting screw lock nut. Turn steering wheel about 1/4 turn away from center position.

3) Measure torque required to rotate steering wheel through high spot at center position. If reading is not to specifications, readjust sector shaft adjusting screw to obtain proper torque reading.

4) Place front wheels in straight ahead position. With steering gear and steering wheel centered, install steering arm on sector and torque retaining nut.

REMOVAL & INSTALLATION

NOTE: **Steering column must be completely detached from floor and instrument panel before removing steering gear.**

Removal

Disconnect negative battery terminal. Remove steering column. From under vehicle remove steering arm retaining nut and lock washer. Remove steering arm with tool (C-4150). Remove steering gear-to-frame retaining nuts and remove gear.

Installation

1) Position gear on frame and install retaining nuts. Rotate worm shaft by hand and center sector shaft to mid-point of its travel. Align master serrations on sector shaft with splines in steering arm.

2) Install steering arm lock washer and nut and tighten. Install steering column. Connect battery.

OVERHAUL

STEERING GEAR ASSEMBLY

NOTE: **Thoroughly the clean entire outside surface of steering gear before disassembly to avoid contaminating worm shaft and ball nut assembly with dirt.**

Disassembly

1) Loosen sector shaft adjusting screw lock nut and back out screw 2 turns. Remove sector shaft oil seal. Position worm shaft in straight ahead position.

2) Remove sector shaft cover bolts and remove sector shaft. Remove lock nut from sector shaft adjusting screw and remove screw. Slide adjustment screw and shim out of slot in end of sector shaft.

3) Loosen worm shaft bearing adjuster lock nut with a soft drift punch and remove lock nut. Hold worm shaft from turning while unscrewing adjuster. Slide worm shaft adjuster off shaft.

NOTE: **Handle adjuster carefully to avoid damaging threads. Be sure that ball nut does not run down to either end of worm shaft as ball guide ends can be damaged.**

4) Carefully remove worm and ball nut assembly. Remove sector shaft needle bearing by placing gear housing in an arbor press and inserting tool (C-3786) in lower end of housing. Press both bearings through housing.

CHRYSLER RECIRCULATING BALL (Cont.)

5) The sector shaft cover assembly, including a needle bearing and bushing, is serviced as an assembly. Remove worm shaft oil seal with a blunt punch. Remove worm shaft spacer and upper bearing cup in same manner, being careful not to cock bearing cup.

6) Remove lower bearing cup by positioning locking head jaws of remover tool (C-3868) behind bearing cup and expanding remover head. Withdraw bearing cup by turning remover screw nut in a clockwise direction while holding center screw.

Cleaning and Inspection

1) Wash all parts in clean solvent and dry with compressed air. Test operation of ball nut assembly on worm shaft. If it does not travel smoothly or there is roughness, assembly must be replaced.

2) Inspect sector shaft for wear and check fit of shaft in housing bearings. DO NOT screw worm shaft adjuster into housing without lubrication, or when threads are dirty or damaged. Replace sector shaft and worm shaft oil seals whenever unit is disassembled.

Reassembly

1) Press lower sector shaft bearing into housing to 1/2" below end of bore. Press upper needle bearing into housing bore so it is flush with end of bore surface.

2) Press worm shaft bearing cup and spacer into adjuster nut. Install worm shaft oil seal in adjuster with metal retainer UP. Drive seal into place with sleeve so seal is slightly below end of bore in adjuster.

3) Lubricate all moving parts and seals with steering gear lubricant. Clamp housing in vise with worm bearing adjuster opening UP. Place a thrust bearing in lower cup in housing.

4) Hold ball nut from turning and insert worm shaft and ball nut assembly into housing with end of worm resting in thrust bearing. Place upper thrust bearing on worm shaft. Lubricate threads on adjuster and threads in housing.

5) Place tape over worm shaft splines and slide adjuster assembly over shaft. Thread adjuster into housing torque adjuster nut to 50 ft. lbs. (68 N.m) while rotating wormshaft. Loosen adjuster so no bearing preload exists.

6) Adjust worm shaft bearing preload to 1-4.5 INCH lbs. (.1-.5 N.m). Tighten bearing adjuster lock nut and retest preload. Pack worm shaft cavities in housing with steering gear lubricant. Slide sector shaft adjusting screw and shim into slot in end of shaft.

7) Sector shaft adjusting screw must have .004" (.102 mm) maximun end play. If clearance is not within specifications, shims are available in 3 thicknesses. Start sector shaft and adjuster screw into bearing housing cover.

8) Using a screwdriver through hole in cover, turn screw counterclockwise to pull shaft into cover. Install adjusting screw lock nut, but do not tighten. Rotate worm shaft to centralize ball nut. Place new cover gasket on housing cover.

9) Lubricate sector shaft and sector teeth and carefully install shaft and cover assembly into housing. Ensure that some lash exists between sector shaft teeth and ball nut rack. Install and tighten cover bolts.

10) Press sector shaft seal into gear housing with lip of seal facing housing. Adjust worm bearing preload. Adjust ball nut rack and sector mesh.

SECTOR SHAFT OIL SEAL REPLACEMENT

1) Sector shaft oil seal can be replaced with steering gear in vehicle or on bench. If replacement is done in vehicle, clean exposed portion of sector shaft before replacing oil seal.

2) Remove steering gear arm retaining nut and lock washer. Remove steering gear arm. Replace oil seal with special tool (C-3880). Install steering arm and torque nut.

TIGHTENING SPECIFICATIONS

Application	Ft. Lbs. (N.m)
Housing Cover Bolts	25 (34)
Sector Shaft Adj. Screw Lock Nut	35 (48)
Steering Arm Retaining Nut	175 (238)
Steering Gear-to-Frame Bolts	100 (136)

ADJUSTMENT SPECIFICATIONS

Application	INCH Lbs. (N.m)
Ball Nut Rack & Sector Mesh	
Gear in Vehicle	8.2-11.3 (.9-1.3)
Gear Removed From Vehicle	7.5-11.5 (.8-1.3)
Worm Bearing Preload	1.0-4.5 (.1-.5)

Manual Steering Gears
KOYO RECIRCULATING BALL

Ford (Bronco II, "F" 2WD Pickup, Ranger & Van)

DESCRIPTION & OPERATION

The steering gear is of the worm and recirulating ball type. A ball nut is used which has threads that mate to the threads of the wormshaft via continuous rows of ball bearings between the two. As the steering wheel is rotated, the wormshaft rotates, causing the ball nut to move up or down the wormshaft.

The gear teeth on the ball nut are meshed with the gear teeth on the sector shaft. Thus, the movement of the ball nut causes the sector shaft to rotate and swing the Pitman arm.

Proper mesh engagement between the sector and ball nut is obtained by an adjusting screw which moves the sector shaft axially. The worm thrust bearing adjuster can be turned to provide proper preloading of the worm thrust bearings.

There are two types of manual ball nut gears: A constant (24:1) ratio and a varible (20-24:1) ratio. Gears may be distinguised from one another by a model number stamped on the sector cover. "SMK-A" designates a constant ratio gear, while a "SMK-B" code is a varible ratio gear.

Fig. 1: Koyo Recirulating Ball Steering Gear

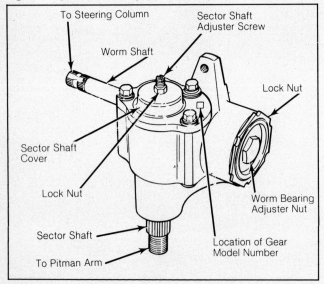

To Steering Column
Sector Shaft Adjuster Screw
Worm Shaft
Lock Nut
Sector Shaft Cover
Lock Nut
Sector Shaft
To Pitman Arm
Worm Bearing Adjuster Nut
Location of Gear Model Number

"SMK-A" is a constant ratio gear, and "SMK-B" is a varible ratio gear.

ADJUSTMENTS

PRELIMINARY

1) Worm bearing preload must be adjusted before the meshload. While meshload may be adjusted with the steering gear installed, worm preload cannot be adjusted in the vehicle.

2) Disconnect the Pitman arm at the ball stud. Lubricate the wormshaft seal with a drop of automatic transmission fluid. Remove the horn pad. Turn the steering wheel slowly to one stop.

3) Place an INCH lb. torque wrench on the steering wheel nut. Measure the torque required to rotate the steering wheel at a constant speed for approximately 1 1/2 turns.

4) If preload is not within 2-6 INCH lbs. (22-68 N.cm) on Bronco II and Ranger or 5-9 INCH lbs. (60-100 N.cm) on Pickups and Vans, readjust the preload. If preload is within specifications, check meshload.

5) Place an INCH lb. torque wrench on the steering wheel nut. Measure the highest torque required to rotate the steering wheel back and forth approximately 90° either way across the center position.

6) The meshload must be 4-10 INCH lbs. (45-113 N.cm) on Bronco II and Ranger or 9-14 INCH lbs. (102-158 N.cm) on Pickups and Vans. Meshload must also be at least 2 INCH lbs. (23 N.cm) over the preload. Meshload can be adjusted in the vehicle.

WORM BEARING PRELOAD & MESHLOAD

1) Remove steering gear from vehicle. See REMOVAL & INSTALLATION in this article. Tighten the sector cover bolts to 40 ft. lbs. (53 N.m). Loosen preload adjuster locknut and screw.

2) Tighten worm bearing adjuster until all end play has been removed. Lubricate wormshaft seal with a drop of automatic transmission fluid. Turn worm shaft carefully to the right stop.

3) Using an INCH lb. torque wrench, measure the torque required to rotate worm shaft to the left, in a constant motion, for approximately 1 1/2 turns.

4) Turn adjuster nut to obtain a preload of 5-6 INCH lbs. (56-68 N.cm) on Bronco II and Ranger or 7-9 INCH lbs. (79-102 N.cm) on Pickups and Vans. Tighten adjuster nut. Rotate the wormshaft to the center position.

5) Using an INCH lbs. torque wrench, measure the highest reading while the wormshaft is turned approximately 90° either way across center.

6) If the highest reading is not within 9-10 INCH lbs. (102-113 N.cm) on Bronco II and Ranger or 12-14 INCH lbs. on Pickups and Vans, turn sector shaft adjusting screw as required.

7) Meshload must be at least 4 INCH lbs. (45 N.cm) over the preload. Hold the sector shaft adjusting screw and torque the locknut to 25 ft. lbs. (34 N.m).

REMOVAL & INSTALLATION

STEERING GEAR

Removal

1) Disengage the flex coupling shield from the steering gear input shield and slide it up the intermediate shaft. Remove the flex coupling-to-steering gear bolt.

2) Remove steering gear input shaft shield. Remove the Pitman arm nut and washer. Remove the Pitman arm using puller (T64P-3590-F). Remove the steering gear-to-frame attaching bolts and remove gear.

Installation

1) Center the wormshaft in the steering gear. Ensure that the flat on the gear input shaft is facing straight up and aligns with the flat on the flex coupling. Install steering gear to the side rail and torque bolts to specifications.

2) Align the two blocked teeth on the Pitman arm with the four missing teeth on the sector shaft. Install nut and tighten. Install flex coupling-to-steering gear bolt. Snap the flex coupling shield to the steering gear input shaft shield.

KOYO RECIRCULATING BALL (Cont.)

OVERHAUL

DISASSEMBLY

1) Place steering gear in a vise, clamping onto one mounting tab or a holding fixture. Worm shaft should be in a horizontal position, and centered in the steering box.

2) Remove the sector shaft cover bolts. Lift the sector shaft and cover out of the gear. Remove the cover from the shaft by turning the screw clockwise. Keep the shim with the screw.

3) Loosen lock nut on worm shaft adjuster, and remove the adjuster plug and the wormshaft thrust bearing. Pull the wormshaft and ball nut assembly from the housing.

4) DO NOT allow ball nut to run down to either end of the wormshaft as ball guide ends may be damaged. Pry out and discard both sector shaft and worm shaft seals.

NOTE: **Individual parts are not available for service. If worm cannot rotate freely in the ball nut, replace the entire assembly.**

5) Remove the wormshaft adjuster nut bearing cup with a slide hammer. Remove the bearing cup from the housing using a bearing driver or socket.

6) The sector shaft cover bushing is not serviceable. The entire sector cover assembly is serviced as a unit. Sector shaft needle bearing is serviced only as a unit with the housing. DO NOT attempt to remove sector needle assembly.

CLEANING & INSPECTION

1) Wash parts with clean solvent and blow dry with air. Inspect bearings and races for signs or wear. Any parts that show signs of wear should be replaced.

2) Inspect sector shaft fit at side cover bushing. If bushing is worn, a new side cover and bushing assembly should be installed. Check ball nut and worm shaft assembly for wear and straightness.

3) Inspect wormshaft and ball nut for tightness or binding by turning the wormshaft in the ball nut. If ball nut and wormshaft is defective, replace as an assembly.

4) Inspect the housing for cracks or damage. Inspect the needle bearing inside the housing for defects. Replace the housing if any defects are found. Inspect steering gear teeth for chipping, excessive wear and surface breakdown.

5) Check the clearance between the sector adjusting screw head and the bottom of the sector shaft T-slot. If clearance is more than .004" (.10 mm), replace shim to obtain desired clearance.

6) Steering gear lash adjuster shims are available in .078" (1.95 mm), .080" (2.00 mm), .082" (2.05 mm), .084" (2.10 mm) and .086" (2.15 mm). Hold sector adjuster screw and turn sector shaft.

7) Sector must turn freely. If sector does not turn freely, increase T-slot clearance by replacing shims. *See Fig. 3.*

Fig. 2: Exploded View of Koyo Recirculating Ball Steering Gear

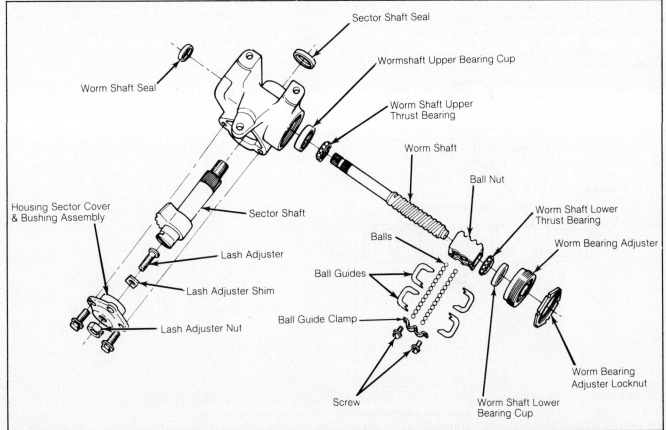

KOYO RECIRCULATING BALL (Cont.)

Fig. 3: Checking Sector Shaft T-Slot Clearance

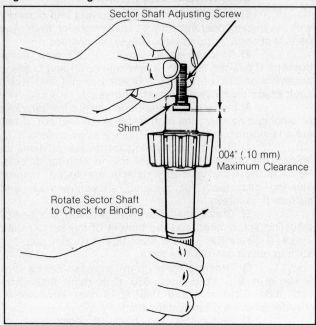

Clearance may be adjusted by replacing shims.

REASSEMBLY

1) All seals, bushings, and worm shaft bearing cups should be installed. Clamp the housing in a vise with the wormshaft bore horizontal and the sector cover opening up.

2) Apply steering gear lubricant to the wormshaft bearings, sector shaft needle bearings and sector cover bushing. Slip thrust bearing over worm shaft splined end and position correctly. *See Fig. 4*

Fig. 4: Installing Wormshaft Thrust Bearing

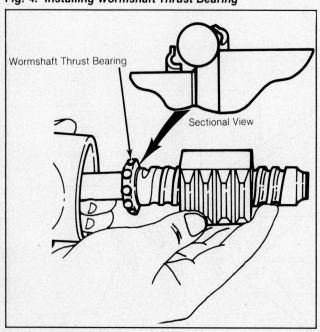

Lubricate bearing before assembly.

3) Install wormshaft and ball nut, splined end first, into housing. Place remaining wormshaft bearing into

adjuster plug bearing cup. Install adjuster plug and lock nut into the housing.

4) Screw adjuster nut down until nearly all end play has been removed. Lubricate the steering gear by rotating the wormshaft until the ball nut is the end of its travel.

5) Pack as much grease as possible into the housing without losing it out the sector shaft opening. Rotate ball nut to the other end of its travel and pack more grease into the housing.

6) Rotate the ball nut until it is in the center of its travel. Insert the sector shaft assembly, containing the adjusting screw, into the housing. Center tooth of the sector gear must engage the center rack tooth space in the ball nut.

7) Pack the housing with grease. Apply a thin bead of sealant to the sector shaft cover and install on the housing. Engage the sector adjuster screw with the tapped hole in the center of the sector cover by turning the screw counterclockwise.

8) Turn the screw until the sector cover is flush with the housing. Install the sector cover bolts but do not tighten unless there is a lash between the sector shaft and wormshaft.

9) Torque the sector cover bolts to specifications. Adjust the steering gear preload and meshload. See ADJUSTMENTS in this article.

TIGHTENING SPECIFICATIONS

Application	Ft. Lbs. (N.m)
Coupling-to-Steering Gear Shaft Bolt	35 (47)
Pitman Arm-to-Sector Shaft Nut	230 (312)
Sector Cover Bolts	40 (54)
Sector Shaft Lock Nut	25 (34)
Steering Gear-to-Frame Bolts	66 (88)
Worm Bearing Adjuster Nut	187 (253)

SAGINAW RECIRCULATING BALL

**Chrysler Corp. (Except Van Models),
Ford (Except Bronco II & Ranger),
General Motors, Jeep**

DESCRIPTION & OPERATION

Steering gear is a recirculating ball type and consists of a ball nut connected to steering worm and in mesh with sector gear. Gears are basically the same for all models and service procedures will apply to all gears unless noted otherwise.

Precision finished helical grooves within ball nut match helical grooves in worm. Ball bearings roll within grooves when steering wheel is turned. There are two complete circuits using tubular ball guides to deflect balls away from their helical path at one end of groove and guide them back to other end.

When steering wheel is turned to right, nut moves upward; when turned to left, nut moves downward. The teeth on sector (forged as part of pitman shaft) and the ball nut are so designed that a tighter fit exists between the two when the front wheels are straight ahead.

Proper engagement between sector and ball nut is obtained by adjusting screw, which moves pitman shaft endwise, permitting desired engagement of tapered teeth of the ball nut and sector gear. Worm bearing adjuster can be turned to provide proper preloading of the upper and lower bearings.

ADJUSTMENT

PRELIMINARY

Worm bearing preload adjustment MUST be made first; then, make over-center preload adjustment. DO NOT reverse the order of adjustment. Adjustment of steering gear can be made on or off vehicle in most cases.

When making the worm bearing preload adjustment with gear on vehicle, the pitman arm must be disconnected or the steering linkage disconnected from the pitman arm.

The torque wrench can be connected directly to the worm shaft (input shaft) or to steering wheel retaining nut (steering column drag is negligible). When making the over-center preload adjustment, torque wrench is attached to the sector shaft (after removing pitman arm) or the steering wheel nut.

WORM BEARING PRELOAD

1) Loosen over-center preload adjuster screw. Tighten worm bearing adjuster until all end play has been removed; then loosen 1/4 turn and tighten lock nut. Turn worm shaft carefully to either stop. Do not jam into stop as damage to gear could result.

2) Rotate worm shaft back from stop about 1/2 turn. Using an INCH lb. torque wrench, measure the torque required to keep worm shaft in motion about one revolution.

3) Adjust rotating torque to specifications, using worm bearing adjuster. Tighten lock nut, and recheck turning torque. Adjust as necessary. Proceed to Over-Center Preload adjustment procedure.

WORM BEARING PRELOAD

Application	INCH Lbs. (N.m)
All Manufacturers	5-8 (.6-.9)

Fig. 1: Adjustment Points for Steering Gear

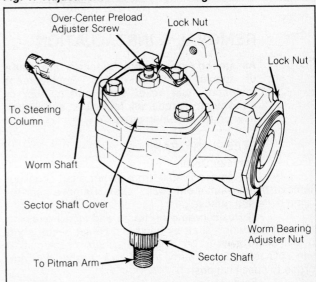

Worm bearing preload must be adjusted before over-center preload.

OVER-CENTER PRELOAD

1) With worm bearing preload adjusted, turn worm shaft slowly from stop-to-stop while counting total number of turns. Then, turn shaft half-way back to exact center position.

2) Loosen lock nut and turn over-center adjustment screws in until all lash is taken out of shaft. Tighten lock nut. Rotate worm shaft slightly off center (45-90°), then attach an INCH lbs. torque wrench to worm shaft.

3) Using torque wrench as a lever, rotate worm shaft back through center position and record rotating torque. If rotating torque is not to specifications, repeat procedure.

Fig. 2: Cross Section of Steering Gear

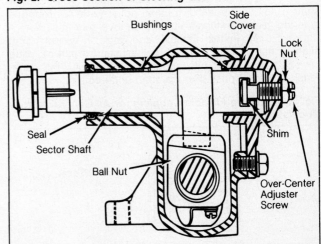

Manual Steering Gears

SAGINAW RECIRCULATING BALL (Cont.)

OVER-CENTER ADJUSTMENT INCH LBS. (N.m)

Application	Preload
Chrysler Corp.	14 (1.6)
Ford	10-16 (1.1-1.8)
All Other Manufacturers	16 (1.8)

REMOVAL & INSTALLATION

NOTE: All steering component fasteners are made of special quality materials. Replacement fasteners must be of same part number or equivalent. Torque all fasteners and install new cotter pin when used.

STEERING GEAR

Chrysler Corp.

1) Remove 2 bolts from sector shaft coupling. Remove pitman arm from sector shaft. Remove gear-to-frame bolts and remove gear.

2) Position gear on frame and install retaining bolts. Rotate worm shaft by hand and center sector shaft to mid point of its travel. Align serration on sector shaft with splines in pitman arm. Install lock washer and nut, torque to specifications.

Ford

1) Raise vehicle on hoist. Disconnect flex-coupling from steering shaft. Disconnect drag link from pitman arm. Remove pitman arm-to-sector shaft nut, and remove pitman arm.

2) Remove bolts attaching steering gear-to-frame side rails, and lower steering gear from vehicle. Remove coupling-to-gear attaching bolt and remove coupling.

3) To install, center worm shaft of steering gear and install gear onto frame side rail. Tighten bolts. Connect pitman arm to the sector shaft and drag link to pitman arm. Torque nuts, and install cotter pins. Attach flex coupling-to-steering shaft flange.

General Motors

1) Set front wheels in straight-ahead position. Remove flexible coupling-to-steering shaft flange bolts or lower universal joint pinch bolt. Mark position of universal yoke-to-worm shaft.

2) Mark relationship of pitman arm-to-sector shaft. Remove pitman arm using puller (J-6632). Remove steering gear mounting bolts and remove gear assembly.

3) Install flexible coupling on worm shaft aligning flat on coupling with flat on shaft. Push coupling on shaft until shaft hits shoulder and install pinch bolt. Pinch bolt must pass through shaft undercut.

Fig. 3: Adjusting Flexible Coupling for All General Motors Models

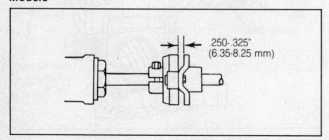

.250-.325"
(6.35-8.25 mm)

4) Place gear in position, guiding coupling bolt into steering shaft flange. Install gear-to-frame bolts and torque to specification.

5) If flexible coupling alignment pin plastic spacers are used, make sure they are bottomed on pins, then tighten flange bolt nuts and remove plastic spacers. Spacers aid in centering pins and maintain correct coupling-to-flange dimension.

6) Check that flexible coupling-to-steering shaft flange dimension is .250-.325" (6.35-8.25 mm). *See Fig. 3.* If flexible coupling alignment pin plastic spacers are not used, center pins in slots in steering shaft flange and tighten flange bolt nuts.

NOTE: Plastic spacers must be removed before driving vehicle.

Jeep

1) Remove intermediate shaft-to-worm shaft coupling clamp bolt and disconnect intermediate shaft. Remove pitman arm nut and washer. Pull pitman arm off shaft using puller (J-6632).

2) On Cherokee, Truck and Wagoneer models, remove steering gear-to-frame rail bolts and remove steering gear from vehicle. On "CJ" and Scrambler models, raise left side of vehicle slightly to release tension from left front spring. Place safety stand under frame.

3) Remove bolts securing steering gear lower bracket to the frame. Remove bolts securing steering gear upper bracket to the crossmember. Remove steering gear from vehicle. To install, apply Loctite to frame end crossmember bolts, reverse removal procedure.

SECTOR SHAFT SEAL

NOTE: For models not listed, seal replacement procedure was not available from manufacturer.

General Motors

1) On 4WD models, gear must be removed from vehicle to replace seal. On all others, remove pitman arm from sector shaft. Rotate steering wheel from stop-to-stop while counting number of turns. Turn wheel back half way, placing gear at center of travel.

2) Remove bolts attaching side cover to housing, and lift sector shaft and side cover assembly from housing. Pry sector shaft seal from housing using a screwdriver. Be careful not to scratch housing bore.

3) Inspect gear lubricant for contamination, if lubricant is contaminated in any way, gear should be completely overhauled. Lubricate new sector shaft seal with steering gear lubricant (GM 4673M). Position seal in sector shaft bore, and tap it into place using a socket.

4) Remove over-center adjuster lock nut. Remove side cover from sector shaft assembly by turning over-center adjuster screw clockwise. Install sector shaft in gear so center tooth of sector enters center tooth space of ball nut.

5) Fill gear housing with lubricant and install new side cover gasket on gear housing. Install side cover over sector shaft by reaching through cover hole with a screwdriver.

6) Turn over-center adjuster screws counterclockwise until screw bottoms; then back off screw 1/4 turn. Install over-center adjuster lock nut. Adjust worm bearing and over-center preload.

SAGINAW RECIRCULATING BALL (Cont.)

Jeep

1) Mark pitman arm and sector shaft for reassembly reference. Remove pitman arm using puller. Remove seal from sector shaft using a pointed tool or small bladed screwdriver.

2) Inspect condition of gear lubricant. If contaminated, remove overhaul gear. Wrap pitman arm shaft splines with shim stock to protect replacement seal during installation.

3) Lubricate lip of replacement seal with chassis lubricant, slide seal over shim stock and seat seal in gear housing. Tap seal into place with small plastic hammer. Align index marks, install pitman arm and tighten.

OVERHAUL

DISASSEMBLY

All Models

1) Place steering gear in a vise, clamping onto one mounting tab or a suitable holding fixture. Worm shaft should be in a horizontal position. Loosen over-center preload adjuster lock nut, and turn adjuster a few turns out.

2) Loosen lock nut on worm shaft adjuster, and turn adjuster out a few turns. Rotate worm shaft from stop-to-stop, counting number of turns. Then turn shaft back 1/2 the number of turns to center sector shaft.

3) Place a pan under assembly to catch oil, and remove 3 self-locking bolts holding side cover to the housing. Tap on end of sector shaft with a mallet and lift side cover and sector shaft assembly from gear housing.

4) If sector does not clear opening easily, turn worm shaft by hand until sector can be removed. Remove worm shaft adjuster and lock nut assembly with lower worm shaft bearing.

CAUTION: DO NOT allow ball nut to run down to either end of the wormshaft as ball guide ends may be damaged.

5) Remove worm shaft and ball nut assembly from housing while housing is in a horizontal position to prevent ball nut from running down worm shaft. Remove upper bearing from worm guide.

6) Using screwdriver, pry lower bearing retainer from worm adjuster assembly and remove bearing. Remove over-center adjuster lock nut and screw.

7) Slide screw and shim out slot in end of sector shaft. Pry out and discard both sector shaft and worm shaft seals.

CLEANING & INSPECTION

Wash parts with clean solvent and blow dry with air. Inspect bearings and races for signs or wear. Any parts that show signs of wear should be replaced.

Inspect sector shaft fit at side cover bushing. If bushing is worn, a new side cover and bushing assembly should be installed. Check ball nut and worm shaft assembly for wear and straightness.

COMPONENT SERVICE

Sector Shaft & Worm Shaft Seals

Pry out seals using a screwdriver. Before installing new seals, check condition of sector shaft bushings and upper worm shaft bearing race. Use a socket (pressing outer diameter of seal) to replace seal. Avoid installing seal in a cocked position.

Sector Shaft Bushing

Support steering gear in a arbor press and drive sector shaft bushing from housing. Press new bushing into position reversing removal procedure. Replacement bushings are machined to size and need no reaming.

Ford Motor Company steering gears use needle bearings in place of bushings. Removal and stallation is the same as bushings.

Worm Shaft Bearing Race (In Adjuster)

Remove worm shaft bearing race using a slide hammer or a hammer and punch. Press bearing in place using an arbor press.

Fig. 4: Removing Worm Shaft Bearing Race from Adjuster

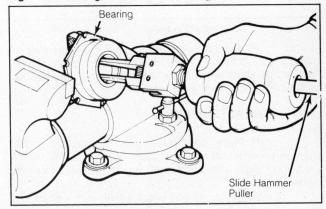

Install new race using arbor press.

Worm Shaft Bearing Race (In Housing)

Drive out housing bearing race with a hammer and punch. Press new race in using an arbor press.

Ball Nut & Worm Shaft Assembly

Ball nut disassembly is not necessary unless there is indication of binding or tightness when rotating worm. If disassembly is required, proceed as follows:

1) This step will let loose about 50 ball bearings; be ready to catch them ALL. Remove clamp that retains ball guides and pull guides from ball nut while catching balls in clean pan. Turn nut over and rotate worm until all balls have fallen into pan.

2) Note relation of worm to ball nut and remove worm from ball nut. Wash parts and inspect worm, nut grooves, and ball bearings for indentations. Check ball guides for damage at ends where they deflect or pick up balls from helical path on worm.

3) To reassemble ball nut and worm shaft, insert ball nut over worm so that shallow end of ball nut teeth are on left side (looking from steering wheel end of worm shaft). Align grooves in worm and nut by sighting through ball guide holes.

4) There are 2 types of ball guides: those with holes in middle and those with no hole. If ball guides have hole in middle, insert ball guides into holes in ball nut. Divide balls into 2 equal groups and insert each group into a ball guide, while slowly turning worm shaft.

5) If guides have no hole, separate the halves and fill half of each set with balls. Cover with the remaining half and plug ends with grease to prevent balls from falling out.

Fig. 5: Filling Ball Circuits Through Holes in Ball Guides

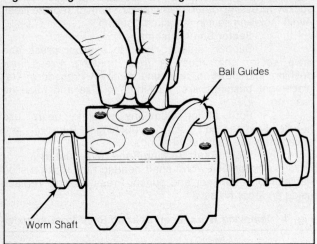

Rotate worm while installing balls.

6) Fill each circuit in ball nut with half of remaining balls in one circuit, and half in the other. Do not turn worm shaft while installing. Insert ball guides. On both types, install ball guide retainer.

REASSEMBLY
All Models

1) Place gear housing in a vise with worm shaft bore horizontal and side cover opening facing up. All seals, bushings, and worm shaft bearing races should be installed.

2) Slip upper ball bearing over worm shaft and insert worm and nut assembly into housing feeding end of

Fig. 7: Filling Ball Circuits Through Holes in Ball Nut

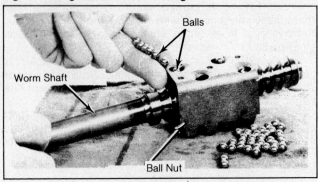

Do not rotate worm while installing balls.

shaft through upper ball bearing race and seal. Place ball bearing in adjuster race and press stamped retainer into place with a socket.

3) Install adjuster and lock nut into housing carefully guiding worm shaft into bearing until nearly all end play is removed from worm shaft. Position over-center adjuster (with shim) in slotted end of sector shaft.

4) Check end clearance, which should not exceed .002" (.05 mm). If clearance is greater than specified, a steering gear over-center adjuster shim kit is available.

5) Lubricate gear as follows: Rotate worm shaft until ball nut is at end of travel, while forcing as much grease as possible into housing without losing it out sector shaft opening. Rotate worm until ball is at other end, and apply more lubricant.

Fig. 6: Exploded View of Recirculating Ball Steering Gear

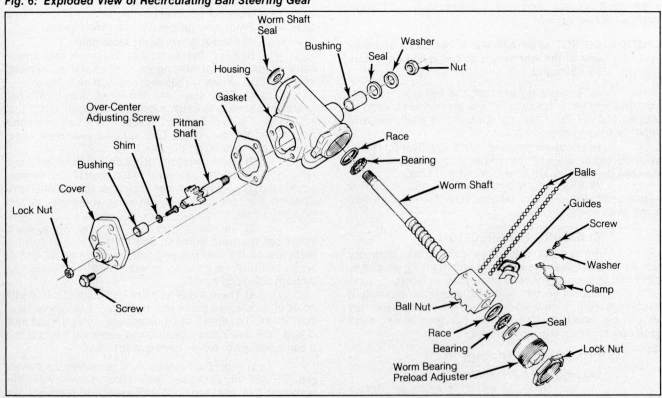

General Motors model is shown.

SAGINAW RECIRCULATING BALL (Cont.)

Fig. 8: Checking Over-Center Adjuster Clearance

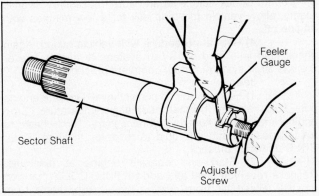

Feeler
Gauge

Sector Shaft

Adjuster
Screw

Clearance should be .002" (.05 mm).

6) Rotate worm until ball is at center. This will help sector and ball nut engage properly. Insert sector shaft and over-center adjuster screw (without side cover) into housing so center tooth of sector teeth enters center tooth space in ball nut.

7) Apply more lubricant into housing. Install side cover gasket. Install side cover over sector shaft by reaching through cover with a screwdriver.

8) Turn over-center adjuster screw counterclockwise until screw bottoms; then back off screw 1/2 turn. Loosely install a new lock nut onto adjuster screw.

9) Install and tighten side cover bolts to specifications. Adjust worm bearing preload and over-center preload as previously outlined. See Adjustments in this article.

TIGHTENING SPECIFICATIONS

Application	Ft. Lbs. (N.m)
Worm Bearing Preload Adj. Lock Nut	
Jeep	90 (122)
All Other Manufacturers	85 (116)
Over-Center Preload Adj. Lock Nut	
Chrysler Corp.	35 (48)
Jeep	23 (31)
All Other Manufacturers	25 (34)
Side Cover Bolts	
Chrysler Corp.	25 (34)
General Motors	45 (61)
All Other Manufacturers	30 (41)
Flexible Coupling Bolts	
General Motors	20 (27)
Jeep	45 (61)
All Other Manufacturers	30 (41)
Pitman Arm-to-Sector Shaft	
Chrysler Corp.	175 (238)
Ford	170-210 (231-286)
All Other Manufacturers	185 (252)
Steering Gear-to-Frame	
Chrysler Corp.	100 (136)
Ford	70 (95)
General Motors	80 (109)
Jeep (Cherokee, Truck & Wagoneer)	70 (95)
Steering Bracket-to-Frame ("CJ" & Scrambler Models)	
Bracket-to-Toe Plate	55 (75)
Bracket-to-Gear	70 (95)

Power Steering General Servicing

ALL MODELS

Chrysler Corp., Ford,
General Motors, Jeep

LUBRICATION

SERVICE INTERVALS

Chrysler Corp.
Check fluid every oil change.
Ford
Check with required maintenance checks.
General Motors
Check with every oil change.
Jeep
Check the fluid every 5,000 miles (8045 km.) or 5 months.

CHECKING FLUID LEVEL

Chrysler Corp.
Check fluid with engine at normal operating temperature. Fluid level should read "FULL" on dipstick.
Ford
With fluid at normal operating temperature, and system properly bled, shut off engine. Fluid level on dipstick should read between "HOT" mark and end of dipstick.

General Motors & Jeep
Check fluid level with engine stopped and fluid hot or cold. Fluid level should be to "FULL HOT" or "FULL COLD" mark on dipstick. On models with remote reservoir, keep fluid level 0.5-1.0" from top of reservoir with wheels fully to the left.

RECOMMENDED FLUID

Application	Fluid Type
Chrysler Corp.	Power Steering Fluid (2084329)
Ford .... ¹	Power Steering Fluid (C1AZ-19582-A,C,D)
General Motors	Power Steering Fluid (1050017)
Jeep	² Power Steering Fluid

¹ — Automatic Transmission Fluid.
² — AMC/Jeep Power Steering Fluid or equivalent.

REFILLING & BLEEDING SYSTEM

Chrysler Corp.
Fill pump reservoir with power steering fluid, start engine and check for leaks. Bleed system by turning wheels from stop-to-stop several times. Shut off engine and check fluid level.
Ford
Fill pump reservoir with fluid and run engine until fluid reaches operating temperature of 165-175°F (74-80°C). Turn steering wheel all the way to the left then all the way to the right several times without hitting stops. Check fluid and add if necessary.
General Motors
1) Fill reservoir to correct level. Let oil settle for 2 minutes. Start engine and run for 2 seconds. Check reservoir and add oil if necessary. Repeat procedure until level in reservoir remains constant after running engine.

2) Raise front of vehicle so that both wheels are off ground. Start engine and increase engine speed to 1500 RPM. Turn wheels right and left, lightly contacting stops. Check fluid and add if necessary.

3) Lower vehicle and turn wheels right and left on ground. Check fluid level and add if necessary. If oil is foamy, allow vehicle to stand still for a few minutes with engine off.

4) Repeat procedure with vehicle raised. Again check fluid level and for air in system. If level is low or there is air in system, repeat complete procedure.
Jeep
1) Fill reservoir to correct level. Operate engine until fluid reaches normal operating temperature. Stop engine and correct fluid level if necessary. Turn wheels to full left position and add fluid to reservoir to fill to "FULL COLD" mark on dipstick.

2) Start and operate engine at fast idle. Recheck reservoir level and add to "FULL COLD" mark on dipstick. Bleed air from system by turning wheels from side-to-side without contacting stops. Maintain fluid level just above pump body.

3) Fluid with air in it will have bubbles in it and will have a Light Tan or Tan-Orange appearance. When air is removed, return wheels to straight ahead position and operate engine an additional 2-3 minutes and then stop engine.

4) Road test vehicle and recheck fluid level. Level should be at "FULL HOT" position after system has stabilized. Add as necessary but do not overfill.

SERVICE

BELT TENSION
Tension in Lbs. (Kg.) using Strand Tension Gauge

Application	New Belt	Used Belt
Chrysler Corp. .... ¹		¹
Ford		
1/4" Belt	80	60
	(36.2)	(27)
All Other Belts	140	110
	(64)	(50)
General Motors		
5/16" Belt	80 Max.	50 Min.
	(36 Max.)	(23 Min.)
3/8" Belt	140 Max.	70 Min.
	(63 Max.)	(32 Min.)
15/32" Belt	165 Max.	90 Min.
	(75 Max.)	(41 Min.)
Jeep	² 125-155	² 90-115
	² (57-70)	² (41-52)

¹ — Belt deflection should be 1/4" to 5/16".
² — Calif. models tension is 180-200 lbs. new, 140-160 Lbs. used.

TESTING

PRESSURE TEST

1) With belt tension correct, disconnect power steering pump pressure hose, keeping hose end raised to prevent fluid loss. Connect pressure hose of gauge to power steering pump fitting and connect second hose from valve side of tester to steering gear inlet.

2) Open valve and run engine until fluid reaches normal operating temperature of 170°F (77°C). Check fluid level and add if necessary.

ALL MODELS (Cont.)

NOTE: For testing Ford vehicles, Power Steering Analyzer D79-33610-A with flow meter is necessary.

3) If testing Chrysler vehicle, skip intermediate steps and proceed to step **13)**. On all other vehicles, note pressure reading with valve open and engine idling. Pressure should be 80-125 psi (5.6-8.8 kg/cm²).

4) On Ford vehicles, note flow. If flow is less than 2 gals/min. (7.6 L/min.), pump may require repair. At this point, however, continue test.

5) If pressure is above 150 psi (10.5 kg/cm²) on Ford or 200 psi (14 kg/cm²) on all other vehicles, check hoses for restrictions and poppet valve (Saginaw gears) for proper assembly.

6) On Ford vehicles, partially close valve to build pressure up to 740 psi (51.8 kg/cm²) for Ford pumps and 620 psi (43 kg/cm²) for Saginaw pumps.

7) If flow drops below 1.7 gals./min. (6.4 L/min.) for Ford or 1.8 gals./min. (6.8 L/min.) for Saginaw pumps, disassemble pump and replace cam pack.

8) On all vehicles, close gate valve completely and reopen 3 times. Record highest reading each time. DO NOT close valve for more than 5 seconds. On Ford vehicles, increase engine speed to 1500 RPM and record flow.

9) On all models, if pressure is less than specification, replace flow control valve. If within specifications on General Motors and Jeep but readings are not within 50 psi (3.5 kg/cm²) of each other, remove flow control valve and clean or replace.

10) If above specifications on Ford, or if flow varies from step **7)** reading by more than 1 gal./min. (3.8 L/min.), remove flow control valve and clean or replace.

11) On all models, with valve open, turn steering wheel all the way from right-to-left stops and record pressure. DO NOT hold wheel against stops more than 5 seconds. Pressure should be the same as recorded in Pressure Test Specifications.

12) Note that on Ford vehicles flow should drop 0.5 gal./min. (1.9 L/min.) If pump output cannot be matched in either side of gear, gear is leaking internally and must be overhauled. Shut off engine and remove tester, reconnecting hoses.

13) On Chrysler vehicles, idle engine at 600-800 RPM and with valve open, note pressure while turning wheels from side-to-side to stops. DO NOT hold wheel against stops for more than 5 seconds. A pressure of at least 900 psi (63 kg/cm²) should be read.

14) If pressure is low, system is not operating properly. Momentarily close valve and note pressure. If pressure is less than 900 psi (63 kg/cm²), pump is faulty. If pressure is 900 psi (63 kg/cm²) but was low at previous reading, steering gear is at fault.

PRESSURE TEST SPECIFICATIONS

Application	Idle Pressure psi (kg/cm²)	Relief Pressure psi (kg/cm²)
Chrysler Corp.	[1] 900 (63)	1200-1300 (84-91)
Ford	80-125 (6-9)	[2] 1350-1450 (95-102)
General Motors C10/30	80-125 (6-9)	1200-1300 (77-84)
G10/30	80-125 (6-9)	[3] 900-1000 (63-70)
Jeep CJ & Scrambler	80-125 (6-9)	1100-1200 (77-84)
Cherokee, Truck & Wagoneer	80-125 (6-9)	1400-1500 (98-105)

[1] — Steering wheel turned to extreme right or left position.

[2] — Saginaw pump. With Ford pump, 1400-1500 psi (98-105 kg/cm²).

[3] — G30 with hydroboost, pressure is 1350-1450 psi (95-102 kg/cm²).

Power Steering Gears

CHRYSLER CORP. CONSTANT CONTROL

Dodge Vans & Plymouth Wagons

DESCRIPTION

Constant ratio power steering gear consists of a gear box housing containing a sector shaft with forged sector gear, a rack-piston with gear teeth broached into the side of piston, and a worm shaft. Piston teeth and sector gear are in constant mesh with each other.

Worm shaft connects rack-piston to steering shaft through a flexible coupling. Worm shaft is geared to rack-piston through recirculating ball contact. Steering control valve, mounted to top of steering gearbox, directs flow of fluid through the system.

Fluid is supplied to the steering gear by an engine driven, constant displacement pump through a high pressure hose. Fluid is returned to pump reservoir from steering gear through a return hose.

LUBRICATION

See Power Steering General Servicing article in this Section.

TROUBLE SHOOTING & TESTING

See Power Steering General Servicing article in this Section.

ADJUSTMENT

SECTOR SHAFT PRELOAD

1) Disconnect steering center link from pitman arm. Start engine and run at idle speed, while turning steering wheel from stop-to-stop, counting number of turns from one stop to the other. Turn wheel back exactly 1/2 number of turns to center gear.

2) Loosen sector shaft adjuster screw until backlash is evident in pitman arm. Tighten adjuster until backlash just disappears, then continue tightening 3/8-1/2 turn from this position. Hold adjuster in position and torque lock nut.

CONTROL VALVE CENTERING

1) Loosen control valve mounting screws. Torque screws to 7 ft. lbs. (10 N.m) to prevent fluid leakage during centering operation. Start engine.

2) Tap on head or end plug of control valve assembly until unit is not self steering. Turn steering wheel from stop-to-stop several times to expel all air from system. Check fluid level in pump reservoir.

3) With steering wheel in center position, start and stop engine several times. Tap on valve end plug or valve head until there is no movement of steering wheel when engine is started or stopped.

4) When steering wheel movement no longer exists, valve is centered. Torque valve body attaching screws.

Fig. 1: Cutaway View of Steering Gear Assembly

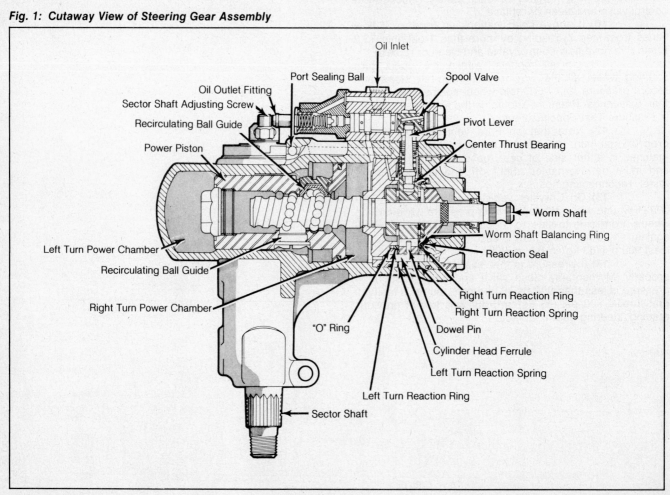

CHRYSLER CORP. CONSTANT CONTROL (Cont.)

REMOVAL & INSTALLATION

STEERING GEAR

NOTE: To avoid damage to collapsible steering column, it is recommended that column be completely detached from floor and instrument panel before steering gear is removed. See column removal under STEERING COLUMNS in this Section.

Removal

Remove battery cable and steering column. Disconnect power steering lines and cap all lines and fittings. Remove pitman arm with tool (C-4150). Remove bolts or nuts from steering gear and remove gear.

Installation

1) Position gear on frame and install retaining nuts or bolts. Rotate worm shaft by hand to center sector shaft. Align serrations on sector shaft with splines in pitman arm and install pitman arm.

2) Install and align steering column. Connect power steering lines and fill steering pump with fluid. Start engine and turn wheel from stop-to-stop to bleed system of air. Stop engine and fill steering pump if necessary.

OVERHAUL

STEERING GEAR

Disassembly

1) Clean exterior of gear, then clamp in a soft-jawed vise. Rotate input shaft from stop-to-stop several times to drain fluid.

2) Remove attaching screws, control valve, and "O" rings from housing. Remove pivot lever and spring by prying carefully under spherical head with a screwdriver.

CAUTION: Use care not to collapse slotted end of valve lever as this will destroy bearing tolerances of spherical head.

3) Loosen sector shaft adjuster lock nut, then use a spanner wrench to remove sector shaft cover spanner nut. Rotate input shaft until sector teeth are in center position.

4) Loosen steering power train retaining nut with a spanner wrench. Position a holding tool (C-3786) on threaded end of sector shaft. Slide tool into housing until both tool and shaft are engaged with bearings.

5) Rotate input shaft to full left turn position in order to compress power train components. Remove power train retaining nut and housing end tang washer.

6) Compress power train fully. Pry on rack-piston teeth with a screwdriver, using sector shaft as a fulcrum, and remove complete power train assembly. *See Fig. 2.*

CAUTION: It is important that cylinder head, center race and spacer assembly, and housing head be maintained in close contact with each other to eliminate the possibility of reaction rings becoming disengaged from grooves in cylinder head and housing head, and to prevent center spacer from separating from center race and becoming cocked in housing.

Fig. 2: Removing Powertrain Assembly

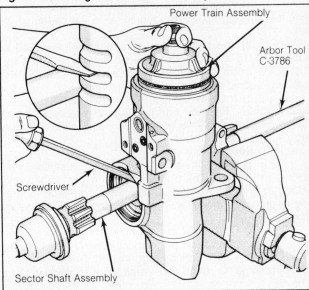

Power Train Assembly

Arbor Tool C-3786

Screwdriver

Sector Shaft Assembly

Turn wormshaft to the left to compress the powertrain components.

7) Position power train assembly vertically in a soft-jawed vise. Raise housing head until input shaft oil seal just clears end of input shaft. Position arbor tool (C-3929) on top of input shaft and extending into oil seal.

8) Keeping arbor in position, pull up on housing head until arbor is fully positioned in bearing. Remove head and arbor as a unit.

CAUTION: If input shaft oil seal is to be replaced, perform operation with housing head assembled in steering gear housing.

9) Remove large "O" ring from groove in housing head. Remove reaction seal by directing compressed air into ferrule chamber. Inspect all grooves for burrs. Make sure passage from ferrule chamber to upper reaction chamber is unobstructed.

10) Remove reaction spring, reaction ring, worn balancing ring, and spacer. While holding worm shaft from turning, turn nut to release staked portions from knurled section of shaft.

11) Wire brush knurled section, and blow out nut and worm shaft to remove metal particles. Remove nut, upper thrust bearing race and upper thrust bearing.

12) Remove center bearing race, lower thrust bearing and lower thrust bearing race. Remove lower reaction ring and spring. Remove cylinder head assembly.

13) Remove "O" rings from outer grooves in cylinder head. Remove reaction "O" ring from groove in face of cylinder head by directing compressed air into oil hole between two "O" ring grooves.

14) Remove snap ring, sleeve, and rectangular oil seal ring from cylinder head counterbore. Test operation of worm shaft. Torque required to rotate worm shaft through its travel in or out of rack piston must not exceed 1 1/2 INCH lbs. (.2 N.m).

NOTE: Worm and piston are serviced as an assembly and should not be disassembled.

Inspection

1) Place the piston in a soft jawed vise with the rack teeth facing up. Worm should be in the center of its travel.

2) The vertical side play must be measured at a point 2 5/16" (59 mm) from the piston flange. When the end of the worm is lifted with a force of 1 lb. (2.2 kg), the side play should not exceed .008" (.2 mm).

3) Inspect condition of teflon piston ring for wear and cuts. Replace with new rubber sealing ring and cast iron piston ring if necessary. To install, slide new ring into place in piston groove.

Reassembly

1) Then place piston and ring assembly into holding fixture (C-3676), with lower part of piston and ring resting against land of tool. Press down on piston to seat ring in groove, forcing open ends of ring out for ease of locking ring.

2) Clamp piston assembly in a soft-jawed vise with worm shaft pointing up. Inspect cylinder head ferrule oil passage for obstructions, and inspect lands for burrs. Lubricate large "O" rings and install them in cylinder head grooves.

3) Install worm sleeve seal, sleeve and snap ring, making sure snap ring is fully seated in groove. Install lower reaction "O" ring in cylinder head groove. Slide cylinder head assembly, ferrule end up, onto worm shaft.

CAUTION: Check worm shaft seal ring, making sure gap is closed to avoid damaging the ring as the cylinder head moves against the piston flange.

4) Lubricate power train parts with power steering fluid and install in the following order; lower thrust bearing and race, lower reaction spring, lower reaction ring, center bearing race, upper thrust bearing, upper thrust race and thrust bearing adjusting nut.

5) Ensure small hole in reaction spring is over ferrule. Lower reaction ring must be installed with flange up so ring protrudes through reaction spring and contacts the reaction "O" ring in the cylinder head.

6) Turn worm shaft 1/2 turn clockwise. Hold shaft in this position using the splined nut, Tool C-3637, and socket wrench. Tighten adjusting nut to 50 ft. lbs. (68 N.m) to prestretch the threads. Hold shaft in position as outlined while performing the following adjustment.

7) Loosen the adjusting nut. Place several rounds of cord around center bearing race and attach a spring scale. Pull on cord causing bearing race to rotate.

8) Tighten adjusting nut while pulling on cord with spring scale. Adjusting nut is properly tightened when reading on spring scale is 16-24 oz. (4.4-6.7 N) with bearing race turning.

9) Stake upper part of worm shaft bearing adjusting nut into knurled area of shaft. Hold a 1/4" flat end punch on centerline of worm shaft end at a slight angle to nut flange. If adjusting nut moves, strike it in the opposite direction to regain proper preload.

10) After retesting for proper preload, stake the nut at 3 more locations 90° apart around upper part of nut. To test total staking, apply 20 ft. lbs. (27 N.m) of torque in each direction. If nut does not move, staking operation is correct.

11) Position spacer assembly over center race, engaging dowel pin of spacer in slot of race, and slot of spacer centered over cylinder head ferrule. This aligns valve pivot lever hole in center bearing race with valve pivot lever hole in center bearing spacer assembly.

NOTE: The small "O" ring for the ferrule groove should not be installed until after upper reaction spring and spacer have been installed.

12) Install upper reaction ring on center race, and spacer, with flange down against spacer. Install upper reaction spring over reaction ring, with cylinder head ferrule through hole in reaction spring. Install worm balancing ring (without flange) inside upper reaction ring.

13) Lubricate ferrule "O" ring, and install in groove on cylinder head ferrule. If oil seal was removed from housing head, install new seal using seal installer (C-3650) to drive seal in until tool bottoms on support.

14) Lubricate and install reaction seal in groove in face of housing head with flat side of seal out. Install "O" ring in groove in housing head.

Fig. 3: Exploded View of Reaction Seal and Ring

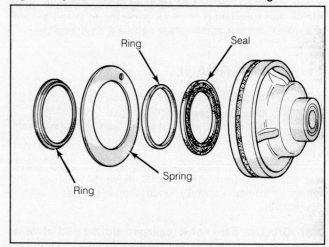

15) Slide housing head and arbor assembly over worm shaft, engaging cylinder head ferrule and "O" ring and making sure reaction rings enter circular groove in housing head.

16) Lubricate power train bore of housing and install power train assembly while noting the following: Keep worm turned fully counterclockwise to keep reaction rings from coming out of their grooves.

17) Piston teeth must be facing to the right, and valve lever hole in center race and spacer must be in the "up" position. Ensure cylinder head is bottomed on housing shoulder.

18) Align valve lever hole in center bearing race and center spacer with lever hole in gear housing. Install valve pivot lever, double bearing end first, through hole in housing until engaged in center race and spacer.

CAUTION: Slots in valve lever must be parallel to worm shaft in order to engage anti-rotation pin in center race.

19) Lightly tap on end of lever to seat lower pivot pin in center race. Center lever in hole by turning housing head by tapping on a reinforcing rib with a hammer and drift. Install housing head tang washer to index with groove in housing.

Power Steering Gears

CHRYSLER CORP. CONSTANT CONTROL (Cont.)

Fig. 4: Exploded View of Steering Gear Components

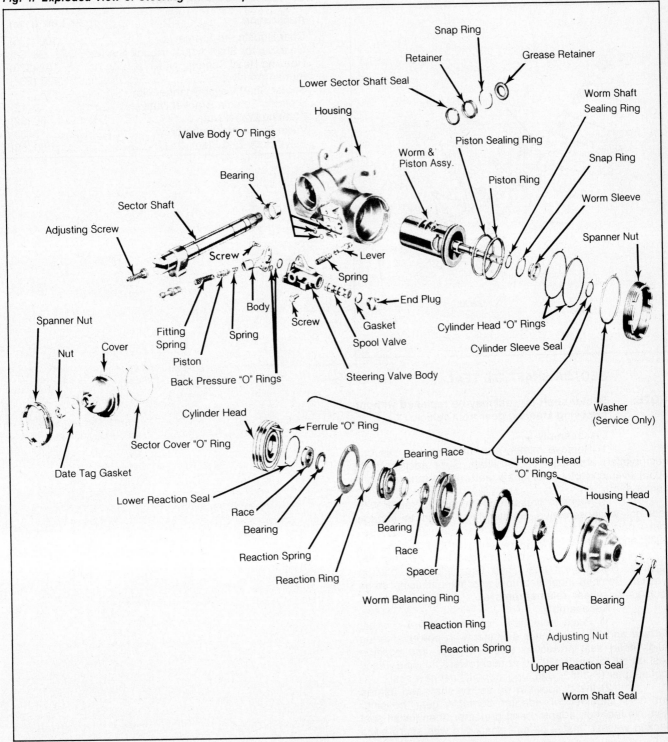

20) Install and torque spanner nut. Ensure valve lever remains centered in hole in housing. Turn worm shaft until piston bottoms in both directions, and note valve lever action.

21) Lever must center in hole and snap back to its center position when worm tension is relieved. Install valve lever spring, small end first.

22) Set power piston at center of travel, install sector shaft and cover assembly, and center sector teeth with piston rack teeth. Make sure "O" ring is properly installed on cover. Install sector cover lock nut.

23) Install control valve body on housing, making sure valve pivot lever enters hole in valve spool. Be sure "O" ring seals are in place. Torque control valve attaching screws. Install new sector shaft seal, seal back-up washer and snap ring. Install new grease retainer.

Power Steering Gears

CHRYSLER CORP. CONSTANT CONTROL (Cont.)

Fig. 5: Disassembled View of Control Valve Assembly

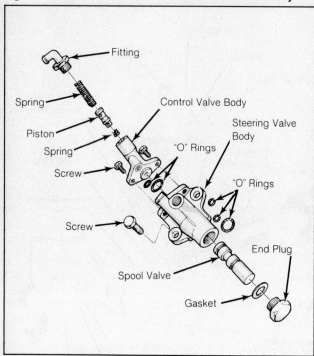

TIGHTENING SPECIFICATIONS

Application	Ft. Lbs. (N.m)
Gear Housing-to-Frame	100 (136)
Gear Sector Shaft Adjuster Lock Nut	28 (38)
Housing Head Spanner Nut	162 (220)
Pitman Arm Nut	175 (238)
Sector Shaft Cover Spanner Nut	155 (211)
Steering Column Bracket Nuts	9 (12)
Steering Wheel Nut	60 (82)
Valve Body Attaching Screw	17 (23)
Valve Body End Plug	50 (68)

SECTOR SHAFT OIL SEAL

NOTE: Sector shaft oil seal may be replaced without removing steering gear from vehicle.

Disassembly

1) Remove pitman arm attaching nut. Disconnect pitman arm from sector shaft. Slide adapter (SP-3056) over end of sector shaft, and thread tool nut onto sector shaft.

2) Maintain pressure on threaded adapter with tool nut while screwing adapter far enough to engage metal portion of grease retainer. Place 2 half rings (SP-1932) and tool retainer ring over both portions of tool.

3) Turn tool nut counterclockwise to remove retainer. Remove oil seal snap ring, and seal backup washer. Remove inner seal in same manner using same tools as for grease retainer removal.

Reassembly

1) Place new seal, lip facing down, on flat surface and lubricate inner diameter with power steering fluid. Insert seal protective sleeve in seal, and position seal on sector shaft with lip of seal toward housing. Place tool adapter (S-3052) with long step against new seal.

2) Install tool nut on sector shaft and tighten nut until shoulder of adapter contacts gear housing. Remove tool nut, adapter, and protector, then install seal backup washer. Install oil seal snap ring with sharp edge out.

3) Fill housing cavity outside retainer and snap ring with a multi-purpose chassis grease. Position oil seal in housing bore. Position adapter tool (SP-3052) with short step of lip against seal.

4) Install tool nut on sector shaft, then tighten until shoulder contacts gear housing. Remove tool, and position steering gear and steering wheel in straight ahead position. Install pitman arm and attaching nut.

Power Steering Gears

FORD TORSION BAR

Bronco, Bronco II, Pickup, Ranger & Van Models

DESCRIPTION

Torsion bar type power steering unit consists of a worm and one-piece rack-piston, which is meshed to gear teeth on sector shaft. Hydraulic control valve, input shaft, and torsion bar assembly are mounted to end of worm shaft and operated by twisting action of torsion bar.

One-piece rack-piston, worm and sector shaft are mounted in one housing, while valve spool is mounted in an attached housing. This allows internal passage of fluid between valve and cylinder, thus eliminating the need for all external lines and hoses, except for pressure and return hoses between pump and gearbox assembly.

LUBRICATION

Check fluid level in pump reservoir every 5000 miles. Steering gear and fluid must be at normal operating temperature. If necessary, add power steering fluid to bring level to proper mark on dipstick.

ADJUSTMENT

OVERCENTER POSITION

1) Disconnect pitman arm from sector shaft. Disconnect fluid return line at pump reservoir, and cap reservoir return line pipe. Place end of return line in clean container and cycle steering wheel in both directions several times to discharge all fluid from steering gearbox.

2) Remove horn button from steering wheel, and turn steering wheel until positioned 45° from left steering stop. Using an INCH-lb. torque wrench on steering wheel attaching nut, measure force required to turn steering shaft 1/8 turn from 45° position.

3) Turn steering wheel back to center position and measure force required to move steering shaft back and forth across center position.

Fig. 1: Ford Torsion Bar Steering Gear Assembly

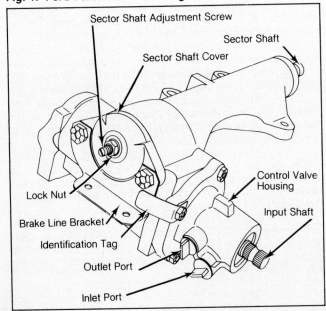

Sector Shaft Adjustment Screw
Sector Shaft
Sector Shaft Cover
Control Valve Housing
Input Shaft
Lock Nut
Brake Line Bracket
Identification Tag
Outlet Port
Inlet Port

4) Loosen lock nut and turn adjusting screw until reading across center position is 14-18 INCH lbs. (1.6-2.0 N.m) greater than reading across 45° position. Tighten lock nut while holding adjusting screw in place. Replace pitman arm and reconnect hoses.

TESTING

VALVE SPOOL CENTERING

1) Install a 0-2000 psi pressure gauge and valve assembly between power steering pump and high pressure line. Open gauge valve completely, and remove horn button from steering wheel. Attach an INCH-lb. torque wrench to steering wheel attaching nut.

2) Power steering fluid must be at normal operating temperature and at correct level. Steering wheel must be in centered position and engine at normal operating temperature.

3) Set engine idle to 1000 RPM. Using torque wrench, rotate steering shaft to either side of center to obtain gauge reading of 250 psi (17.5 kg/cm²) in each direction.

4) Torque reading should be same in both directions when 250 psi (17.5 kg/cm²) is reached. If difference between readings exceeds 6 INCH lbs. (.68 N.m), steering gear must be removed and the shaft and control assembly replaced.

NOTE: **When performing test off vehicle, use same procedure, except take torque and pressure readings at right and left stops instead of either side of center.**

REMOVAL & INSTALLATION

STEERING GEAR

Removal

1) Disconnect hydraulic lines at power steering gear, and cap lines. Plug ports in steering gear to prevent entry of foreign matter. Remove splash shield from flex coupling. Disconnect flex coupling at steering gear.

2) Raise vehicle and remove pitmam arm, attaching nut and washer. Using puller, remove pitman arm from sector shaft, being careful not to damage seals.

3) Support steering gear and remove steering gear attaching bolts. Work the steering gear free of the flex coupling and remove steering gear from vehicle.

Installation

1) Slide flex coupling into position on steering shaft assembly and turn steering wheel so spokes are in horizontal position. Center steering gear input shaft with indexing flat forward.

2) Install gearbox input shaft into flex coupling and into place on frame. Install and tighten attaching bolts. With wheels in straight ahead position, install pitman arm on sector shaft. Install washer and nut on pitman arm and tighten.

3) Install splash shield. Connect and tighten pressure and return lines to steering gear. Disconnect coil wire. Fill reservoir to proper level. Turn ignition on and turn steering wheel left to right to distribute fluid. Check fluid and add if necessary.

Power Steering Gears

FORD TORSION BAR (Cont.)

OVERHAUL

NOTE: If complete gearbox assembly is not to be overhauled, remove unit to be overhauled and proceed to disassembly and reassembly of that unit.

STEERING GEAR

Disassembly

1) Drain steering gear completely, and mount gear in a soft-jawed vise. Remove lock nut and washer from adjusting screw. Turn input shaft to either stop, then turn shaft back 2 turns to center gear.

2) Remove sector shaft cover attaching bolts. Tap lower end of sector shaft with a soft faced hammer to loosen shaft in bore, then lift shaft and cover assembly from housing. Discard cover "O" ring.

3) Turn sector shaft cover counterclockwise to remove it from adjusting screw. Remove valve housing attaching bolts and identification tag. Lift valve housing from steering gear housing while holding piston to prevent it from rotating off worm shaft.

4) Remove valve housing and control valve gasket. Discard gasket. With piston held so that ball guide faces up, remove ball guide clamp screws and ball guide clamp.

5) Over a clean container, place finger over opening in ball guide, turn piston so ball guide faces down and let guide tubes fall into container.

6) Rotate input shaft stop to stop until all balls fall from the piston into the container. Remove valve assembly from piston. Inspect piston bore to make sure all balls have been removed.

7) Install valve body assembly in bench mounted holding fixture (T57L-500-B) or vise. Loosen hex head race nut screw from the bearing race nut. *See Fig. 2.* Carefully slide input shaft, worm and valve assembly out of valve housing.

Fig. 2: Removing Worm Bearing Race Nut

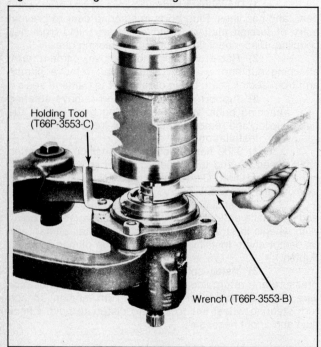

Holding Tool (T66P-3553-C)

Wrench (T66P-3553-B)

CAUTION: Due to close clearance, cocking of spool may cause it to jam in housing.

Reassembly

1) Mount valve housing in a holding fixture with flanged end upward. Apply a light coat of lubricant to Teflon rings on valve sleeve, then carefully install worm and valve in housing.

2) Install race nut in housing and tighten securely. Install Allen head race nut set screw through housing and tighten. Place piston on bench with ball guide holes facing up.

3) Insert worm shaft into piston so that the first groove is in line with the hole nearest the center of the piston. Place the ball guide in the piston. Place a minimum of 27 ball bearings in the ball guide while turning worm counterclockwise as viewed from input end of shaft.

Fig. 3: Installing Piston on Worm Shaft

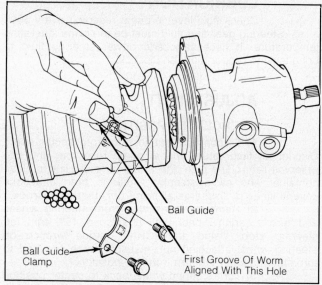

Ball Guide

Ball Guide Clamp

First Groove Of Worm Aligned With This Hole

Rotate worm while installing balls.

4) If all balls have not been fed into the guide upon reaching the left stop, rotate the input shaft in one direction and then the other while inserting the remaining balls. DO NOT rotate the input shaft more than 3 turns from the left stop or the balls will fall out of the circuit.

5) Secure guides in ball nut with guide clamp. Apply petroleum jelly to Teflon seal on piston and place a new "O" ring on valve housing. Slide piston and valve into gear housing, using care not to damage Teflon seal.

6) Align oil passage in valve housing with passage in gear housing. Place new "O" ring in oil passage hole of gear housing. Install identification tag on housing on upper right valve housing bolt.

7) Loosely install housing attaching bolts, rotate the ball nut so that teeth are in same place as sector teeth and tighten valve housing bolts. Position sector shaft cover "O" ring in steering gear housing. Turn input shaft as necessary to center piston.

8) Apply petroleum jelly to sector shaft journal, and position sector shaft and cover assembly in gear housing. Install and tighten cover attaching bolts. Adjust steering overcenter position. See Overcenter Position Adjustment in this article.

FORD TORSION BAR (Cont.)

STEERING GEAR HOUSING
Disassembly & Reassembly

1) Remove snap ring from lower end of housing. Using a puller or slide hammer, remove dust seal and pressure seal from housing. Lubricate new seals and sector shaft seal bore with Lubriplate.

2) Place dust seal on tool (T77L-3576-A) so the raised lip of the seal is toward the tool. Place pressure seal on tool so lip is away from tool. Flat back side of pressure seal should be against flat side of dust seal.

3) Insert tool into sector shaft bore and drive in until seals clear snap ring groove. Do not bottom seals against bearing. Install snap ring in housing groove.

CONTROL VALVE HOUSING
Disassembly

1) Remove dust seal from rear of valve housing using slide hammer. Discard seal. Remove snap ring from valve housing. Invert valve housing.

2) Using input shaft bearing/seal tool (T65P-3524-A2 & T65-3524-A3) in valve body assembly opposite oil seal end, tap bearing and seal out of housing.

3) Discard seal. Remove fluid inlet and outlet tube seats with tube seat remover (T74P-3504-L) if damaged.

Reassembly

1) Coat fluid inlet and outlet tube seats with Vaseline and install them in the housing. Install bearing with metal side covering rollers facing outward. Press bearing into housing.

2) Dip a new oil seal in power steering fluid and place in housing with metal side out. Drive seal into housing until outer edge does not quite clear snap ring groove.

3) Install snap ring in housing. Place the dust seal in the housing with dished rubber side out. Drive into place until seal is located behind undercut in input shaft.

WORM & VALVE SLEEVE
Disassembly & Reassembly

1) Remove rings from sleeve with a small knife. Mount worm end of worm and valve sleeve assembly in a soft-jawed vise. Install a mandrel tool (T75L-3517-A1) over the sleeve. Install rings one at a time with the aid of a driver tool (T75L-3517-A2).

Fig. 4: Disassembled View of Control Valve Housing

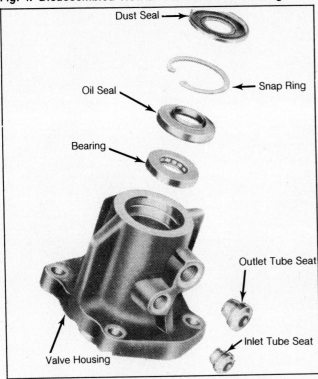

Fig. 5: Disassembled View of Ball Nut & Housing

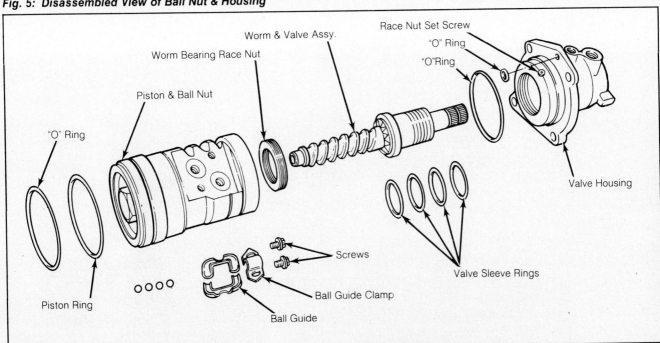

Power Steering Gears

FORD TORSION BAR (Cont.)

2) Rapidly push down on pusher tool to force ring down ramp and into fourth groove of valve sleeve. Repeat three more times, each time adding spacers (Tool T75L-3517-A3) under mandrel tool to line up next groove.

3) After all sleeve rings are installed, install sizing tool (T75L-3517-A4) carefully over valve sleeve rings. Be sure rings are not bent over as tube is slid over them. Remove sizing tool and check condition of rings. They must turn freely.

TIGHTENING SPECIFICATIONS

Application	Ft. Lbs. (N.m)
Piston End Cap	70-110 (95-150)
Rack Retaining Nut	1
Sector Shaft Adj. Screw Lock Nut	35-45 (48-61)
Sector Shaft Cover Bolts	55-70 (75-95)
Valve Housing-to-Gear Bolts	35-50 (48-68)

	INCH Lbs. (N.m)
Allen Head Race Nut Set Screw	15-25 (1.6-2.8)
Ball Return Guide Clamp Screw	42-70 (4.7-7.9)

1 - Tool used with torque wrench will affect observed reading at torque wrench. To obtain required torque wrench reading, multiply length of torque wrench by desired torque (72 ft. lbs.; 98 N.m), and divide this product by total length of torque wrench and tool.

Power Steering Gears

SAGINAW ROTARY VALVE

Chrysler Corp. (Exc. Van), General Motors, Jeep

DESCRIPTION

Steering gear is a recirculating ball type, available in either a constant or a variable ratio design. Steel balls work as rolling thread between steering gear worm shaft and rack-piston nut. Worm shaft thrust is taken by a thrust bearing and two races at the lower end, and by a bearing in the adjuster plug at the upper end.

This design puts spring pressure on worm shaft to prevent loss of thrust bearing preload. The adjuster plug provides initial preload adjustment and service adjustment (when repairing gear). As worm shaft is turned right, the rack-piston is moved upward in gear.

As worm shaft is turned left, the rack-piston is moved downward in gear. The rack-piston teeth mesh with the sector, which is forged as part of the sector shaft. Rotating the worm shaft moves the sector shaft, which turns the wheels through mechanical linkage. *See Fig. 1.*

LUBRICATION, TESTING & TROUBLE SHOOTING

See Power Steering General Servicing article in this section.

ADJUSTMENT

THRUST BEARING PRELOAD

1) This procedure is to be performed with steering gear removed from vehicle. Remove adjuster plug lock nut. Turn adjuster plug clockwise with a spanner wrench till plug is seated in housing. This will require 20-30 ft. lbs. (27-41 N.m) of torque.

2) Place an index mark on housing opposite one spanner wrench hole in adjuster plug. Measure 1/2" (13 mm) counterclockwise from mark and again mark housing. Rotate plug counterclockwise until hole in adjuster lines up with second mark.

3) Tighten lock nut, making sure adjuster remains in position. Attach an INCH lb. torque wrench to end of input shaft. Turn input shaft to right stop, then back 1/4 turn.

4) Using torque wrench measure rotational torque required to turn shaft. Reading should be taken with beam of torque wrench near vertical while turning it counterclockwise at an even rate. Torque reading should be 4-10 INCH Lbs. (.4-1.1 N.m). *See. Fig. 2.*

NOTE: **If reading does not fall within this range, the adjuster plug may have turned while lock nut was being tightened. Steering gear may be incorrectly assembled or worm shaft thrust bearings and races may be defective. Repair as required and readjust preload.**

Fig. 1: Exploded View of Saginaw Rotary Valve Power Steering Gear

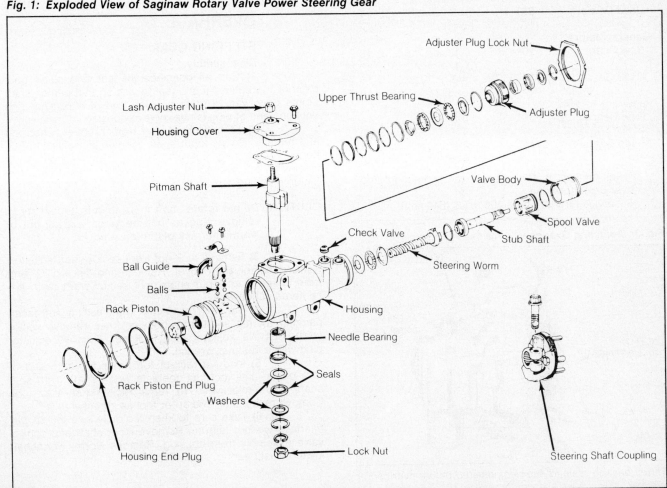

Power Steering Gears

SAGINAW ROTARY VALVE (Cont.)

Fig. 2: Measuring Thrust Bearing Preload

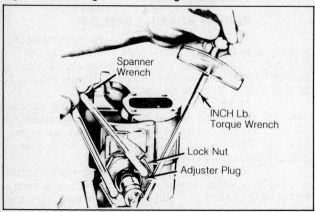

Preload should be 4-10 INCH Lbs. (.4-1.1 N.m).

OVERCENTER PRELOAD TORQUE

1) Loosen adjuster screw lock nut. Back off adjuster screw until stopped, then turn in 1 full turn. Rotate input shaft from stop to stop counting the number of turns. Turn shaft half way back, to center position.

OVER-CENTER PRELOAD INCH LBS. (N.m)

Application	Arc	Over-Center	[1] Total
Chrysler Corp.			
New Gears	90°	4-8	14
		(.5-.9)	(1.5)
Used Gears [2]	90°	4-5	14
		(.5-.6)	(1.5)
General Motors			
New Gears	20°	6-10	18
		(.7-1.1)	(2)
Used Gears	20°	4-5	18
		(.5-.6)	(2)
Jeep			
New Gears	45°	4-8	14
		(.4-.9)	(1.5)
Used Gears	45°	4-5	14
		(.5-.6)	(1.5)

[1] - Total preload is the sum of thrust bearing and over-center preload.
[2] - In service for more than 400 miles (640 km.).

Fig. 3: Adjusting Over-center Preload

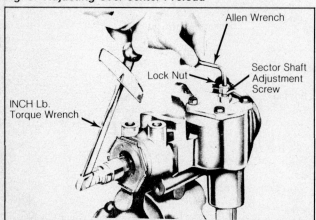

Thrust bearing preload must be adjusted before over-center preload.

2) Attach an INCH lb. torque wrench to input shaft. Refer to *Overcenter Preload Specifications* and turn shaft from side to side through the specified arc on each side of center. Note torque reading going over center. *See Fig. 3.*

REMOVAL & INSTALLATION

NOTE: **To avoid damage, collapsible steering column should be completely removed from vehicle before steering gear is removed.**

STEERING GEAR
Removal
1) Raise and support vehicle. Place drain pan under steering gear assembly. Center steering gear. Disconnect hydraulic hoses from gear and cap ends. Disconnect steering linkage from pitman arm and remove arm from gear.

2) Remove flexible coupling clamp bolt and bolts retaining steering gear to frame. Disconnect gear from flexible coupling and remove gear from vehicle. On Jeep "CJ" and Scrambler models, remove steering gear and mounting bracket as an assembly.

Installation
To install, reverse removal procedure. Fill power steering pump reservoir with fluid and bleed air from system. *See Power Steering General Service.*

OVERHAUL

STEERING GEAR
Disassembly
1) Cap all openings in gear and clean gear exterior throughly. Mount gear in vise so that pitman shaft points downward. Rotate housing end plug retainer ring until one end of plug is over hole in housing.

2) Force end of ring from groove in housing and remove. Rotate input shaft counterclockwise to force housing end plug out of housing. Rotate input shaft clockwise 1/2 turn to draw rack-piston inward. Remove piston end plug.

CAUTION: **Do not rotate shaft more than is necessary to remove plug as ball bearings will fall out of worm and rack piston assembly.**

3) Remove lock nut from sector shaft adjuster. Remove sector shaft cover. Remove and discard "O" ring from cover. Turn input shaft until sector shaft teeth are centered in housing.

4) Tap end of sector shaft with a soft-faced hammer to free shaft from housing, then remove sector shaft. Remove adjuster plug lock nut. Remove adjuster plug with a spanner wrench.

5) Insert a rack-piston arbor tool into end of rack-piston until tool just contacts worm shaft. Turn stub shaft counterclockwise to force rack-piston onto tool. Remove rack-piston and arbor tool as an assembly.

6) Take care to keep tool fully inserted so ball bearings will not fall out. Remove input shaft and control valve assembly from housing. Remove worm, wormshaft lower thrust bearing, and races from housing.

SAGINAW ROTARY VALVE (Cont.)

Reassembly

1) Lubricate all parts with clean power steering fluid before reassembly. Install lower thrust bearing and races on worm. *See Fig. 4.*

Fig. 4: Reassembly of Valve Body & Worm Shaft Assembly

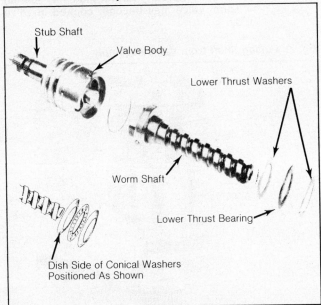

Cupped side of thrust washers must face toward stub shaft.

NOTE: If conical thrust races are used, make sure tapered surfaces are parallel to each other and that cupped sides face toward stub shaft.

2) Install stub shaft cap "O" ring in valve body. Align valve body drive pin on worm with narrow pin slot in valve body. Worm drive lugs must engage in stub shaft cap.

3) Install valve body and worm assembly into housing. Perform installation by pressing directly on the valve body only. This will prevent the stub shaft "O" ring from disengaging from the valve body.

4) The valve body is correctly seated when the fluid return port in the housing is fully visible. Make sure worm locating pin is fully engaged in valve body. Place seal protector over input shaft, install a new adjuster plug "O" ring, then install adjuster plug.

5) Remove seal protector from housing and loosely install adjuster plug lock nut. Insert arbor tool and rack-piston into housing. Align worm and rack-piston and turn stub shaft clockwise to engage worm. Maintain pressure on arbor tool until worm is fully engaged.

6) Turn input shaft clockwise until middle rack groove in rack-piston is aligned with center of sector shaft roller bearing. Remove arbor tool.

7) Install a new sector shaft cover gasket. Thread sector shaft cover onto adjuster screw until bottomed. Back off 1 1/2 turns. Install sector shaft so that center gear tooth meshes with center groove in rack-piston. Install cover attaching bolts.

8) Install adjuster lock nut halfway onto sector shaft. Install piston and plug in rack-piston. Install housing end plug "O" ring, end plug and retainer ring. Adjust worm bearing preload and over-center preload at this time.

ADJUSTER PLUG
Disassembly

1) Remove thrust bearing retainer ring with a screwdriver, taking care not to score needle bearing bore. Discard retainer ring. Remove thrust bearing spacer, thrust bearing and bearing races.

2) Remove and discard adjuster plug "O" ring, then remove input shaft seal retainer. Remove and discard dust seal. Pry input shaft seal from adjuster plug.

3) Inspect needle bearing in adjuster plug. If necessary, remove bearing by pressing out from spacer end. *See Fig. 5.*

Inspection

Inspect thrust bearing for cracks and rollers for pitting, scoring, or cracking. Check thrust races and spacer for damage or damage. Replace parts as necessary.

Fig. 5: Exploded View of Adjuster Plug Assembly

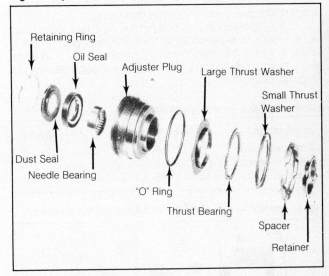

Reassembly

1) Press roller bearing into adjuster plug (identification end facing tool) until bearing bottoms on input shaft seal bore. Install input shaft seal with spring in seal facing adjuster plug.

2) Install dust seal into adjuster plug. Rubber face of seal must face away from plug. Install retainer ring. Install adjuster plug "O" ring.

3) Assemble thrust bearing, thrust bearing race, and thrust bearing spacer on adjuster plug. Using a brass or wooden dowel, press bearing retainer into needle bearing bore.

RACK-PISTON & WORM
Disassembly

Remove worm, lower thrust bearing and bearing races from rack piston. Remove piston ring and back-up "O" ring from rack-piston. Remove ball return guide clamp, ball return guide and all ball bearings from rack-piston.

Inspection

1) Clean and dry all parts. Inspect worm and rack-piston grooves for scoring. Inspect ball bearings for damage. If any ball bearings are damaged, replace entire set. Check ball guides for pinching of ends.

2) Inspect lower thrust bearing races for cracking, scoring, or pitting. Replace the wormshaft and rack-piston as an assembly if either part is damaged. Inspect the rack-piston teeth for chips, cracks, dents or scoring.

Reassembly

1) Install "O" ring and piston ring onto the rack-piston using care not to twist them. Install worm into rack-piston until worm is against piston shoulder. Install ball bearings into rack-piston while slowly rotating worm counterclockwise.

NOTE: See following table for number of balls to be installed. BE SURE to install light and dark colored balls alternately, as black balls are .0005" smaller than silver balls.

2) Install correct number of balls in ball guide. Bearings in guide must be in sequence with bearings in rack-piston. Hold balls in place with chassis lubricant and install return ball guide assembly into position.

3) Install clamp and tighten attaching bolts. See Fig. 6. Insert rack-piston arbor tool into rack-piston until it contacts worm. Maintain pressure on arbor tool, and back worm out of rack-piston. DO NOT allow ball bearings to drop out of circuits.

RACK PISTON & WORM ASSEMBLY BALL BEARINGS

Application	Rack-Piston	Guide
Chrysler Corp.	19	5
General Motors	17	7
Jeep	18	6

Fig. 6: Installing Ball Bearing into Rack-Piston Assembly

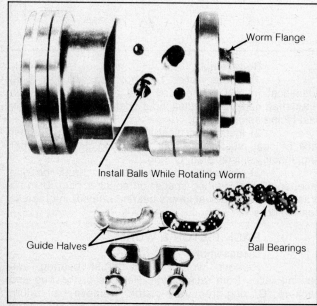

Worm Flange

Install Balls While Rotating Worm

Guide Halves

Ball Bearings

Alternate light and dark colored balls when installing.

ROTARY VALVE

NOTE: Complete valve assembly is balanced during assembly. If replacement of any part other than rings or seals is necessary, replace complete assembly.

Disassembly

1) Remove and discard stub shaft cap "O" ring. Invert valve and lightly tap end of stub shaft against wood block until shaft cap is free of valve body. Pull stub shaft outward until drive pin hole is visible. See Fig. 7.

NOTE: Do not pull shaft any further than 1/4" (6 mm) or spool valve may become cocked in valve body.

Fig. 7: Pulling Shaft from Valve Assembly

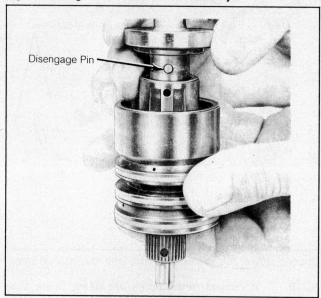

Disengage Pin

Depress pin to remove stub shaft from valve body.

2) Disengage drive pin and carefuly remove stub shaft from valve body and spool assembly with a twisting motion. If binding occurs, realign valve and try removal again.

Fig. 8: Exploded View of Valve Body Assembly

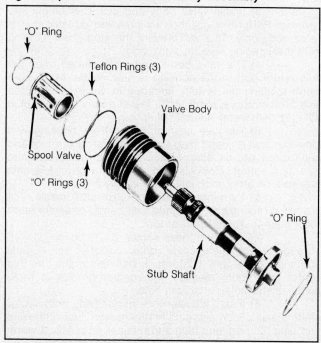

"O" Ring

Teflon Rings (3)

Valve Body

Spool Valve

"O" Rings (3)

"O" Ring

Stub Shaft

CAUTION: Do not force stub shaft or spool out of valve body.

3) Remove spool valve from valve body with twisting motion. Remove and discard all "O" rings and Teflon rings.

Reassembly

1) Lubricate all valve body components with power steering fluid. Install replacement backup "O" rings in seal grooves and install replacement seal rings over backup rings. Take care not to damage seal rings during installation.

NOTE: **Teflon seal rings may appear to be distorted after installation. However, heat of operation will straighten them.**

2) Lubricate replacement spool valve damper "O" ring with petroleum jelly. Install on spool valve. Carefully insert spool valve into valve body.

3) Push spool valve through valve body until locating pin hole is visible at opposite end of valve body and spool valve is flush with notched end of valve. Install stub shaft in spool valve and valve body.

4) Be sure stub shaft locating pin is aligned with spool valve locating hole. Align notch in stub shaft cap with stub shaft locating pin and press sub shaft and spool valve into valve body. Install stub shaft cap "O" ring into valve body. *See Fig. 9.*

CAUTION: Before installing assembled valve body into gear housing, be sure valve body stub shaft locating pin is fully engaged in stub shaft cap notch. Do not allow stub shaft to disengage from valve body pin.

Fig. 9: Aligning Pin and Notch for Input (Stub) Shaft

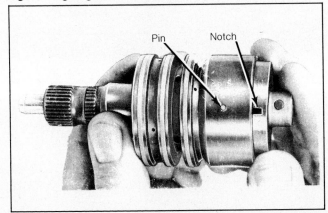

Stub shaft locating pin must align with spool valve locating hole.

STEERING GEAR HOUSING
Disassembly

1) Remove sector shaft seal retaining ring and remove lower steel washer. Remove lower seal, spacer washer and upper seal from housing. Press sector shaft bearing out of housing from lower end.

2) To remove hose connector seat, tap out seat using a 5/16"-18 thread tap. Thread connector seats ONLY 2-3 threads. Install a bolt with a flat washer and nut into the seat.

3) Hold bolt from turning and tighten nut to extract seat from housing. Some Jeep steering gear units have metric thread fittings and hose fittings which use "O" ring seals instead of connector seats. Remove check valve and spring from inlet port and discard.

Fig. 10: Gear Housing Seals and Bearing

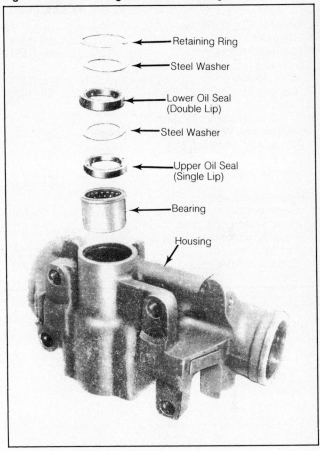

- Retaining Ring
- Steel Washer
- Lower Oil Seal (Double Lip)
- Steel Washer
- Upper Oil Seal (Single Lip)
- Bearing
- Housing

Inspection

1) Replace the housing if bore is severly worn, scored or pitted. Minor scratches may be removed with crocus cloth. Inspect the housing ball plug for fluid leakage. Seat the ball plug with blunt punch.

2) Spray the ball area with Loctite Solvent 7559 and dry with compressed air. Cover the ball area with Loctite Sealant 290. Allow sealant to cure for 2 hours before assembling gear.

3) Inspect all retaining ring, bearing and seal surfaces in the housing. Replace the housing if any surface is worn or damaged.

Reassembly

1) Working from upper end, press a new bearing into housing until it is seated .030" (.76 mm) below shoulder in housing bore. Lubricate new seal with power steering fluid.

2) Install single lipped seal and spacer washer only far enough to provide clearance for next seal, washer and retaining ring. DO NOT bottom the seal against the housing counterbore.

3) Install double lipped seal and steel washer. Install retaining ring. DO NOT allow seals to contact one another. To ensure proper seal action, be sure there is clearance between them.

4) If port seat was removed, position NEW spring, check valve, and a new seat over opening in housing. Drive into place using a brass drift.

TIGHTENING SPECIFICATIONS

Application	Ft. Lbs. (N.m)
Adjuster Plug Lock Nut	
Chrysler Corp.	85 (116)
General Motors	80 (108)
Gear-to-Frame Attaching Bolts	
Chrysler Corp.	100 (136)
General Motors	80 (108)
Jeep	
"CJ" & Scrambler Models	55 (75)
Cherokee, Wagoneer & Truck Models	70 (95)
Pitman Arm Attaching Nut	
Chrysler Corp.	175 (237)
General Motor	180 (244)
Jeep	185 (250)
Rack Piston End Plug	
Chrysler Corp.	50 (68)
General Motors & Jeep	75 (102)
Sector Shaft Adjuster Lock Nut	
Chrysler Corp.	28 (38)
General Motors	20 (27)
Jeep	33 (45)

Power Steering Pumps

FORD C-II

Bronco, Bronco II, "F" Models & Ranger

DESCRIPTION

C-II power steering pump is a belt driven, slipper type integral pump with a fiber glass nylon reservoir. Reservoir is attached to rear side of pump housing front plate. Pump body is encased within housing and reservoir.

Hoses are attached with quick disconnect fittings, located below filler neck at outboard side of reservoir. A pressure sensitive identification tag is attached to reservoir, indicating basic model number.

LUBRICATION, TROUBLE SHOOTING & TESTING

See Power Steering General Servicing article in this section.

REMOVAL & INSTALLATION

Removal

1) Disconnect fluid return hose at reservoir and drain fluid. Remove pressure hose from pump. Remove bolts from pump adjustment bracket and loosen pump enough to remove drive belt.

2) Remove pump and adjustment bracket from support bracket. Remove pulley from pump with appropriate pulley puller and remove adjustment bracket attaching bolts. Remove pump.

Installation

1) Install adjustment bracket on pump and tighten bolts. Install pulley on pump with appropriate pulley installer. Place pump with adjustment bracket and pulley on support bracket. Install and tighten adjustment bracket-to-support bracket bolts.

2) Install and adjust belt on pulley, then tighten adjustment bracket bolts. Install hoses to pump, fill reservoir and start engine, turning wheel from stop-to-stop to remove air from system.

OVERHAUL

Disassembly

1) Remove pulley from pump using installer/remover tool (T75L-3733-A). Remove outlet fitting, flow control valve, spring and reservoir. Place a "C" clamp in vise.

2) Install lower support plate tool (T78P-3733-A1) over pump rotor shaft. Install upper compressor plate tool (T78P-3733-A2) into upper portion of "C" clamp. Place the pump assembly into "C" clamp with rotor shaft facing down. See Fig. 1.

3) Tighten "C" clamp until slight bottoming of valve cover is felt. Insert small drift through hole in side of pump housing plate and push inward on valve cover retaining ring. Remove retaining ring. See Fig. 2.

4) Remove pump from clamp. Remove valve cover and "O" ring seal. Push on rotor shaft and remove. Remove upper plate, rotor and slippers. Remove cam insert and two dowel pins.

5) Remove lower plate and Belleville spring by lightly tapping housing on flat surface, remove "O" ring.

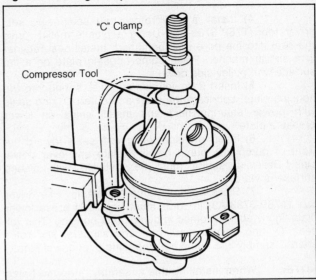

Fig. 1: Installing Compressor Plate Tools

DO NOT overtighten "C" clamp.

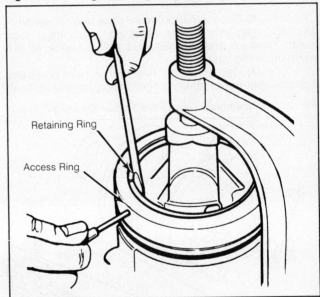

Fig. 2: Removing Retaining Ring

Use screwdriver to pry out retaining ring.

Remove rotor shaft seal and seal retainer with a screwdriver.

Reassembly

1) Place the rotor on rotor shaft splines, with triangle detent in rotor counterbore facing upward. Install retaining ring in groove in end of rotor shaft. Place the insert cam over the rotor with recessed flat toward reservoir.

2) With rotor extended half way out of cam, insert a spring into a rotor spring pocket. Work in the rotor cavity directly below recessed flat on the cam. Use one of the slippers to compress the spring and install slipper with groove facing upward.

3) Hold cam stationary and turn rotor either direction one space at a time and install another spring and slipper until all 10 rotor cavities have been filled. Be

careful when turning rotor that springs and slipper do not fall out.

4) Install a new rotor shaft seal using seal driver tool (T78P-3733-A3). Using a plastic mallet, drive the seal into the bore until bottomed. Install seal retainer in a similar manner. Place pump housing plate on a flat surface with pulley side down.

5) Insert 2 dowel pins and disc spring into the housing plate. Lubricate the inner and outer "O" ring seals with power steering fluid and install seals on lower pressure plate.

6) Insert pressure plate with seals toward the front of pump into pump housing plate and over dowel pins. Belleville spring must be installed with dished surface upward.

7) Place assembly into "C" clamp. Use driver tool (T78P-3733-A3) in rotor shaft hole and press lower plate lightly until bottomed in pump plate housing. This will seat "O" ring. Install cam, rotor and slippers, and rotor shaft assembly into pump housing plate over dowel pins.

NOTE: When installing this assembly, stepped holes must be used for dowel pins, and recessed notch in cam insert must face reservoir and be approximatly 180° opposite square pump mounting boss.

8) Place upper pressure plate over dowel pins. Side of plate with square recessed notch must face toward reservoir and be positioned 180° opposite square pump mounting boss.

9) Place a new "O" ring seal on valve cover and lubricate with power steering fluid. Insert valve cover over dowel pins. Be sure outlet fitting hole in valve cover is directly in line with square mounting boss of pump housing plate.

10) Place the entire assembly in "C" clamp tool. Compress valve cover into pump housing plate, until retaining ring groove is exposed in pump housing plate.

NOTE: Be sure plastic baffle is securely in place in valve cover. If not, apply petroleum jelly to baffle and install.

11) Install valve cover retaining ring with ends near access hole in pump housing plate. Remove pump assembly from "C" clamp. Place a new "O" ring seal on pump housing plate. Lubricate seal with power steering fluid. Install power steering reservoir.

12) Install flow control spring and flow control valve in valve cover. Place new "O" ring seals on outlet fitting and lubricate with power steering fluid. Install outlet fitting into valve cover and tighten. Install pulley.

TIGHTENING SPECIFICATIONS

Application	Ft. Lbs. (N.m)
Adjustment Bracket-to-Support	30-45 (41-61)
Pressure Hose-to-Rear Fitting	14-29 (19-39)
Pump-to-Adjusting Bracket	30-45 (41-61)
Pump Outlet-to-Pump Valve Cover	25-34 (34-46)
Return Hose-to-Gear Fitting	17-32 (23-44)
Return Line-to-Frame	11-16 (15-22)

Fig. 3: Disassembled View of C-II Power Steering Pump

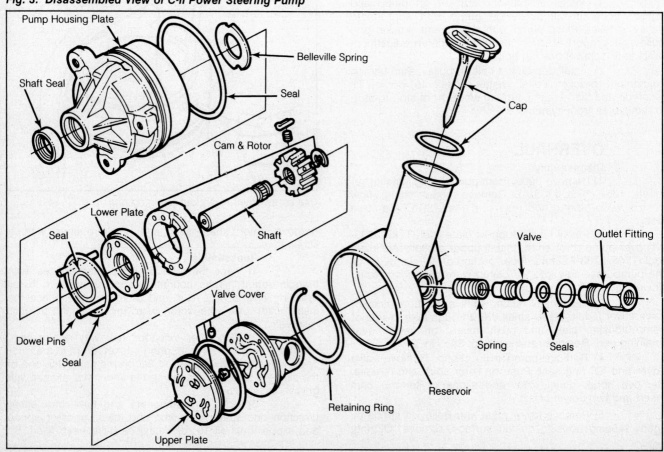

Power Steering Pumps

SAGINAW VANE TYPE

Chrysler Corp., Ford (Van Models Only), General Motors & Jeep

DESCRIPTION

The Saginaw vane type power steering pump can be identified by the "ham can" shape of the fluid reservoir. Internally, rectangular pumping vanes carried by a shaft driven rotor move fluid from intake to pressure cavities of cam ring.

As rotor begins to rotate, centrifugal force throws vanes against inside surface of cam ring to pick up residual oil, which is then forced into high pressure area. As more oil is picked up by the vanes, oil is forced into the cavities of the thrust plate and through the 2 cross-over holes in the cam ring and pressure plate (which empty into high pressure area between pressure plate and housing end plate).

Filling high pressure area causes oil to flow under vanes in slots of rotor, forcing vanes to follow inside oval surface of cam ring. As vanes rotate to small area of cam ring, oil is forced out from between vanes.

LUBRICATION, TROUBLE SHOOTING & TESTING

See Power Steering General Servicing article in this section.

REMOVAL & INSTALLATION

POWER STEERING PUMP

Loosen pump adjusting bolt (or nut) and pump mounting bolts, then withdraw pump drive belt. Disconnect pressure and return hoses from pump and cap ends to prevent loss of fluid and entry of dirt.

Remove bolts attaching pump mounting bracket to engine, and withdraw pump, pulley and mounting bracket as an assembly. To install, reverse removal procedure and bleed hydraulic system.

OVERHAUL

CAUTION: When clamping pump in vise, be careful not to exert excessive force on front hub or pump as bushing may become distorted.

Disassembly

1) Do not use a hammer to remove pulley. Drain pump reservoir, clean exterior of unit and remove mounting bracket(s). Using a puller, withdraw pulley from shaft. *See Fig. 1.*

2) Clamp pump (with shaft pointing downward) in a soft jawed vise, making sure vise grips pump at square boss and shaft housing. Remove pressure line union and "O" ring seal. Remove reservoir retaining studs.

3) Tap against filler tube with plastic hammer to loosen reservoir on pump body. Remove reservoir from body, then withdraw and discard "O" ring seals.

4) Using a 1/8" diameter punch, tap end plate retaining ring around until one end of ring is near hole in pump body. Insert punch in hole far enough to disengage ring from groove in pump bore, then use a screwdriver and pry ring out of body. *See Fig. 2.*

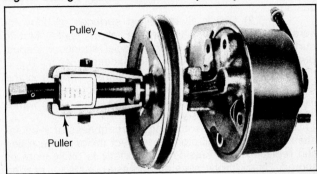

Fig. 1: Using Puller to Remove Pump Pulley

DO NOT use hammer to remove pulley.

5) Tap end plate with a soft faced hammer to break it loose; the spring, located under the end plate, should push plate up. Remove spring. Remove pump from vise.

Fig. 2: Removing Retaining Ring for Pump End Plate

Push In With Punch To Disengage Ring From Groove

Tap end plate with a soft-faced hammer to break it loose from housing.

6) Place pump in inverted position on flat surface, and tap end of drive shaft with soft-faced hammer to loosen pressure plate, rotor, and thrust plate assembly from body.

7) Lift pump body off rotor assembly (flow control valve and spring should also slide out of bore). Remove and discard end plate and pressure plate "O" rings. Pry drive shaft oil seal from body using a screwdriver.

8) Inspect seal bore in housing for burrs, nicks, or score marks that would allow oil to by-pass outer seal surface. Lift pressure plate and cam ring from rotor, then remove rotor vanes.

9) Clamp drive shaft in soft-jawed vise, with rotor and thrust plate facing up, and remove rotor lock ring from shaft. Use care not to nick shaft or rotor. Slide rotor and thrust plate off shaft, and remove shaft from vise.

Cleaning & Inspection

1) Clean all pump components (except drive shaft seal) in clean solvent and blow dry. Inspect flow

Power Steering Pumps

SAGINAW VANE TYPE (Cont.)

control valve assembly for wear, scoring, burrs or other damage.

2) Check all machined surfaces of body for scratches or burrs which might allow leaks. Mating surfaces on "O" rings require special attention. Inspect pump body drive shaft bushing for excessive wear.

3) If replacement is required, replace pump body and bushing as an assembly. Inspect end cover for nicks and burrs on surface for "O" ring, then polish with a fine oil stone if necessary.

4) Inspect rotor ring for roughness or irregularities. Use a small oil stone to correct minor irregularities and replace ring if outside cam surface is badly worn or scored. Check thrust plate and pressure plate for scoring and wear.

5) To remove light scoring, carefully lap with crocus cloth until surface is smooth and flat. Clean surface thoroughly. Check fit of vanes in rotor to ensure that they slide freely but fit snugly into slots.

6) If vanes are excessively loose in slots, the rotor and/or vanes require replacement. Scoring on rotor may be removed by careful laping using crocus cloth, and then cleaning thoroughly.

Reassembly

1) Lubricate all "O" rings and seal areas with power steering fluid. On Jeep models, use petroleum jelly to lubricate "O" rings. Place pump body on a flat surface. Drive a new shaft seal in until it bottoms on shoulder in bore.

2) Lubricate seal with power steering fluid, then clamp body in vise with shaft pointing downward. Install end plate and pressure plate "O" rings in groove on body. Install body to reservoir "O" rings and install on pump body.

3) With drive shaft clamped, splined end up, in a soft-jawed vise, install thrust plate on shaft with smooth,

ported side up. Slide rotor over splines with counter bore of rotor facing down.

4) Install rotor lock ring making sure it is seated in groove. Install two dowel pins in holes in pump cavity. Carefully insert drive shaft, rotor, and thrust plate assembly in pump cavity, indexing location holes with dowel pins.

NOTE: **Always use a new full diameter locking ring.**

5) Slide cam ring over rotor and onto dowel pins, with arrow on ring facing toward rear of housing. Install vanes in rotor slots with radius edge facing out towards cam ring inner surface. Position pressure plate on dowel pins with circular spring depression toward the rear of housing.

6) Place a 1 1/4" socket in groove of pressure plate, and seat entire assembly on "O" ring in pump cavity by pressing down on socket with both thumbs. Place

Fig. 4: Pressing Pump Pulley into Position

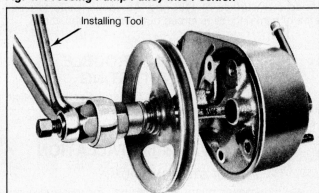

Installing Tool

DO NOT hammer pulley on shaft.

Fig. 3: Exploded View of Power Steering Pump

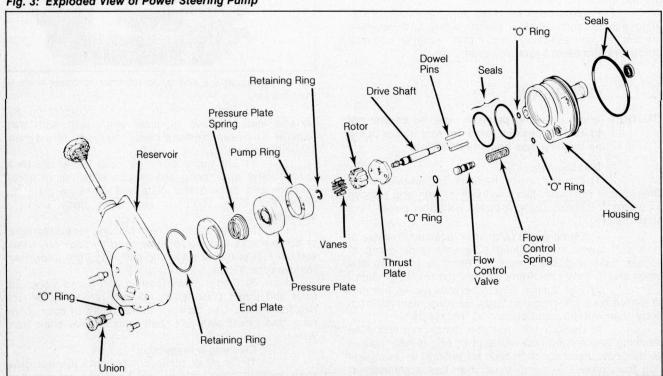

Retaining Ring

Pressure Plate Spring

Pump Ring

Reservoir

"O" Ring

Union

Retaining Ring

End Plate

Pressure Plate

Vanes

Rotor

Thrust Plate

"O" Ring

Drive Shaft

Dowel Pins

Seals

Flow Control Valve

"O" Ring

Flow Control Spring

Seals

"O" Ring

Housing

SAGINAW VANE TYPE (Cont.)

spring in groove in pressure plate and position end cover lip edge up over spring.

7) Press end cover down below retaining ring groove with thumb or arbor press. Install retaining ring, making sure ring is seated in groove. Care should be taken to prevent cocking end cover in bore or distorting assembly.

8) Using a punch, tap retaining ring ends around in groove until opening is opposite flow control valve bore. This is necessary for maximum retention of retaining ring.

9) Install new reservoir "O" ring, mounting stud "O" rings, and flow control valve "O" ring on pump body, then carefully position reservoir on pump body. Align mounting stud holes until studs can be started in threads.

10) Using a soft-faced hammer, tap reservoir down on pump and install flow control valve spring and valve assembly slotted end up. Install new "O" ring seal on pressure hose fitting, making sure it is installed on the UPPER groove.

CAUTION: It is possible to install pressure hose "O" ring in lower groove. This will restrict relief outlet orifice.

11) Install pressure hose fitting and tighten mounting studs. Tighten hose fitting and rear mounting studs. Remove pump assembly from vise and install mounting bracket and drive pulley.

TIGHTENING SPECIFICATIONS

Application	Ft. Lbs. (N.m)
Hose Fittings	
Gear End	
Chrysler Corp.	25 (34)
Ford	20-30 (27-41)
Jeep	25-35 (34-48)
Pump End	
Chrysler Corp.	35 (48)
Ford	20-35 (27-48)
Jeep	25-35 (34-48)
Bracket Bolts	
All Models	35 (48)

CONTENTS

SECTION 14

TRANSMISSION SERVICING

NOTE: ALSO SEE GENERAL INDEX.

IMPORTANT: Because of the many model names used by vehicle manufacturers, accurate identification of models is important. See Model Identification at the front of this publication.

Transmission Application

AUTOMATIC TRANSMISSIONS

MANUFACTURER & MODEL	TRANSMISSION MODEL
CHRYSLER CORP. Ram Van, Voyager Wagon, 2WD Pickup, 4WD Pickup, 2WD Ramcharger, 4WD Ramcharger	Chrysler Corp. Loadflite A-727
Ram Van, Voyager Wagon, 2WD Pickup	Chrysler Corp. Loadflite A904T
Ram Van, Voyager Wagon, 2WD Ramcharger	Chrysler Corp. Loadflite A999
FORD Ranger	Ford C-3
"F" 100 Pickup	Ford C-4
Bronco II, "F" 100 Pickup, Ranger	Ford C-5
Bronco, "E" 100/350 Van, "F" 100/350 Pickup	Ford C-6
"F" 100/250 Pickup	Ford Automatic Overdrive
GENERAL MOTORS S10 Pickup & Blazer	Turbo Hydra-Matic 200C
C10 2WD Pickup & Suburban	Turbo Hydra-Matic 350
C20 2WD Pickup & Suburban, C30 2WD Pickup, G30 Van, K20 4WD Pickup & Suburban, K30 4WD Pickup, P30 Parcel Delivery Van	Turbo Hydra-Matic 400
C10/20 2WD Pickup & Suburban, G20/30 Van, S10 Blazer & Pickup, K10 4WD Blazer, Pickup & Suburban, K20 4WD Pickup & Suburban	Turbo Hydra-Matic 700-R4
JEEP Cherokee, CJ7, J10 Pickup, Scrambler, Wagoneer	Jeep 999
Cherokee, J10/20 Pickup, Wagoneer	Jeep 727

MANUAL TRANSMISSIONS

MANUFACTURER & MODEL	TRANSMISSION MODEL
CHRYSLER CORP. 2WD Pickups, 4WD Pickups, 4WD Ramcharger	New Process 435 4-Speed
Ram Van, Voyager Wagon, 1/2 Ton 2WD Pickup	New Process A833 4-Speed Overdrive
FORD Bronco II, Ranger,	Ford 4-Speed
Bronco II, Ranger,	Ford 5-Speed
"E" 100/350 Van, "F" 100/350 Pickup	Ford 303 3-Speed
Bronco, "F" 100/350 Pickup	New Process 435 4-Speed
Bronco, "F" 100/350 Pickup	Warner T18 4-Speed
Bronco, "F" 100/250 Pickup	Ford SROD 4-Speed
"F" 250/350 Pickup	Warner T19B 4-Speed
"E" 100/150 Van	Ford 4-Speed Overdrive
GENERAL MOTORS C10 Pickup, G10/30 Van	GM 76 MM 3-Speed
K10 4WD Blazer, Pickup & Suburban, K20 4WD Pickup & Suburban, K30 4WD Pickup	Muncie 117 MM 4-Speed
S10 Blazer & Pickup	Isuzu 77.5 MM 4-Speed
S10 Blazer & Pickup	GM 77 MM 4-Speed
C10/30 Pickup & Suburban, G10/30 Van, K10/30 4WD Blazer, Pickup & Suburban S10 Blazer & Pickup	New Process 89 MM 4-Speed Overdrive GM 77 MM 5-Speed
JEEP CJ5, CJ7, Scrambler	Borg-Warner T4 4-Speed
Cherokee, CJ5, CJ7, J10 Pickup, Scrambler	Borg-Warner T5 5-Speed
J20 Pickup	Borg-Warner T18A 4-Speed
Cherokee, CJ5, CJ7, J10 Pickup, Scrambler	Borg-Warner T176 4-Speed

Automatic Transmission Servicing

CHRYSLER CORP.

LUBRICATION

SERVICE INTERVALS

Check fluid level at each engine oil change. Under normal light duty service conditions, service transmission (change fluid, replace filter, and adjust bands) every 37,500 miles. Under normal heavy duty service conditions, service transmission every 24,000 miles. Under severe heavy duty service conditions, transmission should be serviced every 12,000 miles.

CHECKING FLUID LEVEL

All Models

1) Check fluid level with vehicle parked on level surface, parking brake applied, and engine at curb idle speed and normal operating temperature. Move selector lever through all gear ranges, ending in Neutral.

2) Fluid level should be between "FULL" and "ADD ONE PINT" marks on dipstick. Fluid level should never be above "FULL" mark. Make sure dipstick seats properly to seal out water and dirt.

RECOMMENDED FLUID

Use only Dexron II type automatic transmission fluid when topping off or refilling transmission.

CAPACITY

When filling transmission, use capacities listed in table as a guideline, only. Correct fluid level should always be determined by marks on dipstick, rather than by amount of fluid added.

TRANSMISSION REFILL CAPACITIES

Application	Capacity Pints (Liters)
A-727	
Including Converter	
Lock-Up	16.7 (7.9)
Non Lock-Up	17.1 (8.1)
Without Converter	7.7 (3.6)
A-904T & A-999	
Including Converter	17.1 (8.1)

DRAINING & REFILLING

All Models

1) Loosen oil pan bolts. Tap lightly at one corner to break loose and allow fluid to drain. Remove pan. Install new filter on bottom of valve body and tighten retaining screws. Clean oil pan and install with new gasket.

2) Pour 4 quarts of transmission fluid through filler tube. Start engine and allow to run at idle for 2 minutes. With engine at curb idle and parking brake applied, move shift selector lever through all ranges, ending in neutral. Add fluid up to "ADD ONE PINT" mark on dipstick. Do not overfill.

3) Reseat dipstick fully to seal out water and dirt. Recheck fluid level when transmission reaches normal operating temperature.

ADJUSTMENT

KICKDOWN (FRONT) BAND

All Models

1) Locate kickdown band adjusting screw at left side of transmission case, near throttle lever shaft.

Loosen adjusting screw lock nut and back off approximately 5 turns. Make sure adjusting screw turns freely in case. Using special wrench (C-3380-A) with adapter (C-3705), tighten adjusting screw to 48 INCH lbs. (5 N.m). If adapter is not used, tighten adjusting screw to 72 INCH lbs. (8 N.m) which is the true torque.

2) Back off adjusting screw specified number of turns, as given in *Kickdown Band Adjustment Table*. Hold adjusting screw in position and tighten lock nut to 35 ft. lbs. (47 N.m).

Fig. 1: Adjusting Kickdown Band

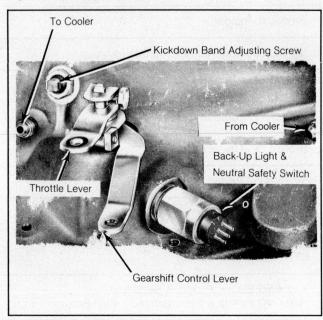

With band properly adjusted, tighten lock nut to 35 ft. lbs. (47 N.m).

KICKDOWN BAND ADJUSTMENT TABLE

Application	Back Off Screw
All Models	2 1/2 Turns

LOW-REVERSE (REAR) BAND

All Models

1) Transmission pan must be removed to adjust band. Remove transmission oil pan and locate low-reverse band adjusting screw on rear servo lever. Loosen adjusting screw lock nut and back off nut approximately 5 turns. Test adjusting screw for free turning in lever. Using special wrench (C3380-A), tighten adjusting screw to 72 INCH lbs. (8 N.m).

2) Back off adjusting screw specified number of turns as given in *Low-Reverse Band Adjustment Table*. Hold adjusting screw in position and tighten lock nut to 30 ft. lbs. (41 N.m). Clean oil pan, install new gasket with pan and refill transmission with fluid.

LOW-REVERSE BAND ADJUSTMENT TABLE

Application	Back Off Screw
Models A-904T and A-999	4 Turns
Model A-727	2 Turns

Fig. 2: Adjusting Low-Reverse Band

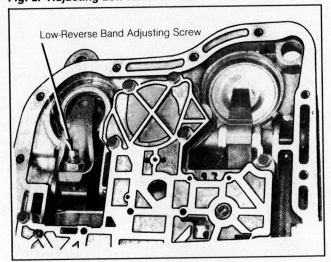

With band properly adjusted, tighten lock nut to 30 ft. lbs. (41 N.m).

TRANSMISSION THROTTLE ROD
All Models

1) With engine at normal operating temperature and carburetor off fast idle cam, adjust idle speed to specifications. Turn off engine and disconnect choke at carburetor or block choke valve in full open position. Open throttle slightly to release fast idle cam and return throttle to curb idle position.

2) Raise vehicle on hoist. Loosen swivel lock screw. Be sure swivel is free to slide along flat end of throttle rod so that preload spring action is not restricted. If necessary, disassemble and clean parts to assure free action.

Fig. 3: Throttle Rod Adjustment Diagram

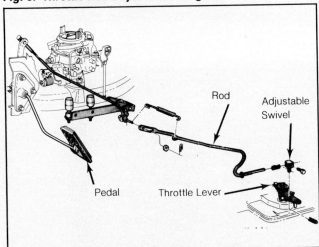

Linkage for vehicles equipped with 3.7L 6-cylinder engine.

3) Hold transmission lever firmly forward, against internal stop. Tighten swivel lock screw to 100 INCH lbs. (11 N.m). Adjustment is complete. Linkage backlash is automatically removed by preload spring.

4) Lower vehicle and reconnect choke. To test linkage, move throttle rod rearward and slowly release it to confirm full forward return.

Fig. 4: Throttle Rod Adjustment Diagram

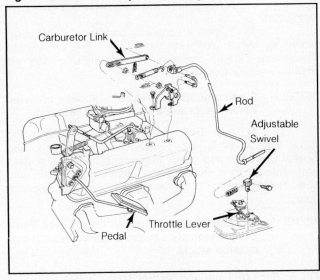

Linkage for vehicles equipped with V8 engines.

SHIFT LINKAGE

1) Ensure that swivel lock bolt is free to move on shift rod. Disassemble and clean components as required.

2) Place shift lever in "P" and move shift control lever on transmission all the way to the rear detent (park) position. Tighten swivel lock bolt.

3) When linkage is properly adjusted, detent positions for neutral and drive will be within limits of shift lever gate stops. Engine must crank in "P" or "N", only.

Fig. 5: Column Shift Linkage Component Diagram

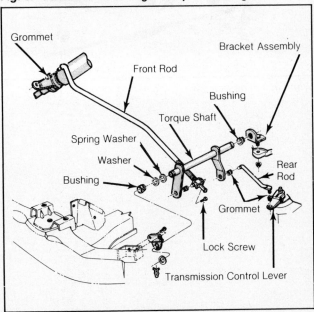

NEUTRAL SAFETY SWITCH
All Models

1) With transmission linkage properly adjusted, switch should allow starter operation in park and neutral only. To test switch, remove wire connector and test for

CHRYSLER CORP. (Cont.)

continuity between center pin of switch and case. Continuity should exist only when transmission is in park or neutral.

2) Check for continuity between 2 outer pins. Continuity should exist with transmission in reverse, only. There should be no continuity between either outside pin and the transmission case.

NOTE: **Be sure gearshift linkage is properly adjusted before replacing a switch which tests bad.**

3) To replace, remove switch from case and allow fluid to drain. Move selector lever to park and neutral positions and check that switch operating fingers are centered in switch opening. Install new switch and seal. Retest switch for continuity and add transmission fluid.

NOTE: **To center switch operation fingers, see Valve Body Assembly section of appropriate transmission article.**

Fig. 6: Back-Up Light and Neutral Safety Switch

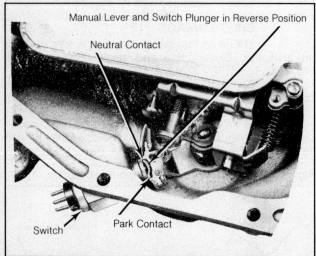

Manual Lever and Switch Plunger in Reverse Position

Neutral Contact

Switch

Park Contact

When installing new switch, tighten to 24 ft. lbs. (33 N.m).

FORD

LUBRICATION

SERVICE INTERVALS

Vehicles used in normal service do not require regularly scheduled maintenance. Fluid level should be checked whenever underhood maintenance is performed, or if leakage is detected. Clutch bands (except AOT) should be adjusted when quality of shifts deteriorates or otherwise indicates improper band adjustment.

On vehicles used for fleet service or those operated under severe conditions, regular transmission fluid changes are required. On 100 series vehicles with 4.9L engines, change fluid every 20,000 miles. On all other models, drain and refill transmission at 22,500 mile intervals.

If vehicle is used for off-highway operation, check fluid level every 1000 miles. If operated in water, check fluid level and condition daily. Drain and refill if necessary.

CHECKING FLUID LEVEL

Check fluid with vehicle on level ground, engine warm at curb idle and transmission fluid at normal operating temperature. Apply parking brake and move transmission selector lever through all ranges, ending in "P". Fluid level should check between "ADD" and "FULL" marks on dipstick (or in crosshatched area). Add fluid through filler tube as needed. DO NOT overfill. When check is complete, seat dipstick fully to seal out water and dirt.

RECOMMENDED FLUID

On C-5 transmissions, use fluid which meets Ford Motor Co. specification ESP-M2C166-H or type H fluid (or equivalent). On all other models, Ford Motor Co. specification ESP-M2C138-CJ, Dexron II, Series D or equivalent must be used.

CAPACITY

Transmission and converter assembly capacities listed are approximate. Determine correct fluid level by mark on dipstick rather than by amount of fluid added.

TRANSMISSION REFILL CAPACITIES

Application	Capacity Quarts (Liters)
C-3 Transmission	8.0 (7.6)
C-5 Transmission	
All Except Bronco II & Ranger	11.0 (10.4)
2WD Ranger	7.5 (7.1)
Bronco II & 4WD Ranger	7.9 (7.5)
C-6 Transmission	
2WD Models	11.8 (11.2)
4WD Models	13.5 (12.8)
AOT Transmission	12.0 (11.4)

DRAINING & REFILLING

1) On C-5 models, disconnect fluid filler tube from oil pan to drain fluid, then remove pan. On all other models, loosen oil pan bolts and tap pan to break gasket seal. Allow fluid to drain, then remove oil pan bolts and oil pan. On all models, clean pan and reinstall with new filter, gasket and pan gasket. On C-5 models, install filler tube.

2) On all models, add 3 quarts transmission fluid through filler tube. Check fluid level as described. When filling a dry transmission and converter, refer to *Transmission Refill Capacity Chart*.

3) Recheck fluid level when transmission is at normal operating temperature. Do not overfill.

ADJUSTMENT

INTERMEDIATE (FRONT) BAND

1) On C-3 transmissions, remove downshift rod from transmission downshift lever. On all models, clean dirt from band adjusting screw area. Remove and discard band adjusting screw lock nut. Install new lock nut.

2) Tighten adjusting screw to 120 INCH lbs. (14 N.m). Then back off screw exact number of turns as indicated in *Intermediate (Front) Band Adjustment* table. Hold adjusting screw in position and tighten new lock nut to 40 ft. lbs. (56 N.m).

3) On C-3 models, re-install downshift rod on transmission downshift lever.

Fig. 1: Adjusting Intermediate Band (C-3 & C-5)

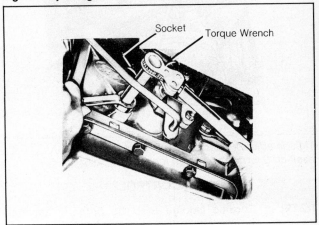

Socket   Torque Wrench

Tighten adjusting screw to 120 INCH lbs. (14 N.m). Back off 2 turns on C-3, 4 1/4 turns on C-5, and tighten lock nut.

Fig. 2: Adjusting Intermediate Band (C-6)

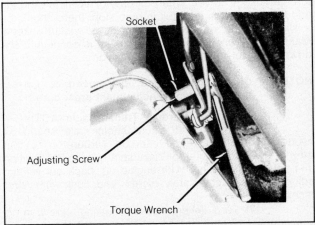

Socket

Adjusting Screw

Torque Wrench

Tighten adjusting screw to 120 INCH lbs. (14 N.m), back off 1 1/2 turns and tighten lock nut.

Ford (Cont.)

INTERMEDIATE (FRONT) BAND ADJUSTMENT

Application	Back Off Turns
C-3	2
C-5	4 1/4
C-6	1 1/2

LOW-REVERSE (REAR) BAND

C-5 Only

Clean all dirt from band adjusting screw area, then remove and discard band adjusting screw lock nut. Install new lock nut on adjusting screw. Tighten screw to 120 INCH lbs. (14 N.m), then back off 3 full turns. Hold screw in position and tighten lock nut to 40 ft. lbs. (54 N.m).

Fig. 3: Adjusting Low-Reverse Band (C-5)

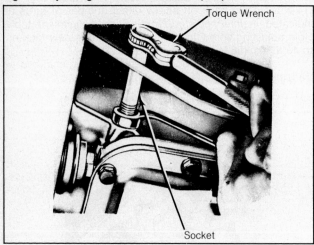

Tighten adjusting screw to 120 INCH lbs. (14 N.m), back off 3 turns and tighten lock nut.

KICKDOWN CONTROL

NOTE: **Throttle linkage must be properly adjusted before attempting to make kickdown control adjustment.**

C-5 & C-6

With throttle pedal held to floor, check for full throttle linkage travel. When carburetor is at full throttle and throttle linkage is at full throttle stop, there should be a slight amount of movement left in downshift linkage. Make sure downshift lever return spring is connected and downshift lever returns to closed position.

NOTE: **Check that engine idle speed is correct before beginning adjustment procedure.**

Automatic Overdrive Transmission (AOT)

1) Check and adjust engine idle speed as needed. Release fast idle cam on carburetor so that throttle lever is at idle stop. Place shift lever in "N" position and set parking brake. With engine off, back out linkage adjusting screw completely (screw end flush with lever face).

2) Turn linkage lever adjusting screw in to obtain .005" (.13 mm) clearance between end of screw and throttle lever. Turn screw in an additional 2-4 turns. Four complete turns are preferred, but as few as 2 is acceptable if travel is limited. However, if 2 complete turns

cannot be made, adjustment of throttle valve control rod on transmission is required.

AOT Throttle Valve (TV) Control Rod

1) Check and adjust engine curb idle speed as needed. With engine off, release fast idle cam so that throttle lever is against idle stop.

2) Place shift lever in neutral and apply parking brake. Set linkage lever adjustment screw at its approximate mid-range.

3) Raise vehicle on hoist. Loosen nut on sliding stud of TV control assembly. Push lower end of control rod to be sure linkage lever at carburetor is against throttle lever. Release force on rod.

4) Push TV control lever on transmission up against internal stop with firm force (about 5 lbs.). Tighten nut on stud.

SHIFT LINKAGE

1) With engine off and parking brake applied, place shift lever in "D". On models with column-mounted shift levers, hold against stop by hanging an 8 lb. weight from the selector lever.

2) Loosen nut on slotted shift rod at transmission. Move shift lever at transmission all the way to the rear, then forward 2 steps (3 steps on Bronco II and Ranger). This places lever in "D" position.

3) On Bronco II and Ranger, apply light forward pressure on shifter control lever. On all models, tighten nut at slotted lever to 144-216 INCH lbs. (16-24 N.m). Remove weight from shift lever. Move lever through all positions making sure transmission is at full detent in each position.

Fig. 4: Shift Linkage on "F" Models

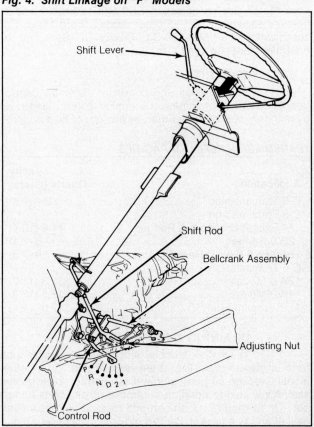

Fig. 5: Shift Linkage on "E" Models

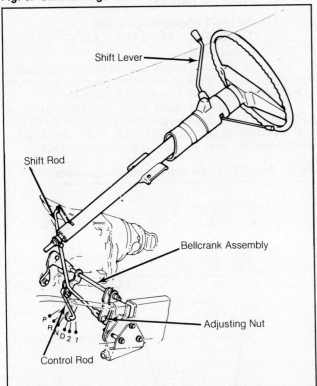

Shift Lever

Shift Rod

Bellcrank Assembly

Adjusting Nut

P R N D 2 1

Control Rod

Fig. 6: Shift Linkage on AOT Models

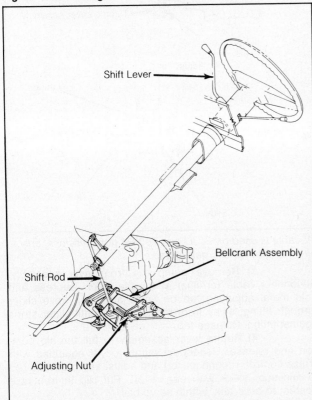

Shift Lever

Bellcrank Assembly

Shift Rod

Adjusting Nut

Fig. 7: Shift Linkage on Bronco II & Ranger

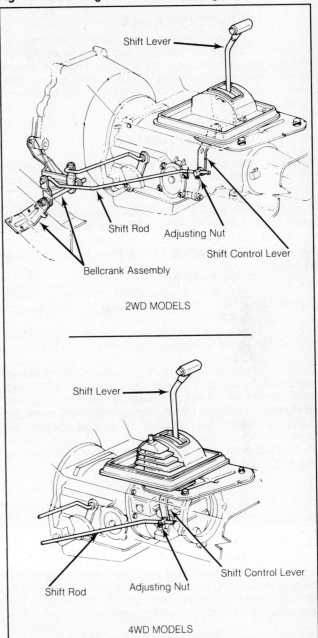

Shift Lever

Shift Rod

Adjusting Nut

Shift Control Lever

Bellcrank Assembly

2WD MODELS

Shift Lever

Shift Rod

Adjusting Nut

Shift Control Lever

4WD MODELS

C-5 shown, all others similar.

NEUTRAL START SWITCH

1) Loosen both neutral safety switch bolts at transmission. Place shifter in "Neutral" position.

2) Slide switch until a .091" (no. 43) drill fits into gauge holes. Drill should rest against case on Bronco II and Ranger models. Tighten switch bolts and remove gauge pin.

3) Check switch operation. Back-up lights should come on with transmission in "R", only. Vehicle should start in "N" or "P", only.

GENERAL MOTORS

LUBRICATION

SERVICE INTERVALS

Check transmission fluid level at each engine oil change. Change transmission fluid and filter at 100,000 mile intervals on vehicles in normal use. If used in severe service conditions (commercial use, trailor pulling, constant stop and go city traffic), change fluid and filter every 15,000 miles.

CHECKING FLUID LEVEL

NOTE: **One pint of fluid will raise level from "ADD" mark to "FULL" mark on dipstick in a hot transmission. Do not overfill.**

With engine at curb idle, move selector lever through all positions, ending in "P". Remove dipstick and touch end cautiously to find out if fluid is cool, warm, or hot. Wipe dipstick clean and check level, by temperature, as follows:

COOL (65-85°F)
Fluid level should check between the two dimples below "ADD" mark on dipstick.

WARM
Fluid level should check close to the "ADD" mark (either above or below) on dipstick.

HOT
Fluid is hot when it cannot be touched comfortably. Fluid level should check between "ADD" and "FULL" marks on dipstick. If vehicle has been operated for an extended period of time at high speed, in city traffic, or pulling a trailer, an accurate fluid level cannot be immediately determined. Transmission must cool for about 30 minutes, after vehicle is parked, before fluid level is checked.

RECOMMENDED FLUID

Use only DEXRON or DEXRON-II automatic transmission fluid, or equivalent.

CAPACITY

The transmission refill capacities given below are approximations, only. Correct fluid level should always be determined by marks on dipstick, rather than by amount added. DO NOT overfill transmission.

TRANSMISSION REFILL CAPACITIES

| | Capacity in Pints (Liters) | |
Application	Drain & Refill	Overhaul
THM 200C	7.0 (3.3)	19.0 (9.0)
THM 350C	6.0 (2.8)	20.0 (9.5)
THM 400	7.0 (3.8)	22.0 (10.4)
THM 700-R4	10.0 (4.7)	23.0 (10.9)

DRAINING & REFILLING

With engine at normal operating temperature, loosen transmission oil pan bolts. Pry pan loose with a large screwdriver and allow fluid to drain. Remove oil pan and gasket. Replace old filter. Install oil pan with new gasket. Add fluid to proper mark on dipstick.

ADJUSTMENT

DETENT (DOWNSHIFT) OR THROTTLE VALVE (TV) CABLE

Diesel Engines

1) Remove cruise control rod (if equipped). Disconnect cable terminal at throttle assembly. Loosen lock nut on pump rod and back off several turns.

2) Rotate throttle lever assembly (at valve body) to full open position and hold. Lengthen pump rod until injection pump lever contacts full throttle stop. Release throttle lever and tighten pump rod lock nut.

Fig. 1: Detent/TV Cable Adjustment Components

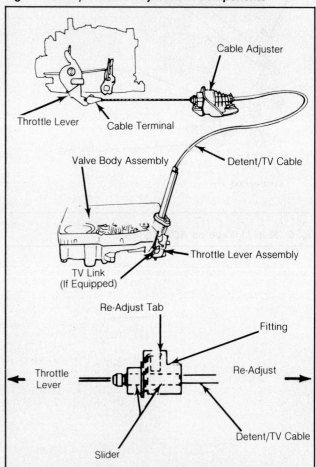

TV cable is used on 200C and 700-R4 transmissions, only. All other models use detent cable.

3) Remove pump rod from lever assembly. Reconnect cable terminal at throttle lever. Depress and hold metal adjusting tab on cable adjuster. Move slider through fitting, away from throttle lever, until slider stops against fitting. Release tab.

4) Rotate lever assembly to full throttle position and release. Reconnect pump rod. If equipped with cruise control, reconnect rod and adjust servo throttle rod to minimum slack with engine off. Put clip in free hole nearest to bellcrank, within servo bail.

Gas Engines

1) Gasoline engine equipped vehicles use "self-adjusting" cables. A brief procedure is required, however, to allow cable to adjust.

GENERAL MOTORS (Cont.)

2) Press tab in cable re-adjuster and move slider back through fitting, away from throttle lever, until slider stops against fitting. Release tab. Move throttle lever to full open position. This automatically adjusts cable. Release lever.

DETENT (DOWNSHIFT) SWITCH
THM 400 Only
With engine off, push detent switch plunger as far forward as possible. This presets switch for adjustment. Depress accelerator pedal to wide open position; switch will self adjust. Operation of detent switch circuit can be checked by connecting a test lamp across switch terminals.

Fig. 2: Detent Switch Installation

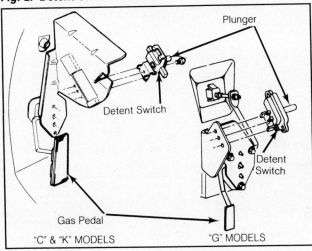

THM 400 transmissions, only.

VACUUM REGULATOR VALVE
Vacuum is regulated at idle and during heavy loads by the vacuum regulator valve. Valve is mounted to the diesel fuel pump and can be identified by the 2 vacuum ports extending from valve chamber.

Diagnosis & Testing
1) Loosely assemble throttle position switch to fuel injection pump with throttle lever in closed position. Attach a continuity meter across terminals (light duty vehicles IGN Pink and EGR Yellow).
2) Insert the proper "switch-closed" gauge block, between gauge boss on injection pump and wide open stop screw on throttle shaft. Rotate and hold throttle lever against gauge block.
3) Rotate throttle switch clockwise (facing throttle switch) until continuity pivot occurs (high meter reading) across terminals. Hold switch body at this position and tighten mounting bolts to 4-5 ft. lbs. (5-7 N.M).

NOTE: Switch point must be set only while rotating switch body in clockwise direction.

4) Release throttle lever and allow it to return to idle position. Remove "switch-closed" gauge block and insert "switch-open" gauge block. Rotate throttle lever against "switch-open" gauge block. There should be no continuity across terminals.

5) If no continuity exists, switch is set properly. However, if there is continuity, then switch must be reset by returning to step **1)** and repeating the entire procedure.

SHIFT LINKAGE
All Except "S" Models
1) Make sure shift tube and lever assembly are free in steering column. Disconnect shift lever rod from swivel at lower column lever. Move transmission lever clockwise to stop, then counterclockwise 2 detents. This is neutral position. Place selector lever in neutral. Locate position using mechanical stops, NOT indicator pointer.

Fig. 3: Shift Linkage Components

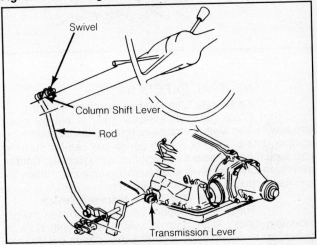

"C" and "K" models, only.

2) Slide swivel and clamp onto shift lever rod. Install grommets, washers and nut (as needed) but do not tighten nut. Hold lower column lever against neutral stop on park side. Tighten swivel nut to 20 ft. lbs. (27 N.m)

Fig. 4: Shift Linkage Components

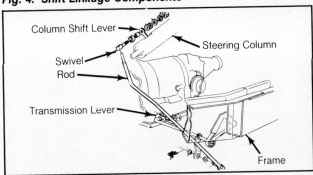

"G" models, only.

"S" Models
1) Make sure shift tube and lever are free in steering column. To adjust linkage, remove screw and spring washer from swivel. Turn transmission lever clockwise to stop, then counterclockwise 2 detents. This is neutral position.
2) Place selector lever in neutral. Locate proper position using mechanical stops, NOT indicator pointer. Hold swivel against shift lever, install spring washer and screw and tighten finger tight. Avoid applying

GENERAL MOTORS (Cont.)

force in either direction (along shift rod or lever) while tightening screw to 20 ft. lbs. (27 N.m).

Fig. 5: Shift Linkage Components

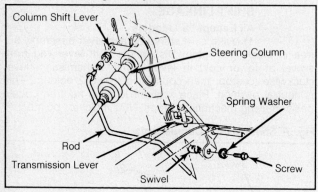

"S" models, only.

NEUTRAL SAFETY SWITCH

All Models With Column Mounted Switch

Place gearshift selector lever in neutral position and loosen switch attaching screws. Rotate switch on column until a .095" (2.5 mm) gauge pin can be inserted into switch gauge hole to a depth of 3/8" (10 mm). Tighten switch attaching screws and remove gauge pin. Check for engine starting in neutral and park only.

All Models With Trans. Mounted Switch

Raise and support vehicle and loosen switch mounting bolts. Align hole in switch lever with hole in switch assemby. Insert a .095" (2.5 mm) gauge pin through switch holes to hold switch in neutral position. With selector lever on transmission in neutral detent position, tighten switch mounting bolts and remove gauge pin. Lower vehicle and check operation of switch.

LUBRICATION

SERVICE INTERVALS

Check fluid level and condition of fluid at each engine oil change. Under light duty service conditions, change fluid, replace filter and adjust bands every 28 months or 27,500 miles. Under heavy duty service conditions, change fluid, replace filter and adjust bands every 12 months or 12,500 miles.

CHECKING FLUID LEVEL

1) Park vehicle on level surface and apply parking brake. With engine at normal operating temperature and idling, move transmission selector lever through all gear ranges, ending in neutral. Check fluid level.

2) Fluid level should be between "FULL" and "ADD ONE PINT" marks on dipstick. Fluid level should never be above "FULL" mark. Make sure dipstick seats properly to seal out water and dirt.

RECOMMENDED FLUID

Use only Dexron or Dexron II type automatic transmission fluid.

CAPACITY

Transmission and converter capacities listed in the *Transmission Refill Capacities* table are approximate only. Fluid level should always be determined by reading on dipstick, rather than amount of fluid added.

TRANSMISSION REFILL CAPACITIES

Application	Capacity Pints (Liters)
All Models	
Including Converter	17.0 (8.0)
Without Converter	8.5 (4.0)

DRAINING & REFILLING

1) Loosen oil pan bolts, tap pan to break it loose and allow fluid to drain. Remove pan. Install new filter on bottom of valve body and tighten retaining screws. Install new "O" ring on fluid pickup pipe (if needed). Clean oil pan and install with a new gasket.

2) Pour 5 quarts of transmission fluid through filler tube. Start engine and allow to run at curb idle for a few minutes. With engine idling and parking brake applied, move shift selector lever through all ranges, ending in neutral. Add fluid up to "ADD ONE PINT" mark on dipstick.

3) With transmission at normal operating temperature, check fluid level. Fluid should be between "ADD" and "FULL" marks on dipstick. Transmission must NOT be overfilled. Seat dipstick fully to seal out water and dirt.

ADJUSTMENT

KICKDOWN (FRONT) BAND

1) Locate kickdown band adjusting screw on left side of case, near throttle lever shaft. Loosen adjusting screw lock nut and back off approximately 5 turns. Make sure adjusting screw turns freely in case.

2) Using adapter tool (J-24063) and 5/16" square socket, tighten screw to 36 INCH lbs. (4 N.m). If

adapter is not used, tighten screw to 72 INCH lbs. (8 N.m). Back off screw 2 1/2 turns. Hold adjusting screw in position and tighten lock nut to 35 ft. lbs. (48 N.m).

Fig 1: Kickdown Band Adjusting Screw Location

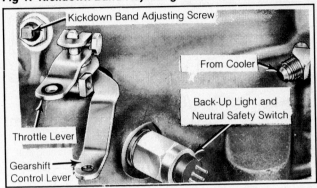

Adjust band every 27,500 miles in light duty service, every 12,500 miles for heavy duty service.

LOW REVERSE (REAR) BAND

1) Raise vehicle, drain transmission fluid and remove oil pan. Locate adjusting screw on rear servo lever. Loosen adjusting screw lock nut and back off about 5 turns. Tighten screw to 41 INCH lbs. (4.6 N.m).

2) Back off screw specified number of turns. See *Low-Reverse Band Adjustment Table*. Hold adjusting screw in position and tighten lock nut to 35 ft. lbs. (48 N.m). Install oil pan and fill transmission with fluid.

LOW-REVERSE BAND ADJUSTMENT TABLE

Application	Back Off Screw
Model 727	2 Turns
Model 999	4 Turns

Fig. 2: Adjusting Low-Reverse Band

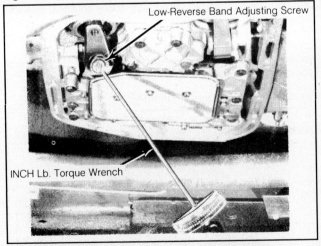

Band should be adjusted whenever oil pan is removed.

TRANSMISSION THROTTLE LINKAGE
6-Cyl. Models With 999 Transmission

1) Disconnect throttle control rod spring. Use spring to hold adjusting link in forward position, against nylon washer. Block choke open and release fast idle cam.

Automatic Transmission Servicing

JEEP (Cont.)

2) Raise vehicle. Loosen both retaining bolts on adjusting link clamp. DO NOT remove spring clip or nylon washer.

Fig. 3: Throttle Linkage Adjustment

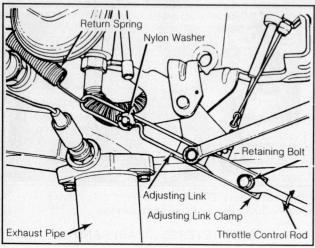

6-cylinder models with 999 transmission.

3) Use a spare spring to hold transmission throttle lever against forward stop.

4) Push adjusting link to eliminate lash and pull clamp to rear so that bolt in rod bottoms in rear of slot in rod. Tighten forward clamp retaining bolt.

5) Pull throttle control rod to the rear so that bolt in rod bottoms in front of slot and tighten rear retaining bolt. Remove spare spring. Lower vehicle and reconnect throttle control rod spring.

6-Cyl. Models With 727 Transmission

1) Disconnect throttle control rod spring. Use spring to hold transmission throttle control lever forward, against stop. Block choke open and release fast idle cam.

2) On carburetors equipped wih throttle operated solenoid valve, turn key to "ON" position to energize solenoid. Open throttle half-way to allow solenoid to lock. Return throttle to idle position.

3) Loosen retaining bolt on throttle control adjusting link. DO NOT remove spring clip or nylon washer. Pull on end of link to eliminate lash. Tighten link retaining bolt. Reconnect throttle control rod spring.

Fig. 4: Throttle Linkage Adjustment

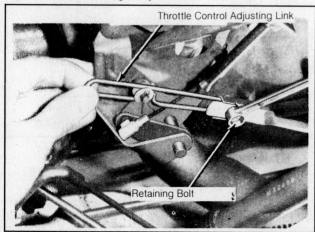

6-cylinder models with 727 transmission.

V8 Models

1) Disconnect throttle control rod spring. Use spring to hold transmission throttle valve control lever against forward stop. Block choke open and release fast idle cam.

Fig. 5: Throttle Linkage Adjustment

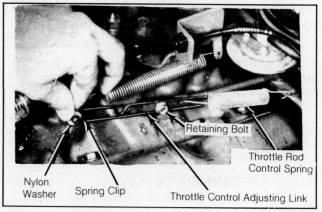

All models equipped with V8 engines.

2) On carburetors equipped wih throttle operated solenoid valve, turn key to "ON" position to energize solenoid. Open throttle half-way to allow solenoid to lock. Return throttle to idle position.

3) Loosen retaining bolt on throttle control rod adjusting link. Remove spring clip and slide nylon washer to rear of link. Push on end of link to eliminate lash and tighten retaining bolt. Install nylon washer and spring clip. Reconnect throttle control rod spring.

NEUTRAL SAFETY SWITCH

1) Switch combines functions of neutral safety switch and back-up light switch. With transmission linkage properly adjusted, switch should allow starter operation in "P" and "N" only.

2) To test switch, remove wire connector and test for continuity between center pin of switch and case. Continuity should only exist when transmission is in "P" or "N". Check for continuity between 2 outer pins. Continuity should exist with transmission in "R" only. There should be

Fig. 6: Back-Up Light/Neutral Safety Switch Location

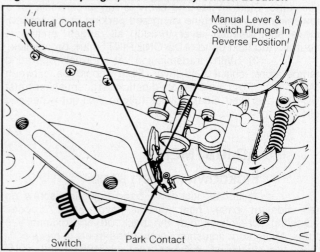

When installing switch, tighten to 24 ft. lbs. (33 N.m).

JEEP (Cont.)

no continuity between either outer pin and transmission case. If these conditions are not met, the switch should be replaced.

3) Remove switch from case and allow fluid to drain into a container. Move selector lever to "P" and "N" positions and check that switch operating fingers are centered in switch opening. Install switch and new seal and tighten. *See Fig. 6.*

SHIFT LINKAGE

1) Loosen shift rod trunnion jam nuts at transmission lever. Remove lock pin retaining shift rod to bellcrank. Disengage trunnion and shift rod. Place selector lever in "P" position and lock steering column. Move transmission shift lever to full rear (Park) position.

2) Adjust shift rod trunnion to obtain free pin fit in bellcrank arm. Tighten jam nuts. Make sure gearshift linkage lash is eliminated by pulling downward on shift rod and pushing upward on outer bellcrank when tightening jam nuts.

3) Check steering column lock for ease of operation. Check that engine starts in "N" or "P", only. If starter engages in any drive gear, or does not work in "N" or "P", check for proper shift linkage adjustment or faulty neutral safety switch.

Fig. 7: Exploded View of Shift Linkage Assemblies

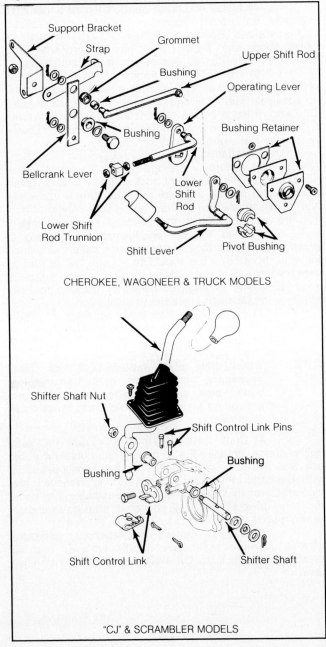

Support Bracket
Strap
Grommet
Upper Shift Rod
Bushing
Operating Lever
Bushing
Bushing Retainer
Bellcrank Lever
Lower Shift Rod
Lower Shift Rod Trunnion
Shift Lever
Pivot Bushing

CHEROKEE, WAGONEER & TRUCK MODELS

Shifter Shaft Nut
Shift Control Link Pins
Bushing
Bushing
Shift Control Link
Shifter Shaft

"CJ" & SCRAMBLER MODELS

CHRYSLER CORP.

TRANSFER CASE

MODEL NP-205
Removal

1) Raise vehicle, remove plug and drain transfer case. Replace plug. Disconnect speedometer cable. Remove skid plate, crossmember and strut rods as needed. Disconnect propeller shafts and wire out of way. Do not allow propeller shafts to hang free, as damage to universal joints may result.

2) Disconnect shift lever rod from shift rail link. Support transfer case and remove transfer case-to-transmission adapter bolts. Move transfer case to rear until input shaft clears adapter. Lower transfer case from vehicle.

Installation

Reverse removal procedures to install transfer case. Ensure that all attaching bolts are tight. Fill transfer case with lubricant.

MODEL NP-208
Removal

1) Raise vehicle, remove plug and drain transfer case. Mark front and rear output shaft yokes and propeller shafts for reassembly reference. Disconnect speedometer cable and indicator switch wires. Disconnect shift lever link from operating lever.

2) Support transfer case with transmission jack and remove crossmember. Disconnect front and rear propeller shafts at yokes and wire to frame.

3) If necessary, disconnect parking brake cable guide from pivot on right frame rail. Remove bolts attaching exhaust pipe support bracket to transfer case. Remove transfer case-to-transmission bolts. Move assembly to the rear until clear of output shaft. Lower transfer case from vehicle.

4) Remove all gasket material from rear of transmission adapter housing.

Installation

Install new transmission-to-transfer case gasket with sealer on both sides. Align transfer case with transmission. Rotate transfer case output shaft until transmission output shaft engages transfer case input shaft. Move transfer case until case seats flush against transmission. Install transfer case attaching bolts. Reverse removal procedures to complete installation.

TRANSMISSION

ALL MODELS

NOTE: **Transmission and converter must be removed and installed as an assembly to prevent damage to converter drive plate, front pump bushing, and oil seal. DO NOT allow weight of transmission to rest on plate during removal or installation.**

Removal

1) Remove transfer case from 4WD vehicles. Disconnect negative battery cable. Disconnect lower exhaust system as needed for removal clearance. Remove engine-to-transmission struts (if equipped). Disconnect cooler lines at transmission. Remove starter, cooler line bracket and converter access cover.

2) Loosen oil pan bolts, tap pan to break loose and allow fluid to drain. Reinstall pan. Rotate crankshaft clockwise with socket on vibration damper bolt to gain access to converter-to-drive plate bolts. Remove bolts. Mark propeller shaft for reassembly reference and remove from vehicle.

NOTE: **Crankshaft flange bolt circle, inner and outer circle of holes in drive plate and tapped holes in converter all have 1 hole offset so parts can only be installed in original position.**

3) Disconnect wiring connector from back-up light/neutral safety switch. Disconnect gearshift rod and torque shaft assembly from transmission. Disconnect transmission throttle rod from lever. Remove linkage bellcrank assembly, if equipped. Remove oil filler tube. Disconnect speedometer cable.

4) Install an engine support fixture under rear of engine. Raise transmission with service jack to relieve load on suports. Remove bolts securing crossmember to transmission and frame, then remove crossmember. Remove all converter housing-to-engine attaching bolts.

5) Carefully work transmission and converter assembly rearward off engine block dowel pins, disengaging converter hub from end of crankshaft. Attach a small "C" clamp on edge of converter housing to hold converter in place while transmission is being removed. Lower transmission and remove from vehicle.

Installation

1) Before installing converter, rotate front pump rotors with alignment tool (C3881) until 2 small holes in tool handle are vertical. Slide torque converter over input and reaction shafts, making sure converter hub slots are vertical, and fully engage pump inner rotor lugs.

2) Test for full engagement by placing a straightedge across face of transmission case. Surface of converter front cover lug should be at least 1/2" to rear of straightedge when converter is fully engaged. Attach a small "C" clamp to edge of converter housing to hold converter in place while installing transmission.

3) Inspect converter drive plate for distortion or cracks and replace if necessary. Install drive plate and tighten bolts to 55 ft. lbs. (75 N.m).

NOTE: **When drive plate replacement has been necessary, make sure both transmission dowel pins are in engine block and are protruding far enough to hold transmission in alignment.**

4) Coat converter hub hole in crankshaft with multi-purpose grease. Place transmission assembly on jack and position under vehicle. Make sure marks on converter and drive plate (made during removal) are aligned. Carefully work transmission assembly into position over dowels. Install all converter housing-to-engine retaining bolts. Tighten bolts to 30 ft. lbs. (41 N.m).

5) Reverse removal procedures to complete installation. Adjust shift and throttle linkages and fill transmission with fluid. On 4WD models, install transfer case.

CHRYSLER CORP. (Cont.)

TIGHTENING SPECIFICATIONS

Application	Ft. Lbs. (N.m)
Converter Housing-to-Engine	30 (41)
Cooler Line Fitting	15 (20)
Drain & Fill Plugs	
NP-205 Transfer Case	130 (41)
NP-208 Transfer Case	18 (24)
Oil Pan Bolts	13 (18)
Torque Converter-to-Drive Plate Bolts	22 (30)
Transfer Case-to-Transmission	40 (54)

FORD

TRANSFER CASE

NP-208 (BRONCO, F-150 & F-250)
Removal

1) Raise and support vehicle. Remove drain plug and drain fluid from transfer case. Replace plug. Disconnect 4WD indicator switch connector at transfer case. Disconnect speedometer driven gear from transfer case rear bearing retainer.

2) Remove transmission shift lever-to-transfer case retaining nut. Remove skid plate from frame. Support transfer case with transmission jack. Disconnect front and rear propeller shafts from transfer case output shaft yokes and wire out of way. Do not allow shafts to hang free as damage to universal joints may result.

3) Remove transfer case-to-transmission adapter bolts. Remove gasket between transfer case and adapter and lower transfer case out of vehicle.

Installation

To install transfer case, reverse removal procedures. Fill case with 7 pints (3.3 liters) of Dexron II type automatic transmission fluid.

BORG-WARNER 1345 (F-250 & F-350)
Removal

1) Raise vehicle. Remove drain plug and drain fluid from transfer case. Replace plug. Disconnect 4WD indicator switch connector at transfer case. If equipped, remove skid plate.

2) Disconnect front and rear propeller shafts from transfer case output shaft yokes, and wire out of way. Do not allow shafts to hang free as damage to universal joints may result.

3) Disconnect speedometer driven gear from rear bearing retainer. Remove retaining clips and shift rod from transfer case control and transfer case shift levers. Disconnect vent hose from case.

4) Remove heat shield. Support transfer case with transmission jack, remove transfer case-to-transmission adapter bolts and slide transfer case off of transmission output shaft (towards rear). Lower transfer case out of vehicle and remove gasket from between transfer case and adapter.

Installation

Reverse removal procedures to install transfer case. Fill case with 6.5 pints (3.1 liters) of Dexron II type automatic transmission fluid.

BORG-WARNER 13-50 (BRONCO II & RANGER)
Removal

1) Raise vehicle. Remove skid plate (if equipped). Remove drain plug and drain fluid from case. Replace plug. Disconnect 4WD indicator switch connector at transfer case. Disconnect front propeller shaft from front axle. Loosen front shaft boot clamp and slide out propeller shaft and boot as an assembly.

2) Disconnect rear propeller shaft from transfer case. Disconnect speedometer driven gear from transfer case rear cover. Disconnect vent hose from control lever.

3) Loosen or remove large and small bolts (1 each) retaining shifter to extension housing. Pull on control lever until bushing slides off transfer case shift lever pin. Unscrew shift lever from control lever, as needed.

4) Remove heat shield from transfer case. Support transfer case with jack and remove transfer case-to-transmission extension housing bolts (5). Slide transfer case to the rear and off of transmission output shaft. Lower case from vehicle. Remove gasket from between transfer case and extension housing.

Installation

Reverse removal procedures to install transfer case, noting the following:

1) When installing shift lever assembly, tighten large bolt first, then small bolt.

2) When installing vent assembly, White marking on hose should be positioned in notch in shifter with upper end of hose 2 inches above top of shifter, inside of shift lever boot.

3) Before installing front propeller shaft into transfer case, lubricate female splines of transfer case input shaft with multi-purpose grease.

4) Fill transfer case to bottom of fill plug hole with Dexron-II automatic transmission fluid.

TRANSMISSION

C-3 (BRONCO II & RANGER)
Removal

1) Disconnect battery negative cable. Raise vehicle. Loosen transmission pan bolts, tap edge of pan to break seal and allow fluid to drain. Replace pan after fluid

FORD (Cont.)

has drained. Remove converter drain plug access cover. Remove adapter plate bolts from lower end of converter housing.

2) Remove flywheel-to-converter attaching nuts and converter drain plug. Allow fluid to drain from converter, then reinstall and tighten drain plug. Mark propeller shaft for reassembly. Disconnect shaft at rear axle and slide out of transmission.

3) Remove speedometer cable from extension housing. Disconnect shift rod at manual lever and downshift rod at downshift lever. Remove starter-to-converter housing bolts and position starter out of way. DO NOT allow starter to hang by cables.

4) Disconnect neutral start switch connector from switch. Remove vacuum line from vacuum modulator. Raise slightly and support transmission with transmission jack. Remove rear mount-to-crossmember bolts.

5) Remove crossmember-to-frame side support bolts and remove crossmember insulator, support and damper. Lower jack under transmission and allow transmission to hang. Position a second jack at front of engine and raise enough to gain access to 2 top converter housing-to-engine bolts. DO NOT remove bolts at this time.

6) Disconnect transmission cooler lines and plug connections. Remove lower converter housing-to-engine bolts. Remove transmission filler tube. Raise transmission jack up to transmission and secure transmission to jack with safety chain.

7) Remove 2 top converter housing-to-engine bolts. Move transmission rearward and down to remove from vehicle.

Installation

Reverse removal procedures to install, noting the following: Ensure full converter engagement in transmission before installing transmission. During installation, keep transmission in a "nose-up" position at all times to prevent disengagement of the torque converter and pump gear.

C-5 (BRONCO II, RANGER & F-100)
Removal

1) Disconnect battery negative cable. On 4WD vehicles, remove filler tube bracket bolt from valve cover bracket. On all models, raise and support vehicle. Drain transmission fluid and replace pan. Remove converter drain plug access cover. On 2WD models, remove adapter plate bolts from lower end of converter housing.

2) On all models, remove flywheel-to-converter attaching nuts and converter drain plug. Allow fluid to drain from converter, then reinstall and tighten drain plug. On 2WD models, mark propeller shaft for reassembly. Disconnect shaft at rear axle and slide out of transmission.

3) On all models, disconnect battery cable from starter motor and remove starter. Disconnect neutral start switch wires at connector. Remove rear mount-to-crossmember nuts and 2 crossmember-to-frame bolts. Remove right and left gussets. On 4WD vehicles, remove rear insulator-to-extension housing bolts (2).

4) On all models, disconnect throttle valve (TV) linkage rod from transmission TV lever. Disconnect manual rod from manual lever at transmission. On 4WD models, disconnect downshift and manual linkage rods from levers on transmission. Remove vacuum hose from diaphragm unit. Remove vacuum line from retaining clip.

5) On all models, remove bellcrank housing-to-converter housing bolts (2). Remove transfer case (4WD models). Raise transmission enough to allow removal of crossmember. Remove rear mount from crossmember, then remove crossmember.

6) Lower transmission as needed to disconnect oil cooler lines. Disconnect cooler lines. Disconnect speedometer cable from extension housing. On 2WD models, remove transmission filler tube-to-engine bolt and lift filler tube out of transmission.

7) On all models, secure transmission to jack with safety chain. Remove converter housing-to-engine bolts. Carefully remove transmission and converter assembly from vehicle.

Installation

To install transmission, reverse removal procedures, noting the following:

1) Ensure that converter is fully engaged with pump gear before installation.

2) When installing filler tube, install a new "O" ring on bottom of tube.

3) On 2WD models, when installing damper assembly over engine rear support studs, make sure that the painted surface of the damper is facing forward when installed in vehicle.

4) Before installing rear propeller shaft, apply a small amount of multi-purpose grease to splines of yoke.

C-6 (ALL "E" MODELS)
Removal

1) Working inside vehicle, remove engine compartment cover and disconnnect electrical leads at plug connector. Remove flex hose from air cleaner heat tube (V8 models only), then remove upper converter housing-to-engine attaching bolts. Remove fluid filler tube-to-engine bolt.

2) Raise vehicle, drain transmission pan and remove converter drain plug access cover. Remove converter-to-flywheel attaching nuts and converter drain plug. Drain fluid and replace drain plug.

3) Disconnect propeller shaft. Remove filler tube. Disconnect starter cable and remove starter. Position an engine support bar to side rail and oil pan flanges. Disconnect oil cooler lines and vacuum lines from transmission.

4) Remove speedometer driven gear from extension housing and manual and downshift linkage rods from transmission control levers. Support transmission with transmission jack and secure with safety chain.

5) Remove bolts and nuts securing rear mount to crossmember and bolts retaining crossmember to side rails. Remove 2 support inserts, raise transmission with jack and remove crossmember. Remove remaining converter housing-to-engine bolts and lower assembly out of vehicle.

Installation

Reverse removal procedures to install, noting the following: Be sure that converter is fully engaged with pump gear during installation. Always use a new "O" ring on the end of the fluid filler tube. When installation is complete, fill transmission with Dexron II type automatic transmission fluid.

FORD (Cont.)

C-6 (BRONCO & "F" MODELS)
Removal
1) Disconnect negative cable from battery. Remove 2 upper converter housing-to-engine bolts. Raise vehicle, drain transmission pan and remove converter drain plug access cover.

2) Remove converter-to-flywheel attaching nuts and converter drain plug. Allow fluid to drain, then reinstall and tighten converter drain plug. On 2WD models, disconnect propeller shaft at rear axle and slide shaft out of transmission.

3) On all models, disconnect speedometer cable from extension housing. Disconnect downshift and manual linkage rods from levers at transmission. Disconnect oil cooler lines from transmission.

4) Remove vacuum line from vacuum unit. Remove vacuum line retaining clip. Disconnect starter cable from starter and remove starter. On 4WD models, remove transfer case.

5) On all models, remove 2 rear crossmember-to-frame attaching bolts. Remove 2 rear support-to-extension housing attaching bolts and 6 bolts securing second crossmember to frame side rails.

6) Raise transmission with a transmission jack and remove both crossmembers. Secure transmission to the jack with safety chain. Remove remaining converter housing-to-engine attaching bolts. Move transmission away from engine, lower the jack and remove converter and transmission assembly from vehicle.

Installation
Reverse removal procedure to install, noting the following: Make sure that torque converter is fully engaged in transmission before and during installation. When installing fluid filler tube, always use a new "O" ring on end of tube. When installation is complete, fill transmission with Dexron II type automatic transmission fluid.

AUTOMATIC OVERDRIVE ("F" MODELS)
Removal
1) Disconnect negative battery cable. Raise vehicle and drain transmission fluid. Remove converter drain plug access cover. Remove converter-to-flywheel attaching nuts and torque converter drain plug. Drain converter, then reinstall and tighten converter drain plug.

2) Disconnect propeller shaft from rear axle and remove shaft from transmission. Disconnect starter cable and remove starter. Disconnect neutral start switch wires at connector.

3) Remove rear mount-to-crossmember bolts and crossmember-to-frame bolts. Remove bolts securing engine rear support to extension housing. Disconnect TV linkage rod and manual rod from transmission levers.

4) Remove bellcrank bracket-to-converter housing bolts (2). Raise transmission with jack and remove crossmember. Lower transmission enough to remove oil cooler lines.

5) Disconnect speedometer cable from extension housing. Remove bolt securing filler tube to engine and remove filler tube. Secure transmission to jack with safety chain. Remove converter housing-to-engine bolts. Move transmission to rear and down to remove from vehicle.

Installation
Reverse removal procedures to install transmission, noting the following: Ensure that converter is fully seated in transmission before and during installation procedure. Install new "O" ring on end of fluid filler tube before installing tube. When installation is complete, fill transmission with Dexron II type automatic transmission fluid.

TIGHTENING SPECIFICATIONS

Application	Ft. Lbs. (N.m)
Converter Housing-to-Engine	
C-3	28-38 (38-51)
C-5	
Bronco II, Ranger & All 3.8L V6	28-38 (38-51)
All Others	40-50 (55-67)
C-6	
Gas Engines	40-50 (55-67)
Diesel Engines	50-65 (67-87)
AOT	40-50 (55-67)
Converter-to-Flywheel	
C-3	27-49 (37-66)
All Others	20-30 (28-40)
Starter Mounting Bolts	
Bronco II & Ranger	15-20 (20-27)
All Other Models	
Gas Engine	40-50 (56-70)
Diesel Engine	50-65 (70-91)
Control Lever-to-Transfer Case	
(Bronco II & Ranger)	
Large Bolt	70-90 (95-112)
Small Bolt	31-42 (42-57)

GENERAL MOTORS

TRANSFER CASE

"S" SERIES
Removal
1) With transfer case shift lever in "4 Hi" position, disconnect negative battery cable. Raise vehicle and remove skid plate. Drain transfer case. Mark front and rear output shaft yokes and propeller shafts for reassembly reference and remove shafts.

2) Disconnect speedometer cable and vacuum harness from transfer case. Remove shift lever from case. Remove catalytic converter hanger bolts at converter.

Raise transmission and transfer case assembly with jack and remove transmission mount bolts. Remove mount.

3) Lower complete assembly. Support transfer case alone and remove transmission-to-transfer case bolts. Remove shift lever bracket from transfer case adapter in order to reach upper left attaching bolt.

4) Separate transfer case from transmission adapter and remove from vehicle.
Installation
Reverse removal procedures to install. Always use a new gasket between the transfer case and adapter.

Automatic Transmission Removal

GENERAL MOTORS (Cont.)

TRANSMISSIONS

ALL EXCEPT "S" & "K" SERIES
Removal

1) Disconnect negative battery cable. Remove air cleaner and disconnect TV or detent cable at carburetor. Remove dipstick and filler tube support bracket bolt. Raise and support vehicle. Mark propeller shaft for reassembly reference and remove from vehicle.

2) Disconnect speedometer cable and shift linkage and all electrical leads from transmission. Remove transmission support brackets (if present) and flywheel inspection cover.

3) Mark flex plate and torque converter for reassembly in same position and remove torque converter-to-flex plate bolts. Disconnect catalytic converter support bracket (if equipped).

4) Remove transmission rear mount bolts. Support transmission with jack and raise slightly. Remove transmission support-to-frame bolts and insulators. Remove support.

5) Lower transmission enough to remove oil cooler lines and TV or detent cable from transmission. Disconnect lines and cable. Support engine with jack and remove transmission-to-engine bolts.

6) Disconnect transmission assembly from engine. Install torque converter retaining tool (J-21366) and remove transmission from vehicle.

Installation

To install, reverse removal procedure and note the following: Before installing flex plate-to-converter bolts, make certain that the weld nuts on converter are flush with the flex plate and the converter rotates freely by hand in this position. Install converter-to-flex plate bolts (3) and tighten finger tight before tightening to proper specification.

"K" SERIES
Removal

1) Disconnect negative battery cable. Remove air cleaner and disconnect TV or detent cable at carburetor. Remove transfer case shift lever knob and boot. Raise and support vehicle.

2) Mark propeller shafts for reassembly reference and remove from vehicle. Disconnect speedometer cable, shift linkage and all electrical leads from transmission and transfer case. Disconnect transfer case shift linkage.

3) Remove transmission support strut rods and flywheel inspection cover. Mark flex plate and converter for reassembly reference. Remove torque converter-to-flex plate retaining bolts.

4) Disconnect transmission oil cooler lines from transmission. Support transmission and transfer case assembly with a jack and remove transfer case-to-frame bracket bolts. Remove mount bolts and crossmember.

5) Remove transmission/transfer case assembly mounting bolts and remove assembly from vehicle. Separate transmission from transfer case.

Installation

Reverse removal procedures to install, noting the following: Before installing flex plate-to-converter bolts, make certain that the weld nuts on converter are flush with the flex plate and the converter rotates freely by hand in this position. Then, hand start all 3 bolts and tighten finger tight before tightening to specifications.

"S" SERIES

NOTE: If vehicle is a 4WD model, refer to Transfer Case removal procedures and remove case.

Removal

1) Disconnect negative battery cable. Remove air cleaner and disconnect TV cable at carburetor. On models with 1.9L 4-cylinder engine, remove upper starter retaining nut. On all models, raise and support vehicle.

2) Mark propeller shaft for reassembly reference and remove shaft. Disconnect speedometer cable, shift linkage and all electrical leads from transmission. Remove brake line to crossmember clips and remove crossmember (4WD only).

3) Remove transmission support brace bolts and converter cover (if equipped). Remove exhaust crossover pipe and converter attaching bolts. Remove crossover and converter as an assembly.

4) Remove flywheel inspection plate and mark flex plate and torque converter for reassembly reference. Remove torque converter-to-flex plate bolts. Disconnect catalytic converter support bracket.

5) Place a jack under transmission and raise slightly. Remove transmission support-to-mount bolt and support-to-frame bolts and insulators. Remove left body mounting bolts and loosen radiator support mount bolt.

6) Raise cab on left side as needed to remove upper transmission-to-engine bolts. Support cab with wood block between body and frame. Slide transmission support towards rear and lower transmission enough to remove oil cooler lines and TV cable. Disconnect lines and cable.

7) Support engine with jack and remove remaining transmission-to-engine bolts. Slide transmission away from engine and install torque converter retaining tool (J-21366) to prevent converter damage as transmission is removed from vehicle. Remove transmission.

Installation

Reverse removal procedures to install, noting the following: Before installing flex plate-to-converter bolts, make certain that the weld nuts on converter are flush with the flex plate and the converter rotates freely by hand in this position. Then, hand start all 3 bolts and tighten finger tight before tightening to specifications.

TIGHTENING SPECIFICATIONS

Application	Ft. Lbs. (N.m)
Transmission-to-Engine	
"S" Series	
1.9L 4-Cylinder	25 (35)
2.8L V6	55 (75)
All Others	35 (50)
Converter-to-Flex Plate	
"S" Series	35 (50)
All Others	35 (45)
Transmission-to-Mount	
"S" Series	35 (50)
All Others	35 (48)
Transfer Case-to-Adapter	
"S" Series	20-25 (27-34)
All Others	25 (35)
Transmission-to-Adapter	25 (35)

JEEP

REMOVAL

ALL MODELS

1) Disconnect fan shroud and transmission fill tube upper bracket. Raise vehicle. Remove converter inspection cover and fill tube. Remove starter.

2) Mark propeller shafts for reassembly. Disconnect shafts at transfer case and wire to frame rails. Do not allow shafts to hang free as damage to universal joints may result. On V8 models, disconnect exhaust pipes from exhaust manifolds. Drain transfer case lubricant on Cherokee, Wagoneer and Truck models. Disconnect speedometer cable from transmission.

3) Disconnect all shift and throttle linkages and wiring from transmission and transfer case. Mark converter drive plate and converter for reassembly and remove torque converter-to-drive plate bolts. Rotate crankshaft to gain access to bolts.

4) Suport transmission/transfer case assembly with jack and secure with chain. Remove bolts and rear crossmember. Lower transmission enough to disconnect cooler lines at transmission. Remove transmission-to-engine retaining bolts and slowly slide transmission assembly away from engine.

5) Hold converter in position while lowering transmission assembly from vehicle. Separate transmission from transfer case.

INSTALLATION

ALL MODELS

Reverse removal procedures to install, noting the following: Do not tighten exhaust pipe attaching bolts until crossmember has been installed and transmission jack has been removed. Make sure all index marks made at removal are aligned. Tighten all bolts to specification and fill transmission and transfer case with fluid.

TIGHTENING SPECIFICATIONS

Application	Ft. Lbs. (N.m)
Cooler Line Nuts	25 (34)
Torque Converter-to-Drive Plate	22 (30)
Transfer Case-to-Transmission	40 (54)
Transmission-to-Engine	30 (41)

Manual Transmission Servicing

CHRYSLER CORP.

LUBRICATION

SERVICE INTERVALS

NOTE: There are 2 light duty truck emission control standards classifications: Light Duty and Heavy Duty. Light Duty refers to vehicles up to 8500 lbs. GVW; Heavy Duty refers to vehicles over 8500 lbs. GVW.

Transmission

1) Check fluid level whenever vehicle is serviced. On vehicles used in normal service with heavy duty emissions, transmission should be drained and refilled every 36,000 miles.

2) On vehicles containing light duty emissions, transmission should be drained and refilled every 37,500 miles. On vehicles used under severe conditions, drain and refill transmission every 18,000 miles.

Shift Linkage for Overdrive 4-Speed

1) Gearshift control mechanism should be lubricated every 22,500 miles or every 2 years. Lubricate more frequently if shift effort or noise is apparent. The 4-speed gearshift linkage has a grease fitting located on left side of mechanism. Lubricate linkage from under vehicle.

2) Use a high pressure grease gun to lubricate linkage with multipurpose grease. Lubricate until grease is visible on operating levers.

NOTE: Vehicle must be in reverse gear position, engine OFF, when lubricating gearshift control mechanism.

CHECKING FLUID LEVEL

Check lubricant level at filler plug hole on side of transmission. Lubricant should be level with bottom of filler plug hole. Add lubricant as needed to bring to correct level.

RECOMMENDED FLUID

New Process 435 4-Speed

Either multipurpose gear lubricants meeting API specification GL-5 or engine oils labeled for API Service "SF" may be used.

If multipurpose gear lubricant is used and the minimum anticipated atmospheric temperature is:
- Above 90°F (32°C), use SAE 140.
- As low as -10°F (-23°C), use SAE 90.
- Below -10°F (-23°C), use SAE 80.

If engine oil is used, and the minimum anticipated atmospheric temperature is:

- Above 32°F (0°C), use SAE 50.
- Below 32°F (0°C), use SAE 30.

Overdrive 4-Speed

Use Dexron II Automatic Transmission Fluid. If gear rattle is apparent during idle or acceleration, multipurpose gear lubricant SAE 90, SAE 75W, 75W-80, SAE 80W-90 or SAE 85W-90 may be used.

CAPACITY

TRANSMISSION REFILL CAPACITIES

Application	Capacity Pints (Liters)
4-Speed Overdrive	7.0 (3.3)
NP-435	7.0 (3.3)

ADJUSTMENT

SHIFT LINKAGE

Overdrive 4-Speed

1) Install floor shift lever aligning tool to hold levers in neutral crossover position. See Fig. 1. Remove all rods from transmission shift levers and place levers in neutral detent positions.

2) Rotate shift rods until they are centered in transmission lever mounting holes, starting with 1st-2nd shift rod. Replace all washers and clips. Remove aligning tool and test shifting action.

Fig. 1: Overdrive 4-Speed Gearshift Linkage Adjustment

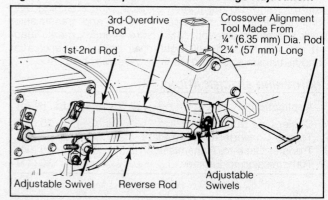

Rotate shift rods until they are exactly centered in transmission lever mounting holes.

FORD

LUBRICATION

SERVICE INTERVALS

Check fluid level whenever malfunction is suspected, leakage is observed, or after vehicle operation in water. Periodic draining and refilling is not required.

CHECKING FLUID LEVEL

Check lubricant level at transmission filler plug hole. It should be level with bottom of filler hole. Add lubricant as needed.

RECOMMENDED FLUID

All transmissions except Warner T19B should use 80W multi-purpose gear lubricant meeting Ford specification ESP-M2C83-C, or equivalent. Warner T19B transmissions use SAE 30 or SAE 50 engine oil, depending upon ambient air temperatures. If vehicle will be operated at temperatures below 0°F (-18°C), SAE 30 should be used. SAE 50 should be used if temperatures are consistently above 0°F (-18°C).

FORD (Cont.)

CAPACITY

Capacities given below are approximate. Correct fluid level should be determined by level at filler plug hole, rather than by amount added.

TRANSMISSION REFILL CAPACITIES

Application	Capacity Pints (Liters)
Ford 3-Speed	3.5 (1.6)
New Process 435	
With Extension	7.0 (3.3)
Without Extension	6.5 (3.0)
Warner T-18	7.0 (3.3)
Warner T-19B	7.0 (3.3)
4-Speed Overdrive	4.5 (2.1)
4-Speed Single Rail Overdrive	4.5 (2.1)
Bronco II & Ranger 4-Speed	
Diesel Engine	3.2 (1.5)
Gas Engine	3.0 (1.4)
5-Speed Overdrive	3.0 (1.4)

ADJUSTMENT

SHIFT LINKAGE

Shift linkage may be adjusted on the 3-Speed and 4-Speed Overdrive transmissions, only. All other models use internal shift linkage which cannot be adjusted.

3-Speed

1) Insert a 3/16" gauge pin through steering column shift levers and plastic spacer.

2) Loosen shift rod lock nuts at transmission shift levers. Place both shift levers in neutral position. Tighten lock nuts and remove gauge pin. Check shift linkage operation for smoothness.

4-Speed Overdrive

1) Disconnect all 3 shift rods and insert a 1/4" diameter pin in alignment hole in shifter assembly. Align 1-2 (rear) and 3-4 (front) shift levers in neutral position. Turn Reverse (middle) lever counterclockwise to neutral position.

2) Rotate transmission output shaft to be sure all levers are in neutral. Then turn reverse lever fully clockwise to reverse position. This causes the interlock system to align 1-2 and 3-4 rails in precise neutral positions. Install 1-2 and 3-4 shift rods on shift levers and tighten lock nuts.

3) Rotate reverse lever back to neutral position. Install reverse shift rod and lock nut. Remove alignment pin and check for proper linkage operation.

GENERAL MOTORS

LUBRICATION

SERVICE INTERVALS

NOTE: There are 2 light duty truck emission control standards classifications: Light Duty and Heavy Duty. Light Duty refers to vehicles up to 8500 lbs. GVW; Heavy Duty refers to vehicles over 8500 lbs. GVW.

On "S" models with 4-speed transmission, change transmission fluid after the first 7500 miles and at 35,000 mile intervals thereafter. On all other light duty vehicles, check transmission fluid level every 12 months or 7500 miles. On heavy duty vehicles, check fluid level every 12 months or 6000 miles. Periodic draining and refilling is not required.

CHECKING FLUID LEVEL

Check lubricant level at transmission filler plug hole. Lubricant should be level with bottom of hole. Add as needed.

RECOMMENDED FLUID

In all except Isuzu and 5-speed transmissions, use only SAE 80W or SAE 80W-90 GL-5 multipurpose gear lubricant, or equivalent. Isuzu and 5-speed models use only Dexron II automatic transmission fluid, or equivalent.

CAPACITY

The capacities listed in the following chart are approximations only. Correct fluid level should be determined by level at filler plug hole, rather than by amount added.

TRANSMISSION REFILL CAPACITIES

Application	Capacity Pints (Liters)
3-Speed (76 MM)	3.0 (1.4)
4-Speed (117 MM)	8.0 (3.7)
4-Speed w/Overdrive (89 MM)	4.5 (2.1)
"S" Models	1

1 — Add fluid to bottom of filler plug hole.

ADJUSTMENT

SHIFT LINKAGE
All With Shifter on Column

1) Place gear selector lever in reverse position. Turn transmission shift lever fully clockwise to forward stop. Turn ignition switch to "LOCK" position. Attach primary shift rod to column shift lever with retainer. See Fig. 1.

2) Slide swivel on to end of shift rod and insert swivel into transmission shift lever. Loosely assemble with bolt and washer. Turn column shift lever down as far as possible and tighten bolt.

3) Turn ignition switch to "UNLOCK" position and move gear selector lever to neutral. Turn transmission shift lever and cross shaft lever clockwise to full forward positions, then back 1 detent to neutral.

Manual Transmission Servicing

GENERAL MOTORS (Cont.)

Fig. 1: Adjusting Shift Linkage

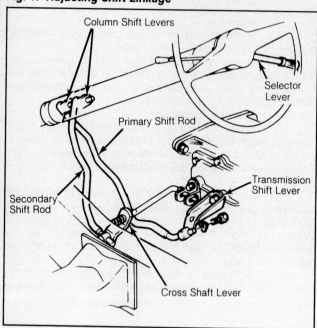

3-Speed with column mounted shifter.

4) Align gauge holes in column shift levers (3) and insert 1/4" gauge pin through holes. Repeat adjustment procedure with secondary shift rod. Remove gauge pin and check for proper linkage operation. Ignition switch should turn to "LOCK" position with shifter in reverse position, only.

All With Floor-Mounted Shifter

1) Disconnect all shift rods from transmission shift levers. With shift selector lever in neutral position, insert a 1/4" diameter pin through alignment holes in shifter assembly.

2) Align all shift levers at transmission in neutral position. Rotate transmission output shaft to be sure all levers are in neutral. Loosen lock nuts on shift rod ends and align rod ends with shift lever holes. Install shift rods in levers, tighten lock nuts and install lock pins.

3) Remove alignment pin and check for proper linkage operation.

JEEP

LUBRICATION

SERVICE INTERVALS

Under normal driving conditions, check fluid level every 5000 miles. Under severe driving conditions, check fluid level every 3000 miles. Transmission lubricant should be changed at 27,500 mile intervals.

CHECKING FLUID LEVEL

Check lubricant level at transmission filler plug hole. Lubricant should be level with bottom of hole. Add lubricant as needed.

RECOMMENDED FLUID

T4 & T5 Transmissions
Use Jeep Automatic Transmission Fluid or equivalent, labeled Dexron II.
T-176 & T-18A Transmissions
Use only SAE 85W-90 API GL-5 gear lubricant.

NOTE: Do not use gear lubricants containing lead, chlorine or sulphur compounds in T-176 and T-18 transmissions.

CAPACITY

Capacities given below are approximate. Correct fluid level should be determined by level at filler plug hole.

TRANSMISSION REFILL CAPACITIES

Application	Capacity Pints (Liters)
4-Speed	
T4	3.5 (1.7)
T-18A	6.5 (3.1)
T-176	3.5 (1.7)
5-Speed	
T5	4.0 (1.9)

SHIFT LINKAGE

NOTE: All Jeep models use transmission shift linkage which does not require external adjustment

CHRYSLER CORP.

TRANSFER CASE

MODEL NP-205

Removal

1) Raise vehicle, remove plug and drain transfer case. Replace plug. Disconnect speedometer cable. Remove skid plate, crossmember and strut rods as needed. Disconnect propeller shafts and wire out of way. Do not allow propeller shafts to hang free, as damage to universal joints may result.

2) Disconnect shift lever rod from shift rail link. Support transfer case and remove transfer case-to-transmission adapter bolts. Move transfer case to rear until input shaft clears adapter. Lower transfer case from vehicle.

Installation

Reverse removal procedures to install transfer case. Ensure that all attaching bolts are tight. Fill transfer case with lubricant.

MODEL NP-208

Removal

1) Raise vehicle, remove plug and drain transfer case. Mark front and rear output shaft yokes and propeller shafts for reassembly reference. Disconnect speedometer cable and indicator switch wires. Disconnect shift lever link from operating lever.

2) Support transfer case with transmission jack and remove crossmember. Disconnect front and rear propeller shafts at yokes and wire to frame.

3) If necessary, disconnect parking brake cable guide from pivot on right frame rail. Remove bolts attaching exhaust pipe support bracket to transfer case. Remove transfer case-to-transmission bolts. Move assembly to the rear until clear of output shaft. Lower transfer case from vehicle.

4) Remove all gasket material from rear of transmission adapter housing.

Installation

Install new transmission-to-transfer case gasket with sealer on both sides. Align transfer case with transmission. Rotate transfer case output shaft until transmission output shaft engages transfer case input shaft. Move transfer case until case seats flush against transmission. Install transfer case attaching bolts. Reverse removal procedures to complete installation.

TRANSMISSION

ALL MODELS

Removal

1) Disconnect negative battery cable. Remove retaining screws from floor pan and slide boot up and off shift lever.

2) On models equipped with New Process 435 transmission, remove shift lever retainer by pressing down, rotating retainer clockwise and releasing.

3) On models equipped with Overdrive 4-Speed transmission, remove shift lever by inserting a .010" (.25 mm) feeler gauge between floor shift assembly and shift lever, and disengaging internal spring clip.

Fig. 1: Removing Overdrive 4-Speed Shift Lever

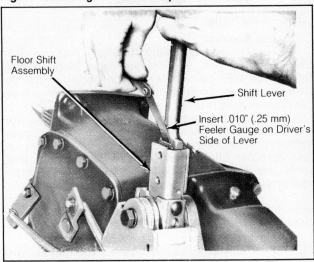

Floor Shift Assembly

Shift Lever

Insert .010" (.25 mm) Feeler Gauge on Driver's Side of Lever

Insert feeler gauge to remove spring clip.

4) Remove bolts and washers securing shift lever to mounting plate on extension housing and remove.

5) On all models, drain fluid from transmission. On 4WD models, remove transfer case. On all vehicles, remove propeller shaft from transmission at rear universal joint. Disconnect speedometer cable and back-up light switch. Install engine support fixture (C-3487-A).

6) On models equipped with New Process 435 transmission, place adapters (DD-1279) firmly over frame rails. On all models, make sure support ends of engine fixture tool are up against underside of oil pan flange.

7) Raise engine slightly with support fixture. On models with Overdrive 4-Speed transmission, disconnect extension housing from removable center crossmember.

8) On all models, support transmission with a jack and remove crossmember. Remove transmission-to-clutch housing bolts. Slide transmission rearward until drive pinion shaft clears clutch disc, then lower and remove transmission.

Installation

Reverse removal procedures to install, noting the following: apply a small amount of high-temperature grease to the pilot shaft bushing in the flywheel and on pinion bearing retainer release bearing sleeve area before installing transmission. As transmission is installed, engage pinion shaft with clutch disc by slowly turning shaft to engage teeth. DO NOT allow transmission to hang free once clutch disc has been engaged.

TIGHTENING SPECIFICATIONS

Application	Ft. Lbs. (N.m)
Transfer Case-to-Transmission	40 (54)
Transmission Case-to-Clutch Housing	
Overdrive 4-Speed	50 (68)
NP-435	105 (142)
Crossmember-to-Frame	30 (41)
Ext. Housing-to-Rear Mount Bolt	50 (68)

Manual Transmission Removal

FORD

TRANSFER CASE

NP-208
Removal

1) Raise and support vehicle. Remove drain plug and drain fluid from transfer case. Replace plug. Disconnect 4WD indicator switch connector at transfer case. Disconnect speedometer driven gear from transfer case rear bearing retainer.

2) Remove transmission shift lever-to-transfer case retaining nut. Remove skid plate from frame. Support transfer case with transmission jack. Disconnect front and rear propeller shafts from transfer case output shaft yokes and wire out of way. Do not allow shafts to hang free as damage to universal joints may result.

3) Remove transfer case-to-transmission adapter bolts. Remove gasket between transfer case and adapter and lower transfer case out of vehicle.

Installation

To install transfer case, reverse removal procedures. Fill case with 7 pints (3.3 liters) of Dexron II type automatic transmission fluid.

BORG-WARNER 1345
Removal

1) Raise vehicle. Remove drain plug and drain fluid from transfer case. Replace plug. Disconnect 4WD indicator switch connector at transfer case. If equipped, remove skid plate.

2) Disconnect front and rear propeller shafts from transfer case output shaft yokes and wire out of way. Do not allow shafts to hang free as damage to universal joints may result.

3) Disconnect speedometer driven gear from rear bearing retainer. Remove retaining clips and shift rod from transfer case control and transfer case shift levers. Disconnect vent hose from case.

4) Remove heat shield. Support transfer case with transmission jack, remove transfer case-to-transmission adapter bolts and slide transfer case off of transmission output shaft. Lower transfer case out of vehicle and remove gasket from between transfer case and adapter.

Installation

Reverse removal procedures to install transfer case. Fill case with 6.5 pints (3.1 liters) of Dexron II type automatic transmission fluid.

BORG-WARNER 1350
Removal

1) Raise vehicle. Remove skid plate (if equipped). Remove drain plug and drain fluid from case. Replace plug. Disconnect 4WD indicator switch connector at transfer case. Disconnect front propeller shaft from front axle. Loosen front shaft boot clamp and slide out propeller shaft and boot as an assembly.

2) Disconnect rear propeller shaft from transfer case. Disconnect speedometer driven gear from transfer case rear cover. Disconnect vent hose from control lever.

3) Loosen or remove large and small bolts (1 each) retaining shifter to extension housing. Pull on control lever until bushing slides off transfer case shift lever pin. Unscrew shift lever from control lever, as needed.

4) Remove heat shield from transfer case. Support transfer case with jack and remove transfer case-to-transmission extension housing bolts (5). Slide transfer case to the rear and off of transmission output shaft. Lower case from vehicle. Remove gasket from between transfer case and extension housing.

Installation

Reverse removal procedures to install transfer case, noting the following:

1) When installing shift lever assembly, tighten large bolt first, then small bolt.

2) When installing vent assembly, White marking on hose should be positioned in notch in shifter with upper end of hose 2 inches above top of shifter, inside of shift lever boot.

3) Before installing front propeller shaft into transfer case, lubricate female splines of transfer case input shaft with multipurpose grease.

4) Fill transfer case to bottom of fill plug hole with Dexron II automatic transmission fluid.

TRANSMISSION

BRONCO II & RANGER
Removal

1) Place shift lever in neutral position. Remove boot retainer screws and bolts attaching retainer cover to gearshift lever retainer. Disconnect clutch master cylinder push rod from clutch pedal.

2) Pull gearshift lever assembly, shim and bushing straight up and away from lever retainer. Disconnect negative cable from battery. Raise and support vehicle.

3) Disconnect propeller shaft at rear axle and remove shaft. Remove clutch housing dust shield and slave cylinder. Wire to one side. Disconnect speedometer cable, starter motor cable and backup light wiring.

4) Place jack and wood block under engine oil pan to support engine. On 4WD vehicles, remove transfer case. On all models, remove starter. Place transmission jack under transmission.

5) Remove bolts, lockwashers and flat washers attaching transmission to engine rear plate. Remove transmission mount-to-crossmember bolts. Remove nuts attaching crossmember to frame. Remove crossmember.

6) Lower jack under engine. Work transmission to the rear until input shaft clears clutch housing. Remove transmission.

Installation

Reverse removal procedures to install.

3-SPEED ("E" MODELS)
Removal

1) Raise and support vehicle. Remove lower extension housing-to-transmission bolt to drain lubricant. Disconnect propeller shaft from flange at transmission and wire out of way. Do not allow shaft to hang free as damage to universal joint may result.

2) Disconnect speedometer cable and shift control rods from transmission shift levers. Place jack under transmission and secure transmission to jack with safety chain.

3) Raise transmission slightly and remove 4 bolts retaining transmission extension housing to insulator and retainer assembly. Remove transmission-to-clutch housing bolts. Install engine support bar on frame, under engine, and lower transmission out of vehicle.

FORD (Cont.)

Installation

Reverse removal procedures to install. Fill transmission with lubricant. Adjust clutch and shift linkages.

3-SPEED ("F" MODELS)

Removal

1) Raise vehicle and support on safety stands. Support engine with jack and wood block under oil pan. To drain fluid from transmission, remove lower extension housing-to-transmission bolt.

2) Place jack under transmission and secure transmission to jack with safety chain. Disconnect shift linkage at transmission. Disconnect speedometer cable and back-up switch wires.

3) Disconnect propeller shaft and wire out of way. Do not allow shaft to hang free as damage to universal joint may result. Raise transmission and remove rear support, insulator and retainer.

4) Remove transmission-to-clutch housing attaching bolts. Move transmission rearward until input shaft clears clutch housing. Lower transmission out of vehicle. Do not depress clutch pedal at any time while transmission is out of vehicle.

Installation

Reverse removal procedures to install, noting the following: Apply a thin film of multi-purpose grease to the release bearing inner hub surfaces, release lever fulcrum and fork, and the transmission front bearing retainer. With installation complete, fill transmission with lubricant. Adjust clutch and shift linkage.

4-SPEED OVERDRIVE

Removal

1) Raise and support vehicle. Mark propeller shaft position for reassembly reference. Disconnect propeller shaft from rear axle and slide shaft out of transmission. Disconnect speedometer cable and shift rods. Remove bolts connecting shift control to transmission case.

2) Remove rear transmission support-to-crossmember bolts. Support engine with transmission jack and raise transmission enough to take weight off number 3 crossmember. Remove bolts holding crossmember to frame side supports. Remove crossmember.

3) Place jack under rear of engine and raise high enough to remove weight from forward crossmember. Remove crossmember. With transmission supported by and secured to transmission jack, remove clutch housing-to-transmission bolts.

4) Move transmission to the rear until input shaft clears clutch housing and remove transmission. Do not depress clutch pedal while transmission is out of vehicle.

Installation

Reverse removal procedures to install.

S.R.O.D. 4-SPEED

1) Raise vehicle and support on safety stands. Drain transmission and transfer case (if equipped). On 4WD vehicles, remove retaining clips and shift rod from transfer case control lever and transfer case shift lever. Disconnect vent hose from transfer case.

2) On all models, mark propeller shaft position for reassembly reference. Disconnect propeller shaft from rear "U" joint flange. Remove propeller shaft. Disconnect

speedometer cable and backup light switch. Remove screws holding shift lever to turret and remove shift lever.

3) Support engine with transmission jack, and remove extension housing-to-engine support bolts. Raise engine enough to remove weight from crossmember. Remove bolts securing crossmember to frame side supports. Remove crossmember.

4) On 4WD vehicles, remove transfer case. On all models, support transmission with jack and remove transmission-to-flywheel housing bolts. Move transmission rearward, until input shaft clears flywheel housing. Remove transmission. Do not depress clutch pedal at any time while transmission is out of vehicle.

Installation

Reverse removal procedures to install.

NP 435

Removal

1) Remove floor mat. Remove shift lever, shift ball and boot as an assembly. On 4WD models, remove transfer case shift lever, shift ball and boot as an assembly. Remove floor pan transmission cover or weather pad on F150-350 models. Remove seat if necessary.

2) To remove gearshift lever and knob, first remove inner cap with puller (T73T-7220-A or equivalent). Remove seat and spring. Remove gearshift lever. Disconnect back-up light.

3) Raise vehicle. Disconnect speedometer cable and rear propeller shaft. Wire shaft out of way. On 4WD models, drain transfer case, remove front propeller shaft from case and wire out of way.

4) Remove cotter pin holding shift link and remove link. Remove bolts holding bracket to transfer case. Position transmission jack under transfer case.

5) Remove transfer case-to-transmission bolts and remove transfer case. On all models, place transmission jack under transmission and lift slightly. Remove transmission-to-insulator, insulator-to-crossmember and crossmember-to-frame bolts. Remove insulator and crossmember.

6) Remove transmission-to-clutch housing bolts and lower transmission out of vehicle.

Installation

Reverse removal procedures to install.

WARNER T-18 (2WD MODELS)

Removal

1) Working from inside vehicle, remove floor mat and body floor pan cover. Remove gearshift lever, shift ball and boot as an assembly. Remove weather pad. Raise and support vehicle. Disconnect speedometer cable.

2) Disconnect back-up light switch from rear of gear shift housing cover. Disconnect propeller shaft from transmission and wire out of way. Do not allow shaft to hang free as damage to universal joint may result. Disconnect clutch linkage.

3) Remove skid plate (if equipped) and heat shield. Support transmission with jack. Remove crossmember gusset-to-frame bolts and gusset-to-crossmember bolts. Remove transmission-to-insulator bolts. Raise transmission and remove insulator-to-crossmember bolts. Remove insulator

4) Remove right gusset, crossmember-to-frame bolts and crossmember. Remove transmission-to-

Manual Transmission Removal

FORD (Cont.)

clutch housing bolts. Move transmission away from clutch housing until input shaft clears housing. Lower transmission out of vehicle.

Installation

Reverse removal procedures to install, noting the following: When installing shift lever, shift ball and boot assembly, lubricate the spherical ball seat with multipurpose grease.

WARNER T-18 (4WD MODELS)

Removal

1) Working from inside vehicle, remove floor mat and access cover to floor pan. Place shift lever in reverse position and remove cover, insulator and dust cover. Remove transfer case shift lever, shift ball and boot as an assembly.

2) Remove transmission shift lever, shift ball and boot as an assembly. Raise vehicle. Remove drain plug and allow transmission to drain. Replace plug. Disconnect front and rear propeller shafts from transfer case and wire out of way. Do not allow shafts to hang free as damage to universal joint may result.

3) Remove shift link retainer ring and remove shift link from transfer case. Disconnect speedometer cable. Place transmission jack under transfer case. Remove transfer case-to-transmission bolts and lower transfer case out of vehicle.

4) Remove rear support bracket-to-transmission bolts (8), position transmission jack under transmission and remove rear support bracket and brace. Remove transmission-to-clutch housing bolts (4) and remove transmission.

Installation

Reverse removal procedures to install.

WARNER T19B (2WD MODELS)

Removal

1) Working from inside vehicle, remove floor mat and body floor pan cover. Remove gearshift lever, shift ball and boot as an assembly. Remove weather pad.

2) Raise vehicle. Place transmission jack under transmission and disconnect speedometer cable. Disconnect back-up light switch from rear of gear shift housing cover. Disconnect propeller shaft and clutch linkage. Wire out of way.

3) Remove transmission rear insulator and lower retainer. Remove skid plate (if equipped) and heat shield. Remove upper gusset bolts and gusset-to-crossmember bolts. Remove left side gusset.

4) Remove transmission-to-support plate bolts, raise transmission slightly and remove support plate-to-crossmember bolts. Remove support plate and right gusset. Remove crossmember-to-frame bolts and remove crossmember.

5) Remove transmission-to-clutch housing bolts. Move transmission to the rear until input shaft clears housing and remove transmission.

Installation

Reverse removal procedures to install transmission, noting the following: When installing the shift lever, shift ball and boot assembly, lubricate spherical ball seat with multipurpose grease.

WARNER T19B (4WD MODELS)

Removal

1) Working from inside vehicle, remove floor mat and access cover to floor pan (shift lever in reverse when removing cover). Remove insulator and dust cover. Remove transfer case shift lever, shift ball and boot as an assembly.

2) Remove transmission shift lever, shift ball and boot as an assembly. Raise vehicle. Drain transmission and replace drain plug. Disconnect front and rear driveshafts from transfer case and wire out of way.

3) Remove shift link retainer ring and remove link from transfer case. Disconnect speedometer cable. Place transmission jack under transfer case and remove transfer case-to-transmission bolts (6). Lower transfer case out of vehicle.

4) Remove rear support bracket-to-transmission bolts (8). Place transmission jack under transmission and remove rear support bracket and brace. Remove transmission-to-clutch housing bolts (4) and remove transmission.

Installation

Reverse removal procedures to install.

TIGHTENING SPECIFICATIONS

Application	Ft. Lbs. (N.m)
Transmission-to-Clutch Housing	
Bronco II & Ranger	30-40 (42-56)
All Others	
3-Speed	42-50 (59-70)
4-Speed	35-50 (49-70)
Transfer Case-to-Transmission	
NP-208	20-25 (28-35)
Borg-Warner 1345	25-43 (35-60)
Borg-Warner 13-50	25-35 (35-49)
Insulator-to-Crossmember	
3-Speed	50-70 (70-98)
4-Speed Overdrive	50-70 (70-98)
Bronco II & Ranger	71-94 (98-132)
All Others	
2WD	50-70 (70-98)
4WD	35-45 (49-63)
Insulator-to-Transmission	
3-Speed ("E" Models)	50-70 (70-98)
4-Speed Overdrive	50-70 (70-98)
SROD 4-Speed (2WD)	40-60 (56-84)
T19B 4-Speed	45-60 (63-84)
All Others	60-80 (84-112)

GENERAL MOTORS

TRANSFER CASE

"S" SERIES
Removal

1) Disconnect negative battery cable. Place transfer case in "4 Hi" position. Raise vehicle and remove skid plate. Drain transfer case. Mark front and rear output shaft yokes and propeller shafts for reassembly reference and remove shafts.

2) Disconnect speedometer cable and vacuum harness from transfer case. Remove shift lever from case. Remove catalytic converter hanger bolts at converter. Raise transmission and transfer case assembly with jack and remove transmission mount bolts. Remove mount.

3) Lower complete assembly, support transfer case only and remove transmission-to-transfer case attaching bolts. Separate transfer case from extension housing and remove from vehicle.

Installation

Reverse removal procedures to install. Always use a new gasket between the transfer case and the extension housing.

TRANSMISSION

ALL EXCEPT "S" & "K" SERIES
Removal

1) On models with 117 MM 4-speed, remove attaching screws from shift lever boot retainer. Slide boot assembly up shift lever and remove lever. To remove shift lever, push down on collar and turn counter-clockwise.

2) On all models, raise and support vehicle under frame. Drain fluid from transmission. Disconnect speedometer cable at transmission. Remove shift controls from transmission (if not already removed). Remove parking brake lever, controls, and back-up switch wire as needed.

3) Disconnect propeller shaft at transmission and position support under transmission assembly. Disconnect exhaust pipes from exhaust manifolds as needed. Remove frame crossmember and flywheel inspection plate.

4) On 117 MM 4-speed, remove top 2 transmission-to-clutch housing bolts and install guide pins. On all models, remove all transmission-to-clutch housing attaching bolts, slide transmission rearward until input shaft is clear of clutch hub and remove assembly from vehicle. Remove guide pins if used.

NOTE: **Support clutch release bearing and support assembly when removing transmission main drive gear from flywheel housing. This will prevent release bearing from falling out of flywheel housing.**

Installation

Apply a light coating of high temperature grease to main drive gear bearing retainer and splined portion of transmission main drive gear shaft. Reverse removal procedures to complete installation.

ALL "K" SERIES
Removal

1) On models with 117 MM 4-speed, remove attaching screws from shift lever boot retainer. Slide boot

assembly up shift lever and remove lever. To remove shift lever, push down on collar and turn counter-clockwise.

2) On all models, raise and support vehicle under frame. Drain fluid from transmission and transfer case. Disconnect speedometer cable. Disconnect front and rear propeller shafts at transfer case and wire out of way. Disconnect transfer case shift lever.

3) Position support under transfer case. Remove transfer case-to-adapter bolts and remove transfer case. Disconnect shift control rods from shifter levers if not already removed. Separate exhaust pipes from exhaust manifolds as needed.

4) Support rear part of engine and remove 2 adapter bolts. Remove crossmember. Remove 2 top transmission-to-clutch housing cap screws. Insert 2 guide pins (J-1126 on 117 MM, J-2216 all others) in holes. Remove 2 lower transmission-to-clutch housing cap screws.

5) Slide transmission and adapter assembly rearward until clutch gear is free of splines in clutch disc. Guide pins will support transmission and prevent damage to clutch disc. Remove transmission and adapter as an assembly. Remove adapter from transmission.

Installation

Apply a light coating of high temperature grease to main drive gear bearing retainer and splined portion of transmission main drive gear shaft. Reverse removal procedures to complete installation.

ALL "S" SERIES

NOTE: **If vehicle is a 4WD model, refer to Transfer Case removal procedures and remove case.**

Removal

1) Disconnect negative battery cable. On 77.5 MM 4-speed, remove upper starter motor nut. On all models, remove shift lever boot screws and slide boot up shift lever. Shift transmission into neutral and remove shift lever bolts at transmission. Remove shift lever.

2) Disconnect electrical connector and clip at transmission, if present. Raise vehicle and remove propeller shaft. Disconnect exhaust pipe at manifold, if needed.

3) Disconnect speedometer cable, electrical connector and clutch cable at transmission. Support transmission on jack and remove mount attaching bolts. Remove catalytic converter hanger. Remove crossmember attaching bolts and crossmember. Remove flywheel inspection cover.

4) On 77.5 MM 4-speed, remove lower starter motor attaching bolt. Remove body mounting bolts on left side of body and loosen radiator support bolt. Raise cab on left side as needed to remove upper bell housing attaching bolts. Support cab with wood block between frame and cab.

5) Remove transmission-to-engine bolts on all models. Remove transmission.

Installation

Reverse removal procedures to install transmission, noting the following: On 77 MM 4-speed, coat main drive gear bearing retainer and splined portion of transmission main drive gear with high temperature grease before installation.

Manual Transmission Removal

GENERAL MOTORS (Cont.)

TIGHTENING SPECIFICATIONS

Application	Ft. Lbs. (N.m)
Transmission-to-Clutch Housing	
"S" Series	
1.9L 4-Cylinder	25 (35)
2.8L V6	55 (75)
All Others	75 (102)
Crossmember-to-Frame	
"S" Series	25 (35)
All Others	55-65 (75-88)
Crossmember-to-Mount	
"S" Series	25 (35)
All Others	40-45 (54-61)
Mount-to-Transmission Bolt	35 (50)
Radiator Support Mounting Bolt	45-60 (60-84)
Cab Mounting Bolts	45-60 (60-84)
Transfer Case-to-Extension Housing	
"S" Series	19-29 (26-40)
All Others	26-40 (36-56)
Adapter-to-Transmission	
"S" Series	20-25 (28-35)
All Others	26-40 (36-56)

JEEP

ALL MODELS

1) Remove screws attaching shift lever boot to floorpan. Slide boot over lever. On models with T4 or T5 transmission, remove shift lever and lever housing from transmission.

2) On models equipped with T-18A transmission, unthread shift lever cap and remove cap, gasket, spring seat, spring and shift lever as an assembly. Remove shift lever locating pins from housing.

3) On models with T-176 transmission, press and turn shift lever retainer counterclockwise to release lever. Remove lever, boot, spring and seat as an assembly.

4) On all models, raise vehicle and support with safety stands. Disconnect rear propeller shaft from transfer case and wire out of way. Do not allow shaft to hang free, as damage to universal joint may result.

5) On Cherokee, Wagoneer and Truck models, disconnect front parking brake cable at equalizer. Remove rear cable clip from crossmember. On all models, place a jack under clutch housing to support engine. Remove rear crossmember from frame.

6) Disconnect speedometer cable, back-up light switch wire and 4WD indicator switch wire. Disconnect transfer case vent hose. Disconnect front propeller shaft and wire out of way.

7) On "CJ" and Scrambler models, remove transfer case shift lever by removing shifter shaft retaining nut. Remove cotter pins retaining shift control link pins in shift rods and remove pins. Remove shifter shaft and disengage shift lever from shift control links. Move lever out of the way.

NOTE: **On some models, shifter shaft must be unthreaded from shift lever in order to be removed. On other models, shaft can be removed by sliding it out of lever.**

8) On Cherokee, Wagoneer and Truck models, remove cotter pin and washers connecting link to shift lever. Separate link from lever. On all models, support transmission and transfer case with jack.

9) Remove bolts securing transmission to clutch housing and remove transmission and transfer case. Separate transfer case and transmission.

Installation

Reverse removal procedures to install transmission. Adjust clutch and shift linkage.

TIGHTENING SPECIFICATIONS

Application	Ft. Lbs. (N.m)
Transmission-to-Clutch Housing	55 (75)
Transmission Cover Bolts	55-65 (75-88)
Housing-to-Transmission Case	40-45 (54-61)
Crossmember Attaching Bolts	34-40 (47-54)
Filler Plug	13-15 (18-20)

METRIC CONVERSIONS

Metric conversions are making life more difficult for the mechanic. In addition to doubling the number of tools required, metric-dimensioned nuts and bolts are used alongside English components in many new vehicles. The mechanic has to decide which tool to use, slowing down the job. The tool problem can be solved by trial and error, but some metric conversions aren't so simple.

Converting temperature, lengths or volumes requires a calculator and conversion charts, or else a very nimble mind. Conversion charts are only part of the answer though, becuase they don't help you "think" metric, or "vizualize" what you are converting. The following examples are intended to help you "see" metric sizes:

LENGTH

Meters are the standard unit of length in the metric system. The smaller units are 10ths (decimeter), 100ths (centimeter), and 1000ths (millimeter) of a meter. These common examples might help you to visualize the metric units:

* A meter is slightly longer than a yard (about 40 inches).
* An aspirin tablet is about one centimeter across (.4 inches).
* A millimeter is about the thickness of a dime.

VOLUME

Cubic meters and centimeters are used to measure volume, just as we normally think of cubic feet and inches. Liquid volume measurements include the liter and milliliter, like the English quarts or ounces.

* One teaspoon is about 5 cubic centimeters.
* A liter is about one quart.
* A liter is about 61 cubic inches.

WEIGHT

The metric weight system is based on the gram, with the most common unit being the kilogram (1000 grams). Our comparable units are ounces and pounds:

* A kilogram is about 2.2 pounds.
* An ounce is about 28 grams.

TORQUE

Torque is somewhat complicated. The term describes the amount of effort exerted to turn something. A chosen unit of weight or force is applied to a lever of standard length. The resulting leverage is called torque. In our standard system, we use the weight of one pound applied to a lever a foot long—resulting in the unit called a foot-pound. A smaller unit is the inch-pound (the lever is one inch long). Metric units include the meter kilogram (lever one meter long with a kilogram of weight applied) and the Newton-meter(lever one meter long with force of one Newton applied). Some conversions are:

* A meter kilogram is about 7.2 foot pounds.
* A Newton-meter is about 1.4 foot pounds.
* A centimeter kilogram (cmkg) is equal to .9 inch pounds.

PRESSURE

Pressure is another complicated measurement. Pressure is described as a force or weight applied to a given area. Our common unit is pounds per square inch. Metric units can be expressed in several ways. One is the kilogram per square centimeter (kg/cm²). Another unit of pressure is the Pascal (force of one Newton on an area of one square meter), which equals about 4 ounces on a square yard. Since this is a very small amount of pressure, we usually see the kiloPascal, or kPa (1000 Pascals). Another common automotive term for pressure is the bar (used by German manufacturers), which equals 10 Pascals. Thoroughly confused? Try the examples below:

* Atmospheric pressure at sea level is about 14.7 psi.
* Atmospheric pressure at sea level is about 1 bar.
* Atmospheric pressure at sea level is about 1 kg/cm².
* One pound per square inch is about 7 kPa.

If all of these examples leave you still confused, then just use the conversion chart that follows. If you think these examples over for a while, you will begin to see the relationships betweeen the two systems of measurement. The result will be more ease in using both English and metric units!

Mitchell Manuals also offers audio visual presentations for mechanic training and microfiche products. For details on ordering, please contact:

MITCHELL MANUALS, INC.
P.O. Box 26260
San Diego, CA 92126

BONUS SECTION

MEDIUM & HEAVY DUTY TRUCK ENGINE SPECIFICATIONS

CONTENTS

Medium & Heavy Duty Tune-Up

ALL MODELS

ENGINE	IGNITION TIMING		DISTRIBUTOR		SPARK PLUGS		CARBURETOR	No.
	Man. Trans.	Auto. Trans.	Cam Angle	Point Gap	Type	Gap	Make & Type	
CHRYSLER CORP								
360"-3 V8	4°B②	4°B②	①	①	CH RF-10	.035"	Holley 2245	1
446" V8	5°B	5°B	①	①	CH RBN-13Y	.035"	Holley 4150G	2
FORD								
370" V8								
2-Bbl	6°B	6°B	①	①	MC ASF-32	.044"	Holley 2300EG	3
4-Bbl	6°B②	6°B②	①	①	MC ASF-32	.044"	Holley 4180EG	4
429" V8	6°B	6°B	①	①	MC ASF-32	.044"	Holley 4180EG	5
477" & 534" V8	10°B	10°B	①	①	MC BYSF-31-4	.040"	Holley 4150EG	6
GENERAL MOTORS								
292" 6 Cyl	8°B	8°B	①	①	AC R44T	.035"	Roch 1ME	7
350" V8	4°B	4°B	①	①	AC R44T	.045"	Roch 2G	8
366" V8	8°B	8°B	①	①	AC R43T	.045"	Holley 4150EG	9
427" & 454" V8	8°B	8°B	①	①	AC R42T	.045"	Holley 4150EG	10
IHC								
345" V8	TDC	TDC	①	①	CH RJ6	.030"	Holley 2300EG	11
392" V8	TDC	TDC	①	①	CH RJ6	.030"	Holley 2300EG	12
404" V8								
2-Bbl	9°B	9°B	①	①	CH RBN-13Y	.030"	Holley 2300EG	13
4-Bbl	9°B	9°B	①	①	CH RBN-13Y	.030"	Holley 4150G	14
446" V8	5°B	5°B	①	①	CH RBN-13Y	.030"	Holley 4150G	15
537" V8	7°B	7°B	①	①	CH RBN-11Y	.030"	Holley 4150G	16

IGNITION TIMING: B — BTDC; **A** — ATDC.

SPARK PLUGS: AL — Autolite; **CH** — Champion; **MC** — Motorcraft.

CARBURETORS: Roch — Rochester.

ALL MODELS (Cont.)

No.	HOT IDLE		FAST IDLE			Remarks
	Man. Trans.	Auto. Trans.	Man. Trans.		Auto. Trans.	
			RPM	Cam Step	RPM	
1	700③	700③	1600	High	1600	①Electronic Ignition.
2	650	650	2400	.....	2400	②On models with carb TQ9261S, set at 10°.
						③On models with carb TQ9261S, set to 750 RPM.
3	600	600	2200	High	2200	①Electronic Ignition.
4	600	600	2500	High	2500	②Calif models, 2°.
5	600	600	2700	High	2700	
6	600	600	2500	High	2500	
7	700	700	2400	High	2400	①Electronic Ignition.
8	700	700	②	②	②	②See Tune-Up Decal.
9	700	700	2200	High	2200	
10	700	700	2200	High	2200	
11	650	650	2000	.....	2000	①Electronic Ignition.
12	650	650	2000	.....	2000	
13	550	650	1800	.....	1800	
14	550	650	2400	.....	2400	
15	650	650	2400	.....	2400	
16	525	625	2000	.....	2000	

Medium & Heavy Duty Gas

CHRYSLER CORP.

GENERAL SPECIFICATIONS

Engine	Net HP At RPM	Torque (Ft. Lbs. at RPM)	Compr. Ratio	Bore	Stroke	Displ. Cu. Ins.
318"-3	160@4000	180@3600	8.5:1	3.910"	3.310"	318.31"
360"-3	180@3600	260@2000	8.40:1	4.000"	3.580"	360.10"
413"-3	220@3200	325@2000	7.54:1	4.180"	3.750"	413.40"

VALVES

Engine & Valve	Head Diam.	Face Angle	Seat Angle	Seat Width	Stem Diameter	Stem Clearance	Valve Lift
318"-3							
Int.	1.806-1.816"	45°	45°	.080-.105"	.3720-.3730"	.017" Max.	.373"
Exh.	1.512-1.522"	45°	45°	.090-.100"	.3710-.3720"	.017" Max.	.400"
360"-3							
Int.	1.875-1.885"	45°	45°	.065-.085"	.3720-.3730"	.017" Max.	.410"
Exh.	1.595-1.605"	43°	43°	.040-.060"	.3710-.3720"	.017" Max.	.400"
413"							
Int.	1.875-1.885"	45°	45°	.063-.094"	.3720-.3730"	.0010-.0020"	.360"
Exh.	1.495-1.505"	45°	45°	.094-.109"	.4330-.4340"	.0030-.0050"	.360"

VALVE SPRINGS

Engine	Free Length	PRESSURE (LBS.)	
		Valve Closed	Valve Open
318"-3			
Int.	2.000"	78-88@1.687"	170-184@1.313"
Exh.	1.813"	78-88@1.687"	170-184@1.313"
360-3"			
Int.	2.000"	78-88@1.687"	170-184@1.313"
Exh.	2.000"	78-88@1.687"	170-184@1.313"
413"			
Int.	2.313"	75-85@1.859"	173-187@1.469"
Exh.	2.125"	80-90@1.750"	168-182@1.328"

CAMSHAFT

Engine	Journal Diam.	Clearance	Lobe Lift
318"-3 & 360"-3	.....	005" Max.	.....
No. 1	1.9980-1.9990"		
No. 2	1.9820-1.9830"		
No. 3	1.9670-1.9680"		
No. 4	1.9510-1.9520"		
No. 5	1.5605-1.5615"		
413"		.001-.003"	.....
No. 1	2.0000"		
No. 2	1.9840"		
No. 3	1.9690"		
No. 4	1.9530"		
No. 5	1.7500"		

CRANKSHAFT MAIN & CONNECTING ROD BEARINGS

Engine	MAIN BEARINGS				CONNECTING ROD BEARINGS		
	Journal Diam.	Clearance	Thrust Bearing	Crankshaft End Play	Journal Diam.	Clearance	Side Play
318"-3	2.4995-2.5005"	.0005-.0015"	No. 3	.002-.007"	2.1235-2.1245"	.0010-.0020"	.006-.014"
360"-3	2.8095-2.8105"	.0005-.0015"	No. 3	.002-.007"	2.1240-2.1250"	.0005-.0025"	.006-.014"
413"	2.7495-2.7505"	.0015-.0025"	No. 3	.002-.009"	2.3740-2.3750"	.0010-.0020"	.009-.017"

CHRYSLER CORP. (Cont.)

PISTONS, PINS, RINGS

Engine	PISTONS	PINS		RINGS		
	Clearance	Piston Fit	Rod Fit	Rings	End Gap	Side Clearance
318"-3	.0005-.0015"	.00045-.00075"	.0007-.0014"	1&2	.010-.020"	.0015-.0030"
				3	.015-.055"	.0005-.0050"
360"-3	.0005-.0015"	.00025-.00075"	.0007-.0017"	1&2	.010-.020"	.0015-.0030"
				3	.015-.055"	.0005-.0050"
413"	.0003-.0013"	.00045-.00075"	.0007-.0014"	1&2	.013-.023"	.0010-.0025"
				3	.013-.025"	.0010-.0025"

OIL PUMP SPECIFICATIONS

318" & 360"

Pump Cover Wear	.0015"Max.
Clearance Over Rotors	.004"Max.
Outer Rotor Diameter	2.469"Min.
Inner & Outer Rotor Thickness	.649"Min.
Outer Rotor-to-Pump Body	.014"Max.
Relief Valve Spring .... 16.2-17.2lbs. @1.344"	

413"

Pump Cover Wear	.0015"Max.
Outer Rotor Thickness	.943"Min.
Inner Rotor Thickness	.942"Min.
Outer Rotor Diameter	2.469"Min.
Outer Rotor-to-Pump Body	.014"Max.
Clearance Over Rotors	.004"Max.
Tip Clearance Betwen Rotors	.010"Max.
Relief Valve Spring .... 22.3-23.3lbs. @1.549"	

TIGHTENING SPECIFICATIONS

318" & 360"

Application	Ft. Lbs.
Cylinder Head Bolts①	95
Main Bearing Cap Bolts	85
Connecting Rod Cap Nuts	45
Vibration Damper-to-Crankshaft Bolt	100
Flywheel Bolts	55

① — See cylinder head tightening sequence.

413"

Application	Ft. Lbs.
Cylinder Head Bolts①	70
Main Bearing Cap Bolts	85
Connecting Rod Cap Nuts	45
Vibration Damper-to-Crankshaft Bolt	135
Flywheel Bolts	5

① — See cylinder head tightening sequence.

CYLINDER HEAD TIGHTENING SEQUENCE

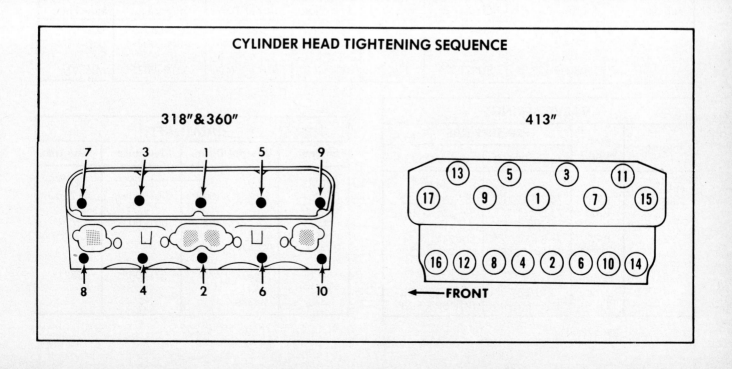

318" & 360"   413"

← FRONT

Medium & Heavy Duty Gas

FORD

GENERAL SPECIFICATIONS

Engine	Net HP At RPM	Torque (Ft. Lbs. at RPM)	Compr. Ratio	Bore	Stroke	Displ. Cu. Ins.
300″	119@3200	243@1200	8.9:1	4.00″	3.98″	300″
370″ 2V	174@3600	274@2200	8.4:1	4.05″	3.59″	370″
370″ 4V	196@3600	293@2600	8.0:1	4.05″	3.59″	370″
429″	223@4000	343@2700	8.0:1	4.36″	3.59″	429″
475″	.....	.....	.....	4.50″	3.75″	475″
477″	210@3200	393@2300	7.2:1	4.50″	3.75″	477″
534″	227@3200	431@2100	7.3:1	4.50″	4.20″	534″

PISTONS, PINS, RINGS

Engine	PISTONS Clearance	PINS Piston Fit	PINS Rod Fit	RINGS Rings	RINGS End Gap	RINGS Side Clearance
300″	.0014-.0022″	.0002-.0004″	Press Fit	1	.010-.020″	.0019-.0036″
				2	.010-.020″	.0020-.0040″
				3	.010-.035″	①
370″	.0018-.0039″	.0003-.0006″	Press Fit	1	.010-.022″	.0019-.0039″
				2	.010-.023″	.0020-.0040″
				3	②	.0015-.0030″③
429″	.0019-.0037″	.0003-.0006″	Press Fit	1	.013-.025″	.0019-.0036″
				2	.010-.020″	.0020-.0040″
				3	.013-.028″	.0020-.0035″
475″, 477″, 534″	.0028-.0034″	.0003-.0005″	.0002-.0004″	1	.018-.028″	.0029-.0046″
				2	.015-.025″	.0029-.0046″
				3	.013-.028″	.0014″-.0031″

① — Ring should be snug fit in groove with no visible side play.
② — Steel rail type ring, gap not measured.
③ — On 370″ 2V, ring should be snug fit in groove with no visible side play.

CRANKSHAFT MAIN & CONNECTING ROD BEARINGS

Engine	MAIN BEARINGS Journal Diam.	MAIN BEARINGS Clearance	MAIN BEARINGS Thrust Bearing	MAIN BEARINGS Crankshaft End Play	CONNECTING ROD BEARINGS Journal Diam.	CONNECTING ROD BEARINGS Clearance	CONNECTING ROD BEARINGS Side Play
300″	2.3982-2.3990″	.0008-.0015″	No. 3	.004-.008″	2.1228-2.1236″	.0008-.0015″	.006-.013″
370″, 429″	2.9994-3.0002″	.0008-.0026″	No. 3	.004-.008″	2.4992-2.5000″	.0008-.0028″	.010-.020″
475″, 477″, 534″	3.1246-3.1254″	.0019-.0028″	No. 3	.004-.008″	2.7092-2.7100″	.0019-.0037″	.006-.014″

VALVE SPRINGS

Engine	Free Length	PRESSURE (LBS.) Valve Closed	PRESSURE (LBS.) Valve Open
300″			
Int.	1.99″	76-84@1.70″	187-207@1.30″
Exh.	1.87″	77-85@1.58″	12-202@1.18″
370″, 429″			
Int.	1.97″	76-84@1.72″	218-241@1.26″
Exh.	1.97″①	76-84@1.78″	218-241@1.52″
475″, 477″, 534″			
Int.	2.02″	73-81@1.70″	171-189@1.28″
Exh.	2.02″	73-81@1.70″	171-189@1.28″

① — 370″ 2V is 2.03″

CAMSHAFT

Engine	Journal Diam.	Clearance	Lobe Lift
300″	2.017-2.018″	.001-.003″	.249″
370″, 429″ 475, 477″	2.1238-2.1348″	.001-.003″	.2526″①
No. 1	2.474-2.475″	.001-.003″	.2777″
No. 2, 3, 4, 5	2.370-2.371″		
534″			
No. 1	2.474-2.475″	.001-.002″	.2777″
No. 2, 3, 4, 5	2.370-2.371″		

① — Exhaust lobe lift is .265″

FORD (Cont.)

VALVES

Engine & Valve	Head Diam.	Face Angle	Seat Angle	Seat Width	Stem Diameter	Stem Clearance	Valve Lift
300″							
Int.	1.772-1.790″	44°	45°	.060-.080″	.3416-.3423″	.0010-.0027″	403″
Exh.	1.551-1.569″	44°	45°	.070-.090″	.3416-.3423″	.0010-.0027″	.403″
370″ 2V							
Int.	1.779-1.789″	44°	45°	.060-.080″	.3711-.3718″	.0010-.0027″	.4377″
Exh.	1.557-1.567″	44°	45°	.070-.090″	.3701-.3708″	.0020-.0037″	.4809″
370″ 4V							
Int.	1.779-1.789″	44°	45°	.060-.080″	.3717-.3718″	.0010-.0027″	.4377″
Exh.	1.557-1.567″	44°	45°	.090-.100″	.3703-.3712″	.0016-.0035″	.4809″
429″							
Int.	2.059-2.069″	44°	45°	.060-.080″	.3711-.3718″	.0010-.0027″	.4377″
Exh.	1.667-1.677″	44°	45°	.093-.108″	.3703-.3712″	.0016-.0035″	.4809″
475″, 477″							
Int.	2.015-2.025″	44°	45°	.090-.105″	.4349-.4358″	.0010-.0026″	.4388″
Exh.	1.630-1.640″	44°	45°	.100-.115″	.4335-.4344″	.0024-.0040″	.4388″
534″							
Int.	2.015-2.025	44°	45°	.090-.105″	.4358-.4359″	.0010-.0026″	.4388″
Exh.	1.630-1.640″	44°	45°	.100-.115″	.4335-.4344″	.0024-.0040″	.4388″

OIL PUMP SPECIFICATIONS

300″

Relief Valve Spring Tension	20.6-22.6lbs @ 2.49″
Shaft-to-Housing Clearance	.0015-.0029″
Relief Valve Clearance	.0015-.0029″
Rotor Assembly End Clearance	.004″ Max.
Outer Race-to-Housing Clearance	.001-.013″

370 & 429″

Relief Valve Spring Tension	11.1-11.8lbs @ 1.56″
Shaft-to-Housing Clearance	.0015-.0030″
Relief Valve Clearance	.0015-.0030″
Rotor Assembly End Clearance	.004″ Max.
Outer Race-to-Housing Clearance	.001-.013″

475″, 477″ & 534″

Relief Valve Spring Tension	10.7-11.9lbs. @ 1.07″
Shaft-to-Housing Clearance	.0015-.0030″
Relief Valve Clearance	.0015-.0030″
Rotor Assembly End Clearance	.004″ Max.
Outer Race-to-Housing Clearance	.006-.011″

TIGHTENING SPECIFICATIONS
300″

Application	Ft. Lbs.
Cylinder Head Bolts①	
Step One	55
Step Two	65
Step Three	70-85
Manifold-to-Cylinder Head	22-32
Intake manifold-to-Exhaust Manifold	28-33
Main Bearing Cap Bolts	60-70
Connecting Rod Cap Nuts	40-45
Vibration Damper	130-150
Flywheel Bolts	75-85

370″ & 429″

Application	Ft. Lbs.
Cylinder Head Bolts①	
Step One	70-80
Step Two	100-110
Step Three	130-140
Manifold-to-Cylinder Head — Intake	22-32
Manifold-to-Cylinder Head — Exhaust	28-33
Main Bearing Cap Bolts	95-105
Connecting Rod Cap Nuts	45-50
Vibration Damper-to-Crankshaft	150-175
Flywheel Bolts	75-85

475″, 477″ & 534″

Application	Ft. Lbs.
Cylinder Head Bolts①	
Step One	140
Step Two	160
Step Three	180
Manifold-to-Cylinder Head — Intake	25-32
Manifold-to-Cylinder Head — Exhaust	22-32
Main Bearing Cap Bolts	150-165
Connecting Rod Cap Nuts	60-65
Damper-to-Crankshaft	130-175
Flywheel-to-Crankshaft	75-85

① — See cylinder head tightening sequence.

Medium & Heavy Duty Gas
FORD (Cont.)

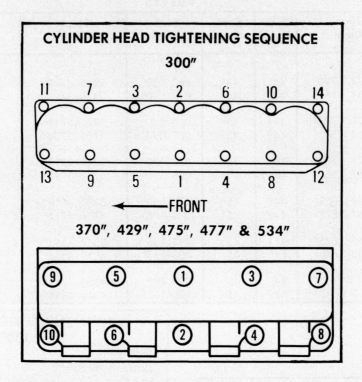

CYLINDER HEAD TIGHTENING SEQUENCE

300"

370", 429", 475", 477" & 534"

Medium & Heavy Duty Gas

GENERAL MOTORS

GENERAL SPECIFICATIONS

Engine	Net HP At RPM	Torque (Ft. Lbs. at RPM)	Compr. Ratio	Bore	Stroke	Displ. Cu. Ins.
292"	125@3600	225@1600	7.8:1	3.875"	4.12"	292"
350"	161@3600	275@2400	8.0:1	4.000"	3.48"	350"
366"	190@4000	305@2400	7.6:1	3.937"	3.76"	366"
427"	210@3800	340@2400	7.5:1	4.250"	3.76"	427"
454"	210@3800	340@2800	7.9:1	4.250"	4.00"	454"

VALVES

Engine & Valve	Head Diam.	Face Angle	Seat Angle	Seat Width	Stem Diameter	Stem Clearance	Valve Lift
292"							
Int.	1.72"	45°	46°	.031-.063"	.3410-.3417"	.0010-.0027"	.....
Exh.	1.50"	5°	46°	.063-.094"	.3410-.3417"	.0015-.0032"	.....
350"							
Int.	1.94"	45°	46°	.031-.063"	.3410-.3417"	.0010-.0027"	.....
Exh.	1.50"	45°	46°	.0630.094"	.3410-.3417"	.0010-.0027"	.....
366"							
Int.	.....	45°	46°	.031-.063"	.....	.0010-.0027"	.....
Exh.	.....	45°	46°	.363-.094"	.....	.0012-.0029"	.....
427"							
Int.	.....	45°	46°	.031-.063"	.....	.0010-.0027"	.....
Exh.	.....	45°	46°	.063-.094"	.....	0014-.0029"	.....
454"							
Int.	.....	45°	46°	.031-.063"	.3715-.3722"	.0010-.0027"	.....
Exh.	.....	45°	46°	.063-.094"	.3713-.3720"	.0014-.0027"	.....

VALVE SPRINGS

Engine	Free Length	PRESSURE (LBS.) Valve Clossed	PRESSURE (LBS.) Valve Open
292"	1.90"	85-93@1.69"	174-184@1.30"
350	2.03"	76-84@1.69"	194-206@1.25"
366"	2.05"	84-96@1.80"	210-230@1.40"
427"	2.05"	84-96@1.80"	210-230@1.40"
454"	2.05"	84-96@1.80"	210-230@1.40"

CAMSHAFT

Engine	Journal Diam.	Clearance	Lobe Lift
292"	1.8682-1.8692"	.....	.2315"
350"	1.8682-1.8692"	.....	.2600"
366"	1.9487-1.9497"	.....	.2343"
427"	1.9487-1.9497"	.....	.2343"
454"	1.9482-1.9492"	.....	.2588"

PISTONS, PINS, RINGS

Engine	PISTONS Clearance	PINS Piston Fit	PINS Rod Fit	RINGS Rings	RINGS End Gap	RINGS Side Clearance
292"	.0026-.0036"	.00015-.00025"	.0008-.0016"	1	.010-.020"	.0020-.0040"
				2	.010-.020"	.0020-.0040"
				3	.015-.055"	.0050-.0055"
350"	.0016-.0026"	.00016-.00026"	.0008-.0016"	1	.010-.020"	.0012-.0032"
				2	.013-.025"	.0012-.0032"
				3	.015-.055"	.0020-.0070"
366"	.0030-.0040"	.00025-.00035"	.0008-.0021"	1	.010-.020"	.0018-.0032"
				2	.010-.020"	.0018-.0032"
				3	.010-.030"	.0025-.0035"
427"	.0039-.0049"	.00025-.00035"	.0008-.0021"	1	.010-.020"	.0018-.0032"
				2	.010-.020"	.0018-.0032"
				3	.010-.030"	.0005-.0065"
454"	.0034-.0044"	.00025-.00035"	.0013-.0021"	1	.010-.020"	.0018-.0032"
				2	.010-.020"	.0018-.0032"
				3	.010-.030"	.0020-.0035"

CRANKSHAFT MAIN & CONNECTING ROD BEARINGS

| Engine | MAIN BEARINGS | | | | CONNECTING ROD BEARINGS | | |
	Journal Diam.	Clearance	Thrust Bearing	Crankshaft End Play	Journal Diam.	Clearance	Side Play
292"	2.2983-2.2993"	.0008-.0034"	No. 7	.002-.006"	2.0990-2.1000"	.0007-.0027"	.006-.017"
350"							
No. 1	2.4484-2.4493"	.0008-.0020"	No. 5	.002-.006"	2.1990-2.2000"	.0013-.0035"	.008-.014"
No. 2, 3, 4	2.4481-2.4493"	.0011-.0023"					
No. 5	2.4479-2.4488"	.0017-.0033"					
366"							
No. 1, 2, 3, 4	2.7481-2.7490"	.0013-.0025"	No. 5	.006-.010"	2.1990-2.2000"	.0013-.0035"	.013-.023"
No. 5	2.7473-2.7483"	.0029-.0045"					
427"							
No. 1, 2, 3, 4	2.7481-2.7490"	.0013-.0025"	No. 5	.006-.010"	2.1990-2.2000"	.0014-.0030"	.013.023"
No. 5	2.7473-2.7483"	.0029-.0045"					
454"							
No. 1	2.7485-2.7495"	.0013-.0025"	No. 5	.006-.010"	2.1990-2.2000"	.0014-.0030"	.013-.023"
No. 2, 3, 4	2.7481-2.7490"	.0013-.0025"					
No. 5	2.7478-2.7488"	.0024-.0040"					

TIGHTENING SPECIFICATIONS
292"

Application	Ft. Lbs
Cylinder Head Bolts①	95
Intake Manifold-to-Head	35
Exhaust Manifold Bolts	30
Main Bearing Cap Bolts	65
Connecting Rod Cap Nuts	40
Flywheel Bolts	110
Harmonic Balancer Bolt	60

① — See cylinder head tightening sequence.

350"

Application	Ft. Lbs.
Cylinder Head Bolts①	65
Intake Manifold	30
Exhaust Manifold	②20
Main Bearing Cap Bolts	70
Connecting Rod Cap Nuts	45
Flywheel Bolts	60

① — See cylinder head tightening sequence.
② — Tighten two center bolts to 30 ft. lbs.

366", 427" & 454"

Application	Ft. Lbs.
Cylinder Head Bolts①	80
Intake Manifold	30
Exhaust Manifold	20
Main Bearing Cap Bolts	110
Connecting Rod Cap Nuts	50
Flywheel Bolts	65
Torsional Damper	85

① — See cylinder head tightening sequence.

CYLINDER HEAD TIGHTENING SEQUENCE

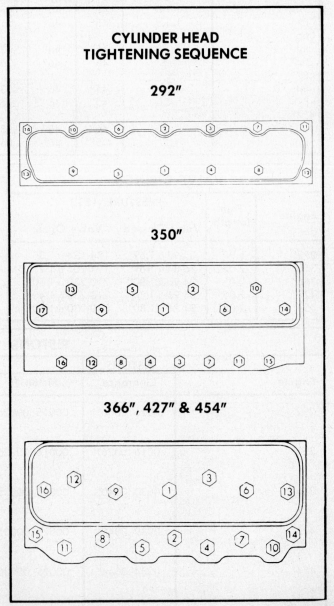

292"

350"

366", 427" & 454"

INTERNATIONAL HARVESTER

GENERAL SPECIFICATIONS

Engine	Net HP At RPM	Torque (Ft. Lbs. at RPM)	Compr. Ratio	Bore	Stroke	Displ. Cu. Ins.
345"①	282@2200	154@3600	8.28:1	3.880"	3.66"	345.00"
392"	302@2800	185@3600	8.00:1	4.120"	3.66"	390.90"
404" 2V②	326@2200	189@3600	8.00:1	4.125"	3.74"	399.80"
404" 4V	336@2600	206@3600	8.00:1	4.125"	3.74"	399.80"
446"③	385@2600	227@3600	8.00:1	4.125"	4.18"	446.89"
478"	384@2200	209@3400	7.60:1	4.500"	3.75"	477.20"
537" 2V	410@1800	203@3200	7.50:1	4.625"	4.00"	537.60"
537" 4V	236@3200	429@2200	7.50:1	4.625"	4.00"	537.20"
549"	227@3200	446@2000	7.60:1	4.500"	4.31"	548.70"

① — Calif. models 115 HP, 281 ft. lbs. torque.
② — Calif. models 183 HP, 323 ft. lbs. torque.
③ — Calif. models 221 HP, 380 ft. lbs. torque.

VALVES

Engine & Valve	Head Diam.	Face Angle	Seat Angle	Seat Width	Stem Diameter	Stem Clearance	Valve Lift
345"							
Int.	.....	45°	45°	.063-.094"	.3720-.3730"	.0010-.0035"	.440"
Int.	.....	45°	45°	.078-.109"	.3715-.3725"	.0015-.0040"	.395"
392"							
Int.	.....	30°	30°	.063-.094"	.3720-.3730"	.0010-.0035"	.440"
Exh.	.....	45°	45°	.078-.109"	.4140-.4150"	.0015-.0040"	.395"
404"							
Int.	.....	45°	45°	.060-.090"	.37215-.37285"	.00115-.00285"	.435"
Exh.	.....	45°	45°	.085-.105"	.37165-.37265"	.00165-.00235"	.435"
446"							
Int.	.....	45°	45°	.060-.090"	.37215-.37285"	.00115-.00285"	.435"
Exh.	.....	45°	45°	.085-.105"	.37165-.37235"	.00165-.00235"	.435"
478"							
Int.	.....	15°	15°	.063-.094"	.4340-.4350"	.0015-.0040"	.....
Exh.	.....	45°	45°	.094-.125"	.4330-.4340"	.0025-.0050"	.....
537"							
Int.	.....	15°	15°	.060-.090"	.4341-.4349"	.0016-.0034"	.465"
Exh.	.....	45°	45°	.090-.120"	.4338-.4345"	.0020-.0037"	.465"
549"							
Int.	.....	15°	15°	.063-.094"	.4340-.4350"	.0015-.0040"	.....
Exh.	.....	45°	45°	.094-.125"	.4330-.4340"	.0025-.0050"	.....

CRANKSHAFT MAIN & CONNECTING ROD BEARINGS

Engine	MAIN BEARINGS				CONNECTING ROD BEARINGS		
	Journal Diam.	Clearance	Thrust Bearing	Crankshaft End Play	Journal Diam.	Clearance	Side Play
345"	2.7484-2.7494"	.0010-.0040"	No.3	.0044-.0094"	2.3730-2.3740"	.0011-.0036"	.008-.016"
392"	2.7484-2.7494"	.0010-.0040"	No.3	.0044-.0094"	2.3730-2.3740"	.0011-.0036"	.008-.016"
404"	3.1228-3.1236"	.0010-.0036"	No.3	.0025-.0085"	2.4980-2.4990"	.0011-.0036"	.008-.020"
446"	3.1228-3.1236"	.0010-.0036"	No.3	.0025-.0085"	2.4980-2.4990"	.0011-.0036"	.008-.020"
478"	3.1230-3.1240"	.0014-.0044"	No.3	.0040-.0090"	2.6230-2.6240"	.0017-.0042"	.010-.018"
537"	3.1235-3.1245"	.0015-.0035"	No.3	.0060-.0120"	2.6230-2.6240"	.0011-.0036"	.008-.018"
549"	3.1230-3.1240"	.0014-.0044"	No.3	.0040-.0090"	2.6230-2.6240"	.0017-.0042"	.010-.018"

Medium & Heavy Duty Gas
INTERNATIONAL HARVESTER (Cont.)

PISTONS, PINS, RINGS

Engine	PISTONS Clearance	PINS Piston Fit	PINS Rod Fit	RINGS Rings	RINGS End Gap	RINGS Side Clearance
345"	.0035"	.0005-.0009"	.0006-.0012"	1 & 2 3	.010-.020" .015-.055"	.0015-.0030" .0000-.0084"
392"	.0035"	.0005-.0009"	.0006-.0012"	1 & 2 3	.013-.023" .013-.028"	.0015-.0030" .0020-.0035"
404"	.0012-.0017"	.0002-.0006"	.0004-.0008"	1 & 2 3	.013-.023" .013-.023"	.0020-.0040 .0020-.0040
446"	.0012-.0017"	.0002-.0006"	.0004-.0008"	1 & 2 3	.013-.023" .013-.023"	.0020-.0040" .0020-.0040"
478"	.0020"	.0001-.0004"	.0008-.0011"	1 & 2 3	.013-.025" .013-.028"	.0035-.0050" .0010-.0030"
537"	.0012-.0022"	.0001-.0004"	.0008-.0011"	1 2 3	.012-.022" .014-.024" .012-.022"	.0020-.0040" .0020-.0040" .0020-.0040"
549"	.0020"	.0001-.0004"	.0008-.0011"	1,2 & 3 4	.013-.025" .013-.028"	.0035-.0050" .0010-.0030"

VALVE SPRINGS

Engine	Free Length	PRESSURE (LBS.) Valve Closed	PRESSURE (LBS.) Valve Open
345"	2.065"	.....	188.1 @ 1.429"
392"	2.065"	.....	188.1 @ 1.429"
404"	2.065"	.....	188.1 @ 1.429"
446"	2.065"	.....	188.1 @ 1.429"
478"			
Inner	2.281"	.....	79-87 @ 1.538"
Outer	2.563"	.....	112-121 @ 1.663"
537"	2.075"	.....	200 @ 1.397"
549"			
Inner	2.281"	.....	79-87 @ 1.538"
Outer	2.563"	.....	112-121 @ 1.663"

CAMSHAFT

Engine	Journal Diam.	Clearance	Lobe Lift
345" & 392"	.....	.0015-.0035"	.....
No. 1	2.0990-2.1000"		
No. 2	2.0890-2.0900"		
No. 3.	2.0790-2.0800"		
No. 4	2.0690-2.0700"		
No. 5	2.0590-2.0600"		
404"	2.0990-2.1000"	.0010-.0035"	.....
446"	2.0990-2.1000"	.0010-.0035"	.....
478" & 549"	.....	.0010-.0030"	.....
No. 1	2.3470-2.3480"		
No. 2	2.3160-2.3170"		
No. 3	2.2900-2.2910"		
No. 4	2.2470-2.2480"		

OIL PUMP SPECIFICATIONS

345" & 392"

Gear End Play	.0015-.0060"
Gear Side Clearance	.0007-.0027"
Shaft Clearance	.0010-.0025"
Gear Backlash	.0107"
Pressure Regulator Spring	1.812" @ 13.33 lbs.

404" & 446"

Body Gear End Clearance	.0015-.0065"
Body-to-Gear Clearance	.0014-.0054"
Pump Shaft Diameter	.4885-.4890"
Shaft Clearance in Body	.0010-.0025"
Body Gear Backlash	.0107" Max.
Idler Shaft Diameter	.4845-.4855"
Idler Gear Clearance on Shaft	.0015-.0040"

INTERNATIONAL HARVESTER (Cont.)

OIL PUMP SPECIFICATIONS (Cont.)

537"

Body-to-Gear End Clearance	.0030-.0045"
Body-to-Gear Clearance	.0007-.0027"
Gear Backlash	.0005-.0065"

478" & 549"

Body Gear End Clearance	.0015-.0090"
Pump Body-to-Gear Clearance	.0046-.0086"
Pump Shaft Diameter	.4905-.4910"
Pump Shaft Clearance in Bore	.0015-.0030"
Body Gear Backlash	.0030-.0150"

TIGHTENING SPECIFICATIONS

345" & 392"

Application	Ft. Lbs.
Cylinder Head Bolts①	90-100
Main Bearing Cap Bolts	75-85
Connecting Rod Cap Nuts	②45-55
Crankshaft Pulley Bolt	100-110
Flywheel Bolts	45-55

① — See cylinder head tightening sequence.

② — Tighten V-392 engine to 40-45 ft. lbs.

478" & 549"

Application	Ft. Lbs.
Cylinder Head Bolts①	80-90
Main Bearing Cap Bolts	100-110
Connecting Rod Cap Nuts	60-70
Flywheel-to-Crankshaft	90-100

① — See cylinder head tightening sequence.

404" & 446"

Application	Ft. Lbs.
Cylinder Head Bolts①	②90-100
Main Bearing Cap Bolts	90-110
Connecting Rod Cap Nuts	38-44
Crankshaft Vibration Damper	80-100
Flywheel Bolts	45-60

① — See cylinder head tightening sequence.

② — On engines below serial number 38949, tighten to 80-90 ft. lbs.

537"

Application	Ft. Lbs.
Cylinder Head Bolts①	80-90
Main Bearing Cap Bolts	125-130
Connecting Rod Cap Nuts	65-70
Crankshaft Pulley	260-290
Flywheel-to-Crankshaft	110-120
Idler Pulley	70-85

① — See cylinder head tightening sequence

CYLINDER HEAD TIGHTENING SEQUENCE

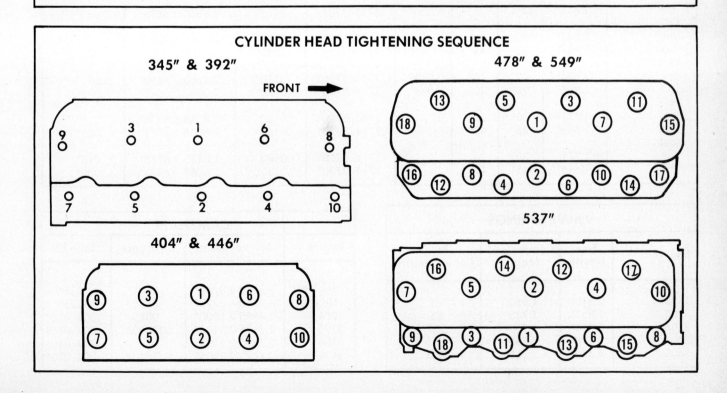

Medium & Heavy Duty Diesel

CATERPILLAR

GENERAL SPECIFICATIONS

Engine	Cycle	Displ. Cu. Ins.	Compr. Ratio	Bore	Stroke	Firing Order	Inj. Timing ①
1693	4	893"	16.0:1	5.40"	6.50"	1,5,3,6,2,4	11.0°
3208	4	636"	16.4:1	4.50"	5.00"	1,2,7,3,4,5,6,8	16.0°
3306	4	638"	17.5:1	4.75"	6.00"	1,5,3,6,2,4	13.5°
3406	4	893"	14.5:1	5.40"	6.50"	1,5,3,6,2,4	10.0°
3408	4	1099"	16.5:1	5.40"	6.00"	1,8,4,3,6,5,7,2	①11.00°

① — Unless noted otherwise, all Injection Timing is BTDC.
② — Direct Injection Turbocharged Model is 28°BTDC.

NORMAL OPERATING SPECIFICATIONS

Engine	Idle RPM	Max. RPM	Oil Temp.	Oil Press.	Coolant Temp.	Compression Pressure (PSI) @ RPM (Sea Level)
1693	550	2100	210°	45-65	210°	.....
3208	650	3070	210°	55-85	210°	.....
3306	600	2400	210°	45-60	210°	.....
3406	600	2300	210°	45-70	210°	.....
3408	700	2340	210°	55-69	210°	.....

VALVES & SEATS

Engine	Head Diameter	Face Angle	Seat Angle	Seat Width	Stem Diameter	Stem Clearance	Valve Seat Insert O.D.	Valve Clearance
1693								
Int.	1.771"	44¼°	45°	.060"	.3715-.3725"	.0007"	1.8115-1.8125"	.018"
Exh.	1.646"	44¼°	45°	.060"	.3715-.3725"	.0007"	1.6865-1.6875"	.030"
3208								
Int.	2.094"	30°	30°	.120"	.3720-.3730"	.0200"	2.0400-2.0500"	.015"
Exh.	1.804"	45°	45°	.105"	.3710-.3720"	.0200"	1.9115-1.9125"	.025"
3306								
Int.	2.094"	29°	30°	.076"	.3714-.3720"	.0170"	2.1280-2.1290"	.015"
Exh.	1.896"	29°	30°	.076"	.3714-.3720"	.0170"	2.0030-2.0040"	.025"
3406								
Int.	1.771"	30°	30°	.....	.3714-.3720"	.0180"	1.8115-1.8125"	.015"
Exh.	1.646"	45°	45°	.....	.3714-.3720"	.0180"	1.6865-1.6875"	.030"
3408								
Int.	1.771"	30°	30°	.....	.3714-.3720"	.0180"	1.8115-1.8125"	.015"
Exh.	1.646"	45°	45°	.....	.3714-.3720"	.0180"	1.6865-1.6875"	.030"

VALVE SPRINGS

Engine	Free Length	Compressed Length	Lbs. @ Comp. Length
1693	2.310"	1.950"	35
3208	1.855"	1.715"	35
3306	2.050"	1.766"	57.7
3406	2.470"	2.165"	77.5
3408	2.470"	2.165"	77.5

CAMSHAFT

Engine	Journal Diam.	Clearance	Lobe Lift
1693			
No.1,2,3	2.8750-2.8760"	.010"	.025"
No.4	1.8710-1.8720"	.010"	.025"
3208	2.4995-2.5000"	.007"	.004-.010"
3306	2.3105-2.3115"	.002-.006"	.004-.010"
3406	2.7495-2.7505"	.....	.004-.010"
3408	2.7495-2.7505"	.....	.004-.010"

CATERPILLAR (Cont.)

ROCKER ARMS & VALVE BRIDGES

Engine	Rocker Shaft O.D.	Rocker Arm I.D.	Rocker Arm Clearance	Bridge Guide O.D.	Bridge I.D.	Bridge Height Above Head
1693	.....	.....	.....	.....	.....	.....
3208	.8580-.8588″	.8595-.8611″	.005″	.....	.....	.....
3306	.7240-.7250″	.7258-.7268″	.008″	.....	.....	.....
3406	.9740-.9750″	.9760-.9770″	.010″	.4333-.4335″	.4338.4362″	2.080-2.120″
3408	.9740-.9750″	.9760-.9770″	.010″	.4333-.4335″	.4338.4362″	2.080-2.120″

PISTONS, PINS, RINGS

Engine	PISTONS	PINS		RINGS		
	Clearance	Piston Fit	Rod Fit	Rings	End Gap	Side Clearance
1693	.....	.003-.011″	.0009-.0019″	1	.021-.036″	.0057-.0071″
				2	.035-.050″	.0030-.0048″
				3	.015-.030″	.0015-.0030″
3208	.....	.003″	.003″	1	.015-.030″	.0030-.0055″
				2	.010-.025″	.0015-.0035″
3306	.....	.003-.013″	.003″	1	.0175-.0325″	.0028-.0046″
				2	.0175-.0325″	.0023-.0041″
				3	.0130-.0280″	.0015-.0035″
3406	.....	.003-.013″	.003″	1	.021-.036″	①
				2	.035-.050″	①
				3	.015-.030″	.010-.030″
3408	.....	.003-.011″	.003″	1	.021-.036″	①
				2	.035-.050″	①
				3	.015-.030″	.010-.030″

① — Ring should be a snug fit in groove, with no visible side play.

CRANKSHAFT & MAIN BEARINGS

Engine	Journal Diameter	Bearing Clearance	Crankshaft End Play	Thrust Location	Thrust Washer Thickness	Number of Main Bearings
1693	4.4995-4.5005″	.0035-.0066″	.0060-.0180″	.....	.....	7
3208	3.4990-3.5000″	.0060″	.0030-.0090″	.....	.....	5
3306	3.4984-3.5000″	.0030-.0065″	.0025-.0145″	Front	.1835-.1865″	7
3406	4.7495-4.7508″	.0037-.0068″	.0060-.0200″	Center	.....	7
3408	4.7492-4.7508″	.0036-.0073″	.0060-.0200″	Center	.....	5

CYLINDER LINER & BORE

Engine	Type	Liner Bore	Liner Protrusion
1693	Wet	5.400-5.402″	.002-.007″
3208	.....	①4.500-4.510″	.....
3306	Wet	4.750-4.752″	.001″
3406	Wet	5.400-5.402″	.002-.008″
3408	Wet	5.400-5.402″	.002-.008″

CONNECTING RODS & BEARINGS

Engine	Journal Diameter	Bearing Clearance	Sideplay
1693	3.5395-3.5405″	.003-.006″	.....
3208	2.7496-2.7504″	.007″	.....
3306	2.9984-2.3000″	.0030-.0066″	.....
3406	3.8195-3.8205″	.003-.006″	.....
3408	3.8192-3.8208″	.0028-.0066″	.....

① — Liners not used on Model 3208

Medium & Heavy Duty Diesel

CATERPILLAR (Cont.)

OIL PUMP SPECIFICATIONS

1693

Type	Gear
Shaft Diameter	1.2275-1.2281″
Bore in Bushings	1.2300-1.2310″
Clearance Between Gear and Cover	.001-.004″
Relief Valve Spring	
Compressed Length	4.02″@34 lbs.
Free Length	4.38″

3208

Type	Rotary
Clearance Pump Gear Rotor Tip	.002-.006″
Relief Valve Spring	
Compressed Length	2.579″@37.3 lbs.
Free Length	3.500″

3306

Type	Gear
Bore in Idler Gear Bearing	1.1236-1.1284″
Idler Shaft Diameter	1.1250-1.1260″
Clearance Bearing-to-Shaft	.0006-.0064″
Drive Shafts Diameter	.8745-.8749″
Drive Shaft Bearings I.D.	.8760-.8766″
Clearance Drive Shafts-to-Bearings	.0011-.0022″
Clearance all Gears and Housing	.0032-.0068″

3406

Type	Gear
Drive Shaft Diameter	.8745-.8749″
Drive Shaft Bearing Bore	.8760-.8766″
Idler Shaft Bearing Bore	.8760-.8766″
Gear Length	3.1245-3.1255″
Gear Bore Depth	3.1292-3.1308″
Pressure Relief Valve Spring	
Length Compressed @110 lbs.	4.640″
Free Length	6.020″

3408

Type	Gear
Drive Shaft Diameter	.8745-.8749″
Drive Shaft Bearing Bore	.8760-.8766″
Idler Shaft Diameter	.8745-.8749″
Idler Shaft Bearing Bore	.8760-.8766″
Gear Length	3.1240-3.1260″
Gear Bore Depth	3.1292-3.1308″
Pressure Relief Valve Spring	
Length Compressed @110lbs.	4.640″
Free Length	6.020″

TIGHTENING SPECIFICATIONS

1693

Application	Ft. Lbs.
Cylinder Head Bolts①	
Step One	200
Step Two	330
Step Three	330
Main Bearing Cap Bolts②	75
Connecting Rod Cap Bolts③	50
Vibration Damper-to-Crankshaft	138-159
Flywheel Bolts④	375

① — See cylinder head tightening sequence.
② — Mark each bolt and cap, tighten bolt 120°.
③ — Mark each bolt and nut, tighten nut 180°.
④ — Engine with brakesaver, without brakesaver 265 Ft.Lbs.

3208

Application	Ft. Lbs.
Cylinder Head Bolts①	
Step One — Bolts 1-18	60
Step Two — Bolts 1-18	95
Step Three — Bolts 1-18	95
Bolts 19-22	32
Main Bearing Caps②	30
Connecting Rod Caps③	30
Pulley and Damper	460
Flywheel Bolts	55
Fuel Injection Pump	70

① — See cylinder head tightening sequence.
② — Mark each bolt and cap, tighten bolts 120°.
③ — Mark each bolt and nut, tighten nuts 60°.

3306

Application	Ft. Lbs.
Cylinder Head Bolts①	
Step One — All Numbered Bolts	115
Step Two — All Numbered Bolts	175
Step Three — All Numbered Bolts	175
Step Four — All Bolts in Letter Sequence	22
Step Five — All Bolts in Letter Sequence	32
Step Six — All Bolts in Letter Sequence	32
Main Bearing Caps②	30
Connecting Rod Caps③	30
Crankshaft Hub and Damper	230

① — See cylinder head tightening sequence.
② — Mark each bolt and cap, tighten bolts 90°.
③ — Mark each bolt and nut, tighten nuts 90°.

CATERPILLAR (Cont.)

TIGHTENING SPECIFICATIONS (Cont.)

3406

Application	Ft. Lbs.
Cylinder Head Bolts①	
Step One — Bolts 1-20	200
Step Two — Bolts 1-20	330
Step Three — Bolts 1-20	330
Step Four — Install Rocker Arm Groups	
Step Five — Bolts 21-26	200
Step Six — Bolts 21-26	330
Step Seven — Bolts 21-26	330
Step Eight — Tighten Remaining 12 Bolts	32
Main Bearing Caps②	190
Connecting Rod Caps③	60
Flywheel-to-Crankshaft Bolts	210

① — See cylinder head tightening sequence.
② — Mark each bolt and cap, tighten bolts 120°.
③ — Mark each bolt and nut, tighten nuts 120°.

3408

Application	Ft. Lbs.
Cylinder Head Bolts①	
Step One — Bolts 1-14	200
Step Two — Bolts 1-14	330
Step Three — Bolts 1-14	330
Step Four — Install Rocker Arms	
Step Five — Bolts 15-18	200
Step Six — Bolts 15-18	330
Step Seven — Bolts 15-18	330
Step Eight — Nine Small Bolts	32
Main Bearing Caps②	190
Connecting Rod Caps③	60
Flywheel Bolts	200
Vibration Damper	100

① — See cylinder head tightening sequence.
② — Mark each bolt and cap, tighten bolts 120°.
③ — Mark each bolt and nut, tighten nuts 120°.

CYLINDER HEAD TIGHTENING SEQUENCE

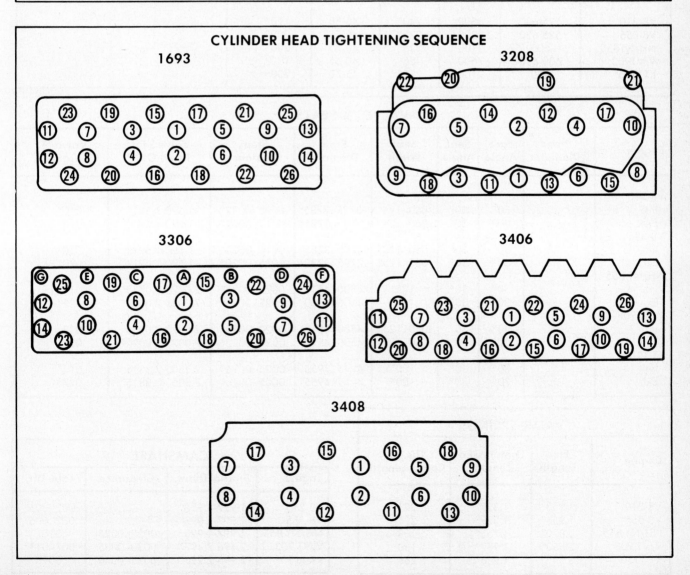

1693   3208   3306   3406   3408

Medium & Heavy Duty Diesel
CUMMINS

GENERAL SPECIFICATIONS

Engine	Cycle	Displ. Cu. Ins.	Compr. Ratio	Bore	Stroke	Firing Order ②	Inj. Timing ①
V8-210	4	504"	17.0:1	4.625"	3.750"	1,5,4,8,6,3,7,2	③24.5°
V8-555	4	555"	17.0:1	4.625"	4.125"	1,5,4,8,6,3,7,2	④22.5°
NH/NT 855	4	855"	15.8:1	5.4995"	6.000"	R-1,5,3,6,2,4	20.0°
						L-1,4,2,6,3,5	
V/VT 903	4	903"	15.5:1	5.4995"	4.750"	1,5,4,8,6,3,7,2	21.0°
KT 1150	4	1150"	14.5:1	6.250"	6.250"	1,5,3,6,2,4	⑤.2032"

① — Unless noted otherwise, all Injection Timing is BTDC.
② — R- Right-hand rotation. L- Left-hand rotation.
③ — "H" Model is 15.5°BTDC.
④ — "H" Model is 14.5°BTDC.
⑤ — Piston travel with 0.1080" push rod travel.
   Use of special tools required.

NORMAL OPERATING SPECIFICATIONS

Engine	Idle RPM	Max. RPM	Oil Temp.	Oil Press.	Coolant Temp.	Compression Pressure (PSI) @ RPM (Sea Level)
V8-210	525-600	3300	240°	40-58	190°	.....
V8-555	525-620	3300	225°	40-75	200°	.....
NH/NT855	600	2100	225°	40-75	200°	.....
V/VT903	600-650	2600	225°	40-65	190°	.....
KT1105	600	2100	225°	45-70	200°	.....

VALVES & SEATS

Engine	Head Diameter	Face Angle	Seat Angle	Seat Width	Stem Diameter	Stem Clearance	Valve Seat Insert O.D.	Valve Clearance
V8-210								
Int.	.....	30°	30°	.060-.125"	.3795-.3785"	.0015-.0022"	1.690-1.691"	.010"
Exh.	.....	30°	30°	.060-.125"	.3795-.3785"	.0015-.0022"	1.690-1.691"	.020"
V8-555								
Int.	.....	30°	30°	.060-.125"	.3795-.3785"	.0015-.0020"	1.690-1.691"	.010"
Exh.	.....	30°	30°	.060-.125"	.3795-.3785"	.0015-.0020"	1.690-1.691"	.020"
NH/NT 855								
Int.	.....	30°	30°	.125"	.4500-.4510"	.0022-.0025"	2.0025-2.0035"	.014"
Exh.	.....	30°	30°	.125"	.4500-.4510"	.0022-.0025"	2.0025-2.0035"	.029"
V/VT 903								
Int.	.....	30°	30°	.060-.125"	.4500-.4510"	.0020-.0022"	2.0025-2.0035"	.012"
Exh.	.....	30°	30°	.060-.125"	.4500-.4510"	.0020-.0022"	2.0025-2.0035"	.025"
KT 1150								
Int.	.....	30°	30°	.100"	.4945-.4955"	.0005-.0016"	2.3805-2.3815"	.014"
Exh.	.....	30°	30°	.100"	.4945-.4955"	.0005-.0016"	2.3805-2.3815"	.027"

VALVE SPRINGS

Engine	Free Length	Compressed Length	Lbs. @ Comp. Length
V8-210	1.953"	1.329"	221
V8-555	1.953"	1.329"	221
NH/NT 855	2.890"	1.765"	108
V/VT 903	2.350"	1.287"	136
KT 1150	3.349"	1.908"	266

CAMSHAFT

Engine	Journal Diam.	Clearance	Lobe Lift
V8-210	1.997-1.998"	.....	.002-.006"
V8-555	1.997-1.998"	.....	.002-.006"
NH/NT 855	1.997-1.998"	.0020-.0025"	.010"
V/VT 903	2.496-2.497"	.0030-.0035"	.007-.011"
KT 1150	2.996-2.997"	.0035-.0040"	.009"

CUMMINS (Cont.)

ROCKER ARMS & VALVE BRIDGES

Engine	Rocker Shaft O.D.	Rocker Arm I.D.	Rocker Arm Clearance	Bridge Guide O.D.	Bridge I.D.	Bridge Height Above Head
V8-210	1.1230-1.1240"	1.1245-1.1280"	.0015-.0040"	.3750-.3755"	.376-.378"	2.040-2.060"
V8-555	1.1230-1.1240"	1.1245-1.1280"	.0015-.0040"	.3750-.3755"	.376-.378"	2.040-2.060"
NH/NT 855	1.1230-1.1240"	1.1245-1.1275"	.0015-.0035"	.4330-.4335"	.440-.442"	1.860-1.880"
V/VT 903	1.1855-1.1865"	1.1875-1.1905"	.0020-.0040"	.4330-.4335"	.434-.436"	1.860-1.880"
KT 1150	1.3720-1.3725"	1.3755-1.3765"	.0015-.0040"	.4330-.4335"	.434-.436"	2.350-2.370"

PISTONS, PINS, RINGS

Engine	PISTONS Clearance	PINS Piston Fit	Rod Fit	RINGS Rings	End Gap	Side Clearance
V8-210	.0085-.0110"	.0003"	Press Fit	1	.013"	.005"
				2	.025"	.005"
				3	.010"	.005"
V8-555	.0085-.0110"	.0003"	Press Fit	1	.013"	.005"
				2	.025"	.005"
				3	.010"	.005"
NH/NT 855	.0125-.0130"	.0002"	Press Fit	1	.023"	.005"
				2	.019"	.005"
				3	.019"	.005"
				4	.010"	.005"
V/VT 903	.0095-.0120"	.0003"	Press Fit	1	.017"	.005"
				2	.013"	.005"
				3	.010"	.005"
KT 1150	.0112-.0115"	.0003"	Press Fit	1	.025"	.005"
				2	.025"	.005"
				3	.012"	.005"

CRANKSHAFT & MAIN BEARINGS

Engine	Journal Diameter	Bearing Clearance	Crankshaft End Play	Thrust Location	Thrust Washer Thickness	Number of Main Bearings
V8-210	3.4990-3.5000"	.0015-.0045"	.004-.014"	No.5	.1490-.1510"	5
V8-555	3.4990-3.5000"	.0015-.0045"	.004-.014"	No.5	.1490-.1510"	5
NH/NT 855	4.4985-4.5000"	.0015-.0050"	.007-.022"	No.7	.2450-.2470"	7
V/VT 903	3.7490-3.7500"	.0020-.0090"	.005-.015"	Front	.1505-.1735"	5
KT 1150	5.4985-5.5000"	.0026-.0065"	.004-.016"	No.6	.1505-1735"	7

CYLINDER LINER & BORE

Engine	Type	Liner Bore	Liner Protrusion
V8-210	Wet	4.6245-4.6260"	.006-.009"
V8-555	Wet	4.6245-4.6260"	.006-.009"
NH/NT 855	Wet	5.4995-5.5010"	.003-.006"
V/VT 903	Wet	5.4995-5.5010"	.003-.006"
KT 1150	Wet	6.2495-6.2550"	.003-.006"

CONNECTING RODS & BEARINGS

Engine	Journal Diameter	Bearing Clearance	Sideplay
V8-210	2.4990-2.5000"	.0015-.0045"	.008-.018"
V8-555	2.7490-2.7500"	.0015-.0045"	.008-.018"
NH/NT 855	3.1235-3.1250"	.0015-.0045"	.....
V/VT 903	3.1240-3.1250"	.0050"	.005-.020"
KT 1150	3.9985-4.0000"	.0050"	.....

Medium & Heavy Duty Diesel
CUMMINS (Cont.)

OIL PUMP SPECIFICATIONS

V8-210 & V8-555

Type	Gear
Idler Gear Bushing I.D.	.6195-.6205″
Pump Drive Shaft Bushing I.D.	.6165-.6175″
Drive Shaft Diameter	.6150-.6155″
Idler Shaft Diameter	.6180-.6185″
Driven-to-Idler Gear Backlash	.016-.020″

NH/NT 855

Type	Gear
Bushings I.D.	.8400-.8405″
Idler and Drive Shaft Diameter	.8375-.8380″
Driven Shaft Protrusion	.580-.610″
Drive Shaft Protrusion	.050-.070″
Drive Shaft End Play	.004-.010″
Pressure Relief Valve Open	130PSI

V903 & VT903

Type	Gear
Shaft Bores	.8770-.8775″
Drive Shaft Diameter	.8740″ min
Idler Shaft Diameter	.8750″ min
Pump Gears	2.397″ min
Gear Housing Diameter	2.415″ max
Gear Housing Depth	1.252″ max
Clearance Driven Gear From Shaft End	.5450-.5750″
Clearance Scavenger Drive Gear-to-Body	.0020-.0040″
Clearance Drive Gear From Shaft End	1.232-1.290″
Clearance Main Drive Gear From Shaft End	.0000-.0200″

KT1150

Type	Gear
Bushing I.D.	.8765-.8775″
Idler Shaft Diameter	.8745-.8750″
Drive Shaft Diameter	.8745-.8750″
Clearance Drive Gear-to-Body	.1300-.1500″
Shaft Protrusion From Mounting Surface	1.030-1.050″
Drive Shaft End Clearance	.0025-.0065″

TIGHTENING SPECIFICATIONS

V8-210

NOTE — *Use minimum two steps to torque all nuts and bolts.*

Application	Ft. Lbs.
Cylinder Head Bolts①	110-115
Main Bearing Cap Bolts	175-185
Connecting Rod Cap Nuts	55
Flywheel Bolts	100-105
Pulley-to-Crankshaft	90-100

① — See cylinder head tightening sequence.

TIGHTENING SPECIFICATIONS (Cont.)

V8-555

NOTE — *Use minimum two steps to torque all nuts and bolts.*

Application	Ft. Lbs.
Cylinder Head Bolts①	135-140
Main Bearing Cap Bolts	165-175
Connecting Rod Cap Nuts	85-90
Flywheel Bolts	135-140
Vibration Damper-to-Crankshaft	135-140

① — See cylinder head tightening sequence.

NH/NT 855

NOTE — *Use minimum two steps to torque all nuts and bolts.*

Application	Ft. Lbs.
Cylinder Head Bolts①	280-300
Main Bearing Cap Bolts	300-310
Connecting Rod Cap Nuts	140-150
Flywheel Bolts	200-220
Vibration Damper and Pulley-to-Crankshaft	180-200

① — See cylinder head tightening sequence.

V903 & VT903

NOTE — *Use minimum two steps to torque all nuts and bolts.*

Application	Ft. Lbs.
Cylinder Head Bolts①	280-300
Main Bearing Cap Bolts	340-350
Connecting Rod Cap Nuts	95-100
Flywheel Bolts	200-210
Vibration Damper and Pulley-to-Crankshaft	200-205

① — See cylinder head tightening sequence.

KT1150

NOTE — *Use minimum two steps to torque all nuts and bolts.*

Application	Ft. Lbs.
Cylinder Head Bolts①	
Cadium Plated	250-260
Lubrited	350-370
Main Bearing Cap Bolts	440-450
Connecting Rod Cap Nuts	210-220
Flywheel Bolts	200-220
Vibration Damper and Pulley-to-Crankshaft	320-340

① — See cylinder head tightening sequence.

CUMMINS (Cont.)

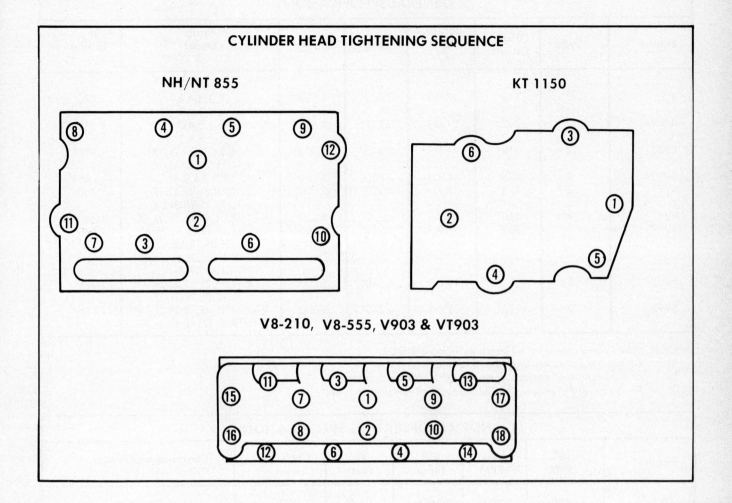

CYLINDER HEAD TIGHTENING SEQUENCE

NH/NT 855

KT 1150

V8-210, V8-555, V903 & VT903

Medium & Heavy Duty Diesel

DETROIT DIESEL

GENERAL SPECIFICATIONS

Engine	Cycle	Displ. Cu. Ins.	Compr. Ratio ③	Bore	Stroke	Firing Order ②	Inj. Timing ①
4-53	2	212″	17.0:1	3.875″	4.500″	R-1,3,4,2 L-1,2,4,3	1.470″
4-53N	2	212″	21.0:1	3.875″	4.500″	R-1,3,4,2 L-1,2,4,3	1.470″
6V53	2	318″	21.0:1	3.875″	4.500″	R-1L,3R,3L,2R,2L,1R L-1L,1R,2L,2R,3L,3R	1.470″
6-71N	2	426″	18.7:1	4.250″	5.000″	1,5,3,6,2,4	④1.460″
6V71	2	426″	18.7:1	4.250″	5.000″	R-1L,3R,3L,2R,2L,1R L-1L,1R,2L,2R,3L,3R	1.460″
8V71	2	568″	18.7:1	4.250″	5.000″	R-1L,3R,3L,4R,4L,2R,2L,1R	1.460″
12V71	2	852″	18.7:1	4.250″	5.000″	R-1L,5L,3R,4R,3L,4L,2R,6R, 2L,6L,1R,5R L-1L,5R,1R,6L,2L,6R,2R,4L, 3L,4R,3R,5L	1.460″
6V92	2	552″	19.0:1	4.840″	5.000″	R-1L,3R,3L,2R,2L,1R L-1L,1R,2L,2R,3L,3R	1.484″
8V92	2	736″	19.0:1	4.840″	5.000″	R-1L,3R,3L,4R,4L,2R,2L,1R L-1L,1R,2L,2R,4L,4R,3L,3R	1.484″

① — Unless noted otherwise, all Injection Timing is BTDC.
② — R-Right-hand rotation. L-Left-hand rotation.
③ — All Turbocharged engines have a 17.0:1 compression ratio.
④ — Timing on all 71 series engines with advanced camshaft is 1.484″.

NORMAL OPERATING SPECIFICATIONS

Engine	Idle RPM	Max. RPM	Oil Temp.	Oil Press.	Coolant Temp.	Compression Pressure (PSI) @ RPM (Sea Level)
4-53	600	2800	240°	40-60	185°	540-590@600
4-53N	600	2800	240°	40-60	185°	540-590@600
6V53	600	2800	240°	40-60	185°	430-480@600
6-71N	600	2100	225°	40-60	185°	515-565@600
V71	600	2300	235°	50-70	185°	425-475@600
8V71	600	2300	235°	50-70	185°	425-475@600
12V71	600	2300	235°	50-70	185°	425-475@600
6V92	600	2100	235°	50-70	185°	430-480@600
8V92	600	2100	235°	50-70	185°	430-480@600

ROCKER ARMS & VALVE BRIDGES

Engine	Rocker Shaft O.D.	Rocker Arm I.D.	Rocker Arm Clearance	Bridge Guide O.D.	Bridge I.D.	Bridge Height Above Head
4-53	.8735-.8740″	.8750-.8760″	.0010-.0025″	.....	.....	.....
4-53N	.8735-.8740″	.8750-.8760″	.0010-.0025″	.....	.....	.....
6V53	.8735-.8740″	.8750-.8760″	.0010-.0025″	.....	.....	.....
6-71N	.8735-.8740″	.8750-.8760″	.0010-.0025″	.....	.....	2.040″
6V71	.8735-.8740″	.8750-.8760″	.0010-.0025″	.....	.....	2.040″
8V71	.8735-.8740″	.8750-.8760″	.0015-.0025″	.....	.....	2.040″
12V71	.8735-.8740″	.8750-.8760″	.0010-.0025″	.....	.....	2.040″
6V92	.8735-.8740″	.8750-.8760″	.0010-.0025″	.....	.....	2.040″
8V92	.8735-.8740″	.8750-.8760″	.0010-.0025″	.....	.....	2.040″

DETROIT DIESEL (Cont.)

VALVES & SEATS

Engine ①	Head Diameter	Face Angle	Seat Angle	Seat Width	Stem Diameter	Stem Clearance	Valve Seat Insert O.D.	Valve Clearance
4-53	0.910″	30°	30°	.0468-.0781″	.2480-.2488″	.0017-.0035″	1.1615″	.025″
4-53N	0.910″	30°	30°	.0468-.0781″	.2480-.2488″	.0017-.0035″	1.1615″	.025″
6V53	0.910″	30°	30°	.0468-.0781″	.2480-.2488″	.0017-.0035″	1.1615″	.025″
6-71N								
2V	1.180″	30°	30°	.0625-.0937″	.3417-.3425″	.0002-.0038″	1.6260-1.6270″	.013″
4V	1.180″	30°	30°	.0468-.0937″	.3100-.3105″	.0002-.0035″	1.2600-1.2610″	.013″
6V71								
2V	0.980″	30°	30°	.0630-.0940″	.3417-.3425″	.0020-.0038″	1.6260-1.6270″	.011″
4V	0.980″	30°	30°	.0470-.0940″	.3100-.3105″	.0020-.0035″	1.2600-1.2610″	.015″
8V71								
2V	0.980″	30°	30°	.0630-.0940″	.3417-.3425″	.0020-.0038″	1.6260-1.6270″	.011″
4V	0.980″	30°	30°	.0470-.0940″	.3100-.3105″	.0020-.0035″	1.2600-1.2610″	.015″
12V71								
2V	0.980″	30°	30°	.0630-.0940″	.3417-.3425″	.0020-.0038″	1.6260-1.6270″	.011″
4V	0.980″	30°	30°	.0470-.0490″	.3100-.3105″	.0020-.0035″	1.2600-1.2610″	.015″
6V92	1.300″	30°	31°	.078″	.3100-.3108″	.0017-.0035″	1.4420″	.015″
8V92	1.300″	30°	31°	.078″	.3100-.3108″	.0017-.0035″	1.4420″	.015″

① — Detroit Diesel engines do not use intake valves, specifications given are for exhaust valves only.

VALVE SPRINGS

Engine	Free Length	Compressed Length	Lbs. @ Comp. Length
4-53	.....	1.930″	25
4-53N	.....	1.930″	25
6V53	.....	1.930″	25
6-71N			
2V	.....	2.200″	25
4V	.....	1.800″	25
6V71			
2V	.....	2.200″	25
4V	.....	1.800″	25
8V71			
2V	.....	2.200″	25
4V	.....	1.800″	25
12V71			
2V	.....	2.200″	25
4V	.....	1.800″	25
6V92	.....	1.800″	25
8V92	.....	1.800″	25

CAMSHAFT

Engine	Journal Diam.	Clearance	Lobe Lift
4-53	2.1820-2.1825″	.0045-.0060″	.005-.015″
4-53N	2.1820-2.1825″	.0045-.0060″	.005-.015″
6V53	2.1820-2.1825″	.0045-.0060″	.005-.015″
6-71N			
No.1-5	1.4970-1.4975″	.0025-.0040″	.004-.012″
No.2-3-4	1.4980-1.4985″	.0025-.0050″	
6V71			
No.1-5	1.4970-1.4975″	.0025-.0040″	.004-.012″
No.2-3-4	1.4980-1.4985″	.0025-.0050″	
8V71			
No.1-5	1.4960-1.4965″	.0035-.0050″	.004-.012″
No.2-3-4	1.4980-1.4985″	.0025-.0050″	
12V71			
No.1-5	1.4970-1.4975″	.0025-.0040″	.004-.012″
No.2-3-4	1.4980-1.4985″	.0025-.0050″	
6V92			
No.1-5	1.4970-1.4975″	.0025-.0040″	.004-.012″
No.2-3-4	1.4980-1.4985″	.0025-.0050″	
8V92			
No.1-5	1.4960-1.4965″	.0035-.0050″	.004-.012″
No.2-3-4	1.4980-1.4985″	.0025-.0050″	

Medium & Heavy Duty Diesel

DETROIT DIESEL (Cont.)

PISTONS, PINS, RINGS						
	PISTONS	PINS		RINGS		
Engine	Clearance	Piston Fit	Rod Fit	Rings	End Gap	Side Clearance
4-53	.0031-.0068"	.0025-.0034"	.0010-.0019"	Chrome		
				1	.020-.046"	.0030-.0060"
				2	.020-.046"	.0070-.0100"
				3	.020-.046"	.0050-.0080"
				4	.020-.046"	.0050-.0080"
				5	.010-.025"	.0015-.0055"
				6	.010-.025"	.0015-.0055"
				Iron		
				1	.020-.036"	.0030-.0060"
				2	.020-.036"	.0070-.0100"
				3	.020-.036"	.0050-.0080"
				4	.020-.036"	.0050-.0080"
				5	.010-.025"	.0015-.0055"
				6	.010-.025"	.0015-.0055"
4-53N	.0031-.0068"	.0025-.0034"	.0010-.0019"	Chrome		
				1	.020-.046"	.0030-.0060"
				2	.020-.046"	.0070-.0100"
				3	.020-.046"	.0050-.0080"
				4	.020-.046"	.0050-.0080"
				5	.010-.025"	.0015-.0055"
				6	.010-.025"	.0015-.0055"
				Iron		
				1	.020-.036"	.0030-.0060"
				2	.020-.036"	.0070-.0100"
				3	.020-.036"	.0050-.0080"
				4	.020-.036"	.0050-.0080"
				5	.010-.025"	.0015-.0055"
				6	.010-.025"	.0015-.0055"
6V53	.0031-.0068"	.0025-.0034"	.0010-.0019"	Chrome		
				1	.020-.046"	.0030-.0060"
				2	.020-.046"	.0070-.0100"
				3	.020-.046"	.0050-.0080"
				4	.020-.046"	.0050-.0080"
				5	.010-.025"	.0015-.0055"
				6	.010-.025"	.0015-.0055"
				Iron		
				1	.020-.036"	.0030-.0060"
				2	.020-.036"	.0070-.0100"
				3	.020-.036"	.0050-.0080"
				4	.020-.036"	.0050-.0080"
				5	.010-.025"	.0015-.0055"
				6	.010-.025"	.0015-.0055"
6-71N Trunk Type	.0040-.0078"	.0025-.0034"	.0015-.0024"	1	.023-.038"	.0040-.0060"
				2	.018-.043"	.0100-.0130"
				3	.018-.043"	.0040-.0070"
				4	.018-.043"	.0040-.0070"
				5	.008-.023"	.0015-.0055"
				6	.008-.023"	.0015-.0055"
Crosshead Type	.0045-.0083"	①.0870-.0880"	.....	1	.023-.038"	.0010-.0050"
				2	.018-.043"	.0100-.0130"
				3	.018-.043"	.0040-.0070"
				4	.002-.021"	.0005-.0030"
				②5	.008-.023"	.0010-.0035"
				②6	.008-.023"	.0015-.0055"

① — Thickness of slipper bushing at center on all Crosshead type pistons.
② — Ring end gap for rings 5 and 6 on turbocharged engines is .005-.014".

DETROIT DIESEL (Cont.)

| | PISTONS | PINS | | RINGS | | |
Engine	Clearance	Piston Fit	Rod Fit	Rings	End Gap	Side Clearance
6V71 Trunk Type	① .0040-.0078"	.0025-.0034"	.0015-.0024"	1 2 3 4 5 6	.023-.038" .018-.043" .018-.043" .018-.043" .008-.023" .008-.023"	.0040-.0070" .0095-.0130" .0075-.0110" .0055-.0090" .0015-.0055" .0015-.0055"
6V71N Trunk Type	① .0040-.0078"	.0025-.0034"	.0015-.0024"	1 2 3 4 5 6	.023-.038" .018-.043" .018-.043" .018-.043" .008-.023" .008-.023"	.0040-.0070" .0100-.0130" .0040-.0070" .0040-.0070" .0015-.0055" .0015-.0055"
6V71N&T Crosshead Type	.0045-.0083"	① .0870-.0880"	.....	1 2 3 4 5 6	.023-.038" .018-.043" .018-.043" .002-.021" .008-.023" .008-.023"	.0010-.0050" .0100-.0130" .0040-.0070" .0005-.0030" .0010-.0035" .0015-.0055"
8V71 Trunk Type	① .0040-.0078"	.0025-.0034"	.0015-.0024"	1 2 3 4 5 6	.023-.038" .018-.043" .018-.043" .018-.043" .008-.023" .008-.023"	.0040-.0070" .0095-.0130" .0075-.0110" .0055-.0090" .0015-.0055" .0015-.0055"
8V71N Trunk Type	① .0040-.0078"	.0025-.0034"	.0015-.0024"	1 2 3 4 5 6	.023-.038" .018-.043" .018-.043" .018-.043" .008-.023" .008-.023"	.0040-.0070" .0100-.0130" .0040-.0070" .0040-.0070" .0015-.0055" .0015-.0055"
8V71N&T Crosshead Type	.0045-.0083"	① .0870-.0880"	.....	1 2 3 4 5 6	.023-.038" .018-.043" .018-.043" .002-.021" .008-.023" .008-.023"	.0010-.0050" .0100-.0130" .0040-.0070" .0005-.0030" .0010-.0035" .0015-.0055"
12V71 Trunk Type	② .0040-.0078"	.0025-.0034"	.0015-.0024"	1 2 3 4 5 6	.023-.038" .018-.043" .018-.043" .018-.043" .008-.023" .008-.023"	.0040-.0070" .0095-.0130" .0075-.0110" .0055-.0090" .0015-.0055" .0015-.0055"
12V71N Trunk Type	② .0040-.0078"	.0025-.0034"	.0015-.0024"	1 2 3 4 5 6	.023-.038" .018-.043" .018-.043" .018-.043" .008-.023" .008-.023"	.0040-.0070" .0100-.0130" .0040-.0130" .0040-.0130" .0015-.0055" .0015-.0055"

① — Thickness of slipper bushing at center on all Crosshead type pistons.

② — With 70 mm injectors, clearance is .0045-.0083".

Medium & Heavy Duty Diesel

DETROIT DIESEL (Cont.)

PISTONS, PINS, RINGS						
	PISTONS	PINS		RINGS		
Engine	Clearance	Piston Fit	Rod Fit	Rings	End Gap	Side Clearance
12V71N&T Crosshead Type	.0045-.0083"	①.0870-.0880"	.....	1	.023-.038"	.0010-.0050"
				2	.018-.043"	.0100-.0130"
				3	.018-.043"	.0040-.0070"
				4	.002-.021"	.0005-.0030"
				5	.008-.023"	.0010-.0035"
				6	.008-.023"	.0015-.0055"
6V92	.0120"	①.0870-.0880"	.....	1	.025-.040"	.0010-.0050"
				2	.025-.040"	.0100-.0130"
				3	.025-.040"	.0040-.0070"
				4	.002-.017"	.0005-.0030"
				5	.010-.020"	.0010-.0040"
				6	.010-.020"	.0015-.0055"
8V92	.0120"	①.0870-.0880"	.....	1	.025-.040"	.0010-.0050"
				2	.025-.040"	.0100-.0130"
				3	.025-.040"	.0040-.0070"
				4	.002-.017"	.0005-.0030"
				5	.010-.020"	.0010-.0040"
				6	.010-.020"	.0015-.0055"

① — Thickness of slipper bushing at center on all Crosshead type pistons.

CRANKSHAFT & MAIN BEARINGS						
Engine	Journal Diameter	Bearing Clearance	Crankshaft End Play	Thrust Location	Thrust Washer Thickness	Number of Main Bearings
4-53	2.9990-3.0000"	.0010-.0040"	.004-.011"	No.5	.119-.122"	5
4-53N	2.9990-3.0000"	.0010-.0040"	.004-.011"	No.5	.119-.122"	5
6V53	3.4990-3.5000"	.0010-.0040"	.004-.011"	No.4	.119-.122"	4
6-71N	3.4990-3.5000"	.0014-.0044"	.004-.014"	No.7	.119-.122"	7
6V71	4.4990-4.5000"	.0016-.0050"	.004-.014"	No.4	.119-.122"	4
8V71	4.4990-4.5000"	.0016-.0050"	.004-.014"	No.5	.119-.122"	5
12V71	4.4990-4.5000"	.0016-.0050"	.004-.014"	No.7	.119-.122"	7
6V92	4.4990-4.5000"	.0016-.0050"	.004-.011"	No.4	.119-.122"	4
8V92	4.4990-4.5000"	.0016-.0050"	.004-.011"	No.5	.119-.122"	5

CONNECTING RODS & BEARINGS			
Engine	Journal Diameter	Bearing Clearance	Sideplay
4-53	2.4990-2.5000"	.0015-.0045"	.006-.012"
4-53N	2.4990-2.5000"	.0015-.0045"	.006-.012"
6V53	2.7490-2.7500"	.0011-.0041"	.008-.016"
6-71N	2.7514-2.7534"	.0014-.0044"	.006-.012"
6V71	2.9990-3.0000"	.0014-.0044"	.008-.016"
8V71	2.9990-3.0000"	.0014-.0044"	.008-.016"
12V71	2.9990-3.0000"	.0014-.0044"	.008-.016"
6V92	2.9990-3.0000"	.0010-.0040"	.004-.011"
8V92	2.9990-3.0000"	.0010-.0040"	.004-.011"

CYLINDER LINER & BORE			
Engine	Type	Liner Bore	Liner Protrusion ①
4-53	Wet	3.8752-3.8767"	.0465-.0500"
4-53N	Wet	3.8752-3.8767"	.0465-.0500"
6V53	Wet	3.8752-3.8767"	.0465-.0500"
6-71N	Wet	4.2495-4.2511"	.0450-.0500"
6V71	Wet	4.2495-4.2511"	.0450-.0500"
8V71	Wet	4.2495-4.2511"	.0450-.0500"
12V71	Wet	4.2495-4.2511"	.0450-.0500"
6V92	Wet	4.8395-4.8411"	.0418-.0482"
8V92	Wet	4.8395-4.8411"	.0418-.0482"

① — All measurements are DEPTH BELOW block surface.

DETROIT DIESEL (Cont.)

OIL PUMP SPECIFICATIONS

4-53, 4-53N & 6V53

Type	Rotary
Clearance Between Inner and Outer Rotors at Each Lobe	.0040-.0110"
Depth Between Face and Rotors	.0010-.0035"
Pressure Relief Valve Opening	52psi

6-71N

Type	Gear
Shaft Bore	.6213-.6225"
Shaft Diameter	.6230"
Clearance Body Bushing	.0008-.0025"
Clearance Cover Bushing	.0010-.0027"
Distance Gear From Shaft End	6.4690"
Clearance Driven Gear-to-Housing	.0050"
Pressure Relief Regulator Opening	50psi
Pressure Relief Valve Opening	105psi

6V71 & 8V71

Type	Gear
Clearance Drive Shaft-to-Bushing	.0010-.0025"
Shaft Shoulder Below Front Cover	.0000-.0200"
Pressure Relief Valve Opening	100psi

12V71

Type	Gear
Shaft Bore	.8787-.8799"
Shaft Diameter	.8781"
Clearance Shaft-to-Bushing	.0015-.0032"
Gear Backlash	.0060-.0120"
Pressure Regulator Valve Opening	50psi
Pressure Relief Valve Opening	120psi

6V92 & 8V92

Type	Gear
Clearance Drive Shaft-to-Bushing	.0010-.0025"
Shaft Shoulder Below Front Cover	.0000-.0200"
Pressure Relief Valve Opening	100psi

TIGHTENING SPECIFICATIONS

Application	Ft. Lbs.
Cylinder Head Bolts①	170-180
Main Bearing Bolts	120-130
Flywheel Bolts	110-120
Crankshaft End Bolt	200-220
Camshaft and Balance Shaft Nut	300-325
Connecting Rod Nuts	40-45

① — See cylinder head tightening sequence.

TIGHTENING SPECIFICATIONS (Cont.)

6-71N

NOTE — *Aluminum engine only.*

Application	Ft. Lbs.
Cylinder Head Nuts①	140-160
Main Bearing Nuts	120-140
Flywheel Bolts	150-160
Crankshaft End Bolt	290-310
Camshaft and Balance Shaft Nut	300-325
Connecting Rod Nuts	60-70

① — See cylinder head tightening sequence.

6-71N

NOTE — *Cast iron engine only.*

Application	Ft. Lbs.
Cylinder Head Bolts①	175-185
Main Bearing Bolts	180-190
Main Bearing Nuts	155-185
Flywheel Bolts	180-190
Crankshaft End Bolt	290-310
Connecting Rod Nut	60-70
Crosshead Piston Pin to Connecting Rod Bolt	55-60

① — See cylinder head tightening sequence.

6V71, 8V71 & 12V71

Application	Ft. Lbs.
Cylinder Head Bolts①	175-185
Main Bearing Bolts	180-190
Flywheel Bolts	180-190
Crankshaft End Bolt	290-310
Camshaft and Balance Shaft Nut	300-325
Connecting Rod Nuts	60-70
Crosshead Piston Pin to Connecting Rod Bolt	55-60

① — See cylinder head tightening sequence.

6V92 & 8V92

Application	Ft. Lbs.
Cylinder Head Bolts①	230-240
Main Bearing Bolts	230-240
Flywheel Bolts	180-190
Crankshaft End Bolt	290-310
Camshaft Nut	300-325
Connecting Rod Nut	60-70
Crosshead Piston Pin to Connecting Rod Bolt	55-60

① — See cylinder head tightening sequence.

Medium & Heavy Duty Diesel
DETROIT DIESEL (Cont.)

CYLINDER HEAD TIGHTENING SEQUENCE

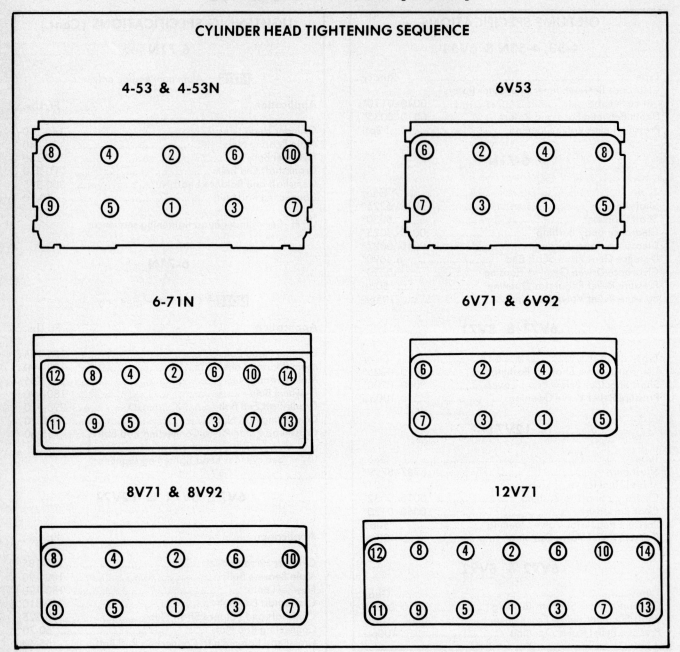

Medium & Heavy Duty Diesel

INTERNATIONAL HARVESTER

GENERAL SPECIFICATIONS							
Engine	Cycle	Displ. Cu. Ins.	Compr. Ratio	Bore	Stroke	Firing Order	Inj. Timing ①
D-150	4	461"	17.0:1	4.125"	4.313"	1,8,7,3,6,5,4,2	.207"
D-170	4	549"	17.0:1	4.500"	4.313"	1,8,7,3,6,5,4,2	.207"
D-190	4	549"	17.0:1	4.500"	4.313"	1,8,7,3,6,5,4,2	.207"
DT-466	4	466"	15.1:1	4.300"	5.350"	1,5,3,6,2,4	②13.0°
V-800	4	798"	16.0:1	5.313"	4.500"	1,8,7,3,6,5,4,2	22.0°

① — Unless noted otherwise, all Injection Timing is BTDC.
② — Timing for Model DTI-466, Intercooled is 15.0° static.

NORMAL OPERATING SPECIFICATIONS						
Engine	Idle RPM	Max. RPM	Oil Temp.	Oil Press.	Coolant Temp.	Compression Pressure (PSI) @ RPM (Sea Level)
D-150	550-600	3000	220°	45-60	190°	375-425@ ①
D-170	550-600	3000	220°	45-60	190°	375-425@ ①
D-190	550-600	3000	220°	45-60	190°	375-425@ ①
DT-466	675	2920	230°	40-65	202°	.....
DTI-466	675	2935	230°	40-60	202°	.....
V-800	625-675	2860	220°	45-65	190°	400-470@234

① — Cranking Speed.

VALVES & SEATS								
Engine	Head Diameter	Face Angle	Seat Angle	Seat Width	Stem Diameter	Stem Clearance	Valve Seat Insert O.D.	Valve Clearance
D-150								
Int.	1.1810"	45°	45°	.080-.090"	.3725-.3730"	.0080-.0230"	.....	.014"
Exh.	1.030"	45°	45°	.080-.090"	.3720-.3725"	.0080-.0230"	.....	.016"
D-170								
Int.	1.990"	45°	45°	.080-.090"	.3725-.3730"	.0080-.0230"	.....	.014"
Exh.	1.740"	45°	45°	.080-.090"	.3720-.3725"	.0080-.0230"	.....	.016"
D-190								
Int.	1.990"	45°	45°	.080-.090"	.3725-.3730"	.0080-.0230"	.....	.014"
Exh.	1.740"	45°	45°	.080-.090"	.3720-.3725"	.0080-.0230"	.....	.016"
DT-466								
Int.	1.965-1.975"	30°	30°	.075-.085"	.3718-.3725"	.0015-.0032"	1.996-1.997"	①.019-.021"
Exh.	1.595-1.605"	45°	45°	.075-.085"	.3718-.3725"	.0015-.0032"	1.624-1.625"	①.024-.026"
V-800								
Int.	1.500"	30°	30°	.080"	.3718-.3725"	.0015-.0032"	.....	.013"
Exh.	1.260"	30°	30°	.080"	.3718-.3725"	.0015-.0032"	.....	.025"

① — Clearance is with engine cold.

Medium & Heavy Duty Diesel

INTERNATIONAL HARVESTER (Cont.)

VALVE SPRINGS

Engine	Free Length	Compressed Length	Lbs. @ Comp. Length
D-150	2.075"	1.397"	200
D-170	2.075"	1.397"	200
D-190	2.075"	1.397"	200
DT-466	2.340"	1.552"	156-165
V-800	1.835"	1.571"	58-62

CAMSHAFT

Engine	Journal Diam.	Clearance	Lobe Lift
D-150, D-170 & D-190			
No.1	2.346-2.347"	.0015-.0035"	.0035-.0115"
No.2	2.315-2.316"	.0015-.0035"	.0035-.0115"
No.3	2.289-2.290"	.0015-.0035"	.0035-.0115"
No.4	2.246-2.247"	.0015-.0035"	.0035-.0115"
DT-466	2.2814-2.2825"	.0020-.0066"	.0050-.0130"
V-800	2.346-2.347"	.0020-.0065"	.0050-.0130"

ROCKER ARMS & VALVE BRIDGES

Engine	Rocker Shaft O.D.	Rocker Arm I.D.	Rocker Arm Clearance	Bridge Guide O.D.	Bridge I.D.	Bridge Height Above Head
D-150	.....	.....	.0011-.0045"	.....	.....	1.219"
D-170	.....	.....	.0011-.0045"	.....	.....	1.219"
D-190	.....	.....	.0011-.0045"	.....	.....	1.219"
DT-466	.8491-.8501"	.851-.853"	.0009-.0039"	.....	.....	.....
V-800	.9990-1.0010"	.....	.....	.....	.....	0.910"

PISTONS, PINS, RINGS

Engine	PISTONS Clearance	PINS Piston Fit	PINS Rod Fit	RINGS Rings	RINGS End Gap	RINGS Side Clearance
D-150	.0055-.0065"	.0009-.0015"	Press Fit	1	.013-.023"	.0035-.0050"
				2	.013-.023"	.0035-.0050"
				3	.013-.028"	.0015-.0030"
D-170	.0060-.0070"	.0009-.0015"	Press Fit	1	.013-.023"	.0035-.0050"
				2	.013-.023"	.0035-.0050"
				3	.013-.028"	.0015-.0030"
D-190	.0060-.0070"	.0009-.0015"	Press Fit	1	013-.023"	.0035-.0050"
				2	.013-.023"	.0035-.0050"
				3	.013-.028"	.0015-.0030"
DT-466	.0045-.0065"	.0005-.0010"	.0006-.0010"	1	.016-.026"	.0000-.0280"
				2	.020-.030"	.0045-.0215"
				3	.010-.020"	.002-.004"
V-800	.0060-.0090"	.0005-.0011"	Press Fit	1	.018-.028"	.0020-.0040"
				2	.020-.030"	.0000-.0150"
				3	.008-.018"	.0015-.0035"

CRANKSHAFT & MAIN BEARINGS

Engine	Journal Diameter	Bearing Clearance	Crankshaft End Play	Thrust Location	Thrust Washer Thickness	Number of Main Bearings
D-150	3.123-3.1240"	.0018-.0048"	.004-.010"	No.3	.....	5
D-170	3.123-3.1240"	.0018-.0048"	.004-.010"	No.3	.....	5
D-190	3.123-3.1240"	.0018-.0048"	.004-.010"	No.3	.....	5
DT-466	3.3742-3.3755"	.0018-.0051"	.006-.012"	No.7	.....	7
V-800	3.7477-3.7490"	.0026-.0059"	.003-.011"	No.5	.....	5

Medium & Heavy Duty Diesel

INTERNATIONAL HARVESTER (Cont.)

CYLINDER LINER & BORE

Engine	Type	Liner Bore	Liner Protrusion
D-150	①	.....	.....
D-170	①	.....	.....
D-190	①	.....	.....
DT-466	Wet	4.300-4.301″	.002-.005″
V-800	Wet	5.3125-5.3135″	.003-.006″

① — Liners are not used.

CONNECTING RODS & BEARINGS

Engine	Journal Diameter	Bearing Clearance	Sideplay
D-150	2.753-2.754″	.0018-.0048″	.....
D-170	2.753-2.754″	.0018-.0048″	.....
D-190	2.753-2.754″	.0018-.0048″	.....
DT-466	2.9977-2.9990″	.0018-.0051″	.007-.015″
V-800	2.9972-2.9982″	.0026-.0059″	.....

OIL PUMP SPECIFICATIONS

D-150, D-170 & D-190

Type	Gear
Shaft Diameter	.4905-.4912″
Clearance in Bore	.0013-.0030″
Clearance Gear-to-Housing	.0014-.0054″
Gear Backlash	.0005-.0065″

DT-466

Type	Gerotor
End clearance, outer rotor-to-housing	.0015-.0040″
End clearance, inner rotor-to-housing	.0018-.0044″
Radial clearance, outer rotor and housing	.0055-.0085″

V-800

Type	Gear
Drive Shaft Diameter	.7385-.7390″
Idler Shaft Diameter	.5901-.5904″
Running Clearance	.0020-.0035″
Clearance Gear-to-Housing	.0040-.0055″
Pumping Gears Backlash	.0080-.0120″
Idler and Crankshaft Gears Backlash	.0040-.0140″
Drive Shaft End Play	.003-.006″

TIGHTENING SPECIFICATIONS

D-150, D-170 & D-190

NOTE — *Use minimum two steps to torque all nuts and bolts.*

Application	Ft. Lbs.
Cylinder Head Bolts①	110
Main Bearing Cap Bolts	130
Connecting Rod Cap Bolts	55
Crankshaft Pulley Nut	150
Flywheel Bolts	110

① — See cylinder head tightening sequence.

DT-466

Application	Ft. Lbs.
Cylinder Head Bolts①	165
Main Bearing Cap Bolts	115
Connecting Rod Cap Bolts	130
Crankshaft Pulley Bolts	125
Flywheel Bolts	125

① — See cylinder head tightening sequence and tighten in minimum of two steps.

V-800

NOTE — *Use minimum two steps to torque all nuts and bolts.*

Application	Ft. Lbs.
Cylinder Head Bolts①	220
Main Bearing Cap Bolts	390
Connecting Rod Cap Nuts	130
Vibration Damper-to-Crankshaft Nut	350
Flywheel Bolts	235

① — See cylinder head tightening sequence.

Medium & Heavy Duty Diesel
INTERNATIONAL HARVESTER (Cont.)

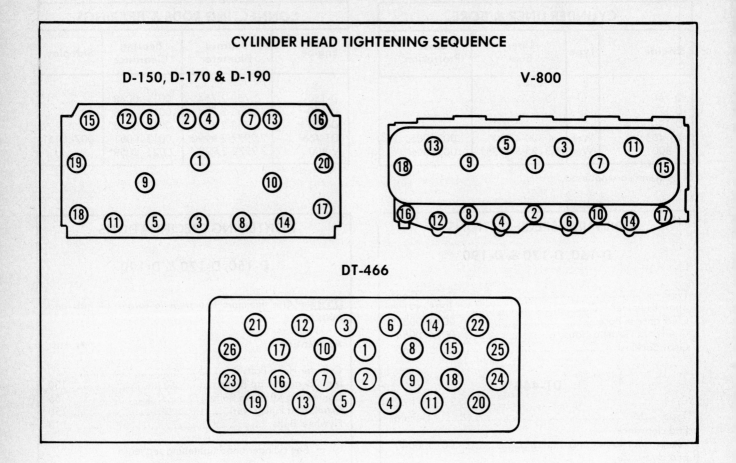

CYLINDER HEAD TIGHTENING SEQUENCE

D-150, D-170 & D-190

V-800

DT-466

Medium & Heavy Duty Diesel

MACK

GENERAL SPECIFICATIONS

Engine	Cycle	Displ. Cu. Ins.	Compr. Ratio	Bore	Stroke	Firing Order	Inj. Timing ①
END475	4	475"	16.5:1	4.530"	4.920"	1,5,3,6,2,4	24.0°
ENDT475	4	475"	15.5:1	4.530"	4.920"	1,5,3,6,2,4	25.0°
ENDT673	4	672"	16.11:1	4.875"	6.000"	1,5,3,6,2,4	29.0°
ENDT673C	4	672"	14.99:1	4.875"	6.000"	1,5,3,6,2,4	28.0°
ENDT673E	4	672"	16.11:1	4.875"	6.000"	1,5,3,6,2,4	30.0°
ENDT/B675	4	672"	14.99:1	4.875"	6.000"	1,5,3,6,2,4	29.0°
ENDT/B676	4	672"	14.99:1	4.875"	6.000"	1,5,3,6,2,4	22.0°
END707	4	707"	15.21:1	5.000"	6.000"	1,5,3,6,2,4	30.0°
ENDT/B865	4	866"	15.7:1	5.250"	5.000"	1,5,4,8,6,3,7,2	25.0°
ENDT/B866	4	866"	15.7:1	5.250"	5.000"	1,5,4,8,6,3,7,2	25.0°

① — Unless otherwise noted, all Injection Timing is BTDC.

NORMAL OPERATING SPECIFICATIONS

Engine	Idle RPM	Max. RPM	Oil Temp.	Oil Press.	Coolant Temp.	Compression Pressure (PSI) @ RPM (Sea Level)
END475	450	2600	.....	75	①170°	490-540@1000
ENDT475	500	2600	.....	75	①170°	430-470@1000
ENDT673	500-575	2280	.....	45-75	①170°	575@1000
ENDT673C	525-575	2280	.....	40-75	①170°	460@1000
ENDT673E	500-575	2280	.....	40-75	①170°	530@1000
ENDT/B675	500-575	2270	.....	40-75	①170°	460-1000
ENDT/B676	525-575	2310	.....	40-94	①170°	460@1000
END707	525-575	2285	.....	45-75	①170°	530@1000
ENDT/B865	600-650	2650	.....	40-95	①170°	②530@1000
ENDT/B866	600-650	2500	.....	40-95	①170°	③540@1000

① — Thermostat open temperature.
② — Prior to engine serial no. T865-7WO-030, 485@1000.
③ — Prior to engine serial no. T866-7WO-515, 485@1000.

ROCKER ARMS & VALVE BRIDGES

Engine	Rocker Shaft O.D.	Rocker Arm I.D.	Rocker Arm Clearance	Bridge Guide O.D.	Bridge I.D.	Bridge Height Above Head
END475	.8654-.8656"	.8661-.8669"	.0005-.0015"	.....	.....	.....
ENDT475	.8654-.8656"	.8661-.8669"	.0005-.0015"	.....	.....	.....
ENDT673	1.1286-1.1291"	1.1296-1.1301"	.0005-.0015"	.....	.....	.....
ENDT673C	1.1286-1.1291"	1.1296-1.1301"	.0005-.0015"	.....	.....	.....
ENDT673E	1.1286-1.1291"	1.1296-1.1301"	.0005-.0015"	.....	.....	.....
ENDT/B675	1.1286-1.1291"	1.1296-1.1301"	.0005-.0015"	.....	.....	.....
ENDT/B676	1.1286-1.1291"	1.1296-1.1301"	.0005-.0015"	.....	.....	.....
END707	1.1286-1.1291"	1.1296-1.1301"	.0005-.0015"	.....	.....	.....
ENDT/B865	1.1286-1.1291"	1.1296-1.1301"	.0005-.0015"	.....	.....	.....
ENDT/B866	1.1286-1.1291"	1.1296-1.1301"	.0005-.0015"	.....	.....	.....

Medium & Heavy Duty Diesel
MACK (Cont.)

VALVES & SEATS								
Engine	Head Diameter	Face Angle	Seat Angle	Seat Width	Stem Diameter	Stem Clearance	Valve Seat Insert O.D.	Valve Clearance
END475 Int.	2.170″	30°	29½°	.047-.059″	.....	.0060″	.....	.012″Hot .014″Cold
Exh.	1.854″	30°	29½°	.047-.059″	.....	.0060″	.....	.016″Hot .018″Cold
ENDT475 Int.	2.170″	30°	29½°	.047-.059″	.....	.0060″	.....	.012″Hot .014″Cold
Exh.	1.854″	30°	29½°	.047-.059″	.....	.0060″	.....	.026″Hot .028″Cold
ENDT673 Int.	2.050″	30°	30°	.063-.094″	.4965-.4975″	.0030-.0050″	2.4405-2.4415″	.014″Hot .016″Cold
Exh.	1.690″	30°	30°	.063-.094″	.4955-.4965″	.0030-.0050″	2.0855-2.0865″	.022″Hot .024″Cold
ENDT673C Int.	2.050″	30°	30°	.063-.094″	.4965-.4975″	.0030-.0050″	2.4405-2.4415″	.014″Hot ①.016″Cold
Exh.	1.690″	30°	30°	.063-.094″	.4955-.4965″	.0030-.0050″	2.0855-2.0865″	.022″Hot .024″Cold
ENDT673E Int.	2.050″	30°	30°	.063-.094″	.4965-.4975″	.0030-.0050″	2.4405-2.4415″	.014″Hot ①.016″Cold
Exh.	1.690″	30°	30°	.063-.094″	.4955-.4965″	.0030-.0050″	2.0855-2.0865″	.022″Hot .024″Cold
ENDT/B675 Int.	2.050″	30°	30°	.063-.094″	.4965-.4975″	.0030-.0050″	2.4405-2.4415″	.014″Hot ①.016″Cold
Exh.	1.690″	30°	30°	.063-.094″	.4955-.4965″	.0030-.0050″	2.0855-2.0865″	.022″Hot .024″Cold
ENDT/B676 Int.	2.050″	30°	30°	.063-.094″	.4965-.4975″	.0020-.0040″	2.4405-2.4415″	.014″Hot ①.016″Cold
Exh.	1.690″	30°	30°	.063-.094″	.4955-.4965″	.0030-.0050″	2.0855-2.0865″	.022″Hot .024″Cold
END707 Int.	2.050″	30°	30°	.063-.094″	.4965-.4975″	.0020-.0040″	2.4405-2.4415″	.014″Hot ①.016″Cold
Exh.	1.690″	30°	30°	.063-.094″	.4955-.4965″	.0020-.0040″	2.0855-2.0865″	.022″Hot .024″Cold
ENDT/B865 Int.	2.050″	30°	30°	.063-.094″	.4965-.4975″	.0020-.0040″	2.4370-2.4380″	.015″Hot ①.016″Cold
Exh.	1.690″	30°	30°	.063-.094″	.4955-.4965″	.0030-.0050″	2.1760-2.1770″	.024″Hot .026″Cold
ENDT/B866 Int.	2.050″	30°	30°	.063-.094″	.4965-.4975″	.0020-.0040″	2.4370-2.4380″	.015″Hot ①.016″Cold
Exh.	1.690″	30°	30°	.063-.094″	.4955-.4965″	.0030-.0050″	2.1760-2.1770″	.024″Hot .026″Cold

① — Set valve clearance COLD STATIC ONLY on all B&C model engines which are equipped with Dynatard Engine Brake.

CAMSHAFT			
Engine	Journal Diam.	Clearance	Lobe Lift
END475			
No.1	2.6825"	.0020-.0030"	.004-.010"
No.2	2.6800"	.0015-.0030"	.004-.010"
No.3	2.6750"	.0015-.0030"	.004-.010"
No.4	2.3600"	.0015-.0030"	.004-.010"
ENDT475			
No.1	2.6825"	.0020-.0030"	.004-.010"
No.2	2.6800"	.0015-.0030"	.004-.010"
No.3	2.6750"	.0015-.0030"	.004-.010"
No.4	2.3600"	.0015-.0030"	.004-.010"
ENDT673			
No.1-6	2.4390-2.4400"	.0015-.0045"	.008-.014"
No.7	2.2510-2.2520"	.0015-.0045"	.008-.014"
ENDT673C			
No.1-6	2.4390-2.4400"	.0015-.0045"	.008-.014"
No.7	2.2510-2.2520"	.0015-.0045"	.008-.014"
ENDT673E			
No.1-6	2.4390-2.4400"	.0015-.0045"	.008-.014"
No.7	2.2510-2.2520"	.0015-.0045"	.008-.014"
ENDT/B675			
No.1-6	2.4390-2.4400"	.0015-.0045"	.008-.014"
No.7	2.2510-2.2520"	.0015-.0045"	.008-.014"
ENDT/B676			
No.1-6	2.4390-2.4400"	.0010-.0050"	.008-.014"
No.7	2.2510-2.2520"	.0015-.0030"	.008-.014"
END707			
No.1-6	2.4390-2.4400"	.0020-.0040"	.008-.014"
No.7	2.2510-2.2520"	.0015-.0030"	.008-.014"
ENDT/B865	2.4390-2.4400"	.0010-.0050"	.008-.014"
ENDT/B866	2.4390-2.4400"	.0010-.0050"	.008-.014"

VALVE SPRINGS			
Engine	Free Length	Compressed Length	Lbs. @ Comp. Length
END475			
Inner	2.313"	1.250"	45
Outer	2.594"	1.406"	106
ENDT475			
Inner	2.313"	1.250"	45
Outer	2.594"	1.406"	106
ENDT673			
Inner	3.031"	2.031"	77.2
Outer	3.406"	2.156"	99
ENDT673C			
Inner	3.031"	2.031"	77.2
Outer	3.406"	2.156"	99
ENDT673E			
Inner	3.031"	2.031"	77.2
Outer	3.406"	2.156"	99
ENDT/B675			
Inner	3.031"	2.031"	77.2
Outer	3.406"	2.156"	99
ENDT/B676			
Inner	3.031"	2.031"	77.2
Outer	3.406"	2.156"	99
END707			
Inner	3.031"	2.156"	77.2
Outer	3.406"	2.156"	99
ENDT/B865	3.125"	2.563"	90
ENDT/B866	3.125"	2.563"	90

CYLINDER LINER & BORE			
Engine	Type	Liner Bore	Liner Protrusion
END475	Dry	4.5270"	.0027-.0040"
ENDT475	Dry	4.5270"	.0027-.0040"
ENDT673	Dry	4.8670-4.8770"	.0035-.0075"
ENDT673C	Dry	4.8670-4.8770"	.0035-.0075"
ENDT673E	Dry	4.8670-4.8770"	.0035-.0075"
ENDT/B675	Dry	4.8670-4.8770"	.0035-.0075"
ENDT/B676	Dry	4.8760-4.8770"	.0035-.0075"
END707	Dry	5.0010-5.0020"	.0035-.0075"
ENDT/B865	Wet	5.2415-5.2425"	.0005-.0045"
ENDT/B866	Wet	5.2415-5.2425"	.0005-.0045"

CONNECTING RODS & BEARINGS			
Engine	Journal Diameter	Bearing Clearance	Sideplay
END475	2.9510"	.0020-.0040"	.008-.010"
ENDT475	2.9510"	.0020-.0040"	.008-.010"
ENDT673	2.9970-2.9980"	.0011-.0036"	.006-.012"
ENDT673C	2.9970-2.9980"	.0011-.0036"	.006-.012"
ENDT673E	2.9970-2.9980"	.0011-.0036"	.006-.012"
ENDT/B675	2.9970-2.9980"	.0011-.0036"	.006-.012"
ENDT/B676	2.9970-2.9980"	.0011-.0039"	.007-.012"
END707	2.9970-2.9980"	.0011-.0031"	.007-.012"
ENDT/B865	3.7470-3.7480"	.0016-.0046"	.007-.0015"
ENDT/B866	3.7470-3.7480"	.0016-.0046"	.007-.015"

Medium & Heavy Duty Diesel
MACK (Cont.)

CRANKSHAFT & MAIN BEARINGS						
Engine	Journal Diameter	Bearing Clearance	Crankshaft End Play	Thrust Location	Thrust Washer Thickness	Number of Main Bearings
END475	3.3465"	.0020-.0045"	.002-.010"	No.7	.....	7
ENDT475	3.3465"	.0020-.0045"	.002-.010"	No.7	.....	7
ENDT673①	3.9980-3.9990"	.0020-.0050"	.004-.010"	No.4	.090-.103"	7
ENDT/B675	3.9980-3.9990"	.0020-.0050"	.004-.010"	No.4	.090-.103"	7
ENDT/B676	3.9980-3.9990"	.0020-.0050"	.004-.010"	No.4	.090-.103"	7
END707	3.9980-3.9990"	.0020-.0050"	.004-.010"	No.4	.090-.103"	7
ENDT/B865	3.9980-3.9990"	.0026-.0056"	.004-.010"	No.3	.....	5
ENDT/B866	3.9980-3.9990"	.0026-.0056"	.004-.010"	No.3	.....	5

① — ENDT673 E&C Models have same specifications.

PISTONS, PINS, RINGS						
	PISTONS	PINS		RINGS		
Engine	Clearance	Piston Fit	Rod Fit	Rings	End Gap	Side Clearance
END475	.0060"	.0015-.0050"	.0005-.0015"	1	.020-.028"	①
				2	.012-.024"	.0025"
				3	.012-.024"	.0020"
				4	.012-.024"	.0016"
				5	.012-.024"	.0016"
ENDT475	.0060"	.0015-.0050"	.0005-.0015"	1	.020-.028"	①
				2	.012-.024"	.0025"
				3	.012-.024"	.0020"
				4	.012-.024"	.0016"
				5	.012-.024"	.0016"
ENDT673	.0075-.0085"	.0003"	.0011-.0016"	1	.013-.025"	①
				2	.013-.025"	①
				3	.013-.025"	.0020-.0060"
				4	.013-.025"	.0010-.0045"
ENDT673C	.0075-.0085"	.0003"	.0011-.0016"	1	.013-.025"	①
				2	.013-.025"	①
				3	.013-.025"	.0020-.0060"
				4	.013-.025"	.0010-.0045"
ENDT673E	.0075-.0085"	.0003"	.0011-.0016"	1	.013-.025"	①
				2	.013-.025"	①
				3	.013-.025"	.0020-.0060"
				4	.013-.025"	.0010-.0045"
ENDT/B675	.0075-.0085"	.0003"	.0011-.0016"	1	.013-.025"	①
				2	.013-.025"	①
				3	.013-.025"	.0020-.0060"
				4	.013-.025"	.0010-.0045"
ENDT/B676	.0015-.0060"	.0011-.0039"	.0011-.0016"	1	.013-.025"	.0057"
				2	.013-.025"	.0052"
				3	.013-.025"	.0015-.0035"
END707	.0090-.0100"	.0001-.0002"	.0008-.0012"	1	.013-.025"	①
				2	.013-.025"	①
				3	.013-.025"	①
				4	.013-.025"	.0010-.0045"
ENDT/B865	.0080"	.0004-.0007"	.0008-.0055"	1	.020-.030"	.0060"
				2	.020-.030"	.0060"
				3	.016-.026"	.0060"
				4	.018-.028"	.0040-.0050"

① — Ring should be snug in groove with no visible side play.

MACK (Cont.)

OIL PUMP SPECIFICATIONS

END475, ENDT475

```
Type ............................................. Rotor
Clearance Bushing-to-Inner Rotor Shaft ..... .0015-.0025"
Drive Gear-to-Idler Gear Backlash ............ .0020-.0040"
Idler Gear-to-Crankshaft Gear Backlash .... .0020-.0040"

Type ............................................. Gear
Clearance Pump Gear-to-Housing ............ .0020-.0040"
```

ENDT673, ENDT673C, ENDT673E ENDT/B675

```
Type ............................................. Gear
Clearance Gear-to-Side, Cavity ................ .0035-.0060"
Clearance Gear-to-Cover ....................... .0025-.0050"
Pump Gear Backlash ........................... .0235-.0295"
Pump Gear-to-Pump Driven Gear Backlash  .0072-.0138"
Pump Spring
   Compressed Length @40 lbs. ................ 3.078"
   Free Length ................................. 3.875"
Pressure Relief Valve Opening ........... 65-100psi
```

ENDT/B676

```
Type ............................................. Gear
Clearance Gear-to-Side, Cavity ................ .0035-.0060"
Clearance Gear-to-Cover ....................... .0025-.0050"
Pump Gear Backlash ........................... .0235-.0295"
Pump Gear-to-Pump Driven Gear Backlash  .0072-.0138"
Pump Spring
   Compressed Length @40 lbs. ................ 3.078"
   Free Length ................................. 3.469"
Pressure Relief Valve Opening ........... 65-100psi
```

END707

```
Type ............................................. Gear
Clearance Gear-to-Housing Side ............... .0025-.0045"
Clearance Gear-to-Housing End ............... .0015-.0020"
Gear Backlash ............................... .0270"max
Pump Spring
   Compressed Length @40 lbs. ................ 3.078"
   Free Length ................................. 3.469"
```

ENDT/B865, ENDT/B866

```
Type ............................................. Gear
Drive Gear-to-Idler Gear Backlash ............ .0050-.0070"
Clearance Gear-to-Housing Cover ............ .0025-.0050"
Clearance Gear-to-Side, Cavity ............... .0035-.0060"
Pump Gear Backlash ........................... .0250-.0290"
Idler Gear-to-Crankshaft Gear Backlash .... .0032-.0058"
Idler Gear Bushing Bore ..................... 1.0015-1.0025"
Idler Gear End Clearance .................... .0015-.0040"
Pump Spring
   Compressed Length @72.75 lbs. ............ 3.085"
   Free Length ................................. 4.275"
Relief Valve Spring
   Compressed Length @29.7 lbs. ............. 3.875"
   Free Length ................................. 4.875"
```

TIGHTENING SPECIFICATIONS

NOTE — *Use minimum two steps to torque all nuts and bolts.*

END475, ENDT475

Application	Ft. Lbs.
Cylinder Head Nuts①	140
Main Bearing Cap Nuts	150
Connecting Rod Bearing Cap Bolts	80
Vibration Damper-to-Crankshaft	542
Camshaft Gear Retaining Nut	220
Flywheel Bolts	149

① — See cylinder head tightening sequence.

ENDT673, ENDT673C, ENDT673E ENDT/B675

Application	Ft. Lbs.
Cylinder Head Nuts①	175
Main Bearing Cap Bolts	
11/16" Bolt	200
5/8" Bolt	150
Connecting Rod Bearing Cap Bolts	150
Vibration Damper-to-Crankshaft	300
Flywheel Bolts	150-175

① — See cylinder head tightening sequence.

ENDT/B676

Application	Ft. Lbs.
Cylinder Head Nuts①	175
Main Bearing Cap Bolts	
11/16" Bolt	200
5/8" Bolt	150
Connecting Rod Bearing Cap Bolts	150
Vibration Damper-to-Crankshaft	300
Flywheel Bolts	150

① — See cylinder head tightening sequence.

END707

Application	Ft. Lbs.
Cylinder Head Nuts①	175
Main Bearing Cap Bolts	200
Connecting Rod Bearing Cap Bolts	150
Vibration Damper-to-Crankshaft	275
Flywheel Bolts	150-175

① — See cylinder head tightening sequence.

ENDT/B865, ENDT/B866

Application	Ft. Lbs.
Cylinder Head Bolts①	225
Main Bearing Cap Bolts	350
Connecting Rod Bearing Cap Bolts	150
Vibration Damper-to-Crankshaft	300
Flywheel Bolts	150

① — See cylinder tightening sequence.

Medium & Heavy Duty Diesel
MACK (Cont.)

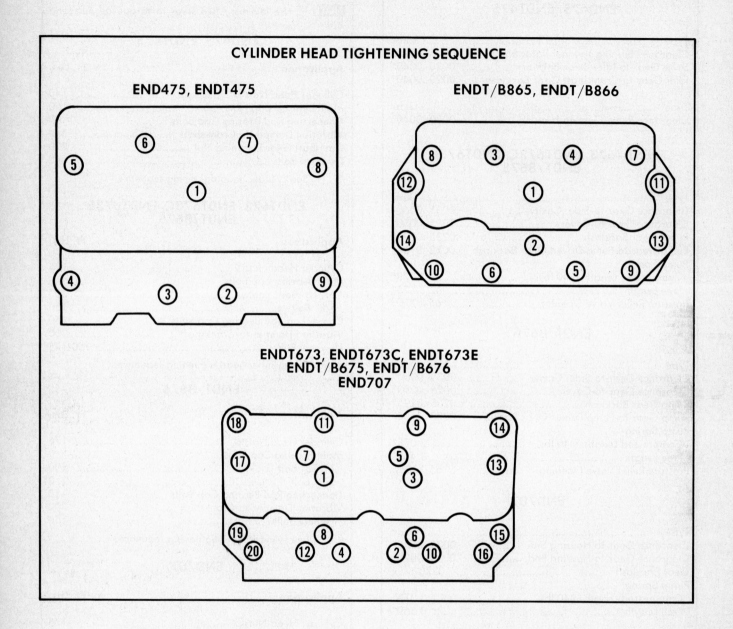

CYLINDER HEAD TIGHTENING SEQUENCE

END475, ENDT475

ENDT/B865, ENDT/B866

ENDT673, ENDT673C, ENDT673E
ENDT/B675, ENDT/B676
END707

Medium & Heavy Duty Diesel
PERKINS

GENERAL SPECIFICATIONS

Engine	Cycle	Displ. Cu. Ins.	Compr. Ratio	Bore	Stroke	Firing Order	Inj. Timing ①
6-354	4	354"	16.0:1	3.875"	5.00"	1,5,3,6,2,4	24.0°

① — Unless noted otherwise, all Injection Timing is BTDC.

NORMAL OPERATING SPECIFICATIONS

Engine	Idle RPM	Max. RPM	Oil Temp.	Oil Press.	Coolant Temp.	Compression Pressure (PSI) @ RPM (Sea Level)
6-354	500-550	3100	.....	25-50	.....	430@375

VALVES & SEATS

Engine	Head Diameter	Face Angle	Seat Angle	Seat Width	Stem Diameter	Stem Clearance	Valve Seat Insert O.D.	Valve Clearance
6-354 Int.	.....	45°	45°	.094"	.3725-.3735"	.0015-.0035"	.....	.010"
Exh.	.....	45°	45°	.109"	.3720-.3730"	.0020-.0040"	.....	.010"

VALVE SPRINGS

Engine	Free Length	Compressed Length	Lbs. @ Comp. Length
6-354 Inner	.....	1.5625"	13.4-17.4
Outer	.....	1.7800"	38-42

CAMSHAFT

Engine	Journal Diam.	Clearance	Lobe Lift
6-354		①.0025-.0055"	.3005-.3035"
No.1	1.9965-1.9975"		
No.2	1.9865-1.9875"		
No.3	1.9765-1.9775"		
No.4	1.9665-1.9675"		

① — No. 1 journal only is .0025-.0045".

ROCKER ARMS & VALVE BRIDGES

Engine	Rocker Shaft O.D.	Rocker Arm I.D.	Rocker Arm Clearance	Bridge Guide O.D.	Bridge I.D.	Bridge Height Above Head
6-354	.7485-.7495"	.7505-.7520"	.0010-.0035"	.....	.....	.....

Medium & Heavy Duty Diesel
PERKINS (Cont.)

CRANKSHAFT & MAIN BEARINGS

Engine	Journal Diameter	Bearing Clearance	Crankshaft End Play	Thrust Location	Thrust Washer Thickness	Number of Main Bearings
6-354	2.9985-2.9990"	.0025-.0045"	.002-.014"	4	.089-.091"	7

PISTONS, PINS, RINGS

Engine	PISTONS Clearance	PINS Piston Fit	PINS Rod Fit	RINGS Rings	RINGS End Gap	RINGS Side Clearance
6-354	.0059-.0074"	Push Fit	.00075-.00170"	1	.015-.019"	.0019-.0039"
				2	.011-.016"	.0019-.0039"
				3	.011-.016"	.0019-.0039"
				4	.011-.016"	.0025-.0045"
				5	.011-.016"	.0025-.0045"

CYLINDER LINER & BORE

Engine	Type	Liner Bore	Liner Protrusion
6-354	Dry	3.8770-3.8785"	①.030-.035"

① Engine No. 8123411 is flush to .010" below face of block.

CONNECTING RODS & BEARINGS

Engine	Journal Diameter	Bearing Clearance	Sideplay
6-354	2.4990-2.4995"	.0015-.0030"	.0095-.0130"

OIL PUMP SPECIFICATIONS

Type	Rotor
Outer Rotor Diameter	2.2530-2.2540"
Rotor Shaft Bore Diameter	.6875-.6885"
Rotor Shaft Diameter	.6855-.6860"
Shaft Clearance	.0015-.0030"
Rotor Depth	2.1250-2.1260"
Clearance Between Inner and Outer Rotors	.0040"
Rotor End Clearance	.0025"

TIGHTENING SPECIFICATIONS

Application	Ft. Lbs.
Cylinder Head Nuts①	
7/16"	55-60
1/2"	75-80
Main Bearing Cap Bolts	145-150
Connecting Rod Cap Nuts	65-70
Flywheel-to-Crankshaft Bolts	75
Crankshaft End Bolt	250

① — See cylinder head tightening sequence.

CYLINDER HEAD TIGHTENING SEQUENCE

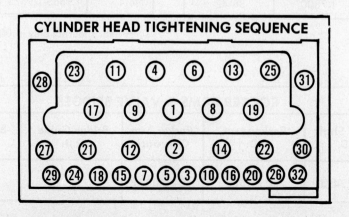

Notes

Notes

Notes

Notes

Notes

Notes

Notes

Latest Changes & Corrections

FOR 1983 & EARLIER MODELS

NOTE: The Latest Changes and Corrections represent a collection of last minute 1983 information which arrived too late to be included into the regular data pages. In addition, we have included information on prior year models which we have received since last year's edition.

TUNE-UP
SECTION 1

FORD MOTOR CO.

1. 1983 FORD RANGER WITH 2.0 & 2.3L ENGINES AND ALL CALIBRATIONS EXCEPT 3-41P-R15: ENGINE LOADING, BLACK SMOKE AND ROUGH RUNNING DURING COLD DRIVE — Complaints about loading on cold driveaway can be fixed by changing the choke setting to one notch leaner than the original production setting. The Carter YFA carburetor employs an index plate to determine choke setting. The following chart should be used for identifying the indexing plate and the original setting.

CARTER YFA CHOKE IDENTIFICATION

Color	Setting	Part No.
Orange	Index	E3PZ-9A539-C
Gray	1NR	E3PZ-9A539-F
Yellow	2NR	E3PZ-9A539-A
Green	3NR	E3PZ-9A539-G
Black	4NR	E3PZ-9A539-B

For example, if the original index plate is a Yellow (2NR), the change would be to a Gray (1NR).

After determining the correct index plate, remove and replace the existing choke plate with the corrected plate.

2. 1983 FORD "E" AND "F" SERIES TRUCKS WITH 6.9L DIESEL ENGINE: DIESEL DYNAMIC TIMING PROBE — The following information details the installation of the magnetic timing pick-up into the holding tube, and also servicing for a missing or loose engine timing quadrant holding tube.

Installing Magnetic Pick-Up

When installing the magnetic pick-up into the holding tube in the timing quadrant, the pick-up must be inserted until it contacts the vibration damper. If the end of the pick-up is not close enough to the damper, no reading will be obtained. Pick-up should be within .015" of damper.

The snap ring on the pick-up probe must be inside of the timing quadrant. If the snap ring will not enter the holding tube, replace it with a rubber "O" ring.

Missing Timing Holding Tube

1) If the magnetic timing probe holding tube is loose or breaks off, the tube can be reinstalled and brazed in place.

2) If the tube is missing or heavily damaged, the zero offset hole (.375" at TDC) can be used for the magnetic timing pick-up as follows:

3) Wrap tape around the pick-up until it is a snug fit in the zero offset hole. Install the luminosity probe into no. 8 cylinder instead of no. 1 cylinder.

4) Set the timing meter for minus 90° instead of minus 20°. Meter readings set at this position on no. 8 cylinder will be the same as those set at minus 20° in no. 1 cylinder.

GENERAL MOTORS

3. 1982 GENERAL MOTORS TRUCKS WITH 6.2L DIESEL ENGINES: OIL FILL RATE — Engine damage could occur on these models when using a power fill method of adding engine oil if the fill rate is too fast. Since the 6.2L lubrication system is a closed system, the rate of fill must be limited to prevent oil being drawn into the intake manifold and cylinder through the crankcase ventilation system. Engine damage can occur if oil enters the cylinders.

Do not exceed an oil fill rate of 7 qts. in 2 minutes. Also, remove the oil level dipstick during filling operation, and ensure that dipstick is seated when replacing. Depending upon ambient temperature and the viscosity of the oil being used, adjustments to fill equipment pressure may be required to limit flow rate.

4. 1981-82 GENERAL MOTORS TRUCKS WITH 5.0L LE9 ENGINES AND ELECTRONIC SPARK CONTROL: ABNORMAL COMBUSTION — Some vehicles may experience preignition or poor performance under moderately severe conditions. As a result of the preignition, the ESC retards the spark timing giving a marked loss of power and reduction of performance. The preignition may not be corrected by the spark retard, and continued operation could cause internal engine damage. To reduce the chances of this happening, the spark plugs should be changed to a colder heat range type. A/C R44TS spark plugs are recommended for use.

JEEP

5. 1981-83 JEEP MODELS WITH 6-CYLINDER ENGINES AND COMPUTERIZED ENGINE CONTROLS: SERPENTINE DRIVE BELTS — The serpentine drive belt used on some of these models can be expected to develop some random cracks in one or more of the belt ribs during the life of the belt. These random cracks are a normal development during the latter part of the belt's life. The cracks do not affect the belt performance and improve flexibility. The only time belt replacement is warranted for cracks is when the cracks are at or near the full depth of the belt, or if the cracks run parallel to the belt ribs.

COMPUTERIZED ENGINE CONTROLS
SECTION 1A

CHRYSLER CORP.

1. 1981 CHRYSLER CORP. FEDERAL TRUCKS WITH 5.2L ENGINE AND 2-BBL. CARBURETOR: SPARK KNOCK — Some of these models may develop a spark knock during light acceleration. This may be caused by too much vacuum being applied to the vacuum transducer.

Latest Changes & Corrections

FOR 1983 & EARLIER MODELS (Cont.)

This allows the fuel control computer to advance ignition timing, creating a spark knock problem. This can be corrected by installing a field fix package (4240177) as follows:

1) Locate the vacuum hose that leads to the fuel control computer. Remove a 2" section of hose about 4" from the computer.

2) Install the vacuum reducer valve from the kit with the vent end of the valve toward the computer.

3) Install a new vacuum hsse routing label over the old one. Road test the vehicle to ensure the problem has been corrected.

FUEL SYSTEMS SECTION 2

CHRYSLER CORP.

1️⃣ 1982 CHRYSLER CORP. TRUCKS AND VANS WITH 3.7L ENGINES: FAILED POWER VALVE VACUUM DIAPHRAGM — If a vehicle shows increased fuel consumption, develops a miss at idle and has a sooty No. 6 spark plug, if may be caused by a failed power valve vacuum diaphragm.

Using a hand vacuum pump, apply vacuum to the power valve external nipple on carburetor air horn. Vacuum should hold. If diaphragm will not hold vacuum, it should be replaced as outlined.

1) Remove carburetor air horn. Remove 2 screws on diaphragm retainer. Remove old diaphragm, being careful not to lose the spring under the diaphragm.

2) Install new diaphragm (4131115), being sure to install spring under diaphragm. Repeat vacuum test on new diaphragm. It should hold vacuum.

3) Replace carburetor air horn using new gasket (4186146). Be careful when inserting accelerator pump in pump well as this causes fuel to raise accelerator pump check ball and weight which may be trapped between air horn and main body.

4) Remove and discard the external vacuum hose from air horn to vacuum tee on No. 6 runner of intake manifold. Use a 3/16" rubber cap to plug nipple.

5) Cut vacuum hose at base of carburetor 1 1/2" from from carburetor flange end. This section of hose also supplies vacuum to choke vacuum kick diaphragm and EGR amplifier.

6) Install a vacuum tee in hose just cut. Cut a 16" length of 5/16" vacuum hose and install it between the vacuum tee and air horn vacuum nipple.

7) Check action of throttle linkage and choke linkage before starting engine. Start engine and check for proper operation. It may be necessary to reset idle speed.

FORD MOTOR CO.

2️⃣ 1982 FORD "F" SERIES TRUCKS: CARBURETORS WITH PASSENGER CAR FLOAT SYSTEMS — A number of light truck carburetors (E2TE-9150-BAA) with build codes L2G28 and L2G29 were built with passenger car short floats, instead of truck long floats. The inlet system components affected are the float, damper spring, float retainer and air horn gasket. Identical parts must be used when servicing these carburetors. Correct part numbers are listed below.

1982 "F" SERIES CARBURETOR PARTS

Part	Part No.
Float Assembly	D9AZ-9550-B
Damper Spring	E2TZ-9F570-A
Air Horn Gasket	E2ZZ-9561-B
Float Retainer	D9AZ-9599-A

3️⃣ 1980-83 FORD "E" AND "F" MODELS OVER 8500 GVW WITH ELECTRIC FUEL PUMPS: SPECIAL FUEL HOSE MATERIAL — Fuel hoses on models with electric fuel pumps are made of a special fluro-elastomer material that provides longer life when used in the vapor return system. Any service replacement of this hose must be made with the same type of hose. Hose that is 5/16" in diameter and Yellow striped is part number E0TZ-9324-A, and 3/8" hose with Red stripe is part number E0TZ-9324-B.

GENERAL MOTORS

4️⃣ 1982-83 GENERAL MOTORS TRUCKS WITH 6.2L DIESEL ENGINES: FUEL INJECTION NOZZLE USAGE — Because of design changes between 1982 and 1983 diesel fuel injection nozzles, care should be used when replacing these nozzles. Nozzles released for 1983 are similar in appearance to 1982 nozzles, except that 1983 nozzles have a fine thread pitch instead of a coarse pitch. Also, a new shorter nozzle is used on "G" model vans.

General Motors 6.2L Diesel Injection Nozzles

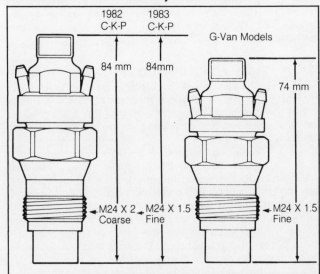

EMISSION CONTROL SECTION 3

FORD MOTOR CO.

1️⃣ ALL FORD LIGHT TRUCKS WITH 4.9L ENGINES: HEAVY WHITE SMOKE FROM EXHAUST — A heavy white smoke from exhaust may appear during extended idle after a stabilized drive period. This may be

FOR 1983 & EARLIER MODELS (Cont.)

caused by the thermactor air system not venting the thermactor air during extended idle (more than 150 seconds). This causes catalyst to burn off fuel residue, producing white smoke. Correct as follows:

1) Check that all vacuum lines are properly routed, connections are secure and hoses are not crimped or broken.

2) With engine at normal operating temperature and transmission in Neutral, accelerate to about 1500 RPM, then return to idle and begin timing.

3) If, after 150 seconds, the thermactor by-pass valve vents, the thermactor system is okay.

4) If thermactor does not vent, remove the Red/White delay valve and the in-line vacuum reservoir.

5) Check vacuum system to thermactor by-pass valve for vacuum to ensure there is no blockage.

6) Replace vacuum delay valve with new valve (D8AZ-9E487-B). Eliminate the vacuum reservoir and replace it with a 7/32" vacuum line and a 1/4" X 1/4" connector. Do not re-use the short vacuum hose.

7) Install a fuel vacuum separator assembly (D4FZ-9C369-A) at the third port of the carburetor. With all steps completed, re-test system to ensure proper function of by-pass valve.

2▷ 1983 FORD RANGER WITH MCU ENGINE CONTROL SYSTEM: EXHAUST SYSTEM RATTLE — Exhaust system rattles on these models may be caused by a broken Managed Thermactor Air (MTA) tube support bracket at catayltic converter inlet pipe. The following

"L" Bracket Dimensions for 1983 Ranger

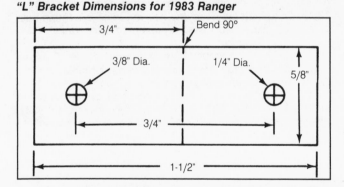

procedures explain the fabrication of a new support bracket to replace a broken one.

1) Fabricate an "L" bracket from 1/8" metal stock to the dimensions shown in the illustration.

2) Loosely assemble the fabricated bracket and pipe clamp to the MTA tube as shown in the illustration. The MTA tube clamp at catalytic converter may have to be loosened to achieve proper fit.

3) Tighten clamp and bracket bolt when proper alignment is achieved.

"L" Bracket Installation on 1983 Ranger

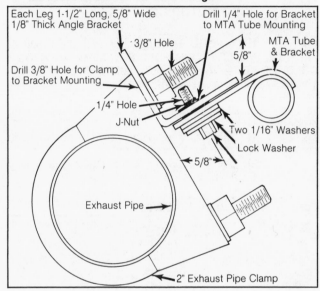

GENERAL MOTORS

3▷ 1982 GENERAL MOTORS "S" MODEL TRUCKS WITH 2.8L V6 ENGINES: AIR SYSTEM NOISE — Some models may exhibit a noise coming from the AIR system check valve. To correct this, a new check valve (22035420) is available which has a thinner valve spring which opens at a lower flow rate than previous valves. This valve will eliminate the noise. Federal vehicles require 2 check valves, California models require 1 valve.

ELECTRICAL SECTION 4

CHRYSLER CORP.

1▷ 1982 CHRYSLER CORP.: DISTRIBUTOR SPECIFICATIONS — A revision has been made to the

1982 distributor specifications listed for Chrysler Corp. The 1982 specifications were provided at distributor RPM, rather than engine RPM. In the table below, distributor specifications have been adjusted.

CHRYSLER CORP. DISTRIBUTOR ADVANCE SPECIFICATIONS
FOR DISTRIBUTOR RPM AND DEGREES, DIVIDE SPECIFICATIONS BY 2

Distributor Part No.	Rot.[1]	AUTOMATIC ADVANCE (Engine Degrees & RPM)						VACUUM ADVANCE (Engine Deg.)			
		Deg.	RPM	Deg.	RPM	Deg.	RPM	Deg.	In. Hg	Deg.	In. Hg
4091661	C	3-6	1100	11-15	1700	22-26	4000	1-4	14	12-16	30
4111501	C	1-3	1400	3-7	1800	15-20	4400	2-5	14	20-24	30
4111950	C	1-5	1300	5-9	1800	16-20	4400	2-5	14	20-24	30
4145602	C	1-5	1800	5-7	2400	11-15	4400	0-2	12	20-24	26
4145751	C	Electronic Spark Advance									

[1] — C=Clockwise, as viewed from rotor end.

FOR 1983 & EARLIER MODELS (Cont.)

▷2️⃣ **1979-82 CHRYSLER CORP. "B" MODEL VANS AND WAGONS: RECURRING NO START CONDITION —** This condition may be caused by an inoperative starter relay. Inspect the relay for icing of the relay contacts or internal corrosion, and replace as required. After replacement, install a starter splash shield (4289138) to prevent failure from reoccuring.

Splash shield is designed to fit over relay housing flange. To install, press relay wiring back against engine compartment dash panel and install shield. Ensure relay shield fully engages relay housing flange.

FORD MOTOR CO.

▷3️⃣ **1983 FORD RANGER WITH 2.0L ENGINE: LACK OF POWER, POOR FUEL ECONOMY AND POOR COLD DRIVE —** Vehicles built before September 27, 1982 may exhibit these symptoms. This can be caused by the distributor mechanical advance. The following in-vehicle test will determine if distributor is functioning properly.

1) Remove and plug vacuum hose which connects to the distributor diaphragm.

2) Using a timing light, check the timing advance at the limits shown in the table.

FORD RANGER TIMING ADVANCE

Engine RPM	Nominal Advance	[1] Tolerance
1000	8°	4°-12°
1500	14°	10°-18°
2000	16°	12°-20°
3000	23°	19°-27°
4000	28°	24°-32°

[1] — Plus or minus 4°.

3) If centrifugal advance is not functioning, replace distributor (E27E-12127-BA) with a new distributor (E3TZ-12127-B).

▷4️⃣ **1981-83 FORD LIGHT TRUCKS WITH EEC-III, 5.0 AND 5.8L ENGINES: DISTRIBUTOR ROTOR ALIGNMENT —** The following procedure clarifies the proper setting of distributor rotor alignment on these vehicles. 1981-83 vehicles with 5.0L engines use a second generation type rotor, while all others use a conventional type rotor.

Rotor Alignment

1) Remove distributor cap and wires and set aside. Remove rotor.

2) Rotate engine until No. 1 piston is on compression stroke. Alignment tool (T79P-12200-A) mounts between the slot on the distributor sleeve and the cut outs on the adapter.

3) Slowly rotate engine until the alignment tool can be installed. With tool installed, read the timing mark on the damper indicated by the timing pointer.

4) If timing reads TDC plus or minus 4°, rotor alignment is satisfactory.

Adjusting Rotor Alignment

1) Remove distributor cap and rotor. Rotate engine so No. 1 piston is on compression stroke.

2) Slowly rotate engine until timing pointer is aligned with TDC plus or minus 4°.

3) Loosen 2 sleeve adjusting screws and rotate sleeve until alignment tool fits into slots in sleeve and adapter.

4) Tighten adjustment screws and remove alignment tool. On 1983 models with conventional rotor, coat top, bottom and edges of rotor blade tip with silicone grease.

5) Reinstall rotor and distributor cap ensuring that wires are firmly seated in cap and on plugs.

▷5️⃣ **1983 FORD F250/350 WITH 6.9L DIESEL ENGINE: BATTERY OVERCHARGING OR DISCHARGING —** A discharged battery or overcharged voltage regulator may be caused by improper installation of the voltage regulator ground screw. The wiring harness has a ground connection for the voltage regulator that is retained by a screw.

The location of the ground connection is on the component platform in the right hand side of the engine compartment. A loose or missing screw may cause the voltage regulator to fail resulting in overcharging with engine running or battery discharge with engine off. Check ground screw for tightness, or if missing, replace screw.

▷6️⃣ **1983 FORD RANGER WITH MANUAL A/C-HEATER SYSTEMS: PUSH BUTTON A/C CONTROL LIGHT BULB REPLACEMENT —** Rangers with manual A/C use a push button with a small light bulb (D3TZ-13466-B) to indicate when the A/C is turned on. If this bulb burns out, use the following replacement procedure.

Removal

1) Disconnect battery ground cable. Remove radio control knobs. Remove 4 screws attaching top of cluster finish panel to upper finish panel pad.

2) Remove cigar lighter and center and left instrument panel trim. Pull headlamp switch to "ON" position and detach left instrument panel trim enough to allow access to cluster finish panel lower attaching screw.

3) Remove 4 screws attaching bottom of cluster finish panel to instrument panel. Lift cluster finish panel away from instrument panel.

4) Remove 4 screws attaching control assembly to instrument panel. Pull control assembly out from instrument panel opening.

5) Rotate bulb plastic base 1/8 turn counterclockwise and lift bulb and base from push button switch. Note routing of bulb wires. Unthread bulb wires from plastic base.

Installation

1) Install bulb in plastic base. Insert bulb and base in push button switch and rotate to lock base in switch. Position control assembly into instrument panel opening and install 4 screws.

2) Install cluster finish panel and 8 screws. Install instrument panel trim by aligning guide pins and snapping retainers into instrument panel attaching holes.

3) Install cigar lighter and radio knobs. Connect battery ground cable. Check A/C-Heater for proper operation. Verify light bulb glows when A/C button is depressed.

FOR 1983 & EARLIER MODELS (Cont.)

7▷ 1982 GENERAL MOTORS CORP.: DISTRIBUTOR SPECIFICATIONS — A revision has been made to the 1982 distributor specifications listed for Delco-Remy (GMC). The 1982 specifications were provided at distributor RPM, rather than engine RPM. In the table below, distributor specifications have been adjusted.

DELCO-REMY (GMC) DISTRIBUTOR ADVANCE SPECIFICATIONS
FOR DISTRIBUTOR RPM AND DEGREES, DIVIDE SPECIFICATIONS BY 2

Distributor [1] Part No.	Rot.[2]	AUTOMATIC ADVANCE (Engine Degrees & RPM)						VACUUM ADVANCE (Engine Deg.)			
		Deg.	RPM	Deg.	RPM	Deg.	RPM	Deg.	In. Hg	Deg.	In. Hg
1103353	CC	0-8	1300	14-18	2400	20-24	4600	0	6-12	20	18-24
1103375	CC	0-6	1400	14-18	2400	20-24	4200	0	6-12	10	14-18
1103376	CC	0-6	1400	12-16	2400	18-22	4200	0	14-18	10	24-28
1103420	CC	0-6	2000	.....	.....	22-26	4000	0	18-22	10	24-28
1103433	CC	0-8	1300	14-18	2400	20-24	4600	0	6-12	24	20-26
1103435	CC	0-8	1300	14-18	2400	20-24	4600	0	4-8	16	10-14
1103436	CC	0-8	1300	14-18	2400	20-24	4600	0	4-8	20	12-18
1103481	CC	0-4	1400	6-10	2000	18-22	4200	0	4-8	16	10-14
1103482	CC	0-4	1400	6-10	2000	18-22	4200	0	4-8	24	14-18
1103483	CC	0-4	1400	6-10	2000	18-22	4200	0	4-8	20	12-18
1103484	CC	0-4	1400	6-10	2000	18-22	4200	0	4-8	12	10-14
1103487	CC	0-4	1200	8-12	2000	12-16	4000	0	4-8	10	10-14
1103488	CC	0-4	1400	6-10	2000	18-22	4200	0	6-10	14	14-18
1110581	C	0	900	14	2200	22	4800	0	3	20	6.5
1110582	C	0	1650	6	2200	14	4800	0	3	20	6.5
1110583 [3]	C	.....						.....	.....	.....	.....
1110598	CC	0-4	1600	4-10	2400	12-16	4000	0	4-8	20	14-18
1110753	CC	0-6	1300	12-18	2400	22-26	4100	0	6-12	10	14-18
1111388	CC	0-6	1300	12-16	2400	22-26	4100	0	4-8	20	12-18

[1] — Part numbers apply to Chevrolet and GMC except for 1110598, used on Jeep 2.5L 4-cylinder engine.
[2] — C=Clockwise; CC=Counterclockwise, as viewed from rotor end.
[3] — HEI-EST distributor does not use vacuum or centrifugal advance mechanisms.

ACCESSORIES & EQUIPMENT SECTION 6

FORD MOTOR CO.

1▷ 1983 FORD "F" SERIES TRUCKS WITH 5.8L ENGINE AND OPTIONAL GAUGE PACKAGE: NO START CONDITION — On models with EEC built before October 11, 1982, a no start condition may be caused by a shorted oil pressure sender switch wire. Service as follows:

1) Inspect the oil pressure sender switch wire located in the left front area of the engine for evidence of chafing on the left exhaust manifold.

2) If the wire is chafed and is shorting through the exhaust manifold, replace the wire and install a tie strap on the wire to prevent the chafing.

3) The tie strap should hold the wire to either the power steering or idler arm bracket.

ENGINES SECTION 7

CHRYSLER CORP.

1▷ 1974-83 CHRYSLER CORP. TRUCKS WITH 3.7L ENGINE: NODULAR IRON EXHAUST MANIFOLD — A new nodular iron exhaust manifold has been released for heavy duty usage on these engines. Manifold can be identified by a triangular identification mark cast into manifold as shown in the illustration.

Chrysler 3.7L Engine Exhaust Manifold Identification

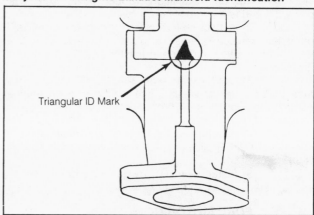

Triangular ID Mark

2▷ 1981-82 CHRYSLER CORP. TRUCKS WITH 3.7L ENGINES: CRANKSHAFT REAR OIL SEAL SERVICING — Crankshaft oil leaks are sometimes difficult to locate on these engines without proper diagnosis. When a leak is suspected, an air test should always be performed to verify location and condition before disassembly. Air tests can be performed as follows:

Leak Test & Seal Removal

1) Use only regulated air adjusted to 4 psi. Do not use regular shop air. Remove crankcase vent valve and cap and plug holes in rocker cover.

2) Remove dipstick. Install a rubber hose to air source and insert hose in dipstick tube. Raise vehicle and remove torque converters or clutch housing cover.

3) Inspect rear of block for evidence of leak. Leakage between rear seal and crank will spray oil in a circular pattern. Leakage from retainer side seals, retainer joint face or around back side of rear seal will tend to run straight down. Other leak paths are porous block iron and rear cam and gallery plugs.

4) Apply air to crankcase while inspecting rear seal area. If leakage is detected, it could be the seal or seal retainer. If no leaks are detected, slowly rotate crank and watch for leakage.

5) If leakage is now detected, crankshaft seal surface is damaged or scratched. Remove air source and remove oil pan.

6) If no leaks are detected with this test, pressurizing the lubrication system is the other method of detecting leaks.

7) With oil pan removed, carefully remove the rear seal retainer. Inspect the retainer for proper sealing of the sides and for correct orientation of the half-round seal. If leak was evident only when crank was rotated, inspect crank for nicks, scratches or cuts in seal area. Minor nicks and scratches can be polished out with emery cloth.

8) Thoroughly clean all old sealer from seal retainer and block. Remove upper half of seal from block. If seal was in backward, this could cause leaks. Check back of seal. If seal was cut or rubber peeled off during installation, this could cause leaks.

Seal Installation

1) Install upper half of seal in block. Make sure stripe on seal is to rear of engine. Make a tool out of plastic to protect back of seal against block surface during installation. If, on installation, rubber peels from seal, discard it and use another new seal.

2) Inspect seal retainer for damage or flaws. If damaged, replace retainer. Apply a 1/8" bead of RTV in bottom of groove, starting and finishing 1/2" from ends of groove.

3) Install lower seal half. Color stripe should face toward rear of vehicle. Install side seal on retainer using Super Bonder (4057988). Apply RTV sealer to top of retainer. DO NOT apply to seal lip surface.

4) Carefully install retainer and seal within 10 minutes of RTV application. Tighten bolts to 30 ft. lbs. (40 N.m).

5) Install new oil pan gasket and oil pan. Fill with oil, start engine and check for leaks.

FORD MOTOR CO.

3> 1983 FORD RANGER WITH 2.2L DIESEL ENGINE: CRANKSHAFT DAMPER REMOVAL — Crankshaft damper removal requires the usage of a tool which attaches to the tapped holes in the crankshaft damper. Engines produced before October 7, 1982 did not have the holes drilled in the damper for the tool. The following procedures describe how to remove the damper if the holes do not exist.

1) Disconnect battery ground cables from both batteries. Remove fan and fan shroud.

2) If equipped, remove power steering and/or air conditioning drive belts. Remove alternator/water pump drive belt.

3) Drain coolant and remove radiator. If equipped, remove air conditioning condensor and move out of way.

4) Place transmission in low gear and apply parking brake. Remove crankshaft damper lock bolt with an impact wrench and 38mm socket.

5) Remove damper from crankshaft using a puller. DO NOT reinstall original damper. Replace it with a damper with drilled holes (part no. E3TZ-6312-C). Reverse removal procedure for remaining components.

GENERAL MOTORS

4> 1983 GENERAL MOTORS "C" AND "K" 10/30 MODELS WITH 6.2L DIESEL ENGINES: ROCKER ARM SHAFT INSTALLATION — Rocker arm shafts on these models may break if installed improperly. Uneven torquing causes stress at bolt holes. Proper methos for tightening is as follows:

1) Set engine balancer timing mark at TDC mark on engine.

2) Rotate engine 3 1/2" counterclockwise to first lower water pump bolt. This will position engine so all valves are closed.

3) Before installing bolts through rocker shaft, be certain that ring around shaft is installed with split at bottom.

4) Snug both bolts on each shaft. Tighten bolts evenly to 35 ft. lbs. (45 N.m)

CLUTCHES
SECTION 8

GENERAL MOTORS

1> 1982-83 GENERAL MOTORS "C" & "K" 10/30 MODELS WITH 6.2L DIESEL AND 4-SPEED OVERDRIVE TRANSMISSION: GROANING NOISE FROM CLUTCH — Some of these models may develop a groaning noise when the clutch pedal is about half way down. This can be corrected as follows:

1) Remove the return spring bracket from the clutch fork. Temporarily install a damper (14066237) under the clutch fork using the return spring mounting bolt.

2) Position the damper under the clutch fork and drill a mounting hole 1/2" inward from the lower edge of the clutch fork. Using a 9/32" drill bit, drill out the remaining damper mounting hole.

3) Remove the damper and then reinstall it in the center of the clutch fork. Install the return spring bracket. Tighten the damper and return spring attaching bolts to 10 ft. lbs. (14 N.m)

DRIVE AXLES
SECTION 9

FORD MOTOR CO.

1> 1980-82 FORD "F" TRUCKS AND BRONCO WITH FOUR-WHEEL DRIVE: INOPERATIVE OR NOISY LOCKING HUBS — Some of these models may have excessive noise in the hub area, or the hubs may be inoperative. This may be caused by the axle shaft retaining snap ring coming out of its retaining groove.

FOR 1983 & EARLIER MODELS (Cont.)

1) To verify that the snap ring has come out of the groove, remove the manual hub lock cap assembly and visually inspect the snap ring position. If snap ring is out of its groove, continue.

2) Remove hub lock body assembly. Remove hub, rotor and spindle. Remove the shaft and joint assembly.

3) Measure the axle shaft spline major diameter immediately outboard of the snap ring groove. Measure inside free diameter (inside diameter) of the snap ring.

4) Compare the 2 measurements. If axle shaft major spline diameter is 1.23-1.25" and snap ring inside diameter is 1.14-1.16", install a new snap ring (D7TZ-1B093-A).

5) If axle shaft major spline diameter is 1.28-1.30" and snap ring inside diameter is 1.19-1.22", install a new snap ring (D8TZ-1B093-A).

6) Reinstall all components that were removed. Check operation of manual hubs to ensure condition has been corrected.

GENERAL MOTORS

[2]

1982 GENERAL MOTORS "C" AND "K" 10 AND "G" 10/20 MODEL TRUCKS: 8 1/2" EATON LOCKING DIFFERENTIAL LOCK SCREW — Whenever service is performed on one of these differential units, and the differential pinion shaft lock screw is removed, it is essential that one of the following procedures be followed.

1) Discard screw that was removed and use a new lock screw with an adhesive patch (14056196) and tighten to 25 ft. lbs. (33 N.m).

2) Clean the used screw and apply Loctite Wick N' Lock adhesive (29014) to threaded area of screw. Install screw and tighten to 25 ft. lbs. (33 N.m). DO NOT use any other adhesive due to temperature considerations.

In both procedures, the vehicle must not be moved for 2 hours to ensure curing of adhesive.

JEEP

[3]

1983 JEEP MODELS WITH AMC REAR AXLE: IMPROPER SEATING OF REAR AXLE YOKE CLAMP STRAPS — On CJ, Cherokee, Scrambler, Wagoneer and J10 truck models, excess material may exist on rear axle yoke clamp strap mounting surfaces. This may result in improper seating of the clamps and/or driveline vibration. The yoke can be inspected and corrected, if required as follows:

Yoke Inspection

1) If the yoke has a White paint mark in the saddle area, or if it does not have a Green paint mark, it must be replaced.

2) If the word "Spicer" is cast into the yoke saddle or the yoke has a Green paint mark in the saddle area, it does not have to be replaced. If vibration occurs, however, some part of system may need correction to eliminate noise.

Yoke Replacement

1) Remove both rear wheels and brake drums. Disconnect propeller shaft from axle yoke. Inspect universal bearing caps for damage. Replace joint if caps or needle bearings are damaged.

2) Measure and record the amount of torque required to rotate the pinion gear using a socket and INCH Lb. torque wrench.

3) Remove the pinion using remover tool (J-8614-01) and socket tool (J-22575). Do not discard the old pinion nut.

4) Position drain pan under axle. If yoke has a White paint mark on saddle, make a corresponding mark on pinion shaft for assembly alignment. If no paint mark, continue.

5) Remove axle yoke. Use remover tools (J-8614-01, 02, 03) if yoke cannot be removed by hand. Inspect pinion seal. Remove if damaged, worn or leaking. If removed, do not install a new seal at this time.

6) If old yoke had a White paint mark on it, go to step **7)**. If no paint mark, proceed to step **8)**.

7) Replace yoke seal if necessary. Align Green paint mark on new yoke with paint mark on pinion shaft and install yoke. Proceed to step **12)**.

8) Position new yoke on pinion shaft and install old pinion nut. Tighten nut finger tight. Reconnect shaft to new yoke and measure runout at rear of shaft with dial indicator. Runout should not exceed .015".

9) If runout exceed specifications, disconnect shaft, turn it 180° reconnect and check runout again. If within specifications, continue to step **12)**. If not within specifications, disconnect shaft and remove yoke.

10) Turn yoke 45°, reinstall and recheck runout. If within specifications, go to step **12)**. If not within specifications, rotate yoke 45° again and recheck runout. Continue to rotate yoke in 45° increments until runout meets specifications.

11) Mark propeller shaft, axle yoke and pinion for reassembly reference. Disconnect shaft, remove and discard old pinion nut. Do not remove yoke unless seal is being replaced.

12) If new seal is being used, install seal and slide yoke onto pinion. Align yoke and pinion using reference marks. Install new pinion nut. Do not overtighten nut, tighten only enough to remove end play.

13) Measure pinion rotating torque. Tighten new pinion nut to the torque recorded during removal, plus 5 INCH Lbs. for correct preload.

14) Connect propeller shaft to yoke. Install brake drums and wheels. Check and adjust lubricant level as needed.

BRAKES
SECTION 10

FORD MOTOR CO.

[1]

1983 FORD RANGER AND 1984 BRONCO II: FRONT DISC CALIPER PIN RETENTION — A new split shell brake caliper pin has been released for these vehicles. This replaces the bolt and nut design previously used. The new pin can be re-used. The following procedures must be used for removal and installation of the pin.

Installation

1) Position the pin with the pin retention tabs oriented adjacent to the spindle groove. Do not use the bolt and nut with the new pin.

2) Tap the pin on the outboard end with a hammer. Continue tapping pin inward until retention tabs contact the spindle face. Repeat procedure for lower pin.

3) Do not allow the retention tabs to be tapped to far inward. If this happens, tap from other side until tabs snap into place. Tabs on each end of caliper pins must be free to catch on spindle flanks.

Removal

1) Clean excess dirt from area around pin tabs. Tap upper caliper pin toward inboard side until pin tabs touch spindle face.

2) Insert a screwdriver into slot provided behind pin tabs on inboard side of the pin.

3) Use needle nose pliers to compress outboard end of pin while prying at same time with screwdriver, until tabs slip into spindle groove.

4) Place one end of a 7/16" punch against end of caliper pin and drive caliper pin out of caliper slide groove.

5) Reverse removal procedure for opposite side.

GENERAL MOTORS

2▷ 1982 GENERAL MOTORS "C" and "K" 30 MODELS: HEIGHT SENSING BRAKE PROPORTIONING VALVE SETTING PROCEDURE — Some of these models have an incorrect setting of the brake proportioning valve. The following procedure should be used to reset the valve setting.

1) Raise vehicle. Allow axle to hang free. Remove nut and disengage lever assembly from valve shaft. Select appropriate plastic adjustment gauge from table below.

BRAKE PROPORTION VALVE ADJUSTMENT GAUGE

Application	Color	Part No.
With Heavy Duty Springs	Green	14061394
Without Heavy Duty Springs		
C30 Models	Black	14061395
K30 Models	Blue	14061396

2) Rotate the valve shaft to permit installation of plastic adjustment gauge. Center the "D" shaped hole of gauge over "D" shaped hole of valve shaft. Ensure gauge tang is positioned in valve mounting hole.

3) Use a "C" clamp or channel lock pliers to seat lever nylon bushing to serrations on valve shaft. Reinstall lever assembly to valve shaft.

4) Resintall valve shaft nut and tighten to 70-98 INCH lbs. (8-11 N.m.) Sever gauge tang from body of adjustment gauge to allow valve assembly to rotate freely. Lower vehicle and test brakes

SUSPENSION SECTION 12

FORD MOTOR CO.

1▷ ALL 1983 FORD TRUCKS: DOG TRACKING AND/OR REAR AXLE SKEWED — A limited number of 1983 vehicles may exhibit dog tracking, where the rear axle is not parallel to the front axle. This is the result of the rear spring center bolt being mislocated. The rear

spring center bolt location should be checked on both springs to determine if there is an out-of-specification condition. The specified distance between the main leaf spring center bolt and the forward spring eye (measured along the radius of the main leaf) is listed in the table. If the vehicle has a spring that has an incorrect dimension, the spring should be replaced.

REAR SPRING CENTER BOLT DIMENSION

Model	Wheelbase Inches	Dimension MM
Ranger	All	650.2
F100/350	117, 133, 135	635
F250/350	137, 161	660.4
E100/150	124	24.9
E100/350	138, 158	23.8

GENERAL MOTORS

2▷ 1982 GENERAL MOTORS "C" & "K" 10 TRUCKS WITH 6.2L DIESEL ENGINE: FRONT SUSPENSION BOTTOMS OUT — If excessive bounce or bottoming out of the front suspension exists, suspension can be improved by installing heavy duty shocks on both front and rear suspension. Part numbers are as follows: For "C" Pickups and Suburban models, use 22017533 for front and 22012145 for rear. For "K" Pickups, Blazer and Suburban models, use 3187843 for front and 3187844 for rear.

JEEP

3▷ 1982 JEEP CJ LIMITED MODELS: SUSPENSION SPRING SQUEAKS AND/OR HARD/STIFF RIDE — These conditions may be caused by improperly installed suspension spring retainers. On some models the retainer tabs were clinched flat against the spring instead of allowing the required spring-to-tab clearance. Correct as follows;

Inspect the spring retainers. If the top of the retainers are flattened against the leaf springs, use a pry bar to bend the retainers upward so there is at least .10-.25" clearance between leaf springs and retainer. Do not use a torch to heat and then bend the retainer.

STEERING SECTION 13

FORD MOTOR CO.

1▷ 1983 FORD BRONCO II AND RANGER WITH 2.8L V6 ENGINE AND POWER STEERING: POWER STEERING GEAR VALVE HOUSING — On these models, one of the lugs on the Ford integral power steering gear valve housing has been removed to increase clearance between the gear assembly and the fuel pump. This affects only models with 2.8L V6 engine.

Whenever replacing a gear assembly, control valve assembly or control valve housing the replacement housing must be the type without a lug on one side. If a housing is installed with a lug on it, it may interfere with fuel pump.

Name _____

Address _____

City _____ State _____ Zip _____

NO POSTAGE
NECESSARY
IF MAILED
IN THE
UNITED STATES

BUSINESS REPLY CARD

FIRST CLASS   PERMIT NO. 3701   SAN DIEGO, CA

POSTAGE WILL BE PAID BY ADDRESSEE

MITCHELL MANUALS, INC.

P.O. Box 26260
San Diego, California 92126

Name _____

Address _____

City _____ State _____ Zip _____

NO POSTAGE
NECESSARY
IF MAILED
IN THE
UNITED STATES

BUSINESS REPLY CARD

FIRST CLASS   PERMIT NO. 3701   SAN DIEGO, CA

POSTAGE WILL BE PAID BY ADDRESSEE

MITCHELL MANUALS, INC.

P.O. Box 26260
San Diego, California 92126

Name _____

Address _____

City _____ State _____ Zip _____

NO POSTAGE
NECESSARY
IF MAILED
IN THE
UNITED STATES

BUSINESS REPLY CARD

FIRST CLASS   PERMIT NO. 3701   SAN DIEGO, CA

POSTAGE WILL BE PAID BY ADDRESSEE

MITCHELL MANUALS, INC.

P.O. Box 26260
San Diego, California 92126

Now . . . Save Time, Expand Your Business, Increase Profits

with Mitchell's time-saving profit builders!

Turn Page →